CAMPERSTOP EUROPE 2018

motorhome stopovers in

Albania
Austria
Belgium
Bosnia-Herzegovina
Croatia
Czech Republic
Denmark
Finland
France
Germany
Greece
Hungary
Ireland
Italy
Luxemburg
Montenegro
Netherlands
Norway
Poland
Portugal
Romania
Slovakia
Slovenia
Spain
Sweden
Switzerland
United Kingdom

Publisher - Herausgeber - Éditeur - Editore Facile Media

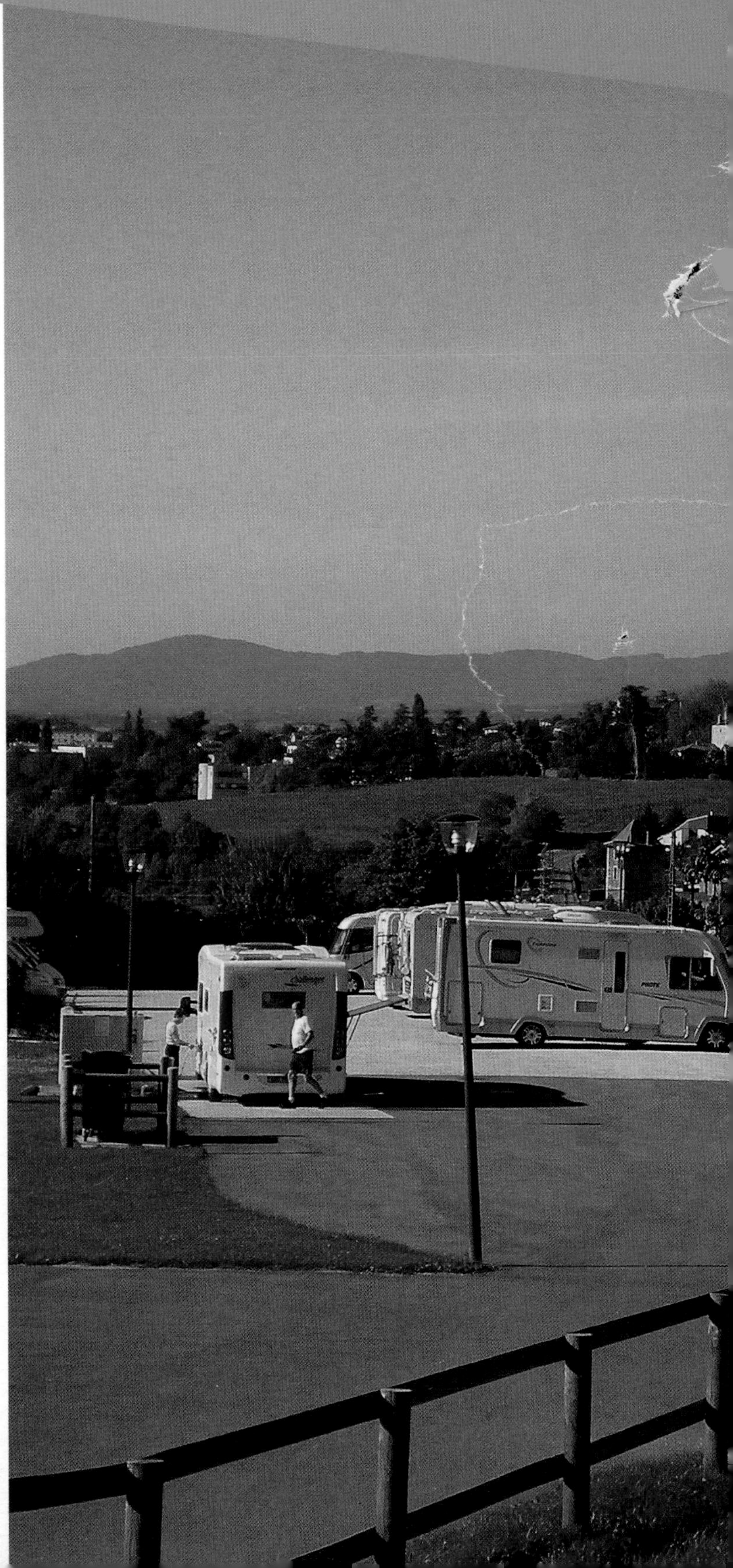

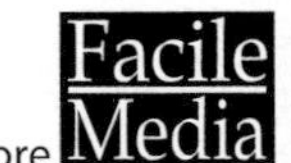

Reliable information

Every summer, 50 teams of Facile Media drive all across Europe to inspect the motorhome stopovers. The inspections take place according to predefined guidelines. The inspections by these specially trained motorhome enthusiasts have made it possible to make the information in the guide as up-to-date as possible. More than 10,000 motorhome stopovers and 7,751 illustrative photos are the result.

Unique way to find the motorhome sites

The motorhome stopovers can be easily located on the 39 maps. Below each map, you'll find a location name index with map referral and a page number where the location can be found in the guide. In addition, the type of motorhome stopover is indicated. In a glance, you'll be able to see whether it is the type of stopover you had in mind. In order to provide you with additional information, the location is described extensively on the relevant page, usually with a picture.

GPS-data sets on your navigation system

In addition to this guide, you can order datasets online, which you can download. The sets can be uploaded to the most common navigation systems. This allows you to drive to the motorhome stopovers listed in this guide without any effort. More information about this is available on page 7.

Preface

COLOPHON

A publication of:

Facile Media b.v., Tilburg
Kraaivenstraat 25-49-AB
NL-5048 AB Tilburg
Tel: +31 412 65 68 85
E-mail: info@camperstop.com
Internet: camperstop.com

Chief editor
Anne van den Dobbelsteen

The draft of this version is saved in October 2017

Comments or suggestions can be sent to the publisher:

Facile Media
Kraaivenstraat 25-49-AB
NL-5048 AB Tilburg
E-mail: info@camperstop.com
Tel.: +31 412 65 68 85

ISBN 978-90-76080-54-3

The world is changing, the digital road has become a motorway and there is no way back. Yet our guides remain popular with the European motorhomers. It still appears to be an indispensable reference book that is often consulted.

The number of motorhomes in Europe continues to rise. Everyone seems to have been motorhoming once or would like to try this soon. It is almost certainly the urge for freedom that makes motorhoming so attractive. Getting up in the morning and not knowing where you will spend the night.

It does not matter if you leave home for a long period or for a short trip nearby, the freedom to go and do what you want gives you a great feeling. Obviously, there are some (inwritten) rules with so many motorhome owners on route. The number of motorhome places is growing significantly, but there are actually not enough.
Popular camperstops face a problem, there are often more motorhomes parked than allowed by the council. In turn this causes inconvenience and therefore some camperstops are closed. A real shame. Try to have an alternative if your first choice of camperstop is not available. To be more secure of a place, it is recommended to go to a camperstop on time.

Our big trip in 2017 went to Greece. It is and remains a lovely holiday country. This time we boarded the ferry in Ancona and after a lovely Greek meal, a shower and a good night's sleep, we disembarked in Igoumenitsa in the morning. Straight in the middle of Greek life. We visited a part of Greece where we have never been before.

The peninsula of Volos and the island of Evia surprised us both. The weather was a bit disappointing but nature however was great. The beaches that we visited were all quiet, attractive and beautifully located. But the mountains on Evia are also very impressive. But always pay attention: the GPS system just sends you onto unpaved roads and then also steeply up the mountain, please do not do this. Do not be tempted, it seems shorter but it is dangerous and you are at risk that your motorhome suffers damages.

This happened to us. Luckily it was only a broken outlet pipe of the oven and because of the rain we believed that this had to be repaired. But where in Greece do you find a company that can do this. Via the office in Oss, we received an address. When we arrived at the repair company the air outlet was repaired immediately. Very convenient this emergency service that can refer you to a repair company. Actually, it should be available to everyone.

After this small repair we went to the Peloponnese via Athens. This part of Greece is familiar territory for us. We stay at camperstops located directly on the beach and we enjoy the beautiful views. Via Ancient Messene, an archaeological place where you drive through the Arcadian Gate with your motorhome, we go to Patras where we take the ferry back to Ancona. Looking back on our trip in Greece we can only say, motor homing is freedom.

I hope that this guide will provide you with inspiration for beautiful motorhome trips. Nearby or far away, short or long, it does not matter as long as you enjoy the freedom.

Anne van den Dobbelsteen
Chief editor

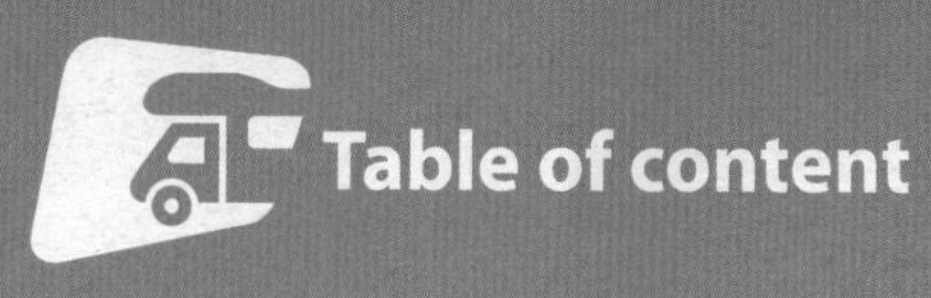

Table of content

How to use the guide

Maps
On pages 12-13 the countries are divided into sections. The number in each box is the number of the map. On the map the red dots indicate the location of the town. Next to each map an index is published with the places on maps. The index shows the name, type of stopover, map code and page number of each location. This way the description of the motorhome stopover can be found quickly and easy.

Searching in a region
In the table of contents, at the beginning of the guide, one can search a region in preferred country. On the page of the region a map indicates the different departments/provinces with a reference to the pages.

Searching for a town
Places identified in this guide can be found under the name of the local town in the alphabetical index at the back. Use the index like a dictionary to look for specific towns, the facilities offered, map references and relevant page numbers.

Country specific rules
When travelling you have to take into account that each country has its own rules and regulations. These rules are written on the first page of each countries section.

Advise
It is recommended not to wait to long to look for an overnight stop. It could be that chosen motorhome stopover is already full and you have to go looking for an alternative.

Type of camperstop

MOTORHOME PARK
This symbol indicates a motorhome park, a park designed for motorhomes with a range of facilities.

OFFICIAL MOTORHOME STOPOVER
This symbol indicates an area suitable for overnight parking.

OVERNIGHT PARKING TOLERATED
In some countries tolerated places are mentioned. This means that it is officially prohibited but is being tolerated by local authorities. Therefore the local or national situation may change at any time. Nevertheless these places are listed because they were frequently being used by motorhomes at the time of writing.

OVERNIGHT STAY IN HARBOUR/MARINA
Motorhome stopover in or near harbour or marina, often with a beautiful view.

OVERNIGHT STAY AT FARM/VINEYARD
Farms and vineyards that welcome motorhomes, you may be encouraged to sample and buy their fare.

OVERNIGHT STAY AT RESTAURANT
Motorhomes are allowed to stopover on the car park of a hotel, restaurant or bar. You should expect to dine or drink in the bar. Some restaurants insist on you having dinner. Sometimes a nominal charge is asked for the overnight stay.

OVERNIGHT STAY AT SPA
A growing number of spas and thermal baths offer stopovers to motorhomes.

OVERNIGHT STAY AT ZOO/MUSEUM/ AMUSEMENT PARK
Motorhomes are allowed to stopover on the car park of a zoo, museum or amusement park. Entrance is not always obligated.

OVERNIGHT STAY AT COMPANY/ENTERPRISE
Overnight stay, mostly inside the gates, at companies/enterprises.

OVERNIGHT STAY OUTSIDE THE CAMPSITE
Motorhomes are allowed to stopover on the parking place outside the gate of a campsite.

CAMPSITE
Overnight stay on a campsite.

CAR-PARK
Motorhome parking bays, suitable for daytime use only. Often in large cities and/or tourist towns, charges may apply.

Blue bar

Type of camperstop
Name of town with particularities like :
town worth visiting, touristic town, shopping town
Map code: 36B1, map 36 (page 80) grid B1

S Wien 36B1
Reisemobilstellplatz Wien, Perfektastraße 49-53, Vienna (Wien).
GPS: n48,13698 e16,31582.

167 € 19 Ch (167x)€ 2/24h WC included
Location: Urban, comfortable.
Surface: grassy/gravel.
01/01-31/12.
Distance: city centre 12km 4km 30m 30m metro 150m, bus 50m 100m.

Contact information Camperstop

Name - Address of the camperstop
GPS coordinates indicated in decimal degrees
- Signposted on the spot
- Signposted in town
- No signs to indicate the motorhome stopover

Payment

- Collector parking fee
- Parking meter
- Reception/office on the spot
- Payment only with a credit/debit card
- Payment with cash and credit/debit card

Description of the Camperstop

Camperstop 'Reisemobilstellplatz Wien', with 167 pitches on grass and gravel, is situated in an urban area and is open all year round. The camperstop is situated 12 kilometers from the city centre; 4 kilometers from the motorway; at 30 meters there is a restaurant and shops; the bus and metro stops are 50-150 meters; 100 meters distance to a cycle route.

167 € 19 : 167 pitches, the price is € 19 per night, all year.

Ch WC **included :** all service included except electricity.

(167x)€ 2/24h : 167 power connections, € 2 per 24 hours.

S Motorhome service facilities

- drinking water
- grey water dump
- Ch chemical toilet disposal point
- charging battery
- power connection available
- WC toilets
- showers
- washing machine/ dryer (price/price) on the spot
- wifi access point
- animals not allowed

GPS-convenience

Downloading GPS-coordinates

Downloads of the gps-coordinates for the motorhome stopovers listed in this guide are available from www.camperstop.com. The files are suitable for most navigation systems. The data that appears on the screen gives the town name and page number in this guide so you can look up the details of the facilities very easily.

The downloadable files list the stopovers and most of the other facilities mentioned in the guide. Therefore it could be a stopover with or without service facilities, a place with service facilities only, but also a tourist information office or a campsite.

You can easily check for your nearest stopover, the navigation system will list the stopovers by distance. Use the guide to see what facilities are available. Once a choice has been made you can navigate to there without a problem.

The costs for downloading are € 3.25 per country/dataset. The Netherlands/Belgium/Luxembourg are sold as one country, also Austria/Switzerland and Spain/Portugal are treated the same.

Full downloading instructions are found on at camperstop.com. There are different downloads of several navigation systems.

Modifications

Active motorhome traveller?

With your help we can ensure that all motorhomers in Europe can use the most recent data regarding the camperstops. So, we like to receive your comments, adjustments and additions. For example, rate adjustments, municipal regulations or beautiful pictures of a camperstop. All data will be processed by us. It will be immediately visible in the Camperstop app and will be published in the next edition of the motorhome guide.

Camperstop-App

The camperstop database is updated throughout the year. You find the latest data in the Camperstop App. The app is available in 5 languages: English, German, French, Dutch and Italian, in the Android and iOs Stores. The entire online use of the app is free, would you like to use the app offline, display weather forecasts or turn off adverts, you can purchase the Camperstop-Pro version in the app.

The most beautiful pictures can win a free Camperstop package!

Send us the most beautiful picture of your motorhome holiday and see it on the cover of the motorhome guide 2019. If your picture is used on one of the covers of the new motor-home guides, you receive a free Camperstop package. This package includes a motorhome guide with your picture and the Camperstop-Pro version for one year (for Android or iOs).

Send your comments - adjustments - pictures to:

info@camperstop.com

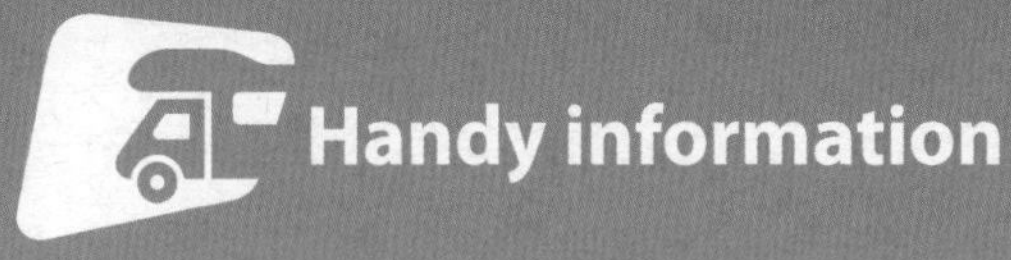

Handy information

Database camperstops from 1996

For more than 20 years the data of motorhome stopovers have been accurately recorded in the database for motorhome stopovers. This is updated every day; adjustments, pictures, new camperstops and places that have unfortunately been closed. Would you like to help keeping the data as up-to-date as possible, please send us your information: info@camperstop.com.

This guide in 5 languages

Did you know that this guide is available for European motorhomers in 5 languages, namely: German, Italian, Dutch, French and English.

Inspection camperstops

Facile Media trains people to inspect motorhome stopovers. Every year about 50 couples travel through Europa to inspect the camperstops.

Datasets for GPS system

Datasets are available for all countries in this guide. These sets can be used in the most common GPS systems. No longer entering (wrong) coordinates, but convenient direct navigation. More information you can find on our website, camperstop.com.

Camperstop app

The latest available data of the camperstops can be found in the Camperstop-App. The app can be downloaded from the Android and Apple stores. The use of the online app is free. If you do not want to use internet when on the road, the offline version is the solution. This pro-version can be purchased in the online app and is valid for 12 months. For more information see: camperstop.com/app.

Surveys

To respond to the wishes of the European motorhome owners, surveys and polls are regularly published on our website camperstop.com. We find your opinion important, so would you please be so kind to fill in a survey to express your vision to us?

Always informed

Register yourself for our newsletter and receive, among others, exclusive benefits, inspiration for your next motorhome trip and much more: camperstop.com/newsletter. You can also follow us on facebook: facebook.com/camperstopeurope.

Your pictures in our guides and app?

Send us your most beautiful pictures of your motorhome holiday and you can win great prices, see camperstop.com.

Driving regulations in Europe

Each country has different driving rules. For motorhomes sometimes there are different regulations. Here below an overview with maximum speed limits for motorhomes.

Per country there are also different rules as for warning triangles, security vests or driving with daily lights. Here below this information at a glance.

	within towns	single carriageway		expressway		motorway		compulsory in your vehicle:
AL Albania	40	80 <3,5T	70 >3,5T	90 <3,5T	70 >3,5T	110 <3,5T	80 >3,5T	
A Austria	50	100 <3,5T	70 >3,5T			130 <3,5T	80 >3,5T	A10-A12-A13-en A14 : 22-05h max. 110km/h.
B Belgium	50	70 Flanders	90 Wallonia			120 <3,5T	90 >3,5T	
BIH Bosnia and Herzegovina	50	80		100 <3,5T	80 >3,5T	130 <3,5T	80 >3,5T	
CH Switzerland	50	80		100		120 <3,5T	100 >3,5T	
CZ Czech Republic	50	90 <3,5T	80 >3,5T	90 <3,5T	80 >3,5T	130 <3,5T	80 >3,5T	
D Germany	50	100 <3,5T	80 >3,5T	130 <3,5T	100 >3,5T	130 <3,5T	100 >3,5T	130km/h is a recommended speed limit.
DK Denmark	50	80 <3,5T	70 >3,5T	110 <3,5T	80 >3,5T	130 <3,5T	80 >3,5T	
ES Spain	50	80		90 <3,5T	80 >3,5T	100 <3,5T	90 >3,5T	
FIN Finland	50	80		100 <3,5T	80 >3,5T	100 <3,5T	80 >3,5T	
F France	50	90 <3,5T	80 >3,5T	110 <3,5T	100 >3,5T	130 <3,5T	110 >3,5T	Speed limits on a dry road. Safety vest also for bicycles.
GB Great Britain	30	60 <3,5T	50 >3,5T	70 <3,5T	60 >3,5T	70		30mph=48km 50mph=80km 60mph=96km 70mph=112km Speed limits in mph.
GR Greece	50	90		110 <3,5T	90 >3,5T	130 <3,5T	90 >3,5T	
HR Croatia	50	90 <3,5T	80 >3,5T	110 <3,5T	80 >3,5T	130 <3,5T	90 >3,5T	Set of spare bulbs.
HU Hungary	50	90 <3,5T	70 >3,5T	110 <3,5T	70 >3,5T	130 <3,5T	80 >3,5T	

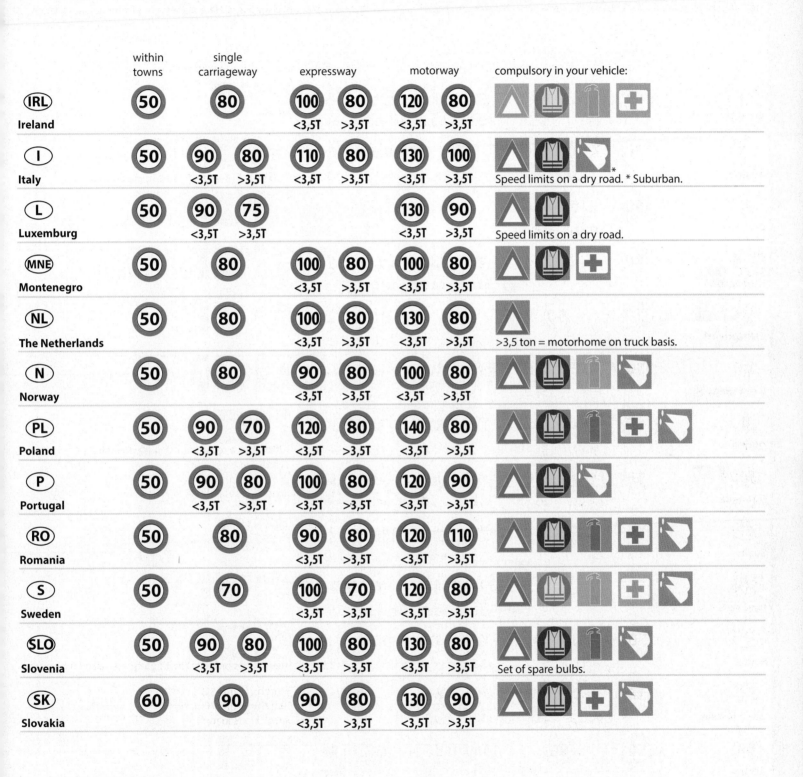

	within towns	single carriageway	expressway	motorway	compulsory in your vehicle:
(IRL) **Ireland**	50	80	100 <3,5T / 80 >3,5T	120 <3,5T / 80 >3,5T	
(I) **Italy**	50	90 <3,5T / 80 >3,5T	110 <3,5T / 80 >3,5T	130 <3,5T / 100 >3,5T	* Speed limits on a dry road. * Suburban.
(L) **Luxemburg**	50	90 <3,5T / 75 >3,5T		130 <3,5T / 90 >3,5T	Speed limits on a dry road.
(MNE) **Montenegro**	50	80	100 <3,5T / 80 >3,5T	100 <3,5T / 80 >3,5T	
(NL) **The Netherlands**	50	80	100 <3,5T / 80 >3,5T	130 <3,5T / 80 >3,5T	>3,5 ton = motorhome on truck basis.
(N) **Norway**	50	80	90 <3,5T / 80 >3,5T	100 <3,5T / 80 >3,5T	
(PL) **Poland**	50	90 <3,5T / 70 >3,5T	120 <3,5T / 80 >3,5T	140 <3,5T / 80 >3,5T	
(P) **Portugal**	50	90 <3,5T / 80 >3,5T	100 <3,5T / 80 >3,5T	120 <3,5T / 90 >3,5T	
(RO) **Romania**	50	80	90 <3,5T / 80 >3,5T	120 <3,5T / 110 >3,5T	
(S) **Sweden**	50	70	100 <3,5T / 70 >3,5T	120 <3,5T / 80 >3,5T	
(SLO) **Slovenia**	50	90 <3,5T / 80 >3,5T	100 <3,5T / 80 >3,5T	130 <3,5T / 80 >3,5T	Set of spare bulbs.
(SK) **Slovakia**	60	90	90 <3,5T / 80 >3,5T	130 <3,5T / 90 >3,5T	

warning triangle

security vest

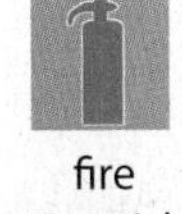
fire extinguisher

first aid kit

daily lights

recommended

Information is based on information available in November 2017.

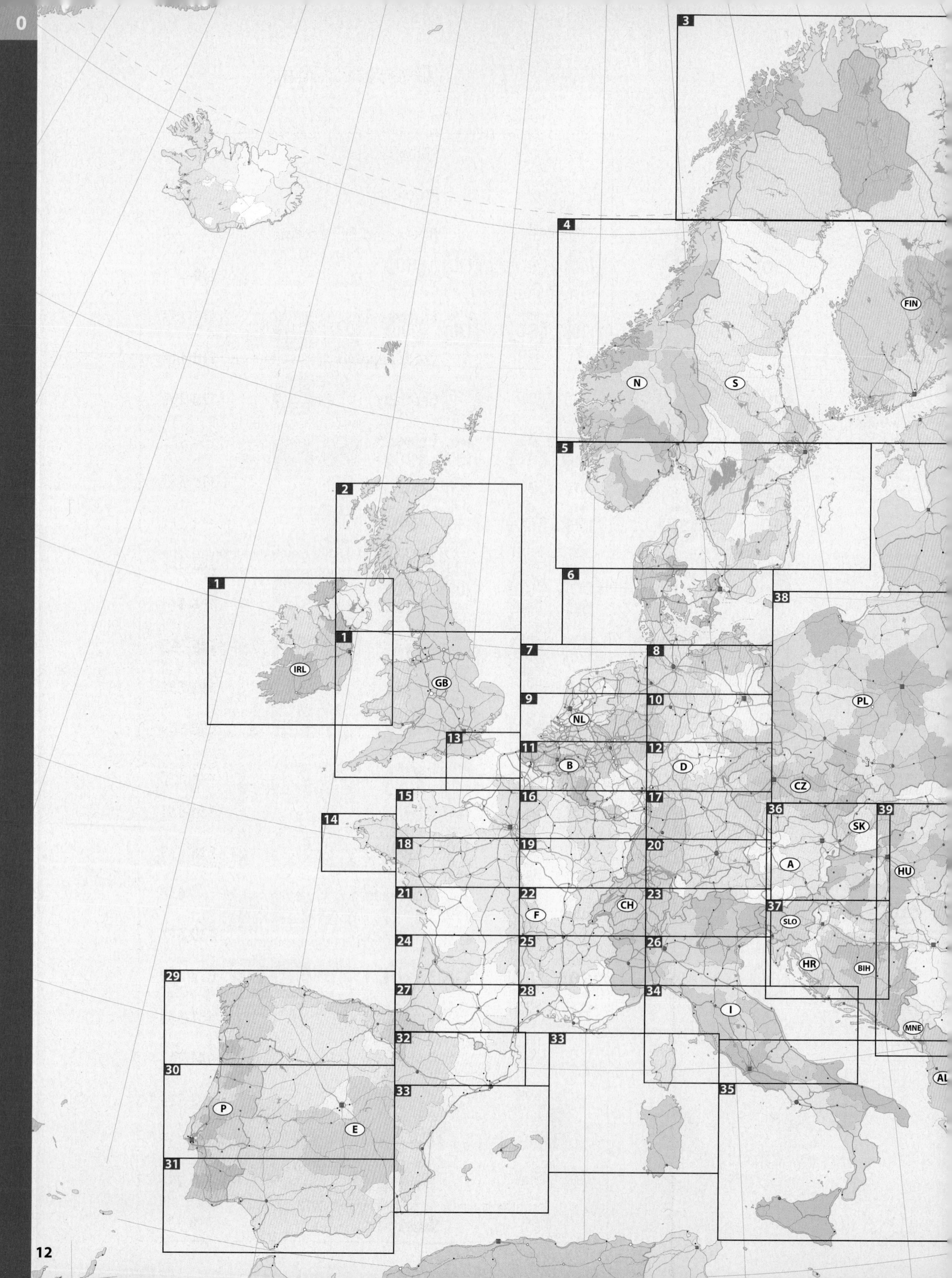

3
4
FIN
N
S
5
2
1
IRL
1
GB
6
38
7
8
9
NL
10
PL
13
11
B
12
D
CZ
15
16
17
36
SK
39
14
18
19
20
A
HU
21
22
F
CH
23
37
SLO
24
25
26
HR
BIH
29
27
28
34
I
MNE
32
33
30
P
E
33
35
AL
31

Overview map

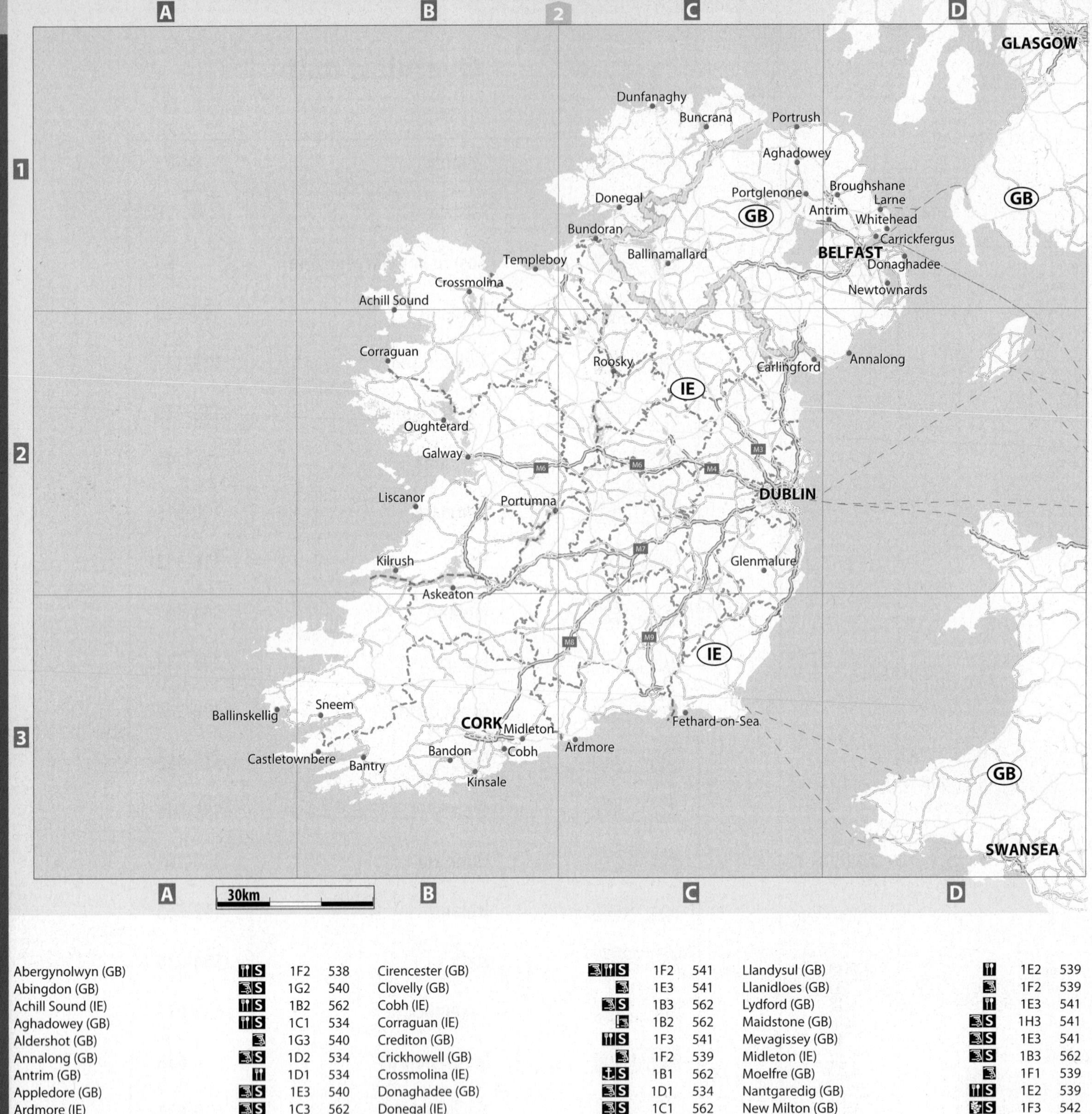

Place	Grid	Page
Abergynolwyn (GB)	1F2	538
Abingdon (GB)	1G2	540
Achill Sound (IE)	1B2	562
Aghadowey (GB)	1C1	534
Aldershot (GB)	1G3	540
Annalong (GB)	1D2	534
Antrim (GB)	1D1	534
Appledore (GB)	1E3	540
Ardmore (IE)	1C3	562
Arundel (GB)	1G3	540
Askeaton (IE)	1B2	562
Ballinamallard (GB)	1C1	534
Ballinskellig (IE)	1A3	562
Bandon (IE)	1B3	562
Bantry (IE)	1B3	562
Bideford (GB)	1E3	540
Bourton-on-the-Water (GB)	1G2	540
Brecon (GB)	1F2	538
Broughshane (GB)	1D1	534
Bude (GB)	1E3	540
Builth Wells (GB)	1F2	539
Buncrana (IE)	1C1	562
Bundoran (IE)	1C1	562
Bury St Edmunds (GB)	1H2	540
Canterbury (GB)	1H3	540
Carlingford (IE)	1C2	562
Carrickfergus (GB)	1D1	534
Castletownbere (IE)	1B3	562
Cheltenham (GB)	1F2	540
Chester (GB)	1F1	541
Cirencester (GB)	1F2	541
Clovelly (GB)	1E3	541
Cobh (IE)	1B3	562
Corraguan (IE)	1B2	562
Crediton (GB)	1F3	541
Crickhowell (GB)	1F2	539
Crossmolina (IE)	1B1	562
Donaghadee (GB)	1D1	534
Donegal (IE)	1C1	562
Dover (GB)	1H3	541
Dunfanaghy (IE)	1C1	562
Fethard-on-Sea (IE)	1C3	562
Galway (IE)	1B2	562
Glenmalure (IE)	1C2	562
Great Missenden (GB)	1G2	541
Hay-on-Wye (GB)	1F2	539
Hayling Island (GB)	1G3	541
Helmsley (GB)	1G1	541
Holsworthy (GB)	1E3	541
Huntingdon (GB)	1G2	541
Ipswich (GB)	1H2	541
Ivybridge (GB)	1E3	541
Kilrush (IE)	1B2	562
Kinsale (IE)	1B3	562
Knighton (GB)	1F2	539
Larne (GB)	1D1	534
Liscanor (IE)	1B2	562
Liverpool (GB)	1F1	541
Llandrindod Wells (GB)	1F2	539
Llandudno Junction (GB)	1F1	539
Llandysul (GB)	1E2	539
Llanidloes (GB)	1F2	539
Lydford (GB)	1E3	541
Maidstone (GB)	1H3	541
Mevagissey (GB)	1E3	541
Midleton (IE)	1B3	562
Moelfre (GB)	1F1	539
Nantgaredig (GB)	1E2	539
New Milton (GB)	1F3	542
New Quay (GB)	1E2	539
Newhaven (GB)	1G3	542
Newnham on Severn (GB)	1F2	542
Newton (GB)	1F2	539
Newtownards (GB)	1D1	534
Oldham (GB)	1F1	542
Oughterard (IE)	1B2	562
Pickering (GB)	1G1	542
Portglenone (GB)	1C1	534
Portrush (GB)	1C1	534
Portumna (IE)	1B2	562
Praa Sands (GB)	1E3	542
Presteigne (GB)	1F2	539
Rake (GB)	1G3	542
Roosky (IE)	1C2	562
Rye (GB)	1H3	542
Scarborough (GB)	1G1	542
Settle (GB)	1F1	542
Sewerby (GB)	1G1	542
Shrewsbury (GB)	1F2	542
Skipton (GB)	1G1	542

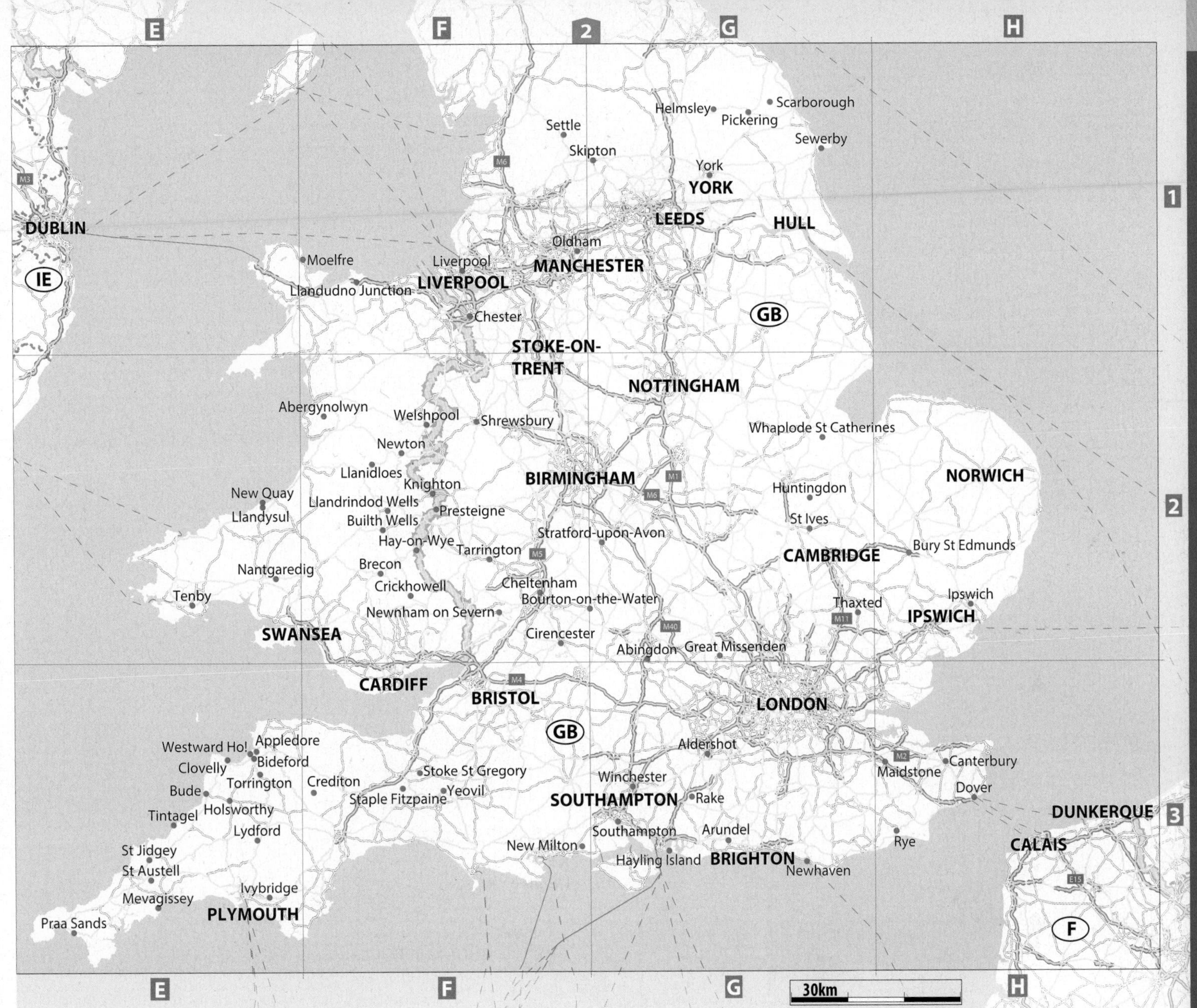
E
F
2
G
H
Helmsley
Scarborough
Pickering
Settle
Sewerby
Skipton
M6
York
YORK
M3
1
DUBLIN
LEEDS
HULL
Oldham
Moelfre
Liverpool
MANCHESTER
IE
Llandudno Junction
LIVERPOOL
Chester
GB
STOKE-ON-
TRENT
NOTTINGHAM
Abergynolwyn
Welshpool
Shrewsbury
Whaplode St Catherines
Newton
M1
NORWICH
Llanidloes
Knighton
BIRMINGHAM
Huntingdon
New Quay
M6
2
Llandrindod Wells
Llandysul
Presteigne
Builth Wells
St Ives
Hay-on-Wye
Stratford-upon-Avon
Bury St Edmunds
Tarrington
M5
CAMBRIDGE
Nantgaredig
Brecon
Crickhowell
Cheltenham
Tenby
Ipswich
Bourton-on-the-Water
Thaxted
Newnham on Severn
M11
IPSWICH
SWANSEA
M40
Cirencester
Abingdon
Great Missenden
CARDIFF
M4
BRISTOL
LONDON
GB
Appledore
Westward Ho!
Aldershot
Bideford
Clovelly
M2
Canterbury
Stoke St Gregory
Maidstone
Torrington
Crediton
Winchester
Bude
Yeovil
Dover
Staple Fitzpaine
SOUTHAMPTON
Rake
Holsworthy
Tintagel
DUNKERQUE
3
Lydford
Southampton
Arundel
New Milton
Rye
CALAIS
St Jidgey
Hayling Island
BRIGHTON
St Austell
Newhaven
Ivybridge
E15
Mevagissey
PLYMOUTH
Praa Sands
F
E
F
G
30km
H

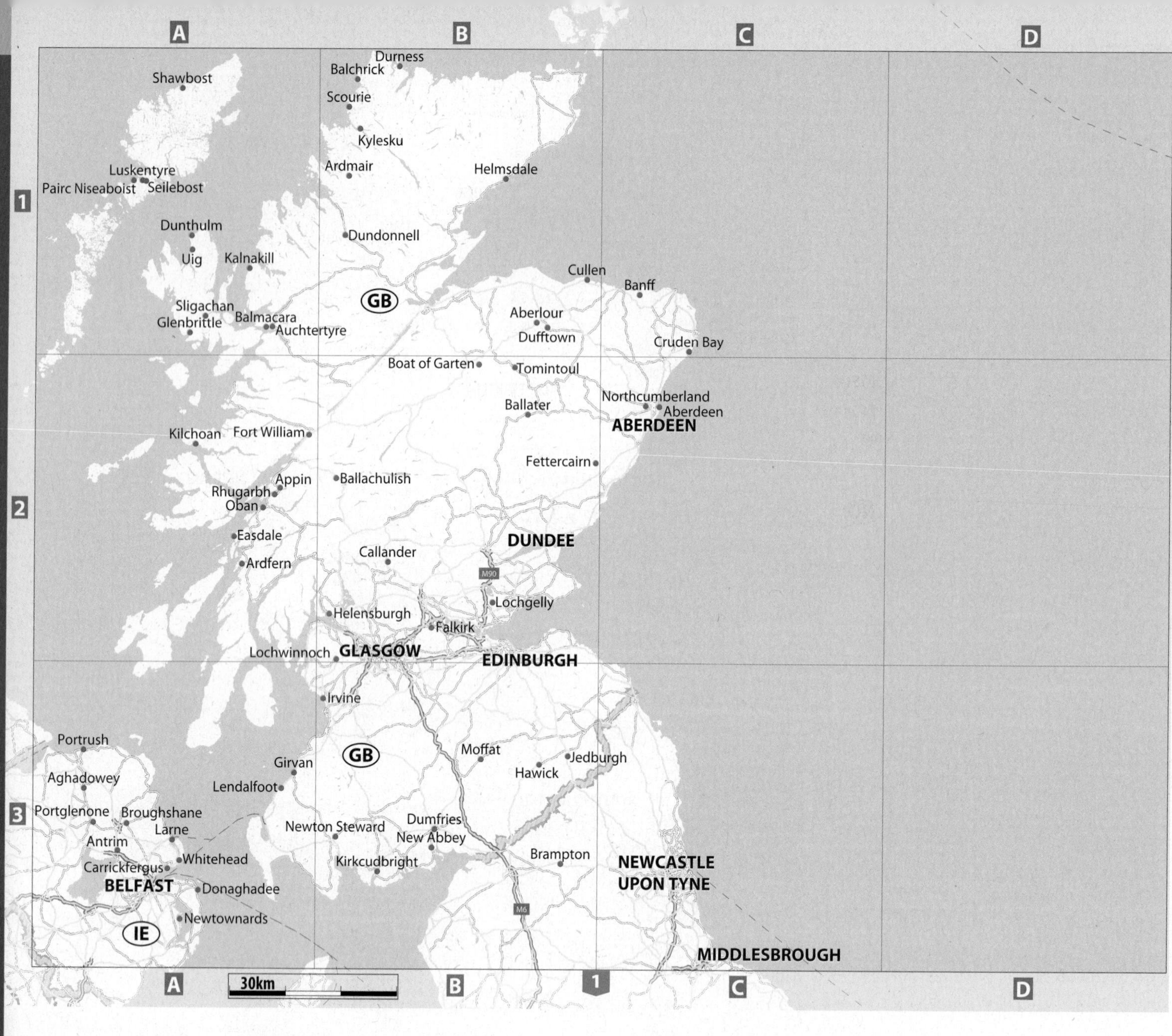

Aberdeen (GB)	2C2	535
Aberlour (GB)	2B1	535
Appin (GB)	2A2	535
Ardfern (GB)	2A2	535
Ardmair (GB)	2B1	535
Auchtertyre (GB)	2A1	535
Balchrick (GB)	2B1	535
Ballachulish (GB)	2B2	535
Ballater (GB)	2B2	535
Balmacara (GB)	2A1	535
Banff (GB)	2C1	535
Boat of Garten (GB)	2B2	535
Brampton (GB)	2B3	540
Callander (GB)	2B2	535
Cruden Bay (GB)	2C1	536
Cullen (GB)	2B1	536
Dufftown (GB)	2B1	536
Dumfries (GB)	2B3	536
Dundonnell (GB)	2B1	536
Dunthulm (GB)	2A1	536
Durness (GB)	2B1	536
Easdale (GB)	2A2	536
Falkirk (GB)	2B2	536
Fettercairn (GB)	2B2	536
Fort William (GB)	2A2	536
Girvan (GB)	2A3	536
Glenbrittle (GB)	2A1	536
Hawick (GB)	2B3	536
Helensburgh (GB)	2B2	537
Helmsdale (GB)	2B1	537
Irvine (GB)	2B3	537
Jedburgh (GB)	2B3	537
Kalnakill (GB)	2A1	537
Kilchoan (GB)	2A2	537
Kirkcudbright (GB)	2B3	537
Kylesku (GB)	2B1	537
Lendalfoot (GB)	2A3	537
Lochgelly (GB)	2B2	537
Lochwinnoch (GB)	2B2	537
Luskentyre (GB)	2A1	537
Moffat (GB)	2B3	537
New Abbey (GB)	2B3	537
Newton Steward (GB)	2B3	538
Northcumberland (GB)	2C2	542
Oban (GB)	2A2	538
Pairc Niseaboist (GB)	2A1	538
Rhugarbh (GB)	2A2	538
Scourie (GB)	2B1	538
Seilebost (GB)	2A1	538
Shawbost (GB)	2A1	538
Sligachan (GB)	2A1	538
Tomintoul (GB)	2B2	538
Uig (GB)	2A1	538

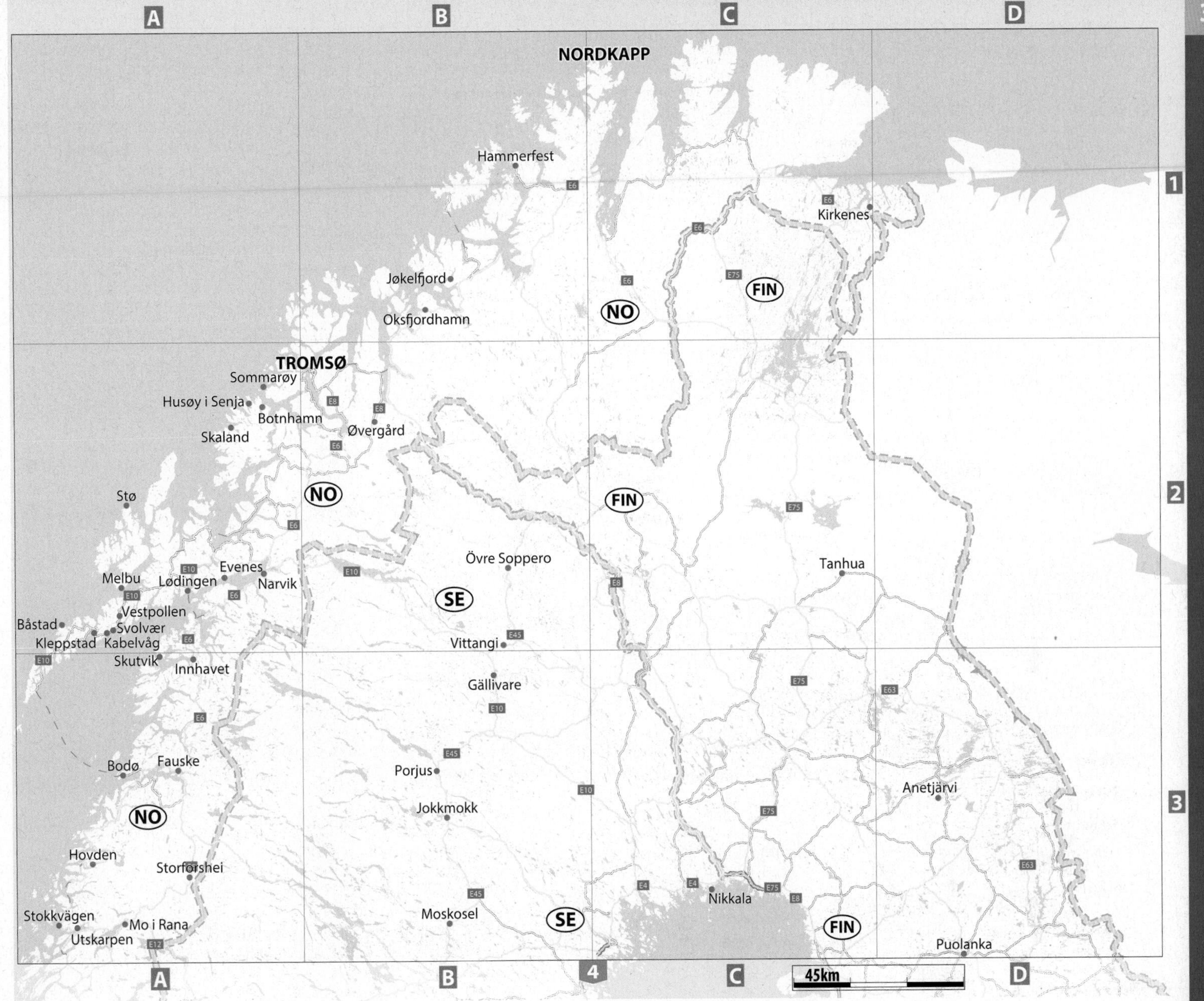

Location		Grid	Page
Anetjärvi (FI)	S	3D3	347
Båstad (NO)	S	3A2	672
Bodø (NO)	S	3A3	672
Botnhamn (NO)	S	3A2	672
Evenes (NO)	S	3A2	672
Fauske (NO)	S	3A3	672
Gällivare (SE)	S	3B3	704
Hammerfest (NO)	S	3B1	672
Hovden (NO)	S	3A3	672
Husøy i Senja (NO)		3A2	673
Innhavet (NO)	S	3A3	673
Jokkmokk (SE)	S	3B3	704
Jøkelfjord (NO)	S	3B1	673
Kabelvåg (NO)	S	3A2	673
Kirkenes (NO)	S	3C1	673
Kleppstad (NO)	S	3A2	673
Lødingen (NO)	S	3A2	673
Melbu (NO)	S	3A2	673
Mo i Rana (NO)	S	3A3	673
Moskosel (SE)	S	3B3	705
Narvik (NO)		3A2	673
Nikkala (SE)	S	3C3	705
Oksfjordhamn (NO)	S	3B1	673
Övre Soppero (SE)		3B2	705
Porjus (SE)		3B3	705
Puolanka (FI)	S	3D3	347
Skaland (NO)	S	3A2	673
Skutvik (NO)		3A3	673
Sommarøy (NO)	S	3A2	673
Stokkvägen (NO)	S	3A3	673
Storforshei (NO)		3A3	673
Stø (NO)	S	3A2	673
Svolvær (NO)	S	3A2	673
Tanhua (FI)	S	3C2	347
Utskarpen (NO)	S	3A3	673
Vestpollen (NO)		3A2	673
Vittangi (SE)		3B2	705
Øvergård (NO)	S	3B2	673

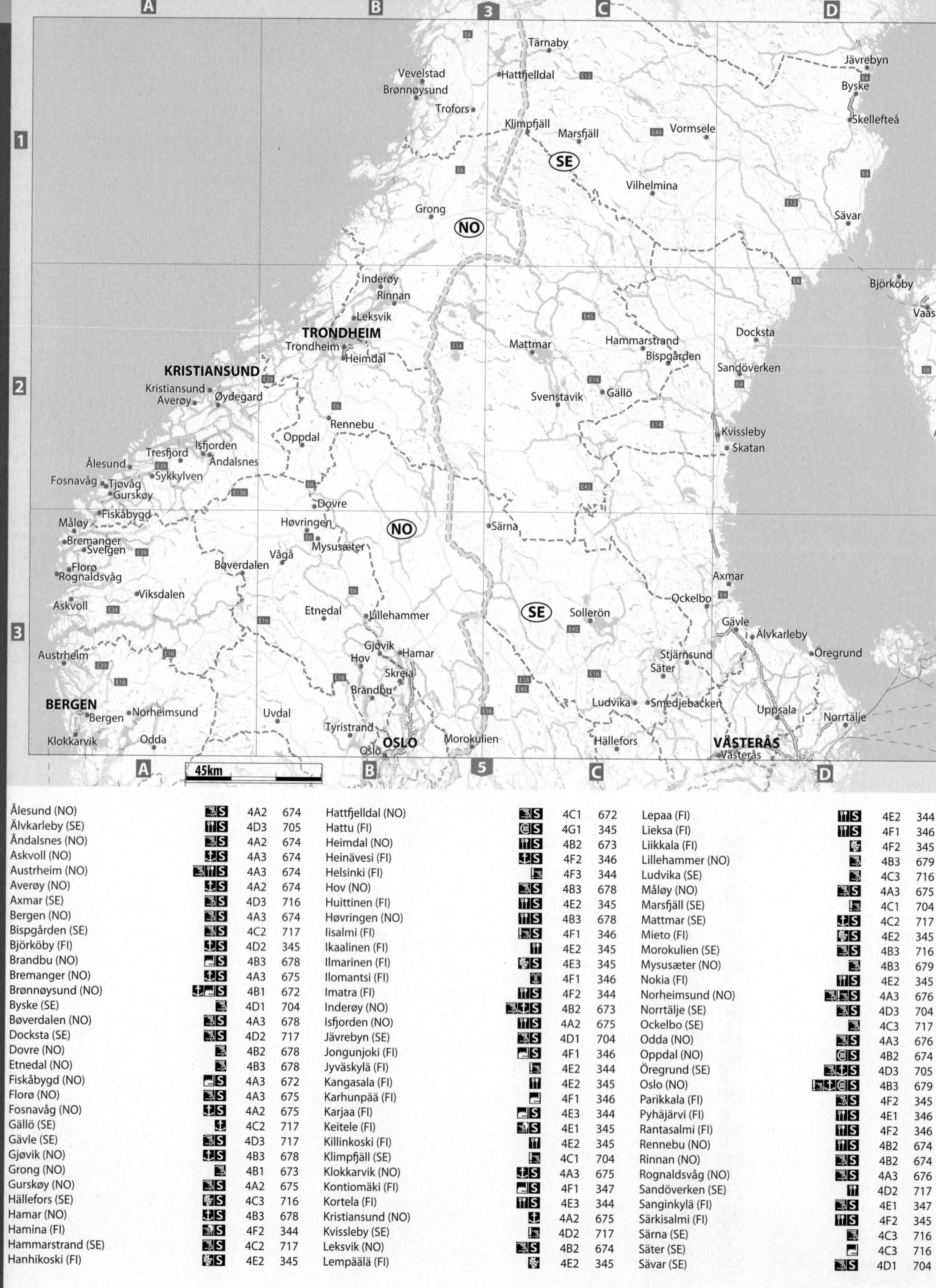

Place	Grid	Page
Ålesund (NO)	4A2	674
Älvkarleby (SE)	4D3	705
Åndalsnes (NO)	4A2	674
Askvoll (NO)	4A3	674
Austrheim (NO)	4A3	674
Averøy (NO)	4A2	674
Axmar (SE)	4D3	716
Bergen (NO)	4A3	674
Bispgården (SE)	4C2	717
Björköby (FI)	4D2	345
Brandbu (NO)	4B3	678
Bremanger (NO)	4A3	675
Brønnøysund (NO)	4B1	672
Byske (SE)	4D1	704
Bøverdalen (NO)	4A3	678
Docksta (SE)	4D2	717
Dovre (NO)	4B2	678
Etnedal (NO)	4B3	678
Fiskåbygd (NO)	4A3	672
Florø (NO)	4A3	675
Fosnavåg (NO)	4A2	675
Gällö (SE)	4C2	717
Gävle (SE)	4D3	717
Gjøvik (NO)	4B3	678
Grong (NO)	4B1	673
Gurskøy (NO)	4A2	675
Hällefors (SE)	4C3	716
Hamar (NO)	4B3	678
Hamina (FI)	4F2	344
Hammarstrand (SE)	4C2	717
Hanhikoski (FI)	4E2	345
Hattfjelldal (NO)	4C1	672
Hattu (FI)	4G1	345
Heimdal (NO)	4B2	673
Heinävesi (FI)	4F2	346
Helsinki (FI)	4F3	344
Hov (NO)	4B3	678
Huittinen (FI)	4E2	345
Høvringen (NO)	4B3	678
Iisalmi (FI)	4F1	346
Ikaalinen (FI)	4E2	345
Ilmarinen (FI)	4E3	345
Ilomantsi (FI)	4F1	346
Imatra (FI)	4F2	344
Inderøy (NO)	4B2	673
Isfjorden (NO)	4A2	675
Jävrebyn (SE)	4D1	704
Jongunjoki (FI)	4F1	346
Jyväskylä (FI)	4E2	344
Kangasala (FI)	4E2	345
Karhunpää (FI)	4F1	346
Karjaa (FI)	4E3	344
Keitele (FI)	4E1	345
Killinkoski (FI)	4E2	345
Klimpfjäll (SE)	4C1	704
Klokkarvik (NO)	4A3	675
Kontiomäki (FI)	4F1	347
Kortela (FI)	4E3	344
Kristiansund (NO)	4A2	675
Kvissleby (SE)	4D2	717
Leksvik (NO)	4B2	674
Lempäälä (FI)	4E2	345
Lepaa (FI)	4E2	344
Lieksa (FI)	4F1	346
Liikkala (FI)	4F2	345
Lillehammer (NO)	4B3	679
Ludvika (SE)	4C3	716
Måløy (NO)	4A3	675
Marsfjäll (SE)	4C1	704
Mattmar (SE)	4C2	717
Mieto (FI)	4E2	345
Morokulien (SE)	4B3	716
Mysusæter (NO)	4B3	679
Nokia (FI)	4E2	345
Norheimsund (NO)	4A3	676
Norrtälje (SE)	4D3	704
Ockelbo (SE)	4C3	717
Odda (NO)	4A3	676
Oppdal (NO)	4B2	674
Öregrund (SE)	4D3	705
Oslo (NO)	4B3	679
Parikkala (FI)	4F2	345
Pyhäjärvi (FI)	4E1	346
Rantasalmi (FI)	4F2	346
Rennebu (NO)	4B2	674
Rinnan (NO)	4B2	674
Rognaldsvåg (NO)	4A3	676
Sandöverken (SE)	4D2	717
Sanginkylä (FI)	4E1	347
Särkisalmi (FI)	4F2	345
Särna (SE)	4C3	716
Säter (SE)	4C3	716
Sävar (SE)	4D1	704

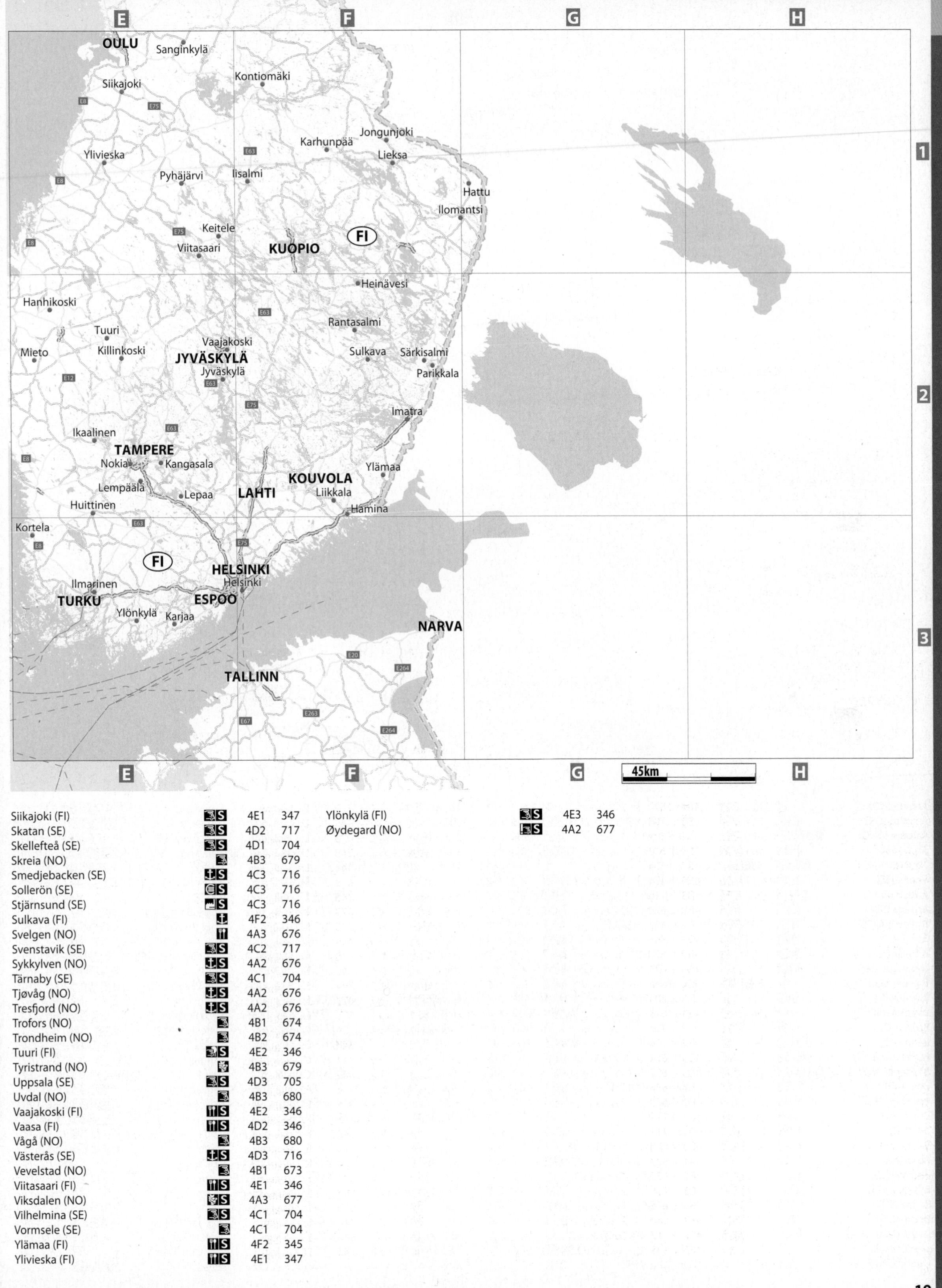
E
F
G
H
1
2
3
OULU
Sanginkylä
Siikajoki
Kontiomäki
E8
E75
Jongunjoki
Karhunpää
Lieksa
Ylivieska
E63
Pyhäjärvi
Iisalmi
Hattu
Ilomantsi
Keitele
E75
Viitasaari
KUOPIO
FI
Heinävesi
Hanhikoski
E63
Rantasalmi
Tuuri
Vaajakoski
Mieto
Killinkoski
JYVÄSKYLÄ
Sulkava
Särkisalmi
Jyväskylä
Parikkala
E12
E63
E75
Imatra
E63
Ikaalinen
TAMPERE
Nokia
Kangasala
Ylämaa
KOUVOLA
Lempäälä
Lepaa
LAHTI
Liikkala
Huittinen
Hamina
Kortela
E63
E8
E75
FI
HELSINKI
Ilmarinen
Helsinki
TURKU
ESPOO
Ylönkylä
Karjaa
NARVA
E20
E264
TALLINN
E263
E67
E264
45km

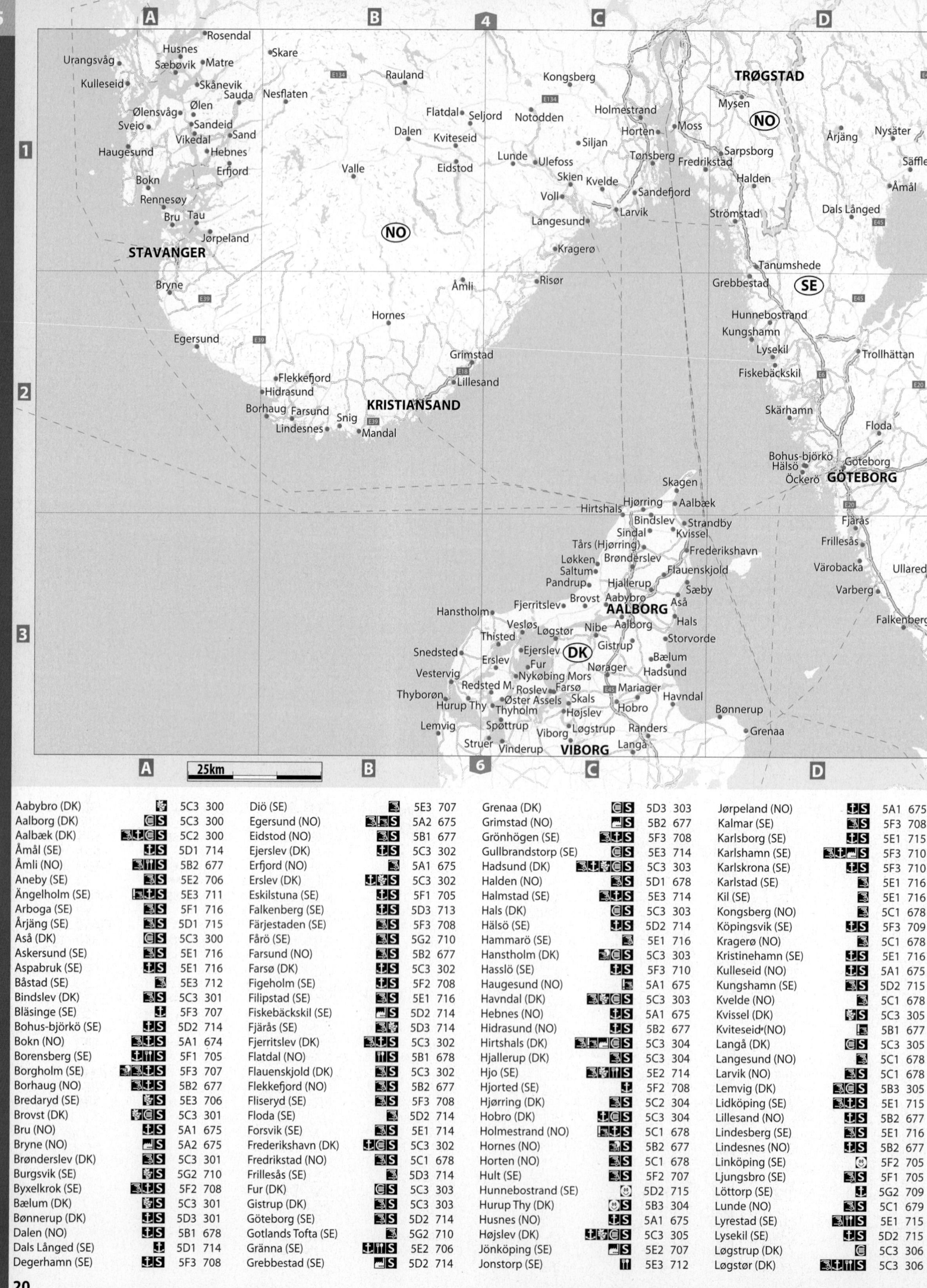

Place	Map	Page
Aabybro (DK)	5C3	300
Aalborg (DK)	5C3	300
Aalbæk (DK)	5C2	300
Åmål (SE)	5D1	714
Åmli (NO)	5B2	677
Aneby (SE)	5E2	706
Ängelholm (SE)	5E3	711
Arboga (SE)	5F1	716
Årjäng (SE)	5D1	715
Aså (DK)	5C3	300
Askersund (SE)	5E1	716
Aspabruk (SE)	5E1	716
Båstad (SE)	5E3	712
Bindslev (DK)	5C3	301
Bläsinge (SE)	5F3	707
Bohus-björkö (SE)	5D2	714
Bokn (NO)	5A1	674
Borensberg (SE)	5F1	705
Borgholm (SE)	5F3	707
Borhaug (NO)	5B2	677
Bredaryd (SE)	5E3	706
Brovst (DK)	5C3	301
Bru (NO)	5A1	675
Bryne (NO)	5A2	675
Brønderslev (DK)	5C3	301
Burgsvik (SE)	5G2	710
Byxelkrok (SE)	5F2	708
Bælum (DK)	5C3	301
Bønnerup (DK)	5D3	301
Dalen (NO)	5B1	678
Dals Långed (SE)	5D1	714
Degerhamn (SE)	5F3	708
Diö (SE)	5E3	707
Egersund (NO)	5A2	675
Eidstod (NO)	5B1	677
Ejerslev (DK)	5C3	302
Erfjord (NO)	5A1	675
Erslev (DK)	5C3	302
Eskilstuna (SE)	5F1	705
Falkenberg (SE)	5D3	713
Färjestaden (SE)	5F3	708
Fårö (SE)	5G2	710
Farsund (NO)	5B2	677
Farsø (DK)	5C3	302
Figeholm (SE)	5F2	708
Filipstad (SE)	5E1	716
Fiskebäckskil (SE)	5D2	714
Fjärås (SE)	5D3	714
Fjerritslev (DK)	5C3	302
Flatdal (NO)	5B1	678
Flauenskjold (DK)	5C3	302
Flekkefjord (NO)	5B2	677
Fliseryd (SE)	5F3	708
Floda (SE)	5D2	714
Forsvik (SE)	5E1	714
Frederikshavn (DK)	5C3	302
Fredrikstad (NO)	5C1	678
Frillesås (SE)	5D3	714
Fur (DK)	5C3	303
Gistrup (DK)	5C3	303
Göteborg (SE)	5D2	714
Gotlands Tofta (SE)	5G2	710
Gränna (SE)	5E2	706
Grebbestad (SE)	5D2	714
Grenaa (DK)	5D3	303
Grimstad (NO)	5B2	677
Grönhögen (SE)	5F3	708
Gullbrandstorp (SE)	5E3	714
Hadsund (DK)	5C3	303
Halden (NO)	5D1	678
Halmstad (SE)	5E3	714
Hals (DK)	5C3	303
Hälsö (SE)	5D2	714
Hammarö (SE)	5E1	716
Hanstholm (DK)	5C3	303
Hasslö (SE)	5F3	710
Haugesund (NO)	5A1	675
Havndal (DK)	5C3	303
Hebnes (NO)	5A1	675
Hidrasund (NO)	5B2	677
Hirtshals (DK)	5C3	304
Hjallerup (DK)	5C3	304
Hjo (SE)	5E2	714
Hjorted (SE)	5F2	708
Hjørring (DK)	5C2	304
Hobro (DK)	5C3	304
Holmestrand (NO)	5C1	678
Hornes (NO)	5B2	677
Horten (NO)	5C1	678
Hult (SE)	5F2	707
Hunnebostrand (SE)	5D2	715
Hurup Thy (DK)	5B3	304
Husnes (NO)	5A1	675
Højslev (DK)	5C3	305
Jönköping (SE)	5E2	707
Jonstorp (SE)	5E3	712
Jørpeland (NO)	5A1	675
Kalmar (SE)	5F3	708
Karlsborg (SE)	5E1	715
Karlshamn (SE)	5F3	710
Karlskrona (SE)	5F3	710
Karlstad (SE)	5E1	716
Kil (SE)	5E1	716
Kongsberg (NO)	5C1	678
Köpingsvik (SE)	5F3	709
Kragerø (NO)	5C1	678
Kristinehamn (SE)	5E1	716
Kulleseid (NO)	5A1	675
Kungshamn (SE)	5D2	715
Kvelde (NO)	5C1	678
Kvissel (DK)	5C3	305
Kviteseid (NO)	5B1	677
Langå (DK)	5C3	305
Langesund (NO)	5C1	678
Larvik (NO)	5C1	678
Lemvig (DK)	5B3	305
Lidköping (SE)	5E1	715
Lillesand (NO)	5B2	677
Lindesberg (SE)	5E1	716
Lindesnes (NO)	5B2	677
Linköping (SE)	5F2	705
Ljungsbro (SE)	5F1	705
Löttorp (SE)	5G2	709
Lunde (NO)	5C1	679
Lyrestad (SE)	5E1	715
Lysekil (SE)	5D2	715
Løgstrup (DK)	5C3	306
Løgstør (DK)	5C3	306

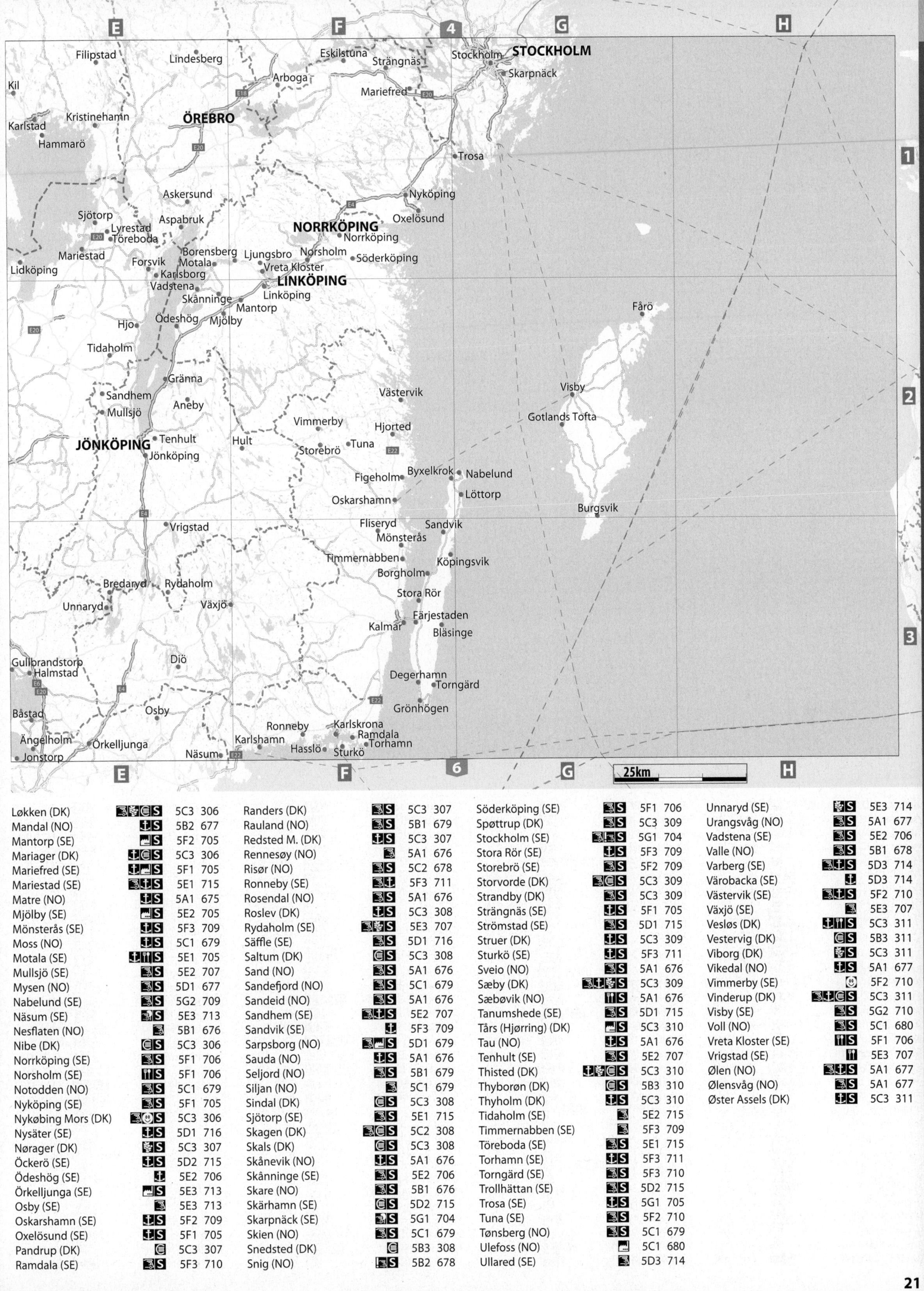
E
F
4
G
H
STOCKHOLM
Stockholm
Skarpnäck
Filipstad
Lindesberg
Eskilstuna
Strängnäs
Arboga
Mariefred
Kil
Karlstad
Kristinehamn
Hammarö
ÖREBRO
Trosa
Askersund
Nyköping
Sjötorp
Lyrestad
Töreboda
Aspabruk
NORRKÖPING
Norrköping
Oxelösund
Mariestad
Lidköping
Forsvik
Borensberg
Motala
Karlsborg
Ljungsbro
Norsholm
Vreta Kloster
Söderköping
Vadstena
LINKÖPING
Linköping
Skänninge
Mantorp
Hjo
Ödeshög
Mjölby
Fårö
Tidaholm
Gränna
Sandhem
Mullsjö
Aneby
Västervik
Visby
Vimmerby
Hjorted
Gotlands Tofta
JÖNKÖPING
Tenhult
Jönköping
Hult
Storebrö
Tuna
Figeholm
Byxelkrok
Nabelund
Löttorp
Oskarshamn
Burgsvik
Vrigstad
Fliseryd
Mönsterås
Sandvik
Timmernabben
Köpingsvik
Borgholm
Bredaryd
Rydaholm
Stora Rör
Unnaryd
Växjö
Kalmar
Färjestaden
Bläsinge
Gullbrandstorp
Halmstad
Diö
Degerhamn
Torngärd
Grönhögen
Båstad
Osby
Ronneby
Karlskrona
Ramdala
Torhamn
Ängelholm
Örkelljunga
Karlshamn
Hasslö
Sturkö
Näsum
Jonstorp
6
25km
1
2
3
E4
E6
E18
E20
E22

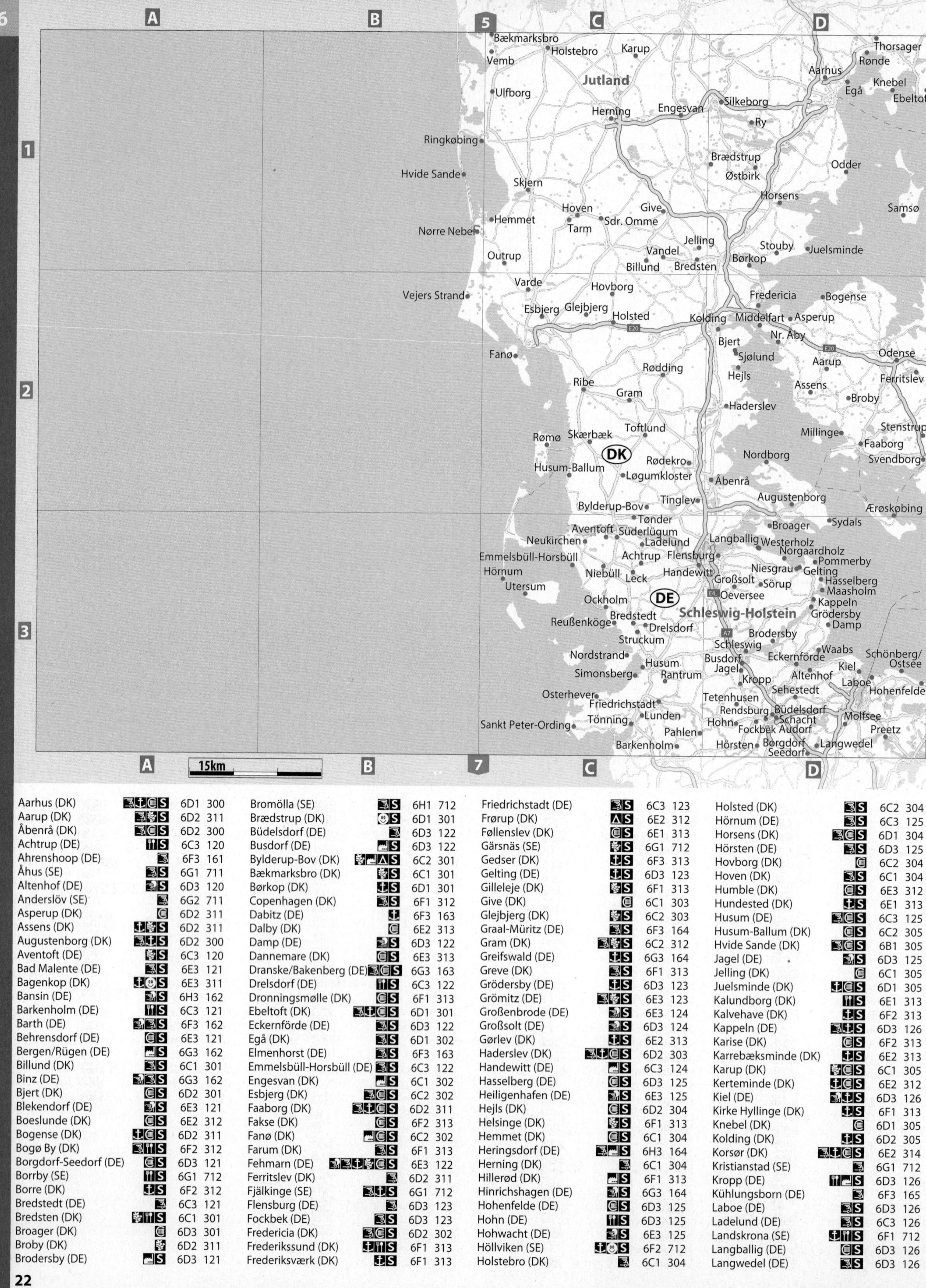

Aarhus (DK)	6D1	300
Aarup (DK)	6D2	311
Åbenrå (DK)	6D2	300
Achtrup (DE)	6C3	120
Ahrenshoop (DE)	6F3	161
Åhus (SE)	6G1	711
Altenhof (DE)	6D3	120
Anderslöv (SE)	6G2	711
Asperup (DK)	6D2	311
Assens (DK)	6D2	311
Augustenborg (DK)	6D2	300
Aventoft (DE)	6C3	120
Bad Malente (DE)	6E3	121
Bagenkop (DK)	6E3	311
Bansin (DE)	6H3	162
Barkenholm (DE)	6C3	121
Barth (DE)	6F3	162
Behrensdorf (DE)	6E3	121
Bergen/Rügen (DE)	6G3	162
Billund (DK)	6C1	301
Binz (DE)	6G3	162
Bjert (DK)	6D2	301
Blekendorf (DE)	6E3	121
Boeslunde (DK)	6E2	312
Bogense (DK)	6D2	311
Bogø By (DK)	6F2	312
Borgdorf-Seedorf (DE)	6D3	121
Borrby (SE)	6G1	712
Borre (DK)	6F2	312
Bredstedt (DE)	6C3	121
Bredsten (DK)	6C1	301
Broager (DK)	6D3	301
Broby (DK)	6D2	311
Brodersby (DE)	6D3	121
Bromölla (SE)	6H1	712
Brædstrup (DK)	6D1	301
Büdelsdorf (DE)	6D3	122
Busdorf (DE)	6D3	122
Bylderup-Bov (DK)	6C2	301
Bækmarksbro (DK)	6C1	301
Børkop (DK)	6D1	301
Copenhagen (DK)	6F1	312
Dabitz (DE)	6F3	163
Dalby (DK)	6E2	313
Damp (DE)	6D3	122
Dannemare (DK)	6E3	313
Dranske/Bakenberg (DE)	6G3	163
Drelsdorf (DE)	6C3	122
Dronningsmølle (DK)	6F1	313
Ebeltoft (DK)	6D1	301
Eckernförde (DE)	6D3	122
Egå (DK)	6D1	302
Elmenhorst (DE)	6F3	163
Emmelsbüll-Horsbüll (DE)	6C3	122
Engesvan (DK)	6C1	302
Esbjerg (DK)	6C2	302
Faaborg (DK)	6D2	311
Fakse (DK)	6F2	313
Fanø (DK)	6C2	302
Farum (DK)	6F1	313
Fehmarn (DE)	6E3	122
Ferritslev (DK)	6D2	311
Fjälkinge (SE)	6G1	712
Flensburg (DE)	6D3	123
Fockbek (DE)	6D3	123
Fredericia (DK)	6D2	302
Frederikssund (DK)	6F1	313
Frederiksværk (DK)	6F1	313
Friedrichstadt (DE)	6C3	123
Frørup (DK)	6E2	312
Føllenslev (DK)	6E1	313
Gärsnäs (SE)	6G1	712
Gedser (DK)	6F3	313
Gelting (DE)	6D3	123
Gilleleje (DK)	6F1	313
Give (DK)	6C1	303
Glejbjerg (DK)	6C2	303
Graal-Müritz (DE)	6F3	164
Gram (DK)	6C2	312
Greifswald (DE)	6G3	164
Greve (DK)	6F1	313
Grödersby (DE)	6D3	123
Grömitz (DE)	6E3	123
Großenbrode (DE)	6E3	124
Großsolt (DE)	6D3	124
Gørlev (DK)	6E2	313
Haderslev (DK)	6D2	303
Handewitt (DE)	6C3	124
Hasselberg (DE)	6D3	125
Heiligenhafen (DE)	6E3	125
Hejls (DK)	6D2	304
Helsinge (DK)	6F1	313
Hemmet (DK)	6C1	304
Heringsdorf (DE)	6H3	164
Herning (DK)	6C1	304
Hillerød (DK)	6F1	313
Hinrichshagen (DE)	6G3	164
Hohenfelde (DE)	6D3	125
Hohn (DE)	6D3	125
Hohwacht (DE)	6E3	125
Höllviken (SE)	6F2	712
Holstebro (DK)	6C1	304
Holsted (DK)	6C2	304
Hörnum (DE)	6C3	125
Horsens (DK)	6D1	304
Hörsten (DE)	6D3	125
Hovborg (DK)	6C2	304
Hoven (DK)	6C1	304
Humble (DK)	6E3	312
Hundested (DK)	6E1	313
Husum (DE)	6C3	125
Husum-Ballum (DK)	6C2	305
Hvide Sande (DK)	6B1	305
Jagel (DE)	6D3	125
Jelling (DK)	6C1	305
Juelsminde (DK)	6D1	305
Kalundborg (DK)	6E1	313
Kalvehave (DK)	6F2	313
Kappeln (DE)	6D3	126
Karise (DK)	6F2	313
Karrebæksminde (DK)	6E2	313
Karup (DK)	6C1	305
Kerteminde (DK)	6E2	312
Kiel (DE)	6D3	126
Kirke Hyllinge (DK)	6F1	313
Knebel (DK)	6D1	305
Kolding (DK)	6D2	305
Korsør (DK)	6E2	314
Kristianstad (SE)	6G1	712
Kropp (DE)	6D3	126
Kühlungsborn (DE)	6F3	165
Laboe (DE)	6D3	126
Ladelund (DE)	6C3	126
Landskrona (SE)	6F1	712
Langballig (DE)	6D3	126
Langwedel (DE)	6D3	126

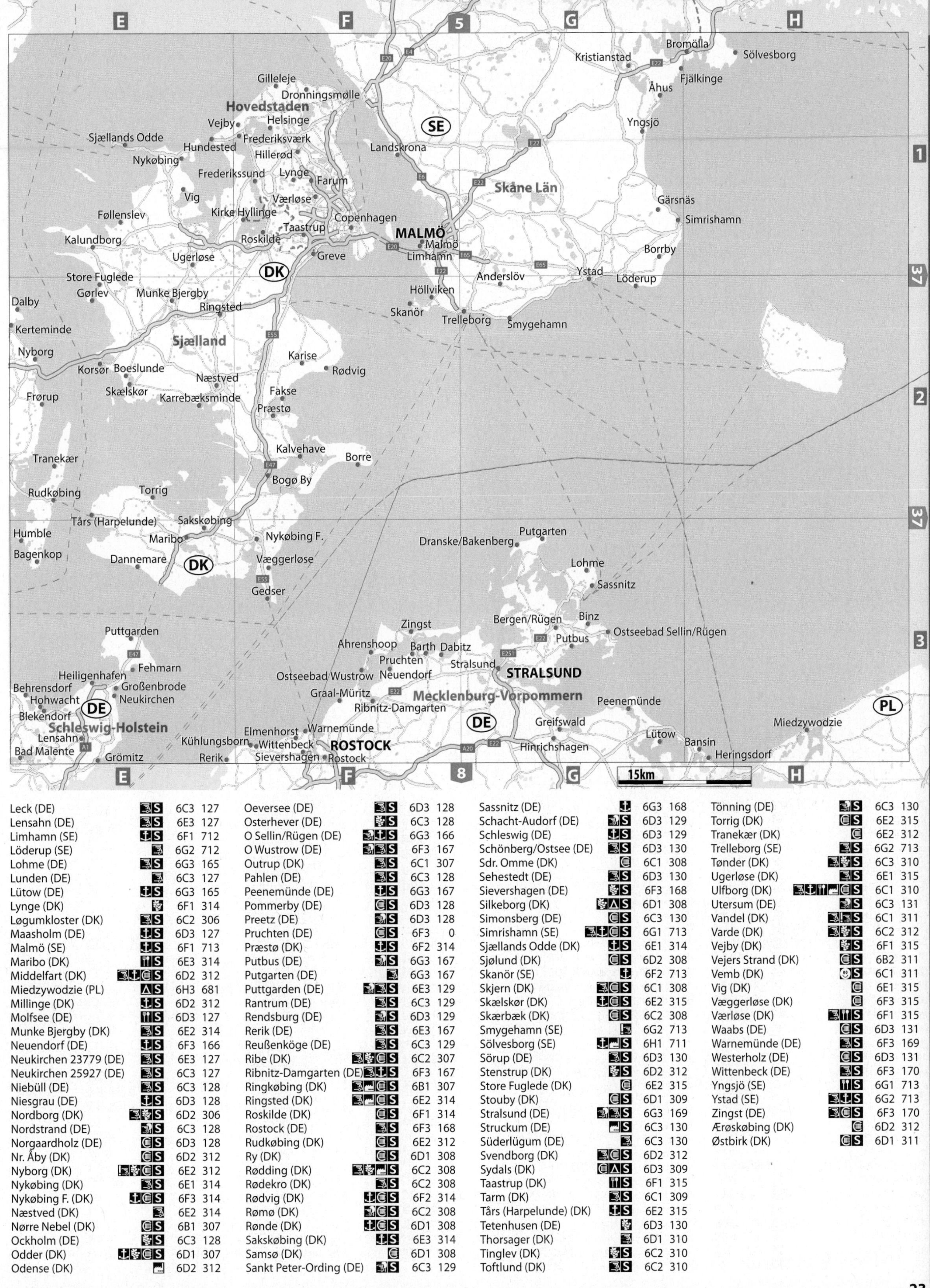

Place	Grid	Page
Leck (DE)	6C3	127
Lensahn (DE)	6E3	127
Limhamn (SE)	6F1	712
Löderup (SE)	6G2	712
Lohme (DE)	6G3	165
Lunden (DE)	6C3	127
Lütow (DE)	6G3	165
Lynge (DK)	6F1	314
Løgumkloster (DK)	6C2	306
Maasholm (DE)	6D3	127
Malmö (SE)	6F1	713
Maribo (DK)	6E3	314
Middelfart (DK)	6D2	312
Miedzywodzie (PL)	6H3	681
Millinge (DK)	6D2	312
Molfsee (DE)	6D3	127
Munke Bjergby (DK)	6E2	314
Neuendorf (DE)	6F3	166
Neukirchen 23779 (DE)	6E3	127
Neukirchen 25927 (DE)	6C3	127
Niebüll (DE)	6C3	128
Niesgrau (DE)	6D3	128
Nordborg (DK)	6D2	306
Nordstrand (DE)	6C3	128
Norgaardholz (DE)	6D3	128
Nr. Åby (DK)	6D2	312
Nyborg (DK)	6E2	312
Nykøbing (DK)	6E1	314
Nykøbing F. (DK)	6F3	314
Næstved (DK)	6E2	314
Nørre Nebel (DK)	6B1	307
Ockholm (DE)	6C3	128
Odder (DK)	6D1	307
Odense (DK)	6D2	312
Oeversee (DE)	6D3	128
Osterhever (DE)	6C3	128
O Sellin/Rügen (DE)	6G3	166
O Wustrow (DE)	6F3	167
Outrup (DK)	6C1	307
Pahlen (DE)	6C3	128
Peenemünde (DE)	6G3	167
Pommerby (DE)	6D3	128
Preetz (DE)	6D3	128
Pruchten (DE)	6F3	0
Præstø (DK)	6F2	314
Putbus (DE)	6G3	167
Putgarten (DE)	6G3	167
Puttgarden (DE)	6E3	129
Rantrum (DE)	6C3	129
Rendsburg (DE)	6D3	129
Rerik (DE)	6E3	167
Reußenköge (DE)	6C3	129
Ribe (DK)	6C2	307
Ribnitz-Damgarten (DE)	6F3	167
Ringkøbing (DK)	6B1	307
Ringsted (DK)	6E2	314
Roskilde (DK)	6F1	314
Rostock (DE)	6F3	168
Rudkøbing (DK)	6E2	312
Ry (DK)	6D1	308
Rødding (DK)	6C2	308
Rødekro (DK)	6C2	308
Rødvig (DK)	6F2	314
Rømø (DK)	6C2	308
Rønde (DK)	6D1	308
Sakskøbing (DK)	6E3	314
Samsø (DK)	6D1	308
Sankt Peter-Ording (DE)	6C3	129
Sassnitz (DE)	6G3	168
Schacht-Audorf (DE)	6D3	129
Schleswig (DE)	6D3	129
Schönberg/Ostsee (DE)	6D3	130
Sdr. Omme (DK)	6C1	308
Sehestedt (DE)	6D3	130
Sievershagen (DE)	6F3	168
Silkeborg (DK)	6D1	308
Simonsberg (DE)	6C3	130
Simrishamn (SE)	6G1	713
Sjællands Odde (DK)	6E1	314
Sjølund (DK)	6D2	308
Skanör (SE)	6F2	713
Skjern (DK)	6C1	308
Skælskør (DK)	6E2	315
Skærbæk (DK)	6C2	308
Smygehamn (SE)	6G2	713
Sölvesborg (SE)	6H1	711
Sörup (DE)	6D3	130
Stenstrup (DK)	6D2	312
Store Fuglede (DK)	6E2	315
Stouby (DK)	6D1	309
Stralsund (DE)	6G3	169
Struckum (DE)	6C3	130
Süderlügum (DE)	6C3	130
Svendborg (DK)	6D2	312
Sydals (DK)	6D3	309
Taastrup (DK)	6F1	315
Tarm (DK)	6C1	309
Tårs (Harpelunde) (DK)	6E2	315
Tetenhusen (DE)	6D3	130
Thorsager (DK)	6D1	310
Tinglev (DK)	6C2	310
Toftlund (DK)	6C2	310
Tönning (DE)	6C3	130
Torrig (DK)	6E2	315
Tranekær (DK)	6E2	312
Trelleborg (SE)	6G2	713
Tønder (DK)	6C3	310
Ugerløse (DK)	6E1	315
Ulfborg (DK)	6C1	310
Utersum (DE)	6C3	131
Vandel (DK)	6C1	311
Varde (DK)	6C2	312
Vejby (DK)	6F1	315
Vejers Strand (DK)	6B2	311
Vemb (DK)	6C1	311
Vig (DK)	6E1	315
Væggerløse (DK)	6F3	315
Værløse (DK)	6F1	315
Waabs (DE)	6D3	131
Warnemünde (DE)	6F3	169
Westerholz (DE)	6D3	131
Wittenbeck (DE)	6F3	170
Yngsjö (SE)	6G1	713
Ystad (SE)	6G2	713
Zingst (DE)	6F3	170
Ærøskøbing (DK)	6D2	312
Østbirk (DK)	6D1	311

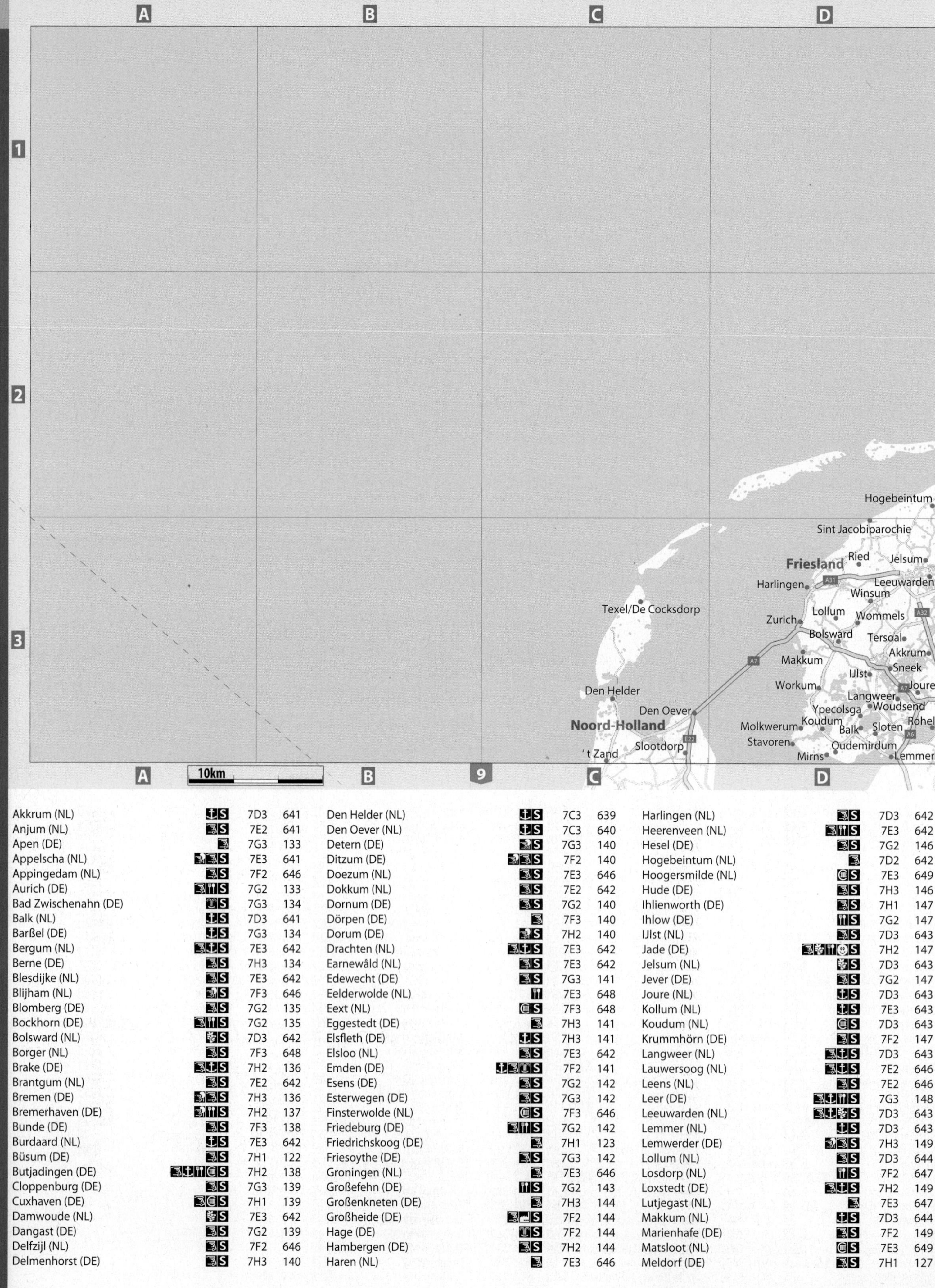

Place	Grid	Page
Akkrum (NL)	7D3	641
Anjum (NL)	7E2	641
Apen (DE)	7G3	133
Appelscha (NL)	7E3	641
Appingedam (NL)	7F2	646
Aurich (DE)	7G2	133
Bad Zwischenahn (DE)	7G3	134
Balk (NL)	7D3	641
Barßel (DE)	7G3	134
Bergum (NL)	7E3	642
Berne (DE)	7H3	134
Blesdijke (NL)	7E3	642
Blijham (NL)	7F3	646
Blomberg (DE)	7G2	135
Bockhorn (DE)	7G2	135
Bolsward (NL)	7D3	642
Borger (NL)	7F3	648
Brake (DE)	7H2	136
Brantgum (NL)	7E2	642
Bremen (DE)	7H3	136
Bremerhaven (DE)	7H2	137
Bunde (DE)	7F3	138
Burdaard (NL)	7E3	642
Büsum (DE)	7H1	122
Butjadingen (DE)	7H2	138
Cloppenburg (DE)	7G3	139
Cuxhaven (DE)	7H1	139
Damwoude (NL)	7E3	642
Dangast (DE)	7G2	139
Delfzijl (NL)	7F2	646
Delmenhorst (DE)	7H3	140
Den Helder (NL)	7C3	639
Den Oever (NL)	7C3	640
Detern (DE)	7G3	140
Ditzum (DE)	7F2	140
Doezum (NL)	7E3	646
Dokkum (NL)	7E2	642
Dornum (DE)	7G2	140
Dörpen (DE)	7F3	140
Dorum (DE)	7H2	140
Drachten (NL)	7E3	642
Earnewâld (NL)	7E3	642
Edewecht (DE)	7G3	141
Eelderwolde (NL)	7E3	648
Eext (NL)	7F3	648
Eggestedt (DE)	7H3	141
Elsfleth (DE)	7H3	141
Elsloo (NL)	7E3	642
Emden (DE)	7F2	141
Esens (DE)	7G2	142
Esterwegen (DE)	7G3	142
Finsterwolde (NL)	7F3	646
Friedeburg (DE)	7G2	142
Friedrichskoog (DE)	7H1	123
Friesoythe (DE)	7G3	142
Groningen (NL)	7E3	646
Großefehn (DE)	7G2	143
Großenkneten (DE)	7H3	144
Großheide (DE)	7F2	144
Hage (DE)	7F2	144
Hambergen (DE)	7H2	144
Haren (NL)	7E3	646
Harlingen (NL)	7D3	642
Heerenveen (NL)	7E3	642
Hesel (DE)	7G2	146
Hogebeintum (NL)	7D2	642
Hoogersmilde (NL)	7E3	649
Hude (DE)	7H3	146
Ihlienworth (DE)	7H1	147
Ihlow (DE)	7G2	147
IJlst (NL)	7D3	643
Jade (DE)	7H2	147
Jelsum (NL)	7D3	643
Jever (DE)	7G2	147
Joure (NL)	7D3	643
Kollum (NL)	7E3	643
Koudum (NL)	7D3	643
Krummhörn (DE)	7F2	147
Langweer (NL)	7D3	643
Lauwersoog (NL)	7E2	646
Leens (NL)	7E2	646
Leer (DE)	7G3	148
Leeuwarden (NL)	7D3	643
Lemmer (NL)	7D3	643
Lemwerder (DE)	7H3	149
Lollum (NL)	7D3	644
Losdorp (NL)	7F2	647
Loxstedt (DE)	7H2	149
Lutjegast (NL)	7E3	647
Makkum (NL)	7D3	644
Marienhafe (DE)	7F2	149
Matsloot (NL)	7E3	649
Meldorf (DE)	7H1	127

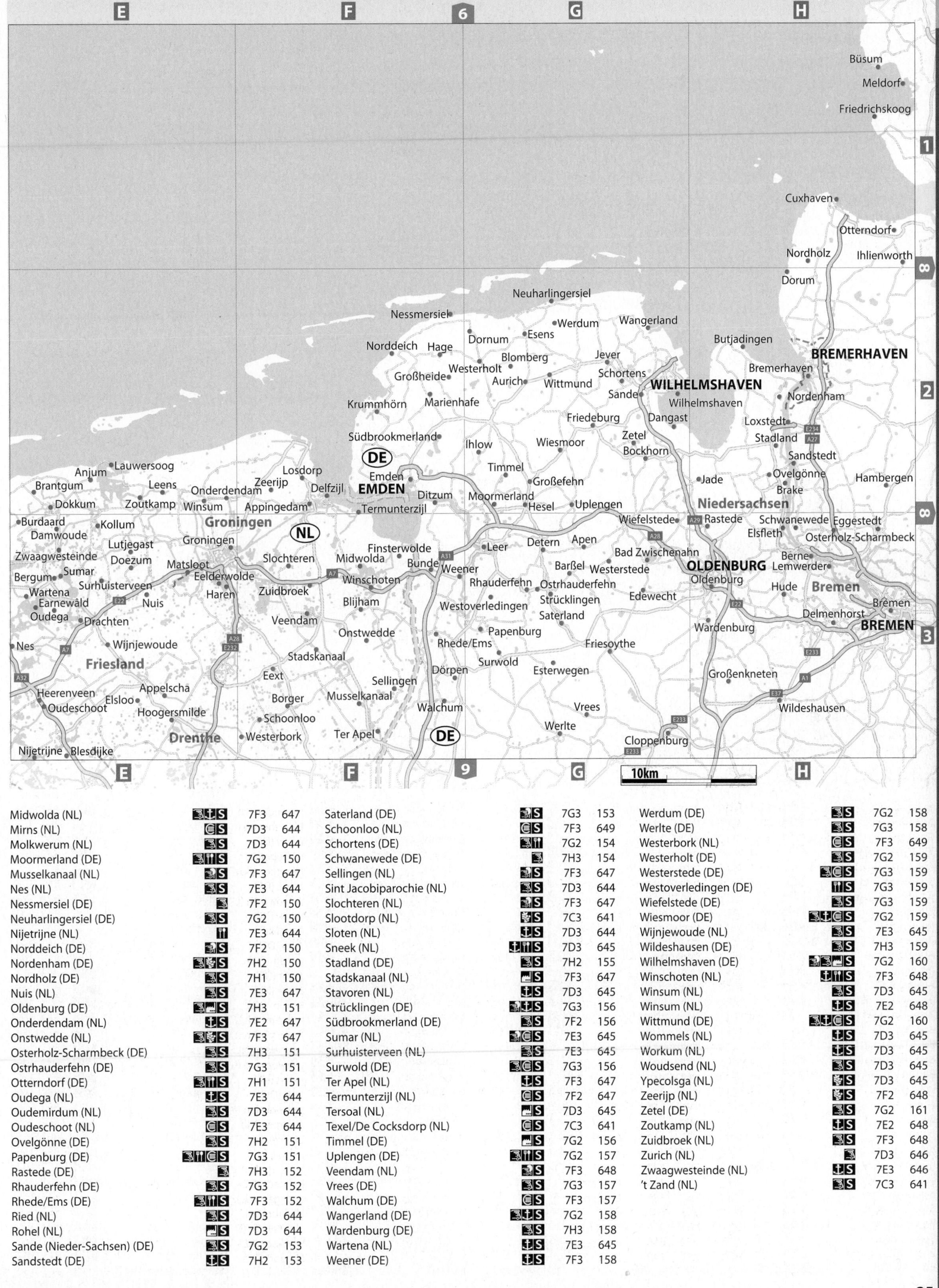

Place	Grid	Page
Midwolda (NL)	7F3	647
Mirns (NL)	7D3	644
Molkwerum (NL)	7D3	644
Moormerland (DE)	7G2	150
Musselkanaal (NL)	7F3	647
Nes (NL)	7E3	644
Nessmersiel (DE)	7F2	150
Neuharlingersiel (DE)	7G2	150
Nijetrijne (NL)	7E3	644
Norddeich (DE)	7F2	150
Nordenham (DE)	7H2	150
Nordholz (DE)	7H1	150
Nuis (NL)	7E3	647
Oldenburg (DE)	7H3	151
Onderdendam (NL)	7E2	647
Onstwedde (NL)	7F3	647
Osterholz-Scharmbeck (DE)	7H3	151
Ostrhauderfehn (DE)	7G3	151
Otterndorf (DE)	7H1	151
Oudega (NL)	7E3	644
Oudemirdum (NL)	7D3	644
Oudeschoot (NL)	7E3	644
Ovelgönne (DE)	7H2	151
Papenburg (DE)	7G3	151
Rastede (DE)	7H3	152
Rhauderfehn (DE)	7G3	152
Rhede/Ems (DE)	7F3	152
Ried (NL)	7D3	644
Rohel (NL)	7D3	644
Sande (Nieder-Sachsen) (DE)	7G2	153
Sandstedt (DE)	7H2	153
Saterland (DE)	7G3	153
Schoonloo (NL)	7F3	649
Schortens (DE)	7G2	154
Schwanewede (DE)	7H3	154
Sellingen (NL)	7F3	647
Sint Jacobiparochie (NL)	7D3	644
Slochteren (NL)	7F3	647
Slootdorp (NL)	7C3	641
Sloten (NL)	7D3	644
Sneek (NL)	7D3	645
Stadland (DE)	7H2	155
Stadskanaal (NL)	7F3	647
Stavoren (NL)	7D3	645
Strücklingen (DE)	7G3	156
Südbrookmerland (DE)	7F2	156
Sumar (NL)	7E3	645
Surhuisterveen (NL)	7E3	645
Surwold (DE)	7G3	156
Ter Apel (NL)	7F3	647
Termunterzijl (NL)	7F2	647
Tersoal (NL)	7D3	645
Texel/De Cocksdorp (NL)	7C3	641
Timmel (DE)	7G2	156
Uplengen (DE)	7G2	157
Veendam (NL)	7F3	648
Vrees (DE)	7G3	157
Walchum (DE)	7F3	157
Wangerland (DE)	7G2	158
Wardenburg (DE)	7H3	158
Wartena (NL)	7E3	645
Weener (DE)	7F3	158
Werdum (DE)	7G2	158
Werlte (DE)	7G3	158
Westerbork (NL)	7F3	649
Westerholt (DE)	7G2	159
Westerstede (DE)	7G3	159
Westoverledingen (DE)	7G3	159
Wiefelstede (DE)	7G3	159
Wiesmoor (DE)	7G2	159
Wijnjewoude (NL)	7E3	645
Wildeshausen (DE)	7H3	159
Wilhelmshaven (DE)	7G2	160
Winschoten (NL)	7F3	648
Winsum (NL)	7D3	645
Winsum (NL)	7E2	648
Wittmund (DE)	7G2	160
Wommels (NL)	7D3	645
Workum (NL)	7D3	645
Woudsend (NL)	7D3	645
Ypecolsga (NL)	7D3	645
Zeerijp (NL)	7F2	648
Zetel (DE)	7G2	161
Zoutkamp (NL)	7E2	648
Zuidbroek (NL)	7F3	648
Zurich (NL)	7D3	646
Zwaagwesteinde (NL)	7E3	646
't Zand (NL)	7C3	641

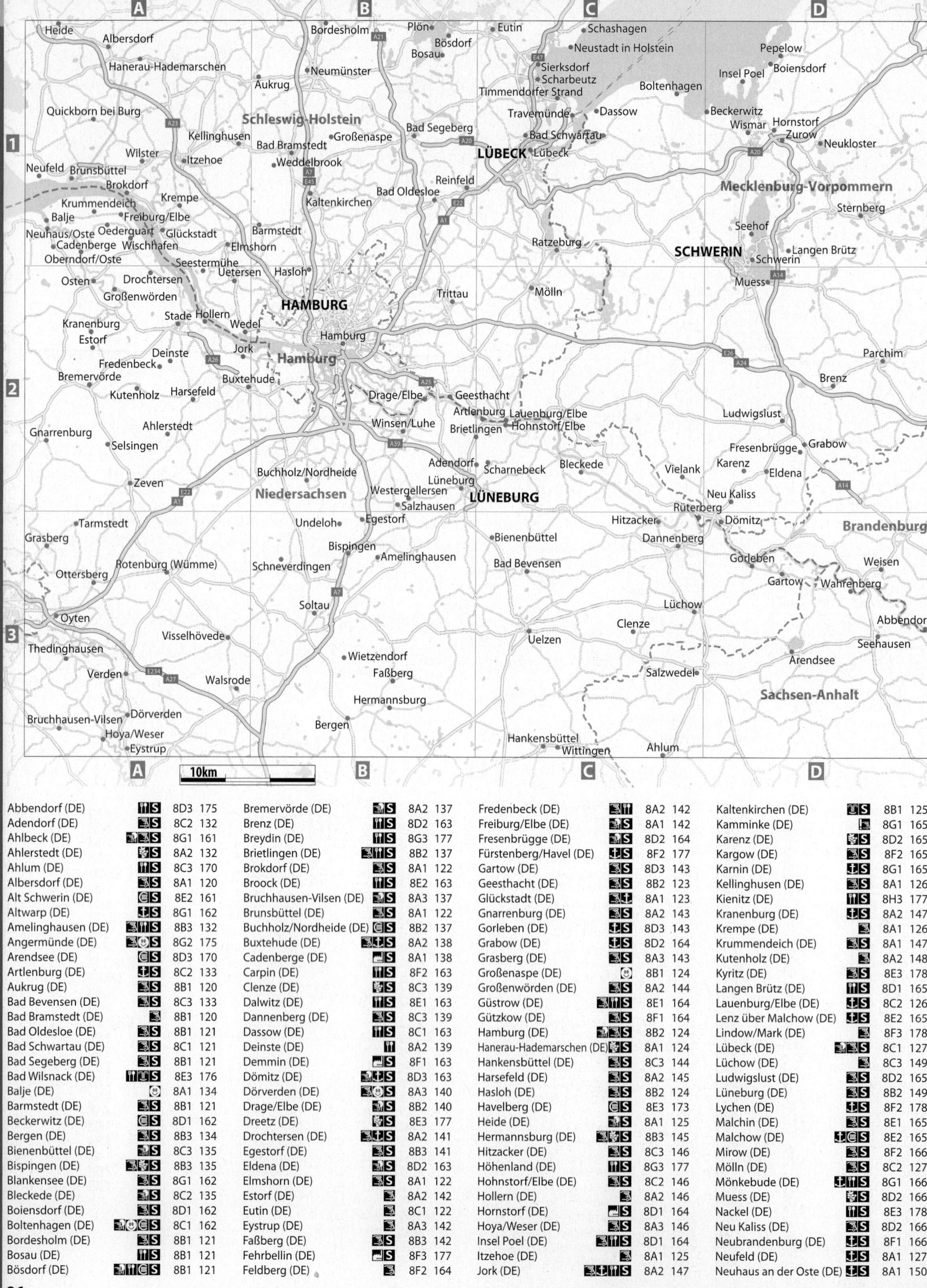

A
B
C
D
1
2
3
Heide
Albersdorf
Hanerau-Hademarschen
Bordesholm
Plön
Bösdorf
Bosau
Eutin
Schashagen
Neustadt in Holstein
Sierksdorf
Scharbeutz
Timmendorfer Strand
Pepelow
Boiensdorf
Insel Poel
Boltenhagen
Neumünster
Aukrug
Quickborn bei Burg
Schleswig-Holstein
Kellinghusen
Großenaspe
Bad Bramstedt
Bad Segeberg
Travemünde
Dassow
Beckerwitz
Wismar
Hornstorf
Zurow
Neukloster
Bad Schwartau
LÜBECK
Lübeck
Wilster
Itzehoe
Weddelbrook
Neufeld
Brunsbüttel
Brokdorf
Reinfeld
Bad Oldesloe
Krempe
Kaltenkirchen
Mecklenburg-Vorpommern
Krummendeich
Balje
Freiburg/Elbe
Neuhaus/Oste
Oederquart
Glückstadt
Cadenberge
Wischhafen
Barmstedt
Elmshorn
Oberndorf/Oste
Seestermühe
Uetersen
Hasloh
Ratzeburg
Seehof
Sternberg
SCHWERIN
Schwerin
Langen Brütz
Muess
Osten
Drochtersen
Großenwörden
Trittau
Mölln
HAMBURG
Stade
Hollern
Wedel
Kranenburg
Estorf
Hamburg
Deinste
Jork
Fredenbeck
Bremervörde
Buxtehude
Parchim
Brenz
Kutenholz
Harsefeld
Drage/Elbe
Geesthacht
Artlenburg
Lauenburg/Elbe
Hohnstorf/Elbe
Brietlingen
Winsen/Luhe
Ludwigslust
Gnarrenburg
Ahlerstedt
Selsingen
Fresenbrügge
Grabow
Karenz
Eldena
Adendorf
Scharnebeck
Bleckede
Vielank
Buchholz/Nordheide
Lüneburg
Westergellersen
Salzhausen
LÜNEBURG
Niedersachsen
Neu Kaliss
Rüterberg
Dömitz
Zeven
Tarmstedt
Undeloh
Egestorf
Hitzacker
Dannenberg
Brandenburg
Grasberg
Bienenbüttel
Bispingen
Amelinghausen
Bad Bevensen
Gorleben
Weisen
Ottersberg
Rotenburg (Wümme)
Schneverdingen
Gartow
Wahrenberg
Soltau
Lüchow
Abbendorf
Oyten
Clenze
Visselhövede
Uelzen
Seehausen
Thedinghausen
Arendsee
Wietzendorf
Verden
Faßberg
Salzwedel
Walsrode
Sachsen-Anhalt
Hermannsburg
Dörverden
Bruchhausen-Vilsen
Bergen
Hoya/Weser
Hankensbüttel
Eystrup
Wittingen
Ahlum
A21
A23
A7
E45
A20
E47
A1
E22
A26
A25
E26
A24
A39
A14
E234
A27
10km

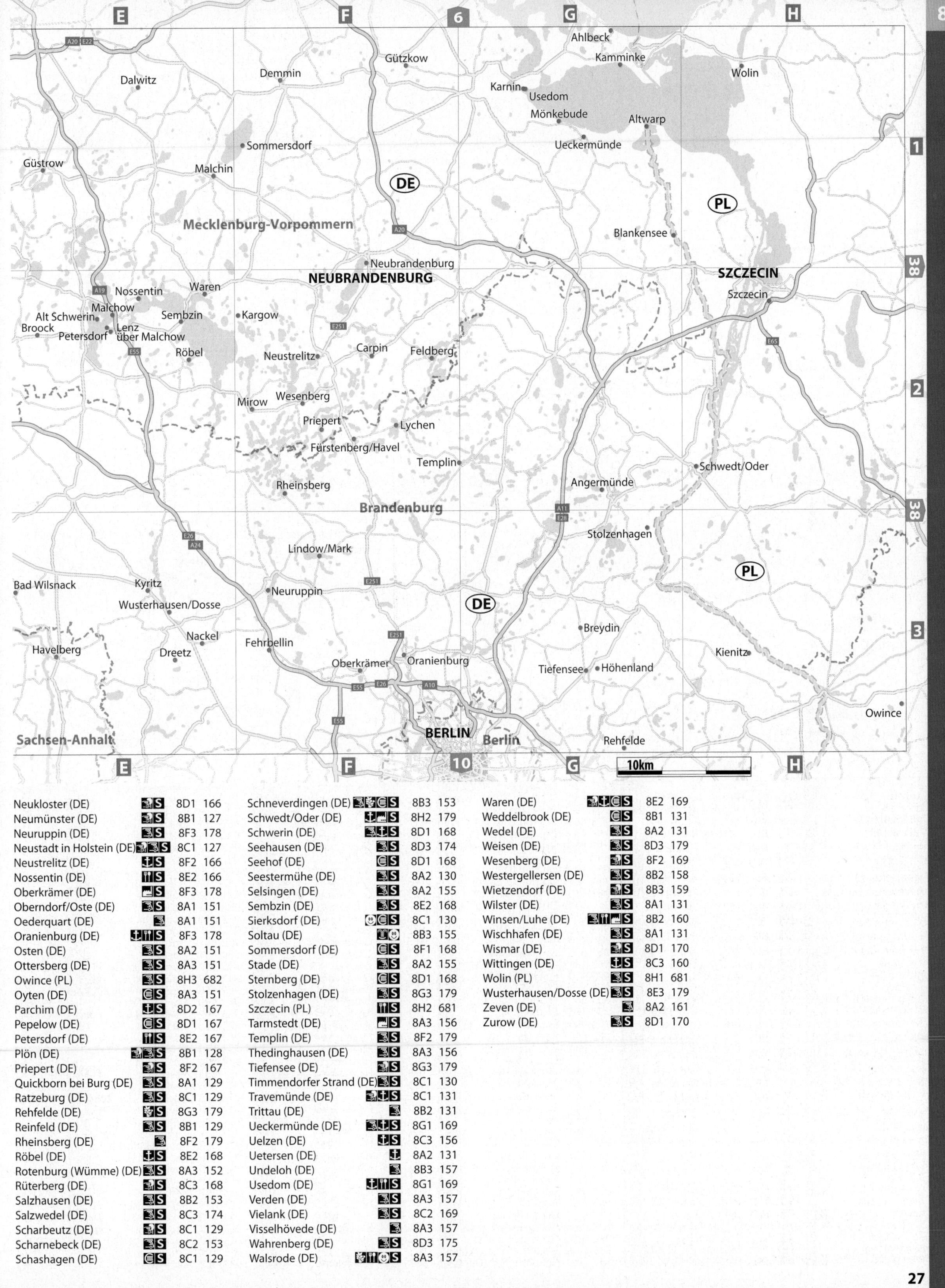

E
F
6
G
H
Ahlbeck
Kamminke
Gützkow
Wolin
Dalwitz
Demmin
Karnin
Usedom
Mönkebude
Altwarp
Ueckermünde
Sommersdorf
1
Güstrow
Malchin
DE
PL
Mecklenburg-Vorpommern
Blankensee
Neubrandenburg
NEUBRANDENBURG
38
SZCZECIN
Szczecin
Nossentin
Waren
Malchow
Alt Schwerin
Sembzin
Kargow
Broock
Petersdorf
Lenz über Malchow
Röbel
Neustrelitz
Carpin
Feldberg
2
Mirow
Wesenberg
Priepert
Lychen
Fürstenberg/Havel
Templin
Schwedt/Oder
Rheinsberg
Angermünde
Brandenburg
38
Stolzenhagen
Lindow/Mark
PL
Bad Wilsnack
Kyritz
Neuruppin
Wusterhausen/Dosse
DE
Breydin
3
Nackel
Havelberg
Dreetz
Fehrbellin
Kienitz
Oberkrämer
Oranienburg
Tiefensee
Höhenland
Owince
BERLIN
Berlin
Sachsen-Anhalt
Rehfelde
E
F
10
G
10km
H

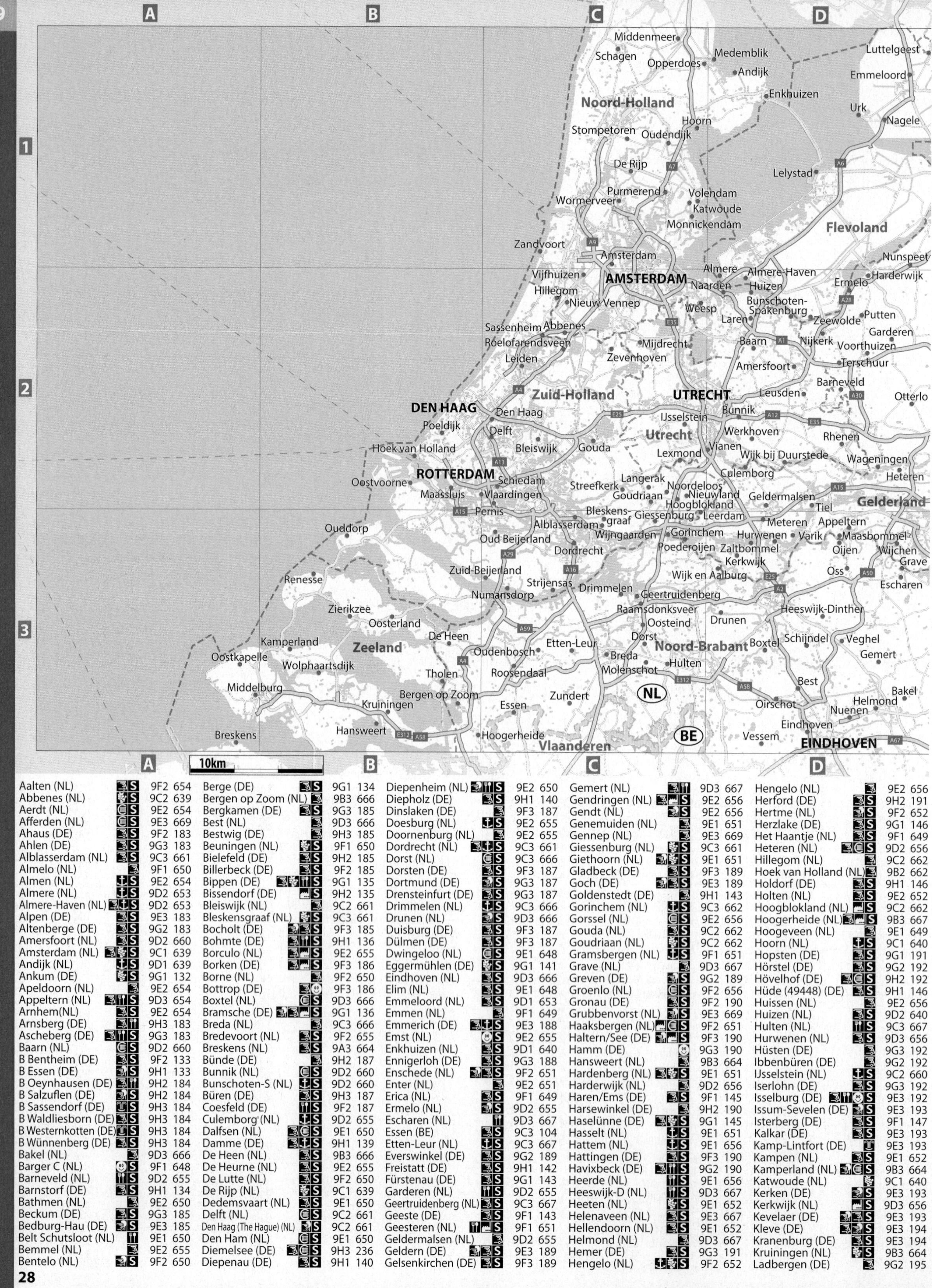
A
B
C
D
1
2
3
Middenmeer
Schagen
Opperdoes
Medemblik
Andijk
Enkhuizen
Luttelgeest
Emmeloord
Urk
Nagele
Noord-Holland
Hoorn
Stompetoren
Oudendijk
De Rijp
Lelystad
Purmerend
Wormerveer
Volendam
Katwoude
Monnickendam
Flevoland
Zandvoort
Amsterdam
AMSTERDAM
Vijfhuizen
Hillegom
Nieuw Vennep
Almere
Almere-Haven
Naarden
Huizen
Weesp
Bunschoten-Spakenburg
Laren
Zeewolde
Putten
Ermelo
Harderwijk
Nunspeet
Garderen
Voorthuizen
Terschuur
Sassenheim
Abbenes
Roelofarendsveen
Leiden
Mijdrecht
Zevenhoven
Baarn
Nijkerk
Amersfoort
Barneveld
Leusden
Otterlo
DEN HAAG
Den Haag
Zuid-Holland
UTRECHT
IJsselstein
Bunnik
Poeldijk
Delft
Bleiswijk
Gouda
Utrecht
Werkhoven
Rhenen
Hoek van Holland
Lexmond
Vianen
Wijk bij Duurstede
Wageningen
ROTTERDAM
Oostvoorne
Schiedam
Streefkerk
Langerak
Noordeloos
Nieuwland
Hoogblokland
Culemborg
Heteren
Maassluis
Vlaardingen
Goudriaan
Geldermalsen
Tiel
Gelderland
Pernis
Bleskens-graaf
Giessenburg
Leerdam
Meteren
Appeltern
Alblasserdam
Wijngaarden
Gorinchem
Hurwenen
Varik
Maasbommel
Ouddorp
Oud Beijerland
Dordrecht
Poederoijen
Zaltbommel
Oijen
Wijchen
Kerkwijk
Grave
Zuid-Beijerland
Renesse
Strijensas
Drimmelen
Wijk en Aalburg
Oss
Escharen
Numansdorp
Geertruidenberg
Zierikzee
Raamsdonksveer
Heeswijk-Dinther
Oosterland
Oosteind
Drunen
De Heen
Dorst
Schijndel
Veghel
Kamperland
Zeeland
Oudenbosch
Etten-Leur
Noord-Brabant
Boxtel
Gemert
Oostkapelle
Breda
Hulten
Wolphaartsdijk
Molenschot
Tholen
Roosendaal
Best
Bakel
Middelburg
NL
Helmond
Bergen op Zoom
Zundert
Oirschot
Kruiningen
Essen
Nuenen
Eindhoven
Breskens
Hansweert
Hoogerheide
BE
Vessem
Vlaanderen
EINDHOVEN
10km

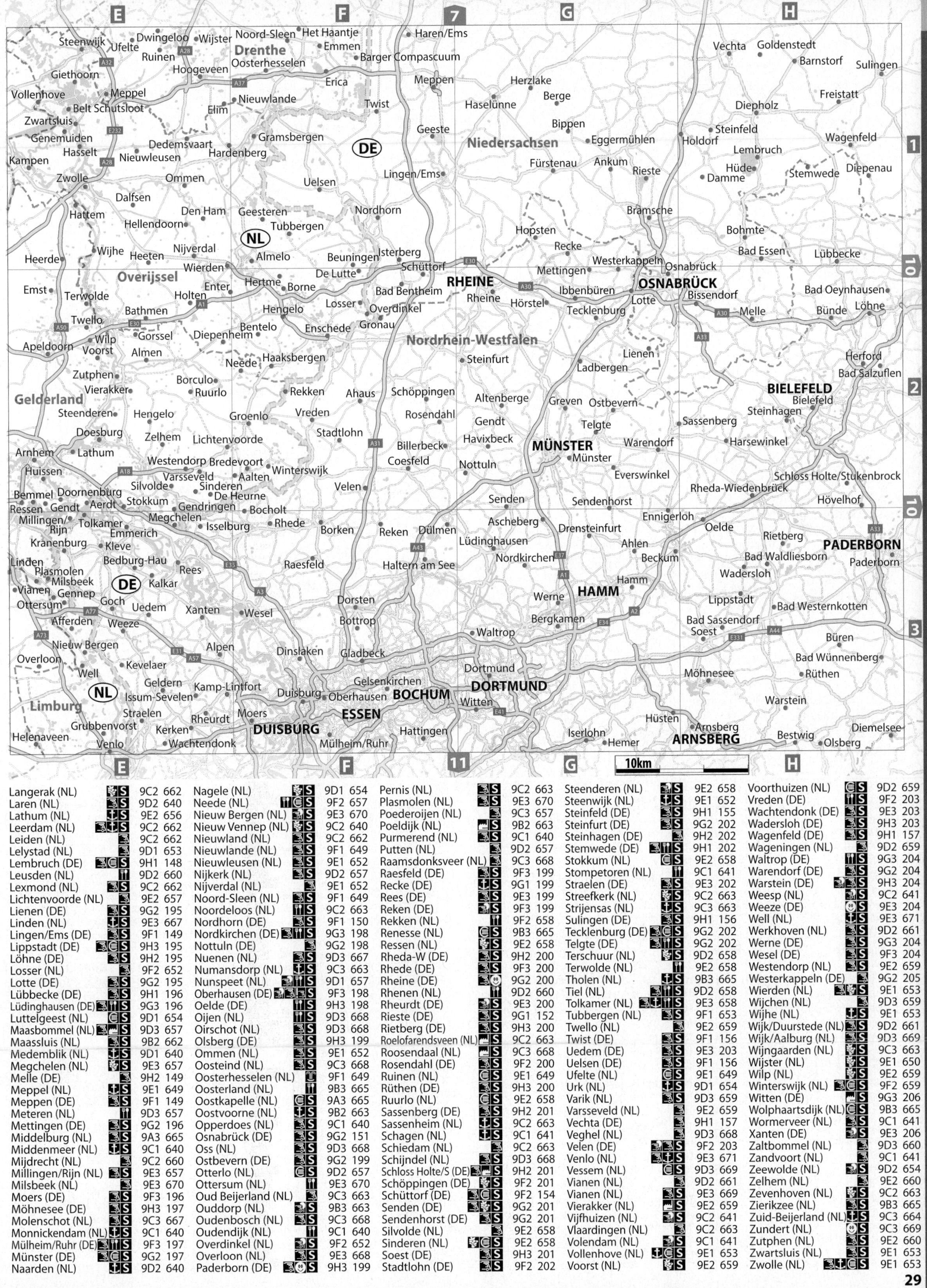
E
F
7
G
H
Drenthe
Overijssel
Gelderland
Limburg
Niedersachsen
Nordrhein-Westfalen
NL
DE
Steenwijk
Dwingeloo
Wijster
Noord-Sleen
Het Haantje
Haren/Ems
Emmen
Barger Compascuum
Ufelte
Ruinen
Hoogeveen
Oosterhesselen
Erica
Meppen
Herzlake
Berge
Haselünne
Giethoorn
Vollenhove
Meppel
Belt Schutsloot
Elim
Nieuwlande
Twist
Zwartsluis
Genemuiden
Hasselt
Kampen
Dedemsvaart
Nieuwleusen
Hardenberg
Gramsbergen
Geeste
Bippen
Eggermühlen
Fürstenau
Ankum
Rieste
Zwolle
Ommen
Uelsen
Lingen/Ems
Dalfsen
Hattem
Den Ham
Hellendoorn
Geesteren
Tubbergen
Nordhorn
Bramsche
Hopsten
Recke
Heerde
Wijhe
Heeten
Nijverdal
Wierden
Almelo
Beuningen
Isterberg
Schüttorf
RHEINE
Rheine
Mettingen
Westerkappeln
Osnabrück
OSNABRÜCK
Emst
Terwolde
Holten
Enter
Hertme
Borne
De Lutte
Bad Bentheim
Hörstel
Ibbenbüren
Lotte
Bissendorf
Melle
Twello
Bathmen
Hengelo
Losser
Overdinkel
Tecklenburg
Apeldoorn
Wilp
Voorst
Gorssel
Diepenheim
Bentelo
Enschede
Gronau
Almen
Neede
Haaksbergen
Steinfurt
Ladbergen
Lienen
Zutphen
Vierakker
Borculo
Ruurlo
Rekken
Ahaus
Schöppingen
Altenberge
Greven
Ostbevern
Steenderen
Groenlo
Vreden
Rosendahl
Gendt
Telgte
Sassenberg
Doesburg
Zelhem
Lichtenvoorde
Stadtlohn
Billerbeck
Havixbeck
MÜNSTER
Münster
Warendorf
Arnhem
Lathum
Westendorp
Bredevoort
Winterswijk
Coesfeld
Nottuln
Everswinkel
Huissen
Varsseveld
Aalten
Silvolde
Sinderen
De Heurne
Velen
Senden
Sendenhorst
Bemmel
Doornenburg
Ressen
Aerdt
Stokkum
Gendringen
Bocholt
Millingen/Rijn
Tolkamer
Megchelen
Emmerich
Isselburg
Rhede
Borken
Reken
Dülmen
Ascheberg
Drensteinfurt
Lüdinghausen
Kranenburg
Kleve
Nordkirchen
Ahlen
Beckum
Linden
Plasmolen
Milsbeek
Bedburg-Hau
Rees
Raesfeld
Haltern am See
Vianen
Gennep
Kalkar
Ottersum
Goch
Uedem
Xanten
Wesel
Dorsten
Werne
HAMM
Hamm
Afferden
Weeze
Bottrop
Bergkamen
Waltrop
Nieuw Bergen
Alpen
Dinslaken
Gladbeck
Overloon
Well
Kevelaer
Dortmund
Geldern
Kamp-Lintfort
Gelsenkirchen
DORTMUND
Issum-Sevelen
Duisburg
Oberhausen
BOCHUM
Witten
Straelen
Rheurdt
Moers
ESSEN
Grubbenvorst
Kerken
DUISBURG
Hattingen
Helenaveen
Venlo
Wachtendonk
Mülheim/Ruhr
Iserlohn
Hemer
Vechta
Goldenstedt
Barnstorf
Sulingen
Freistatt
Diepholz
Steinfeld
Holdorf
Wagenfeld
Lembruch
Hüde
Damme
Stemwede
Diepenau
Bohmte
Bad Essen
Lübbecke
Bad Oeynhausen
Bünde
Löhne
Herford
Bad Salzuflen
BIELEFELD
Bielefeld
Steinhagen
Harsewinkel
Schloss Holte/Stukenbrock
Rheda-Wiedenbrück
Hövelhof
Ennigerloh
Oelde
Rietberg
PADERBORN
Paderborn
Bad Waldliesborn
Wadersloh
Lippstadt
Bad Westernkotten
Bad Sassendorf
Soest
Büren
Bad Wünnenberg
Möhnesee
Rüthen
Warstein
Hüsten
Arnsberg
ARNSBERG
Bestwig
Diemelsee
Olsberg
10
11
1
2
3
10km

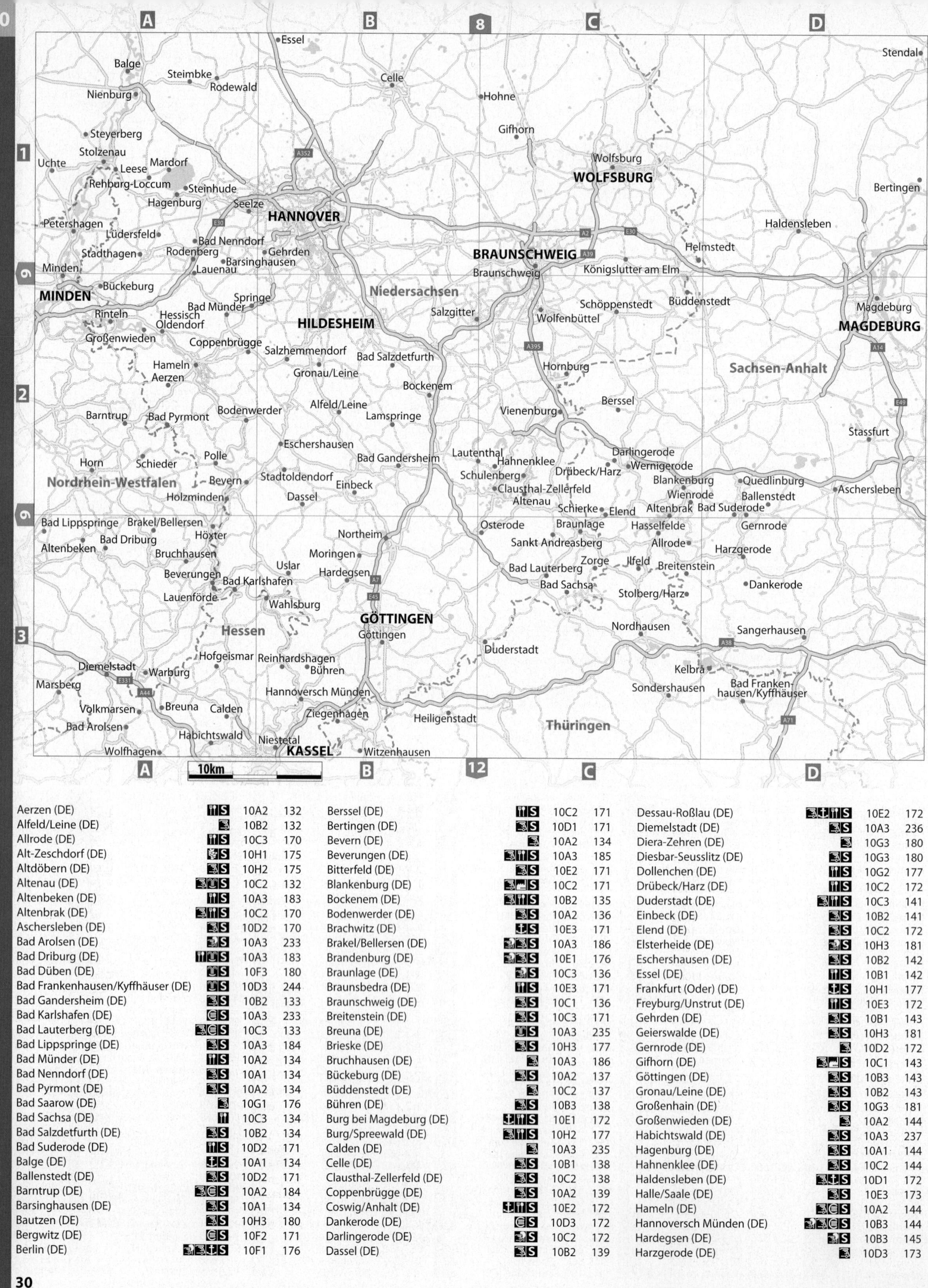
A
B
8
C
D
Essel
Stendal
Balge
Steimbke
Rodewald
Celle
Nienburg
Hohne
Gifhorn
Steyerberg
1
Stolzenau
Uchte
Leese
Mardorf
Wolfsburg
WOLFSBURG
Rehburg-Loccum
Steinhude
Bertingen
Hagenburg
Seelze
HANNOVER
Petershagen
Haldensleben
Lüdersfeld
Bad Nenndorf
Helmstedt
Stadthagen
Rodenberg
Gehrden
BRAUNSCHWEIG
Barsinghausen
9
Minden
Lauenau
Königslutter am Elm
Braunschweig
Bückeburg
Niedersachsen
MINDEN
Springe
Schöppenstedt
Büddenstedt
Rinteln
Bad Münder
Salzgitter
Magdeburg
Hessisch Oldendorf
HILDESHEIM
Wolfenbüttel
MAGDEBURG
Großenwieden
Coppenbrügge
Salzhemmendorf
Bad Salzdetfurth
Hameln
Hornburg
Sachsen-Anhalt
Aerzen
Gronau/Leine
2
Bockenem
Berssel
Barntrup
Bad Pyrmont
Bodenwerder
Alfeld/Leine
Vienenburg
Lamspringe
Stassfurt
Eschershausen
Lautenthal
Darlingerode
Polle
Bad Gandersheim
Hahnenklee
Wernigerode
Horn
Schieder
Schulenberg
Drübeck/Harz
Blankenburg
Quedlinburg
Nordrhein-Westfalen
Bevern
Stadtoldendorf
Einbeck
Clausthal-Zellerfeld
Wienrode
Aschersleben
Holzminden
Dassel
Altenau
Ballenstedt
Schierke
Elend
Altenbrak
Bad Suderode
9
Bad Lippspringe
Brakel/Bellersen
Osterode
Braunlage
Hasselfelde
Gernrode
Höxter
Northeim
Altenbeken
Bad Driburg
Sankt Andreasberg
Allrode
Bruchhausen
Moringen
Harzgerode
Uslar
Zorge
Ilfeld
Breitenstein
Beverungen
Hardegsen
Bad Lauterberg
Bad Karlshafen
Bad Sachsa
Dankerode
Lauenförde
Stolberg/Harz
Wahlsburg
GÖTTINGEN
Hessen
Nordhausen
Sangerhausen
3
Göttingen
Duderstadt
Hofgeismar
Reinhardshagen
Diemelstadt
Warburg
Bühren
Kelbra
Marsberg
Hannoversch Münden
Sondershausen
Bad Frankenhausen/Kyffhäuser
Volkmarsen
Breuna
Calden
Ziegenhagen
Heiligenstadt
Thüringen
Bad Arolsen
Habichtswald
Niestetal
Wolfhagen
KASSEL
Witzenhausen
A
10km
B
12
C
D

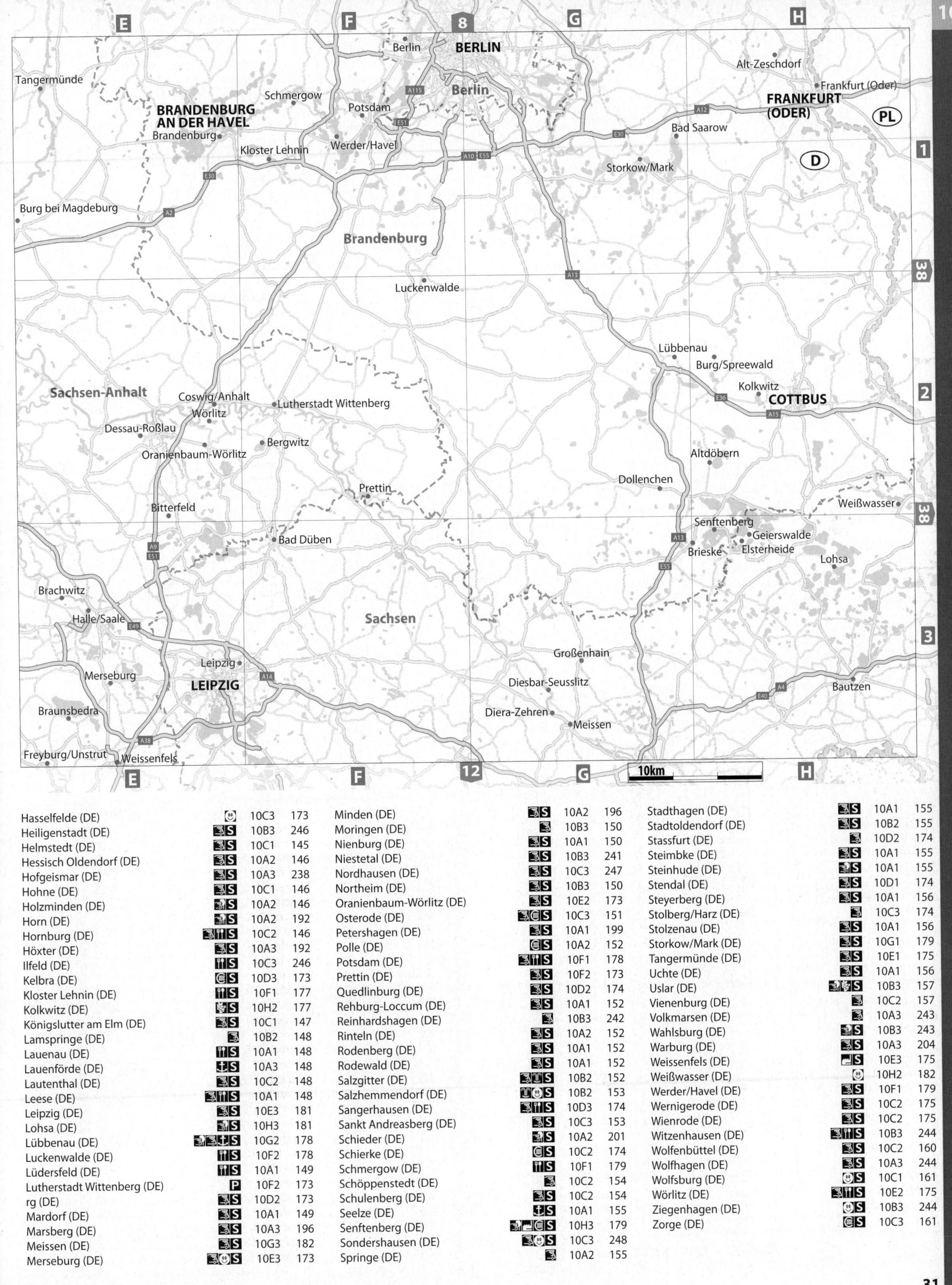

E
F
8
G
H
Berlin
BERLIN
Berlin
Alt-Zeschdorf
Tangermünde
Schmergow
Potsdam
Frankfurt (Oder)
FRANKFURT (ODER)
PL
BRANDENBURG AN DER HAVEL
Brandenburg
Bad Saarow
Kloster Lehnin
Werder/Havel
D
Storkow/Mark
1
Burg bei Magdeburg
Brandenburg
A115
A12
E51
E30
A10
E55
A2
A13
38
Luckenwalde
Lübbenau
Burg/Spreewald
Kolkwitz
COTTBUS
E36
A15
2
Sachsen-Anhalt
Coswig/Anhalt
Wörlitz
Lutherstadt Wittenberg
Dessau-Roßlau
Bergwitz
Oranienbaum-Wörlitz
Altdöbern
Dollenchen
Prettin
Weißwasser
Bitterfeld
Senftenberg
Geierswalde
Elsterheide
Brieske
Bad Düben
A9
E51
Lohsa
Brachwitz
Halle/Saale
E49
Sachsen
3
Großenhain
Leipzig
LEIPZIG
A14
Merseburg
Diesbar-Seusslitz
Bautzen
A4
E40
Braunsbedra
Diera-Zehren
Meissen
A38
Freyburg/Unstrut
Weissenfels
12
10km

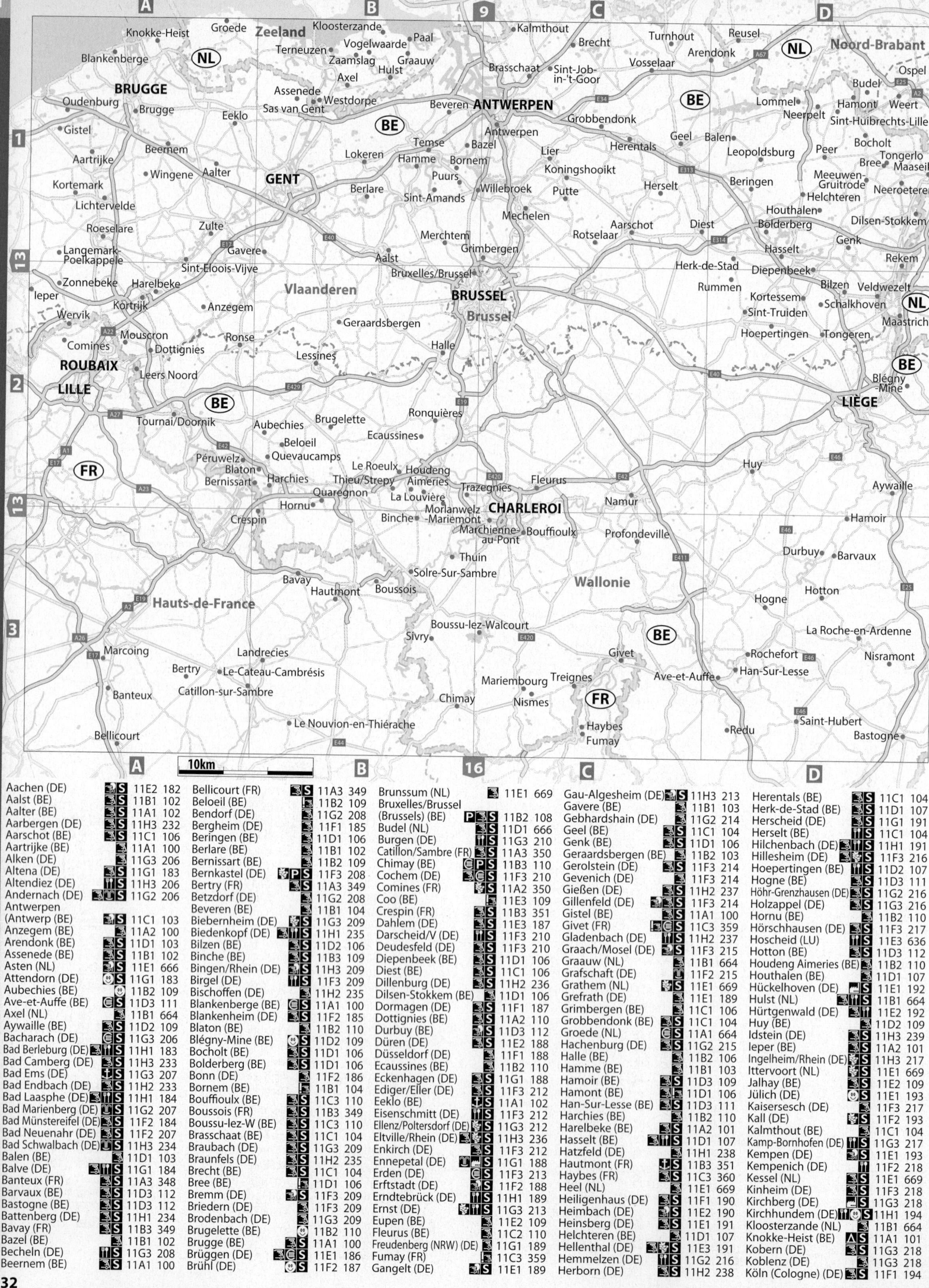

Place	Grid	Page
Aachen (DE)	11E2	182
Aalst (BE)	11B1	102
Aalter (BE)	11A1	102
Aarbergen (DE)	11H3	232
Aarschot (BE)	11C1	106
Aartrijke (BE)	11A1	100
Alken (DE)	11G3	206
Altena (DE)	11G1	183
Altendiez (DE)	11H3	206
Andernach (DE)	11G2	206
Antwerpen (Antwerp (BE)	11C1	103
Anzegem (BE)	11A2	100
Arendonk (BE)	11D1	103
Assenede (BE)	11B1	102
Asten (NL)	11E1	666
Attendorn (DE)	11G1	183
Aubechies (BE)	11B2	109
Ave-et-Auffe (BE)	11D3	111
Axel (NL)	11B1	664
Aywaille (BE)	11D2	109
Bacharach (DE)	11G3	206
Bad Berleburg (DE)	11H1	183
Bad Camberg (DE)	11H3	233
Bad Ems (DE)	11G3	207
Bad Endbach (DE)	11H2	233
Bad Laasphe (DE)	11H1	184
Bad Marienberg (DE)	11G2	207
Bad Münstereifel (DE)	11F2	184
Bad Neuenahr (DE)	11F2	207
Bad Schwalbach (DE)	11H3	234
Balen (BE)	11D1	103
Balve (DE)	11G1	184
Banteux (FR)	11A3	348
Barvaux (BE)	11D3	112
Bastogne (BE)	11D3	112
Battenberg (DE)	11H1	234
Bavay (FR)	11B3	349
Bazel (BE)	11B1	102
Becheln (DE)	11G3	208
Beernem (BE)	11A1	100
Bellicourt (FR)	11A3	349
Beloeil (BE)	11B2	109
Bendorf (DE)	11G2	208
Bergheim (DE)	11F1	185
Beringen (BE)	11D1	106
Berlare (BE)	11B1	102
Bernissart (BE)	11B2	109
Bernkastel (DE)	11F3	208
Bertry (FR)	11A3	349
Betzdorf (DE)	11G2	208
Beveren (BE)	11B1	104
Biebernheim (DE)	11G3	209
Biedenkopf (DE)	11H1	235
Bilzen (BE)	11D2	106
Binche (BE)	11B3	109
Bingen/Rhein (DE)	11H3	209
Birgel (DE)	11F3	209
Bischoffen (DE)	11H2	235
Blankenberge (BE)	11A1	100
Blankenheim (DE)	11F2	185
Blaton (BE)	11B2	110
Blégny-Mine (BE)	11D2	109
Bocholt (BE)	11D1	106
Bolderberg (BE)	11D1	106
Bonn (DE)	11F2	186
Bornem (BE)	11B1	104
Bouffioulx (BE)	11C3	110
Boussois (FR)	11B3	349
Boussu-lez-W (BE)	11C3	110
Brasschaat (BE)	11C1	104
Braubach (DE)	11G3	209
Braunfels (DE)	11H2	235
Brecht (BE)	11C1	104
Bree (BE)	11D1	106
Bremm (DE)	11F3	209
Briedern (DE)	11F3	209
Brodenbach (DE)	11G3	209
Brugelette (BE)	11B2	110
Brugge (BE)	11A1	100
Brüggen (DE)	11E1	186
Brühl (DE)	11F2	187
Brunssum (NL)	11E1	669
Bruxelles/Brussel (Brussels) (BE)	11B2	108
Budel (NL)	11D1	666
Burgen (DE)	11G3	210
Catillon/Sambre (FR)	11A3	350
Chimay (BE)	11B3	110
Cochem (DE)	11F3	210
Comines (FR)	11A2	350
Coo (BE)	11E3	109
Crespin (FR)	11B3	351
Dahlem (DE)	11E3	187
Darscheid/V (DE)	11F3	210
Deudesfeld (DE)	11F3	210
Diepenbeek (BE)	11D1	106
Diest (BE)	11C1	106
Dillenburg (DE)	11H2	236
Dilsen-Stokkem (BE)	11D1	106
Dormagen (DE)	11F1	187
Dottignies (BE)	11A2	110
Durbuy (BE)	11D3	112
Düren (DE)	11E2	188
Düsseldorf (DE)	11F1	188
Ecaussines (BE)	11B2	110
Eckenhagen (DE)	11G1	188
Ediger/Eller (DE)	11F3	212
Eeklo (BE)	11A1	102
Eisenschmitt (DE)	11F3	212
Ellenz/Poltersdorf (DE)	11G3	212
Eltville/Rhein (DE)	11H3	236
Enkirch (DE)	11F3	212
Ennepetal (DE)	11G1	188
Erden (DE)	11F3	213
Erftstadt (DE)	11F2	188
Erndtebrück (DE)	11H1	189
Ernst (DE)	11G3	213
Eupen (BE)	11E2	109
Fleurus (BE)	11C2	110
Freudenberg (NRW) (DE)	11G1	189
Fumay (FR)	11C3	359
Gangelt (DE)	11E1	189
Gau-Algesheim (DE)	11H3	213
Gavere (BE)	11B1	103
Gebhardshain (DE)	11G2	214
Geel (BE)	11C1	104
Genk (BE)	11D1	106
Geraardsbergen (BE)	11B2	103
Gerolstein (DE)	11F3	214
Gevenich (DE)	11F3	214
Gießen (DE)	11H2	237
Gillenfeld (DE)	11F3	214
Gistel (BE)	11A1	100
Givet (FR)	11C3	359
Gladenbach (DE)	11H2	237
Graach/Mosel (DE)	11F3	215
Graauw (NL)	11B1	664
Grafschaft (DE)	11F2	215
Grathem (NL)	11E1	669
Grefrath (DE)	11E1	189
Grimbergen (BE)	11C1	106
Grobbendonk (BE)	11C1	104
Groede (NL)	11A1	664
Hachenburg (DE)	11G2	215
Halle (BE)	11B2	106
Hamme (BE)	11B1	103
Hamoir (BE)	11D3	109
Hamont (BE)	11D1	106
Han-Sur-Lesse (BE)	11D3	111
Harchies (BE)	11B2	110
Harelbeke (BE)	11A2	101
Hasselt (BE)	11D1	107
Hatzfeld (DE)	11H1	238
Hautmont (FR)	11B3	351
Haybes (FR)	11C3	360
Heel (NL)	11E1	669
Heiligenhaus (DE)	11F1	190
Heimbach (DE)	11E2	190
Heinsberg (DE)	11E1	191
Helchteren (BE)	11D1	107
Hellenthal (DE)	11E3	191
Hemmelzen (DE)	11G2	216
Herborn (DE)	11H2	238
Herentals (BE)	11C1	104
Herk-de-Stad (BE)	11D1	107
Herscheid (DE)	11G1	191
Herselt (BE)	11C1	104
Hilchenbach (DE)	11H1	191
Hillesheim (DE)	11F3	216
Hoepertingen (BE)	11D2	107
Hogne (BE)	11D3	111
Höhr-Grenzhausen (DE)	11G2	216
Holzappel (DE)	11G3	216
Hornu (BE)	11B2	110
Hörschhausen (DE)	11F3	217
Hoscheid (LU)	11E3	636
Hotton (BE)	11D3	112
Houdeng Aimeries (BE)	11B2	110
Houthalen (BE)	11D1	107
Hückelhoven (DE)	11E1	192
Hulst (NL)	11B1	664
Hürtgenwald (DE)	11E2	192
Huy (BE)	11D2	109
Idstein (DE)	11H3	239
Ieper (BE)	11A2	101
Ingelheim/Rhein (DE)	11H3	217
Ittervoort (NL)	11E1	669
Jalhay (BE)	11E2	109
Jülich (DE)	11E1	193
Kaisersesch (DE)	11F3	217
Kall (DE)	11F2	193
Kalmthout (BE)	11C1	104
Kamp-Bornhofen (DE)	11G3	217
Kempen (DE)	11E1	193
Kempenich (DE)	11F2	218
Kessel (NL)	11E1	669
Kinheim (DE)	11F3	218
Kirchberg (DE)	11G3	218
Kirchhundem (DE)	11H1	194
Kloosterzande (NL)	11B1	664
Knokke-Heist (BE)	11A1	101
Kobern (DE)	11G3	218
Koblenz (DE)	11G3	218
Köln (Cologne) (DE)	11F1	194

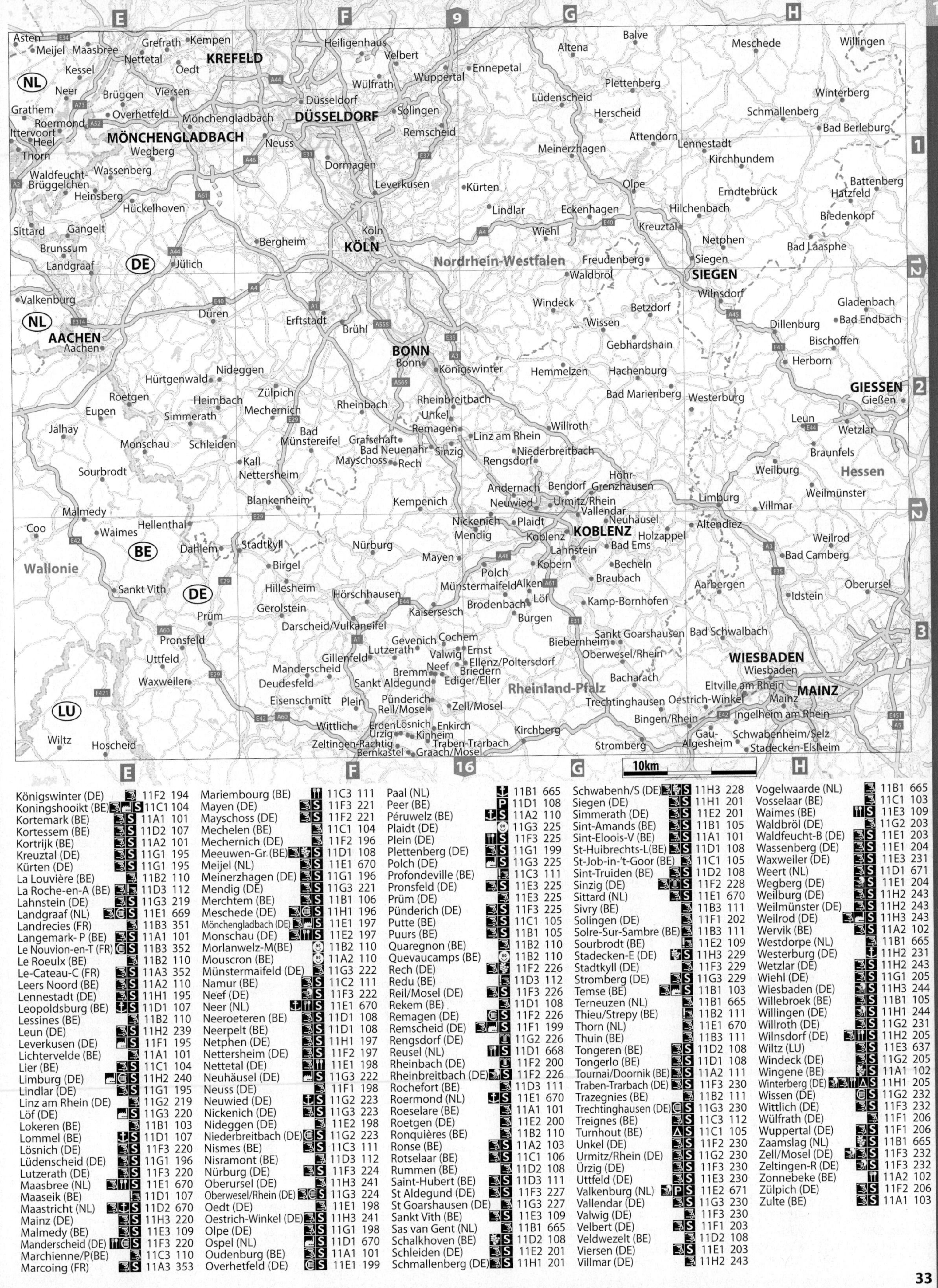
E
F
9
G
H
Asten
Meijel
Maasbree
Grefrath
Kempen
Nettetal
KREFELD
Oedt
Kessel
NL
Neer
Brüggen
Viersen
Grathem
Roermond
Overhetfeld
Mönchengladbach
Ittervoort
Heel
Thorn
MÖNCHENGLADBACH
Wegberg
Waldfeucht-
Brüggelchen
Wassenberg
Heinsberg
Hückelhoven
Sittard
Gangelt
Brunssum
Landgraaf
DE
Jülich
Heiligenhaus
Velbert
Wülfrath
Wuppertal
Ennepetal
Düsseldorf
DÜSSELDORF
Solingen
Remscheid
Neuss
Dormagen
Leverkusen
Kürten
Bergheim
Köln
KÖLN
Altena
Balve
Plettenberg
Lüdenscheid
Herscheid
Meinerzhagen
Attendorn
Lennestadt
Kirchhundem
Olpe
Lindlar
Eckenhagen
Wiehl
Kreuztal
Nordrhein-Westfalen
Freudenberg
Waldbröl
Meschede
Willingen
Winterberg
Schmallenberg
Bad Berleburg
Erndtebrück
Battenberg
Hatzfeld
Hilchenbach
Biedenkopf
Netphen
Siegen
SIEGEN
Bad Laasphe
1
12
Valkenburg
NL
AACHEN
Aachen
Düren
Erftstadt
Brühl
BONN
Bonn
Königswinter
Windeck
Betzdorf
Wissen
Gebhardshain
Hemmelzen
Hachenburg
Bad Marienberg
Westerburg
Wilnsdorf
Gladenbach
Bad Endbach
Dillenburg
Bischoffen
Herborn
GIESSEN
Gießen
2
Nideggen
Hürtgenwald
Roetgen
Eupen
Heimbach
Zülpich
Simmerath
Mechernich
Rheinbach
Rheinbreitbach
Unkel
Remagen
Linz am Rhein
Willroth
Jalhay
Monschau
Schleiden
Bad Münstereifel
Grafschaft
Bad Neuenahr
Sinzig
Niederbreitbach
Rengsdorf
Leun
Wetzlar
Braunfels
Sourbrodt
Kall
Nettersheim
Mayschoss
Rech
Höhr-Grenzhausen
Andernach
Bendorf
Neuwied
Urmitz/Rhein
Vallendar
Limburg
Weilburg
Hessen
Weilmünster
Villmar
Blankenheim
Kempenich
Malmedy
Coo
Waimes
Hellenthal
BE
Dahlem
Stadtkyll
Nürburg
Nickenich
Mendig
Plaidt
Koblenz
KOBLENZ
Neuhäusel
Holzappel
Altendiez
Weilrod
Lahnstein
Bad Ems
Bad Camberg
Wallonie
Mayen
Birgel
Polch
Kobern
Becheln
Braubach
Aarbergen
Oberursel
Idstein
Sankt Vith
DE
Hillesheim
Münstermaifeld
Alken
Löf
Kamp-Bornhofen
Prüm
Gerolstein
Hörschhausen
Kaisersesch
Brodenbach
Burgen
Darscheid/Vulkaneifel
Pronsfeld
Gevenich
Cochem
Sankt Goarshausen
Bad Schwalbach
Biebernheim
3
Uttfeld
Lutzerath
Valwig
Ernst
Ellenz/Poltersdorf
Oberwesel/Rhein
WIESBADEN
Wiesbaden
Gillenfeld
Manderscheid
Bremm
Neef
Briedern
Waxweiler
Deudesfeld
Sankt Aldegund
Ediger/Eller
Bacharach
Rheinland-Pfalz
Eltville am Rhein
Mainz
MAINZ
Eisenschmitt
Plein
Pünderich
Reil/Mosel
Zell/Mosel
Trechtinghausen
Oestrich-Winkel
LU
Wittlich
Erden
Lösnich
Enkirch
Kinheim
Ürzig
Bingen/Rhein
Ingelheim am Rhein
Wiltz
Hoscheid
Zeltingen-Rachtig
Bernkastel
Graach/Mosel
Traben-Trarbach
Kirchberg
Stromberg
Gau-Algesheim
Schwabenheim/Selz
Stadecken-Elsheim
16
10km

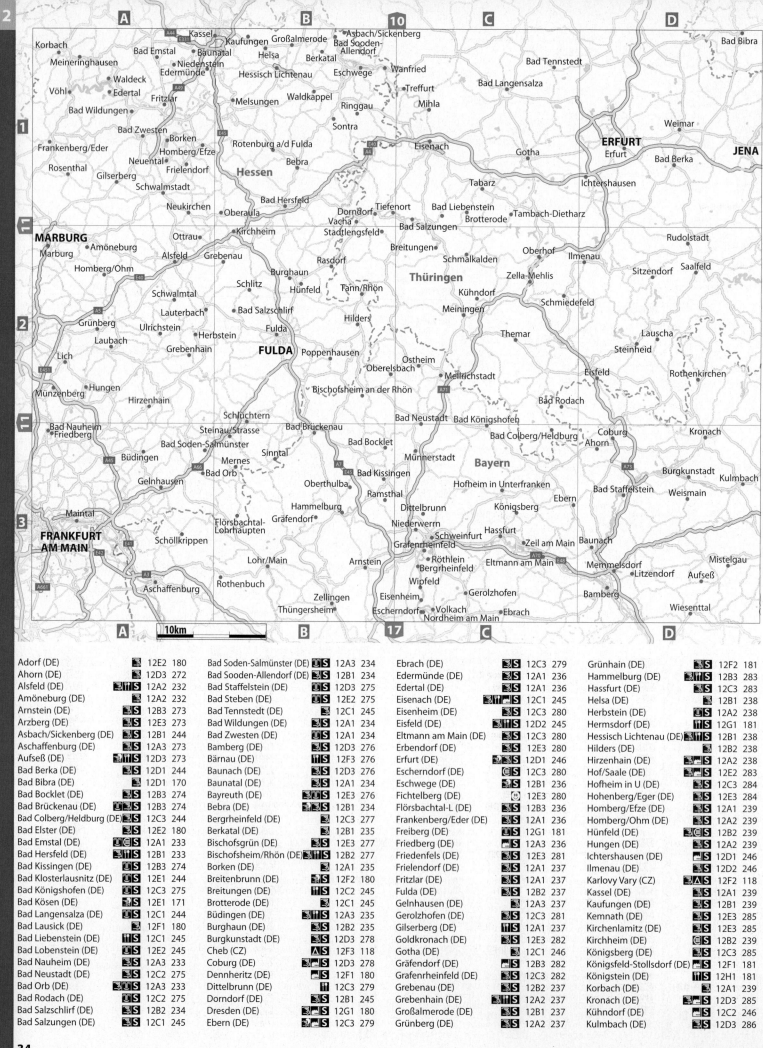

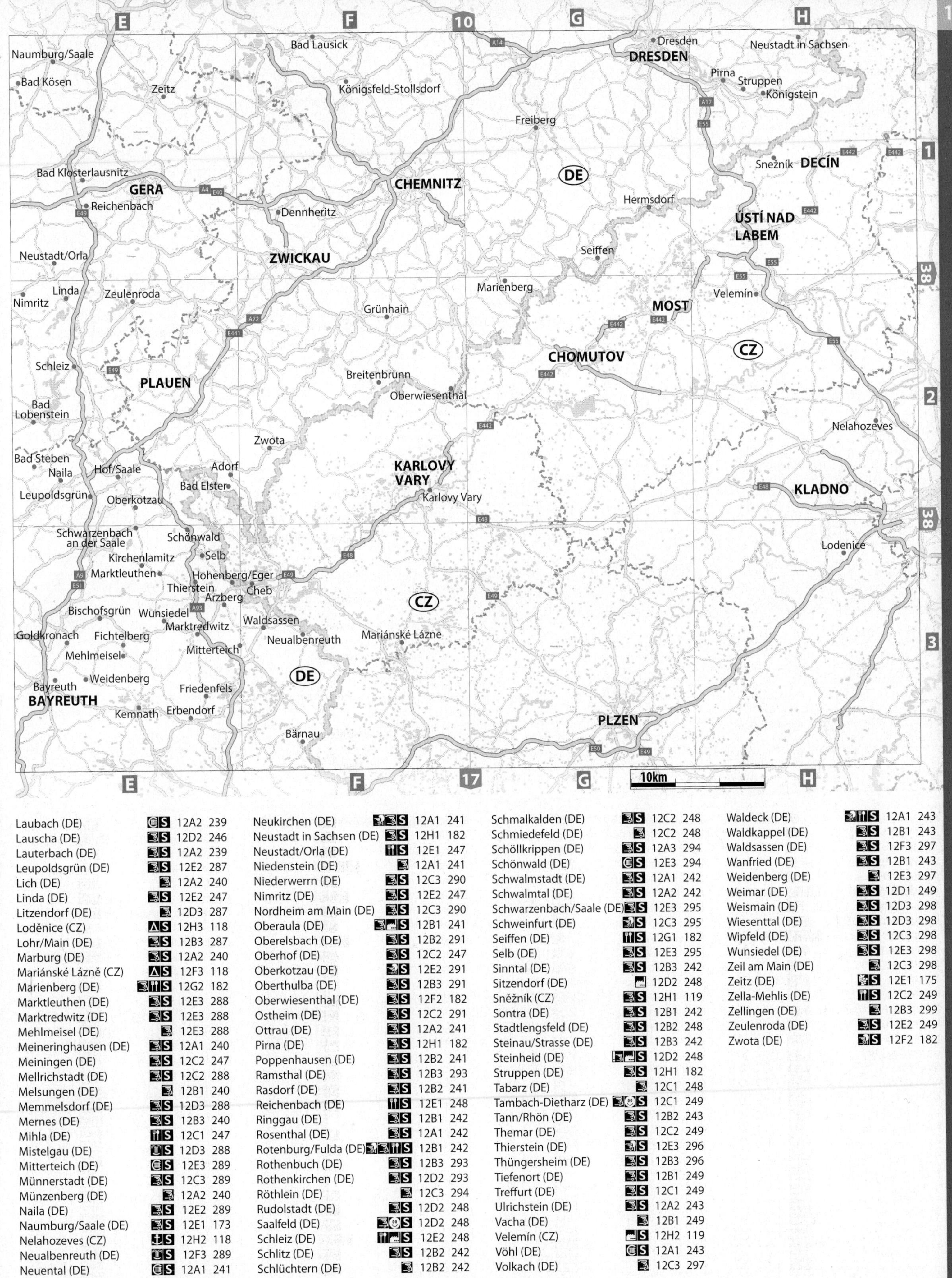
E
F
10
G
H
Naumburg/Saale
Bad Kösen
Zeitz
Bad Lausick
Königsfeld-Stollsdorf
Dresden
DRESDEN
Neustadt in Sachsen
Pirna
Struppen
Königstein
Freiberg
Sneżník
DECÍN
1
Bad Klosterlausnitz
GERA
Reichenbach
CHEMNITZ
Dennheritz
DE
Hermsdorf
ÚSTÍ NAD
LABEM
Neustadt/Orla
ZWICKAU
Seiffen
38
Linda
Nimritz
Zeulenroda
Grünhain
Marienberg
MOST
Velemín
CHOMUTOV
CZ
Schleiz
PLAUEN
Breitenbrunn
Oberwiesenthal
2
Bad
Lobenstein
Nelahozeves
Zwota
Bad Steben
Naila
Hof/Saale
Adorf
KARLOVY
VARY
Karlovy Vary
KLADNO
Leupoldsgrün
Bad Elster
Oberkotzau
Schwarzenbach
an der Saale
Schönwald
Kirchenlamitz
Selb
Lodenice
Marktleuthen
Hohenberg/Eger
Thierstein
Cheb
Arzberg
CZ
Bischofsgrün
Wunsiedel
Marktredwitz
Waldsassen
Goldkronach
Fichtelberg
Neualbenreuth
Mariánské Lázne
3
Mehlmeisel
Mitterteich
Bayreuth
Weidenberg
DE
BAYREUTH
Friedenfels
Kemnath
Erbendorf
PLZEN
Bärnau
E
F
17
G
10km
H

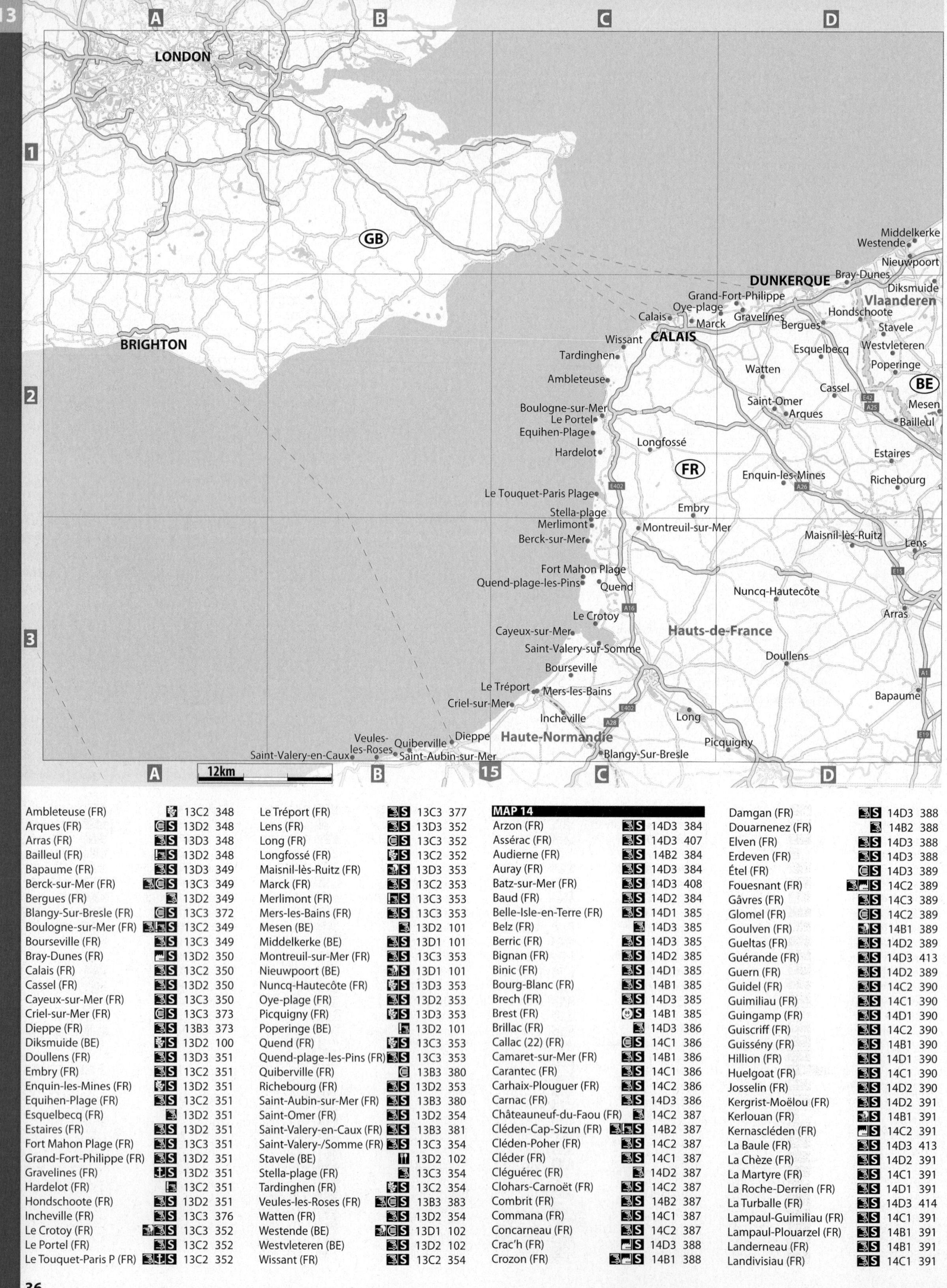
A
B
C
D
LONDON
1
GB
BRIGHTON
2
3
Middelkerke
Westende
Nieuwpoort
Bray-Dunes
DUNKERQUE
Diksmuide
Vlaanderen
Grand-Fort-Philippe
Oye-plage
Calais
Marck
Gravelines
Hondschoote
Bergues
Stavele
Wissant
CALAIS
Esquelbecq
Westvleteren
Tardinghen
Poperinge
Watten
Ambleteuse
BE
Cassel
Saint-Omer
Mesen
Boulogne-sur-Mer
Arques
Le Portel
Bailleul
Equihen-Plage
Longfossé
Hardelot
Estaires
FR
Enquin-les-Mines
Richebourg
Le Touquet-Paris Plage
Embry
Stella-plage
Merlimont
Montreuil-sur-Mer
Maisnil-lès-Ruitz
Berck-sur-Mer
Lens
Fort Mahon Plage
Quend-plage-les-Pins
Quend
Nuncq-Hautecôte
Le Crotoy
Arras
Cayeux-sur-Mer
Hauts-de-France
Saint-Valery-sur-Somme
Doullens
Bourseville
Le Tréport
Mers-les-Bains
Bapaume
Criel-sur-Mer
Incheville
Long
Veules-les-Roses
Quiberville
Dieppe
Haute-Normandie
Picquigny
Saint-Valery-en-Caux
Saint-Aubin-sur-Mer
Blangy-Sur-Bresle
12km
15

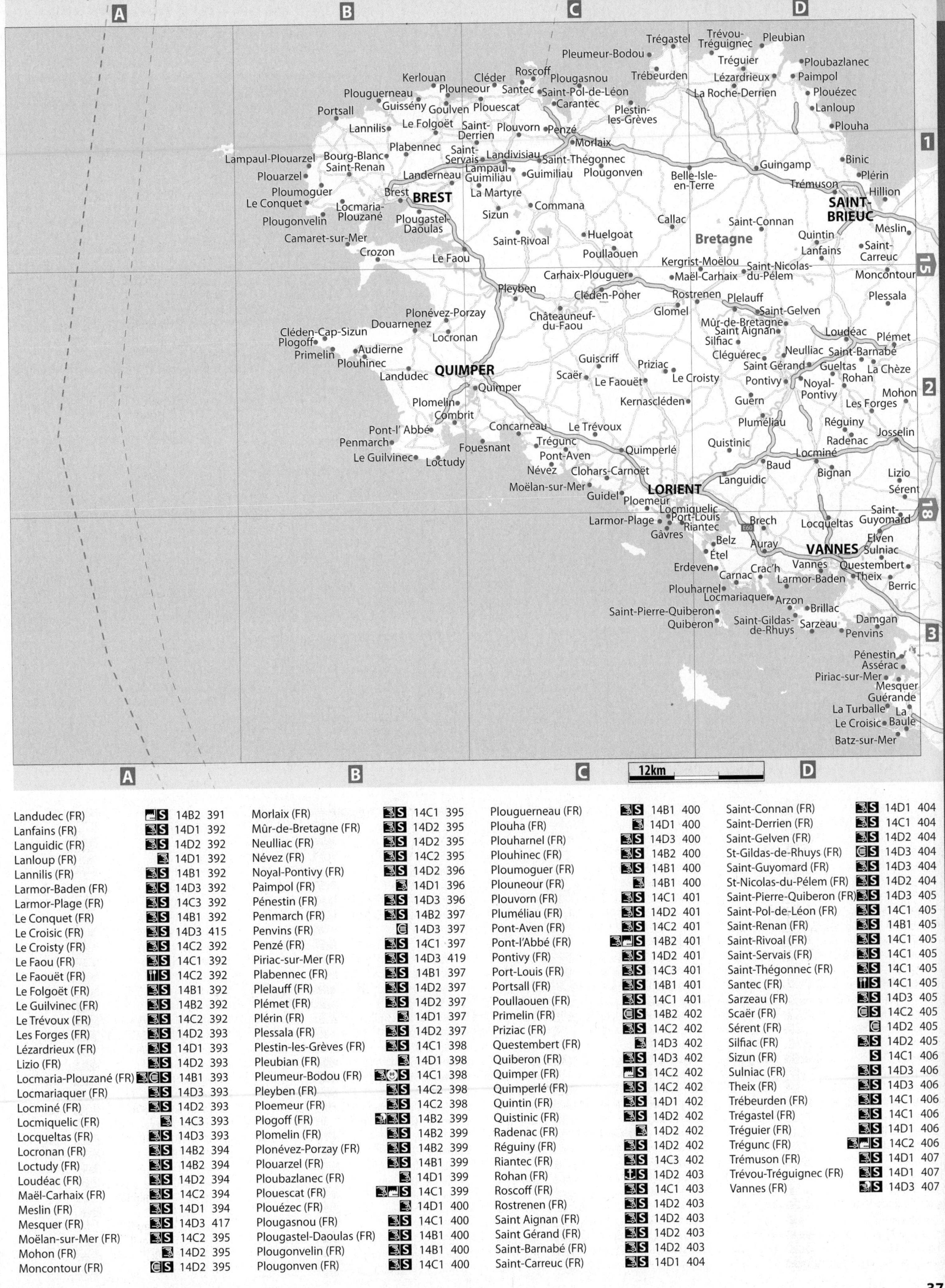
A
B
C
D
1
2
3
15
18
12km
Trégastel
Trévou-Tréguignec
Pleubian
Pleumeur-Bodou
Tréguier
Ploubazlanec
Kerlouan
Cléder
Roscoff
Plougasnou
Trébeurden
Lézardrieux
Paimpol
Plouguerneau
Plouneour
Santec
Saint-Pol-de-Léon
La Roche-Derrien
Plouézec
Guissény
Goulven
Plouescat
Carantec
Plestin-les-Grèves
Lanloup
Portsall
Lannilis
Le Folgoët
Saint-Derrien
Plouvorn
Penzé
Plouha
Plabennec
Saint-Servais
Morlaix
Lampaul-Plouarzel
Bourg-Blanc
Landivisiau
Saint-Thégonnec
Binic
Saint-Renan
Lampaul-Guimiliau
Guimiliau
Plougonven
Guingamp
Plérin
Plouarzel
Landerneau
Belle-Isle-en-Terre
Trémuson
Hillion
Ploumoguer
Brest
BREST
La Martyre
SAINT-BRIEUC
Le Conquet
Locmaria-Plouzané
Commana
Plougonvelin
Plougastel-Daoulas
Sizun
Callac
Saint-Connan
Meslin
Camaret-sur-Mer
Saint-Rivoal
Huelgoat
Bretagne
Quintin
Crozon
Le Faou
Poullaouen
Lanfains
Saint-Carreuc
Kergrist-Moëlan
Saint-Nicolas-du-Pélem
Carhaix-Plouguer
Maël-Carhaix
Moncontour
Pleyben
Cléden-Poher
Rostrenen
Plelauff
Plessala
Glomel
Saint-Gelven
Plonévez-Porzay
Châteauneuf-du-Faou
Mûr-de-Bretagne
Douarnenez
Saint Aignan
Loudéac
Plémet
Cléden-Cap-Sizun
Locronan
Silfiac
Plogoff
Audierne
Cléguérec
Neulliac
Saint-Barnabé
Primelin
Plouhinec
Guiscriff
Priziac
Saint Gérand
Gueltas
La Chèze
Landudec
QUIMPER
Scaër
Le Faouët
Le Croisty
Pontivy
Rohan
Quimper
Noyal-Pontivy
Mohon
Plomelin
Kernascléden
Guern
Les Forges
Combrit
Pluméliau
Réguiny
Pont-l'Abbé
Concarneau
Le Trévoux
Radenac
Josselin
Penmarch
Trégunc
Quistinic
Fouesnant
Quimperlé
Locminé
Le Guilvinec
Loctudy
Pont-Aven
Baud
Névez
Clohars-Carnoët
Bignan
Lizio
Moëlan-sur-Mer
LORIENT
Languidic
Sérent
Guidel
Ploemeur
Locmiquelic
Saint-Guyomard
Larmor-Plage
Port-Louis
Brech
Locqueltas
Riantec
Gâvres
E60
Belz
Elven
Auray
VANNES
Sulniac
Étel
Erdeven
Crac'h
Vannes
Questembert
Carnac
Larmor-Baden
Theix
Berric
Plouharnel
Locmariaquer
Arzon
Saint-Pierre-Quiberon
Brillac
Quiberon
Saint-Gildas-de-Rhuys
Sarzeau
Damgan
Penvins
Pénestin
Assérac
Piriac-sur-Mer
Mesquer
Guérande
La Turballe
La Baule
Le Croisic
Batz-sur-Mer

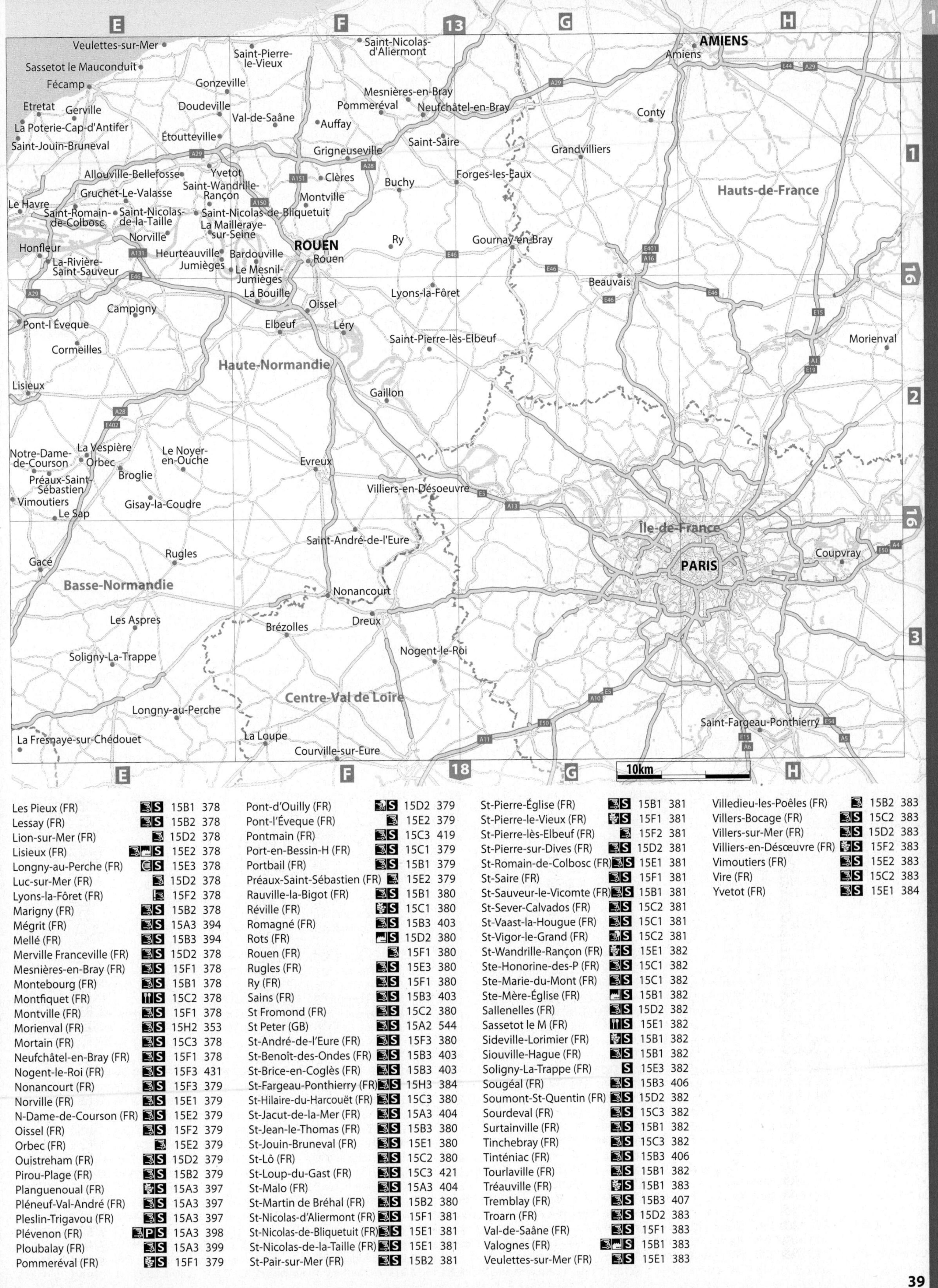
E
F
13
G
H
Veulettes-sur-Mer
Saint-Pierre-le-Vieux
Saint-Nicolas-d'Aliermont
AMIENS
Amiens
Sassetot le Mauconduit
Fécamp
Gonzeville
Mesnières-en-Bray
Etretat
Gerville
Doudeville
Pommeréval
Neufchâtel-en-Bray
Conty
La Poterie-Cap-d'Antifer
Val-de-Saâne
Auffay
Saint-Jouin-Bruneval
Étoutteville
Saint-Saire
Gigneuseville
Grandvilliers
Allouville-Bellefosse
Yvetot
Clères
Buchy
Forges-les-Eaux
Saint-Wandrille-Rançon
Gruchet-Le-Valasse
Montville
Hauts-de-France
Le Havre
Saint-Romain-de-Colbosc
Saint-Nicolas-de-la-Taille
Saint-Nicolas-de-Bliquetuit
La Mailleraye-sur-Seine
Norville
Ry
Gournay-en-Bray
Honfleur
ROUEN
Heurteauville
Bardouville
Rouen
La-Rivière-Saint-Sauveur
Jumièges
Le Mesnil-Jumièges
Beauvais
La Bouille
Lyons-la-Fôret
Oissel
Campigny
Pont-l Éveque
Elbeuf
Léry
Saint-Pierre-lès-Elbeuf
Morienval
Cormeilles
Haute-Normandie
Lisieux
Gaillon
Notre-Dame-de-Courson
La Vespière
Orbec
Le Noyer-en-Ouche
Evreux
Broglie
Préaux-Saint-Sébastien
Villiers-en-Désoeuvre
Vimoutiers
Gisay-la-Coudre
Le Sap
Île-de-France
Saint-André-de-l'Eure
Coupvray
Gacé
Rugles
PARIS
Basse-Normandie
Nonancourt
Les Aspres
Dreux
Brézolles
Nogent-le-Roi
Soligny-La-Trappe
Centre-Val de Loire
Longny-au-Perche
Saint-Fargeau-Ponthierry
La Fresnaye-sur-Chédouet
La Loupe
Courville-sur-Eure
18
10km
1
2
3
16

A B 11 C D

Malzy Luzoir Revin Monthermé Bohan Bogny-sur-Meuse Alle-sur-Semois Rochehaut
SAINT-QUENTIN
CHARLEVILLE-MÉZIÈRES
Poupehan Bouillon Herbeumont Charleville-Mézières
Rozoy-sur-Serre Sedan BE Wallonie
Beautor Tergnier Launois-sur-Vence Wadelincourt
Mouzon
Coucy-le-Château-Auffrique Laôn Avioth FR
Blérancourt Chavignon Bruyères-et-Montberault Longwy
Stenay
Hauts-de-France
Longuyon
Vouziers Dun-sur-Meuse
Damvillers
Longpont Azannes-et-Soumazannes
REIMS Consenvoye
Villers-Côtterets Reims
Grand Est Avocourt
Neuilly-Saint-Front Chamery Vauquois Thierville-sur-Meuse
Verdun
Suippes
Villers-sous-Châtillon Saint-Imoges Les Islettes Nixéville-Blercourt Bonzée
Mutigny Dieue-sur-Meuse
Mareuil-sur-Ay La Cheppe
Château-Thierry La Chapelle-Monthodon Épernay Beaulieu-en-Argonne Souilly
Nubécourt Vigneulles-lès-Hattonchâtel
Avize Seuil-d'Argonne Issoncourt La Croix-sur-Meuse
Saint-Cyr-sur-Morin Heudicourt sous les Côtes
Villeneuve-Renneville-Chevigny Nonsard Lamarche
Beaunay Laheycourt Saint-Mihiel
La Gault-Soigny Revigny-sur-Ornain Marbotte
Contrisson Val-d'Ornain
Fains-Veel
Bar-le-Duc Commercy
Esternay Sézanne
Île-de-France Longeville-en-Barrois
Tannois
Haironville Montplonne Velaines Void-Vacon
Mailly-le-Camp Saint-Dizier Nant-le-Grand Ligny-en-Barrois
Sapignicourt Ancerville
Sainte-Marie-du-Lac-Nuisement Sainte-Livière Vaucouleurs
Provins Montigny-lès-Vaucouleurs
Morley Champougny
Nogent-sur-Seine Giffaumont-Champaubert Maxey-sur-Vaise
Chavanges Gondrecourt-le-Château
A 10km B 19 C D

1 2 3 15 15
E44 A29 E46 E17 A26 A34 E411 E25 E50 A4 E54

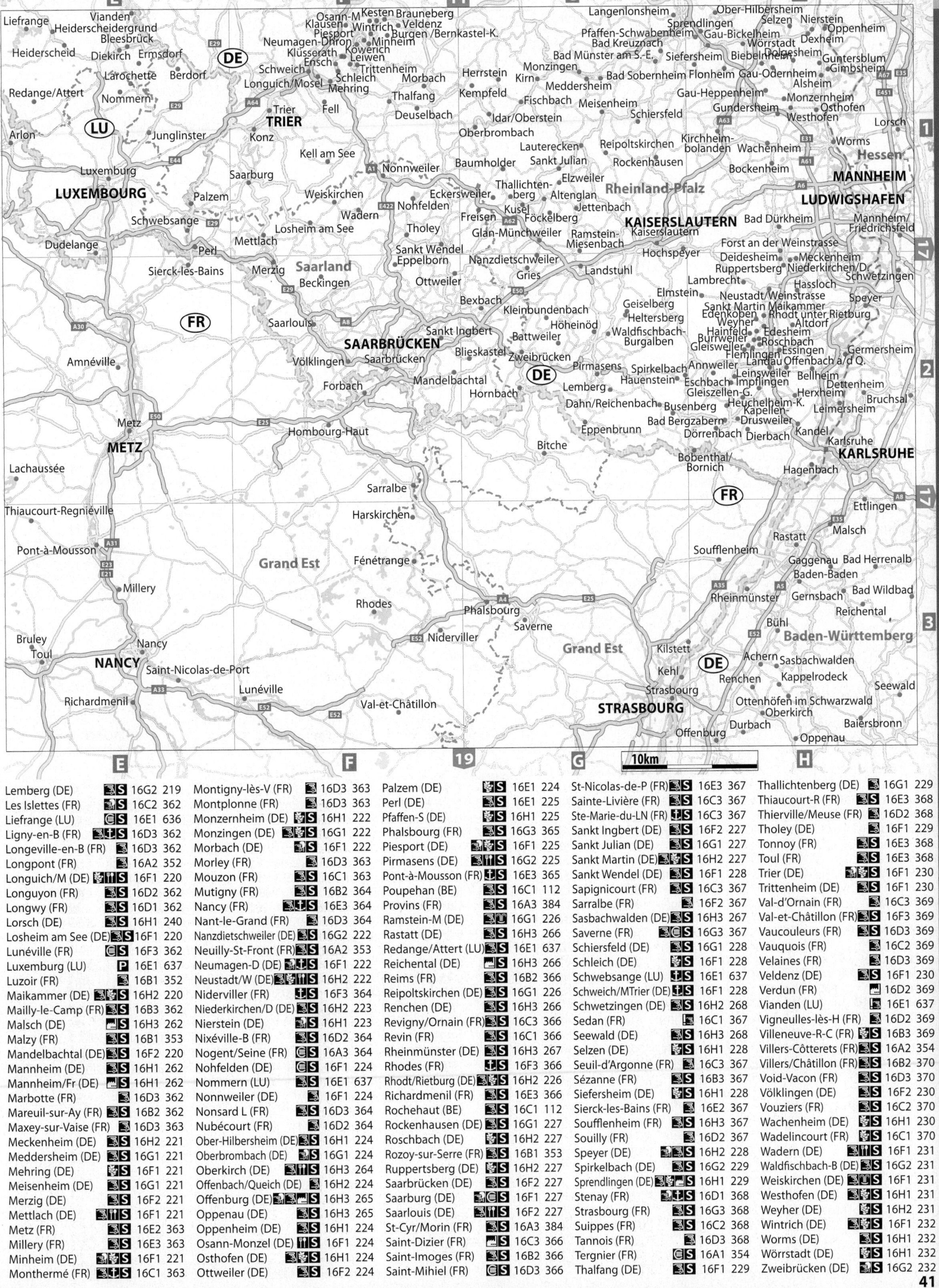

Place	Grid	Page
Lemberg (DE)	16G2	219
Les Islettes (FR)	16C2	362
Liefrange (LU)	16E1	636
Ligny-en-B (FR)	16D3	362
Longeville-en-B (FR)	16D3	362
Longpont (FR)	16A2	352
Longuich/M (DE)	16F1	220
Longuyon (FR)	16D2	362
Longwy (FR)	16D1	362
Lorsch (DE)	16H1	240
Losheim am See (DE)	16F1	220
Lunéville (FR)	16F3	362
Luxemburg (LU)	16E1	637
Luzoir (FR)	16B1	352
Maikammer (DE)	16H2	220
Mailly-le-Camp (FR)	16B3	362
Malsch (DE)	16H3	262
Malzy (FR)	16B1	353
Mandelbachtal (DE)	16F2	220
Mannheim (DE)	16H1	262
Mannheim/Fr (DE)	16H1	262
Marbotte (FR)	16D3	362
Mareuil-sur-Ay (FR)	16B2	362
Maxey-sur-Vaise (FR)	16D3	363
Meckenheim (DE)	16H2	221
Meddersheim (DE)	16G1	221
Mehring (DE)	16F1	221
Meisenheim (DE)	16G1	221
Merzig (DE)	16F2	221
Mettlach (DE)	16F1	221
Metz (FR)	16E2	363
Millery (FR)	16E3	363
Minheim (DE)	16F1	221
Monthermé (FR)	16C1	363
Montigny-lès-V (FR)	16D3	363
Montplonne (FR)	16D3	363
Monzernheim (DE)	16H1	222
Monzingen (DE)	16G1	222
Morbach (DE)	16F1	222
Morley (FR)	16D3	363
Mouzon (FR)	16C1	363
Mutigny (FR)	16B2	364
Nancy (FR)	16E3	364
Nant-le-Grand (FR)	16D3	364
Nanzdietschweiler (DE)	16G2	222
Neuilly-St-Front (FR)	16A2	353
Neumagen-D (DE)	16F1	222
Neustadt/W (DE)	16H2	222
Niderviller (FR)	16F3	364
Niederkirchen/D (DE)	16H2	223
Nierstein (DE)	16H1	223
Nixéville-B (FR)	16D2	364
Nogent/Seine (FR)	16A3	364
Nohfelden (DE)	16F1	224
Nommern (LU)	16E1	637
Nonnweiler (DE)	16F1	224
Nonsard L (FR)	16D3	364
Nubécourt (FR)	16D2	364
Ober-Hilbersheim (DE)	16H1	224
Oberbrombach (DE)	16G1	224
Oberkirch (DE)	16H3	264
Offenbach/Queich (DE)	16H2	224
Offenburg (DE)	16H3	265
Oppenau (DE)	16H3	265
Oppenheim (DE)	16H1	224
Osann-Monzel (DE)	16F1	224
Osthofen (DE)	16H1	224
Ottweiler (DE)	16F2	224
Palzem (DE)	16E1	224
Perl (DE)	16E1	225
Pfaffen-S (DE)	16H1	225
Phalsbourg (FR)	16G3	365
Piesport (DE)	16F1	225
Pirmasens (DE)	16G2	225
Pont-à-Mousson (FR)	16E3	365
Poupehan (BE)	16C1	112
Provins (FR)	16A3	384
Ramstein-M (DE)	16G1	226
Rastatt (DE)	16H3	266
Redange/Attert (LU)	16E1	637
Reichental (DE)	16H3	266
Reims (FR)	16B2	366
Reipoltskirchen (DE)	16G1	226
Renchen (DE)	16H3	266
Revigny/Ornain (FR)	16C3	366
Revin (FR)	16C1	366
Rheinmünster (DE)	16H3	267
Rhodes (FR)	16F3	366
Rhodt/Rietburg (DE)	16H2	226
Richardmenil (FR)	16E3	366
Rochehaut (BE)	16C1	112
Rockenhausen (DE)	16G1	227
Roschbach (DE)	16H2	227
Rozoy-sur-Serre (FR)	16B1	353
Ruppertsberg (DE)	16H2	227
Saarbrücken (DE)	16F2	227
Saarburg (DE)	16F1	227
Saarlouis (DE)	16F2	227
St-Cyr/Morin (FR)	16A3	384
Saint-Dizier (FR)	16C3	366
Saint-Imoges (FR)	16B2	366
Saint-Mihiel (FR)	16D3	366
St-Nicolas-de-P (FR)	16E3	367
Sainte-Livière (FR)	16C3	367
Ste-Marie-du-LN (FR)	16C3	367
Sankt Ingbert (DE)	16F2	227
Sankt Julian (DE)	16G1	227
Sankt Martin (DE)	16H2	227
Sankt Wendel (DE)	16F1	228
Sapignicourt (FR)	16C3	367
Sarralbe (FR)	16F2	367
Sasbachwalden (DE)	16H3	267
Saverne (FR)	16G3	367
Schiersfeld (DE)	16G1	228
Schleich (DE)	16F1	228
Schwebsange (LU)	16E1	637
Schweich/MTrier (DE)	16F1	228
Schwetzingen (DE)	16H2	268
Sedan (FR)	16C1	367
Seewald (DE)	16H3	268
Selzen (DE)	16H1	228
Seuil-d'Argonne (FR)	16C3	367
Sézanne (FR)	16B3	367
Siefersheim (DE)	16H1	228
Sierck-les-Bains (FR)	16E2	367
Soufflenheim (FR)	16H3	367
Souilly (FR)	16D2	367
Speyer (DE)	16H2	228
Spirkelbach (DE)	16G2	229
Sprendlingen (DE)	16H1	229
Stenay (FR)	16D1	368
Strasbourg (FR)	16G3	368
Suippes (FR)	16C2	368
Tannois (FR)	16D3	368
Tergnier (FR)	16A1	354
Thalfang (DE)	16F1	229
Thallichtenberg (DE)	16G1	229
Thiaucourt-R (FR)	16E3	368
Thierville/Meuse (FR)	16D2	368
Tholey (DE)	16F1	229
Tonnoy (FR)	16E3	368
Toul (FR)	16E3	368
Trier (DE)	16F1	230
Trittenheim (DE)	16F1	230
Val-d'Ornain (FR)	16C3	369
Val-et-Châtillon (FR)	16F3	369
Vaucouleurs (FR)	16D3	369
Vauquois (FR)	16C2	369
Velaines (FR)	16D3	369
Veldenz (DE)	16F1	230
Verdun (FR)	16D2	369
Vianden (LU)	16E1	637
Vigneulles-lès-H (FR)	16D2	369
Villeneuve-R-C (FR)	16B3	369
Villers-Côtterets (FR)	16A2	354
Villers/Châtillon (FR)	16B2	370
Void-Vacon (FR)	16D3	370
Völklingen (DE)	16F2	230
Vouziers (FR)	16C2	370
Wachenheim (DE)	16H1	230
Wadelincourt (FR)	16C1	370
Wadern (DE)	16F1	231
Waldfischbach-B (DE)	16G2	231
Weiskirchen (DE)	16F1	231
Westhofen (DE)	16H1	231
Weyher (DE)	16H2	231
Wintrich (DE)	16F1	232
Worms (DE)	16H1	232
Wörrstadt (DE)	16H1	232
Zweibrücken (DE)	16G2	232

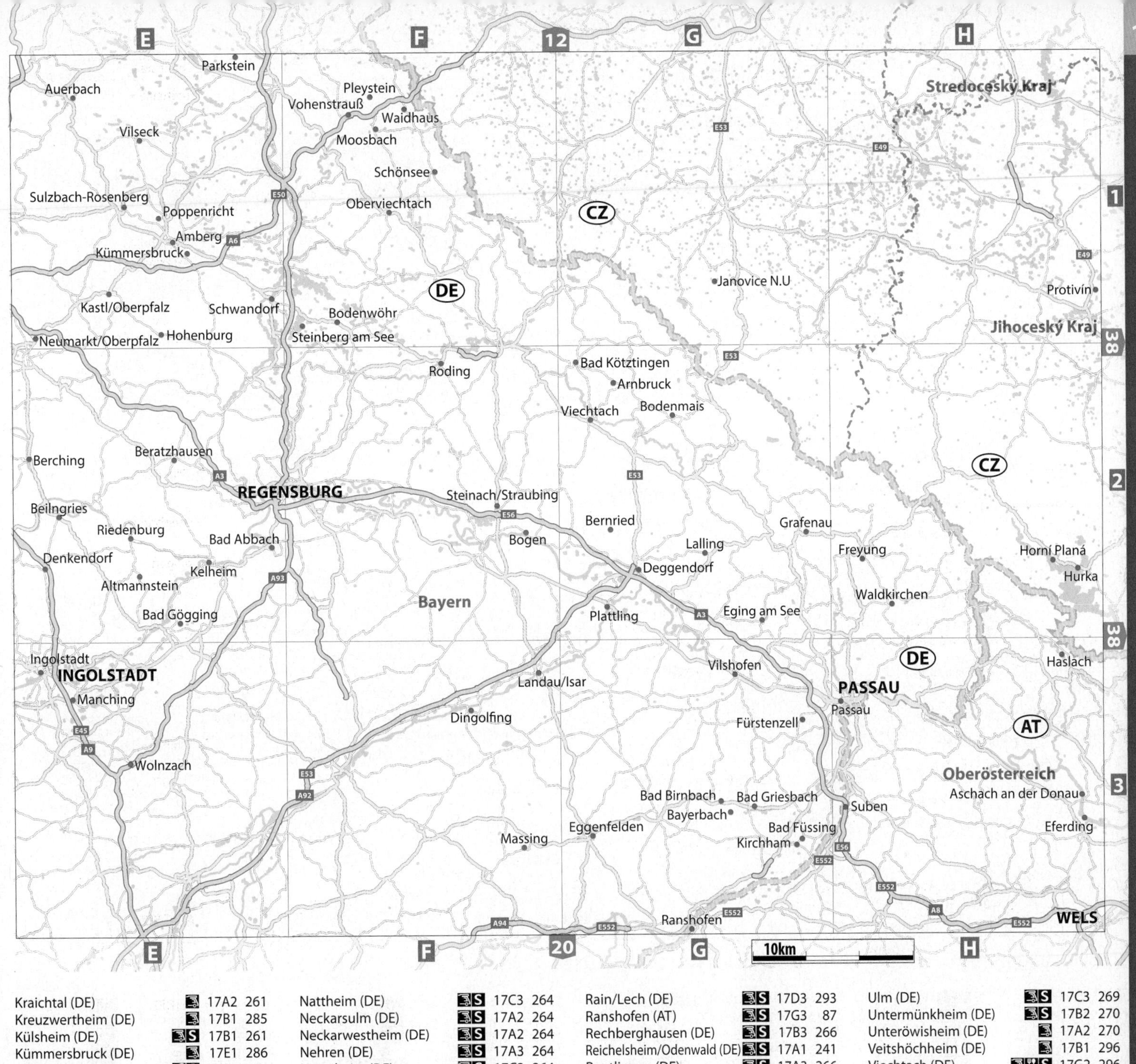

E
F
12
G
H
1
2
3
38
38
20
Parkstein
Auerbach
Pleystein
Vohenstrauß
Waidhaus
Vilseck
Moosbach
Schönsee
Sulzbach-Rosenberg
Poppenricht
Oberviechtach
Amberg
Kümmersbruck
CZ
DE
Janovice N.U
Stredoceský Kraj
Protivín
Jihoceský Kraj
Kastl/Oberpfalz
Schwandorf
Bodenwöhr
Neumarkt/Oberpfalz
Hohenburg
Steinberg am See
Roding
Bad Kötztingen
Arnbruck
Viechtach
Bodenmais
Berching
Beratzhausen
REGENSBURG
Steinach/Straubing
Beilngries
Riedenburg
Bad Abbach
Bogen
Bernried
Grafenau
Lalling
Freyung
Horní Planá
Hurka
Denkendorf
Kelheim
Deggendorf
Altmannstein
Bayern
Waldkirchen
Bad Gögging
Plattling
Eging am See
Ingolstadt
INGOLSTADT
Manching
Vilshofen
Landau/Isar
PASSAU
Passau
Haslach
Dingolfing
Fürstenzell
AT
Wolnzach
Oberösterreich
Aschach an der Donau
Bad Birnbach
Bad Griesbach
Suben
Bayerbach
Eggenfelden
Bad Füssing
Eferding
Massing
Kirchham
Ranshofen
WELS
E50
E53
E49
A6
A3
E56
A93
E45
A9
A92
A94
E552
A8
10km

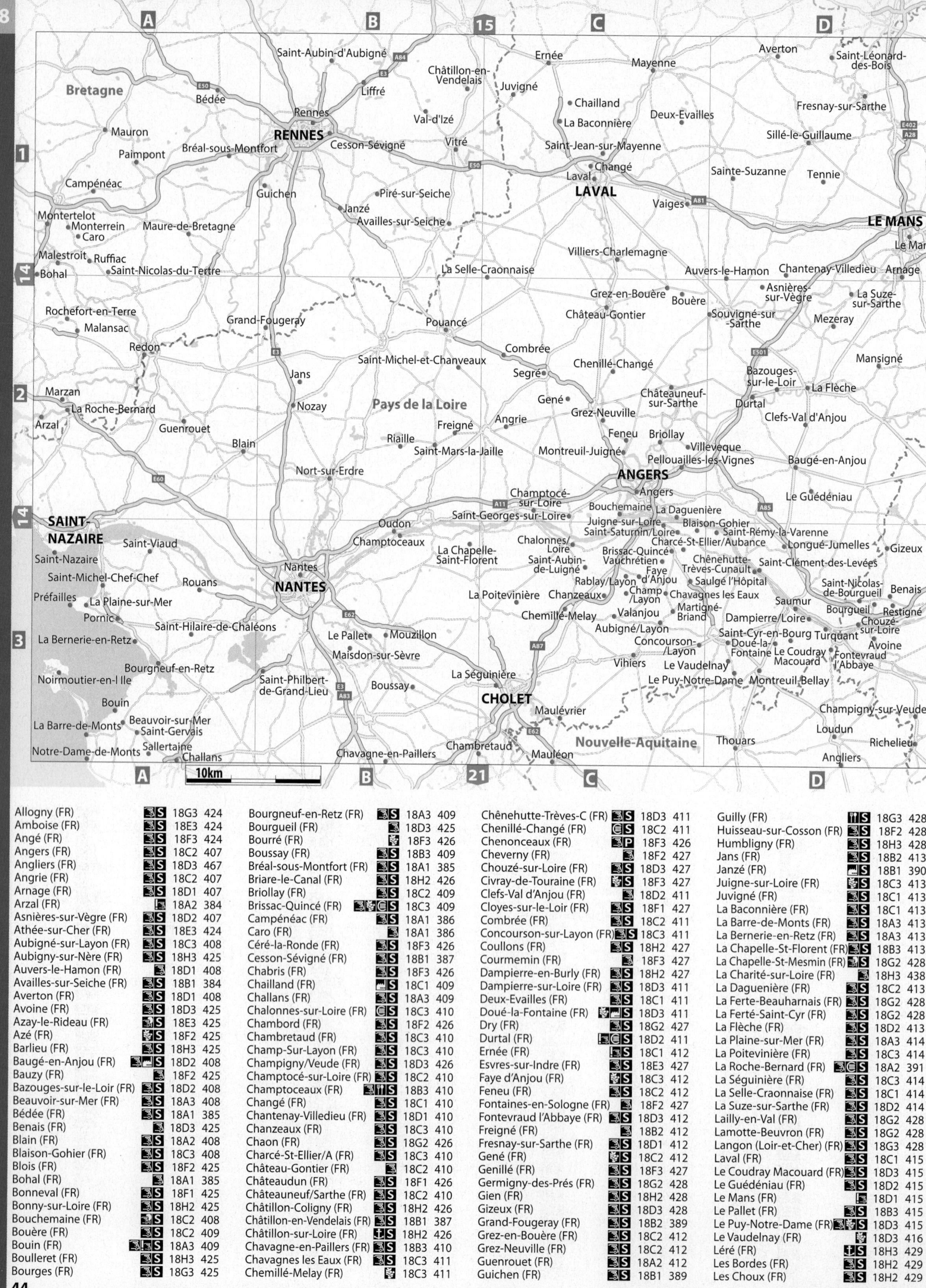

Place	Map	Page
Allogny (FR)	18G3	424
Amboise (FR)	18E3	424
Angé (FR)	18F3	424
Angers (FR)	18C2	407
Angliers (FR)	18D3	467
Angrie (FR)	18C2	407
Arnage (FR)	18D1	407
Arzal (FR)	18A2	384
Asnières-sur-Vègre (FR)	18D2	407
Athée-sur-Cher (FR)	18E3	424
Aubigné-sur-Layon (FR)	18C3	408
Aubigny-sur-Nère (FR)	18H3	425
Auvers-le-Hamon (FR)	18D1	408
Availles-sur-Seiche (FR)	18B1	384
Averton (FR)	18D1	408
Avoine (FR)	18D3	425
Azay-le-Rideau (FR)	18E3	425
Azé (FR)	18F2	425
Barlieu (FR)	18H3	425
Baugé-en-Anjou (FR)	18D2	408
Bauzy (FR)	18F2	425
Bazouges-sur-le-Loir (FR)	18D2	408
Beauvoir-sur-Mer (FR)	18A3	408
Bédée (FR)	18A1	385
Benais (FR)	18D3	425
Blain (FR)	18A2	408
Blaison-Gohier (FR)	18C3	408
Blois (FR)	18F2	425
Bohal (FR)	18A1	385
Bonneval (FR)	18F1	425
Bonny-sur-Loire (FR)	18H2	425
Bouchemaine (FR)	18C2	408
Bouère (FR)	18C2	409
Bouin (FR)	18A3	409
Boulleret (FR)	18H3	425
Bourges (FR)	18G3	425
Bourgneuf-en-Retz (FR)	18A3	409
Bourgueil (FR)	18D3	425
Bourré (FR)	18F3	426
Boussay (FR)	18B3	409
Bréal-sous-Montfort (FR)	18A1	385
Briare-le-Canal (FR)	18H2	426
Briollay (FR)	18C2	409
Brissac-Quincé (FR)	18C3	409
Campénéac (FR)	18A1	386
Caro (FR)	18A1	386
Céré-la-Ronde (FR)	18F3	426
Cesson-Sévigné (FR)	18B1	387
Chabris (FR)	18F3	426
Chailland (FR)	18C1	409
Challans (FR)	18A3	409
Chalonnes-sur-Loire (FR)	18C3	410
Chambord (FR)	18F2	426
Chambretaud (FR)	18C3	410
Champ-Sur-Layon (FR)	18C3	410
Champigny/Veude (FR)	18D3	426
Champtocé-sur-Loire (FR)	18C2	410
Champtoceaux (FR)	18B3	410
Changé (FR)	18C1	410
Chantenay-Villedieu (FR)	18D1	410
Chanzeaux (FR)	18C3	410
Chaon (FR)	18G2	426
Charcé-St-Ellier/A (FR)	18C3	410
Château-Gontier (FR)	18C2	410
Châteaudun (FR)	18F1	426
Châteauneuf/Sarthe (FR)	18C2	410
Châtillon-Coligny (FR)	18H2	426
Châtillon-en-Vendelais (FR)	18B1	387
Châtillon-sur-Loire (FR)	18H2	426
Chavagne-en-Paillers (FR)	18B3	410
Chavagnes les Eaux (FR)	18C3	411
Chemillé-Melay (FR)	18C3	411
Chênehutte-Trèves-C (FR)	18D3	411
Chenillé-Changé (FR)	18C2	411
Chenonceaux (FR)	18F3	426
Cheverny (FR)	18F2	427
Chouzé-sur-Loire (FR)	18D3	427
Civray-de-Touraine (FR)	18F3	427
Clefs-Val d'Anjou (FR)	18D2	411
Cloyes-sur-le-Loir (FR)	18F1	427
Combrée (FR)	18C2	411
Concourson-sur-Layon (FR)	18C3	411
Coullons (FR)	18H2	427
Courmemin (FR)	18F3	427
Dampierre-en-Burly (FR)	18H2	427
Dampierre-sur-Loire (FR)	18D3	411
Deux-Evailles (FR)	18C1	411
Doué-la-Fontaine (FR)	18D3	411
Dry (FR)	18G2	427
Durtal (FR)	18D2	411
Ernée (FR)	18C1	412
Esvres-sur-Indre (FR)	18E3	427
Faye d'Anjou (FR)	18C3	412
Feneu (FR)	18C2	412
Fontaines-en-Sologne (FR)	18F2	427
Fontevraud l'Abbaye (FR)	18D3	412
Freigné (FR)	18B2	412
Fresnay-sur-Sarthe (FR)	18D1	412
Gené (FR)	18C2	412
Genillé (FR)	18F3	427
Germigny-des-Prés (FR)	18G2	428
Gien (FR)	18H2	428
Gizeux (FR)	18D3	428
Grand-Fougeray (FR)	18B2	389
Grez-en-Bouère (FR)	18C2	412
Grez-Neuville (FR)	18C2	412
Guenrouet (FR)	18A2	412
Guichen (FR)	18B1	389
Guilly (FR)	18G3	428
Huisseau-sur-Cosson (FR)	18F2	428
Humbligny (FR)	18H3	428
Jans (FR)	18B2	413
Janzé (FR)	18B1	390
Juigne-sur-Loire (FR)	18C3	413
Juvigné (FR)	18C1	413
La Baconnière (FR)	18C1	413
La Barre-de-Monts (FR)	18A3	413
La Bernerie-en-Retz (FR)	18A3	413
La Chapelle-St-Florent (FR)	18B3	413
La Chapelle-St-Mesmin (FR)	18G2	428
La Charité-sur-Loire (FR)	18H3	438
La Daguenière (FR)	18C2	413
La Ferte-Beauharnais (FR)	18G2	428
La Ferté-Saint-Cyr (FR)	18G2	428
La Flèche (FR)	18D2	413
La Plaine-sur-Mer (FR)	18A3	414
La Poitevinière (FR)	18C3	414
La Roche-Bernard (FR)	18A2	391
La Séguinière (FR)	18C3	414
La Selle-Craonnaise (FR)	18C1	414
La Suze-sur-Sarthe (FR)	18D2	414
Lailly-en-Val (FR)	18G2	428
Lamotte-Beuvron (FR)	18G2	428
Langon (Loir-et-Cher) (FR)	18G3	428
Laval (FR)	18C1	415
Le Coudray Macouard (FR)	18D3	415
Le Guédéniau (FR)	18D2	415
Le Mans (FR)	18D1	415
Le Pallet (FR)	18B3	415
Le Puy-Notre-Dame (FR)	18D3	415
Le Vaudelnay (FR)	18D3	416
Léré (FR)	18H3	429
Les Bordes (FR)	18H2	429
Les Choux (FR)	18H2	429

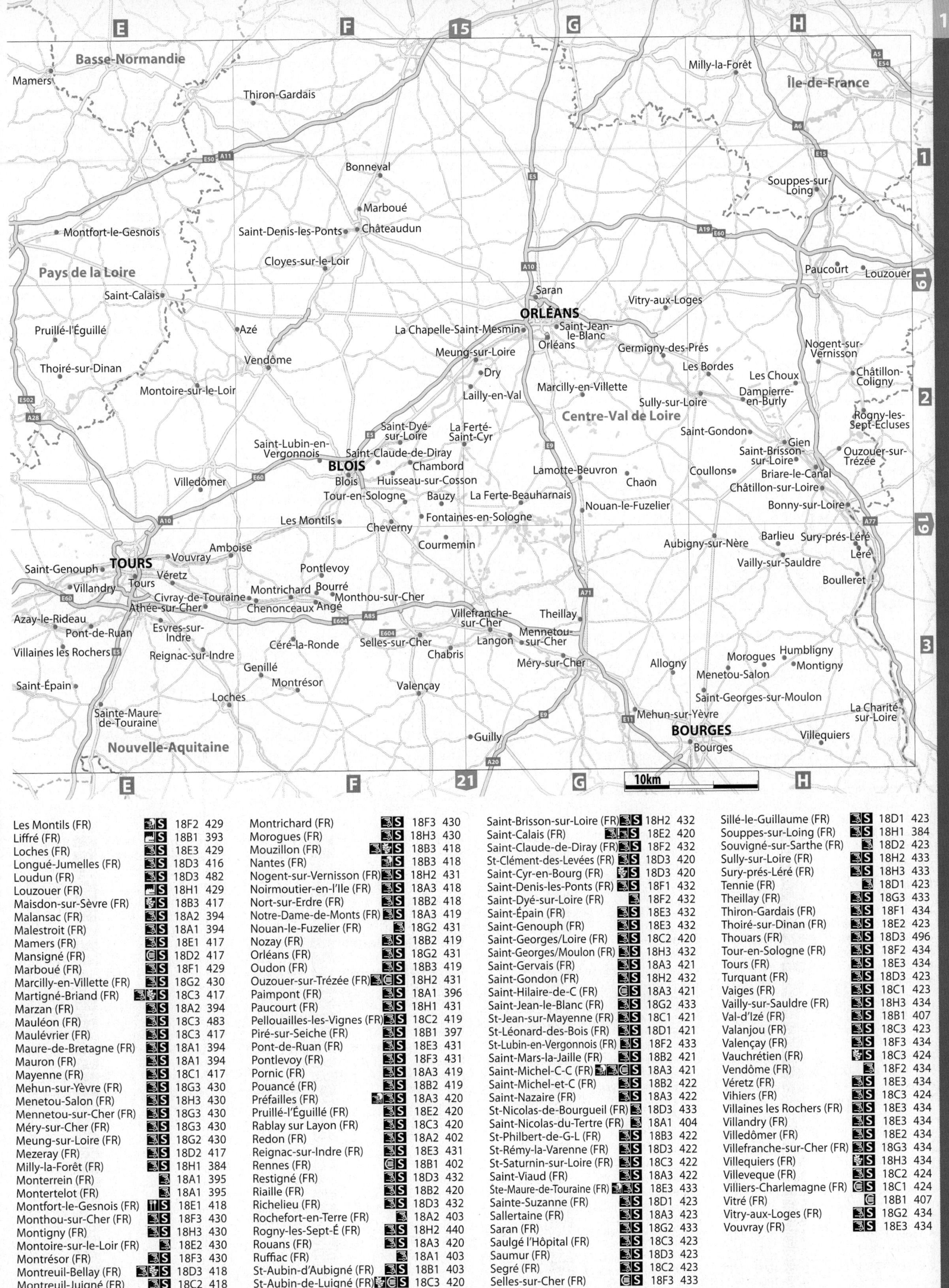

E
F
15
G
H
Basse-Normandie
Mamers
Thiron-Gardais
Milly-la-Forêt
Île-de-France
1
Bonneval
Souppes-sur-Loing
Marboué
Montfort-le-Gesnois
Saint-Denis-les-Ponts
Châteaudun
Cloyes-sur-le-Loir
Pays de la Loire
Paucourt
Louzouer
19
Saint-Calais
Saran
ORLÉANS
Vitry-aux-Loges
Pruillé-l'Éguillé
Azé
La Chapelle-Saint-Mesmin
Saint-Jean-le-Blanc
Orléans
Germigny-des-Prés
Nogent-sur-Vernisson
Vendôme
Meung-sur-Loire
Les Bordes
Les Choux
Châtillon-Coligny
Thoiré-sur-Dinan
Dry
Marcilly-en-Villette
Montoire-sur-le-Loir
Lailly-en-Val
Sully-sur-Loire
Dampierre-en-Burly
2
Rogny-les-Sept-Écluses
Centre-Val de Loire
Saint-Dyé-sur-Loire
La Ferté-Saint-Cyr
Saint-Gondon
Saint-Lubin-en-Vergonnois
Saint-Claude-de-Diray
Gien
Saint-Brisson-sur-Loire
Ouzouer-sur-Trézée
BLOIS
Chambord
Lamotte-Beuvron
Coullons
Briare-le-Canal
Blois
Huisseau-sur-Cosson
Chaon
Villedômer
Châtillon-sur-Loire
Tour-en-Sologne
Bauzy
La Ferte-Beauharnais
Nouan-le-Fuzelier
Bonny-sur-Loire
Les Montils
Fontaines-en-Sologne
Cheverny
Barlieu
Sury-près-Léré
19
Courmemin
Aubigny-sur-Nère
Léré
Amboise
Vouvray
Vailly-sur-Sauldre
Saint-Genouph
TOURS
Pontlevoy
Véretz
Boulleret
Villandry
Tours
Montrichard
Bourré
Cirvay-de-Touraine
Monthou-sur-Cher
Athée-sur-Cher
Chenonceaux
Angé
Theillay
Villefranche-sur-Cher
Azay-le-Rideau
Mennetou-sur-Cher
Pont-de-Ruan
Esvres-sur-Indre
Langon
3
Céré-la-Ronde
Selles-sur-Cher
Humbligny
Villaines les Rochers
Chabris
Reignac-sur-Indre
Allogny
Morogues
Montigny
Méry-sur-Cher
Genillé
Menetou-Salon
Saint-Épain
Montrésor
Valençay
Saint-Georges-sur-Moulon
Loches
Mehun-sur-Yèvre
La Charité-sur-Loire
Sainte-Maure-de-Touraine
BOURGES
Villequiers
Nouvelle-Aquitaine
Guilly
Bourges
E
F
21
G
10km
H

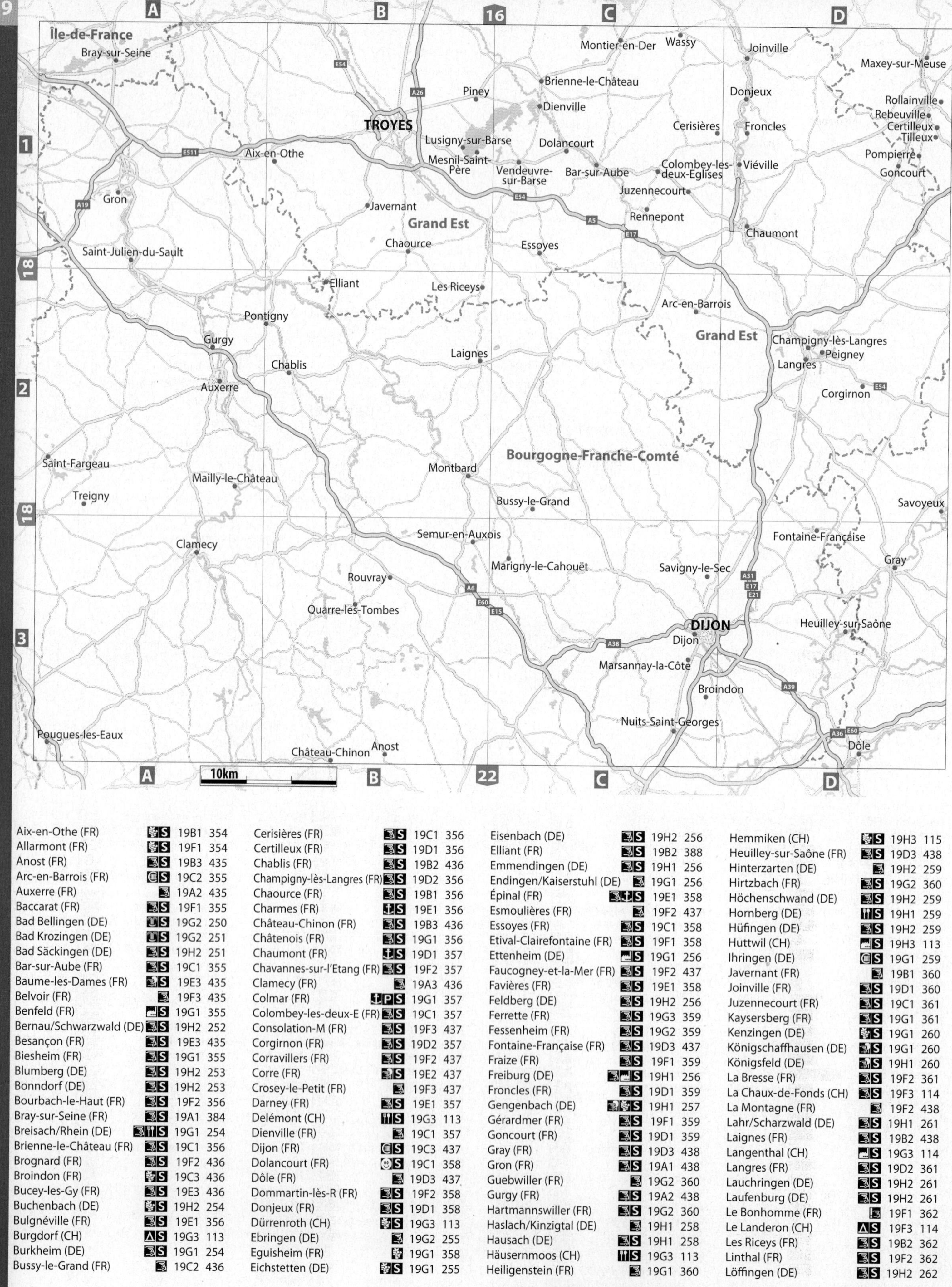

A
B
16
C
D
Île-de-France
Bray-sur-Seine
Montier-en-Der
Wassy
Joinville
Maxey-sur-Meuse
Brienne-le-Château
Piney
Donjeux
Rollainville
Rebeuville
Certilleux
Tilleux
Dienville
TROYES
Cerisières
Froncles
Lusigny-sur-Barse
Dolancourt
Aix-en-Othe
Mesnil-Saint-Père
Vendeuvre-sur-Barse
Bar-sur-Aube
Colombey-les-deux-Eglises
Viéville
Pompierre
Goncourt
Juzennecourt
Gron
Javernant
Rennepont
Grand Est
Chaumont
Chaource
Essoyes
Saint-Julien-du-Sault
Elliant
Les Riceys
Arc-en-Barrois
Pontigny
Grand Est
Champigny-lès-Langres
Peigney
Gurgy
Laignes
Langres
Chablis
Auxerre
Corgirnon
Bourgogne-Franche-Comté
Saint-Fargeau
Montbard
Mailly-le-Château
Treigny
Bussy-le-Grand
Savoyeux
Semur-en-Auxois
Fontaine-Française
Clamecy
Marigny-le-Cahouët
Savigny-le-Sec
Gray
Rouvray
Quarre-les-Tombes
DIJON
Dijon
Heuilley-sur-Saône
Marsannay-la-Côte
Broindon
Nuits-Saint-Georges
Pougues-les-Eaux
Château-Chinon
Anost
Dôle
A
10km
B
22
C
D
1
2
3
18
18
E54
A26
E511
A19
A5
E17
E54
A6
E60
E15
A38
A31
E17
E21
A39
A36
E60

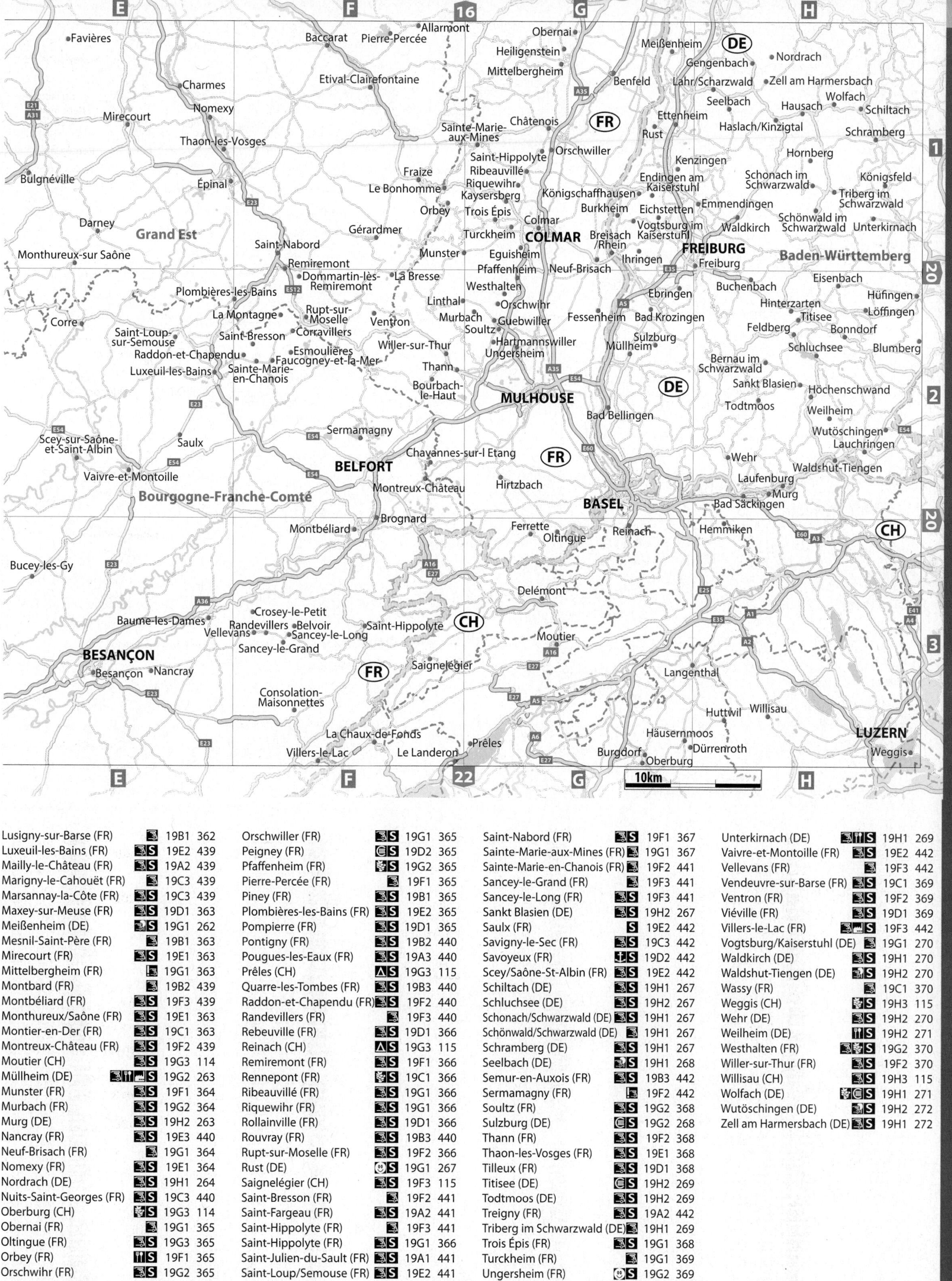
E
F
16
G
H
Favières
Baccarat
Pierre-Percée
Allarmont
Obernai
Heiligenstein
Mittelbergheim
Meißenheim
DE
Gengenbach
Nordrach
Etival-Clairefontaine
Benfeld
Lahr/Scharzwald
Zell am Harmersbach
Charmes
Seelbach
Wolfach
Hausach
Schiltach
Nomexy
Mirecourt
Sainte-Marie-aux-Mines
Châtenois
FR
Ettenheim
Rust
Haslach/Kinzigtal
Schramberg
Thaon-les-Vosges
Saint-Hippolyte
Orschwiller
Hornberg
1
Kenzingen
Fraize
Ribeauvillé
Endingen am Kaiserstuhl
Schonach im Schwarzwald
Königsfeld
Bulgnéville
Épinal
Le Bonhomme
Riquewihr
Kaysersberg
Königschaffhausen
Triberg im Schwarzwald
Burkheim
Eichstetten
Emmendingen
Orbey
Trois Épis
Colmar
Schönwald im Schwarzwald
Unterkirnach
Darney
Grand Est
Gérardmer
Turckheim
COLMAR
Breisach /Rhein
Vogtsburg im Kaiserstuhl
Waldkirch
Saint-Nabord
FREIBURG
Baden-Württemberg
Monthureux-sur Saône
Munster
Eguisheim
Ihringen
Remiremont
Pfaffenheim
Neuf-Brisach
Freiburg
20
Dommartin-lès-Remiremont
La Bresse
Eisenbach
Plombières-les-Bains
Westhalten
Buchenbach
Hüfingen
Ebringen
Linthal
Hinterzarten
Rupt-sur-Moselle
Orschwihr
Löffingen
La Montagne
Titisee
Corre
Ventron
Murbach
Guebwiller
Fessenheim
Bad Krozingen
Feldberg
Saint-Loup-sur-Semouse
Saint-Bresson
Corravillers
Soultz
Bonndorf
Hartmannswiller
Sulzburg
Esmoulières
Willer-sur-Thur
Müllheim
Schluchsee
Blumberg
Raddon-et-Chapendu
Faucogney-et-la-Mer
Ungersheim
Bernau im Schwarzwald
Thann
Luxeuil-les-Bains
Sainte-Marie-en-Chanois
Sankt Blasien
Bourbach-le-Haut
DE
Höchenschwand
MULHOUSE
2
Todtmoos
Weilheim
Bad Bellingen
Sermamagny
Wutöschingen
Scey-sur-Saône-et-Saint-Albin
Saulx
Lauchringen
Chavannes-sur-l Etang
FR
Wehr
BELFORT
Waldshut-Tiengen
Vaivre-et-Montoille
Laufenburg
Montreux-Château
Hirtzbach
Murg
Bourgogne-Franche-Comté
BASEL
Bad Säckingen
Brognard
20
Montbéliard
Ferrette
Reinach
Hemmiken
CH
Oltingue
Bucey-les-Gy
Delémont
Crosey-le-Petit
Baume-les-Dames
Randevillers
Belvoir
Saint-Hippolyte
CH
Vellevans
Sancey-le-Long
Moutier
3
Sancey-le-Grand
BESANÇON
FR
Saignelégier
Langenthal
Besançon
Nancray
Consolation-Maisonnettes
Huttwil
Willisau
LUZERN
La Chaux-de-Fonds
Häusernmoos
Prêles
Dürrenroth
Villers-le-Lac
Le Landeron
Burgdorf
Weggis
Oberburg
E
F
22
G
10km
H

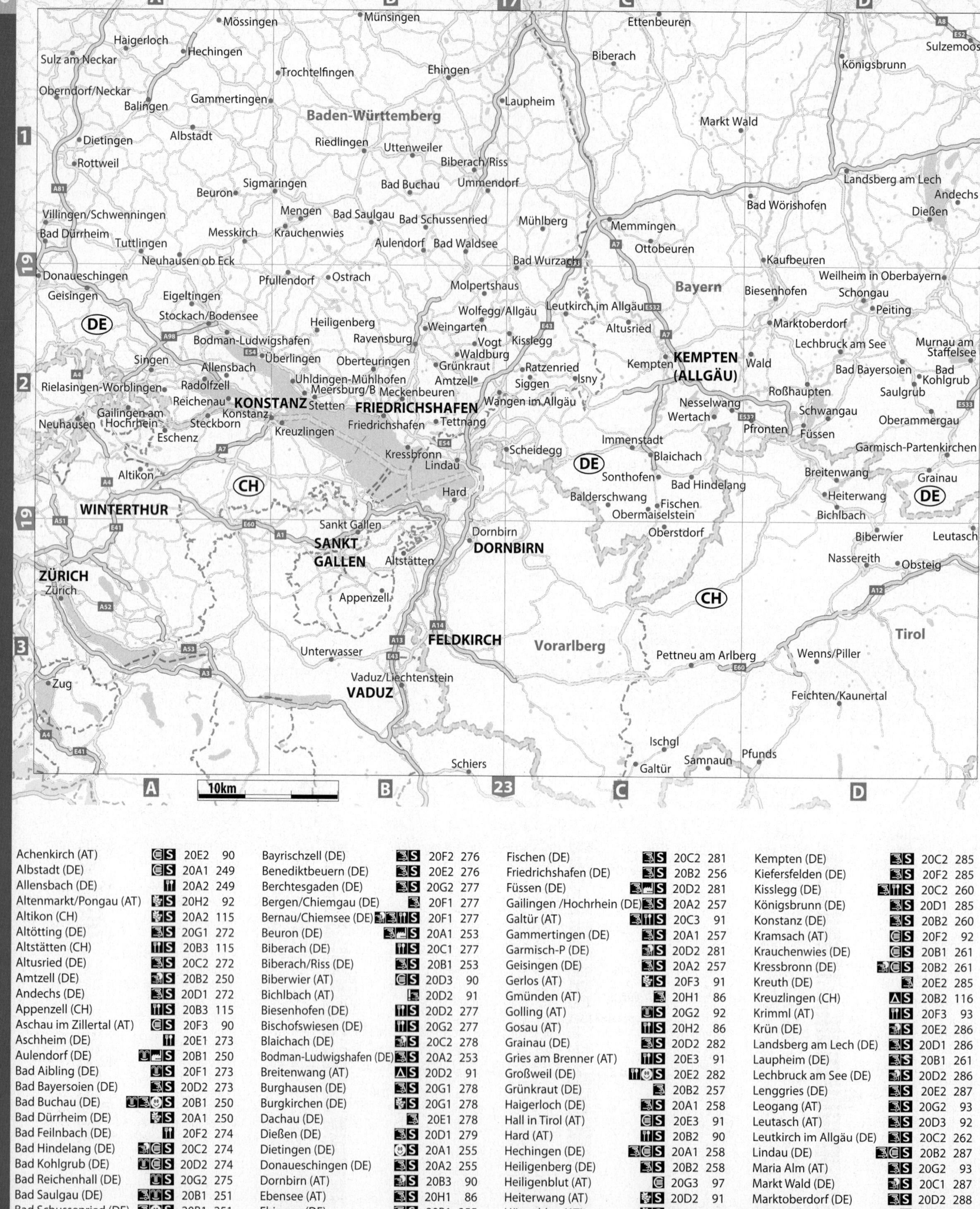

A
B
17
C
D
1
2
3
19
23
Mössingen
Münsingen
Ettenbeuren
Haigerloch
Hechingen
Sulz am Neckar
Biberach
Sulzemoos
Königsbrunn
Trochtelfingen
Ehingen
Oberndorf/Neckar
Balingen
Gammertingen
Laupheim
Baden-Württemberg
Markt Wald
Dietingen
Albstadt
Riedlingen
Uttenweiler
Rottweil
Biberach/Riss
Landsberg am Lech
Andechs
Beuron
Sigmaringen
Bad Buchau
Ummendorf
Dießen
Bad Wörishofen
Villingen/Schwenningen
Mengen
Bad Saulgau
Bad Schussenried
Mühlberg
Memmingen
Bad Dürrheim
Tuttlingen
Messkirch
Krauchenwies
Aulendorf
Bad Waldsee
Ottobeuren
Neuhausen ob Eck
Bad Wurzach
Kaufbeuren
Donaueschingen
Pfullendorf
Ostrach
Weilheim in Oberbayern
Geisingen
Eigeltingen
Molpertshaus
Bayern
Biesenhofen
Schongau
Stockach/Bodensee
Wolfegg/Allgäu
Leutkirch im Allgäu
Peiting
DE
Heiligenberg
Weingarten
Altusried
Marktoberdorf
Bodman-Ludwigshafen
Ravensburg
Vogt
Kisslegg
Lechbruck am See
Murnau am Staffelsee
Singen
Allensbach
Überlingen
Oberteuringen
Waldburg
Grünkraut
Ratzenried
Kempten
KEMPTEN (ALLGÄU)
Wald
Bad Bayersoien
Bad Kohlgrub
Rielasingen-Worblingen
Radolfzell
Uhldingen-Mühlhofen
Amtzell
Siggen
Isny
Meersburg/B
Meckenbeuren
Roßhaupten
Saulgrub
Reichenau
KONSTANZ
Stetten
FRIEDRICHSHAFEN
Wangen im Allgäu
Nesselwang
Schwangau
Gailingen am Hochrhein
Konstanz
Wertach
Oberammergau
Neuhausen
Steckborn
Friedrichshafen
Tettnang
Pfronten
Füssen
Eschenz
Kreuzlingen
Immenstadt
Kressbronn
Scheidegg
Blaichach
Garmisch-Partenkirchen
Lindau
Altikon
CH
Sonthofen
Bad Hindelang
Breitenwang
Grainau
Hard
Balderschwang
Heiterwang
WINTERTHUR
Fischen
Obermaiselstein
Bichlbach
Sankt Gallen
Dornbirn
Oberstdorf
Biberwier
Leutasch
SANKT GALLEN
DORNBIRN
Altstätten
Nassereith
Obsteig
ZÜRICH
Zürich
Appenzell
FELDKIRCH
Vorarlberg
Tirol
Unterwasser
Pettneu am Arlberg
Wenns/Piller
Zug
Vaduz/Liechtenstein
VADUZ
Feichten/Kaunertal
Ischgl
Pfunds
Schiers
Samnaun
Galtür
10km

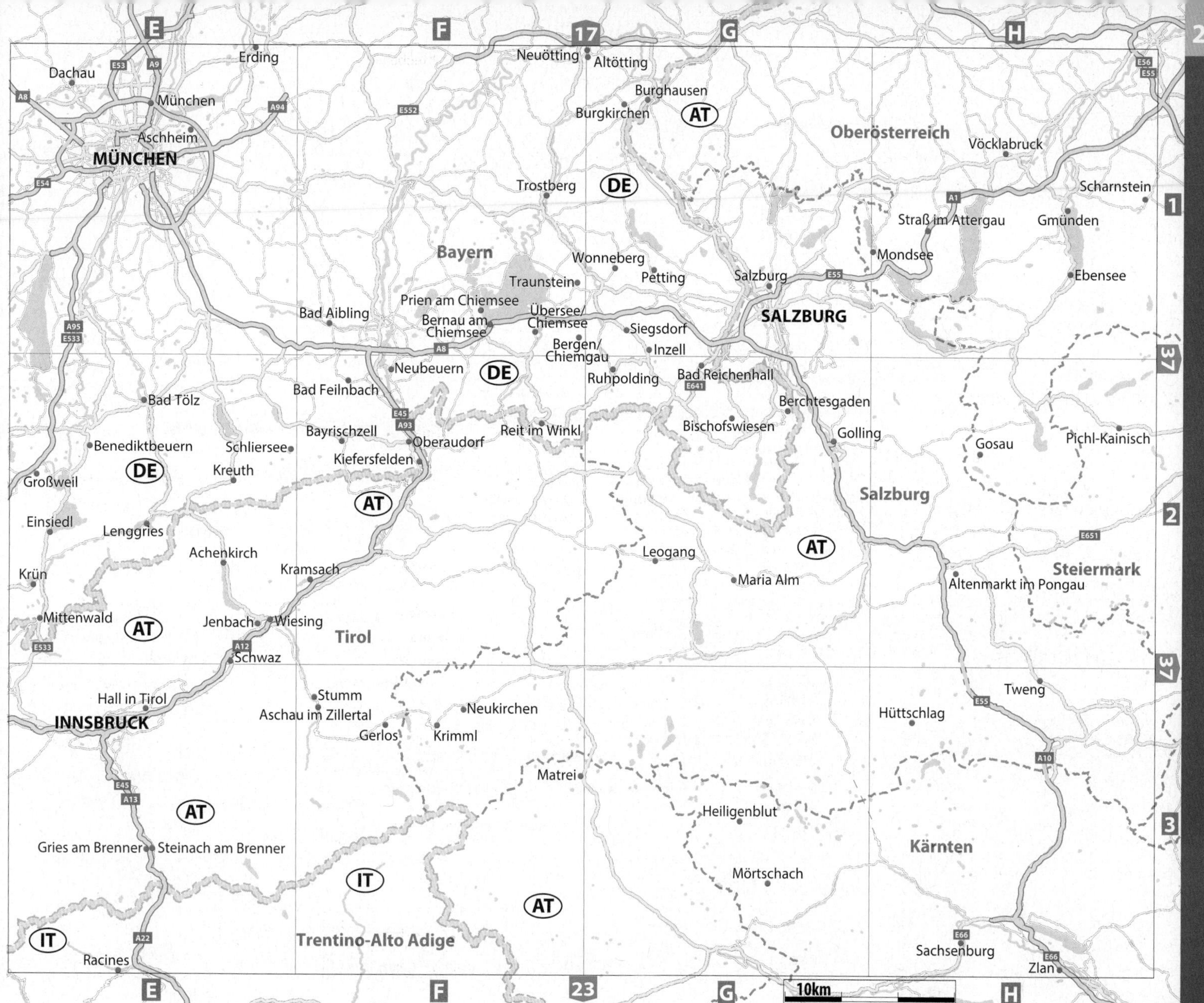
E
F
17
G
H
Dachau
Erding
Neuötting
Altötting
München
Burghausen
Burgkirchen
AT
Aschheim
MÜNCHEN
Oberösterreich
Vöcklabruck
Trostberg
DE
Scharnstein
1
Straß im Attergau
Gmünden
Bayern
Wonneberg
Mondsee
Traunstein
Petting
Salzburg
Ebensee
Prien am Chiemsee
Bad Aibling
Bernau am Chiemsee
Übersee/Chiemsee
SALZBURG
Siegsdorf
Bergen/Chiemgau
Inzell
Neubeuern
DE
Ruhpolding
Bad Reichenhall
37
Bad Feilnbach
Bad Tölz
Berchtesgaden
Bayrischzell
Reit im Winkl
Bischofswiesen
Golling
Benediktbeuern
Schliersee
Oberaudorf
Gosau
Pichl-Kainisch
Kiefersfelden
DE
Kreuth
Großweil
AT
Salzburg
2
Einsiedl
Lenggries
AT
Achenkirch
Leogang
Kramsach
Maria Alm
Steiermark
Krün
Altenmarkt im Pongau
Mittenwald
AT
Jenbach
Wiesing
Tirol
Schwaz
37
Tweng
Stumm
Hall in Tirol
Neukirchen
Hüttschlag
Aschau im Zillertal
INNSBRUCK
Gerlos
Krimml
Matrei
AT
Heiligenblut
3
Gries am Brenner
Steinach am Brenner
Kärnten
IT
Mörtschach
AT
IT
Trentino-Alto Adige
Sachsenburg
Racines
Zlan
E
F
23
G
10km
H

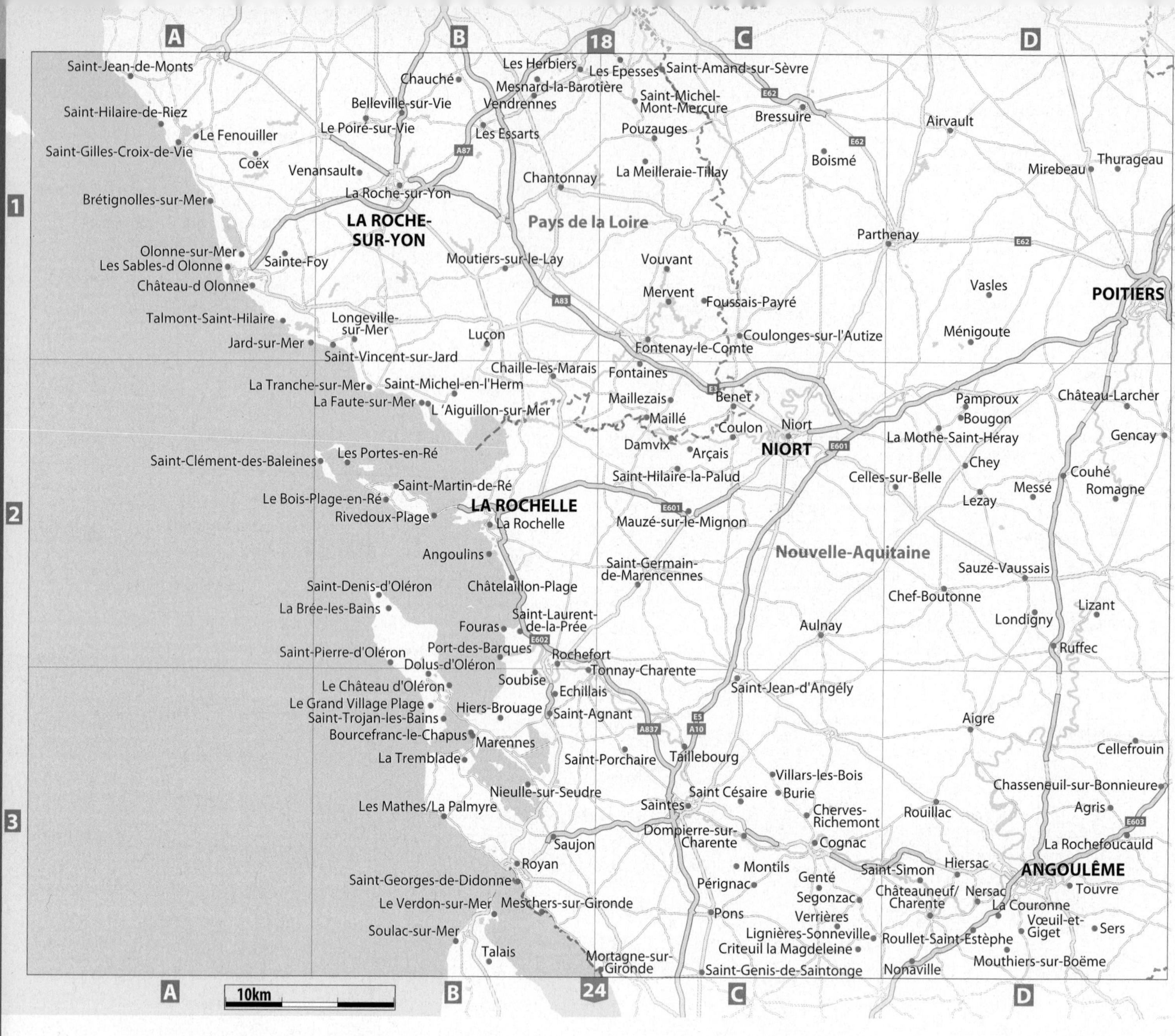

A
B
18
C
D
Saint-Jean-de-Monts
Chauché
Les Herbiers
Les Epesses
Saint-Amand-sur-Sèvre
Mesnard-la-Barotière
Saint-Hilaire-de-Riez
Belleville-sur-Vie
Vendrennes
Saint-Michel-Mont-Mercure
Bressuire
Airvault
Le Fenouiller
Le Poiré-sur-Vie
Les Essarts
Pouzauges
Saint-Gilles-Croix-de-Vie
Coëx
Venansault
Boismé
Thurageau
Mirebeau
Chantonnay
La Meilleraie-Tillay
1
Brétignolles-sur-Mer
La Roche-sur-Yon
LA ROCHE-SUR-YON
Pays de la Loire
Parthenay
Olonne-sur-Mer
Les Sables-d Olonne
Sainte-Foy
Moutiers-sur-le-Lay
Vouvant
Château-d Olonne
Mervent
Foussais-Payré
Vasles
POITIERS
Talmont-Saint-Hilaire
Longeville-sur-Mer
Jard-sur-Mer
Luçon
Coulonges-sur-l'Autize
Ménigoute
Fontenay-le-Comte
Saint-Vincent-sur-Jard
Chaille-les-Marais
Fontaines
La Tranche-sur-Mer
Saint-Michel-en-l'Herm
Maillezais
Benet
Pamproux
Château-Larcher
La Faute-sur-Mer
L 'Aiguillon-sur-Mer
Maillé
Bougon
Coulon
Niort
Damvix
La Mothe-Saint-Héray
Gencay
Arçais
NIORT
Saint-Clément-des-Baleines
Les Portes-en-Ré
Chey
Couhé
Celles-sur-Belle
Saint-Hilaire-la-Palud
Saint-Martin-de-Ré
Messé
Romagne
Le Bois-Plage-en-Ré
LA ROCHELLE
Lezay
2
Rivedoux-Plage
La Rochelle
Mauzé-sur-le-Mignon
Nouvelle-Aquitaine
Angoulins
Saint-Germain-de-Marencennes
Sauzé-Vaussais
Saint-Denis-d'Oléron
Châtelaillon-Plage
Chef-Boutonne
La Brée-les-Bains
Saint-Laurent-de-la-Prée
Lizant
Londigny
Fouras
Aulnay
Saint-Pierre-d'Oléron
Port-des-Barques
Ruffec
Rochefort
Dolus-d'Oléron
Tonnay-Charente
Soubise
Le Château d'Oléron
Echillais
Saint-Jean-d'Angély
Le Grand Village Plage
Hiers-Brouage
Saint-Agnant
Saint-Trojan-les-Bains
Aigre
Bourcefranc-le-Chapus
Marennes
Cellefrouin
La Tremblade
Saint-Porchaire
Taillebourg
Villars-les-Bois
Nieulle-sur-Seudre
Saint Césaire
Burie
Chasseneuil-sur-Bonnieure
Les Mathes/La Palmyre
Saintes
Cherves-Richemont
Rouillac
Agris
3
Dompierre-sur-Charente
Saujon
Cognac
La Rochefoucauld
Royan
Montils
Hiersac
Saint-Simon
ANGOULÊME
Saint-Georges-de-Didonne
Pérignac
Genté
Châteauneuf/Charente
Nersac
Touvre
Segonzac
La Couronne
Le Verdon-sur-Mer
Meschers-sur-Gironde
Pons
Verrières
Vœuil-et-Giget
Sers
Soulac-sur-Mer
Lignières-Sonneville
Roullet-Saint-Estèphe
Talais
Criteuil la Magdeleine
Mortagne-sur-Gironde
Mouthiers-sur-Boëme
Saint-Genis-de-Saintonge
Nonaville
A
10km
B
24
C
D

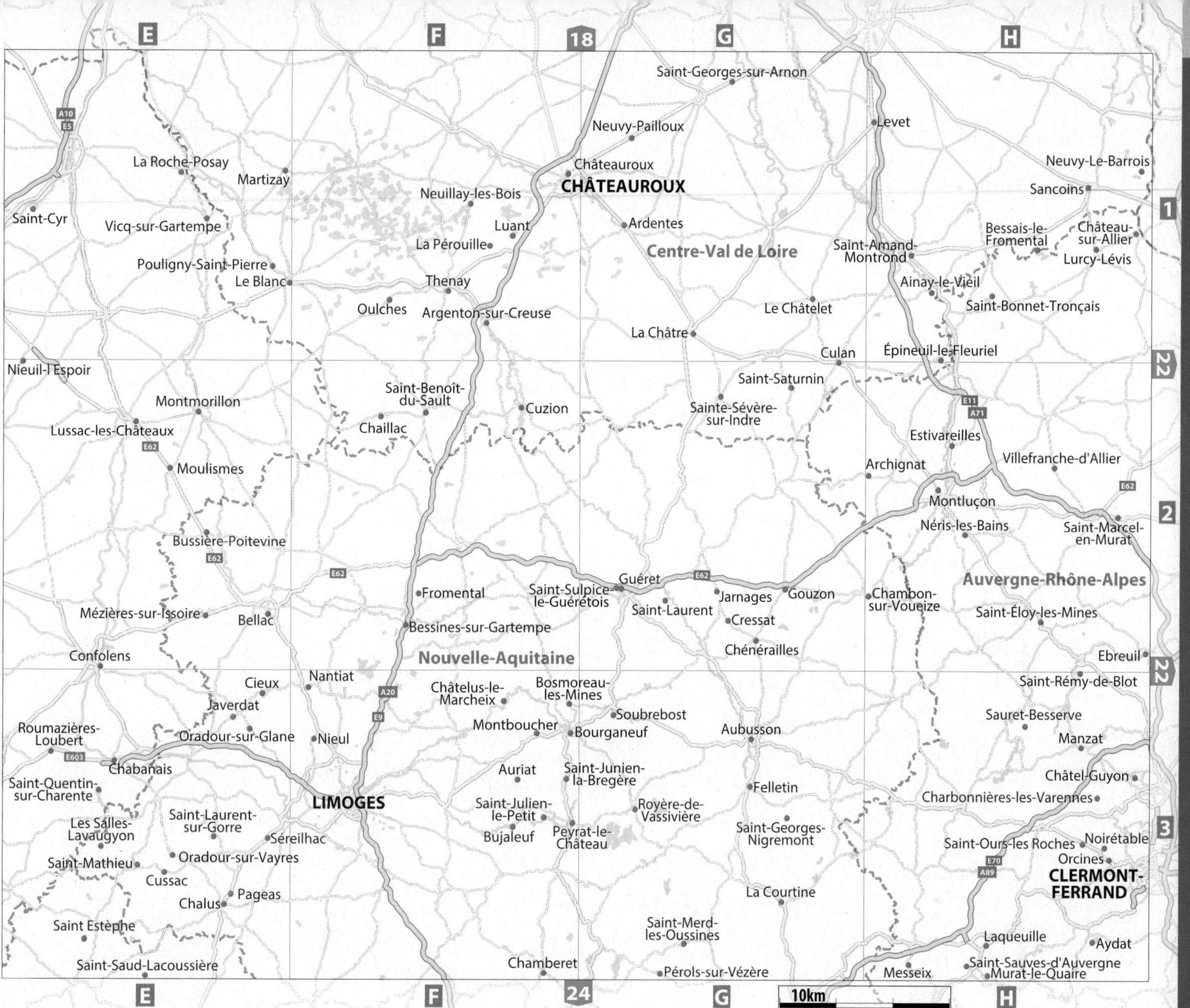
E
F
18
G
H
Saint-Georges-sur-Arnon
Neuvy-Pailloux
Levet
A10
E5
La Roche-Posay
Martizay
Châteauroux
CHÂTEAUROUX
Neuvy-Le-Barrois
Sancoins
Neuillay-les-Bois
Saint-Cyr
Vicq-sur-Gartempe
Luant
Ardentes
Bessais-le-Fromental
Château-sur-Allier
1
La Pérouille
Centre-Val de Loire
Saint-Amand-Montrond
Lurcy-Lévis
Pouligny-Saint-Pierre
Le Blanc
Thenay
Ainay-le-Vieil
Oulches
Argenton-sur-Creuse
Le Châtelet
Saint-Bonnet-Tronçais
La Châtre
Culan
Épineuil-le-Fleuriel
Nieuil-l'Espoir
22
Saint-Saturnin
Saint-Benoît-du-Sault
Montmorillon
Cuzion
Sainte-Sévère-sur-Indre
E11
A71
Chaillac
Lussac-les-Châteaux
E62
Estivareilles
Moulismes
Archignat
Villefranche-d'Allier
Montluçon
2
Néris-les-Bains
Saint-Marcel-en-Murat
Bussière-Poitevine
Guéret
Auvergne-Rhône-Alpes
Fromental
Saint-Sulpice-le-Guérétois
Jarnages
Gouzon
Chambon-sur-Voueize
Mézières-sur-Issoire
Saint-Laurent
Saint-Éloy-les-Mines
Bellac
Cressat
Bessines-sur-Gartempe
Chénérailles
Nouvelle-Aquitaine
Confolens
Ebreuil
Cieux
Nantiat
Châtelus-le-Marcheix
Bosmoreau-les-Mines
Saint-Rémy-de-Blot
22
A20
Javerdat
Soubrebost
Sauret-Besserve
E9
Roumazières-Loubert
Montboucher
Bourganeuf
Aubusson
Manzat
Oradour-sur-Glane
Nieul
E603
Chabanais
Auriat
Saint-Junien-la-Bregère
Châtel-Guyon
Saint-Quentin-sur-Charente
Felletin
Charbonnières-les-Varennes
LIMOGES
Saint-Julien-le-Petit
Royère-de-Vassivière
Les Salles-Lavauguyon
Saint-Laurent-sur-Gorre
Saint-Georges-Nigremont
Noirétable
3
Bujaleuf
Peyrat-le-Château
Séreilhac
Saint-Ours-les Roches
Orcines
Saint-Mathieu
Oradour-sur-Vayres
E70
A89
CLERMONT-FERRAND
Cussac
La Courtine
Pageas
Chalus
Saint Estèphe
Saint-Merd-les-Oussines
Laqueuille
Aydat
Saint-Saud-Lacoussière
Chamberet
Pérols-sur-Vézère
Messeix
Saint-Sauves-d'Auvergne
Murat-le-Quaire
E
F
24
G
10km
H

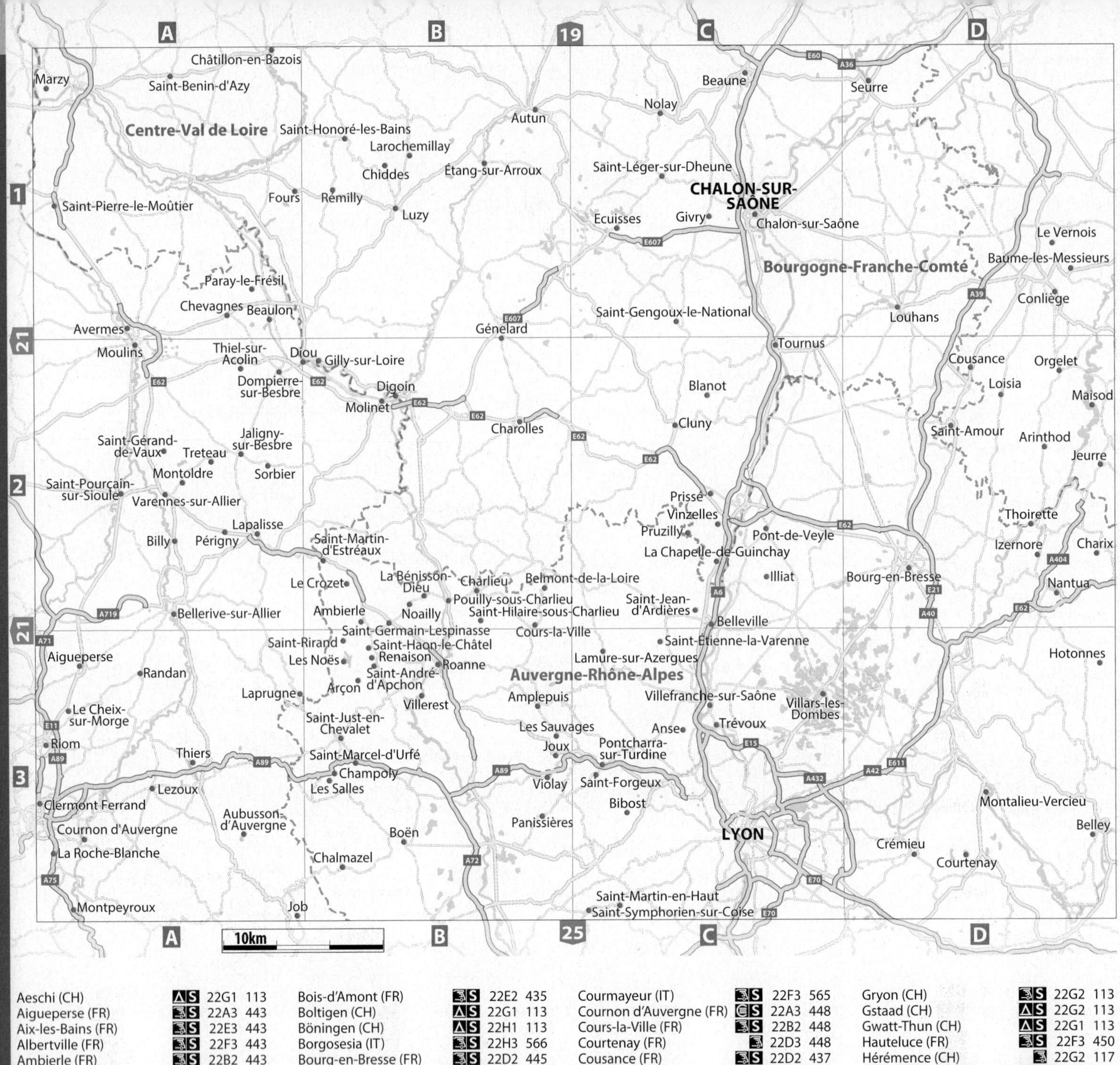
A
B
19
C
D
1
2
3
21
25
10km
Marzy
Châtillon-en-Bazois
Saint-Benin-d'Azy
Centre-Val de Loire
Saint-Honoré-les-Bains
Larochemillay
Chiddes
Étang-sur-Arroux
Autun
Nolay
Beaune
Seurre
Saint-Léger-sur-Dheune
Saint-Pierre-le-Moûtier
Fours
Remilly
Luzy
CHALON-SUR-SAÔNE
Ecuisses
Givry
Chalon-sur-Saône
Le Vernois
Baume-les-Messieurs
Bourgogne-Franche-Comté
Paray-le-Frésil
Chevagnes
Beaulon
Saint-Gengoux-le-National
Louhans
Conliège
Avermes
Moulins
Thiel-sur-Acolin
Diou
Gilly-sur-Loire
Génelard
Tournus
Cousance
Orgelet
Dompierre-sur-Besbre
Digoin
Molinet
Blanot
Loisia
Maisod
Charolles
Cluny
Saint-Amour
Arinthod
Saint-Gérand-de-Vaux
Treteau
Jaligny-sur-Besbre
Sorbier
Jeurre
Saint-Pourçain-sur-Sioule
Montoldre
Varennes-sur-Allier
Prissé
Vinzelles
Pruzilly
Thoirette
Lapalisse
Billy
Périgny
Saint-Martin-d'Estréaux
La Chapelle-de-Guinchay
Pont-de-Veyle
Izernore
Charix
Le Crozet
La Bénisson-Dieu
Charlieu
Belmont-de-la-Loire
Illiat
Bourg-en-Bresse
Nantua
Bellerive-sur-Allier
Ambierle
Noailly
Pouilly-sous-Charlieu
Saint-Hilaire-sous-Charlieu
Saint-Jean-d'Ardières
Belleville
Saint-Germain-Lespinasse
Cours-la-Ville
Saint-Étienne-la-Varenne
Aigueperse
Saint-Rirand
Les Noës
Saint-Haon-le-Châtel
Renaison
Roanne
Lamure-sur-Azergues
Hotonnes
Randan
Saint-André-d'Apchon
Arçon
Auvergne-Rhône-Alpes
Laprugne
Villerest
Amplepuis
Villefranche-sur-Saône
Villars-les-Dombes
Le Cheix-sur-Morge
Saint-Just-en-Chevalet
Les Sauvages
Anse
Trévoux
Riom
Thiers
Saint-Marcel-d'Urfé
Joux
Pontcharra-sur-Turdine
Champoly
Lezoux
Les Salles
Violay
Saint-Forgeux
Clermont Ferrand
Bibost
Montalieu-Vercieu
Aubusson-d'Auvergne
Panissières
Belley
Cournon d'Auvergne
Boën
LYON
Crémieu
La Roche-Blanche
Chalmazel
Courtenay
Saint-Martin-en-Haut
Montpeyroux
Job
Saint-Symphorien-sur-Coise
E60
A36
E607
A39
E62
A6
A404
E21
A40
A719
A71
E11
A89
E15
E611
A42
A432
A72
A75
E70

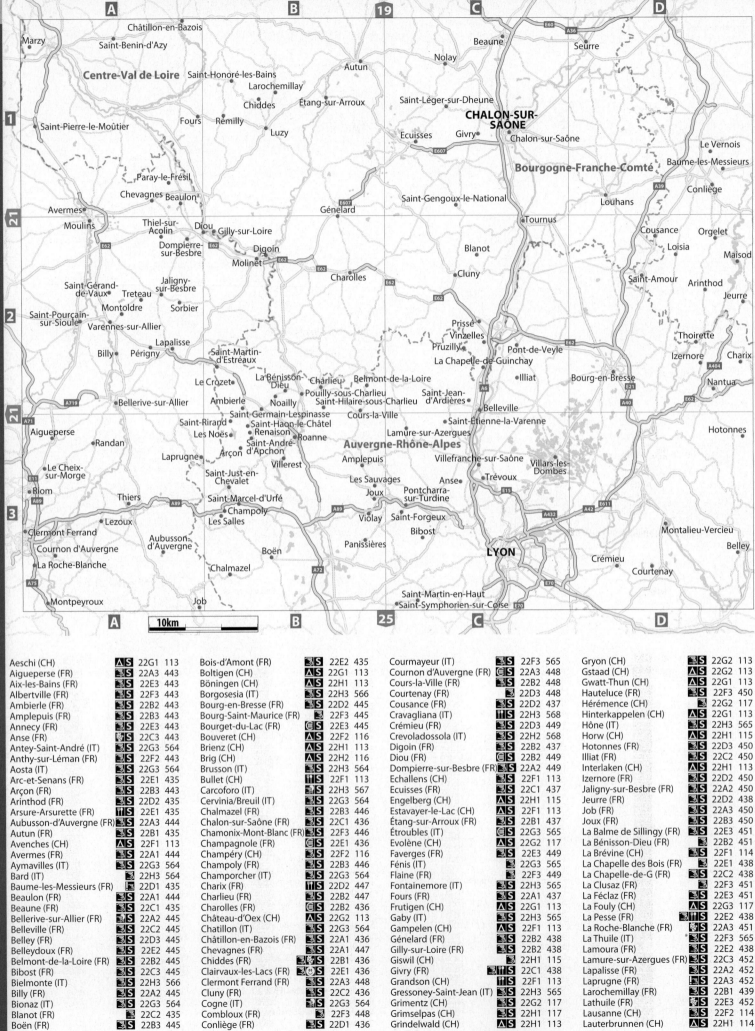

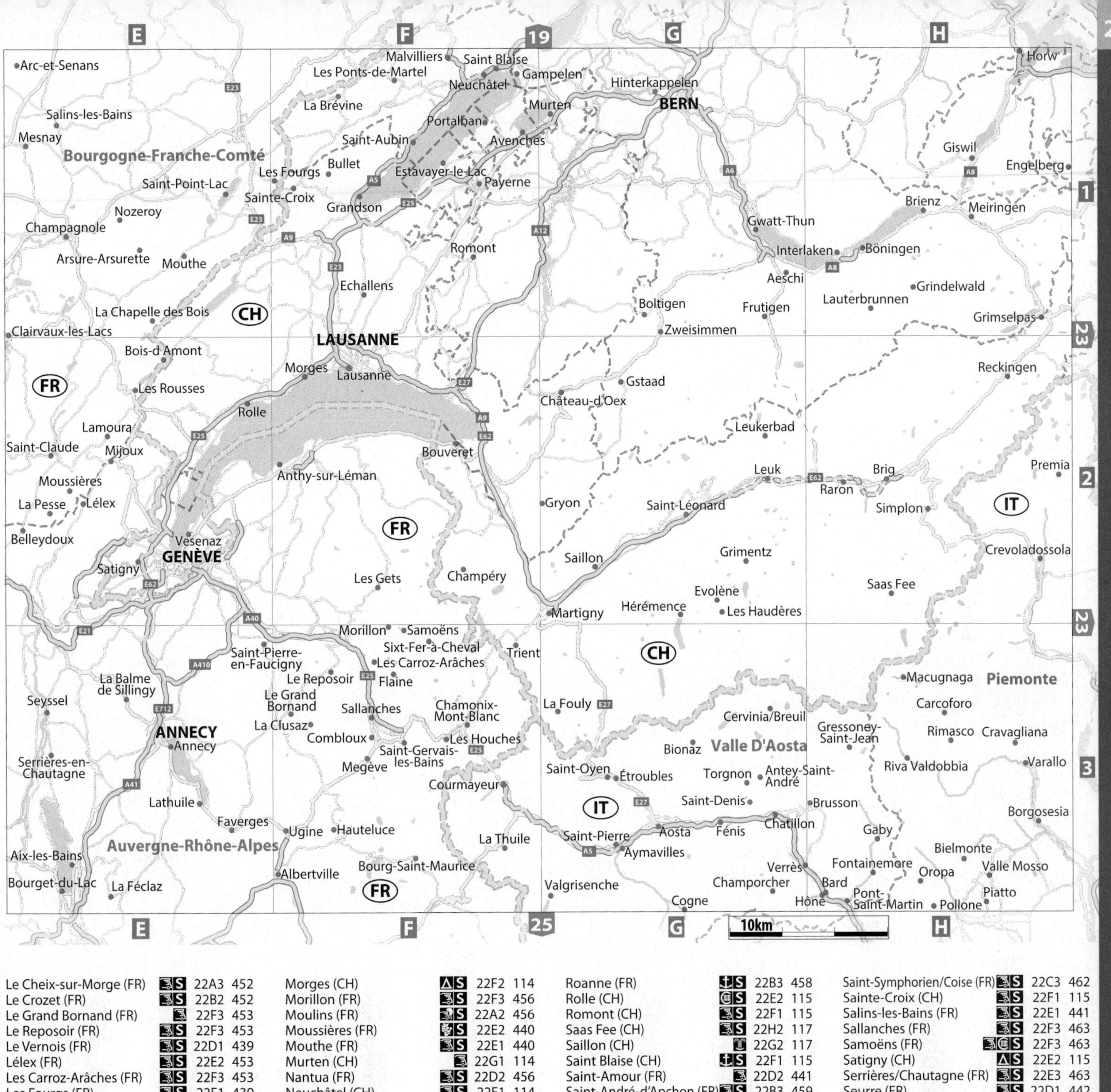

Place	Grid	Page
Le Cheix-sur-Morge (FR)	22A3	452
Le Crozet (FR)	22B2	452
Le Grand Bornand (FR)	22F3	453
Le Reposoir (FR)	22F3	453
Le Vernois (FR)	22D1	439
Lélex (FR)	22E2	453
Les Carroz-Arâches (FR)	22F3	453
Les Fourgs (FR)	22F1	439
Les Gets (FR)	22F2	453
Les Haudères (CH)	22G2	117
Les Houches (FR)	22F3	453
Les Noës (FR)	22B3	454
Les Ponts-de-Martel (CH)	22F1	114
Les Rousses (FR)	22E2	439
Les Salles (FR)	22B3	454
Les Sauvages (FR)	22B3	454
Leuk (CH)	22G2	117
Leukerbad (CH)	22G2	117
Lezoux (FR)	22A3	454
Loisia (FR)	22D2	439
Louhans (FR)	22D1	439
Luzy (FR)	22B1	439
Macugnaga (IT)	22H3	569
Maisod (FR)	22D2	439
Malvilliers (CH)	22F1	114
Martigny (CH)	22G2	117
Marzy (FR)	22A1	439
Megève (FR)	22F3	454
Meiringen (CH)	22H1	114
Mesnay (FR)	22E1	439
Mijoux (FR)	22E2	455
Molinet (FR)	22B2	455
Montalieu-Vercieu (FR)	22D3	455
Montoldre (FR)	22A2	455
Montpeyroux (FR)	22A3	455
Morges (CH)	22F2	114
Morillon (FR)	22F3	456
Moulins (FR)	22A2	456
Moussières (FR)	22E2	440
Mouthe (FR)	22E1	440
Murten (CH)	22G1	114
Nantua (FR)	22D2	456
Neuchâtel (CH)	22F1	114
Noailly (FR)	22B2	456
Nolay (FR)	22C1	440
Nozeroy (FR)	22E1	440
Orgelet (FR)	22D2	440
Oropa (IT)	22H3	571
Panissières (FR)	22B3	457
Paray-le-Frésil (FR)	22A1	457
Payerne (CH)	22F1	114
Périgny (FR)	22A2	457
Piatto (IT)	22H3	571
Pollone (IT)	22H3	571
Pont-de-Veyle (FR)	22C2	457
Pont-Saint-Martin (IT)	22H3	565
Pontcharra/Turdine (FR)	22C3	457
Portalban (CH)	22F1	114
Pouilly-sous-Charlieu (FR)	22B2	457
Premia (IT)	22H2	572
Prissé (FR)	22C2	440
Pruzilly (FR)	22C2	440
Randan (FR)	22A3	458
Raron (CH)	22H2	117
Reckingen (CH)	22H2	117
Rémilly (FR)	22B1	440
Renaison (FR)	22B3	458
Rimasco (IT)	22H3	572
Riom (FR)	22A3	458
Riva Valdobbia (IT)	22H3	572
Roanne (FR)	22B3	458
Rolle (CH)	22E2	115
Romont (CH)	22F1	115
Saas Fee (CH)	22H2	117
Saillon (CH)	22G2	117
Saint Blaise (CH)	22F1	115
Saint-Amour (FR)	22D2	441
Saint-André-d'Apchon (FR)	22B3	459
Saint-Aubin (CH)	22F1	115
Saint-Benin-d'Azy (FR)	22A1	441
Saint-Claude (FR)	22E2	441
Saint-Denis (IT)	22G3	565
Saint-Étienne-la-V (FR)	22C3	459
Saint-Forgeux (FR)	22C3	460
Saint-Gengoux-le-N (FR)	22C1	441
Saint-Gérand-de-Vaux (FR)	22A2	460
Saint-Germain-L (FR)	22B2	460
Saint-Gervais/Bains (FR)	22F3	460
Saint-Haon-le-Châtel (FR)	22B3	460
Saint-Hilaire/Charlieu (FR)	22B2	460
Saint-Honoré/Bains (FR)	22B1	441
Saint-Jean-d'Ardières (FR)	22C2	460
Saint-Just/Chevalet (FR)	22B3	461
Saint-Léger/Dheune (FR)	22C1	441
Saint-Léonard (CH)	22G2	117
Saint-Marcel-d'Urfé (FR)	22B3	461
Saint-Martin-d'Estréaux (FR)	22B2	461
Saint-Martin-en-Haut (FR)	22C3	461
Saint-Oyen (IT)	22G3	565
Saint-Pierre (IT)	22G3	565
Saint-Pierre/Faucigny (FR)	22E3	461
Saint-Pierre-le-Moûtier (FR)	22A1	441
Saint-Point-Lac (FR)	22E1	441
Saint-Pourçain/Sioule (FR)	22A2	462
Saint-Rirand (FR)	22B3	462
Saint-Symphorien/Coise (FR)	22C3	462
Sainte-Croix (CH)	22F1	115
Salins-les-Bains (FR)	22E1	441
Sallanches (FR)	22F3	463
Samoëns (FR)	22F3	463
Satigny (CH)	22E2	115
Serrières/Chautagne (FR)	22E3	463
Seurre (FR)	22D1	442
Seyssel (FR)	22E3	463
Simplon (CH)	22H2	117
Sixt-Fer-à-Cheval (FR)	22F3	463
Sorbier (FR)	22A2	463
Thiel-sur-Acolin (FR)	22A2	464
Thiers (FR)	22A3	464
Thoirette (FR)	22D2	442
Torgnon (IT)	22G3	565
Tournus (FR)	22C2	442
Treteau (FR)	22A2	465
Trévoux (FR)	22C3	465
Trient (CH)	22F3	117
Ugine (FR)	22F3	465
Valgrisenche (IT)	22G3	565
Valle Mosso (IT)	22H3	574
Varallo (IT)	22H3	574
Varennes-sur-Allier (FR)	22A2	465
Verrès (IT)	22G3	565
Vesenaz (CH)	22E2	115
Villars-les-Dombes (FR)	22C3	466
Villefranche/Saône (FR)	22C3	466
Villerest (FR)	22B3	466
Vinzelles (FR)	22C2	442
Violay (FR)	22B3	466
Zweisimmen (CH)	22G1	115

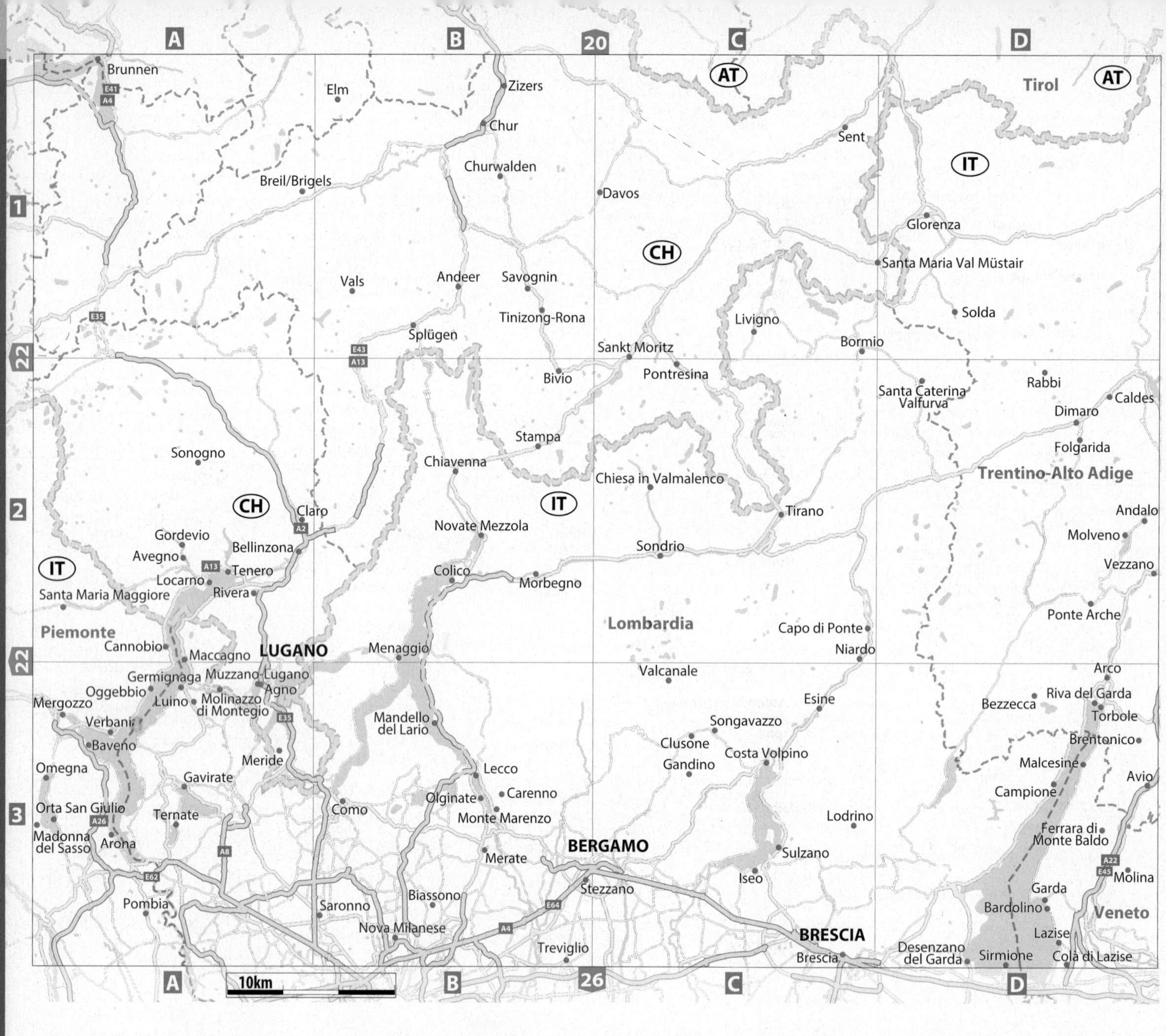
A
B
20
C
D
Brunnen
E41
A4
Elm
Zizers
Chur
AT
Tirol
AT
Sent
Churwalden
IT
Breil/Brigels
Davos
1
Glorenza
CH
Santa Maria Val Müstair
Vals
Andeer
Savognin
Solda
E35
Tinizong-Rona
Livigno
Splügen
Bormio
22
E43
A13
Sankt Moritz
Pontresina
Bivio
Santa Caterina Valfurva
Rabbi
Caldes
Dimaro
Stampa
Folgarida
Sonogno
Chiavenna
Trentino-Alto Adige
Chiesa in Valmalenco
CH
Claro
IT
2
Tirano
Andalo
A2
Novate Mezzola
Gordevio
Bellinzona
Molveno
Avegno
A13
Tenero
Sondrio
IT
Colico
Vezzano
Locarno
Morbegno
Santa Maria Maggiore
Rivera
Ponte Arche
Lombardia
Piemonte
Capo di Ponte
Cannobio
Maccagno
LUGANO
Menaggio
Niardo
22
Germignaga
Muzzano-Lugano
Valcanale
Arco
Oggebbio
Agno
Riva del Garda
Mergozzo
Luino
Molinazzo di Montegio
Esine
Bezzecca
Torbole
Verbania
E35
Mandello del Lario
Songavazzo
Brentonico
Baveno
Clusone
Costa Volpino
Meride
Malcesine
Omegna
Gandino
Lecco
Gavirate
Avio
Carenno
Campione
3
Orta San Giulio
Ternate
Como
Olginate
Lodrino
A26
Monte Marenzo
Ferrara di Monte Baldo
Madonna del Sasso
Arona
A8
Merate
BERGAMO
Sulzano
A22
E45
Molina
E62
Iseo
Stezzano
Garda
Pombia
Biassono
Saronno
E64
Bardolino
Veneto
Nova Milanese
A4
BRESCIA
Lazise
Treviglio
Desenzano del Garda
Brescia
Sirmione
Colà di Lazise
A
10km
B
26
C
D

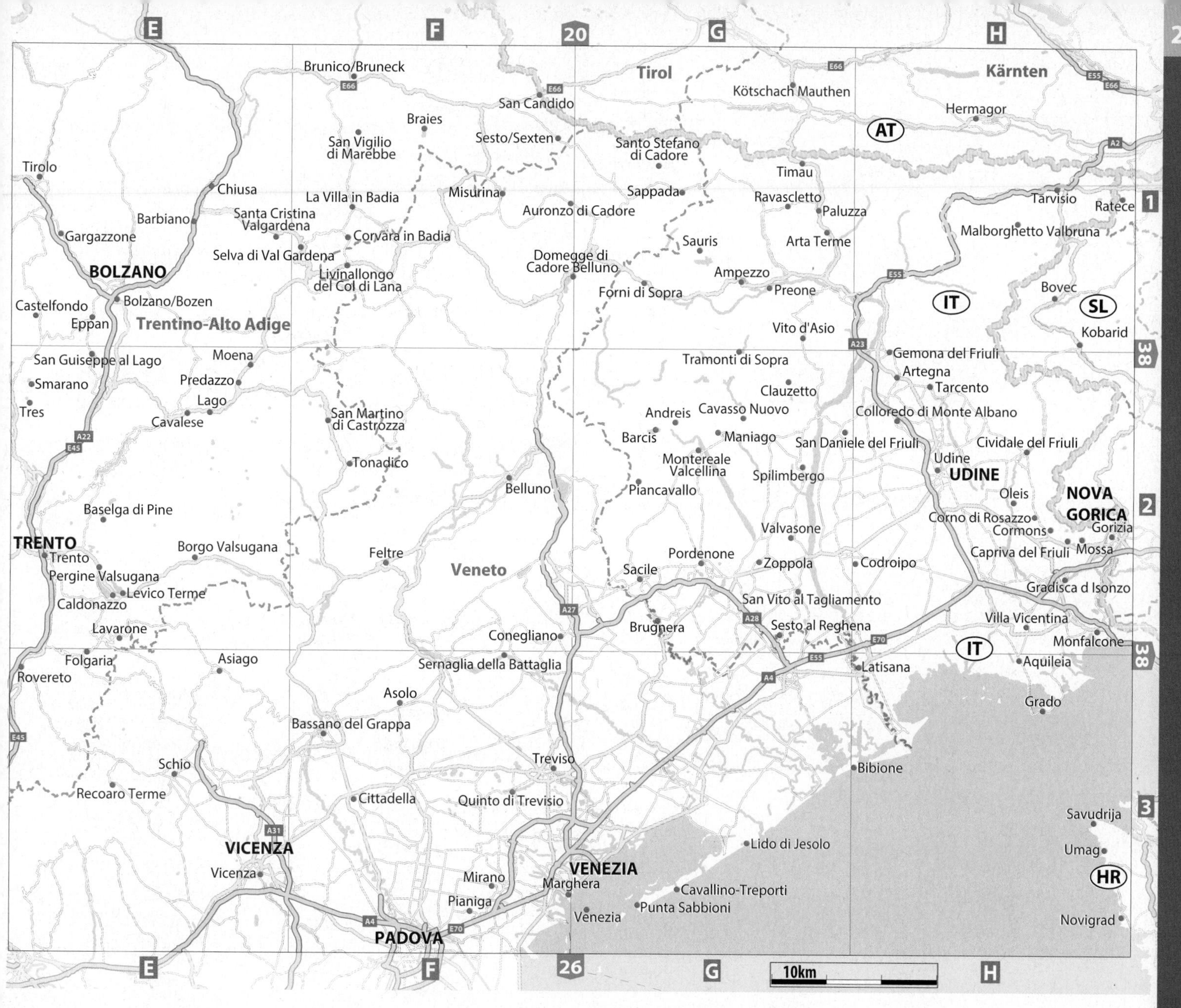
E
F
20
G
H
Brunico/Bruneck
Tirol
Kötschach Mauthen
Kärnten
San Candido
Hermagor
Braies
San Vigilio di Marebbe
Sesto/Sexten
Santo Stefano di Cadore
AT
Tirolo
Timau
Chiusa
La Villa in Badia
Misurina
Sappada
Ravascletto
Tarvisio
Ratece
1
Barbiano
Santa Cristina Valgardena
Auronzo di Cadore
Paluzza
Gargazzone
Corvara in Badia
Sauris
Arta Terme
Malborghetto Valbruna
Selva di Val Gardena
Domegge di Cadore Belluno
BOLZANO
Livinallongo del Col di Lana
Ampezzo
Forni di Sopra
Preone
Bovec
Castelfondo
Bolzano/Bozen
IT
SL
Eppan
Trentino-Alto Adige
Vito d'Asio
Kobarid
Moena
Tramonti di Sopra
Gemona del Friuli
38
San Guiseppe al Lago
Artegna
Smarano
Predazzo
Clauzetto
Tarcento
Lago
Tres
Cavalese
San Martino di Castrozza
Andreis
Cavasso Nuovo
Colloredo di Monte Albano
Barcis
Maniago
San Daniele del Friuli
Cividale del Friuli
Montereale Valcellina
Udine
Tonadico
UDINE
Spilimbergo
Belluno
Piancavallo
Oleis
NOVA GORICA
2
Baselga di Pine
Corno di Rosazzo
Gorizia
Valvasone
Cormons
TRENTO
Borgo Valsugana
Capriva del Friuli
Mossa
Trento
Feltre
Pordenone
Veneto
Zoppola
Codroipo
Pergine Valsugana
Sacile
Gradisca d Isonzo
Levico Terme
San Vito al Tagliamento
Caldonazzo
Villa Vicentina
Lavarone
Brugnera
Sesto al Reghena
Conegliano
Monfalcone
Folgaria
Asiago
IT
Sernaglia della Battaglia
Latisana
Aquileia
Rovereto
Asolo
Grado
Bassano del Grappa
Schio
Treviso
Bibione
Recoaro Terme
Cittadella
Quinto di Trevisio
3
Savudrija
Lido di Jesolo
VICENZA
Umag
Vicenza
VENEZIA
Mirano
HR
Marghera
Cavallino-Treporti
Pianiga
Punta Sabbioni
Venezia
Novigrad
PADOVA
E
F
26
G
10km
H

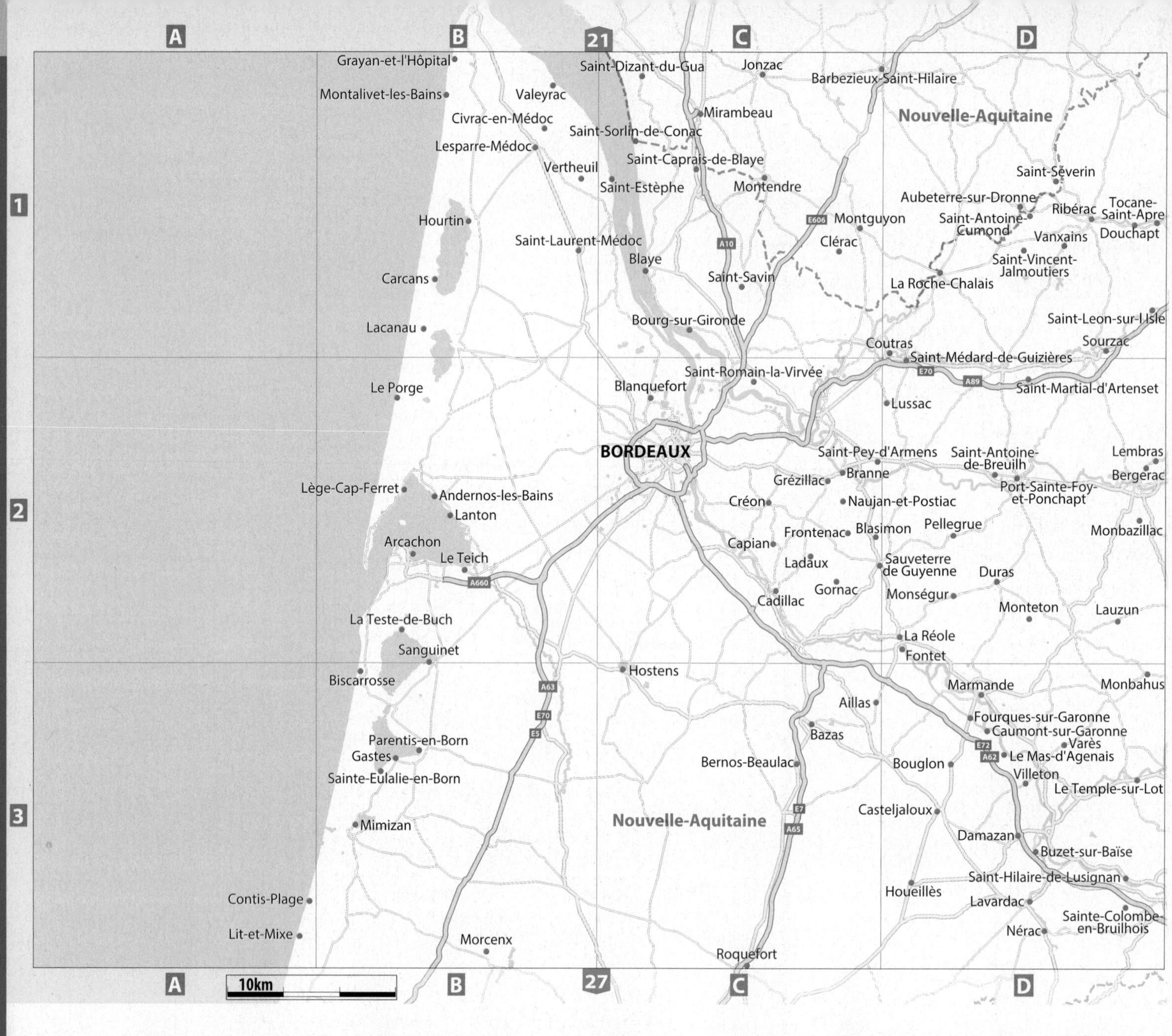

A
B
C
D
21
27
1
2
3
10km
Grayan-et-l'Hôpital
Montalivet-les-Bains
Valeyrac
Civrac-en-Médoc
Lesparre-Médoc
Vertheuil
Saint-Estèphe
Saint-Dizant-du-Gua
Saint-Sorlin-de-Conac
Saint-Caprais-de-Blaye
Jonzac
Mirambeau
Montendre
Barbezieux-Saint-Hilaire
Nouvelle-Aquitaine
Saint-Séverin
Aubeterre-sur-Dronne
Ribérac
Tocane-Saint-Apre
Saint-Antoine-Cumond
Vanxains
Douchapt
Saint-Vincent-Jalmoutiers
La Roche-Chalais
Montguyon
Clérac
Hourtin
Saint-Laurent-Médoc
Blaye
Carcans
Saint-Savin
Lacanau
Bourg-sur-Gironde
Coutras
Saint-Médard-de-Guizières
Saint-Leon-sur-l'Isle
Sourzac
Saint-Martial-d'Artenset
Saint-Romain-la-Virvée
Blanquefort
Le Porge
Lussac
BORDEAUX
Saint-Pey-d'Armens
Saint-Antoine-de-Breuilh
Lembras
Bergerac
Grézillac
Branne
Port-Sainte-Foy-et-Ponchapt
Lège-Cap-Ferret
Andernos-les-Bains
Lanton
Créon
Naujan-et-Postiac
Frontenac
Blasimon
Pellegrue
Monbazillac
Arcachon
Le Teich
Capian
Ladaux
Sauveterre de Guyenne
Duras
Gornac
Cadillac
Monségur
Monteton
Lauzun
La Teste-de-Buch
La Réole
Fontet
Sanguinet
Hostens
Biscarrosse
Marmande
Monbahus
Aillas
Fourques-sur-Garonne
Caumont-sur-Garonne
Varès
Bazas
Le Mas-d'Agenais
Parentis-en-Born
Gastes
Bernos-Beaulac
Bouglon
Villeton
Sainte-Eulalie-en-Born
Le Temple-sur-Lot
Casteljaloux
Mimizan
Nouvelle-Aquitaine
Damazan
Buzet-sur-Baïse
Saint-Hilaire-de-Lusignan
Houeillès
Lavardac
Contis-Plage
Sainte-Colombe-en-Bruilhois
Nérac
Lit-et-Mixe
Morcenx
Roquefort
A10
E606
E70
A89
A660
A63
E5
E72
A62
E7
A65

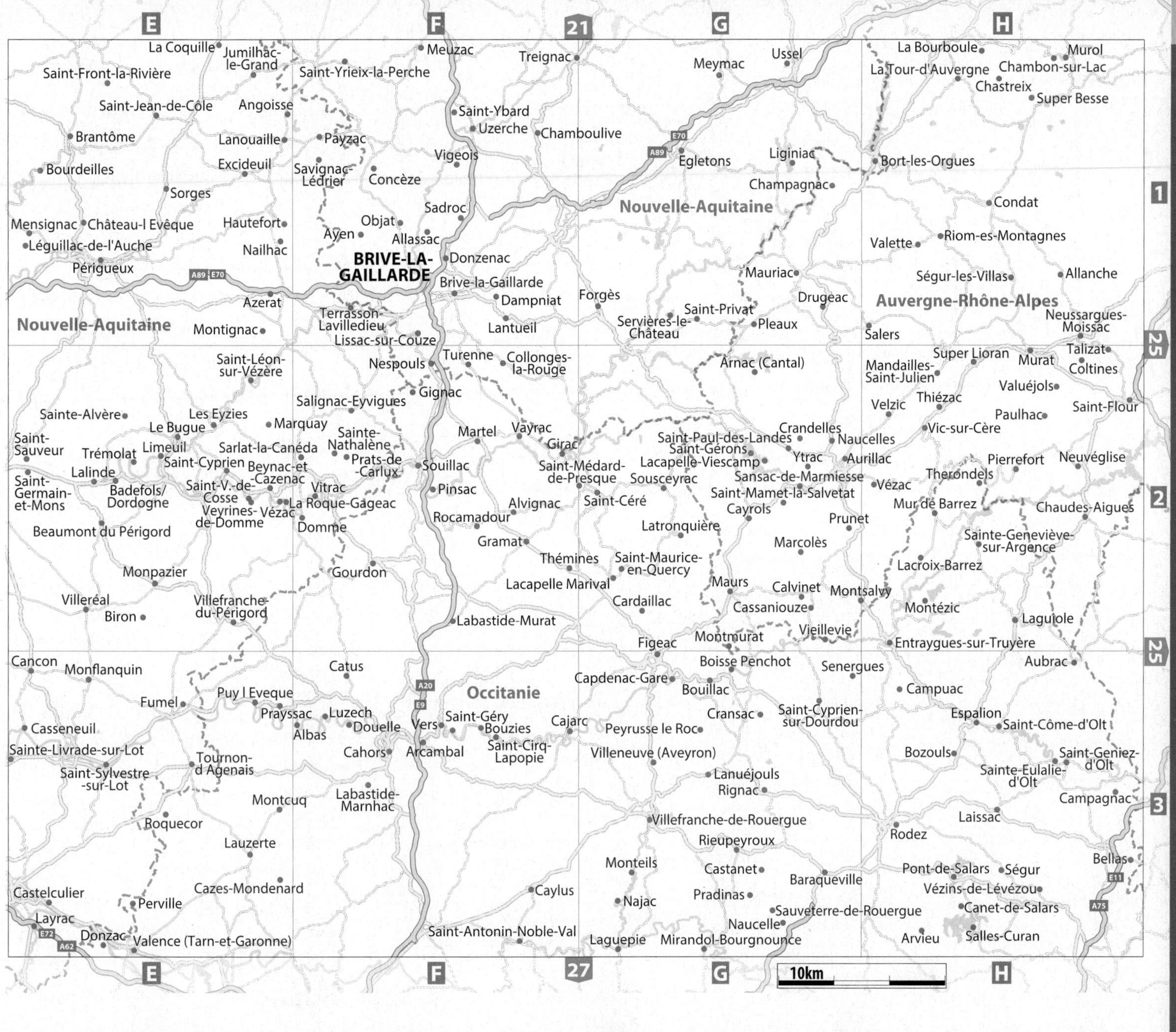
E
F
21
G
H
La Coquille
Jumilhac-le-Grand
Meuzac
Treignac
Meymac
Ussel
La Bourboule
Murol
Saint-Front-la-Rivière
Saint-Yrieix-la-Perche
La Tour-d'Auvergne
Chambon-sur-Lac
Chastreix
Super Besse
Saint-Jean-de-Côle
Angoisse
Saint-Ybard
Uzerche
Chamboulive
Brantôme
Lanouaille
Payzac
Vigeois
Egletons
Liginiac
Bort-les-Orgues
Bourdeilles
Excideuil
Savignac-Lédrier
Concèze
Champagnac
Sorges
Sadroc
Nouvelle-Aquitaine
Condat
1
Mensignac
Château-l Evêque
Hautefort
Objat
Ayen
Allassac
Valette
Riom-es-Montagnes
Léguillac-de-l'Auche
Nailhac
BRIVE-LA-GAILLARDE
Donzenac
Périgueux
Mauriac
Ségur-les-Villas
Allanche
Brive-la-Gaillarde
Azerat
Dampniat
Forgès
Drugeac
Auvergne-Rhône-Alpes
Terrasson-Lavilledieu
Saint-Privat
Nouvelle-Aquitaine
Montignac
Lantueil
Servières-le-Château
Pleaux
Neussargues-Moissac
Lissac-sur-Couze
Salers
Saint-Léon-sur-Vézère
Turenne
Collonges-la-Rouge
Arnac (Cantal)
Super Lioran
Murat
Talizat
Nespouls
Mandailles-Saint-Julien
Coltines
Gignac
Valuéjols
Salignac-Eyvigues
Velzic
Thiézac
Saint-Flour
Sainte-Alvère
Les Eyzies
Marquay
Paulhac
Le Bugue
Sainte-Nathalène
Martel
Vayrac
Crandelles
Vic-sur-Cère
Saint-Sauveur
Trémolat
Limeuil
Sarlat-la-Canéda
Prats-de-Carlux
Girac
Saint-Paul-des-Landes
Naucelles
Saint-Cyprien
Beynac-et-Cazenac
Souillac
Saint-Gérons
Pierrefort
Neuvéglise
Lalinde
Saint-Médard-de-Presque
Lacapelle-Viescamp
Ytrac
Aurillac
Saint-Germain-et-Mons
Badefols/Dordogne
Saint-V.-de-Cosse
Vitrac
Sousceyrac
Sansac-de-Marmiesse
Vézac
Therondels
Veyrines-de-Domme
Vézac
La Roque-Gageac
Pinsac
Saint-Mamet-la-Salvetat
Mur de Barrez
Chaudes-Aigues
2
Alvignac
Saint-Céré
Cayrols
Beaumont du Périgord
Domme
Rocamadour
Latronquière
Prunet
Sainte-Geneviève-sur-Argence
Gramat
Marcolès
Thémines
Saint-Maurice-en-Quercy
Lacroix-Barrez
Monpazier
Gourdon
Lacapelle Marival
Maurs
Calvinet
Montsalvy
Villeréal
Villefranche-du-Périgord
Cardaillac
Cassaniouze
Montézic
Biron
Laguiole
Labastide-Murat
Vieillevie
Figeac
Montmurat
Entraygues-sur-Truyère
25
Cancon
Monflanquin
Catus
Boisse Penchot
Senergues
Aubrac
Capdenac-Gare
Puy l Eveque
Occitanie
Bouillac
Campuac
Fumel
Prayssac
Luzech
Cransac
Saint-Cyprien-sur-Dourdou
Espalion
Casseneuil
Albas
Douelle
Vers
Saint-Géry
Bouzies
Cajarc
Peyrusse le Roc
Saint-Côme-d'Olt
Sainte-Livrade-sur-Lot
Cahors
Arcambal
Saint-Cirq-Lapopie
Villeneuve (Aveyron)
Bozouls
Saint-Geniez-d'Olt
Tournon-d'Agenais
Saint-Sylvestre-sur-Lot
Lanuéjouls
Sainte-Eulalie-d'Olt
Rignac
Montcuq
Labastide-Marnhac
Campagnac
Villefranche-de-Rouergue
Laissac
3
Roquecor
Rodez
Rieupeyroux
Lauzerte
Bellas
Monteils
Castanet
Pont-de-Salars
Ségur
Baraqueville
Cazes-Mondenard
Vézins-de-Lévézou
Castelculier
Caylus
Perville
Najac
Pradinas
Sauveterre-de-Rouergue
Canet-de-Salars
Layrac
Naucelle
Donzac
Valence (Tarn-et-Garonne)
Saint-Antonin-Noble-Val
Laguepie
Mirandol-Bourgnounce
Arvieu
Salles-Curan
E
F
27
G
10km
H

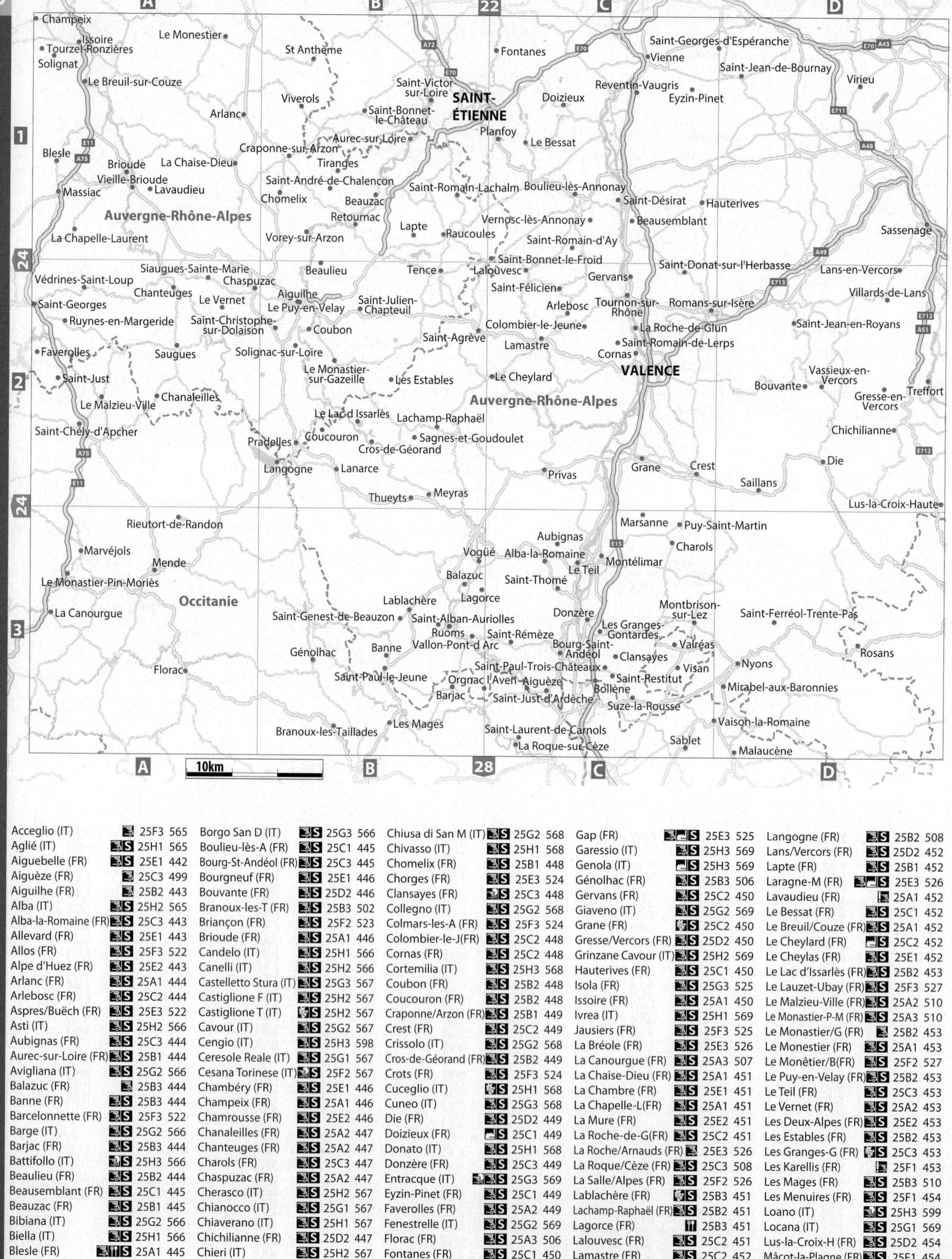

Place	Grid	Page
Acceglio (IT)	25F3	565
Agliè (IT)	25H1	565
Aiguebelle (FR)	25E1	442
Aiguèze (FR)	25C3	499
Aiguilhe (FR)	25B2	443
Alba (IT)	25H2	565
Alba-la-Romaine (FR)	25C3	443
Allevard (FR)	25E1	443
Allos (FR)	25F3	522
Alpe d'Huez (FR)	25E2	443
Arlanc (FR)	25A1	444
Arlebosc (FR)	25C2	444
Aspres/Buëch (FR)	25E3	522
Asti (IT)	25H2	566
Aubignas (FR)	25C3	444
Aurec-sur-Loire (FR)	25B1	444
Avigliana (IT)	25G2	566
Balazuc (FR)	25B3	444
Banne (FR)	25B3	444
Barcelonnette (FR)	25F3	522
Barge (IT)	25G2	566
Barjac (FR)	25B3	444
Battifollo (IT)	25H3	566
Beaulieu (FR)	25B2	444
Beausemblant (FR)	25C1	445
Beauzac (FR)	25B1	445
Bibiana (IT)	25G2	566
Biella (IT)	25H1	566
Blesle (FR)	25A1	445
Bollène (FR)	25C3	523
Borgo San D (IT)	25G3	566
Boulieu-lès-A (FR)	25C1	445
Bourg-St-Andéol (FR)	25C3	445
Bourgneuf (FR)	25E1	446
Bouvante (FR)	25D2	446
Branoux-les-T (FR)	25B3	502
Briançon (FR)	25F2	523
Brioude (FR)	25A1	446
Candelo (IT)	25H1	566
Canelli (IT)	25H2	566
Castelletto Stura (IT)	25G3	567
Castiglione F (IT)	25H2	567
Castiglione T (IT)	25H2	567
Cavour (IT)	25G2	567
Cengio (IT)	25H3	598
Ceresole Reale (IT)	25G1	567
Cesana Torinese (IT)	25F2	567
Chambéry (FR)	25E1	446
Champeix (FR)	25A1	446
Chamrousse (FR)	25E2	446
Chanaleilles (FR)	25A2	447
Chanteuges (FR)	25A2	447
Charols (FR)	25C3	447
Chaspuzac (FR)	25A2	447
Cherasco (IT)	25H2	567
Chianocco (IT)	25G1	567
Chiaverano (IT)	25H1	567
Chichilianne (FR)	25D2	447
Chieri (IT)	25H2	567
Chiusa/Pesio (IT)	25H3	568
Chiusa di San M (IT)	25G2	568
Chivasso (IT)	25H1	568
Chomelix (FR)	25B1	448
Chorges (FR)	25E3	524
Clansayes (FR)	25C3	448
Collegno (IT)	25G2	568
Colmars-les-A (FR)	25F3	524
Colombier-le-J(FR)	25C2	448
Cornas (FR)	25C2	448
Cortemilia (IT)	25H3	568
Coubon (FR)	25B2	448
Coucouron (FR)	25B2	448
Craponne/Arzon (FR)	25B1	449
Crest (FR)	25C2	449
Crissolo (IT)	25G2	568
Cros-de-Géorand (FR)	25B2	449
Crots (FR)	25F3	524
Cuceglio (IT)	25H1	568
Cuneo (IT)	25G3	568
Die (FR)	25D2	449
Doizieux (FR)	25C1	449
Donato (IT)	25H1	568
Donzère (FR)	25C3	449
Entracque (IT)	25G3	569
Eyzin-Pinet (FR)	25C1	449
Faverolles (FR)	25A2	449
Fenestrelle (IT)	25G2	569
Florac (FR)	25A3	506
Fontanes (FR)	25C1	450
Frabosa Soprana (IT)	25H3	569
Gap (FR)	25E3	525
Garessio (IT)	25H3	569
Genola (IT)	25H3	569
Génolhac (FR)	25B3	506
Gervans (FR)	25C2	450
Giaveno (IT)	25G2	569
Grane (FR)	25C2	450
Gresse/Vercors (FR)	25D2	450
Grinzane Cavour (IT)	25H2	569
Hauterives (FR)	25C1	450
Isola (FR)	25G3	525
Issoire (FR)	25A1	450
Ivrea (IT)	25H1	569
Jausiers (FR)	25F3	525
La Bréole (FR)	25E3	526
La Canourgue (FR)	25A3	507
La Chaise-Dieu (FR)	25A1	451
La Chambre (FR)	25E1	451
La Chapelle-L(FR)	25A1	451
La Mure (FR)	25E2	451
La Roche-de-G(FR)	25C2	451
La Roche/Arnauds (FR)	25E3	526
La Roque/Cèze (FR)	25C3	508
La Salle/Alpes (FR)	25F2	526
Lablachère (FR)	25B3	451
Lachamp-Raphaël (FR)	25B2	451
Lagorce (FR)	25B3	451
Lalouvesc (FR)	25C2	451
Lamastre (FR)	25C2	452
Lanarce (FR)	25B2	452
Langogne (FR)	25B2	508
Lans/Vercors (FR)	25D2	452
Lapte (FR)	25B1	452
Laragne-M (FR)	25E3	526
Lavaudieu (FR)	25A1	452
Le Bessat (FR)	25C1	452
Le Breuil/Couze (FR)	25A1	452
Le Cheylard (FR)	25C2	452
Le Cheylas (FR)	25E1	452
Le Lac d'Issarlès (FR)	25B2	453
Le Lauzet-Ubay (FR)	25F3	527
Le Malzieu-Ville (FR)	25A2	510
Le Monastier-P-M (FR)	25A3	510
Le Monastier/G (FR)	25B2	453
Le Monestier (FR)	25A1	453
Le Monêtier/B(FR)	25F2	527
Le Puy-en-Velay (FR)	25B2	453
Le Teil (FR)	25C3	453
Le Vernet (FR)	25A2	453
Les Deux-Alpes (FR)	25E2	453
Les Estables (FR)	25B2	453
Les Granges-G (FR)	25C3	453
Les Karellis (FR)	25F1	453
Les Mages (FR)	25B3	510
Les Menuires (FR)	25F1	454
Loano (IT)	25H3	599
Locana (IT)	25G1	569
Lus-la-Croix-H (FR)	25D2	454
Mâcot-la-Plagne (FR)	25F1	454
Maglione (IT)	25H1	569

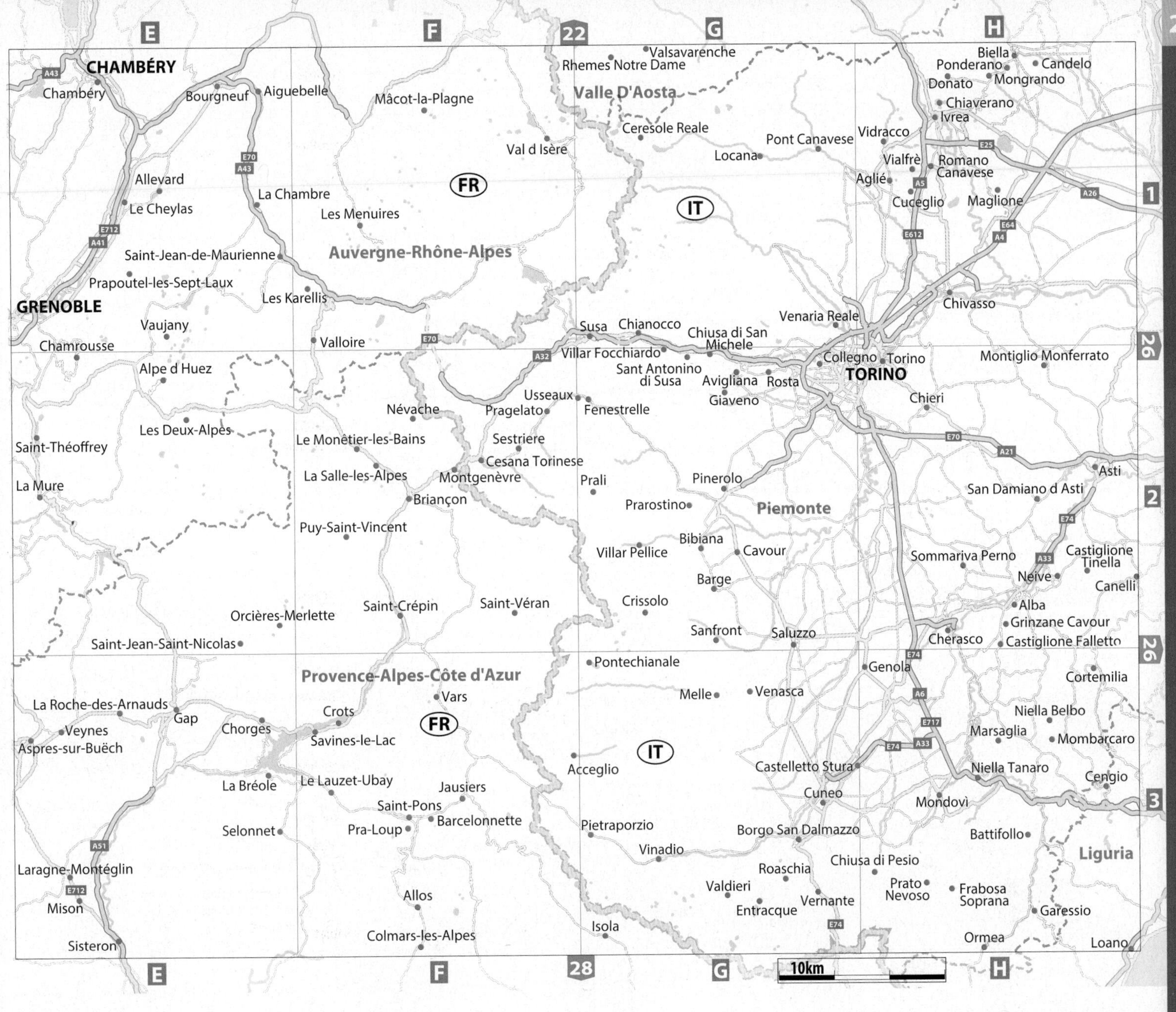
E
F
22
G
H
CHAMBÉRY
Chambéry
Bourgneuf
Aiguebelle
Mâcot-la-Plagne
Rhemes Notre Dame
Valsavarenche
Valle D'Aosta
Ceresole Reale
Val d Isère
Locana
Pont Canavese
Vidracco
Biella
Ponderano
Candelo
Donato
Mongrando
Chiaverano
Ivrea
Vialfrè
Romano Canavese
Agliè
Cuceglio
Maglione
Allevard
Le Cheylas
La Chambre
FR
Les Menuires
IT
Saint-Jean-de-Maurienne
Auvergne-Rhône-Alpes
Prapoutel-les-Sept-Laux
GRENOBLE
Les Karellis
Chivasso
Vaujany
Chamrousse
Valloire
Susa
Chianocco
Chiusa di San Michele
Venaria Reale
Villar Focchiardo
Sant Antonino di Susa
Avigliana
Rosta
Collegno
Torino
TORINO
Montiglio Monferrato
Alpe d Huez
Usseaux
Pragelato
Fenestrelle
Giaveno
Chieri
Névache
Saint-Théoffrey
Les Deux-Alpes
Le Monêtier-les-Bains
Sestriere
Cesana Torinese
La Salle-les-Alpes
Montgenèvre
Prali
Pinerolo
Asti
La Mure
Briançon
Prarostino
Piemonte
San Damiano d Asti
Puy-Saint-Vincent
Villar Pellice
Bibiana
Cavour
Sommariva Perno
Castiglione Tinella
Barge
Neive
Canelli
Orcières-Merlette
Saint-Crépin
Saint-Véran
Crissolo
Alba
Grinzane Cavour
Sanfront
Saluzzo
Cherasco
Castiglione Falletto
Saint-Jean-Saint-Nicolas
Pontechianale
Genola
Provence-Alpes-Côte d'Azur
Cortemilia
Vars
Melle
Venasca
La Roche-des-Arnauds
Niella Belbo
Gap
Crots
FR
Veynes
Chorges
Marsaglia
Mombarcaro
Aspres-sur-Buëch
Savines-le-Lac
IT
Castelletto Stura
Niella Tanaro
Acceglio
Cengio
La Bréole
Le Lauzet-Ubay
Jausiers
Cuneo
Mondovì
Saint-Pons
Barcelonnette
Selonnet
Pra-Loup
Pietraporzio
Borgo San Dalmazzo
Battifollo
Vinadio
Liguria
Laragne-Montéglin
Roaschia
Chiusa di Pesio
Valdieri
Prato Nevoso
Frabosa Soprana
Allos
Entracque
Vernante
Mison
Garessio
Isola
Colmars-les-Alpes
Ormea
Sisteron
Loano
28
10km
1
2
3
26

A
B
23
C
D
1
25
2
3
34
16km
NOVARA
MILANO
Milano
Vercelli
Certosa di Pavia
Lombardia
Pizzighettone
Cremona
Monticelli d'Ongina
Peschiera del Garda
Monzambano
Veneto
Borghetto di Valeggio sul Mincio
Mantova
Casale Monferrato
Sartirana Lomellina
PIACENZA
Sabbioneta
Guastalla
Occimiano
Mirabello Monferrato
Soragna
Fontanellato
Ruino
Alessandria
ALESSANDRIA
Volpedo
Varzi
Gropparello
Salsomaggiore Terme
PARMA
Parma
Carpi
Piemonte
Collecchio
Sala Baganza
Reggio nell'Emilia
REGGIO NELL' EMILIA
Nizza Monferrato
Novi Ligure
Emilia Romagna
Farini
Langhirano
Marzaglia
Acqui Terme
Tagliolo Monferrato
Ovada
Casaleggio Boiro
Terenzo
Vezzano Sul Crostolo
Castellarano
Torriglia
Berceto
Castelnovo ne Monti
Serramazzoni
Liguria
Giusvalla
Pontinvrea
Pavullo nel Frignano
GENOVA
Celle Ligure
San Rocco
Toscana
Sestola
Sestri Levante
Vado Ligure
Deiva Marina
Levanto
Fivizzano
Equi Terme
San Romano in Garfagnana
Castelnuovo di Garfagnana
Cutigliano
Finale Ligure
Pietra Ligure
LA SPEZIA
La Spezia
Castelnuovo Magra
Barga
Gallicano
A4
E64
E62
A58
E70
A26
A22
E45
A21
A21DIR
E35
E74
A1
E62
A7
E25
E31
A15
A10
E80
E717
A6
A12

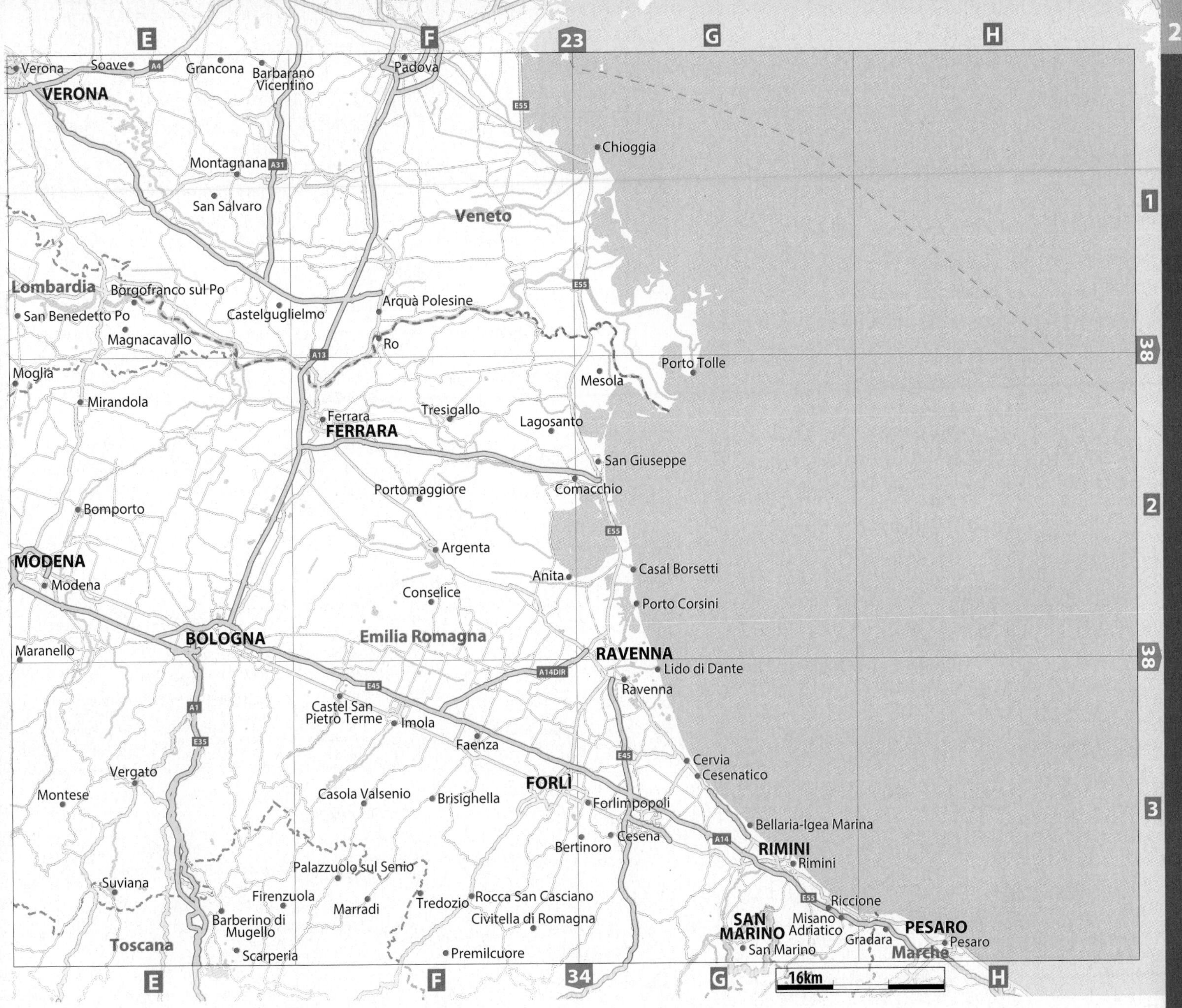
E
F
23
G
H
Verona
Soave
A4
Grancona
Barbarano Vicentino
Padova
VERONA
E55
Chioggia
Montagnana
A31
San Salvaro
Veneto
1
Lombardia
Borgofranco sul Po
San Benedetto Po
Castelguglielmo
Arquà Polesine
E55
Magnacavallo
Ro
A13
Moglia
Mesola
Porto Tolle
38
Mirandola
Ferrara
FERRARA
Tresigallo
Lagosanto
San Giuseppe
Comacchio
Portomaggiore
Bomporto
2
E55
Argenta
MODENA
Modena
Anita
Casal Borsetti
Conselice
Porto Corsini
BOLOGNA
Emilia Romagna
Maranello
RAVENNA
Lido di Dante
38
A14DIR
Ravenna
E45
A1
Castel San Pietro Terme
Imola
Faenza
E35
E45
Cervia
Cesenatico
Vergato
Montese
Casola Valsenio
Brisighella
FORLÌ
Forlimpopoli
3
Bellaria-Igea Marina
A14
Cesena
Bertinoro
RIMINI
Rimini
Palazzuolo sul Senio
Suviana
Firenzuola
Marradi
Tredozio
Rocca San Casciano
E55
Riccione
Barberino di Mugello
Civitella di Romagna
SAN MARINO
Misano Adriatico
Gradara
PESARO
Pesaro
Toscana
San Marino
Marche
Scarperia
Premilcuore
E
F
34
G
16km
H

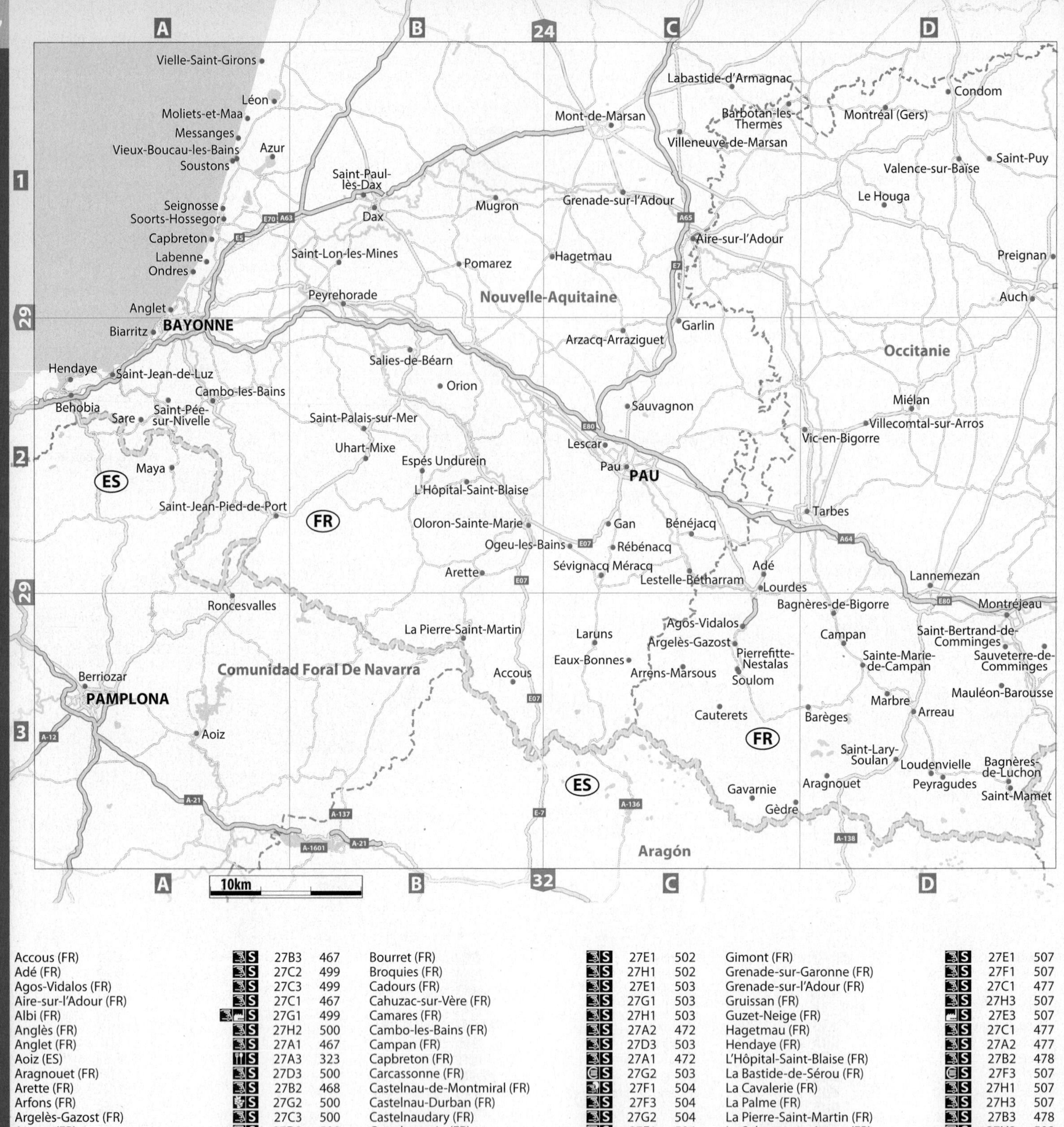

A
B
24
C
D
1
2
3
29
29
32
Vielle-Saint-Girons
Léon
Moliets-et-Maa
Messanges
Vieux-Boucau-les-Bains
Azur
Soustons
Seignosse
Soorts-Hossegor
Capbreton
Labenne
Ondres
Anglet
Biarritz
BAYONNE
Hendaye
Saint-Jean-de-Luz
Behobia
Sare
Saint-Pée-sur-Nivelle
Cambo-les-Bains
Maya
ES
Saint-Jean-Pied-de-Port
FR
Roncesvalles
Berriozar
PAMPLONA
Aoiz
Comunidad Foral De Navarra
Saint-Paul-lès-Dax
Dax
E70
A63
E5
Saint-Lon-les-Mines
Peyrehorade
Salies-de-Béarn
Orion
Saint-Palais-sur-Mer
Uhart-Mixe
Espés Undurein
L'Hôpital-Saint-Blaise
Oloron-Sainte-Marie
Ogeu-les-Bains
E07
Arette
La Pierre-Saint-Martin
Accous
Mugron
Pomarez
Hagetmau
Nouvelle-Aquitaine
Mont-de-Marsan
Grenade-sur-l'Adour
Labastide-d'Armagnac
Barbotan-les-Thermes
Villeneuve-de-Marsan
A65
Aire-sur-l'Adour
E7
Garlin
Arzacq-Arraziguet
Sauvagnon
E80
Lescar
Pau
PAU
Gan
Bénéjacq
Rébénacq
Sévignacq Méracq
Lestelle-Bétharram
Adé
Lourdes
Laruns
Eaux-Bonnes
Agos-Vidalos
Argelès-Gazost
Arrens-Marsous
Pierrefitte-Nestalas
Soulom
Cauterets
Gavarnie
Gèdre
ES
A-136
E-7
Aragón
Condom
Montréal (Gers)
Saint-Puy
Valence-sur-Baïse
Le Houga
Preignan
Auch
Occitanie
Miélan
Villecomtal-sur-Arros
Vic-en-Bigorre
Tarbes
A64
Lannemezan
Montréjeau
Bagnères-de-Bigorre
Campan
Saint-Bertrand-de-Comminges
Sainte-Marie-de-Campan
Sauveterre-de-Comminges
Mauléon-Barousse
Marbre
Arreau
Barèges
FR
Saint-Lary-Soulan
Loudenvielle
Peyragudes
Bagnères-de-Luchon
Saint-Mamet
Aragnouet
A-138
A-12
A-21
A-137
A-1601
10km

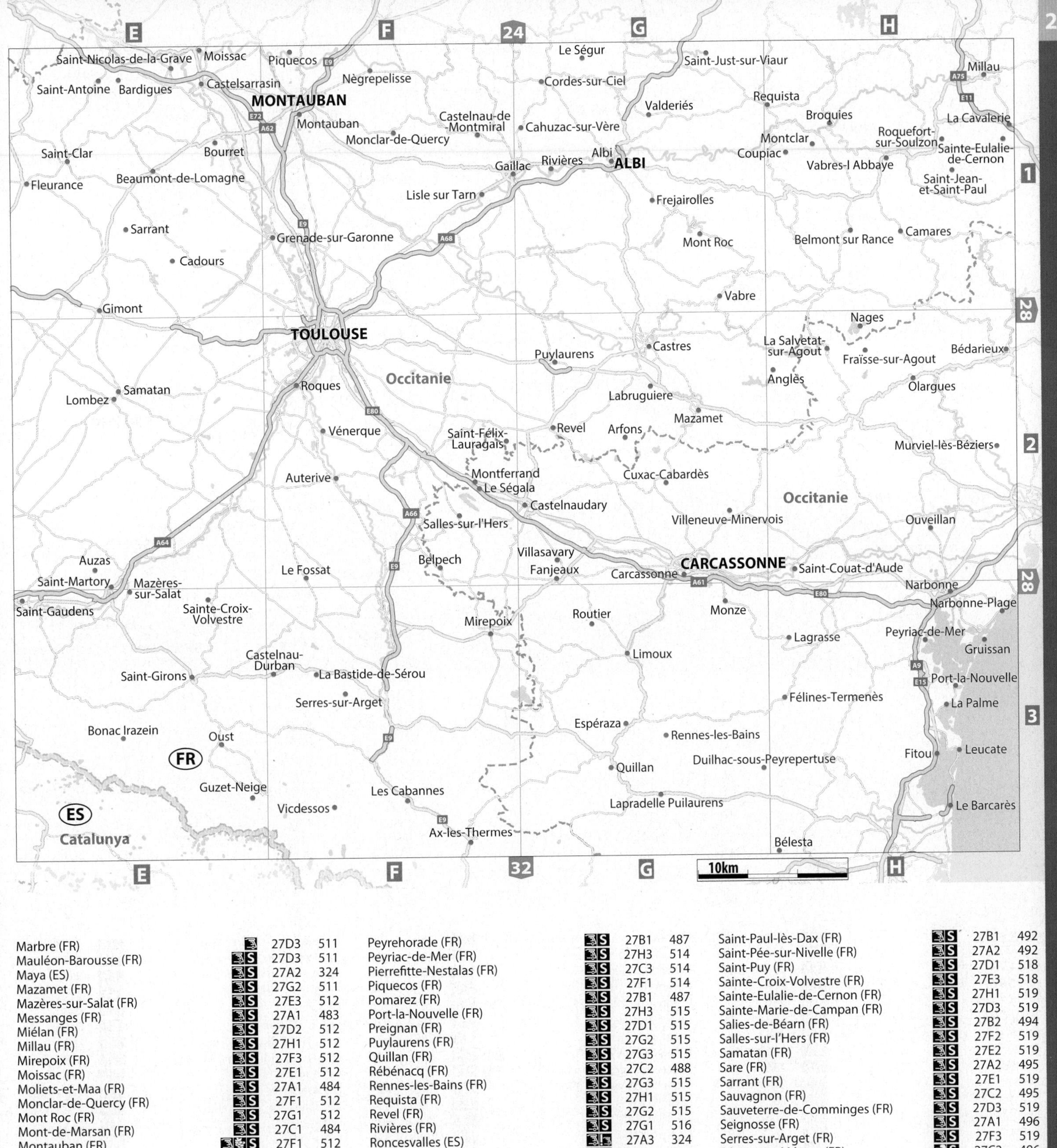
E
F
24
G
H
Saint-Nicolas-de-la-Grave
Moissac
Piquecos
Le Ségur
Saint-Just-sur-Viaur
Millau
Saint-Antoine
Bardigues
Castelsarrasin
Nègrepelisse
Cordes-sur-Ciel
MONTAUBAN
Valderiés
Requista
Broquies
La Cavalerie
Montauban
Castelnau-de-Montmiral
Cahuzac-sur-Vère
Montclar
Roquefort-sur-Soulzon
Monclar-de-Quercy
Coupiac
Sainte-Eulalie-de-Cernon
Saint-Clar
Bourret
Albi
Gaillac
Rivières
ALBI
Vabres-l Abbaye
Fleurance
Beaumont-de-Lomagne
Saint-Jean-et-Saint-Paul
Lisle sur Tarn
Frejairolles
Sarrant
Grenade-sur-Garonne
Mont Roc
Belmont sur Rance
Camares
Cadours
Vabre
Gimont
Nages
TOULOUSE
La Salvetat-sur-Agout
Castres
Puylaurens
Fraïsse-sur-Agout
Bédarieux
Samatan
Roques
Occitanie
Anglès
Olargues
Lombez
Labruguiere
Mazamet
Vénerque
Saint-Félix-Lauragais
Revel
Arfons
Murviel-lès-Béziers
Montferrand
Le Ségala
Auterive
Cuxac-Cabardès
Castelnaudary
Occitanie
Salles-sur-l'Hers
Villeneuve-Minervois
Ouveillan
Auzas
Villasavary
Belpech
CARCASSONNE
Saint-Couat-d'Aude
Saint-Martory
Mazères-sur-Salat
Le Fossat
Fanjeaux
Carcassonne
Narbonne
Saint-Gaudens
Sainte-Croix-Volvestre
Monze
Narbonne-Plage
Routier
Mirepoix
Lagrasse
Peyriac-de-Mer
Gruissan
Castelnau-Durban
Limoux
Saint-Girons
La Bastide-de-Sérou
Port-la-Nouvelle
Serres-sur-Arget
Félines-Termenès
La Palme
Bonac Irazein
Espéraza
Oust
Rennes-les-Bains
Leucate
FR
Fitou
Quillan
Duilhac-sous-Peyrepertuse
Guzet-Neige
Les Cabannes
ES
Vicdessos
Lapradelle Puilaurens
Le Barcarès
Catalunya
Ax-les-Thermes
Bélesta
E
F
32
G
10km
H
1
2
3
28

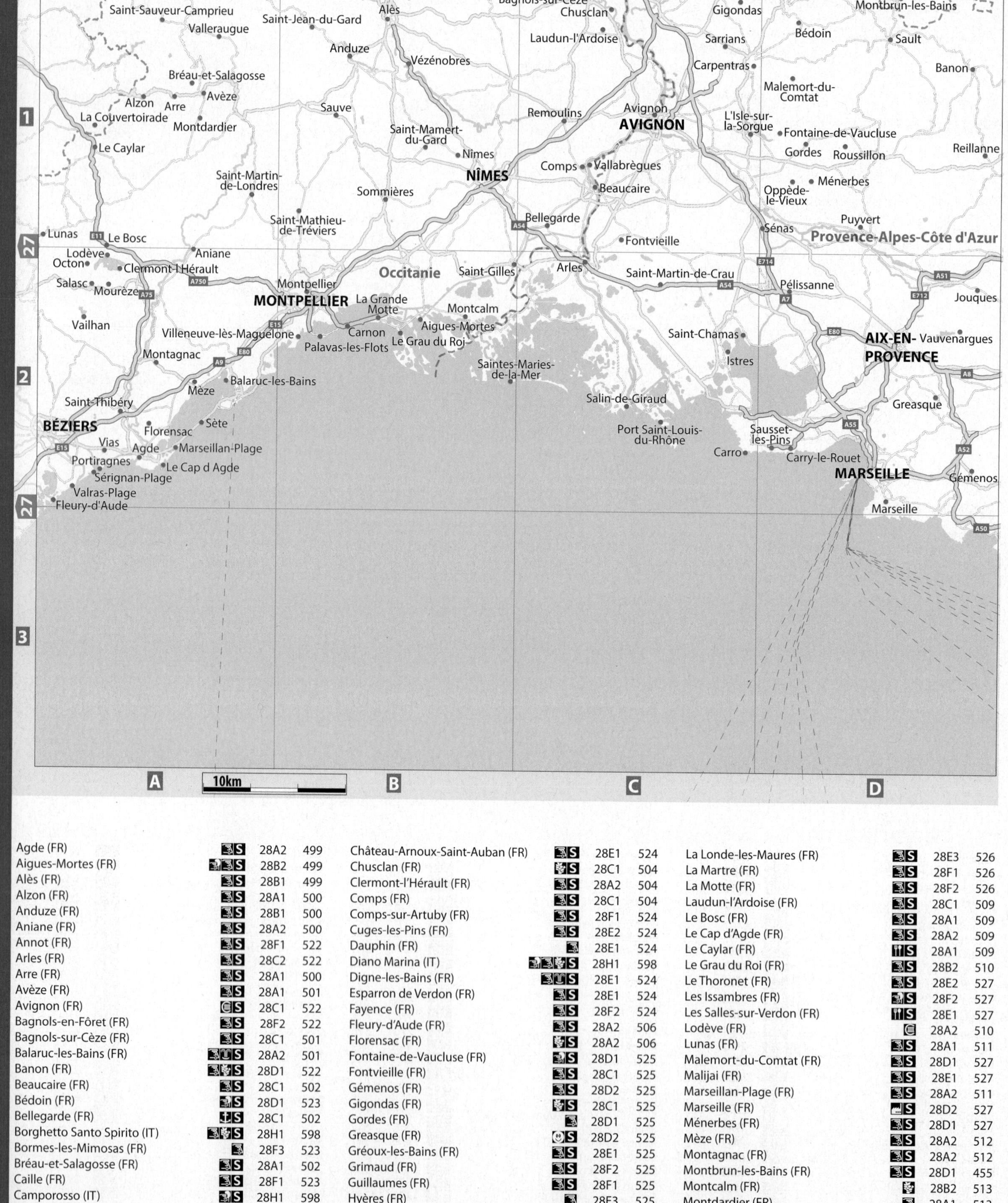

Place	Grid	Page
Agde (FR)	28A2	499
Aigues-Mortes (FR)	28B2	499
Alès (FR)	28B1	499
Alzon (FR)	28A1	500
Anduze (FR)	28B1	500
Aniane (FR)	28A2	500
Annot (FR)	28F1	522
Arles (FR)	28C2	522
Arre (FR)	28A1	500
Avèze (FR)	28A1	501
Avignon (FR)	28C1	522
Bagnols-en-Fôret (FR)	28F2	522
Bagnols-sur-Cèze (FR)	28C1	501
Balaruc-les-Bains (FR)	28A2	501
Banon (FR)	28D1	522
Beaucaire (FR)	28C1	502
Bédoin (FR)	28D1	523
Bellegarde (FR)	28C1	502
Borghetto Santo Spirito (IT)	28H1	598
Bormes-les-Mimosas (FR)	28F3	523
Bréau-et-Salagosse (FR)	28A1	502
Caille (FR)	28F1	523
Camporosso (IT)	28H1	598
Carnon (FR)	28B2	503
Carpentras (FR)	28C1	523
Carro (FR)	28C2	523
Carry-le-Rouet (FR)	28D2	523
Castellane (FR)	28F1	523
Cavalière (FR)	28F3	524
Cervo (IT)	28H1	598
Château-Arnoux-Saint-Auban (FR)	28E1	524
Chusclan (FR)	28C1	504
Clermont-l'Hérault (FR)	28A2	504
Comps (FR)	28C1	504
Comps-sur-Artuby (FR)	28F1	524
Cuges-les-Pins (FR)	28E2	524
Dauphin (FR)	28E1	524
Diano Marina (IT)	28H1	598
Digne-les-Bains (FR)	28E1	524
Esparron de Verdon (FR)	28E1	524
Fayence (FR)	28F2	524
Fleury-d'Aude (FR)	28A2	506
Florensac (FR)	28A2	506
Fontaine-de-Vaucluse (FR)	28D1	525
Fontvieille (FR)	28C1	525
Gémenos (FR)	28D2	525
Gigondas (FR)	28C1	525
Gordes (FR)	28D1	525
Greasque (FR)	28D2	525
Gréoux-les-Bains (FR)	28E1	525
Grimaud (FR)	28F2	525
Guillaumes (FR)	28F1	525
Hyères (FR)	28E3	525
Imperia (IT)	28H1	599
Istres (FR)	28C2	525
Jouques (FR)	28D2	526
L'Isle-sur-la-Sorgue (FR)	28C1	526
La Couvertoirade (FR)	28A1	507
La Crau (FR)	28E3	526
La Grande Motte (FR)	28B2	507
La Londe-les-Maures (FR)	28E3	526
La Martre (FR)	28F1	526
La Motte (FR)	28F2	526
Laudun-l'Ardoise (FR)	28C1	509
Le Bosc (FR)	28A1	509
Le Cap d'Agde (FR)	28A2	509
Le Caylar (FR)	28A1	509
Le Grau du Roi (FR)	28B2	510
Le Thoronet (FR)	28E2	527
Les Issambres (FR)	28F2	527
Les Salles-sur-Verdon (FR)	28E1	527
Lodève (FR)	28A2	510
Lunas (FR)	28A1	511
Malemort-du-Comtat (FR)	28D1	527
Malijai (FR)	28E1	527
Marseillan-Plage (FR)	28A2	511
Marseille (FR)	28D2	527
Ménerbes (FR)	28D1	527
Mèze (FR)	28A2	512
Montagnac (FR)	28A2	512
Montbrun-les-Bains (FR)	28D1	455
Montcalm (FR)	28B2	513
Montdardier (FR)	28A1	513
Montpellier (FR)	28B2	513
Mourèze (FR)	28A2	513
Moustiers-Sainte-Marie (FR)	28E1	528
Nîmes (FR)	28B1	514
Octon (FR)	28A2	514
Ollioules (FR)	28E3	528
Oppède-le-Vieux (FR)	28D1	528

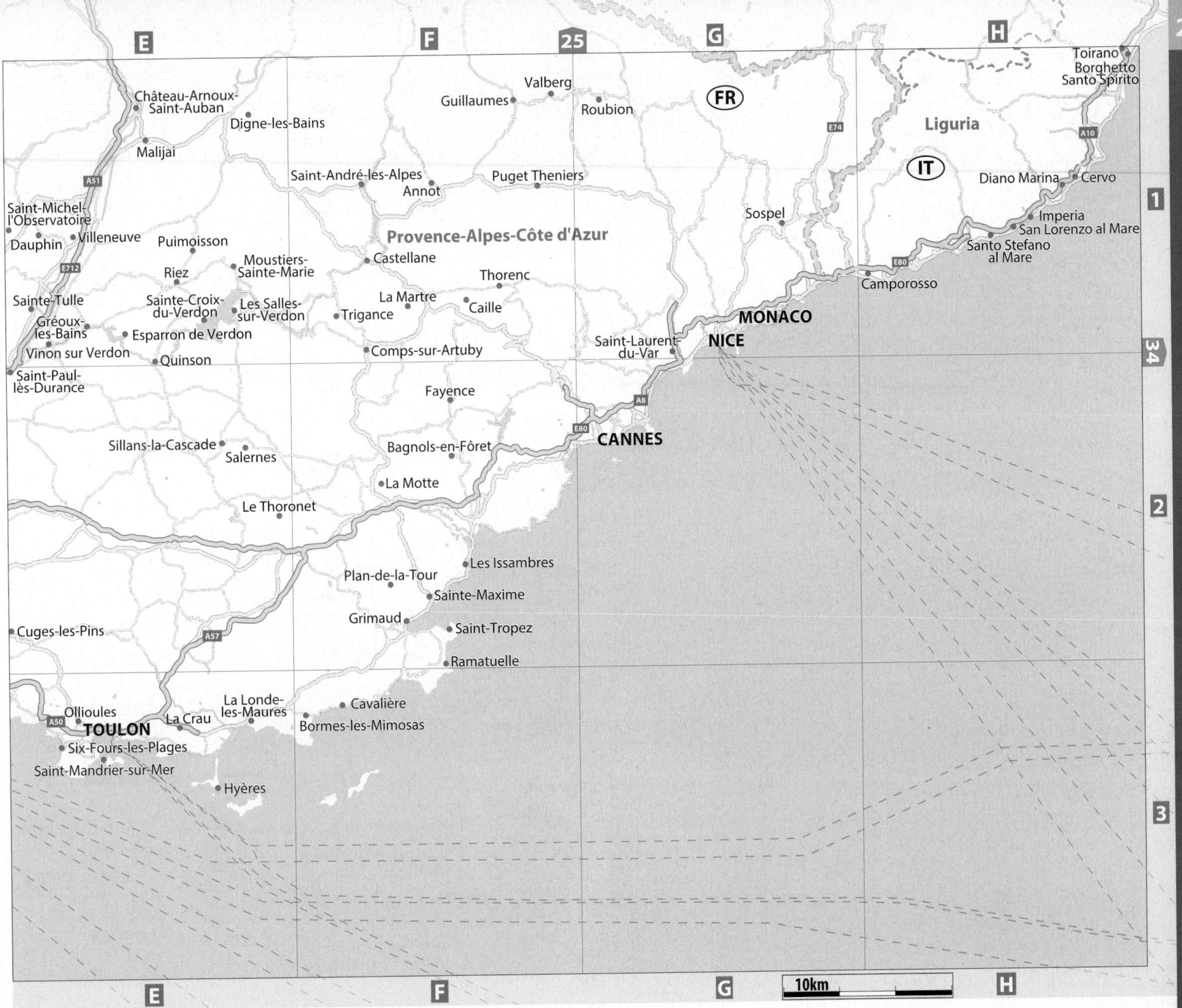

E
F
25
G
H
Château-Arnoux-Saint-Auban
Digne-les-Bains
Malijai
Guillaumes
Valberg
Roubion
FR
Liguria
IT
Toirano
Borghetto Santo Spirito
Saint-André-les-Alpes
Annot
Puget Theniers
Diano Marina
Cervo
Saint-Michel-l'Observatoire
Dauphin
Villeneuve
Puimoisson
Provence-Alpes-Côte d'Azur
Sospel
Imperia
San Lorenzo al Mare
Santo Stefano al Mare
Riez
Moustiers-Sainte-Marie
Castellane
Thorenc
Camporosso
Sainte-Tulle
Sainte-Croix-du-Verdon
Les Salles-sur-Verdon
La Martre
Trigance
Caille
MONACO
Gréoux-les-Bains
Esparron de Verdon
Vinon sur Verdon
Quinson
Comps-sur-Artuby
Saint-Laurent-du-Var
NICE
Saint-Paul-lès-Durance
Fayence
CANNES
Sillans-la-Cascade
Salernes
Bagnols-en-Fôret
La Motte
Le Thoronet
Les Issambres
Plan-de-la-Tour
Sainte-Maxime
Grimaud
Saint-Tropez
Cuges-les-Pins
Ramatuelle
Ollioules
TOULON
La Crau
La Londe-les-Maures
Cavalière
Bormes-les-Mimosas
Six-Fours-les-Plages
Saint-Mandrier-sur-Mer
Hyères
10km
1
2
3
34
A51
E712
E74
A10
E80
A8
A57
A50

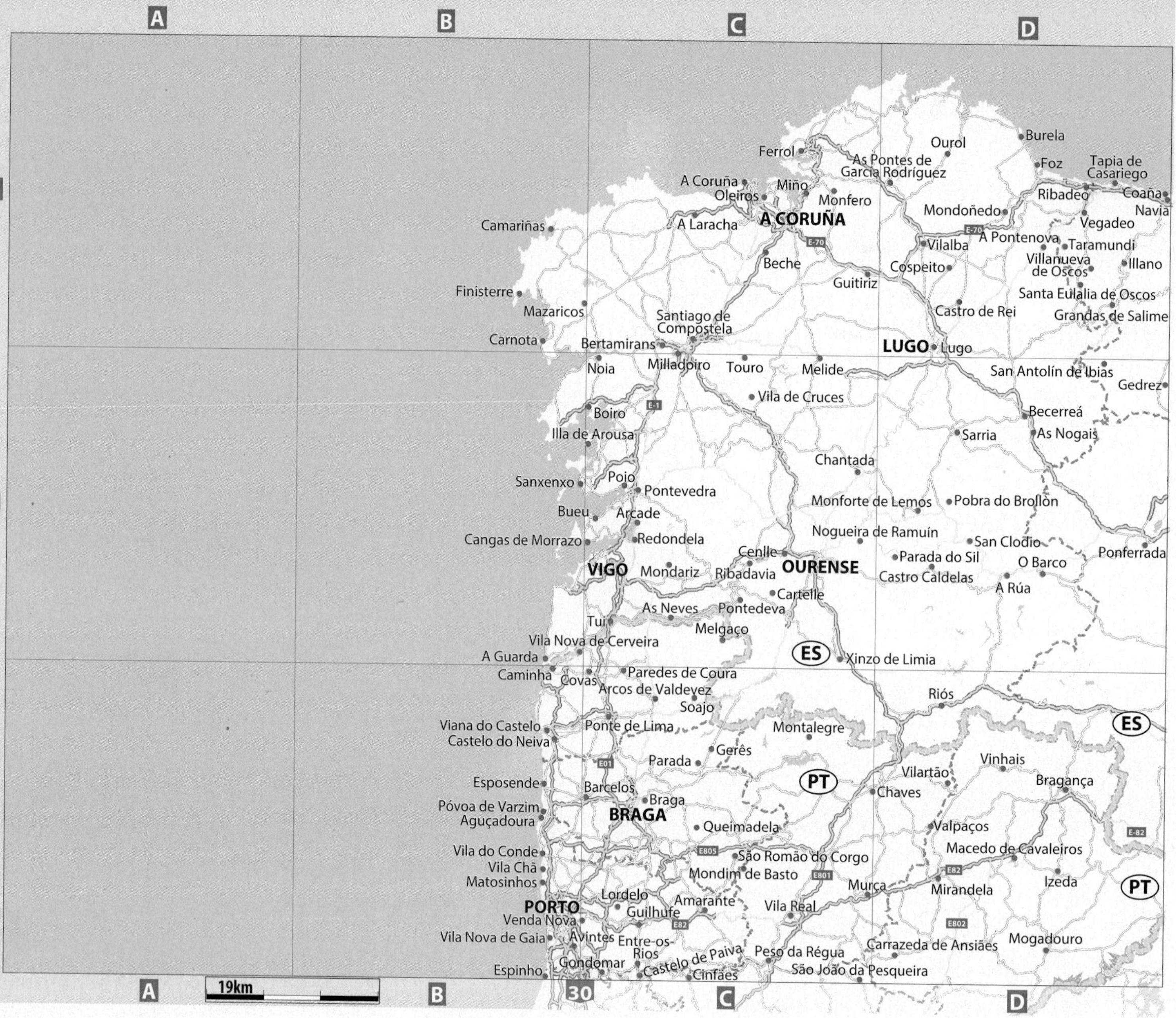

A Coruña (ES) 29C1 316
A Guarda (ES) 29B2 316
A Laracha (ES) 29C1 316
A Pontenova (ES) 29D1 316
A Rúa (ES) 29D2 316
Aguçadoura (PT) 29B3 684
Aguilar de Campoo (ES) 29F2 335
Agurain (ES) 29H2 316
Amarante (PT) 29C3 684
Ampudia (ES) 29F3 335
Amurrio (ES) 29H2 316
Añana (ES) 29G2 316
Arcade (ES) 29C2 316
Arcos de Valdevez (PT) 29C3 684
Arnedillo (ES) 29H3 323
Arrigorriaga (ES) 29H2 317
Arróniz (ES) 29H2 323
As Neves (ES) 29C2 317
As Nogais (ES) 29D2 317
As Pontes de García R (ES) 29D1 317
Astorga (ES) 29E2 335
Astudillo (ES) 29F3 335
Avintes (PT) 29B3 684
Ayegui (ES) 29H2 323
Bakio (ES) 29H2 317
Baltanàs (ES) 29F3 335
Barcelos (PT) 29C3 684
Barrio Cosío (ES) 29F2 317
Bárzana (ES) 29E1 317
Beasain (ES) 29H2 317
Becerreá (ES) 29D2 317
Becerril de Campos (ES) 29F3 335
Beche (ES) 29C1 317
Bergara (ES) 29H2 317
Bermeo (ES) 29H2 317
Bertamirans (ES) 29C1 317
Bilbao (ES) 29H2 317
Boiro (ES) 29C2 317
Braga (PT) 29C3 685
Bragança (PT) 29D3 685
Bretocino (ES) 29E3 335
Bueu (ES) 29C2 317
Burela (ES) 29D1 317
Burgos (ES) 29G3 335
Cabárceno (ES) 29G2 318
Camariñas (ES) 29B1 318
Caminha (PT) 29B3 685
Candás (ES) 29E1 318
Cangas de Morrazo (ES) 29C2 318
Cangas de Onís (ES) 29F1 318
Cangas del Narcea (ES) 29E1 318
Carnota (ES) 29B1 318
Carrazeda de Ansiães (PT) 29D3 685
Carrión de los Condes (ES) 29F3 336
Cartelle (ES) 29C2 318
Cascante (ES) 29H3 323
Castelo de Paiva (PT) 29C3 688
Castelo do Neiva (PT) 29B3 685
Castro Caldelas (ES) 29D2 318
Castro de Rei (ES) 29D1 318
Cenlle (ES) 29C2 318
Cervera de Pisuerga (ES) 29F2 336
Chantada (ES) 29C2 318
Chaves (PT) 29C3 685
Cinfães (PT) 29C3 689
Coaña (ES) 29D1 318
Colombres (ES) 29F1 318
Colunga (ES) 29F1 318
Cospeito (ES) 29D1 318
Covas (PT) 29C3 685
Cudillero (ES) 29E1 318
Duruelo de la Sierra (ES) 29G3 336
Elorrio (ES) 29H2 318
Eltziego (ES) 29H3 318
Entre-os-Rios (PT) 29C3 685
Espinho (PT) 29B3 685
Espinosa de los M (ES) 29G2 336
Esposende (PT) 29B3 685
Falces (ES) 29H3 323
Ferrol (ES) 29C1 318
Finisterre (ES) 29B1 319
Foncastín (ES) 29F3 336
Foz (ES) 29D1 319
Frómista (ES) 29F3 336
Fuente Dé (ES) 29F2 319
Gedrez (ES) 29D2 319
Gerês (PT) 29C3 686
Gijón (ES) 29E1 319
Gondomar (PT) 29C3 686
Gorliz (ES) 29H2 319
Gozon (ES) 29E1 319
Grado (ES) 29E1 319
Grandas de Salime (ES) 29D1 319
Guilhufe (PT) 29C3 686
Guitiriz (ES) 29C1 319
Haro (ES) 29H2 324
Hernani (ES) 29H2 319
Herrera de Pisuerga (ES) 29F2 336
Hontoria del Pinar (ES) 29G3 336
Huergas de Babia (ES) 29E2 336
Illa de Arousa (ES) 29C2 319
Illano (ES) 29D1 319
Irura (ES) 29H2 324
Izeda (PT) 29D3 686
Labastida (ES) 29H3 319
Lanestosa (ES) 29G2 319
Langreo (ES) 29E1 319
Legazpi (ES) 29H2 319
Lekeitio (ES) 29H2 319
León (ES) 29E2 337
Liérganes (ES) 29G2 319
Llanes (ES) 29F1 320
Logroño (ES) 29H3 324
Lordelo (PT) 29C3 686
Lugo (ES) 29D1 320
Lugones (ES) 29E1 320
Macedo de Cavaleiros (PT) 29D3 686
Matosinhos (PT) 29B3 686
Mazaricos (ES) 29B1 320
Melgaço (PT) 29C2 686
Melide (ES) 29C2 320
Mieres (ES) 29E1 320
Milladoiro (ES) 29C1 320
Miño (ES) 29C1 320

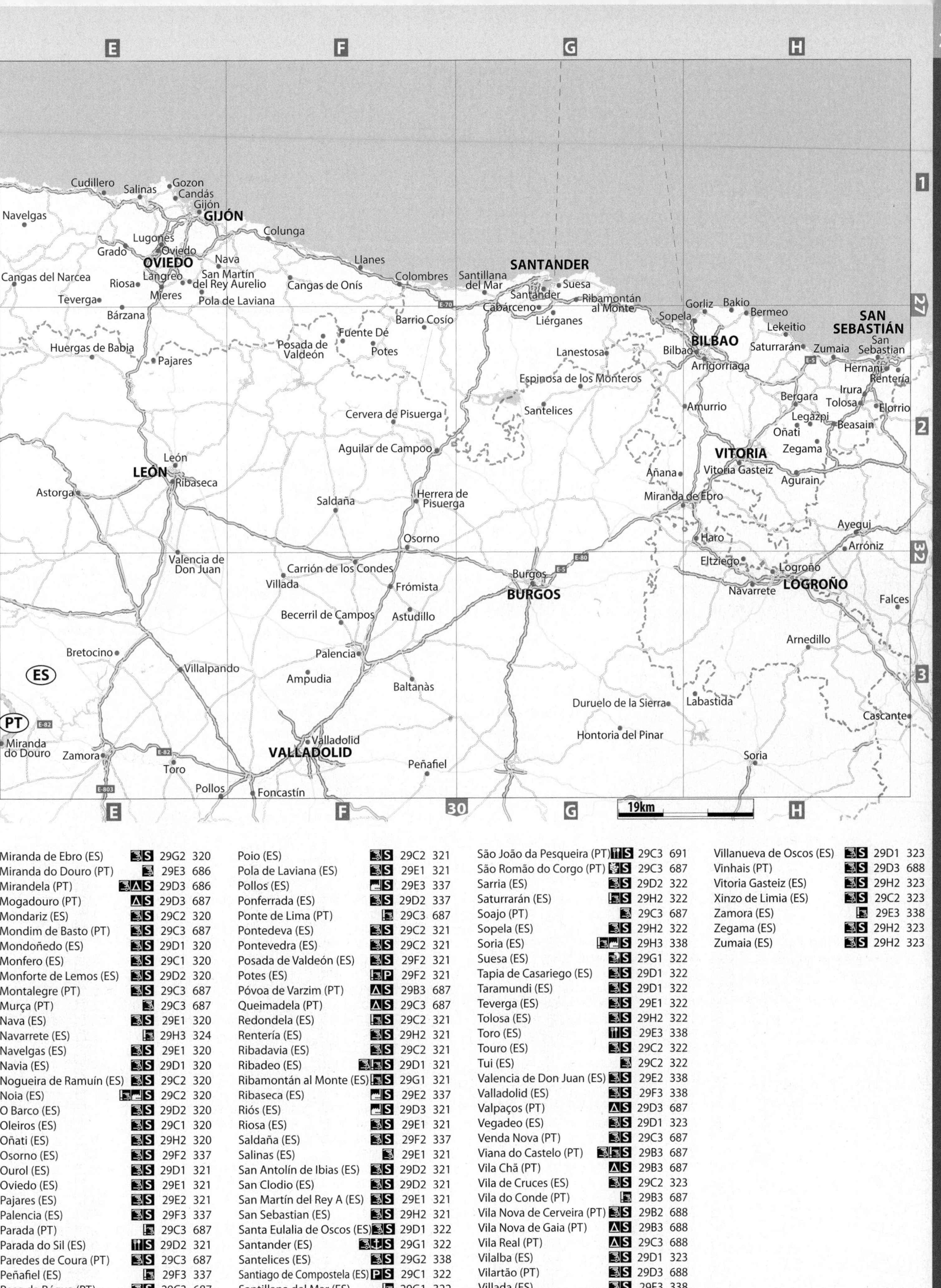

E
F
G
H
1
2
3
27
32
30
Cudillero
Salinas
Gozon
Candás
Gijón
GIJÓN
Navelgas
Lugones
Colunga
Grado
Oviedo
OVIEDO
Nava
Llanes
Cangas del Narcea
Riosa
Langreo
San Martín del Rey Aurelio
Cangas de Onís
Colombres
Santillana del Mar
SANTANDER
Suesa
Teverga
Mieres
Pola de Laviana
Santander
Ribamontán al Monte
Cabárceno
Liérganes
Gorliz
Bakio
Bermeo
SAN SEBASTIÁN
Bárzana
Barrio Cosío
Sopela
Lekeitio
Fuente Dé
Huergas de Babia
Posada de Valdeón
Potes
Lanestosa
Bilbao
BILBAO
Saturrarán
Zumaia
San Sebastian
Pajares
Arrigorriaga
Hernani
Espinosa de los Monteros
Rentería
Irura
Bergara
Tolosa
Amurrio
Cervera de Pisuerga
Santelices
Elorrio
Legazpi
Oñati
Beasain
Aguilar de Campoo
VITORIA
Zegama
León
LEÓN
Añana
Vitoria Gasteiz
Agurain
Ribaseca
Astorga
Saldaña
Herrera de Pisuerga
Miranda de Ebro
Ayegui
Osorno
Haro
Arróniz
Valencia de Don Juan
Elztiego
Carrión de los Condes
Burgos
Logroño
Villada
Frómista
BURGOS
Navarrete
LOGROÑO
Falces
Becerril de Campos
Astudillo
Arnedillo
Bretocino
Palencia
Villalpando
ES
Ampudia
Baltanàs
Duruelo de la Sierra
Labastida
PT
Cascante
Miranda do Douro
Valladolid
Hontoria del Pinar
Zamora
VALLADOLID
Soria
Toro
Peñafiel
Pollos
Foncastín
E-70
E-5
E-80
E-82
E-803
19km

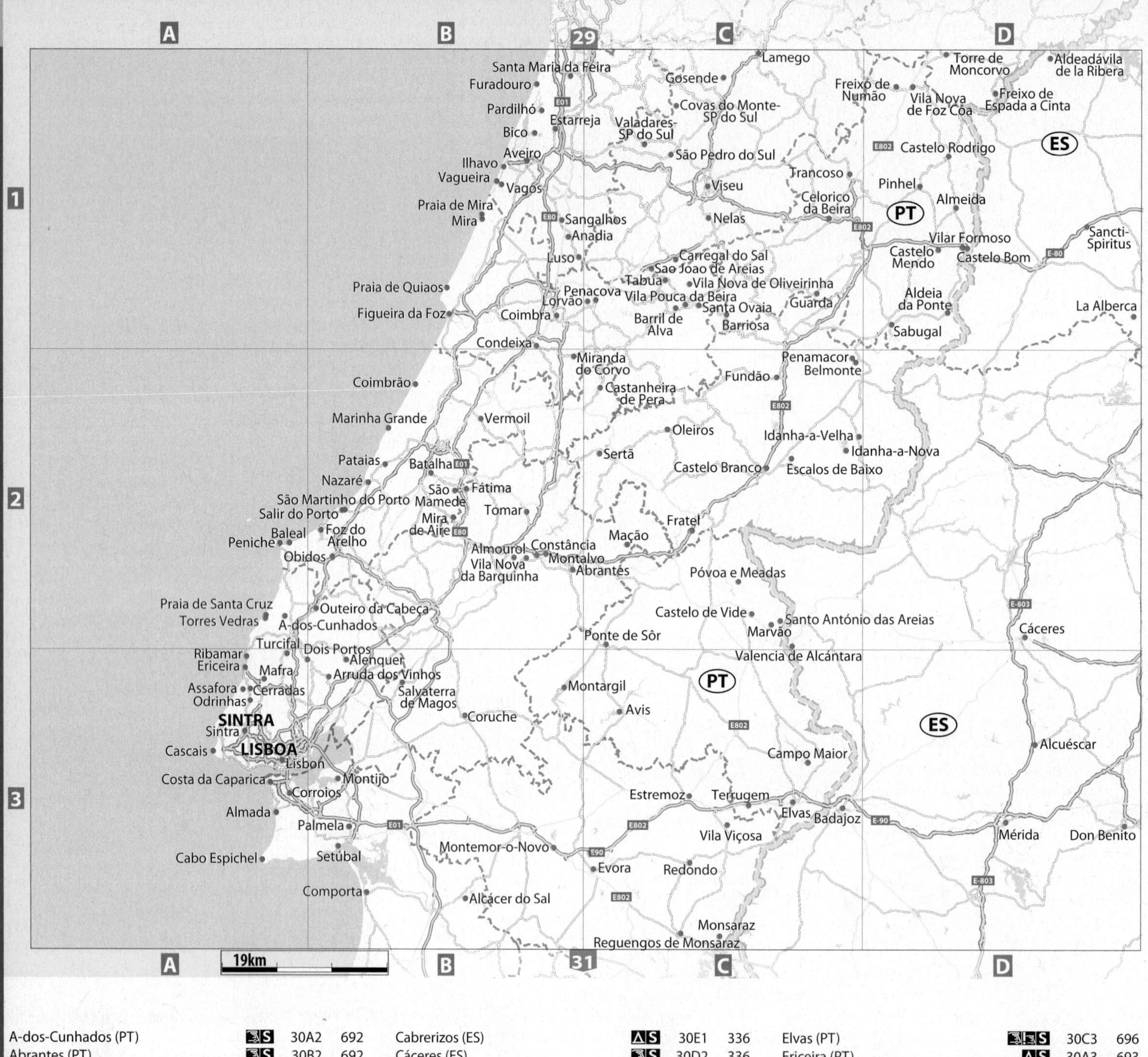
A
B
29
C
D
1
2
3
Santa Maria da Feira
Furadouro
Pardilhó
Estarreja
Bico
Aveiro
Ilhavo
Vagueira
Vagos
Praia de Mira
Mira
Lamego
Gosende
Covas do Monte-SP do Sul
Valadares-SP do Sul
São Pedro do Sul
Viseu
Nelas
Freixo de Numão
Torre de Moncorvo
Vila Nova de Foz Côa
Aldeadávila de la Ribera
Freixo de Espada a Cinta
Castelo Rodrigo
ES
Trancoso
Pinhel
Celorico da Beira
PT
Almeida
Sangalhos
Anadia
Luso
Carregal do Sal
São João de Areias
Tabua
Vila Nova de Oliveirinha
Penacova
Lorvão
Vila Pouca da Beira
Santa Ovaia
Barril de Alva
Barriosa
Guarda
Vilar Formoso
Castelo Mendo
Castelo Bom
Sancti-Spiritus
Aldeia da Ponte
Sabugal
La Alberca
Praia de Quiaos
Figueira da Foz
Coimbra
Condeixa
Miranda do Corvo
Castanheira de Pera
Fundão
Penamacor
Belmonte
Coimbrão
Marinha Grande
Vermoil
Oleiros
Idanha-a-Velha
Idanha-a-Nova
Sertã
Castelo Branco
Escalos de Baixo
Pataias
Batalha
Nazaré
Fátima
São Mamede
São Martinho do Porto
Salir do Porto
Mira de Aire
Tomar
Baleal
Peniche
Foz do Arelho
Obidos
Fratel
Mação
Almourol
Constância
Vila Nova da Barquinha
Montalvo
Abrantes
Póvoa e Meadas
Praia de Santa Cruz
Torres Vedras
Outeiro da Cabeça
A-dos-Cunhados
Castelo de Vide
Santo António das Areias
Marvão
Cáceres
Ponte de Sôr
Valencia de Alcántara
Turcifal
Dois Portos
Ribamar
Ericeira
Alenquer
Mafra
Arruda dos Vinhos
Assafora
Cerradas
Odrinhas
Salvaterra de Magos
Montargil
PT
Avis
SINTRA
Sintra
Coruche
ES
Cascais
LISBOA
Lisbon
Campo Maior
Alcuéscar
Costa da Caparica
Montijo
Corroios
Estremoz
Terrugem
Almada
Elvas
Badajoz
Palmela
Vila Viçosa
Mérida
Don Benito
Cabo Espichel
Setúbal
Montemor-o-Novo
Evora
Redondo
Comporta
Alcácer do Sal
Monsaraz
Reguengos de Monsaraz
19km
31

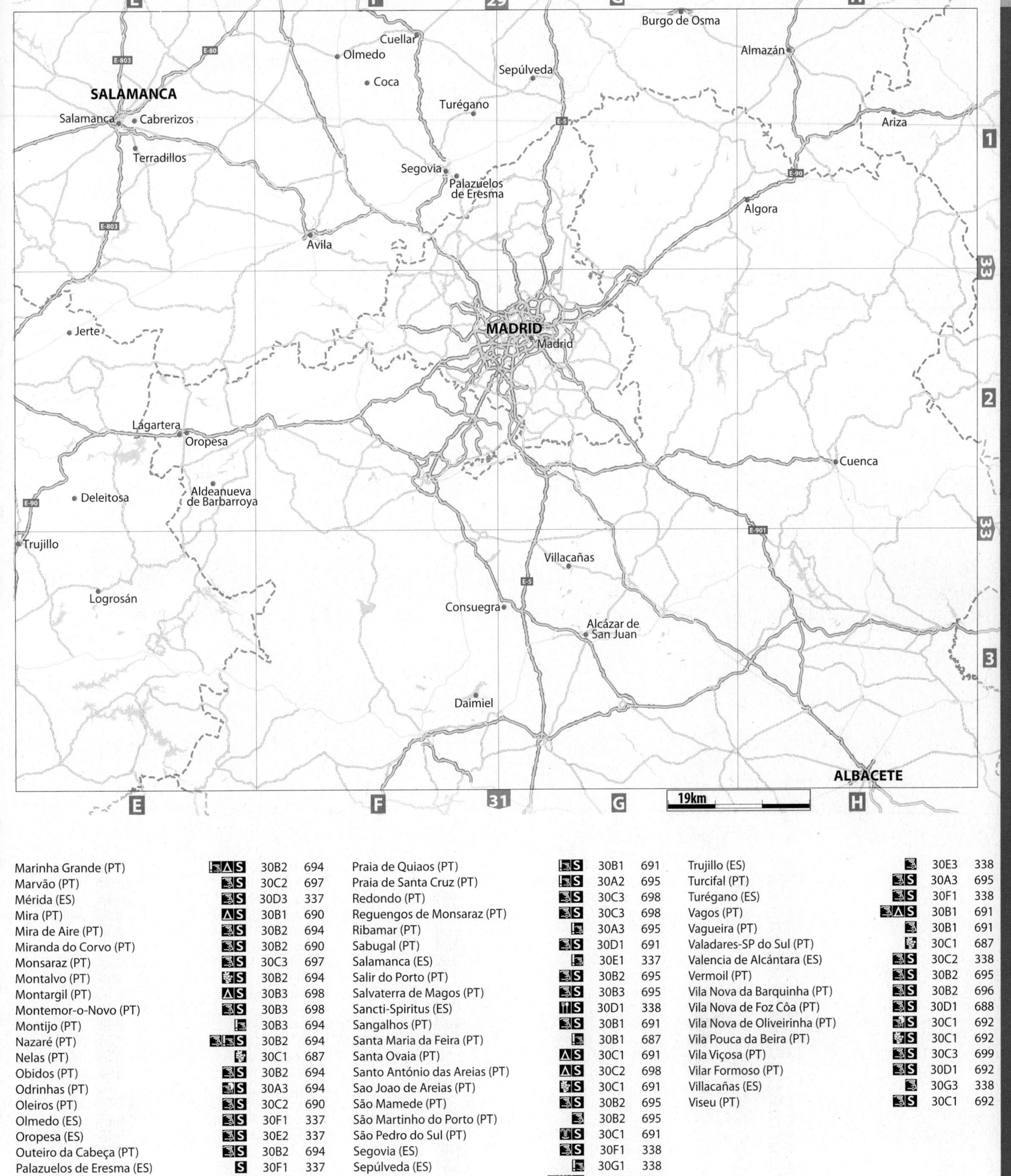
E
F
29
G
H
Burgo de Osma
Cuellar
Olmedo
Almazán
E-803
E-80
Sepúlveda
Coca
SALAMANCA
Turégano
Salamanca
Cabrerizos
E-5
Ariza
1
Terradillos
Segovia
Palazuelos de Eresma
E-90
Algora
E-803
Avila
33
Jerte
MADRID
Madrid
2
Lagartera
Oropesa
Cuenca
Aldeanueva de Barbarroya
E-90
Deleitosa
33
E-901
Trujillo
Villacañas
E-5
Logrosán
Consuegra
Alcázar de San Juan
3
Daimiel
ALBACETE
E
F
31
G
19km
H

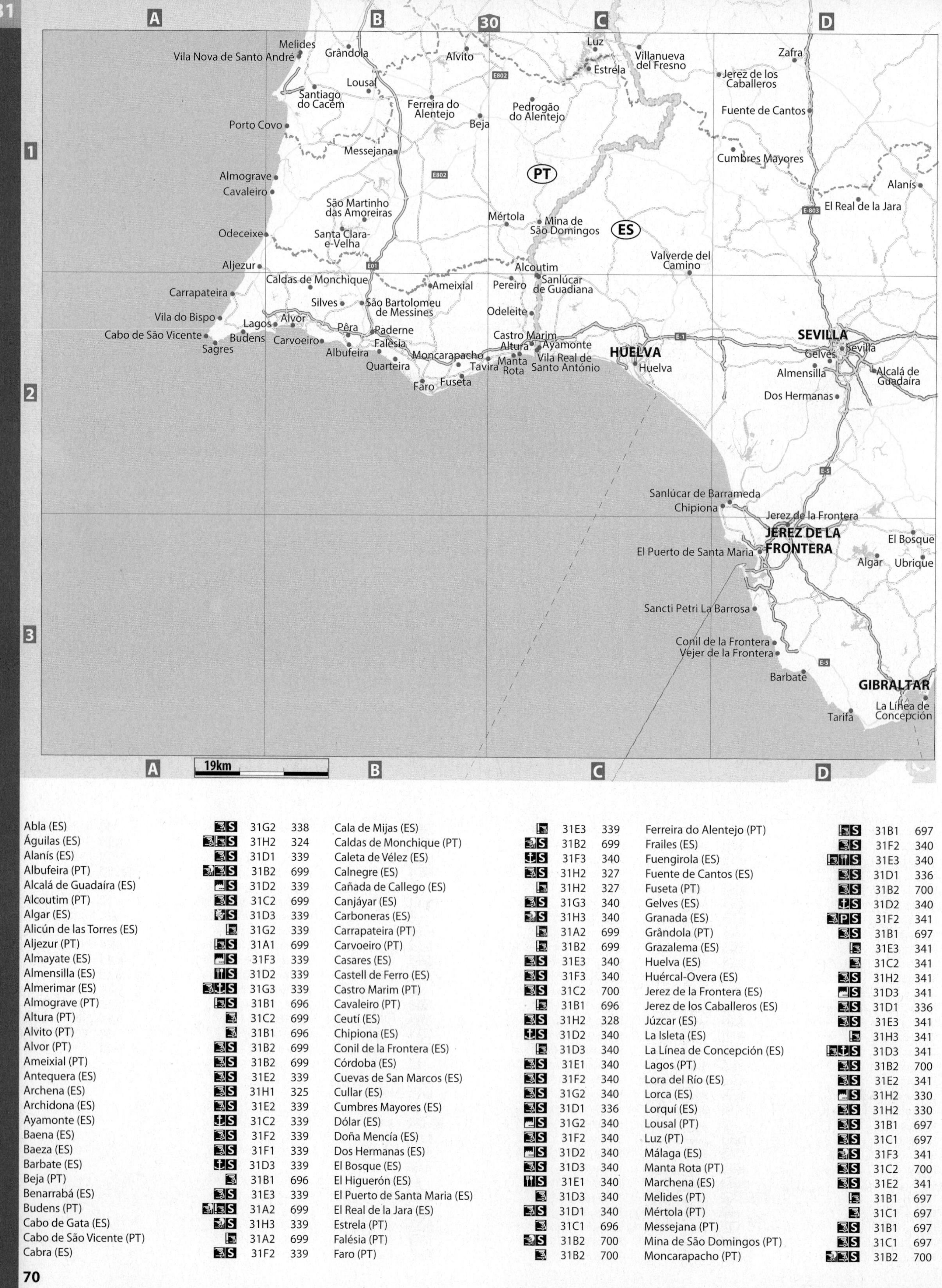
A
B
30
C
D
1
2
3
Melides
Vila Nova de Santo André
Grândola
Alvito
Luz
Villanueva del Fresno
Zafra
Estrela
Jerez de los Caballeros
Lousal
Santiago do Cacém
Ferreira do Alentejo
Pedrogão do Alentejo
Beja
Fuente de Cantos
Porto Covo
Messejana
Cumbres Mayores
Almograve
PT
Alanís
Cavaleiro
El Real de la Jara
São Martinho das Amoreiras
Mértola
Mina de São Domingos
ES
Odeceixe
Santa Clara-e-Velha
Valverde del Camino
Aljezur
Alcoutim
Caldas de Monchique
Ameixial
Pereiro
Sanlúcar de Guadiana
Carrapateira
Silves
São Bartolomeu de Messines
Odeleite
Vila do Bispo
Lagos
Alvor
Pêra
Paderne
Cabo de São Vicente
Budens
Carvoeiro
Falésia
Castro Marim
Altura
Ayamonte
SEVILLA
Sagres
Albufeira
Moncarapacho
Manta Rota
Vila Real de Santo António
HUELVA
Gelves
Sevilla
Quarteira
Tavira
Huelva
Almensilla
Alcalá de Guadaira
Faro
Fuseta
Dos Hermanas
Sanlúcar de Barrameda
Chipiona
Jerez de la Frontera
JEREZ DE LA FRONTERA
El Bosque
El Puerto de Santa Maria
Algar
Ubrique
Sancti Petri La Barrosa
Conil de la Frontera
Vejer de la Frontera
Barbate
GIBRALTAR
La Línea de Concepción
Tarifa
19km

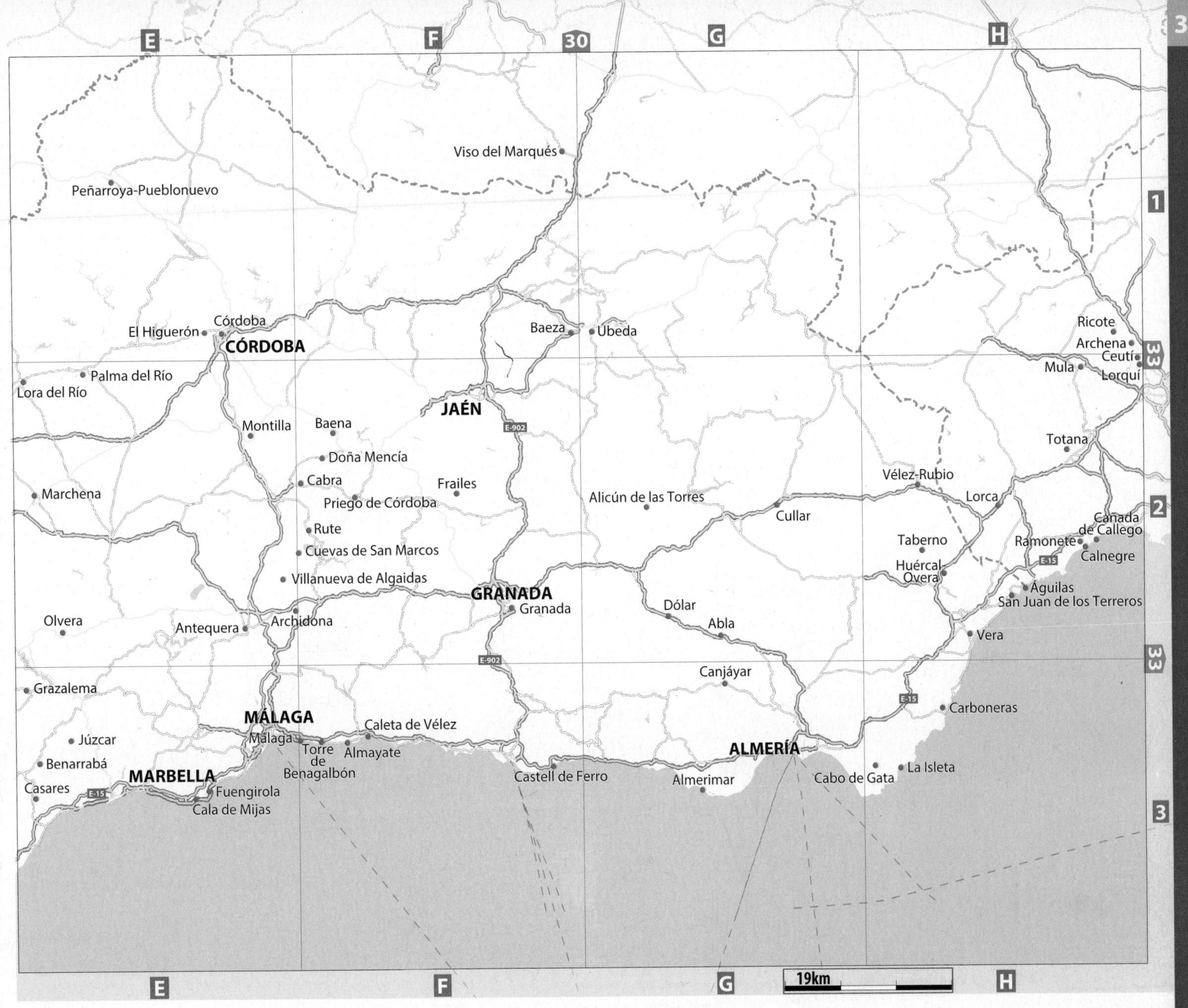
E
F
30
G
H
Viso del Marqués
Peñarroya-Pueblonuevo
1
El Higuerón
Córdoba
CÓRDOBA
Baeza
Úbeda
Ricote
Archena
Ceutí
Mula
Lorquí
33
Palma del Río
Lora del Río
JAÉN
E-902
Montilla
Baena
Doña Mencía
Totana
Cabra
Frailes
Vélez-Rubio
Marchena
Priego de Córdoba
Alicún de las Torres
Lorca
Cullar
2
Cañada de Callego
Rute
Taberno
Ramonete
Calnegre
Cuevas de San Marcos
Huércal-Overa
E-15
Villanueva de Algaidas
Águilas
GRANADA
San Juan de los Terreros
Olvera
Antequera
Archidona
Granada
Dólar
Abla
Vera
E-902
Canjáyar
33
Grazalema
E-15
Carboneras
MÁLAGA
Caleta de Vélez
Júzcar
Málaga
Torre de Benagalbón
Almayate
ALMERÍA
Benarrabá
MARBELLA
La Isleta
Casares
E-15
Fuengirola
Castell de Ferro
Almerimar
Cabo de Gata
Cala de Mijas
3
E
F
G
19km
H

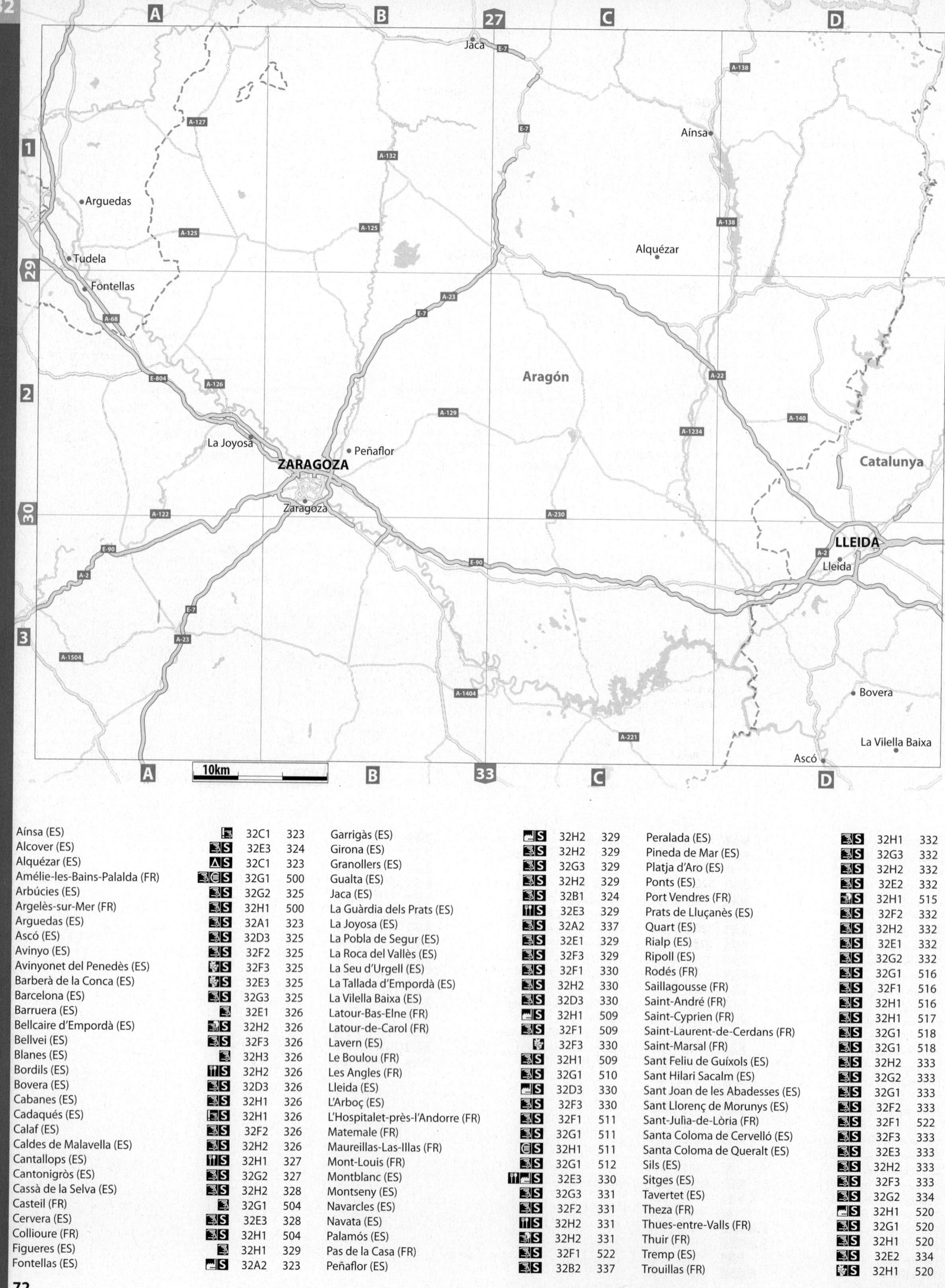

A
B
27
C
D
Jaca
E-7
A-138
A-127
E-7
Aínsa
1
A-132
Arguedas
A-125
A-125
A-138
Alquézar
Tudela
29
Fontellas
A-23
E-7
A-68
Aragón
A-22
E-804
A-126
2
A-129
A-140
A-1234
La Joyosa
Peñaflor
ZARAGOZA
Catalunya
Zaragoza
30
A-122
A-230
LLEIDA
E-90
A-2
Lleida
E-90
A-2
E-7
3
A-23
A-1504
A-1404
Bovera
A-221
La Vilella Baixa
Ascó
A
10km
B
33
C
D

E
F
27
G
H
PERPIGNAN
Rodés
Vinça
Thuir
Theza
Trouillas
Saint-Cyprien
Latour-Bas-Elne
Argelès-sur-Mer
Saint-André
Collioure
Port Vendres
Le Boulou
Saint-Marsal
Occitanie
L'Hospitalet-près-l'Andorre
Les Angles
Matemale
Vernet-les-Bains
Casteil
Mont-Louis
Thues-entre-Valls
ANDORRA LA VELLA
Pas de la Casa
Sant-Julià-de-Lòria
Barruera
Rialp
Latour-de-Carol
Saillagousse
FR
Amélie-les-Bains-Palalda
Maureillas-Las-Illas
Cantallops
Saint-Laurent-de-Cerdans
La Seu d'Urgell
La Pobla de Segur
ES
Cabanes
Peralada
Cadaqués
Sant Joan de les Abadesses
Figueres
Navata
Tremp
Sant Llorenç de Morunys
Ripoll
Garrigàs
La Tallada d Empordà
Catalunya
Cantonigròs
Bellcaire d'Empordà
Bordils
Gualta
Tavertet
Prats de Lluçanès
Girona
Ponts
Vic
Quart
Avinyo
Sant Hilari Sacalm
Cassà de la Selva
Caldes de Malavella
Viladrau
Palamós
Arbúcies
Sils
Platja d'Aro
Navarcles
Calaf
Sant Feliu de Guíxols
Cervera
La Roca del Vallès
Montseny
Blanes
Granollers
Pineda de Mar
Santa Coloma de Queralt
La Guàrdia dels Prats
Barberà de la Conca
Lavern
Barcelona
Montblanc
Vallirana
BARCELONA
Avinyonet del Penedès
Vilafranca del Penedès
Santa Coloma de Cervelló
Alcover
L'Arboç
Sitges
Bellvei
33
10km
1
2
3

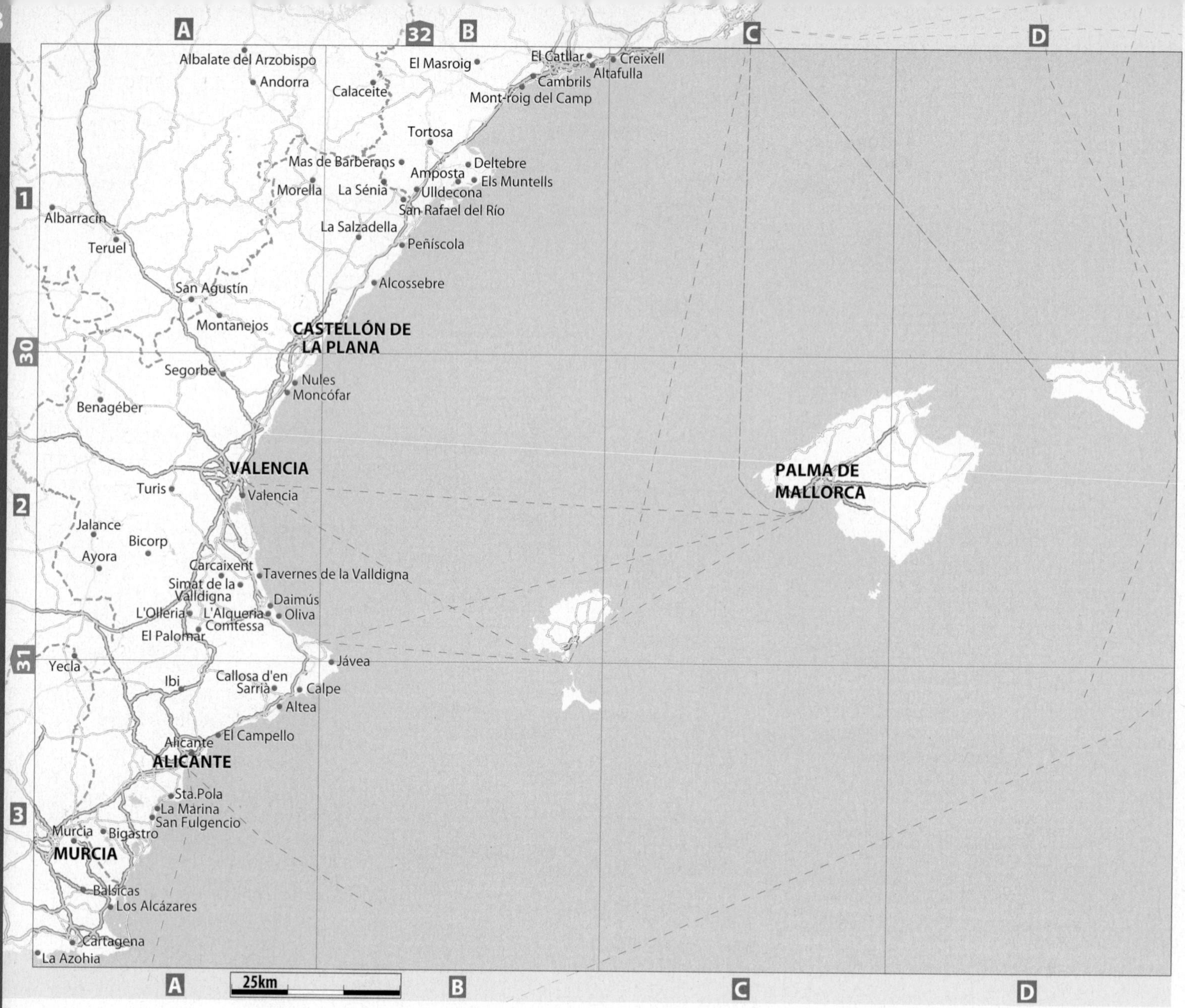

A B C D 32 30 31 1 2 3

Albalate del Arzobispo
Andorra
Calaceite
El Masroig
El Catllar
Creixell
Altafulla
Cambrils
Mont-roig del Camp
Tortosa
Mas de Barberans
Amposta
Deltebre
Els Muntells
Morella
La Sénia
Ulldecona
San Rafael del Río
Albarracín
Teruel
La Salzadella
Peñíscola
Alcossebre
San Agustín
Montanejos
CASTELLÓN DE LA PLANA
Segorbe
Nules
Moncófar
Benagéber
VALENCIA
Turis
Valencia
PALMA DE MALLORCA
Jalance
Bicorp
Ayora
Carcaixent
Tavernes de la Valldigna
Simat de la Valldigna
Daimús
L'Olleria
L'Alqueria Comtessa
Oliva
El Palomar
Yecla
Jávea
Ibi
Callosa d'en Sarrià
Calpe
Altea
Alicante
El Campello
ALICANTE
Sta.Pola
La Marina
San Fulgencio
Murcia
Bigastro
MURCIA
Balsicas
Los Alcázares
Cartagena
La Azohia
25km

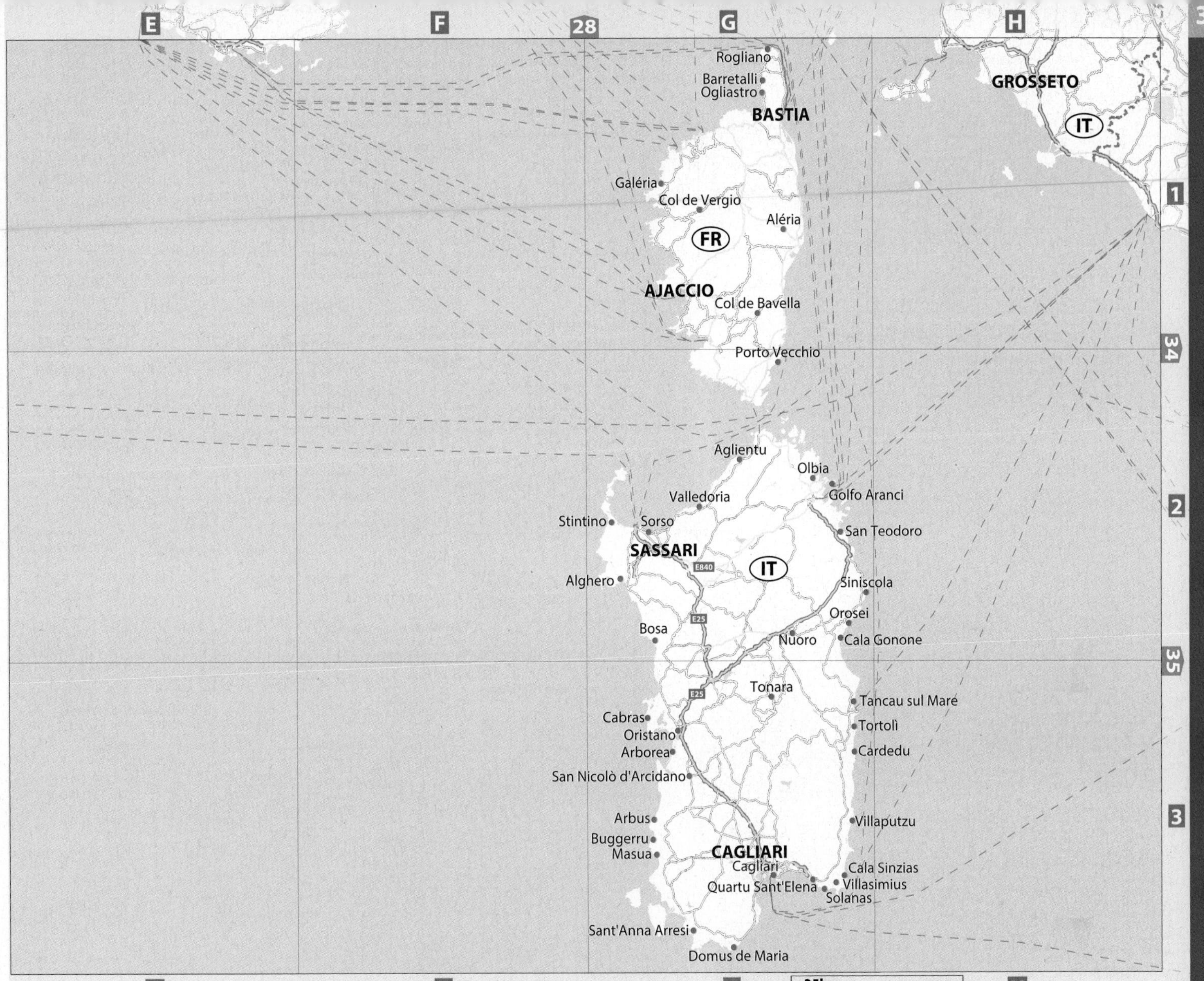

Tortolì (IT)	33G3	631
Tortosa (ES)	33B1	334
Turis (ES)	33A2	334
Ulldecona (ES)	33B1	334
Valencia (ES)	33A2	334
Valledoria (IT)	33G2	632
Villaputzu (IT)	33G3	632
Villasimius (IT)	33G3	632
Yecla (ES)	33A2	334

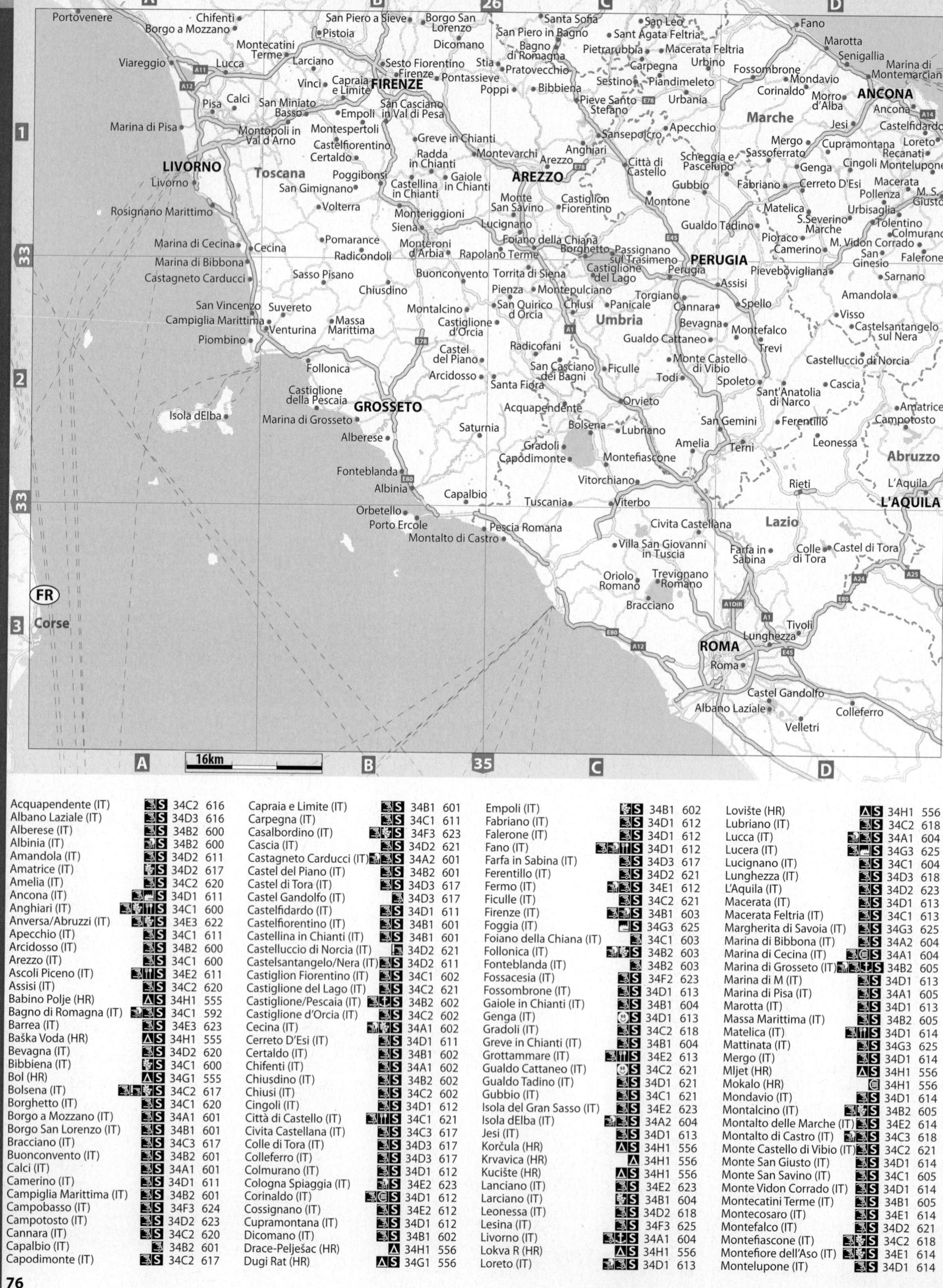
A
B
26
C
D
1
2
3
33
FR
Corse
Portovenere
Chifenti
Borgo a Mozzano
San Piero a Sieve
Borgo San Lorenzo
Pistoia
Dicomano
Santa Sofia
San Piero in Bagno
Bagno di Romagna
San Leo
Sant Agata Feltria
Pietrarubbia
Macerata Feltria
Carpegna
Urbino
Fano
Marotta
Senigallia
Marina di Montemarciano
Montecatini Terme
Viareggio
Lucca
Larciano
Sesto Fiorentino
Stia
Pratovecchio
Pontassieve
Firenze
FIRENZE
Vinci
Capraia e Limite
Poppi
Bibbiena
Sestino
Piandimeleto
Fossombrone
Mondavio
Corinaldo
Morro d'Alba
ANCONA
Ancona
Pisa
Calci
San Miniato Basso
Empoli
San Casciano in Val di Pesa
Pieve Santo Stefano
Urbania
Marche
Jesi
Castelfidardo
Marina di Pisa
Montopoli in Val d'Arno
Montespertoli
Castelfiorentino
Certaldo
Greve in Chianti
Sansepolcro
Apecchio
Mergo
Cupramontana
Loreto
Recanati
LIVORNO
Livorno
Toscana
Poggibonsi
San Gimignano
Radda in Chianti
Castellina in Chianti
Gaiole in Chianti
Montevarchi
Arezzo
AREZZO
Anghiari
Città di Castello
Scheggia e Pascelupo
Sassoferrato
Genga
Cingoli
Montelupone
Gubbio
Fabriano
Cerreto D'Esi
Macerata
Pollenza
M.S. Giusto
Rosignano Marittimo
Volterra
Monteriggioni
Siena
Monte San Savino
Castiglion Fiorentino
Montone
Matelica
S.Severino Marche
Urbisaglia
Tolentino
Colmurano
Lucignano
Gualdo Tadino
Pioraco
Camerino
M. Vidon Corrado
San Ginesio
Falerone
Marina di Cecina
Cecina
Pomarance
Radicondoli
Monteroni d'Arbia
Rapolano Terme
Foiano della Chiana
Borghetto
Passignano sul Trasimeno
Castiglione del Lago
PERUGIA
Perugia
Pievebovigliana
Marina di Bibbona
Castagneto Carducci
Sasso Pisano
Chiusdino
Buonconvento
Torrita di Siena
Pienza
Montepulciano
Assisi
Sarnano
Amandola
San Vincenzo
Suvereto
Campiglia Marittima
Venturina
Massa Marittima
Montalcino
Castiglione d'Orcia
San Quirico d'Orcia
Chiusi
Panicale
Torgiano
Cannara
Spello
Umbria
Bevagna
Montefalco
Visso
Castelsantangelo sul Nera
Piombino
Gualdo Cattaneo
Trevi
Castel del Piano
Radicofani
Monte Castello di Vibio
Castelluccio di Norcia
Follonica
Arcidosso
Santa Fiora
San Casciano dei Bagni
Ficulle
Todi
Spoleto
Cascia
Castiglione della Pescaia
GROSSETO
Sant'Anatolia di Narco
Amatrice
Isola dElba
Marina di Grosseto
Acquapendente
Orvieto
Campotosto
Saturnia
Bolsena
Lubriano
San Gemini
Ferentillo
Alberese
Gradoli
Capodimonte
Montefiascone
Amelia
Terni
Leonessa
Abruzzo
Fonteblanda
Albinia
Vitorchiano
Rieti
L'Aquila
Capalbio
Tuscania
Viterbo
L'AQUILA
Orbetello
Porto Ercole
Civita Castellana
Lazio
Pescia Romana
Montalto di Castro
Villa San Giovanni in Tuscia
Farfa in Sabina
Colle di Tora
Castel di Tora
Oriolo Romano
Trevignano Romano
Bracciano
Tivoli
Lunghezza
ROMA
Roma
Castel Gandolfo
Albano Laziale
Colleferro
Velletri
16km
35
A11
A12
A1
A14
A24
A25
A1DIR
E45
E78
E80

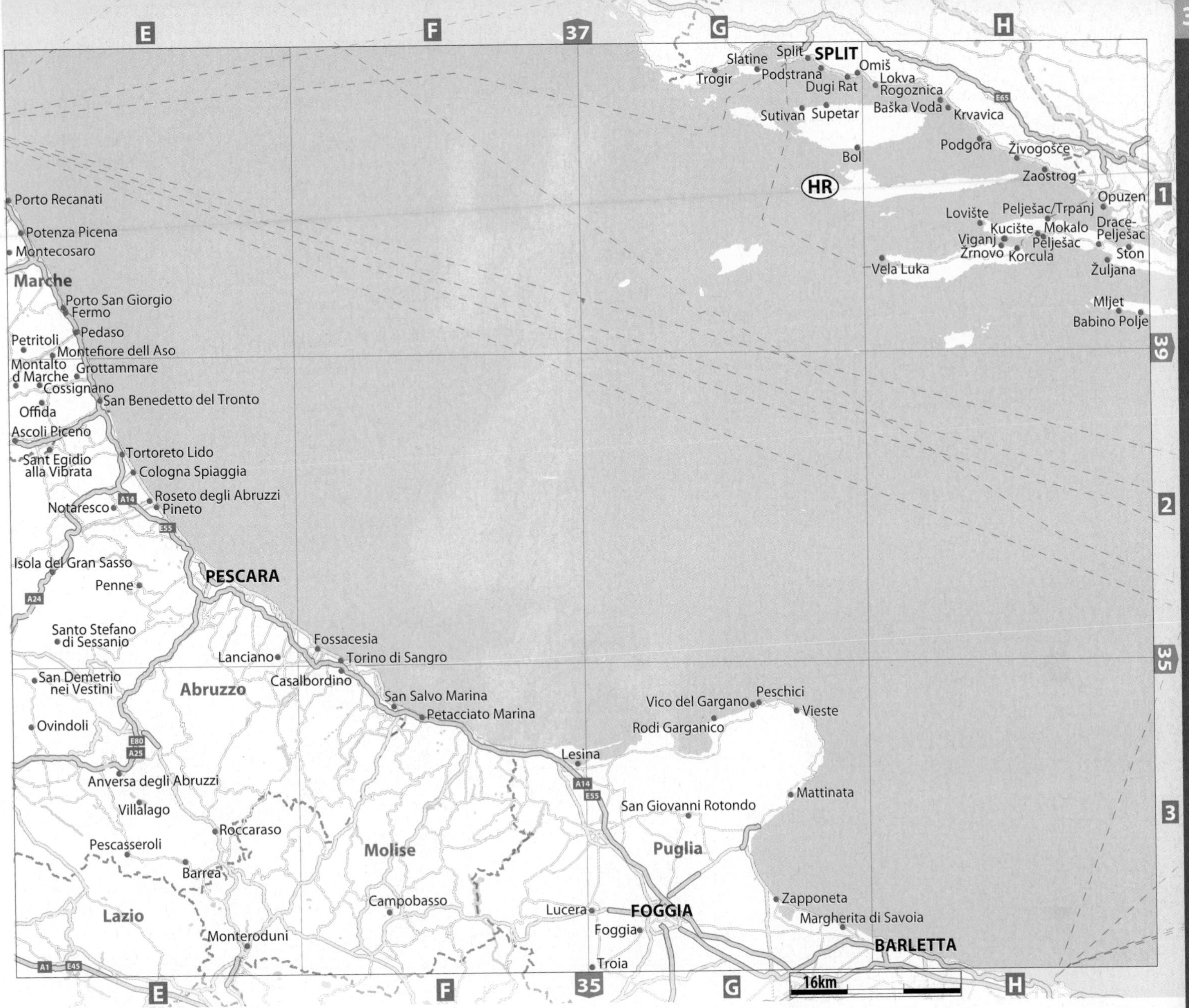
E
F
37
G
H
Slatine
Split
SPLIT
Omiš
Trogir
Podstrana
Lokva
Dugi Rat
Rogoznica
Sutivan
Supetar
Baška Voda
Krvavica
Bol
Podgora
Živogošće
HR
Zaostrog
Opuzen
1
Loviště
Pelješac/Trpanj
Kucište
Mokalo
Drace-
Pelješac
Viganj
Pelješac
Žrnovo
Korcula
Ston
Vela Luka
Žuljana
Mljet
Babino Polje
39
Porto Recanati
Potenza Picena
Montecosaro
Marche
Porto San Giorgio
Fermo
Pedaso
Petritoli
Montefiore dell Aso
Montalto
d Marche
Grottammare
Cossignano
San Benedetto del Tronto
Offida
Ascoli Piceno
Tortoreto Lido
Sant Egidio
alla Vibrata
Cologna Spiaggia
Roseto degli Abruzzi
Pineto
Notaresco
2
Isola del Gran Sasso
Penne
PESCARA
Santo Stefano
di Sessanio
Fossacesia
Lanciano
Torino di Sangro
35
San Demetrio
nei Vestini
Abruzzo
Casalbordino
San Salvo Marina
Petacciato Marina
Peschici
Vico del Gargano
Vieste
Rodi Garganico
Ovindoli
Lesina
Anversa degli Abruzzi
Mattinata
San Giovanni Rotondo
3
Villalago
Roccaraso
Pescasseroli
Molise
Puglia
Barrea
Zapponeta
Campobasso
Lucera
FOGGIA
Margherita di Savoia
Lazio
Foggia
Monteroduni
BARLETTA
Troia
16km
E
F
35
G
H

A
B
34
C
D
1
33
33
3
34km
LATINA
Lazio
Nettuno
Latina
Terracina
San Felice Circeo
Gaeta
Cassino
Mondragone
Baia e Latina
Casalbore
Benevento
NAPOLI
Pozzuoli
Napoli
Bacoli
Pompei
Cava de Tirreni
Tramonti
Pontecagnano Faiano
Contursi Terme
Battipaglia
Paestum
Campania
Case del Conte
Palinuro
Marina di Camerota
Sala Consilina
Grumento Nova
Basilicata
Puglia
BARI
Bari
Monopoli
Castellana Grotte
Torre Canne di Fasano
Putignano
Alberobello
Brindisi
BRINDISI
Matera
Massafra
TARANTO
LECCE
Torre dell'Orso
San Pietro in Bevagna
Lequile
Melendugno
Otranto
Metaponto
Santa Maria al Bagno
Gallipoli
Nova Siri
Marina di Felloniche
Praia a Mare
Morano Calabro
Trebisacce
Scalea
Cirella
Corigliano Calabro
Santa Maria del Cedro
Rossano
Cittadella del Capo
Camigliatello Silano
Cirò Marina
Calabria
Amantea
CATANZARO
Crotone
Cropani Marina
Catanzaro Marina
Palmi
MESSINA
Furnari
Terme Vigliatore
Oliveri
Roccalumera
Bova Marina
Condofuri Marina
San Vito Lo Capo
Palermo
PALERMO
Castelluzzo
Scopello
Reitano
Francavilla di Sicilia
Motta Camastra
Taormina
Giardini Naxos
Castelbuono
Trapani
Marsala
Castellammare del Golfo
Caccamo
Gangi
MARSALA
Sicilia
Montevago
San Giovanni La Punta
Camporotondo Etneo
CATANIA
Sutera
Enna
Caltanissetta
Piazza Armerina
Augusta
Ribera
Mineo
Montallegro
Realmonte
Agrigento
Caltagirone
SIRACUSA
Porto Empedocle
Licata
GELA
Piano San Paolo
Siracusa
Noto
Marina di Ragusa
Pozzallo
Pachino
Scicli
Ispica
Portopalo di Capo Passero

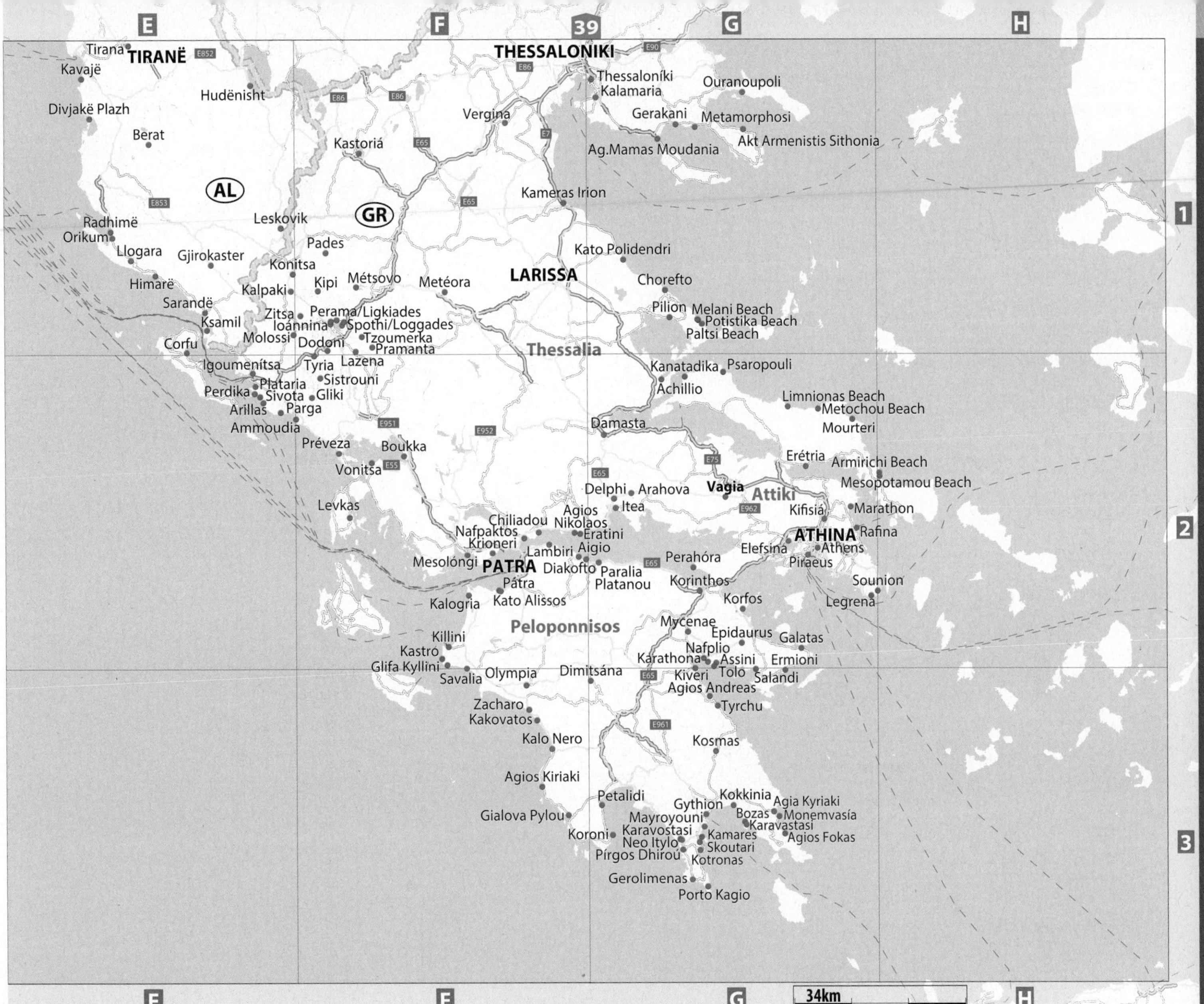
E
F
39
G
H
1
2
3
34km
Tirana
TIRANË
Kavajë
Divjakë Plazh
Hudënisht
Berat
AL
GR
Radhimë
Orikum
Llogara
Gjirokaster
Himarë
Sarandë
Ksamil
Corfu
Leskovik
Pades
Konitsa
Kalpaki
Kipi
Métsovo
Meteóra
Zitsa
Perama/Ligkiades
Ioánnina
Spothi/Loggades
Molossi
Dodoni
Tzoumerka
Pramanta
Igoumenitsa
Tyria
Lazena
Plataria
Sistrouni
Perdika
Sivota
Gliki
Arillas
Parga
Ammoudia
Préveza
Boukka
Vonitsa
Levkas
THESSALONIKI
Thessaloníki
Kalamaria
Vergina
Kastoriá
Ouranoupoli
Gerakani
Metamorphosi
Ag.Mamas Moudania
Akt Armenistis Sithonia
Kameras Irion
Kato Polidendri
LARISSA
Chorefto
Pilion
Melani Beach
Potistika Beach
Paltsi Beach
Thessalia
Kanatadika
Psaropouli
Achillio
Limnionas Beach
Metochou Beach
Mourteri
Damasta
Erétria
Armirichi Beach
Mesopotamou Beach
Delphi
Arahova
Vagia
Attiki
Itea
Agios Nikolaos
Kifisiá
Marathon
Chiliadou
Nafpaktos
Krioneri
Eratini
ATHINA
Rafina
Athens
Piraeus
Elefsina
Mesolóngi
PATRA
Lambiri
Aigio
Diakofto
Paralia Platanou
Perahóra
Pátra
Korinthos
Sounion
Legrena
Kalogria
Kato Alissos
Korfos
Peloponnisos
Mycenae
Epidaurus
Galatas
Killini
Kastro
Nafplio
Glifa Kyllini
Karathona
Assini
Ermioni
Savalia
Olympia
Dimitsána
Kiveri
Tolo
Salandi
Agios Andreas
Tyrchu
Zacharo
Kakovatos
Kalo Nero
Kosmas
Agios Kiriaki
Petalidi
Kokkinia
Gythion
Agia Kyriaki
Gialova Pylou
Mayroyouni
Bozas
Monemvasía
Karavostasi
Karavastasi
Koroni
Neo Itylo
Kamares
Agios Fokas
Pírgos Dhiroú
Skoutari
Kotronas
Gerolimenas
Porto Kagio
E852
E853
E86
E90
E65
E75
E951
E952
E55
E962
E961

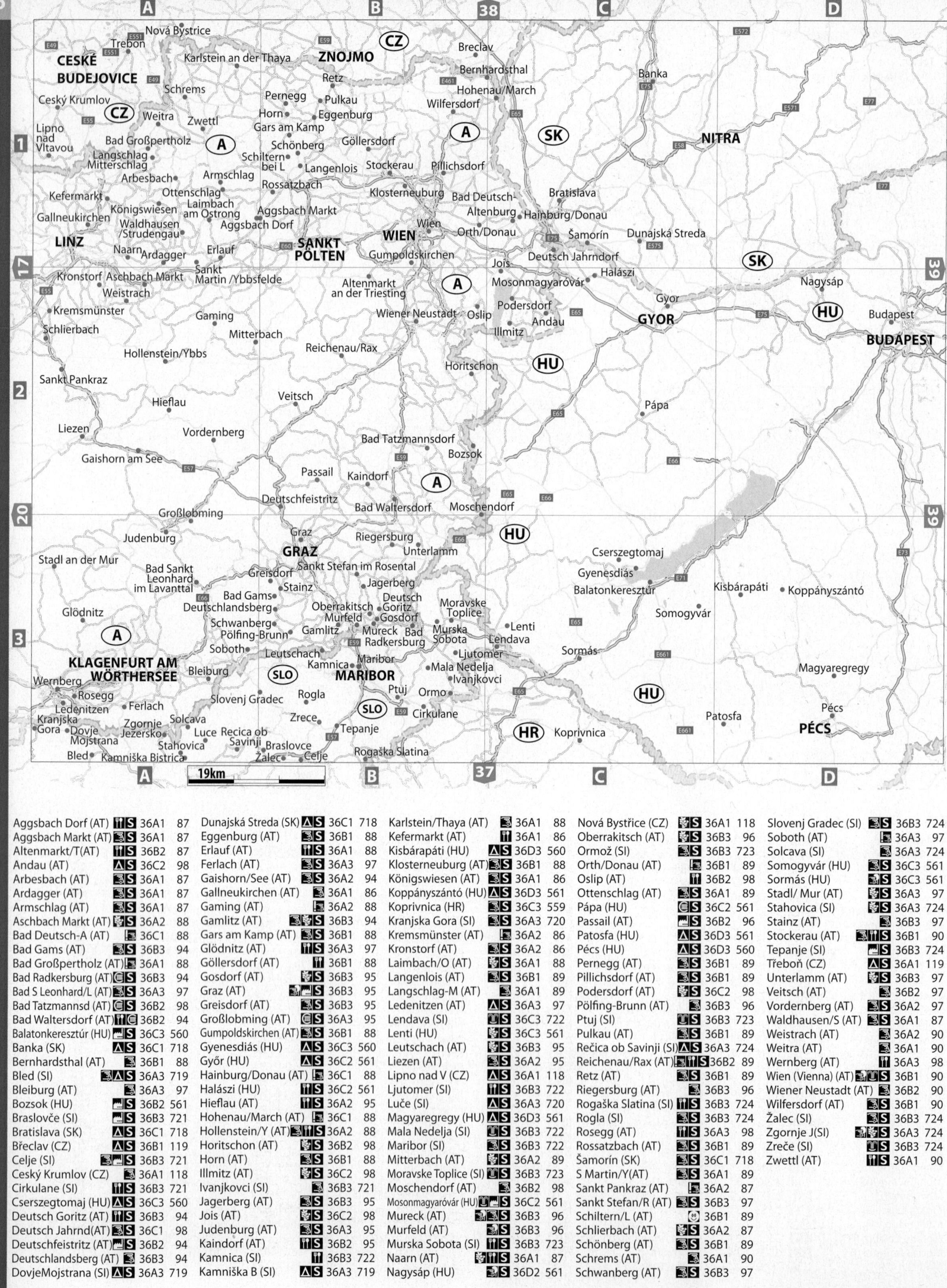

A
B
38
C
D
Nová Bystrice
Trebon
CESKÉ BUDEJOVICE
Karlstein an der Thaya
ZNOJMO
CZ
Breclav
Bernhardsthal
Banka
Retz
Schrems
Hohenau/March
Cesky Krumlov
Pernegg
Pulkau
Wilfersdorf
CZ
Weitra
Zwettl
Horn
Eggenburg
Lipno nad Vltavou
Gars am Kamp
A
SK
NITRA
1
Bad Großpertholz
A
Schönberg
Göllersdorf
Langschlag
Mitterschlag
Schiltern bei L
Langenlois
Stockerau
Pillichsdorf
Arbesbach
Armschlag
Rossatzbach
Kefermarkt
Ottenschlag
Klosterneuburg
Bad Deutsch-Altenburg
Bratislava
Gallneukirchen
Königswiesen
Laimbach am Ostrong
Aggsbach Markt
Aggsbach Dorf
Hainburg/Donau
Waldhausen /Strudengau
Wien
Orth/Donau
Šamorín
Dunajská Streda
LINZ
SANKT PÖLTEN
WIEN
Naarn
Ardagger
Erlauf
Gumpoldskirchen
Deutsch Jahrndorf
Jois
SK
17
Sankt Martin /Ybbsfelde
Halászi
39
Kronstorf
Aschbach Markt
Altenmarkt an der Triesting
A
Mosonmagyaróvár
Nagysáp
Weistrach
Gyor
Kremsmünster
Podersdorf
Gaming
Wiener Neustadt
Oslip
Andau
HU
Budapest
Schlierbach
GYOR
Mitterbach
Illmitz
BUDAPEST
Reichenau/Rax
Hollenstein/Ybbs
Horitschon
HU
Sankt Pankraz
2
Veitsch
Pápa
Hieflau
Liezen
Vordernberg
Bad Tatzmannsdorf
Bozsok
Gaishorn am See
Passail
Kaindorf
A
Deutschfeistritz
Bad Waltersdorf
Moschendorf
20
Großlobming
39
Graz
Riegersburg
HU
Judenburg
GRAZ
Unterlamm
Cserszegtomaj
Stadl an der Mur
Bad Sankt Leonhard im Lavanttal
Greisdorf
Sankt Stefan im Rosental
Gyenesdiás
Stainz
Jagerberg
Balatonkeresztúr
Kisbárapáti
Koppányszántó
Bad Gams
Deutsch Goritz
Moravske Toplice
Deutschlandsberg
Oberrakitsch
Glödnitz
Murfeld
Gosdorf
Somogyvár
Schwanberg
Pölfing-Brunn
Gamlitz
Mureck
Bad Radkersburg
Murska Sobota
Lenti
A
3
Lendava
Soboth
Leutschach
Ljutomer
Sormás
KLAGENFURT AM WÖRTHERSEE
Bleiburg
Kamnica
Maribor
Mala Nedelja
Magyaregregy
SLO
MARIBOR
Ivanjkovci
Wernberg
Ptuj
Ormo
HU
Rosegg
Slovenj Gradec
Rogla
Ledenitzen
Ferlach
Kranjska Gora
Zrece
SLO
Cirkulane
Pécs
Zgornje Jezersko
Solcava
Patosfa
Dovje Mojstrana
Luce
Recica ob Savinji
Tepanje
HR
Koprivnica
PÉCS
Stahovica
Braslovce
Bled
Kamniška Bistrica
Žalec
Celje
Rogaška Slatina
A
19km
B
37
C
D

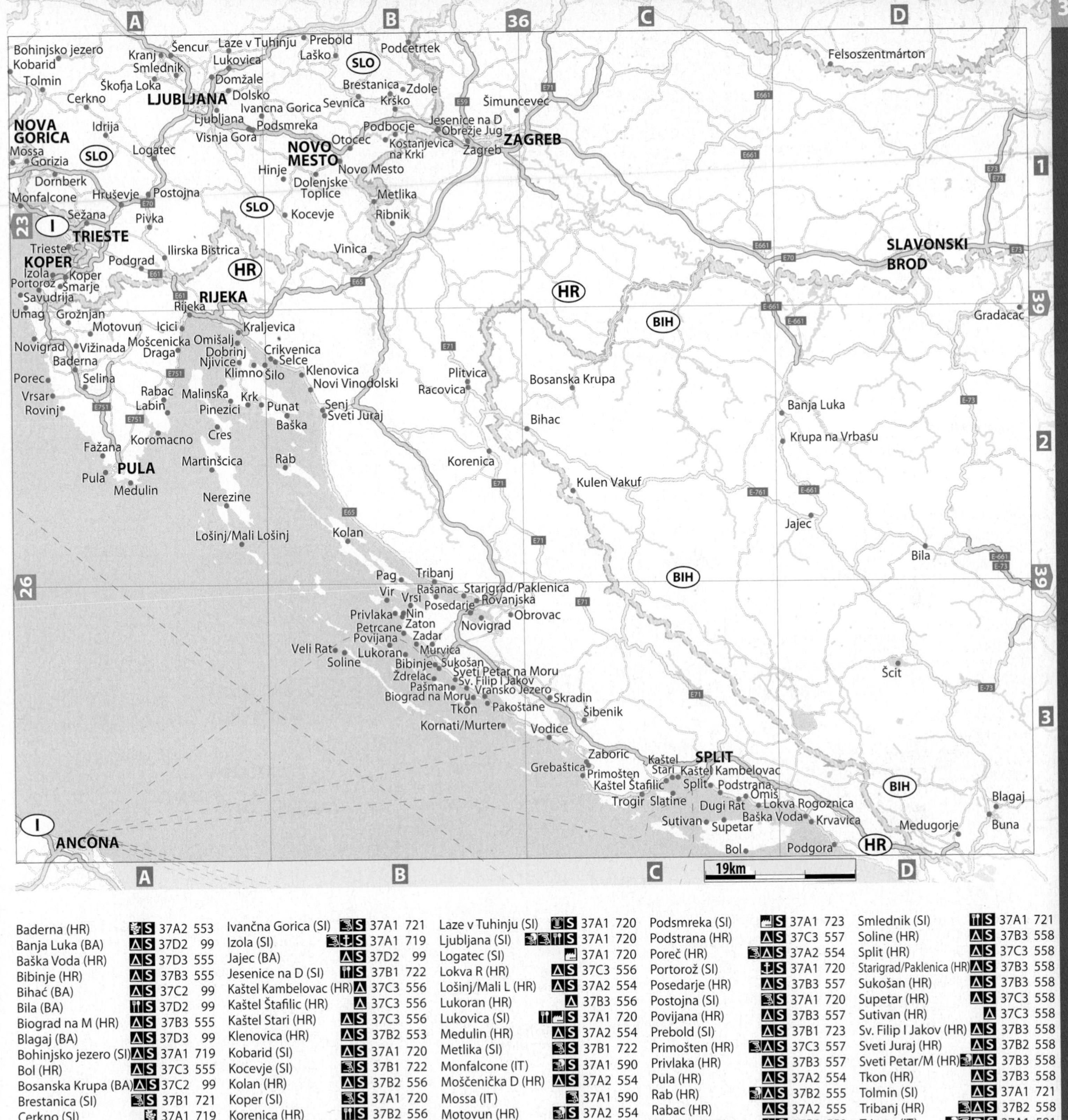

Place	Map	Page
Baderna (HR)	37A2	553
Banja Luka (BA)	37D2	99
Baška Voda (HR)	37D3	555
Bibinje (HR)	37B3	555
Bihać (BA)	37C2	99
Bila (BA)	37D2	99
Biograd na M (HR)	37B3	555
Blagaj (BA)	37D3	99
Bohinjsko jezero (SI)	37A1	719
Bol (HR)	37C3	555
Bosanska Krupa (BA)	37C2	99
Brestanica (SI)	37B1	721
Cerkno (SI)	37A1	719
Cres/Cres (HR)	37A2	553
Cres/Martinščica (HR)	37A2	553
Cres/Nerezine (HR)	37A2	553
Crikvenica (HR)	37B2	553
Dobrinj (HR)	37A2	553
Dolenjske T (SI)	37B1	721
Dolsko (SI)	37A1	721
Domžale (SI)	37A1	719
Dornberk (SI)	37A1	719
Dugi Rat (HR)	37C3	556
Fažana (HR)	37A2	553
Felsőszentmárton (HU)	37D1	561
Gorizia (IT)	37A1	589
Grebaštica (HR)	37C3	556
Grožnjan (HR)	37A2	553
Hinje (SI)	37B1	721
Hruševje (SI)	37A1	719
Ičiči (HR)	37A2	553
Idrija (SI)	37A1	719
Ilirska Bistrica (SI)	37A1	719
Ivančna Gorica (SI)	37A1	721
Izola (SI)	37A1	719
Jajec (BA)	37D2	99
Jesenice na D (SI)	37B1	722
Kaštel Kambelovac (HR)	37C3	556
Kaštel Štafilic (HR)	37C3	556
Kaštel Stari (HR)	37C3	556
Klenovica (HR)	37B2	553
Kobarid (SI)	37A1	720
Kocevje (SI)	37B1	722
Kolan (HR)	37B2	556
Koper (SI)	37A1	720
Korenica (HR)	37B2	556
Kornati/Murter (HR)	37B3	556
Koromačno (HR)	37A2	553
Kostanjevica na K(SI)	37B1	722
Kraljevica (HR)	37A2	553
Kranj (SI)	37A1	720
Krvavica (HR)	37D3	556
Krk/Baška (HR)	37B2	553
Krk/Klimno (HR)	37A2	553
Krk/Krk (HR)	37A2	553
Krk/Malinska (HR)	37A2	554
Krk/Njivice (HR)	37A2	554
Krk/Omišalj (HR)	37A2	554
Krk/Pinezici (HR)	37A2	554
Krk/Punat (HR)	37A2	554
Krk/Šilo (HR)	37A2	554
Krško (SI)	37B1	722
Krupa na Vrbasu (BA)	37D2	99
Kulen Vakuf (BA)	37C2	99
Labin (HR)	37A2	554
Laško (SI)	37B1	722
Laze v Tuhinju (SI)	37A1	720
Ljubljana (SI)	37A1	720
Logatec (SI)	37A1	720
Lokva R (HR)	37C3	556
Lošinj/Mali L (HR)	37A2	554
Lukoran (HR)	37B3	556
Lukovica (SI)	37A1	720
Medulin (HR)	37A2	554
Metlika (SI)	37B1	722
Monfalcone (IT)	37A1	590
Moščenička D (HR)	37A2	554
Mossa (IT)	37A1	590
Motovun (HR)	37A2	554
Murvica (HR)	37B3	556
Nin (HR)	37B3	556
Novi Vinodolski (HR)	37B2	554
Novigrad (Dalm) (HR)	37B3	556
Novigrad (Istria) (HR)	37A2	554
Novo Mesto (SI)	37B1	723
Obrežje Jug (SI)	37B1	723
Obrovac (HR)	37B3	556
Omiš (HR)	37C3	556
Otočec (SI)	37B1	723
Pag (HR)	37B2	557
Pakoštane (HR)	37B3	557
Pašman (HR)	37B3	557
Petrcane (HR)	37B3	557
Pivka (SI)	37A1	723
Plitviča (HR)	37B2	559
Podbočje (SI)	37B1	723
Podčetrtek (SI)	37B1	723
Podgora (HR)	37D3	557
Podgrad (SI)	37A1	720
Podsmreka (SI)	37A1	723
Podstrana (HR)	37C3	557
Poreč (HR)	37A2	554
Portorož (SI)	37A1	720
Posedarje (HR)	37B3	557
Postojna (SI)	37A1	720
Povijana (HR)	37B3	557
Prebold (SI)	37B1	723
Primošten (HR)	37C3	557
Privlaka (HR)	37B3	557
Pula (HR)	37A2	554
Rab (HR)	37B2	555
Rabac (HR)	37A2	555
Racovica (HR)	37B2	559
Ražanac (HR)	37B3	557
Ribnik (HR)	37B1	555
Rijeka (HR)	37A2	555
Rovanjska (HR)	37B3	557
Rovinj (HR)	37A2	555
Savudrija (HR)	37A1	555
Šćit (BA)	37D3	99
Selce (HR)	37B2	555
Selina (HR)	37A2	555
Šenčur (SI)	37A1	721
Senj (HR)	37B2	557
Sevnica (SI)	37B1	724
Sežana (SI)	37A1	721
Šibenik (HR)	37C3	557
Šimunčevec (HR)	37B1	559
Škofja Loka (SI)	37A1	721
Skradin (HR)	37C3	557
Slatine (HR)	37C3	558
Šmarje (SI)	37A1	721
Smlednik (SI)	37A1	721
Soline (HR)	37B3	558
Split (HR)	37C3	558
Starigrad/Paklenica (HR)	37B3	558
Sukošan (HR)	37B3	558
Supetar (HR)	37C3	558
Sutivan (HR)	37C3	558
Sv. Filip I Jakov (HR)	37B3	558
Sveti Juraj (HR)	37B2	558
Sveti Petar/M (HR)	37B3	558
Tkon (HR)	37B3	558
Tolmin (SI)	37A1	721
Tribanj (HR)	37B2	558
Trieste (IT)	37A1	591
Trogir (HR)	37C3	558
Umag (HR)	37A1	555
Veli Rat (HR)	37B3	558
Vinica (SI)	37B1	724
Vir (HR)	37B3	558
Visnja Gora (SI)	37A1	724
Vižinada (HR)	37A2	555
Vodice (HR)	37C3	558
Vransko Jezero (HR)	37B3	558
Vrsar (HR)	37A2	555
Vrsi (HR)	37B3	558
Zaboric (HR)	37C3	558
Zadar (HR)	37B3	558
Zagreb (HR)	37B1	559
Zaton (HR)	37B3	559
Zdole (SI)	37B1	724
Ždrelac (HR)	37B3	559

Place	Map	Page
Bad Muskau (DE)	38A3	180
Biskupice (PL)	38A2	682
Brezno (SK)	38C4	718
Červená Řečice (CZ)	38A4	119
Czaplinek (PL)	38A1	681
Dobre Miasto (PL)	38B1	682
Ebersbach/Sachsen (DE)	38A3	181
Gaj (PL)	38C4	683
Gdańsk (Danzica) (PL)	38B1	681
Gierloz (PL)	38C1	682
Golčův Jeníkov (CZ)	38A4	118
Gora Swietej Anny (PL)	38B3	683
Görlitz (DE)	38A3	181
Haligovce (SK)	38C4	718
Hernádvécse (HU)	38C4	560
Hluboká nad Vltavou (CZ)	38A4	118
Karpacz (PL)	38A3	683
Kraków (Cracovia) (PL)	38C4	683
Kutná Hora (CZ)	38A4	118
Lipce Reymontowskie (PL)	38C2	683
Liptovský Ján (SK)	38C4	718
Löbau (DE)	38A3	181
Malbork (PL)	38B1	681
Mikolajki (PL)	38C1	682
Milolyn (PL)	38B1	682
Miroslawiec (PL)	38A2	681
Mrągowo (PL)	38C1	682
Naklo (PL)	38B3	683
Nové Město pod Smrkem (CZ)	38A3	118
Oderwitz (DE)	38A3	182
Osetno (PL)	38B1	682
Oswiecim (PL)	38B4	683
Parchowo (PL)	38A1	682
Paslek (PL)	38B1	682
Piecki (PL)	38C1	682
Pieniezno (PL)	38B1	682
Poznań (PL)	38A2	682
Prague (Praga) (CZ)	38A4	118
Řásná (CZ)	38A4	119
Sękowa (PL)	38C4	683
Snina (SK)	38D4	718
Sorkwity (PL)	38C1	682
Svitavy (CZ)	38A4	119
Tolkmicko (PL)	38B1	682
Toruń (PL)	38B2	682
Uciechów (PL)	38A3	683
Uherský Brod (CZ)	38B4	119
Varín (SK)	38B4	718
Velká Jesenice (CZ)	38A4	119
Vyšný Medzev (SK)	38C4	718
Vysoké Tatry (SK)	38C4	718
Warszawa (Varsavia) (PL)	38C2	682
Wetlina (PL)	38D4	683
Wieliczka (PL)	38C4	683
Wierzbna (PL)	38A2	682
Zagaje (PL)	38A1	682
Žďár nad Sázavou (CZ)	38A4	119
Zittau (DE)	38A3	182
Łukta (PL)	38B1	682

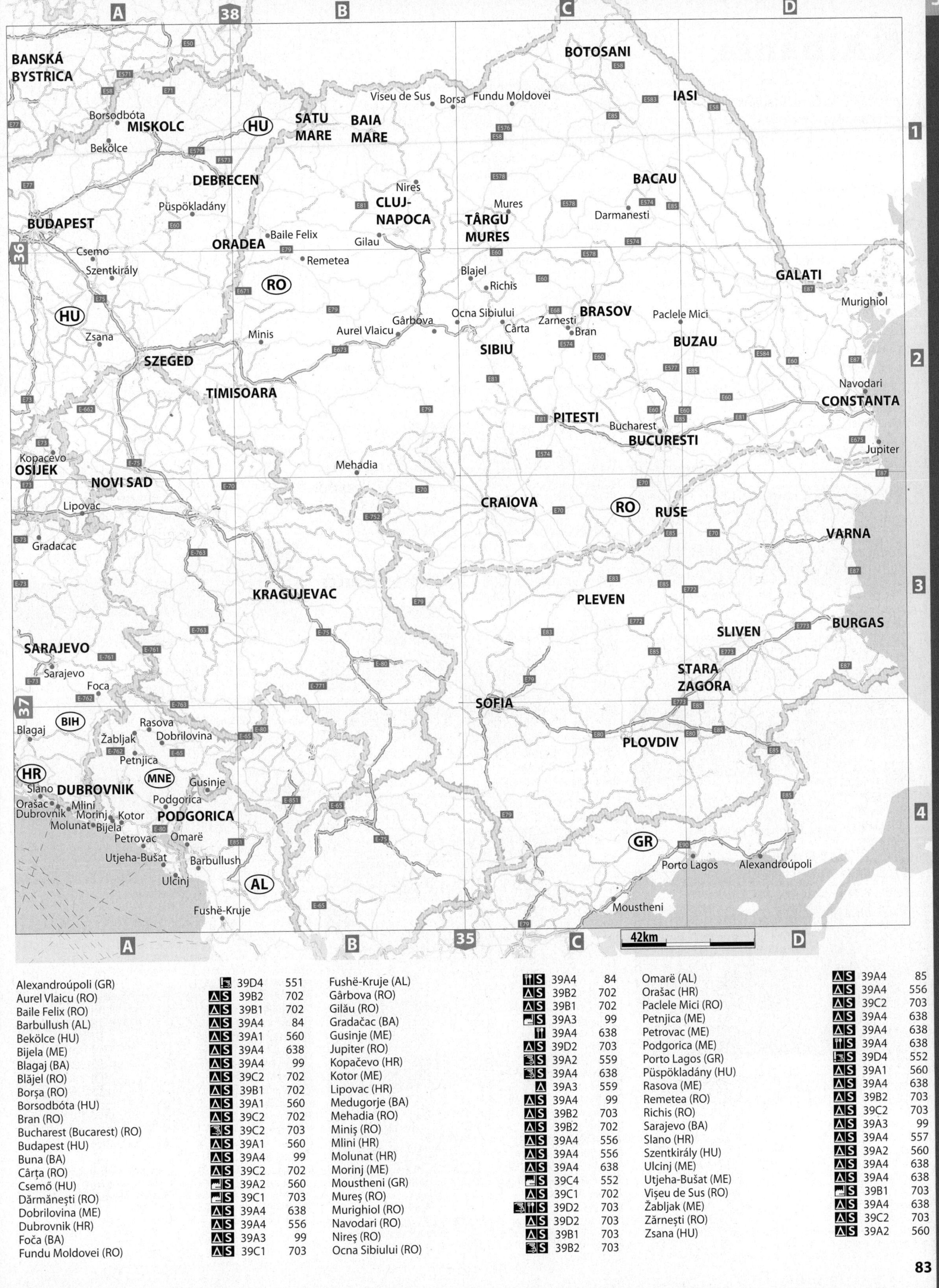

A
B
C
D
38
1
2
3
4
36
37
35
BANSKÁ BYSTRICA
Borsodbóta
MISKOLC
Bekölce
HU
SATU MARE
BAIA MARE
Viseu de Sus
Borsa
Fundu Moldovei
BOTOSANI
IASI
DEBRECEN
Püspökladány
BUDAPEST
Nires
CLUJ-NAPOCA
Mures
TÂRGU MURES
BACAU
Darmanesti
ORADEA
Baile Felix
Gilau
Remetea
Csemo
Szentkirály
RO
Blajel
Richis
GALATI
Murighiol
Gârbova
Ocna Sibiului
Zarnesti
BRASOV
Paclele Mici
Aurel Vlaicu
Cârta
Bran
Minis
Zsana
SIBIU
BUZAU
SZEGED
TIMISOARA
Navodari
CONSTANTA
PITESTI
Bucharest
BUCURESTI
Jupiter
Kopacevo
OSIJEK
Mehadia
NOVI SAD
CRAIOVA
RUSE
Lipovac
VARNA
Gradacac
KRAGUJEVAC
PLEVEN
BURGAS
SLIVEN
SARAJEVO
Sarajevo
Foca
STARA ZAGORA
SOFIA
BIH
Blagaj
Rasova
Žabljak
Dobrilovina
Petnjica
PLOVDIV
HR
MNE
Gusinje
Slano
DUBROVNIK
Orašac
Mlini
Dubrovnik
Morinj
Kotor
Podgorica
PODGORICA
Molunat
Bijela
Petrovac
Omarë
Utjeha-Bušat
Barbullush
GR
Porto Lagos
Alexandroúpoli
Ulcinj
AL
Fushë-Kruje
Moustheni
42km

Albania

Capital: Tirana
Government: parliamentarian republic
Official Language: Albanian
Population: 3.038.594 (2016)
Area: 28.748 km²

General information
Dialling code: 0355
General emergency: 112
Currency: Lek (ALL) € 1 = 134 ALL, 100 ALL = € 0,75
£1 = 151 ALL, 100 ALL = £0.66 (October 2017)
Credit cards are accepted in the main cities.

Regulations for overnight stays
Wild camping is allowed with permission from land owner/manager or local government.

Additional public holidays 2018
March 14 Dita e Verës (Summer Day)
March 21 Nowruz (Iranian New Year)
March 30 Good Friday
October 19 Mother Teresa Day
November 28 Independence Day
November 29 Liberation Day

Time Zone
Winter (Standard Time) GMT+1
Summer (DST) GMT+2

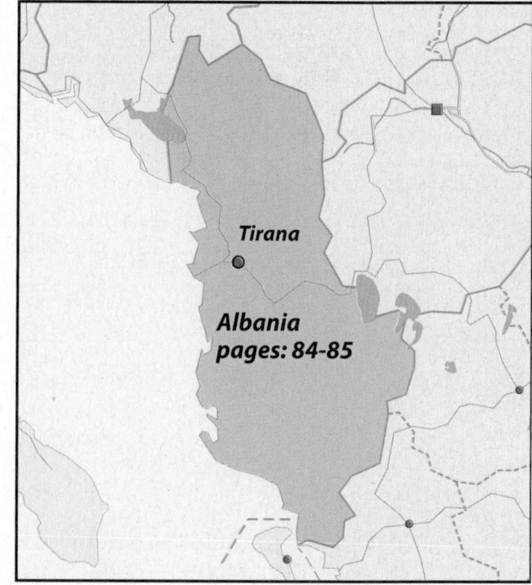

AL

Barbullush 39A4
Restaurant/Camping Albania, Barbullush 4022.
GPS: n41,92386 e19,54186.

€ 12 Ch € 2/day WC € 3,50 included.
Location: Rural. **Surface:** grassy. 01/01-31/12.
Distance: Skodër 20km.

Berat 35E1
Berat Caravan Camping, Ura Vajgurore. **GPS**: n40,77914 e19,85848.

30 € 17 Ch WC included. **Surface:** grassy.
01/01-31/12.
Distance: city centre Berat 18km on the spot on the spot.

Divjakë Plazh 35E1
Bar/Rest/Hotel Adrian Satka. **GPS**: n40,97156 e19,48036.

. 01/01-31/12.

Fushë-Kruje 39A4
Hotel Nordpark, Rruga Nacionale. **GPS**: n41,47078 e19,69875.

€ 19 Ch WC included. 01/01-31/12.
Remarks: Incl. access swimming pool.

Gjirokaster 35E1
Viroi, SH4. **GPS**: n40,10308 e20,12289.

2 free. 01/01-31/12.
Distance: 3km on the spot.

Himarë 35E1
Camping Kranea, Livadh Beach. **GPS**: n40,10734 e19,72739.

€ 14 € 2 € 3. 01/01-31/12.

Himarë 35E1
Camping Moskato, Livadh Road. **GPS**: n40,10986 e19,72280.

25 € 13 Ch WC included € 2/time.
01/01-31/12.

Hudënisht 35E1
Peshku, SH3. **GPS**: n40,96725 e20,64274.
€ 5-12 Ch WC included € 2.
Surface: grassy.
01/01-31/12.
Distance: 100m.
Remarks: Lake Ohrid, free use of sun beds and beach chairs.

Kavajë 35E1
Camp Pa Emer, Rrakull-Karpen. **GPS**: n41,18138 e19,47750.

34 € 18 Ch WC included.
Surface: grassy/gravel. 01/04-01/11.
Distance: 1km on the spot on the spot.

Ksamil 35E1
Sunset, SH81. **GPS**: n39,77908 e20,00831.

20 € 10 Ch WC included.
Surface: metalled. 01/01-31/12.
Distance: Sarandë 10km on the spot on the spot 1km.

Leskovik 35E1
Farma Sotira, SH75, Leskovik > Ersekë 15km.
GPS: n40,21477 e20,64611.

20 € 10 Ch WC included. **Location:** Rural, isolated.
Surface: grassy. 01/04-01/11.
Distance: on the spot on the spot on the spot on the spot.

Llogara 35E1
Hotel Hamiti, SH8. **GPS**: n40,21035 e19,57924.
€ 5. 01/01-31/12.

ΔS Omarë 39A4

Lake Shkodra Resort, Rruga E Liqenit.
GPS: n42,13836 e19,46562.
€ 12, Jul/Aug € 14 Ch € 2 WC € 3,95 included.
Surface: grassy. 01/04-15/11.
Distance: Skodër 10km lake with sandy beach on the spot on the spot.
Remarks: Free use of sun beds and beach chairs, canoe and bicycle rental.

ΔS Orikum 35E1

Camping Dion. **GPS**: n40,34407 e19,48280.

12 € 10 Ch included. **Surface:** metalled.
01/01-31/12.
Distance: 500m on the spot on the spot.
Remarks: S 148.

S Radhimë 35E1

Rezidenca Cekodhima, SH8. **GPS**: n40,37706 e19,47872.

20 € 20 Ch WC .
Surface: gravel. 01/01-31/12.
Distance: pebbled beach on the spot.

S Sarandë 35E1

Hotel Mediterrane, Rruga Skënderbeu. **GPS**: n39,87041 e20,01854.

10 € 15 included WC . **Location:** Urban.
Surface: asphalted. 01/01-31/12.
Distance: city centre 1km 600m on the spot.

S Tirana 35E1

Hotel Baron, Rruga e Elbasanit. **GPS**: n41,29947 e19,85012.

6 € 15 Ch WC included.
Surface: metalled. 01/01-31/12.
Distance: centre 4km on the spot.

AL

Austria

Capital: Vienna
Government: federal, parliamentarian, democratic republic
Official Language: German
Population: 8,711,770 (2016)
Area: 83,871 km²

General information
Dialling code: 0043
General emergency: 112
Currency: Euro

Regulations for overnight stays
In general overnight parking is allowed, except: Tyrol, Vienna, nature reserves and in areas where locally prohibited. No "camping" activities allowed and disposal wastewater must be at official places.

Additional public holidays 2018
January 6 Epiphany
May 1 Labor Day
May 31 Corpus Christi
August 15 Assumption of the Virgin Mary
October 26 National Holiday
November 1 All Saints' Day
December 8 Immaculate Conception

Time Zone
Winter (Standard Time) GMT+1
Summer (DST) GMT+2

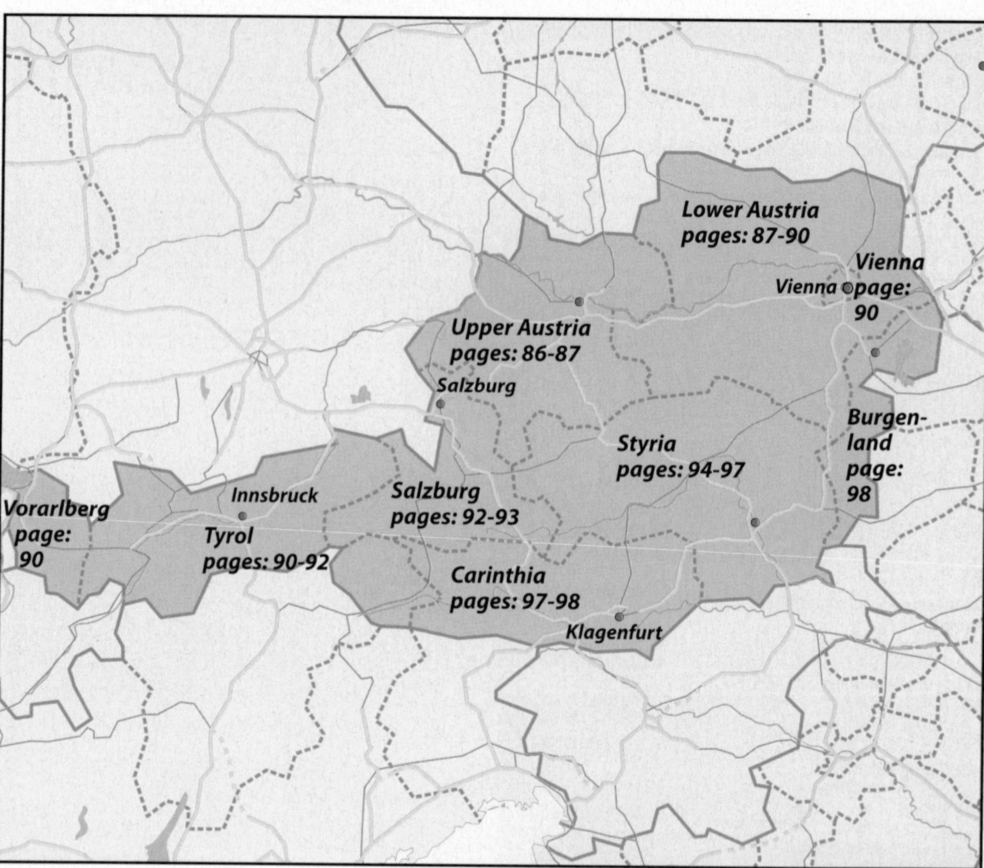

Upper Austria

Aschach an der Donau 17H3
Schopperplatz. **GPS**: n48,37417 e14,02824.
4 € 12/24h Ch included.
Location: Quiet. 01/01-31/12.
Distance: 300m on the spot.
Remarks: At Danube cycle route, water closed during wintertime.

Ebensee 20H1
Am Traunsee, Trauneck. **GPS**: n47,81283 e13,77730.

10 € 12/24h € 0,50/50liter Ch (12x)€ 3 WC.
Location: Rural, simple, quiet. **Surface:** asphalted.
01/01-31/12.
Distance: 500m on the spot 300m.
Remarks: At lake, max. 3 days.

Ebensee 20H1
Freizeitanlage Rindbach, Strandbadstraße.
GPS: n47,80934 e13,79002.

30 € 12 € 1/25liter (4x)€ 1/h. **Location:** Rural, simple, quiet. **Surface:** grassy. 01/04-31/10.
Distance: 1,4km.
Remarks: At lake.

Eferding 17H3
Brandstatt, Pupping. **GPS**: n48,33503 e14,02698.
. 01/01-31/12.
Remarks: On the Danube river.

Gallneukirchen 36A1
Freizeitcentrum, Veitsdorfer Weg 10. **GPS**: n48,36045 e14,40797.

10 free. **Location:** Rural, simple.
Surface: asphalted. 01/01-31/12.
Distance: 1km on the spot 1km.

Gmünden 20H1
Parkplatz des Toscanapark, Scharnsteiner Straße.
GPS: n47,91186 e13,78708.
5 free. **Surface:** asphalted. 01/01-31/12.
Distance: 1km 200m.

Gosau 20H2
Gasthaus Echo, Echoweg 9. **GPS**: n47,55171 e13,51345.
10 free € 5 . **Location:** Rural, simple, isolated, quiet.
Surface: asphalted. 01/05-31/10.
Distance: 400m on the spot.

Gosau 20H2
Hotel Gosauschmied, Gosau 57. **GPS**: n47,55072 e13,51607.
10 € 10 Ch on demand. **Surface:** asphalted.
01/01-31/12.
Distance: 3km on the spot 3km on the spot 500m on the spot.

Haslach 17H3
Gasthof Furtmühle, Schwackerreith 20, St.Oswald.
GPS: n48,60497 e14,01967.
15 free against payment. 01/01-31/12 Tue.
Distance: on the spot.

Kefermarkt 36A1
Schloßbrauerei Weinberg, Weinberg 2. **GPS**: n48,44856 e14,53957.

5 guests free. **Location:** Rural, simple.
Surface: asphalted. 01/01-31/12.
Distance: 800m on the spot.

Königswiesen 36A1
Freibad, Badgasse 4. **GPS**: n48,40450 e14,84080.

3 € 2 + € 2/pp Ch WC free.
Location: Rural, simple, quiet. **Surface:** asphalted. 01/04-31/10.
Distance: 500m 10m Freibadbuffet 300m.
Remarks: Parking swimming pool.

Kremsmünster 36A2
Parkplatz Benediktiner Stift, Fuxjägerstraße.
GPS: n48,05407 e14,12607.
. 01/01-31/12.
Distance: 500m 500m.

Kronstorf 36A2
Stellplatz Metzenhof, Dörfling 2. **GPS**: n48,12828 e14,43432.

10 € 18, 2 pers.incl WC included. **Location:** Rural, comfortable, isolated, quiet. **Surface:** gravel/metalled.
01/03-30/11.
Distance: on the spot on the spot.
Remarks: At golf court.

Mondsee 20H1

Geflügelhof Schweighofer, Schwand 10.
GPS: n47,88186 e13,31105.

5 € 13, 2 pers.incl Ch WC included. **Location:** Rural, quiet. **Surface:** grassy. 01/01-31/12.
Distance: 3km 2km 3km.

Naarn 36A1

Bauernhof Mostschenke, Dirnwagram 1.
GPS: n48,21750 e14,61972.

5 € 10 Ch € 2/day WC included. **Location:** Rural, simple.
Surface: asphalted. 01/01-31/12.
Distance: 2km on the spot 2km.
Remarks: Arrival <19.30h, max. 4 days.

Naarn 36A1

Gasthof zur Post, Marktplatz 1. **GPS**: n48,22579 e14,60662.

5 € 6, 2 pers.incl. **Location:** Simple, noisy.
Surface: asphalted. 01/01-31/12 Thu.
Distance: on the spot on the spot.

Ranshofen 17G3

Gasthof Putscher, Scheuhub 2. **GPS**: n48,23228 e12,99893.
5 € 15, 2 pers.incl Ch € 2. **Surface:** grassy.
01/01-31/12.
Distance: 2km on the spot 2km 2km.

Sankt Pankraz 36A2

Parkplatz Klauser Stausee, Klaus an der Pyhmbahn.
GPS: n47,82733 e14,15703.
. 01/01-31/12.
Remarks: Along river.

Scharnstein 20H1

Camping Schatzlmühle, Viechtwang 1A.
GPS: n47,91578 e13,97353.

5 € 10 Ch included € 3 € 2 € 2. **Location:** Rural, quiet.
Surface: grassy/gravel. 01/05-31/10.
Distance: 2km on the spot 600m on the spot on the spot on the spot.

Schlierbach 36A2

Bauernhof Eisterer, Föhrenweg 7. **GPS**: n47,95083 e14,08639.
3 € 6,50 + € 4/pp Ch € 2,50/day . **Location:** Rural, comfortable. **Surface:** grassy. 01/01-31/12.

Straß im Attergau 20H1

Landgasthof Rosslwirt, Halt 4. **GPS**: n47,90488 e13,44677.

6 guests free free. **Location:** Rural, simple, quiet.
Surface: grassy/gravel. 01/01-31/12.
Distance: on the spot.

Suben 17H3

Hotel Suben, Etzelshofen 125. **GPS**: n48,40149 e13,42582.
40 € 10 Ch included. **Location:** Motorway, simple, noisy.
01/01-31/12.
Distance: on the spot on the spot.

Vöcklabruck 20H1

Hallenbad am Freizeitgelände, Hausruckstraße.
GPS: n48,01107 e13,65299.

6 free Ch . **Location:** Rural, simple. **Surface:** metalled.
01/01-31/12.
Distance: 500m.
Remarks: Max. 48h.

Waldhausen im Strudengau 36A1

Badesee, Schloßberg. **GPS**: n48,28420 e14,95883.

6 voluntary contribution € 1/10minutes Ch € 1/8h.
Location: Rural, isolated, quiet. **Surface:** gravel.
01/01-31/12.
Distance: 2km on the spot on the spot 2km 2km.

Lower Austria

Aggsbach Dorf 36A1

Gasthof Pension zur Kartause, Aggsbach-Dorf 38.
GPS: n48,29638 e15,42604.
10 free . **Location:** Rural, isolated, quiet. **Surface:** grassy.
01/01-31/12.
Distance: on the spot.

Aggsbach Markt 36A1

Badestrand. GPS: n48,29814 e15,40497.

26 € 11,50 Ch € 1/24h WC .
Location: Comfortable. **Surface:** gravel. 01/03-31/10.
Distance: 500m 50m Donaustüberl 500m.
Remarks: On the Danube river.

Altenmarkt an der Triesting 36B2

Gasthof Zum Kleinen Semmering, Hafnerberg 15.
GPS: n48,01762 e16,01383.

10 free WC.
Location: Rural, simple. **Surface:** gravel. 01/01-31/12.
Distance: 2,3km on the spot 2,3km.

Arbesbach 36A1

Am Ganser. **GPS**: n48,49123 e14,95683.

15 € 5 Ch included. **Location:** Rural, simple.
Surface: gravel. 01/01-31/12.
Distance: 500m on the spot 500m 500m 500m.
Remarks: Check in at town hall.

Ardagger 36A1

Stellplatz am Donauwellenpark, Markt 39.
GPS: n48,17981 e14,82579.

10 free € 2 Ch (6x)€ 1/kWh.
Location: Rural, simple. 01/01-31/12.
Distance: 100m 7km 100m 100m on the spot.
Remarks: At Danube cycle route.

Armschlag 36A1

Mohndorf. **GPS**: n48,45222 e15,21944.

5 € 7, 2 pers.incl. Ch included. **Location:** Rural, simple.
Surface: asphalted. 01/01-31/12.

AT

Distance: on the spot on the spot 2km Mohnstrudelwandernetz.

S Aschbach Markt 36A2

Fam. Edtbauer, Auckental 1 u. 2. **GPS:** n48,10682 e14,69988.

8 free € 2. **Location:** Rural, quiet. 15/04-30/10.
Distance: 7km 3km 7km.

Bad Deutsch-Altenburg 36C1

Parking Donaupromenade, Donaupromenade.
GPS: n48,14110 e16,90090.

. **Location:** Rural, simple.
Surface: asphalted. 01/01-31/12.
Distance: 500m on the spot 1km 1km.

Bad Großpertholz 36A1

Busparkplatz Naturpark Nordwald, Scheiben.
GPS: n48,61765 e14,81548.
. **Location:** Rural. **Surface:** asphalted. 01/01-31/12.

Bernhardsthal 36B1

Am Bernhardsthaler Teich, Schulstrasse.
GPS: n48,69402 e16,87481.

5 free. **Surface:** grassy.
01/01-31/12.
Distance: 500m on the spot on the spot weekends only.

S Eggenburg 36B1

Stellplatz an der Stadtmauer, Erzherzog-Karl-Ring 19.
GPS: n48,64513 e15,81745.
8 € 4 € 1/10minutes Ch (8x)€ 1/8h.
Location: Rural, comfortable. **Surface:** gravel. 01/04-31/10.
Distance: on the spot 4km creek 300m 200m 500m on the spot 300m.

S Erlauf 36A1

Plaikawirt, Plaika 1, Bergland. **GPS:** n48,16866 e15,16436.

10 guests free € 2/100liter € 2/24h.
Location: Rural, quiet.
Surface: asphalted. 01/01-31/12 Mo.
Distance: 2km on the spot on the spot.

Gaming 36A2

Kartause. **GPS:** n47,92463 e15,08223.
. 01/01-31/12.

S Gars am Kamp 36B1

Sport- und Erlebnisbad, Gföhler Strasse/Strandgasse, Thunau am Kamp. **GPS:** n48,59300 e15,65723.

5 € 16 Ch WC included.
Location: Comfortable. 01/01-31/12.
Distance: 200m on the spot 200m.
Remarks: At swimming pool.

Göllersdorf 36B1

Parkplatz Barbara Heuriger, Spitalgasse 467.
GPS: n48,49667 e16,11171.

10 free. **Location:** Rural, simple.
Surface: gravel. 01/01-31/12.
Distance: 500m 1km on the spot 1km.

Gumpoldskirchen 36B1

Brunngasse. **GPS:** n48,04212 e16,27820.

10 free. **Location:** Rural, simple.
Surface: asphalted. 01/01-31/12.
Distance: 500m 500m.
Remarks: Max. 8M.

S Gumpoldskirchen 36B1

Neustiftgasse. **GPS:** n48,04423 e16,27552.
Ch. 01/01-31/12.

Hainburg/Donau 36C1

Parkplatz an der Donau, Donaulande 4.
GPS: n48,15110 e16,94440.

. **Location:** Rural, simple.
Surface: asphalted. 01/01-31/12.
Distance: 500m on the spot on the spot 500m.

Hohenau/March 36C1

Freizeitzentrum, Kindergartenstrasse. **GPS:** n48,61095 e16,91010.

free. **Surface:** asphalted. 01/01-31/12.
Remarks: Swimming pool 200m.

S Hollenstein/Ybbs 36A2

Der Wentsteinhammer, Wenten 1. **GPS:** n47,76884 e14,77270.
3 € 5 Ch .
Location: Rural, isolated, quiet. 01/01-31/12.
Distance: 4km.

S Hollenstein/Ybbs 36A2

Gasthof Staudach, Walcherbauer 5. **GPS:** n47,80703 e14,76687.
8 € 13-18, 4 pers.incl Ch WC included.
Surface: grassy. 01/04-31/10.
Distance: 200m 10m 200m on the spot.

S Horn 36B1

Wohnmobil-Stellplatz Horn, Höhe Spitalgasse 49.
GPS: n48,67246 e15,66108.

4 free, tourist tax € 1,60/pp € 1/50liter Ch € 1/8h.
Surface: gravel/sand. 01/01-31/12.
Distance: 1km 500m 500m.
Remarks: Max. 5 nights.

Karlstein an der Thaya 36A1

Sieghartser Straße. **GPS:** n48,88186 e15,40442.
. **Surface:** grassy. 01/01-31/12.
Distance: 200m 200m.
Remarks: At tennis-court.

S Klosterneuburg 36B1

Euromobil Campers, Bahnhofplatz 16, Kritzendorf.
GPS: n48,33582 e16,29863.

4 free Ch. **Location:** Simple.
Surface: asphalted. 01/01-31/12.
Distance: 12,5km 300m 500m.
Remarks: Lock-up parking, guarded.

S Laimbach am Ostrong 36A1

Bauernhof Stoiber, Wagmühle 34. **GPS:** n48,31711 e15,12565.

5 € 12 included. **Location:** Rural, simple.
Surface: grassy. 01/01-31/12.
Distance: 300m 300m 300m.

S **Langenlois** 36B1

Reisemobilstellplatz Langenlois, Krumpöckallee 21.
GPS: n48,47063 e15,69782.

7 € 8 + € 1,50/pp € 1/10minutes Ch (7x)€ 1/8h.
Location: Rural, simple, quiet.
Surface: metalled. 01/01-31/12.
Distance: 1,5km 1km 1km.

Langschlag-Mitterschlag 36A1

Freizeitanlage Frauenwieserteich, Böhmerwald-Bundesstraße.
GPS: n48,58038 e14,83507.

10 free. **Location:** Rural, simple, isolated, quiet.
Surface: grassy/gravel.
01/01-31/12.
Distance: 5km on the spot on the spot on the spot 5km.

S **Mitterbach** 36A2

Biobauernhof Sepplbauer, Bergstraße 11. **GPS**: n47,83216 e15,30648.
10 € 6 € 2. **Location:** Rural, isolated, quiet.
Surface: grassy. 01/05-30/09.
Distance: 4km.

Orth/Donau 36B1

P2, Am Rosenhügel. **GPS**: n48,14523 e16,70383.

4 free. **Location:** Urban, simple.
Surface: grasstiles. 01/01-31/12.
Distance: on the spot 3km 250m 1,2km.

S **Ottenschlag** 36A1

Florianigasse. **GPS**: n48,42361 e15,22750.

8-10 € 5 € 1/10minutes Ch € 1/8h. **Location:** Rural, simple. **Surface:** gravel. 01/01-31/12.
Distance: 500m Gaststätte 500m.

S **Pernegg** 36B1

Freizeitanlage Gallien, Gallien 1. **GPS**: n48,71333 e15,66139.
20 € 15 + € 5/pp Ch WC included. **Location:** Rural, comfortable. 01/01-31/12.
Distance: on the spot on the spot.

S **Pillichsdorf** 36B1

Am Tennisclub, Bahnstraße 8A. **GPS**: n48,36167 e16,53750.

8 free, use facilities € 10 Ch WC .
Location: Simple. 01/01-31/12.
Distance: 500m, Vienna 15km 300m 500m on the spot.
Remarks: Use facilities clubhouse possible.

S **Pulkau** 36B1

Rat-Cumfe Straße. **GPS**: n48,70430 e15,86637.

8 € 5 € 1/10minutes Ch € 1/6h.
Location: Urban, simple. **Surface:** gravel. 01/01-31/12.
Distance: 500m 300m on the spot on the spot.

Reichenau/Rax 36B2

Kaiserbrunn, Bundesstraße Höllental 27. **GPS**: n47,73480 e15,79188.

free. **Surface:** metalled. 01/01-31/12.

S **Reichenau/Rax** 36B2

Gasthof Flackl Wirt, Hinterleiten 12. **GPS**: n47,69056 e15,82778.

5 € 14/pp breakfast incl according consumption WC at restaurant. **Location:** Rural. **Surface:** grassy/gravel. 01/01-31/12.
Distance: 1,5km on the spot.

S **Retz** 36B1

Parkplatz Alter Sportplatz, Jahnstraße. **GPS**: n48,75382 e15,95105.

2 € 3 € 1/10minutes Ch € 1/8h. **Location:** Simple.
Surface: asphalted. 01/04-31/10 last weekend of Sep.
Distance: 500m 500m.

S **Rossatzbach** 36B1

Wohnmobilplatz Artner, Aggsteiner-Bundesstraße.
GPS: n48,38750 e15,51722.

12 € 10 Ch (12x) WC included.
Location: Rural, comfortable. **Surface:** gravel. 01/01-31/12.
Distance: 300m on the spot 100m 1,5km.
Remarks: Vinotheek 300m.

S **Sankt Martin am Ybbsfelde** 36A1

Gemeindeparkplatz, St. Martin. **GPS**: n48,16465 e15,01995.

5 free € 5/day Ch (2x)€ 5/day.
Location: Rural, simple, quiet. **Surface:** grasstiles. 01/01-31/12.
Distance: on the spot on the spot 200m on the spot.
Remarks: Parking in front of church.

Schiltern bei Langenlois 36B1

Erlebnisgärtner Kittenberger, Laabergstraße 15.
GPS: n48,51180 e15,63277.

3 free. **Location:** Simple, isolated. 01/01-31/12.
Distance: 500m.

S **Schönberg** 36B1

Freizeitzentrum, Badgasse. **GPS**: n48,52063 e15,69377.

5 € 5, first night free WC .
Location: Rural, simple. **Surface:** asphalted. 15/05-31/08.
Distance: 200m 300m 200m Kamptalradweg.
Remarks: Along river, use sanitary only during opening hours swimming pool.

AT

Schrems 36A1

Parkplatz Stadthalle, Doktor-Karl-Renner-Straße.
GPS: n48,79167 e15,07120.

3 free. **Location:** Urban, simple, central.
Surface: asphalted. 01/01-31/12.
Distance: on the spot on the spot 100m.

Stockerau 36B1

Hallenbad Wellness Oase, Pestalozzigasse.
GPS: n48,39385 e16,21912.

6 free € 2 Ch WC sanitary in swimming pool.
Location: Comfortable. **Surface:** gravel. 01/01-31/12.
Distance: 1,5km 500m 50m.

Stockerau 36B1

Alte Au, Zum Spitzgarten. **GPS**: n48,38366 e16,20394.

3 free. **Location:** Urban, simple.
Surface: asphalted. 01/01-31/12.
Distance: 1km 50m.
Remarks: At sports centre.

Weistrach 36A2

Parkplatz Sportplatz. **GPS**: n48,05475 e14,58167.

10 free. **Location:** Rural, simple.
Surface: asphalted. 01/01-31/12.
Distance: 200m on the spot 200m.
Remarks: Near sports fields.

Weitra 36A1

Freizeitzentrum Hausschachen, Promenade.
GPS: n48,70414 e14,89343.

10 free. **Location:** Simple, quiet. **Surface:** gravel.
01/01-31/12.

Distance: 600m 600m.
Remarks: Max. 1 night.

Wiener Neustadt 36B2

Parkplatz Stadion, Stadionstrasse. **GPS**: n47,82156 e16,25629.

20 . **Location:** Urban. **Surface:** asphalted. 01/01-31/12.
Distance: 500m on the spot.

Wilfersdorf 36B1

Schloss Wilfersdorf, Parkplatz am Schloss.
GPS: n48,58600 e16,64514.

3 € 4 WC. 01/01-31/12.
Distance: 100m 300m on the spot.
Remarks: Check in at Schloss, 10-16h tue/su.

Zwettl 36A1

Wirtshaus zur Minidampfbahn, 47, Teichhäuser bei Zwettl.
GPS: n48,66278 e15,15444.

10 € 5 Ch € 2,50. **Location:** Rural, simple, quiet.
Surface: grassy. 01/01-31/12.
Distance: 2km 200m on the spot 2,5km.

Vienna

Wien 36B1

Reisemobilstellplatz Wien, Perfektastraße 49-53, Vienna (Wien).
GPS: n48,13698 e16,31582.

167 € 19 Ch (167x)€ 2/24h WC included .
Location: Urban, comfortable.
Surface: grassy/gravel.
01/01-31/12.
Distance: city centre 12km 4km 30m 30m metro 150m, bus 50m 100m.

Wien 36B1

Kurpark Oberlaa, Filmteichstrasse 5, Vienna (Wien).
GPS: n48,15215 e16,40363.

free. **Location:** Urban, simple. **Surface:** grasstiles. 01/01-31/12.
Distance: centre > bus 68A Reumannplatz > tram U1 Stefansdom.
Remarks: No camping activities.

Tourist information Vienna (Wien):
Overnight parking prohibited.
Tourist-Info, Albertinaplatz 1, info.wien.at/. Imperial city, many curiosities, capital of the classic music.
Wien-Karte. Card gives 72h entrance to public transport and discounts on museums, curiosities. Available at Tourist-Info and hotels. € 24,90.
Spanische Hofreitschule, Michaelerplatz 1. Spanish Riding School, morning-training can be visited without reservation. 10-12.
Kunsthistorisches Museum, Maria Theresien-Platz. Important painting collection.
Tue-Su 10-18h, Thu 10-21h.
€ 15.
Wurstelprater. Amusement park. 15/03-15/10 10-24h.

Vorarlberg

Dornbirn 20B3

Stellplatz Mathis, Obere Härte 27. **GPS**: n47,40577 e9,72492.
3 (7-8-10m) € 17 + € 1,10/pp tourist tax Ch included.
Location: Comfortable. **Surface:** grasstiles.
01/01-31/12.
Distance: on the spot 2km on the spot on the spot.

Hard 20B2

Gasthaus Sternen, Landstraße 49. **GPS**: n47,48442 e9,68698.
8 customers free . **Surface:** asphalted. 01/01-31/12 Mo.
Distance: Bregenz 4,5km on the spot.

Tyrol

Achenkirch 20E2

Wohnmobilhafen Achensee, Achenkirch 17.
GPS: n47,49947 e11,70655.

10 from € 14 + € 1,50/pp tourist tax, € 1 Umwelttaxe Ch € 3,50/24h WC included. **Location:** Rural, comfortable, quiet.
Surface: grasstiles/metalled. 01/01-31/12.
Distance: on the spot on the spot.
Remarks: Max. 1 night, dog € 4,50, extra pers € 7, electricity winter € 0,70/kWh.

Aschau im Zillertal 20F3

Reisemobilhafen Aufenfeld, Aufenfeldweg.
GPS: n47,26318 e11,90063.

10 € 17 Ch WC . **Location:** Rural. **Surface:** grassy.
01/01-31/12.
Remarks: Quick-Stop: >19h - <9h.

Biberwier 20D3

Wohnmobilhafen Arienberg, Marienbergstrasse 15.
GPS: n47,37472 e10,89223.

AT

18 € 15, 2 pers.incl, tourist tax € 2/pp Ch € 2,50/24h included. **Location:** Rural, comfortable. **Surface:** grassy/gravel. 01/01-31/12.
Distance: on the spot 2km on the spot on the spot.

Bichlbach 20D2

Almkopfbahn. **GPS**: n47,42367 e10,78116.

15 free. 01/01-31/12.
Distance: 5km on the spot on the spot on the spot.

Breitenwang 20D2

Seespitze. **GPS**: n47,47438 e10,78515.
€ 22,50-31 Ch WC . 01/01-31/12.

Breitenwang 20D2

Sennalpe. **GPS**: n47,48639 e10,83972.
€ 14. 15/12-15/10.

Feichten/Kaunertal 20D3

Kaunertal. **GPS**: n47,05333 e10,75056.
60 € 20,50 Ch WC . 01/05-30/09.

Galtür 20C3

Bergbahnen, Silvretta-Bundesstraße, B188, Wirl.
GPS: n46,96570 e10,16390.

€ 20, summer free Ch.
Location: Rural. **Surface:** gravel. winter.
Distance: 100m on the spot on the spot on the spot.
Remarks: Free skibus to Ischgl.

Galtür 20C3

Zeinissee, Zeinisjochstrasse. **GPS**: n46,97824 e10,12738.

€ 23-25,50 incl. 2 pers, dog € 3 € 0,70/kWh WC included against payment. **Location:** Rural. **Surface:** grassy/gravel.
Whitsuntide-05/10.
Distance: Galtür 8,5km on the spot.
Remarks: Silvrettacard incl., one night stay + € 5.

Gerlos 20F3

Bauernhof Schönachhof, Schönachtal 242. **GPS**: n47,22639 e12,05476.

24 € 20, winter € 30 + tourist tax, dog € 4 Ch WC .
Location: Isolated. 01/01-31/12.
Tourist information Gerlos:
Activ Wellness. Free wellness program. 01/07-30/09.

Gries am Brenner 20E3

Gasthof Humler-Hof, Nößlach 483. **GPS**: n47,06660 e11,47187.
50 € 10 WC included. 01/01-31/12.
Distance: Gries 5km 1km on the spot.

Hall in Tirol 20E3

Wohnmobilpark, Scheidensteinstraße 24.
GPS: n47,28444 e11,49665.

10 € 10-15 + € 1/pp + tourist tax Ch included.
Location: Urban. **Surface:** metalled. 01/01-31/12.
Distance: 400m 200m Gaststätte 300m.
Remarks: Max. 1 night.

Heiterwang 20D2

Ferienhof Sunnawirt, Mühle 4. **GPS**: n47,44951 e10,74812.

AT

30 € 7 + tourist tax € 2/pp Ch € 3.
Surface: grassy/gravel. 01/01-31/12.
Distance: 200m Heiterwanger See 1,6km 200m 200m on the spot 3km on the spot.
Remarks: Bread-service.

S Ischgl 20C3
Mathoner Straße 5, Ischgl-Mathon. **GPS**: n46,98967 e10,24751.

8 € 15 + tourist tax Ch (8x).
Location: Rural, simple. **Surface:** gravel. 01/01-31/12.
Distance: 1km 100m.
Remarks: Free skibus to Ischgl and Galtür.

S Jenbach 20E2
Gasthof Rieder, Fischl 3. **GPS**: n47,40131 e11,77500.

3 free. **Location:** Rural, simple, isolated. **Surface:** asphalted.
01/01-31/12.
Remarks: Guests only.

S Kramsach 20F2
Camping & Appartements Seehof, Moosen 42.
GPS: n47,46206 e11,90733.
10 € 18-25 2 pers.incl, dog € 3-3,50 Ch (10x)€ 3/4kWh, 16Amp WC included € 4/4 € 3/day.
Location: Rural. **Surface:** asphalted. 01/01-31/12.
Distance: 3km Reintalersee on the spot on the spot free on the spot on the spot on the spot. **Remarks:** Tariff on presentation of the most recent guide or Camperstop-App.

S Leutasch 20D3
Am Kreithlift, Weidach 381. **GPS**: n47,36392 e11,16657.
20 € 26, 2 pers.incl Ch WC included.
Surface: asphalted/gravel. 15/12-15/03.
Distance: 1,5km on the spot on the spot on the spot.
Remarks: Loipenplakette, drying room for skis and sauna included.

Matrei 20F3
Matreier Tauernhaus, Nähe Tauer 22. **GPS**: n47,11833 e12,49778.
20 € 10/24h. **Surface:** gravel. 25/05-15/10.
Distance: on the spot on the spot.

S Nassereith 20D3
Roßbach, Roßbach 325. **GPS**: n47,31046 e10,85524.

€ 20,50 Ch WC. **Surface:** grassy. 01/01-31/12.
Distance: 500m.

S Obsteig 20D3
Gasthof zum Lenz, Gschwent 282. **GPS**: n47,30930 e10,94482.

6 € 15 Ch included. **Location:** Rural, simple, isolated.
Surface: grassy/gravel. 01/01-31/12.
Distance: on the spot on the spot.

S Pettneu am Arlberg 20C3
Camping Arlberg, Pettneu am Arlberg 235. **GPS**: n47,14506 e10,33816.

54 € 15, winter € 23 + tourist tax, dog € 3 Ch included € 1/2kWh. **Location:** Luxurious. **Surface:** grassy/metalled.
01/01-31/12.
Distance: 1km 250m on the spot.
Remarks: Bread-service, winter: skibus, summer: hiking bus.

S Pfunds 20D3
Wohnmobilplatz Via Claudiasee, Rauth 714.
GPS: n46,95429 e10,51171.

10 € 10 + € 1,50/pp tourist tax, dog € 1,50 € 1/80liter Ch € 0,60/kWh WC sanitary € 3/pp from € 0,50.
Location: Rural, comfortable.
Surface: grassy/metalled.
01/01-31/12.
Distance: 2km on the spot 200m on the spot on the spot.
Remarks: Bread-service.

S Schwaz 20E2
Wohnmobilstellplatz Königfeld, Königfeldweg.
GPS: n47,34655 e11,70436.

10 € 6 € 2 Ch. **Location:** Urban, simple, central.
Surface: asphalted. 01/01-31/12.
Distance: 500m 1,9km Gaststätte 50m 50m.
Remarks: Max. 3 nights.

Tourist information Schwaz:
Schwazer Silberbergwerk. 01/05-30/09 9-17, 01/10-30/04 10-16h.

S Steinach am Brenner 20E3
Gasthaus Wolf, Brennerstraße 36. **GPS**: n47,06704 e11,48574.
5 guests free. **Surface:** asphalted. 01/01-31/12.
Distance: 2km on the spot.

S Stumm 20F3
Gasthof Rißbacher Hof, Ahrnbachstraße 37.
GPS: n47,27951 e11,89347.

3 € 15 WC. **Location:** Rural, simple.
Surface: asphalted. 01/01-31/12 Wed.

S Wenns/Piller 20D3
Gasthof Sonne, Piller 41. **GPS**: n47,13581 e10,69390.

3 € 5, guests free. **Location:** Rural, simple, isolated.
Surface: gravel. 01/01-31/12.
Distance: on the spot 50m.
Remarks: Altitude 1350m.

S Wiesing 20E2
Inntal. **GPS**: n47,40585 e11,80536.

€ 20-24,50 Ch WC. 01/01-31/12.

Salzburg

S Altenmarkt im Pongau 20H2
Stellplatz Kellerbauer, Kellerdörfl 18. **GPS**: n47,37043 e13,42903.

10 € 11 Ch (15x)€ 3/24h,16Amp WC € 2/2 included.
Location: Comfortable, isolated, quiet. **Surface:** grassy/gravel.
01/01-31/12.
Distance: 1,2km 4km 2km 1,2km on the spot 1km.

S Golling 20G2
Wohnmobil-Park Aqua Salza, Möslstraße 199.
GPS: n47,59543 e13,17222.

15 € 9,90 + € 1/pp tourist tax € 1/80liter Ch € 0,50/kWh.
Location: Rural, quiet. **Surface:** asphalted.
01/01-31/12.
Distance: 500m 300m 300m 200m.
Remarks: Max. 5 days, check in on arrival.

S Hüttschlag 20H3

Bauernhof Stockham-Camping, See 5. **GPS**: n47,14775 e13,28947.

5 € 15,60, 2 pers.incl Ch € 1,50 WC € 1. 01/04-31/10.

Distance: 6km 150m 6km.

S Krimml 20F3

Hotel Krimmlerfälle, Wasserfallstraße 42.

GPS: n47,21827 e12,17543.

10 € 20, dog € 4 Chincluded (4x).

Location: Rural, simple. **Surface:** grassy/gravel. 15/05-25/10.

Distance: 500m on the spot.

S Leogang 20G2

Leoganger Bergbahnen, Hütten 39. **GPS**: n47,43963 e12,72040.

50 € 8 + € 1,50/pp tourist tax Ch (50x)€ 2/24h WC.

Location: Rural, comfortable, quiet.

Surface: grassy/gravel. 01/01-31/12.

Distance: 3,5km on the spot on the spot.

S Maria Alm 20G2

Wohnmobilstellplatz Stegerbauer, Stegen 16.

GPS: n47,39765 e12,90350.

10 € 12-14 + € 1,50/pp tourist tax Ch (10x)€ 2.

Surface: gravel. 01/01-31/12.

Distance: 1km on the spot 500m 1km 200m on the spot 1km on the spot.

Remarks: Bread-service.

S Neukirchen 20F3

Panoramastellplatz, Scheffau 96. **GPS**: n47,23862 e12,24083.

17 € 8, discount for clients Ch € 3/24h WC.

Location: Rural, isolated, quiet.

Surface: gravel. 01/01-31/12.

Distance: 4km on the spot Tauernradweg on the spot on the spot on the spot.

Remarks: Bread-service.

S Salzburg 20G1

Reisemobil - Stellplatz Salzburg, Carl-Zuckmayer-Straße 26.

GPS: n47,83586 e13,05997.

106 € 21 Ch (106x),6Amp WC included € 2.

Location: Rural. **Surface:** grassy. 01/01-31/12.

Distance: on the spot 1,5km 10m 150m on the spot 50m.

Tourist information Salzburg:

Salzburg Card, Tourismus Information. Card gives entrance to museums, public transport etc.

Tourismus Salzburg, Altstadt, Mozartplatz; Hauptbahnhof, Bahnsteig 2a; Autobahn A10, Abfahrt Süd, www.salzburg.info. City, UNESCO's List of World Heritage, also Mozart city.

Festung Hohensalzburg, Mönchsberg 34. High fortress. 15/6-14/9 9-18, 15/9-14/6 9.30-17h.

Mozart-Wohnhaus, Makartplatz 8. Former dwellinghouse of the Mozart family. 9-18h, 01/07-31/08 9-19h.

Mozarts Geburtshaus, Getreidegasse 9. Life and work of Mozart. 9-18h, 01/07-31/08 9-19h.

Salzburger Trachten, Griesgasse 23. History of the costumes. Tue-Fri 10-12h, 14-16h.

Schloß Hellbrunn. Italian villa with park.

Schloß Mirabell.

Nonnberg. Convent.

S Tweng 20H3

Landhotel Postgut, Tweng 2. **GPS**: n47,19058 e13,60210.

AT

10 € 20 included. **Surface:** metalled. 01/01-31/12.
Distance: on the spot on the spot on the spot on the spot.
Remarks: Breakfast-service, sauna incl..

Styria

Bad Gams 36B3

Freizeitzentrums GamsBad, Bad Gams 2.
GPS: n46,86730 e15,22743.

6 € 5 Ch. **Surface:** grasstiles/metalled. 01/01-31/12.
Distance: 200m on the spot 200m 100m 200m.
Remarks: Check in at Gamsbad.

Bad Radkersburg 36B3

Camping Alt-Weindörfl, Altneudörfl 144. **GPS**: n46,69444 e15,98991.
25 € 5 + € 3/pp WC included.
Surface: gravel. 01/03-31/10.
Distance: 750m on the spot 750m.

Bad Waltersdorf 36B2

Gasthof Erhardt, Am Waltersdorfberg 99.
GPS: n47,16687 e15,98921.

4 € 8, guests free. **Location:** Rural, simple.
Surface: grasstiles. 01/01-31/12.
Distance: 1,8km 3,2km on the spot.

Bad Waltersdorf 36B2

Thermenland Camping, Campingplatzweg 316.
GPS: n47,16246 e16,02296.
10 Mondscheinplätze € 9,50/18-9h, 2 pers. incl. + tourist tax.
01/01-31/12.
Distance: 1,6km 3km Stüberl.

Deutsch Goritz 36B3

Pechmann's Alte Ölmühle, Ratschendorf 188.
GPS: n46,75072 e15,81337.
15 customers free according consumption.
Surface: metalled. 01/01-31/12.
Distance: 850m on the spot.

Deutschfeistritz 36B2

Sportclub Union, Am Quellengrund 11. **GPS**: n47,20116 e15,32710.

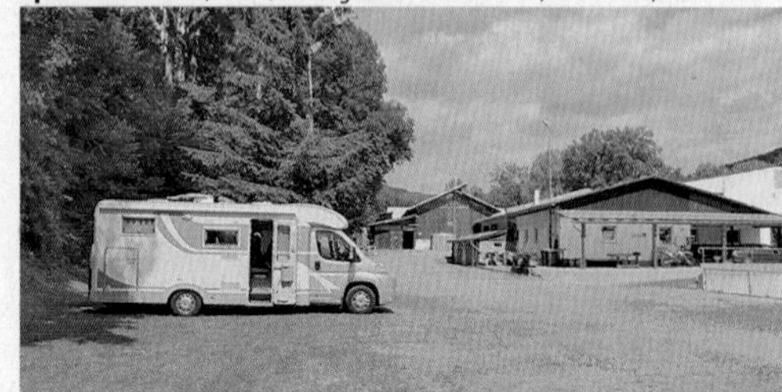

20 € 15, 2 pers.incl Ch € 3 WC included.
Surface: grassy. 01/04-31/10.

Remarks: At manege, check in on arrival, bread-service.

Deutschlandsberg 36B3

Koralmhalle, Höhe Frauentalerstraße 51.
GPS: n46,81783 e15,22248.

2 free. **Surface:** asphalted. 01/01-31/12.
Distance: 200m on the spot 100m on the spot.
Remarks: Max. 3 days.

Gaishorn am See 36A2

Sportzentrum, Sieberer Weg, B113. **GPS**: n47,48583 e14,54803.
10 € 10 + € 1,20/pp Ch (6x)€ 1 WC included.
Surface: gravel. 15/04-30/09.
Distance: 500m 4,6km Gaishorner See 100m 150m 500m.

Gamlitz 36B3

Wohnmobilstellplatz Gamlitz, Untere Hauptstraße 455.
GPS: n46,72028 e15,56833.

30 € 20 € 1/100liter Ch € 1/2kWh WC.
Location: Rural, comfortable. **Surface:** gravel.
01/04-31/10.

Distance: 1km 5km on the spot on the spot on the spot.
Remarks: Parking at Motorikpark.

Gamlitz 36B3

Buschenschank Loar-Moar, Untere Hauptstraße 21.
GPS: n46,72196 e15,56495.

9 € 22 Ch WC included.
Location: Rural. **Surface:** grassy. 01/05-31/10.
Distance: 900m 5,5km.

Gosdorf 36B3

Hof Schönwetter, Haus 5. **GPS**: n46,72630 e15,79652.
6 € 10. **Surface:** grassy. 01/01-31/12.
Distance: 500m 2km.

Graz 36B3

Reisemobil Stellplatz Graz, Martinhofstraße 3.
GPS: n47,02472 e15,39694.

160 € 21 Ch (160x) WC included € 2/2 € 2/day.
Location: Urban. **Surface:** grassy/gravel. 01/01-31/12.
Distance: on the spot 3,5km on the spot on the spot 200m 250m 200m on the spot on the spot.
Remarks: Website: www.reisemobilstellplatz-graz.at, video surveillance.

Graz 36B3

Stellplatz Wölfl, Steinfeldgasse 47. **GPS**: n47,06527 e15,42046.
5 € 12 € 2/day.
Location: Simple. **Surface:** asphalted. 01/01-31/12 Sa-Su.
Distance: 1,5km 3,7km.
Remarks: At motorhome dealer, check in during opening hours.

Tourist information Graz:
Freilichtmuseum, Stübing. Open air museum. 18/03-31/10.
Schloß Eggenberg, Eggenberger Allee 90. 01/04-31/10 Tue-Su 10-17h. € 11,50. Schlossbergbahn, Kaiser-Franz-Josef-Kai. Mountain railway, gradient 61%.

Greisdorf 36B3

Greisdorf, St. Stefan ob Stainz. **GPS**: n46,92734 e15,21589.

10 € 15 Ch included (4x) € 1/2kWh,10Amp.
Location: Rural. **Surface:** gravel. 23/04-04/11.
Distance: 550m 7km 550m 6km 100m.

Großlobming 36A3

Murinsel, Teichweg 1. **GPS**: n47,19326 e14,80422.
16 € 9/18-10h 2 pers.incl, 1 hour € 1 Ch included.
Surface: grassy. 01/01-31/12.
Remarks: Reservation in winter peak season.

Hieflau 36A2

Gasthaus zum Harmonika Wald, Wandau 9.
GPS: n47,62255 e14,75411.
5 guests free included.
Surface: asphalted. 01/01-31/12 Wed.
Distance: 1,8km on the spot.

Jagerberg 36B3

Am Freibad. **GPS**: n46,85152 e15,74655.

6 free € 0,50/60liter Ch. **Location:** Rural, simple.
Surface: asphalted/gravel. 01/01-31/12.
Distance: 500m 500m 500m.

Jagerberg 36B3

Kindergarten Vorplatz, Jagerberg 98.
GPS: n46,85692 e15,74292.

15 free Ch (1x).
Location: Rural, simple. **Surface:** gravel. 01/01-31/12.
Distance: 400m 400m 400m 400m.

Judenburg 36A3

Erlebnisbad, Fichtenhainstraße. **GPS**: n47,16407 e14,65308.

5 € 5 Ch WC free. **Surface:** gravel. 01/01-31/12.
Distance: 500m 200m 200m.
Remarks: Check in at swimming pool.

Kaindorf 36B2

Buschenschank Schleiss, Obertiefenbach 42.
GPS: n47,23839 e15,84498.

4 € 6, guests free Ch.
Location: Rural, simple. **Surface:** asphalted. 01/03-15/12.
Distance: on the spot.

Leutschach 36B3

Weinbau Peter Grill, Kranach 48. **GPS**: n46,68478 e15,47191.
4 free free € 3. **Surface:** grassy. Easter-01/11.
Distance: 4,5km.

Leutschach 36B3

Weingut oberGuess, Schloßberg 9. **GPS**: n46,63898 e15,45872.
10 guests free Ch. 08/04-12/11.
Distance: 6km.

Liezen 36A2

Sportzentrum, Friedau. **GPS**: n47,56500 e14,23333.

3 free € 1 € 1. **Surface:** gravel. 01/01-31/12.
Distance: 1km 5,3km 300m 1km on the spot.

AT

AT

Mureck 36B3

Reisemobil - Stellplatz Mureck, Austraße 9.
GPS: n46,70489 e15,77240.

82 € 21 Ch (82x),6 Amp WC included € 2/2 € 2.
Location: Rural, comfortable, luxurious, quiet.
Surface: grassy. 01/01-31/12.
Distance: on the spot 9,5km 150m 150m 250m on the spot 150m on the spot on the spot.

Mureck 36B3

Ölmühle Sixt, Oberrakitsch 53. **GPS**: n46,73818 e15,74574.

10 € 13 Ch included WC.
Surface: gravel. 01/03-31/10.
Distance: 600m.
Remarks: Bread-service.

Murfeld 36B3

Gasthof Dorfheuriger Rom Thomas, Dorfstrasse 1, Unterschwarza.
GPS: n46,71557 e15,67624.

40 € 13 Ch WC included.
Location: Comfortable. **Surface:** grassy. 01/01-31/12.
Distance: 200m 2,5km on the spot.
Remarks: Check in at restaurant, bread-service, wifi code: Camping01, entrance code: camp1.

Oberrakitsch 36B3

Ölmühle Sixt, Oberrakitsch 115. **GPS**: n46,73863 e15,74605.

10 € 10 Ch WC included.
Location: Rural, simple. **Surface:** gravel. 01/01-31/12.
Distance: 1km on the spot 1km 3km 4km.
Remarks: Bread-service.

Passail 36B2

Almenland Stellplatz, Auen 61. **GPS**: n47,28217 e15,55711.

4 free € 0,50/60liter Ch € 0,50/kWh.
Location: Rural, comfortable. **Surface:** asphalted. 01/01-31/12.
Distance: Passail 3,5km.

Pichl-Kainisch 20H2

Sportstüberl Andrea, Pichl 57. **GPS**: n47,56711 e13,85207.
3 guests free. **Surface:** metalled. 01/01-31/12 Wed.

Pölfing-Brunn 36B3

Kipferlbad, Badstraße 13. **GPS**: n46,72422 e15,29268.

10 free. **Location:** Rural, simple.
Surface: grassy. 01/01-31/12.
Distance: 1km on the spot on the spot 1km 1km.

Riegersburg 36B3

P Seebad. **GPS**: n46,99677 e15,94107.

10 free. **Location:** Rural, simple.
Surface: asphalted. 01/01-31/12.
Distance: 500m on the spot 500m.
Remarks: Swimming pool available.

S **Sankt Stefan im Rosental** 36B3

Schichenauerstraße 6. **GPS**: n46,90634 e15,71431.

15 free € 1/100liter Ch (6x)€ 0,50/kWh.
Location: Rural, comfortable. **Surface:** gravel. 01/01-31/12.
Distance: 200m 200m 200m.

S **Schwanberg** 36B3

Freibad, Badstraße. **GPS**: n46,76361 e15,20639.

4 free, 16/05-14/09 € 6 Ch included.
Surface: gravel. 01/01-31/12.
Distance: 500m on the spot on the spot 500m 500m.

Soboth 36A3

Parkplatz Soboth-Stausee. GPS: n46,68142 e15,03805.

free. **Location:** Rural, simple.
Surface: asphalted. 01/01-31/12.
Distance: 5km on the spot 200m on the spot.
Remarks: Parking at artificial lake.

S **Stadl an der Mur** 36A3

Da' Bräuhauser, Steindorf 23. **GPS**: n47,08885 e13,98824.
15 € 16-19 + € 1,20/pp tourist tax, dog € 1,50 Chincluded € 0,60/kWh.
Surface: grassy. 01/01-31/12.
Distance: 500m.
Remarks: Breakfast-service.

Stainz 36B3

Ettendorfer Straße 3. **GPS**: n46,89377 e15,26823.

10 free. **Surface:** metalled. 01/01-31/12.
Distance: 100m 100m 100m.

Stainz 36B3

TSV Stelzl, Bad-Gamser-Straße 21. **GPS**: n46,88498 e15,25471.
10. **Location:** Rural, isolated, quiet. 01/01-31/12.
Distance: 1,2km on the spot.
Remarks: At fish lake.

Tourist information Stainz:
Region Süd-Weststeiermark, Hauptplatz 34, www.stainz.at. Das Land des Schilcher, country of the Austrian rosé wine.
Der Stainzer Flascherlzug. Narrow-gauge steam train. 01/05-31/10 Sa/Su/holidays 15h.
Ren(nt)t a Traktor, Anton Nettwall, Sommereben 95, St. Stefan ob Stainz. With a tractor through Schilcherland.
€ 58 1/2 day.

S **Unterlamm** 36B3

Sieglhof, Magland 44. **GPS**: n46,98152 e16,09172.

10 € 5 on demand. **Location:** Rural, simple.
Surface: grassy/gravel. 01/01-31/12 Tue + Wed.
Distance: 4km on the spot 1,5km on the spot.

Veitsch 36B2

Marktgemeindeamt, Obere Hauptstraße 18.
GPS: n47,57896 e15,48961.

2 free. **Surface:** asphalted. 01/01-31/12.
Distance: 300m 100m 100m 100m.

S **Vordernberg** 36A2

Hauptplatz 2. **GPS**: n47,48617 e14,99202.

6 free € 1/10minutes Ch € 1/8h. **Surface:** gravel.
01/04-31/10.
Distance: 500m 500m 500m on the spot.

Carinthia

S **Bad Sankt Leonhard im Lavanttal** 36A3

Bachwegbrücke. GPS: n46,96037 e14,79358.

8 € 4 Chincluded. 01/01-31/12.
Remarks: Parking behind Spar-supermarket.

Bleiburg 36A3

Grabenstraße. **GPS**: n46,59095 e14,79550.

4 free. **Surface:** grasstiles. 01/01-31/12.
Distance: 100m on the spot 200m.

S **Ferlach** 36A3

Messeparkplatz Schloß Ferlach, Messeplatz 5.
GPS: n46,52633 e14,29750.

30 € 4/24h € 1/10minutes Ch (10x)€ 1/10h.
Location: Urban, simple. **Surface:** metalled. 01/01-31/12.
Distance: 500m on the spot 300m 300m 300m.
Remarks: Max. 24h, no camping activities.

S **Glödnitz** 36A3

Gasthof Hochsteiner, Laas Straß2 9. **GPS**: n46,87226 e14,11655.
20 € 3, guests free WC.
Surface: asphalted. 01/01-31/12 Restaurant: Mo.
Distance: on the spot.

Heiligenblut 20G3

Möllfluss-Camping, Pockhorn 25. **GPS**: n47,02371 e12,86180.
€ 19,90 + tourist tax. **Surface:** asphalted.
15/06-01/09.

S **Hermagor** 23H1

Schluga, Vellach 15. **GPS**: n46,63147 e13,39532.

6 € 14 2 pers.incl, dog € 3,10 Ch (6x)€ 2,72 WC included.
Surface: gravel. 01/01-31/12.
Distance: winter free shuttle to piste.
Remarks: Peak season max. 3 days, max. 7 days.

Tourist information Hermagor:
Presseggersee. Nature reserve, no motor boats allowed.

S **Kötschach-Mauthen** 23G1

Gasthof Gailberghöhe, Gailberg 3. **GPS**: n46,71525 e12,96753.

70 € 14,50, 2 pers.incl. Ch WCincluded.
Surface: asphalted/gravel. 01/05-15/11, 15/12-15/03.
Distance: 7km on the spot 7km 2km 7km.

S **Ledenitzen** 36A3

Ferien am Walde. GPS: n46,57000 e13,95242.
220 € 13-18 Ch WC. 01/05-01/10.

S **Mörtschach** 20G3

Gasthaus Schwaiger, Mörtschach 35. **GPS**: n46,92287 e12,91348.

AT

4 guests free. **Surface:** grassy. 01/05-31/10.
Distance: on the spot.

Rosegg 36A3
Gasthof Roseggerhof, Schulweg 4. **GPS**: n46,59026 e14,02037.

30 € 10,50-12 + € 1,20/pp tourist tax € 2 included.
Location: Rural, simple. **Surface:** grassy.
01/04-31/10.
Distance: 8km on the spot bakery 150m.

Sachsenburg 20H3
Restaurant Auszeit, Obergottesfeld 79. **GPS**: n46,79959 e13,35137.

10 guests free.
Location: Rural, simple. **Surface:** gravel.
01/01-31/12 week after Easter, week after All Saints' Day.
Distance: 9km on the spot.

Wernberg 36A3
Landgasthof Fruhmann, Triester Straße 1.
GPS: n46,62501 e13,92933.

5 guests free. **Location:** Rural, simple.
Surface: gravel. 01/01-31/12.
Distance: Villach 6,5km 1,2km on the spot bakery + butcher.

Zlan 20H3
Nagelerhof, Ziebl 4. **GPS**: n46,74042 e13,57707.

8 € 17,20 + € 1,50/pp tourist tax Ch € 1,50 WC included.
Location: Simple. **Surface:** grassy. 01/03-31/10.
Distance: 8km.
Remarks: Not suitable for motorhomes +7m.

Burgenland

Andau 36C2
Pusztasee. GPS: n47,77426 e17,01307.
150 € 19-23 Ch. 15/04-15/10.

Bad Tatzmannsdorf 36B2
Thermencamping, Am Campingplatz 1, Oberschützen.
GPS: n47,33912 e16,21892.

15 € 13-20,20 + € 1,50/pp tourist tax Ch € 0,52/kWh WC included. **Location:** Rural, comfortable.
Surface: gravel. 01/01-31/12.
Distance: 1,5km 500m 450m.

Deutsch Jahrndorf 36C1
Deutsch Jahrndorf, Söldnergasse 19. **GPS**: n48,00777 e17,11073.

17 voluntary contribution Ch.
Location: Rural, simple. **Surface:** grassy. 01/04-31/10.
Distance: 500m 500m 500m.
Remarks: Max. 3 nights.

Horitschon 36B2
Weingut Duschanek, Hauptstraße 104. **GPS**: n47,59162 e16,53493.

10 € 5, guests free included € 3/24h WC.
Location: Simple. **Surface:** metalled. 01/01-31/12.
Distance: 600m on the spot 600m on the spot.

Illmitz 36C2
Wohnmobilstellplatz Pustablick, Ufergasse 42.
GPS: n47,75851 e16,79606.

5 voluntary contribution € 2.
Location: Rural, simple. **Surface:** grassy. 01/04-01/11.
Distance: 900m 900m bakery 500m.

Jois 36C2
Bioweingut Edelhof, Hauptplatz 6. **GPS**: n47,95922 e16,79012.

3 € 15 Ch included. **Location:** Rural, simple.
Surface: grassy/gravel. 01/03-31/10.
Remarks: In the courtyard of a medieval farmstead.

Moschendorf 36B2
P Weinmuseum-Kulturverein Moschendorf, Moschendorf 95.
GPS: n47,05784 e16,47713.

free. **Location:** Urban, simple.
Surface: asphalted. 01/01-31/12.
Distance: on the spot.

Oslip 36B2
Kulturzentrum Gasthof Cselly Mühle, Sachsenweg 63.
GPS: n47,84119 e16,62510.

10 free. **Location:** Rural, simple, isolated.
Surface: grassy. 01/01-31/12.
Distance: 1,2km on the spot.
Remarks: Check in on arrival.

Podersdorf 36C2
Weingut Schaller, Frauenkirchnerstraße 20.
GPS: n47,85032 e16,83934.

8 € 8 Ch included € 2/24h. **Location:** Rural, simple.
Surface: grassy. 01/04-30/11. **Distance:** 300m.
Remarks: When buying wine 1 night free.

Podersdorf 36C2
Weingut Sloboda, Alte Satz 1. **GPS**: n47,85020 e16,83091.

11 € 10 Ch WC included.
Location: Rural, comfortable, quiet. **Surface:** grassy. 01/03-31/10.
Distance: 500m 13,5km 500m Neusiedler See on the spot 1km.
Remarks: When buying wine 1 night free.

AT

Bosnia and Herzegovina

Capital: Sarajevo
Government: Federation
Official Language: Bosnien, Croatien and Serbian
Population: 3,861,912 (2016)
Area: 51,209 km²

General information
Dialling code: 0387
General emergency: 112
Currency: convertible Mark (BAM) also the Euro is accepted as currency.
Credit cards are accepted in the main cities.

Regulations for overnight stays
Wild camping is not allowed.

Additional public holidays 2018
March 1 Independence Day
May 1 Labour Day
May 9 Victory Day
November 25 Statehood Day

Time Zone
Winter (Standard Time) GMT+1
Summer (DST) GMT+2

S Banja Luka 37D2

Kamp Olimp. **GPS**: n44,71114 e17,16642.
10 € 15 Ch included. **Surface:** grassy. 01/01-31/12.
Distance: 8km on the spot on the spot.

S Bihać 37C2

Kamp Orljani. **GPS**: n44,80145 e15,90643.
120 € 18,50 Ch included .
Surface: grassy/gravel. 01/05-01/11.
Distance: 3,5km on the spot 100m.

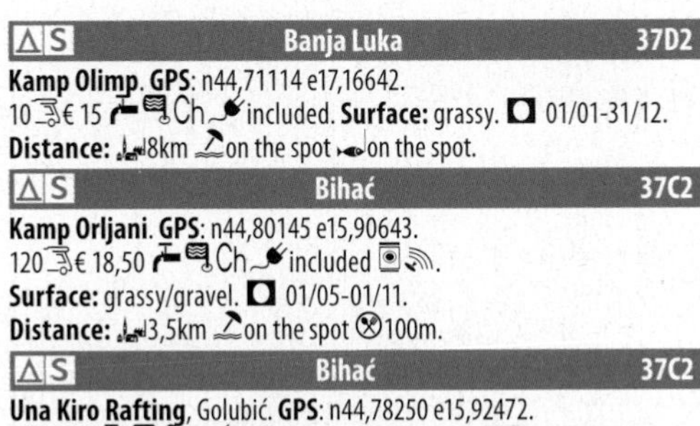

S Bihać 37C2

Una Kiro Rafting, Golubić. **GPS**: n44,78250 e15,92472.
9 € 17 Ch included. **Surface:** grassy. 01/04-01/11.
Distance: 5km on the spot on the spot on the spot.

S Bila 37D2

Motel Carousel. **GPS**: n44,17886 e17,75475.
15 € 15 Ch included. **Surface:** grassy. 01/01-31/12.
Distance: 1km on the spot.

S Blagaj 39A4

Autocam Blagaj. **GPS**: n43,25682 e17,87936.
25 € 20 Ch included.
Surface: grassy. 01/04-01/10.
Distance: Mostar 12km on the spot.

S Blagaj 39A4

Mail Wimbledon. **GPS**: n43,26317 e17,87799.
60 € 18 Ch € 3 included.
Surface: grassy/gravel. 01/01-31/12.
Distance: Mostar 10km 150m 100m.

S Blagaj 39A4

River Camp Aganovac. **GPS**: n43,25724 e17,88774.
8 € 20 Ch included.
Surface: grassy/sand. 01/01-31/12.
Distance: on the spot on the spot 200m 150m.

S Bosanska Krupa 37C2

Una Camping. **GPS**: n44,91484 e16,15696.
€ 16 Ch included. **Surface:** grassy. 01/05-01/10.
Distance: on the spot on the spot.

S Buna 39A4

River Camp Half Island. **GPS**: n43,24166 e17,83861.

20 € 17 Ch included.
Surface: grassy. 01/04-01/10.
Distance: on the spot on the spot 500m 500m.
Remarks: Only cash payment.

S Foča 39A3

Auto Camp Drina. **GPS**: n43,52948 e18,78254.
15 € 17 Ch included.
Surface: grassy. 01/05-15/09.
Distance: 3km on the spot on the spot on the spot.

S Gradačac 39A3

Hipodrom Vuković. **GPS**: n44,91860 e18,41893.
€ 20 Ch included.
Location: Rural. **Surface:** grassy/sand. 01/04-01/11.
Distance: on the spot.

S Jajec 37D2

Autocamp Plivsko Jezero. **GPS**: n44,35103 e17,22682.

40 € 21 Ch included . **Surface:** grassy. 15/04-31/10.
Distance: 5km 100m 100m on the spot.

S Krupa na Vrbasu 37D2

Camp Krupa. **GPS**: n44,61616 e17,14837.
80 € 12 Ch included. **Surface:** grassy. 01/05-01/10.
Distance: on the spot on the spot 200m.

S Kulen Vakuf 37C2

RC Discover Bihac. **GPS**: n44,56909 e16,08338.

25 € 5 + € 5/pp Ch WC included.
Surface: grassy/gravel. 01/04-30/10.
Distance: on the spot on the spot on the spot.

S Medugorje 39A4

Camp Zemo. **GPS**: n43,19432 e17,67612.
45 € 10 Ch included.
Surface: gravel. 01/01-31/12.
Distance: 100m 100m.

S Sarajevo 39A3

Oaza Resort. **GPS**: n43,82799 e18,29659.

350 € 20,90 Chincluded € 2,60.
Surface: grassy. 01/01-31/12.
Distance: 10km 100m 800m.

S Ščit 37D3

Konoba Gaj. **GPS**: n43,80230 e17,52560.
5 € 10 Ch included. **Location:** Rural. 01/01-31/12.
Distance: on the spot on the spot on the spot.

BA

Belgium

Capital: Brussels
Government: Constitutional monarchy
Official Language: Dutch/Flemish, French and German
Population: 11,409,077 (2016)
Area: 30,528 km²

General information
Dialling code: 0032
General emergency: 112
Currency: Euro

Regulations for overnight stays
Wild camping is forbidden.

Additional public holidays 2018
May 1 Labour Day
July 11 Feast Flemish Community
July 21 National Day
August 15 Assumption Day
September 27 Feast of the Walloon Region
November 1 All Saints' Day
November 11 Armistice Day 1918

Time Zone
Winter (Standard Time) GMT+1
Summer (DST) GMT+2

West Flanders

Aartrijke 11A1
Sint-Aarnoutstraat. **GPS**: n51,11341 e3,08983.

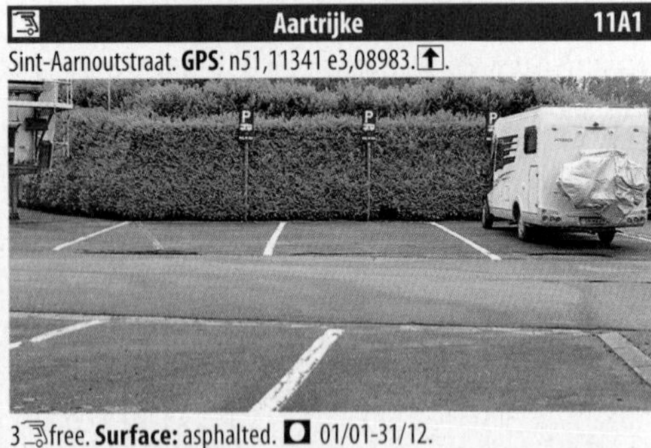

3 free. **Surface:** asphalted. 01/01-31/12.
Distance: 400m 80m 50m.

Anzegem 11A2
Vital Moreelsplein, Tiegemberg. **GPS**: n50,81712 e3,46666.
3 free. **Surface:** unpaved. 01/01-31/12.
Distance: Anzegem 3km 200m.

Beernem 11A1
Kanaaloever Beernem, Oude Vaartstraat.
GPS: n51,13482 e3,33427.

6 € 10/24h Ch (4x)WC included,sanitary at harbour building. **Location:** Rural. **Surface:** metalled.
01/01-31/12.
Distance: 1,9km.

Remarks: Max. 72h, only exact change.

Blankenberge 11A1
Kampeerautoterrein De Wielen, Zeebruggelaan 135.
GPS: n51,31106 e3,15154.
26 € 20-23 Ch included € 0,50 € 4/3.
Surface: grassy/metalled. 01/01-31/12.
Distance: 2km 2km.

Tourist information Blankenberge:
Dienst Toerisme, Koning Leopold III-plein. Lively bathing resort.
Sea Life Centre, Koning Albert I Laan 116. Underwaterworld.
10-18h.
Serpentarium, Zeedijk 147. World of the reptiles. Easter-Oct 10-18h, 01/07-31/08 10-21h.

Brugge 11A1
Bargeweg. **GPS**: n51,19633 e3,22544.

59 € 19, 01/04-30/09 € 25 € 0,50 Ch included.
Location: Urban, simple, central. **Surface:** metalled. 01/01-31/12.
Distance: within walking distance on the spot.
Remarks: Arrival <22h, max 3,5t, monitored parking.

Tourist information Brugge:
Brugge City Card gives for free entrance on among other things 27 museums, boat trips and many discounts on purchases. € 47.
Toerisme Brugge, 't Zand 34, www.brugge.be. City with medieval character, hiking itinerary available at Tourist office.
Brouwerij Halve Maan, Walplein 26. Town brewery. 11-16u. € 8,50.
Lamme Goedzak, Noorweegsekaai 31. Boat excursion from Bruges to Damme with the `Lamme Goedzak', departure Noorweegse Kaai.
01/04-30/09 10-16.
Diamantmuseum, Katelijnestraat 43. Diamond museum. 10.30-17.30h.
Boudewijn Seapark, Alfons De Baeckerstraat 12, Sint-Michiels. Attractions park with dolphinarium, seal island etc., in winter large skating rink covered.
01/07-31/08 10-18h.

Diksmuide 13D2
't Nesthof, Zijdelingstraat 2a. **GPS**: n51,07178 e2,86422.

14 € 9/night € 1 Ch € 2/24h.
Location: Rural, isolated, quiet. **Surface:** grassy. 01/04-01/10.
Distance: 5km on the spot on the spot.
Remarks: Bread-service.

Gistel 11A1
Sportstraat. **GPS**: n51,16112 e2,96495.

2 free Ch free. **Surface:** metalled. 01/01-31/12.
Distance: 1km 3,3km on the spot on the spot.

Remarks: Parking behind swimming pool, key service at swimming pool, many walking and bicycle area.

S Harelbeke 11A2

Kampeerautoterrein De Dageraad, Stasegemsesteenweg 21.
GPS: n50,84396 e3,31057.

8 € 5/24h Ch included WC € 1,25 free.
Surface: metalled. 01/01-31/12.
Distance: 1,6km 4,5km 700m 100m.
Remarks: Parking next to midget golf, service during opening hours: 8-20h.

S Ieper 11A2

Kampeerautoterrein Zillebekevijver, Zillebekevijverdreef.
GPS: n50,83578 e2,90504.

17 € 8/24h € 1/100liter Ch included.
Location: Rural, comfortable. **Surface:** grasstiles/metalled.
01/01-31/12.
Distance: 2,5km 500m 1,5km 1km on the spot on the spot.
Remarks: Max. 48h.

S Knokke-Heist 11A1

Holiday, Natiënlaan 72. **GPS**: n51,33612 e3,28866.
10 € 18-24 Ch WC free. **Surface:** metalled.
01/01-31/12.
Distance: 1km on the spot 100m.

S Kortemark 11A1

Sporthal Kortemark, Ichtegemstraat 2a. **GPS**: n51,03201 e3,04168.

2 free € 2 € 2 Ch. **Surface:** metalled. 01/01-31/12.
Distance: 500m on the spot.
Remarks: Max. 48h.

S Kortrijk 11A2

Kampeerautoterrein Broeltorens, Damkaai.
GPS: n50,83120 e3,26818.

8 € 10/24h Ch included.
Location: Urban. **Surface:** metalled. 01/01-31/12.
Distance: centre 400m 100m.

Tourist information Kortrijk:
Dienst Toerisme, Begijnhofpark, www.kortrijk.be. Historical little town with Beguine convent.

S Langemark- Poelkappele 11A1

Boezingestraat 51a. **GPS**: n50,90944 e2,91763.

8 € 12/24h Ch (4x)included € 1.
Location: Urban, simple. **Surface:** grasstiles.
01/01-31/12.
Distance: on the spot on the spot.
Remarks: Max. 72h, check in at reception sports centre.

Lichtervelde 11A1

O.C. De Schouw, Twee Lindenstraat. **GPS**: n51,02389 e3,13493.

2 free. **Surface:** metalled. 01/01-31/12.
Distance: 600m 600m 300m on the spot on the spot on the spot.
Remarks: Max. 48h.

Mesen 13D2

Kerkstraat. **GPS**: n50,76391 e2,89825.

3 free. **Surface:** metalled. 01/01-31/12.
Distance: on the spot frituur 200m 100m.
Remarks: In front of church, max. 24h.

S Middelkerke 13D1

Camperpark Poldervallei, Westendelaan 178.
GPS: n51,16684 e2,78246.

16 € 16-22 Ch included.
Surface: asphalted. 01/01-31/12.
Distance: 500m 500m.
Remarks: Nearby camp site.

S Nieuwpoort 13D1

De Zwerver, Brugsesteenweg 29, N367. **GPS**: n51,12988 e2,76576.

28 € 16,50/24h, then € 0,50/h € 0,50/50liter Ch included, 10Amp WC € 4. **Surface:** grassy. 01/01-31/12.

Distance: 800m 3,3km 4km.

S Oudenburg 11A1

Carpool, Stationsstraat. **GPS**: n51,19387 e3,00567.

free € 2 € 2 Ch. **Surface:** metalled. 01/01-31/12.
Distance: 800m.
Remarks: P service max. 30 min.

Tourist information Oudenburg:
Wed-afternoon.

Poperinge 13D2

Oudstrijdersplein. **GPS**: n50,85333 e2,72332.

. 01/01-31/12 Fri.
Distance: 500m 50m.

Roeselare 11A1

O.L. Vrouwenmarkt. **GPS**: n50,94786 e3,13450.

1 free. **Surface:** metalled. 18-9h, 01/01-31/12h.
Distance: 200m on the spot.
Remarks: Max. 1 night.

Roeselare 11A1

Trakelweg. **GPS**: n50,94438 e3,13320.

10 free. **Location:** Urban. **Surface:** asphalted. 01/01-31/12.
Distance: 1km on the spot on the spot.
Remarks: No camping activities.

S Sint-Eloois-Vijve 11A1

Kampeerautoterrein Leiekamper, Leiesas 15.
GPS: n50,90879 e3,40468.

8 € 5 € 1/100liter included,16Amp. 01/01-31/12.
Distance: 400m 400m 1km on the spot on the spot.
Remarks: Max. 72h.

BE

Stavele 13D2

Hof van Commerce, IJzerstraat 16. **GPS**: n50,94313 e2,67206.
guests free. **Surface:** gravel.
01/01-31/12 15/08-14/09.
Distance: on the spot on the spot on the spot.

S Wervik 11A2

Kampeerautoterrein De Balokken, De Balokken.
GPS: n50,77456 e3,03705.

8 € 10/72h € 1/100liter Ch included.
Surface: grasstiles. 01/01-31/12.
Distance: 1km on the spot on the spot cafetaria 700m bakery on the spot on the spot.
Remarks: On leisure island, max. 72h.

S Westende 13D1

Camperpark Westende, Heidestraat 18. **GPS**: n51,15597 e2,76623.

30 € 18-22, 2 pers. incl. Ch WC included .
01/01-31/12.
Distance: on the spot 1km 300m 400m.
Remarks: Discount longer stays, swimming pool (summer).

S Westende 13D1

Kompas kampeerautoterrein, Strandjuttersdreef.
GPS: n51,15594 e2,76019.

35 20h € 12,50-19, 44h € 21-29 Ch included .
Surface: grasstiles/metalled. 01/01-31/12.
Distance: on the spot 1km Taverne, Frituur on the spot.

S Westende 13D1

Poldervallei, Westendelaan 178. **GPS**: n51,16675 e2,78242.
15 € 16-22 Ch included.
Surface: asphalted. 01/01-31/12.
Distance: 1km.

S Westvleteren 13D2

Camperpunt Sixtusbos, Nachtegaalstraat 2. **GPS**: n50,89844 e2,71033.

18 € 10 Chincluded € 2. **Location:** Rural.
Surface: grassy/gravel. 01/01-31/12.
Distance: 5km 950m on the spot.
Remarks: Bread-service, narrow entrance.

S Wingene 11A1

Smart - ijs, Noordakkerstraat 1a. **GPS**: n51,07377 e3,26515.

6 € 8, discount for clients Ch included.
Location: Rural. **Surface:** gravel. 01/01-31/12.
Distance: 2km 1,5km bike junction on the spot.
Remarks: Max. 72h.

Zonnebeke 11A2

Café De Dreve, Lange Dreef 16. **GPS**: n50,85410 e2,97924.

free. **Surface:** gravel. 01/01-31/12.
Distance: Zonnebeke 2,7km 3,5km A19 snacks on the spot on the spot.
Remarks: Passendalemuseum-Zonnebeke.

East Flanders

S Aalst 11B1

Zwembadlaan 2. **GPS**: n50,93825 e4,05829.

2 free € 5,50 Ch € 5,50/1h.
Surface: metalled.
01/01-31/12.
Distance: city centre ± 1km 3,8km on the spot on the spot on the spot.
Remarks: Only 2 plots indicated, more plots permitted.

Tourist information Aalst:
Thu-morning.

Aalter 11A1

Vaart-Zuid, Bellem. **GPS**: n51,09821 e3,49365.

25 free. **Surface:** asphalted. 01/01-31/12.
Distance: Canal.

Aalter 11A1

Vaart-Noord, Bellem. **GPS**: n51,09875 e3,49468.

25 free. **Surface:** asphalted. 01/01-31/12.
Distance: 600m 500m.

Aalter 11A1

Bellemdorpweg, Bellem. **GPS**: n51,09323 e3,48308.

2 free. **Surface:** asphalted. 01/01-31/12.
Distance: 500m.
Remarks: At football ground.

S Aalter 11A1

Wingenestraat, Maria Aalter. **GPS**: n51,09915 e3,37141.
2 free € 1 . **Surface:** metalled. 01/01-31/12.
Distance: on the spot.
Remarks: Near church.

Tourist information Aalter:
Kasteel Poeke, Kasteelstraat 26, Poeke. weekend, holidays, 01/04-31/10 Su 14-17h.
Wed-morning.

S Assenede 11B1

Kapelledreef. **GPS**: n51,23067 e3,74891.

4 € 10/72h € 1/60liter Ch WC € 1.
Location: Urban, comfortable, quiet. **Surface:** grassy.
01/01-31/12 Service: winter.
Distance: 500m 600m on the spot on the spot.
Remarks: Behind gymnasium, max. 72h, payment only with coins, sanitary during opening hours gymnasium.

Bazel 11B1

Sporthal De Dulpop, Beekdam 1. **GPS**: n51,14778 e4,30583.

10 free. **Location:** Rural, simple. **Surface:** asphalted.
01/01-31/12.
Distance: 200m 6km 3km 500m 500m on the spot on the spot.
Remarks: Barn-museum 200m.

Berlare 11B1

Donklaan, Berlare-Overmere. **GPS**: n51,04258 e3,98293.

4 free. **Surface:** grasstiles. 01/01-31/12.
Distance: 9km Donkmeer on the spot.

S Eeklo 11A1

Jachthaven Eeklo, Nijverheidskaai. **GPS**: n51,17884 e3,54959.

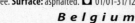

12 € 10/24h € 0,50/130liter Ch € 5/24h,6Amp WC.
Surface: grasstiles/metalled. 01/01-31/12.
Distance: 1,5km 1,5km 800m.
Remarks: Check in at harbourmaster, use sanitary only during opening hours.

Tourist information Eeklo:
Provinciaal Domein "Het Leen", Gentsesteenweg 80. Nature reserve. 9-12h, 13-17h Mo.

Gavere 11B1

Sportdreef. **GPS**: n50,92823 e3,65810.

12 free. **Surface:** asphalted. 01/01-31/12.
Distance: on the spot.
Remarks: Behind sports complex.

Geraardsbergen 11B2

Jeugdherberg 't Schipken, Kampstraat 59.
GPS: n50,79500 e3,90412.

4 free. **Surface:** grassy. 01/01-31/12.
Distance: Geraardsbergen 3,7km on the spot.
Remarks: Max. 1 night.

Tourist information Geraardsbergen:
Provinciaal Domein "de Gavers", Onkelzelestraat 280. Recreation area; swimming, watersports, fishing, boat trips and tennis.Free entrance, payment per attraction.

Hamme 11B1

Camperplaats Mirabrug, Hamveer. **GPS**: n51,10418 e4,14246.

2 free. **Location:** Rural, simple, quiet. **Surface:** metalled.
01/01-31/12.
Distance: 1km 400m 500m on the spot on the spot.
Remarks: Max. 48h.

Lokeren 11B1

Veerstraat. **GPS**: n51,11013 e3,97163.

5 free. **Location:** Urban, noisy. **Surface:** metalled.
01/01-31/12.
Distance: 1,5km, bakery 500m.
Remarks: Parking in front of church, max. 48h.

Lokeren 11B1

Verloren Bos, Aardeken. **GPS**: n51,10981 e3,99525.

2 free. **Location:** Rural, simple. **Surface:** unpaved.
01/01-31/12.
Distance: 500m 600m.

Tourist information Lokeren:
Stationsplein. Flea market. Su 7-12h.
Molsbroek. Protected European Nature Reserve, 80ha marsh area with many birds, asphalted hiking trail. Su 14-17h, 01/07-31/08 Wed-Su 14-17h.

S Ronse 11A2

Engelsenlaan/Boulevard des Anglais. **GPS**: n50,74447 e3,58794.

4 free free. **Surface:** asphalted. 01/01-31/12.
Distance: 1km 200m on the spot. **Remarks:** Behind swimming pool, entrance code available at swimming pool.

Temse 11B1

De Zaat, Nagelheetmakerslaan 1. **GPS**: n51,12466 e4,21007.
20 free. **Location:** Urban. **Surface:** grasstiles/metalled.
01/01-31/12.
Distance: 400m 250m.
Remarks: Behind police station, temporary stopover.

S Temse 11B1

Camperbedrijf Alpha Motorhomes, Kapelanielaan 13a, N16.
GPS: n51,13699 e4,18017.

free Chfree. **Surface:** metalled. 01/01-31/12.
Distance: city centre 3km.

Tourist information Temse:
Grote Markt. Fri-morning.

Vosselaar 11C1

Sportcentrum Diepvenneke, Diepvenneke 43.
GPS: n51,30142 e4,89418.

2 free. **Surface:** metalled. 01/01-31/12.
Distance: city centre 1,5km.

S Zulte 11A1

Leihoekstraat, Machelen. **GPS**: n50,96103 e3,48352.

8 € 8/72h € 1 Ch included.
Surface: metalled. 01/01-31/12.
Distance: 150m 50m 150m on the spot.
Remarks: Max. 72h.

Antwerp

S Antwerpen 11C1

Vogelzang, Vogelzanglaan 7-9. **GPS**: n51,18983 e4,40074.

115 € 8, Jun/Jul/Aug € 10 € 1 Ch (30x)€ 1/kWh.
Location: Simple. **Surface:** grassy/metalled.
04/01-22/12.
Distance: city centre 3km 1km 3km 500m 1km 3km 150m.

Tourist information Antwerp (Antwerpen):
Antwerp City Card. Antwerp City Card gives free City tour, entrance to museums, churches and many discounts on purchases. from € 27.
Toerisme Antwerpen, Grote Markt, 13, www.visitantwerpen.be. Large port city, worth seeing is the city centre.
Dageraadsplaats. Thu 8-13h.
Lijnwaadmarkt. Antiques market. Easter-Oct Sa 9-17h.
St. Andriesplaats. Tue 8-13h.
St. Jansplein. Wed, Fri 8-13h.
St. Jansvliet. Bric-a-brac market. Su 9-17h.
Theaterplein. Exotic market. Sa.
Vogelenmarkt, Theaterplein. Famous flea market. Su-morning.

S Arendonk 11D1

De Vloed. **GPS**: n51,32253 e5,08610.

10 free. **Location:** Urban. **Surface:** asphalted.
01/01-31/12.
Distance: 400m on the spot 100m.
Remarks: Parking in front of swimming pool, max. 24h, water during openinghours swimming pool.

Balen 11D1

Vrijetijdscentrum De Kruierie, Berg. **GPS**: n51,17043 e5,16255.
2 free. **Location:** Urban. **Surface:** asphalted. 01/01-31/12.
Distance: 400m 200m 500m.

Remarks: Max. 24h.

Beveren 11B1

De Meerminnen, Klapperstraat. **GPS**: n51,21201 e4,24377.
2 free. **Location:** Urban. **Surface:** asphalted. 01/01-31/12.

Bornem 11B1

Kasteel d'Ursel, Koningin Astridlaan. **GPS**: n51,10294 e4,27261.

5 free. **Location:** Rural. **Surface:** unpaved.
01/01-31/12.
Remarks: Parking next to castle, open 8-21h.

Brasschaat 11C1

P5b, Elshoutbaan 17. **GPS**: n51,28555 e4,50325.

15 free € 1/100liter Ch € 0,50/kWh.
Location: Rural. **Surface:** forest soil. 01/01-31/12.
Distance: 1,7km 6km 500m 500m on the spot on the spot.
Remarks: Parking sports and recreation centre, max. 72h.

Tourist information Brasschaat:
Armand Reusensplein. Mo 8-13h.

Brecht 11C1

Mudeausstraat. **GPS**: n51,34814 e4,64123.

2 free at townhall.
Location: Urban. **Surface:** metalled. 01/01-31/12.
Distance: on the spot 1,2km 150m 150m.
Remarks: Max. 48h.

Brecht 11C1

Schoolstraat. **GPS**: n51,34992 e4,64577.

10 free. **Surface:** grassy/metalled. 01/01-31/12.
Distance: 800m 1,5km.

Essen 9C3

Kerkeneind, N133. **GPS**: n51,47086 e4,46401.

2 free Chfree. **Location:** Urban, simple, central, quiet.
Surface: metalled. 01/01-31/12.
Distance: 500m 150m on the spot on the spot.
Remarks: Max. 24h.

Geel 11C1

Parking Pas, Fehrenbachstraat. **GPS**: n51,15828 e4,99158.
3 € 5 Ch € 1/kWh.
Surface: metalled. 01/01-31/12.
Distance: city centre 200m 400m.
Remarks: At swimming pool, service 100m.

Grobbendonk 11C1

Vaartkom. **GPS**: n51,18954 e4,73638.

5 free € 1/5minutes Ch€ 1 (6x)€ 1.
Surface: asphalted. 01/01-31/12.
Distance: 200m 3,6km frituur 200m.

Herentals 11C1

Herenhoutseweg. **GPS**: n51,16586 e4,82664.

free free. **Surface:** asphalted. 01/01-31/12.
Distance: 1,5km 2,8km bakery 200m.
Remarks: Parking multipurpose area, next to footballstadium VC Herentals.

Herentals 11C1

Jachthaven, Noordervaart 45. **GPS**: n51,17666 e4,85694.
€ 10 € 0,50/kWh. **Surface:** metalled. 01/01-31/12.
Distance: 3,9km on the spot.

Tourist information Herentals:
Augustijnenlaan. Su-morning.
Grote Markt. Fri-morning.

Herselt 11C1

Taverne Herberg Mie Maan, Diestsebaan 28.
GPS: n51,06025 e4,92897.

6 free . **Surface:** gravel. 01/01-31/12.
Distance: 3km on the spot 3km.
Remarks: Restaurant visit appreciated, intersection hiking and biking trails.

Kalmthout 11C1

Kalmthoutse Heide, Heibloemlaan. **GPS**: n51,37688 e4,44911.

2 free. **Location:** Rural, simple, isolated, quiet. **Surface:** grasstiles.
01/01-31/12.
Distance: city centre 2km 50m on the spot on the spot.
Remarks: Parking nature reserve, max. 24h.

Koningshooikt 11C1

Donderheide. **GPS**: n51,08439 e4,56541.

free. **Surface:** unpaved. 01/01-31/12.
Distance: on the spot.
Remarks: In front of 'Het Fort'.

Koningshooikt 11C1

Motorhomes Konings, Sander de Vosstraat 141.
GPS: n51,08774 e4,62816.

€ 2,50 € 2 € 2,50. **Surface:** asphalted. 01/01-31/12.
Remarks: Apply during openinghours.

Lier 11C1

Parking Mol Poort, Aarschotsesteenweg 2. **GPS**: n51,12525 e4,57332.

2 free € 1 Ch .
Surface: asphalted. 01/01-31/12.
Distance: 1km 1km 1km on the spot on the spot on the spot.

Tourist information Lier:
Dienst Toerisme, Grote Markt 57. City with old centre worth a visit.
City walls, prison tower and Zimmertoren.
10-12h, 14-17/18h.
Grote Markt/Eikelstraat. Sa 8-13h.
Kerststallentocht. Dec.

Mechelen 11C1

Douaneplein. **GPS**: n51,02667 e4,50058.
5 . **Surface:** gravel. 01/01-31/12.
Distance: centre 1,2km 200m.
Remarks: Nearby sports park, max. 24h.

Tourist information Mechelen:
Dienst Toerisme Stad Mechelen, Hallestraat 2-4, www.mechelen.be/. Historical city, city of carillons.
Brouwerijmuseum Het Anker. Old brewery, 1369. 01/04-30/09 14-18h, guided tour 15h. € 3,30.
De Nekker. Sports and recreation area with ponds, sports grounds etc. Dierenpark Planckendael. Zoo. 10-18h.
Technopolis. Interactively "discover" museum.
Caroluswandeling. City walk along historical bldg. And breweries,

information Dienst Toerisme.

S Putte 11C1

Ixenheuvel, Heuvel. **GPS**: n51,04678 e4,62564.

2 free Chfree. **Location:** Simple. **Surface:** asphalted.
01/01-31/12.
Distance: 1,5km.
Remarks: Max. 48h.

S Puurs 11B1

Eeuwfeeststraat/ Kerkhofstraat. **GPS**: n51,07476 e4,28337.

2 free Chfree. **Surface:** metalled. 01/01-31/12.
Distance: 5,3km.
Remarks: Max. 48h, intersection hiking and biking trails.

S Sint-Amands 11B1

Parking Noord, Emile Verhaerenstraat. **GPS**: n51,05906 e4,20206.

2 free Ch free. **Surface:** metalled. 01/01-31/12.
Distance: on the spot 200m 200m 300m on the spot on the spot.
Remarks: Max. 48h.

Sint-Job-in-'t-Goor 11C1

Vaartlaan. **GPS**: n51,30151 e4,56888.

2 free. **Location:** Urban. **Surface:** metalled. 01/01-31/12.
Distance: 50m 50m 50m.
Remarks: Max. 48h.

S Turnhout 11C1

Baalse Hei, Roodhuisstraat. **GPS**: n51,35385 e4,95591.

7 € 16-28 Ch € 1,20 WC free.
Location: Rural. 15/01-15/12.
Distance: 3km on the spot on the spot on the spot.
Tourist information Turnhout: Begijnhof. Beguine convent.
Tue-Sa 14-17h, Su 11-17h Christmas.

S Willebroek 11B1

Dijlelaan. **GPS**: n51,06028 e4,34472.

3 free € 1 € 1 Ch.
Surface: metalled. 01/01-31/12.
Distance: 300m.
Remarks: Max. 2 nights.

Flemish Brabant

S Aarschot 11C1

Demervallei. **GPS**: n50,98285 e4,83809.

free Ch free. 01/01-31/12.
Distance: 500m on the spot.
Remarks: Max. 48h.

S Diest 11C1

De Halve Maan, Omer Vanaudenhovelaan 48.
GPS: n50,98607 e5,06373.

4 € 15 Ch (4x)included WC. **Location:** Comfortable, quiet. **Surface:** grassy/gravel. 01/03-31/10.
Distance: 1,2km, beguine convent 350m 20m 200m 100m 100m.
Remarks: Check in at pay desk recreation centre, max. 3 nights.

Tourist information Diest:
Begijnhof. Beguine convent. Art studios open: sa/so afternoon and in july/aug each afternoon. Beguine convent daily, Angel convent Sa/Su 14.30-17h, church Easter-Oct Su 14-17h.

Grimbergen 11C1

K.S.C. Grimbergen, Brusselsesteenweg. **GPS**: n50,92787 e4,36610.

10 free. **Location:** Simple. **Surface:** asphalted. 01/01-31/12.
Distance: 1km 1km > Brussels.

Tourist information Grimbergen:
Gemeentelijke Dienst voor Toerisme, Prinsenstraat 22. Well-known for the Abbey beer, info at the beer museum.
Abdijkerk. Abbey-church. 10-12h, 13-17h.
Jaarmarkt. Village festival with among other things fair, cattle market. 1st weekend Sep.

Halle 11B2

Parking Nederhem, Jean Laroystraat 12. **GPS**: n50,73945 e4,24203.
free. 01/01-31/12.
Distance: centre 600m.

S Merchtem 11B1

Brusselsesteenweg. **GPS**: n50,95553 e4,24011.

4 free.
Surface: metalled. 01/01-31/12.
Distance: 300m Good bus connection for Brussels.

Remarks: Next to cemetery and sports fields, no camping activities.

S Rotselaar 11C1

Recreatiedomein Sportoase Ter Heide, Vakenstraat 18.
GPS: n50,96217 e4,72288.

4 free € 1/100liter Ch € 1/kWh WC.
Surface: gravel. 01/01-31/12.
Distance: 2km 100m 100m 500m 2km 200m on the spot on the spot.

Limburg

Beringen 11D1

P Koolmijnmuseum, Koolmijnlaan. **GPS**: n51,07048 e5,22097.
2 free. **Surface:** metalled. 01/01-31/12 events.
Distance: 2,3km.
Remarks: Max. 24h.

S Bilzen 11D2

Parking Lanakerdij, Lanakerdij. **GPS**: n50,86985 e5,52215.

2 free € 2/4minutes Ch (5x)€ 2/12h.
Surface: asphalted. 01/01-31/12.
Distance: 300m 3km 300m 300m on the spot on the spot.
Remarks: Max. 24h.

Tourist information Bilzen:
Landcommanderij Alden Biesen, Kasteelstraat 6. Tue-Su 10-17h. € 3.
Zuivelhoeve 't Wanthof. Dairy farm. Tue-Fri 10-22h, Sa-Su 9-23h.
Markt. Wed.

S Bocholt 11D1

Heuvelzicht, Schipperstraat 1. **GPS**: n51,17722 e5,58500.

7 € 10/24h € 0,50 Ch WCincluded € 1.
Surface: metalled.
01/01-31/12.
Distance: on the spot 50m 100m 50m 50m.
Remarks: Parking marina at Zuidwillemsvaart, max. 48h.

S Bolderberg 11D1

Domein Bovy, Galgeneinde. **GPS**: n50,98690 e5,27048.

3 free € 2 Ch € 2/1h.
Location: Rural. **Surface:** metalled.
01/01-31/12.

Distance: 500m 150m 500m on the spot on the spot.
Remarks: Estate with i.e. restaurant, bar, brasserie, marked hiking trails, herb garden, petting zoo, old tools.

Bree 11D1

N721, Opitter. **GPS**: n51,11788 e5,64524.

5 free. **Surface:** metalled. 01/01-31/12.
Distance: on the spot on the spot.
Remarks: Parking next to church, in front of petrol station, max. 48h.

Tourist information Bree:
Vrijthof. Fri.
Sint-Antoniuskapel, Opitter.

S Diepenbeek 11D1

Demerstrand, Stationsstraat 27. **GPS**: n50,91323 e5,42189.

4 free Chfree € 2/8h.
Surface: asphalted. 01/01-31/12.
Distance: 500m 250m 1km.
Remarks: At gymnasium, max. 48h, video surveillance.

Dilsen-Stokkem 11D1

De Wissen, Maaspark 3. **GPS**: n51,02361 e5,74945.

3 free. **Location:** Rural. **Surface:** gravel. 01/01-31/12.
Distance: 500m on the spot on the spot Taverne Maascentrum 500m on the spot on the spot on the spot.
Remarks: Parking at tourist office De Wissen, starting point of cycle routes.

S Genk 11D1

Parking Kattevennen, Kattevennen. **GPS**: n50,95728 e5,53337.

8 € 5 Ch.
Surface: asphalted. 01/01-31/12.
Distance: 3km taverne on the spot on the spot on the spot.
Remarks: Max. 24h, mountainbike and hiking trails, national park Hoge Kempen.

Tourist information Genk:
Zondagsmarkten. Flea market. 01/06-31/08 9-13h.

Hamont 11D1

Michielsplein, Achel. **GPS**: n51,25421 e5,48128.

4 free. **Location:** Urban. **Surface:** metalled. 01/01-31/12.
Distance: on the spot on the spot on the spot.
Remarks: At bicycle trail Limburgse Kempen, behind church of Achel, max. 24h, market Tuesday 8-13h.

Hamont 11D1

Kerkplein. **GPS:** n51,25152 e5,54612.

5 free. **Location:** Urban. **Surface:** metalled. 01/01-31/12.
Distance: on the spot 50m 50m 50m on the spot.
Remarks: Behind church, max. 24h.

Hamont 11D1

Stadpark. GPS: n51,25085 e5,55200.

5 free. **Location:** Rural. **Surface:** grasstiles/grassy.
01/01-31/12.
Distance: 200m.
Remarks: Large parking in the centre behind tennis-courts, max. 24h.

Tourist information Hamont:
VVV, Generaal Dempseylaan 1, www.hamontachel.com.
Historical little town.
Mo-Fri 9-12h, 13-16h, Sa 9-12h.

Hasselt 11D1

Sporthal Alverberg, Herkenrodesingel. **GPS:** n50,93871 e5,32081.

>5 free € 2 Ch. **Surface:** asphalted. 01/01-31/12.
Distance: city centre 3km Carrefour on the spot.

Hasselt 11D1

Bakkerslaan. **GPS:** n50,92141 e5,32562.

3 free. **Location:** Urban, simple. **Surface:** grasstiles/grassy.
01/01-31/12.
Distance: 2km 600m 500m 500m on the spot.

Hasselt 11D1

Restaurant Aan het Water, Overdemerstraat 20, Kuringen.
GPS: n50,94663 e5,30877.

8 guests free. **Surface:** grassy.
01/01-31/12 Tue, Wed, 26/09-06/10.
Distance: on the spot bakery 50m.

Helchteren 11D1

Parking de Dool, Sportstraat. **GPS:** n51,06087 e5,38650.

10 free. **Surface:** asphalted. 01/01-31/12.
Distance: 1km 500m 500m.
Remarks: Next to castle.

Herk-de-Stad 11D1

Park Olmenhof, Pikkeleerstraat. **GPS:** n50,93361 e5,16654.

7 free € 1/100liter Ch € 0,60/kWh WC.
Location: Rural, simple. **Surface:** asphalted. 01/01-31/12.
Distance: 400m 7km 50m 300m on the spot.
Remarks: At football ground, max. 48h.

Hoepertingen 11D2

De Verborgen Parel, Hoenshovenstraat 5.
GPS: n50,80224 e5,29073.
6 € 7,50 Ch included.
Location: Simple. **Surface:** grassy. 01/01-31/12.
Distance: 1,5km on the spot 1,5km on the spot on the spot.
Remarks: Bread-service, use of sauna against payment.

Houthalen 11D1

Parking Kelchterhoef, Kelchterhoefstraat.
GPS: n51,03015 e5,44063.

4 free. **Location:** Rural. **Surface:** grasstiles/metalled.
01/01-31/12.
Distance: 6km on the spot on the spot on the spot.
Remarks: In front of abbey farm.

Kortessem 11D2

Kapittelstraat. **GPS:** n50,85724 e5,39126.

5 free (10x). **Surface:** asphalted. 01/01-31/12.
Distance: 200m 200m bakery 200m on the spot.
Remarks: At gymnasium, max. 2 nights.

Tourist information Kortessem:
't Rood Kasteel, Guigoven. Former medieval water castle.

Leopoldsburg 11D1

Jachthaven, Antwerpsesteenweg 129. **GPS:** n51,12892 e5,25028.

22 € 10 included WC € 1.
Surface: asphalted. 01/01-31/12.
Distance: 2km on the spot on the spot 2km.
Remarks: Check in at harbourmaster.

Lommel 11D1

Taverne Haven de Meerpaal, Boskantstraat 60.
GPS: n51,24266 e5,36891.

10 € 10 € 0,50 Ch (6x)€ 1 WC € 1 € 5.
Surface: asphalted. 01/01-31/12.
Distance: 500m on the spot on the spot on the spot.
Remarks: Near marina.

Maaseik 11D1

Sportlaan P4. **GPS:** n51,10108 e5,78964.

20 free. **Surface:** asphalted. 01/01-31/12.
Distance: historical centre 200m.

Tourist information Maaseik:

BE

Marktplein. Wed 9-12h.

Meeuwen-Gruitrode 11D1

CC Gruitrode, Royerplein 1, Gruitrode. **GPS**: n51,08939 e5,58949.

8 free. **Surface:** metalled. 01/01-31/12.
Distance: 200m on the spot 200m 200m on the spot.
Remarks: Max. 24h.

Meeuwen-Gruitrode 11D1

Ophovenstraat. **GPS**: n51,06404 e5,56442.

16 € 8 Chincluded € 1. **Location:** Rural, isolated, quiet. **Surface:** metalled. 01/04-31/12.
Distance: 6,5km on the spot on the spot.

Neeroeteren 11D1

Komweg. **GPS**: n51,08375 e5,70284.

6 € 8 € 1/150liter Ch.
Surface: metalled. 01/01-31/12.
Remarks: At football ground.

Neerpelt 11D1

De Welvaart, Jaak Tassetstraat. **GPS**: n51,23333 e5,43164.

8 € 6/24h Ch included.
Surface: metalled. 01/01-31/12.
Distance: 500m.
Remarks: At the canal, parking marina, max. 48h, checked, coin waste dump € 1.

Peer 11D1

P1 Aan den Boogaard. GPS: n51,13193 e5,45741.
free. 01/01-31/12.
Distance: 100m.
Remarks: Max. 24h.

Peer 11D1

P2 Noordervest. GPS: n51,13422 e5,45511.
free. 01/01-31/12.
Distance: 150m.
Remarks: Max. 24h.

Rekem 11D1

Kanaalstraat. **GPS**: n50,92177 e5,70493.

10 free. **Location:** Rural. **Surface:** gravel. 01/01-31/12.
Distance: 1km on the spot on the spot 500m 1km 100m on the spot on the spot.
Remarks: Max. 48h, walking and bicycle area.

Tourist information Rekem:

Oud-Rekem with museum-church, city walls and castle, marked walking route 2km.

Rummen 11D2

Ketelstraat. **GPS**: n50,89285 e5,16037.

4 free. **Surface:** gravel. 01/01-31/12.
Distance: on the spot 300m 250m on the spot on the spot.
Remarks: At gymnasium.

Schalkhoven 11D2

Nollekes Winning, Schalkhovenstraat 79. **GPS**: n50,84531 e5,44687.

9 voluntary contribution Ch WC.
Surface: grasstiles/metalled. 01/01-31/12.
Distance: 200m on the spot.
Remarks: Sale of wines.

Sint-Huibrechts-Lille 11D1

De Bosuil, Bosuilstraat 4. **GPS**: n51,22371 e5,49502.

32 € 6 Ch included.
Location: Quiet. **Surface:** grassy. 01/01-31/12.
Distance: 1,5km on the spot on the spot on the spot.
Remarks: Check in on arrival.

Sint-Truiden 11D2

Domein Terbiest, Hasseltsesteenweg. **GPS**: n50,82946 e5,20547.
30 free Chfree. **Surface:** metalled.
01/04-31/05, 01/09-30/09.
Distance: city centre 2km.
Remarks: Check in at tourist office.

Tourist information Sint-Truiden:

Toerisme Sint-Truiden, Stadhuis, Grote Markt, www.sint-truiden.be. Abbey-town.

Grote Markt, Groenmarkt, Trudoplein, Minderbroedersplein. Sa 7.30-13h.

Veemarkt, Speelhoflaan. Antiques and flea market. Sa 6-12h.

Tongeren 11D2

Pliniuspark, Fonteindreef. **GPS**: n50,78626 e5,45256.

25 € 10/24h € 0,50/100liter Ch € 0,50/kWh.
Location: Rural. **Surface:** grasstiles/metalled. 01/01-31/12.
Distance: 2km on the spot on the spot.
Remarks: At swimming pool, max. 24h.

Tourist information Tongeren:

Dienst Toerisme, Stadhuisplein 9, www.tongeren.be. Oldest city of Belgium with numerous historico-cultural heritage.

Maastrichterstraat, Schiervelstraat, Clarissenstraat. Biggest antique market in the Benelux, also all antique stores open. Su 6-13h.

Tongerlo 11D1

De Kieper, Keyartstraat. **GPS**: n51,12397 e5,65449.

4 free € 1/100liter € 1.
Location: Rural. **Surface:** metalled. 01/01-31/12.
Distance: 10 min walking on the spot on the spot.

Veldwezelt 11D2

Omstraat 20. **GPS**: n50,86195 e5,62696.

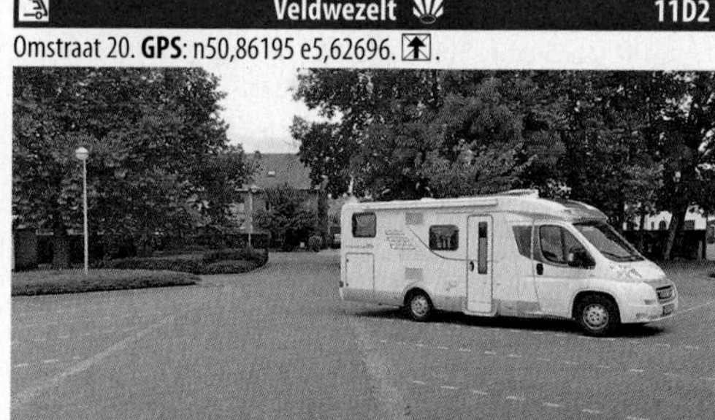

5 free. **Surface:** metalled. 01/01-31/12.
Distance: 800m 200m 500m.
Remarks: Parking gymnasium.

Brussels

Bruxelles/Brussel 11B2

Bruparck, Wemmel/Heizel, Brussels (Bruxelles/Brussel).
GPS: n50,89745 e4,33826.
01/01-31/12.
Remarks: Max. 24h. Ring road Brussels exit 8.

Bruxelles/Brussel 11B2

Auberge de Jeunesse Génération Europe, Rue de l'Eléphant 4, Brussels (Bruxelles/Brussel). **GPS**: n50,85317 e4,33479.
5 € 30 Ch included WC. 01/01-31/12.
Distance: on the spot.

Bruxelles/Brussel 11B2

Heizel/Heysel Metro, Brussels (Bruxelles/Brussel).
GPS: n50,89736 e4,33827.
01/01-31/12.
Remarks: Nearby Bruparck.

Tourist information Brussels (Bruxelles/Brussel):

Brussels City Card gives for free entrance on public transport and museums and many discounts on purchases. € 22.

Bureau van Toerisme, Office de Tourisme, Grote Markt 1, Grand Place, visit.brussels. Capital of Belgium, with a history of more than 1000 years. A lot of buildings worth seeing and historical places.

Koninklijke Serres van Laken, Les serres royales à Laeken. Park, garden, nature area.

Basiliek van Koekelberg, basilique de Koekelberg. The fifth largest church of the world. Wed, Thu, Sa, Su 14-16h. € 5.

Autoworld, Jubelpark 11, Parc du Cinquantenaire. Motorcar history from 1886 up to 1970s. 01/04-30/09 10-18, 01/10-31/03 10-17.

Museum van de stad Brussel Broodhuis, Musée de la ville Bruxelles,

BE

Grote Markt 44, Grand Place. History of the city. Tue-Su 10-17h.
Grote Zavel, Place du Grand Sablon. Antiques and book market. Sa 9-17h, Su 9-14h.
Vossenplein. Flea market. 6-14h.
Grote Markt, Grand place. Flowers and plant market. 8-18h.
Kunstmarkt, marché d'art, Boterstraat, rue au Beurre. Painters and portraitists. 11-18h.
Atomium, Bruparck, Boulevard du Centenaire, Laeken. Built for the occasion of the 1958 Brussels World Fair, symbolising a crystallised iron molecule to the scale of its atoms enlarged 160 thousand million times. 10-18h.
Bruparck, Boulevard du Centenaire 20, Laeken. Family park with among other things Mini-Europe, paradise pool and The Village with restaurants, cafés and shops. 01/01-31/12.
Mini-Europe, Bruparck, Boulevard du Centenaire, Laeken. Europe in miniature, 350 monuments.
Oceade, Bruparck, Boulevard du Centenaire, Laeken. Subtropical leisure pool park. holidays, Sa-Su 10-22h.

Liège

S Aywaille 11D2

Esplanade du Fair-Play, Rue de la Heid. **GPS**: n50,47583 e5,67809.

8 € 8/48h, incl. 1 coin (water or 2h electricity) € 2 Ch (4x) € 2/2h. **Surface:** metalled. 01/01-31/12.
Distance: 300m 200m.
Remarks: At recreation area.

S Blégny-Mine 11D2

Domaine de Blégny-Mine, Rue Lambert Marlet. **GPS**: n50,68617 e5,72367.

8 free Chfree (8x)€ 2/12h. **Location:** Rural, comfortable, isolated, quiet. **Surface:** gravel. 01/01-31/12.
Distance: 4,6km on the spot on the spot on the spot.
Remarks: At former coalmine, UNESCO World Heritage, access € 9,30, 1 day all inclusive € 29,50, coins electricity at reception park.

Coo 11E3

Petit Coo. **GPS**: n50,39222 e5,87531.
€ 5. **Location:** Simple. **Surface:** asphalted. 01/01-31/12.
Distance: 150m 150m.
Remarks: Water falls Coo 250m.

Eupen 11E2

Langesthal 164. **GPS**: n50,62180 e6,09148.

free. **Surface:** asphalted. 18-10h.
Distance: Eupen 4km 150m Taverne.
Remarks: At weir, isolated.

Tourist information Eupen:
Benedenstad. Wed 7-12.30h.
Eupen/Keltenis. Flea market. Su 7-16h.

S Hamoir 11D3

Complexe Sportif, Quai du Batty. **GPS**: n50,42463 e5,53522.

10 € 8/24h Chincluded. **Location:** Urban, comfortable.
Surface: grassy/gravel. 01/01-31/12.
Distance: 200m on the spot on the spot 200m 200m.
Remarks: Along the Ourthe river, max. 24h.

Huy 11D2

Avenue Godin Parnajon. **GPS**: n50,52379 e5,24310.

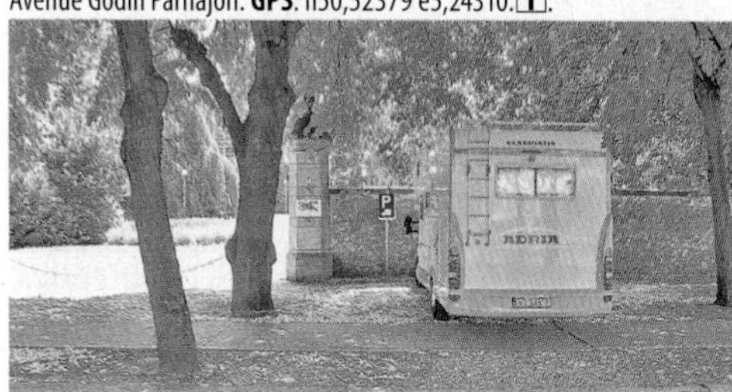

2 free. **Location:** Urban, central, noisy. **Surface:** asphalted. 01/01-31/12.
Distance: 500m on the spot 500m.
Remarks: Parking in front of restaurant Quick.

Huy 11D2

Quai de Namur. **GPS**: n50,51673 e5,23453.

2 free. **Location:** Urban, central, noisy. **Surface:** asphalted. 01/01-31/12.
Distance: 500m on the spot on the spot 500m.
Remarks: Under the citadel, along the Meuse River, in front of Hôtel du Fort to the right to the quay.

Tourist information Huy:
Office du Tourisme, Quai de Namur,1, www.huy.be. Tourist town, citadel above the city.
Fort en museum. Easter-Sep 10-17/18/19h.

S Jalhay 11E2

Baraque de La Gileppe. **GPS**: n50,58759 e5,96980.
4 free free. 01/01-31/12.
Distance: 3,5km on the spot on the spot.
Remarks: At artificial lake.

S Malmedy 11E3

Avenue de la Gare, N62. **GPS**: n50,42282 e6,03080.

30 € 5/24h Ch (8x).
Surface: gravel/metalled. 01/01-31/12.
Distance: 300m 300m bakery 100m, supermarket 800m on the spot on the spot on the spot Waimes 5km.
Remarks: At cycle route (former railroad).

Tourist information Malmedy:
Place St. Géréon. Fri 7-13h.
Hautes Fagnes. Nature reserve Hautes Fagnes.

S Sankt Vith 11E3

An den Weyern, Rodter Strasse 9a. **GPS**: n50,28091 e6,12240.

20 free € 1/4minutes . **Location:** Urban, simple.
Surface: asphalted. 01/01-31/12.
Distance: 500m on the spot on the spot.
Remarks: At sports centre.

Sourbrodt 11E2

Signal de Botrange, Rue de Botrange. **GPS**: n50,50148 e6,09312.

20 free. **Location:** Rural, simple, noisy. **Surface:** gravel. 01/01-31/12.
Distance: on the spot on the spot on the spot.

S Waimes 11E3

La Faitafondue, Rue de Merkem 4. **GPS**: n50,39532 e6,07024.

10 € 9, free with a meal WC. **Location:** Rural, comfortable. **Surface:** gravel. 01/01-31/12 Wed.
Distance: 4km 6km on the spot on the spot 200m.

Hainaut

Aubechies 11B2

Parking Archéosite, Rue de l'Abbaye 1Y. **GPS**: n50,57419 e3,67546.
2 free. **Surface:** gravel. 01/01-31/12.
Remarks: At museum.

Tourist information Aubechies:
Archéosite d'Aubechies. Archeological open air museum. Mo-Fri 9-17h, 01/04-31/10 9-18h.

Beloeil 11B2

Château Beloeil, Rue de la Hunelle. **GPS**: n50,55128 e3,73280.
free. **Surface:** unpaved. 01/01-31/12.
Remarks: Parking castle.

Tourist information Beloeil:
Château de Beloeil, www.beloeil.be/. 01/06-30/09 10-19h, 01/04-31/05 Sa/Su/holidays 10-19h.

Bernissart 11B2

Musée de l'Iguanodon, Ruelle des Médecins. **GPS**: n50,47530 e3,64958.

free. 01/01-31/12.
Distance: 6km.
Remarks: Parking 100m of dinosaur museum.

S Binche 11B3

Pastures, Rue des Pastures. **GPS**: n50,41413 e4,17070.

BE

50 free Ch (2x). **Surface:** asphalted. 01/01-31/12.
Distance: on the spot.
Remarks: Parking just outside centre.

Tourist information Binche:
Office du Tourisme, Parc communal, rue des Promenades, 2, www.binche.be. Medieval city with ramparts.

Blaton 11B2
Place de Feignies. **GPS:** n50,50179 e3,66135.

free. 01/01-31/12.
Distance: 200m.
Remarks: Nearby Romanesque church.

Bouffioulx 11C3
Maison de la Poterie, Rue du Général Jacques.
GPS: n50,39024 e4,51406.
3 € 0,50 Ch. **Surface:** metalled. 01/01-31/12.
Remarks: Next to Centre d'Interprétation de la Poterie, coins at Maison de la Poterie.

Boussu-lez-Walcourt 11C3
Les Lacs de l'Eau d'Heure, Route de la Plate Taille.
GPS: n50,19265 e4,37958.

20 € 10 Chfree. **Surface:** asphalted. 01/01-31/12.
Distance: on the spot on the spot on the spot on the spot.

Brugelette 11B2
Pairi Daiza, Domaine de Cambron. **GPS:** n50,58892 e3,88670.

€ 7. **Surface:** gravel/sand. 01/04-31/10.
Remarks: Max. 1 night.

Tourist information Brugelette:
Parc Paradisio, Domaine de Cambron. Park with bird paradise and monkey island. 26/03-06/11 10-18.

Chimay 11B3
Communal de Chimay, Allée des Princes 1. **GPS:** n50,04557 e4,30956.
7 € 5 Ch included.
Surface: grassy/metalled. 01/01-31/12.
Distance: on the spot 300m 200m.

Chimay 11B3
Place Froissart. **GPS:** n50,04728 e4,31307.
. 01/01-31/12.

Chimay 11B3
Place Léopold. **GPS:** n50,04747 e4,31784.
. 01/01-31/12 Fri.

Dottignies 11A2
Rue des Écoles. **GPS:** n50,72821 e3,30011.

4 free free. **Surface:** asphalted. 01/01-31/12.
Distance: 500m 1,3km.
Remarks: Square behind fire-station.

Ecaussines 11B2
Château de la Folie, Rue de la Folie. **GPS:** n50,57443 e4,17851.
free. 01/01-31/12.
Distance: 800m.

Ecaussines 11B2
Eglise Sainte Aldegonde, Rue Jacquemart Boulle 28, Ecaussines-Lalaing. **GPS:** n50,57085 e4,18107.
free. 01/01-31/12.
Distance: 500m.

Fleurus 11C2
Parking Gare, Avenue de la Gare. **GPS:** n50,48215 e4,54433.
. 01/01-31/12.

Fleurus 11C2
Stade Communal, Rue de Fleurjoux. **GPS:** n50,47852 e4,55237.

free. 01/01-31/12.

Harchies 11B2
Place du Rivage. **GPS:** n50,47106 e3,69619.
. 01/01-31/12.

Hornu 11B2
Le Site du Grand Hornu, Rue Sainte-Louise 82.
GPS: n50,43488 e3,83707.

free. 01/01-31/12.
Distance: 1km.

Tourist information Hornu:
Grand-Hornu. Old industrial mining complex, a remarkable reminder of the Industrial Revolution. Tue-Fri 10-18h. € 8.

Houdeng Aimeries 11B2
Musée de la Mine de Bois-du-Luc, Rue Saint-Patrice.
GPS: n50,47081 e4,14952.
free. 01/01-31/12.

La Louvière 11B2
Boulevard de Roi Baudouin. **GPS:** n50,46619 e4,19055.
10 free. 01/01-31/12.
Remarks: P Station Sud.

Tourist information La Louvière:
Ascenseur Funiculaire de Strépy-Thieu, Strépy-Bracquegnies. Draw-works, 19th century. 01/02-27/11 9.30-18.30.
Rue du Marché. Sa 8-13h.

Le Roeulx 11B2
Grand Place. **GPS:** n50,50019 e4,10919.
. 01/01-31/12.

Le Roeulx 11B2
Place de la Chapelle. **GPS:** n50,50294 e4,10874.
. 01/01-31/12.
Distance: 100m.
Remarks: Next to church.

Le Roeulx 11B2
Place de la Tannée. **GPS:** n50,50339 e4,10819.
.

Le Roeulx 11B2
Place du Château. **GPS:** n50,50406 e4,11024.
. 01/01-31/12.
Remarks: Parking at castle.

Leers Noord 11A2
La Maison du Canal, Rue du Canal 6. **GPS:** n50,69089 e3,25728.

3 free Chfree.
Location: Rural, quiet. **Surface:** gravel. 01/01-31/12.
Distance: on the spot on the spot on the spot on the spot.
Remarks: Tarerne closed on Monday.

Lessines 11B2
Rue des 4 fils Aymon. **GPS:** n50,71280 e3,83403.
free. **Location:** Quiet. **Surface:** unpaved. 01/01-31/12.
Distance: 400m on the spot on the spot.

Marchienne-au-Pont 11C3
Musée d'Histoire et d'Archéologie Industrielle, 134 rue de la Providence. **GPS:** n50,41301 e4,40450.
free. 01/01-31/12.
Remarks: In front of museum.

Morlanwelz-Mariemont 11B2
Musée Alex Louis Martin, Place de Carnières, 52, Carnières.
GPS: n50,44402 e4,25416.
10 free. 01/01-31/12.

Mouscron 11A2
Musée du Folklore, Rue des Brasseurs, 3. **GPS:** n50,74217 e3,21795.
free.
01/01-31/12.
Remarks: Possibility make a reservation tel 02.56.33.23.36.

Péruwelz 11A2
Port de plaisance, Rue de la Boitérie. **GPS:** n50,51864 e3,60904.
10 € 6 WC .
Surface: asphalted/gravel. 01/02-30/11.

Quaregnon 11B2
La Grand Place. **GPS:** n50,44369 e3,86428.
2 . 01/01-31/12.

Quevaucamps 11B2
Musée de la Bonneterie, Rue Paul Pastur.
GPS: n50,52671 e3,68776.

2 free. 01/01-31/12.
Remarks: Parking in front of museum, via N527.

Ronquières 11B2
Grande tour et promenade en Bateau Mouche, Rue Rosemont.
GPS: n50,60636 e4,22249.

BE

20 free. 01/01-31/12.
Distance: on the spot on the spot.

Sivry 11B3

Observatoire de Sivry, Route de Mons 52. **GPS**: n50,17897 e4,22646.
2 . 01/01-31/12.
Remarks: Centre for nature studies.

Solre-Sur-Sambre 11B3

Château-Fort, Rue du Chateau Fort. **GPS**: n50,30918 e4,15585.
free. 01/01-31/12.
Remarks: At castle.

Thieu/Strepy 11B2

Rue Saint-Géry. **GPS**: n50,47156 e4,09069.
+10 free. **Surface:** metalled. 01/01-31/12.
Distance: on the spot on the spot on the spot.

Thuin 11B3

Drève des Alliés. **GPS**: n50,33951 e4,29860.
. 01/01-31/12.
Remarks: Max. 24h.

Thuin 11B3

L'Abbaye d'Aulnes, Rue Vandervelde. **GPS**: n50,36592 e4,33324.
free. 01/01-31/12.
Remarks: Near abbey, max. 24h.

Thuin 11B3

Place du Chapitre. **GPS**: n50,33980 e4,28724.
. 01/01-31/12.
Remarks: Max. 24h.

Tournai/Doornik 11A2

Maison de la Culture, Avenue des Frères Rimbaud, Tournai (Tournai/Doornik). **GPS**: n50,60432 e3,38199.

15-20 free Ch free. **Surface:** metalled.
01/01-31/12.
Distance: 5 min walking 5 min walking 5 min walking on the spot.

Trazegnies 11B2

Place Albert I 32. **GPS**: n50,46248 e4,33025.
. 01/01-31/12.
Distance: 1,5km.
Remarks: Parking at castle.

Namur

Alle-sur-Semois 16C1

Recreatiecentrum Recrealle, restaurant les Pierres du Diable, Rue Léon Henrard 16. **GPS**: n49,84648 e4,97579.

10 free. **Location:** Rural, simple. **Surface:** unpaved.
01/01-31/12.
Distance: 700m on the spot fishing permit obligatory on the spot 700m.

Tourist information Alle-sur-Semois:

Recrealle. Canoe rent; departures for canoe and kayaks, fishing and swimming possibilities, bowling, tennis, play ground, restaurant.

Ave-et-Auffe 11D3

Le Roptai, Rue du Roptai 34. **GPS**: n50,11144 e5,13373.

10 € 15-20 Ch (10x)€ 3/24h WC included € 1 € 4 € 1/3h. **Location:** Rural, comfortable, quiet. **Surface:** grassy/gravel.
08/01-31/12.
Distance: 4km 2km 1km 5km 1km on the spot.
Remarks: Bread-service, Han 5km.

Bohan 16C1

Rue de Monts les Champs. **GPS**: n49,86918 e4,88628.
4 € 11,40 Ch . **Surface:** metalled. 01/01-31/12.
Distance: 600m 600m.

Han-Sur-Lesse 11D3

Rue de la Lesse. **GPS**: n50,12751 e5,18819.

40 € 7,50-11 Ch WC included. **Location:** Urban.
Surface: asphalted. 01/01-31/12. **Distance:** 300m 200m 200m on the spot. **Remarks:** Parking nearby caves and centre.

Tourist information Han-Sur-Lesse:

Tourist centre around the caves.

Grottes de Han. Caves, son-et-lumière and boat trip on underground river. 01/04-31/10 10-16/18h, 01/11-31/03 11.30-16h.

Réserve d'Animaux. European animals alive today and those which lived previously in this area. 01/03-31/12 10-17h, 01/07-31/08 9.30-18h.

Hogne 11D3

Aire del Foy, 16 rue de Serinchamps. **GPS**: n50,24981 e5,27933.
25 € 5-10 Ch 16Amp WC .
Surface: grassy. 01/03-31/10.
Distance: on the spot.

Mariembourg 11C3

Brasserie des Fagnes, 26, route de Nismes. **GPS**: n50,08403 e4,52377.
20 guests free. **Surface:** grassy/gravel. 01/01-31/12.
Distance: 3km on the spot.

Namur 11C2

Tabora, Place André Ryckmans.
GPS: n50,46770 e4,85056.

8 free Ch € 7,50. **Surface:** asphalted. 01/01-31/12.
Distance: 1km 1km 1km 200m.
Remarks: Behind gymnasium.

Nismes 11C3

Rue Longue. **GPS**: n50,07387 e4,54863.

± 8 € 5 € 2/100liter Ch € 2/h.
Surface: asphalted. 01/01-31/12.
Distance: on the spot 100m bakery 100m on the spot on the spot.
Remarks: Coins at tourist info.

Profondeville 11C3

Chaussée de Namur. **GPS**: n50,37644 e4,87106.

4 free. **Surface:** asphalted. 01/01-31/12.
Distance: 50m 150m 50m.
Remarks: Max. 24h.

Rochefort 11D3

Route de Marche. **GPS**: n50,15800 e5,22639.

10 free. **Location:** Urban, simple. **Surface:** metalled.
01/01-31/12.
Distance: 200m 200m 200m.

Saint-Hubert 11D3

Chemin des Etangs/ Rue de Lavaux. **GPS**: n50,02689 e5,38088.

3 free Ch free. **Location:** Urban, simple. **Surface:** gravel.
01/01-31/12.
Distance: 500m 500m 500m on the spot on the spot.
Remarks: Max. 48h, 10 parking places tolerated, European campital of hunting, events: 1st weekend September and November 1st Saint Hubert.

Saint-Hubert 11D3

Fourneau Saint Michel, Rue Saint Hubert.
GPS: n50,08480 e5,33902.

10 free Ch free (4x)€ 1/h. **Location:** Rural, simple.
Surface: asphalted/grassy. 01/01-31/12.
Distance: St Hubert 9km 200m on the spot.

BE

Remarks: At open air museum from Fourneau Saint-Michel.

S Treignes 11C3

Rue de la Gare. **GPS**: n50,09085 e4,68182.

3 free € 2 Ch € 2. **Surface:** gravel. 01/01-31/12.
Distance: 900m.
Remarks: At former station, coins at tourist info Nismes, steam train museum.

Luxembourg

S Arlon 16E1

Casserne Callemeyn, Drève des Espagnols, N882.
GPS: n49,68990 e5,81929.

5 free.
Location: Urban, simple. **Surface:** asphalted. 01/01-31/12.
Distance: 600m 5,8km.
Remarks: At fire-station.

Tourist information Arlon:
Parc Archéologique, Rue des Thermes. Archeological site. 9-12h, 14-17h.
Flea market. 01/03-31/10 1st Su of the month 7-19h.

S Barvaux 11D3

Petit Barvaux. **GPS**: n50,35223 e5,49501.

20 € 10/24h € 2 Ch.
Surface: grasstiles.
01/01-31/12.
Distance: 300m Delhaize 50m Ravel-route on the spot.
Remarks: Along the Ourthe river, max. 24h, coins at tourist info.

Tourist information Barvaux:
Labyrinthus, Rue Basse Commene. Labyrinth park. Jul/Aug 10-19h, Sep 11-17h.
Domaine de Hottemme. Nature reserve with visitor centre. 10.30-17h, summer 10.30-18h. € 2.

S Bastogne 11D3

Avenue Albert I. **GPS**: n49,99825 e5,71526.

10 free free. **Location:** Urban, simple, central.
Surface: asphalted. 01/01-31/12.
Distance: 300m 3km 300m 300m.

S Bouillon 16C1

Parking du stade, Rue de la Poulie. **GPS**: n49,79106 e5,05767.

10 free Ch € 1/kWh.
Surface: gravel. 01/01-31/12.
Distance: 1,3km 1,3km 1,5km.
Remarks: Max. 24h, coins at tourist info.

S Durbuy 11D3

P Mobilhome Le Vedeur, Rue Fond de Vedeur.
GPS: n50,35780 e5,45672.

50 € 21, 2 pers.incl Ch WC included.
Location: Comfortable. **Surface:** gravel. 01/01-31/12.
Distance: 750m on the spot fishing permit obligatory 750m 750m on the spot.

Tourist information Durbuy:
Confiturerie Saint Amour, Rue St Amour 13. Production of traditional products. 10-18h 01/10-31/03 Mo. free.
Diamour, Rue de la Prevoté 2. Centre of diamonds and goldsmithing. 10.30-19.30h Tue-Wed. free.
Parc des Topiaires, Rue Haie Himbe. Model garden. 10-18h 01/01-31/01. € 4,50.
Antiques and flea market. 01/03-30/09, 9-17h, 2nd Sa of the month.

S Herbeumont 16D1

Avenue de Combattants. **GPS**: n49,77729 e5,23700.

50 free Chfree.
Location: Rural. **Surface:** asphalted/grassy.
01/01-31/12.
Distance: 500m 500m.
Remarks: Parking of old station.

Tourist information Herbeumont:
Royal Syndicat d'Initiative, Avenue des Combattants, 7, www.herbeumont.be. Beautiful position in the Ardennes landscape. Ruins of medieval castle, free entry.
Au cœur de l'Ardoise, Rue du Babinay 1, Bertrix. Slate mine. sa-su 10-18h, wed 14h. € 9,50.

S Hotton 11D3

Haie Notre Dame. **GPS**: n50,26937 e5,45738.
6 € 10 Ch. **Surface:** asphalted. 01/01-31/12.
Distance: 800m 800m RAVeL.
Remarks: At cemetery.

Tourist information Hotton:
Grottes de Hotton, Chemin du spéléoclub 1. Caves. 01/04-31/10 10-17h, 01/07-31/08 10-18h.

La Roche-en-Ardenne 11D3

Mâboge. **GPS**: n50,16749 e5,62597.
50 free. **Surface:** grassy. 01/01-31/12.
Distance: on the spot on the spot.
Remarks: Along river, max. 24h.

La Roche-en-Ardenne 11D3

Rue du Harzé. **GPS**: n50,19075 e5,57432.

5 free. **Location:** Urban, simple. **Surface:** asphalted.
01/01-31/12.
Distance: 500m 500m 500m on the spot.
Remarks: Parking at sports park..

Nisramont 11D3

Barrage de Nisramont, Rue de barrage. **GPS**: n50,14089 e5,67118.

10 free. **Location:** Simple, isolated, quiet. **Surface:** metalled.
01/01-31/12.
Distance: 3,7km 15km on the spot on the spot on the spot on the spot. **Remarks:** At artificial lake.

S Poupehan 16C1

Rue du Pont. **GPS**: n49,80886 e5,00418.

20 free Chfree. **Location:** Rural, simple, quiet.
Surface: gravel. 01/01-31/12.
Distance: on the spot on the spot 200m 300m on the spot on the spot.
Remarks: Along the Semois river, next to sports fields, max. 24h, canoe rental.

Redu 11D3

Rue de Saint Hubert. **GPS**: n50,00877 e5,16348.

10 free. **Location:** Rural, simple. **Surface:** gravel.
01/01-31/12. **Distance:** on the spot.

S Rochehaut 16C1

Le Palis, Le Routi 25. **GPS**: n49,84156 e5,01073.

39 € 12-15 Ch (39x)included. **Location:** Rural.
Surface: grassy/metalled. 01/01-31/12.
Distance: 100m 500m 100m 100m 300m on the spot on the spot.
Remarks: Video surveillance.

BE

Switzerland

Capital: Bern
Government: Direct democracy, Federal republic
Official Language: German, French, Italian, Romansh
Population: 8,179,294 (2016)
Area: 41,284 km^2

General information
Dialling code: 0041
General emergency: 112
Currency: Swiss franc (CHF)
CHF 1 = € 0,87, € 1 = CHF 1,16
CHF 1 = £0.76, £1 = CHF 1,32 (October 2017)

Regulations for overnight stays
Overnight parking is allowed, max 15 hours.

Additional public holidays 2018
May 31 Corpus Christi
August 1 National Day

Time Zone
Winter (Standard Time) GMT+1
Summer (DST) GMT+2

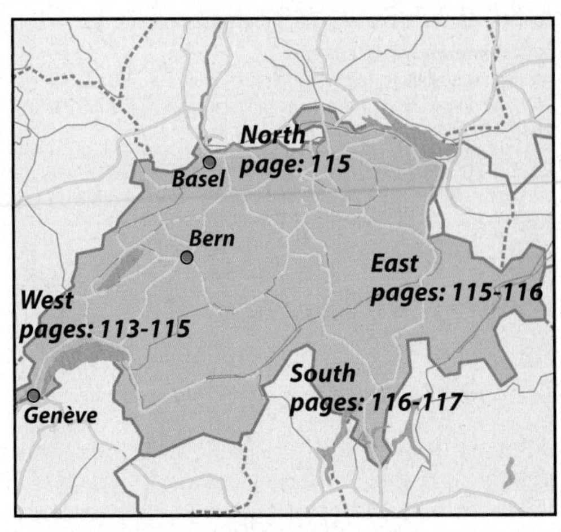

Switzerland West

Aeschi 22G1
Panorama, Scheidgasse 272. **GPS**: n46,65399 e7,70070.
50 CHF 22,40-31,20 Ch WC. 15/05-15/10.

Avenches 22F1
Port-Plage. **GPS**: n46,90351 e7,04918.
300 CHF 45 Ch WC. 01/04-01/10.

Boltigen 22G1
Jaunpass. **GPS**: n46,59208 e7,33758.
117 Ch WC. 01/01-31/12.

Böningen 22H1
Seeblick, Campingstrasse 14. **GPS**: n46,68987 e7,89398.
105 CHF 41,80 Ch WC. Easter-01/10.

Brienz 22H1
Aaregg. **GPS**: n46,74859 e8,04957.
180 CHF 30-45 Ch WC.
24/03-31/10.
Tourist information Brienz:
Alpen Region Brienz-Meiringen-Hasliberg, Bahnhofstrasse 22, Meiringen, www.alpenregion.ch. Village of wood-cutters.
during school hours 01/07-31/08.
Brienz Rothorn Bahn. Steam rack-railway.
01/06-31/10 8.45h.
CHF 57-88.
Freilichtmuseum Ballenberg. Open air museum.
15/04-31/10 10-17h.

Bullet 22F1
Restaurant Les Cluds, Les Cluds. **GPS**: n46,84248 e6,55991.

4 CHF 10 Ch (4x)included.
Location: Rural, simple, isolated, quiet. **Surface:** asphalted.
01/01-31/12 Restaurant: Mo.
Distance: on the spot on the spot on the spot.
Remarks: Max. 2 nights, pay at restaurant.

Burgdorf 19G3
Waldegg, Waldeggweg. **GPS**: n47,05407 e7,62895.
CHF 28-31,50 Ch WC. 01/04-31/10.

Château-d'Oex 22G2
Le Berceau. **GPS**: n46,46673 e7,12529.
70 CHF 38,50 Ch WC. 01/01-31/12.

Delémont 19G3
Place de Parc Gros-Pré Monsieur, Route de Porrentruy.
GPS: n47,36289 e7,34008.

10 free Ch free. **Surface:** gravel. 01/01-31/12.
Distance: 200m.

Dürrenroth 19G3
Reisemobilstellplatz Blueberry Hill, Brunnen 54.
GPS: n47,06563 e7,76553.

5 CHF 10 CHF 2. **Location:** Rural, comfortable, quiet.
Surface: gravel. 01/01-31/12.
Distance: Dürrenroth 3,5km on the spot on the spot.
Remarks: Panoramic view.

Echallens 22F1
Chemin du Pont. **GPS**: n46,63945 e6,64096.

5 free Ch free.
Location: Rural, simple. **Surface:** asphalted. 01/01-31/12.
Distance: 700m 300m 700m.
Remarks: Max. 1 night.

Estavayer-le-Lac 22F1
Nouvelle-Plage. **GPS**: n46,85602 e6,84801.
30 CHF 27-46,60 Ch WC. 01/04-01/11.

Frutigen 22G1
Grassi. **GPS**: n46,58178 e7,64213.
68 CHF 26 Ch. 01/01-31/12.

Gampelen 22F1
Fanel, Seestraße. **GPS**: n47,00154 e7,03957.
CHF 42-52 Ch. 24/03-09/10.

Grandson 22F1
Le Pécos, Chemin du Pécos 3. **GPS**: n46,80371 e6,63575.
4 CHF 26 Ch WC. 01/04-01/10.
Remarks: Next to campsite.

Grindelwald 22H1
Eigernordwand. **GPS**: n46,62135 e8,01683.
CHF 34 Ch.
01/01-31/12.
Tourist information Grindelwald:
Jungfraubahn. Train journey to the highest train station of Europe.

Gryon 22G2
Place de la Barboleuse. **GPS**: n46,28222 e7,07028.

4 CHF 2,80/pp, Summer CHF 5,30/pp Ch (4x)CHF 5.
Location: Rural, simple, quiet. **Surface:** asphalted.
01/01-31/12.
Distance: 200m 3,5km on the spot 100m.
Remarks: To be paid at office de tourisme.

Gstaad 22G2
Bellerive. **GPS**: n46,48106 e7,27328.
CHF 27,50-30 Ch. 01/01-31/12.

Gwatt-Thun 22G1
Betllereiche. **GPS**: n46,72749 e7,62760.
CHF 42-62 Ch WC. 24/03-09/10.

Häusernmoos 19G3
Restaurant Koi-Gartenteich, Huttwilstrasse 22.
GPS: n47,07890 e7,74935.
4 CHF 10, overnight stay free Ch CHF 4 included, at restaurant. 01/01-31/12 Restaurant: Mo-Tue.
Distance: on the spot 2km.

Hinterkappelen 22G1
Kappelenbrucke, Wohlenstrasse 62. **GPS**: n46,96433 e7,38361.
70 Ch WC. 01/01-31/12.

Huttwil 19H3
FLYER Stellplatz, Schwende 1. **GPS**: n47,11527 e7,86795.

16 free Ch free.
Location: Rural. **Surface:** gravel. 01/01-31/12.
Distance: 500m.
Remarks: E-bike factory, guided tour Tuesdays 14.30h.

Interlaken 22H1
Hobby, Lehnweg 16. **GPS**: n46,68424 e7,83022.
80 CHF 29,40-40 Ch WC. 01/04-30/09.

Interlaken 22H1
Lazy-Rancho, Lehnweg 6. **GPS**: n46,68583 e7,83095.

CH

90 CHF 33-51 Ch WC . Easter-01/10.

Tourist information Interlaken:

Heimwehfluhbahn. Telpher carrier from 1906. 24/03-23/10 10-17. JungfrauPark. Attractions and themepark. 01/05-23/10 11-18u 25/12-01/01.

S La Brévine 22F1

Les Varodes. **GPS**: n46,97195 e6,58860.

10 free Ch (2x)WCfree. **Location:** Rural, simple, isolated, quiet. **Surface:** asphalted. 01/01-31/12.
Distance: 3km on the spot 1,5km on the spot on the spot on the spot.
Remarks: Parking at Lac des Tailleres.

S La Chaux-de-Fonds 19F3

Bois du Couvent. **GPS**: n47,09334 e6,83593.

2 free Ch (4x)free. **Location:** Rural, simple.
Surface: gravel. 01/05-30/09.
Distance: 1,3km 350m 700m on the spot.
Remarks: In front of campsite du Bois du Couvent.

Tourist information La Chaux-de-Fonds:

Tourisme neuchâtelois - Montagnes, Espacité 1, Place Le Corbusier. Capital of the clock industry.

Musée International d'Horlogerie, Rue des Musée 29. Watch museum. 10-17h Mo, 25/12-01/01.

Musée paysan et artisanal, Rue des Crêtets 148. The farmers' life and old crafts industry. 01/04-31/10 14-17h, 01/11-28/02 Wed, Sa, Su 14-17h Mo, 01/03-31/03.

S Langenthal 19G3

Lexa-Wohnmobile, Bern-Zürichstrasse 49b.
GPS: n47,22461 e7,77944.

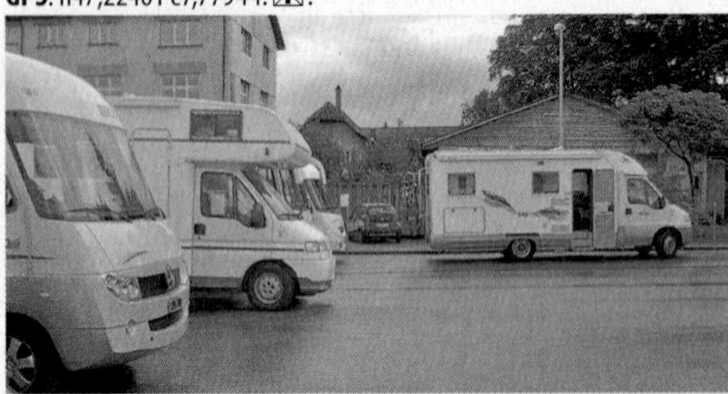

5 free Ch free. **Surface:** asphalted. 01/01-31/12.
Distance: 2km.
Remarks: At motorhome dealer.

S Lausanne 22F2

Vidy, Chemin du Camping 3. **GPS**: n46,51734 e6,59777.

10 CHF 23,60 or € 20 Ch WC included CHF 4,35/4h **Location:** Urban, simple, central. **Surface:** grassy/metalled.
01/01-31/12.
Distance: on the spot on the spot.
Remarks: Next to campsite the Vidy, pay at reception, service passerby CHF 3, free bus to centre.

Tourist information Lausanne:

Lausanne Tourisme, Avenue de Rhodanie 2, www.lausanne-tourisme.ch. Parking at the port, rack-railway to city centre.

Musée Olympique, Quai d'Ouchy 1. All about the Olympic games. 01/05-14/10 9-18h, 14/10-30/04 10-18h Mo, 01/10-30/04.

S Lauterbrunnen 22H1

Jungfrau. **GPS**: n46,58834 e7,90882.
CHF 42,80 Ch WC . 01/01-31/12.

S Lauterbrunnen 22H1

Schützenbach. **GPS**: n46,59047 e7,91194.
Ch WC . 01/01-31/12.

Tourist information Lauterbrunnen:

Jungfraubahn, Grindelwald. Train journey to the highest train station of Europe.

Klöppelstube, Altes Schulhaus. Making of bobbin lace. Fri 13.30-16.30h. free.

Trümmelbachfälle, Lauterbrunnen dir Stechelberg. Underground waterfalls. 01/04-30/11 9-17h.

S Le Landeron 19F3

Camp des Pêches. **GPS**: n47,05257 e7,06993.
CHF 38 Ch WC . 01/04-15/10.

Tourist information Le Landeron:

Restaurant Le Carnotzet, Rue de la Gare 22. Restaurant with regional specialities. Tue-Sa 11-14h, 17-23h Mo, Su.

S Les Ponts-de-Martel 22F1

Rue du Bugnon. **GPS**: n46,99644 e6,73065.

3 free Ch (2x)free. **Location:** Rural, simple.
Surface: asphalted. 01/01-31/12.
Distance: 600m 700m.
Remarks: At community centre.

S Malvilliers 22F1

Hotel-Restaurant La Croisée, Route de Neuchâtel.
GPS: n47,03200 e6,86779.

5 CHF5 Ch (4x)included. **Location:** Simple, noisy.
Surface: asphalted. 01/01-31/12.
Distance: 100m on the spot.

S Meiringen 22H1

Alpencamping, Brüningstrasse 46. **GPS**: n46,73448 e8,17122.
8 CHF 27,90 Ch WC included. **Surface:** grassy.
01/01-31/12.
Distance: 1km 1km.
Remarks: Max. 3 nights.

S Morges 22F2

Le Petit Bois. **GPS**: n46,50446 e6,48894.
170 CHF 56 Ch WC . 01/04-01/10.
Remarks: Service at entrance campsite.

S Moutier 19G3

Chemin de la Piscine. **GPS**: n47,27365 e7,37923.

5 free Ch free. **Location:** Urban, simple, quiet.
Surface: asphalted. 01/01-31/12.
Distance: 1km.
Remarks: At swimming pool.

Murten 22G1

Lac de Morat, Ryf. **GPS**: n46,93240 e7,11967.

30 CHF 1/h, overnight stay free. **Location:** Urban, simple, central.
Surface: grasstiles. 01/01-31/12.
Distance: on the spot on the spot on the spot.

S Neuchâtel 22F1

Route des Falaises. **GPS**: n47,00145 e6,95735.

8 free Ch (4x)free. **Location:** Simple, noisy.
Surface: grasstiles.
01/01-31/12.
Distance: city centre 2km 300m 100m.
Remarks: Max. 2 days, max. 7m.

Tourist information Neuchâtel:

Le Creux-du-Van, Val-de-Travers. Nature reserve. 01/01-31/12.

S Oberburg 19G3

Reisemobilstellplätze Kürbishof, Krauchthalstrasse 40.
GPS: n47,03807 e7,62079.
5 CHF 13 or € 9 Ch WC against payment.
01/01-31/12. **Distance:** 600m 300m.
Remarks: Payment also in euros.

S Payerne 22F1

Place de la Concorde. **GPS**: n46,81976 e6,93757.

2 free Ch (2x)free. **Location:** Urban, simple, central, noisy. **Surface:** asphalted. 01/01-31/12.
Distance: on the spot on the spot on the spot.

S Portalban 22F1

Route du Port. **GPS**: n46,92131 e6,95614.

CH

25 CHF 20, 2 pers.incl Ch (30x) WC included.
Location: Rural, simple. **Surface:** grasstiles.
01/01-31/12.
Distance: on the spot 200m on the spot on the spot.
Remarks: In harbour, near campsite, check in at reception.

Prêles 19G3

Prêles, Route de la Neuveville 61. **GPS**: n47,08569 e7,11714.
CHF 37,50 Ch WC. 01/04-15/10.

Rolle 22E2

Camping de Rolle Aux Vernes, Chemin de la Plage.
GPS: n46,46191 e6,34630.
5 CHF 18-30 + CHF 8,50-10/pp tourist tax CHF 3.
Surface: asphalted. 01/03-01/10.
Distance: 500m.
Remarks: Max. 48h.

Romont 22F1

Promenade des Avoines. **GPS**: n46,69753 e6,91774.

2 CHF 1,35 tourist tax Ch (4x)free.
Location: Rural, simple, noisy. **Surface:** grasstiles.
01/01-31/12.
Distance: on the spot 100m 700m.
Remarks: Max. 24h.

Saignelégier 19F3

Chemin de la Tuilerie. **GPS**: n47,25223 e7,00347.

10 free Ch free. **Location:** Rural, simple, noisy.
Surface: grasstiles. 01/01-31/12.
Distance: 700m on the spot 200m.

Saint Blaise 22F1

Chemin des Pêcheurs. **GPS**: n47,01139 e6,98778.

12 CHF 16/24h Ch (4x) WC included.
Location: Urban, simple, central, noisy. **Surface:** asphalted.
01/01-31/12.
Distance: Neuchâtel 5km 300m 250m 500m 600m.

Saint-Aubin 22F1

Port de St-Aubin-Sauges. **GPS**: n46,89181 e6,77427.

10 CHF 20 Ch (6x) WC included.
Location: Simple, quiet. **Surface:** asphalted. 01/01-31/12.
Distance: 600m on the spot on the spot 400m 400m.
Remarks: Parking port, nearby the capitainerie.

Sainte-Croix 22F1

Grand-Rue, L'Auberson. **GPS**: n46,82019 e6,47230.

4 free Ch (4x)free. **Location:** Rural, simple.
Surface: asphalted. 01/01-31/12.
Distance: 2km on the spot 3km.

Satigny 22E2

Bois de Bay, Route du Bois-de-Bay 19. **GPS**: n46,20087 e6,06619.
Ch WC. 01/01-31/12.

Vesenaz 22E2

Pointe a la Bise. **GPS**: n46,24517 e6,19331.
105 CHF 62 Ch WC. 28/03-05/10.

Zweisimmen 22G1

Vermeille, Eygässli 2. **GPS**: n46,56265 e7,37766.
25 CHF 24,80-30,30 Ch. 01/01-31/12.

Switzerland North

Altikon 20A2

Stellplatz auf dem Bauernhof, Feldistrasse 18.
GPS: n47,57337 e8,78391.
3 CHF 10 CHF 1 Ch CHF 4 CHF 2. **Surface:** metalled.
01/01-31/12.
Distance: 200m 200m.
Remarks: Max. 48h.

Brunnen 23A1

Hopfraeben. **GPS**: n46,99700 e8,59300.
40 CHF 23-39 Ch WC. 01/05-01/10.

Engelberg 22H1

Eienwäldli, Wasserfallstraße 108. **GPS**: n46,81009 e8,42243.
130 CHF 28-36 Ch WC. 01/01-31/12.

Giswil 22H1

Stellplatz an der Kirche, Panoramastrasse. **GPS**: n46,83230 e8,17900.
3 free. **Surface:** asphalted. 01/01-31/12.
Distance: on the spot on the spot on the spot.
Remarks: Max. 1 night.

Hemmiken 19H3

Stellplatz Bauernhof, Asphof 50. **GPS**: n47,49682 e7,88749.
3 CHF 20 Ch. **Location:** Isolated, quiet.
Surface: unpaved. 01/01-31/12.
Distance: 1,4km.

Horw 22H1

Steinibachried. **GPS**: n47,01100 e8,31100.
CHF 38-50 Ch. 24/03-09/10.

Reinach 19G3

Waldhort, Heideweg 16. **GPS**: n47,49923 e7,60296.
CHF 36 Ch WC. 04/03-28/10.

Weggis 19H3

Bauernhof Gerberweid, Eichistrasse 2. **GPS**: n47,03888 e8,41446.

15 CHF 6-10 + CHF 6/pp + CHF 2,70/pp tourist tax CHF 1 Ch
CHF 3 CHF 2. **Surface:** grassy. 01/04-15/10.
Distance: 2km 1km 1km 500m on the spot.

Willisau 19H3

Bisangmatt. **GPS**: n47,11937 e7,99829.

4 CHF 5 (4x)included. **Surface:** metalled. 01/01-31/12.
Distance: 800m 800m 800m.
Remarks: At fire-station.

Zug 20A3

Zugersee, Chamer Fussweg 36. **GPS**: n47,17758 e8,49358.
CHF 40 Ch WC. 24/03-09/10.
Remarks: Max. ^3.17m.

Switzerland East

Altstätten 20B3

Gasthausziel, Trogenerstrasse 99. **GPS**: n47,38892 e9,53457.
6 CHF 10, guests free Ch CHF 5/day.
01/01-31/12 Wed-Thu.
Distance: 3km on the spot.

Andeer 23B1

Sut Baselgia. **GPS**: n46,60651 e9,42630.
CHF 30 Ch WC. 01/01-31/12.

Appenzell 20B3

Restaurant Eggli, Egglistrasse. **GPS**: n47,32104 e9,46565.
10 guests free Ch.
Surface: asphalted. 01/01-31/12.
Remarks: The most beautiful panorama of Appenzell.

Bivio 23B2

Wohnmobil-Stellplatz Tua. **GPS**: n46,46304 e9,65597.

20 CHF 10-15 + CHF 2,50/pp tourist tax Ch CHF 7/day.
Location: Isolated, quiet. **Surface:** grasstiles.
01/01-31/12.
Distance: Savognin 18km on the spot Savognin 18km on the spot.
Remarks: Parking ski-lifts.

Breil/Brigels 23A1

Wohnmobil-Stellplatz Brigels. **GPS**: n46,77104 e9,06770.

20 CHF 25 CHF 2/50liter Ch CHF 3/day.
Surface: metalled. 01/01-31/12.

CH

Distance: 600m on the spot Imbiss on the spot, restaurants 600m 600m on the spot on the spot nearby.
Remarks: At Brigeler See.

Chur 23B1
Stellplätze Camp Au, Felsenaustrasse 61. **GPS**: n46,86187 e9,50756.
CHF 15 + CHF 1,20/pp tourist tax Ch WC.
01/01-31/12.
Distance: 3km 2km on the spot on the spot.
Remarks: Max. 1 night, oldest city of Switzerland.

Churwalden 23B1
Pradafenz, Girabodawag 34. **GPS**: n46,77690 e9,54121.
50 CHF 35,60 Ch WC. 01/01-31/12.

Davos 23C1
Rinerlodge Talstation, Landwasserstrasse.
GPS: n46,74150 e9,77814.
10 CHF 26-32 Ch CHF 2.
Surface: gravel.
01/01-31/12.
Distance: 1km on the spot on the spot on the spot on the spot.
Remarks: Max. 24h.

Tourist information Davos:
Davos Alpengarten. Botanical garden. 01/05-30/09 9-17h.
Berghaus Stafelalp, Frauenkirch. 250 Year old inn where they still cook on a wood oven and shimmer paraffin lamps are lit.

Elm 23B1
Sportbahnen Elm, Schiesserblock. **GPS**: n46,91332 e9,16228.
50 free. **Surface:** metalled. 01/03-30/11.
Distance: 650m 650m on the spot on the spot.

Eschenz 20A2
Hüttenberg. **GPS**: n47,64436 e8,85935.
8 CHF 20 Ch WC included.
Location: Rural. **Surface:** grassy/metalled.
01/01-31/12.
Remarks: 01/04-31/10 Quickstop >19h <10h, payment also in euros.

Kreuzlingen 20B2
Fischerhaus, Promenadestraße 52. **GPS**: n47,64745 e9,19898.
CHF 41-51 Ch WC. 23/03-16/10.

Neuhausen 20A2
Parkplatz Fischacker, Nohlstrasse. **GPS**: n47,67373 e8,60866.

50 first hour CHF 5, than CHF 2/h Ch WC.
Surface: grassy/metalled. 01/01-31/12.
Distance: 200m on the spot 200m 1km.

Tourist information Neuhausen:
Der Rheinfall. Water falls.

Pontresina 23C2
Plauns. **GPS**: n46,46200 e9,93400.
Ch. 01/06-15/10, 15/12-15/04.

Samnaun 20C3
Wohnmobilstellplatz Samnaun-Ravaisch, Sportplatzweg 13.
GPS: n46,94906 e10,36705.

18 CHF 13-38/day, CHF 6/pp Ch WC included.
01/01-31/12.
Distance: 750m 200m on the spot.
Remarks: At football ground, bread-service.

Sankt Gallen 20B3
Paul-Grüninger-Stadion, Grütlistrasse. **GPS**: n47,43361 e9,40464.
2 CHF 2/9-19h, CHF 1/19-8h CHF 1/100liter CHF 0,50/kWh.
Surface: asphalted. 01/01-31/12.

Distance: 2km 300m.
Remarks: Next to sports fields.

Sankt Moritz 23C1
Olympiaschanze. **GPS**: n46,47800 e9,82600.
125 CHF 45 Ch WC. 20/05-03/10.

Tourist information Sankt Moritz:
Clean Energy Tour. Hiking trail, nature, energy, climate and weather adventure. Sign up at Kur- und Verkehrsverein St. Moritz. 15/06-01/10 Wed 13.45h duration 2,5 hours.

Santa Maria Val Müstair 23D1
Hotel Stelvio, Via Veglia 107. **GPS**: n46,60123 e10,42226.
10 € 20 Ch. **Location:** Rural. **Surface:** metalled.
01/01-31/12.
Distance: on the spot on the spot on the spot on the spot on the spot.
Remarks: Max. 3 nights.

Savognin 23B1
Veia Sandeilas. **GPS**: n46,59660 e9,59226.
15 CHF 15 + CHF 8/pp CHF 1 Ch CHF 2,50.
Surface: gravel. 01/01-31/12.
Distance: 500m.
Remarks: Near the chair-lift, summer: parking at campsite Julia.

Schiers 20B3
Restaurant Prättigauerhof, Flurystrasse 19. **GPS**: n46,97034 e9,68752.
2 free, use of a meal obligated.
Surface: metalled. 01/01-31/12 Sa + Su.
Distance: 300m on the spot 100m.

Sent 23C1
Camping Sur En. **GPS**: n46,81852 e10,36596.
10 CHF 15 + CHF 2,50/pp tourist tax CHF 3.
Surface: grassy/gravel. 01/01-31/12.
Distance: on the spot.
Remarks: Max. 1 night, 17-10h.

Splügen 23B1
Auf dem Sand. **GPS**: n46,54922 e9,31399.
CHF 40 Ch WC. 01/01-31/12.

Steckborn 20A2
Wohnmobilplatz Steckborn, Schützengraben.
GPS: n47,66813 e8,98462.

8 CHF 12/24h Ch (8x)included.
Surface: gravel. 01/01-31/12.
Distance: 400m 200m 400m 300m.

Tinizong-Rona 23B1
Stellplatz Restaurant dalla Punt, Julierstrasse.
GPS: n46,56124 e9,62396.
20 CHF 20 Ch WC included.
Location: Comfortable, noisy. **Surface:** gravel. 01/01-31/12.
Distance: on the spot on the spot on the spot on the spot on the spot.

Unterwasser 20B3
Hotel Restaurant Post, Dorfstrasse 16. **GPS**: n47,19673 e9,30949.
8 CHF 15 + CHF 2,60/pp tourist tax, guests free Ch (6x).
Surface: asphalted. 01/01-31/12.
Distance: 300m on the spot 300m on the spot.

Vaduz/Liechtenstein 20B3
Rheinparkstadion, Rheindamm. **GPS**: n47,14022 e9,50945.

10 CHF 0,50/h, 19-7h free Ch WC free. **Surface:** asphalted.
01/01-31/12.
Distance: 1,8km on the spot.
Remarks: Along the Rhine river, parking near stadium, max. 24h.

Tourist information Vaduz/Liechtenstein:
Liechtenstein Tourismus, Städtle 37, www.vaduz.li. Monarchy on the Austrian-Swiss border.
Kunstmuseum Lichtenstein, Städtle 32. Tue-Su 10-17h.
Erlebniswelt Neuguthof, Neugutweg 30. Maize labyrinth with wild-west city. 15/06-30/09 Wed 13-18h, Sa-Su 10-20h, holidays Mo-Fri 10-20h, Sa-Su 10-22h.

Vals 23B1
Stellplatz Vals, Vallée. **GPS**: n46,60891 e9,17438.

9 CHF 17 + CHF 3,40/pp tourist tax WC included.
Surface: metalled. summer.
Distance: 300m on the spot 300m 300m on the spot.
Remarks: Parking funicular railway.

Zizers 23B1
K. Lüthi, Rappagugg. **GPS**: n46,91937 e9,56270.
5 free Ch. **Surface:** metalled. 01/01-31/12.
Distance: 1,6km on the spot.
Remarks: At motorhome dealer.

Zürich 20A3
Camping Zürich, Seestrasse 559. **GPS**: n47,33641 e8,53960.
01/01-31/12.

Tourist information Zürich:
Zürich Tourismus, Im Hauptbahnhof, www.zuerich.com. Historical city with large pedestrian area.

Switzerland South

Agno 23A3
Eurocampo, Via di Molinnazzo. **GPS**: n45,99556 e8,90621.
CHF 30-34 Ch WC. 01/04-31/10.

Avegno 23A2
Piccolo Paradiso, Via Cantonale 13. **GPS**: n46,20100 e8,74300.
280 CHF 27-46 Ch WC. 20/03-25/10.

Bellinzona 23A2
Centro Sportivo, Viale Giuseppe Motta. **GPS**: n46,20116 e9,01729.

7 CHF 20 CHF 1/20liter Ch.
Location: Noisy. **Surface:** asphalted. 01/01-31/12.
Distance: 1,5km 4km.
Remarks: Max. 48h.

Tourist information Bellinzona:
Castelgrande, Via Salita Castelgrande 18. 11-16h, Apr/Jun/Sep/Oct 10-18h, Jul/Aug 10-19h.
Castello di Montebello, Via Artore 4. 01/03-30/11 10-18h.
Castello di Sasso Corbaro. 01/04-30/11 10-18h.
Palestra di Roccia San Paolo, Palazo Civico. Climbing garden for beginners and experienced, 30.000^{2}m, 23 climbing trails.

Bouveret 22F2
Rive Bleue. **GPS**: n46,38645 e6,86041.
CHF 28,20-37,20 Ch WC. 25/03-16/10.

Brig 22H2
Brigerbad. **GPS**: n46,30209 e7,93102.
400 CHF 29-33 Ch WC. 30/04-02/11.

Champéry 22F2
Route de la Fin. **GPS**: n46,17592 e6,87076.

CH

6 CHF 18 + CHF 2,20/pp Ch (4x)included.
Location: Rural, simple. **Surface:** asphalted. 01/01-31/12.
Distance: 100m on the spot 200m 200m.
Remarks: Parking supermarket, nearby the télépherique.

S Claro 23A2

Swissvan, A Torascia 3. **GPS:** n46,24528 e9,02806.
6 € 18 Ch included.
Surface: gravel. 01/01-31/12.
Distance: 1km 1km 1km 300m on the spot.

S Evolène 22G2

Evolène. GPS: n46,11075 e7,49654.
CHF 29,40 Ch WC. 01/01-31/12.

S Gordevio 23A2

Bella Riva. GPS: n46,22159 e8,74194.
Ch WC. 01/04-01/10.

S Grimentz 22G2

Aire camping-car l'Ilôt Bosquet, Route de Moiry.
GPS: n46,17432 e7,57271.

20 CHF 15 Ch included.
Location: Rural, simple, quiet. **Surface:** unpaved. 01/01-31/12.
Distance: on the spot on the spot on the spot on the spot nearby nearby.
Remarks: Pay and coins at tourist office, public transport, free entrance swimming pool (summer).

Tourist information Grimentz:
Grimentz/St.Jean Tourisme, www.grimentz.ch. Many signposted cycle and hiking routes.
La Maison bourgeoisiale. Life of the citizens of Grimentz. guided tour Mo. free.

S Grimselpas 22H1

Berghotel Grimselblick, Grimselpasshöhe.
GPS: n46,56115 e8,33673.
20 CHF 20, guests free. **Location:** Rural. **Surface:** asphalted.
14/06-31/10.
Distance: on the spot.
Remarks: Service at hotel.

Hérémence 22G2

Val des Hérémence, Parking B,C,D en E, Le Chargeur.
GPS: n46,08882 e7,40362.

15 free. **Surface:** unpaved. 01/01-31/12.
Remarks: At artificial lake.

S La Fouly 22G3

Les Glaciers. GPS: n45,93351 e7,09361.
Ch WC. 15/05-30/09.

S Les Haudères 22G2

Molignon. GPS: n46,09061 e7,50776.
CHF 14,50-30,60 Ch WC. 01/01-31/12.

S Leuk 22G2

Hexenplatzstrasse. **GPS:** n46,31082 e7,63436.
4 CHF 15/24h Ch. **Location:** Central, noisy.
Surface: asphalted. 01/01-31/12.
Distance: 400m on the spot on the spot 400m 400m.

Leukerbad 22G2

Winterstellplatz, Parkplatz Fischweiher. **GPS:** n46,38215 e7,63232.

30 CHF 10/24h. **Location:** Rural, simple. **Surface:** gravel/sand.
01/11-15/04.
Distance: 150m 600m 100m.
Remarks: Payment only with coins.

Locarno 23A2

Parco della Pace, Via Gioacchino Respini.
GPS: n46,16011 e8,80255.

50 CHF 5/6h. **Surface:** gravel. 01/01-31/12.
Distance: 900m 100m 100m.
Remarks: Max. 24h.

Tourist information Locarno:
Rasa. Touristic car-free miniature village, can be reached by first taking the Centrovall-track, till Verdasio, then the small telpher carrier to Rasa.
Tenero-Locarno-Tenero. Free boat service. 31/05-30/09.

S Martigny 22G2

Les Neuvilles, Rue du Levant 68. **GPS:** n46,09787 e7,07930.
70 CHF 32-48 Ch WC. 07/04-15/10.

Tourist information Martigny: Gorges du Durnand. Hiking trail through the gorge of the river Durnand.

S Meride 23A3

Parco al Sole. GPS: n45,88806 e8,94944.
CHF 38-56 Ch WC. 15/04-25/09.

S Molinazzo di Montegio 23A3

Tresiana. GPS: n45,98990 e8,81576.
95 CHF 26-46 Ch WC. 19/03-23/10.

S Muzzano-Lugano 23A3

Piodella di Agnuzzo. GPS: n45,99463 e8,90857.
200 CHF 45 Ch WC. 01/01-31/12.

S Raron 22H2

Santa Monica, Kantonstrasse 56. **GPS:** n46,30007 e7,82374.
CHF 23-29 Ch WC. 01/01-31/12.

S Reckingen 22H2

Camping Augenstern, Im Ellbogen 21. **GPS:** n46,46500 e8,24500.
50 CHF 29-35 Ch WC. 01/05-18/10 and 15/12-15/03.

S Rivera 23A2

Area Camper Tamaro, Monte Ceneri 19. **GPS:** n46,13926 e8,90675.
80 3-72h CHF 1/h Ch included.
Surface: grassy/gravel. 01/01-31/12, 24/24h.
Distance: on the spot.
Remarks: Video surveillance.

S Saas Fee 22H2

Parkplatz P4. GPS: n46,11090 e7,93208.

50 CHF 26/24h Ch included CHF 2 WC.
Location: Rural, simple, isolated, quiet. **Surface:** grassy/gravel.
01/01-31/12 Service: winter.
Distance: 100m 200m 900m 200m.

Saillon 22G2

Bains de Saillon, Route du Centre Thermal 16.
GPS: n46,17353 e7,19372.
12 free. **Surface:** grassy. 01/01-31/12.
Distance: 4km.
Remarks: Max. 48h.

Tourist information Saillon:
Sentier des Vitraux. Hiking trail, 45 minutes, through wine region.

S Saint-Léonard 22G2

Place du Lac Souterrain. **GPS:** n46,25564 e7,42600.

15 CHF 10/night Ch (4x) WC included.
Location: Rural, simple, central, quiet. **Surface:** asphalted/grassy.
01/01-31/12 service: 01/11-19/03.
Distance: 5,5km 300m.
Remarks: Pay in at kiosk.

S Simplon 22H2

Col du Simplon, Simplonstrasse. **GPS:** n46,24944 e8,03056.

18 free Ch WC free. **Location:** Rural, simple, isolated.
Surface: asphalted. 01/01-31/12.
Distance: 200m.

S Sonogno 23A2

Camper Area Sonogno, Cioss. **GPS:** n46,35058 e8,78846.
15 € 16/night Ch included.
Location: Rural, isolated, quiet. **Surface:** grassy. 01/01-31/12.
Distance: 200m 200m 200m.

S Stampa 23B2

Tankstelle Esso, Strada Principale. **GPS:** n46,34593 e9,59660.
8 CHF 8 CHF 3 Ch CHF 3.
Surface: grassy. 01/01-31/12.
Distance: on the spot.
Remarks: Max. 24h.

S Tenero 23A2

Lido Mappo, Via Mappo. **GPS:** n46,17692 e8,84433.
CHF 36-56 Ch. 18/03-23/10.

S Tenero 23A2

Tamaro, Via Mappo 32. **GPS:** n46,17525 e8,84779.
CHF 36 Ch WC. 15/03-01/11.

S Trient 22F3

Place de Repos Du Peuty, Le Peuty. **GPS:** n46,04645 e6,99499.

6 CHF 3/pp free.
Location: Rural, simple, isolated, quiet. **Surface:** grassy.
01/01-31/12.
Distance: 1,5km on the spot.

CH

Czech Republic

Capital: Prague
Government: parliamentary constitutional republic
Official Language: Czech
Population: 10.644.842 (2016)
Area: 78,866 km²

General information
Dialling code: 00420
General emergency: 112
Currency: Koruna(CZK)
€ 1 = 26 CZK, 1 CZK = € 0,04
£1 = 29 CZK, 10 CZK = £0.34 (October 2017)
Credit cards are accepted almost everywhere.

Regulations for overnight stays
Wild camping is not allowed.

Additional public holidays 2018
May 1 Labour Day
May 8 Liberation Day
July 5 St. Cyril & St. Methodius Day
July 6 Jan Hus Day
September 28 St. Wenceslas Day
October 28 Independent Czechoslavak State Day
November 17 Freedom and Democracy Day

Time Zone
Winter (Standard Time) GMT+1
Summer (DST) GMT+2

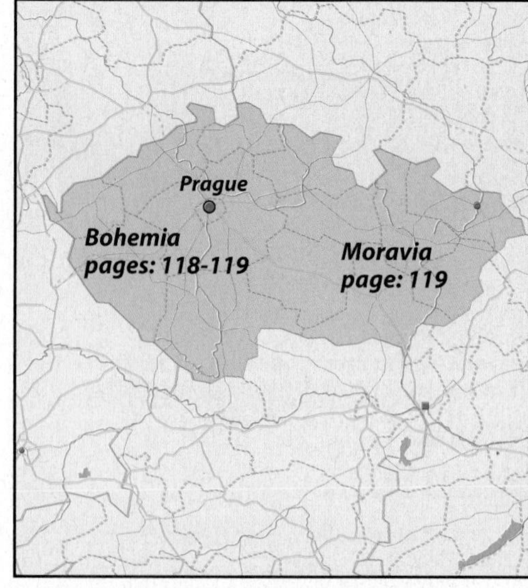

Bohemia

Ceský Krumlov 36A1
Camper - Ceský Krumlov, Chvalšinská 227. **GPS**: n48,81606 e14,30916.

15 € 15. **Location:** Urban, noisy. **Surface:** grassy/sand.
01/01-31/12.
Distance: 100m on the spot on the spot on the spot.

Cheb 12F3
Camping Briza, Bříza 19. **GPS**: n50,09124 e12,28210.
40 € 13,90 (24x)€ 4,20 WC . **Surface:** grassy.
02/04-31/10.
Distance: on the spot on the spot on the spot on the spot.

Golčův Jeníkov 38A4
Mamolina, Římovice 9. **GPS**: n49,80428 e15,44581.
20 Ch . 01/01-31/12.

Hluboká nad Vltavou 38A4
Camping Kostelec, Kostelec 8. **GPS**: n49,13863 e14,47408.

25 € 12,11, 01/07-27/08 € 24,85 Ch € 4/day WCincluded € 0,50 € 5,50 . **Surface:** grassy. 29/04-07/09.
Distance: 200m on the spot on the spot on the spot on the spot.
Remarks: Bread-service.

Horní Planá 17H2
Caravan Camping Horní Planá, Jiráskova. **GPS**: n48,76086 e14,02588.
160 € 15-18 Ch WC included.
Surface: asphalted/grassy. 15/04-29/10.
Distance: on the spot on the spot on the spot 500m 600m on the spot on the spot.

Hůrka 17H2
Jezerní penzion, Hurka 52. **GPS**: n48,74239 e14,08705.

30 Ch WC . **Surface:** grassy.
Distance: on the spot on the spot on the spot on the spot.

Janovice N.U 17G1
Camping U Dvou Orechu, Splz 13- Strzov. **GPS**: n49,28137 e13,24008.

10 € 19/22 Ch WC included. **Surface:** grassy/metalled.
01/05-15/09.
Distance: 3km 3km 500m on the spot on the spot.

Karlovy Vary 12F2
Nakladni. **GPS**: n50,23438 e12,86782.
15 € 20 Ch included € 1. **Surface:** metalled.
01/03-01/11.
Distance: 500m 200m 600m.

Karlovy Vary 12F2
U. Podjezdu 1616/5. **GPS**: n50,21992 e12,83688.
10 Chincluded € 2,50. **Surface:** grassy.
01/03-01/11.
Distance: 400m.

Kutná Hora 38A4
Autocamp Transit, K Malínskému Mostu 35. **GPS**: n49,96467 e15,30273.

40 € 10-11 WC . **Location:** Rural. **Surface:** grassy.
01/04-30/09.
Distance: 3km on the spot.
Remarks: Max. 2 nights.

Lipno nad Vltavou 36A1
Camping Hotel Panorama, Lipno nad Vltavou 22.
GPS: n48,63869 e14,22484.
40 € 10,50-17,50 Ch WC included.
Location: Rural. **Surface:** grassy/metalled. 01/04-01/10.
Distance: on the spot on the spot on the spot on the spot.
Remarks: Bread-service.

Loděnice 12H3
Camp Valek, Chrustenice 155. **GPS**: n50,01065 e14,14889.
100 € 13,80-16,48 Ch WC included.
Location: Rural. **Surface:** grassy. 01/05-30/08.
Distance: on the spot on the spot on the spot on the spot.
Remarks: Bread-service.

Mariánské Lázně 12F3
Camping Stanowitz, Stanoviště 9. **GPS**: n49,94404 e12,72811.

25 € 15 Ch € 3,80 WC included . **Location:** Rural.
Surface: grassy. 01/04-31/10.
Distance: 3km on the spot on the spot on the spot.

Nelahozeves 12H2
Marina Vltava, Dvořákova stezka. **GPS**: n50,25898 e14,30230.
15 € 6 € 2/100liter € 2 € 2 . **Surface:** grasstiles.
01/01-31/12.
Distance: on the spot on the spot 300m on the spot on the spot.

Nová Bystřice 36A1
Farma Alpaka, Dobrá Voda čp 20. **GPS**: n49,06400 e15,10481.
10 € 8 Ch . **Location:** Rural. **Surface:** gravel.
01/01-31/12.
Distance: 6km.
Remarks: Bread-service.

Nové Město pod Smrkem 38A3
Ludvikov Horses&Holiday, Ludvikov pod Smrkem 9.
GPS: n50,91579 e15,20486.
15 € 13 Ch included WC . **Location:** Rural.
Surface: grassy. 01/01-31/12.
Distance: on the spot on the spot 10km.

Prague 38A4
Nonstop Parking Praha, Izraelská 6. **GPS**: n50,07978 e14,48246.
100 € 15 Ch WC .
Location: Urban. **Surface:** metalled.
01/01-31/12.
Distance: on the spot on the spot on the spot.
Remarks: 24/24 surveillance.

Prague 38A4
Camp Drusus, K Řeporyjím 4. **GPS**: n50,04357 e14,28455.
70 € 16-20 Ch WC included. **Location:** Rural.
Surface: grassy. 01/04-05/10.
Distance: 100m on the spot on the spot.
Remarks: Bread-service.

Prague 38A4

Camp Herzog, Trojská 602/161. **GPS**: n50,11719 e14,42717.
20 € 14 Ch € 3,50 WC included.
Location: Urban. **Surface:** grassy.
01/01-31/12.
Distance: 4,2km 500m.

Prague 38A4

Caravan Camping Císařská Louka, Císařská louka 16.
GPS: n50,05584 e14,41336.
40 € 16,50 Ch WC € 3,50 included. **Location:** Urban, noisy. **Surface:** grassy. 01/01-31/12.
Distance: 4km 750m on the spot.
Remarks: Bread-service.

Prague 38A4

Dana Troja, Trojská 357/129. **GPS**: n50,11716 e14,43176.
15 € 19 Ch € 3 WC € 2,50 included.
Location: Urban. **Surface:** grassy.
01/01-31/12.
Distance: 4km 200m.

Protivín 17H1

Camping U Serifa, Chelčického 889/2. **GPS**: n49,19046 e14,22004.

38 € 9 € 3 WC. **Location:** Rural, quiet. **Surface:** grassy.
01/04-15/09.
Distance: 300m on the spot on the spot 400m on the spot on the spot.

Sněžník 12H1

Stellplatz Sněžník, Jílové. **GPS**: n50,79647 e14,08425.

15 € 5/5h, then € 0,60/h € 0,10/10liter Ch € 0,60/kWh.
01/01-31/12.
Distance: 50m.

Svitavy 38A4

U Stadion, U Stadionu. **GPS**: n49,75146 e16,46521.
6 free Chfree € 0,25/kWh. **Location:** Urban.
Surface: metalled. 01/01-31/12.
Distance: on the spot.
Remarks: At stadium.

Třeboň 36A1

Autocamp Třeboň, Domanín 285. **GPS**: n48,99287 e14,76675.

100 € 13,20 WC. **Location:** Rural. **Surface:** grassy.
28/04-01/10.
Distance: 200m on the spot on the spot on the spot on the spot on the spot.

Velemín 12H2

Finaso, Velemin 198. **GPS**: n50,53639 e13,97333.

6 free Chfree € 0,50/kWh. **Location:** Simple.
Surface: metalled. 01/01-31/12.

Velká Jesenice 38A4

Stellplatz Rozkoš, Vodní nádrž Rozkoš . **GPS**: n50,36444 e16,05944.
16 € 11 Ch included. **Location:** Rural.
01/01-31/12.
Distance: on the spot on the spot.

Moravia

Břeclav 36B1

Autokemp Apollo, Slovácká 722/4. **GPS**: n48,78583 e16,82620.

70 € 15 WC included. **Location:** Rural. **Surface:** grassy.
01/05-30/09.
Distance: on the spot on the spot on the spot on the spot on the spot.
Remarks: Bread-service.

Červená Řečice 38A4

Camping Kovarna, Červená Řečice 63. **GPS**: n49,51922 e15,15661.
39 € 15 Ch € 3,75 WC included. **Location:** Rural.
Surface: grassy. 01/06-26/08.
Distance: on the spot 5km 2km on the spot on the spot.
Remarks: Bread-service.

Řásná 38A4

Camp Velkopařezitý, Řásná 10. **GPS**: n49,22792 e15,38426.
€ 9,70 € 3 WC € 1/5minutes.
Location: Rural. **Surface:** grassy.
Distance: 1km 200m 200m 100m on the spot on the spot.

Uherský Brod 38B4

Aquapark Delfin, Slovácké náměstí 2377.
GPS: n49,01960 e17,64828.
2 free. **Location:** Urban. **Surface:** metalled. 01/01-31/12.
Distance: 100m 150m.

Žďár nad Sázavou 38A4

Autokempink Pilák. **GPS**: n49,59077 e15,92072.

€ 10 WC € 0,80. **Location:** Rural, quiet. **Surface:** grassy.
01/05-30/09.
Distance: on the spot on the spot on the spot on the spot on the spot.

CZ

Germany

Capital: Berlin
Government: Federal republic
Official Language: Germany
Population: 81,000,000 (2016)
Area: 357,121 km^2

General information
Dialling code: 0049
General emergency: 112
Currency: Euro

Regulations for overnight stays
Overnight stays on the public highway are allowed, if there is no local prohibition, but no "camping" activities are allowed.

Additional public holidays 2018
January 6 Epiphany
March 30 Good Friday
April 2 Easter Monday
May 1 Labor Day
May 21 White Monday
May 31 Corpus Christi
August 15 Assumption of the Virgin Mary
October 3 Day of German Unity
November 1 All Saints' Day

Time Zone
Winter (Standard Time) GMT+1
Summer (DST) GMT+2

Schleswig-Holstein/ Hamburg

Achtrup 6C3

Landgasthof Achtruper Stuben, Ladelunderstrasse 24.
GPS: n54,79337 e9,02676.

3 free, water/electricity free. **Location:** Simple.
01/01-31/12 Mo-Tue.
Distance: 5km on the spot 5km.
Remarks: Along through road.

Albersdorf 8A1

Freitzeitbad Albersdorf, Weg zur Badeanstalt 18.
GPS: n54,15135 e9,28055.

6 € 15 swimming pool incl Ch (6x)included.
Location: Rural, isolated, quiet. **Surface:** grassy.
01/05-31/08.
Distance: 1km 100m 300m on the spot on the spot.
Remarks: Parking at swimming pool, max. 3 days.

Altenhof 6D3

Wohnmobilpark Ostsee 'Grüner Jäger', Grünen Jäger.
GPS: n54,44392 e9,90526.

80 € 8 Chincluded (40x)€ 4/24h WC € 1.
Location: Rural, simple, isolated, quiet. **Surface:** grassy.
01/01-31/12.
Distance: Eckernförde 6km 2km on the spot 6km 200m busstop -> Kiel on the spot on the spot.
Remarks: Check in at restaurant Grüner, bread-service.

Aukrug 8B1

Parkplatz am Freibad, Zum Sportplatz 1.
GPS: n54,07441 e9,79160.

10 € 8 Ch (10x)included. **Location:** Rural.
Surface: grassy/metalled. 01/01-31/12.
Distance: 1km 800m 1km on the spot on the spot.
Remarks: Max. 5 days, check in and key service at pay-desk of swimming pool.

Aventoft 6C3

Wohnmobillstellplatz Zu den Fuchswiesen, Revtoftweg 1.
GPS: n54,87661 e8,84562.

15 € 5 Chincluded € 1,50/24h.
Location: Rural, simple, isolated, quiet. **Surface:** asphalted/grassy.
01/01-31/12.
Distance: 3km 3km 3km on the spot.
Remarks: Bread-service.

Bad Bramstedt 8B1

Parkplatz P7, Am Bahnhof, König Christian Strasse.
GPS: n53,92167 e9,88967.

5 free. **Location:** Urban, simple, central, noisy. **Surface:** metalled.
01/01-31/12.
Distance: centre 500m 500m 500m on the spot.
Remarks: At station, max. 1 night, service at camping Roland, Kielerstrasse.

Bad Malente 6E3

Parkplatz Krützen, Sebastian-Kneipp-Straße.
GPS: n54,17198 e10,54919.

4 € 5 + € 2/pp tourist tax € 1 € 1 Ch. **Location:** Rural, simple. **Surface:** metalled. 01/01-31/12.
Distance: on the spot 500m 1km.
Remarks: Max. 24h.

Bad Oldesloe 8B1

Wohnmobilplatz Exer, Am Bürgerpark.
GPS: n53,81101 e10,36915.

8 free € 1/10minutes Ch (8x)€ 2/10h WC.
Location: Urban, simple, quiet. **Surface:** metalled.
01/01-31/12.
Distance: on the spot 3km on the spot 400m.
Remarks: Max. 3 nights, bread-service.

Bad Schwartau 8C1

Landschaftsschutzgebiet Riesebusch. **GPS**: n53,92405 e10,69795.
15 € 5/24h, tourist tax € 1,65/pp € 1/90liter Ch € 1/8h.
01/01-31/12.
Distance: 1,5km 1,5km.
Remarks: Max. 72h.

Bad Segeberg 8B1

Kalkbergblick, Kastanienweg 1b. **GPS**: n53,93872 e10,31423.

25 € 8 Chincluded (15x)€ 2/12h,6 Amp.
Location: Rural, comfortable, quiet. **Surface:** gravel.
01/01-31/12.
Distance: 500m A7 3km 600m Segerberger See 600m 500m 500m on the spot on the spot.
Remarks: Jun/Aug Karl May Spiele, open air theater.

Barkenholm 6C3

Gaststätte Jägerstuben, Dorfstraße 28. **GPS**: n54,23497 e9,17484.

6 € 5, free with a meal free € 1/day.
Location: Rural, simple, isolated. **Surface:** grasstiles.
01/01-31/12 Wed.
Distance: 8km on the spot.
Remarks: Wifi at restaurant.

Barmstedt 8B1

Parkplatz am Rondeel, Platz Roissy-en-Brie.
GPS: n53,78640 e9,76420.

5 € 5 Ch WC included. **Location:** Urban, simple.
Surface: metalled. 01/01-31/12.
Distance: on the spot on the spot 500m on the spot on the spot.
Remarks: To be paid at swimming pool, key electricity at pool.

Behrensdorf 6E3

Campingpark Waldesruh, Neuland. **GPS**: n54,35754 e10,60216.

23 € 11-13, 2 pers. incl., dog € 1,50 Ch € 0,40/kWh WC.
Location: Rural, comfortable. **Surface:** grassy. 01/04-31/10.
Distance: 2km on the spot on the spot on the spot on the spot.
Remarks: Dog € 1,50/night.

Blekendorf 6E3

Am Sehlendorfer Strand, Strandstrasse 24.
GPS: n54,30571 e10,69358.

40 € 15,50 € 1 Ch included WC.
Location: Rural, comfortable. **Surface:** grassy.
01/01-31/12.
Distance: 1km on the spot on the spot on the spot 5km.

Bordesholm 8B1

Festplatz, Kielerstrasse. **GPS**: n54,18389 e10,02667.

6 free. **Location:** Rural, simple, quiet. **Surface:** grassy/sand.
01/01-31/12.
Distance: 1,5km 4km.
Remarks: Max. 18h, service at petrol station.

Bordesholm 8B1

Shell tankstelle, Bahnofstrasse 78. **GPS**: n54,17343 e10,03497.
Ch. 01/01-31/12.

Borgdorf-Seedorf 6D3

Seecampingplatz BUM, Hauptstrasse 99. **GPS**: n54,18256 e9,88422.
12 € 13,50 Ch € 3,50.
Surface: grassy. 01/01-31/12.
Distance: 3km.

Bosau 8B1

Dat Gröne Huus, Stadtbeker Strasse 97. **GPS**: n54,09198 e10,42886.

3 € 5, guests free € 3 . **Location:** Rural, simple, quiet.
Surface: gravel. 01/04-30/11.
Distance: 100m Großer Plöner See on the spot on the spot 1km.
Remarks: Bread-service.

Bösdorf 8B1

Wohnmobilcamp Augustfelde, Vierer See, Augustfelde.
GPS: n54,12898 e10,45506.

16 € 11,50-13,50 Ch (16x)WCincluded € 0,75.
Surface: grassy. 01/04-25/10.
Distance: on the spot on the spot on the spot on the spot.

Bösdorf 8B1

Landhaus zur Tenne, Hörn 6. **GPS**: n54,12792 e10,50194.
10 € 6 Chincluded € 2/day. **Surface:** grassy/gravel.
01/01-31/12.
Distance: on the spot on the spot.

Bösdorf 8B1

Campingpark Gut Ruhleben, Missionsweg 2, Ruhleben.
GPS: n54,14308 e10,45021.

10 € 11-13 Ch € 2,50 included. **Location:** Rural, simple. **Surface:** grassy/gravel. 01/04-30/09.
Remarks: Max. 3 nights.

Bredstedt 6C3

Süderstraße. **GPS**: n54,61307 e8,97082.

15 free. **Location:** Rural, simple, quiet. **Surface:** asphalted.
01/01-31/12.
Distance: 900m Aldi 650m.
Remarks: Nearby sports complex, nearby swimming pool.

Brodersby 6D3

Ferienhof Lassen, Gross Brodersbyer Weg 5.
GPS: n54,53850 e9,71402.

DE

2 € 10 Ch (1x),16Amp included.
Location: Rural, simple, quiet. **Surface:** grassy. 01/01-31/12.
Distance: 500m 2km 500m.

S Brokdorf 8A1

Stellplatz Brokdorf, Dorfstrasse 53. **GPS**: n53,86417 e9,31667.

30 € 5, 01/03-31/10 € 10 € 1/70liter € 1 Ch (30x)€ 0,50/kWh WC included € 1.
Location: Rural, comfortable. **Surface:** metalled. 01/01-31/12.
Distance: 800m 400m on the spot 500m on the spot on the spot.
Remarks: Max. 3 days.

S Brunsbüttel 8A1

An der Braake, Am Freizeitbad. **GPS**: n53,89832 e9,13138.

12 € 3 € 2 Ch. **Location:** Rural, comfortable, central, quiet.
Surface: grassy/metalled. 01/01-31/12.
Distance: 500m 500m 500m on the spot.
Remarks: To pay at swimming pool.

Büdelsdorf 6D3

Hermann-Ehlers-Platz, Agnes Miegel Strasse.
GPS: n54,31583 e9,69306.

10 free. **Location:** Urban, simple, central.
Surface: metalled. 01/01-31/12.
Distance: on the spot 1km 1,5km.
Remarks: Max. 1 night.

S Busdorf 6D3

Autohof Wikingerland, Wittgenstein 2. **GPS**: n54,47736 e9,54454.

6 free € 1/80liter € 1/time Ch€ 1/time (6x) WC .
Location: Rural, simple, noisy. **Surface:** asphalted.
01/01-31/12.

Distance: on the spot on the spot.
Remarks: At petrol station, special part for motor homes.

S Büsum 7H1

Wohnmobilstellplatz Nordsee, Dr. Martin Bahr Strasse.
GPS: n54,12889 e8,86889.

100 € 11, 01/03-31/10 € 15 € 0,50/50liter Ch (100x) included WC€ 0,50 € 1/4minutes € 0,50/day.
Location: Rural, comfortable, isolated, quiet. **Surface:** grassy.
01/01-31/12.
Distance: 1km 500m 300m on the spot on the spot.
Remarks: Key shower at Imbiss.

S Damp 6D3

Wohnmobilpark Damp, Parkstrasse 2.
GPS: n54,57742 e10,01572.

80 € 13 + € 1/pp tourist tax € 0,10/10liter Ch (60x)€ 0,60/kWh,6Amp WC € 1/4minutes included.
Location: Rural, comfortable, quiet. **Surface:** grassy/gravel.
01/01-31/12.
Distance: 600m 500m 500m 500m 150m on the spot.

S Drelsdorf 6C3

Drelsdörper Krog, Dorfstrasse 23. **GPS**: n54,60555 e9,03555.

10 € 5, guests free € 2 WC. **Location:** Rural, central, noisy.
Surface: grassy. 01/01-31/12.
Distance: 200m on the spot 2km.
Remarks: Along through road.

S Eckernförde 6D3

Wohnmobilstellplatz am Noor, Kakabellenweg.
GPS: n54,46443 e9,83402.

49 € 14 excl. tourist tax € 1/100liter Ch € 0,50/kWh WC € 2/2 included. **Location:** Urban, comfortable, central, quiet. **Surface:** grassy. 01/01-31/12.
Distance: 1km on the spot on the spot 500m on the spot on the spot on the spot.

S Elmshorn 8A1

Stellplatz Elmshorn, Nordufer. **GPS**: n53,75157 e9,65268.

4 free € 1/80liter Ch WC. **Location:** Urban, simple, central, quiet. **Surface:** metalled. 01/01-31/12.
Distance: 800m on the spot on the spot on the spot.

S Emmelsbüll-Horsbüll 6C3

Stellplatz am Badedeich, Südwesthörner Strasse.
GPS: n54,79686 e8,66075.

3 free € 1. **Location:** Rural, simple, isolated, quiet.
Surface: grassy/gravel. 01/01-31/12.
Distance: on the spot on the spot.
Remarks: Max. 5 days.

Eutin 8C1

Elisabethstrasse. **GPS**: n54,13507 e10,60935.

6 free. **Location:** Urban. **Surface:** asphalted. 01/01-31/12.
Distance: on the spot 300m.
Remarks: Parking at station.

Eutin 8C1

Forsthaus am Ukleisee, Zum Ukleisee 23, Sielbeck.
GPS: n54,18181 e10,64137.
€ 5. **Surface:** grassy/gravel. 01/01-31/12.

S Fehmarn 6E3

Wohnmobilpark Wulfener Hals, Wulfener-Hals-Weg 16, Wulfen.
GPS: n54,40687 e11,17489.

100 from € 12,90-49 Ch € 4,20 WC € 0,90 .
Location: Rural, luxurious. **Surface:** grassy. 01/01-31/12.
Distance: on the spot.
Remarks: Bike/car rental.

S Fehmarn 6E3

Hintz-Heizungsbau, Landkirchenerweg 1b, Burg.
GPS: n54,44228 e11,18967.

DE

16 € 10 € 1 Ch (16x)€ 5. **Location:** Simple, quiet.
Surface: metalled. 01/01-31/12.
Distance: on the spot.

Fehmarn 6E3

Parkplatz Ost, Osterstrasse, Burg. **GPS**: n54,43754 e11,19990.

30 € 8 (21-8h).
Location: Urban, simple. **Surface:** metalled. 01/01-31/12.
Distance: 100m.

Fehmarn 6E3

Kommunal- und Yachthafen Burgstaaken, Burgstaaken/Am Binnensee. **GPS**: n54,42028 e11,19224.

15 € 10 21-08h.
Location: Rural, simple. **Surface:** metalled. 01/01-31/12.
Distance: 100m 100m.

Fehmarn 6E3

Ferienhof Wachtelberg. **GPS**: n54,44653 e11,26039.
4 € 13, 2 pers.incl, extra pers € 5 WC included.
Surface: grassy. 01/01-31/12.
Distance: 1km.

Fehmarn 6E3

Camping Strukkamphuk, Strukkamp. **GPS**: n54,41239 e11,10223.

21 € 14,50-31 Ch WC included.
Location: Rural, simple. **Surface:** grassy. 01/01-31/12.
Distance: 10m.

Flensburg 6D3

Am Industriehafen, dir Flensburg Mürwick.
GPS: n54,80430 e9,44334.

12 free. **Location:** Urban, simple, isolated, quiet.
Surface: gravel. 01/01-31/12.
Distance: 1,5km on the spot on the spot.
Remarks: Max. 1 night.

Fockbek 6D3

Am Freibad, Grosse Rheie 17a. **GPS**: n54,30187 e9,60456.

3 free Chfree WC. **Location:** Rural, simple, isolated, quiet.
Surface: grassy/gravel. 01/04-31/10.
Distance: 800m 800m 800m on the spot on the spot.
Remarks: Parking swimming pool, max. 24h.

Friedrichskoog 7H1

P2, Nordseestrasse. **GPS**: n54,03272 e8,84833.

30 € 10/24h Chincluded.
Location: Rural, comfortable, isolated, quiet.
Surface: asphalted/grassy. 01/03-31/10.
Distance: 1km 550m 800m on the spot.
Remarks: Bread-service.

Friedrichstadt 6C3

Friedrichstädter Wohnmobilstellplatz, Halbmond 5.
GPS: n54,37256 e9,08868.

65 € 13 € 0,10/10liter Ch € 0,60/kWh WCfree € 1
€ 3,50/3,50 included. **Location:** Rural, luxurious.
Surface: grassy/gravel. 01/01-31/12.
Distance: 300m on the spot 300m.

Geesthacht 8B2

Alter Schiffsanleger 777, Elbuferstrasse.
GPS: n53,42574 e10,37907.

16 € 7 € 1/100liter Ch (12x)€ 0,50/kWh.
Location: Rural, simple.
Surface: grasstiles/metalled. 01/01-31/12.
Distance: 1,5km on the spot on the spot 1,5km 2km on the spot on the spot on the spot.
Remarks: Along the river Elbe, max. 3 days.

Gelting 6D3

Yachthafen Gelting-Wackerballig, Strandweg, Wackerballig.
GPS: n54,75564 e9,87842.

12 € 8 € 0,10/10liter Ch € 1,50/night WC € 0,50.
Location: Rural, simple, quiet. **Surface:** grassy/gravel.
01/04-31/10.
Distance: 1,5km on the spot on the spot 2km on the spot.
Remarks: Key sanitary building/waste dump at harbour master, caution € 20.

Glückstadt 8A1

Park & Ride platz, Pentzstrasse. **GPS**: n53,78776 e9,43145.

10 free. **Location:** Urban, simple.
Surface: asphalted. 01/01-31/12.
Distance: 900m 200m on the spot on the spot.

Glückstadt 8A1

Am Außenhafen, Am Hafen. **GPS**: n53,78560 e9,41088.

16 € 10. **Location:** Rural, comfortable.
Surface: metalled. 01/01-31/12 high water.
Distance: 1km on the spot on the spot on the spot on the spot on the spot.
Remarks: Along the river Elbe, money in envelope in mail box.

Grödersby 6D3

WSG Arin/Grödersby, Friedenshöher Straße 21.
GPS: n54,63444 e9,92944.

20 € 15 Ch WC € 3/2 included.
Location: Rural, simple, quiet.
Surface: gravel/metalled. 01/05-30/09.
Distance: 200m on the spot on the spot 200m on the spot on the spot.
Remarks: Bicycle rental.

Grömitz 6E3

Großraumparkplatz, Gildestraße 14. **GPS**: n54,14490 e10,95262.

DE

60 € 15, 01/11-14/03 € 6 € 0,50 Ch (20x)€ 1/kWh.
Location: Rural, simple. **Surface:** metalled.
01/01-31/12 water disconnected in winter.
Distance: 200m on the spot 200m 500m.

Grömitz 6E3

Wohnmobilstellplatz am Lensterstrand, Blankwasserweg.
GPS: n54,15650 e10,99134.

50 free, 15/03-31/10 € 10 WC. **Location:** Rural.
Surface: grassy. 01/01-31/12 water disconnected in winter.
Distance: on the spot on the spot.
Remarks: Max. 24h.

Grömitz 6E3

Wohnmobilplatz Kattenberg, Kattenberg 8, Cismar.
GPS: n54,18637 e10,96541.

5 € 8 Ch € 2. **Surface:** grassy. 01/04-31/10.
Distance: Grömitz 5km 1,3km.

Großenaspe 8B1

Wildpark Eekholt, Eekhol 1. **GPS:** n53,94819 e10,02916.

10 free. **Location:** Rural, simple, isolated, quiet.
Surface: grassy/sand. 01/01-31/12.
Distance: 4km Grossenaspe Kiek ut Stuben, Game preserve > Wildpark.

Großenbrode 6E3

Wassersportzentrum, Am Kai 29. **GPS:** n54,35583 e11,07798.

50 € 10-12 € 0,50/100liter Ch € 1/kWh WC € 0,50 .
Location: Rural. **Surface:** grassy/metalled.
01/01-31/12.
Distance: 300m on the spot 2km.

Großenbrode 6E3

Wohnmobilhafen Reise, Südstrand 1.
GPS: n54,36170 e11,08567.

36 € 10-14 Ch WC included € 0,50 € 3/day.
Location: Rural, comfortable. **Surface:** gravel. 01/01-31/12.
Distance: 300m on the spot 500m on the spot.
Remarks: Bread-service.

Großsolt 6D3

Stellplatz Mühlenbrück, Flensburger strasse, Mühlenbrück.
GPS: n54,70853 e9,52243.

13 € 10 Ch (13x)€ 2/day WC € 0,50.
Location: Rural, comfortable, quiet. **Surface:** gravel.
01/03-01/10.
Distance: 200m.

Hamburg 8B2

Elbepark-Bunthaus, Moorwerder Hauptdeich 33.
GPS: n53,46194 e10,06265.

80 € 12-19, 2 pers.incl Ch (70x) WC included € 0,50/5minutes € 1 .
Location: Rural, comfortable, quiet. **Surface:** asphalted.
15/03-05/10.
Distance: 15km on the spot on the spot.
Remarks: Several locations, bread-service, possibility for reservation.

Hamburg 8B2

Wohnmobilhafen Hamburg, Grüner Deich 8, Hammerbrook.
GPS: n53,54360 e10,02570.

60 € 19 Ch WC included.
Location: Urban, simple, central, noisy. **Surface:** gravel.
01/01-31/12.
Distance: 4km 200m.

Hamburg 8B2

Heiligengeistfeld. **GPS:** n53,55523 e9,97361.

30 € 18 € 5/day € 5/day included.
Location: Urban, simple. **Surface:** gravel/sand.
01/01-31/12 during event.
Distance: on the spot 300m 300m.
Remarks: Accessible via entrance C, max. 3 nights, possibility for reservation, special part for motor homes.

Hamburg 8B2

Am Strand Pauli, St. Pauli Hafenstraße.
GPS: n53,54598 e9,96099.
20 € 12,50, weekend € 19,50.
Surface: asphalted.
01/01-31/12.
Distance: Hamburg Altstadt 2,4km on the spot many restaurant 100m 600m.

Tourist information Hamburg:

Hamburg-card. Card offers free entrance to public transport and museums, discounts on boat trips, zoo etc. Available at Tourist Information. € 9,90 1 day, € 25,50/3 days, 1 adult max. 3 childeren.
Sankt Pauli. City district with well-known Reeperbahn.
Flohschanze, Rinderschlachthalle St Pauli. Antiques and flea market.
Sa 8-16h.
Tierpark Hagenbeck, Stellingen. Zoo.
Antikpassage, Klosterwall 9-21. Arcade with 39 antique stores.
Tue-Fri 12-18h, Sa 10-16h.

Handewitt 6C3

Scandinavian Park, Scandinavian-Park. **GPS:** n54,77857 e9,33528.

40 free Ch WC € 0,50/time .
Location: Urban, simple, central, quiet. **Surface:** asphalted.
01/01-31/12.
Distance: 2km on the spot on the spot.
Remarks: At shopping centre, service at petrol station.

Hanerau-Hademarschen 8A1

Ferienhof Sievers, Wilhelmsburg. **GPS:** n54,12360 e9,38627.

5 € 10 Ch (6x) WC included.
Location: Rural, comfortable, isolated, quiet.
Surface: grasstiles/grassy. 01/01-31/12.
Distance: 2km 500m on the spot on the spot.

Hasloh 8B2

Stellplatz Tante Henni, Garstedter Weg 36a.
GPS: n53,69251 e9,92608.

21 € 17 Ch (21x) WC € 1 included. **Location:** Rural, comfortable, quiet. **Surface:** grassy. 01/01-31/12.
Distance: on the spot on the spot 4km 1,5km 1,5km 800m on the spot on the spot.
Remarks: Check in on arrival.

Hasselberg 6D3

Ostseecamping Gut Oehe, Drecht 6. **GPS**: n54,71590 e9,99030.

10 € 11 WC included. **Location:** Rural, simple, quiet.
Surface: grassy. 01/04-30/09.
Distance: 3km on the spot on the spot on the spot.

Heide 8A1

Wohnmobilplatz Heide, Langvogt-Johannsen-strasse.
GPS: n54,20181 e9,11319.

16 € 7 € 1/100liter € 1 Ch € 1/2kWh
Location: Urban, comfortable, central, noisy.
Surface: grasstiles/metalled. 01/01-31/12.
Distance: 800m 5,5km 100m 300m.
Remarks: At swimming pool, use of sauna against payment.

Heiligenhafen 6E3

Reisemobilstellplatz Heilgenhafen, Eichholzweg 26.
GPS: n54,37721 e10,95548.

99 € 13-16 + € 3/pp tourist tax € 1/100liter Ch € 0,50/kWh, + € 0,50 WC € 2/2 included.
Location: Urban. **Surface:** metalled. 01/01-31/12.
Distance: 1km on the spot.

Hohenfelde 6D3

Campingpark Ostseestrand, Strandstraße.
GPS: n54,38588 e10,49152.

25 € 15-21, dog € 2 Ch WC included
Location: Rural, luxurious. **Surface:** grassy. 01/04-15/10.
Distance: 1km beach 150m 150m on the spot on the spot.

Hohenfelde 6D3

Wohnmobilplatz Radeland, Strandstraße 18.
GPS: n54,38278 e10,49295.

20 € 6, dog € 1,50 € 2 Ch € 0,70/kWh WC € 3/day.
Location: Rural. **Surface:** grassy/sand. 01/04-30/09.
Distance: 300m.

Hohn 6D3

Rosenhof Hohn, Westende 12. **GPS**: n54,29944 e9,49622.

5 € 10 Ch . **Location:** Rural, simple, isolated, quiet.
Surface: grassy. 01/04-31/10.
Distance: 800m on the spot 1km on the spot.

Hohwacht 6E3

Parkplatz Alt-Hohwacht, Strandstrasse.
GPS: n54,31902 e10,67529.

19 € 10 € 1/80liter € 1 Ch (20x) € 1/kWh.
Location: Urban. **Surface:** metalled. 01/01-31/12.
Distance: on the spot on the spot.

Hörnum 6C3

Zeltplatz. **GPS**: n54,76385 e8,28335.
30 € 18 € 0,50 € 0,50 Ch € 0,45/kWh WC .
Surface: sand. 01/01-31/12.
Distance: on the spot on the spot 750m.

Hörsten 6D3

Reisemobilstellplatz NOK, Schachtholm 1.
GPS: n54,22499 e9,60243.

49 € 10 € 1/75liter € 1/time Ch € 1/time (48x) € 0,50/kWh, 16Amp WC included. **Location:** Rural, comfortable, isolated, quiet. **Surface:** grassy. 16/03-15/11 and 30/12-02/01.
Distance: on the spot 700m on the spot on the spot.
Remarks: At the canal, bread-service.

Husum 6C3

Loof's Wohnmobilhafen, Dockkoogstrasse 7.
GPS: n54,47451 e9,04249.

30 € 12 € 1 € 2 Ch € 2 (30x) € 3 WC included € 0,50.
Location: Urban, simple, central, quiet. **Surface:** gravel.
01/01-31/12.
Distance: 200m 200m 200m 200m 200m on the spot on the spot.

Husum 6C3

Wohnmobilplatz Am Dockkoog, Dockoogstrasse 17.
GPS: n54,47888 e9,01138.

25 € 13 Ch WC included .
Location: Rural, simple, quiet. **Surface:** grassy. Easter-15/10.
Distance: 500m 200m 200m on the spot on the spot on the spot.
Remarks: Max. 3 nights, sanitary at campsite.

Itzehoe 8A1

Malzmüllerwiesen, Schuhmacherallee.
GPS: n53,91970 e9,51815.

5 free (4x) € 0,50/kWh.
Location: Rural, simple, central, quiet. **Surface:** metalled/sand.
01/01-31/12 during event.
Distance: 600m 20m on the spot on the spot.

Jagel 6D3

Wohnmobilhafen Jagel, Bundesstrasse 13.
GPS: n54,45448 e9,53654.

31 € 10 Ch € 2/night WC . **Location:** Rural, comfortable, quiet. **Surface:** grassy. 01/01-31/12.
Distance: 250m 4,5km 400m.

Kaltenkirchen 8B1

Reisemobilstellplatz Holstentherme, Norderstrasse 8.
GPS: n53,84056 e9,94650.

DE

20 free € 1/80liter € 1 Ch€ 1 € 0,50/kWh.
Location: Urban, quiet. **Surface:** grassy/gravel. 01/01-31/12.
Distance: 1,5km 1km on the spot 1,5km on the spot.
Remarks: Coins available at pay-desk of theTherme.

S Kappeln 6D3

Aral-Tankstelle, Eckernförder Strasse 9/B. **GPS:** n54,65688 e9,94480.

10 € 5 € 0,50/80liter € 0,50/time Ch€ 0,50/time € 5/night
Location: Urban, simple, quiet. **Surface:** metalled. 01/01-31/12.
Distance: 300m 2km on the spot 500m.
Remarks: At petrol station, caution key electricity € 25.

S Kappeln 6D3

Anker Yachting, Am Hafen 23A. **GPS:** n54,66612 e9,93698.

50 € 12 Ch € 2/4kWh WC € 1
Location: Rural, comfortable, central, quiet. **Surface:** gravel.
15/02-15/11.
Distance: 1km 1km 300m on the spot.
Remarks: Near marina, caution key electricity € 5.

S Kellinghusen 8A1

Am Freibad, Jacob-Fleischer-Strasse 6. **GPS:** n53,94715 e9,71035.

6 free € 0,50/100liter Ch€ 0,50 (4x)€ 1/h WC use sanitary facilities at swimming pool.
Location: Rural, simple, quiet. **Surface:** gravel. 01/01-31/12.
Distance: centre 500m 500m 500m on the spot.
Remarks: Check in at swimming pool.

S Kiel 6D3

Wohnmobilstellplatz Kiel, Förde und Kanalblick, Mecklenburgstrasse 58. Kiel-Wik. **GPS:** n54,36362 e10,14705.

32 € 12-15 Ch (33x)€ 3,50/24h WC € 1/5minutes € 3/1.
Location: Urban, simple, central, noisy.
Surface: metalled.
01/01-31/12.
Distance: 6,5km Imbiss on the spot 1,5km on the spot on the spot.
Remarks: Check in and pay at reception, bread-service.

S Kiel 6D3

Olympiahafen Schilksee, Soling 26. **GPS:** n54,43033 e10,16634.

20 € 10 € 0,50/3minutes € 1 Ch WC.
Surface: metalled. 01/01-31/12 last 2 weeks of Jun.
Distance: 13km 400m 400m.
Remarks: Check in and coins service at harbourmaster.

Tourist information Kiel:

Schleswig-Holsteinisches Freilichtmuseum, Hamburger Landstraße 97, Molfsee. Open air museum.
01/04-31/10 daily 9-18h, 01/11-31/03 Su/holidays 11-16h. € 8, family card € 17.

Krempe 8A1

Am Schul- und Sportzentrum, Am Freibad.
GPS: n53,83356 e9,49447.

3 free. **Location:** Rural, simple, quiet. **Surface:** gravel.
01/01-31/12.
Distance: 200m.

S Kropp 6D3

Hotel Wikingerhof, Tetenhusener Chaussee 1.
GPS: n54,40837 e9,51042.

12 free WC. **Location:** Urban, simple, central, quiet.
Surface: metalled. 01/04-31/10.
Distance: 300m on the spot 300m.

S Kropp 6D3

Garage Audi-VW Thomsen, Werkstrasse 2.
GPS: n54,41381 e9,52878.

4 € 5 € 0,50/80liter € 0,50/time Ch€ 0,50/time
Location: Urban, simple, quiet. **Surface:** metalled.
01/01-31/12.
Distance: 300m 300m 300m.
Remarks: Max. 3 days, service at petrol station.

S Laboe 6D3

Ostseebad Laboe Ehrenmal, Steinerweg/Prof. Munzerring.
GPS: n54,41029 e10,23289.

18 € 12 € 1/5minutes € 1 Ch. **Location:** Urban, simple.
Surface: grassy. 01/01-31/12.
Distance: 1km 400m 400m on the spot 1km.

S Ladelund 6C3

Am Naturbad, Stato. **GPS:** n54,84919 e9,03629.

5 € 10 Ch WC included. **Location:** Rural, comfortable, isolated, quiet. **Surface:** grassy. 01/01-31/12.
Distance: 1km on the spot.

S Langballig 6D3

Campingplatz Langballigau, Strandweg 3, Langballigau.
GPS: n54,82234 e9,65969.

50 € 11, dog € 1 Chincluded € 2,50/night WC € 1 € 1.
Location: Rural, simple. **Surface:** grassy/gravel.
01/01-31/12.
Distance: 100m on the spot.

S Langwedel 6D3

Caravanpark am Brahmsee, Mühlenstraße 30a.
GPS: n54,21462 e9,91943.

20 € 15 € 1/80liter Ch € 2,50/24h,6 Amp WC sanitary at campsite. **Location:** Rural, comfortable, quiet.
Surface: grassy/gravel. 01/01-31/12.
Distance: 600m 3km Brahmsee 500m 500m 7km.
Remarks: Check in at reception campsite, bread-service.

S Lauenburg/Elbe 8C2

Marina Lauenburg/Yachthafen, Hafenstrasse 14.
GPS: n53,37156 e10,56527.

20 € 10 € 1/100liter (8x)€ 1/kWh WC€ 0,50 € 1 € 4/4.
Location: Rural, comfortable.
Surface: metalled.

DE

01/01-31/12.
Distance: 10 min walking on the spot 10 min walking.

Leck 6C3

Reisemobilhafen Leck, Am Stadion 3. **GPS**: n54,76704 e8,98123.

20 € 5 € 1/80liter (20x)€ 0,50/kWh WC € 2.
Location: Urban, comfortable, central, quiet.
Surface: grassy/gravel. 01/01-31/12.
Distance: 1km 2km 100m 1km on the spot on the spot.
Remarks: At swimming pool, to be paid at swimming pool.

Lensahn 6E3

Reisemobilplatz Lensahn, Dr. Julius-Stinde strasse.
GPS: n54,21446 e10,87745.

15 € 8 € 1/80liter € 1 Ch (4x)€ 2.
Location: Rural, simple. **Surface:** grasstiles. 01/01-31/12.
Distance: 1,5km on the spot 200m 2,5km.

Lübeck 8C1

Wohnmobil Treff Lübeck, An der Hülshorst 11.
GPS: n53,89510 e10,71088.

40 € 11/day Ch WCincluded € 1/5minutes .
Location: Urban, luxurious, quiet. **Surface:** gravel. 02/01-31/10.
Distance: 4,5km 5km 100m 50m.

Lübeck 8C1

Wohnmobilstellplatz Lübeck Marienbrücke P4, Lastadie.
GPS: n53,87147 e10,67904.

16 free, 18-10h. **Location:** Urban, simple.
Surface: asphalted.
01/01-31/12.
Distance: 500m 2km on the spot on the spot.
Remarks: Max. 24h.

Tourist information Lübeck:
Museum Holstentor, Holstentorplatz. Historical museum. 10-16/17h. € 7, family card € 15.
Niederegger Einkaufserlebnis, Café und Marzipan-Museum, Breite strasse 89. Marzipan, Lübecker speciality, museum, café and shop.

Lunden 6C3

Wollersumer Straße. **GPS**: n54,33280 e8,99697.

10 free. **Location:** Rural, simple. **Surface:** grassy/gravel.
01/01-31/12 high water.
Distance: 1,7km on the spot.

Maasholm 6D3

Stellplatz am Yachthafen, Uleweg 31. **GPS**: n54,68334 e9,99436.

40 € 12 Ch € 2/night WC € 0,50 € 2 .
Location: Rural, comfortable, central, quiet.
Surface: grassy/gravel. 01/01-31/12.
Distance: 100m 5km on the spot on the spot 100m 300m.
Remarks: Parking marina.

Meldorf 7H1

Reisemobil-Stellplatz am Deich, Deichstraße 2.
GPS: n54,09409 e8,95070.

80 € 8 (18x)€ 3 WC € 2.
Location: Rural, comfortable, isolated, quiet.
Surface: grassy/metalled. Easter-31/10.
Distance: 7km on the spot Imbiss 10-18 uur on the spot on the spot.

Molfsee 6D3

Freilichtmuseum/Restaurant Drathenhof, Hamburger Landstrasse 99. **GPS**: n54,27411 e10,07571.

20 free, use of a meal desired WC at restaurant.
Location: Central. **Surface:** gravel. 01/01-31/12.
Distance: on the spot on the spot on the spot on the spot on the spot.
Remarks: At open air museum.

Mölln 8C2

Alt Möllner strasse. **GPS**: n53,62564 e10,68314.

24 € 7 (20x)included. **Location:** Rural. **Surface:** gravel.
01/01-31/12.
Distance: 1km 250m 300m.
Remarks: Service: Vorkamp 19, GPS N53,62024, E10,67701.

Neufeld 8A1

SBC Neufeld, An'n Hoven. **GPS**: n53,90677 e9,02042.

20 € 8 (20x)€ 2/day WC included. **Location:** Rural, comfortable, quiet. **Surface:** grassy. 01/04-31/10.
Distance: on the spot on the spot on the spot.

Neukirchen 23779 6E3

Wohnmobilhafen Seepark Sütel, Sütel.
GPS: n54,33359 e11,06620.

30 € 12-14, 2 pers. incl included.
Surface: grassy. 01/01-31/12.
Distance: 500m 750m on the spot on the spot.
Remarks: Bread-service in summer period.

Neukirchen 25927 6C3

Sportzentrum, Kirchenweg 2. **GPS**: n54,86602 e8,73304.

4 free . **Location:** Rural, simple, quiet.
Surface: concrete. 01/01-31/12.
Distance: 500m 500m 350m.
Remarks: Max. 4 days.

Neumünster 8B1

Bad am Stadtwald, Hansaring 177. **GPS**: n54,08078 e9,96064.

22 € 10 € 0,50/100liter € 0,50 Ch (22x)€ 0,50/kWh WC € 1 . **Location:** Rural, comfortable, central, quiet.
Surface: grassy/gravel. 01/01-31/12.
Distance: 2km A7 1 km on the spot 300m on the spot.
Remarks: Check in at swimming pool.

Neustadt in Holstein 8C1

Wohnmobilstellplatz Ostsee, Auf der Pelzer Wiese 45, Pelzerhaken.
GPS: n54,08889 e10,87250.

DE

90 € 14 + tourist tax (summer) € 1/100liter € 1 Ch (90x) € 1/2kWh WC € 2. **Location:** Rural, luxurious, noisy.
Surface: grassy. 01/03-31/12.
Distance: 900m 150m 900m 400m on the spot.

Neustadt in Holstein 8C1

P5, Am Binnenwasser. **GPS**: n54,11096 e10,81496.

10 Mo-Fr € 5/24h, Sa-Su free (2x)€ 0,50/kWh.
Location: Urban, simple. **Surface:** metalled. 01/01-31/12.
Distance: on the spot.

Niebüll 6C3

Parkplatz, Lornsenstrasse 19. **GPS**: n54,78901 e8,82546.

25 € 5 € 1/5minutes € 1 Ch (12x)€ 1/8h free.
Location: Urban, simple, central, quiet. **Surface:** grassy.
01/01-31/12 1st week in June.
Distance: on the spot 200m 300m.
Remarks: Parking swimming pool, max. 24h.

Niesgrau 6D3

Wohnmobilstellplatz Gelting-Mole, Gelting-Mole 1.
GPS: n54,75194 e9,86242.

23 € 15 Ch WC included .
Location: Rural. **Surface:** metalled. 01/01-31/12.
Distance: on the spot on the spot 100m.
Remarks: Check in at harbourmaster.

Nordstrand 6C3

Wohnmobilplatz Margarethenruh, Süderhafen 8.
GPS: n54,46944 e8,91000.

21 € 20,50, 2 pers. incl Ch € 3,20/24h WC included € 3/3 . **Location:** Rural, comfortable, central, quiet.
Surface: grassy/gravel. 01/01-31/12.
Distance: 3km 300m 150m 3km.

Nordstrand 6C3

Womoland, Norderquerweg 2. **GPS**: n54,51736 e8,93012.

44 € 7 + € 4/pp Ch € 0,60/kWh WC included.
Location: Comfortable, isolated, quiet.
Surface: grassy/gravel.
15/03-31/10.
Distance: 10km 6km on the spot on the spot 6km.
Remarks: Bread-service.

Tourist information Nordstrand:
Former Wadden island.

Norgaardholz 6D3

Campingplatz Nordstern, Nordstern 1. **GPS**: n54,78528 e9,79889.

10 € 8 Ch (10x)€ 2/night WC € 1,use sanitary € 4/night € 3 € 2/24h. **Location:** Rural, simple, isolated, quiet.
Surface: gravel/metalled. 01/04-30/09.
Distance: on the spot on the spot on the spot on the spot on the spot.

Ockholm 6C3

Wohnmobilstellplätze Altes Pastorat Ockholm, Baderstrasse 5/6.
GPS: n54,66517 e8,82940.

5 € 9 Ch (5x)€ 2/24h WC included € 5/5.
Location: Rural, simple, isolated, quiet. **Surface:** grassy/gravel.
01/01-31/12.
Distance: 100m on the spot.
Remarks: Along through road, bread-service.

Oeversee 6D3

Wohnmobilstellplatz Schnell, Frörupsand 2.
GPS: n54,69253 e9,43252.

20 € 6 Ch € 1/night WC free.
Location: Rural, simple, quiet. **Surface:** grassy. 01/01-31/12.
Distance: 400m 500m 400m.

Osterhever 6C3

Stellplatz Norderheverkoog, Norderheverkoogstraße 12, Norderheverkoog. **GPS**: n54,39656 e8,76163.

10 € 10 Ch (10x)WC included € 1.
Location: Rural, isolated, quiet. **Surface:** grassy.
01/04-31/10.
Distance: 1km 2km 1km on the spot on the spot.
Remarks: Bread-service, bicycle rental.

Pahlen 6C3

Fischerstrasse 17. **GPS**: n54,27101 e9,30015.

12 € 6 + € 1/pp (12x)WC included. **Location:** Rural, comfortable, quiet. **Surface:** grassy. 01/01-31/12.
Distance: 200m 50m 50m 200m 200m.

Plön 8B1

Wohnmobilhafen Plön, Ascheberger straße 76.
GPS: n54,14709 e10,39841.

14 € 17, dog € 3 Ch WC included.
Location: Comfortable, noisy. **Surface:** grassy/gravel.
01/04-15/12.
Distance: 1,5km on the spot.
Remarks: Max. 4 nights.

Plön 8B1

Womo-Stop Kleinen Plöner See, Hamburgerstrasse/Aschenberg strasse, B430. **GPS**: n54,15278 e10,40417.

11 € 5 € 1/1 € 0,50 Ch. **Location:** Simple.
Surface: asphalted. 01/01-31/12.
Distance: on the spot.
Remarks: In front of passage to beach, max. 24h.

Pommerby 6D3

Wohnmobilhafen Ostseesonne, Gammeldam 6.
GPS: n54,76335 e9,97097.
30 € 10-12 Ch € 3/night. **Location:** Rural, simple, quiet. **Surface:** grassy. 01/04-31/10.
Distance: on the spot on the spot on the spot on the spot.

Preetz 6D3

Wohnmobilpark Preetz, Kahlbrook 25a.
GPS: n54,22811 e10,28616.

DE

10 € 15 included WC . Surface: gravel. 01/01-31/12 service 01/11-31/03.
Distance: 10min on the spot on the spot.
Remarks: Bread-service, canoe and bicycle rental.

S Puttgarden 6E3

Wohnmobilplatz Johannisberg, Johannisbergstrasse.
GPS: n54,50054 e11,17938.

50 € 10-15 € 0,10/10liter € 2 Ch € 0,50/kWh WC € 1 € 3,50/2. **Location:** Rural, simple, quiet.
Surface: grassy/metalled. 01/01-31/12.
Distance: 2,5km 800m 800m on the spot.
Remarks: In nature reserve Am Grüner Brink, bread-service.

S Puttgarden 6E3

Bade- und Surfstrand Grüner Brink, Krögenweg.
GPS: n54,51174 e11,18285.
30 € 9 € 2,50 Ch. **Surface:** gravel. 01/01-31/12.
Distance: on the spot.

S Quickborn bei Burg 8A1

Am Helmschen-Bach, Hauptstraße 2. **GPS**: n54,01165 e9,21648.

5 € 6 included € 0,50/kWh. **Location:** Rural, comfortable, quiet. **Surface:** grassy. 01/04-30/09.
Distance: 300m on the spot.

S Rantrum 6C3

Reisemobilhafen Rantrum, Bannony. **GPS**: n54,43369 e9,12743.

13 € 10 Ch (12x) WC included. **Location:** Rural, simple, isolated, quiet. **Surface:** gravel. 01/01-31/12.
Distance: 8km 30km 300m.
Remarks: At swimming pool.

S Ratzeburg 8C1

Hallenbad Aqua Siwa, Fischerstrasse 43.
GPS: n53,69567 e10,77598.

12 € 8/24h € 1/80liter Ch € 0,50/kWh.
Location: Urban, simple, central, noisy. **Surface:** gravel.
01/01-31/12.
Distance: 500m on the spot on the spot on the spot.

S Reinfeld 8B1

Am Herrenteich, Karpfenplatz. **GPS**: n53,83024 e10,48362.

5 free € 0,50/70liter € 0,50 Ch € 0,50/kWh.
Location: Urban, simple, quiet.
Surface: metalled. 01/01-31/12.
Distance: 500m 200m 400m.

S Rendsburg 6D3

Wohnmobil-Hafen Eiderblick, An der Untereider 9.
GPS: n54,30406 e9,65610.

40 € 15 € 1/75liter Ch (45x) € 0,50/kWh WC included against payment. **Location:** Urban, luxurious, central, quiet.
Surface: gravel. 01/01-31/12.
Distance: 800m on the spot 800m on the spot on the spot on the spot.
Remarks: Bread-service, internetcafé.

Tourist information Rendsburg:
- Eiserne Lady. Train-bridge North Sea-Baltic Canal, 42m high.
- Blue Line. City walk 3 km.
- Hausbrauerei Niewarker, Paradeplatz. Guided tour and tastery.

S Reußenköge 6C3

Amsinck Haus, Sönke Nissenkoog 36a. **GPS**: n54,61666 e8,87027.

11 € 7 (6x) € 2/24h WC included € 3.
Location: Rural, comfortable, isolated, quiet. **Surface:** asphalted.
01/04-31/10.
Distance: 4km 4km.
Remarks: Bicycle rental.

S Sankt Peter-Ording 6C3

Reisemobilhafen St.Peter-Ording, Am Ketelskoog.
GPS: n54,30881 e8,63522.

70 € 16 € 2/50liter Ch (70x) € 0,60/kWh WC € 0,20 € 1 € 1/h.
Location: Rural, comfortable. **Surface:** gravel. 01/01-31/12.
Distance: 300m 1km 300m 300m.
Remarks: Arrival <22h, market Wednesday.

Tourist information Sankt Peter-Ording:
- Westküstenpark, Wohldweg 6. Animal park. summer 9.30-18h, winter 11h-sunset.

S Schacht-Audorf 6D3

WohnmobilPark Schacht-Audorf, K76. **GPS**: n54,30611 e9,71250.

41 € 10 € 0,50/100liter Ch (33x) € 0,60/kWh WC € 1 € 1/6minutes .
Location: Rural, comfortable, quiet.
Surface: gravel. 01/01-31/12.
Distance: 700m A7 2km 800m 1km on the spot on the spot.
Remarks: At the canal, max. 3 nights, payment only with coins.

S Scharbeutz 8C1

Womohafen Scharbeutzer Strand, Hamburger Ring 6-8.
GPS: n54,03112 e10,75242.

90 € 10,40 + € 2,80/pp + tourist tax € 1/100liter Ch (2x) € 1/kWh € 2 .
Location: Rural, simple. 01/01-31/12.
Distance: 300m 300m, dog friendly beach 1km 400m.

S Schashagen 8C1

Ostsee-Campingplatz Kagelbusch, Strandweg/Kagelbusch.
GPS: n54,12570 e10,92789.
€ 12 € 1. 01/01-31/12.
Distance: 500m.

S Schashagen 8C1

Wohnmobilpark Ostseeblick, Biesdorf.
GPS: n54,11934 e10,92108.

30 € 7, 01/04-30/09 € 14,50-16,50, 2 pers. incl., dog € 2,50-3,50 € 1/80liter Ch € 0,50/kWh WC .
Location: Rural, comfortable, quiet. **Surface:** grasstiles.
01/01-31/12 Service: winter.
Distance: 300m.

S Schleswig 6D3

Am Schleswig Stadthafen, Am Hafen 5. **GPS**: n54,51203 e9,56802.

DE

45 € 16 Ch (30x),10Amp WC € 2,50/2,50 included.
Location: Urban, comfortable, central. **Surface:** gravel/metalled.
01/03-15/11.
Distance: 150m 5km on the spot on the spot 50m 500m nearby 50m.
Remarks: Max. 48h, check in at harbourmaster, caution key € 20.

Schleswig — 6D3

Wiking-Yachthafen, Wikingeck 11. **GPS**: n54,50670 e9,54733.

8 € 12 € 1 € 1 Ch € 0,40/kWh WC € 2.
Location: Urban, simple, quiet.
Surface: metalled.
01/05-30/09.
Distance: 2km on the spot on the spot on the spot on the spot on the spot.
Remarks: Check in at harbourmaster.

Tourist information Schleswig:
Tourist Information Schleswig, Plessenstrasse 7. Historical city, founded by the Vikings, Haithabu.
Schloß Gottorf. Regional museum, archeological museum and museum for art and culture.
Museum am Danewerk, Ochsenweg 5, Dannewerk. Fortifications, 650-1200.
winter 10-16h, 01/04-31/10 Tue-Fri 9-17h, Sa-Su 10-18h.
Wikinger Museum Haithabu, Haddeby-Busdorf. All about the life of the Vikings.
01/04-31/10 9-17h, 01/11-31/03 Tue-Su 10-16h.

Schönberg/Ostsee — 6D3

Brasilien, Seesternweg. **GPS**: n54,42408 e10,39116.

40 € 9, 15/05-15/09 € 11 Ch included.
Location: Rural, simple. **Surface:** grassy. 01/01-31/12.
Distance: 200m 200m.

Schönberg/Ostsee — 6D3

Stellplatz Mittelstrand, Mittelstrand.
GPS: n54,42233 e10,39573.

50 € 9, 01/05-30/09 € 11 Ch € 2 WC included.
Location: Rural. **Surface:** grassy. 01/01-31/12.
Distance: 200m 200m on the spot.
Remarks: Bread-service in summer period.

Seestermühe — 8A2

Achtern Diek. **GPS**: n53,70333 e9,56232.

4 € 2 € 2 € 2 Ch € 2 € 2/day € 1,50.
Location: Rural. **Surface:** metalled. 01/01-31/12.
Distance: 200m.

Sehestedt — 6D3

Wohnmobilstellplatz Sehestedt, Fährstrasse 1.
GPS: n54,36466 e9,81973.

13 € 7/24h € 0,50/80liter Ch.
Surface: gravel. 01/01-31/12.
Distance: 750m A7 13km on the spot 200m.
Remarks: Directly at North Sea-Baltic canal.

Sierksdorf — 8C1

Hansa-Park, Am Fahrenkrog 1. **GPS**: n54,07417 e10,77522.
100 € 6/24h. **Surface:** asphalted. 15/04-31/10.
Distance: 1km on the spot 750m 800m on the spot.

Sierksdorf — 8C1

Wohnmobilstellplatz Hof Sierksdorf, Altonaer Straße.
GPS: n54,06013 e10,75737.
15 € 11 excl. tourist tax € 1 € 1 Ch € 0,50/kWh WC.
Location: Simple. **Surface:** gravel. 01/04-30/09.
Distance: beach 100m.

Simonsberg — 6C3

Nordsee Camping Zum Seehund, Lundenbergweg 4.
GPS: n54,45515 e8,96958.

15 € 15-21 Ch WC included € 3 free.
Location: Rural, comfortable, isolated, quiet.
Surface: gravel. Easter-31/10.
Distance: 3km 500m on the spot on the spot on camp site on the spot on the spot.
Remarks: Use steam bath, sauna, fitness-studio incl.

Sörup — 6D3

Südensee, Seeblick. **GPS**: n54,71086 e9,66511.

5 € 4 Ch € 2/night WC.
Location: Rural, simple, quiet. **Surface:** gravel. 01/04-31/10.
Distance: 500m on the spot on the spot kiosk on the spot on the spot.
Remarks: Parking at small lake.

Struckum — 6C3

Marschblick, Kennedy Weg 3. **GPS**: n54,58597 e8,99117.

30 € 10 Ch WC included € 3.
Location: Rural, simple, quiet. **Surface:** asphalted.
01/01-31/12.
Distance: 100m 8km 750m 1,5km 100m on the spot.
Remarks: Money in envelope in mail box.

Süderlügum — 6C3

Wohnmobilplatz Mehrzweckhalle, Jahnstrasse.
GPS: n54,87472 e8,90306.

5 free. **Location:** Rural, simple, central, quiet. **Surface:** metalled.
01/01-31/12.
Distance: 500m 300m.
Remarks: Max. 7m.

Tetenhusen — 6D3

Heuherberge Tetenhusen, Sein 10. **GPS**: n54,34795 e9,50330.

6 € 12 included WC € 2. **Location:** Rural, simple, isolated, quiet. **Surface:** grassy. 01/01-31/12.
Distance: 300m on the spot 250m on the spot.
Remarks: Breakfast-service, canoe rental.

Timmendorfer Strand — 8C1

Am Vogelpark, P4, Bäderrandstraße, B76.
GPS: n53,99136 e10,81439.

50 € 7,50 + € 3/pp tourist tax € 0,50/120liter Ch € 1/kWh.
Location: Rural, simple. **Surface:** grassy/sand.
01/01-31/12.
Distance: 180m.
Remarks: Max. 1 night.

Tönning — 6C3

Wohnmobilplatz Eiderblick - Kapitänshaus, Am Strandweg.
GPS: n54,30920 e8,93684.

DE

50 € 12 2p incl. + tourist tax € 1/100liter Ch € 0,60/kWh included € 4/3 € 1/2h. **Location:** Rural, luxurious, isolated, quiet. **Surface:** grassy. 01/01-31/12.
Distance: 500m on the spot on the spot on the spot.
Remarks: Along the Eider river, swimming pool 200m.

Travemünde 8C1

Wohnmobilparkplatz Kowitzberg, Kowitzberg.
GPS: n53,97598 e10,87830.

49 15/5-14/9 € 12, 15/9-14/5 € 8 € 1/100liter Ch (48x) € 1/5kWh. **Location:** Rural, simple. **Surface:** grassy. 01/01-31/12.
Distance: 2,5km 800m 800m 300m 250m 50m.

Travemünde 8C1

Parkplatz am Fischerreihafen, Auf dem Baggersand 15.
GPS: n53,95556 e10,86139.

90 € 12-15 € 1/35liter Ch (5x)€ 3/kWh WC € 2.
Location: Urban, simple. **Surface:** grassy/gravel.
01/01-31/12.
Distance: beach 800m max. 500m express bus Altstadt Lubeck.
Remarks: Parking fishing port, bicycle rental.

Trittau 8B2

Zum Schützenplatz. **GPS**: n53,61063 e10,40843.

5 free WC. **Location:** Urban, simple, central, quiet.
Surface: asphalted. 01/01-31/12.
Distance: 500m 500m 500m 50m.
Remarks: Next to swimming pool.

Uetersen 8A2

Am Stichhafen, Ziegelei. **GPS**: n53,67977 e9,66861.

4 free. **Location:** Urban, simple. **Surface:** metalled.
01/01-31/12.
Distance: 400m 7,4km 300m.

Utersum 6C3

Wohnmobilstellplatz Föhr, Strunwai 14. **GPS**: n54,71593 e8,40117.
€ 15 € 0,50/100liter Ch WC € 0,50. **Surface:** grassy.
15/03-15/11.
Distance: 400m.

Waabs 6D3

Gut Ludwigsburg. **GPS**: n54,50350 e9,95767.

18 € 15 Ch 16Amp WC included € 4/24h.
Location: Rural, simple, isolated, quiet. **Surface:** grassy.
01/04-30/09.
Distance: on the spot on the spot on the spot on the spot.

Weddelbrook 8B1

Campingplatz Vogelzunge, Schulstraße 19.
GPS: n53,89995 e9,82657.

6 € 10 Chincluded € 0,50/4h WC € 1/4minutes.
Location: Rural, simple, quiet.
Surface: grassy. 01/01-31/12.
Distance: 300m on the spot.
Remarks: At lake, check-in and key at reception.

Wedel 8A2

Am Freibad. **GPS**: n53,57860 e9,69520.

20 € 10 € 1/10minutes Ch (14x)€ 1/8h WC.
Location: Rural, simple, quiet. **Surface:** grassy/metalled.
01/01-31/12 during event.
Distance: 800m.
Remarks: Max. 3 days, to be paid at swimming pool.

Westerholz 6D3

Campingplatz Fördeblick, Kummle 1. **GPS**: n54,81998 e9,66686.

45 € 10 € 1/time Ch € 3/night,6Amp WC € 1 against payment included. **Location:** Rural, simple, quiet.
Surface: grassy/gravel. 01/04-30/09.
Distance: 2,5km 100m 1,5km 2,5km on the spot.
Remarks: At Flensborg Fjord, max. 24h.

Wilster 8A1

Colosseumplatz, Etatsrätin-Doos-Straße 14-17.
GPS: n53,92419 e9,37449.

15 free € 1/5minutes Ch€ 1 (4x)€ 0,50/kWh.
Location: Urban, simple, central, quiet. **Surface:** grassy/gravel.
01/01-31/12 fair.
Distance: 200m 100m on the spot on the spot.

Wischhafen 8A1

Alter Hafen, Hafenstraße 10. **GPS**: n53,77278 e9,32278.

8 free (6x)€ 1/kWh. **Location:** Rural, simple.
Surface: grassy/gravel. 01/01-31/12.
Distance: 500m 1km.

Wischhafen 8A1

Ziegelstraße, Gewerbegebiet Wischhafen.
GPS: n53,76417 e9,32111.

3 free Chfree.
Location: Rural, simple. **Surface:** gravel. 01/01-31/12.
Distance: 1km 200m.

Wischhafen 8A1

Süder-Elbe, Glückstädter Straße. **GPS**: n53,78678 e9,34017.

15 free. **Location:** Rural, simple, isolated.
Surface: gravel. 01/01-31/12.
Distance: 3km 150m.
Remarks: Parking at ferry-boat.

Wischhafen 8A1

Unterm Deich 7. **GPS**: n53,77528 e9,32111.

6 free. **Location:** Rural, simple. **Surface:** grassy. 01/01-31/12.
Distance: 300m on the spot 1km.

DE

Lower Saxony/Bremen

Adendorf 8C2

Freizeitzentrum, Scharnebecker Weg. **GPS**: n53,28925 e10,45398.

30 € 8 € 1/10minutes Ch (4x)€ 1/8h,01/10-30/04 € 2/8h.
Location: Rural, simple, noisy. 01/01-31/12.
Distance: 500m.
Remarks: Parking sports centre, max. 3 days, swimming pool and sauna on site.

Aerzen 10A2

Restaurant Waldquelle, Waldquelle 1.
GPS: n52,05952 e9,26146.

5 € 5 (1x)€ 2/day.
Location: Rural, isolated. **Surface:** gravel. 01/01-31/12 Tue.
Distance: 2km 1km 500m on the spot.
Remarks: Check in at hotel, bread-service and breakfast buffet.

Ahlerstedt 8A2

Ahlerstedt Ottendorf, Rickstücken 2. **GPS**: n53,38908 e9,41017.

25 € 8 Ch included.
Location: Rural, simple. **Surface:** metalled. 01/01-31/12.
Distance: 3km 3km.

Alfeld/Leine 10B2

Bornstrasse. **GPS**: n51,98586 e9,82769.

4 free. **Location:** Simple. **Surface:** metalled. 01/01-31/12.
Distance: on the spot 80m 200m.
Remarks: Parking in city centre behind the evangelical church.

Altenau 10C2

Alter Bahnhof Altenau, Rothenbergerstrasse 52.
GPS: n51,79879 e10,43320.
30 € 6 + € 3,87/pp € 1/65liter Ch (20x)€ 3,50/day,10Amp WC € 1 € 2,50/2,50 included. **Location:** Quiet.
Surface: gravel. 01/01-31/12.
Distance: 1km on the spot 1km on the spot on the spot 2km on the spot.
Remarks: Bread-service, shuttle bus.

Altenau 10C2

Kristall-Saunatherme Heißer Brocken, Karl-Reinecke-Weg 35.
GPS: n51,79836 e10,44408.

20 € 10 + € 2/pp tourist tax € 0,50/40liter Ch € 0,50/kWh € 1,50. **Location:** Rural, quiet. **Surface:** metalled.
01/01-31/12.
Distance: 1,5km on the spot on the spot on the spot.
Remarks: Pay at pay-desk of theTherme.

Amelinghausen 8B3

Lopausee, Auf der Kalten Hude. **GPS**: n53,13324 e10,23441.

50 € 5, 1/9-1/7 € 3,50 Chincluded. **Location:** Simple, isolated, quiet. **Surface:** gravel/sand. 01/01-31/12.
Distance: 1km 100m 100m 1km 1km on the spot on the spot.
Remarks: Bread-service in summer period, ticket available at petrol stations, kiosk Lopausee, pay-desk Waldbad and tourist office.

Amelinghausen 8B3

Waldbad, Zum Lopautal. **GPS**: n53,12402 e10,23018.

40 € 8 Ch included.
Location: Comfortable. 01/01-31/12.
Distance: 1km 500m 1km 1km on the spot on the spot.
Remarks: Bread-service in summer period, incl. access swimming pool.

Amelinghausen 8B3

Kronsbergheide, Hochseilgarten. **GPS**: n53,13500 e10,23389.

10 € 5, 1/9-1/7 € 3,50.
Location: Rural, simple, isolated, quiet. 01/01-31/12.
Distance: 1km 500m on the spot 1km 1km on the spot on the spot.
Remarks: Ticket available at petrol stations, kiosk Lopausee, pay-desk Waldbad and tourist office.

Amelinghausen 8B3

Schwindbeckerheide, Steinbeckerstrasse, Soderstorf.
GPS: n53,12247 e10,09934.

15 € 5, 1/9-1/7 € 3,50. **Location:** Rural, simple, isolated.
Surface: metalled/sand. 01/01-31/12.
Distance: 6km on the spot on the spot.
Remarks: Ticket available at petrol stations, kiosk Lopausee, pay-desk Waldbad and tourist office.

Amelinghausen 8B3

Landgasthaus Eichenkrug, Unter den Eichen 10, Dehnsen.
GPS: n53,12804 e10,16817.

4 € 6 included.
Location: Simple, isolated. **Surface:** metalled. 01/01-31/12.
Distance: 4km on the spot 4km on the spot on the spot.
Remarks: Max. 3 nights.

Amelinghausen 8B3

Schenck's Hotel & Gasthaus, Lüneburgerstrasse 48.
GPS: n53,12568 e10,21426.

15 € 10 € 0,80/kWh,+ € 1,50 WCincluded.
Location: Simple, central. **Surface:** metalled.
01/01-31/12.
Distance: on the spot on the spot on the spot on the spot on the spot.

Tourist information Amelinghausen:
Oldendorfer Totenstatt. Hunnebed cineraria from the ice-age.
guided tour 01/05-30/09.

Ankum 9G1

Ferienhof Buse-Glass, Tütingen 5. **GPS**: n52,51431 e7,86842.

DE

5 € 15 WC included.
Location: Quiet. **Surface:** grassy. 01/01-31/12.
Distance: 2,5km 500m 2,5km.

Apen 7G3

Am Drahkamp, Edewechter Strasse, Godensholt.
GPS: n53,16999 e7,83356.
free. **Location:** Rural. 01/01-31/12.
Distance: Apen 6km 900m.

Apen 7G3

Am Freibad, Hauptstraße, Hengstforde. **GPS:** n53,21795 e7,78706.

10 free. **Location:** Rural, simple. **Surface:** metalled.
01/05-15/09.
Distance: 5,8km 50m.
Remarks: Along railwayline, swimming pool Hengstforde.

Apen 7G3

Viehmarktplatz, Hauptstraße. **GPS:** n53,21820 e7,80221.

10 free. **Location:** Simple. **Surface:** metalled.
01/01-31/12.
Distance: 100m 5km on the spot.
Remarks: Max. 2 days.

Artlenburg 8C2

Am Sportboothafen, Am Deich 9. **GPS:** n53,37680 e10,48550.

30 € 10-15 Ch WC. **Location:** Comfortable, quiet.
Surface: grassy. 15/04-15/10.
Distance: 500m on the spot on the spot 500m 500m 500m.
Remarks: Along the river Elbe.

Aurich 7G2

Familienbad De Baalje, Tannenbergstraße.
GPS: n53,46540 e7,47568.

20 € 10 € 1/100liter Ch € 1/time (24x)€ 1/kWh € 1.
Location: Urban, comfortable, quiet. **Surface:** metalled.
01/01-31/12.
Distance: 500m 100m.
Remarks: Check in and pay at pay desk swimming pool.

Aurich 7G2

An den Kiesgruben, Tannenhausen. **GPS:** n53,52173 e7,47834.

5 free. **Surface:** unpaved. 01/01-31/12.
Distance: 1km 10m on the spot.
Remarks: At the lake of Tannenhausen.

Aurich 7G2

Landgasthof Alte Post, Essenerstrasse. **GPS:** n53,54573 e7,60736.

6 € 6, guests € 3 € 1 Ch WC.
Surface: metalled. 01/01-31/12.
Distance: on the spot.
Remarks: Caution key electricity € 10.

Bad Bentheim 9F2

Am Mühlenberg, Mühlenberg. **GPS:** n52,29360 e7,10095.

10 € 8 € 1/80liter Ch € 0,50/kWh WC.
Location: Rural. **Surface:** metalled. 01/01-31/12.
Distance: 200m 50m 200m on the spot on the spot.

Bad Bentheim 9F2

Am Schloßpark, Funkenstiege. **GPS:** n52,30328 e7,15448.

35 € 9/24h € 1/80liter Ch (36x)€ 0,50/kWh WC.
Surface: metalled. 01/01-31/12.
Distance: 200m 100m.

Bad Bevensen 8C3

Am Waagekai. **GPS:** n53,07417 e10,60139.

30 € 5,40 + € 3/pp tourist tax Ch included € 1.
Location: Rural, simple, quiet. **Surface:** gravel/sand.
01/01-31/12.
Distance: 1km on the spot 1km 600m on the spot on the spot.

Bad Essen 9H1

Wohnmobilstellplatz Falkenburg, Falkenburg 3.
GPS: n52,32352 e8,36384.

50 € 7 € 1/100liter Ch € 2/4kWh WC € 0,50.
Location: Rural, comfortable, quiet. **Surface:** grassy/metalled.
01/03-30/10.
Distance: 1,2km 900m 300m.
Remarks: At the Mittelland canal, near marina, bread-service (weekend).

Bad Gandersheim 10B2

Wohnmobil-Stellplatz Rio Gande, An der Wiek.
GPS: n51,87191 e10,01881.

24 € 7/24h, tourist tax incl € 1/100liter Ch (14x)€ 0,50/kWh. **Location:** Rural, simple. **Surface:** gravel.
01/01-31/12.
Distance: 400m 100m 200m on the spot on the spot.
Remarks: Max. 3 nights, bread-service only in summer.

Bad Lauterberg 10C3

Erlebnisbad Vitamar, Mast Tal 1. **GPS:** n51,63358 e10,48661.

5 free € 1 € 1 Ch € 1. **Location:** Simple, quiet.
Surface: metalled. 01/01-31/12.
Distance: 1,5km 30km on the spot 1,5km on the spot.

Bad Lauterberg 10C3

Wiesenbeker Teich, Wiesenbek 75. **GPS:** n51,61719 e10,49074.

DE

4 € 13 Ch included.
Location: Isolated, quiet. **Surface:** gravel.
01/01-31/12.
Distance: 2km 30km on the spot on the spot on the spot 2km 2km on the spot.
Remarks: Check in and pay at reception campsite, max. 1 night.

S Bad Münder 10A2

Rhomelbad, Lindenallee. **GPS**: n52,19305 e9,47111.

5 free Ch.
Location: Simple. **Surface:** metalled. 01/01-31/12.
Distance: 400m on the spot 400m 200m.

S Bad Nenndorf 10A1

Wohnmobilstellplatz am Schulzentrum, Bahnhofstrasse 77.
GPS: n52,34294 e9,37666.

8 free € 2/45liter Ch (8x)€ 1/6h WC.
Location: Simple. **Surface:** gravel/metalled. 01/01-31/12.
Distance: 700m 3,4km on the spot on the spot on the spot.
Remarks: At sports centre, use sanitary only during opening hours swimming pool.

S Bad Pyrmont 10A2

Reisemobilhafen in den Emmerauen, Hauptmann Boelke-Weg.
GPS: n51,98092 e9,25108.
65 € 11 + € 2,30-3,20/pp tourist tax € 0,10/10liter Ch (60x)€ 0,60/kWh WC included.
Location: Urban, central. **Surface:** grassy/gravel.
01/01-31/12.
Distance: historical centre 400m 200m 400m 100m.
Remarks: Bread-service, e-bike rental, free shuttle to spa resort, free entrance swimming pool.

Tourist information Bad Pyrmont:
Bad Pyrmont Tourismus GmbH, Europa-Platz 1, www.badpyrmont.de. Health resort.

Bad Sachsa 10C3

Harzer Schnitzelhaus & Waffelbäckerei, Schützenstrasse 13.
GPS: n51,59778 e10,55056.

2 guests free. **Location:** Rural, simple, central. **Surface:** asphalted.
01/01-31/12.
Distance: on the spot on the spot 100m.
Remarks: Max. 2 days.

S Bad Salzdetfurth 10B2

Am Solebad, Solebadstraße, Detfurth.
GPS: n52,07193 e10,01859.

10 € 5/24h € 1/50liter Ch € 1/6h WC € 3.
Location: Rural. **Surface:** asphalted.
01/01-31/12.
Distance: 2km Bistro 50m 100m on the spot on the spot.
Remarks: Use sanitary only during opening hours swimming pool, market Friday-morning.

S Bad Zwischenahn 7G3

Wohnmobilstellplatz Am Badepark, Am Badepark 1.
GPS: n53,18722 e8,00021.

50 € 14 tourist tax incl € 0,50/100liter Ch (35x)€ 0,60/kWh WC (spa resort) included.
Location: Urban, simple. **Surface:** metalled. 01/01-31/12.
Distance: 350m 6,8km on the spot on the spot 100m 500m on the spot.

S Balge 10A1

Stellplatz Marina Mehlbergen, Werderstraße.
GPS: n52,68788 e9,17779.
20 € 10 Ch (16x)€ 0,50/kWh WC included.
Surface: metalled. 01/01-31/12.
Distance: 2km on the spot on the spot 2km 2km 1km on the spot on the spot.
Remarks: Check in on arrival.

Balje 8A1

Am Natureum, Neuenhof 8, Neuhaus. **GPS**: n53,81958 e9,03867.

6 free. **Location:** Rural, simple, isolated. **Surface:** grassy.
01/01-31/12.
Distance: 4km on the spot 4km 4km.

S Barnstorf 9H1

Wohnmobilstellplatz Midden int Dörp, Rathausweg/Brinkstraße.
GPS: n52,71170 e8,50780.
3 free Ch. **Surface:** metalled. 01/01-31/12.
Distance: on the spot 100m 300m.

S Barßel 7G3

Am Bootshafen, Deichstrasse. **GPS**: n53,16754 e7,73441.

18 €6 Ch (34x)€ 2/24h WC € 1 included.
Location: Urban, simple. **Surface:** grasstiles. 01/01-31/12.
Distance: 500m on the spot on the spot 500m.

S Barsinghausen 10A1

Wohnmobilstellplatz am Besucherbergwerk Klosterstollen, Conrad-Bühreweg. **GPS**: n52,29858 e9,46943.

5 € 6,50 (5x)included.
Location: Rural, simple. **Surface:** gravel. 01/01-31/12.
Distance: 300m nearby 300m.
Remarks: Max. 3 days, visit coalmine possible.

S Berge 9G1

Stift Börstel, Börstel 5. **GPS**: n52,64957 e7,69438.
2 € 5, in envelope in mail box € 2 € 2. **Surface:** metalled.
01/01-31/12.
Distance: city centre Haselünne 7km 3km 7km 150m.
Remarks: Near abbey, max. 2 nights.

Berge 9G1

Dorfteich Berge, Schienenweg 19. **GPS**: n52,62011 e7,75099.
2 free. 01/01-31/12.
Distance: 400m 400m 300m 150m.

S Bergen 8B3

Stellplatz am Ziegeleiweg, Ziegeleiweg. **GPS**: n52,81273 e9,96457.

6 € 3,50 € 1 Ch included.
Surface: gravel.
01/01-31/12.
Distance: nearby 300m 450m 250m.
Remarks: Caution key € 20 at town hall.

Tourist information Bergen:
Wildpark Lüneburger Heide, Nindorf. Game preserve.
01/03-31/10 8-19h, 01/11-28/02 9.30-16.30h.

S Berne 7H3

Fähranleger Motzen, Motzener Strasse. **GPS**: n53,17972 e8,55778.

4 free € 1/60liter Ch (4x)€ 1/6h.
Location: Urban, simple, isolated, noisy. **Surface:** gravel/sand.
01/01-31/12.
Distance: 3,5km on the spot 1km 100m 100m.
Remarks: Parking at ferry-boat at river Weser.

Bevern 10A2

Schwimm- und Freizeitzentrum, Jahnstrasse.
GPS: n51,85750 e9,50805.

5 free. **Location:** Rural, simple. **Surface:** asphalted.
01/01-31/12.

DE

Distance: 1,2km 500m 500m.

S Bienenbüttel 8C3

Wohnmobilstellplatz Ilmenauwiese, Niendorfer strasse, K42.
GPS: n53,14514 e10,49051.

12 € 6/24h € 1/10minutes Ch (14x)€ 1/8h WC free € 0,50. **Location:** Rural, comfortable, quiet. **Surface:** metalled.
01/01-31/12.
Distance: 500m on the spot on the spot 500m 500m special sculpture route.

Bippen 9G1

Dorfteich, Hauptstrasse. **GPS**: n52,58209 e7,73887.
2 free. 01/01-31/12.
Distance: 1km.

S Bippen 9G1

Ferienhof Nyenhuis, Hallweg 8. **GPS**: n52,59360 e7,73005.

20 € 13 WC € 2,50.
Location: Rural, simple, quiet. **Surface:** grassy. 01/01-31/12.
Distance: 1km.

S Bippen 9G1

Gasthof Mol, Einigkeitsstraße 20, Lonnerbecke.
GPS: n52,54337 e7,67118.
10 free Service € 7/day Service € 7/day.
01/01-31/12.
Distance: on the spot.

S Bippen 9G1

Hotel-Restaurant-Café Sülte Mühle, Ölmühle 1, Lonnerbecke.
GPS: n52,54972 e7,69594.
2 free € 2. 01/01-31/12.
Distance: on the spot.

S Bispingen 8B3

Parkplatz Oberhaverbeck, Oberhaverbeck. **GPS**: n53,14281 e9,91998.

30 € 3/day, € 6/night € 1/10minutes Ch (8x)€ 1/10h.
Location: Rural, simple, isolated. **Surface:** grassy/gravel.
01/01-31/12 Service: winter.
Distance: 6km 350m 6km 100m on the spot on the spot.
Remarks: In nature reserve the the Lüneburg Heide (heath).

Bispingen 8B3

Parking Rathaus, Borsteler Straße 4-6. **GPS**: n53,08499 e9,89789.

5 free. **Location:** Simple, central. **Surface:** metalled.
01/01-31/12.
Distance: on the spot 1km 100m 100m on the spot on the spot.

S Bispingen 8B3

Reiter- und Ferienhof Cohrs, Volkwardingen 1, Moorweg.
GPS: n53,13409 e10,00047.

10 € 14 Ch included WC € 3.
Location: Comfortable, isolated, quiet.
Surface: grassy. 01/01-31/12.
Distance: 3km 5,5km 500m 5km on the spot.
Remarks: Bread-service.

S Bissendorf 9H2

Reisemobil-Center Veregge & Welz, Gewerbepark 14, A30 Abfahrt Bissendorf. **GPS**: n52,24026 e8,13977.

6 free € 1/5minutes Ch (4x)€ 1/6h. **Location:** Urban, simple, quiet. **Surface:** metalled.
01/01-31/12.
Distance: 1km 650m 800m 800m.

S Bleckede 8C2

Campingpark Elbtalaue, Am Waldbad 23.
GPS: n53,25948 e10,80526.

5 € 10/night € 1/80liter Ch € 0,70/kWh WC sanitary € 3,50/pp € 3,50/3 € 4/day. **Location:** Rural, luxurious, isolated, quiet. **Surface:** grassy. 01/03-31/10.
Distance: 2km 300m 800m 6km 50m on the spot on the spot.
Remarks: Bread-service, dog € 3,50, possibility for reservation, free entrance swimming pool.

S Blomberg 7G2

Dorfplatz Blomberg, Hauptstrasse. **GPS**: n53,57718 e7,55815.

20 free € 1 Ch € 1 (12x)€ 1/kWh WC.
Location: Rural, comfortable, quiet. **Surface:** grassy/metalled.
01/01-31/12 service 01/11-31/03.
Distance: on the spot 200m 200m 50m.

Bockenem 10B2

Am Freibad, In den Reesen. **GPS**: n52,00787 e10,13610.

5 free. **Location:** Rural, simple, quiet. **Surface:** gravel.
01/01-31/12.
Distance: 800m 200m 300m.

S Bockenem 10B2

Hotel Sauer am Aral Autohof, Allensteiner strasse 7.
GPS: n52,00224 e10,13379.

20 guests free € 1,50 Ch (8x)€ 2,50 WC € 1,50.
Location: Rural, simple.
Surface: metalled. 01/01-31/12.
Distance: 300m on the spot 500m.

S Bockhorn 7G2

Reisemobilplatz Germer, Am Geeschendamm 1.
GPS: n53,38575 e8,00857.

30 € 7 € 1,50 Ch (15x)€ 0,75/kWh WC € 2.
Location: Comfortable. **Surface:** grassy. 01/01-31/12.
Distance: 400m 700m on the spot on the spot.

Bockhorn 7G2

Erlebnisbad, Urwaldstrasse 35a. **GPS**: n53,39876 e7,99410.

5 free. **Location:** Rural, simple.
Surface: gravel. 01/01-31/12.
Distance: on the spot.
Remarks: Parking swimming pool, max. 1 day.

S Bockhorn 7G2

Gaststätte Altdeutsche Diele, Landesstrasse 11, Steinhausen.
GPS: n53,41404 e8,03466.

3 free (3x)against payment. **Location:** Simple.
Surface: metalled. 01/01-31/12.

DE

Bockhorn 7G2

Zum Sandkrug, Sandkrugsweg 21,Grabstede.
GPS: n53,35893 e8,00186.

4 free. **Location:** Rural, simple, quiet.
Surface: grassy. 01/01-31/12.
Distance: on the spot.

Bodenwerder 10A2

Wohnmobilstellplatz Bodenwerder, Am Mühlentor.
GPS: n51,98037 e9,51795.

25 € 6, tourist tax € 1/pp € 2/10minutes Ch € 2,50/day WC € 1,50.
Location: Urban, simple. **Surface:** grassy. 01/01-31/12.
Distance: 200m Weser 200m 200m 500m 200m.
Remarks: Check in and pay at kiosk.

Bohmte 9H1

Golfclub Arenshorst, Arenshorster Kirchweg 2.
GPS: n52,35651 e8,28450.

3 guests free. **Location:** Rural, simple.
Surface: grassy/metalled. 01/01-31/12.
Distance: 3km on the spot 3km.

Bohmte 9H1

Landgasthaus Gieseke-Asshorn, Bremer strasse 55.
GPS: n52,36674 e8,31261.

4 guests free free. **Location:** Urban, quiet.
Surface: metalled. 01/01-31/12.
Distance: 50m on the spot 200m.

Brake 7H2

City-Parkplatz, Breite Strasse. **GPS**: n53,32534 e8,47982.

2 free. **Location:** Urban, simple, central, noisy. **Surface:** metalled.
01/01-31/12.
Distance: on the spot on the spot 200m 200m on the spot.
Remarks: Key at aparthotel Panorama (50m).

Brake 7H2

Am Binnenhafen, Hafenstrasse. **GPS**: n53,32802 e8,48296.

4 free € 1/10minutes Ch (4x)€ 1/6h.
Location: Urban, simple, central, noisy. **Surface:** grasstiles.
01/01-31/12.
Distance: on the spot 1km 100m 200m 200m on the spot.

Bramsche 9G1

Wohnmobilstellplatz Waldwinkel, Zum Dreschhaus 4.
GPS: n52,39591 e8,10244.

60 € 7 € 0,10/10liter Ch (80x)€ 2 WC € 1.
Location: Rural, comfortable, quiet. **Surface:** grassy.
01/01-31/12.
Distance: 3,5km 100m 3,5km on the spot on the spot.
Remarks: Next to campsite Waldwinkel.

Bramsche 9G1

Hasebad, Malgartener strasse 49. **GPS**: n52,41493 e7,99423.

6 free. **Location:** Urban, simple, quiet.
Surface: metalled. 01/01-31/12.
Distance: 500m.

Bramsche 9G1

Reisemobile Lewandowsky, Am Kanal 1b.
GPS: n52,38524 e7,92958.

2 free Ch free € 2/day.
Location: Rural, simple. **Surface:** gravel. 01/01-31/12.
Distance: 1km 1km 1km.
Remarks: Also repairs possible, service during opening hours, walking and bicycle area.

Braunlage 10C3

Schützenplatz, Schützenstrasse 21. **GPS**: n51,71658 e10,60847.

85 € 10 + € 2,20/pp tourist tax € 1/80liter Ch € 0,50/kWh WC included € 1,50 € 3.
Location: Rural, luxurious, quiet. **Surface:** gravel. 01/01-31/12.
Distance: 400m Café Restaurant Hubertushöhe on the spot on the spot on the spot.
Remarks: Bread-service.

Braunschweig 10C1

Theodor-Heuss-Straße. **GPS**: n52,24964 e10,51835.

16 free € 1/10minutes Ch (16x)€ 1/8h.
Location: Urban, simple, noisy. **Surface:** asphalted.
01/01-31/12.
Distance: 2km 400m 200m on the spot.
Remarks: Max. 2 nights.

Bremen 7H3

Wohnmobil Oase Bremen, Schoster born, via Emil von Behringstrasse.
GPS: n53,06778 e8,86333.

8 € 15 + tourist tax € 1/pp € 2 Ch WC included € 1,50,use luxurious bathroom € 5, sauna € 5 € 6.
Location: Urban, comfortable, central. **Surface:** gravel.
01/01-31/12.
Distance: 4km on the spot 50m Tram on the spot.
Remarks: Motorhome < 7m.

Bremen 7H3

Am Kuhhirten, Kurhirtenweg. **GPS**: n53,06500 e8,81871.

70 € 15 € 1/100liter Ch (70x)€ 0,50/kWh WC € 1/24h € 1/5minutes. **Location:** Urban, comfortable, central.
Surface: gravel. 01/01-31/12.
Distance: Old city centre 1,3km 500m on the spot 800m Tram 700m on the spot.
Remarks: Bread-service.

Bremen 7H3

Bremer Schweiz, Im Pohl, Lesum. **GPS**: n53,16765 e8,69560.

DE

7 € 5/24h € 1/10minutes Ch (8x)€ 1/8h.
Location: Urban, comfortable, quiet. **Surface:** gravel.
01/01-31/12.
Distance: on the spot 2,4km on the spot 300m on the spot on the spot.

S Bremen 7H3

Maritime Meile, Schulkenstrasse. **GPS**: n53,17298 e8,60906.

5 € 5 + tourist tax € 1/80liter Ch (4x)€ 1/8h.
Location: Urban, comfortable, central, quiet.
Surface: asphalted.
01/01-31/12.
Distance: Bremen 20km 100m 100m 200m on the spot.

Tourist information Bremen:
Tourist Information, Obernstrasse en Hauptbahnhof, www.bremen-tourism.de. Hanseatic city and second harbour of Germany.
Böttcherstrasse. Pedestrian passage.
Weserpromenade Schlachte. Antiques and flea market. Sa 8-14h.

S Bremerhaven 7H2

Reisemobil-Parkplatz Doppelschleuse, An der Neuen Schleuse.
GPS: n53,53230 e8,57607.

63 € 10 € 1/80liter Ch (40x)€ 0,50/kWh WC € 0,50 € 0,50. **Location:** Urban, comfortable, central, quiet.
Surface: asphalted. 01/01-31/12.
Distance: 1km 8km 1km 1,5km 1,2km on the spot.
Remarks: Bread-service.

S Bremerhaven 7H2

Reisemobil-Parkplatz Fischereihafen, Hoebelstrasse, Fischereihafen 1. **GPS**: n53,52634 e8,57610.

47 € 10, tourist tax incl € 1/100liter Ch (36x)€ 0,50/kWh WC included € 0,50. **Location:** Urban, luxurious, central, quiet.
Surface: asphalted/metalled. 01/01-31/12.
Distance: 4km on the spot on the spot 500m 500m 200m 200m.
Remarks: At harbour, caution key sanitary € 5.

S Bremerhaven 7H2

Havenhostel Bremerhaven, Bürgermeister-Smidt-Straße 209.
GPS: n53,55932 e8,56793.

20 € 15 Ch included WC € 2/2. **Surface:** grassy.
01/01-31/12.
Distance: 1km on the spot.
Remarks: Check in at reception, breakfast-service.

S Bremervörde 8A2

Wohnmobilstation Bremervörde, Kiebitzweg 1.
GPS: n53,49453 e9,15576.
40 € 9,50, 01/11-28/02 € 6,50 Ch (21x)€ 3/day,10Amp WC € 1 included. **Location:** Rural, comfortable, quiet.
Surface: metalled. 01/01-31/12.
Distance: 1,5km 100m 100m 300m 1km 1,5km on the spot on the spot.

S Brietlingen 8B2

Reihersee, Grosse strabe. **GPS**: n53,34344 e10,45844.

50 € 8 € 2,50 . **Location:** Rural, simple, isolated.
Surface: grassy. 01/03-31/10.
Distance: on the spot.

S Brietlingen 8B2

Landhotel Franck, Bundesstrasse 31b. **GPS**: n53,32951 e10,44491.

5 guests free (1x)€ 5/night.
Location: Rural, simple, quiet. 01/01-31/12.
Distance: on the spot on the spot 500m.

S Bruchhausen-Vilsen 8A3

Reisemobilstellplatz Bruchhausen-Vilsen, Bollenstrasse.
GPS: n52,82671 e8,99536.

40 € 6 € 1/100liter Ch (24x) WC included .
Surface: gravel. 01/01-31/12.
Distance: 200m 200m 200m.
Remarks: Max. 3 days.

S Buchholz/Nordheide 8B2

Campingplatz Nordheide, Weg zum Badeteich 20.
GPS: n53,28202 e9,87495.

12 € 12-15 Ch (6x)€ 2 WC included .
Location: Rural, comfortable. **Surface:** metalled/sand.
01/01-31/12.
Distance: 200m on the spot on the spot 200m.

S Bückeburg 10A2

Am Schloss, Georgstrasse/Liebesallee. **GPS**: n52,25777 e9,04583.

20 € 7/24h € 1/8minutes Ch (24x)€ 1/12h.
Location: Urban, quiet. **Surface:** gravel/metalled.
01/01-31/12.
Distance: 500m 500m 500m 200m on the spot.

S Bückeburg 10A2

Neumarktplatz, Unterwallweg 5c. **GPS**: n52,26326 e9,05040.

15 free € 1/80liter Ch (6x)€ 0,50/kWh.
Location: Urban, simple. **Surface:** gravel. 01/01-31/12.
Distance: 250m 250m 250m on the spot.

Büddenstedt 10C2

Am Sportplatz. **GPS**: n52,17567 e11,01843.

3 free. **Location:** Rural, simple, quiet.
Surface: asphalted. 01/01-31/12.
Distance: 1km on the spot 2km.
Remarks: Parking swimming pool.

Büddenstedt 10C2

Parking K22, Barneberger Straße, Offleben.
GPS: n52,13738 e11,04409.

2 free. **Location:** Rural, simple. **Surface:** asphalted.
01/01-31/12.

DE

Distance: 500m 500m 500m.

Bühren 10B3

Alter Festplatz, Im Teich. **GPS**: n51,48378 e9,67451.

20 € 2 € 2 Ch. **Location:** Rural, isolated.
Surface: grassy. 01/01-31/12.
Distance: 700m 5km on the spot on the spot.

Bunde 7F3

Am Friedhofsweg. **GPS**: n53,18500 e7,26639.

15 € 5 € 1 € 1.Ch € 1/10h.
Location: Central. **Surface:** grasstiles. 01/01-31/12.
Distance: 100m 2,3km 350m 200m 100m.
Remarks: At townhall, max. 3 days.

Bunde 7F3

Freizeitgelände, Denkmalstrasse 11, Ditzumerverlaat.
GPS: n53,26028 e7,26861.

10 € 3/24h € 0,50 Ch (8x)€ 1/8h.
Surface: metalled. 01/01-31/12 during event.
Distance: 250m on the spot on the spot 350m 250m.
Remarks: Max. 3 days.

Bunde 7F3

Möhlenlandbad, Kellingwold 25. **GPS**: n53,18683 e7,27418.

10 € 3.
Location: Simple, quiet. **Surface:** metalled. 01/01-31/12.
Distance: 500m 3km 600m 1,5km.
Remarks: At swimming pool.

Butjadingen 7H2

Henken's Stellplatz, Am Hafen 6, Fedderwardersiel.
GPS: n53,59581 e8,35669.

80 € 6 + tourist tax € 0,95-2,30/pp € 0,01/1liter Ch € 1/24h (48x)€ 2,50/day. **Location:** Rural, comfortable, central, quiet.
Surface: grassy. 01/03-31/10.
Distance: 500m on the spot on the spot on the spot on the spot 500m on the spot on the spot.
Remarks: Bread-service.

Butjadingen 7H2

Freizeithafen Fedderwardersiel, Sielstraße.
GPS: n53,59518 e8,35700.

45 € 12, 2 pers.incl, tourist tax € 2,3/0pp, dog € 0,50 Ch € 1,50 (20x)€ 2,50/day WC € 0,50/3minutes € 6.
Location: Rural, comfortable, isolated, quiet. **Surface:** grassy.
01/04-31/10.
Distance: 800m on the spot on the spot 800m 800m on the spot on the spot on the spot.

Butjadingen 7H2

Hof Iggewarden, Iggewarden 1. **GPS**: n53,58622 e8,32653.

20 € 8 € 1/100liter Ch (2x)included WC.
Location: Rural, comfortable, isolated, quiet.
Surface: gravel. 01/05-30/09.
Distance: 2km 2km on the spot on the spot 300m on the spot on the spot.

Butjadingen 7H2

Knaus Campingpark Burhave, An der Nordseelagune 1.
GPS: n53,58306 e8,37000.

125 € 14,50 + € 2,30/pp tourist tax € 1/70liter Ch € 0,70/kWh WC € 3,50,sanitary € 3,50/pp € 4/day.
Surface: grassy. 15/04-15/10.
Distance: 1km on the spot 200m 1km.

Buxtehude 8A2

Pfingstmarktplatz, Cuxhavenerstrasse, Neukloster, B73.
GPS: n53,47974 e9,63528.

40 free € 1/100liter Ch € 2.
Location: Rural, simple. **Surface:** asphalted.
01/01-31/12 week before/after Whitsuntide.
Distance: 3km Imbiss bakery 200m.
Remarks: Key shower at Imbiss.

Buxtehude 8A2

Stellplatz am Schützenplatz, Genslerweg.
GPS: n53,47139 e9,69528.

30 € 5 € 1/100liter Ch (18x)€ 1/kWh.
Location: Urban, central. **Surface:** gravel. 01/01-31/12.
Distance: nearby Old city centre 50m bakery 50m on the spot on the spot.

Buxtehude 8A2

Wassersportverein Hansa, Am Hafen 5. **GPS**: n53,47871 e9,70359.
5 € 5 included .
Location: Urban. **Surface:** grassy/metalled. 01/05-30/09.
Distance: city centre 2km 350m 200m.

Tourist information Buxtehude:
Das Fleth. Old inland-port.

Cadenberge 8A1

Reisemobilvermietung Hennig, Alter Postweg 1.
GPS: n53,76686 e9,05681.

4 € 5 € 0,50/100liter € 1,50/24h.
Location: Rural, simple. **Surface:** grassy. 01/01-31/12.
Distance: 50m on the spot 50m.

Celle 10B1

Schützenplatz, Hafenstraße. **GPS**: n52,62794 e10,07348.

5 free € 1/100liter Ch WC.
Surface: grassy/metalled. 01/01-31/12.
Distance: 150m 100m 1km.

Celle 10B1

Am Badeland, Langensalzaplatz. **GPS**: n52,61842 e10,08052.

3 free. **Surface:** metalled. 01/01-31/12.
Distance: on the spot 700m 700m.

Clausthal-Zellerfeld 10C2

Busbahnhof, Bahnhofstraß 5. **GPS**: n51,81360 e10,33602.

DE

4 tourist tax € 1,50 WC. **Location:** Rural, simple.
Surface: metalled. 01/01-31/12.
Distance: on the spot 200m 600m on the spot on the spot on the spot.
Remarks: Pay at tourist office.

S Clenze 8C3

Regenbogen-Hof, Mützen. **GPS**: n52,94079 e10,93899.

5 € 7/pp Ch WC included. **Location:** Rural, simple, isolated, quiet. **Surface:** grassy. 01/01-31/12.
Distance: 3km on the spot 3km on the spot.
Remarks: Arrival <22h.

S Cloppenburg 7G3

Am Stadtpark, Hagenweg. **GPS**: n52,84649 e8,04687.

3 € 5, tourist tax incl € 1/80liter Ch free € 0,50/kWh.
Location: Urban, simple. **Surface:** metalled.
01/01-31/12.
Distance: 100m 2km 100m 300m.
Remarks: Max. 3 days.

Cloppenburg 7G3

Museumsdorf Cloppenburg, Bether Straße.
GPS: n52,85197 e8,05335.

20 free. **Location:** Rural, simple. **Surface:** metalled.
01/01-31/12.
Distance: 900m 1km.
Remarks: Parking in front of museum village, max. 24h.

S Coppenbrügge 10A2

Parkplatz am Frei- und Hallenbad, Felsenkellerweg.
GPS: n52,11613 e9,53676.

11 € 3,50 € 2,50 Ch (12x) € 1 WC included.
Location: Rural, simple. **Surface:** grassy/gravel.
01/01-31/12.
Distance: 1,5km 500m 500m on the spot on the spot.
Remarks: Check in at campsite, use sanitary only during opening hours swimming pool.

S Cuxhaven 7H1

Duhner Allee, Duhnen. **GPS**: n53,88284 e8,64814.

60 € 8, peak season € 10 Ch included € 2/day WC € 0,50 € 1. **Location:** Simple. **Surface:** asphalted. 01/01-31/12.
Remarks: Beach parking, in front of campsite am Bäderring.

S Cuxhaven 7H1

Elbe-Ferry, Am Fährhafen. **GPS**: n53,87508 e8,70315.

100 € 10-13, tourist tax incl € 1/80liter Ch (100x) € 1/kWh.
Location: Urban, simple. **Surface:** asphalted.
01/01-31/12.
Distance: 1km 500m 900m.
Remarks: Bread-service.

S Cuxhaven 7H1

Privatparkplatz Kugelbake Halle, Nordfeldstraße.
GPS: n53,89033 e8,67703.

80 € 8 Ch WC included.
Location: Urban, simple. **Surface:** metalled. 01/01-31/12.
Distance: 200m 100m.

S Cuxhaven 7H1

Campingplatz Finck, Am Sahlenburger Strand 25.
GPS: n53,86039 e8,59167.

16 € 17, tourist tax incl Ch (16x)included WC € 0,50 .
Location: Comfortable. 15/03-31/10.
Distance: 3km on the spot on the spot on camp site 100m.
Remarks: Sanitary at campsite.

S Damme 9H1

Stellplatz am Flugplatz, Am Flugplatz 8.
GPS: n52,49055 e8,17925.

12 € 10 € 0,50/80liter Ch (12x) € 0,50/kWh WC € 1.
Location: Luxurious. **Surface:** grassy/gravel. 01/01-31/12.
Distance: 1.4km on the spot 100m.
Remarks: Parking airport Damme.

Damme 9H1

Parkplatz Altes Amtsgericht, Ohlkensbergweg 10.
GPS: n52,52389 e8,19488.
5 free. **Surface:** metalled. 01/01-31/12.
Distance: 300m 400m 100m 150m.

S Damme 9H1

Olgahafen, Dümmerstrasse, Dümmerlohausen.
GPS: n52,52917 e8,31098.

12 free € 1 Ch (12x) € 1/kWh. **Location:** Rural, simple, quiet. **Surface:** gravel. 01/01-31/12.
Distance: 100m 100m on the spot bakery.
Remarks: At lake Dümmer, max. 3 days.

S Dangast 7G2

Sielstrasse 30. **GPS**: n53,44539 e8,10979.

40 € 9, tourist tax excl (14x)included.
Location: Simple. **Surface:** grassy. 15/04-15/10.
Distance: on the spot on the spot on the spot.

S Dannenberg 8C3

Bäckergrund 32. **GPS**: n53,10062 e11,10903.
4 Ch. 01/04-30/09.
Distance: 300m 850m.

S Dassel 10B2

Am Badesee in der Ortschaft, Lauenberg.
GPS: n51,75750 e9,76389.

8 free, 01/05-01/10 € 5 € 1/80liter Ch € 1/8h included,01/05-30/09. **Location:** Rural, isolated, quiet.
Surface: asphalted. 01/01-31/12.
Distance: 8,5km on the spot 300m 300m 300m on the spot on the spot.

S Dassel 10B2

Am Sollingbad, An der Badeanstalt. **GPS**: n51,80722 e9,68917.

5 free WC . **Location:** Rural, isolated. 01/01-31/12.
Distance: Old city centre 500m 500m 1km on the spot on the spot.
Remarks: Use sanitary only during opening hours swimming pool.

Deinste 8A2

Gut Deinster Mühle, Im Mühlenfeld 30. **GPS**: n53,53132 e9,43301.

DE

15 free. **Surface:** grassy. 01/01-31/12.
Distance: on the spot 400m bakery on the spot on the spot.
Remarks: Golf court.

Delmenhorst 7H3

Reisemobilhafen Delmenhorst, An den Graften.
GPS: n53,04722 e8,62278.

8 free Chfree (4x)€ 1/kWh.
Location: Urban, simple, central, quiet. **Surface:** gravel/sand.
01/01-31/12 during event.
Distance: on the spot 2,8km on the spot 200m.
Remarks: Max. 7 days.

Detern 7G3

Reisemobilhafen Detern, Alte Heerstrasse 6, Stickhausen.
GPS: n53,21560 e7,64743.

40 € 8 € 1/100liter Ch (44x)€ 2/24h WC € 1/6minutes € 2 € 1/24h. **Location:** Urban, luxurious.
Surface: asphalted/gravel. 01/01-31/12.
Distance: on the spot 6km on the spot on the spot on the spot on the spot on the spot.
Remarks: Behind tourist info, bread-service.

Diepenau 9H1

Stellplatz am Bahnhof, Am Bahnhof. **GPS:** n52,42470 e8,74106.

5 free € 1 Ch (5x)€ 1/8h.
Surface: metalled. 01/01-31/12.
Distance: 500m 500m 500m.

Diepenau 9H1

Wohnmobilstellplatz Am Tor zum Moor, Steinbrinkerstrasse 8.
GPS: n52,47664 e8,74016.

30 € 8 Ch included. **Surface:** grassy/metalled.
01/04-31/10.
Distance: on the spot on the spot 1km.

Diepholz 9H1

Parkplatz Am Heldenhain, Am Heldenhaim (B69).
GPS: n52,61250 e8,37056.

20 free € 1/80liter Ch (20x)€ 0,50/kWh free.
Location: Urban. **Surface:** grassy. 01/01-31/12.
Distance: 500m 500m 500m.
Remarks: Max. 3 days.

Ditzum 7F2

Ankerplatz Blank, Pogumer Straße. **GPS:** n53,31489 e7,27619.

14 € 7/24h € 1/100liter Ch (10x)€ 1/2kWh WC € 0,50 .
Surface: metalled. 01/01-31/12.
Distance: 100m 300m 300m 100m on the spot.

Ditzum 7F2

Reisemobilstellplatz Ditzum, Am Deich.
GPS: n53,31555 e7,28666.

45 € 7/night € 1/100liter Ch (45x)€ 1/2kWh.
Surface: metalled.
01/01-31/12.
Distance: 100m 100m 100m 100m 300m.
Remarks: Bread-service, waste dump € 1, shower € 1.

Dornum 7G2

Schöpfwerkstraße, Dornumersiel. **GPS:** n53,67272 e7,48092.

30 € 9, Nordsee-ServiceCard incl (12x)€ 1/8h.
Location: Rural, simple, quiet. **Surface:** metalled.
01/01-31/12.
Distance: 500m 100m 100m.

Dornum 7G2

Schützenplatz. **GPS:** n53,64829 e7,42367.

30 € 9, Nordsee-ServiceCard incl € 1/65liter Ch € 1/8h.
Location: Urban, simple, quiet. **Surface:** grassy.
01/01-31/12.
Distance: on the spot 300m 50m.

Remarks: Max. 1 night.

Dornum 7G2

Wohnmobilstellplatz Nordseeblick. GPS: n53,67912 e7,47767.

38 € 13 Nordsee-ServiceCard incl € 2/100liter Ch € 1/kWh WC . **Location:** Rural, comfortable, quiet.
Surface: grasstiles. 24/03-03/10.
Distance: 900m 200m 200m 500m 500m.
Remarks: Swimming pool.

Dörpen 7F3

Festplatz, Veeneweg. **GPS:** n52,97115 e7,33425.

5 free. **Location:** Simple. **Surface:** grassy/metalled.
01/01-31/12 1st week in June: fair.
Distance: 500m on the spot 500m on the spot.
Remarks: Max. 4 nights.

Dorum 7H2

Wohnmobilhafen Grube-Petrat, Am Neuen Deich 2a.
GPS: n53,73838 e8,51966.

20 € 12,50 + € 2 tourist tax, 01/05-15/09 € 14 + € 3,40 tourist tax Ch included WC € 1 .
Location: Simple. **Surface:** metalled. 01/01-31/12.
Distance: on the spot on the spot on the spot.
Remarks: Check in at Deichhotel, bread-service.

Dörverden 8A3

In der Worth. **GPS:** n52,84529 e9,22568.

5 free € 1/80liter (5x)€ 1/8h.
Location: Urban, simple, quiet. **Surface:** gravel. 01/01-31/12.
Distance: 200m 200m 200m Bremen/Hanover 100m 1km.
Remarks: Behind town hall, max. 3 nights.

Dörverden 8A3

Wolfcenter, Kasernenstraße, Barme. **GPS:** n52,82635 e9,21417.
10 free. **Location:** Simple. **Surface:** concrete.
01/01-31/12.
Distance: Dörverden 3km on the spot Aldi 3km.
Remarks: Parking wolf park.

Drage/Elbe 8B2

Reisemobilplatz Stover Strand, Stover Strand 10.
GPS: n53,42467 e10,29213.

DE

100 € 13, dog € 2 € 1/80liter Ch (100x)€ 0,50/kWh WC € 0,50/4minutes € 4/4 € 2/h. **Location:** Comfortable. **Surface:** grassy. 01/01-31/12.
Distance: on the spot on the spot on the spot on the spot 500m on the spot on the spot.
Remarks: Next to campsite.

Drochtersen 8A2

Wohnmobilstellplatz Krautsand, Hinterm Elbdeich, Krautsand. **GPS:** n53,75167 e9,39028.

10 € 10 WC included. **Location:** Rural, simple. **Surface:** grassy/metalled. 15/04-03/10.
Distance: Elbestrand 300m.

Drochtersen 8A2

Hallenbad Drochtersen, Am Sportplatz. **GPS:** n53,70548 e9,38215.

6 free. **Location:** Simple. **Surface:** metalled. 01/01-31/12.
Distance: 1km 1km.
Remarks: Parking at swimming pool.

Drochtersen 8A2

Am Alten Hafen, Asseler Sand. **GPS:** n53,69418 e9,43928.

6 free. **Location:** Rural, simple. **Surface:** gravel. 01/01-31/12.
Distance: 500m 1km.

Duderstadt 10C3

P&R Parkplatz, Adenauerring. **GPS:** n51,51043 e10,27278.

20 free € 1/120liter € 1 Ch € 1 (4x)€ 0,50/kWh. **Location:** Rural, quiet. **Surface:** gravel. 01/01-31/12.
Distance: 800m 17km 800m 200m 100m.
Remarks: Coins available at the shop.

Duderstadt 10C3

Eichsfeldhalle, August Werner Allee. **GPS:** n51,50662 e10,25890.

5 free. **Location:** Rural, simple. **Surface:** gravel. 01/01-31/12.
Distance: 900m 17km 900m 900m 700m.
Remarks: Max. 1 night.

Duderstadt 10C3

Hotel Rosenthaler Hof, Rosenthaler Str. 31. **GPS:** n51,51556 e10,21194. 35 € 15, 2 pers.incl Ch (50x) included . **Surface:** metalled. 01/01-31/12.
Distance: 5km on the spot.

Tourist information Duderstadt:
Gästeinformation der Stadt Duderstadt, Marktstrasse 66, www.duderstadt.de. Old part of town with half-timbered houses.

Edewecht 7G3

Am Marktplatz, Rathhausstrasse. **GPS:** n53,12834 e7,98201.

20 € 5/24h € 1/80liter Ch (8x)€ 1/6h. **Location:** Urban, simple. **Surface:** grassy. 01/01-31/12.
Distance: on the spot 400m Aldi 50m.

Egestorf 8B3

Naturerlebnisbad Acquadies, Ahornweg 5. **GPS:** n53,19796 e10,05455.

30 € 8 € 1 Ch (20x)€ 2/10h WC € 2. **Location:** Simple, quiet. **Surface:** gravel/metalled. 01/01-31/12.
Distance: 1km 2,2km on the spot 700m 1km.
Remarks: At swimming pool, shower during opening hours.

Eggermühlen 9G1

Reiterhotel Vox, OT Bockraden 1. **GPS:** n52,57278 e7,79553.

8 € 25, clients € 7,50 Ch WC included. **Location:** Rural. **Surface:** grassy. 01/01-31/12.
Distance: 3km 3km.

Eggestedt 7H3

Eggestedt, Betonstrasse/Habichthorsterweg. **GPS:** n53,22819 e8,63902.

8 free. **Location:** Simple, isolated, noisy. **Surface:** metalled/sand. 01/01-31/12.
Distance: 4km 400m.

Einbeck 10B2

Am Schwimmbad, Ochsenhofweg. **GPS:** n51,82433 e9,86464.

30 € 5 € 1/60liter € 1 Ch (18x)€ 0,50/kWh. **Location:** Simple. **Surface:** gravel. 01/01-31/12.
Distance: 800m 500m 500m on the spot on the spot.
Remarks: Parking at swimming pool, free entrance swimming pool.

Tourist information Einbeck:
Alte Marktplatz. Wed + Sa morning.

Elsfleth 7H3

Im Hafen, An der Kaje. **GPS:** n53,23771 e8,46545.

28 € 8/24h € 1/80liter Ch (16x)€ 1/12h WC € 2. **Location:** Urban, comfortable, central, noisy. **Surface:** concrete. 01/01-31/12.
Distance: 150m 900m on the spot 100m 500m on the spot on the spot.

Emden 7F2

Alter Binnenhafen, Am Eisenbahndock. **GPS:** n53,36306 e7,20778.

29 € 9 € 0,50/100liter € 0,50 Ch (36x)€ 0,50/kWh WC € 0,50 € 1 € 3/1. **Location:** Urban, comfortable, central. **Surface:** metalled. 01/01-31/12.
Distance: 500m 500m 500m.
Remarks: Pay at harbourmaster, charging point for electric bicycles.

Emden 7F2

Wohnmobilstellplatz Knock, Jannes Ohling Strasse 39. **GPS:** n53,35559 e7,00367.

20 € 6,50/night. **Location:** Rural, simple, quiet. **Surface:** metalled.

DE

01/01-31/12.
Distance: 13km on the spot 500m 13km.
Remarks: Beautiful view.

Emden 7F2

Außenhafen Emden, An der Nesserlanderschleuse.
GPS: n53,33798 e7,18395.
10 € 5. **Surface:** asphalted. 01/01-31/12.
Distance: 3,5km on the spot on the spot.

Emden 7F2

Friesen Therme, Theaterstraße 2. **GPS**: n53,37530 e7,20203.

4 free (4x)€ 0,50/kWh. **Location:** Urban, simple.
Surface: metalled. 01/01-31/12.
Distance: 1,5km 400m.

Eschershausen 10B2

Reisemobil-Stellplatz am Angerplatz, Angerweg.
GPS: n51,92965 e9,62806.

10 free € 1/100liter € 1 Ch (6x)€ 0,50/kWh.
Surface: metalled. 01/01-31/12.
Distance: 1km 350m 1km.

Esens 7G2

Wohnmobil-Stellplatz Esens, Schützenplatz.
GPS: n53,63921 e7,61077.

20 € 2 + € 2,80/pp tourist tax Ch included.
Location: Rural, comfortable, quiet.
Surface: grassy. 01/01-31/12.
Distance: 500m 50m 200m.
Remarks: Max. 2 nights.

Essel 10B1

Hotel Heide-Kröpke, Esseler Damm 1. **GPS**: n52,73240 e9,69419.

5 free (3x) . **Surface:** grassy.
01/01-31/12.
Distance: on the spot 9km.
Remarks: Use of a meal desired, bird reserve Ostenholzer-Moor.

Esterwegen 7G3

Am Erikasee. **GPS**: n52,99366 e7,66768.

6 free € 1/100liter Ch (8x)€ 1/2kWh WC .
Location: Rural, simple, isolated.
Surface: gravel/metalled. 01/01-31/12.
Distance: 2km 100m Imbiss 80m.
Remarks: Walking and bicycle area.

Estorf 8A2

Wohnmobilstellplatz Gräpel - An der Prahmfähre, Zum Hafen 21.
GPS: n53,56596 e9,17315.
3 free. **Surface:** gravel. 01/01-31/12.
Distance: on the spot.
Remarks: Along the Oste river.

Eystrup 8A3

Bahnhofstrasse 21. **GPS**: n52,78004 e9,21840.

5 free. **Surface:** grassy. 01/01-31/12.
Distance: 100m.
Remarks: Max. 5 days.

Faßberg 8B3

Am Schützenplatz, Moorweg. **GPS**: n52,90518 e10,16991.

50 € 2 € 1 ChWC. **Surface:** grassy.
01/01-31/12 marksmen's festival end of September.
Distance: 700m 700m 700m.

Faßberg 8B3

Parkplatz Heidesee, Unterlüßerstraße, L280, Müden.
GPS: n52,87889 e10,12472.

30 € 2 € 1 Ch € 1. **Surface:** grassy.
01/01-31/12 end Sep.
Distance: 500m 1km.

Faßberg 8B3

Parkplatz am Wildpark, Willinghäuser Kirchweg, Müden.
GPS: n52,87222 e10,10861.

15 € 2/night. **Surface:** grassy. 01/01-31/12.
Distance: 1km 1km on the spot.

Fredenbeck 8A2

Dinghornerstraße 21. **GPS**: n53,52146 e9,39598.
5 free. **Surface:** grassy/gravel. 01/01-31/12.
Distance: on the spot on the spot on the spot.

Fredenbeck 8A2

Restaurant Niedersachsenschänke, Schwingestraße 33.
GPS: n53,52646 e9,39314.
5 free. **Surface:** grassy. 01/01-31/12.
Distance: 300m on the spot 300m on the spot on the spot.

Freiburg/Elbe 8A1

Stellplatz am Freizeitcentrum, Am Bassin 25.
GPS: n53,82285 e9,29305.

30 € 8 Ch WCincluded € 1.
Location: Rural, simple. **Surface:** metalled.
01/01-31/12.
Distance: 200m 50m 300m 400m.
Remarks: Find more possibilities on the city plan.

Freistatt 9H1

Freistätter Feldbahn, Badeweg. **GPS**: n52,62613 e8,65147.
6 € 7 Ch included. 01/01-31/12.
Distance: 1km 400m.

Friedeburg 7G2

Schützenplatz. **GPS**: n53,45488 e7,83349.

20 free Chfree (6x)€ 1/8h.
Location: Urban, simple. **Surface:** grassy. 01/01-31/12.
Distance: 15/05-15/09 400m.
Remarks: Max. 3 days.

Friedeburg 7G2

Gasthaus Wilken am See, Friedeburger Straße 19.
GPS: n53,45794 e7,88265.

10 € 5 included. **Location:** Rural, simple, quiet.
Surface: grassy. 01/01-31/12.
Distance: on the spot on the spot.
Remarks: At lake.

Friesoythe 7G3

Am Aquaferrum, Thüler Straße 28A. **GPS**: n53,01149 e7,86152.

DE

5 free € 1/100liter Ch€ 3 (8x)€ 6/24h.
01/01-31/12.
Distance: 900m 900m 800m.
Remarks: At swimming pool.

S Fürstenau 9G1

Schlossinsel Fürstenau, Schlossplatz 1. **GPS**: n52,51638 e7,67333.

2 free € 3 Ch € 2/day.
Location: Quiet. **Surface:** metalled. 01/01-31/12.
Distance: 100m 100m 100m on the spot on the spot.
Remarks: Next to castle.

S Gartow 8D3

Imbiss am See, Springstraße 88. **GPS**: n53,02944 e11,44944.

20 € 5 included20liter WC.
Surface: gravel/metalled. 01/03-30/10.
Distance: 1km on the spot on the spot on the spot.
Remarks: Imbiss 11-21h.

S Geeste 9F1

Am Speicherbecken, Biener Straße 13. **GPS**: n52,59407 e7,27417.

50 free WCfree. **Location:** Quiet.
Surface: grassy/metalled. 01/01-31/12.
Distance: 2km 200m 100m 4km on the spot on the spot.
Remarks: Max. 1 night.

Geeste 9F1

P Biotop/Ausblick, Osterbrocker Strasse. **GPS**: n52,59840 e7,29279.

4 free. **Surface:** metalled. 01/01-31/12.
Distance: 1,5km 1,5km on the spot on the spot.
Remarks: Max. 1 night, hiking area.

S Gehrden 10B1

An den Sporthallen, Lange Feldstraße 12.
GPS: n52,31197 e9,60971.

2 free (2x)€ 0,50/kWh.
Location: Simple. **Surface:** metalled. 01/01-31/12.
Distance: centre 700m 200m.

S Gifhorn 10C1

Frei- und Hallenbad Allerwelle, Konrad Adenauerstrasse.
GPS: n52,48437 e10,55407.
12 € 5/24h € 1/90liter Ch (12x)€ 1/8h WC.
Location: Rural, comfortable, quiet. **Surface:** grasstiles.
01/01-31/12.
Distance: 200m 100m 250m 200m 200m on the spot on the spot.
Remarks: Max. 3 days.

S Gifhorn 10C1

Fischer Camping + Gas, Schmiedeweg 4, Wische.
GPS: n52,50863 e10,48462.

8 free € 0,50/50liter Ch (8x).
Location: Rural, simple, isolated. **Surface:** grassy. 01/01-31/12.
Distance: 3km 500m 3km.
Remarks: Accessory shop.

S Gnarrenburg 8A2

Parkplatz Brillit, Alte Strasse, Brillit. **GPS**: n53,41390 e9,00007.

15 free Chfree. **Location:** Rural, simple.
Surface: gravel. 01/01-31/12.
Distance: 1km 3km 1km on the spot on the spot.
Remarks: At community centre.

S Gnarrenburg 8A2

Schulzentrum, Brilliterweg. **GPS**: n53,39000 e9,00028.

15 free Chfree. **Surface:** metalled. 01/01-31/12.
Distance: 1km 500m.
Remarks: Sports centre.

Goldenstedt 9H1

Haus im Moor, Arkeburger Straße 22. **GPS**: n52,72777 e8,39120.
6 free. 01/01-31/12.
Distance: 8,5km.

S Gorleben 8D3

Am Sportboothafen, Ringstraße. **GPS**: n53,04972 e11,35111.

5 € 7,50 € 1/10minutes (4x)€ 1/10h WC € 1,50.
Location: Rural, comfortable, quiet.
Surface: grasstiles. 01/05-30/09.
Distance: on the spot on the spot 500m.
Remarks: Bakery 500m.

S Göttingen 10B3

Reisemobilhafen Eiswiese, Windausweg 6.
GPS: n51,52320 e9,92965.

28 € 9 € 1/100liter Ch (24x)€ 0,50/kWh WC € 1/15h.
Location: Comfortable. **Surface:** gravel. 01/01-31/12.
Distance: 500m 5,2km 100m 20-400m 100m 500m 100m.
Remarks: Max. 3 nights.

S Grasberg 8A3

P&R, Wörpedorfer Straße. **GPS**: n53,18411 e8,98433.

10 free € 1 Ch (8x)€ 1/6h.
Location: Simple. **Surface:** gravel. 01/01-31/12.
Distance: on the spot on the spot on the spot > Bremen.

S Gronau/Leine 10B2

Kuhmasch. **GPS**: n52,08265 e9,77034.

4 € 5 € 1,50 WC. **Location:** Rural, simple.
Surface: grassy. 01/01-31/12.
Distance: 200m 300m 300m on the spot.
Remarks: Check in at swimming pool, caution key electricity € 10.

S Großefehn 7G2

Ostfriesen-Bräu Bagband, Voerstad 8, Badband.
GPS: n53,35034 e7,61060.

4 € 7 16Amp WC. **Location:** Simple, quiet.
Surface: metalled. 01/01-31/12.

Distance: 10km on the spot 3km.

Großenkneten 7H3

Dorfplatz, Bahnhofstrasse, Huntlosen. **GPS**: n52,99145 e8,28658.

6 free. **Location:** Rural, simple.
Surface: grasstiles. 01/01-31/12.
Distance: on the spot 50m 1km.

Großenkneten 7H3

Wilhelm-Wellman-Platz, Ahlhorner Strasse/markt.
GPS: n52,94274 e8,25751.

6 free. **Location:** Rural, simple.
Surface: grasstiles. 01/01-31/12.
Distance: 200m 200m on the spot.

Großenwieden 10A2

Am Steinbrink, Hessisch Oldendorf. **GPS**: n52,17191 e9,18982.

4 free. **Location:** Rural. **Surface:** gravel. 01/01-31/12.
Distance: 3,8km Gasthaus/Biergarten 300m Weserradweg on the spot.

Großenwörden 8A2

Deichstraße 21. **GPS**: n53,67757 e9,25769.
3 € 5 € 1 € 1/kWh.
Surface: grasstiles. 01/01-31/12.
Distance: 200m.
Remarks: Along the Oste river.

Großheide 7F2

Moormuseum, Kirchweg, Berumerfehn.
GPS: n53,56040 e7,34713.

6 free. **Location:** Urban, simple, quiet.
Surface: metalled. 01/01-31/12.
Distance: on the spot on the spot 2km.
Remarks: Max. 2 nights.

Großheide 7F2

P Freizeitanlage Am Kiessee, Doornkaatsweg.
GPS: n53,58718 e7,36560.

15 free. **Location:** Rural, simple, quiet. **Surface:** gravel.
01/01-31/12.
Distance: on the spot.

Großheide 7F2

AC Dehne, Dorfstraße 86. **GPS**: n53,56254 e7,36077.

20 € 4 Ch (9x)€ 1 € 1. **Location:** Rural, comfortable, quiet. **Surface:** grassy. 01/01-31/12.
Distance: on the spot.

Hage 7F2

Kurzentrum, Wichter Weg, Blandorf-Wichte.
GPS: n53,60501 e7,31950.

12 € 9 € 0,50/80liter Ch € 1/2kWh included.
Location: Rural, comfortable, quiet. **Surface:** metalled.
01/01-31/12.

Hagenburg 10A1

Grillplatz, Steinhuder-Meer-Straße. **GPS**: n52,43684 e9,32388.

8 free (8x)€ 1/6h. **Location:** Rural, isolated.
Surface: gravel. 01/01-31/12.
Distance: 500m Lake Steinhude 1,1km 200m.
Remarks: At sports park.

Hahnenklee 10C2

Am Bocksberg. **GPS**: n51,85757 e10,34176.
free € 2/60liter Ch. **Location:** Rural, comfortable, quiet.
Surface: concrete. 01/01-31/12.
Distance: 500m 1km 500m on the spot on the spot on the spot.

Hambergen 7H2

Festplatz, Kirchweg/Am Langenend. **GPS**: n53,31050 e8,82389.

20 € 3,50 Ch (6x)included. **Location:** Urban, simple.
Surface: gravel/sand. 01/01-31/12.
Distance: on the spot 50m 50m 1km on the spot on the spot.
Remarks: Caution key service € 25.

Hameln 10A2

Wohnmobilstellplatz Hameln, Ruthenstrasse 14.
GPS: n52,09623 e9,35853.

27 € 8/24h € 1/100liter Ch (27x)€ 1/8h.
Location: Urban, simple. **Surface:** metalled. 01/01-31/12.
Distance: 1km 600m 600m 800m Weser-Radweg.

Hameln 10A2

Campingplatz Hameln, Uferstraße 80. **GPS**: n52,10932 e9,34768.
30 € 12 Ch. 01/01-31/12.
Distance: 2km 800m on the spot.

Hankensbüttel 8C3

Parkplatz Am Boldhamm, Wiesenweg.
GPS: n52,73111 e10,61417.

10 € 6 Ch included.
Location: Rural. **Surface:** grassy.
01/04-30/09.
Distance: 900m 1km 1km.
Remarks: Service: Mo/Fr 6-12h, Sa/Su 8-10h.

Tourist information Hankensbüttel:
Otter-Zentrum. Zoo. 15/03-31/10 9.30-18h, 01/11-14/03 9.30-17h 15/12-15/01.

Hannoversch Münden 10B3

Am Weserstein, Tanzwerder. **GPS**: n51,42000 e9,64888.

30 € 6/24h € 1 Ch (16x)€ 1/8h.
Location: Central. **Surface:** metalled.
01/01-31/12 Easter Market, service: 01/11-31/03.
Distance: 900m 100m on the spot on the spot.
Remarks: 01/11/- 31/03 no service.

Hannoversch Münden 10B3

Am Hochbad, Rattwerder. **GPS**: n51,40595 e9,64643.

15 free. **Location:** Rural. **Surface:** asphalted. 01/01-31/12.
Distance: 1,7km 1km on the spot.
Remarks: At swimming pool.

Hannoversch Münden 10B3

Am Werraweg, Werraweg. **GPS**: n51,41701 e9,66176.

10 free. **Location:** Simple. **Surface:** gravel. 01/01-31/12.
Distance: 700m 600m 600m on the spot.
Remarks: Along the Werra river.

S Hannoversch Münden 10B3

Grüne Insel Tanzwerder, Tanzwerder 1. **GPS**: n51,41694 e9,64751.

20 € 6 + € 4,50/pp, dog € 2 Ch included (6x) € 0,60/kWh,+ € 2 WC € 3/h.
Location: Simple. **Surface:** grassy.
01/01-31/12.
Distance: 100m 150m 150m on the spot on the spot.
Remarks: Max. 3t.

Tourist information Hannoversch Münden:
Touristik Naturpark Münden e.V, Rathaus, www.hann-muenden.net/spontan. Old city centre with 430 half-timbered houses.

S Hardegsen 10B3

Wohnmobilhafen Steinbreite, Alte Uslarer Straße 1.
GPS: n51,65093 e9,82267.

15 € 6 € 1/100 Ch (16x) € 1/8h WC € 2/day € 2 € 2,50/day. **Location:** Comfortable. **Surface:** grasstiles.
01/01-31/12.
Distance: 500m 500m 800m on the spot on the spot.

S Haren/Ems 9F1

Am Schloss Danken, Am Tiergarten. **GPS**: n52,79724 e7,20530.

22 € 12/24h Ch (18x) WC included € 1.
Location: Rural, simple. **Surface:** grassy/gravel.
21/03-25/10.
Distance: 1km 2,8km on the spot on the spot on the spot on the spot.

Haren/Ems 9F1

Stellplatz an der Ems, Schleusenstraße. **GPS**: n52,78890 e7,24744.
15 free. **Surface:** grasstiles. 01/01-31/12.
Distance: 500m 550m.

S Harsefeld 8A2

Klosterpark, Kirchenstrasse. **GPS**: n53,45384 e9,50344.

5 free (10x).
Location: Rural, simple. 01/01-31/12.
Distance: 100m 100m 100m 100m on the spot on the spot.
Remarks: Caution key electricity € 10 at hotel, parking park of monastery, max. 5 days.

S Haselünne 9G1

Erholungsgebiet am See. **GPS**: n52,67060 e7,49907.
free Ch. **Surface:** metalled. 01/01-31/12.
Distance: centre 1,2km on the spot on the spot 1,2km.

S Haselünne 9G1

Sportzentrum, Lingener Strasse 28. **GPS**: n52,66778 e7,48222.

4 free Ch. **Location:** Simple, quiet.
Surface: metalled. 01/01-31/12.
Distance: 400m 400m 400m 100m on the spot.
Remarks: Parking swimming pool.

S Haselünne 9G1

Dröge-Polle, Poller Straße 19. **GPS**: n52,65123 e7,49849.
3 € 5,50 WC included . **Location:** Rural. **Surface:** grassy.
01/01-31/12.

S Helmstedt 10C1

Am Maschweg, Maschweg. **GPS**: n52,23535 e11,01128.

25 free € 1/3minutes € 1/4h.
Location: Rural, simple. **Surface:** metalled. 01/01-31/12.
Distance: 500m 800m 50m 200m on the spot on the spot.
Remarks: Other parking in case of festivities.

Helmstedt 10C1

Brunnentheater, Brunnenweg 6A, Bad Helmstedt.
GPS: n52,23676 e11,06411.

5 free. **Location:** Rural, simple, isolated, quiet.
Surface: asphalted. 01/01-31/12.
Distance: 4km 500m 4km on the spot on the spot.

S Hermannsburg 8B3

Parkplatz Waldschwimmbad, Lotharstrasse 66.
GPS: n52,82718 e10,10807.

3 free € 1 € 1 Ch. **Surface:** metalled. 01/01-31/12.
Distance: 500m 100m.
Remarks: Parking at swimming pool.

S Hermannsburg 8B3

Schützenplatz, Lotharstraße 75. **GPS**: n52,82787 e10,10963.

40 € 2 Ch. **Surface:** grassy. 01/01-31/12.
Distance: 500m on the spot.
Remarks: Max. 1 night, service at Waldbad (50m).

Hermannsburg 8B3

Grillplatz Bonstorf, Schulstrasse. **GPS**: n52,86492 e10,05134.

4 free. **Surface:** grassy. 01/01-31/12.
Distance: 5km 5km 5km.
Remarks: Parking sports park.

Hermannsburg 8B3

Parkplatz am Feuerwehrhaus, Weesenerstrasse, Weesen.
GPS: n52,83645 e10,13692.

3 free. **Surface:** grassy. 01/01-31/12.
Distance: 500m 50m.
Remarks: Parking fire-station.

Hermannsburg 8B3

Parkplatz Örtzetal-Halle, Lutterweg. **GPS**: n52,83363 e10,09579.

3 free. **Surface:** metalled. 01/01-31/12.
Distance: 1km 600m 100m.

S Hermannsburg 8B3

Lutter Hof, Waldstrasse, Lutter. **GPS**: n52,84188 e10,09894.

DE

5 € 5 according consumption included.
Surface: grassy. 01/01-31/12.
Distance: 2km 2km 2km.

S Herzlake 9G1

Hasetal, Im Mersch. **GPS**: n52,68211 e7,60780.

30 free Ch WC free. **Surface:** grassy. 15/03-15/11.
Distance: 700m 200m.
Remarks: Parking sports centre.

S Hesel 7G2

Dorfplatz, Kirchstrasse. **GPS**: n53,30497 e7,59174.

12 € 4 Ch included € 1/8h.
Location: Rural, simple, quiet. **Surface:** metalled. 01/01-31/12.
Distance: on the spot on the spot 1km on the spot on the spot.
Remarks: Pay at tourist office.

S Hessisch Oldendorf 10A2

Südwall P1, Weserstraße. **GPS**: n52,16693 e9,25049.

4 free € 0,50/5minutes € 0,50 Ch € 0,50.
Location: Rural, simple. **Surface:** grassy/gravel.
01/01-31/12.
Distance: 400m 500m 500m Weserradweg 1km.
Remarks: Max. 5 days.

Hessisch Oldendorf 10A2

Steinbrink, Am Steinbrink. **GPS**: n52,17222 e9,19056.
4 free. **Surface:** gravel. 01/01-31/12.
Distance: 200m 200m 200m.

S Hitzacker 8C3

Bleichwiesen, K36, Elbufferstrasse. **GPS**: n53,15074 e11,04941.

40 free € 2/70liter Ch (17x)€ 2/6h WC.

Location: Rural, comfortable. **Surface:** metalled.
01/01-31/12.
Distance: 200m 450m.
Remarks: Max. 2 nights.

S Hohne 10C1

Am Waldbad, Am Schwimmbad 23. **GPS**: n52,59340 e10,37398.

4 € 5 Ch (4x) WC included.
Location: Rural, comfortable, quiet. **Surface:** gravel. 01/01-31/12.
Distance: 1km 50m 200m.
Remarks: Max. 7 days, caution key € 50, use sanitary only during opening hours swimming pool.

S Hohnstorf/Elbe 8C2

Wohnmobilstellplatz Hohnstorf, Schulstraße 1.
GPS: n53,36234 e10,56223.

9 € 8/24h € 1/100liter Ch (3x)€ 1/10h.
Location: Comfortable. **Surface:** metalled. 01/01-31/12.
Distance: on the spot 500m 500m.
Remarks: Along the river Elbe.

S Holdorf 9H1

Zeltplatz Heidesee, Zum Heidesee 53. **GPS**: n52,57788 e8,11424.

60 € 9 Ch included € 2 against payment.
Surface: grasstiles.
01/03-15/10.
Distance: 1,5km 3,4km Sandy beach on the spot 1,5km.
Remarks: At tennis-courts, bread-service.

Hollern 8A2

Am Deich, Twielenfleth. **GPS**: n53,60417 e9,55917.

15 € 5/24h.
Location: Rural, simple. **Surface:** metalled. 01/01-31/12.
Distance: 200m Imbiss 300m.
Remarks: Along the river Elbe.

S Holzminden 10A2

Mobilcamping Holzminden, Stahler Ufer 16.
GPS: n51,82681 e9,43909.

145 € 5-8,50 € 1/100liter Ch (150x)€ 0,60/kWh WC € 0,50/4minutes.
Location: Comfortable. **Surface:** grassy. 01/01-31/12.
Distance: 550m 100m 100m 100m 200m on the spot on the spot.
Remarks: At swimming pool, bread-service.

Hornburg 10C2

Am Freibad, Bgm. Löhdenstrasse. **GPS**: n53,10350 e9,56874.
8 free. **Location:** Urban. **Surface:** metalled. 01/01-31/12.

S Hornburg 10C2

Iberg-Gaststätte, Schützenallee 1. **GPS**: n52,03133 e10,59677.

20 € 2 (6x)€ 1/night. **Location:** Rural, simple, quiet.
Surface: grassy/metalled. 01/01-31/12.
Distance: 600m 5km on the spot 1km on the spot.

S Hoya/Weser 8A3

Reisemobilstellplatz Weserblick, Stettiner Straße.
GPS: n52,80106 e9,13987.

10 voluntary contribution € 1/150liter Ch.
Surface: grassy/gravel. 01/01-31/12.
Distance: 500m 100m 500m 700m.

S Hude 7H3

Wohnmobilstellplatz Hude, Schützenstrasse.
GPS: n53,10758 e8,45867.

10 € 5 € 1 Ch (12x)€ 0,50/kWh.
Location: Urban, quiet. **Surface:** gravel. 01/01-31/12.
Distance: on the spot on the spot 400m on the spot on the spot 1km.

S Hüde (49448) 9H1

Freizeitarena Dümmer See, Rohrdommelweg 33.
GPS: n52,50176 e8,35425.

DE

50 € 10 Ch € 3/day WC included.
Location: Rural, quiet. **Surface:** grassy. 15/04-01/11.
Distance: 150m 150m bakery 300m on the spot.

S **Ihlienworth** 7H1

Auf der Schöpfwerkinsel, Hauptstrasse 40.
GPS: n53,74539 e8,91831.
9 free € 1 free Ch€ 1 € 1/kWh. **Location:** Rural, simple.
Surface: grassy/metalled. 01/03-30/10.
Distance: on the spot on the spot 500m.

S **Ihlow** 7G2

Straub's Bürgerstuben, 1.Kompanieweg 3, Ihlowerfehn.
GPS: n53,41153 e7,44013.

6 free € 1/5minutes Ch€ 1/time (4x)€ 0,50/kWh.
Location: Rural, simple, quiet. **Surface:** metalled.
01/01-31/12 Wed.
Distance: on the spot on the spot on the spot.

S **Isterberg** 9F1

Am Isterberger Waldhaus, Lehmstrasse. **GPS:** n52,35167 e7,14906.
30 € 7 € 2 Ch € 1. 01/01-31/12.
Distance: on the spot.

S **Jade** 7H2

Bäderstraße, Sehestedt. **GPS:** n53,43605 e8,29553.
10 € 10 Chincluded € 2/night WC.
Location: Rural. **Surface:** grassy/gravel. 01/05-30/09.
Distance: 500m on the spot.
Remarks: At lake.

S **Jade** 7H2

Quittenweg, Süderschweiburg. **GPS:** n53,39139 e8,26639.

8 free € 1 Ch (8x)€ 1/8h. **Location:** Rural, comfortable, isolated. **Surface:** gravel/metalled. 01/01-31/12.
Distance: 800m 500m 1km 800m on the spot on the spot.

S **Jade** 7H2

Drei Eichen, Kreuzmoorstrasse 28. **GPS:** n53,31531 e8,23084.

10 € 10 Ch (3x)WCincluded against payment.
Location: Rural, simple, quiet. **Surface:** grassy/gravel.
01/01-31/12.
Distance: 4km.
Remarks: At manege.

S **Jade** 7H2

Schützenhof, Am Schützenplatz, Vareler Strasse.
GPS: n53,34111 e8,18667.

10 guests free on demand (3x)€ 2/night.
Location: Simple. **Surface:** metalled. 01/01-31/12.
Distance: on the spot on the spot on the spot.
Remarks: Parking of Shooting Club.

Jade 7H2

Jaderpark, Tiergartenstrasse 69, Jaderberg.
GPS: n53,32679 e8,18521.

20 free. **Location:** Simple. **Surface:** gravel.
01/01-31/12.
Distance: on the spot on the spot.
Remarks: Parking Jarderpark, zoo and adventure park, max. 1 night.

S **Jever** 7G2

Jahnstrasse. **GPS:** n53,57733 e7,89074.

20 € 8 € 2 Ch (20x)€ 2.
Surface: metalled. 01/01-31/12.
Distance: Old city centre 750m 100m.
Remarks: Sports centre, max. 3 days, coins at petrol station Henn.

Tourist information Jever:
Schloßmuseum. Castle, English gardens and museum. Tue-Su 10-18h, 01/07-31/08 Mo-Su 10-18h.
Frisiesches Brauhaus. Brewery with museum. Guided tour 2 hours, 2 drinks included. Mo-Fri 9.30-16.30h, Sa 9.30-12.30h.

S **Jork** 8A2

Festplatz, Schützenhofstrasse/Festplatzweg.
GPS: n53,53100 e9,68336.

80 € 7 € 1/100liter ChWC € 0,50.
Location: Rural, simple. **Surface:** metalled. 01/01-31/12.
Distance: 200m 200m 200m.
Remarks: Parking event ground, max. 24h.

Jork 8A2

Stellplatz Lühe-Anleger, Fährstraße, Grünendeich.
GPS: n53,57271 e9,63129.
10 € 10/24h. **Surface:** gravel. 01/01-31/12.

S **Jork** 8A2

Am Yachthafen, Neuenschleuse. **GPS:** n53,55375 e9,66858.

18 € 7 € 1/90liter Ch (18x)€ 0,50/kWh WC € 2.
Location: Urban, simple. **Surface:** unpaved.
01/01-31/12.
Distance: Jork 3km on the spot on the spot on the spot.
Remarks: Along the river Elbe.

S **Jork** 8A2

Stubbe's Gasthaus, Lühe 46. **GPS:** n53,56861 e9,63333.

14 € 10 € 2 . **Location:** Rural, comfortable.
Surface: grassy. 01/01-31/12.
Distance: on the spot.
Remarks: Bread-service, picnic area Am Gartenteich.

S **Königslutter am Elm** 10C1

P1 Niedernhof, Amtsgarten. **GPS:** n52,25009 e10,81996.

5 free € 1/5minutes € 1 (4x)€ 1/8h.
Location: Urban, comfortable, central, noisy. **Surface:** asphalted.
01/01-31/12.
Distance: 500m 7km 100m 100m 100m 900m 900m.

S **Kranenburg** 8A2

Fährverein Brobergen, Fährstraße, 21726. **GPS:** n53,59708 e9,17080.
5 € 10 WC included. **Location:** Isolated, quiet.
01/05-30/09.
Distance: 1km on the spot on the spot.

S **Krummendeich** 8A1

Stellplatz Krummendeich, Osterwechtern.
GPS: n53,83145 e9,20231.

6 free WC€ 0,50 € 0,50.
Location: Rural, simple. **Surface:** gravel. 01/01-31/12.
Distance: 100m 300m.

S **Krummhörn** 7F2

Reisemobilhafen Greetsiel, Mühlenstrasse 3, Greetsiel.
GPS: n53,49711 e7,10181.

DE

55 € 11, 2 pers.incl € 2/90liter Ch (40x)€ 1/8h.
Location: Rural, comfortable, quiet. **Surface:** gravel.
01/01-31/12.
Distance: 250m 250m.

Kutenholz 8A2

Festhalle, Bürgermeister-Schmetjen-Platz. **GPS**: n53,48163 e9,31486.
10 free. 01/01-31/12.
Distance: 800m 500m on the spot on the spot.

Lamspringe 10B2

Am Bahnhof. **GPS**: n51,95404 e10,00656.

3 free. **Location:** Rural, isolated.
Surface: gravel. 01/01-31/12.
Distance: 750m 1km 400m 250m Radweg zur Kunst on the spot.
Remarks: Max. 3 days.

Lauenau 10A1

Brauhaus Felsenkeller, Feggendorfer Straße 10.
GPS: n52,27914 e9,36906.

5 free free. **Location:** Rural, simple.
Surface: gravel. 01/01-31/12.
Distance: 500m 2,4km on the spot on the spot.
Remarks: Check in at restaurant.

Lauenförde 10A3

Yachthafen Dreiländereck, Würgasser Straße.
GPS: n51,65045 e9,37983.

50 € 8 Chincluded (35x)€ 2,20/day WC € 0,50 € 2,50 € 4,95.
Location: Rural, comfortable. **Surface:** gravel. 01/04-01/11.
Distance: 3km on the spot 3km on the spot on the spot.
Remarks: Bread-service.

Lautenthal 10C2

Kaspar Bitter Strasse 7b. **GPS**: n51,87020 e10,28729.

25 € 4 + € 1/pp tourist tax € 1/60liter € 2 Ch€ 2 (8x)€ 1/6h. **Location:** Rural, comfortable, quiet. **Surface:** gravel.
01/01-31/12.
Distance: 300m 300m 500m 50m.

Leer 7G3

P9, Große Bleiche. **GPS**: n53,22577 e7,44686.

6 free € 1/100liter € 1 Ch (6x)€ 1/24h WC€ 0,50 € 1.
Location: Urban, simple.
Surface: metalled.
01/01-31/12.
Distance: 200m on the spot 2km on the spot on the spot.
Remarks: Max. 3 nights, caution key sanitary € 30, sanitary at offices Bruchbrücke.

Leer 7G3

Am Hafen, Nessestrasse. **GPS**: n53,22527 e7,45472.

10 free WC€ 0,50 € 1. **Location:** Urban, simple.
Surface: asphalted/gravel. 01/01-31/12.
Distance: 500m 300m 2km.
Remarks: Max. 3 nights, caution key sanitary € 30, sanitary at offices Bruchbrücke.

Leer 7G3

Segelnverein, Segelerweg 3. **GPS**: n53,21907 e7,44793.

3 € 8 Chincluded € 0,30/kWh WC € 1.
Location: Simple, quiet. **Surface:** metalled. 01/01-31/12.

Leer 7G3

Landgaststätte zur Jümme-Fähre, Amdorfer Straße 101.
GPS: n53,22429 e7,52593.

guests free € 2/24h. **Location:** Rural, quiet. **Surface:** grassy.
01/01-31/12.
Distance: 3km on the spot on the spot on the spot 3km on the spot on the spot.
Remarks: Along river.

Leer 7G3

Windmühlenhof Eiklenborg, Logabirumer Straße, Logabirum.
GPS: n53,24745 e7,51582.

5 € 12 Ch WC € 2,50.
Surface: grassy/metalled. 01/01-31/12.
Remarks: Near old Dutch windmill.

Leese 10A1

Wohnmobilhafen Leeser See, Mühlenberg. **GPS**: n52,50616 e9,10360.
8 free € 1/10minutes Ch € 1/6h.
Surface: gravel. 01/03-31/10.
Distance: on the spot bakery 500m.

Leese 10A1

Loccumer Straße. **GPS**: n52,50272 e9,11733.

4 free. **Surface:** metalled. 01/01-31/12.
Distance: 200m on the spot 200m.

Leese 10A1

Rasthaus Leeser Tanger, Bahlweg. **GPS**: n52,49372 e9,12055.

8 € 15, discount for clients included.
Surface: metalled. 01/01-31/12.
Distance: 800m on the spot.

Lembruch 9H1

Stellplatz Dümmer-See Lembruch, Seestraße.
GPS: n52,52439 e8,36703.

20 free. **Location:** Rural. **Surface:** grassy. 01/01-31/12.
Distance: 300m 100m.

Lembruch 9H1

Campingplatz Seeblick, Birkenallee. **GPS**: n52,52583 e8,36056.

20 € 9 Ch on camp site € 5,50.
Location: Rural. **Surface:** grassy. 01/01-31/12.
Distance: 50m 50m.
Remarks: Max. 1 night.

S Lemwerder 7H3

Reisemobilhafen Peter-Baxmann-Platz, Schulstrasse 44.
GPS: n53,15784 e8,61783.

50 € 3/24h Ch included (40x)€ 1/8h.
Location: Urban, comfortable, isolated, quiet. **Surface:** gravel.
01/01-31/12.
Distance: on the spot 200m 500m 500m 300m.
Remarks: Nearby swimming pool.

Lemwerder 7H3

Vulkanparkplatz an der Weser, Uferweg.
GPS: n53,17000 e8,60028.

5 free. **Location:** Urban, simple, quiet.
Surface: asphalted/metalled. 01/01-31/12.
Distance: 2km on the spot 2km 2km on the spot on the spot.

S Lingen/Ems 9F1

Linus Bad, Teichstrasse. **GPS**: n52,51863 e7,30606.

30 € 5 € 1 Ch (16x)€ 0,50/kWh.
Location: Rural. **Surface:** gravel. 01/01-31/12.
Distance: 1km 600m 600m on the spot on the spot.
Remarks: At swimming pool, max. 3 days.

Loxstedt 7H2

Stotel, Alte Schulstraße 75. **GPS**: n53,44067 e8,59356.

4 free. **Location:** Urban, simple, quiet. **Surface:** grassy.
01/01-31/12.

Distance: 600m 1km Stoteler See 100m on the spot.

S Loxstedt 7H2

Am Bootshafen, Fährstrasse. **GPS**: n53,44438 e8,49942.

5 € 5 (6x)€ 0,50/kWh. **Location:** Rural, simple.
Surface: gravel/sand. 01/04-15/10.
Distance: 300m on the spot on the spot on the spot.
Remarks: Along the Weser river.

Lüchow 8C3

Parkstraße. **GPS**: n52,96983 e11,14594.

2 free. **Location:** Urban, simple.
Surface: asphalted/metalled. 01/01-31/12.
Distance: 900m 900m 1,7km.
Remarks: Max. 3 nights.

S Lüdersfeld 10A1

Heinrichs'Reisemobil Stellplatz, Am Hülsebrink 10+11.
GPS: n52,35972 e9,25512.

45 € 6 Ch (8x)included. **Location:** Rural, simple.
Surface: gravel. 01/01-31/12.
Distance: 500m on the spot.
Remarks: Check in at hotel, bread-service.

S Lüneburg 8B2

Am Sülzwiesen, Pieperweg. **GPS**: n53,24556 e10,39694.

53 € 10 € 1/10minutes Ch (40x)€ 1/8h,01/10-30/04 € 2/8h.
Location: Rural, comfortable, isolated, quiet.
Surface: metalled. 01/01-31/12.
Distance: 1km 300m.
Remarks: Max. 1 night.

S Mardorf 10A1

Wohnmobilstellplatz Steinhuder Meer, Rote-Kreuz-Strasse 16.
GPS: n52,48704 e9,30065.

60 € 7 € 1/100liter Ch (60x)€ 3.
Surface: grassy. 01/01-31/12.
Distance: 1km 300m 1km.
Remarks: Bread-service.

S Marienhafe 7F2

Rechtsupweg, Poststrasse. **GPS**: n53,52658 e7,32550.

20 free against payment. **Location:** Rural, simple, quiet.
Surface: gravel. 01/01-31/12.
Distance: 150m 150m 150m.

S Marienhafe 7F2

Tjücher Moortun. **GPS**: n53,52835 e7,28168.

5 € 5 € 1/100liter Ch (5x)€ 1/24h.
Location: Rural, comfortable, quiet. **Surface:** gravel.
01/01-31/12.
Distance: 400m on the spot Lidl 400m.

Marienhafe 7F2

Dorfplatz Leezdorf, Sträkweg. **GPS**: n53,54802 e7,29354.

4 free. **Location:** Urban, simple, quiet.
Surface: metalled. 01/01-31/12.
Distance: on the spot 150m on the spot.

Melle 9H2

Am Wellenbad 43. **GPS**: n52,20497 e8,32368.

10 free. **Location:** Simple, quiet. **Surface:** metalled.
01/01-31/12.
Distance: on the spot 1,2km nearby 300m.
Remarks: Parking swimming pool.

S Meppen 9F1

Reisemobilplatz am Hallenbad, An der Bleiche.
GPS: n52,69107 e7,28399.

DE

10 € 8, swimming pool incl. 1 pers € 2/100liter Ch (4x) € 2/24h. **Surface:** metalled. 01/01-31/12.
Distance: 200m on the spot 300m.
Remarks: Parking swimming pool, max. 2 nights.

Tourist information Meppen:
Tue-Sa morning.

Moormerland 7G2

Am Rathaus, Theodor Heussstrasse 12, Warsingsfehn.
GPS: n53,30826 e7,48613.

4 free. **Location:** Urban, simple.
Surface: metalled. 01/01-31/12.
Distance: 50m 50m 50m.
Remarks: Parking townhall, max. 3 nights.

Moormerland 7G2

Bei Cassi, Deichlandstraße 10, Rorinchem.
GPS: n53,32010 e7,35473.

15 € 5, free with a meal € 1 Ch € 2 € 1.
Surface: gravel. 01/04-31/10 Restaurant: Mo.
Distance: on the spot.

Moringen 10B3

Domänenhof, Amtsfreiheit. **GPS**: n51,69833 e9,86861.

3 free. **Location:** Rural, simple.
Surface: gravel. 01/01-31/12.
Distance: on the spot 5,5km 300m.
Remarks: At city park.

Nessmersiel 7F2

Strandstrasse. **GPS**: n53,68369 e7,35963.

25 € 10. **Location:** Rural, simple. **Surface:** grassy/gravel.
01/01-31/12.

Distance: 2km on the spot.

Neuharlingersiel 7G2

Wohnmobilstellplatz am Ostanleger, Am Hafen Ost.
GPS: n53,70173 e7,70741.

23 € 12 + € 1-2,50/pp tourist tax € 1/100liter included WC.
Location: Rural, comfortable, quiet. **Surface:** metalled.
01/01-31/12.
Distance: 500m 800m on the spot 1km.
Remarks: Max. 3 nights.

Neuhaus an der Oste 8A1

Am Yachthafen. GPS: n53,80348 e9,04013.
13 € 9 Ch € 2/day € 2 € 7,50. **Location:** Rural.
Surface: grassy. 01/03-30/10.
Distance: on the spot on the spot.

Nienburg 10A1

Reisemobilstellplatz Nienburg/Weser, Oyler Straße.
GPS: n52,64094 e9,20137.

25 € 5 € 1/120liter Ch (16x)€ 1/8h.
Surface: gravel. 01/01-31/12.
Distance: 600m on the spot on the spot 300m 500m.
Remarks: Along the river Weser.

Norddeich 7F2

Wohnmobilhafen Norddeich, Itzendorferstrasse.
GPS: n53,61014 e7,15777.

100 € 11/24h, 2 pers. + tourist tax, incl. 30% discount Erlebnisbad Ocean Wave Chincluded (96x)€ 1/2kWh WC € 1.
Location: Rural, comfortable, quiet. **Surface:** metalled.
01/01-31/12.
Distance: 100m 100m 100m 500m 100m.

Norddeich 7F2

Womo Park Norddeich, Deichstraße 24. **GPS**: n53,60166 e7,13527.

60 € 13, tourist tax excl., dog € 3 € 1/100liter Ch € 1/kWh WC € 1 € 3/1,50.
Location: Rural, comfortable, quiet. **Surface:** gravel. 01/01-31/12.
Distance: 2km beach 1,5km, beach (dog allowed) 1km on the spot 500m 100m.
Remarks: Bread-service.

Nordenham 7H2

Freizeitbad Störtebeker, Atenser Allee.
GPS: n53,49478 e8,47368.

15 € 6 € 1/liter Ch (16x)€ 0,50/kWh € 2,at sauna.
Location: Urban, comfortable, noisy. **Surface:** grasstiles.
01/01-31/12.
Distance: 1km 2km on the spot 400m on the spot on the spot.
Remarks: Max. 3 days, bread-service.

Nordenham 7H2

Volkers, Deichstrasse 158. **GPS**: n53,54003 e8,50905.

6 € 8 € 1/100 Ch (16x)€ 0,50/kWh WC € 1/4minutes on demand. **Location:** Rural, comfortable, quiet.
Surface: gravel. 01/01-31/12.
Distance: 2km 100m 500m on the spot.
Remarks: Grill and picknic area.

Nordholz 7H1

Wuster Strasse 12, Spieka. **GPS**: n53,75772 e8,59409.

5 € 5 + tourist tax € 1/100liter € 1 Ch (5x)€ 1/2kWh.
Location: Rural, simple.
Surface: metalled. 01/01-31/12.
Distance: on the spot 100m.

Nordhorn 9F1

Vechtesee, Heseperweg. **GPS**: n52,43683 e7,08190.

35 € 5 € 1/80liter € 1/5h.
Location: Rural. **Surface:** grassy/metalled. 01/01-31/12.
Distance: 400m 300m 300m on the spot on the spot.

Northeim 10B3

Grosser Freizeitsee, Am Nordhafen. **GPS**: n51,72920 e9,96286.

DE

10 € 6 € 0,50/50liter Ch (8x)€ 1/kWh.
Location: Rural, simple, noisy. **Surface:** gravel.
01/01-31/12.
Distance: 5km 3km on the spot 2km.

Oberndorf/Oste 8A1

Wohnmobilplatz Bentwisch, Hoffmann-von-Fallersleben-Straße 10.
GPS: n53,75398 e9,15054.

8 € 5 € 2/100liter Ch (6x)€ 2/8h WC € 0,50 € 0,50.
Location: Rural, comfortable. **Surface:** grassy/gravel.
01/01-31/12.
Distance: 2km 100m 100m on the spot.

Oederquart 8A1

Am Sportplatz. **GPS**: n53,80411 e9,24485.
6 free. **Surface:** metalled. 01/01-31/12.
Remarks: At sports centre.

Oldenburg 7H3

Am Küstenkanal, Westfalendamm. **GPS**: n53,12927 e8,21465.

3 voluntary contribution. **Location:** Rural, simple.
Surface: gravel. 01/01-31/12.
Distance: on the spot 1km on the spot 100m 400m.
Remarks: Alternative: in front of campsite Am Flötenteich, 53,166944 8,235, 2 pitches free.

Oldenburg 7H3

Hymer Zentrum Fassbender, Sieben Berge. **GPS**: n53,19187 e8,22574.
4 free € 0,50 Ch € 1. **Location:** Simple. **Surface:** metalled.
01/01-31/12.
Distance: 50m.

Osnabrück 9G2

Wohnmobilplatz Nettebad, Im Haseesch 6.
GPS: n52,30194 e8,05031.

5 € 10 € 1/100liter Ch € 1/6h. **Location:** Urban, simple, quiet. **Surface:** grassy/metalled. 01/01-31/12.
Distance: on the spot on the spot.
Remarks: At swimming pool, max. 24h.

Osten 8A2

Festhalle, Altendorf 13. **GPS**: n53,69602 e9,18813.

10 € 8 Ch (2x)included.
Location: Rural, simple. **Surface:** metalled. 01/01-31/12.
Distance: on the spot on the spot 500m.

Remarks: Pay at Hotel Fährkrug.

Osterholz-Scharmbeck 7H3

August-Schlüter-Turnhalle, Lange Strasse 28.
GPS: n53,22562 e8,79000.

4 free € 1/100liter . **Location:** Urban, simple, central.
Surface: metalled. 01/01-31/12.
Distance: on the spot on the spot on the spot.

Osterode 10C3

Aloha-Aqualand, Schwimmbadstraße.
GPS: n51,72263 e10,24998.

7 € 8-12 € 1/75liter € 1 Ch (11x)€ 1,50/8h.
Location: Rural, noisy. **Surface:** metalled. 01/01-31/12.
Distance: 1km 200m 500m.
Remarks: Max. 2 nights, discount at swimming pool.

Osterode 10C3

Campingplatz Eulenburg, Scheerenberger Straße 100.
GPS: n51,72766 e10,28347.

13 € 10, 2 pers.incl € 1/100liter Ch (12x)€ 1/kWh WC € 0,70/4minutes € 4/day. **Location:** Rural, comfortable, quiet.
Surface: gravel. 01/01-31/12.
Distance: 2km on the spot 2,5km on the spot on the spot on the spot on the spot.
Remarks: Bread-service, swimming pool incl.

Ostrhauderfehn 7G3

Reisemobilhafen Ostrhauderfehn, Hauptstrasse 115.
GPS: n53,13872 e7,62318.

32 € 7 Ch (12x)€ 1/2kWh WC € 0,50 € 2 included.
Location: Comfortable. **Surface:** grassy/metalled.
01/01-31/12 during fair in June.
Distance: 100m 100m 100m.
Remarks: Caution key € 10, sanitary at bar.

Otterndorf 7H1

Schützenplatz, Fröbelweg. **GPS**: n53,80861 e8,89444.

8 free. **Location:** Rural, simple.
Surface: metalled. 01/01-31/12.
Distance: on the spot 200m.

Otterndorf 7H1

Seglertreff, Schleuse 5. **GPS**: n53,82250 e8,89472.

12 free, 01/04-31/10 € 7 + tourist taks Ch € 2,50/24h WC € 1,50.
Location: Rural, comfortable. **Surface:** metalled. 01/01-31/12.
Distance: 2km 50m on the spot on the spot 2km on the spot on the spot.

Ottersberg 8A3

Am Sportzentrum, Fährwisch. **GPS**: n53,10721 e9,13558.

8 free € 1 Ch € 1/8h. **Location:** Simple.
Surface: gravel/sand. 01/01-31/12.
Distance: 500m 200m.

Ovelgönne 7H2

Burgdorf Ovelgönne, Am Sportplatz. **GPS**: n53,34333 e8,42750.

5 free € 1/100liter Ch free. **Location:** Urban, simple, isolated, quiet. **Surface:** gravel. 01/01-31/12.
Distance: 700m 700m 700m on the spot.

Oyten 8A3

KNAUS Reisemobilpark, Oyter See 1. **GPS**: n53,04645 e9,00396.

28 € 22 Ch € 3,50 WC included € 1
Location: Rural, comfortable. **Surface:** metalled.
01/03-01/11.
Distance: 2,5km 3km Oyter See 150m.
Remarks: Caution key € 5, service passerby € 4.

Papenburg 7G3

Roten Kreuz, Rathausstraße. **GPS**: n53,07646 e7,39266.

DE

50 free. **Location:** Urban, simple. **Surface:** grassy/sand.
01/01-31/12.
Distance: on the spot 300m.
Remarks: Nearby hospital.

Papenburg 7G3

Hotel-Restaurant Hilling, Mittelkanal links 94.
GPS: n53,07879 e7,43894.
22 € 8 € 1 € 1 Ch € 0,50/kWh WC € 2,50/time included. **Location:** Rural, comfortable, quiet.
Surface: grassy/gravel. 01/01-31/12.
Distance: on the spot 500m on the spot on the spot.

Papenburg 7G3

Poggenpoel, Zum Poggenpoel. **GPS:** n53,06526 e7,42630.

20 € 10 € 3/100liter € 3 Ch (8x)€ 2,50/24h WC € 2.
Location: Rural, simple.
Surface: gravel. 01/01-31/12.
Distance: 3,5km Badesee 500m.
Remarks: At lake, max. 3 nights.

Polle 10A2

Weserpromenade, Mühlenweg 2. **GPS:** n51,89871 e9,40830.

15 € 8 + € 1/pp tourist tax Ch included € 2,50.
Location: Rural, simple. **Surface:** grassy. 01/01-31/12.
Distance: 100m on the spot on the spot 100m 100m Weser-Radweg.
Remarks: Along the Weser river, check in at campsite, bread-service.

Rastede 7H3

Mühlenstraße. **GPS:** n53,24806 e8,20944.

4 free. **Location:** Urban, simple.
Surface: metalled. 01/01-31/12.
Distance: 1km 2,7km 1km 2km.
Remarks: Use sanitary only during opening hours swimming pool.

Rehburg-Loccum 10A1

Wohnmobilstellplatz Rehburg, Auf der Bleiche 14.
GPS: n52,47370 e9,23227.

8 € 5 € 1/100liter Ch € 1/12h.
Location: Rural. **Surface:** gravel. 01/01-31/12.
Distance: 500m 4km 500m 400m on the spot on the spot.

Tourist information Rehburg-Loccum:
Dinosaurierpark Münchehagen. Attractions park around the dinosaur. 12/03-30/10 9-18.

Rhauderfehn 7G3

Paddel- und Pedalstation, Am Siel 8. **GPS:** n53,13878 e7,58689.

16 € 8 € 1/100liter Ch (16x)€ 1/8h WC € 1,50 included. **Location:** Rural, luxurious, quiet.
Surface: grassy. 01/01-31/12.
Distance: 500m on the spot on the spot 50m on the spot on the spot.
Remarks: Caution key sanitary € 10, canoe and bicycle rental.

Rhede/Ems 7F3

Emspark, Am Sportplatz 6. **GPS:** n53,05853 e7,27621.

5 free. **Location:** Simple. **Surface:** metalled.
01/01-31/12.
Distance: 500m 500m 500m.
Remarks: Parking in front of sports park.

Rhede/Ems 7F3

Gasthof Prangen, Kirchstraße 25. **GPS:** n53,05943 e7,26923.

10 guests free free. **Location:** Urban, simple, quiet.
Surface: grassy/gravel. 01/01-31/12.
Distance: on the spot on the spot 100m on the spot.

Rieste 9G1

Reisemobilhafen am Alfsee Center, Westerfeldstraße 76.
GPS: n52,49309 e7,98953.
30 € 8-15 € 0,50/kWh. 01/01-31/12.

Rieste 9G1

Wohnmobilstellplätze-Alfsee, Bootshafenstraße 4.
GPS: n52,47824 e7,98961.
10 € 12, dog € 1,50 € 1/100liter Ch € 0,50 WC.
Location: Isolated, quiet. **Surface:** grassy/metalled. 01/01-31/12.
Distance: on the spot.
Remarks: Caution key sanitary € 10.

Rinteln 10A2

Reisemobilplatz am Weseranger, Dankerser strasse.
GPS: n52,19226 e9,07842.

40 free € 4/100liter € 4 Ch € 2 (36x)€ 1/kWh,16Amp.
Location: Rural, simple. **Surface:** grassy/gravel.
01/01-31/12.
Distance: 600m on the spot on the spot 100m 400m 400m Weserradweg on the spot.
Remarks: Max. 3 days.

Rodenberg 10A1

Rikes Wohnmobilstellplatz am Deister, Gottlieb Daimler Straße 11.
GPS: n52,30690 e9,36757.

8 € 6 € 1/100liter Ch € 0,50/kWh.
Surface: gravel. 01/01-31/12.
Distance: centre 1,2km.
Remarks: Bread-service.

Rodewald 10A1

Am Freibad, Im Zentrum. **GPS:** n52,66369 e9,48020.

6 voluntary contribution € 0,50/100liter (10x)€ 0,50/kWh.
Surface: grasstiles. 01/01-31/12.
Distance: 200m on the spot on the spot.

Rotenburg (Wümme) 8A3

Am Weichelsee, Bremer Straße. **GPS:** n53,11960 e9,38230.

20 € 5 Ch (20x)€ 3.
Location: Rural, simple. **Surface:** metalled.
01/01-31/12.
Distance: 2km on the spot Strandhaus 2km on the spot.
Remarks: Check in at StrandHouse.

Salzgitter 10B2

Reisemobilstellplatz am Salzgittersee, Zum Salzgittersee.
GPS: n52,15222 e10,31306.

DE

18 free € 2/100liter Ch (14x)€ 1/6h.
Location: Rural, comfortable. **Surface:** grassy/metalled.
01/01-31/12.
Distance: 1km on the spot 500m 1km on the spot on the spot on the spot.
Remarks: Max. 4 days, boat rental.

Salzgitter 10B2

Thermalsolebad, Parkallee 3, Salzgitter-Bad.
GPS: n52,03724 e10,38351.

6 free. **Location:** Rural, simple, quiet.
Surface: metalled. 01/01-31/12.
Distance: 1,5km on the spot 1,5km on the spot on the spot on the spot.
Remarks: Max. 4 days, use sanitary only during opening hours swimming pool, against payment, no camping activities.

Salzhausen 8B2

Am Waldbad, Schwienbrink. **GPS**: n53,22199 e10,17841.

6 free € 1/10minutes Ch (4x)€ 1/12h.
Location: Rural, simple. **Surface:** gravel. 01/01-31/12.
Distance: 1km 500m.

Salzhemmendorf 10B2

Ith-Sole-Therme, In der Saale-Aue. **GPS**: n52,07093 e9,58564.

20 € 7,50 € 0,20/20liter € 1 Ch (20x)€ 1/kWh included.
Location: Rural, quiet. **Surface:** grassy/gravel. 01/01-31/12.
Distance: 400m 300m on the spot.
Remarks: Check in at pay-desk of the Therme.

Salzhemmendorf 10B2

Rasti-land, Quanthofer strasse 9. **GPS**: n52,09706 e9,66451.

5 free. **Location:** Isolated. **Surface:** gravel/sand.
01/01-31/12.
Distance: 1km.
Remarks: Bus parking amusement park.

Tourist information Salzhemmendorf:
Rasti-Land, Quanthofer strasse 9. Amusement park. 01/04-31/10 10-17/18h, Apr, Sep: Sa, Su.

Sande (Nieder-Sachsen) 7G2

Am Markt. **GPS**: n53,50251 e8,01113.

4 free. **Location:** Urban, simple. **Surface:** metalled.
01/01-31/12.
Distance: 100m 100m 100m.

Sande (Nieder-Sachsen) 7G2

Jade Weser Airport, Mariensielerstrasse. **GPS**: n53,50788 e8,05245.

2 free. **Location:** Rural, simple.
Surface: grassy/metalled. 01/01-31/12.
Distance: 3km on the spot.

Sande (Nieder-Sachsen) 7G2

Paddel- und Pedalstation, Altmarienhausen.
GPS: n53,51174 e8,01076.
4 free. **Location:** Rural, simple, quiet. **Surface:** gravel.
01/01-31/12.
Distance: 1km Sander See 50m.

Sande (Nieder-Sachsen) 7G2

Sander See, Loppelter Weg. **GPS**: n53,51162 e8,00206.

4 free. **Surface:** metalled. 01/01-31/12.
Distance: 2km on the spot.

Sande (Nieder-Sachsen) 7G2

Freizeitmobile von der Kammer, Huntestraße 1.
GPS: n53,49076 e8,02292.
Ch on demand. 01/03-31/10.

Sandstedt 7H2

Wohnmobilstellplatz Sandstedt, Am Radarturm 5.
GPS: n53,36317 e8,51231.

10 free € 1/100liter € 1 Ch€ 1 (9x)€ 1 WC 150m on campsite. **Location:** Rural, comfortable, isolated, quiet.
Surface: grassy/gravel. 01/04-30/09.
Distance: 500m 3km 100m 950m 3km 500m on the spot on the spot.

Sankt Andreasberg 10C3

Silbererzgrube Samson, Am Samson 4. **GPS**: n51,71398 e10,51625.

20 € 15 Ch (20x)included.
Location: Rural, simple, quiet. **Surface:** gravel. 01/01-31/12.
Distance: 1km 400m 1km on the spot.
Remarks: At Historical Mine of Sllver Ores.

Saterland 7G3

Reisemobilhafen am Maiglöckchensee, Am Sportplatz, Scharrel.
GPS: n53,07060 e7,70116.

28+7 € 5 € 1/100liter € 1 Ch€ 1 (28x)€ 2/24h WC € 0,50 € 2. **Location:** Rural, luxurious, quiet. **Surface:** grassy.
01/01-31/12.
Distance: 300m 50m 50m 1km 500m 500m.

Scharnebeck 8C2

Wohnmobilstellplatz Am Schiffshebewerk, Adendorfer Straße 40.
GPS: n53,29196 e10,49320.

15 € 6/24h, park € 2 € 1/10minutes Ch (8x)€ 1/8h.
Location: Rural, comfortable, isolated, quiet. **Surface:** metalled.
01/01-31/12.
Distance: 1km 200m Aldi 400m.
Remarks: Climbing wall 100m, boat lift Scharnebeck.

Schneverdingen 8B3

Wohnmobil-Park Lüneburger Heide, Badeweg 3, Heber.
GPS: n53,07104 e9,86481.

44 € 16 € 1/80liter Ch (40x),10Amp WC included .
Location: Rural, comfortable.
Surface: grassy/metalled. 01/04-31/10.
Distance: 7km 5km on the spot on the spot on camp site on the spot on the spot.
Remarks: Use sanitary facilities at campsite, car rental, shuttle bus.

Schneverdingen 8B3

Am Quellenbad, Inseler Straße. **GPS**: n53,13110 e9,77280.

DE

10 free, € 2 Ch WC € 1.
Location: Urban, simple. **Surface:** grassy. 01/01-31/12.
Distance: 2km on the spot on the spot on the spot.
Remarks: Max. 2 nights, use sanitary only during opening hours swimming pool.

Schneverdingen 8B3

Parkplatz Festhalle, Im Osterwald. **GPS**: n53,11893 e9,80681.

10 free. **Location:** Simple. **Surface:** metalled.
01/01-31/12.
Distance: 2km 2km.
Remarks: Max. 2 nights, entrance via Festhalle.

Schneverdingen 8B3

Walter-Peters-Park, Verdener Straße. **GPS**: n53,11307 e9,78799.
2 free. 01/01-31/12.
Distance: 100m.
Remarks: Nearby police station.

Schneverdingen 8B3

Mariechens Hoff, Voßbarg 15, Reinsehlen.
GPS: n53,17122 e9,83316.

8 € 8 Ch included (8x)€ 0,40/kWh. **Location:** Rural, simple, isolated, quiet. **Surface:** grassy. 01/01-31/12.
Distance: 7km 15km 3km 4km on the spot on the spot.

Schneverdingen 8B3

Reisemobilhafen Lüneburgerheide, Badeweg 3, Heber.
GPS: n53,07108 e9,86464.

5 € 12 Ch (5x)included WC € 2,50.
Location: Rural, luxurious, quiet. **Surface:** grasstiles/metalled.
01/04-31/10.
Distance: 5km on camp site on the spot on the spot.
Remarks: Sanitary at campsite.

Schöppenstedt 10C2

Elm-Asse-Platz, Schützenplatz am Berge.
GPS: n52,14756 e10,77737.

15 free. **Location:** Rural, simple, noisy.
Surface: asphalted. 01/01-31/12.
Distance: 600m 1km 1km.
Remarks: Next to sports fields.

Tourist information Schöppenstedt:
The region of Till Eulenspiegel. Tills-Tauf-Tour: cycle and hiking routesin the country of Jester Till, start at the Till Eulenspiegel museum.
Tue-Fri 14-17h, Sa/Su/holidays 11-17h.
Till Eulenspiegelmuseum, Nordstrasse 4a. Tue-Fri 14-17h, Sa/Su/holidays 11-17h Mo.

Schortens 7G2

Aqua-toll, Beethovenstrasse. **GPS**: n53,53961 e7,93780.

2 free. **Surface:** metalled. 01/01-31/12.
Distance: 200m 25m.
Remarks: Parking swimming pool, max. 6,5m.

Schortens 7G2

Reisemobilstellplatz Fair-Cafe, Birkenstraße.
GPS: n53,55281 e7,97650.

6 guests free. **Surface:** unpaved. 01/01-31/12.
Distance: 3km 100m.

Schulenberg 10C2

Wiesenbergstrasse. **GPS**: n51,83535 e10,43464.

20 € 5 + € 1,50/pp tourist tax € 1/80liter Ch (6x)€ 0,60/kWh WC. **Location:** Rural, comfortable, quiet.
Surface: gravel. 01/01-31/12.
Distance: on the spot on the spot 6km on the spot on the spot.
Remarks: Check in at tourist office, view at Okerstausee.

Schüttorf 9F2

Am Kuhmplatz, Graf-Egbert-Straße. **GPS**: n52,32123 e7,22642.

10 free Ch free. **Location:** Rural, simple.
Surface: gravel. 01/01-31/12.
Distance: 2,4km 100m.
Remarks: Parking swimming pool.

Schüttorf 9F2

Quendorfer See, Weiße Riete 3. **GPS**: n52,33892 e7,22665.
€ 5 Ch included. **Surface:** gravel. 01/04-31/10.
Distance: 450m 450m.

Schwanewede 7H3

Am Markt, Am Markt. **GPS**: n53,22412 e8,59644.

3 free. **Location:** Simple, central.
Surface: metalled. 01/01-31/12.
Distance: on the spot on the spot on the spot.

Schwanewede 7H3

Brücke zu Harriersand, Inselstraße. **GPS**: n53,26489 e8,49762.

5 free. **Location:** Rural, simple, isolated.
Surface: grassy. 01/01-31/12.
Distance: 7km.

Schwanewede 7H3

Löhnhorst, Hammersbeckerweg/Am Fosshall.
GPS: n53,20355 e8,62453.

2 free. **Location:** Rural, simple, isolated, quiet.
Surface: metalled. 01/01-31/12.
Distance: 6km 6km 6km.

Schwanewede 7H3

Wohnmobilstellplatz, Klint, Neuenkirchen.
GPS: n53,23670 e8,50919.

5 free. **Location:** Rural, simple, quiet. **Surface:** unpaved.
01/01-31/12.

Distance: 500m.
Remarks: Dead end street.

S Seelze 10A1

Marina Rasche Werft, Werftstraße 10. **GPS**: n52,39560 e9,56435.

13 € 6,50 Chincluded (13x)€ 3 WC € 2.
Surface: gravel/metalled. 01/04-15/10.
Distance: 2km 4,5km on the spot.
Remarks: Bread-service, boat rental.

S Selsingen 8A2

Wohnmobilstation, Im Sick. **GPS**: n53,37573 e9,20681.

25 free Chfree. **Location:** Rural, simple. **Surface:** metalled.
01/01-31/12.
Distance: 500m 500m 100m.

Soltau 8B3

Soltau Therme, Stubbendorffweg. **GPS**: n52,99301 e9,84443.

10 free. **Location:** Simple, central, quiet.
Surface: metalled. 01/01-31/12.
Distance: 1km on the spot on the spot on the spot.
Remarks: Max. 1 night.

Soltau 8B3

Heidepark. GPS: n53,02166 e9,87370.

100 € 6. **Location:** Rural, simple, isolated.
Surface: grasstiles.
19/03-30/10.
Remarks: Parking amusement park.

Tourist information Soltau:
Heidepark. Amusement park.
01/03-31/10 9-18h, 01/07-15/08 Sa 9-21h.

Springe 10A2

Alter Museumshof, Auf dem Burghof. **GPS**: n52,20765 e9,55717.

5 free. **Location:** Simple. **Surface:** asphalted. 01/01-31/12.
Distance: Old city centre 200m 300m 800m.

S Stade 8A2

Wohnmobilstellplatz Am Schiffertor, Schiffertorsstrasse 21.
GPS: n53,60278 e9,46667.

79 € 9,50/24h € 1/80liter Ch € 0,50/kWh WC .
Location: Urban, central.
Surface: gravel. 01/01-31/12.
Distance: 500m 700m on the spot.

S Stadland 7H2

Am Sportplatz, Hauptstrasse, Seefeld. **GPS**: n53,45639 e8,35778.

5 free € 1/10minutes (4x)€ 1/8h.
Location: Urban, simple, quiet. **Surface:** asphalted. 01/01-31/12.
Distance: on the spot on the spot on the spot on the spot on the spot.
Remarks: Next to sports fields.

S Stadland 7H2

Deichparkplatz, Fährstrasse, Kleinensiel. **GPS**: n53,44250 e8,47833.

5 free € 1/100liter (4x)€ 1. **Location:** Rural, simple, isolated, quiet. **Surface:** gravel. 01/01-31/12.
Distance: 500m 200m Weserstrand 300m on the spot.

S Stadland 7H2

Rathausplatz, Am Markt, Rodenkirchen. **GPS**: n53,39944 e8,45444.

10 free € 1/10minutes Ch (4x)€ 1/8h.
Location: Urban, simple, central, quiet. **Surface:** grasstiles/metalled.
01/01-31/12 Thu 5-13h market.
Distance: on the spot 500m 500m on the spot on the spot.

S Stadland 7H2

Birkenweg, Kleinensiel. **GPS**: n53,44194 e8,47444.
Chfree. **Location:** Urban. 01/01-31/12.

S Stadthagen 10A1

Reisemobilplatz am Tropicana, Jahnstraße 2.
GPS: n52,32236 e9,18896.

15 free € 1/100liter Ch (4x)€ 1/2kWh WC .
Location: Rural, quiet. **Surface:** gravel. 01/01-31/12.
Distance: 2km 1km 500km on the spot on the spot.
Remarks: Max. 3 days, service at Tropicana.

S Stadtoldendorf 10B2

Mobilcamping unter den Homburg, Linnenkämper Strasse 33.
GPS: n51,87777 e9,63500.

30 € 5/day € 1 € 1 Ch (25x)€ 2/day.
Location: Simple. **Surface:** grassy. 01/01-31/12.
Distance: 1km on the spot 800m 800m.
Remarks: Check in at restaurant.

S Steimbke 10A1

Klostergarten. **GPS**: n52,65989 e9,38707.
8 voluntary contribution (8x). 01/01-31/12.
Distance: 400m on the spot.

S Steinfeld 9H1

Zur Schemder Bergmark, Dammer Strasse.
GPS: n52,58308 e8,21476.

10 free € 1/100liter € 0,50 Ch € 0,50.
Location: Rural, quiet. **Surface:** metalled. 01/01-31/12.
Distance: 500m 500m.
Remarks: Parking swimming pool, max. 3 days.

S Steinhude 10A1

Wohnmobilstellplatz Steinhude, Am Bruchdamm.
GPS: n52,44874 e9,35478.

168 € 11 € 1 € 1 Ch (168x)€ 0,60/kWh WC € 1/5minutes
€ 2,50/2,50. **Surface:** grassy. 01/01-31/12.
Distance: 500m 500m 500m 500m.
Remarks: Max. 3 nights, bread-service.

Tourist information Steinhude:
Marina on lake of the same name.

DE

Steyerberg 10A1

Wohnmobilstellplatz Steyerberg, Kleine Straße 7.
GPS: n52,56655 e9,02505.
4 free € 1 Ch€ 1 (8x)€ 1/8h. **Surface:** gravel.
01/01-31/12.
Distance: on the spot.

Stolzenau 10A1

Reisemobilstellplatz Stolzenau, Weserstrasse.
GPS: n52,51021 e9,08104.

24 € 4 € 1/60liter Ch (24x)€ 2/12h.
Surface: grasstiles. 01/01-31/12 service 01/11-31/03.
Distance: 250m on the spot on the spot 300m 300m.
Remarks: Along the Weser river.

Strücklingen 7G3

Reisemobilpark Sagter Ems, Haupstrasse.
GPS: n53,12166 e7,66761.

55 € 7 € 1/100liter Ch € 0,50/kWh € 1/10minutes € 3 included. **Location:** Rural, comfortable. **Surface:** grassy/gravel.
01/01-31/12.
Distance: on the spot on the spot 500m on the spot on the spot.

Strücklingen 7G3

Reisemobilplatz Am Bootshafen, Hauptstrasse 640.
GPS: n53,12819 e7,66762.

15 € 5 € 1/100liter € 1 Ch€ 1 € 2/24h WC€ 1 € 1.
Location: Rural, simple, quiet. **Surface:** grassy/gravel.
01/01-31/12.
Distance: 100m on the spot on the spot on the spot on the spot 100m.
Remarks: Canoe and bicycle rental.

Südbrookmerland 7F2

Grosses Meer, Langerweg. **GPS**: n53,44454 e7,30808.

30 € 9 € 0,50/100liter € 0,50 Ch€ 0,50 € 1/2kWh WC included. **Location:** Rural, comfortable, quiet.
Surface: metalled. 01/01-31/12.
Distance: on the spot on the spot.
Remarks: Caution key sanitary € 50.

Sulingen 9H1

Am Stadtsee, Kornstraße. **GPS**: n52,67653 e8,80127.

20 free € 1/5minutes € 1 Ch€ 1.
Surface: metalled. 01/01-31/12.
Distance: 600m 300m.

Surwold 7G3

Privatplatz Klapper, Papenburgerstrasse 57.
GPS: n53,01774 e7,48470.

10 € 10 Ch (4x)€ 2/24h WC € 2.
Location: Rural, simple. **Surface:** grassy. 01/01-31/12.
Distance: 1km 1,5km 1km 1km.
Remarks: Swimming pool and picnic area available.

Surwold 7G3

Erholungsgebiet Surwolds Wald, Waldstrasse.
GPS: n52,96743 e7,51535.

20 € 8 € 1/100liter Ch € 3 WC € 2.
Surface: grassy. 01/01-31/12.
Distance: 800m 250m.

Tarmstedt 8A3

Landtechniek Grabau, Bahnhofstraße.
GPS: n53,22421 e9,08728.

15 € 6 Chincluded according consumption.
Location: Simple. **Surface:** metalled. 01/01-31/12.
Distance: on the spot 500m on the spot.

Thedinghausen 8A3

Reisemobilstellplatz Erbhof, Braunschweiger Straße 45.
GPS: n52,96188 e9,03020.

8 € 5 € 1/10minutes Ch (8x)€ 1/6h WC.
Surface: grasstiles. 01/01-31/12.
Distance: 500m on the spot on the spot.

Timmel 7G2

Ferienhof Welsch, Ulbagrgerstrasse 17. **GPS**: n53,36492 e7,52840.

8 € 6 € 1/100liter Ch € 0,50/kWh € 2,50 free.
Location: Comfortable, quiet. **Surface:** grassy. 01/01-31/12.
Distance: 500m 250m 500m 200m 200m.

Twist 9F1

Am Hallenbad. **GPS**: n52,64719 e7,08918.

6 free € 1/100liter Ch (8x)€ 1/2kWh.
Surface: metalled. 01/01-31/12.
Distance: on the spot on the spot.
Remarks: Barefoot path.

Uchte 10A1

Balkenkamp. **GPS**: n52,49761 e8,90618.

3 free € 1 Ch € 1/8h.
Surface: metalled. 01/01-31/12.
Distance: 100m 500m 100m.

Uelsen 9F1

Festplatz, Hardinghauserstrasse. **GPS**: n52,49575 e6,88840.

10 free € 2 ChWC. **Surface:** asphalted. 01/01-31/12.

Uelzen 8C3

Im Sportboothafen, Riedweg 7. **GPS**: n52,95722 e10,59444.

6 € 8 + € 1/pp € 1/70liter € 1 Ch (8x)€ 1/6h,16Amp WC included € 2,50/2,50.
Location: Rural, simple, quiet. **Surface:** metalled. 01/01-31/12.
Distance: 2,5km on the spot on the spot on the spot 2km on the spot on the spot.
Remarks: Max. 3 nights, free bicycles available, playground.

DE

Undeloh 8B3

Am Naturschutzpark, Wilseder Straße. **GPS**: n53,19253 e9,97709.

30 € 3/day, € 6/night. **Location:** Rural, simple.
Surface: unpaved. 01/01-31/12.
Distance: 500m 100m on the spot.
Remarks: In nature reserve the the Lüneburg Heide (heath).

Uplengen 7G2

Remelser Paddel- & Pedalstation, Uferstrasse.
GPS: n53,30123 e7,75151.

5 € 5 Ch (4x)€ 1/12h.
Surface: metalled. 01/01-31/12.
Distance: 500m 50m 500m.
Remarks: Max. 3 days, canoe and bicycle rental.

Uplengen 7G2

Schützenplatz, Schützenstraße. **GPS**: n53,30719 e7,74708.

10 € 5 Ch included € 1/12h. **Location:** Urban, simple.
Surface: grasstiles. 01/01-31/12 10/06-25/06.
Distance: 500m 500m 600m 600m.
Remarks: Max. 3 nights.

Uplengen 7G2

Zum grünen Jäger, Hollener Straße 36. **GPS**: n53,27825 e7,75244.

10 free free € 5.
Location: Rural, quiet. **Surface:** metalled. 01/01-31/12.
Distance: 4km 3km on the spot 4km on the spot on the spot.
Remarks: Restaurant closed on Monday.

Uslar 10B3

Reisemobilpark am Badeland, Zur Schwarzen Erde.
GPS: n51,66753 e9,62831.

20 € 6 + reduction swimming pool € 1/10minutes Ch € 1/8h WC € 0,50.
Location: Quiet. **Surface:** grasstiles. 01/01-31/12.
Distance: 1km on the spot 500m on the spot.

Uslar 10B3

Am Lindenhof, Lindenhof 1. **GPS**: n51,67213 e9,62952.

5 first night € 8, € 2 each additional night Ch included € 0,50/kWh. **Location:** Rural, simple.
Surface: grassy/gravel.
01/01-31/12.
Distance: 2,5km 2,5km 2,5km on the spot.

Tourist information Uslar:
Market, city centre. Fri 9-13h.
Alaris Schmetterlingspark. Butterfly park in tropical rain forest.
18/03-01/10 9.30-17.30, 02/10-01/11 9.30-16.30.
Uslarer Badeland. Swimming pool complex. Sa 13-19h, Su 10-18h, Tue-Fri 15-20h.

Vechta 9H1

Am Hallenwellen- und Freibad, Dornbusch.
GPS: n52,74000 e8,29639.

10 free. **Location:** Urban, simple.
Surface: grassy/metalled. 01/01-31/12.
Distance: 1km 1km 1km.
Remarks: Parking swimming pool, max. 3 days, service Bokenerd-damm 40.

Vechta 9H1

Oldenburgerstraße. **GPS**: n52,73245 e8,28833.

5 free. **Location:** Urban, simple.
Surface: metalled. 01/01-31/12.
Distance: on the spot on the spot on the spot.

Verden 8A3

Conrad-Wode-Straße. **GPS**: n52,92572 e9,22738.
14 € 6/24h € 1/90liter Ch (18x)€ 1/8h.
Location: Urban, comfortable, central.
Surface: grassy.
01/01-31/12.
Distance: 350m 300m 300m 300m.

Tourist information Verden:
Reiterstadt, horse city of international reputation.
Deutsches Pferdemuseum, Holzmarkt 9 . Horse museum. Tue-Su 10-17h.
Verdener Bauernmarkt. Sa 8-13h.

Vienenburg 10C2

Schacht I. **GPS**: n51,95705 e10,56772.

4 free. **Location:** Rural, simple, quiet.
Surface: metalled. 01/01-31/12.
Distance: 700m 700m 600m on the spot on the spot.
Remarks: At Vienenburg Lake, max. 24h.

Visselhövede 8A3

Zu den Visselwiesen, Wüstenhof 1. **GPS**: n52,98530 e9,57772.

8 free. **Location:** Urban, simple.
Surface: metalled. 01/01-31/12.
Distance: on the spot 100m 200m.

Vrees 7G3

Herzog-Arenberg-Straße 5. **GPS**: n52,88972 e7,77488.
6 free € 1/100liter Ch € 1/2kWh. 01/01-31/12.
Distance: on the spot 350m.

Wagenfeld 9H1

Hallen-Freibad, Schulstraße 12. **GPS**: n52,54531 e8,59634.
20 € 7 Ch included. 01/01-31/12.
Distance: 300m 300m.
Remarks: At swimming pool.

Wagenfeld 9H1

Ströher Lokschuppen, Bahnhofstraße 29, Ströhen.
GPS: n52,53954 e8,68465.
25 € 4 € 1,50 € 1,50 Ch € 1 € 3.
Surface: grassy. 01/01-31/12.
Distance: on the spot bakery.

Walchum 7F3

Marinapark Emstal, Steinbilder Straße. **GPS**: n52,92680 e7,29624.

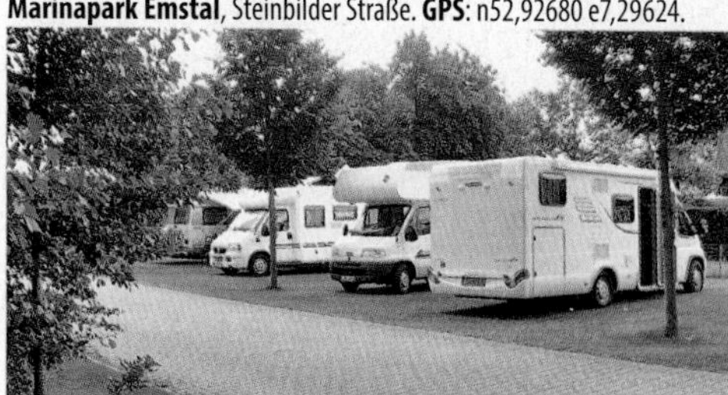

10 € 10 Ch (6x) WC € 1,50.
Location: Rural. **Surface:** grassy. 01/01-31/12.
Distance: fishing permit obligatory 300m on the spot on the spot on the spot.

Walsrode 8A3

Ferienhof Wiechers, Klein Eilstorf 6. **GPS**: n52,81462 e9,47898.
3 € 15 + € 3/pp. **Surface:** grassy. 01/01-31/12.

Walsrode 8A3

Forellenhof, Hünzingen 3. **GPS**: n52,89855 e9,59122.

10 € 15 (2x) included.
Location: Rural, simple, isolated, quiet. **Surface:** grasstiles/grassy.
01/01-31/12.
Distance: 3km on the spot 3km.

DE

Remarks: Free with a meal.

S **Walsrode** 8A3

Weltvogelpark, Am Vogelpark. **GPS**: n52,88425 e9,59720.

20 free Ch (12x)€ 1/8h. **Location:** Rural, simple, central. **Surface:** grassy. 01/01-31/12. **Distance:** 2,5km on the spot 2,5km. **Remarks:** Max. 1 night.

Tourist information Walsrode:

Weltvogelpark. Bird park and botanical garden. 01/03-31/10 10-17h.

S **Wangerland** 7G2

Am Hallenwellenbad, Hooksiel. **GPS**: n53,63435 e8,03532.

18 € 10, dog € 3 € 1/100liter Ch (12x)€ 0,50/kWh included. **Location:** Rural, simple, quiet. **Surface:** metalled. 01/01-31/12. **Distance:** 1km 100m. **Remarks:** To be paid at swimming pool.

S **Wangerland** 7G2

An der Ostdüne, Bäderstrasse, Hooksiel. **GPS**: n53,64103 e8,03514.

75 € 17 + € 2,90/pp tourist tax, dog € 3,10 Ch WC included. **Location:** Rural, comfortable, quiet. **Surface:** grassy/gravel. 01/04-30/10. **Distance:** 1,7km beach ±250m on the spot.

S **Wangerland** 7G2

Bismarckstraße 30. **GPS**: n53,66497 e7,92751.

12 € 3/pp tourist tax € 1/80liter Ch (12x)€ 0,50/kWh. **Location:** Rural, comfortable, quiet. **Surface:** gravel. 01/01-31/12. **Distance:** 750m on the spot 750m 1km. **Remarks:** Max. 2 nights.

S **Wangerland** 7G2

Nordsee-Camping-Schillig, Jadestraße, Schillig. **GPS**: n53,69986 e8,02338.

80 € 13 + € 2,90/pp tourist tax, dog € 3,10 Ch (80x) WC included. **Location:** Rural, comfortable, quiet. **Surface:** grassy. 01/04-31/10. **Distance:** 200m on the spot.

S **Wangerland** 7G2

Wangermeer, Jelliestede. **GPS**: n53,66962 e7,90975.

10 free (4x)€ 0,50/kWh. **Location:** Rural, simple, quiet. **Surface:** grassy/sand. 01/01-31/12. **Distance:** 800m on the spot 100m. **Remarks:** Max. 2 days.

S **Wangerland** 7G2

Am Yachthafen, Zum Hafen, Horumersiel. **GPS**: n53,68293 e8,02091.

22 € 12 € 1 Ch WC included. **Location:** Rural, comfortable, central, quiet. **Surface:** concrete. 01/04-30/10. **Distance:** 600m on the spot on the spot.

S **Wardenburg** 7H3

Keilstrasse, Astrup. **GPS**: n53,04770 e8,21197.

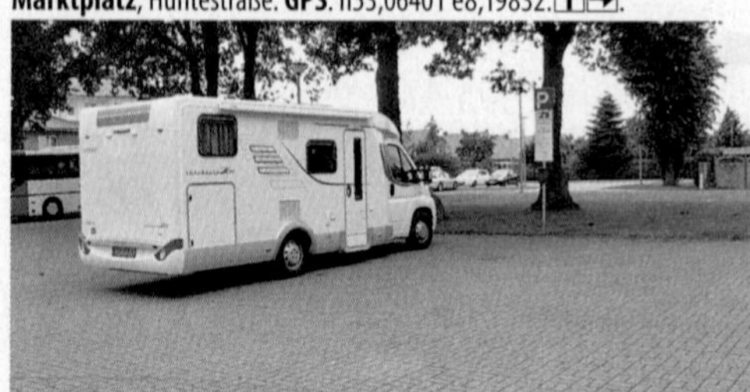

5 free (3x). **Location:** Urban, simple. **Surface:** grassy. 01/01-31/12. **Distance:** 2,5km.

Wardenburg 7H3

Marktplatz, Huntestraße. **GPS**: n53,06401 e8,19832.

3 free. **Location:** Urban, simple. **Surface:** metalled. 01/01-31/12. **Distance:** on the spot 3,6km.

S **Weener** 7F3

Am Alten Hafen, Panneborgstrasse. **GPS**: n53,16953 e7,36167.

45 € 7,50/24h € 1/100liter Ch (45x)€ 2,50/24h WC € 1. **Location:** Urban, comfortable. **Surface:** asphalted. 01/01-31/12 during harbor festival 3rd week of June. **Distance:** on the spot on the spot on the spot. **Remarks:** Max. 3 days.

S **Weener** 7F3

Am Yachthafen, Am Marina-Park. **GPS**: n53,16570 e7,36480.

24 € 7,50 € 1/24h Ch € 2,50 WC € 1. **Location:** Simple, quiet. **Surface:** metalled. 01/04-30/09. **Distance:** centre 1,2km 50m.

S **Werdum** 7G2

Raiffeisenplatz. **GPS**: n53,65823 e7,71515.

15 € 10 € 0,50 Ch (6x)€ 0,50/kWh. **Location:** Rural, simple, quiet. **Surface:** gravel. 01/01-31/12. **Distance:** on the spot on the spot. **Remarks:** Pay at tourist office.

S **Werlte** 7G3

Kreutzmanns Mühle, Kirchstraße 28. **GPS**: n52,85463 e7,68155.

6 free € 1/100liter Ch (8x)€ 1/2kWh. **Location:** Urban, comfortable. **Surface:** metalled. 01/01-31/12. **Distance:** 200m 200m 200m.

S **Westergellersen** 8B2

Turniergelände Luhmühlen, Westergellerser Heide. **GPS**: n53,23306 e10,21623.

35 € 8 € 1 Ch (35x)€ 1/8h WC. **Location:** Rural, comfortable, isolated, quiet. **Surface:** grassy. 01/01-31/12. **Distance:** 4km 1,5km 4km 4km 2km. **Remarks:** Key sanitary building at Autohaus.

DE

Westerholt 7G2

Schützenplatz, Nordener Straße. **GPS**: n53,58918 e7,45327.

6 free € 1/5minutes € 1/time Ch € 1/time (12x) € 1/2kWh. **Location:** Rural, comfortable, quiet. **Surface:** metalled. 01/01-31/12. **Distance:** 400m 400m on the spot on the spot. **Remarks:** Max. 3 days.

Westerholt 7G2

Sportzentrum. **GPS**: n53,59120 e7,44852.

10 free Ch. **Location:** Rural, simple, quiet. **Surface:** metalled. 01/01-31/12. **Distance:** 500m 750m 800m.

Westerstede 7G3

Albert-Post-Platz, Auf der Lohe. **GPS**: n53,25883 e7,92685.

5 free. **Location:** Urban, simple. **Surface:** metalled. 01/01-31/12. **Distance:** 100m 2km 250m. **Remarks:** Max. 3 days.

Westerstede 7G3

Badesee Karlshof, Bekassinenweg. **GPS**: n53,18811 e7,86954.

5 free. **Location:** Rural, simple, isolated. **Surface:** gravel. 01/01-31/12. **Distance:** Badesee. **Remarks:** Max. 3 days.

Westerstede 7G3

Hössensportanlage, Jahnallee. **GPS**: n53,25369 e7,91229. 5 free. **Surface:** grasstiles. 01/01-31/12. **Distance:** 1km 500m 500m. **Remarks:** At swimming pool, max. 3 days.

Westerstede 7G3

Wohnmobilhafen Westerstede, Süderstraße 2. **GPS**: n53,24968 e7,93438.

50 € 9 Ch WC included. **Location:** Urban, comfortable, quiet. **Surface:** grassy/gravel. 01/01-31/12. **Distance:** 800m 1,4km McDonalds 200m.

Westoverledingen 7G3

Reisemobilhafen zur Mühle, Mühlenstrasse 214, Steenfelderfehn. **GPS**: n53,12944 e7,44051.

30 € 6 Ch (18x) WC included. **Location:** Rural, simple. **Surface:** grassy/metalled. 01/01-31/12. **Distance:** on the spot 1km on the spot on the spot.

Westoverledingen 7G3

Schützenplatz Flachsmeer, Papenburger strasse 74, Flachsmeer. **GPS**: n53,12700 e7,46367.

10 € 6 Ch (10x) included. **Location:** Rural, simple. **Surface:** grassy. 01/01-31/12. **Distance:** on the spot on the spot 100m.

Wiefelstede 7G3

Wohnmobilstellplatz am Bernsteinsee, Dorfstrasse 11, Conneforde. **GPS**: n53,32657 e8,06362.

30 € 6 € 1 € 2 Ch (25x) € 0,50/kWh WC € 0,50 on camp site. **Location:** Rural, comfortable. **Surface:** grassy. 01/01-31/12. **Distance:** on the spot on the spot. **Remarks:** In front of campsite, caution sepkey € 5.

Wiefelstede 7G3

Freibad Wiefelstede, Alter Damm 11. **GPS**: n53,26146 e8,10713.

10 free. **Location:** Rural, simple, quiet. **Surface:** metalled. 01/01-31/12. **Distance:** 500m on the spot 1,5km.

Wiesmoor 7G2

Auf dem Marktplatz. **GPS**: n53,41351 e7,73511.

5 € 7 (4x) included. **Location:** Urban, simple, quiet. **Surface:** metalled. 01/01-31/12. **Distance:** on the spot 100m 800m. **Remarks:** Pay in at kiosk.

Wiesmoor 7G2

Bootshafen Ottermeer, Am Stadion. **GPS**: n53,40951 e7,71841.

14 € 5,50 Ch included. **Surface:** grassy/metalled. 01/01-31/12. **Distance:** 1,5km. **Remarks:** Key service at Gastätte (12-19h).

Wiesmoor 7G2

Campingplatz Ottermeer, Am Ottermeer 52. **GPS**: n53,41570 e7,70930.

4 € 15, dog € 2 Ch € 2,50 WC € 3 included. **Location:** Simple, quiet. **Surface:** grasstiles. 01/01-31/12. **Distance:** 1,5km.

Wietzendorf 8B3

Übernachtungsoase Südsee Camp, Südsee camp 1, K41. **GPS**: n52,93120 e9,96474.

40 € 15 € 1/100liter € 0,50/kWh WC. **Location:** Comfortable. **Surface:** metalled. 01/01-31/12. **Distance:** 2km 100m on the spot. **Remarks:** Caution key service € 3.

Wildeshausen 7H3

Am Krandel, Krandelstrasse. **GPS**: n52,90042 e8,42728.

19 € 5/24h € 1/80liter Ch (20x) included € 2. **Location:** Rural, simple. **Surface:** grassy/metalled. 01/01-31/12.

DE

Distance: 500m 4,4km 400m 700m.
Remarks: Parking at swimming pool.

S Wilhelmshaven 7G2

Wohnmobilhafen Nautimo, Friedenstrasse 99.
GPS: n53,53546 e8,10104.

26 € 8 € 1/100liter Ch (26x)€ 1/6h,10Amp WC € 1 € 2/h. **Location:** Rural, comfortable, quiet.
Surface: metalled. 01/01-31/12.
Distance: 2km 3km 4km 1,5km on the spot 200m 1,5km 100m on the spot on the spot.
Remarks: Max. 7 days.

S Wilhelmshaven 7G2

Wohnmobilstellplatz Schleuseninsel, Schleussenstrasse 37.
GPS: n53,51478 e8,15218.

30 € 10, trailer € 5 € 1/100liter Ch (28x)€ 3/24h WC € 3/time . **Location:** Rural, comfortable, quiet.
Surface: gravel. 01/01-31/12.
Distance: 2,5km on the spot 250m Jadebus.

S Wilhelmshaven 7G2

Am Freibad Nord, Möwenstraße 30. **GPS:** n53,57032 e8,10368.

6 € 6, free with use of swimming pool (6x)€ 1/6h WC € 1.
Location: Rural, simple, quiet.
Surface: gravel. 01/05-31/08.
Distance: 1,5km.
Remarks: Use sanitary only during opening hours swimming pool.

S Wilhelmshaven 7G2

Reisemobilstellplatz Wilhelmshaven Südstadt, Banterweg 12.
GPS: n53,51559 e8,09072.

16 € 10 Ch (16x)included .
Location: Urban, simple, noisy. **Surface:** gravel. 01/01-31/12.
Remarks: Motorhome washing place.

Wilhelmshaven 7G2

Fliegerdeich West, Fliegerdeich. **GPS:** n53,50996 e8,12718.

40 € 0,75/h, € 12/day. **Location:** Rural, simple, quiet.
Surface: metalled. 01/01-31/12.
Distance: 2,5km sea nearby.
Remarks: No camping activities.

S Wilhelmshaven 7G2

Wohnmobilstellplatz Jade, Bunsenstraße 10.
GPS: n53,51047 e8,08879.

10 € 10 (10x)WC included.
Location: Rural, comfortable, noisy. **Surface:** gravel.
01/01-31/12 water: 01/11-31/03.
Distance: 5km 1km 2km.

Tourist information Wilhelmshaven:
Aquarium Wilhelmshaven, Südstrand 123. Sea aquarium.
10-18h.

Winsen/Luhe 8B2

Festplatz Bleiche, Tönnhäuserweg. **GPS:** n53,36452 e10,21228.

10 free. **Location:** Simple, central.
Surface: asphalted. 01/01-31/12.
Distance: 100m 100m 100m.

Winsen/Luhe 8B2

GreenEagle Golf, Radbrucher Straße 200. **GPS:** n53,32278 e10,22778.
15 free, playing golf obligatory. **Location:** Simple.
Surface: gravel. 01/01-31/12.
Distance: 6km 2,2km on the spot.

Winsen/Luhe 8B2

Grube's Fischerhütte, Hoopter Elbdeich 32. **GPS:** n53,39474 e10,17159.
5 free. **Surface:** asphalted/metalled. 01/01-31/12.
Distance: 4,5km on the spot 300m 400m.
Remarks: Max. 1 night, restaurant closed on Monday.

S Winsen/Luhe 8B2

Freizeit Center Albrecht, Porchestrasse 15, Gewerbegebiet Lühdorf.
GPS: n53,33750 e10,21947.

10 free € 1 € 2 Ch (11x) WC.
Location: Rural, simple. **Surface:** metalled. 01/01-31/12.
Distance: 4,5km on the spot.

S Wittingen 8C3

Wittinger Sporthafen, Am Sporthafen 1.
GPS: n52,72706 e10,66187.

20 € 9 + € 0,50/pp Ch (20x)WC included € 2,50/2,50.
Location: Rural, comfortable. **Surface:** grassy. 01/04-01/10.
Distance: 4km on the spot on the spot on the spot 4km 200m on the spot.
Remarks: Near marina.

S Wittmund 7G2

Am Gulfhof, Funnixer Riege 11. **GPS:** n53,64202 e7,78566.

8 € 9 Ch included. **Location:** Rural, simple, quiet.
Surface: grassy. 01/01-31/12.

Wittmund 7G2

Schützenplatz, Auricherstrasse. **GPS:** n53,55763 e7,69156.
15 free. **Surface:** grassy. 01/01-31/12.
Distance: 800m bakery 200m.

S Wittmund 7G2

Wohnmobilstellplatz an der Mole, Am Harlesiel 20.
GPS: n53,70941 e7,80839.

54 € 13 + € 2,50/pp tourist tax, dog € 2 Ch (18x)€ 3 WC .
Location: Rural, comfortable, quiet.
Surface: metalled. 15/03-31/10.
Distance: on the spot on the spot on the spot.
Remarks: Caution key electricity € 10.

S Wittmund 7G2

Campingplatz Harlesiel, Am Harlesiel, Carolinensiel-Harlesiel.
GPS: n53,70797 e7,80649.

50 € 13 + € 2,50/pp tourist tax, dog € 2 Ch (40x)€ 3 WC .
Location: Rural, comfortable, quiet.
Surface: asphalted. 15/03-31/10.
Distance: 500m 100m 100m on the spot.

S Wolfenbüttel 10C2

Alte Spinnerei, Am Seeligerpark. **GPS:** n52,16228 e10,52632.
10 free € 1 (3x)€ 1. **Surface:** metalled. 01/01-31/12.
Distance: 800m 300m.
Remarks: Max. 3 days, quiet at night, crowdy during the day.

S Wolfenbüttel 10C2

Sporthalleninsel, Vor dem Wehre. **GPS:** n52,16168 e10,52646.

DE

2 free € 1/80liter (4x)€ 1/8h. **Location:** Urban, central, noisy. **Surface:** metalled. 01/01-31/12.
Distance: 250m 500m 500m 200m.
Remarks: Along railwayline.

Wolfenbüttel 10C2

Wohnmobilpark Stadtbad Okeraue, Harztorwall 21.
GPS: n52,15680 e10,54024.
44 € 12, 2 pers.incl Ch (44x)included WC.
Surface: grassy. 01/01-31/12.
Remarks: Next to swimming pool.

Wolfsburg 10C1

Autostadt P2, Berliner Brücke. **GPS**: n52,43485 e10,79716.

9 € 3/day, € 6/24h included.
Location: Urban, noisy. **Surface:** asphalted. 01/01-31/12.
Distance: 2km on the spot 2km.

Tourist information Wolfsburg:
Autostadt. Of the Volkswagen-concern; with pavilion of several car makes, car tower of 20 floors, test driving. 9-20h.

Zetel 7G2

Johann Quathamer, Fuhrenkampstrasse 60.
GPS: n53,40084 e7,91893.

15 € 8 € 1/100liter Ch (15x)WCincluded € 1.
Location: Rural, comfortable, quiet. **Surface:** grassy.
01/01-31/12.
Distance: 4km 3km 3km.

Zetel 7G2

Markthamm, Neuenburger Strasse. **GPS**: n53,41706 e7,97000.

40 free Chfree (6x)€ 1/kWh.
Location: Urban, simple, central. **Surface:** grasstiles.
01/01-31/12.
Distance: on the spot Imbiss.
Remarks: Parking centre, max. 2 days, service Kläranlage open: Mo/Tue 11-23h, Thu/Sa 11-23h, Su 16-23h.

Zetel 7G2

Driefeler Esch. **GPS**: n53,41835 e7,98445.

10 free. **Location:** Simple. **Surface:** gravel. 01/01-31/12.
Remarks: Parking swimming pool, max. 48h.

Zetel 7G2

Schulmuseum Bohlenbergerfeld, Wehdestrasse.
GPS: n53,41322 e7,92143.

10 free. **Location:** Rural, simple, isolated.
Surface: grassy/gravel. 01/01-31/12.
Distance: 2,5km.
Remarks: At museum.

Zetel 7G2

Urwald, Urwaldstrasse, Neuenburg. **GPS**: n53,39293 e7,96547.

20 free. **Location:** Rural, simple, quiet.
Surface: unpaved. 01/01-31/12.
Remarks: Max. 1 day.

Zetel 7G2

Kläranlage, Moorstraße. **GPS**: n53,42302 e7,97937.
Chfree. 01/01-31/12.
Remarks: Mo/Thu 7-16h, Fri 7-13h, Sa/Su 9-9.30h.

Zeven 8A2

Viehmarktplatz, Meyerstrasse/Godenstedterstrasse.
GPS: n53,29764 e9,27514.

4 free. **Location:** Simple. **Surface:** metalled.
01/01-31/12.
Distance: 500m.

Zorge 10C3

Campingplatz im Waldwinkel, Kunzental 2.
GPS: n51,64188 e10,64881.

30 € 9,50, 2 pers.incl € 0,20/10liter Ch (15x)€ 2/day WC € 1/pp. **Location:** Rural, simple, quiet. **Surface:** grassy/gravel.
01/01-31/12.
Distance: 1,5km on the spot 6km 300m on the spot on the spot.
Remarks: Max. 2 nights.

Mecklenburg-Western Pomerania

Ahlbeck 8G1

Caravanplatz Am Wiesenrand, Gothenweg 5a.
GPS: n53,94100 e14,17600.

27 € 11-13,50 Ch € 0,50/kWh WCincluded € 1 € 3/2 € 3,50/3h. **Location:** Rural, comfortable, quiet.
Surface: grassy. 01/03-31/10.
Distance: 10min 10min 500m 200m.
Remarks: Bread-service, possibility for reservation.

Ahlbeck 8G1

Wohnmobilstellplatz Rauthe, Waldstrasse 7.
GPS: n53,93660 e14,18660.

30 € 16 Ch (30x)WCincluded € 2 € 4.
Location: Urban, central. **Surface:** grassy.
01/01-31/12.
Distance: on the spot 5 min 200m 200m.

Ahlbeck 8G1

Parkplatz an der Grenze, Swinemüdestrasse.
GPS: n53,92380 e14,21280.

30 € 5 + € 2,50/pp. **Location:** Urban, simple.
Surface: metalled. 01/01-31/12.
Distance: 3km.
Remarks: Max. 24h.

Ahrenshoop 6F3

Dorfstraße. **GPS**: n54,39155 e12,43914.

10 € 6/day, € 25/night. **Location:** Rural, simple, isolated, noisy.
Surface: gravel. 01/01-31/12.
Distance: 2km beach 50m.

Alt Schwerin 8E2

Insel Camping Werder, Wendorf 8. **GPS**: n53,48696 e12,31833.

DE

13 € 15,80 € 0,50/40liter Ch € 2 WC € 1 € 3/3 included. **Location:** Rural, luxurious, quiet. **Surface:** grassy.
01/01-31/12.
Distance: 4km on the spot on the spot 1km 3,5km.
Remarks: Max. 9m, dog € 2/day.

Altwarp 8G1

Hafen, Seestrasse. **GPS**: n53,73905 e14,27147.

40 € 9,50, dog € 2 Ch € 2/24h WC included € 1 € 2/1.
Location: Rural, luxurious, quiet. **Surface:** grassy/metalled.
01/01-31/12.
Distance: 500m 300m on the spot 300m 400m 300m on the spot on the spot.
Remarks: At tourist office.

Bansin 6H3

Waldparkplatz Bansin, Am Heuberg 1. **GPS**: n53,98834 e14,11291.

100 € 5-6 + € 3-3,50/pp, dog € 1,50 Ch € 2,70/24h WC included € 1 € 4,50/3. **Location:** Rural, comfortable, isolated.
Surface: grassy/metalled. 01/05-30/09.
Distance: 3km 400m on the spot.

Barth 6F3

Segelverein, Am Westhafen. **GPS**: n54,37130 e12,72510.

20 € 10 Ch € 2 WC € 1.
Surface: grassy. 01/05-01/10.
Distance: on the spot on the spot on the spot.
Remarks: Caution key sanitary € 20.

Barth 6F3

Wohnmobilparkplatz Barth, Am Osthafen.
GPS: n54,36965 e12,73251.

10 € 7 (8x)€ 0,50/kWh. **Location:** Urban, simple, noisy.
Surface: metalled. 01/01-31/12.
Distance: 300m 300m 300m on the spot on the spot.

Beckerwitz 8D1

Ostseecamping Beckerwitzer Strand, Ostseestrasse 10.
GPS: n53,94137 e11,31682.

12 € 6-8 € 1 Ch € 2,60/night WC € 0,50 € 3,50/3,50.
Location: Rural, comfortable. **Surface:** grassy. 01/04-10/10.
Distance: on the spot on the spot on the spot 4km on the spot on the spot.

Bergen/Rügen 6G3

Wohnmobilstellplatz Rügen, Tilzower Weg 32a.
GPS: n54,40281 e13,42781.
20 € 14 € 1/60liter Ch (16x)€ 2/24h,25Amp WC € 2/6minutes € 4/4 included.
Location: Comfortable. **Surface:** metalled. 01/01-31/12.
Distance: 1km 400m 500m, bakery 300m 100m on the spot.
Remarks: Car rental.

Binz 6G3

Wohnmobil-Oase Rügen, Proraer Chaussee 60.
GPS: n54,44819 e13,56181.

150 € 13-16 € 1/50liter € 1 Ch € 0,50 € 1/kWh WC € 0,20 € 0,50/minutes € 4/4 according consumption.
Location: Luxurious, isolated, quiet. **Surface:** grassy/gravel.
15/04-15/10.
Distance: Binz 6km 1,5km on the spot 6km on the spot.
Remarks: Bread-service.

Binz 6G3

Parkplatz Zentrum, Proraer Chaussee 5.
GPS: n54,40278 e13,60194.

60 € 17/24h. **Location:** Urban, simple. **Surface:** grassy/metalled.
01/01-31/12.
Distance: on the spot 50m on the spot.
Remarks: Next to petrol station.

Blankensee 8G1

Reisemobilplatz Lühn, Am Achterfeld 1.
GPS: n53,51787 e14,31844.
4 € 4 € 2 € 2 Ch € 0,50/kWh WC. **Location:** Quiet.
Surface: grassy. 01/01-31/12.
Distance: 800m 600m 5km.

Boiensdorf 8D1

Am Strand, Bungalowsiedlung. **GPS**: n54,02412 e11,54744.

35 € 8/24h € 0,20/10liter € 2 Ch € 2/day WC € 0,50.
Location: Rural, comfortable, quiet. **Surface:** grassy.
01/01-31/12.
Distance: on the spot on the spot 50m on the spot on the spot.

Boltenhagen 8C1

Krämer's Wohnmobilhafen, Ostsee-allee 58b.
GPS: n53,98122 e11,21908.

45 € 10-14, 2 pers.incl € 0,20/20liter Ch € 2,50/day WC € 0,50. **Location:** Urban, comfortable, central, noisy.
Surface: grassy/gravel. 01/01-31/12.
Distance: 800m 200m 200m 100m 700m on the spot on the spot on the spot.
Remarks: Bread-service in summer period, bicycle rental.

Boltenhagen 8C1

Wohnmobilpark Boltenhagen, Ostsee-allee 58.
GPS: n53,98133 e11,21854.

50 € 9-13 + € 2,10/pp tourist tax € 2,50 Ch € 2,50/day WC € 1 € 5.
Location: Urban, simple, noisy. **Surface:** grassy. 01/01-31/12.
Distance: 700m 200m 200m on the spot 700m on the spot on the spot.

Boltenhagen 8C1

Swin Golf Boltenhagen, Ausbau 15, Redewisch.
GPS: n54,00851 e11,17180.

10 € 13-15 € 2/day. **Location:** Rural, comfortable, quiet. **Surface:** grassy. 01/04-31/10.

DE

Distance: on the spot on the spot on the spot.
Remarks: At golf court.

S Boltenhagen 8C1

Regenbogen Boltenhagen, Ostseeallee 54.
GPS: n53,98196 e11,21714.

20 € 20 WC included € 4/3 € 1/h.
Location: Urban, comfortable, central, noisy.
Surface: grassy/metalled. 01/01-31/12.
Distance: 600m 200m 200m on the spot 100m on the spot on the spot on the spot.
Remarks: Max. 1 night, check in at reception.

S Brenz 8D2

Landhaus Böttcher, Parchimer strasse 11.
GPS: n53,38688 e11,67103.

5 € 10, guests free € 1,50 (4x)€ 2/day WC included.
Location: Rural, simple. **Surface:** grassy/metalled.
01/01-31/12.
Distance: on the spot 3km on the spot 5km 200m.

S Broock 8E2

Hotel-Restaurant Am Worns-Berg, Am Worns-Berg 1.
GPS: n53,46734 e12,10698.

6 € 5, free with a meal Ch € 2 WC € 1,50.
Surface: grassy/gravel.
01/01-31/12.
Distance: 5km 1,5km 1,5km on the spot 5km 500m.

S Carpin 8F2

Landgasthof Am Schlesersee, Hauptstrasse 25.
GPS: n53,35424 e13,24028.

10 € 5, free with a meal € 5 WC included.
Surface: metalled. 01/01-31/12.
Distance: 500m on the spot on the spot on the spot 4km.
Remarks: Max. 1 night.

Dabitz 6F3

Hafen Dabitz, Boddenstraße. **GPS**: n54,36217 e12,80610.

5 € 6/night. **Location:** Rural, simple, quiet.
Surface: concrete. 01/01-31/12.
Distance: 500m on the spot on the spot on the spot on the spot.

S Dalwitz 8E1

Ferien Gut Dalwitz, Dalwitz 46. **GPS**: n53,93484 e12,53830.

2 € 10 € 1 WC € 3/3.
Location: Rural. **Surface:** grassy. 01/01-31/12.
Distance: 15km on the spot on the spot.
Remarks: Parking estate.

S Dassow 8C1

Reisemobilplatz Ostseestrand, Straße des Friedens 14, Rosenhagen.
GPS: n53,96040 e10,94430.

10 € 10 Ch € 3 WC included € 3. **Location:** Rural, comfortable, quiet. **Surface:** grassy. 01/01-31/12.
Distance: 1km 500m.
Remarks: At Café Strandgut.

S Demmin 8F1

Kanuhaus Demmin, Meyenkrebs 15. **GPS**: n53,91806 e13,02833.

2 € 6-8,40 WC included € 1/3minutes.
Location: Simple. **Surface:** grassy. 01/04-31/10.
Distance: 1km on the spot 400m 500m.

S Dömitz 8D3

WasserWanderZentrum Dömitz, An der Schleuse 1.
GPS: n53,14078 e11,25908.

30 € 10 € 1,50/150liter Ch € 2/day WC € 1.
Location: Rural, comfortable, quiet. **Surface:** grassy. 01/01-31/12.
Distance: 400m on the spot on the spot 100m 800m.

S Dömitz 8D3

Dömitzer Hafen, Hafenplatz 3. **GPS**: n53,13724 e11,26034.

22 € 8 € 1/50liter (10x)€ 2/day WC € 1.
Location: Rural, comfortable, quiet. **Surface:** grassy.
01/01-31/12.
Distance: 1km 10m 10m 200m 800m 600m.
Remarks: Bread-service.

S Dranske/Bakenberg 6G3

MC Burgstaedt Wohnmobilstellplatz, Nonnevitz 23a.
GPS: n54,67139 e13,29278.

12 € 19-25 € 3/day WC included. **Location:** Rural, simple, isolated, quiet. **Surface:** grassy. 15/05-31/10.
Distance: 6km 100m 300m 300m.
Remarks: Dog € 2/day.

S Dranske/Bakenberg 6G3

Küstencamp, Nonnevitz 23. **GPS**: n54,66288 e13,26929.

15 € 13,50-15 Ch € 3,20/day WC included € 1/2minutes € 3/3. **Location:** Rural, comfortable, isolated, quiet.
Surface: metalled. 01/01-31/12.
Distance: 7km 400m 400m 500m.
Remarks: Bread-service, car rental.

S Eldena 8D2

Bootshafen und Campingplatz Eldena, Am Bootshafen 1.
GPS: n53,23163 e11,42422.

12 € 10,50 Ch WC included € 1,10 € 3,50/3,50.
Location: Rural, comfortable, quiet.
Surface: grassy. 01/04-31/10.
Distance: 400m 10m 10m 50m 400m on the spot.

S Elmenhorst 6F3

Firma Stuhr, Haupstrasse 47. **GPS**: n54,15882 e12,00464.

DE

20 € 8 Ch € 2 WC. **Location:** Rural, simple, quiet.
Surface: grassy. 01/01-31/12.
Distance: 1km 1,3km 1km 500m 200m.
Remarks: Use sanitary € 2/pp per day.

S Elmenhorst 6F3

Stellplatz Elmenhorst, Gewerbeallee 3a.
GPS: n54,15250 e12,01667.

24 € 10 € 1/100liter Ch € 0,50/kWh WC € 2 free.
Location: Quiet. **Surface:** metalled. 01/01-31/12.
Distance: 300m.

Feldberg 8F2

Weidendamm 1. **GPS**: n53,33583 e13,44176.

10 € 10 + € 1,50/pp tourist tax. **Location:** Urban, simple.
Surface: grassy/metalled. 01/01-31/12.
Distance: on the spot 150m 400m.

S Fresenbrügge 8D2

Wohnmobilhafen an der Edle, Eldeufer 1.
GPS: n53,26355 e11,54243.

23 € 10 Ch included € 2/day WC € 1/pp.
Location: Rural, comfortable, isolated, quiet.
Surface: grassy. 01/01-31/12.
Distance: on the spot on the spot 2km 2km on the spot on the spot.

S Graal-Müritz 6F3

Strandmitte, Buchenkampweg. **GPS**: n54,25663 e12,25005.

20 € 15/24h, tourist tax € 2/pp € 1/100liter.
Location: Rural, simple, quiet. **Surface:** grassy/metalled.
01/01-31/12.
Distance: 500m on the spot on the spot 500m 500m

on the spot on the spot.
Remarks: Max. 3 days.

S Grabow 8D2

Stadthafen, Canalstrasse. **GPS**: n53,27738 e11,55949.

18 € 5 € 0,50/125liter € 0,50 Ch € 2 WC € 0,50 € 1.
Location: Urban. **Surface:** metalled.
01/01-31/12, service: 8-9.30h and 18.30-20h.
Distance: 200m on the spot on the spot 100m 50m.

S Greifswald 6G3

Am Museumhafen, Marienstraße 10. **GPS**: n54,09887 e13,38945.

20 € 15 Ch WC included. **Location:** Urban, simple.
Surface: metalled.
01/03-30/11.
Distance: 300m 300m 1km.

Tourist information Greifswald:
Fischerdorf Greifswald-Wieck. Fishermen's village worth seeing.

Güstrow 8E1

Gleviner Platz. **GPS**: n53,79117 e12,18054.

3 free. **Location:** Urban. **Surface:** asphalted. 01/01-31/12.
Distance: 400m 5km 5km 100m 100m.

S Güstrow 8E1

Hotel Am Tierpark, Verbindungschaussee 7.
GPS: n53,79159 e12,21577.
30 € 15, 2 pers.incl + tourist tax € 2,50/pp Ch (30x) included WC use sanitary € 2,50/pp.
Location: Rural. **Surface:** grassy. 01/01-31/12.
Distance: 5km on the spot 5km station 2km.
Remarks: Bread-service + breakfast-service, discount on access sauna/wellness.

S Gützkow 8F1

Rittergut Schloss Pentin, Zum Bollwerk 11.
GPS: n53,91824 e13,46763.

10 € 10 € 0,50/80liter Ch € 0,50/kWh € 1.
Location: Rural, simple.
Surface: grassy/gravel. 01/01-31/12.
Distance: 1km 400m.
Remarks: Bread-service, nature reserve.

S Heringsdorf 6H3

Blasendorff, Labahnstrasse 10. **GPS**: n53,95940 e14,15680.

3 € 10 € 0,50/40liter € 1,50 € 1,80.
Location: Urban, simple. **Surface:** grassy. 01/01-31/12.
Distance: 10min 300m 300m 300m.

S Heringsdorf 6H3

Korbwerk, Waldbühnenweg 2, Heringsdorf Seebad.
GPS: n53,95056 e14,16611.
15 € 12 Ch WC included. **Surface:** gravel.
01/01-31/12.
Distance: 500m 600m 200m 200m.

S Hinrichshagen 6G3

Reisemobilstellplatz Wöller, Chausseestraße 12.
GPS: n54,07450 e13,35230.

50 € 10 Ch included WC. **Location:** Comfortable.
Surface: grassy/gravel. 01/01-31/12.
Distance: 3,5km 1,8km 800m.
Remarks: Use sanitary € 5/motorhome, in winter limited services, service passerby € 5.

S Hornstorf 8D1

Gartencenter Offermann, Dorfstraße 1. **GPS**: n53,89473 e11,54159.

20 € 10 Ch included. **Location:** Rural, simple, noisy.
Surface: concrete. 01/01-31/12.

S Insel Poel 8D1

Strandparkplatz Timmendorf, Tau n Lüchttorm.
GPS: n53,99287 e11,38058.

60 € 5/day, € 4/night + € 2/pp tourist tax € 0,50/80liter Ch (64x)€ 2/2kWh € 1.
Location: Rural, simple, quiet. **Surface:** grassy. 01/01-31/12.
Distance: 150m 500m 200m 300m on the spot on the spot.
Remarks: Check in at kosk, caution key sanitary € 10.

S Insel Poel 8D1

Poeler Forellenhof, Niendorf 13. **GPS**: n53,99454 e11,44714.

DE

16 € 13, 2 pers.incl € 2/100liter WC included € 2,60/2,60. **Location:** Rural, simple. **Surface:** concrete. 01/01-31/12. **Distance:** 1,5km on the spot on the spot on the spot 1,5km on the spot on the spot.
Remarks: Check in at restaurant, steam bath and sauna, fish smoke-house.

Kamminke 8G1

Ortstraße. **GPS**: n53,86750 e14,20480.

15 € 8. **Surface:** grassy. 01/01-31/12.
Distance: on the spot on the spot.

Karenz 8D2

Reiterhof am Steinberg, Grebserstrasse 1. **GPS**: n53,23638 e11,34836.

3 € 10 € 1 Ch € 1,50 WC. **Location:** Rural, simple, isolated. **Surface:** grassy. 01/01-31/12.
Distance: 1km 1km 300m.
Remarks: Parking at manege.

Kargow 8F2

Reisemobilstellplatz Ziegenwiese, Schwarzenhof 7.
GPS: n53,46433 e12,79925.

10 € 7,50 € 3 Ch € 1,50. **Location:** Rural, quiet.
Surface: grassy. 01/01-31/12.
Distance: 1km 1km 200m 4km.

Karnin 8G1

Hafen, Karnin 14a. **GPS**: n53,84450 e13,85860.

3 € 10 € 0,50/100liter Ch € 1 € 0,50/kWh WC € 1 € 4. **Location:** Rural, quiet. **Surface:** metalled.
01/01-31/12.
Distance: 6km 500m 6km on the spot on the spot on the spot.

Remarks: Intersection hiking and biking trails.

Kühlungsborn 6F3

Hafenstrasse. **GPS**: n54,15051 e11,76329.

20 € 8/24h. **Location:** Urban, simple, noisy.
Surface: concrete. 01/01-31/12.
Distance: 500m on the spot on the spot on the spot.

Langen Brütz 8D1

Landhaus Bondzio, Hauptstrasse 21a. **GPS**: n53,65722 e11,55737.

4 € 12 WC included € 2. **Location:** Rural, simple.
Surface: asphalted/grassy. 01/01-31/12 Restaurant: Mo.
Distance: 150m on the spot 50m.

Lenz über Malchow 8E2

Lenzer Hafen, Zum Hafen 1. **GPS**: n53,46793 e12,34929.

25 € 13,30-16,30 € 2 Ch € 0,50 € 1/2kWh WC € 1,50 € 3 included. **Location:** Rural, quiet.
Surface: grasstiles.
01/03-31/10.
Distance: 5km on the spot on the spot on the spot 5km.
Remarks: Parking eastern bank Plauersee.

Lohme 6G3

Wohnmobilstellplatz Dorfladen, Arkonastrasse 4.
GPS: n54,58300 e13,61150.

35 € 14 - € 17,50 € 1/90liter Ch € 2 € 1/2kWh WC € 2/5minutes € 3/3 included.
Location: Rural, comfortable. **Surface:** grassy/metalled.
01/01-31/12.
Distance: on the spot 200m on the spot on the spot on the spot.
Remarks: Dog € 1,50/night, breakfast-service, discount longer stays.

Lohme 6G3

Zum Königsstuhl, Stubbenkammerstraße 57, Hagen.
GPS: n54,56220 e13,62590.

40 € 10,50 + € 1/pp tourist tax € 1/100liter Ch € 2,50/24h WC € 0,50 € 1/4minutes.
Location: Rural. **Surface:** grassy/metalled. 01/01-31/12.
Distance: on the spot 600m on the spot.

Ludwigslust 8D2

Am Schloss, Friedrich-Naumann-Allee. **GPS**: n53,32735 e11,49080.

20 € 7/24h € 1/100liter € 1 Ch € 1 WC.
Location: Rural, simple, quiet. **Surface:** gravel/sand.
01/01-31/12.
Distance: 600m 500m 600m.
Remarks: Coins at the shops.

Lütow 6G3

Yachtlieger Achterwasser, Netzelkow. **GPS**: n54,02690 e13,90950.

22 € 1/m + € 1/pp Ch (20x)€ 0,25/kWh WC € 2.
Surface: grassy. 01/01-31/12.
Distance: on the spot on the spot on the spot.
Remarks: Bread-service, bike/car rental.

Malchin 8E1

Malchiner Kanu-club, Am Kanal 2. **GPS**: n53,74417 e12,76611.

8 € 10 Ch € 1 WC included € 0,50 € 3/2.
Location: Comfortable, quiet. **Surface:** grassy. 01/05-30/09.
Distance: 500m on the spot on the spot 500m 500m.
Remarks: Dog € 4.

Malchow 8E2

Marina Malchow, Ziegeleiweg 5. **GPS**: n53,46432 e12,42417.

20 € 10-20 excl. tourist tax Ch € 2,50 WC included € 2,50. **Location:** Rural, comfortable, quiet.
Surface: grassy. 01/05-30/09.
Distance: 2km 4km on the spot on the spot 2km 4km

DE

250m.
Remarks: Bread-service.

Malchow 8E2

Wohnmobilstellplatz Am Plauer See, Zum Plauer See 1.
GPS: n53,49192 e12,37268.

5 € 10-12, 2 pers.incl Ch (5x)€ 3,30 WC included.
Location: Rural, quiet. **Surface:** grassy. 01/01-31/12.
Distance: 5km on the spot on the spot on the spot on the spot.
Remarks: Use sanitary € 2/pp per day.

Mirow 8F2

Schloßstraße 1A. **GPS**: n53,27623 e12,81348.

8 free € 1 € 1 Ch€ 1 (8x) WC€ 0,50.
Location: Simple. **Surface:** grasstiles/metalled.
01/01-31/12.
Distance: 400m 200m 400m.

Mönkebude 8G1

Stettinger Haff, Am Hafen. **GPS**: n53,77174 e13,96868.

25+15 € 8,50-10 + € 1/pp tourist tax, dog € 2 € 0,50/100liter Ch € 2/24h WC € 1 € 3,50/3 € 4/4h.
Location: Rural, comfortable. **Surface:** grassy.
01/01-31/12.
Distance: 50m on the spot on the spot 50m.
Remarks: Peak season: sanitary installation, nov/apr service only on demand.

Mönkebude 8G1

Gastätte Kregelin's Bistro, Hauptstrasse.
GPS: n53,76663 e13,97614.

4 guests free. **Surface:** metalled. 01/01-31/12.
Distance: on the spot.

Muess 8D2

Feriendorf Muess, Alte Crivitzer Landstrasse 6.
GPS: n53,59995 e11,47940.

15 € 10, 01/03-30/09 € 20, dog € 1 Ch WC included,winter fee no shower € 2/1,70.
Location: Rural, comfortable.
Surface: grassy. 01/01-31/12.
Distance: 100m 100m 100m 100m 100m on the spot.
Remarks: At open air museum, check in at reception, bicycle rental.

Neu Kaliss 8D2

Find 's Hier, An der Elde 2. **GPS**: n53,17810 e11,29720.

13 € 9 Chincluded € 2/night WC € 1.
Location: Rural, simple, isolated, quiet. **Surface:** grassy.
01/01-31/12.
Distance: on the spot on the spot on the spot 400m 400m.

Neubrandenburg 8F1

Wassersportzentrum Tollensesee, Augustastrasse 7.
GPS: n53,53861 e13,25665.

30 € 10 € 1 Ch€ 1 € 0,50/kWh WC € 1 € 2/day.
Location: Quiet. **Surface:** grassy/metalled. 15/03-31/10.
Distance: 2km on the spot on the spot 200m 500m.
Remarks: Water sports centre.

Neuendorf 6F3

Wohnmobilstellplatz Saal Neuendorf, Am Hafen.
GPS: n54,33516 e12,52812.

36 € 10 included WC€ 0,20 € 1 on demand.
Location: Rural, simple, quiet. **Surface:** grassy.
01/04-31/10.
Distance: 100m on the spot on the spot Imbiss kiosk 400m on the spot on the spot.

Neukloster 8D1

Wohnmobilpark Neuklostersee, Alte Gärtnerei 3.
GPS: n53,86121 e11,69536.

69 € 9,50 € 1,50 Ch € 1/2kWh WC € 2 € 4/2.
Location: Rural, comfortable, quiet. **Surface:** gravel.
16/03-31/10.
Distance: 500m on the spot 50m 500m 1,2km 500m on the spot on the spot.

Neustrelitz 8F2

Parkplatz Am Stadthafen, Zierker Nebenstrasse 6.
GPS: n53,36568 e13,05551.

25 € 8 € 0,50/80liter € 0,50 Ch€ 0,50 € 0,50/kWh WC€ 0,20 € 0,50 € 2.
Location: Urban, comfortable, quiet. **Surface:** metalled.
01/01-31/12.
Distance: on the spot 100m, swimming 1km 200m 100m 200m 200m on the spot on the spot.
Remarks: Coins at harbourmaster (200m), historical centre.

Nossentin 8E2

Am Fleesensee, Am Park 33. **GPS**: n53,51866 e12,46766.

5 € 8 Ch WCincluded .
Surface: grassy. 01/04-31/10.
Distance: 5km 100m 100m on the spot 5km.

Ostseebad Sellin/Rügen 6G3

Reisemobilhafen Sellin, Kiefernweg 4b. **GPS**: n54,37170 e13,70165.

50 € 13-15 € 0,50/60liter Ch (50x)€ 0,50/kWh WCincluded € 0,50/2minutes.
Surface: grassy/metalled. 15/03-15/11.
Distance: 300m 1km 1km 200m 300m 300m.

Ostseebad Sellin/Rügen 6G3

Hafen Seedorf, Seedorf 8. **GPS**: n54,35410 e13,65359.

5 € 10 on demand € 0,50/kWh € 0,50/2minutes.

DE

Location: Rural, simple, quiet. **Surface:** metalled.
01/05-15/10.
Distance: 250m 250m 250m.

Ostseebad Wustrow 6F3

Surfcenter Wustrow, An der Nebelstation 2.
GPS: n54,34080 e12,38040.

30 € 16-29, dog € 2,50-5 Ch € 2,50/day WC € 0,50 € 1/2minutes included. **Location:** Rural, simple, quiet.
Surface: asphalted. 01/04-31/10.
Distance: 1km 50m on the spot on the spot on the spot.

Ostseebad Wustrow 6F3

Hafenstraße. **GPS**: n54,34363 e12,40053.

30 € 4/day, € 10/night. **Location:** Rural, simple, quiet.
Surface: grassy/sand. 01/01-31/12.
Distance: 400m 1,5km on the spot on the spot on the spot on the spot.
Remarks: Max. 1 night.

Parchim 8D2

Yachthafen, Am Fischerdamm. **GPS**: n53,42594 e11,84494.

10 € 6 € 0,50/50liter Ch € 0,50 € 0,50/kWh WC € 0,50 € 0,50. **Location:** Urban, comfortable, central. **Surface:** metalled.
01/01-31/12.
Distance: 100m on the spot on the spot 100m 100m.

Peenemünde 6G3

Fährstrasse 9. **GPS**: n54,13611 e13,76252.
80 € 8-10 € 1 € 1 Ch € 1 € 2 WC € 2 € 3/3h.
Location: Rural. **Surface:** grassy.
01/01-31/12 15/06-19/06.
Distance: 1km 1km 100m 100m 800m on the spot on the spot.

Pepelow 8D1

Wohnmobilpark Am Salzhaff, Seeweg 1.
GPS: n54,03805 e11,58441.

39 € 10-15, 2 pers.incl Ch € 3,30/night WC € 2,50/pp € 3/3 included. **Location:** Rural, luxurious, quiet.
Surface: grassy. 01/01-31/12.
Distance: 700m on the spot on the spot on the spot on the spot on the spot on the spot.

Petersdorf 8E2

Hotel Haus Waldesruh, Lenzerstrasse 19.
GPS: n53,45892 e12,36060.

10 € 7,50 € 1 Ch € 2 WC € 1,50 € 1,50/1,50.
Location: Rural. **Surface:** grassy. 01/01-31/12.
Distance: 7km 600m 600m on the spot 7km.
Remarks: Bowling, use of sauna against payment.

Priepert 8F2

Wohnmobilpark Am Großen Priepertsee, An der Freiheit 8.
GPS: n53,22043 e13,04201.

30 € 7 Chincluded € 2,25 WC € 3/day € 1 € 5.
Location: Rural, comfortable, quiet.
Surface: grassy. 01/01-31/12.
Distance: on the spot 70m 70m 500m 12km.

Pruchten 6F3

NATURCAMP Pruchten, Am Campingplatz 1. **GPS**: n54,37947 e12,66131.
70 € 17, 01/06-31/08 € 23 Ch (70x)€ 2,90/4kWh WC € 4/4 included. **Location:** Comfortable, luxurious, quiet. **Surface:** grassy. 01/04-31/10.
Distance: 800m 600m 600m on the spot on the spot on the spot on the spot.
Remarks: Bicycle rental.

Putbus 6G3

Im-Jaich OHG, Am Yachthafen 1, Lauterbach.
GPS: n54,34278 e13,50167.

14 € 16-18 € 0,50/50liter WC € 0,50 € 4/3 included. **Location:** Luxurious. **Surface:** gravel. 01/01-31/12.
Distance: 500m on the spot on the spot on the spot 800m.
Remarks: Bread kiosk, seaview.

Putbus 6G3

Wohnmobilstellplatz Lauterbach, Chausseestrasse 14.
GPS: n54,34639 e13,49889.

26 € 13-15 € 0,60/50liter Ch € 0,70/kWh WC € 0,30 € 2/5minutes € 4/4 € 1/day. **Location:** Rural, luxurious, quiet.
Surface: grassy/metalled. 15/03-15/10.
Distance: 1km 400m 400m 100m.
Remarks: Max. 8M.

Putgarten 6G3

Kap Arkona, Varnkevitzer Weg. **GPS**: n54,67190 e13,40800.

30 € 5, ^3,10m € 15.
Location: Simple. **Surface:** asphalted. 01/01-31/12.
Distance: 100m Imbiss 6km.

Rerik 6E3

Wohnmobilhafen Ostseebad Rerik, Straße am Zeltplatz 8.
GPS: n54,11332 e11,63037.

35 € 14, Jul-Aug € 23 Ch WC € 0,30 € 3/3 included. **Location:** Rural, comfortable, quiet.
Surface: grassy. 01/01-31/12.
Distance: sandy beach 600m on the spot on the spot on the spot on the spot on the spot.
Remarks: Check in at reception.

Ribnitz-Damgarten 6F3

Gänsewiese, Am See 50. **GPS**: n54,24513 e12,42265.

25 free, night € 8 € 0,50/100liter Ch € 0,50/12h WC.
Location: Rural, simple, quiet. **Surface:** grasstiles/grassy.
01/01-31/12.
Distance: 500m on the spot on the spot 500m 500m on the spot on the spot.

Ribnitz-Damgarten 6F3

Hafen Ribnitz, Am See 44. **GPS**: n54,24536 e12,42921.

DE

10 free, night € 10 WC € 1/3minutes.
Location: Urban, simple, quiet. **Surface:** concrete.
01/01-31/12.
Distance: 100m on the spot on the spot on the spot 200m on the spot on the spot.

Röbel 8E2

Am Seglerhafen, Müritzpromenade 20. **GPS**: n53,38734 e12,61755.

40 € 12 Ch € 2 WC included € 1 € 2/day.
Location: Comfortable.
Surface: grasstiles/metalled. 01/04-31/10.
Distance: 2km on the spot 300m 1km.

Rostock 6F3

Mühlendamm. **GPS**: n54,08444 e12,15361.
24 € 10 Ch (24x)included. **Surface:** metalled.
01/01-31/12.
Distance: 1km 1,5km 450m on the spot.

Rostock 6F3

Am Stadthafen, Warnowufer. **GPS**: n54,09297 e12,12878.

25 € 12. **Location:** Urban, simple.
Surface: asphalted/metalled. 01/01-31/12.
Distance: on the spot on the spot on the spot.

Tourist information Rostock:
www.rostock.de. Hanseatic city with historical centre.

Rüterberg 8C3

Wohmobilparkplatz Dorfrepublik Rüterberg, Ringstraße 2.
GPS: n53,15294 e11,18511.

10 € 5/24h+ € 0,50/pp € 1/50liter € 1 Ch € 1 € 1,50/kWh WC € 1. **Location:** Rural, simple, central, quiet.
Surface: grassy. 01/01-31/12.
Distance: 10m 50m.
Remarks: Bread-service.

Sassnitz 6G3

Hafenstraße. **GPS**: n54,51436 e13,64568.
15 € 20.
Location: Urban. **Surface:** metalled. 01/01-31/12.
Distance: on the spot on the spot 100m 100m.

Schwerin 8D1

Am Hauptbahnhof, Wismarsche Straße. **GPS**: n53,63692 e11,40893.

4 € 8/24h € 1/80liter Ch (4x)€ 1/2kWh.
Location: Urban, simple, central, noisy.
Surface: metalled. 01/01-31/12.
Distance: on the spot on the spot on the spot on the spot.

Schwerin 8D1

Am Stadthafen, Schliemannstraße. **GPS**: n53,62977 e11,41966.

10 € 16/24h (8x)€ 0,50/kWh. **Location:** Urban, simple, central, noisy. **Surface:** metalled.
01/01-31/12.
Distance: on the spot 8km on the spot on the spot on the spot on the spot on the spot.
Remarks: No camping activities.

Schwerin 8D1

Marina-Nord Schwerin, Buchenweg 19.
GPS: n53,64584 e11,43264.

16 € 10 + € 1/pp Ch (14x)€ 0,50/kWh WC € 1,50 € 1/24h. **Location:** Rural, comfortable, quiet. **Surface:** grassy.
15/04-15/10.
Distance: 4km 5km on the spot on the spot on the spot 1km 100m on the spot on the spot.
Remarks: Check in at reception, bread-service.

Schwerin 8D1

Sportbootzentrum Ziegelsee, Güstrower Straße 88.
GPS: n53,64823 e11,43004.

10 € 12/24h € 0,50/70liter Ch € 1/24h WC € 1/6minutes € 5/5. **Location:** Rural, comfortable, quiet.
Surface: concrete. 01/04-30/10.
Distance: 2km 8km on the spot on the spot 2km 300m on the spot on the spot on the spot.

Seehof 8D1

Campingplatz Seehof, Am Zeltplatz 1. **GPS**: n53,69676 e11,43658.

10 € 15-24, 2 pers.incl Ch WC included € 1 € 3,50/3,50.
Location: Rural, comfortable. **Surface:** grassy. 01/01-31/10.
Distance: 1,2km on the spot on the spot on the spot on the spot on the spot on the spot.
Remarks: Bike/boat rental.

Sembzin 8E2

Rasthof Sembzin, Dorfstrasse 2. **GPS**: n53,46445 e12,60386.

16 € 8 Ch included WC € 1/24h.
Location: Noisy. **Surface:** grassy/gravel. 01/04-31/10.
Distance: 8km on the spot 1,5km.
Remarks: € 8 voucher restaurant, use sanitary € 2/pp per day, swimming pool incl.

Sievershagen 6F3

Ferienhof Dubberke, Alt Sievershagen 16.
GPS: n54,11480 e12,03481.

7 € 10 Ch WC included € 1. **Location:** Rural, comfortable, quiet. **Surface:** grassy. 01/01-31/10.
Distance: 500m, Rostock 5km 2km 800m 800m on the spot on the spot.

Sommersdorf 8F1

Wohnmobilpark Sommersdorf, Am Kummerower See.
GPS: n53,79824 e12,87576.

28 € 8-12, 2 pers. incl Ch € 3/day WC € 1 included.
Location: Rural, comfortable, isolated, quiet.
Surface: grassy. 01/01-31/12.
Distance: 1km on the spot on the spot 1km.
Remarks: Use sanitary € 2/pp per day.

Sternberg 8D1

Sternberger, Maikamp 11. **GPS**: n53,71318 e11,81236.

15 € 14-18 Ch € 3/day WC included € 2.
Location: Rural. **Surface:** grassy. 01/04-31/10.
Distance: 1km on the spot on the spot on the spot 500m 500m.

Stralsund 6G3

An der Rügenbrücke, Werftstraße 9a. **GPS**: n54,30222 e13,09889.

40 € 15, 2 pers.incl € 1/50liter € 1 Ch € 1 (40x)€ 0,50/kWh WC included € 1 € 3/3 € 4,95/day. **Location:** Comfortable, noisy. **Surface:** grassy/gravel. 01/01-31/12.
Distance: 1,8km 1,8km 200m on the spot.
Remarks: Bread-service.

Stralsund 6G3

Wohnmobilstellplatz-Stralsund, Boddenweg 3.
GPS: n54,27605 e13,10822.
18 € 15 € 1/100liter Ch € 0,50/kWh WC included .
Surface: gravel. 01/01-31/12.
Distance: city centre 5km 200m.
Remarks: Bread-service, bicycle rental.

Ueckermünde 8G1

An der Uecker, Ueckerstrasse 125. **GPS**: n53,73470 e14,04930.

13 € 8 + € 1/pp tourist tax Ch included. **Location:** Urban, simple. **Surface:** grassy/metalled.
01/01-31/12.
Distance: Old city centre 200m 200m 100m.

Ueckermünde 8G1

See Sport, Grabenstrasse. **GPS**: n53,73917 e14,04944.
€ 6 € 0,50/100liter € 0,50/kWh WC € 0,50/2minutes.
Location: Urban, central. **Surface:** grassy.
01-01/31/12.
Distance: 200m on the spot 200m 500m.

Ueckermünde 8G1

See Sport, Grabenstrasse. **GPS**: n53,73917 e14,04944.

€ 6 € 0,50/100liter € 0,50/kWh WC € 0,50/2minutes.
Location: Urban, central. **Surface:** grassy.
01-01/31/12.
Distance: 200m on the spot 200m 500m.

Usedom 8G1

Am Hafen Usedom, Peenestraße. **GPS**: n53,87099 e13,92679.

20 € 10 € 0,50/50liter Ch € 0,50/kWh WC € 0,50 € 2.
Location: Rural, simple. **Surface:** metalled.
01/01-31/12.
Distance: 600m on the spot on the spot 1,3km.
Remarks: At former fishing-port.

Usedom 8G1

Gaststätte Haffschänke, Dorfstraße 19, Karnin.
GPS: n53,84348 e13,86537.

20 € 7 Ch € 3 WC € 2,50.
Surface: grassy. 01/01-31/12.
Distance: on the spot on the spot on the spot.

Vielank 8C2

Vielanker Brauhaus, Lindenplatz 1. **GPS**: n53,23443 e11,14023.

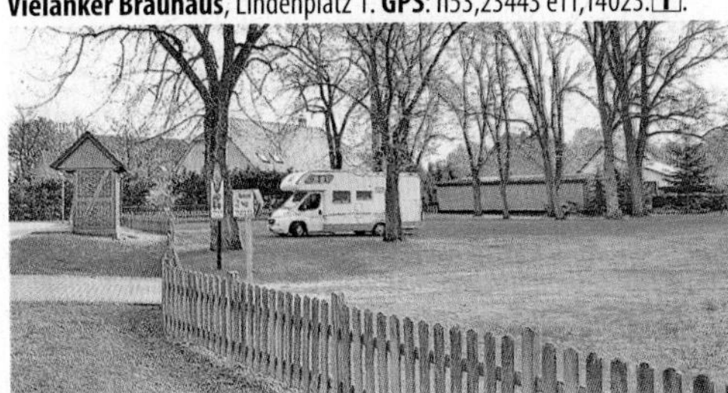

12 free € 3 WC. **Location:** Rural, simple, quiet.
Surface: grassy. 01/01-31/12.
Distance: 20m on the spot.
Remarks: Check in at reception.

Waren 8E2

Blumen und Parken, Mecklenburgerstrasse.
GPS: n53,51363 e12,69431.

40 € 9,50 + € 1,50/pp tourist tax Ch € 0,50/kWh WC included € 1/5minutes. **Location:** Urban, simple.
Surface: grassy/gravel. 01/01-31/12.
Distance: 100m 1km 1km 1km 1km on the spot.

Waren 8E2

Wohnmobilpark Kamerun, Zur Stillen Bucht 3, Müritz.
GPS: n53,51175 e12,65174.

65 € 11-16,30 excl. tourist tax Ch € 3,30 WC € 0,75 included. **Location:** Rural, comfortable, quiet. **Surface:** grassy.
01/01-31/12.
Distance: 3km on the spot on the spot on the spot on the spot 500m.
Remarks: Use sanitary € 2/pp per day.

Waren 8E2

Parkplatz Am Hafen, Strandstrasse 3b. **GPS**: n53,51194 e12,68583.

20 € 13 Ch included.
Location: Urban. **Surface:** metalled. 01/01-31/12.
Distance: on the spot on the spot on the spot on the spot on the spot.

Waren 8E2

Campingplatz Ecktannen, Fontanestraße 66.
GPS: n53,49944 e12,66361.

17 € 14-18, 2 pers. incl Ch WC € 2,60/2,60 included. **Location:** Comfortable, quiet.
Surface: grasstiles/metalled.
01/01-31/12.
Distance: 3,5km 500m 500m Bistro 3km on the spot.

Warnemünde 6F3

Am Bahnhof. **GPS**: n54,17762 e12,09002.

100 € 6/3h, € 12/12h, € 16/24h € 0,50/100liter.
Location: Urban, simple, central, noisy.
Surface: grassy/metalled. 01/01-31/12.
Distance: on the spot on the spot on the spot on the spot on the spot on the spot on the spot.

Warnemünde 6F3

Parkplatz Strand-Mitte, Parkstrasse 46. **GPS**: n54,17643 e12,05765.

100 € 10/24h. **Location:** Urban, simple, noisy.
Surface: metalled. 01/01-31/12.
Distance: 2,5km 100m 400m 2km on the spot on the spot on the spot.

Wesenberg 8F2

Stellplatz Marina Wesenberg, Ahrensberger Weg 11.
GPS: n53,27666 e12,98694.

DE

34 € 16, 2 pers.incl Ch WC included.
Surface: grassy. 01/04-30/09.
Distance: 1km on the spot on the spot 1,5km 2,5km 1km.

Wismar 8D1

Wohnmobilpark Westhafen Wismar, Schiffbauerdamm 12.
GPS: n53,89430 e11,45151.

65 € 7/12h, € 10/24h € 1/100liter Ch € 1/8h WC € 1.
Location: Urban, simple, central, noisy. **Surface:** asphalted/gravel.
01/01-31/12.
Distance: 800m 500m 300m, Burger King 400m 300m 800m 100m.
Remarks: Caution key sanitary € 10.

Wittenbeck 6F3

Sanddornstrand, Bäderweg. **GPS:** n54,14513 e11,79277.

150 € 12-14 Ch (60x)€ 0,60/kWh WC € 0,50 included.
Location: Rural, simple, quiet. **Surface:** grassy/metalled.
01/03-31/10.
Distance: 1km on the spot on the spot on the spot 2,5km 50m on the spot on the spot.
Remarks: Bread-service.

Zingst 6F3

Strandübergang 6, Straminke. **GPS:** n54,44070 e12,70750.

40 € 10-15 + € 2,80/pp + tourist tax € 1/100liter € 3/day WC € 1.
Location: Rural, simple, quiet. **Surface:** grassy. 01/04-31/10.
Distance: 500m on the spot 500m 500m 1km 1km on the spot on the spot.

Zingst 6F3

Wohnmobilhafen Am Freesenbruch, Am Bahndamm 1.
GPS: n54,44060 e12,66058.

40 € 12 + € 9/pp, dog € 4 Ch € 2,30/day WC included € 3/3. **Location:** Rural, comfortable, noisy. **Surface:** grassy.
01/01-31/12.
Distance: 1,5km 50m on the spot on the spot on the spot on the spot.
Remarks: Bread-service.

Zurow 8D1

Urlaub am Schloss, Kastanienallee 56, Krassow.
GPS: n53,87379 e11,56618.

10 € 5 € 1 Ch € 2/day WC € 2.
Location: Rural, simple, quiet. **Surface:** grassy/metalled.
01/01-31/12.
Distance: 1,5km 1km 3km 100m on the spot on the spot.
Remarks: Caution key sanitary € 10.

Saxony Anhalt

Ahlum 8C3

Fischerhütte Ahlumer See, Am Mühlenberg 63.
GPS: n52,69541 e11,00583.

100 € 10, 2 pers.incl Ch € 3 WC included.
Surface: grassy. 01/01-31/12.
Distance: on the spot on the spot on the spot.
Remarks: Bread-service.

Allrode 10C3

Hotel Harzer Land, Teichstraße 28. **GPS:** n51,67774 e10,96478.

25 € 15,50 Ch WC included.
Surface: grassy. 01/01-31/12.
Distance: on the spot on the spot.
Remarks: Breakfest-service, swimming pool and sauna on site.

Altenbrak 10C2

Bodewiese, Am Bielstein. **GPS:** n51,72569 e10,94196.

8 € 5, overnight stay free. **Location:** Rural, simple.
Surface: metalled. 01/01-31/12.
Distance: 100m on the spot 100m 200m on the spot.

Altenbrak 10C2

Hotel Zur Talsperre, Oberbecken 1, Wendefurth.
GPS: n51,73434 e10,90690.

20 € 10 excl. tourist tax (20x)€ 0,50/kWh WC included.
Location: Rural, simple, isolated. **Surface:** asphalted/grassy.
01/01-31/12.
Distance: on the spot.

Arendsee 8D3

Im kleinen Elsebusch, Lüchower strasse 6a.
GPS: n52,87656 e11,46121.

10 € 13 € 1,50 € 1,50 Ch.
Surface: grassy. 01/01-31/12.
Distance: 2,5km on the spot 2,5km.

Aschersleben 10D2

Sport- und Freizeitzentrum Ballhaus, Seegraben.
GPS: n51,76101 e11,45760.

8 free € 1/15minutes € 2 Ch € 2 (12x)€ 1/6h.
Location: Urban, comfortable, central, quiet.
Surface: asphalted. 01/01-31/12.
Distance: 1km 200m 200m on the spot on the spot on the spot.
Remarks: Caution key € 15, key at reception desk BallHaus.

Bad Bibra 12D1

Parkplatz am Schwimmbad, B 176. **GPS:** n51,21214 e11,60002.

20 € 3. **Location:** Rural, simple, isolated, quiet.
Surface: gravel/metalled. 01/01-31/12.

Distance: 1,5km 200m 1,5km.
Remarks: At swimming pool.

Bad Bibra 12D1

Parkplatz Bürgergarten, Haus des Gastes.
GPS: n51,20526 e11,57929.

10 € 3. **Location:** Urban, simple, central, quiet.
Surface: gravel/metalled. 01/01-31/12 Acsension.
Distance: 200m 250m 500m.

Bad Kösen 12E1

Am Saalebogen, Stendorf 14. **GPS**: n51,11356 e11,69609.

15 € 8 Ch (15x)€ 2/day WC included € 1.
Location: Rural, comfortable, quiet. **Surface:** grasstiles/metalled.
01/01-31/12.
Distance: 3km 200m bakery 200m on the spot on the spot.

Bad Suderode 10D2

Restaurant Am Kurpark, Jägerstrasse 7. **GPS**: n51,72685 e11,12078.

4 € 10, € 13 service incl Ch € 5/day.
Location: Urban, comfortable, central, quiet.
Surface: grasstiles/grassy. 01/01-31/12.
Distance: 100m on the spot 200m 200m on the spot on the spot.

Ballenstedt 10D2

Verkehrslandeplatz Ballenstedt/Quedlinburg, Asmusstedt 13.
GPS: n51,74190 e11,23427.

32 € 9 Ch (16x) WC included. **Location:** Rural, simple, quiet. **Surface:** grasstiles/metalled. 01/01-31/12.
Distance: 2km on the spot 2km 200m.

Bergwitz 10F2

Camping Bergwitzsee, Strandweg. **GPS**: n51,79439 e12,57773.

20 € 6 € 3 Ch. **Location:** Rural, simple, isolated, quiet.
Surface: grassy/sand. 01/01-31/12.
Distance: 1km 50m 50m 300m 1,5km.
Remarks: Check in at reception campsite, service on campsite.

Berssel 10C2

Gasthof Zum Schloß, Am Schloß 1. **GPS**: n51,95266 e10,76027.

5 free on demand. **Location:** Rural, simple, quiet.
Surface: metalled. 01/01-31/12.
Distance: 200m on the spot on the spot on the spot.

Bertingen 10D1

Hotel La Porte, Im Wald 2. **GPS**: n52,35994 e11,82264.

30 € 8,50 Ch included.
Location: Rural. **Surface:** grassy. 01/01-31/12.
Distance: on the spot 5km.
Remarks: Bread-service, barbecue place.

Bitterfeld 10E2

Spaßbad Woliday, Reudener Straße, Bitterfeld-Wolfen.
GPS: n51,67102 e12,24842.

10 € 13 WC included.
Surface: grasstiles. 01/01-31/12.
Distance: 1,2km on the spot 900m.
Remarks: Incl. access swimming pool.

Blankenburg 10C2

Am Schnappelberg, Schnappelberg 2. **GPS**: n51,78862 e10,96036.

4 € 6 € 1 € 2/night WC. **Location:** Urban, simple, central, quiet. **Surface:** asphalted. 01/01-31/12.
Distance: 500m 300m on the spot.

Blankenburg 10C2

Busparkplatz, Am Schnappelberg. **GPS**: n51,78884 e10,96076.

6 € 4/24h (6x)€ 1/kWh. **Location:** Urban, simple, quiet.
Surface: metalled. 01/01-31/12.
Distance: 400m 300m 200m on the spot on the spot.

Blankenburg 10C2

Teichwirtschaft, Harzstraße 31a, Timmenrode.
GPS: n51,76874 e10,99134.

10 € 9, 2 pers. incl € 1 Ch € 1 € 1.
Location: Rural, simple, quiet. **Surface:** grassy/metalled.
01/01-31/12.
Distance: Blankenburg 5km on the spot on the spot.
Remarks: Fishpond, playground.

Brachwitz 10E3

Marina Saale-Ufer, An der Fähre. **GPS**: n51,53270 e11,87059.

30 € 5 (4x)€ 0,50/kWh WC. **Location:** Rural, comfortable, quiet. **Surface:** grassy. 01/01-31/12.
Distance: 500m on the spot 500m.

Braunsbedra 10E3

Mobilpark am Geiseltalsee, Schortauer Weg.
GPS: n51,29421 e11,85346.

25 € 10 Ch € 1/kWh WC included € 3 against payment. **Location:** Urban, comfortable, quiet.
Surface: grassy/metalled. 01/01-31/12.
Distance: 700m on the spot 500m.
Remarks: Bread-service + breakfast-service.

Breitenstein 10C3

Hauptstrasse, L236. **GPS**: n51,61756 e10,94957.

8 free € 1 Ch (4x)€ 1/8h.
Location: Rural, simple, quiet. **Surface:** gravel. 01/01-31/12.
Distance: 400m Sportgaststätte.

DE

Remarks: Next to sports fields.

Burg bei Magdeburg 10E1

Wassersportfreunde Burg, Am Kanal 20a.
GPS: n52,28329 e11,84808.

6 € 18 € 1/100liter WC included.
Surface: grassy. 01/05-30/09.
Distance: 1km on the spot.

Burg bei Magdeburg 10E1

Eschenhof, Parchauer Chaussee 5. **GPS**: n52,28718 e11,86583.

15 € 12 2 pers.incl, dog € 1 Ch WC included.
Surface: grassy. 01/01-31/12.
Distance: 2km on the spot 1km.

Coswig/Anhalt 10E2

Marina Coswig, Post Elbstrasse 22. **GPS**: n51,88071 e12,43552.

40 € 11, dog € 1,50 € 1/100liter Ch € 0,60/kWh WC € 1/4minutes. **Location:** Comfortable, quiet.
Surface: gravel. 01/01-31/12.
Distance: 750m on the spot on the spot 150m on the spot.
Remarks: Breakfest-service.

Coswig/Anhalt 10E2

Hotel Zur Fichtenbreite, Fichtenbreite 5.
GPS: n51,88723 e12,40749.

15 € 5 Chincluded (4x)€ 2,50/day € 3,50
Location: Rural, simple, noisy. **Surface:** grassy.
01/01-31/12 24/12.
Distance: 2km 500m on the spot 2km.
Remarks: Bread-service, bicycle rental.

Dankerode 10D3

Campingplatz Panoramablick, Hinterdorf 79.
GPS: n51,58832 e11,14189.

12 € 10 excl. tourist tax € 1 € 1 Ch€ 1 (6x)€ 2,50 WC € 1 € 0,50. **Location:** Rural, simple, isolated, quiet.
Surface: grassy. 01/04-30/10.
Distance: 500m on the spot 500m on the spot on the spot.

Darlingerode 10C2

Wohnmobilpark Harzblick, Hinter den Gärten 11.
GPS: n51,85278 e10,73667.

25 € 8 € 1/80liter Ch (12x)€ 0,60/kWh € 1/day.
Location: Rural, comfortable, quiet.
Surface: grassy/gravel. 01/01-31/12.
Distance: 600m 500m 500m 500m on the spot on the spot.

Dessau-Roßlau 10E2

Flugplatz Hugo Junkers, Alte Landesbahn 27.
GPS: n51,83447 e12,18289.

8 € 11 Ch WC included .
Location: Rural, comfortable, isolated, quiet.
Surface: grassy/metalled. 01/01-31/12.
Distance: 5km 1km 1km.
Remarks: Arrival < 19h, max. 8M, bicycle rental.

Dessau-Roßlau 10E2

Seesport Dessau, Leopoldshafen 4. **GPS**: n51,85648 e12,21992.
10 € 12, 2 pers.incl € 1 Ch € 1 € 1. **Surface:** grassy.
01/01-31/12.
Distance: 5km 500m 500m.

Dessau-Roßlau 10E2

Bowling Treff, Hermann-Wäschke-Weg 17. **GPS**: n51,89889 e12,25667.

50 € 10 € 1/80liter Ch € 2/24h.
Surface: grassy/gravel. 01/01-31/12.
Distance: 2,5km 1km 800m 300m.
Remarks: At bowling centre.

Dessau-Roßlau 10E2

Elbzollhaus, Elbzollhaus 1. **GPS**: n51,87931 e12,23840.
8 € 10 WC included. **Location:** Central. **Surface:** grassy.
01/01-31/12.
Distance: 1,5km Elbe river 200m 650m Rewe 650m station 1km.
Remarks: Breakfast-service.

Dessau-Roßlau 10E2

Hotel Garni Kochstedt, Königendorfer Str. 36.
GPS: n51,79621 e12,17666.
€ 20, 2 pers.incl Ch WC included.
Surface: grassy. 01/01-31/12.
Distance: 1,5km.
Remarks: Breakfast-service.

Drübeck/Harz 10C2

Zur Waldschänke, Tänntalstraße 6. **GPS**: n51,84564 e10,71415.

8 first day € 10, then € 5 Ch included.
Location: Rural, simple, quiet. **Surface:** grassy/gravel.
01/01-31/12 Restaurant: Mo-Tue.
Distance: 1,5km on the spot 2km.
Remarks: Breakfast-service.

Elend 10C2

Waldbad Schenke, Am Waldbad 1. **GPS**: n51,74612 e10,69531.

10 € 5-10 + € 1,50/pp tourist tax (5x)€ 1.
Location: Rural, simple, quiet. **Surface:** grassy/metalled.
01/01-31/12.
Distance: 600m on the spot 500m on the spot on the spot.

Freyburg/Unstrut 10E3

Stellplatz Schleusenblick, Wasserstraße 22.
GPS: n51,21049 e11,76979.

8 € 19, 2 pers.incl, tourist tax € 1,50/pp Ch WCincluded € 2/day. **Location:** Urban, comfortable, central, quiet.
Surface: metalled. 01/01-31/12.
Distance: 100m 50m 300m.
Remarks: Along the Unstrut river, barbecue place.

Gernrode 10D2

Osterteich, Osterallee. **GPS**: n51,72449 e11,16007.

20 free. **Location:** Rural, simple, isolated, quiet.
Surface: metalled. 01/01-31/12.
Distance: 1,5km 300m 1,5km on the spot.
Remarks: Next to train stop Selketalbahn.

Haldensleben 10D1

Am Stendaler Turm, Bornsche Strasse. **GPS**: n52,29291 e11,41342.

10 free. **Surface:** concrete. 01/01-31/12.
Distance: 200m 250m 150m Aldi.

Haldensleben 10D1

Am Sportboothafen, Kronesruhe. **GPS**: n52,27933 e11,40240.

15 € 10 € 1/100liter € 1 Ch. € 0,50/kWh WC € 1/4minutes. **Location:** Rural. **Surface:** grassy.
15/04-31/10.
Distance: 2km 14km on the spot on the spot 200m.
Remarks: Bread-service.

Halle/Saale 10E3

Parkplatz, Fährstraße. **GPS**: n51,50210 e11,95397.

3 € 4,50 € 1/80liter Ch. € 1/8h WC against payment.
Location: Urban, simple, central, noisy. **Surface:** metalled.
01/01-31/12.
Distance: 2km 7km 200m 500m on the spot.
Remarks: Max. 5 days, green zone: environmental badge obligatory.

Halle/Saale 10E3

P25, An der Stadtschleuse. **GPS**: n51,48065 e11,96183.

10 free. **Location:** Urban, simple, central, noisy.
Surface: metalled. 01/01-31/12.
Distance: Old city centre 500m 12km on the spot 600m on the spot. **Remarks:** Along railwayline, green zone: environmental badge obligatory.

Harzgerode 10D3

Parkplatz Wallgarten, Wallstrasse. **GPS**: n51,64210 e11,13983.

5 free. **Location:** Urban, simple, quiet.
Surface: metalled. 01/01-31/12.
Distance: 100m 1km 3km 100m 100m 100m 1km.

Hasselfelde 10C3

P Pullman City/Westernstadt, Im Rosentale.
GPS: n51,70179 e10,86604.

10 € 5. **Location:** Rural, simple, quiet.
Surface: gravel. 15/04-31/10.
Distance: 1km on the spot 900m.

Havelberg 8E3

Campinginsel, Spülinsel 6. **GPS**: n52,82830 e12,06853.

24 € 6 € 1 € 3 Ch. (24x)€ 1/kWh.
Location: Rural. **Surface:** metalled. 01/01-31/12.
Distance: 1km 700m.
Remarks: Bread-service in summer period.

Kelbra 10D3

Seecamping Südharz, L1040, Lange Straße 150.
GPS: n51,42583 e11,00287.

15 € 10-12 2 pers.incl, dog € 2 Ch. (16x)included against payment. **Location:** Rural. **Surface:** gravel.
01/01-31/12.
Distance: 2,5km on the spot on the spot on the spot.
Remarks: Boat rental.

Lutherstadt Wittenberg 10F2

Platz der Jugend. **GPS**: n51,86712 e12,63120.

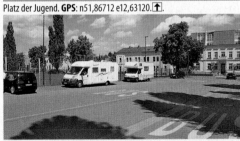

5 free. **Location:** Urban, simple, noisy.
Surface: metalled. 01/01-31/12.
Distance: centre 500m 150m 150m.
Remarks: Max. 8h, overnight stay allowed.

Magdeburg 10D2

Stellplatz Petriförde, Petriförder 1. **GPS**: n52,13289 e11,64714.

50 € 8 € 1 € 1 Ch. **Location:** Urban. **Surface:** metalled.
01/01-31/12.
Distance: on the spot 850m 700m 850m.
Remarks: Along the river Elbe, bar.

Merseburg 10E3

Am Saaleufer, Brühl. **GPS**: n51,35491 e12,00234.

3 free. **Location:** Urban, simple.
Surface: metalled. 01/01-31/12.
Distance: 500m 350m 500m Saale-Rad-Wanderweg on the spot.

Merseburg 10E3

Luftfahrt und Technik-museum Merseburg, Kastanienpromenade 50. **GPS**: n51,36004 e11,97044.

6 € 8, guests free € 3 Ch. **Location:** Rural, simple, quiet.
Surface: gravel/metalled. 01/01-31/12.
Distance: 1km 1,5km.

Naumburg/Saale 12E1

Altstadtparkplatz Vogelwiese, Luisenstraße.
GPS: n51,14861 e11,81391.

15 € 10 € 0,50/80liter Ch. (6x)€ 0,50/kWh WC.
Surface: gravel. 01/01-31/12.
Distance: 500m 50m 500m 50m.
Remarks: Max. 3 days.

Oranienbaum-Wörlitz 10E2

Jugendverkehrsschule Oranienbaum, Dessauer Strasse 47.
GPS: n51,80279 e12,39023.

6 € 7,50 Ch. (6x) WC included € 1/day.
Location: Rural, comfortable, quiet.
Surface: gravel/metalled. 01/01-31/12.
Distance: 1km.

Prettin 10F2

Bade- und Angelsee, Hinterfährstraße. **GPS**: n51,66485 e12,90551.

DE

5 € 6 + € 2,80/pp Chincluded € 0,30/kWh.
Surface: gravel. 01/04-31/10.
Distance: 1,5km on the spot 1km 1km.

Quedlinburg 10D2

An den Fischteichen. GPS: n51,79308 e11,14863.

20 € 10 + € 5/pp tourist tax € 1/80liter (8x)€ 1/6h. **Location:** Urban, comfortable, central, quiet.
Surface: grasstiles/metalled. 01/01-31/12.
Distance: 350m 300m 250m 150m.

Quedlinburg 10D2

Marschlinger Hof. GPS: n51,79138 e11,13965.

6 € 15/24h € 1/80liter Ch (4x)€ 1/6h WC.
Location: Urban, comfortable, central, quiet.
Surface: metalled. 01/01-31/12.
Distance: 100m 50m 400m 200m.
Remarks: Max. 7m.

Quedlinburg 10D2

Schloßparkplatz, Schenkgasse. **GPS:** n51,78755 e11,13507.

6 € 10/24h + tourist tax € 2,50/pp € 1/80liter Ch (4x)€ 2/8h . **Location:** Urban, comfortable, quiet.
Surface: metalled. 01/01-31/12.
Distance: on the spot 100m.
Remarks: At bowling centre.

Quedlinburg 10D2

Wohnmobilparkplatz Familie Jahnke, Feldmark links der Bode 17.
GPS: n51,80373 e11,17548.

10 € 10 € 2/day WCincluded .
Location: Rural, simple, quiet. **Surface:** concrete. 01/01-31/12.
Distance: 2,5km 650m.

Remarks: Barbecue place, use of sauna against payment.

Salzwedel 8C3

Stellplatz der Hansestadt Salzwedel, Dämmchenweg 41.
GPS: n52,85049 e11,13911.

6 € 3 Ch € 2 WC € 2,sanitary € 2.
Location: Urban. **Surface:** metalled. 01/01-31/12.
Distance: historical centre 1km 100m.
Remarks: Caution € 10.

Sangerhausen 10D3

An der Walkmühle, Taubenberg. **GPS:** n51,49056 e11,31127.

50 free. **Surface:** sand. 01/01-31/12.
Distance: 2km on the spot 1,5km.

Sangerhausen 10D3

P7, An der Probstmühle. **GPS:** n51,47707 e11,30798.

20 free. **Location:** Rural. **Surface:** grassy/gravel.
01/01-31/12.
Distance: 500m 200m 100m.

Sangerhausen 10D3

Markl's Pferdestall, Walkberg 1. **GPS:** n51,49417 e11,31361.
3 free on demand.
Location: Rural. **Surface:** gravel. 01/01-31/12 Mo.
Distance: 1,5km on the spot 2km.

Sangerhausen 10D3

Rosarium, Sotterhäuser Weg. **GPS:** n51,47245 e11,31798.
€ 5 Ch. **Surface:** metalled. 15/04-15/10.
Remarks: Check in at shop.

Schierke 10C2

Campingplatz Am Schierker Stern, Hagenstrasse.
GPS: n51,75696 e10,68398.

6 € 10 excl. tourist tax Chincluded (6x)against payment.
Location: Rural, simple, quiet. **Surface:** gravel/metalled.
01/01-31/12.
Distance: 1km on the spot on the spot on the spot on the spot on the spot.

Seehausen 8D3

Stellplatz Seehausen, Arendseer Str. 6. **GPS:** n52,89068 e11,75119.

12 € 5 € 2 Ch (3x)€ 2. **Location:** Rural.
Surface: metalled. 01/01-31/12.
Distance: 100m 300m 200m.
Remarks: Check in at tourist office.

Stassfurt 10D2

Neumarkt, Lehrter Straße. **GPS:** n51,85424 e11,58284.

6 free. **Location:** Urban, simple, central, quiet.
Surface: gravel. 01/01-31/12.
Distance: on the spot on the spot 100m station 700m on the spot on the spot.
Remarks: Along the Bode river.

Stendal 10D1

Nordwall-Schützenplatz. **GPS:** n52,61116 e11,86121.

20 free € 1/80liter Ch.
Surface: grassy/metalled. 01/01-31/12.
Distance: on the spot 500m bakery 50m 200m.

Stolberg/Harz 10C3

Am Bahnhof. **GPS:** n51,56727 e10,95696.

5 free, tourist tax € 2/pp. **Location:** Rural, simple, quiet.
Surface: asphalted. 01/01-31/12.
Distance: centre 800m 750m 350m.
Remarks: Max. 2 days, pay at tourist office.

Stolberg/Harz 10C3

Am Rittertor, Rittergasse. **GPS:** n51,57655 e10,94539.

5 free, tourist tax € 2/pp.
Location: Rural, simple, quiet. **Surface:** asphalted. 01/01-31/12.
Distance: 1km on the spot 2km.
Remarks: Max. 2 days, pay at tourist office.

DE

Stolberg/Harz 10C3

Freizeitbad Thyragrotte, Thyratal 5. **GPS**: n51,56378 e10,95796.

3 free. **Location:** Rural, simple. **Surface:** asphalted. 01/01-31/12.
Distance: city centre 1km 1km 200m on the spot.
Remarks: Max. 2 days, pay at tourist office, swimming pool.

Tangermünde 10E1

Tangerplatz, Klosterberg. **GPS**: n52,53774 e11,96803.

30 € 8/24h, € 14/48h Ch included.
Surface: metalled. 01/01-31/12.
Distance: 700m 150m 700m 550m.
Remarks: Max. 2 days.

Wahrenberg 8D3

Stellplatz Storchenwiese, Eichenwinkel 34.
GPS: n52,98342 e11,67362.

8 € 5 € 1/100liter Ch € 2 (6x) € 2,50,16Amp.
Location: Rural. **Surface:** grassy. 01/01-31/12.
Distance: Elbe 600m on the spot on the spot.

Weissenfels 10E3

Caravan- und Freizeitmarkt Gerth, Drei Wege 5.
GPS: n51,19822 e11,99875.

7 free € 1/80liter Ch (4x) € 1/stay.
Location: Urban, simple, noisy. **Surface:** asphalted. 01/01-31/12.
Distance: 4km on the spot on the spot Saale-Radwanderweg on the spot.

Wernigerode 10C2

Am Katzenteich. **GPS**: n51,83882 e10,78168.

20 € 5/stay € 1/40liter Ch (20x) € 1/kWh WC € 0,50.
Location: Comfortable, quiet. **Surface:** metalled. 01/01-31/12.
Distance: 500m 200m 500m on the spot on the spot on the spot.

Wernigerode 10C2

Schlossparkplatz am Anger, Halberstädler strasse 1.
GPS: n51,83807 e10,79535.

24 € 5 + € 2,50 tourist tax, overnight stay free € 2 Ch WC € 0,50. **Location:** Urban, simple, central, quiet.
Surface: metalled. 01/01-31/12, service 9-18h.
Distance: 300m 200m 600m on the spot on the spot.

Wienrode 10C2

Unterm Tappenstieg, Harzstraße L93. **GPS**: n51,75860 e10,97998.
1 € 8 € 1 Ch € 2. **Location:** Rural. **Surface:** grassy.
01/01-31/12.
Distance: 900m.

Wörlitz 10E2

Seeparke, Seespitze, K2376. **GPS**: n51,84899 e12,41296.

24 € 5 day/€ 5 night free (24x) € 3 WC € 0,50 € 0,50.
Location: Rural, comfortable, quiet. **Surface:** metalled.
01/01-31/12.
Distance: 800m 500m 800m 800m on the spot on the spot.
Remarks: Parking at the edge the Wörlitzer park, pay in at kiosk, max. 24h, caution key sanitary € 15.

Wörlitz 10E2

Hotel Coswiger Elbterrasse, Elbterrasse 1.
GPS: n51,87750 e12,45097.

10 € 5, guests free. **Location:** Rural, simple, quiet.
Surface: grassy. 01/01-31/12.
Distance: 1,5km on the spot on the spot 4km.
Remarks: Along the river Elbe, check in at hotel, guests free.

Zeitz 12E1

Obsthof Martin, Kloster Posa 1. **GPS**: n51,05836 e12,15797.

20 € 5 Ch included (4x) € 3/day.
Location: Rural, comfortable, quiet. **Surface:** grassy. 01/01-31/12.
Distance: 1,5km 200m 1km.
Remarks: Regional products.

Brandenburg/Berlin

Abbendorf 8D3

Gasthaus Dörpkrog an Diek, Am Deich 7.
GPS: n52,89663 e11,90975.

6 € 5 Ch WC included. 01/01-31/12.
Distance: on the spot.
Remarks: Bread-service.

Alt-Zeschdorf 10H1

Reiterhof Blumrich, Falkenhagerweg 11.
GPS: n52,42649 e14,42328.

30 € 10 Ch included.
Surface: grassy. 01/01-31/12 winter Mo.
Distance: 1,5km.
Remarks: At manege, bread-service.

Altdöbern 10H2

Q1 Rasthof Altdöbern, Senftenberger strasse 11.
GPS: n51,64523 e14,03544.

20 € 10 Ch WC included.
Location: Rural. **Surface:** metalled. 01/01-31/12.
Distance: 500m on the spot 500m.
Remarks: Bread kiosk.

Angermünde 8G2

Parkplatz Am Oberwall, Oberwall 5. **GPS**: n53,01501 e14,00371.

5 free € 1/100liter (8x) € 1/2kWh.
Location: Urban, simple, central. **Surface:** metalled. 01/04-31/10.
Distance: on the spot on the spot on the spot Historische Stadtkerne Märkischer Landweg.
Remarks: Near city wall.

Angermünde 8G2

NABU-Erlebniszentrum Blumberger Mühle, Blumberger Mühle 2.
GPS: n53,03572 e13,96806.

DE

10 free. **Location:** Rural, simple, isolated, quiet.
Surface: grassy/metalled. 01/01-31/12.
Distance: 4km near fish pond on the spot on the spot on the spot.
Remarks: At biosphere reserve.

Bad Saarow 10G1

Parkplatz Strolin, Silbergerstrasse. **GPS**: n52,28726 e14,03895.

4 free. **Surface:** metalled. 01/01-31/12.
Distance: 1km 100m 100m on the spot.
Remarks: Max. 24h.

Bad Saarow 10G1

Saarow-Therme, Ringstrasse. **GPS**: n52,29399 e14,06243.

6 free. **Surface:** metalled. 01/01-31/12.
Distance: on the spot 300m 400m.

Bad Wilsnack 8E3

Bauernhof Nickel, An der Kirche 8. **GPS**: n52,96523 e11,85283.
2 € 12/night included. **Surface:** grassy.
01/01-31/12.
Distance: 250m.
Remarks: Barbecue place.

Bad Wilsnack 8E3

Kur- und Gradier-Therme Bad Wilsnack, Am Kähling.
GPS: n52,96316 e11,95007.

80 € 13,50 + € 1/pp tourist tax Ch (43x) WC included.
Location: Urban. **Surface:** grassy/sand.
01/01-31/12 24/12.
Distance: 500m 200m 500m.
Remarks: Check in at pay-desk of the Therme, bread-service, discount on access sauna/wellness.

Berlin 10F1

Historisches Fährhaus Berlin, Muggelbergallee 1, Berlin-Köpenick.
GPS: n52,41851 e13,58734.

15 € 19-23 incl. 2 pers, dog € 3 Ch (15x)€ 5/24h WC included € 1/5minutes € 5/stay. **Location:** Urban, luxurious, quiet. **Surface:** grassy/gravel. 01/01-31/12.
Distance: on the spot 8km on the spot on the spot on the spot 100m, supermarket 750m 1km tram 100m.
Remarks: Possibility for reservation, sauna € 5.

Berlin 10F1

WohnmobilPark Berlin, Waidmannsluster Damm 12-14.
GPS: n52,59559 e13,28910.

90 € 10-23, 2 pers.incl, € 1/pp tourist tax, dog € 2 € 1/100liter Ch € 4/24h,3Amp WC sanitary € 5/day € 4/4 .
Location: Urban, central. **Surface:** grassy/metalled.
01/01-31/12.
Distance: centre Berlin 16km 600m on the spot on the spot metro 1km.
Remarks: Key sanitary building € 4/day, hotline-Nr.: 0176 – 99 55 25 00.

Berlin 10F1

Reisemobilhafen Berlin Spandau, Askanierring 70.
GPS: n52,55309 e13,20050.

180 € 16 2p incl. + tourist tax € 1, dog € 2 € 0,10/10liter Ch WC included € 1/5minutes € 2/24h.
Location: Urban, simple, central, noisy. **Surface:** grassy/gravel.
01/01-31/12.
Distance: on the spot 100m 900m on the spot 300m.
Remarks: Near approach route of airport, 23-5h quiet, check in at kosk, outside environmental zone. In area of the former English barracks 'Alexander Barracks', A10 exit Berlin-Spandau, follow road till cross roads Heerstraße/Gatowerstraße,here to the left, at Flakenseerplatz straight on, Neuendorferstraße, before Hohenzollernring to the left.

Berlin 10F1

Köpenicker Hof, Stellingdamm 15, Berlin-Köpenick.
GPS: n52,45929 e13,58532.

40 € 12-18 2 pers. Incl., dog € 3 € 1/80liter Ch € 0,50/kWh WC included . **Location:** Simple, quiet.
Surface: grassy/metalled. 01/01-31/12.
Distance: on the spot on the spot Tram (centre 300m).
Remarks: Caution key sanitary building € 20, bread-service, dog € 1,50/night.

Berlin 10F1

Wohnmobil-Oase-Berlin, Hochstraße 4. **GPS**: n52,50861 e13,20444.
100 € 23-32 + € 1/pp tourist tax, dog € 2,50 € 1/100liter Ch included WC sanitary € 2/day.
Location: Urban. **Surface:** asphalted.
01/01-31/12.
Distance: on the spot 600m 300m.
Remarks: Bread-service, barbecue place.

Berlin 10F1

Marina Lanke Berlin, Scharfe Lanke 109-131.
GPS: n52,50344 e13,18801.

20 € 1,50-2m + € 3,50/pp, dog € 2 Ch WC included € 3/2 . **Location:** Urban. **Surface:** asphalted. 01/05-15/10.
Distance: centre Berlin 16km on the spot on the spot 1km on the spot.
Remarks: Check in at harbourmaster.

Berlin 10F1

Marina Wendenschloss, Wendenschlossstrasse 350-354.
GPS: n52,42558 e13,58384.

10 € 15-20 Ch WC included € 1/5minutes .
Location: Simple, quiet. **Surface:** grassy/metalled.
01/04-31/10.
Distance: 18km city centre on the spot on the spot 100m Tram 200m.
Remarks: Outside environmental zone, barbecue place, boat rental.

Berlin 10F1

Sunset Marina, Siemenswerderweg 42.
GPS: n52,50646 e13,20206.
25 € 10-12 + € 5/pp € 4/night WC.
Surface: grassy.
01/03-31/10.
Distance: 8km 600m 500m.

Tourist information Berlin:

Berlin Card gives for free entrance on public transport and museums and many discounts on purchases. from € 42.

Tourist Info, Europacenter, Eingang Budapester strasse 3; Brandenburgertor, Südflügel; Fernsehturm, Alexanderplatz, http://www.visitberlin.de/. Documentation available, via Internet.

Haus am Checkpoint Charly, Friedrichstrasse 44. At the former border crossing. History of the Wall is told with photographs.
9-22h.

Zeughaus. German historical museum.

Alexanderplatz. The old historical centre of Berlin.

Brandenburger Tor. Built in 1791 as a triumphal arch after the construction of the Berlin Wall the arch remained as a symbol of the German separation. free.

Schloß Charlottenburg, Spandauer Damm 10-22. Summer residence of the Prussian kings. Tue-Su 10-18h 01/11-31/03. € 10.

Arkonaplatz. Flea market. Su 10-16h.

Ostbahnhof. Antiques and flea market. Su 9-17h.

Strasse des 17. Juni. Arts and fleamarket. Sa-Su 10-17h.

Zoologischer Garten, Hardenbergplatz 8. City-zoo. 01/04-30/09 9-18.30h, 01/10-31/10 9-18h, 01/11-28/02 9-17h.

Brandenburg 10E1

Am Brandenburger Dom, Grillendamm.
GPS: n52,41724 e12,56576.

DE

60 € 10 € 1/100liter Ch (26x)€ 1/kWh WC € 1/4minutes.
Location: Urban, simple, noisy. **Surface:** asphalted.
01/01-31/12.
Distance: Neustadt 15min, Altstadt 15min on the spot Imbiss on the spot on the spot on the spot.

S Brandenburg 10E1

Wassersportzentrum Alte Feuerwache, Franz Zieglerstrasse 27.
GPS: n52,40485 e12,54868.

30 € 12 Ch € 1/day WC € 1 included.
Location: Urban, simple, central, noisy. **Surface:** grassy/metalled.
01/01-31/12.
Distance: 500m on the spot 500m on the spot on the spot on the spot.
Remarks: Bread-service, boat rental, bike and e-bike rental.

S Breydin 8G3

Landhotel Trampe, Am Landhotel 1. **GPS**: n52,76898 e13,84030.
7 € 10 € 2 Ch included. **Location:** Rural.
Surface: grasstiles. 01/01-31/12.
Distance: 500m on the spot.

S Brieske 10H3

Reimann, Brieske Dorf 27. **GPS**: n51,49203 e13,94743.

20 € 6 Ch (12x)€ 2 WC included.
Surface: grassy. 01/01-31/12.
Distance: 200m 9,3km on the spot 2km.
Remarks: Bread-service.

S Burg/Spreewald 10H2

Hagens Insel - Wasserwanderrastplatz, Weidenweg 4.
GPS: n51,86138 e14,11527.

10 € 10 Ch WC included.
Location: Rural. **Surface:** grassy. 01/01-31/12.
Distance: 3km 2km.

S Burg/Spreewald 10H2

Landgasthof zur Wildbahn, Wildbahnweg 20.
GPS: n51,85104 e14,09384.

9 € 20, 2 pers. incl., dog € 2 WC included.
Surface: metalled. 01/03-30/10.

S Dollenchen 10G2

Gasthaus Stuckatz, Hauptstrasse 29. **GPS**: n51,60745 e13,86226.

20 € 9, 2 pers. incl Ch € 1 WC included.
Location: Rural. **Surface:** grassy. 01/01-31/12.
Distance: on the spot on the spot 3km on the spot.
Remarks: Barbecue place, bike and e-bike rental, charging point for electric bicycles.

S Dreetz 8E3

Reiterhof Müller, Schulstrasse 61. **GPS**: n52,79796 e12,46874.

10 € 14 Ch included WC. **Location:** Rural, simple, isolated, quiet. **Surface:** grassy. 01/01-31/12.
Distance: 800m 300m 500m 500m.

S Fehrbellin 8F3

FF Freizeitmobile, Gewerbepark 29. **GPS**: n52,79770 e12,78624.

10 € 7,50 Ch included € 2,50/day WC free.
Location: Urban, simple, quiet.
Surface: grassy.
01/01-31/12.
Distance: 1km 2km 1km 1km on the spot on the spot.
Remarks: Accessory shop.

S Frankfurt (Oder) 10H1

Marina Winterhafen, Hafenstraße 2. **GPS**: n52,35497 e14,55021.
7 € 15, 2 pers.incl Ch included € 0,50/kWh WC .
Location: Comfortable, quiet. **Surface:** grassy. 01/01-31/12.
Distance: 1km on the spot on the spot 400m on the spot on the spot.
Remarks: Check in on arrival.

S Fürstenberg/Havel 8F2

Marina Fürstenberg, Ravensbrücker Dorfstrasse 26.
GPS: n53,19489 e13,14895.

50 € 9 Ch included € 2,50/day WC € 1,50 free.
Location: Rural, comfortable, quiet. **Surface:** grassy.
01/01-31/12.
Distance: 1km on the spot on the spot on the spot 1km on the spot on the spot.
Remarks: Wifi code at harbour master, boat rental, near the former women's concentration camp Ravensbrück.

S Höhenland 8G3

Das Forsthaus, Bahnhofstraße 13. **GPS**: n52,68433 e13,88171.

8 € 11 Ch WC included € 5/day.
Location: Rural, comfortable, quiet. **Surface:** grasstiles.
01/01-31/12.
Distance: 3km on the spot on the spot on the spot.
Remarks: Bread-service.

S Kienitz 8H3

Ferienhaus Marth, Kienitzeroderstrasse 20.
GPS: n52,67616 e14,39890.

8 € 10 Ch € 1,50 WC included € 1,50.
Surface: grassy. 01/04-30/09.
Distance: 3km 3km.

S Kloster Lehnin 10F1

Hotel Seehof, Am See 51. **GPS**: n52,34924 e12,70374.

15 € 10, guests free Ch € 2/day WC included € 2.
Location: Rural, comfortable. **Surface:** grassy/metalled.
01/01-31/12.
Distance: 1,8km on the spot on the spot on the spot on the spot.
Remarks: Check in at hotel.

S Kolkwitz 10H2

Bauernhof Korreng, Papitzerstrasse 48. **GPS**: n51,76676 e14,22410.

DE

3 € 10 Ch WC included. **Location:** Rural.
Surface: grassy. 01/03-31/10.
Distance: 2,5km 400m.

Kyritz 8E3

Parkplatz Wässering, Graf-von-der-Schulenburg-Straße.
GPS: n52,94044 e12,40053.

15 free € 1/100liter Ch € 1/8h WC € 0,50 € 1.
Location: Urban, comfortable, noisy. **Surface:** grasstiles.
01/01-31/12.
Distance: city centre 100m on the spot 250m 250m.

Lindow/Mark 8F3

Am Wutzsee. **GPS**: n52,97205 e12,98924.

3 free, tourist tax € 0,50/pp. **Location:** Urban, simple, noisy.
Surface: metalled. 01/01-31/12.
Distance: on the spot on the spot 150m 150m on the spot on the spot.
Remarks: Max. 1 night, pay at tourist office.

Lübbenau 10G2

Autocamping im Spreewald, Chausseestrasse 17a, Lübbenau-Zerkwitz.
GPS: n51,86559 e13,93324.

6 € 15/24h, 2 pers.incl + tourist tax € 1,50, dog € 1 € 1,50 Ch WC included. **Surface:** grasstiles/grassy.
Easter-31/10.
Distance: 2,5km 1,5km 500m on the spot on the spot.

Lübbenau 10G2

Spreewald Wohnmobilpark, Dammstraße 62.
GPS: n51,86219 e13,97090.
30 € 16,50-18,50, 2 pers.incl + tourist tax € 2/pp Ch € 1,50 € 1 included.
Location: Rural. **Surface:** grassy. Easter-15/10.
Distance: on the spot 100m on the spot station 1km.

Lübbenau 10G2

Am Bahnhof, Bahnhofstraße (B115). **GPS**: n51,86139 e13,96361.

10 € 8 € 1/80liter Ch (10x)€ 0,50/kWh.
Location: Urban. **Surface:** asphalted. 01/01-31/12.
Distance: 800m 3,3km 350m 50m on the spot.
Remarks: Along railwayline, max. 2 days.

Lübbenau 10G2

Kahnfährhafen Leipe, Dorfstrasse 34, Leipe.
GPS: n51,85301 e14,05023.

4 € 5. **Surface:** metalled. 01/01-31/12.
Distance: 11,6km.

Luckenwalde 10F2

Waldidyll im Elsthal, Elsthal 6. **GPS**: n52,07511 e13,16908.
10 € 10 Ch WC included. **Surface:** sand.
01/01-31/12.
Distance: on the spot.
Remarks: Max. <>2.35m.

Lychen 8F2

Marina-Yachthafen Lychensee, Schlüsstrasse 7.
GPS: n53,21187 e13,29686.

6 € 10 Ch € 2,50/day WC € 1.
Location: Rural, simple, quiet. **Surface:** grassy. 15/04-15/10.
Distance: 700m 650m.
Remarks: Check in at harbourmaster, boat rental.

Nackel 8E3

Gaststätte Birkenhof, Segeletzerstrasse 2.
GPS: n52,82503 e12,56528.

3 € 3 € 3 Ch WC included.
Location: Rural, simple, isolated, quiet. **Surface:** metalled.
01/01-31/12 Tue.
Distance: 5km on the spot on the spot on the spot.

Neuruppin 8F3

Sportcenter Neuruppin, Trenckmannstraße 14.
GPS: n52,91573 e12,80365.

30 € 6 WC € 2,50 . **Location:** Urban, simple, quiet.
Surface: grasstiles. 01/01-31/12.
Distance: on the spot Neuruppiner See 500m on the spot 200m, bakery 400m on the spot on the spot.
Remarks: Check in at sport centre.

Oberkrämer 8F3

Bäckerei Plentz, Dorfstraße 43. **GPS**: n52,73643 e13,08540.

4 € 8 Ch WC included.
Location: Rural, simple, quiet. **Surface:** metalled. 01/01-31/12.
Distance: on the spot 1km 700m 500m train 500m on the spot on the spot.
Remarks: Along railwayline, in front of bakery, max. 48h.

Oranienburg 8F3

Am Schlosshafen, Rungestrasse 47. **GPS**: n52,75760 e13,23879.

36 € 15, dog € 2 € 1,50/80liter Ch (16x)€ 1/kWh WC € 0,50 € 1/5minutes € 5.
Location: Rural, comfortable, central, quiet. **Surface:** metalled.
01/01-31/12.
Distance: 600m on the spot 600m 600m on the spot on the spot.
Remarks: Tallycard: service, electricity, sanitary building, caution € 10.

Oranienburg 8F3

Motel Havelidyll, Havelhausener Brücke 1, Havelhausen.
GPS: n52,72161 e13,25047.

5 € 15, 2 pers.incl, dog € 2,50 Ch WC included.
Location: Rural, simple, isolated, quiet. **Surface:** grassy.
01/04-15/11.
Distance: 10km 4km on the spot on the spot 900m 900m.

Potsdam 10F1

Am Krongut, Potsdamer Straße 196. **GPS**: n52,41332 e13,02905.

DE

11 € 10/24h. Location: Urban, simple.
Surface: concrete. 01/01-31/12.
Distance: city centre 2km 100m 500m Tram 300m.

Potsdam 10F1

Historische Mühle von Sanssouci, Maulbeerallee 5.
GPS: n52,40562 e13,03453.

5 € 2/h, max. € 20/24h. **Location:** Urban, simple.
Surface: metalled. 01/01-31/12.
Distance: 2km on the spot 500m.

Potsdam 10F1

Zum Alten Krug, Hauptstraße 2. **GPS**: n52,45606 e12,96616.
8 free Ch against payment.
Surface: gravel. 01/01-31/12 Mo.
Distance: on the spot on the spot on the spot.
Remarks: Playground.

Tourist information Potsdam:
Filmpark Babelsberg, Großbeerenstrasse 200. Attractions park concerning the film. 23/03-31/10 10-18.

Rehfelde 8G3

Campershof, Alt Werder 8. **GPS**: n52,52093 e13,94080.

12 € 8,50 Chincluded € 1/day WC € 2,50.
Location: Rural, comfortable, quiet. **Surface:** grassy.
01/01-31/12.
Distance: 2km 2km 2km on the spot on the spot.
Remarks: Bread-service.

Rheinsberg 8F2

Friedrichszentrum 1. **GPS**: n53,10317 e12,89459.
4 free. **Location:** Urban. **Surface:** asphalted. 01/01-31/12.
Distance: 500m on the spot.

Schmergow 10F1

Zum fröhlichen Landmann, Ziegeleiweg 17.
GPS: n52,45416 e12,80553.

30 € 7,50 Ch € 1/2kWh included.
Location: Rural, simple, isolated.
Surface: grassy. 01/04-31/10.
Distance: 500m on the spot 500m 400m.

Schwedt/Oder 8H2

Wassersportzentrum Schwedt, Wasserplatz 4.
GPS: n53,05759 e14,29861.

30 € 5 + € 5/pp, dog € 1 Ch WC included.
Location: Urban. **Surface:** grassy.
01/01-31/12 Mo.
Distance: 1km on the spot on the spot 500m on the spot on the spot.
Remarks: Check in at harbourmaster or bar, breakfest-service.

Schwedt/Oder 8H2

Uckermark-Wohnmobile, Am Wasserplatz 4.
GPS: n53,05813 e14,29788.
8 € 10 Ch included4kWh WC € 2.
Surface: grassy. 01/01-31/12.
Distance: on the spot 300m 300m.
Remarks: At motorhome dealer, barbecue place, bicycle rental.

Senftenberg 10H3

Wohnmobilstellplatz Buchwalde, Buchwalder Straße 52.
GPS: n51,51256 e14,02278.
12 € 15 Chincluded € 2 WC € 0,50.
Location: Rural. **Surface:** gravel. 01/04-01/11.
Distance: 2km Senftenberger See on the spot on the spot on the spot.
Remarks: Max. 4 nights, caution key sanitary € 20, barbecue place, playground.

Senftenberg 10H3

Reimann-Mobile, Brieske Dorf 27. **GPS**: n51,49069 e13,94885.
20 € 6 Chincluded (12x)€ 2 WC. **Location:** Rural.
Surface: grassy. 01/01-31/12.
Distance: 4km on the spot 2km on the spot.
Remarks: Bread-service, playground.

Senftenberg 10H3

Familienpark Senftenberger See, Straße zur Südsee 1.
GPS: n51,49206 e14,04650.
5 € 19 Ch included € 0,50.
Location: Rural. **Surface:** unpaved. 01/01-31/12.
Distance: 8km on the spot 300m on the spot on the spot.
Remarks: Max. 1 night.

Stolzenhagen 8G3

Am Kietz, Kietz 9. **GPS**: n52,94916 e14,10833.

20 € 7,50 Ch (10x)€ 2,50/day WCincluded € 2,50/pp.
Location: Rural, comfortable, quiet. **Surface:** grassy/metalled.
01/01-31/12.
Distance: on the spot Imbiss 600m Oder-Neiße-Radweg on the spot.
Remarks: Directly on the canal, check in at Imbiss, bread-service.

Storkow/Mark 10G1

An der Schleuse, Kirchstrasse. **GPS**: n52,25792 e13,93178.
5 € 10 included. **Surface:** grasstiles. 01/01-31/12.
Distance: 200m 300m 500m.
Remarks: At the Storkower Canal, max. 36h.

Templin 8F2

Alter Knehdenerstrasse. **GPS**: n53,12359 e13,49423.

40 free € 1/60liter Ch. **Location:** Urban, simple, quiet.
Surface: asphalted/metalled. 01/01-31/12.
Distance: 300m 300m 300m on the spot on the spot.

Tiefensee 8G3

Reisemobilplatz, Country Camping Tiefensee, Schmiedeweg 1.
GPS: n52,68302 e13,84292.

64 € 16,50 incl. 2 pers, dog € 1,50 Ch (51x)WCincluded € 0,50 € 2,50. **Location:** Rural, comfortable, quiet.
Surface: grassy. 01/01-31/12.
Distance: on the spot on the spot on the spot on the spot on the spot on the spot on the spot on the spot.
Remarks: Check in at reception campsite.

Weisen 8D3

Wohnmobilstellplatz Am Biotop, Heinrich-Heine-Strasse 4.
GPS: n53,02062 e11,78086.

8 € 5 Chincluded. **Location:** Rural.
Surface: gravel. 01/04-30/09.
Distance: 300m 200m 300m.

Werder/Havel 10F1

An der Föhse. **GPS**: n52,37807 e12,93704.

25 € 7 + € 1,50/pp tourist tax € 0,50/80liter Ch (8x)€ 0,50/kWh WC € 0,50.
Location: Urban, simple. **Surface:** gravel. 01/01-31/12.
Distance: on the spot on the spot on the spot on the spot 100m on the spot.
Remarks: Check in at harbourmaster.

Wusterhausen/Dosse 8E3

Dossehalle, Zur Dossehalle 6. **GPS**: n52,89337 e12,46537.

3 free € 1/25liter Ch € 1/8h. **Location:** Urban, simple,

DE

quiet. **Surface:** asphalted. 01/01-31/12.
Distance: centre 500m 450m.

Saxony

Adorf 12E2

Waldbad, Waldbadstrasse 5. **GPS**: n50,30778 e12,25056.

3 free. **Surface:** metalled. 01/03-30/11.
Distance: 1km 500m.
Remarks: Max. 24h.

Tourist information Adorf:
TouristInfo, Freiberger Str. 8.

S Bad Düben 10F3

Im Kurgebiet, Parkstraße 1. **GPS**: n51,60139 e12,58247.

4 free, tourist tax € 1,20-1,50/pp € 1/80liter € 1 Ch€ 1 WC.
Location: Rural, simple, isolated. **Surface:** metalled.
01/01-31/12.
Distance: 750m 1,4km 1,4km.

S Bad Elster 12E2

Albertbad, Austus-Klingner Straße. **GPS**: n50,28545 e12,24034.
5 € 8 + € 2,20/pp tourist tax € 1/100liter included.
Location: Rural. **Surface:** metalled. 01/01-31/12.
Distance: 1km 250m.
Remarks: Check in at pay desk swimming pool, caution € 20, swimming pool and sauna on site.

Bad Lausick 12F1

Freizetbad Am Riff, Am Riff 3. **GPS**: n51,14321 e12,65383.

10 free. **Location:** Rural, simple, central, quiet.
Surface: grasstiles. 01/01-31/12.
Distance: 100m 100m on the spot on the spot.
Remarks: At swimming pool.

S Bad Muskau 38A3

Am Fürst-Pückler-Park, Bautzener Straße 39.
GPS: n51,53382 e14,71838.

25 € 8, € 12 service incl. + € 1,25/pp tourist tax Ch (25x) WC. **Location:** Urban, comfortable, central, quiet.
Surface: grasstiles/metalled. 01/01-28/12.
Distance: 400m 4km 2km on the spot on the spot.

S Bautzen 10H3

Schliebenstraße. **GPS**: n51,18168 e14,41482.

4 free € 1 € 1 (4x)€ 0,50/kWh.
Surface: metalled. 01/01-31/12.
Distance: 1,2km 1km.
Remarks: Max. 2 nights.

S Breitenbrunn 12F2

Sportpark Rabenberg, Rabenbergweg. **GPS**: n50,45556 e12,74417.

15 € 8,50 + € 8,50/pp Chincluded € 2/day WC € 1.
Surface: metalled. 01/01-31/12.
Distance: 5km 5km 5km.
Remarks: Arrival <22h, dog € 2/day.

S Dennheritz 12F1

Caravan Service Bressler, Zwickauerstrasse 78.
GPS: n50,80889 e12,48667.

6 € 5/night € 1 Ch (4x)€ 0,50/kWh. **Surface:** metalled.
01/01-31/12.
Distance: 2km 800m 3km.
Remarks: At motorhome dealer.

S Diera-Zehren 10G3

Zum Zuessenhaus, Elbstraße 10. **GPS**: n51,19500 e13,41917.

10 € 5. **Location:** Rural, simple. **Surface:** grassy/metalled.
01/01-31/12.

S Diesbar-Seusslitz 10G3

Parkplatz Am Schloss, An der Weinstraße.
GPS: n51,24111 e13,41575.

6 € 4 (9-19h), overnight stay free (6x)€ 1/6h.
Location: Rural, simple, quiet. **Surface:** metalled. 01/01-31/12.
Distance: 100m 200m on the spot on the spot.

S Dresden 12G1

Parkplatz Grosse Meissner, Wiesentor Strasse.
GPS: n51,05639 e13,74306.

60 € 18/24h € 2/100liter Ch€ 2 (14x)€ 5/day WC.
Location: Urban, simple, central.
Surface: asphalted. 01/01-31/12.
Distance: 100m on the spot on the spot on the spot.

S Dresden 12G1

Sachsenplatz Dresden, Käthe-Kollwitz-Ufer 4.
GPS: n51,05700 e13,75990.
150 € 10 (25x)€ 5/24h. **Location:** Urban, central.
01/01-31/12.
Distance: Old city centre 2,2km 300m Aldi 700m 500m.

S Dresden 12G1

Werner Knopf, B6, Meissner Landstrasse.
GPS: n51,08131 e13,65563.

7 € 5/6m + € 1/m € 2 (8x)€ 2/night € 1,50.
Location: Urban, simple, quiet. **Surface:** grasstiles.
01/03-30/10.
Distance: 6km 500m on the spot.
Remarks: Gate closes at 22h.

S Dresden 12G1

Wohnmobilstellplatz am Blüherpark, Zinzendorfstraße 7.
GPS: n51,04426 e13,74371.

50 € 14 € 1 € 1 € 3/night,16Amp € 2/day.
Location: Urban, comfortable, central.
Surface: grassy/metalled. 01/01-31/12.
Distance: 1km 5km 500m 450m.
Remarks: Check in at Cityherberge, Lingnerallee 3, 24/24.

S Dresden 12G1

Wohnmobilstellplatz Dresden, Kesselsdorfer Straße 153.
GPS: n51,03988 e13,66949.

5 € 12 Ch (5x)€ 2,50/night € 2/pppd.
Location: Urban, comfortable, central. **Surface:** gravel/metalled.
01/01-31/12.
Distance: centre Dresden 4km 4km on the spot 200m 800m.
Remarks: At Wellnesshotel Landlust.

DE

Dresden 12G1

CaravaningPark Schaffer, Kötzschenbroderstrasse 125.
GPS: n51,08639 e13,68222.

100 € 15 € 0,50/60liter € 0,50 Ch€ 0,50 (100x)€ 0,50/kWh WC € 0,50.
Location: Urban, comfortable.
Surface: grassy.
01/01-31/12.
Distance: Dresden 5km 2km 200m 500m 200m 500m.
Remarks: Bread-service, repair possibilities motorhome, access <19h.

Tourist information Dresden:
Dresden-City-Card. Card gives among other things for free public transport, entrance to many museums, discounts on boat trips, restaurants etc.
01/01-31/12. € 35/48h.
Tourist Information, Prager strasse; Schinkelwache/Theaterplatz, www.dresden.de. Former residence city with many curiosities.
Striezelmarkt, Altstadt. Christmas fair.
advent season.

Ebersbach/Sachsen 38A3

Fest- und Parkplatz am Freibad, Kottmarsdorfer Strasse 1.
GPS: n51,00972 e14,59806.

7 € 5, € 10 service incl Ch WC. **Location:** Rural, simple, isolated, quiet. **Surface:** metalled. 01/01-31/12.
Distance: 1km 500m 1km on the spot.

Elsterheide 10H3

Wohnmobilstellplatz Lothar Meusel, Am Hochwald 27, Tätzschwitz.
GPS: n51,48304 e14,10750.

14 € 8,50 € 1 Ch included WC€ 2,50/day.
Location: Rural, comfortable, isolated, quiet.
Surface: grasstiles/grassy. Easter-31/10.
Distance: 3km 8-10km on the spot.

Freiberg 12G1

Am Johannisbad, Lessingstraße. **GPS**: n50,91461 e13,33368.

10 first night € 10, € 7,50 second night € 1/80liter € 1 Ch€ 1 (10x)€ 0,50/kWh WC. **Location:** Urban, simple, central, quiet. **Surface:** metalled. 01/01-31/12.
Distance: Altstadt 900m 150m Kaufland 500m on the spot.

Geierswalde 10H3

Ferien- und Freizeitpark Geierswalde See, Promenadeweg 1-3.
GPS: n51,49372 e14,13481.

100+ € 6 € 2/day Ch € 3 WC. **Location:** Rural, simple, isolated, quiet. **Surface:** grassy. 01/01-31/12.
Distance: 500m Geierswaldesee 300m 1km 5km on the spot.

Görlitz 38A3

Reisemobil & Caravans Hoke, Zittauer Strasse 62.
GPS: n51,13907 e14,97947.
4 € 8/24h Ch included. **Location:** Urban.
Surface: metalled. 01/01-31/12.
Distance: 2km 400m 500m 50m.
Remarks: At motorhome dealer.

Großenhain 10G3

Carl-Maria-von-Weber-Allee. **GPS**: n51,29032 e13,53584.
5 € 5, 15/09-15/05 free € 1/70liter € 1 € 1/4h.
Surface: metalled. 01/01-31/12.
Distance: 500m 100m.
Remarks: To pay at swimming pool.

Grünhain 12F2

Freizeitpark, Auer Strasse 82, Haus des Gastes, Grünhain-Beierfeld.
GPS: n50,58139 e12,79167.

6 € 10 € 1 € 1,customers free Ch € 1,50/day WC € 1.
Surface: metalled. 01/01-31/12.
Distance: 1km on the spot 3km.

Hermsdorf 12G1

Ski- & Sporthotel SWF, Bahnhofstraße 7.
GPS: n50,73241 e13,66400.

8 € 5, tourist tax € 0,50/pp € 2 € 2 Ch € 0,50/kWh.
Location: Rural, simple, isolated, quiet.
Surface: gravel/metalled. 01/01-31/12.
Distance: on the spot on the spot on the spot on the spot.

Königsfeld-Stollsdorf 12F1

Spreer's Ferienhaus, Hauptstrasse 28. **GPS**: n51,04861 e12,74500.

5 € 8 Ch € 2. 01/01-31/12.
Distance: 4km 4km.

Königstein 12H1

Panoramhotel Lilienstein, Ebenheit 7. **GPS**: n50,92505 e14,07546.

10 € 22 included € 5.
Location: Rural, simple, isolated, quiet. **Surface:** grassy/gravel.
Easter-15/11.
Distance: on the spot on the spot.
Remarks: Bread-service and breakfast buffet.

Leipzig 10E3

Reisemobilhafen Leipzig „Parc Fermé", Im Dölitzer Holz 20.
GPS: n51,28525 e12,38352.

30 € 11,50 € 1 Ch (12x)€ 3,50/day free.
Location: Rural, comfortable, quiet. **Surface:** gravel/metalled.
01/01-31/12.
Distance: 5,5km 2,5km 100m Tram 850m.
Remarks: Can be reached without environmental: from the direction Goethesteig.

Leipzig 10E3

Stellplatz Melinenburg, Stöhrerstraße 3.
GPS: n51,36648 e12,42717.

20 € 10, 2 pers.incl, extra pers € 1, dog € 1 € 1 € 1 Ch€ 1 (8x)€ 2/day. **Location:** Urban, comfortable, central, quiet.
Surface: concrete. 01/01-31/12.
Distance: 4,5km 1,2km 200m.
Remarks: Bread-service, outside environmental zone.

Löbau 38A3

Am Löbauer Berg, Beethovenstraße. **GPS**: n51,09508 e14,68088.

3 free (3x)against paymentkWh. **Location:** Rural, simple, isolated, quiet. **Surface:** grasstiles/metalled. 01/01-31/12.
Distance: 1km.

Lohsa 10H3

Dreiweibern See, Am strand Weißkollm 1.
GPS: n51,40782 e14,40008.

DE

14 € 10 € 1/80liter Ch (14x) WC included.
Location: Rural, comfortable, isolated, quiet.
Surface: grasstiles/grassy. 01/01-31/12.
Distance: 1,5km on the spot Imbiss on the spot.

S Marienberg 12G2
Ratsseite-Wiesenweg, Pobershau. **GPS**: n50,63250 e13,20896.
10 € 3 + € 1/pp tourist tax € 1 € 1. 01/04-31/10.
Distance: Marienberg 5km 200m.

S Marienberg 12G2
Tourismuszentrum Rätzteich, Gelobtland 27c.
GPS: n50,62417 e13,17861.

4 € 3 € 1 € 1 Ch € 1 € 1.
Surface: metalled. 01/01-31/12.
Distance: 5km on the spot 500m 5km on the spot on the spot 3km on the spot.
Remarks: Recreation area.

S Marienberg 12G2
Drei Brüder Höhe. **GPS**: n50,65660 e13,12437.
10 € 6/pp WC included. **Location:** Isolated.
01/04-31/10.
Distance: on the spot.

S Meissen 10G3
Wellenspiel, Berghausstraße 2. **GPS**: n51,17444 e13,49861.
19 € 5 € 2/day. **Location:** Rural, simple, quiet.
Surface: grassy/metalled. 01/01-31/12.
Distance: 900m.
Remarks: At swimming pool, caution key € 20.

Meissen 10G3
An der Elbe, Hochuferstraße. **GPS**: n51,16806 e13,47361.

20 € 5. **Location:** Urban, simple, central.
Surface: metalled. 01/01-31/12.
Distance: 800m on the spot 800m 300m on the spot.

S Neustadt in Sachsen 12H1
Mariba, Götzingerstraße 12. **GPS**: n51,02465 e14,20893.
3 free € 5. **Location:** Urban. **Surface:** concrete.
01/01-31/12.
Distance: on the spot 300m 600m on the spot.
Remarks: At paradise pool, max. 2 days.

S Neustadt in Sachsen 12H1
Waldbad Polenz, Flämmigtweg 3. **GPS**: n51,01964 e14,17960.
10 € 7,50/night € 2 € 2. **Location:** Rural. **Surface:** grassy.
01/01-31/12.
Distance: 800m.
Remarks: Check in and pay at kiosk, swimming pool.

S Oberwiesenthal 12F2
OTG Tennishalle, Vierenstrasse 11a. **GPS**: n50,42722 e12,96944.

20 € 18, 01/11-31/03 € 25, tourist tax excl Ch WC included
€ 1. **Location:** Urban. **Surface:** metalled.
01/01-31/12.
Distance: 1km on the spot 1,5km 250m.
Remarks: At sports centre, check in at reception tennishall < 22h, bread-service.

Oderwitz 38A3
Rodelpark Oberoderwitz, Spitzbergstraße 4a.
GPS: n50,96528 e14,70111.

5 free. **Location:** Rural, simple, isolated, quiet.
Surface: gravel/metalled. 01/01-31/12.
Distance: 600m on the spot.

S Pirna 12H1
Schloßpark Pirna, Schloßpark 13a. **GPS**: n50,95998 e13,95232.

8 € 12 Ch included € 1/kWh.
Location: Quiet. **Surface:** metalled. 01/01-31/12.
Distance: 2,5km 500m.

Pirna 12H1
Elbeparkplatz, Hauptplatz 14. **GPS**: n50,96654 e13,93775.

15 free. **Surface:** asphalted. 01/01-31/12.
Distance: 650m on the spot 350m on the spot.
Remarks: Along the river Elbe, max. 24h.

S Seiffen 12G1
Berghof, Kurhausstrasse 36. **GPS**: n50,64605 e13,48114.

20 guests free Ch against payment free.
Location: Rural. **Surface:** asphalted. 01/03-30/11.
Distance: 2,5km on the spot 300m.
Remarks: Bread-service.

S Seiffen 12G1
Waldgasthof Bad Einsiedel, Badstraße 1. **GPS**: n50,64669 e13,48651.
20 € 10, 2 pers.incl. + tourist tax € 2 Ch included.
Location: Rural. **Surface:** grassy. 01/01-31/12 Tue.
Distance: 2,5km on the spot.

S Struppen 12H1
Camping-Stellplatz Struppen, Kirchberg 20.
GPS: n50,93814 e14,01307.

30 € 10, 18/03-05/11 € 13 + tourist tax € 0,75/pp € 1/100liter Ch (30x) € 0,60/kWh € 1 € 3/3.
Location: Luxurious. **Surface:** grassy/metalled. 01/01-31/12.
Distance: 500m 500m.

Weißwasser 10H2
Am Tierpark, Teichstraße 56. **GPS**: n51,51205 e14,63665.

10 free. **Location:** Urban, simple, central. **Surface:** metalled.
01/01-31/12.
Distance: 500m on the spot 500m 500m on the spot.

S Zittau 38A3
Zittau Am Dreiländereck, Brückenstrasse 23.
GPS: n50,89457 e14,82143.

100 € 7 € 1/10minutes Ch (32x) € 1/6h WC.
Location: Urban, comfortable, central, quiet.
Surface: grassy. 01/01-31/12.
Distance: 1,5km 200m 100m on the spot.
Remarks: Three Countries' Corner Germany-Czech Republic-Poland.

S Zwota 12F2
Natur Camping Platz, Merkneukirchner Strasse 79.
GPS: n50,35111 e12,38111.

40 € 15 € 1,50 € 1 Ch (16x) WC included.
Location: Rural. **Surface:** grassy. 01/01-31/12.
Distance: Klingenthal 6km 6km.

North Rhine Westphalia

S Aachen 11E2
Aachen-Camping, Branderhofer Weg 11.
GPS: n50,76111 e6,10306.

DE

46 € 17 Ch WC € 1 included. Location: Urban, luxurious, central, quiet. **Surface:** metalled. 01/01-31/12.
Distance: 2,3km 800m 800m 300m.
Remarks: Baker 8.30-09.00.

S Ahaus 9F2

Am Aquahaus, Vredener Dyk. **GPS:** n52,07778 e6,98361.

7 free € 0,50/40liter Ch (8x)€ 0,50/kWh,16Amp WC.
Location: Rural, simple, isolated. **Surface:** metalled.
01/01-31/12.
Distance: 2km 1,5km on the spot.
Remarks: Max. 3 nights.

S Ahaus 9F2

Kirmesplatz, Schlossstrasse. **GPS:** n52,07450 e7,00299.

10 free € 0,50/80liter Ch (6x)€ 0,50,16Amp WC.
Location: Rural, simple, isolated. **Surface:** metalled.
01/01-31/12 during event.
Distance: on the spot 600m 600m.
Remarks: Parking centre, max. 3 nights.

S Ahlen 9G3

Parkbad Ahlen, Dolbergerstrasse 66. **GPS:** n51,75559 e7,89694.

4 € 8/24h Ch included. **Location:** Rural, comfortable, quiet. **Surface:** metalled. 01/01-31/12.
Distance: centre 300m 100m 300m on the spot on the spot.
Remarks: Max. 3 nights, caution key service € 10, 50% discount at swimming pool.

S Alpen 9E3

Reisemobilstellplatz An der Motte, Burgstrasse 66.
GPS: n51,57985 e6,51846.

11 € 7,50 Ch included.
Location: Rural, comfortable. **Surface:** gravel. 01/01-31/12.
Distance: 500m 2,5km 700m 500m.
Remarks: At tennis-courts.

S Altena 11G1

Sauerlandhalle Pragpaul, Hermann Vossstrasse 14.
GPS: n51,30861 e7,66056.

8 free € 1 € 1 Ch (6x)€ 1/kWh. **Location:** Rural, simple, quiet. **Surface:** asphalted/gravel. 01/01-31/12.
Distance: 2km 10km nearby 2km on the spot on the spot.

S Altenbeken 10A3

Landhaus Friedenstal, Hüttenstrasse 42. **GPS:** n51,75992 e8,95111.

5 € 5 (5x)€ 2,50/24h WC on demand,at restaurant.
Location: Simple, central. **Surface:** grassy/gravel.
01/01-31/12.
Distance: 200m on the spot 200m.

S Altenberge 9G2

Sportpark Grosseberg, Sportzentrum. **GPS:** n52,05528 e7,47056.

15 free € 0,50/60liter Ch. **Location:** Rural, isolated, quiet.
Surface: metalled. 01/01-31/12 water disconnected in winter.
Distance: 1,6km nearby 1,5km.
Remarks: Parking sports centre.

Arnsberg 9H3

An der Schlacht. **GPS:** n51,40174 e8,06574.
4 free. **Location:** Simple. **Surface:** gravel. 01/01-31/12.
Distance: 3,3km Lidl 50m.

Arnsberg 9H3

Wohnmobilstandort Neheim Jahnallee, Jahnallee 38, Neheim.
GPS: n51,44855 e7,95105.
free. 01/01-31/12.
Distance: city centre 1km on the spot 3km.

Ascheberg 9G3

Appelhof, Appelhofstraße. **GPS:** n51,79003 e7,61902.

4 free. **Location:** Rural, simple, central, quiet.
Surface: metalled. 01/01-31/12.
Distance: on the spot on the spot on the spot.

S Ascheberg 9G3

Gasthaus Eickholt, Frieport 22, Davensberg. **GPS:** n51,82619 e7,59391.

6 € 5, free with a meal € 3/24h WC free.
Location: Simple. **Surface:** grassy. 01/01-31/12 Mo.
Distance: 800m 1km on the spot 1km 800m on the spot.
Remarks: Swingolf.

S Attendorn 11G1

Atta Höhle, Finnentroper Straße 39. **GPS:** n51,12489 e7,91421.
6 € 7,50 Ch included.
Surface: metalled. 01/01-31/12.
Distance: 500m 600m Lidl 400m 600m.
Remarks: Parking at the caves.

S Bad Berleburg 11H1

Bismarckstraße. **GPS:** n51,04986 e8,39406.
3 free € 2/80liter Ch € 1/6h.
Surface: metalled. 01/01-31/12.
Distance: 500m 500m.

S Bad Berleburg 11H1

Hotel-Restaurant Erholung - Laibach, Auf dem Laibach 1.
GPS: n51,06776 e8,44527.

5 free with a meal (1x)€ 5/day WC.
Surface: asphalted. 01/01-31/12.
Distance: 5km on the spot 5km on the spot on the spot on the spot 1,5km.

S Bad Berleburg 11H1

Pension-Bauernladen Schmelzhütte, K52 Hoheleye.
GPS: n51,13874 e8,45742.

6 € 10 Ch € 2.
Surface: asphalted. 01/01-31/12 Mo.
Distance: 1km on the spot 1km.
Remarks: Bread-service.

Bad Driburg 10A3

Sachsenklause, Westenfeldmark 6. **GPS:** n51,73118 e9,00646.
5 free. **Location:** Rural. **Surface:** metalled. 01/01-31/12.
Distance: 6km on the spot 6km.

S Bad Driburg 10A3

P Driburg Therme, Georg-Nave-Strasse 24.
GPS: n51,74194 e9,02542.

15 € 7 + tourist tax € 2,60/pp Ch (10x)€ 3/24h WC.
Location: Rural, simple, quiet. **Surface:** asphalted.

DE

01/01-31/12.
Distance: 1km on the spot 1km on the spot on the spot on the spot.
Remarks: Max. 7m, caution € 10, key electricity at pay-desk, discount on access terme.

S Bad Laasphe 11H1
Mühlenstrasse. **GPS:** n50,92412 e8,41146.

7 € 9/24h € 0,50/80liter Ch (6x)€ 0,50/kWh.
Surface: asphalted. 01/01-31/12.
Distance: 500m 500m 500m.
Remarks: Parking at town hall.

S Bad Laasphe 11H1
Hotel Jagdhof Glashütte, Glashütterstrasse 20, Volkholz.
GPS: n50,92008 e8,28070.

6 € 13,80, guests free WC.
Location: Rural. **Surface:** grassy. 01/01-31/12 23-24/12.
Distance: 4km on the spot on the spot 4km 1,5km.

Bad Laasphe 11H1
Restaurant-Café Marburger, Hesselbacher Straße 21.
GPS: n50,88558 e8,36338.
6 guests free. 01/01-31/12 Mo.
Distance: on the spot.

S Bad Lippspringe 10A3
Arminiuspark, Burgstraße 10. **GPS:** n51,78124 e8,82447.

11 € 6,50 Ch.
Location: Urban, quiet. **Surface:** metalled. 01/01-31/12.
Distance: 300m 350m on the spot on the spot.
Remarks: Pay at tourist office.

S Bad Münstereifel 11F2
Wohnmobilpark Bad Münstereifel, Dr.-Greve-Straße 16.
GPS: n50,54600 e6,76514.

26 € 7, tourist tax € 1/pp € 1/100liter € 1 Ch (30x)included WC € 1,80.
Location: Rural, comfortable, quiet. **Surface:** grassy/metalled.
01/01-31/12.
Distance: 350m on the spot 100m.
Remarks: Pay and coins at swimming pool, 20% discount pool.

Bad Oeynhausen 9H2
Südbahnstraße/Detmolder Straße. **GPS:** n52,19680 e8,80038.
3 free. **Surface:** asphalted. 01/01-31/12.
Remarks: Max. 2 days.

Bad Oeynhausen 9H2
Siekmeiers Hof, Volmerdingsener strasse 111.
GPS: n52,24679 e8,78394.

10 guests free. **Location:** Urban, quiet. **Surface:** gravel.
01/01-31/12 Mon, Tue.
Distance: on the spot on the spot 1km.

S Bad Salzuflen 9H2
Wohnmobil-Park Flachsheide, Forsthausweg.
GPS: n52,09868 e8,74569.

25 € 7, tourist tax € 2,90/pp Ch WC included.
Location: Rural, quiet. 01/01-31/12.
Distance: 1,5km 5,5km on the spot 500m 1,5km free.

S Bad Sassendorf 9H3
Kurcamping Rumkerhof, Weslarnerstrasse 30.
GPS: n51,59581 e8,17909.

90 € 9, tourist tax excl Ch (93x)€ 0,50/kWh included.
Surface: gravel. 01/01-31/12.
Distance: 1,3km 1,3km.
Remarks: Waste dump € 0,50, bread-service.

S Bad Waldliesborn 9H3
Wohnmobilpoint, Quellenstraße. **GPS:** n51,71759 e8,33587.

10 € 4,40 + € 7,55/pp € 2/100liter Ch (8x)€ 2/24h.
Location: Rural, quiet. **Surface:** gravel. 01/01-31/12.
Distance: 400m 200m 400m 400m.
Remarks: Discount on access terme.

S Bad Westernkotten 9H3
Wohnmobilplatz An den Sole-Thermen, Mühlenweg 1.
GPS: n51,63126 e8,35195.

46 € 8, tourist tax € 2/pp € 1/100liter Ch € 0,50/kWh.
Surface: grassy. 01/01-31/12.
Distance: 600m 800m bakery 300m.
Remarks: Bread-service.

S Bad Wünnenberg 9H3
Wohnmobilhafen, In den Erlen. **GPS:** n51,52058 e8,70133.

12 € 5 € 1/100liter Ch (12x)€ 1/24h.
Location: Urban, central.
Surface: gravel. 01/01-31/12.
Distance: 100m 400m 100m 400m on the spot on the spot.

S Balve 11G1
Am Hallenbad, In der Murmke 9. **GPS:** n51,32729 e7,86920.

3 free € 1/80liter Ch € 1/kWh.
Location: Urban, simple. **Surface:** metalled. 01/01-31/12.
Distance: 600m 600m 600m on the spot on the spot.

S Balve 11G1
Haus Recke Hönnetal, Binolen 1. **GPS:** n51,37037 e7,86108.
3 € 10, guests free Ch. 01/01-31/12.
Distance: on the spot on the spot.

S Barntrup 10A2
Freibad Barntrup, Badeanstaltsweg. **GPS:** n51,98790 e9,10990.

5 € 6 € 1/100liter Ch € 1/kWh.
Location: Rural, simple. **Surface:** asphalted. 01/01-31/12.
Distance: 450m 450m 450m 450m.
Remarks: To be paid at campsite Teutoburger Wald.

S Barntrup 10A2
Ferienpark Teutoburger Wald, Badeanstaltsweg 4.
GPS: n51,98768 e9,11027.

DE

9 € 15, tourist tax € 1/pp, dog € 2,25 Ch WC € 5/5 included. **Location:** Rural, luxurious, quiet.
Surface: grassy/metalled. 01/04-31/10.
Distance: 450m 450m 450m 450m on the spot on the spot.

S Beckum 9G3

Am Hallenbad, Paterweg 4. **GPS**: n51,75129 e8,03585.

3 free € 0,50/100liter Ch (2x)€ 0,50/kWh.
Location: Urban, simple, noisy. **Surface:** metalled.
01/01-31/12.
Distance: 1km 4km 1km 1km.

S Bedburg-Hau 9E3

Womo-Moyland, Moyländer Allee 3a, Moyland.
GPS: n51,75562 e6,24381.

50 € 7 € 0,50/100liter Ch (40x)€ 3/24h included.
Location: Rural, comfortable, isolated, quiet. **Surface:** forest soil.
01/01-31/12.
Distance: Kleve 8km 2,5km 300m on the spot.
Remarks: Golf court 500m, Schloss Moyland 300m.

Tourist information Bedburg-Hau:
Schloß Moyland, Am Schloss 4. Castle. Tue-Fri 11-18h, Sa-Su 10-18h, 01/04-30/09 Tue-Su 11-17h. Mon.

Bergheim 11F1

Stellplatz Paffendorf, Königsstrasse/Kastanienallee.
GPS: n50,96389 e6,61194.

8 free. **Location:** Rural, simple, quiet. **Surface:** asphalted.
01/01-31/12.
Distance: Bergheim 2km 2,3km 300m 500m.
Remarks: Max. 2 days, castle Paffendorf 100m.

S Bergkamen 9G3

Wohnmobilhafen Marina Rünthe, Hafenweg, Rünthe.
GPS: n51,64106 e7,64309.

18 € 8/24h € 1/80liter Ch (18x)€ 0,50/kWh.
Location: Rural, quiet. **Surface:** grassy/gravel. 01/01-31/12.
Distance: 500m 3,8km 1km.
Remarks: Max. 3 days, only exact change.

Bergkamen 9G3

Freizeitzentrum Im Häupen, Häupenweg 29.
GPS: n51,61300 e7,63075.

5 free. **Location:** Rural, simple, central. **Surface:** asphalted.
01/01-31/12.
Distance: 500m 3,4km 500m 500m.
Remarks: Max. 72h.

Bestwig 9H3

Besucherbergwerk, Ziegelwiese, Ramsbeck.
GPS: n51,31821 e8,40318.

10 free. **Location:** Simple. **Surface:** metalled.
01/01-31/12.
Distance: 800m.

Bestwig 9H3

Ludwigstrasse. **GPS**: n51,36064 e8,40165.

4 free. **Location:** Simple. **Surface:** metalled.
01/01-31/12.
Distance: on the spot 300m 200m.

S Beverungen 10A3

Wohnmobilhafen Weser, Am Hakel. **GPS**: n51,66167 e9,37639.

10 free € 1/100liter Ch€ 1 (12x)€ 1/6h.
Location: Urban, simple. **Surface:** grassy/metalled.
01/01-31/12 service: 01/11-01/03.
Distance: on the spot on the spot on the spot on the spot on the spot.
Remarks: Next to Festplatz.

Beverungen 10A3

Schützenstrasse. **GPS**: n51,66201 e9,37548.
10 free. **Surface:** metalled. 01/01-31/12.
Distance: on the spot 200m 600m on the spot.
Remarks: Along river, max. 72h.

S Beverungen 10A3

Alte Linde, Würrigser Straße 4. **GPS**: n51,64530 e9,41734.
8 € 10 included € 2/24h. **Surface:** grassy.
01/01-31/12.
Distance: 5km on the spot Weserradweg R 99 200m.
Remarks: Discount at restaurant.

S Bielefeld 9H2

Am Johannisberg, Dornbergerstrasse. **GPS**: n52,02270 e8,51155.

10 € 5/24h € 0,50/40liter Ch (10x)€ 1/2kWh.
Location: Rural, comfortable, quiet. **Surface:** metalled.
01/01-31/12.
Distance: 2km Imbiss 2km 2km.
Remarks: Max. 5 days.

S Billerbeck 9F2

Am Freibad, Osterwickerstrasse. **GPS**: n51,97928 e7,28190.

11 € 5 € 1/100liter Ch (8x)€ 1/2kWh,16Amp.
Location: Urban, simple. **Surface:** gravel. 01/01-31/12.
Distance: 500m 500m.
Remarks: At swimming pool.

S Billerbeck 9F2

Am Konzert Theater, Osterwicker Straße 39.
GPS: n51,95322 e7,17390.

12 free € 1/100liter Chfree (12x)€ 1/2kWh € 1.
Location: Rural, simple. **Surface:** gravel/metalled.
01/01-31/12.
Distance: 800m 800m 100m.

S Blankenheim 11F2

An der Weiherhalle, Koblenzerstrasse. **GPS**: n50,43499 e6,65439.

15 € 5/24h € 1/80liter Ch (12x)€ 2/10h.
Location: Rural, simple. **Surface:** metalled.
01/01-31/12.
Distance: 150m.

S Bocholt 9F3

WoMo Park am Aasee, Uhlandstraße 39.
GPS: n51,83496 e6,63146.

50 € 6 € 0,50/50liter Ch€ 0,50 (44x)€ 0,50/kWh WC€ 0,50 € 1 € 3,50/2,50 € 1/24h. **Location:** Rural, comfortable, noisy.

DE

Surface: metalled. 01/01-31/12.
Distance: 800m 300m 300m 300m 300m 200m on the spot on the spot.
Remarks: Service passerby € 2.

S Bocholt 9F3

Inselbad Bahia, Hemdenerweg 169. **GPS**: n51,86265 e6,61002.

10 free € 1/72liter € 1 Ch€ 1.
Location: Rural, simple, quiet. **Surface:** grasstiles.
01/01-31/12.
Distance: 2,5km 450m 1km on the spot.
Remarks: Max. 72h, coins at swimming pool, first coin € 3, next € 0,50.

Bocholt 9F3

Euregio-Gymnasium, Unter den Eichen, Blücherstrasse.
GPS: n51,84884 e6,63700.

10 free. **Location:** Urban, simple, noisy. **Surface:** metalled.
01/01-31/12.
Distance: 1km 700m on the spot.
Remarks: Parking 'Stadtswald', max. 3 nights.

Tourist information Bocholt:
Rathaus - Gasthausplatz. Thu-evening.

Bonn 11F2

An der Rheinaue, Ludwig-Erhard-Allee. **GPS**: n50,70981 e7,13904.
18 free. **Surface:** asphalted. 01/01-31/12 06/05-07/05.
Distance: centre 4km A565 4,6km 300m 300m line 66 > Bonn centre.

S Borken 9F3

Reisemobilstellplatz am Aquarius-Freizeitbad, Parkstraße.
GPS: n51,83618 e6,86074.

15 € 5/night included Ch € 1/24h.
Location: Rural, simple. **Surface:** grasstiles.
01/01-31/12.
Distance: 1km 4km 1km 800m 500m on the spot on the spot.
Remarks: Parking swimming pool, max. 72h.

Borken 9F3

Festplatz Weseke, Borkenwirther strasse, Weseke.
GPS: n51,90529 e6,85210.

10 free. **Location:** Rural, simple. **Surface:** metalled.
01/01-31/12.

Distance: 500m 500m 500m.
Remarks: Max. 3 nights.

Borken 9F3

Schlossklinik Pröbsting, Pröbstinger Allee.
GPS: n51,83861 e6,80556.

10 free. **Location:** Rural, noisy. **Surface:** metalled.
01/01-31/12.
Distance: Badesee 150m 300m on the spot on the spot.

Borken 9F3

Wasserburg Gemen, Coesfelderstrasse, Gemen.
GPS: n51,86172 e6,86909.

5 free. **Location:** Rural, simple. **Surface:** metalled.
01/01-31/12.
Distance: 1km 500m 500m 1km 1km.
Remarks: Parking sports park, max. 3 nights.

S Borken 9F3

Gestüt Forellenhof Wolter, Zum Homborn 9.
GPS: n51,86245 e6,89797.

15 € 10 Ch (7x)included.
Location: Rural. **Surface:** gravel. 01/01-31/12.
Distance: Borken 3,5km fish pond on the spot.
Remarks: Check in at Gaststätte, € 5 euro discount coupon.

Bottrop 9F3

Hans-Böckler-Straße 165. **GPS**: n51,52966 e6,90404.

5 free. **Location:** Rural, simple, quiet. **Surface:** metalled.
01/01-31/12.
Distance: 2km 1km 3km 400m.
Remarks: At cemetery.

Bottrop 9F3

Movie Park, Kirchhellen, Warner Allee 1.
GPS: n51,62400 e6,97096.

50 € 6/night. **Location:** Rural. **Surface:** metalled.
01/04-31/10.
Distance: 2,7km 100m 2,7km.

Tourist information Bottrop:
Alpincenter, Prosperstrasse. Indoor ski centre.
9-24h. day ticket from € 49, <18h € 25.
Warner Bros Movie World, Kirchhellen. Attractions park concerning the film.

S Brakel/Bellersen 10A3

Wohnmobilhafen Mühlengrund, Meinolfussstrasse 6.
GPS: n51,77217 e9,18804.

23 € 9,50 € 0,50 Ch (23x)included. **Location:** Rural, comfortable, isolated. **Surface:** grasstiles. 01/01-31/12.
Distance: 800m 400m 800m 800m on the spot on the spot.

Brakel/Bellersen 10A3

P9, Bredenweg. **GPS**: n51,71927 e9,18395.
3 free. **Surface:** gravel/metalled. 01/01-31/12.
Distance: 400m 300m 800m.

Bruchhausen 10A3

Bruchhäuserstrasse. **GPS**: n51,70714 e9,29192.

4 free. **Location:** Rural, simple. **Surface:** grassy/gravel.
01/01-31/12.
Distance: 200m 200m 200m.

S Brüggen 11E1

Wohnmobilhafen Brüggen, Bornerstraße 48.
GPS: n51,24264 e6,18955.

30 € 4 Chincluded € 2/24h.
Surface: gravel. 01/01-31/12.
Distance: 500m 100m 50m 50m.
Remarks: Behind Aldi-süd.

S Brüggen 11E1

Freizeitplatz Brachter Wald, St.-Barbara-Straße 40–42, Bracht.
GPS: n51,25713 e6,17022.

DE

14 € 9, 2 pers.incl Ch € 2/day WC included € 1.
Surface: grasstiles. 01/01-31/12.
Distance: 2km on the spot on the spot.

Brühl 11F2

Phantasialand P1, Berggeiststrasse 31-41.
GPS: n50,79919 e6,87875.

10 € 12,50/night WC .
Location: Comfortable, quiet. **Surface:** metalled.
04/04-31/10.
Distance: 100m on the spot.

Tourist information Brühl:
Phantasialand. Large amusement park.
19/03-01/11 9-18h, winter changing visiting hours.

Bünde 9H2

Stadthallen, Steinmeisterstrasse. **GPS**: n52,19869 e8,58986.

5 free. **Location:** Urban, simple. **Surface:** metalled.
01/01-31/12.
Distance: 50m 50m 50m.
Remarks: Max. 72h.

Büren 9H3

Wohnmobilparkplatz Netz - Bürener Land, Fürstenberger Strasse.
GPS: n51,54969 e8,56356.

8 free € 1/10minutes Ch € 1/8h.
Location: Urban, simple. 01/01-31/12.
Distance: on the spot 500m 200m.
Remarks: Parking nearby swimming pool, coins at petrol station.

Büren 9H3

Dorfhalle, Niederhagen, Wewelsburg. **GPS**: n51,60947 e8,65544.
free. 01/01-31/12.
Distance: 600m.

Büren 9H3

Ringelsteiner Wald, Eichenweg, Ringelstein.
GPS: n51,50097 e8,56999.
free. 01/01-31/12.
Distance: 1km 1km on the spot.

Coesfeld 9F2

Brauhaus Stephanus, Overhagenweg 1. **GPS**: n51,93719 e7,15617.

4 guests free . **Location:** Urban, simple, noisy. **Surface:** metalled.
01/01-31/12.
Distance: on the spot 100m on the spot.

Dahlem 11E3

Flugplatz Dahlemer Binz, Dahlemer Binz.
GPS: n50,40663 e6,53700.

3 free € 1/80liter Ch. **Location:** Rural, simple.
Surface: asphalted. 01/01-31/12.
Distance: on the spot.
Remarks: Airport Dahlemer Binz.

Dahlem 11E3

Wohnmobilstellplatz Kronenburger See, Seeuferstrasse 6.
GPS: n50,35785 e6,46989.

12 € 10/24h € 1/120liter Ch (12x)included. **Location:** Rural, simple, quiet. **Surface:** grassy.
01/01-31/12.
Remarks: At artificial lake.

Dinslaken 9F3

Am Rotbachsee, Am Freibad. **GPS**: n51,56707 e6,77807.

10 free. **Location:** Rural, simple. **Surface:** sand.
01/01-31/12.
Distance: 100m 100m 100m on the spot on the spot.

Dormagen 11F1

Parkplatz Flügeldeich, Herrenweg, Feste Zons.
GPS: n51,12553 e6,85001.

3 € 5 € 0,50/kWh. **Surface:** metalled. 01/01-31/12.
Distance: 400m on the spot on the spot 100m 500m.
Remarks: Near the Rhine river, max. 3 days.

Dorsten 9F3

Reisemobilhafen An der Lippe, Zur Lippe.
GPS: n51,66550 e6,96744.

38 € 8/24h € 1/10minutes Ch (34x)€ 1/8h € 2.
Location: Urban, central, quiet. **Surface:** metalled/sand.
01/01-31/12.
Distance: 300m 300m 300m.
Remarks: Bread-service in summer period, charging point for electric bicycles.

Tourist information Dorsten:
Marler Str.. Flea market. 2nd Su of the month, 11-18h.

Dortmund 9G3

Mobil-Camp Wischlingen, Wischlinger Weg 50-61, Wischlingen.
GPS: n51,52001 e7,39868.

50 € 8, 2 pers.incl € 1/80liter Ch (30x)€ 0,50/kWh WC € 1. **Location:** Rural. **Surface:** asphalted. 01/01-31/12.
Distance: 1km 100m Rewe 1km 200m.
Remarks: Former tennis-court in recreation area.

Drensteinfurt 9G3

Am Erlbad, Im Erlfeld 2. **GPS**: n51,78972 e7,74778.

3 free Ch € 3/24h WC included € 3.
Location: Rural, simple, noisy. **Surface:** asphalted/metalled.
01/01-31/12 service: 01/09-30/04.
Distance: 800m 9km 800m.
Remarks: Max. 3 nights, max. 8M, check in at swimming pool, swimming pool incl.

Duisburg 9F3

Landschaftspark Duisburg-Nord, Emscherstraße 71, Meiderich.
GPS: n51,48163 e6,78490.

5 free € 1/100liter Ch € 0,50/time.
Location: Urban, simple. **Surface:** asphalted. 01/01-31/12.
Distance: 1,6km on the spot on the spot.

Dülmen 9F3

Reisemobilstellplatz Hüttendyk, Ecke Halterner Strasse.
GPS: n51,82606 e7,27228.

DE

8 free € 1/80liter Ch (8x)€ 2/8h. **Location:** Rural, simple. **Surface:** metalled. 01/01-31/12.
Distance: 500m 200m 100m.
Remarks: Max. 72h.

S **Dülmen** 9F3

Reisemobilstellplatz Kapellenweg, Kapellenweg.
GPS: n51,82331 e7,27945.

7 free Ch. **Location:** Rural, simple. **Surface:** metalled.
01/01-31/12.
Distance: 500m 600m on the spot on the spot.
Remarks: Max. 72h.

Dülmen 9F3

Reisemobilstellplatz Düb, Nordlandwehr 99.
GPS: n51,84408 e7,27300.

7 free. **Location:** Rural, simple. **Surface:** grasstiles/metalled.
01/01-31/12.
Distance: 2km 1km.
Remarks: Max. 72h.

Dülmen 9F3

Reisemobilstellplatz Hausdulmen, Sandstrasse.
GPS: n51,80707 e7,24746.

20 free. **Location:** Rural, simple, quiet. **Surface:** grassy.
01/01-31/12.
Distance: 2,5km 500m 400m on the spot.
Remarks: Max. 72h.

S **Düren** 11E2

IG Reisemobilhafen Düren, Rurstrasse 188. **GPS**: n50,80861 e6,46556.

20 € 7 Chincluded (18x)€ 2. **Location:** Rural, simple, quiet. **Surface:** gravel. 01/01-31/12.

Distance: 900m Bistro 100m Lidl 500m on the spot.
Remarks: Service passerby € 2.

Düsseldorf 11F1

P Rheinterasse/Tonhalle, Robert-Lehr-Ufer.
GPS: n51,23710 e6,77029.

30 € 2,20/h, max. € 12/24h. **Surface:** metalled. 01/01-31/12 spring fair. **Distance:** Old city centre 1km 50m 1,3km.

Tourist information Düsseldorf:
Tourist Info, Immermannstrasse, Gegenüber Station; Kö-Galerie/Finanzhaus, Berliner Alee; Burgplatz, Berliner Allee, www.duesseldorf-tourismus.de. Historical centre, important city of fashion, all large marks established in the Königsallee, Umweltzone: the green environmental badge is required.
During the Caravan Salon (by the end of August/beginning September) there is a large area for motorhomes available. Free shuttlebus to the exhibition and Old city centre. Also several events on the exhibition grounds.

S **Eckenhagen** 11G1

Rodener Festplatz, Rodener Platz. **GPS**: n50,98667 e7,69361.

5 free Ch. **Location:** Urban, simple, quiet.
Surface: asphalted/gravel. 01/01-31/12.
Distance: 200m 4km 300m 300m on the spot on the spot.
Remarks: Key service at Kurverwaltung.

Emmerich 9E3

Auf dem Eltenberg Hoch Elten, Luitgardisstraße.
GPS: n51,86559 e6,17265.

25 free. **Location:** Rural, simple. **Surface:** grassy.
01/01-31/12.
Distance: 1km 100m 1km on the spot.
Remarks: Service at marina.

Emmerich 9E3

P6, Kleiner Wall, Rheinpromenade. **GPS**: n51,83229 e6,23594.

5 free. **Location:** Urban, simple, central, noisy.
Surface: gravel. 15/03-01/11.
Distance: on the spot on the spot on the spot on the spot.

S **Emmerich** 9E3

Yachthafen, Fackeldeystrasse 15-65. **GPS**: n51,83693 e6,21948.

75 € 12 Ch (80x)4,. WC € 0,50 included.
Location: Rural, luxurious, isolated. **Surface:** grassy.
01/03-30/11.
Distance: 2,5km on the spot on the spot 1,5km on the spot on the spot.
Remarks: Arrival <22h, max. 9m.

S **Ennepetal** 11G1

Am Platsch, Mittelstraße 108. **GPS**: n51,29295 e7,37668.

4 € 3 included. **Surface:** gravel. 01/01-31/12.
Distance: 10,8km 5km 5km on the spot on the spot routes for nordic walking. **Remarks:** Check in at pay-desk of swimming pool, use sanitary only during opening hours swimming pool, on the spot: bistro, pool, sauna and golf court.

S **Ennepetal** 11G1

Firma Möller-Elektronic, Königstrasse 17, Oelkinghausen.
GPS: n51,29086 e7,32050.

5 free Ch € 3. **Location:** Urban, simple, quiet.
Surface: metalled. 01/01-31/12.
Distance: 2km 1km 200m on the spot on the spot.

S **Ennigerloh** 9G3

Am Freibad 3. **GPS**: n51,83304 e8,01629.

2 free € 0,50/50liter Ch € 0,50/kWh.
Location: Rural, simple, noisy. **Surface:** metalled.
01/01-31/12.
Distance: 600m 600m 600m on the spot on the spot.

S **Erftstadt** 11F2

Mobilcamp am Ville-Express, Carl-Schurz-strasse 1a, Liblar.
GPS: n50,81781 e6,81986.

11 € 6 € 1/80liter Ch (11x)€ 0,50/kWh.

DE

Location: Urban, comfortable. **Surface:** metalled.
01/01-31/12.
Distance: 1km 4,4km 500m 200m 1km.

Erndtebrück 11H1

Pension Hofius, Hilchenbachterweg 2, Zinse.
GPS: n51,00599 e8,21224.

3 € 6/24h Ch included. 01/01-31/12.
Distance: 5km on the spot on the spot.
Remarks: Max. 8M.

Everswinkel 9G2

Vitus-Bad, Alverkirchenerstrasse 29. **GPS**: n51,92309 e7,83776.

3 free € 0,50/50liter Ch € 0,50/kWh.
Location: Rural, simple, noisy. **Surface:** metalled.
01/01-31/12.
Distance: 500m on the spot 100m on the spot 100-Schlösser-Route on the spot.
Remarks: Parking swimming pool.

Freudenberg (NRW) 11G1

P3, Lohmühle. **GPS**: n50,89625 e7,87636.

2 free. **Surface:** metalled. 01/01-31/12.
Distance: on the spot 100m 200m.
Remarks: Max. 3 days.

Gangelt 11E1

Rodebachtal, Am Freibad 13. **GPS**: n50,98583 e5,99806.

40 € 10 Ch € 0,40/kWh WC € 0,60/4minutes € 2,40.
Location: Rural, luxurious, quiet. **Surface:** metalled.
01/01-31/12.
Distance: on the spot on the spot on the spot 1,5km on the spot on the spot.
Remarks: Arrival <18h, caution key € 10.

Geldern 9E3

Am Holländer See, Am Holländer See 19.
GPS: n51,51131 e6,32867.

45 € 8/24h, 3 days € 19 € 1/90liter Ch (44x)€ 0,50/kWh.
Location: Comfortable, quiet. **Surface:** grassy/metalled.
01/01-31/12.
Distance: 1km 1km 1km on the spot.
Remarks: Parking centre, bread-service (weekend).

Geldern 9E3

Reisemobilhafen Am Freibad, Am Freibad 16, Walbeck.
GPS: n51,49461 e6,22666.

50 € 8/24h € 1/80liter Ch (36x)€ 0,50/kWh.
Surface: grassy/sand. 01/01-31/12.
Distance: city centre Walbeck 1km, city centre Geldern 6km 1km 1km.
Remarks: At swimming pool.

Geldern 9E3

Reisemobilstellplatz Am Sportplatz, Hülspassweg 20, Veert.
GPS: n51,52960 e6,30347.

30 free. **Surface:** gravel. 01/01-31/12.
Distance: city centre Veert 200m, city centre Geldern 2km 500m.
Remarks: Parking at sports park.

Geldern 9E3

Freizeit-Store Diepers, Liebligstrasse 33. **GPS**: n51,52971 e6,35456.
€ 1 € 1 Ch. 01/01-31/12, during opening hours.

Tourist information Geldern:
Internationaler Wettbewerb der strassenmaler und strassenmusikanten und -theatergruppen, Centrum. International street painting competition, street musicians and theater groups. beginning Sep.
Internationales Reisemobilfest. International festival for motorcaravanners with vast tourist program. Not necessary to book in advance,. last weekend April. free.

Gelsenkirchen 9F3

Stellplatz Nienhausen, Feldmarkstraße 201.
GPS: n51,50167 e7,06333.

20 € 7, 2 pers.incl. € 1/90liter Ch € 1/2kWh € 3.
Location: Rural, central. **Surface:** metalled.
01/01-31/12.
Distance: 2,8km 3,2km 100m 2km Tram 700m.
Remarks: Bread-service.

Gladbeck 9F3

Freitzeitstätte Wittringer Wald, Bohmertstrasse 277.
GPS: n51,55912 e6,98403.

25 free voluntary contribution Ch. **Location:** Rural, simple, quiet. **Surface:** grasstiles/grassy. 01/01-31/12.
Distance: 2km 1km 200m 1km.
Remarks: Green zone: environmental badge obligatory, Wasserschloß Wittringen 450m.

Goch 9E3

Friedensplatz, Thielenstrasse. **GPS**: n51,67556 e6,16639.

70 € 5/24h € 1/100liter Ch (60x)€ 0,50/kWh.
Location: Urban, comfortable, quiet. **Surface:** grassy.
01/01-31/12.
Distance: 700m on the spot 700m 700m 100m.
Remarks: Along the Niers river.

Goch 9E3

Reisemobilstellplatz GochNess, Kranenburger Strasse 20, Kessel.
GPS: n51,70291 e6,08915.

6 free. **Location:** Rural, simple, isolated, quiet.
Surface: grassy.
01/01-31/12.
Distance: 1km 1km 1km.
Remarks: At swimming pool.

Tourist information Goch:
Pilgrimage for motorhomes. last weekend Jun.
Museumscafé Edison, Museum Goch. Collection of gramophones. Su 15-17h.
Herrensitz-Route. Cycle route along the Meuse and the Niers, available at Kultourbühne Goch.
€ 7,90.

Grefrath 11E1

Eissportzentrum Grefrath, Stadionstrasse. **GPS**: n51,34889 e6,33972.

50 free. **Surface:** grasstiles.
01/01-31/12.
Distance: 2km 500m 300m 2km.
Remarks: Niederrheinisches Freilichtmuseum, Open air museum 650m.

Greven 9G2

Reisemobilhafen Camp Marina, Fuestruperstrasse 37, Fuestrup.
GPS: n52,04449 e7,68328.

DE

90 € 11 € 0,50/50liter Ch € 2,50 WC € 1 € 3/2,50.
Location: Comfortable. **Surface:** grassy.
01/01-31/12.
Distance: on the spot Restaurant/Biergarten 3km on the spot on the spot.
Remarks: Marina at canal, bread-service, shopping service.

Gronau 9F2

Erholungsgebiet Dreiländersee, Brechterweg.
GPS: n52,23716 e7,08006.

80 € 8/24, only exact change € 0,50/130liter Ch (32x) € 1/4h WC . **Location:** Rural, simple, isolated.
Surface: grassy/metalled. 01/01-31/12.
Distance: 3km 100m on the spot 200m 50m (camping) on the spot.
Remarks: Near the lake, max. 48h.

Haltern am See 9F3

Wohnmobilpark Haltern am See, Hullerner Straße 45-49.
GPS: n51,74186 e7,20179.

20 € 10/night € 1/100liter Ch (20x)€ 0,50/kWh WC € 1,50 included. **Location:** Rural, comfortable, central.
Surface: grasstiles. 01/01-31/12.
Distance: 1km 300m on the spot 1km 200m.
Remarks: At swimming pool, use sanitary only during opening hours swimming pool, discount at swimming pool.

Haltern am See 9F3

RMS ReisemobileSpezialist, Hellweg 252.
GPS: n51,75589 e7,20127.

4 € 7 € 1/70liter Ch € 3,50. **Location:** Rural, simple, isolated. **Surface:** grassy/gravel. 01/01-31/12.
Distance: Old city centre 1km 800m 800m.

Hamm 9G3

Freizeitpark Maximilian Park, Alter Grenzweg 2.
GPS: n51,68392 e7,88395.

10 free. **Location:** Rural, simple. **Surface:** grassy.
01/01-31/12.
Distance: 300m 300m 300m 200m on the spot on the spot.

Harsewinkel 9H2

Frei- und Hallenbad, Prozessionsweg 8. **GPS**: n51,96556 e8,21935.

6 free. **Location:** Rural, simple, quiet. **Surface:** grassy.
01/01-31/12.
Distance: 200m 100m 200m 200m on the spot.
Remarks: Parking next to swimming pool, max. 48h.

Hattingen 9F3

Roonstrasse. **GPS**: n51,40124 e7,18389.

2 € 4 € 1/80liter . **Location:** Urban, simple, quiet.
Surface: asphalted/metalled. 01/01-31/12.
Distance: 300m 5km 300m 300m.

Hattingen 9F3

Wohnmobilstellplatz Ruhrtal, Ruhrdeich 24.
GPS: n51,40839 e7,18091.

16 € 10/night € 1/90liter Ch (18x)€ 1/2kWh € 1/4minutes free. **Location:** Rural, comfortable, quiet.
Surface: gravel. 01/01-31/12.
Distance: 2,5km 5km on the spot on the spot 500m 1km.
Remarks: Along the Ruhr river, next to midget golf.

Hattingen 9F3

August-Bebel strasse. **GPS**: n51,39833 e7,18028.

2 € 3. **Location:** Urban, simple, central, noisy.
Surface: metalled. 01/01-31/12.
Distance: on the spot 5km on the spot on the spot on the spot.
Remarks: At shopping centre Carré.

Hattingen 9F3

Ruhrgasse, Bahnhofstrasse. **GPS**: n51,40083 e7,17676.

3 free. **Location:** Urban, simple, quiet. **Surface:** gravel.
01/01-31/12.
Distance: 500m 5km 500m 500m.
Remarks: Parking behind the Amtshäusern, only on Sa and Su.

Hattingen 9F3

Wanderparkplatz, Isenbergstrasse. **GPS**: n51,38969 e7,15340.

3 free. **Location:** Rural, simple. **Surface:** gravel.
Mo-Fri, 01/01-31/12.
Distance: 2km 5km 300m 1km on the spot on the spot on the spot.
Remarks: Parking along the Ruhr, max. 2 days.

Havixbeck 9G2

Am Freibad, Kardinal-von-Hartmann-Straße.
GPS: n51,97507 e7,42092.

8 free € 1/80liter Ch (8x)against payment WC.
Location: Simple, quiet. **Surface:** metalled. 01/01-31/12.
Distance: 1km 1km 800m 800m on the spot.
Remarks: Parking at swimming pool, small pitches.

Havixbeck 9G2

Klute's Historischem Brauhaus, Poppenbeck 28.
GPS: n51,98938 e7,39291.

15 guests free (8x)€ 5 . **Location:** Rural, simple, isolated. **Surface:** metalled. 01/01-31/12.
Distance: 2km on the spot 2km.

Heiligenhaus 11F1

Westfalenstrasse/Bahnhofstraße. **GPS**: n51,32853 e6,97327.
3 free .
Location: Simple. **Surface:** metalled. 01/01-31/12.
Distance: 200m 200m 200m 50m.

Heimbach 11E2

Wohnmobilhafen am Nationalpark-Tor, An der Laag 4.
GPS: n50,63683 e6,47265.

DE

19 € 7,50/24h, € 0,45/pp tourist tax € 1/100liter Ch (20x)€ 0,50/kWh.
Location: Rural, simple, noisy. **Surface:** gravel. 01/01-31/12.
Distance: 200m 100m on the spot.
Remarks: Nearby Regioshuttle Rurtallbahn.

S Heinsberg 11E1

Heinsberg am Lago, Fritz-Bauer-Strasse 3.
GPS: n51,07333 e6,09278.

44 P1 € 10/day, P2 € 10/2 days € 1/100liter Ch (31x)€ 0,50/kWh. **Location:** Rural, luxurious, quiet. **Surface:** grasstiles.
01/01-31/12.
Distance: 1km Bagger See on the spot 800m.

S Hellenthal 11E3

Europa-Wohnmobilhafen, Am Weissen Stein, Udenbreth, B265.
GPS: n50,40896 e6,37220.

28 € 10 € 2 Ch (28x)included. **Location:** Rural, simple.
Surface: metalled.
01/01-31/12.
Distance: on the spot on the spot.
Remarks: Service on campsite, winter sports area Hellenthal am Wald.

Hellenthal 11E3

Grenzlandhalle Hellenthal, Aachenerstrasse.
GPS: n50,49251 e6,43651.

15 free. **Location:** Rural, simple. **Surface:** grasstiles.
01/01-31/12.
Distance: 500m on the spot 200m.
Remarks: Service on campsite.

S Hellenthal 11E3

Breuerhof, Zum Wilsamtal 39, Udenbreth.
GPS: n50,41081 e6,38992.

2 € 10 Ch (2x). **Location:** Rural, comfortable, quiet.
Surface: metalled. 01/01-31/12.
Distance: 2km on the spot.
Remarks: Check in at nr. 35.

Tourist information Hellenthal:
Greifvogelstation, Wildfreigehege 1. Predatory bird station.
01/11-31/03 10-17h, 01/04-31/10 9-18h.

S Hemer 9G3

Wohnmobilstellplatz Hemer, Hönnetalstraße.
GPS: n51,37841 e7,77151.

20 € 2/8-20h € 1/100liter Ch€ 1 (12x)€ 0,50/kWh.
Location: Urban, comfortable, quiet. **Surface:** asphalted/grassy.
01/01-31/12.
Distance: 1km 6km 300m bakery 500m on the spot.

S Herford 9H2

H2O, Wiessenstrasse 90. **GPS:** n52,10750 e8,68534.

22 € 5 Ch
Location: Rural, comfortable. **Surface:** metalled. 01/01-31/12.
Distance: on the spot 2km 200m.
Remarks: At swimming pool.

Herford 9H2

Am Stadion, Dennewitzstrasse 15. **GPS:** n52,10474 e8,68931.

10 free. **Location:** Rural, simple. 01/01-31/12.
Distance: 2,5km 3km 350m 350m.

S Herscheid 11G1

Am Warmwasserfreibad, Unterdorfstraße.
GPS: n51,17567 e7,74368.

3 free € 1/10minutes Ch (4x)€ 1/8h.
Location: Rural, comfortable, quiet. **Surface:** gravel.
01/01-31/12.
Distance: 1,2km 10km 400m 650m on the spot.

S Hilchenbach 11H1

Hallenbad Dahlbruch, Bernhard-Weiss-Platz, Dahlbruch.
GPS: n50,97792 e8,05343.

3 free € 1/10minutes .
Surface: asphalted/metalled. 01/01-31/12.
Distance: 400m 300m 400m.
Remarks: Parking behind swimming pool, max. 48h, use sanitary only during opening hours swimming pool, against payment.

S Hilchenbach 11H1

Parkplatz P4, Rothenberger strasse, L728.
GPS: n50,99702 e8,11103.

3 free WC. **Surface:** metalled.
01/01-31/12.
Distance: 100m 200m 100m.
Remarks: Parking in front of shopping centre Gerberpark, max. 48h.

Hilchenbach 11H1

Bürgerhaus, Merklinghäuser weg, Müsen.
GPS: n50,99267 e8,04497.

3 free. **Surface:** asphalted. 01/01-31/12.
Distance: 8km 800m 600m.
Remarks: Max. 48h.

Hilchenbach 11H1

Gillerberg, Gillerbergstraße 28. **GPS:** n50,97175 e8,16130.
3 free. 01/01-31/12.
Distance: 9km on the spot.

S Hilchenbach 11H1

Landhotel Steubers Siebelnhof, Siebelnhoferstrasse, Vormwald.
GPS: n50,98658 e8,13173.
6 € 20,50, use sanitary facilities/swimming pool sauna incl WC included. 01/01-31/12.
Distance: on the spot.

S Hopsten 9G1

Dreifachturnhalle, Rüschendorfer strasse 4.
GPS: n52,38544 e7,60490.

6 free Chfree. **Location:** Rural, simple.
Surface: grassy/metalled. 01/01-31/12.
Distance: 100m 100m 100m on the spot on the spot.

DE

Remarks: Parking at gymnasium, max. 3 days.

S **Horn** 10A2

Wohnmobilhafen am Bad Meinberger Badehaus, Wällenweg, Bad Meinberg. **GPS**: n51,89818 e8,99249.

24 € 7,50 + € 2,60/pp tourist tax € 1/100liter € 0,50 Ch € 0,50/kWh WC € 2,50.
Location: Rural, quiet. **Surface:** grassy/metalled.
01/01-31/12.
Distance: 200m on the spot 200m 100m.
Remarks: Behind spa, bread-service, discount at swimming pool.

S **Hörstel** 9G2

Wohnmobilhafen Riesenbeck, Postdamm-Lazarusbrücke. **GPS**: n52,25574 e7,63387.

18 € 5/24h € 1/2kWh. **Location:** Rural, comfortable, central, noisy. **Surface:** grassy/gravel. 01/01-31/12.
Distance: 700m on the spot on the spot 300m on the spot 100-Schlösser-Route on the spot.
Remarks: Max. 3 nights.

S **Hövelhof** 9H2

P Bahnhof, Westfalenstrasse. **GPS**: n51,82417 e8,66099.

6 free free (6x)€ 1/kWh.
Location: Urban. **Surface:** gravel. 01/01-31/12.
Distance: 500m 4,2km 500m 700m 50m on the spot on the spot.

S **Hövelhof** 9H2

Wohnmobil-stellplatz Apelhof, Paderborner Straße 172. **GPS**: n51,80166 e8,67697.
8 € 8 . **Surface:** grassy. 01/01-31/12.
Distance: 3km 250m 3km.

S **Höxter** 10A3

Freizeitanlage Godelheimer See, Godelheimer Strasse, Höxter-Godelheim. **GPS**: n51,75787 e9,37557.

50 € 7/24h ChWC included. **Location:** Comfortable. **Surface:** grasstiles. 01/01-31/12 service: 01/10-01/04.
Distance: 2km on the spot river 500m on the spot 2km on the spot on the spot.
Remarks: Bread-service, recreation area.

S **Höxter** 10A3

Wohnmobilhafen Floßplatz, Milchweg. **GPS**: n51,77325 e9,38781.

70 € 7/24h € 1/100liter Ch (40x)€ 1/2kWh.
Location: Rural, comfortable, central, quiet.
Surface: grassy/gravel.
01/01-31/12.
Distance: 300m on the spot fishing permit available 100m 500m 500m on camp site 200m on the spot.
Remarks: Parking beside river Weser, bread-service in summer period.

S **Hückelhoven** 11E1

Hückelhovener Ruraue, Rheinstraße 4b. **GPS**: n51,05146 e6,21208.

6 € 4,50 € 0,50/100liter Ch € 0,50/kWh.
Location: Rural, simple, isolated, quiet. **Surface:** metalled.
01/01-31/12 With snow.
Distance: 1,5km.

Hürtgenwald 11E2

Einmünding Kall-Rur, Zerkall. **GPS**: n50,69156 e6,45212.

10 free. **Location:** Rural, simple. **Surface:** gravel.
01/01-31/12.
Distance: 100m on the spot on the spot 200m.
Remarks: Along the river Kall/Rur.

Hürtgenwald 11E2

Parkplatz Burgstrasse, Burgstrasse, Bergstein. **GPS**: n50,69582 e6,43848.

5 free. **Location:** Simple. **Surface:** metalled.
01/01-31/12.

Hürtgenwald 11E2

Soldatenfriedhof, Höhenstrasse, Hürtgen. **GPS**: n50,70552 e6,36063.

9 free. **Location:** Rural, simple, noisy.
Surface: asphalted. 01/01-31/12.

Hürtgenwald 11E2

Landhotel Kallbach, Kallweg 24, Simonskall. **GPS**: n50,66716 e6,35395.

5 € 12. **Location:** Rural, comfortable, quiet.
Surface: metalled. 01/01-31/12.
Distance: 200m on the spot.
Remarks: Discount at restaurant.

Hüsten 9G3

Parkplatz Große Wiese. **GPS**: n51,43151 e8,00475.
4 free. **Surface:** asphalted. 01/01-31/12.
Distance: 2km on the spot on the spot.
Remarks: Next to the Sole-Bad.

Ibbenbüren 9G2

Aseebad, An der Umfluth 99. **GPS**: n52,26181 e7,73171.

30 € 3. **Location:** Comfortable, central, quiet. **Surface:** grassy.
01/01-31/12.
Distance: 2,3km.
Remarks: Parking next to swimming pool, max. 4 nights.

S **Iserlohn** 9G3

Parkplatz Seilerblick, Friesenstraße. **GPS**: n51,38456 e7,71128.

5 free € 1 Ch € 1 (4x)€ 0,50.
Location: Urban, simple, noisy. **Surface:** asphalted. 01/01-31/12.
Distance: 2km 2,5km on the spot on the spot.
Remarks: Next to tennis-court.

S **Isselburg** 9E3

Stellplatz am Stadtturm, Münsterdeich. **GPS**: n51,83452 e6,46477.

6 € 5 € 1/100liter Ch (6x)€ 1/day. **Location:** Rural, simple, quiet. **Surface:** grassy. 01/01-31/12.

DE

Distance: on the spot on the spot 300m 100m.
Remarks: At the Issel, parking centre, max. 72h.

Isselburg 9E3

Hotel Restaurant Brüggenhütte, Hahnerfeld 23, Anholt.
GPS: n51,85301 e6,47187.

5 free. **Location:** Rural, simple, noisy.
Surface: grassy.
01/01-31/12.
Distance: 200m on the spot 2km on the spot.
Remarks: Along through road, behind restaurant, max. 3 days.

Isselburg 9E3

Bürgerhaus, Anholter strasse, Vehlingen. **GPS**: n51,83089 e6,42297.

5 free. **Location:** Rural, simple. **Surface:** gravel.
01/01-31/12.
Distance: 1km on the spot.
Remarks: Max. 2 nights.

Isselburg 9E3

Biotopwildpark Anholter Schweiz, Pferdehorster Str. 1.
GPS: n51,83225 e6,43013.

6 € 7 (6x)included. **Location:** Rural, simple.
Surface: gravel/metalled. 15/03-25/10.
Distance: 1km. **Remarks:** Max. 3 days, check in at pay-desk, caution key electricity € 20.

Isselburg 9E3

Ponyhof Leiting, Alte Bundesstrasse 3, Werth.
GPS: n51,81332 e6,49258.

20 free. **Location:** Rural, simple, quiet. **Surface:** grassy.
01/01-31/12.
Distance: on the spot.
Remarks: Max. 72h.

Issum-Sevelen 9E3

Wohnmobilpark Hexenland-Sevelen, Koetherdyck 18.
GPS: n51,49926 e6,43676.

20 € 9 Ch € 3/24h WC € 1/10minutes.
Surface: gravel. 01/01-31/12.
Distance: Sevelen 1km 200m 100m 1km.

Jülich 11E1

Brückenkopf-Park, Rurauenstrasse 11. **GPS**: n50,92345 e6,34029.

22 € 9,50 € 1/100liter Ch WC .
Location: Simple, noisy. **Surface:** grassy.
01/01-31/12 sanitary building: 1/11-31/3.
Remarks: Parking at the Rur.

Tourist information Jülich:
Old fortress city.

Kalkar 9E3

Reisemobilstellplatz Kalkar, Waysche strasse.
GPS: n51,74008 e6,30101.

35 € 4/24h € 1/30liter € 1 Ch (24x)€ 1/2kWh.
Location: Rural, comfortable, central. **Surface:** grassy/gravel.
01/01-31/12.
Distance: 500m 400m 700m on the spot.
Remarks: Max. 3 nights.

Tourist information Kalkar:
KernWasser Wunderland. Amusement park.

Kall 11F2

Im Kallbachtal, Kapellenstrasse 25, Golbach.
GPS: n50,52784 e6,53681.

6 € 6 € 1 Ch (8x)€ 0,50/kWh.
Location: Rural, simple, quiet. **Surface:** gravel. 01/01-31/12.

Kamp-Lintfort 9E3

Pappelsee, Berthastraße 74. **GPS**: n51,50026 e6,53861.

20 free. **Surface:** asphalted. 01/01-31/12.
Distance: 1,5km 1km 1,5km.
Remarks: Caution € 2,50 to pay-desk of the park.

Tourist information Kamp-Lintfort:
Marktplatz, Eberstrasse. Thu, Sa.
Rathausplatz. Tue 7.30-13h.
Mittelalterlicher Markt, Abteiplatz. Medieval market. 3rd weekend Sep.

Kempen 11E1

Reisemobilpark Kempen am Aqua-sol, Berliner Allee.
GPS: n51,36719 e6,40910.

29 € 8/24h € 1/100liter Ch € 0,50/kWh.
Surface: metalled. 01/01-31/12.
Distance: 1,5km on the spot 1,5km.

Kerken 9E3

Wohnmobilpark Aldekerker Platte, Kempener Straße 9, Aldekerk.
GPS: n51,43551 e6,41902.

30 € 7 Ch included (30x)€ 3. **Location:** Rural, simple, quiet. **Surface:** grassy/gravel. 01/01-31/12.
Distance: 400m 2,5km 2km 2km 400m 500m 300m on the spot on the spot.

Kevelaer 9E3

Den Heyberg, Im Auwelt 45, Twisteden. **GPS**: n51,56345 e6,19418.

150 € 9 Ch (150x)included.
Surface: asphalted/metalled. 01/01-31/12.
Distance: 2km 100m 2km 100m.
Remarks: Bread-service (weekend), barbecue place.

Kevelaer 9E3

Sporthotel Schravelsche Heide, Grotendonkerstrasse 54-58.
GPS: n51,59556 e6,25306.

80 € 9,50 Ch WC € 0,50 included.
Location: Comfortable, quiet. **Surface:** grassy. 01/01-31/12.
Distance: 1,5km 100m 1km.

Kevelaer 9E3

Europaplatz, Bahnhof/Geldernstrasse, B9.
GPS: n51,57904 e6,25192.

DE

3 free. **Surface:** asphalted. 01/01-31/12.
Distance: 500m 500m on the spot.
Tourist information Kevelaer:
Fr 14-18h.

Kirchhundem 11H1

Restaurant Rhein-Weser-Turm, Rhein-Weser-Turm 2.
GPS: n51,07109 e8,19791.

10 € 15 Ch included. 01/01-31/12.
Distance: on the spot.

Kirchhundem 11H1

Restaurant Zur Hahnenquelle, Rhein-Weser-Turm.
GPS: n51,07198 e8,19792.
10 € 8 Ch included. 01/01-31/12.
Distance: on the spot.

Kirchhundem 11H1

PanoramaPark Sauerland Wildpark, Rinsecker Straße 100.
GPS: n51,06972 e8,17417.
10 € 2. 01/01-31/12.

Kleve 9E3

Stellplatz van-den-Bergh-Straße, Van-den-Bergh-Straße.
GPS: n51,78917 e6,14836.

60 € 5 Ch free (30x) € 0,50/kWh.
Location: Urban, simple, noisy. **Surface:** metalled. 01/01-31/12.
Distance: 500m 400m 200m.
Remarks: Behind railway station, max. 72h.

Kleve 9E3

Reisemobilpark Kleve, Landwehr/Spyckstraße.
GPS: n51,80083 e6,13222.

75 € 8,50 € 1 Ch (45x) € 1,50 WC € 0,50 € 1 .
Location: Comfortable. **Surface:** grassy/metalled. 01/01-31/12.
Distance: Kleve-zentrum 1,5km 300m 400m.
Remarks: 4th night free.

Kleve 9E3

Am Willisee, Zyfflicherstrasse 33, Keeken. **GPS**: n51,84013 e6,08307.

25 € 10 Ch (25x) € 2/day WC included.
Location: Luxurious, isolated, quiet. **Surface:** grassy/gravel.
01/01-31/12.
Distance: 900m, Kleve city centre 7km on the spot on the spot 400m 4,2km 150m on the spot on the spot.
Remarks: Fishing permit available.

Kleve 9E3

Parkplatz Sporthalle Kleve-Kellen, Postdeich, Kellen.
GPS: n51,80463 e6,16378.

20 free. **Location:** Rural, simple, quiet. **Surface:** metalled.
01/01-31/12.
Distance: 2,5km Steakhaus 350m 300m on the spot.

Kleve 9E3

Schenkenschanz. **GPS**: n51,83526 e6,11205.

5 free. **Location:** Rural, simple, isolated, quiet. **Surface:** metalled.
01/01-31/12.
Distance: Kleve 6,5km 1km 2,5km.

Kleve 9E3

Stellplatz Reichswalde, Dorfanger, Reichswalde.
GPS: n51,75985 e6,10243.

10 free. **Location:** Urban, simple, quiet. **Surface:** asphalted.
01/01-31/12.
Distance: Kleve 3km 200m 500m on the spot on the spot on the spot.

Kleve 9E3

Stellplatz Rindern, Drusus deich, Rindern.
GPS: n51,81212 e6,12884.

5 free. **Location:** Rural, simple, quiet. **Surface:** metalled.
01/01-31/12.
Distance: Kleve-zentrum 2,3km 450m 400m on the spot on the spot.
Remarks: Behind church.

Kleve 9E3

Tiergarten, Tiergartenstrasse, B9 dir Nijmegen.
GPS: n51,79784 e6,12059.

5 free. **Location:** Motorway, simple. **Surface:** metalled.
01/01-31/12.
Distance: 800m 250m.

Kleve 9E3

Wehrpöhl, Griethausen. **GPS**: n51,82476 e6,16448.

5 free. **Location:** Rural, simple, quiet. **Surface:** asphalted.
01/01-31/12.
Distance: 2,5km 300m 300m on the spot.
Remarks: Access via Brienen.
Tourist information Kleve:
Lichterfest. City celebration. 2nd Sa of the month.
Tiergarten Kleve, Tiergartenstrasse. Animal park.

Köln 11F1

Reisemobilhafen Köln, An der Schanz, Cologne (Köln).
GPS: n50,96256 e6,98601.

65 € 12/24h € 1 Ch (30x) € 0,50/kWh.
Location: Urban, comfortable, quiet. **Surface:** asphalted.
01/01-31/12.
Distance: on the spot 5km 600m 800m metro 10 min walking on the spot on the spot.
Remarks: Along the Rhine river.

Königswinter 11F2

Hauptstrasse, Niederdollendorf. **GPS**: n50,69697 e7,17641.

30 free. **Location:** Urban, simple. **Surface:** asphalted/metalled.
01/01-31/12.
Distance: 400m 9km 800m on the spot on the spot.

Kranenburg 9E3

Am Sportzentrum, Großen Haag, 47599.
GPS: n51,79242 e6,01033.

DE

30 € 4/24h € 0,20/liter € 1 Ch (12x)€ 0,50/kWh.
Location: Rural, simple. **Surface:** grassy. 01/01-31/12.
Distance: 500m 1km 1km 500m 500m on the spot on the spot.
Remarks: Service 500m.

Kreuztal 11G1

Heugraben. **GPS:** n50,95778 e7,99167.

3 free € 1/100liter Ch (4x)€ 1/2kWh.
Surface: metalled. 01/01-31/12.
Distance: 300m 7,5km 300m 300m station 100m.
Remarks: Max. 3 days.

Kürten 11G1

Wohnmobilpark am Splash, Broch 8. **GPS:** n51,05586 e7,28943.

20 € 8 € 2 Ch € 2.
Location: Rural, simple, quiet. **Surface:** gravel.
01/01-31/12.
Distance: 2km 17km on the spot on the spot on the spot.
Remarks: Behind Sauna-/Badeland Splash.

Ladbergen 9G2

Rathauspark, Jahnstrasse. **GPS:** n52,13652 e7,74009.

8 free. **Location:** Rural, simple, quiet. **Surface:** grassy.
01/01-31/12.
Distance: 200m 200m 300m 200m on the spot.
Remarks: Parking behind town hall.

Lennestadt 11H1

Naturerlebnisbad, Fasanenweg 10. **GPS:** n51,11814 e8,16990.
3 free . 01/01-31/12.
Distance: 300m 300m.
Remarks: At swimming pool.

Lennestadt 11H1

Parkplatz P4, An der Sauerlandhalle. **GPS:** n51,10557 e8,08017.

4 free (4x)€ 0,50/4h. **Surface:** asphalted. 01/01-31/12.
Distance: 700m 700m 100m.

Leverkusen 11F1

Camping-Caravaning Meier, Adolf-Kaschny-Straße 9, Küppersteg.
GPS: n51,05211 e7,00003.

10 free € 0,50 Ch€ 0,50.
Location: Urban. **Surface:** gravel. 01/01-31/12.
Distance: 3,2km.
Remarks: Motorhome dealer, accessory shop, repairs.

Lienen 9G2

Hallenfreibad, Holperdorperstrasse 37/39.
GPS: n52,15575 e7,97392.

3 free € 5 Ch WC € 3.
Location: Simple, quiet. **Surface:** metalled. 01/01-31/12.
Distance: 1km 100m 2km on the spot on the spot.
Remarks: Parking in front of swimming pool, max. 3 nights, service to be paid at swimming pool.

Lindlar 11G1

Am Freizeitpark, Brionner Straße. **GPS:** n51,01550 e7,36645.

2 free € 1 Ch (4x)€ 1/6h.
Location: Urban, simple. **Surface:** metalled. 01/01-31/12.
Distance: 1km 16km 1km 1km on the spot on the spot.

Lindlar 11G1

Wohnmobilstellplatz Klause, Gerberstraße 39.
GPS: n51,03079 e7,41562.
3 € 5 € 0,50/40liter Ch € 0,50/kWh.
Surface: metalled. 01/01-31/12.
Distance: 4km 1km.
Remarks: Industrial area.

Lippstadt 9H3

Bückeburger Straße. **GPS:** n51,67348 e8,33336.

11 free € 1/10minutes Chfree € 1.
Location: Urban, comfortable, quiet. 01/01-31/12.
Distance: 1,2km 500m 600m on the spot on the spot.
Remarks: At swimming pool, max. 4 days.

Lippstadt 9H3

Camping Lippstadt, Seeuferstraße 16. **GPS:** n51,70194 e8,40789.
18 € 11, 2 pers. incl., dog € 2,50 € 0,50/50liter Ch € 0,50/kWh WC . **Surface:** grassy/gravel. 01/03-31/10.
Distance: 200m 200m.

Lippstadt 9H3

Campingoase Lange, Dorfstraße 47, Benninghausen.
GPS: n51,66103 e8,24435.

15 € 10, 2 pers.incl Ch included. **Location:** Rural, simple.
Surface: metalled. 01/01-31/12.
Distance: 300m on the spot.

Löhne 9H2

Reisemobilstellplatz, Albert-Schweitzer-strasse 12.
GPS: n52,20399 e8,71892.

18 € 8 Chincluded (18x)€ 1/2kWh.
Location: Rural, quiet. **Surface:** metalled. 01/01-31/12.
Distance: 500m 1km 100m 500m 500m.

Lotte 9G2

Fam. Arendröwer, Am Nordberg 4. **GPS:** n52,26306 e7,89833.

4 € 4 € 2/24 included. **Location:** Simple, isolated, noisy. **Surface:** grassy/metalled. 01/03-01/10.
Distance: 3km 500m 3km.

Lotte 9G2

Tennishalle Lotte, Kornweg 3. **GPS:** n52,27192 e7,92275.

10 free. **Location:** Simple, quiet. **Surface:** gravel/metalled.

DE

01/01-31/12.
Distance: 900m 3,5km 1km 300m.

Lübbecke 9H1

Stellplatz Lübbecke, Rahdener Straße. **GPS**: n52,31019 e8,61839.

4 €6 €3 Ch €3.
Location: Urban, central. **Surface:** metalled. 01/01-31/12.
Distance: 600m 700m 500m on the spot on the spot.
Remarks: Max. 3 days.

Lüdenscheid 11G1

Familienbades Nattenberg, Talstraße 59.
GPS: n51,21042 e7,61803.

4 free € 1/100liter Ch (4x)€ 1/6h. **Location:** Urban, simple.
Surface: metalled. 01/01-31/12.
Distance: city centre 1,6km 4km Burger King 450m Aldi 900m on the spot.

Lüdinghausen 9G3

Parkplatz Aqua-See, Rohrkamp 23. **GPS**: n51,77229 e7,42731.

10 free. **Location:** Rural, simple, quiet. **Surface:** metalled.
01/01-31/12.
Distance: 1,5km 1km on the spot.
Remarks: Parking swimming pool.

Lüdinghausen 9G3

Parkplatz Rosengarten, Am Rosengarten, Seppenrade.
GPS: n51,76407 e7,39728.

2 free. **Location:** Simple, quiet. **Surface:** asphalted.
01/01-31/12.
Distance: 200m 200m 800m.

Marsberg 10A3

Wohnmobilhafen, Am Sportplatz. **GPS**: n51,45974 e8,84864.

4 € 5/24h Ch (4x)included. **Location:** Urban.
Surface: asphalted.
01/01-31/12.
Distance: 100m 200m 200m.
Remarks: Max. 5 days, caution key € 20 (pay-desk of theTherme).

Mechernich 11F2

Mühlental, Elisabethhütte, B477. **GPS**: n50,59686 e6,63207.

20 free. **Location:** Rural, simple, noisy. **Surface:** asphalted.
01/01-31/12.
Distance: 500m.

Mechernich 11F2

Parkplatz Essensgasse, Am Kirchberg, Kommern.
GPS: n50,61376 e6,64479.

8 free. **Location:** Rural, simple, noisy. **Surface:** metalled.
01/01-31/12.
Distance: historical centre 200m.
Remarks: Via B266.

Meinerzhagen 11G1

An der Musikschule, Schulplatz. **GPS**: n51,10865 e7,64329.

3 free (4x)€ 0,50/kWh. **Location:** Urban, simple, quiet.
Surface: asphalted. 01/01-31/12.
Distance: 400m 3km 400m 400m on the spot on the spot.

Meschede 11H1

Am Wofibad, Im Ohl 13, Freienohl. **GPS**: n51,37574 e8,17664.

3 free against payment. **Location:** Simple. **Surface:** metalled.
01/01-31/12.

Meschede 11H1

An der Ruhr, Arnsberger Strasse. **GPS**: n51,34897 e8,27356.

10 free. **Location:** Simple. **Surface:** metalled.
18.30-9.30h.
Distance: 500m on the spot on the spot 500m 500m.
Remarks: At swimming pool.

Meschede 11H1

Knaus Campingpark Hennesee, Mielinghausen 7.
GPS: n51,29846 e8,26366.

17 € 8-10 € 1/60liter € 0,50 Ch€ 0,50 (16x)€ 0,70/kWh
WC sanitary € 2,30-3,50 .
Surface: grassy/metalled. 01/01-31/12.
Distance: 5km 100m 100m on the spot on the spot on the spot on the spot.

Mettingen 9G2

Hallenbad, Bahnhofstrasse 18-20. **GPS**: n52,31738 e7,78312.

2 free WC.
Location: Simple. **Surface:** metalled. 01/01-31/12.
Distance: on the spot 200m 200m on the spot on the spot on the spot.
Remarks: Parking swimming pool, service: Kläranlage, Neuenkirchenerstrasse 208, bicycle rental.

Minden 10A2

Reisemobilstellplatz Kanzlers Weide, Hausbergerstrasse.
GPS: n52,28750 e8,92551.

100 €5 € 1/100liter Ch (18x)€ 0,50/kWh,6Amp.
Location: Urban, simple, quiet. **Surface:** metalled.
01/01-31/12.
Distance: 200m 50m 50m 200m 200m 200m.
Remarks: Max. 3 nights, not during big events.

Moers 9F3

Am Aktivbad Solimare, Filder Straße 144. **GPS**: n51,43897 e6,62004.
11 free Ch .
Location: Urban. **Surface:** asphalted. 01/01-31/12.
Distance: 1km on the spot on the spot.
Remarks: At sports grounds.

Moers 9F3

Freizeitpark Schoßpark, Krefelder straße.
GPS: n51,44659 e6,61642.

4 free. **Location:** Rural. **Surface:** grasstiles.
01/01-31/12.

Distance: 700m 700m 500m.

Möhnesee 9H3

Freizeitanlage Möhnesee-Körbecke, Börnigeweg.
GPS: n51,49160 e8,12555.

20 € 6/24h (8x)€ 2/24h.
Location: Simple. **Surface:** metalled. 01/01-31/12.
Distance: 1km on the spot on the spot 1km on the spot on the spot.
Remarks: Max. 24h.

Möhnesee 9H3

Stockumer Eichen, Stockumer Eichen 1. **GPS**: n51,48668 e8,14981.
20 € 10/24h Ch (12x) WC included. 01/03-01/11.
Distance: 2km Möhnesee on the spot on the spot on the spot.

Möhnesee 9H3

Strandbad, Linkstraße 20, Delecke. **GPS**: n51,49177 e8,08255.
50 € 15 Ch (50x) WC included.
Location: Rural, comfortable, quiet. **Surface:** gravel.
01/03-01/11.
Distance: Möhnesee 3,5km 7km A44 Möhnesee 750m.
Remarks: Cash payment.

Möhnesee 9H3

Wildpark/Freizeitanlage, Alte Feld. **GPS**: n51,47360 e8,19831.

10 free. **Surface:** grassy/gravel. 01/01-31/12.
Distance: 1,5km 300m on the spot.
Remarks: Playground.

Mönchengladbach 11E1

Schloß Wickrath, Neukircherweg, Wickrath.
GPS: n51,12889 e6,42258.

10 free. **Surface:** asphalted. 01/01-31/12.
Distance: 2km 2km 500m.
Remarks: Parking behind castle (500m), max. 2 days.

Mönchengladbach 11E1

Camping-Center Krings, Monschauerstrasse 10/32.
GPS: n51,19454 e6,40884.

15 free Ch free. **Surface:** metalled. 01/01-31/12.
Distance: 3km 1km 500m.
Remarks: Max. 2 nights, service during opening hours.

Monschau 11E2

Biesweg, B258. **GPS**: n50,55389 e6,23194.

4 € 12 € 5/7minutes Ch (4x)€ 5/10h.
Location: Simple, noisy. **Surface:** asphalted. 01/01-31/12.
Distance: 600m 600m 600m.
Remarks: Max. 1 night.

Monschau 11E2

Haus Vennblick, Hauptstrasse 24, Höfen. **GPS**: n50,53934 e6,25292.

8 € 10, guests free. **Location:** Rural, simple, noisy.
Surface: gravel. 01/01-31/12 Wed.
Distance: 300m on the spot 4km on the spot 4km.

Mülheim/Ruhr 9F3

Mintarder Straße 45. **GPS**: n51,41462 e6,86934.

6 free. **Location:** Rural, simple.
Surface: metalled. 01/01-31/12.
Distance: 2,7km 50m 100m on the spot on the spot.
Remarks: Max. 72h.

Mülheim/Ruhr 9F3

Landhaus Dicken, Mintarder Straße 139. **GPS**: n51,39615 e6,89152.
5 free. **Surface:** gravel. 01/01-31/12.
Distance: 4km on the spot.
Remarks: Restaurant closed on Tuesday.

Mülheim/Ruhr 9F3

Hymer Zentrum, Kölner Strasse 35-37. **GPS**: n51,39985 e6,87700.
€ 0,50/80liter Ch. 01/01-31/12.
Remarks: At motorhome dealer.

Münster 9G2

Am Ostbad, Mauritz-Lindenweg. **GPS**: n51,95922 e7,65879.

6 free. **Location:** Urban, simple.
Surface: metalled. 01/01-31/12.
Distance: 2,5km 100m 300m 300m on the spot.
Remarks: At swimming pool, max. 8M.

Münster 9G2

Hafenstraße/Albersloher Weg. **GPS**: n51,95199 e7,63600.

6 € 2/h, overnight stay free. **Location:** Urban, simple, central, noisy.
Surface: asphalted. 01/01-31/12.
Distance: Old city centre 1km on the spot on the spot on the spot.
Remarks: Along railwayline.

Münster 9G2

Campingplatz Münster, Laerer Werseufer.
GPS: n51,94583 e7,69082.

24 € 15 2 pers.incl, dog € 3,50 € 0,50 € 0,50 Ch € 0,50 WC included € 0,50/3 € 3/day.
Location: Rural, simple. **Surface:** gravel. 01/01-31/12.
Distance: Münster 4,5km 100m on the spot 100m on the spot on the spot.
Remarks: Pay at reception campsite.

Netphen 11H1

Freitzeitpark Netphen, P3, Brauersdorferstrasse.
GPS: n50,91250 e8,12567.

3 € 3,50/day € 1/70liter Ch.
Surface: metalled. 01/01-31/12.
Distance: 2km 2km.
Remarks: Max. 3 nights, coins at swimming pool.

Nettersheim 11F2

Wohnmobilhafen Nettersheim, Urftstraße.
GPS: n50,48606 e6,62627.
25 € 8,50/24h € 1 Ch (25x)included.
Location: Rural, simple, quiet. **Surface:** metalled. 01/01-31/12.
Distance: 500m 7,5km on the spot 500m 1,5km 700m on the spot on the spot on the spot.
Remarks: Bread-service.

Nettetal 11E1

Am Nettebruch, Flothender straße/Flothend.
GPS: n51,30188 e6,26715.

5 free. **Surface:** grassy/gravel. 01/01-31/12.
Distance: 1km on the spot on the spot 1km.

Nettetal 11E1

Am Krickenbeck See, Krickenbecker Allee 38. **GPS**: n51,34460 e6,25793.

50 Free, use of a meal desired. **Surface:** asphalted. 01/01-31/12.
Distance: 2km on the spot 2km.

Neuss 11F1

Allrounder Winterworld/Skihalle, An der Skihalle 1.
GPS: n51,17316 e6,64862.

30 free. **Surface:** metalled. 01/01-31/12.
Distance: on the spot indoor ski.

Nideggen 11E2

Parkplatz Danzley, Bahnhofstrasse. **GPS**: n50,69247 e6,47952.

14 free. **Location:** Rural, simple. **Surface:** metalled.
01/01-31/12.
Distance: 500m 500m.

Nordkirchen 9G3

Wohnmobilstellplatz Nordkirchen, Am Gorbach 10a.
GPS: n51,74004 e7,53418.
23 € 10 € 1/100liter Ch € 0,55/kWh included.
Location: Rural, central, quiet. **Surface:** grassy/gravel.
01/01-31/12.
Distance: 600m 450m 600m on the spot on the spot.
Remarks: Castle 500m.

Nordkirchen 9G3

Bikertreff, Berger 25. **GPS**: n51,72484 e7,50726.
20 free Ch . **Surface:** gravel/metalled.
01/03-31/12.
Distance: 2km on the spot.

Nordkirchen 9G3

Hotel Plettenberger Hof, Schlossstrasse 28.
GPS: n51,73659 e7,52819.

2 guests free .
Surface: asphalted. 01/01-31/12.
Distance: 200m on the spot 200m.
Remarks: Breakfast-service, restaurant closed on Monday.

Nottuln 9G2

Wellenfreibad/Hallenbad, Rudolf-Harbigstrasse.
GPS: n51,92410 e7,34514.

5 free. **Location:** Rural, simple. **Surface:** metalled.
01/01-31/12.
Distance: 1,5km bakery 800m on the spot.
Remarks: Parking swimming pool, service during opening hours.

Oberhausen 9F3

Stellplatz Kaisergaten, Am Kaisergarten 28.
GPS: n51,48743 e6,85519.

60 € 7 € 1/100liter Ch (24x)€ 0,50/2h.
Location: Urban, noisy. **Surface:** grassy. 01/01-31/12.
Distance: Oberhausen City 30 min walking 1,6km 1,7km 1,7km 400m.

Oberhausen 9F3

Stellplatz Marina, Heinz-Schleußer-Straße 1.
GPS: n51,49444 e6,88417.

18 € 1,50/m € 2 WC included € 1/4minutes € 1.
Location: Urban, simple. **Surface:** gravel/metalled.
01/01-31/12.
Distance: 1km 200m on the spot 250m 800m.

Oberhausen 9F3

Parking 10 - CentrO, Arenastraße. **GPS**: n51,48930 e6,87063.

40 free. **Surface:** metalled. 01/01-31/12.
Distance: 100m on the spot on the spot.
Remarks: At CentrO.

Tourist information Oberhausen:
CentrO. Large shopping centre, 250 shops, 100 restaurants/bars and a market. 10-20h restaurants till 22h, thu 10-21h.

Oedt 11E1

Wohnmobile-Stellplatz Niers-Perle-Oedt, Mühlengasse.
GPS: n51,32327 e6,37650.

7 free. **Surface:** asphalted. 01/01-31/12.
Distance: 800m 500m 500m.

Oelde 9H3

Pott's Brau und Backhaus, In der Geist 120.
GPS: n51,81192 e8,13103.

6 € 5 € 1/60liter Ch included.
Location: Simple, noisy. **Surface:** grassy/metalled. 02/01-23/12.
Distance: 500m on the spot.
Remarks: Caution key € 35.

Olpe 11G1

Freizeitbad Olpe, Seeweg 5. **GPS**: n51,03242 e7,84163.

DE

10 € 5 € 0,20/liter Ch (4x)€ 1/2kWh WC included,at swimming pool 7-22h. **Location:** Urban. **Surface:** asphalted.
01/01-31/12.
Distance: 500m 2km 250m.
Remarks: On the banks of the Biggesee, max. 3 days.

Olsberg 9H3

Wohnmobilplatz am AquaOlsberg, Zur Sauerlandtherme 1.
GPS: n51,35637 e8,48487.
10 € 8,50/24h, tourist tax € 1,50/pp € 1/80liter € 1/8h.
Surface: grassy. 01/01-31/12.
Distance: on the spot 250m 250m.
Remarks: Discount at swimming pool.

Ostbevern 9G2

Bever Bad, Am Hanfgarten 22. **GPS**: n52,03673 e7,84392.

6+10 € 10, overnight stay only 20-9h free Ch WC included.
Location: Luxurious, quiet. **Surface:** grassy.
01/01-31/12.
Distance: 400m 300m 300m 300m.
Remarks: Parking swimming pool, caution key service € 10, incl. access swimming pool.

Overhetfeld 11E1

Camp Graskamp, Graskamp 19. **GPS**: n51,22259 e6,13977.

5 € 8 Ch WC included.
Surface: grassy. 01/01-31/12.
Distance: 200m 200m on the spot.

Paderborn 9H3

Maspernplatz, P4, Hathumarstrasse. **GPS**: n51,72278 e8,75417.

7 day € 6, weekend free (4x)€ 0,50/h.
Location: Urban, central, noisy. **Surface:** metalled.
01/01-31/12.
Distance: 500m 4km 100m 500m on the spot.

Paderborn 9H3

Rolandsbad, Fürstenweg. **GPS**: n51,72825 e8,74509.

16 € 5/24h € 0,50/60liter Ch (16x)€ 0,50/kWh.
Surface: asphalted. 01/01-31/12.
Distance: centre 700m on the spot on the spot on the spot on the spot.
Remarks: Max. 72h.

Paderborn 9H3

Lippesee-Nordufer, Sennelagerstraße 58, Sande.
GPS: n51,76087 e8,67756.

10 free. **Location:** Rural, simple.
Surface: grassy. 01/01-31/12.
Distance: city centre Paderborn 9km 150m 150m 1km 500m on the spot on the spot.

Paderborn 9H3

Heinz Nixdorf MuseumsForum, Fürstenallee 7.
GPS: n51,73193 e8,73592.
3 free. **Surface:** metalled. 01/01-31/12.
Distance: centre 2,5km on the spot.
Remarks: At museum.

Petershagen 10A1

Am Sportplatz, Hohoffstraße 15. **GPS**: n52,37532 e8,96875.

10 free € 1/90liter (8x)€ 1/kWh.
Location: Urban, quiet. **Surface:** metalled. 01/01-31/12.
Distance: 100m 100m 100m on the spot.
Remarks: Nearby football ground, max. 3 days, check in at tourist office.

Plettenberg 11G1

Aqua Magis, Albert Schweizerstrasse, Böddinghausen.
GPS: n51,23220 e7,85308.

12 free € 1/40liter Ch (8x)€ 0,50 WC .
Location: Rural, comfortable, quiet. **Surface:** metalled.
01/01-31/12.
Distance: on the spot 11km on the spot 200m on the spot on the spot.
Remarks: At paradise pool, max. 48h.

Raesfeld 9F3

Wohnmobilstellplatz Graf Alexander, Südring.
GPS: n51,76523 e6,83035.

8 € 8 € 1/8minutes Ch (8x)€ 1/12h WC .
Location: Rural, simple, quiet. **Surface:** gravel.
01/01-31/12.
Distance: 1km 150m on the spot on the spot.
Remarks: At historic moated castle, max. 2 nights.

Recke 9G1

Yackthafen Marina Recke, Auf der Haar 23.
GPS: n52,35082 e7,71174.

40 € 7 Ch (10x)€ 1,50 WC € 1,50 .
Surface: grassy/metalled. 01/01-31/12.
Distance: 1km, Recke 3,5km on the spot on the spot on the spot 900m 400m on the spot on the spot.
Remarks: At the Mittelland canal, check in at harbourmaster.

Rees 9E3

Stellplatz Rees am Niederrhein, Ebentalstrasse.
GPS: n51,76428 e6,38829.

46 € 6/day Ch included. **Location:** Urban, comfortable, central. **Surface:** grassy. 01/01-31/12.
Distance: 400m.
Remarks: Behind swimming pool, bread-service.

Reken 9F3

Wohnmobilstellplatz Reken, Bergen 2a.
GPS: n51,82864 e7,05895.

20 € 6 € 1/200liter Ch (20x)€ 0,50/kWh.
Location: Rural, comfortable, quiet. **Surface:** grassy.
01/01-31/12.
Distance: 1km 1km 1km on the spot.
Remarks: Max. 2 days, friday market.

Remscheid 11F1

Brückenpark Müngsten, Müngstener Brückenweg.
GPS: n51,16833 e7,13750.

DE

4 free. **Location:** Rural, simple, quiet. **Surface:** gravel.
01/01-31/12.
Distance: 5km 4km 100m 100m on the spot.
Remarks: Max. 1 night.

Remscheid 11F1

Dörperhöhe, Bei Haus nr. 15, Lennep. **GPS**: n51,17986 e7,30205.
4 free. **Surface:** asphalted. 01/01-31/12.
Remarks: Max. 1 night.

Remscheid 11F1

Jahnplatz, Am Stadion, Lennep. **GPS**: n51,19052 e7,26110.
4 free. **Surface:** asphalted. 01/01-31/12.
Distance: historical centre of Lennep 300m.
Remarks: Max. 1 night.

S **Remscheid** 11F1

Garage Pauli GmbH, Lenneperstrasse 152. **GPS**: n51,18020 e7,22591.
3 free Ch free. **Surface:** grasstiles. 01/01-31/12.
Remarks: At motorhome dealer, max. 1 night.

S **Rheda-Wiedenbrück** 9H2

Am Werl, Gütersloherstrasse. **GPS**: n51,85456 e8,29768.

4 free Ch WC. **Location:** Urban. **Surface:** metalled.
01/01-31/12.
Distance: 300m 300m.
Remarks: Max. 3 days.

Rheda-Wiedenbrück 9H2

P Hallenbad, Ostring/Am Hallenbad, Wiederbrück.
GPS: n51,83188 e8,32350.

4 free. **Location:** Urban, quiet. **Surface:** metalled.
01/01-31/12.
Distance: 1km 200m bakery 200m on the spot on the spot.
Remarks: Parking swimming pool.

S **Rhede** 9F3

Reisemobilstellplatz Kettelerplatz, Kettelerstrasse 9.
GPS: n51,83677 e6,69346.

15 free € 1/3minutes Ch (6x)€ 1/stay.
Location: Urban, simple, quiet. **Surface:** grassy. 01/01-31/12.
Distance: 750m 750m 500m.
Remarks: At fire-station.

Rhede 9F3

Hallen- und Freibad, Heideweg 59. **GPS**: n51,83164 e6,68635.

2 free. **Location:** Urban, simple, quiet. **Surface:** metalled.
01/01-31/12.
Distance: 1,5km 600m 1,2km.
Remarks: Parking swimming pool, max. 3 days.

Rheinbach 11F2

Freizeitpark Monte Mare, Münstereifelerstraße 69.
GPS: n50,61883 e6,93262.

4 free. **Location:** Rural, simple. **Surface:** metalled.
01/01-31/12.
Distance: 1,5km on the spot 1,5km.
Remarks: Max. 3 days.

Rheine 9G2

Im Stadtpark, Kopernikusstrasse. **GPS**: n52,28137 e7,45478.

2 free. **Location:** Urban, simple. **Surface:** metalled.
01/01-31/12.
Distance: 500m on the spot 500m 300m on the spot on the spot.

Rheine 9G2

Am Naturzoo, Weihbishof-Dalhaus-strasse.
GPS: n52,29526 e7,41645.

10 free. **Location:** Rural, simple.
Surface: grasstiles. 01/01-31/12.
Distance: 1,5km 5km on the spot 100m.

S **Rheurdt** 9E3

Wohnmobilhafen Ökodorf, St. Nikolausweg 15.
GPS: n51,46382 e6,46780.

21 € 10 Ch included WC. **Surface:** metalled.
01/01-31/12.
Distance: 500m 500m 500m on the spot on the spot.

S **Rietberg** 9H3

Jakobistrasse, Mastholte. **GPS**: n51,75667 e8,39111.

6 free € 0,50/80liter Ch. **Location:** Rural, central.
Surface: asphalted. 01/01-31/12.
Distance: 100m 100m 100m.

S **Rietberg** 9H3

Parkplatz Rottwiese, Jerusalemer Straße.
GPS: n51,80999 e8,41203.
free Ch. **Surface:** gravel. 01/01-31/12.
Distance: centre 1,2km.
Remarks: At museum.

Rietberg 9H3

Am Heimathaus, Langenberger Strasse, Mastholte.
GPS: n51,75765 e8,38945.

2 free. **Location:** Urban. **Surface:** asphalted. 01/01-31/12.
Distance: 100m 100m 100m.

Roetgen 11E2

Am Bahnhof, Bahnhofstrasse. **GPS**: n50,64868 e6,18506.

10 free. **Location:** Rural, simple, noisy.
Surface: gravel/metalled. 01/01-31/12.
Distance: 300m 300m.

S **Rosendahl** 9F2

Wohnmobilplatz Darfeld, Sudetenstrasse, Darfeld.
GPS: n52,02696 e7,26501.

20 free € 1/100liter Ch (12x)€ 1/6h.
Location: Rural, simple.
Surface: grassy/metalled. 01/01-31/12.
Distance: 500m on the spot 500m 1km.

S **Rüthen** 9H3

Auf der Kamp, Auf dem Kamp 1. **GPS**: n51,49523 e8,43293.

DE

12 € 5 € 1 Ch € 1/8h.
Surface: asphalted. 01/01-31/12.
Distance: on the spot 200m.

Sassenberg 9H2

Parkplatz Feldmark, Feldmark. **GPS**: n52,00370 e8,06528.

3 free € 1/80liter Ch. **Location:** Rural, simple.
Surface: metalled. 01/01-31/12.
Distance: 2,5km 100m on the spot on the spot on the spot on the spot.

Schieder 10A2

Freizeitzentrum Schiedersee, Kronenbruch.
GPS: n51,92073 e9,16471.

300 € 10 € 1/100liter Ch € 0,50/kWh
WC € 0,50/5minutes € 2. **Location:** Rural, comfortable, quiet.
Surface: grassy/metalled. 01/01-31/12.
Distance: 1,3km 50m 50m on the spot on the spot on the spot on the spot.
Remarks: Bread-service.

Schleiden 11E2

Wohnmobilhafen am Nationalpark-Eifel, Pfarrer-Kneipp-Straße, Gemünd. **GPS**: n50,57855 e6,49107.

55 € 8, tourist tax € 1/pp Ch included € 1,100m.
Location: Rural, comfortable, quiet. **Surface:** gravel/metalled.
01/01-31/12.
Distance: within walking distance 500m 500m on the spot on the spot.
Remarks: Bread-service.

Schleiden 11E2

Erlebnisfreibad, Im Wiesengrund. **GPS**: n50,52993 e6,47022.

3 free. **Location:** Rural, simple, quiet.
Surface: asphalted. 01/01-31/12.
Remarks: Max. 24h.

Schloss Holte/Stukenbrock 9H2

American Store Niebel, Hauptstraße 65. **GPS**: n51,90722 e8,66444.
25 € 14, dog € 1 Ch included. **Surface:** grassy/metalled.
01/01-31/12.
Distance: 1km 3km 200m 1km.

Schloss Holte/Stukenbrock 9H2

Reisemobilstellplatz Am Sennebach, Liemkerstrasse 27, Liemke.
GPS: n51,86979 e8,61531.

15 € 5 Ch € 2 (18x) € 2. **Location:** Rural, isolated, quiet.
Surface: grasstiles. 01/01-31/12 service: sa/su.
Distance: 5km 1km 1km.
Remarks: Behind Froli Kunstoffwerk Fromme, max. 3 days.

Schmallenberg 11H1

Im Sorpetal, Winkhausen 21. **GPS**: n51,16083 e8,34056.

11 € 9 + € 1,25/pp tourist tax € 0,50/60liter Ch (12x) € 0,50/kWh. **Surface:** grassy. 01/01-31/12.
Distance: on the spot 100m 2km 500m 1km on the spot.
Remarks: Trout pond, golf court 500m, playground.

Schöppingen 9F2

Schulze Althoff, Heven 48. **GPS**: n52,07361 e7,22361.

30 € 20/night, 3p incl., +3p € 4/pp Ch (12x),6Amp
WC included sanitary € 2/pp € 5.
Location: Rural, simple. **Surface:** grassy. 01/01-31/12.
Distance: 2,5km on the spot on the spot 2,5km on the spot.
Remarks: Swimming pool available.

Senden 9G2

Sportpark Senden, Buldenerstrasse 13b. **GPS**: n51,85419 e7,47433.

10 free. **Location:** Simple, noisy. **Surface:** grasstiles.
01/01-31/12.
Distance: on the spot 200m 300m on the spot.
Remarks: Parking at sports park.

Senden 9G2

Wohnmobilstellplatz Steinhoff, Gettrup 37.
GPS: n51,83305 e7,46878.

10 € 6 Ch (6x) € 0,50/kWh. **Location:** Rural, isolated.
Surface: grassy/metalled. 01/01-31/12.
Distance: Senden 4km 2,5km 2,5km.

Sendenhorst 9G2

Westor 31. **GPS**: n51,84286 e7,81849.

3 free € 0,50/40liter Ch € 0,50.
Location: Urban, simple, central, noisy. **Surface:** metalled.
01/01-31/12.
Distance: on the spot 300m 1km on the spot.
Remarks: Max. 3 nights.

Siegen 11H1

An der Alche, Freudenbergerstraße 67. **GPS**: n50,88073 e8,00764.
4 free € 0,50/40liter Ch (4x) € 0,50/kWh.
01/01-31/12.
Distance: 1km 5km 200m 1km.
Remarks: Max. 3 days.

Siegen 11H1

Hallenbad Weidenau, Poststraße 27. **GPS**: n50,89463 e8,02405.

3 free € 1/10minutes Ch (2x) € 1/8h.
Location: Urban. **Surface:** metalled. 01/01-31/12.
Distance: 200m 200m 200m 250m on the spot on the spot.
Remarks: Max. 3 days.

Simmerath 11E2

Wohnmobilhafen Rurseezentrum, Seeufer 1, Rurberg.
GPS: n50,60658 e6,38177.

10 € 8/24h € 2 Ch.
Location: Rural, comfortable. **Surface:** grasstiles. 01/01-31/12.
Distance: 100m 50m.

Soest 9H3

AquaFun, Ardeyweg 35. **GPS**: n51,56944 e8,07778.
9 € 9 € 1/5minutes Ch € 1/2kWh. 01/01-31/12.
Distance: 3,5km 4km 1km 1,5km.
Remarks: At swimming pool, e-bike rental.

Soest 9H3

City Motel, Altes Stellwerk 9. **GPS**: n51,57503 e8,11478.

DE

30 € 8 Ch (14x)€ 0,50/kWh WC € 2 € 3/3 included.
Location: Urban, comfortable, central, quiet. **Surface:** gravel.
01/01-31/12.
Distance: 500m 200m 200m 200m on the spot on the spot.
Remarks: Check in at reception.

Solingen 11F1

Am Brandteich, Gräfrath. **GPS**: n51,21151 e7,07217.

10 free. **Location:** Urban, simple, quiet. **Surface:** concrete.
01/01-31/12.
Distance: on the spot 2,7km on the spot 300m.
Remarks: Parking fire-station, max. 1 night, playground.

Solingen 11F1

Technologiezentrum, Grünewalder Straße 29.
GPS: n51,16250 e7,07889.
4 free. **Surface:** grasstiles. 01/01-31/12.
Distance: 1km 200m 400m 200m.

S **Stadtlohn** 9F2

Freizeit- und Hallenbad, Uferstrasse 29.
GPS: n51,99792 e6,93019.

4 free € 0,50/100liter Ch (4x)€ 1/kWh WC.
Location: Rural, simple, isolated. **Surface:** metalled.
01/01-31/12 water disconnected in winter.
Distance: 800m 1km 800m.
Remarks: Parking swimming pool.

S **Steinfurt** 9G2

Wohnmobilstellplatz Steinfurt, Liedekerkerstrasse 70, Burgsteinfurt.
GPS: n52,14738 e7,34746.

25 free € 1/100liter Ch € 1/2kWh. **Location:** Rural, simple.
Surface: gravel. 01/01-31/12.
Distance: 1km 500m 200m.
Remarks: Parking behind police station, max. 3 nights, voluntary contribution.

Steinfurt 9G2

Am Rathaus, Emsdettener Straße 40. **GPS**: n52,12822 e7,39356.

6 free. **Location:** Urban, simple. **Surface:** asphalted.
01/01-31/12.
Distance: 400m 200m 400m 400m 200m.

Steinhagen 9H2

Am Cronsbach. **GPS**: n51,99998 e8,42351.

2 free. **Location:** Urban, simple. **Surface:** metalled.
01/01-31/12.
Distance: 100m 100m 100m.
Remarks: Max. 2 days.

S **Stemwede** 9H1

Stellplatz Hollenmühle, Hinterm Teich 3, Levern.
GPS: n52,36783 e8,43833.

36 € 14 Ch WC included. **Location:** Rural, comfortable. **Surface:** grassy/gravel. 01/01-31/12.
Distance: on the spot 3,2km.
Remarks: Bread-service.

Stemwede 9H1

Park Stemwederberg, Stemwederbergstrasse/Freudeneck, Westrup.
GPS: n52,43246 e8,43973.

8 free. **Location:** Rural, comfortable. **Surface:** grassy.
01/01-31/12.
Distance: 2km 2km 2km on the spot.

S **Stemwede** 9H1

Hotel-Gasthof Moorhof, Wagenfelderstrasse 34, Oppenwehe.
GPS: n52,49979 e8,53507.

20 € 7, free with a meal included € 2,16Amp.
Location: Rural, quiet. **Surface:** grassy. 01/01-31/12 Mo, Thu.
Distance: on the spot.

S **Straelen** 9E3

Fitnessbad Wasserstraelen, Lingsforterstraße 100.
GPS: n51,45201 e6,25708.

27 € 8 € 1/80liter Ch (30x)€ 0,50/kWh included.
Surface: asphalted. 01/01-31/12.
Distance: 1,2km 1km 1km.
Remarks: Max. 3 days.

Tecklenburg 9G2

Parkplatz Bismarckturm, Am Weingarten.
GPS: n52,22129 e7,79905.

5 € 4.
Location: Simple, quiet. **Surface:** asphalted. 01/01-31/12.
Distance: 800m 200m.

S **Tecklenburg** 9G2

Regenbogen-Camp, Grafenstraße. **GPS**: n52,22941 e7,89052.
4 € 10 > 17h < 13h Ch included. **Location:** Urban, simple, noisy. **Surface:** asphalted. 01/01-31/12.
Distance: Tecklenburg 7km.

S **Telgte** 9G2

Am Dümmert, Emstor. **GPS**: n51,98497 e7,79151.
3 free € 1/100liter Ch € 1/kWh. **Location:** Simple.
Surface: gravel. 01/01-31/12.
Distance: 600m 600m 600m on the spot.

S **Telgte** 9G2

Waldschwimmbad Klatenberge, Waldweg.
GPS: n51,99459 e7,78328.

20 free. **Location:** Rural, simple.
Surface: asphalted. 01/01-31/12.
Distance: 1km 300m 900m on the spot.
Remarks: Parking swimming pool, recreation area.

S **Telgte** 9G2

Altes Gasthus Lauheide, Lauheide 3, K17.
GPS: n51,99862 e7,75319.

80 € 10 Ch included.
Location: Quiet. **Surface:** grassy.
01/01-31/12 Restaurant: Wed.
Distance: 4km on the spot bus 300m on the spot on the spot.

DE

S Uedem 9E3

Reisemobilstellplatz Uedem, Bergstraße 99.
GPS: n51,66173 e6,28734.

26 € 9 Ch WC included. **Location:** Rural, comfortable.
Surface: grassy. 01/01-31/12.
Distance: 1,5km 1,3km on the spot on the spot.

S Velbert 11F1

Unter der Saubrücke, Parkstraße, Velbert-Mitte.
GPS: n51,34097 e7,03050.

6 € 5/24h € 1/100liter Ch € 0,50/kWh.
Location: Urban, simple, quiet. **Surface:** gravel.
01/01-31/12.
Distance: 800m 1,6km 250m on the spot.

S Velbert 11F1

Panoramabad Velbert-Neviges, Wiesenweg.
GPS: n51,30582 e7,08546.

4 free € 1/80liter Ch. **Location:** Urban, simple, quiet.
Surface: concrete. 01/01-31/12.
Distance: 800m nearby 500m.
Remarks: Parking swimming pool, max. 3 nights.

Velbert 11F1

Domparkplatz, Bernsaustrasse Schloss Hardenberg.
GPS: n51,31565 e7,08724.

4 free. **Location:** Urban. **Surface:** gravel.
01/01-31/12.
Distance: 600m on the spot.
Remarks: Max. 3 nights.

Velbert 11F1

Nizzabad, Nizzatal 4, Langenberg. **GPS**: n51,34362 e7,13766.

3 free. **Location:** Simple, quiet. **Surface:** metalled.
01/01-31/12.
Distance: Langenberg 2,5km on the spot.
Remarks: Max. 3 nights.

S Velen 9F2

Erholungsgebiet Waldvelen, Klyer Damm 8-10.
GPS: n51,90167 e7,01167.

30 € 15-18, 2 pers. incl. Ch (50x) WC included
€ 1/4minutes € 4.
Location: Rural, luxurious. **Surface:** grassy. 01/01-31/12.
Distance: 2km 8,5km on the spot on the spot.
Remarks: Bread-service (weekend).

Velen 9F2

Freibad Ramsdorf, Velener Straße, Ramsdorf.
GPS: n51,88955 e6,92503.

5 free. **Location:** Rural, simple, noisy. **Surface:** asphalted.
01/01-31/12.
Distance: Ramsdorf 300m 200m on the spot on the spot.
Remarks: At swimming pool.

S Viersen 11E1

Am Familienbad Ransberg, Heesstraße 80, Viersen-Dülken.
GPS: n51,25083 e6,35291.

9 € 10 € 0,50/100liter Ch (9x)included.
Surface: metalled. 01/01-31/12.
Distance: Dülken 400m, Viersen 3km 400m 2km 100m.
Remarks: Max. 3 days, to be paid at swimming pool.

S Vreden 9F2

Hotel Zum Möwenparadies, Zwillbrockerstrasse 39.
GPS: n52,05305 e6,70733.

10 € 10 Ch WC included.
Location: Simple, isolated. **Surface:** grassy. 01/01-31/12.
Distance: 4km on the spot on the spot on the spot
200m.
Remarks: Trout pond.

S Vreden 9F2

Wohnmobilpark Vreden, Ottensteiner Strasse 59.
GPS: n52,03962 e6,84136.

50 € 8, 4 pers.incl Ch (14x)included WC € 2 € 3/h.
Location: Rural, simple, quiet. **Surface:** grassy.
01/01-31/12.
Distance: 500m on the spot.
Remarks: Breakfast-service, swimming pool € 2/pp.

S Wachtendonk 9E3

Bleiche P4, Achter de Stadt. **GPS**: n51,40601 e6,33170.

24 € 7 € 0,50/60liter € 0,50 Ch (12x)€ 0,50/kWh.
Surface: gravel. 01/01-31/12.
Distance: 400m 100m 400m.
Remarks: Money in envelope in mail box.

S Wadersloh 9H3

Im Klostergarten 18, Liesborn. **GPS**: n51,71414 e8,25960.

4 free € 0,50/80liter Ch (4x)€ 0,50/12h.
Location: Rural. **Surface:** metalled. 01/01-31/12.
Distance: 400m 100m 400m on the spot on the spot.
Remarks: Behind gymnasium.

Waldbröl 11G2

Am Hallenbad, Vennstrassse. **GPS**: n50,87511 e7,60987.

5 free. **Location:** Rural, simple, quiet. **Surface:** metalled.
01/01-31/12.
Distance: on the spot 350m 300m on the spot on the spot.
Remarks: Max. 2 days.

S Waldfeucht-Brüggelchen 11E1

Reisemobilstellplatz Tilder Weg, Tilderweg.
GPS: n51,07076 e5,99454.

18 € 5 € 1/80liter Ch (10x)€ 0,50/kWh.
Location: Rural, simple, quiet. **Surface:** metalled.

DE

01/01-31/12.
Distance: 1km on the spot 500m 100m on the spot.
Remarks: Max. 4 nights, money in envelope in mail box.

S Waltrop 9G3

Restaurant Zur Lohburg, Lohburgerstrass 105, A2 Ausfahrt henreichenburg, Schiffshebewerk. **GPS**: n51,60613 e7,34882.

15 € 5 € 3 Ch € 3 . **Surface:** grassy. 01/01-31/12.
Distance: 1km on the spot 1km.

S Warburg 10A3

Schützenplatz, Paderborner Tor 134. **GPS**: n51,48993 e9,13810.
5 € 5 Ch included.
Surface: metalled. 01/01-31/12 15/09-15/10.
Distance: 500m 100m 200m.
Remarks: Max. 3 days.

S Warendorf 9G2

Parkplatz am Emsseepark, Sassenberger Strasse.
GPS: n51,95447 e7,99904.

14 free € 1/50liter Ch (14x)€ 1/kWh.
Location: Rural, simple, central, quiet.
Surface: metalled. 01/01-31/12.
Distance: 500m on the spot 100m 800m 100m on the spot on the spot.

Warendorf 9G2

Parkplatz Zwischen den Emsbrücken, Am Emswehr.
GPS: n51,95426 e7,99164.

2 free. 01/01-31/12.
Distance: 100m.

S Warstein 9H3

Camperpark zum Bayernstadl, Enkerbruch 12a.
GPS: n51,43041 e8,37432.

40 € 8 € 1/100liter Ch (18x)€ 2/day .
Surface: gravel. 01/01-31/12.
Distance: 1,5km on the spot 1,5km 1,5km.
Remarks: Bread-service.

S Warstein 9H3

Vans in Paradise, Zu Hause im Waldpark. **GPS**: n51,42615 e8,35525.

40 € 15 Ch (76x),16Amp WC included € 2/2.
Location: Isolated, quiet. **Surface:** grassy/gravel. 01/01-31/12.
Distance: 2km small menu 2km 2km.
Remarks: At Warstein brewery, bread-service + breakfast-service.

S Warstein 9H3

Schützenhalle, Schützenstraße 30, Hirschberg.
GPS: n51,43398 e8,27477.
3 free . 01/01-31/12 Whitsuntide.
Distance: 500m, Warstein 12km 500m.

Warstein 9H3

Wohnmobilstellplatz, Dammweg. **GPS**: n51,45103 e8,34750.

5 free. **Location:** Simple.
Surface: gravel/metalled.
01/01-31/12.
Distance: 2km 500m 1km 1km.
Remarks: At sports park.

Tourist information Warstein:
Warsteiner Brauerei, Zu Hause im Waldpark. Guided tour 1.45h, 2 drinks included. daily 12-17, Su 13-15h.

S Wassenberg 11E1

Parkbad Wassenberg, Auf dem Taubenkamp 2.
GPS: n51,09833 e6,14364.

11 € 5/day, € 20/week € 1/100 € 1 Ch € 0,50/kWh.
Location: Rural, comfortable, quiet. **Surface:** metalled.
01/01-31/12.
Distance: 1,5km.
Remarks: To be paid at swimming pool.

S Weeze 9E3

Tierpark Fährsteg, L5 Fährsteg. **GPS**: n51,63074 e6,20086.

13 € 5 € 0,50/kWh. **Location:** Simple. 01/01-31/12.
Distance: 500m 500m.

S Weeze 9E3

Aral, Industriestraße. **GPS**: n51,62029 e6,20972.
€ 1 Ch. 01/01-31/12.

S Wegberg 11E1

Wegberger Reisemobilstellplatz, Schul- und Sportzentrum, Maaseiker Strasse 67. **GPS**: n51,13389 e6,28266.

10 € 8 Ch included.
Surface: grassy/gravel. 01/01-31/12.
Distance: 400m 400m 400m on the spot.
Remarks: To be paid at swimming pool, caution key € 20.

S Werne 9G3

Natur Solebad, Am Hagen. **GPS**: n51,65910 e7,63414.

12 € 5/24h € 1/80liter Ch € 0,50/kWh.
Location: Rural, simple. **Surface:** metalled.
01/01-31/12 15/10-31/10.
Distance: 400m 200m 400m on the spot.
Remarks: Tuesday and Friday market.

S Wesel 9F3

Reisemobilstellplatz Römerwardt, Rheinpromenade.
GPS: n51,66116 e6,59256.

45 € 7, 01/04-31/10 € 9 € 1/80liter Ch € 1/kWh € 1,50.
Location: Rural, comfortable, quiet. **Surface:** grassy/metalled.
01/01-31/12.
Distance: 1,5km 100m 1,5km on the spot on the spot.
Remarks: Check in on arrival, bread-service, bicycle rental, market Wednesday and Saturday.

Westerkappeln 9G2

Am Freibad, Bullerteichstraße 12. **GPS**: n52,31556 e7,88070.

2 free. **Location:** Urban, simple. **Surface:** grasstiles.
01/01-31/12.
Distance: 600m 400m 50m.

Wiehl 11G1

Freizeitpark Wiehl, Brüchnerstrasse. **GPS**: n50,94716 e7,54585.

5 free € 1/80liter Ch.
Location: Simple, central. **Surface:** metalled.
01/01-31/12.
Distance: 300m 5,4km 400m.
Remarks: Parking next to recreation park and disco, max. 3 nights.

Wiehl 11G1

Sportplatz Eichhardt, Friedhofstrasse.
GPS: n50,95110 e7,54482.

3 free. **Location:** Urban. **Surface:** metalled.
01/01-31/12.
Distance: 1km 5,3km 1km 1km.
Remarks: Parking sports park, max. 3 nights.

Tourist information Wiehl:
www.wiehl.de. Small town in the green hills. 180 kilometres marked hiking routes.
Wiehler Dahlienschau. 150 varieties of dahlias.
01/08-31/10 daily 9-19h.
free.
Wiehler Trofsteinhöhle. Caves Temperature is approx. 8°C.
15/03-31/10 10-17h, 01/11-14/03 Sa-Su 11-16h.
Bergische Postkutsche, Nümrecht Post. Ride by mail-coach between Wiehl and Nümbrecht. 01/05-30/09 Fri-Su 10-16h.

Wilnsdorf 11H2

Wielandshof, Bauhofstraße 5. **GPS**: n50,80692 e8,10896.

6 € 5 € 0,50/60liter Ch (8x)€ 1/12h,10Amp.
Surface: gravel. 01/01-31/12.
Distance: 900m 900m 1km.
Remarks: Check in at farm.

Wilnsdorf 11H2

Gästehaus Wilgersdorf, Kalkhain 23. **GPS**: n50,80889 e8,14722.
3 free. 01/01-31/12.
Distance: 4km on the spot 1km.

Windeck 11G2

Am Sportplatz, Im Bungert, Herchen. **GPS**: n50,78025 e7,51308.

5 free (10x)€ 0,50/kWh. **Location:** Rural, simple, quiet.
Surface: gravel. 01/01-31/12.
Distance: 200m 8,5km 200m 200m on the spot on the spot.
Remarks: Parking sports park.

Windeck 11G2

Hallenbad, Bergische strasse 21, Dattenfeld.
GPS: n50,80754 e7,56105.

4 free € 2 € 2 Ch€ 2. **Location:** Rural, simple, quiet.
Surface: metalled. 01/01-31/12.
Distance: 8,5km on the spot on the spot.

Windeck 11G2

Auf dem Greent, Dattenfeld. **GPS**: n50,80697 e7,55495.

50 free. **Location:** Rural, simple, quiet.
Surface: asphalted/grassy. 01/01-31/12.
Distance: 500m 8,5km 500m 500m.
Remarks: Fair ground.

Windeck 11G2

Brunnenweg, Dattenfeld. **GPS**: n50,80486 e7,56087.

5 free. **Location:** Simple, quiet.
Surface: grassy/gravel. 01/01-31/12.
Distance: 200m 8km 200m 150m on the spot on the spot.
Remarks: Recreation park.

Windeck 11G2

Museumsdorf Altwindeck, Im Thal Windeck 17, Alt-Windeck.
GPS: n50,81276 e7,57554.

4 free. **Location:** Rural, simple, quiet.
Surface: gravel. 01/01-31/12.
Distance: 2km 8,5km on the spot 2km on the spot on the spot.
Remarks: Parking museum, max. 3 days.

Winterberg 11H1

Wohnmobilpark Winterberg, Neuastenberger Straße 4a, OT Neuastenberg. **GPS**: n51,15974 e8,48383.

70 € 7,50-13,50 + € 1,95/pp tourist tax € 1/100liter Ch (72x)€ 0,60/kWh WC € 1,50/6minutes € 2,50/2,50 included.
Surface: gravel. 01/01-31/12.
Distance: on the spot on the spot.
Remarks: Bread-service.

Winterberg 11H1

Parkplatz Stadthalle, Schulstrasse. **GPS**: n51,19163 e8,53810.

20 € 8/24h € 0,50/50liter Ch (10x)€ 0,50/3h.
Surface: metalled. 01/01-31/12.
Distance: 1km 1km.

Winterberg 11H1

Bergrestaurant Bobhaus, Auf der Kappe 1. **GPS**: n51,18493 e8,50559.

8 € 12, free with a meal.
Location: Rural. **Surface:** asphalted. 01/01-31/12.
Distance: 2km on the spot on the spot on the spot on the spot on the spot.
Remarks: Parking ski-lift, check in at restaurant.

Winterberg 11H1

Campingplatz Winterberg. **GPS**: n51,18632 e8,50445.

DE

€ 18,50-20,50 Ch (25x)€ 0,55/kWh WC € 1 € 0,50.
Location: Rural, luxurious. **Surface:** metalled. 01/01-31/12.
Distance: 2km on the spot 2km 20m on the spot on the spot on the spot on the spot.
Remarks: Parking at skipistes.

Witten 9G3

Reisemobil-Center, Pferdebachstrasse 150.
GPS: n51,45411 e7,35246.

8 free € 1/80liter Ch. **Surface:** gravel. 01/01-31/12.
Distance: 3km 3km 3km.

Wülfrath 11F1

Parkplatz, Mettmanner Straße 42. **GPS**: n51,28188 e7,02741.

6 free. **Location:** Urban, simple, quiet.
Surface: concrete. 01/01-31/12.
Distance: on the spot 500m 800m.

Wuppertal 11F1

Wohnmobil-Oase Wuppertal, Linderhauser Str. 70.
GPS: n51,29436 e7,24509.
10 € 16 € 2 Ch€ 3 . **Surface:** metalled.
01/01-31/12.
Distance: 3km 200m.

Xanten 9E3

WomoPark-Xanten, Fürstenberg 6. **GPS**: n51,65413 e6,46389.
70 € 12 € 0,50/24h € 0,50 Ch€ 1 (70x)€ 3,50/24h
WC€ 0,75 € 1,75/pppd.
Location: Rural, comfortable, luxurious, quiet. **Surface:** grassy.
01/01-31/12.
Distance: 700m 10km 1,4km 1,4km 800m 300m 300m on the spot on the spot.
Remarks: Check in on arrival.

Zülpich 11F2

Wohnmobilpark Seepark, Eichenallee.
GPS: n50,67660 e6,65867.

27 € 9 € 1 Ch included.
Location: Rural, simple, isolated. **Surface:** grassy. 01/01-31/12.
Distance: 2km 100m 400m 2km.
Remarks: Service nearby tenniscourt 100m.

Rhineland-Palatinate/Saarland

Alken 11G3

Moselstraße 1. **GPS**: n50,25090 e7,44590.

5 free. **Location:** Rural, simple. **Surface:** gravel.
01/01-31/12.
Distance: 200m 100m 200m on the spot.

Altdorf 16H2

Schulstraße. **GPS**: n49,28426 e8,22035.
free. **Surface:** metalled. 01/01-31/12.
Distance: 300m 300m.

Altdorf 16H2

Spelzenhof, Hauptstrasse 77. **GPS**: n49,28869 e8,22028.

6 € 10 included € 2.
Location: Simple. **Surface:** grassy. 01/01-31/12 Mon, Tue.
Distance: nearby 7km 150m 400m nearby.

Altendiez 11H3

Gaststätte Lahnblickhalle, Lahnblick 4.
GPS: n50,36610 e7,98040.

6 € 8 included.
Location: Simple. **Surface:** gravel. 01/01-31/12 Mo.
Distance: on the spot on the spot 500m.
Remarks: At gymnasium, discount at restaurant € 5.

Altenglan 16G1

Draisine, Austrasse. **GPS**: n49,55001 e7,46465.

4 free € 1/80liter Ch (6x)€ 1.
Location: Rural, simple, quiet. **Surface:** gravel. 01/04-31/10.
Distance: 100m 100m on the spot on the spot.

Andernach 11G2

Wohnmobilstellplatz Andernach, Scheidsgasse/Uferstrasse.
GPS: n50,44176 e7,40796.

70 € 7 € 1/100liter Ch (40x)€ 1/2kWh WC€ 0,50.
Surface: metalled. 01/01-31/12.
Distance: on the spot Rhine river 200m 400m.
Remarks: Max. 3 nights.

Andernach 11G2

Wohnmobilstellplatz Monte Mare, Klingelswiese 1.
GPS: n50,42633 e7,38492.

14 € 3 € 1/100liter Ch (16x)€ 0,50/kWh WC .
Surface: concrete. 01/01-31/12.
Distance: 2km Laach Lake 10km 2km 2km on the spot on the spot.
Remarks: Bread-service, discount on access terme.

Tourist information Andernach:
Sa 7-13h.

Annweiler 16H2

Am Kurpark, Bindersbacherstrasse. **GPS**: n49,19624 e7,96817.

10 free € 1/80liter Ch.
Location: Rural, quiet. **Surface:** asphalted. 01/01-31/12.
Distance: 1km 600m.
Remarks: Max. 3 days.

Bacharach 11G3

Reisemobilplatz Sonnenstrand, B9 Leinpfad.
GPS: n50,05487 e7,77123.

30 € 9, dog € 1 € 1 Ch (30x)€ 2,50/24h € 1 € 3/3.
Location: Comfortable, central, quiet. **Surface:** gravel.
01/01-31/12 high water.
Distance: on the spot Rhine river 300m 300m.
Remarks: Bread-service, dog € 1,50/night.

S Bad Bergzabern 16H2

Schloßgärten, Weinbergstrasse 7. **GPS**: n49,10322 e7,99737.

10 € 4 € 1/80liter € 1 Ch € 1.
Location: Urban, simple, central, noisy. **Surface:** metalled.
01/01-31/12 water disconnected in winter.
Distance: on the spot on the spot 200m.

S Bad Bergzabern 16H2

Weingut Hitziger, Liebrauenbergweg 3. **GPS**: n49,10667 e7,99611.

8 € 5 Chincluded € 1/kWh.
Location: Rural, simple, quiet. **Surface:** grassy. 01/01-31/12.
Distance: 1km 2km 2km.

S Bad Dürkheim 16H1

In der Silz, Leistadterstrasse. **GPS**: n49,46944 e8,16722.

170 € 6 € 1/80liter Ch (40x)€ 1/kWh.
Location: Urban, simple. **Surface:** grassy/gravel.
01/01-31/12.
Distance: 300m 100m 300m 200m.
Remarks: Max. 3 days, servicepoint at Knaus Park.

S Bad Dürkheim 16H1

Katharinenhof, In den Kornwiesen 1. **GPS**: n49,46633 e8,20144.

10 € 10, € 18 service incl. + € 1/pp tourist tax Ch WC included.
Location: Rural, quiet. **Surface:** gravel. 01/01-31/12.
Distance: 450m on the spot 600m 1km.
Remarks: Bread-service.

S Bad Dürkheim 16H1

Knaus park, In den Almen 3. **GPS**: n49,47472 e8,19167.

16 € 10 € 1/70liter Ch (8x)€ 0,70/kWh € 3,30/pp.
Location: Rural. **Surface:** gravel/metalled. 01/01-31/12.
Remarks: Sanitary at campsite.

S Bad Ems 11G3

Yachthafen Kutscher's Marina, Nievernerstrasse 20.
GPS: n50,33278 e7,70167.

16 € 10 Ch (20x)€ 0,50/kWh WC € 1,2 x € 0,50.
Location: Comfortable, quiet. **Surface:** gravel. 01/03-15/11.
Distance: on the spot on the spot 1km 300m.
Remarks: Barbecue place.

S Bad Kreuznach 16G1

Wohnmobilstellplatz Salinental, Karlshalle 11, Saline.
GPS: n49,82778 e7,85001.

40 € 13 € 0,50/60liter Ch € 3/night WC € 1.
Location: Rural. **Surface:** gravel. 01/01-31/12.
Distance: 2km on the spot on the spot 200m 2km on the spot.

S Bad Kreuznach 16G1

Weingut Desoi, Am Darmstädter Hof. **GPS**: n49,82803 e7,88934.

3 € 5 included. **Location:** Rural, simple, quiet.
Surface: concrete. 01/01-31/12.
Distance: 1,5km 10km 850m 500m.

S Bad Kreuznach 16G1

Weingut Gut Neuhof, Gut Neuhof. **GPS**: n49,86923 e7,85924.

4 € 10 included. **Location:** Rural, simple, quiet.
Surface: grassy. 01/01-31/12.
Distance: 3km 600m 2,5km.

S Bad Marienberg 11G2

Marienbad, Bismarckstrasse 65. **GPS**: n50,64321 e7,93515.

40 € 10 € 1/80liter Ch (40x)€ 0,50/kWh included.
Location: Luxurious, quiet. **Surface:** metalled. 01/01-31/12.
Distance: 2km Bistro.
Remarks: 10 days € 78, bread-service, free use of sun beds and beach chairs.

S Bad Münster am Stein-Ebernburg 16G1

Reisemobilstellplatz Weingut Rapp, Schlossgartenstrasse 74.
GPS: n49,80800 e7,83208.

3 € 10, dog € 1 € 1/100liter Ch included.
Location: Rural, simple, quiet. **Surface:** gravel.
01/01-31/12.
Distance: 500m 15km 500m 2km.

S Bad Neuenahr 11F2

Am Schwimmbad. **GPS**: n50,53806 e7,10139.

25 € 7 € 0,50 Ch € 1/2kWh € 0,50.
Location: Urban, central. **Surface:** metalled.
01/01-31/12.
Distance: 400m 300m bakery 500m.
Remarks: Along the Ahr river, max. 24h.

S Bad Neuenahr 11F2

Apolinaris-Stadion, Kreuzstrasse. **GPS**: n50,54456 e7,15132.

20 € 5/24h € 1/80liter Ch.
Surface: asphalted. 01/01-31/12.
Distance: 3km.

Bad Neuenahr 11F2

Wohnmobilstellplatz Bachem, St.-Pius-Straße.
GPS: n50,53962 e7,10775.

20 € 5/24h. **Location:** Urban, simple. **Surface:** asphalted.
01/01-31/12.

DE

Distance: 700m 700m.
Remarks: Parking at the Ahr.

S Bad Sobernheim 16G1

Reisemobilstellplatz am Nohfels, Hömigweg 1.
GPS: n49,77910 e7,65800.

39 € 9 € 0,10/10liter Ch (48x)€ 2,50/day,16Amp WC. **Location:** Rural, comfortable, quiet. **Surface:** metalled. 01/01-31/12.
Distance: 500m 100m 100m 200m 500m 300m on the spot on the spot.
Remarks: Bread-service.

S Battweiler 16G2

Flugplatz Pottschütthöhe, Pottschütthöhe.
GPS: n49,26761 e7,49096.

10 € 15 Ch (10x)included. **Location:** Simple, isolated, quiet. **Surface:** grassy/gravel. 01/01-31/12 Mo.
Distance: 2km 10km on the spot.
Remarks: At airfield.

Baumholder 16G1

Freizeitzentrum Am Weiher, Ringstrasse.
GPS: n49,61111 e7,33917.

3 free. **Location:** Rural, simple.
Surface: asphalted. 01/04-31/10.
Distance: 2km on the spot McDonalds 250m 250m.

S Becheln 11G3

Restaurant Zum Wolfsbusch, Emser strasse 1.
GPS: n50,29609 e7,71503.

5 € 2, guests free € 2. **Location:** Simple, quiet.
Surface: gravel/metalled. 01/01-31/12.
Distance: on the spot on the spot 300m.

S Beckingen 16F2

Wohnmobilstellplatz Düppenweiler, Brunnenstrasse 11, Düppenweiler. **GPS**: n49,41414 e6,76973.

20 € 4 € 1/100liter Ch (6x)€ 1/day.
Location: Simple, quiet. **Surface:** metalled. 01/01-31/12.
Distance: on the spot 300m.

S Beckingen 16F2

Landgasthaus Wilscheider Hof, Zum Wilscheider Hof, Düppenweiler.
GPS: n49,42562 e6,76422.

15 € 5 Ch (7x)€ 1/day WC € 1,50. **Location:** Rural, comfortable, isolated, quiet. **Surface:** grassy. 01/01-31/12.
Distance: 1,5km on the spot 1,5km.

S Bellheim 16H2

Wohnmobilstellplatz Bellheim, Auchtweide.
GPS: n49,19552 e8,27466.

8 € 5 WCincluded € 1/pp. **Location:** Simple, isolated, quiet.
Surface: grassy/gravel. 01/05-31/10.
Distance: 700m 3km 750m 1km 200m on the spot on the spot.
Remarks: At tennis-courts, max. 24h, possibility for reservation.

Bendorf 11G2

Wohnmobilstellplatz In der Sayner Hütte, In der Sayner Hütte.
GPS: n50,44139 e7,57972.
6 free. **Surface:** gravel. 01/01-31/12.
Distance: 2km 4km 100m 2km.

S Bernkastel 11F3

Weingut Studert-Prüm im Maximin Hof, Hauptstrasse 150, Wehlen.
GPS: n49,93771 e7,04811.

43 € 10-12 Ch WCincluded. **Location:** Rural, comfortable, quiet. **Surface:** grassy. 01/04-31/10.
Distance: on the spot on the spot on the spot on the spot 2km, bakery 300m on the spot on the spot.

P S Bernkastel 11F3

Nikolausufer. **GPS**: n49,91119 e7,06721.

40 Ch. **Location:** Urban. **Surface:** grasstiles.
01/01-31/12, 10-18h.
Distance: on the spot.
Remarks: Max. 6h.

Betzdorf 11G2

Friedrichstrasse. **GPS**: n50,78636 e7,87781.

1 free. **Location:** Urban, simple, noisy.
Surface: asphalted. 01/01-31/12.
Distance: 500m 200m.
Remarks: Max. 24h.

Betzdorf 11G2

Schützenplatz, Martin-Luther-Strasse. **GPS**: n50,79323 e7,86793.

1 free. **Location:** Urban, simple.
Surface: gravel. 01/01-31/12.
Distance: on the spot on the spot on the spot 1km.
Remarks: Max. 1 night.

Betzdorf 11G2

Vor dem Stadion, Eberhardystrasse. **GPS**: n50,78524 e7,86507.

1 free. **Location:** Urban, simple, central.
Surface: gravel. 01/01-31/12.
Distance: 1km 50m 1km on the spot.
Remarks: Max. 1 night.

S Bexbach 16G2

Bexbacher Reisemobilhafen, Im Blumengarten.
GPS: n49,34161 e7,25698.

35 € 7 € 1/80liter Ch (36x)€ 2,50/night WC.
Location: Rural, luxurious, quiet. **Surface:** grassy. 01/01-31/12.
Distance: 900m 5km on the spot 500m 200m on the spot on the spot.

Remarks: Bread-service.

Biebernheim 11G3

Reiterhof Pabst, Auf dem Flürchen. **GPS:** n50,14127 e7,70828.

20 € 6, 2 pers.incl Ch (6x)€ 2. **Location:** Rural, simple, isolated, quiet. **Surface:** grassy. 01/01-31/12.
Distance: 10km.
Remarks: Bread-service.

Bingen/Rhein 11H3

Wohnmobilpark Bingen, Mainzer Straße, Bingen/Kempten.
GPS: n49,96860 e7,94417.

39 € 7/night Ch € 2,50/24h € 3/3 includedstay.
Location: Comfortable, quiet. **Surface:** grassy/metalled.
01/01-31/12.
Distance: 2,5km 1,5km 800m 2,7km.
Remarks: Bread-service, possibility for reservation.

Birgel 11F3

Historische Wassermühle, Bahnhofstrasse 16.
GPS: n50,32033 e6,61764.

10 € 15, free with a meal > € 15 Ch (2x)included.
Location: Simple, quiet. **Surface:** gravel. 01/01-31/12.
Distance: 500m 25km on the spot 1km.

Blieskastel 16G2

Freizeitanlage Würzbacher Weiher, Marxstraße, Niederwürzbach.
GPS: n49,24674 e7,19226.

10 € 4,50 € 1/10minutes € 1 Ch € 1/4h.
Location: Rural, simple, quiet. **Surface:** grassy/gravel.
01/01-31/12.
Distance: 500m on the spot on the spot 100m 600m 600m.
Remarks: At lake, Würzbacher Weiher.

Blieskastel 16G2

Hotel Restaurant Hubertushof, Kirschendell 32.
GPS: n49,24456 e7,21573.

8 € 5, free with a meal .
Surface: asphalted. 01/01-31/12.
Distance: on the spot on the spot 1km.
Remarks: Arrival < 19h, max. 2 nights, bread-service.

Blieskastel 16G2

Freizeitzentrum Blieskastel, Bliesaue 1, Webenheim.
GPS: n49,23527 e7,26946.

3 free.
Location: Urban, simple, noisy. **Surface:** metalled. 01/01-31/12.
Distance: on the spot 5km on the spot.

Bobenthal/Bornich 16H2

Hotel-Restaurant St. Germanshof, Hauptstrasse 10.
GPS: n49,04749 e7,89985.

4 guests free. **Surface:** metalled. 01/01-31/12 Mo.
Distance: 5km on the spot 7km.

Bockenheim 16H1

Weingut Benss, Am Spiegelpfad 10. **GPS:** n49,59959 e8,17823.

6 free (6x) WC Service € 5. **Location:** Rural, simple, quiet.
Surface: grassy. 01/01-31/12.
Distance: 7km 500m 3km.

Bockenheim 16H1

Weingut W. Kohl, Am Sonnenberg 3. **GPS:** n49,59902 e8,17925.

6 € 10 WC included. **Location:** Rural, simple.
Surface: grassy/metalled. 01/01-31/12.
Distance: 500m 500m 3km 2km.
Remarks: Check in on arrival.

Braubach 11G3

Braubacher Rheintreff, Rheinuferstrasse, B42.
GPS: n50,26972 e7,64750.

30 € 10 Ch WC included € 3. **Location:** Comfortable, quiet. **Surface:** asphalted. 01/01-31/12.
Distance: 300m on the spot on the spot 300m 300m 300m.

Brauneberg 16F1

Wohnmobilplatz Juffer, Moselweinstrasse 61.
GPS: n49,90518 e6,97760.

25 € 10 Ch included.
Surface: metalled. 01/01-31/12.
Distance: 100m on the spot 300m 300m 100m Mosel-Radweg on the spot.
Remarks: Bicycle rental at tourist office.

Bremm 11F3

Weingut Oster-Franzen, Calmontstrasse 96.
GPS: n50,09593 e7,12383.

16 € 14, 2 pers incl € 0,50/60liter Ch (16x)€ 0,50/kWh WC € 1/6minutes,2 x € 0,50 € 3,50 .
Location: Rural, comfortable. **Surface:** gravel. 01/03-30/11.
Distance: on the spot 800m 300m on the spot on the spot.

Briedern 11F3

Wohnmobilstellplatz Briedern, Moselstrasse.
GPS: n50,11165 e7,20867.

15 € 6,50.
Location: Rural, simple. **Surface:** grassy/gravel. 01/01-31/12.
Distance: on the spot 300m 200m on the spot.

Brodenbach 11G3

Moselufer. **GPS:** n50,22471 e7,43930.

2 free. **Location:** Urban, simple. **Surface:** metalled.

DE

01/01-31/12.
Distance: 500m 500m on the spot.

Brodenbach 11G3

Salzwiese 9. **GPS**: n50,22519 e7,44291.

4 free. **Location:** Urban. **Surface:** concrete. 01/01-31/12.
Distance: 400m Moselle river 200m 400m 3,5km.

Burgen 11G3

Hotel Schmause Mühle, Baybachstrasse 50.
GPS: n50,20859 e7,39365.

20 € 8 Ch € 2,50/day WC included € 1. **Location:** Quiet.
01/01-31/12.
Distance: on the spot on the spot 300m.

Burgen bei Bernkastel-Kues 16F1

Weingut Bohn-Leimbrock, Lindenstrasse 6.
GPS: n49,87986 e6,99967.

4 € 8 WC. **Surface:** grassy. 01/01-31/12.
Distance: 150m 50m 2km 50m on the spot on the spot.

Burrweiler 16H2

Wein- und Sektgut Hermann-Bruno Eberle, Böchingerstrasse 1a.
GPS: n49,24649 e8,07989.

3 € 6 WC included.
Location: Rural, quiet. **Surface:** metalled. 01/01-31/12.
Distance: 100m 200m.
Remarks: Arrival <21h.

Burrweiler 16H2

Weingut Diether Bauer, Weinstrasse 52. **GPS**: n49,21982 e8,03059.

3 € 5 WC included. **Location:** Rural, quiet.
Surface: metalled. 01/01-31/12.
Distance: on the spot 300m.

Burrweiler 16H2

Weingut Hertel, Raiffeisenstrasse 2. **GPS**: n49,24861 e8,07705.

3 € 5 included WC on demand.
Location: Rural, simple, quiet. **Surface:** metalled. 01/04-31/10.
Distance: 250m.

Burrweiler 16H2

Weingut Winzerhof, Am Schlossberg 3. **GPS**: n49,25147 e7,07902.

4 € 8 WC included. **Location:** Rural, quiet.
Surface: metalled. 01/01-31/12.
Distance: 1km 300m.

Busenberg 16G2

Weißensteiner Hof, An der B427. **GPS**: n49,12152 e7,83943.

3 guests free on demand. **Location:** Rural, simple.
Surface: asphalted. 01/01-31/12 Mon + Fri.
Distance: 2km on the spot.

Cochem 11F3

Bergstrasse, K59. **GPS**: n50,15028 e7,17083.

4 9-19h € 2,50, overnight stay free.
Surface: grasstiles/metalled. 01/01-31/12.
Distance: 300m 300m.

Cochem 11F3

Moselpromenade, B49. **GPS**: n50,14108 e7,16936.

4 8-19h € 1/h, overnight stay free.
Surface: metalled. 01/01-31/12.
Distance: 600m 600m 700m.
Remarks: Max. 11h.

Cochem 11F3

Wohnmobil-Stellplatz an der Nordbrücke, Moselstrasse, B49.
GPS: n50,15329 e7,16828.

16 8-19h € 1/h, overnight stay free.
Location: Urban, simple. **Surface:** metalled. 01/01-31/12.
Distance: 700m 200m 200m on the spot.
Remarks: Max. 11h.

Cochem 11F3

Wohnmobil-Stellplatz am Freizeitzentrum, Stadionstrasse.
GPS: n50,16051 e7,17956.

50 € 0,50/h.
Surface: gravel/sand. 01/01-31/12.
Distance: 2,5km 400m on the spot.
Remarks: Along the Moselle river, max. 24h, sanitary at campsite.

Darscheid/Vulkaneifel 11F3

Kucher's Landhotel, Karl-Kaufmann-Strasse 2.
GPS: n50,21060 e6,88270.
3 € 15, guests free. **Location:** Luxurious. 01/01-31/12.
Distance: 650m 450m on the spot.
Remarks: Breakfast-service.

Deidesheim 16H2

Weinhaus Villa Giessen, Weinstrasse 3. **GPS**: n49,41210 e8,19105.

3 € 8 included. **Location:** Rural, simple.
Surface: gravel/metalled. 01/01-31/12.
Distance: on the spot 5km 500m 1km 900m.

Deudesfeld 11F3

Meisburgerstrasse. **GPS**: n50,10084 e6,72932.

8 free € 1/120liter € 1 Ch € 0,50/kWh.
Location: Rural, simple, quiet. **Surface:** grassy.
01/01-31/12.
Distance: 300m.

Deudesfeld 11F3

Leyendecker Platz, Mandertscheider Strasse.
GPS: n50,10164 e6,73217.

4 free. **Location:** Rural, simple, quiet. **Surface:** gravel.
01/01-31/12.
Distance: 200m.

Deuselbach 16F1

Wohnmobilstellplatz Erbeskopf, K130. **GPS**: n49,73589 e7,08327.

50 € 4 Ch (5x)€ 3/day WC included € 0,50/5minutes.
Location: Rural, simple, quiet. **Surface:** metalled.
01/01-31/12.
Distance: 10km.

Dexheim 16H1

Weingut Bacchushof, Wörrstädter Strasse 14.
GPS: n49,84812 e8,31144.

5 free. **Location:** Rural, simple. **Surface:** concrete.
01/01-31/12.
Distance: 12km.

Dierbach 16H2

Jahnstrasse. **GPS**: n49,08177 e8,06201.

10 € 5 Ch (5x)included.
Location: Simple, quiet. **Surface:** gravel. 01/01-31/12.
Distance: 700m 12km 1km 3km 50m.
Remarks: At sports centre.

Dierbach 16H2

Weingut Geiger, Hauptstrasse 21. **GPS**: n49,08344 e8,06673.

30 € 10 Ch WC included € 4 € 2/day.
Location: Rural, comfortable, quiet. **Surface:** grassy.
01/03-31/12.
Distance: on the spot 12km 500m.
Remarks: Bread-service, playground.

Dolgesheim 16H1

Weingut Seck, Weinolsheimer Strasse 12. **GPS**: n49,79752 e8,26154.

3 € 5 € 2 Ch € 2 WC included.
Location: Rural, simple, quiet. **Surface:** grassy.
01/01-31/12.
Distance: 200m 13km 300m 2km.

Dörrenbach 16H2

Übergasse. **GPS**: n49,08840 e7,96921.

10 € 6 Ch included.
Location: Rural, quiet. **Surface:** gravel/sand. 01/01-31/12.
Distance: 500m 700m.
Remarks: Next to sports fields.

Eckersweiler 16G1

Am Sportplatz. **GPS**: n49,55646 e7,30577.

4 free. **Location:** Rural, simple, isolated. **Surface:** grassy.
01/01-31/12.
Distance: 1,3km on the spot on the spot.

Edenkoben 16H2

Wohnmobilstellplatz Kirchbergplatz, Bahnhofstraße.
GPS: n49,28234 e8,13116.

40 € 5 € 1/100liter Ch (8x)€ 1/kWh.
Surface: asphalted. 01/01-31/12.
Distance: on the spot 2km 300m Aldi 800m.
Remarks: Max. 3 nights.

Edenkoben 16H2

Brennerei & Weinstube Göring, Blücherstrasse 45.
GPS: n49,27792 e8,13487.

5 € 10 Ch included WC.
Surface: grassy. 01/01-31/12.

Distance: 3km.

Edenkoben 16H2

Weingut Bernd und Herbert Schäfer, Rhodter Strasse 24.
GPS: n49,27844 e8,12572.
3 free € 5. 01/01-31/12.
Distance: 3,5km.

Edenkoben 16H2

Weingut Edel Brauch, St.-Martiner-Strasse 30.
GPS: n49,28901 e8,12236.
4 free € 2 Ch € 2. **Surface:** grassy. 01/01-31/12.
Distance: 1km 3km 1km 1km.

Edenkoben 16H2

Weingut Heinrichshof Fritz-Schneider, Klosterstraße 157a.
GPS: n49,28333 e8,11722.
12 € 14, 2 pers incl Ch included.
Surface: gravel. 01/03-30/11.
Distance: 1km 700m.

Edenkoben 16H2

Gasthof Ziegelhütte, Luitpoldstrasse 75-79. **GPS**: n49,28539 e8,13872.

3 € 5/night. **Surface:** metalled. 01/01-31/12.
Distance: on the spot 1km on the spot on the spot.

Edesheim 16H2

Weingut Boos, Ludwigstrasse 150. **GPS**: n49,25785 e8,11673.

3 € 6 Ch (3x)included.
Location: Rural, simple, quiet. **Surface:** grassy. 01/01-31/12.
Distance: 500m 300m 1km.
Remarks: Bread-service.

Edesheim 16H2

Weingut Braun & Sohn, Ludwigsstrasse 151.
GPS: n49,25761 e8,11587.

3 € 6 Ch included.
Location: Rural, simple, quiet. **Surface:** grassy. 01/01-31/12.
Distance: 300m 300m 2km.

Edesheim 16H2

Weingut Erlenmühle, Erlenmühle 1. **GPS**: n49,25865 e8,11417.

5 € 5 Ch included on demand. **Location:** Rural, simple, quiet. **Surface:** gravel. 01/01-31/12.
Distance: 500m on the spot 1km.
Remarks: Arrival <22h.

DE

Edesheim 16H2

Weingut Rehm, Ludwigstrasse 36. **GPS**: n49,26015 e8,12734.

6 € 12/night (6x) included.
Location: Rural, simple, quiet. **Surface:** grassy.
01/01-31/12.
Distance: on the spot 800m 1km.

Ediger/Eller 11F3

Stellplatz Ediger, Moselweinstrasse. **GPS**: n50,09320 e7,15942.

18 € 5 Ch included. **Location:** Rural, simple.
Surface: gravel/metalled. 01/04-30/11.
Distance: 100m on the spot on the spot on the spot on the spot on the spot.
Remarks: Along the Moselle river in Ediger.

Ediger/Eller 11F3

Stellplatz Moselufer, Eller. **GPS**: n50,09915 e7,14370.

10 € 5. **Location:** Rural, simple. **Surface:** metalled.
01/04-30/11.
Distance: on the spot on the spot on the spot 200m on the spot.
Remarks: Along the Moselle river in Eller.

Eisenschmitt 11F3

Hotel-Restaurant Molitors Mühle, Eichelhütte.
GPS: n50,03681 e6,73766.

5 guests free WC included.
Location: Rural, simple. **Surface:** gravel. 01/01-31/12.
Distance: 1km 6km on the spot on the spot on the spot 1km 300m on the spot.
Remarks: Arrival <23h.

Ellenz/Poltersdorf 11G3

Weingut Loosen, Im Goldbäumchen 4. **GPS**: n50,11389 e7,23528.

14 € 7, 2 pers.incl WC included € 1/5minutes.
Location: Rural, comfortable, quiet. **Surface:** gravel.
01/01-31/12.
Distance: on the spot 150m 500m 1km on the spot on the spot.
Remarks: Along Mosel.

Tourist information Ellenz/Poltersdorf:
Strassenweinfest. Wine-growers and - houses open their doors, wine-tastery. end Sep.
Wein- und Heimatfeste. Traditional wine celebration. last weekend Jul, 1st weekend Aug.

Elmstein 16H2

NaturFreundeHaus Elmstein, Esthaler Strasse 63.
GPS: n49,36133 e7,95123.

12 € 3 € 1 € 2 € 1/pp. **Location:** Rural, simple, central, quiet. **Surface:** gravel. 01/01-31/12.
Distance: 3km on the spot on the spot.
Remarks: Bread-service.

Elmstein 16H2

Stellplatz Elmstein, Bahnhofstrasse 88. **GPS**: n49,34803 e7,94337.

4 free (4x) € 0,50/kWh.
Location: Rural. **Surface:** gravel. 01/01-31/12.
Distance: 500m 100m 500m.

Elmstein 16H2

Wohnmobilplatz Waldesruhe, Schwarzbach 36.
GPS: n49,34037 e7,83397.

10 € 5, free with a meal. **Location:** Rural, simple, isolated, quiet.
Surface: grassy. 01/01-31/12.
Distance: on the spot.
Remarks: To be paid at restaurant, breakfast-service.

Elzweiler 16G1

Stellplatz Elzweiler, Hauptstraße 7. **GPS**: n49,58036 e7,51393.

2 free € 1 Ch free € 1.
Location: Rural. **Surface:** metalled. 01/01-31/12.
Distance: 5km on the spot on the spot.
Remarks: Small pitches.

Enkirch 11F3

Wohnmobilplatz an der Mosel, Moselvorgelände, B53.
GPS: n49,98396 e7,12157.

200 € 7 € 1/80liter Ch (104x) € 1/2kWh WC € 1
€ 1,50/30minutes.
Location: Rural, comfortable, quiet. **Surface:** grassy. Easter-31/10.
Distance: 300m on the spot on the spot 200m on the spot.
Remarks: Along the Moselle river.

Ensch 16F1

Reisemobilplatz An den 2 Pappeln, Am Moselufer/ B53.
GPS: n49,82760 e6,83549.

45 € 5 € 2 Ch (45x) € 2.
Location: Rural. **Surface:** grassy. 01/04-31/10.
Distance: 200m on the spot 300m 500m 100m.
Remarks: Bread-service.

Eppelborn 16F2

Wohnmobilstellplatz Finkenrech, L303.
GPS: n49,43285 e6,99986.
3 € 5 € 0,50. **Location:** Rural, simple, quiet. **Surface:** gravel.
01/01-31/12.
Distance: 3km on the spot.

Eppenbrunn 16G2

Im Sportzentrum. **GPS**: n49,11179 e7,56512.

6 free. **Location:** Rural, simple, quiet.
Surface: metalled.
01/01-31/12.
Distance: 500m on the spot 1km on the spot on the spot.
Remarks: Parking sports centre in nature reserve Pfälzer Wald.

Eppenbrunn 16G2

Neudorfstrasse. **GPS**: n49,11531 e7,55360.

5 free. **Location:** Rural, simple, noisy.
Surface: metalled. 01/01-31/12.
Distance: on the spot 800m 800m 100m on the spot on the spot.

Erden 11F3

Wohnmobilstellplatz Erden, An Moselufer 1.
GPS: n49,97989 e7,02120.

21 € 10 Chincluded (21x)€ 3 € 0,30/minutes on demand. **Location:** Rural. **Surface:** grassy. 01/04-31/10.
Distance: 15km 300m on the spot on the spot.

Ernst 11G3

Wohnmobilstellplatz im Weinberg, Weingartenstrasse 106.
GPS: n50,14339 e7,23237.

30 € 9 Ch included € 5/10h.
Location: Rural, comfortable. **Surface:** gravel. 01/01-31/12.
Distance: 300m on the spot 200m 100m on the spot on the spot.

Ernst 11G3

Mosella Schinkenstube, Weingatenstrasse 97.
GPS: n50,14382 e7,23071.

18 € 10 Ch included.
Location: Rural. **Surface:** grassy. 01/01-31/12.
Distance: 100m on the spot on the spot on the spot.
Remarks: Breakfest-service.

Eschbach 16H2

Weingut Wind, Weinstrasse 3-5. **GPS**: n49,17594 e8,02171.

3 € 5, discount for clients € 1/100liter € 3 WCincluded.
Location: Rural, simple, quiet. **Surface:** gravel.
01/01-31/12.

Distance: on the spot on the spot 250m.
Remarks: Check in on arrival.

Essingen 16H2

Weingut Schweikart Dalberghof, Kirchstrasse 16.
GPS: n49,23478 e8,17524.

3 € 5 € 1/100liter (3x)€ 1/night WC€ 1.
Location: Simple, quiet. **Surface:** grassy. 01/01-31/12.
Distance: on the spot 3km 1km 3km 7km 30m.
Remarks: Sale of wines.

Fell 16F1

Besucherbergwerk, Auf den Schiefergruben, K82.
GPS: n49,75440 e6,79731.

30 free, 01/04-30/11 € 4 € 2.
Location: Isolated, quiet. **Surface:** concrete. 01/01-31/12.
Distance: 2km on the spot on the spot on the spot.
Remarks: Bread-service.

Fischbach 16G1

Wohnmobilpark, Marktstraße 1. **GPS**: n49,74046 e7,40444.

40 € 7 Chincluded (40x)€ 2,50,.
Location: Rural, simple, central. **Surface:** grassy. 01/01-31/12.
Distance: 800m on the spot 300m 1,5km.
Remarks: Bread-service, service passerby € 3.

Fischbach 16G1

Historisches Kupferbergwerk, Hosenbachstraße.
GPS: n49,75398 e7,38287.

15 free. **Location:** Rural, simple, isolated, quiet. **Surface:** gravel.
01/01-31/12.
Distance: 1,7km on the spot.
Remarks: Visitors' center former copper mine.

Flemlingen 16H2

Weingut Eichhorn, Maxstrasse 21. **GPS**: n49,24122 e8,09341.

8 € 5 (10x)€ 3 WCincluded € 2/pp.
Location: Rural, simple, quiet. **Surface:** grassy. 01/01-31/12.
Distance: 200m 6km 500m 400m on the spot on the spot.

Flonheim 16H1

Weingut Meyerhof, Aussiedlerhof. **GPS**: n49,78836 e8,04531.

4 € 8 (4x)included. **Location:** Rural, simple, quiet.
Surface: concrete. 01/01-31/12.
Distance: 700m 4km 100m 100m.
Remarks: Bread-service.

Föckelberg 16G1

Wildpark Potzberg, Auf dem Potzberg. **GPS**: n49,52240 e7,48079.

4 free. **Location:** Rural, simple, quiet.
Surface: asphalted/sand. 01/01-31/12.
Distance: 1km on the spot.

Forst an der Weinstrasse 16H1

Weingut Margarethenhof, Wiesenweg 4. **GPS**: n49,42814 e8,19219.

4 € 10 WCincluded € 4. **Location:** Rural, simple.
Surface: grassy. 01/01-31/12 15/06-17/06, 30/06-02/07.
Distance: 1km 7km 1km on the spot on the spot.

Freisen 16G1

Weiselbergbad, Zum Schwimmbad. **GPS**: n49,53324 e7,26048.

3 € 5 € 2/day. **Location:** Rural, simple, noisy.
Surface: metalled. 01/01-31/12.
Distance: 1km 3km 800m on the spot on the spot.
Remarks: Check in at swimming pool.

Gau-Algesheim 11H3

Reimo Gau-Algesheim, Bingerstrasse 8.
GPS: n49,96331 e8,01213.

DE

38 € 8/night Chincluded (40x)€ 2/24h.
Location: Comfortable, quiet. **Surface:** metalled. 01/01-31/12.
Distance: 800m 2,5km 500m 200m.

Gau-Bickelheim 16H1

Winzerhof Schnabel, Bahnhofstrasse 31.
GPS: n49,83941 e8,02116.

15 € 5 included (8x)€ 3/day. **Location:** Rural.
Surface: grassy/gravel. 01/01-31/12.
Distance: 400m 3km 5km 1km 200m.

Gau-Bickelheim 16H1

Am Autohof, B50. **GPS**: n49,83461 e7,99664.

15 € 10 against payment. **Location:** Motorway, simple, noisy.
Surface: asphalted. 01/01-31/12.
Distance: 5km on the spot on the spot 6km.

Gau-Heppenheim 16H1

Mohrenmühle, Mohrenmühle 2. **GPS**: n49,75170 e8,16335.
3 € 5 . **Location:** Rural. **Surface:** grassy.
01/01-31/12.
Distance: 1,5km on the spot on the spot on the spot.
Remarks: Bread-service.

Gau-Heppenheim 16H1

Weingut Gustavshof, Hauptstrasse 53. **GPS**: n49,74138 e8,17082.

3 € 8 (3x)included. **Location:** Rural, simple, quiet.
Surface: concrete. 01/04-31/10.
Distance: 4km 2km 3km.

Gau-Odernheim 16H1

Petersberghalle, Mühlstraße. **GPS**: n49,78528 e8,19575.

3 free. **Location:** Rural, simple. **Surface:** metalled.
01/01-31/12.
Distance: 200m 400m 200m 100m.
Remarks: Max. 3 days.

Gebhardshain 11G2

Festwiese, Steinebacherstrasse. **GPS**: n50,74412 e7,82079.

5 free. **Location:** Urban, simple, central, quiet.
Surface: asphalted. 01/01-31/12.
Distance: 500m 500m 500m.

Geiselberg 16G2

Grillplatz Geiselberg, Hauptstrasse, K31. **GPS**: n49,32381 e7,70957.

10 free. **Location:** Rural, simple, quiet. **Surface:** gravel.
01/01-31/12.
Distance: 800m 12km 1km 1km.
Remarks: Max. 3 days.

Germersheim 16H2

Carnot'sche Mauer, Rüdolf von Habsburgstrasse.
GPS: n49,22004 e8,37906.

8 € 3/24h € 1/100liter Ch (8x)€ 1/5kWh.
Location: Urban, simple, central. **Surface:** grassy.
01/01-31/12.
Distance: 300m 2km 500m 300m 100m
on the spot.

Gerolstein 11F3

Am Hallen- und Freibad, Raderstrasse 22.
GPS: n50,22096 e6,65387.

25 € 10/24h € 1/100liter Ch (12x)€ 1/day.
Location: Urban, simple. **Surface:** grassy/metalled.
15/03-15/11.
Distance: nearby 25km 500m 1km.
Remarks: At swimming pool.

Gevenich 11F3

Am Sportplatz. **GPS**: n50,14727 e7,08385.

5 free. **Location:** Rural, simple, isolated.
Surface: grassy. 01/01-31/12.
Distance: 1km on the spot.

Gillenfeld 11F3

Wohnmobilhafen Pulvermaar, K14. **GPS**: n50,13294 e6,93218.

30 € 7, 2 pers. incl., dog € 1 € 1/50liter Ch € 0,50/kWh
WC € 2. **Location:** Simple. **Surface:** gravel. 01/01-31/12.
Distance: 3km on the spot on the spot 200m 200m
300m.

Gillenfeld 11F3

Feriendorf Pulvermaar, Vulkanstrasse. **GPS**: n50,13000 e6,93194.

40 € 7, 2 pers.incl. € 1/50liter Ch € 0,50/kWh WC € 2/stay. **Location:** Rural, comfortable, quiet. **Surface:** grassy/gravel.
01/03-30/11.
Distance: 3km 7km on the spot on the spot 150m
150m 200m.

Gimbsheim 16H1

Schwimbadstrasse. **GPS**: n49,77806 e8,38278.

8 € 4/night. **Location:** Rural, simple. **Surface:** asphalted/grassy.
15/05-15/09.
Distance: 500m 300m 300m.

Gimbsheim 16H1

Weingut Falger-Baier, Alsheimerstrasse 25.
GPS: n49,77733 e8,36959.

3 € 5 included. **Location:** Rural, simple.
Surface: concrete. 01/01-31/12.
Distance: 300m Pizzeria 50m 500m.

Glan-Münchweiler 16G1

Am Bahnhof, Bahnhofstraße. **GPS**: n49,46935 e7,44420.

DE

3 free € 1 Ch (4x)€ 1/2h.
Location: Urban, simple, central, noisy. **Surface:** metalled.
01/01-31/12.
Distance: 750m 150m on the spot.

Gleisweiler 16H2

Weingut Kost, Hainbachtalstrasse 3. **GPS:** n49,23862 e8,06737.

3 free free . **Location:** Rural, quiet. **Surface:** grassy.
01/01-31/12.
Distance: 8km on the spot.

Gleiszellen-Gleishorbach 16H2

B 48. **GPS:** n49,13083 e8,01139.
20 free. **Location:** Rural. **Surface:** grassy. 01/01-31/12.
Distance: 300m 300m.

Gleiszellen-Gleishorbach 16H2

Weingut Doll, Im Alten Garten. **GPS:** n49,12580 e8,00671.
1 free . **Location:** Urban. 01/11-31/08.
Distance: on the spot 50m.

Gleiszellen-Gleishorbach 16H2

Weingut Schönlaub, Bergstrasse 14. **GPS:** n49,13131 e8,00465.

2 free free . **Location:** Rural, simple, quiet.
Surface: grassy. 01/01-31/12.
Distance: 15km 50m.
Remarks: Check in at Weingut.

Graach/Mosel 11F3

Wohnmobilpark Sun-Park, Gestade 16a. **GPS:** n49,93322 e7,06249.

140 € 10/day Ch (132x)€ 3/day WC included € 1,50/pp € 2,50.
Location: Rural, simple. **Surface:** grassy/gravel. 27/03-03/11.
Distance: 200m on the spot 200m 2km on the spot on the spot on the spot.
Remarks: Bread-service, video surveillance.

Grafschaft 11F2

Panorama Sauna, Panoramaweg 2. **GPS:** n50,56029 e7,05368.

20 free. **Surface:** gravel. 01/01-31/12.
Distance: 5km 300m 300m.

Gries 16G2

Seestube am Ohmbachsee, Bahnhofstrasse 17b.
GPS: n49,41664 e7,40377.

15 € 6/24h € 1/80liter Ch (6x)€ 0,60/kWh.
Location: Rural, simple, quiet. **Surface:** grassy/gravel.
01/01-31/12.
Distance: 6km on the spot on the spot 50m 2km on the spot on the spot.
Remarks: Bread-service, possibility for reservation.

Gundersheim 16H1

Huppert's Wohnmobile Wingert, Untere Grabenstraße 21.
GPS: n49,69499 e8,20465.

12 € 5 € 3/day. **Location:** Rural, simple.
Surface: gravel/sand. 01/01-31/12.
Distance: 1km on the spot 300m.
Remarks: Max. 3 nights.

Guntersblum 16H1

Am Sportanlage, Alsheimerstrasse 85. **GPS:** n49,78974 e8,34373.

16 € 5 € 1/80liter Ch (12x)€ 0,50/kWh.
Location: Rural. **Surface:** gravel. 01/01-31/12.
Distance: 500m 500m 500m.
Remarks: Max. 72h.

Guntersblum 16H1

Weingut Katharinenhof, Alsheimerstrasse 95.
GPS: n49,78667 e8,34324.

10 € 5 included Ch (7x)€ 2/24h.
Location: Rural, simple, quiet. **Surface:** grassy. 01/01-31/12.
Distance: 1km 1km 1km 2km.

Hachenburg 11G2

P4 - Burggarten, Alexanderring. **GPS:** n50,66250 e7,82694.

8 free € 1/70liter Ch € 1/6h WC.
Location: Urban, simple, quiet. **Surface:** grasstiles. 01/01-31/12.
Distance: 300m 300m 300m on the spot on the spot.
Remarks: June 2014 during inspection service out of order, just electricity, historical centre.

Hagenbach 16H2

Stadtbrauhaus Hagenbach, Stixwörthstrasse 2-4.
GPS: n49,00884 e8,25902.

10 free . **Surface:** grassy/gravel. 01/01-31/12 Mon, Tue.
Distance: 1km 5km on the spot 750m 1km.

Hainfeld 16H2

Modenbach. **GPS:** n49,25730 e8,10328.

20 free. **Location:** Simple, quiet.
Surface: gravel. 01/01-31/12.
Distance: 150m 3km 250m 1km on the spot.

Hainfeld 16H2

Weingut Edgar und Andreas Lutz, Weinstrasse 57.
GPS: n49,25696 e8,09882.
4 € 6, € 8 service incl included WC . **Location:** Simple.
Surface: metalled. 01/01-31/12.
Distance: on the spot 100m.

Hassloch 16H2

Hotel Sägmühle, Sägmühlweg 140. **GPS:** n49,34674 e8,25491.

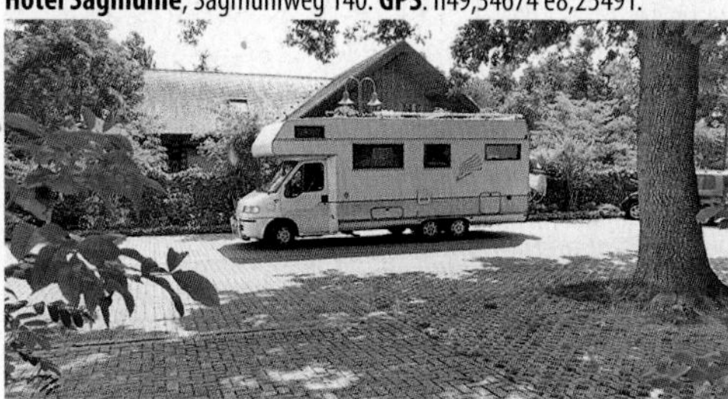

2 € 14, guests free (2x) WC included.
Location: Simple, isolated, quiet. **Surface:** metalled.
01/01-31/12.
Distance: 2km 10km 300m 1,5km 4km.
Remarks: Bicycle rental.

Hassloch 16H2

Badepark Hassloch, Lachener Weg 175. **GPS:** n49,34804 e8,24677.

DE

9 free free. **Location:** Simple, quiet. **Surface:** metalled.
01/01-31/12.
Distance: 2km 10km 50m 200m 100m.
Remarks: Max. 24h.

S Hassloch 16H2

Magin Reisemobile, Hans-Böckler-Strasse 52.
GPS: n49,34968 e8,23935.

8 € 12,50, 2 pers.incl Ch (8x)included.
Location: Urban, simple, quiet.
Surface: gravel/metalled.
01/01-31/12.
Distance: 2km 7km 50m 200m.

Tourist information Hassloch:
Holiday Park. Attractions park with shows. 01/03-31/10 10-18h.

S Hauenstein 16G2

Stellplatz am Deutschen Schumuseum Hauenstein, Turnstrasse 5.
GPS: n49,18896 e7,85669.

16 € 7 Ch included. **Location:** Rural, simple, quiet.
Surface: gravel. 01/01-31/12.
Distance: on the spot 200m 300m.
Remarks: Check in on arrival, pay at pay-desk of the museum.

Heltersberg 16G2

Am Bergbad, Bergstrasse. **GPS**: n49,31654 e7,70380.

5 free. **Location:** Rural, simple, quiet. **Surface:** grassy/gravel.
01/01-31/12.
Distance: 900m 850m.
Remarks: Parking swimming pool.

S Hemmelzen 11G2

Hotel Im Heisterholz, Heisterholzstrasse 10.
GPS: n50,69579 e7,58456.

4 € 12 included. **Location:** Rural, quiet. **Surface:** gravel.
01/01-31/12 Mo.
Distance: 200m on the spot 100m on the spot on the spot.
Remarks: € 2 reduction in restaurant.

S Herrstein 16G1

Wohnmobilstellplatz Herrstein, Brühlstrasse.
GPS: n49,77963 e7,33569.

3 free € 1/80liter € 0,50/kWh WC.
Location: Rural, simple. **Surface:** metalled.
01/01-31/12.
Distance: 300m on the spot.
Remarks: Max. 48h.

Tourist information Herrstein:
Touristinformation Deutsche Edelsteinstraße, Brühlstrasse 16. Renovated mall half-timbered city. 01/05-01/10.

S Herxheim 16H2

Festhalle, Bonifatiusstraße. **GPS**: n49,14463 e8,21656.

8 free Chfree. **Location:** Simple, central.
Surface: grasstiles. 01/01-31/12.
Distance: on the spot 4km 150m 200m 75m on the spot.

S Heuchelheim-Klingen 16H2

Gästehaus am Weingut Kuhn, Hauptstrasse 2.
GPS: n49,14542 e8,05895.
3 € 5 Ch. **Location:** Rural. **Surface:** metalled.
01/01-31/12.
Distance: 14km 300m.

S Heuchelheim-Klingen 16H2

Weingut Arnold, Lindenstraße 57. **GPS**: n49,13917 e8,05683.
1 € 10 Ch. **Surface:** metalled. 01/01-31/12.
Distance: 1km 9km 100m.

S Heuchelheim-Klingen 16H2

Weingut Junghof, Hauptstrasse 21. **GPS**: n49,14572 e8,05580.

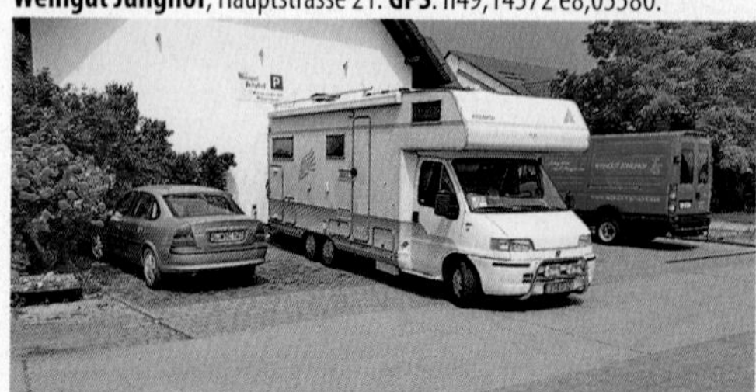

4 € 5, free with a meal € 2/100liter € 2/night.
Location: Simple. **Surface:** grassy/metalled. 01/01-31/12.
Distance: on the spot 14km 500m 2km 500m.

Heuchelheim-Klingen 16H2

Mühlengrund, Untermühle 1. **GPS**: n49,14722 e8,06556.

5 free. **Location:** Rural. **Surface:** gravel. 01/01-31/12 Mon, Tue.
Distance: 1km 9km on the spot.

S Hillesheim 11F3

Markt- und Messeplatz, Am Viehmarkt.
GPS: n50,28895 e6,67239.

6 € 7 Ch (6x) WC included. **Location:** Urban, simple, central. **Surface:** gravel. 01/01-31/12.
Distance: on the spot on the spot 200m.

S Hillesheim 11F3

Wohnmobilstellplatz Birkenhof, Birkenhof 1.
GPS: n50,28639 e6,69083.

8 € 10 (6x)included free.
Location: Rural, simple, quiet. **Surface:** gravel. 01/01-31/12.
Distance: 1,5km 1,5km.
Remarks: Bread-service.

S Hochspeyer 16G1

Am Schwimmbad, Mühlhofstraße. **GPS**: n49,44108 e7,89333.

6 € 5/24h € 1/80liter Ch (12x)€ 0,50/kWh.
Location: Simple, central, quiet. **Surface:** asphalted.
01/01-31/12 01/08-15/08.
Distance: 400m 5km 500m 400m bakery 1km.
Remarks: Max. 3 days.

Höheinöd 16G2

Am Haus des Bürgers, Hauptstrasse 24. **GPS**: n49,28691 e7,60468.

3 free. **Location:** Rural, simple, quiet.
Surface: metalled. 01/01-31/12.
Distance: on the spot 8km.
Remarks: Max. 2 nights.

S Höhr-Grenzhausen 11G2

Martin Lutherstrasse. **GPS**: n50,43943 e7,65984.
5 free € 1/80liter Chfree (11x)€ 1/kWh.
Location: Urban, comfortable, central, quiet. **Surface:** gravel.
01/01-31/12.
Distance: 1km 1km 1km on the spot on the spot on the spot.
Remarks: Service only with 1-euro coins.

S Holzappel 11G3

Stellplatz am Herthasee, Am Herthasee. **GPS**: n50,36135 e7,90274.

DE

12 € 6/24h, € 11/48h, € 15/72h € 1/90liter Ch (12x)€ 1/2kWh. **Location:** Rural, comfortable, quiet.
Surface: grassy.
01/01-31/12.
Distance: 1km on the spot on the spot on the spot 1km.

S Hornbach 16G2

Wohnmobilpark Hornbach, Bahnhofstraße.
GPS: n49,18382 e7,36560.

26 € 8 € 1/60liter Ch (30x)€ 1/2kWh included.
Location: Rural, comfortable, quiet. **Surface:** gravel.
01/01-31/12.
Distance: on the spot 8km on the spot 300m on the spot on the spot.
Remarks: Barbecue place.

S Hörschhausen 11F3

Mechels Hof, Dauner Straße 24. **GPS:** n50,24248 e6,92770.

3 € 5 + € 4/pp, dog € 1 Chincluded (3x)€ 2/24h.
Location: Rural, simple. **Surface:** gravel. 01/01-31/12.
Distance: 9km.
Remarks: Bread-service.

S Idar/Oberstein 16G1

Parking Börse, Hauptstrasse 97. **GPS:** n49,71932 e7,30313.

12 € 6 € 1/100liter ChWC. **Location:** Urban, simple.
Surface: asphalted. 01/01-31/12.
Distance: 300m on the spot 300m.

Tourist information Idar/Oberstein:

Edelsteinminen des Steinkaulenberges. Gem mine.
15/03-15/11 10-18h.
M Deutsches Edelsteinmuseum. Gem museum. 01/05-31/10 9.30-17.30h, 01/11-30/04 10-17h 14/01-01/02.

S Impflingen 16H2

Weingut Junker, Sonnenberghof 1. **GPS:** n49,16242 e8,10728.

3 € 5 included (4x)€ 2 WC.
Location: Simple, quiet. **Surface:** gravel. 01/01-31/12.
Distance: 1km 7km on the spot 3km 200m on the spot on the spot.
Remarks: Breakfest-service.

S Ingelheim am Rhein 11H3

Weingut Menk, Außenliegend 143. **GPS:** n49,97190 e8,09295.

6 € 10 Ch WCincluded. **Location:** Rural, comfortable, quiet. **Surface:** grassy. 01/01-31/12.
Distance: 2km 9km 1,5km 5,5km on the spot.

S Jettenbach 16G1

Freizeitgelände Schwimmbad, Austrasse.
GPS: n49,52919 e7,56453.

6 free Ch.
Location: Simple, quiet. **Surface:** asphalted. 01/01-31/12.
Distance: 500m 800m.
Remarks: Service on demand.

Kaisersesch 11F3

Am Markt. **GPS:** n50,23223 e7,14044.
4 free. **Surface:** asphalted. 01/01-31/12.
Distance: on the spot 1km 300m 500m 1km.

S Kaiserslautern 16G1

Daennerplatz, Mannheimer Straße 208.
GPS: n49,44300 e7,80230.

11 € 10/24h € 1/100liter Ch (12x)€ 2/2kWh.
Location: Urban. **Surface:** metalled. 01/01-31/12.
Distance: 2,5km on the spot on the spot.
Remarks: Free bus to centre.

S Kaiserslautern 16G1

Gasthaus Licht Luft, Entersweilerstraße 51.
GPS: n49,43828 e7,80338.

14 free Chon demand. **Location:** Urban, central, quiet.
Surface: asphalted/gravel. 01/01-31/12.
Distance: 2km 5km on the spot on the spot 3km on the spot on the spot.

Kaiserslautern 16G1

Am Monte Mare, Mailänder Straße 6. **GPS:** n49,45387 e7,81203.

10 free. **Location:** Rural, simple, quiet.
Surface: metalled. 01/01-31/12.
Distance: 4km 1km 300m.

S Kamp-Bornhofen 11G3

Bistro Rheinufer, Rheinuferstrasse 66 A.
GPS: n50,22305 e7,61888.
7 € 8 € 1 € 2,50 WC.
Surface: metalled. 01/01-31/12.
Distance: on the spot on the spot 300m on the spot.
Remarks: Along the Rhine river, toilets only during opening hours restaurant.

S Kandel 16H2

Adams Hof, Rheinzaberner Strasse 1. **GPS:** n49,08902 e8,22194.

30 € 10/night € 2,50 (20x)€ 2,50/12h WC.
Location: Simple, quiet. **Surface:** grassy. 01/01-31/12.
Distance: 1,5km on the spot on the spot 1,5km 1,5km.
Remarks: € 5 voucher Biergarten.

S Kapellen-Drusweiler 16H2

Weingut Manderschied, Dorfstrasse 4. **GPS:** n49,10482 e8,03723.

10 free (3x)free. **Location:** Rural, simple, quiet.
Surface: grassy. 01/01-31/12.
Distance: 500m 500m 2km 500m.

S Kell am See 16F1

Am Camping Hochwald, L 143. **GPS:** n49,63800 e6,80140.

DE

10 € 20, 2 pers.incl Ch WC included.
Location: Rural, quiet. **Surface:** metalled. 01/06-30/08.
Distance: 2km 2km.
Remarks: Free entrance swimming pool.

Kempenich 11F2

Eifel-Gasthof Kleefuß, In der Hardt 1. **GPS**: n50,42209 e7,10951.

4 guests free.
Location: Rural. **Surface:** gravel. 01/01-31/12 Mon, Tue.
Distance: 500m on the spot 1km 300m Steinrausch Erlebnispfad 200m.

Kempfeld 16G1

An der Wildenburg, Wildenburgstraße.
GPS: n49,77588 e7,25423.

3 free. **Location:** Rural. **Surface:** metalled. 01/01-31/12.
Distance: 2km 2km.

Kesten 16F1

Wohnmobilpark Kesten/Mosel, Urmetzgasse/K134.
GPS: n49,90306 e6,96232.

100 € 6/24h € 0,50/50liter Ch included (100x)€ 2/24h, 6Amp. **Surface:** grassy/metalled. 01/04-31/10.
Distance: 300m 10m 10m 300m 1km 300m on the spot on the spot.
Remarks: Parking at the Moselle River, bread-service.

Kinheim 11F3

Am Moselufer, Moselweinstraße, B53. **GPS**: n49,97218 e7,05706.

50 € 8 Ch € 2/day included.
Location: Rural, simple, quiet. **Surface:** grassy. 01/01-31/12.
Distance: 100m on the spot on the spot 150m on the spot on the spot.
Remarks: Parking at the Moselle River.

Tourist information Kinheim:
Tag den offenen Weinkeller. Open wine-cellars. 2nd Thu after Whitsuntide.
Wein- und Frülingsfest. Wine and spring celebration. Whitsuntide.
Winzerfest. Wine festival. 2nd weekend Sep.

Kirchberg 11G3

AMB-Reisemobile, Herbert-Kühn-Straße 10.
GPS: n49,95400 e7,40829.

15 € 6 Ch included. **Location:** Rural, simple.
Surface: grassy. 01/01-31/12.
Distance: 700m 700m 700m 600m on the spot.

Kirchheimbolanden 16H1

Festplatz Herrengarten, Hitzfeldstrasse.
GPS: n49,66667 e8,01501.

8 free € 1/70liter (8x)€ 0,50,16Amp free.
Location: Urban, central, quiet. **Surface:** metalled.
01/01-31/12 2nd weekend May-Aug-Oct.
Distance: 300m 300m on the spot 350m on the spot.
Remarks: Max. 2 nights.

Kirn 16G1

Wohnmobilstellplatz Auf der Kiesel, Fontaine-les-Dijon-Strasse.
GPS: n49,78406 e7,45798.

3 € 1,25/day.
Location: Urban, simple. **Surface:** concrete. 01/01-31/12.
Distance: 300m on the spot on the spot.
Remarks: Monday market.

Klausen 16F1

Zentralparkplatz, Eberhardstrasse/ K51. **GPS**: n49,90550 e6,88104.

5 free. **Surface:** metalled. 01/01-31/12.
Distance: on the spot 2km 400m 400m.

Kleinbundenbach 16G2

Auf der Stampermühle, Stampermühle 1.
GPS: n49,31778 e7,45694.

10 € 7 included. **Location:** Rural, simple, isolated.
Surface: gravel. 01/01-31/12.
Distance: 8km 15km on the spot.

Klüsserath 16F1

Reisemobilpark Klüsserath, B53. **GPS**: n49,84170 e6,85475.

400 € 7,20 € 1/90liter Ch € 1/2kWh .
Surface: grassy. Easter-31/10.
Distance: 9km 500m.
Remarks: Along the Moselle river, bread-service.

Kobern 11G3

Am Kalkofen B416, Kobern-Gondorf. **GPS**: n50,30524 e7,46064.

50 € 5/24h € 1/80liter € 0,10 Ch€ 0,10.
Surface: metalled. 01/01-31/12.
Distance: 300m 8km on the spot on the spot 300m 300m.

Koblenz 11G3

Busparkplatz, Pastor-Klein-Straße. **GPS**: n50,36557 e7,57417.

50 € 5. **Location:** Simple. **Surface:** gravel. 01/01-31/12.
Distance: Old city centre 2km 600m Aldi 500m.

Konz 16F1

An der Saarmündung, Am Moselufer 1. **GPS**: n49,70550 e6,57597.
3 € 8 ChWC against payment .
Surface: grassy. 01/03-31/10.
Distance: on the spot on the spot on the spot 100m 1km 400m on the spot on the spot.
Remarks: Service 100m.

Köwerich 16F1

Weingut Hans Klären-Maringer 'Off'm Herrach', Beethovenstrasse 40. **GPS**: n49,84123 e6,86287.

20 € 8 Ch according consumption WC € 1 € 4. **Location:** Rural. **Surface:** grassy. 01/01-31/12.
Distance: 500m 500m 500m on the spot 2km 100m on the spot.
Remarks: Check in at restaurant, bread-service.

Kusel 16G1

Parkplatz der Tuchfabriken, Trierer Straße 61.
GPS: n49,54016 e7,39626.

3 free Ch Service € 5.
Location: Urban, simple, quiet. **Surface:** asphalted.
01/04-31/10.
Distance: 500m 300m.
Remarks: Max. 3 days, key service at Touristinformation (300m).

Lahnstein 11G3

Wohnmobilstellplatz Kränchen, Johannesstraße 44.
GPS: n50,30939 e7,59833.

60 € 9,50/24h € 1/100liter Ch € 0,50/kWh WC € 1/3minutes.
Location: Rural, simple. **Surface:** gravel. 01/01-31/12.
Distance: 1km 600m 600m 1,5km.

Lahnstein 11G3

Wohnmobilstellplatz Blücherstraße, Blücherstraße 20.
GPS: n50,31335 e7,59331.

10 free. **Location:** Urban, simple, central.
Surface: gravel. 01/01-31/12.
Distance: 2km on the spot on the spot on the spot.
Remarks: Max. 3 days.

Lambrecht 16H2

Blainviller-Straße 1. **GPS**: n49,37030 e8,07448.

7 free € 1 Ch € 1/8h. **Location:** Rural, central, quiet.
Surface: gravel. 01/01-31/12.
Distance: on the spot on the spot 500m 900m on the spot on the spot.
Remarks: Near sports fields.

Landau 16H2

La Ola Das Freizeitbad, Horstring 2. **GPS**: n49,20230 e8,14270.

5 € 10/24h € 4 Ch . **Location:** Simple, quiet.
Surface: metalled. 01/01-31/12.
Distance: 3km 1km 500m 100m.

Landstuhl 16G2

Bahnstraße. **GPS**: n49,41595 e7,57092.

2 free Ch free. **Location:** Urban, simple, noisy.
Surface: metalled. 01/01-31/12.
Distance: on the spot 1,3km 350m Aldi 100m.
Remarks: Max. 3 days.

Langenlonsheim 16G1

Weingut Im Zwölberich, Schützenstrasse 14.
GPS: n49,89672 e7,89466.

5 € 10 included. **Location:** Rural, simple, central, quiet.
Surface: asphalted/grassy. 01/01-31/12.
Distance: 500m 7km 500m 1km.

Lauterecken 16G1

Wohnmobilstellplatz Villa Toskana, Friedhofweg 3a.
GPS: n49,65056 e7,58806.

30 € 8 € 1/80liter Ch (18x) € 1/8h WC € 3 € 1/5minutes.
Location: Comfortable, luxurious, quiet. **Surface:** gravel.
01/01-31/12.
Distance: 300m on the spot 300m on the spot on the spot on the spot.
Remarks: Bread-service.

Leimersheim 16H2

Sport- und Freizeithalle, Rheinstraße 42.
GPS: n49,12534 e8,35457.

5 free . **Location:** Rural, simple, quiet. **Surface:** gravel.
01/01-31/12.

Distance: 500m 4km 100m 100m on the spot 1km on the spot on the spot.
Remarks: At tennis-courts.

Leinsweiler 16H2

Weingut Erlenswein, Wacholderhof. **GPS**: n49,18747 e8,03323.

6 € 10 Ch included. **Location:** Rural, simple, quiet.
Surface: grassy. 01/03-30/11.
Distance: 1km.
Remarks: Check in at Weingut.

Leiwen 16F1

Weingut Heinz Spieles, Schulstrasse 20. **GPS**: n49,82331 e6,87524.

4 € 8, 2 pers.incl € 1 Ch € 1 included.
Surface: grassy/gravel. 01/01-31/12.
Distance: 400m 400m 400m 700m 700m.
Remarks: Breakfast-service.

Leiwen 16F1

Moselblick, Flurgartenstrasse 2/ Weinallee.
GPS: n49,82611 e6,88057.

12 € 10 Ch WC € 1. **Location:** Rural.
Surface: grassy/gravel. 01/01-31/12.
Distance: 500m on the spot on the spot on the spot 300m 500m.

Lemberg 16G2

Lemberger Weiher, Weiherstraße. **GPS**: n49,17284 e7,64731.

5 free, service/electricity incl. € 7 Ch .
Location: Rural. **Surface:** grasstiles. 01/01-31/12.
Distance: 400m 100m 600m on the spot on the spot.
Remarks: Max. 3 days.

Linz am Rhein 11G2

B42 Linzhausenstrasse. **GPS**: n50,56291 e7,27982.

DE

6 free. **Surface:** asphalted. 01/01-31/12.
Distance: 500m on the spot 50m.
Remarks: Along the Rhine river, max. 3 days.

S **Löf** 11G3
SOG Dahmann, In der Mark 2. **GPS**: n50,23194 e7,43750.

9 free Ch (4x)€ 0,50/kWh WC. **Location:** Rural.
Surface: metalled. 01/01-31/12.
Distance: 13km 1km.

S **Longuich/Mosel** 16F1
Feiten, Rioler weg 2. **GPS**: n49,80417 e6,77899.

40 € 8 € 0,50/70liter Ch € 2 WC € 1.
Location: Rural. **Surface:** grassy. 01/01-31/12.
Distance: 300m 2km on the spot on the spot on the spot 1km.
Remarks: Along the Moselle river, playground.

S **Longuich/Mosel** 16F1
WeinKulturgut Longen Schlöder, Kirchenweg 9.
GPS: n49,81023 e6,76427.

8 € 7 € 2 (3x)€ 2,50 WC € 3.
Surface: gravel/metalled. 01/01-31/12 Tue.
Distance: on the spot 1km 150m 150m on the spot 500m.

S **Losheim am See** 16F1
Reisemobilplatz am Stausee, Zum Stausee.
GPS: n49,51999 e6,74123.

8 € 6 € 0,50/70liter Ch WC included.
Location: Rural, simple. **Surface:** grassy/gravel.
01/01-31/12.
Distance: 1km 200m 200m 100m 1km on the spot on the spot.
Remarks: Parking at lake, in front of tourist office.

S **Lösnich** 11F3
Stellplatz am Moselufer, Gestade. **GPS**: n49,97560 e7,04276.

96 € 7 Ch included € 2/day. **Location:** Rural, simple, quiet. **Surface:** grassy. 01/03-01/11.
Distance: on the spot on the spot on the spot on the spot 3km on the spot on the spot.
Remarks: Along the Moselle river, baker every morning.

S **Lutzerath** 11F3
Bürgerhaus zum Üssbachtal, Trierer Strasse.
GPS: n50,13015 e7,01002.

10 € 5/day € 0,50 Ch (6x)€ 0,50/kWh.
Location: Urban, simple. **Surface:** asphalted. 01/01-31/12.
Distance: on the spot on the spot on the spot.
Remarks: Check in at Hotel Restaurant Maas, Trierer Str. 30.

S **Maikammer** 16H2
Sporthalle Kalmit, Johannes Dammstrasse.
GPS: n49,30307 e8,13219.

€ 4/day included. **Surface:** asphalted. 01/01-31/12.
Distance: 100m nearby nearby.

S **Maikammer** 16H2
Weingut Gerald Groß, Bahnhofstraße 24. **GPS**: n49,30649 e8,13742.
2 € 13 WC included. **Surface:** grassy. 01/01-31/12.

S **Maikammer** 16H2
Weingut Hubert Müller, Raiffeisenstrasse 59.
GPS: n49,30737 e8,13646.
3 € 13 WC included.
Surface: gravel. 01/01-31/12.
Distance: on the spot 7km.

S **Maikammer** 16H2
Weingut Schädler, Dieterwiesenstraße. **GPS**: n49,30848 e8,12530.
3 € 7 WC included. 01/01-31/12.
Distance: 500m 1km on the spot on the spot.

S **Maikammer** 16H2
Weingut Ziegler-Ullrich, Weinstraße Nord 46.
GPS: n49,30659 e8,13369.
2 € 5 included. 01/01-31/12.
Distance: on the spot 4km 200m 1km.

S **Mainz** 11H3
Wohnmobilstellplatz Mainz, Dr.-Martin-Luther-King-Weg 21.
GPS: n49,99849 e8,24638.

56 € 10 € 1/90liter Ch € 0,50/kWh,16Amp .
Surface: metalled. 01/01-31/12.
Distance: Old city centre 1,7km 7km 150m Aldi 200m bus 160m.

S **Mandelbachtal** 16F2
Ommersheimer Weiher, L107. **GPS**: n49,21899 e7,16766.

2 free € 1 (2x)€ 1/8h. **Location:** Rural, simple, isolated, quiet.
Surface: asphalted. 01/01-31/12.
Distance: on the spot on the spot.

Mandelbachtal 16F2
Kloster Gräfinthal, Gräfinthal. **GPS**: n49,15975 e7,11924.

2 free. **Location:** Rural, simple, noisy. **Surface:** metalled.
01/01-31/12.
Distance: 100m.
Remarks: Nearby monastery.

S **Manderscheid** 11F3
Hotel Heidsmühle, Mosenbergstrasse 22.
GPS: n50,08504 e6,80021.

20 free (4x)€ 2,50/day. **Location:** Rural, simple, isolated, quiet. **Surface:** grassy/gravel. 01/01-31/12.
Distance: 2km 6km on the spot on the spot on the spot on the spot.

S **Manderscheid** 11F3
Campingplatz Vulkaneifel, Herbstwiese.
GPS: n50,09713 e6,79969.

8 € 7,50/pp, dog € 1,50 € 0,50/100liter Ch € 2,50 WC included . **Location:** Rural, simple, quiet. **Surface:** metalled.
15/03-31/10.
Distance: 800m 800m 800m on camp site on the spot

on the spot.
Remarks: Bread-service.

S **Mayen** 11F3

Wohnmobilstellplatz am Viehmarkt, Polcherstrasse.
GPS: n50,32194 e7,22806.

6 free € 1/80liter Ch WC.
Location: Simple. **Surface:** gravel. 01/01-31/12.
Distance: 100m 4km 100m 100m.
Remarks: Next to event ground, max. 3 nights.

S **Mayschoss** 11F2

Ahruferplatz, Ahr-Rotweinstraße 46. **GPS**: n50,51736 e7,01948.

75 € 6 € 1/100liter Ch (15x)€ 2,50/day WC.
Location: Rural, central.
Surface: asphalted/gravel. 01/01-31/12.
Distance: on the spot 100m 250m bakery 50m.
Remarks: Along the Ahr river, parking at station.

S **Meckenheim** 16H2

Sporthalle Meckenheim, Rödersheimerstraße.
GPS: n49,41167 e8,24056.

10 free (6x)€ 0,50/kWh. **Location:** Rural, simple, quiet.
Surface: gravel. 01/01-31/12.
Distance: 1km 6km 200m 800m 4km on the spot.
Remarks: At gymnasium.

S **Meddersheim** 16G1

Winzergenossenschaft, Naheweinstrasse 63. **GPS**: n49,77988 e7,61347.
8 free free € 3/day. **Location:** Rural, simple, quiet.
Surface: gravel. 01/01-31/12.
Distance: 800m on the spot.
Remarks: Max. 2 nights, gate can be opened manually.

S **Mehring** 16F1

Weingut Zellerhof, Zellerhof 1. **GPS**: n49,79369 e6,81944.

43 € 6 € 0,50/70liter Ch (43x)€ 0,50/kWh WC € 1.
Surface: grassy/metalled. 01/01-31/12.
Distance: 100m 5km on the spot on the spot on the spot 100m.

S **Mehring** 16F1

Wohnmobilstellplatz del Mosel, Moselweinstrasse 2.
GPS: n49,79423 e6,81726.

72 € 8 € 1/100liter Ch (60x)€ 2 WC € 2.
Surface: grassy. 01/01-31/12.
Distance: 100m on the spot 200m.
Remarks: Bread-service.

S **Meisenheim** 16G1

Schwimmbad Meisenheim, In der Heimbach.
GPS: n49,71472 e7,65750.

12 € 5 € 1/100liter € 1 Ch (12x)€ 1/kWh.
Location: Rural, simple, quiet. **Surface:** grassy/gravel.
01/01-31/12 01/07-09/07.
Distance: 1,6km on the spot 500m.

S **Mendig** 11G3

Brauerstraße. **GPS**: n50,37678 e7,28404.

20 free € 1/30liter Ch (12x)€ 0,50/kWh.
Location: Rural, quiet. **Surface:** gravel. 01/01-31/12.
Distance: 200m Vulkanbrauhaus&Felsenkeller 400m.
Remarks: In front of football ground, Vulkanmuseum Lava-Dome 100m.

S **Merzig** 16F2

Das Bad, Saarwiesenring 3. **GPS**: n49,44541 e6,62418.

12 € 7,50 € 1/100liter Ch (12x) WC included.
Location: Rural, simple, quiet. **Surface:** grasstiles.
01/01-31/12.
Distance: 2km 5km on the spot 2km bus 400m.
Remarks: Check in at swimming pool, caution key € 50, use sanitary only during opening hours swimming pool.

S **Mettlach** 16F1

Cloef-Atrium, Alfred-Backer-strasse, Mettlach-Orscholz.
GPS: n49,50394 e6,53225.

10 € 5 WC. **Surface:** gravel. 01/01-31/12.
Distance: 900m 13km 200m 300m bus 300m on the spot.
Remarks: Pay with SMS, max. 24h.

S **Mettlach** 16F1

Mettlacher Abtei-Bräu, P6, Bahnhofstrasse 32.
GPS: n49,49847 e6,59612.

10 € 5 Chfree. **Surface:** gravel. 01/01-31/12.
Distance: 500m 7km on the spot on the spot on the spot aldi 1km 700m.
Remarks: Along the Saar River, pay with SMS.

Mettlach 16F1

Restaurant zum Kaltenborn, Zur Großwies 21, Orscholz.
GPS: n49,50916 e6,53030.

10 € 5. **Surface:** asphalted. 01/01-31/12 Thu.
Distance: on the spot 15km on the spot 200m 400m.

Tourist information Mettlach:
Erlebniszentrum Villeroy&Boch.
Mo-Fr: 9.30-19h, Sa 9.30-18h.
Villeroy&Boch Factory Outlet, Freiherr-vom-Stein-Strasse 4-6.
Mo-Fr: 9.30-19h, Sa 9.30-18h.

S **Minheim** 16F1

Reisemobilpark Sonneninsel, K53. **GPS**: n49,86500 e6,94111.

90 € 6,50 € 1/100liter Ch € 1/2kWh.
Surface: grassy/gravel. 01/01-31/12.
Distance: 10km 400m 3km.
Remarks: Along the Moselle river, next to football ground.

S **Minheim** 16F1

Weingut Thielen-Feilen, Moselweinstraße 11.
GPS: n49,86502 e6,93935.
3 € 8,50 € 2 WC. 01/01-31/12.
Distance: on the spot 300m 300m.

S **Minheim** 16F1

Weinhaus Moselblick, In der Olk 9. **GPS**: n49,86428 e6,93294.

10 € 9 Ch € 1,50/day.
Surface: grassy/gravel. 01/01-31/12.
Distance: 200m 200m 200m 100m on the spot.
Remarks: Breakfast-service.

DE

Monzernheim 16H1

Weingut Helmut Geil, Am Römer 26. **GPS**: n49,72376 e8,22715.

3 € 6 (3x)included. **Location:** Rural, simple, quiet. **Surface:** grassy. 01/01-31/12.
Distance: 8km 4km 4km.
Remarks: Check in at Weingut.

Monzingen 16G1

Parkplatz Festhalle, Rosengartenstrasse 11.
GPS: n49,79438 e7,59075.

3 free. **Location:** Rural, simple, noisy. **Surface:** asphalted. 01/01-31/12.
Distance: on the spot on the spot 1km 350m.

Monzingen 16G1

Weingut Axel Schramm, Soonwaldstrasse 49.
GPS: n49,81088 e7,48058.

3 free free. **Location:** Rural, simple, isolated, quiet. **Surface:** concrete. 01/01-31/12.
Distance: 1,2km 1,5km.

Morbach 16F1

Reisemobilhafen Morbach, Zum Camping 15, Hoxel.
GPS: n49,77855 e7,10695.

40 € 5/night € 1/80liter Ch (40x)€ 2/night.
Location: Rural. **Surface:** grassy. 16/03-15/11.
Distance: 300m 300m.

Münstermaifeld 11G3

An der Stadthalle, An den Gärten 6. **GPS**: n50,24583 e7,36778.

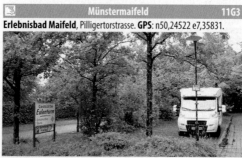

2 free. **Location:** Urban, simple. **Surface:** metalled. 01/01-31/12.
Distance: 800m 800m 800m.

Münstermaifeld 11G3

Erlebnisbad Maifeld, Pilligertorstrasse. **GPS**: n50,24522 e7,35831.

4. **Location:** Rural, simple. **Surface:** metalled. 01/09-15/05.
Distance: 700m 700m 700m.

Nanzdietschweiler 16G2

Hauptstrasse. **GPS**: n49,44083 e7,43500.

2 free € 1/100liter (4x)€ 1/8h. **Location:** Rural, simple, isolated, quiet. **Surface:** metalled. 01/01-31/12.
Distance: 7km on the spot on the spot.

Neef 11F3

Wohnmobilstellplatz Zum Frauenberg, Moseluferstraße.
GPS: n50,09455 e7,13730.

100 € 7 Chincluded (43x)€ 2/24h,10Amp.
Location: Rural, simple. **Surface:** grassy. 01/04-01/11.
Distance: on the spot on the spot 200m 500m on the spot on the spot.
Remarks: Along the Moselle river, nearby sports fields, bread-service.

Neuhäusel 11G3

Wohnmobilstellplatz Efferz, Im Feldchen. **GPS**: n50,38271 e7,70331.

20 € 8 € 1/80liter Ch (12x)€ 1/2kWh WC.
Surface: metalled. 01/01-31/12.
Distance: 250m 250m 250m 100m > Koblenz.
Remarks: Bread-service.

Neumagen-Dhron 16F1

Gaststatte Beim Ketsch, In der Zeil. **GPS**: n49,86449 e6,90321.

100 € 6 Chincluded € 1,50/day WC € 2 € 3 against payment. **Surface:** grassy/gravel. 01/01-31/12.
Distance: 200m on the spot 500m on the spot on the spot.
Remarks: Bread-service.

Neumagen-Dhron 16F1

Yachthafen Neumagen, Moselstrasse 21.
GPS: n49,85188 e6,89232.

40 <9m € 6, >9m € 8 + € 2,50/pp, dog € 2 € 0,50/40liter Ch € 0,60/kWh WC included € 3/24h.
Location: Rural. **Surface:** gravel. 01/01-31/12.
Distance: 100m on the spot on the spot on the spot 1,3km.
Remarks: Check in at harbourmaster, boat rental, bicycle rental.

Neustadt/Weinstrasse 16H2

Dammstrasse-Ost, Hambach. **GPS**: n49,33083 e8,13150.

10 free € 1/100liter € 1 Ch.
Surface: grassy. 01/01-31/12.
Distance: 200m 200m 200m 4km.
Remarks: Next to swimming pool, service 500m.

Neustadt/Weinstrasse 16H2

Reisemobilstellpatz Martin-Luther-Kirche, Martin-Luther-Strasse.
GPS: n49,35485 e8,15255.

30 € 5/24h € 1/8minutes Ch (24x)€ 1/kWh.
Surface: metalled. 01/01-31/12.
Distance: 300m 250m on the spot.

Neustadt/Weinstrasse 16H2

Festplatz Neustadt-Haardt, Am Mandelring, Haardt.
GPS: n49,36731 e8,13917.
2 free. **Location:** Rural, simple. **Surface:** asphalted. 01/01-31/12 Wine festivals.
Distance: 2km 5km 100m.

Neustadt/Weinstrasse 16H2

Parkplatz am Rebenmeer, Am Falltor, Duttweiler.
GPS: n49,30148 e8,21192.

20 free. **Location:** Rural, simple, quiet. **Surface:** gravel/metalled. 01/01-31/12.
Distance: 300m 5km 300m 250m bakery Kraut und Rüben-Radweg.

Neustadt/Weinstrasse 16H2

Wohnmobilstellplatz Gimmeldingen, Peter-Koch-Strasse.
GPS: n49,37771 e8,15448.

DE

2 free. **Location:** Rural, simple. **Surface:** asphalted/metalled.
01/01-31/12.
Distance: 500m 5km on the spot on the spot.

Neustadt/Weinstrasse 16H2

Altes Weingut Steigelmann, Lauterbachstrasse 33, Mussbach.
GPS: n49,37285 e8,17230.
5 € 5 Ch (5x)€ 2. **Location:** Rural. **Surface:** grassy.
01/03-30/11.
Distance: 500m 3km 400m 700m 450m.

Neustadt/Weinstrasse 16H2

Rebenhof Wein- und Sektgut, Andergasse 93, Hambach.
GPS: n49,32157 e8,12241.

5 € 8, 2 pers.incl WC included.
Location: Rural. **Surface:** grasstiles/grassy. 01/01-31/12.
Distance: 5km 100m.

Neustadt/Weinstrasse 16H2

Weingut & Weinschenke Hans Abel, Weinstrasse 103, Hambach.
GPS: n49,33784 e8,13157.
3 free € 2,50. **Surface:** grassy. 01/01-31/12 Thu.
Distance: Old city centre 3km 4,5km 300m bakery 200m bus.

Neustadt/Weinstrasse 16H2

Weingut Andres, Langensteinstrasse 22, Lachen-Speyersdorf.
GPS: n49,33631 e8,20579.
3 free . 01/01-31/12.

Neustadt/Weinstrasse 16H2

Weingut Carl Disson, Andergasse 96, Hambach.
GPS: n49,32123 e8,12220.

4 € 7 WC included.
Location: Rural. **Surface:** grassy. 01/01-31/12.
Distance: 5km 100m.
Remarks: Bread-service, wine tasting.

Neustadt/Weinstrasse 16H2

Weingut Hammer, Zum Klausental 29. **GPS:** n49,32109 e8,13251.
3 € 5 . 01/01-31/12.
Distance: 5km.

Neustadt/Weinstrasse 16H2

Weingut Klohr, An der Eselshaut 67, Mussbach.
GPS: n49,36931 e8,17414.
2 free . 01/01-31/12.
Distance: on the spot 2km 100m 200m 700m.

Neustadt/Weinstrasse 16H2

Weingut Kreiselmaier, Goethestrasse 77, Lachen.
GPS: n49,32255 e8,20061.

3 € 5 € 2/100liter € 2/night.
Location: Rural, simple, quiet. **Surface:** grassy. 01/03-31/10.
Distance: on the spot 4,5km 250m 3km 150m Kraut-und-Rüben-Radweg.
Remarks: Sale of wines.

Neustadt/Weinstrasse 16H2

Weingut Müller-Kern, Andergasse 38, Hambach.
GPS: n49,32266 e8,12681.

3 € 15, 2 pers.incl (3x) WC .
Surface: grassy. 01/01-31/12.
Distance: 4,5km 300m on the spot on the spot.
Remarks: Adjacent walking and bicycle area.

Neustadt/Weinstrasse 16H2

Weingut Rumsauer, Von-Dalheim-Strasse 11, Diedesfeld.
GPS: n49,32010 e8,14037.
2 free . **Surface:** grassy. 01/01-31/12.
Distance: 400m 5km 800m.

Neustadt/Weinstrasse 16H2

Weingut Schäfer, Schiessmauer 56, Mussbach.
GPS: n49,36335 e8,17111.

5 € 15, 2 pers.incl Ch WC included.
Location: Rural. **Surface:** grassy. 01/03-31/10.
Distance: 2km.

Neustadt/Weinstrasse 16H2

Weingut Völcker, An der Eselshaut 15, Mussbach.
GPS: n49,36825 e8,16805.
3 € 5 included. **Location:** Rural. **Surface:** grassy.
01/01-31/12.
Distance: 300m 3km 450m 800m 600m.

Neustadt/Weinstrasse 16H2

Weinhaus Am Herzog, Mandelring 195, Haardt.
GPS: n49,36889 e8,14583.
2 € 20 WC included. **Location:** Rural, simple.
Surface: metalled. 01/01-31/12.
Distance: 4km 500m.
Remarks: Motorhomes <6.5m, bicycle rental.

Neustadt/Weinstrasse 16H2

Weinland Königsbach-Neustadt, Deidesheimer Strasse 12, Königsbach. **GPS:** n49,38712 e8,16239.

5 € 5 included. **Location:** Rural, simple, quiet.
Surface: concrete. 01/01-31/12.
Distance: 6,5km 300m.

Neustadt/Weinstrasse 16H2

Weinland Meckenheim, An der Eselshaut 76, Mussbach.
GPS: n49,37037 e8,17479.
3 € 5 € 2,50 WC. **Surface:** grassy/gravel. 01/01-31/12.
Distance: 400m 2,3km 300m 200m 650m.

Neustadt/Weinstrasse 16H2

Weingut Helbighof, Andergasse 40, Hambach.
GPS: n49,32256 e8,12657.
3 free. 01/01-31/12.
Distance: 4,5km 300m.

Neustadt/Weinstrasse 16H2

Hambacher Schloss, Weinstrasse 110, Hambach.
GPS: n49,33706 e8,13155.
2 free. 01/01-31/12 01/10-31/10.
Distance: 4,5km 200m.

Neuwied 11G2

Yachthafen Neuwied, Rheinstrasse 180. **GPS:** n50,41413 e7,47946.

40 € 7, 2 pers.incl. Ch € 0,50/kWh WC included.
Location: Rural. **Surface:** metalled. 01/01-31/12.
Distance: 2km 16km on the spot 2km 3km.
Remarks: Bread-service, cash payment.

Nickenich 11G3

Wohnmobilstellplatz am Baggerado, Auf dem Teich 1.
GPS: n50,40607 e7,33299.
4 € 7 Ch (4x). **Surface:** metalled. 01/01-31/12.
Distance: 800m 800m.

Niederbreitbach 11G2

Campingplatz Neuerburg, Im Freizeitparkt 1.
GPS: n50,52969 e7,41414.

8 € 7, dog € 1 80liter Ch € 1,50/day € 1 € 4/3.
Location: Rural, comfortable. **Surface:** gravel.
01/01-31/12 sanitary 01/11-31/03.
Distance: 250m 13km on the spot on the spot on the spot on the spot on the spot.
Remarks: Bread-service.

Niederkirchen bei Deidesheim 16H2

Wohnmobilstellplatz Niederkirchen, An de Sportanlage 1.
GPS: n49,40891 e8,22141.

6 free € 1/4h. **Location:** Rural, simple, quiet. **Surface:** gravel.
01/01-31/12.
Distance: 1km 4,5km 1km.
Remarks: Service 300m.

Nierstein 16H1

Mobilstellplatz auf dem Weingut Gehring, Ausserhalb 17.
GPS: n49,85621 e8,32520.

30 € 9 Ch (15x)€ 3/day € 1/6minutes included.
Location: Rural, comfortable, quiet. **Surface:** grassy.
01/01-31/12.
Distance: 1km 11km 3km 1,2km 10m 500m

DE

1,2km 50m 10m.
Remarks: Bread-service.

S Nohfelden 16F1

Campingplatz Bostalsee, P6, L325, Bosen.
GPS: n49,56039 e7,06113.

10 € 12 € 0,50/60liter Ch€ 0,50 € 1/kWh included.
Location: Rural, simple, quiet. **Surface:** metalled.
01/01-31/12.
Distance: 500m 6km 200m € 8/day on the spot 800m on the spot on the spot.

Nonnweiler 16F1

Stellplatz Am Hallenbad, Triererstrasse 2.
GPS: n49,60686 e6,97216.

5 free € 1/100liter (4x)€ 0,50. **Location:** Rural, simple, quiet.
Surface: grassy/metalled. 01/01-31/12.
Distance: on the spot 1km on the spot 800m.
Remarks: Parking swimming pool, max. 48h.

S Nürburg 11F3

Wohnmobilpark Motorsporthotel, Hauptstrasse 34.
GPS: n50,33982 e6,95131.
12 € 10 included on demand. **Location:** Rural, simple.
Surface: grassy. 01/01-31/12.
Distance: on the spot.
Remarks: At racing circuit, pay at hotel.

S Ober-Hilbersheim 16H1

Napoleonshöhe, Sprendlingers Straße. **GPS**: n49,89785 e8,02421.

40 free € 1/90liter Ch (6x)€ 1/8h. **Location:** Rural, simple.
Surface: grassy. 01/01-31/12.
Distance: 500m 300m.

S Oberbrombach 16G1

Wohnmobilstellplatz Höhenblick, Sonnenberger Strasse.
GPS: n49,69481 e7,25960.

75 € 7 Chincluded (45x)€ 2/4kWh. **Location:** Rural, comfortable, quiet. **Surface:** grassy/gravel. 01/01-31/12.
Distance: 400m 4km 1,5km.

S Oberwesel/Rhein 11G3

Stellplatz am Schiffsanleger, B9. **GPS**: n50,10816 e7,72758.
10 € 8/night . **Surface:** metalled. 01/01-31/12.
Distance: 10km on the spot on the spot 200m lidl 1km
600m.
Remarks: Along the Rhine river.

S Oberwesel/Rhein 11G3

Camping Schönburgblick, Am Hafendamm 1.
GPS: n50,10294 e7,73663.

20 € 9 Chincluded € 0,60/kWh WC € 2,50 € 2.
Location: Comfortable, quiet. **Surface:** grassy. 15/03-31/10.
Distance: 800m on the spot on the spot on the spot 200m 400m.
Remarks: Max. 8M, possibility for reservation.

Offenbach an der Queich 16H2

Am Queichtalzentrum, Konrad-Lerch-Ring.
GPS: n49,20056 e8,19478.

2 free. **Location:** Simple. **Surface:** metalled.
01/01-31/12.
Distance: 100m 6km 500m 1km 400m.
Remarks: At sports centre, max. 3 days.

S Oppenheim 16H1

Womoland Oppenheim, An der Festwiese.
GPS: n49,85673 e8,36502.

20 € 7 € 1/50liter Ch € 3/24h.
Location: Rural, simple. **Surface:** grassy.
01/01-31/12 week before/after Whitsuntide.
Distance: 500m 500m 500m.

S Osann-Monzel 16F1

Wohnmobilstellplatz Hotel Moselsteig, Novianderweg 3.
GPS: n49,90865 e6,95776.

8 € 5 € 2 against payment.
Surface: gravel. 01/06-31/10.
Distance: 9km on the spot on the spot on the spot.

S Osthofen 16H1

Festplatz Wonnegauhalle, Herrnsheimer Strasse.
GPS: n49,69913 e8,32691.

15 free Chfree (6x)€ 1/8h. **Location:** Rural, simple.
Surface: gravel. 01/01-31/12.
Distance: 500m 7km 500m.
Remarks: Max. 48h.

Osthofen 16H1

Sommerried Stadion, L439. **GPS**: n49,69222 e8,32805.

10 free. **Location:** Rural, simple. **Surface:** grassy/sand.
01/01-31/12.
Distance: 6km 800m.
Remarks: Max. 48h.

S Osthofen 16H1

Weingut Borntaler Hof, Alter Westhofer Weg.
GPS: n49,69985 e8,29860.

40 € 8 WCincluded . **Location:** Rural, simple.
Surface: grassy/metalled. 01/01-31/12.
Distance: 9km.

S Ottweiler 16F2

Stellplatz Wingertsweiher, Am Wingertsweiher.
GPS: n49,41134 e7,18076.

12 € 5/24h € 1/150liter € 1 Ch (6x)€ 3/8h.
Location: Rural, simple, quiet. **Surface:** grassy/metalled.
01/01-31/12.
Distance: 1,5km on the spot on the spot on the spot 1,5km 1km.
Remarks: Max. 7 days, money in envelope in mail box.

S Palzem 16E1

Weingut E. Pauly, Obermoselstrasse 5.
GPS: n49,56402 e6,37581.

5 € 7 (5x)included WC. **Surface:** gravel/metalled.

DE

01/01-31/12.
Distance: on the spot on the spot 50m 4km 450m.
Remarks: Not suitable for big motorhomes, beautiful view.

Perl 16E1

Am Perlbad, Auf dem Sabel 4. **GPS**: n49,47900 e6,38493.

6 € 5, winter € 3 € 1/6minutes Ch (8x)€ 1/8h.
Surface: metalled. 01/01-31/12.
Distance: 500m 3,5km 500m 500m bus 500m.
Remarks: At swimming pool, to be paid at swimming pool.

Pfaffen-Schwabenheim 16H1

Pferdepension am Sonnenhof, Brühlstraße.
GPS: n49,85224 e7,95951.
10 € 10 WC included. **Location:** Rural, simple, isolated, quiet. **Surface:** concrete. 01/01-31/12.
Distance: 7km on the spot aldi 700m.
Remarks: Breakfast-service.

Piesport 16F1

Piesporter Goldtröpfchen, Moselstrasse.
GPS: n49,87199 e6,92703.

30 € 8 € 1/80liter Ch € 3.
Surface: gravel. 01/01-31/12.
Distance: 100m 11km on the spot on the spot on the spot 500m.
Remarks: Bread-service mo-sa.

Piesport 16F1

Altes Kelterhaus, St. Martinstrasse 33. **GPS**: n49,87872 e6,92590.

7 € 7,50, guests free € 2,50 Ch € 2,50.
Surface: gravel. 01/01-31/12 01/11-28/02: Mo.
Distance: 10km on the spot on the spot.
Remarks: Bicycle rental.

Piesport 16F1

Weingut Heinz Kirsten, In der Noo. **GPS**: n49,88017 e6,92597.

6 € 6 Ch € 1.
Location: Rural. **Surface:** gravel. 01/01-31/12.
Distance: on the spot 7,5km Moselle river 600m Moselle river 600m on the spot on the spot.
Remarks: Check in at Bahnhofstrasse 28.

Piesport 16F1

Weingut Spang, Reisemobilplatz Rebengarten, In den Dur 11.
GPS: n49,88287 e6,92781.

3 € 8, 2 pers.incl included € 0,70/kWh WC € 2,50.
Location: Rural. **Surface:** gravel.
01/03-30/11.
Distance: on the spot 8km 100m 100m 500m 500m.
Remarks: Bread-service + breakfast-service.

Piesport 16F1

Wohnmobilstellplatz Loreleyblick, Loreleyblick 20.
GPS: n49,87323 e6,92535.

5 € 8 Ch (10x) € 1.
Surface: gravel. 01/01-31/12.
Distance: on the spot 11km 1km 300m.
Remarks: Bread-service.

Pirmasens 16G2

Am Messegelände, Zeppelinstraße 11. **GPS**: n49,20446 e7,60885.

8 € 5/24h € 1/100liter Ch € 1/6h.
Location: Urban, simple, noisy. **Surface:** gravel.
01/01-31/12.
Distance: 450m 6km 450m 450m 1km.

Pirmasens 16G2

Forsthaus Beckenhof, Beckenhofer Strasse.
GPS: n49,19604 e7,65635.

10 guests free. **Location:** Rural, simple, quiet. **Surface:** gravel.
01/01-31/12.
Distance: 6km on the spot.

Plaidt 11G3

Wohnmobilstellplatz am Vulkanpark, Rauschermühle 6.
GPS: n50,38790 e7,40444.

10 free. **Location:** Rural. **Surface:** metalled.
01/01-31/12.
Distance: 1km 5km 1km 3km 2km on the spot on the spot.

Plein 11F3

Hotel-Restaurant Waldschlößchen Plein, Zum Waldschlößchen 3.
GPS: n50,03223 e6,88074.
3 guests free . 01/01-31/12 Wed.
Distance: 4km on the spot.

Polch 11G3

Niesmann&Bischoff, Clou-strasse 1. **GPS**: n50,30680 e7,30684.

25 free € 0,50/80liter Ch (12x)€ 0,50/kWh.
Surface: metalled. 01/01-31/12.
Distance: on the spot on the spot.

Pronsfeld 11E3

Am Alten Bahnhof, Bahnhofstrasse. **GPS**: n50,16343 e6,33669.

50 € 6 € 0,50/60liter Ch (24x)€ 0,50/kWh.
Location: Rural, comfortable, quiet. **Surface:** grassy/gravel.
01/01-31/12.
Distance: 600m 7,5km 600m 700m 500m on the spot on the spot.

Prüm 11E3

Wohnmobilstellplatz Prüm, Monthermeerstrasse 3.
GPS: n50,20956 e6,42715.

4 free. **Location:** Urban, simple. **Surface:** gravel.
01/01-31/12.
Distance: 600m 2,2km 500m 500m 200m.

Pünderich 11F3

Wohnmobilstellplatz Pünderich, Moselallee.
GPS: n50,04355 e7,12548.

DE

80 € 6 Ch included (12x)€ 2/24h.
Location: Rural, simple, quiet.
Surface: grassy. 01/04-31/10.
Distance: on the spot on the spot on the spot 300m 500m.

Ramstein-Miesenbach 16G1

City Parkplatz, Talstrasse. **GPS:** n49,45103 e7,55557.

3 free. **Location:** Urban, simple, noisy. **Surface:** gravel.
01/01-31/12.
Distance: on the spot 3,7km 800m aldi 1km 300m.

Ramstein-Miesenbach 16G1

Freizeitbad Azur, Schernauer Strasse 50. **GPS:** n49,44578 e7,56971.

30 free. **Location:** Rural, simple, noisy. **Surface:** metalled.
01/01-31/12.
Distance: 1km 5,5km 350m 1km.

Rech 11F2

Wohnmobilstellplatz Burgwiese, B267. **GPS:** n50,51417 e7,03361.

15 € 6. **Location:** Rural. **Surface:** grassy. 01/01-31/12.
Distance: 500m 11km on the spot on the spot 300m 350m.
Remarks: Along the Ahr river.

Rech 11F2

Im Bungert. **GPS:** n50,51444 e7,03750.
10 € 5. **Location:** Rural, simple. **Surface:** gravel.
01/01-31/12.
Distance: on the spot on the spot on the spot on the spot.

Reil/Mosel 11F3

Am Moselufer, Moselstrasse. **GPS:** n50,02566 e7,11493.

70 € 7 Ch (48x)€ 2 WC included. **Location:** Rural, comfortable, quiet. **Surface:** grassy. 01/03-31/10.
Distance: 500m on the spot 450m.
Remarks: Along the Moselle river.

Reipoltskirchen 16G1

Wasserburg, Kegelbahnstrasse. **GPS:** n49,63448 e7,66373.

7 free € 1/4minutes Ch (4x)€ 1/12h.
Location: Rural, simple, central, quiet. **Surface:** metalled.
01/01-31/12.
Distance: 150m on the spot bakery 100m on the spot.

Reipoltskirchen 16G1

Stellplatz Ausbacherhof, K42, Ausbacherhof.
GPS: n49,61307 e7,65667.

4 free. **Location:** Rural, simple, isolated, quiet.
Surface: grassy/gravel. 01/01-31/12.

Remagen 11F2

Wohnmobilhafen Goldene Meile, Simrockweg 9–13.
GPS: n50,57667 e7,24750.

30 € 12 € 1/90liter Ch (18x)€ 1/6h.
Surface: grassy. 01/04-31/10.
Distance: 10km on the spot on the spot.

Rengsdorf 11G2

Monte Mare, Monte-Mare-Weg 1. **GPS:** n50,50803 e7,48388.

4 free. **Location:** Rural. **Surface:** gravel. 01/01-31/12.
Distance: 600m on the spot 350m.

Rheinbreitbach 11F2

Wohnmobilstellplatz Siebengebirgsblick, Rolandsecker Weg 8.
GPS: n50,62193 e7,22812.

14 € 8 € 1/90liter Ch (12x)€ 1/2kWh.
Location: Simple. **Surface:** grassy/gravel. 01/01-31/12.
Distance: 500m.
Remarks: To be paid at Rolandsecker Weg 8.

Rhodt unter Rietburg 16H2

Theresienstraße. **GPS:** n49,27464 e8,09917.

20 € 4. **Location:** Rural, simple. **Surface:** gravel.
01/01-31/12.
Distance: 100m 5km 500m 600m.

Rhodt unter Rietburg 16H2

Meyer Karl Herman, Edesheimerstrasse 17.
GPS: n49,26883 e8,10868.

6 € 9 (6x)included. **Location:** Rural, simple, quiet.
Surface: gravel. 01/01-31/12.
Distance: 200m 200m 200m.

Rhodt unter Rietburg 16H2

Weingut Fader, Traminerweg 1. **GPS:** n49,26972 e8,11057.

12 € 15 Ch (12x)included.
Location: Rural, simple, quiet. **Surface:** gravel. 01/04-31/10.
Distance: 300m 7km 200m 200m.

Rhodt unter Rietburg 16H2

Weingut Krieger, Edesheimer Straße 7. **GPS:** n49,26917 e8,10778.
2 € 5 included. **Surface:** grassy. 01/01-31/12.
Distance: on the spot 200m 500m.

Rhodt unter Rietburg 16H2

Weingut Krieger, Edesheimerstrasse 7. **GPS:** n49,26961 e8,10803.

2 € 5 free on demand. **Location:** Rural, simple, quiet.
Surface: grassy. 01/01-31/12.
Distance: 100m 6km 200m 200m.

Rhodt unter Rietburg 16H2

Weingut Nichterlein, Mühlgasse 15. **GPS:** n49,27349 e8,10802.

DE

3 € 6 WC included. **Location:** Rural, quiet.
Surface: metalled. 01/01-31/12.
Distance: 300m 5km 200m 400m.

Rhodt unter Rietburg 16H2

Weingut Jürgen Heußler, Weyherer Strasse 34/35.
GPS: n49,27052 e8,10386.

3 € 3, guests free. **Location:** Simple. **Surface:** gravel.
01/01-31/12.
Distance: 300m 6km 100m 350m.

Rockenhausen 16G1

Reisemobilhafen Rockenhausen, Obermühle.
GPS: n49,62136 e7,82146.

5 free € 1/80liter Ch (6x)€ 1/6h.
Location: Rural, simple. **Surface:** gravel. 01/01-31/12.
Distance: 800m on the spot.
Remarks: At swimming pool.

Roschbach 16H2

Weingut Koch, Am Rosenkränzel 13. **GPS**: n49,24736 e8,11532.

3 € 5 included € 2/night WC. **Location:** Rural, quiet.
Surface: grassy. 01/01-31/12.
Distance: 5km 400m.

Ruppertsberg 16H2

Winzerhaus Im Linsenbusch, Hauptstrasse 70.
GPS: n49,39944 e8,20044.

4 € 10 included WC .
Location: Rural, comfortable. **Surface:** grasstiles. 01/01-31/12.
Distance: on the spot 3km on the spot 1km 1,5km.

Saarbrücken 16F2

Reisemobilhafen Calypso, Deutschmühlental 7.
GPS: n49,23027 e6,96222.

20 € 7 + reduction swimming pool Ch included (4x)€ 1/24h. **Location:** Simple, noisy. **Surface:** metalled.
01/01-31/12.
Distance: 700m 100m on the spot 500m on the spot.
Remarks: To pay at swimming pool.

Saarburg 16F1

Reisemobilpark Saarburg, Am Saarufer.
GPS: n49,60158 e6,55442.

100 € 10, 01/11-28/02 € 8 + tourist tax € 0,25/pp
€ 1/100liter Ch (70x)€ 0,50/kWh WC € 1,50 .
Surface: grassy/metalled. 01/01-31/12 Service: winter.
Distance: 850m on the spot on the spot 200m.
Remarks: Bread-service.

Saarburg 16F1

Reisemobilstellplatz Leukbachtal, Leukbachtal 1.
GPS: n49,59921 e6,54130.

20 € 19,50, 2 pers.incl Ch WC included.
Location: Rural, comfortable, quiet. **Surface:** grassy.
01/03-31/10.
Distance: 1km 150m 150m 700m.

Saarlouis 16F2

In den Fliesen, St.Nazairer Allee. **GPS**: n49,32146 e6,74267.

30 free € 1/80liter Ch.
Location: Urban, simple, quiet. **Surface:** metalled. 01/01-31/12.
Distance: 500m 1,5km on the spot on the spot 500m 300m.
Remarks: At sports centre, bread-service.

Saarlouis 16F2

Hotellerie Waldesruh, Siersburger Strasse 8, Wallerfangen.
GPS: n49,34440 e6,67614.

2 € 10, guests free. **Location:** Rural, simple, noisy.
Surface: metalled. 01/01-31/12 Su-Mo.
Distance: 10km on the spot.

Sankt Aldegund 11F3

Am Moselstausee. **GPS**: n50,07899 e7,13119.

40 € 6 Ch included (28x)€ 2/24h. **Location:** Rural, simple.
Surface: grassy/metalled. 01/04-01/12.
Distance: 250m on the spot 250m.
Remarks: Bread-service.

Sankt Goarshausen 11G3

Loreley Besucherzentrum, Auf der Loreley 7.
GPS: n50,14191 e7,73303.

25 € 5. **Location:** Rural, simple, isolated. **Surface:** gravel.
01/01-31/12.
Distance: 600m 600m.

Sankt Ingbert 16F2

Reisemobilplatz 'Das Blau', Spieser Landstraße.
GPS: n49,28652 e7,13194.

8 free € 1/80liter Ch. **Location:** Simple, central, quiet.
Surface: grassy. 01/01-31/12.
Distance: 1,5km 3,5km 100m 1,7km on the spot.
Remarks: Next to parking swimming pool, service 100m.

Sankt Julian 16G1

An der Ölmühle, Mühlstraße (K26). **GPS**: n49,60758 e7,51480.

10 € 5 € 1 Ch € 1/kWh.
Location: Rural, simple, quiet. **Surface:** grassy. 01/04-31/10.
Distance: on the spot 300m.

Sankt Martin 16H2

Edenkoperstrasse. **GPS**: n49,29702 e8,10838.

DE

14 € 6/day. **Surface:** asphalted. 01/01-31/12.
Distance: 5km.
Remarks: Max. 1 night.

S Sankt Martin 16H2

Weingut Schreieck, Friedhofstrasse 8. **GPS**: n49,30113 e8,10560.
17 € 12 Ch WC included. **Location:** Rural.
Surface: grasstiles. 01/01-31/12.
Distance: on the spot 5km 350m.

S Sankt Martin 16H2

Weinkellerei Ziegler, Mühlstrasse 26. **GPS**: n49,29921 e8,10028.
3 € 10 . 01/01-31/12.
Distance: on the spot 5km 550m.

Sankt Martin 16H2

Consulat des Weines, Maikammerer strasse 44.
GPS: n49,29934 e8,10826.
10 € 1/pp tourist tax. 01/01-31/12.
Distance: 4,5km.

Sankt Martin 16H2

Winzer Holger Schneider, Riedweg. **GPS**: n49,29814 e8,10824.

10 free for clients, € 1/pp tourist tax. **Surface:** gravel.
01/01-31/12.
Distance: 300m on the spot.

S Sankt Martin 16H2

Riedweg. **GPS**: n49,29814 e8,10824.
€ 1 Ch. 01/01-31/12.

S Sankt Wendel 16F1

Am Wendelinuspark, Tholeyer Straße. **GPS**: n49,46907 e7,14267.

12 € 5 Ch included.
Location: Urban, simple. **Surface:** metalled. 01/01-31/12.
Distance: 1km on the spot 100m on the spot.
Remarks: Caution key service € 10, tickets Wendelinusbad.

S Schiersfeld 16G1

Sulzbachtal, Bismarkstraße. **GPS**: n49,69274 e7,76895.

8 free € 1 Ch (8x)€ 1/4kWh .
Location: Rural, simple, quiet. **Surface:** gravel. 01/01-31/12.
Distance: 500m 4km bakery 500m Moscheltalradweg on the spot.

S Schleich 16F1

Zum Moselufer, Am Moselufer. **GPS**: n49,81335 e6,84228.

6 € 5 Ch € 2 WC. **Surface:** grassy. 01/01-31/12.
Distance: on the spot on the spot on the spot 200m.
Remarks: Along the Moselle river.

S Schwabenheim/Selz 11H3

Reisemobilstellplatz Schwabenheim, Ingelheimer Straße.
GPS: n49,93284 e8,09430.

10 free (12x)free. **Location:** Rural, comfortable, quiet.
Surface: grasstiles. 01/01-31/12.
Distance: 200m 8,5km 200m on the spot on the spot.
Remarks: Max. 96h free, then € 3/24h.

S Schwabenheim/Selz 11H3

Weingut Schuck Sonnenhof, Ausserhalb 6.
GPS: n49,93130 e8,09117.

3 € 5 (2x)included WC. **Location:** Rural, comfortable, quiet.
Surface: grassy/gravel. 01/01-31/12.
Distance: 500m 9km 50m.

S Schweich/Mosel bei Trier 16F1

Wohnmobilpark zum Fahrturm, Am Yachthafen.
GPS: n49,81455 e6,75038.

40 < 6m € 11 incl. 2 pers, + € 1/m, dog € 2,10 Ch € 0,60/kWh,+ € 1 € 0,50 € 3 against payment.
Surface: grassy. 01/04-31/10.
Distance: on the spot on the spot on the spot on the spot 50m on the spot on the spot.
Remarks: Boat rental.

S Selzen 16H1

Weingut Kapellenhof, Kapellenstrasse 18.
GPS: n49,86484 e8,25528.

4 € 5 (4x)included. **Location:** Rural, simple, quiet.
Surface: grasstiles. 01/01-31/12.
Distance: on the spot 10km 100m 2km.

S Siefersheim 16H1

Weingut Sommer, Mühlweg 19. **GPS**: n49,79850 e7,95245.

6 € 7 Ch (6x)included WC.
Location: Rural, simple. **Surface:** grassy. 01/04-31/10.
Distance: 8km 2km 2km on the spot.

S Sinzig 11F2

Wohnmobilhafen am Sportplatz, Bäderstrasse.
GPS: n50,55128 e7,21731.

10 € 6/24h € 1 Ch (12x)€ 0,50/kWh WC € 1/1,at Freibad. **Location:** Rural, simple. **Surface:** gravel.
01/01-31/12.
Distance: 7km 800m on the spot on the spot.

Sinzig 11F2

Sinziger Schloß, Jahnstrasse. **GPS**: n50,54684 e7,24844.

20 free. **Location:** Urban, simple. **Surface:** metalled.
01/01-31/12.
Distance: 100m on the spot.

S Sinzig 11F2

Wohnmobilhafen am Thermalfreibad, Bäderstrasse.
GPS: n50,54912 e7,21749.

50 € 6/24h € 1 Ch (18x)€ 0,50/kWh € 1/pp.
Location: Rural, simple. **Surface:** metalled.
01/01-31/12.
Distance: 50m on the spot on the spot.

S Speyer 16H2

Techniek Museum Speyer, Geibstrasse. **GPS**: n49,31222 e8,45009.

DE

90 € 22 Ch WC included. **Location:** Comfortable, central, noisy. **Surface:** grassy. 01/01-31/12.
Distance: on the spot 8,5km 150m 200m on the spot on the spot on the spot.
Remarks: Bread-service, discount museum and theater.

S Speyer 16H2

An den Stadtwerken, Industriestraße 21. **GPS**: n49,30329 e8,44817.

10 € 5 € 1 € 1 Ch included. **Location:** Simple.
Surface: asphalted. 01/01-31/12.
Distance: 1,5km 6km 1,5km 1,6km 500m on the spot.
Remarks: Check in at Stadwerke.

Tourist information Speyer:
M Technik Museum Speyer/Imax Filmtheater, Geibstrasse. Mo-Fr 9-18h, Sa-Su 9-17h.

S Spirkelbach 16G2

Grillplatz Spirkelbach. GPS: n49,19454 e7,88208.

4 € 7 Ch WC included. **Location:** Rural, simple, quiet.
Surface: gravel. 01/01-31/12.
Distance: 500m 2km 500m 2km on the spot on the spot.
Remarks: Check in on arrival, tel: 0171 3355971, grill and picknic area, nature reserve Pfalzer Wald.

S Sprendlingen 16H1

Wiesbach, Bachgasse/Bleichstrasse. **GPS**: n49,85424 e7,98538.

24 € 4 € 2/10minutes Ch (24x)€ 2/day. **Location:** Rural, comfortable, quiet. **Surface:** asphalted.
01/01-31/12.
Distance: 700m 3,4km 500m 900m on the spot.
Remarks: Parking at swimming pool, bread-service, entrance swimming pool € 2/day.

S Sprendlingen 16H1

Weingut Annenhof, Außerhalb 13. **GPS**: n49,85778 e7,99278.

4 free WC free. **Location:** Rural, simple. **Surface:** concrete.
01/01-31/12.
Distance: 3km 500m 800m.

S Sprendlingen 16H1

Weingut Hembd, Karlstrasse 24a. **GPS**: n49,86422 e7,98811.

10 € 10 included. **Location:** Rural, simple.
Surface: grassy. 01/01-31/12.
Distance: 4km 500m 500m.

S Sprendlingen 16H1

Eura Mobil Stellplatz, Graf-von-Sponheimstrasse.
GPS: n49,86297 e7,97612.

38 free € 1/100liter Ch (38x)free. **Location:** Rural, simple, quiet. **Surface:** asphalted/metalled. 01/01-31/12.
Distance: 600m 4,4km 300m.
Remarks: Workdays from 9h guided tours (free).

S Stadecken-Elsheim 11H3

Weingut Mengel-Eppelmann, Mühlstrasse 16.
GPS: n49,91575 e8,12107.

5 € 5, free for clients included.
Location: Rural, comfortable, quiet. **Surface:** asphalted.
01/01-31/12.
Distance: on the spot 6km on the spot 1km.
Remarks: Playground.

Stadtkyll 11F3

Kurallee. **GPS**: n50,35290 e6,52820.
6 free. 01/01-31/12.

S Stromberg 11G3

Reisemobilplatz Michelsland, Königsberger Straße.
GPS: n49,94709 e7,78818.

6 € 5 Ch included (6x)€ 0,50/kWh.
Location: Comfortable, quiet. **Surface:** grassy. 01/01-31/12.
Distance: 500m 500m 50m Lidl.

S Thalfang 16F1

Festplatz Thalfang, Talstrasse 2. **GPS**: n49,75103 e6,99902.

40 € 5 Ch (6x)included. **Location:** Simple, quiet.
Surface: grassy/gravel. 01/01-31/12 21/09-30/09.
Distance: 200m on the spot on the spot on the spot 200m 200m on the spot.
Remarks: Max. 4 nights, check in at swimming pool.

Thalfang 16F1

Ferienpark Himmelberg, Birkenweg 73. **GPS**: n49,74835 e6,98721.

2 free. **Location:** Rural, simple. **Surface:** metalled.
01/01-31/12.
Distance: 300m.

Thallichtenberg 16G1

Burg Lichtenberg, K23. **GPS**: n49,55716 e7,35975.

4 free. **Location:** Rural, simple, quiet. **Surface:** asphalted.
01/01-31/12.
Distance: 7km 300m 1km.
Remarks: Max. 3 days.

Tholey 16F1

Parkplatz Am Schaumburg, Am Schaumberg.
GPS: n49,48965 e7,03804.

±20 free. **Location:** Rural, simple, quiet. **Surface:** metalled.
01/01-31/12.
Distance: 500m 100m on the spot on the spot.

DE

Traben-Trarbach 11F3

Wohnmobilstellplatz am Mosel, Rissbacherstraße 155.
GPS: n49,96583 e7,10583.
45 € 12 Ch (45x),6Amp WC included.
Location: Rural, comfortable. **Surface:** grassy/gravel.
01/04-31/12.
Distance: 500m on the spot on the spot 500m 200m 100m on the spot on the spot.
Remarks: Along the Moselle river.

Trechtinghausen 11G3

Camping Marienort, Mainzer Straße. **GPS**: n50,00426 e7,85516.

20 € 15, 2 pers.incl Chincluded € 2/24h WC € 1.
Location: Rural, comfortable, quiet.
Surface: grassy.
01/01-31/12.
Distance: 2km on the spot on the spot on the spot 650m on the spot on the spot.
Remarks: Bread-service, sanitary at campsite, narrow entrance.

Trier 16F1

Reisemobilpark Treviris, In den Moselauen.
GPS: n49,74092 e6,62502.

110 € 0,20/h 10-18h, € 10,60/18-10h € 1/100liter Ch (62x) € 0,70/kWh WC € 0,40 € 1/3minutes.
Location: Urban. **Surface:** grasstiles.
01/01-31/12.
Distance: 3km 6km 400m McDonald's 1km on the spot.
Remarks: Along the Moselle river, bread-service.

Trier 16F1

Weingut Vonnell, Im Tiergarten 12. **GPS**: n49,73840 e6,65914.

15 € 10 included. **Surface:** grassy/gravel.
01/01-31/12.
Distance: 3km 7km 2km 1,5km 3km.
Remarks: Bread-service.

Tourist information Trier:
Tourist Information, An der Porta Nigra, www.trier.de. Old Roman city with the best kept and also largest Roman gate in Europe: Porta Nigra.
Triercard. Free city bus and discount at museums, boat trips, swimming pool etc. € 9,90, family card € 21, 3 days.

Trittenheim 16F1

Moselpromenade Reisemobilplatz Trittenheim, Moselstrasse.
GPS: n49,82436 e6,90295.

30 € 6,50 € 0,50/100liter Ch (30x) € 3/24h.
Location: Rural. **Surface:** grassy/metalled. 01/01-31/12.
Distance: 500m 19km on the spot on the spot 300m 400m.
Remarks: Along the Moselle river, bread-service.

Unkel 11F2

P3, Parkplatz Hallenbad, Kamenerstrasse.
GPS: n50,59776 e7,21962.

6 free € 1/80liter Ch WC. **Location:** Urban.
Surface: asphalted. 01/01-31/12.
Distance: 100m 100m 150m on the spot.

Urmitz/Rhein 11G2

Wohnmobilhafen am Rhein, Kaltenengerser Straße 3.
GPS: n50,41849 e7,52448.

24 € 7,50 € 1/4minutes Ch (24x) € 1/8h WC € 1,50.
Surface: metalled. 01/01-31/12.
Distance: on the spot 5km on the spot on the spot 350m 300m.
Remarks: Along the Rhine river, bread-service.

Ürzig 11F3

Panorama-Mobilstellplatz Ürzig, Moselufer B53.
GPS: n49,97837 e7,00700.

25 € 9,50 Chincluded € 1,50/day.
Location: Comfortable, quiet. **Surface:** grassy. 01/04-31/10.
Distance: 9km on the spot bakery 150m on the spot on the spot.
Remarks: Along the Moselle river.

Uttfeld 11E3

Raffeisenstrasse. **GPS**: n50,12740 e6,27170.
15 € 5 € 0,50/80liter Ch (2x) € 0,50/kWh WC.
Location: Rural, comfortable, isolated, quiet. **Surface:** gravel.
01/01-31/12.
Distance: 6,5km 6,5km on the spot.

Vallendar 11G3

Rheinufer. **GPS**: n50,39749 e7,61277.

3 free . **Location:** Urban, simple.
Surface: asphalted/metalled. 01/01-31/12.
Distance: centre 500m 3km on the spot 200m Aldi 200m.
Remarks: Along railwayline, Max. ^3m.

Valwig 11F3

Moselweinstrasse. **GPS**: n50,14271 e7,21292.

10 € 6. **Location:** Rural, simple. **Surface:** gravel.
01/01-31/12.
Distance: 100m on the spot 100m on the spot on the spot.

Veldenz 16F1

Wohnmobilpark Veldenz, Hauptstrasse, K88.
GPS: n49,89222 e7,01944.

40 € 6 Ch (24x)included € 2.
Location: Rural. **Surface:** grassy. 01/01-31/12.
Distance: 300m 300m 300m 200m.

Völklingen 16F2

Weltkulturerbe Völklinger Hütte, Rathausstraße.
GPS: n49,24730 e6,84492.

10 free € 1/80liter Ch (6x) € 0,25/h.
Location: Urban, simple, central, noisy. **Surface:** asphalted.
01/01-31/12.
Distance: 500m 1,1km 400m 850m on the spot on the spot.
Remarks: Visitors centre Industrial Heritage.

Wachenheim 16H1

Weingut Rudolf Hein, Hauptstrasse 38. **GPS**: n49,63860 e8,16832.

DE

8 € 6 included (6x)€ 2/24h. **Location:** Rural, simple, quiet. **Surface:** grassy. 01/01-31/12.
Distance: 10km 1km 3km 1km.

S Wadern 16F1

An der Stadthalle. **GPS**: n49,54188 e6,89232.

10 free € 0,50 (8x)€ 1/day free.
Location: Urban, simple, central, quiet. **Surface:** metalled.
01/01-31/12.
Distance: on the spot 3km on the spot 100m.
Remarks: Parking in centre.

Wadern 16F1

Noswendeler See, Seestrasse. **GPS**: n49,52021 e6,86387.

5 free. **Location:** Rural, simple. **Surface:** grassy/metalled.
01/01-31/12.
Distance: on the spot on the spot 3km.

Wadern 16F1

Zum Wiesental, Nunkirchen. **GPS**: n49,48866 e6,83575.

5 free. **Location:** Rural, simple, quiet. **Surface:** metalled.
01/01-31/12.
Distance: on the spot on the spot on the spot.

Wadern 16F1

Hotel Pension Steil, Schlossstrasse 2, Lockweiler.
GPS: n49,52765 e6,90158.

4 guests free. **Surface:** metalled. 01/01-31/12.
Distance: 1km on the spot 500m.

Wadern 16F1

Hotel Restaurant Reidelbacher Hof, Reidelbach 5, Reidelbach.
GPS: n49,57706 e6,86808.
5 € 5, guests free. 01/01-31/12.

Distance: 3km 9km on the spot 3km.

Tourist information Wadern:
Tourist Information, Marktplatz 13, www.wadern.de. Nature reserve Saar Hunsrück, many signposted cycle and hiking routes.

S Waldfischbach-Burgalben 16G2

In den Bruchwiesen, Carentaner Platz.
GPS: n49,28155 e7,64772.

6 free € 1/80liter Ch € 1/8h. **Location:** Simple, central, quiet. **Surface:** asphalted. 01/01-31/12.
Distance: 600m 100m.
Remarks: Behind gymnasium.

Waxweiler 11E3

Wohnmobilplatz Waxweiler, Bahnhofstrasse.
GPS: n50,09401 e6,35669.

30 € 5 € 1 Ch € 2. **Location:** Rural, simple, quiet.
Surface: metalled. 01/01-31/12.
Distance: on the spot 1km 500m.

S Weiskirchen 16F1

Wohnmobil Oase Schwarzrinder Seen, Schwarzrinder See 1A.
GPS: n49,52564 e6,83060.
20 € 10 Ch included. **Surface:** gravel/sand.
15/04-31/10.
Distance: on the spot on the spot on the spot on the spot on the spot.
Remarks: Bread-service.

S Weiskirchen 16F1

Am Kurpark, Burgstrasse. **GPS**: n49,55868 e6,81810.

6 € 1,40/pp € 0,50 € 0,50 Ch € 0,50. **Location:** Rural.
Surface: metalled. 01/01-31/12. **Distance:** on the spot 500m 300m. **Remarks:** Parking at the health resort, max. 2-3 days, pay at tourist office.

Westerburg 11H2

Am Segelhafen, Seestrasse, Pottum. **GPS**: n50,59526 e7,99860.

10 free. **Location:** Rural, simple, quiet. **Surface:** metalled.
01/01-31/12.
Distance: 250m on the spot on the spot 250m.

S Westhofen 16H1

Parkplatz Nickelgarten, Am Nickelgarten.
GPS: n49,70559 e8,24672.

15 free (12x)€ 1/8h.
Location: Rural. **Surface:** gravel. 01/01-31/12.
Distance: 100m 4km 100m.
Remarks: Max. 3 days, service at petrol station.

S Westhofen 16H1

Weingut Dreihornmühle, An der Brennerei.
GPS: n49,70375 e8,25288.

3 € 5 € 1/day.
Location: Rural. **Surface:** grassy. 01/01-31/12.
Distance: 600m 600m 150m.
Remarks: Max. 24h.

S Westhofen 16H1

Tankstelle Raiffeisen. **GPS**: n49,70039 e8,24699.
Ch. 01/01-31/12.
Remarks: Coins at petrol station.

S Weyher 16H2

Weingut Möwes, Hübühl 10. **GPS**: n49,26982 e8,08663.

2 € 8 included.
Location: Rural, quiet. **Surface:** metalled. 01/01-31/12.
Distance: 200m 7km 400m.

S Weyher 16H2

Weingut Valentin Ziegler Sohn, Hübühl 9.
GPS: n49,26937 e8,08609.

2 € 5 included on demand WC.
Location: Rural, quiet. **Surface:** grassy. 01/01-31/12.
Distance: 200m 7km 300m.

S Willroth 11G2

Steiger-Mühle, Steinstrasse 18. **GPS**: n50,57176 e7,52995.

15 € 6 € 2,50. **Location:** Rural. **Surface:** metalled.

DE

01/01-31/12.
Distance: 500m 2km on the spot.
Remarks: To be paid at Biergarten.

S Wintrich 16F1

Mosel Stellplatz Wintrich, Moselstrasse.
GPS: n49,88417 e6,94833.
90 € 9 € 1/100liter Ch (90x) WC € 0,50 € 1 included. **Surface:** grassy/gravel. 01/04-31/10.
Distance: on the spot on the spot on the spot 100m 200m 200m on the spot on the spot.
Remarks: Along the Moselle river.

S Wintrich 16F1

Weingut Clemens, Kurfürstenstrasse 11.
GPS: n49,89000 e6,95416.

20 € 6,50-8,50 € 2 Ch € 2 WC.
Surface: gravel/metalled. 01/01-31/12.
Distance: on the spot 800m 800m on the spot 1km Moselradweg on the spot.

S Wissen 11G2

Hahnhof, Nistertalstraße. **GPS**: n50,76106 e7,72083.

25 € 5 Ch € 1/kWh WC € 1,50.
Location: Rural, isolated, quiet. **Surface:** gravel. 01/01-31/12.
Distance: 2,5km on the spot 2,5km on the spot.

S Wittlich 11F3

Zweibächen, Hasenmühlenweg. **GPS**: n49,99470 e6,87595.

30 € 5/24h € 1/80liter Ch. **Location:** Rural, simple.
Surface: grassy. 01/01-31/12.
Distance: 1km 4km 1km 1km.
Remarks: Max. 3 days, to be paid at swimming pool, service 50m.

S Worms 16H1

Wohnmobilhafen, Kastanienallee. **GPS**: n49,63458 e8,37513.

30 € 5/24h € 1 Ch (12x) € 1/8h WC. **Surface:** gravel.
01/01-31/12.
Distance: 15 min walking 7km Rhine promenade 300m 500m on the spot.
Remarks: Along river, service at Gaststätte Hagenbräu 300m from the parking, playground.

S Wörrstadt 16H1

Spargelhof Weinmann, Rommersheimer Strasse 105.
GPS: n49,83446 e8,10673.

3 € 6 (6x)included. **Location:** Rural, simple, central, quiet.
Surface: gravel. 01/01-31/12.
Distance: 300m 4km 300m 300m 1,5km.

S Zell/Mosel 11F3

Wohnmobilstellplatz Römerquelle, Am Freizeitzentrum, Kaimt.
GPS: n50,01632 e7,17662.

70 € 7 € 1/100liter Ch € 1/2kWh. **Location:** Rural, comfortable. **Surface:** grassy/metalled. 01/01-31/12.
Distance: 1km on the spot on the spot 500m 1km.
Remarks: Along the Moselle river, bread-service.

S Zell/Mosel 11F3

Am Fussgängerbrücke. **GPS**: n50,02991 e7,17754.

23 € 7 € 0,50/90liter Ch € 2,at camp site.
Location: Simple, quiet. **Surface:** asphalted. Easter-31/10.
Distance: 300m on the spot on the spot 200m 300m.

S Zeltingen-Rachtig 11F3

Wohnmobilstellplatz Zeltingen, An der Brücke.
GPS: n49,95478 e7,00942.

45 € 9 Ch (34x)included. **Location:** Rural, simple, quiet. **Surface:** grasstiles.
18/03-15/11 high water.
Distance: 50m 9km on the spot 300m 700m on the spot on the spot on the spot.

S Zweibrücken 16G2

Wohnmobilplatz am Freizeitpark an der Schließ, Geschwister-Scholl-Allee 11. **GPS**: n49,25332 e7,37625.
23 € 9-12 € 1/100liter Ch € 0,60/kWh WC included € 2/2. **Surface:** gravel. 01/01-31/12.
Distance: on the spot.
Remarks: Check in at hotel.

Hesse

S Aarbergen 11H3

Im Brühl, Hauptstraße 58, Michelbach. **GPS**: n50,23099 e8,05988.

10 € 5 Ch included.
Location: Rural. **Surface:** metalled. 01/01-31/12.

S Alsfeld 12A2

Erlenstadion, Fulder Weg. **GPS**: n50,74844 e9,27947.

20 € 5 € 1 € 1 Ch € 0,50/kWh.
Location: Simple. **Surface:** metalled. 01/01-31/12.
Distance: 200m 1,8km.

S Alsfeld 12A2

Hotel zum Schäferhof, A20 dir Eudorf. **GPS**: n50,76742 e9,29048.

20 free € 6. **Location:** Urban, simple, quiet. **Surface:** metalled.
01/01-31/12.
Distance: 2km on the spot 500m.
Remarks: Check in at hotel, use of a meal desired.

Amöneburg 12A2

In den Lückeäckern. **GPS**: n50,79554 e8,93135.

4 free. **Location:** Rural, simple. 01/01-31/12.
Distance: Old city centre 1km 500m 500m.
Remarks: Parking tennishall.

DE

Bad Arolsen 10A3

Reisemobilhafen Twistesee, Bericher Seeweg 1, Wetterburg.
GPS: n51,38396 e9,06546.
130 € 12, tourist tax incl € 1/100liter Ch (120x)€ 0,50/kWh, 16Amp WC € 1. **Location:** Rural, comfortable, isolated.
Surface: grassy/gravel. 01/01-31/12.
Distance: 500m 50m 50m 800m 800m on the spot on the spot.
Remarks: Directly at lake, bread-service, dogs beach.

Bad Camberg 11H3

Jahnstraße. **GPS**: n50,29650 e8,26660.

8 free € 1 € 1 Ch € 1/2kWh. **Location:** Urban.
Surface: gravel. 01/01-31/12 water: 01/12-31/03.
Distance: 350m 2,5km 250m.

Bad Emstal 12A1

Am Mineral-Thermalbad, Karlsbader Straße 4, Sand.
GPS: n51,24858 e9,24952.

8 € 7, tourist tax incl € 1/100liter Ch (12x)€ 1/8h.
Location: Rural, comfortable. **Surface:** gravel/metalled.
01/01-31/12.
Distance: 1km on the spot on the spot on the spot.

Bad Emstal 12A1

Erzeberg, Birkenstraße, Balhorn 21. **GPS**: n51,26927 e9,25147.

20 € 10, 2 pers.incl Ch WC € 1 included.
Location: Rural, simple. **Surface:** metalled.
01/01-31/12.
Distance: 100m.
Remarks: Check in at campsite (100m), use pool incl.

Bad Endbach 11H2

Kultur-, Sport- und Freizeitzentrum, Am Bewegungsbad 4.
GPS: n50,75669 e8,47875.

18 € 5 + tourist tax Ch WC included,sanitary at spa resort. **Location:** Rural, simple, quiet.
Surface: grasstiles. 01/01-31/12.
Distance: 1km on the spot 100m.
Remarks: Check in at Lahn-Dill-Bergland-Therme 200m.

Bad Hersfeld 12B1

Geistalbad, Am Schwimmbad. **GPS**: n50,87485 e9,70025.

6 € 5 € 0,50/80liter Ch (6x)€ 0,50/kWh.
Location: Urban, simple. **Surface:** asphalted/metalled.
01/01-31/12 Lullusfest (Oct).
Distance: 50m 3,9km 1km.

Bad Hersfeld 12B1

Acqua-fit, Kolpingstraße 6. **GPS**: n50,86771 e9,72951.
5 free. **Surface:** asphalted. 01/01-31/12.
Distance: 2km.
Remarks: At swimming pool.

Bad Hersfeld 12B1

Auf der Unteraue. **GPS**: n50,85764 e9,69786.

3 free. **Surface:** metalled. 01/01-31/12.
Remarks: At tennis-court.

Bad Hersfeld 12B1

Seilerweg. **GPS**: n50,87092 e9,71179.
free. 01/01-31/12.
Distance: 500m 500m.

Bad Hersfeld 12B1

Waldhotel Glimmesmühle, Hombergerstraße.
GPS: n50,88420 e9,66984.

5 free with a meal included against payment.
Location: Rural, simple. **Surface:** metalled.
01/01-31/12.
Distance: on the spot 2km.

Tourist information Bad Hersfeld:
Lullusfest. Traditional folk festival for the honour of the founder of the city. week 16/10.

Bad Karlshafen 10A3

Am Rechten Weserufer, Am Rechten Weserufer 2.
GPS: n51,64508 e9,44953.

12 € 11, 2 pers.incl € 0,50/100liter Ch (12x)€ 1/2kWh.
Location: Central. **Surface:** grasstiles/grassy.
01/01-31/12.
Distance: on the spot on the spot on the spot on the spot on the spot on the spot.
Remarks: Max. 4 days, check in at reception campsite.

Bad König 17A1

P3, Am Bahndamm. **GPS**: n49,74312 e9,00320.

9 € 5 (9x)included. **Location:** Urban, simple, central, noisy.
Surface: metalled. 01/01-31/12.
Distance: 100m 100m 400m on the spot on the spot on the spot.

Bad Nauheim 12A3

Usa-Wellenbad, Friedberger Strasse 16-20.
GPS: n50,35352 e8,74305.

40 € 5. **Location:** Rural, simple, isolated.
Surface: metalled. 01/01-31/12.
Distance: 1km on the spot 300m on the spot.
Remarks: Check in at Wellenbad, 8-20h.

Bad Orb 12A3

Am Busbahnhof, Austraße. **GPS**: n50,23014 e9,34659.

4 € 7, tourist tax incl Ch (4x) WC included.
Location: Urban, simple, central, noisy. **Surface:** metalled.
01/01-31/12.
Distance: 400m 450m 300m.
Remarks: Historical centre.

Bad Orb 12A3

Am Kurpark, Spessartstraße. **GPS**: n50,21700 e9,35477.

DE

9 € 7 + tourist tax € 2,50/pp € 1/90liter Ch € 1/8h.
Location: Rural, simple, quiet. **Surface:** gravel.
01/01-31/12.
Distance: 1,1km 6km 200m on the spot.

S Bad Salzschlirf 12B2

Riedstraße. **GPS**: n50,62090 e9,50304.

10 free € 1 Ch € 1.
Location: Simple. **Surface:** asphalted. 01/01-31/12.
Distance: 100m 100m.

S Bad Schwalbach 11H3

Wohnmobilstellplatz im Stahlbrunnental, Reitallee 21.
GPS: n50,13988 e8,06362.

4 free € 0,50/50liter Ch € 0,50/kWh. **Location:** Rural, simple. **Surface:** metalled. 01/01-31/12.
Distance: 500m 400m.

S Bad Soden-Salmünster 12A3

Spessart Therme, Parkstraße 12, Bad Soden.
GPS: n50,28544 e9,35917.

33 € 6, tourist tax incl € 1/100liter Ch (33x)€ 1/2kWh.
Location: Rural, luxurious, quiet. **Surface:** metalled.
01/01-31/12.
Distance: 1km 300m 850m.
Remarks: Pay and coins at Spessart Therme.

S Bad Sooden-Allendorf 12B1

Reisemobilhafen Franzrasen, Am Alten Festplatz, Allendorf.
GPS: n51,27149 e9,97209.

100 € 8 € 1/5minutes € 0,50 Ch (40x)€ 0,50/kWh,16Amp € 2,50/30minutes. **Location:** Rural, simple, isolated, quiet.
Surface: grassy/metalled. 01/01-31/12.

Distance: 200m on the spot on the spot.
Remarks: Price including tourist taxes and public transport.

S Bad Wildungen 12A1

Wohnmobilstellplatz Bad Wildungen, Bahnhofstrasse.
GPS: n51,12008 e9,13631.

16 € 5 € 1/45liter Ch (15x)€ 1/2kWh.
Location: Urban, comfortable. **Surface:** grasstiles. 01/01-31/12.
Distance: 1,5km on the spot on the spot.
Remarks: Max. 3 days.

S Bad Wildungen 12A1

Wohnmobilstellplatz Frekot, Wiesenweg 23.
GPS: n51,11134 e9,06677.

15 € 6 Ch € 0,33/kWh WC included € 2.
Location: Rural, simple. **Surface:** grassy. 01/01-31/12.
Distance: 300m.
Remarks: Bread-service.

S Bad Zwesten 12A1

Reisemobilstellplatz, Hardtstrasse 7. **GPS**: n51,05849 e9,17613.

10 € 6 € 1/100liter Ch (8x)€ 1/kWh.
Location: Urban, comfortable. **Surface:** gravel/metalled.
01/01-31/12.
Distance: 400m on the spot 300m.
Remarks: Max. 3 days.

S Battenberg 11H1

Festhalle Battenberg, Festplatzweg. **GPS**: n51,00915 e8,63643.

5 free Ch. **Location:** Rural, simple. **Surface:** gravel/metalled.
01/01-31/12. **Distance:** 1km 1km 1km.
Remarks: At community centre, service: Esso-station, Battenfelderstr. 6.

S Battenberg 11H1

Hallen- und Freibad, Senonchesstraße. **GPS**: n51,01233 e8,63532.

3 free Ch.
Location: Rural, simple. **Surface:** asphalted. 01/01-31/12.
Distance: 300m 100m on the spot on the spot on the spot. **Remarks:** Parking swimming pool, service: Esso-station, Battenfelderstr. 6.

Tourist information Battenberg:
Besucherbergwerk Burgbergstollen. 150 years old mine shaft, can be reached from Marktplatz.
01/05-30/09 1st Su of the month 14-17h.

S Baunatal 12A1

Parkstadion. **GPS**: n51,25769 e9,39851.

16 € 5/24h € 1/100liter Ch (16x)€ 0,50/kWh.
Location: Rural, simple, quiet. **Surface:** grassy/gravel.
01/01-31/12.
Distance: 500m 4km on the spot on the spot.
Remarks: Max. 3 days.

S Bebra 12B1

Natur- und Freizeitpark Fuldaaue Breitenbachen Seen, Hersfelder Straße. **GPS**: n50,95899 e9,78764.

30 € 3, € 18/week € 1/100liter Ch (18x)€ 0,50/kWh.
Location: Comfortable. **Surface:** grassy. 01/01-31/12.
Distance: 1km on the spot on the spot 1km on the spot on the spot.

Bebra 12B1

Am Schwimmbad, Annastrasse 17. **GPS**: n50,97464 e9,79836.

4 free. **Location:** Rural, simple. **Surface:** asphalted.
01/01-31/12.
Distance: 400m.
Remarks: Parking swimming pool.

Bebra 12B1

Mehrzweckparkplatz, Bei der Laufpfütze/Rathausstrasse.
GPS: n50,97000 e9,79000.

10 free. **Location:** Rural, simple. **Surface:** metalled.
01/01-31/12.
Distance: on the spot.

Beerfelden 17A1

Parkplatz NordicCenter, Seeweg. **GPS**: n49,56034 e8,97557.

4 free € 0,50/50liter Ch (4x)€ 0,50/kWh.
Location: Rural, simple, quiet. **Surface:** asphalted.
01/01-31/12.
Distance: 1km on the spot on the spot.

Berkatal 12B1

Am Sportplatz. **GPS**: n51,23763 e9,91504.

3 free. **Location:** Rural, simple, isolated, quiet.
Surface: asphalted. 01/01-31/12.
Distance: 800m 500m on the spot.

Biedenkopf 11H1

Parkplatz Stadtwerke, Mühlweg 6. **GPS**: n50,90925 e8,52687.

4 € 5/24h € 1/12h.
Location: Urban. **Surface:** asphalted. 01/01-31/12.
Distance: 200m.
Remarks: Max. 3 days.

Biedenkopf 11H1

Freizeitzentrum Sackpfeife, An der Berggaststätte.
GPS: n50,94735 e8,53317.

4 € 5/24h.
Location: Rural. **Surface:** concrete.
01/01-31/12.
Distance: on the spot on the spot on the spot.
Remarks: Max. 3 days.

Biedenkopf 11H1

Halbersbacher Parkhotel Biedenkopf, Auf dem Radeköppel 2.
GPS: n50,91183 e8,53515.

5 free with a meal. **Location:** Urban. 01/01-31/12.
Distance: on the spot on the spot 500m 12km 12km.

Bischoffen 11H2

P Aartalsee, Am See. **GPS**: n50,70172 e8,46726.

10 € 3/day, € 5,50/night. **Surface:** grassy/gravel. 01/01-31/12.
Distance: 1,5km.

Borken 12A1

Borkener See, Westrandstrasse. **GPS**: n51,04447 e9,27392.

2 free. **Location:** Rural, simple.
Surface: asphalted. 01/01-31/12.
Distance: 500m 4,5km 100m 1km 500m.
Remarks: At swimming pool.

Borken 12A1

Naturbadesee Stockelache, Kleinengliser Straße.
GPS: n51,06682 e9,24531.
3 € 3. **Surface:** metalled. 01/01-31/12.
Distance: 650m Sandy beach on the spot on the spot Lidl-ReWe 3,7km on the spot on the spot.

Borken 12A1

Singliser See, Main-Weser-Straße 60. **GPS**: n51,05598 e9,31303.
5 € 3. **Location:** Rural. **Surface:** metalled. 01/01-31/12.
Distance: Borken 2,4km on the spot 700m on the spot on the spot.

Braunfels 11H2

Wohnmobilstation Schloss Braunfels, Jahnplatz.
GPS: n50,51478 e8,38609.

4 € 5, € 7,50 service incl Ch . **Location:** Rural, simple, quiet. **Surface:** metalled. 01/01-31/12.
Distance: on the spot 350m on the spot.
Remarks: Pay and key service: Gasthof am Turm, Marktplatz 11, caution € 15.

Breuberg 17A1

Bahnhofstraße 4, Neustadt. **GPS**: n49,81576 e9,04063.

4 free € 1/5minutes Ch€ 1 (4x)€ 0,50/kWh.
Location: Urban, simple, central. **Surface:** asphalted.
01/01-31/12.
Distance: on the spot 300m 550m on the spot.

Breuna 10A3

Märchenlandtherme, Schulstraße. **GPS**: n51,41875 e9,18612.

3 free € 3. **Surface:** gravel. 01/01-31/12.
Distance: 500m 50m.

Büdingen 12A3

Hinter der Meisterei 20. **GPS**: n50,29094 e9,12587.

8 free. **Location:** Rural, simple, quiet.
Surface: metalled. 01/01-31/12.
Distance: Old city centre 750m 500m.
Remarks: At swimming pool.

Büdingen 12A3

Mühltorbrücke. **GPS**: n50,29051 e9,11581.

2 € 5/5h. **Surface:** metalled. 01/01-31/12.
Distance: Old city centre 50m.

Burghaun 12B2

Oberste Straße. **GPS**: n50,69179 e9,73203.

3 free € 1/100liter Ch (4x)€ 0,50/kWh.
Location: Urban, simple. **Surface:** asphalted. 01/01-31/12.
Distance: 800m on the spot on the spot.

Calden 10A3

Waldschwimmbad Calden, Zum Lindenrondell.
GPS: n51,39420 e9,40064.

DE

3 free. **Location:** Rural, simple, isolated. **Surface:** grassy.
01/01-31/12.
Distance: 1km 1,5km 2km.

Diemelsee 9H3

Terrassenparkplatz Hohes Rad, Hohes Rad 1.
GPS: n51,36470 e8,71935.

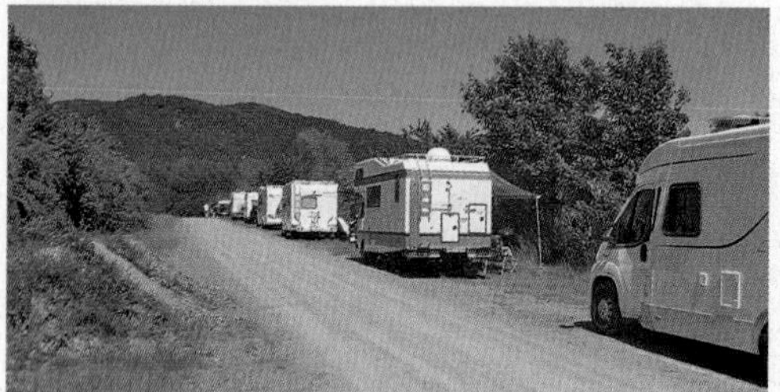

30 € 5 WC. **Location:** Rural, simple.
Surface: grassy/gravel. 01/01-31/12.
Distance: Diemelsee on the spot 500m.

Diemelsee 9H3

Campingpark Hohes Rad, Hohes Rad 1. **GPS:** n51,36355 e8,71830.

5 € 5/pp Ch € 0,53/kWh WC included € 1/day.
Location: Rural, simple. **Surface:** grassy/gravel.
01/01-31/12.
Distance: on the spot on the spot 6km.

Diemelstadt 10A3

Autohof, Kupferkuhle. **GPS:** n51,49034 e9,00885.
10 free € 1 € 1 Ch € 1. **Location:** Motorway.
Surface: asphalted. 01/01-31/12.
Distance: 500m on the spot 600m.

Diemelstadt 10A3

Steinberg. **GPS:** n51,50619 e9,00590.
4 free. **Location:** Rural. **Surface:** metalled. 01/01-31/12.
Distance: 1km 800m 1km.
Remarks: At sports park, swimming pool.

Dillenburg 11H2

Aquarena-Bad, Stadionstrasse. **GPS:** n50,73994 e8,27815.

8 free € 1/90liter Ch (6x)€ 1/8h.
Location: Urban, simple. **Surface:** asphalted. 01/01-31/12.
Distance: 300m.

Edermünde 12A1

Aueweg, Grifte. **GPS:** n51,21252 e9,44905.

12 € 5 € 1/100liter Ch (6x)included15h,then € 1/3h.
Location: Rural, simple. **Surface:** asphalted.
01/01-31/12.
Distance: 300m 1,7km 300m 100m Premium-Radweg R1 on the spot.

Edertal 12A1

Wohnmobilstellplatz Hemfurth/Edersee, Kraftwerkstrasse.
GPS: n51,17022 e9,05096.

30 <8m € 6, >8m € 10 € 1/100liter Ch € 1.
Location: Rural, simple. **Surface:** metalled. 01/01-31/12.
Distance: 500m on the spot 100m 500m.

Edertal 12A1

Wohnmobilstellplatz Rehbach, Am Eschelberg.
GPS: n51,18394 e9,02618.

20 <8m € 6, >8m € 10.
Location: Rural, simple. **Surface:** gravel. 01/01-31/12.
Distance: beach 200m on the spot.

Eltville am Rhein 11H3

Parkplatz Weinhohle, Weinhohle. **GPS:** n50,02832 e8,12406.

+20 € 5 € 1/60liter € 1 Ch.
Location: Urban, simple, central. **Surface:** metalled. 01/01-31/12.
Distance: 200m 400m 50m.

Eltville am Rhein 11H3

Weingut Offenstein Erben, Wiesweg 13. **GPS:** n50,02871 e8,11728.
2 € 15 WC included. **Surface:** metalled. 01/01-31/12.
Distance: 1km.

Eltville am Rhein 11H3

Weinhof Martin, Bachhöller Weg 4, Erbach im Rheingau.
GPS: n50,02365 e8,08815.
4 € 10 Ch WC included.
Surface: metalled. 01/03-23/12.
Distance: 600m 400m.

Erbach 17A1

Alexanderbad, In der Stadtwiese. **GPS:** n49,66349 e8,98863.

10 free € 1/70liter Ch (6x)€ 0,50/kWh.
Location: Urban, simple, quiet. **Surface:** metalled.
01/01-31/12.
Distance: 800m 500m 100m 100m on the spot.
Remarks: Max. 72h.

Eschwege 12B1

Reisemobilhafen Werratalsee, Am werratalsee 2.
GPS: n51,19196 e10,06728.

20 € 10-15 € 1/80liter Ch (18x)€ 0,70/kWh WC use sanitary € 3,30/pp. **Location:** Rural, simple, central, noisy.
Surface: metalled. 01/01-31/12.
Distance: 2km on the spot on the spot.
Remarks: Pay at bistro, service passerby € 4.

Tourist information Eschwege:

Besuchbergwerk Grube Gustav, Höllethal, Meissner, Abterode. Slate mine. 15/03-31/10 Tue-Su/holidays 13-16h.

Flörsbachtal-Lohrhaupten 12B3

Am Schwimbad. GPS: n50,12178 e9,47258.

10 € 9 Ch € 1,50/24h WC included against payment.
Location: Rural, comfortable, quiet. **Surface:** grassy/gravel.
01/01-31/12 Service: winter.
Distance: 1km 100m 1km on the spot on the spot.
Remarks: Check in at Gartenstrasse 10a.

Frankenberg/Eder 12A1

Ederberglandhalle, Teichweg 3. **GPS:** n51,05613 e8,80195.

4 free € 1/25liter Ch (4x)€ 2 WC.
Location: Urban, central. **Surface:** grassy/gravel.
01/01-31/12 water disconnected in winter.
Distance: 500m 200m 100m.
Remarks: Use sanitary only during opening hours swimming pool.

Friedberg 12A3

Engel Caravaning, Dieselstraße 4. **GPS:** n50,34646 e8,75685.

DE

2 voluntary contribution is appreciated € 0,50 Ch (2x).
Location: Urban, simple, central. **Surface:** metalled.
01/01-31/12.
Distance: 800m 100m 800m.
Remarks: Motorhome dealer, accessory shop, closed at night.

S Frielendorf 12A1

Wohnmobilpark Silbersee, Zum Silbersee.
GPS: n50,98389 e9,34667.

50 € 10 Ch included € 2. **Location:** Rural, simple, quiet. **Surface:** grassy/metalled. 01/04-01/11.
Distance: 1km 250m.

S Fritzlar 12A1

Am Grauen Turm. **GPS**: n51,13221 e9,26974.

10 € 7 € 1/90liter Ch € 1/2kWh.
Location: Urban, central. **Surface:** metalled. 01/01-31/12.
Distance: 100m 100m 600m.

Tourist information Fritzlar:
Stadtführingen. Guided tour around the historic city center.
15/03-31/10 Tue-Sa 10.30, Su/holidays 11h. € 4.

S Fulda 12B2

Weimarerstrasse. **GPS**: n50,55685 e9,66663.

30 € 0,10/1h, € 5/24h € 1 Ch € 1/6h
Location: Urban, simple, central.
Surface: asphalted. 01/01-31/12.
Distance: 400m 50m.

Gelnhausen 12A3

Am Hallenbad. **GPS**: n50,20125 e9,17795.

4 free. **Location:** Urban, simple, noisy. **Surface:** asphalted.
01/01-31/12.

Distance: 1km 100m 100m on the spot.
Remarks: Parking at swimming pool.

S Gießen 11H2

Badezentrum Ringallee, Gutfleischstraße.
GPS: n50,58947 e8,68406.

6 € 3 (6x)€ 0,50/kWh. **Location:** Urban, simple.
Surface: metalled. 01/01-31/12.
Distance: 600m 1,5km.

S Gilserberg 12A1

Landgasthof Steller, Marburgerstrasse 3.
GPS: n50,95047 e9,06220.

4 € 5, guests € 2,50 € 2,50 € 2,50 WC.
Location: Urban, simple. **Surface:** asphalted.
01/01-31/12 Wed.
Distance: 250m on the spot on the spot.

S Gladenbach 11H2

Restaurant Rosengarten, Hoherainstrasse 45.
GPS: n50,77462 e8,57952.

3 € 5,50
Location: Urban, simple. **Surface:** grassy. 01/01-31/12.
Distance: 600m on the spot 1km.
Remarks: Pay and key at restaurant.

S Grebenau 12B2

Borngasse 20. **GPS**: n50,74134 e9,47212.

4 free free.
Location: Rural, simple. **Surface:** grassy. 01/01-31/12.
Distance: on the spot 200m 200m.
Remarks: At fire-station.

S Grebenhain 12A2

Reisemobilstellplatz am Kurpark, Hindenburgstraße, Hochwaldhausen. **GPS**: n50,51910 e9,31756.

30 € 6 Ch WC included. **Location:** Rural, simple, central.
Surface: gravel. 01/01-31/12.
Distance: 500m 500m bike-bus 200m Vulkanradweg 200m on the spot.
Remarks: Pay in at kiosk.

S Grebenhain 12A2

Gasthof Zum Felsenmeer, Jean-Berlit-Straße 1.
GPS: n50,51926 e9,31424.

10 € 5 + € 1/pp tourist tax (2x)€ 0,50/kWh,+ € 1.
Location: Rural. **Surface:** grassy. 01/01-31/12.
Distance: on the spot.

S Großalmerode 12B1

Am Mühlgraben, Oststraße. **GPS**: n51,25841 e9,79349.
20 free Ch.
Location: Rural. **Surface:** grassy. 01/01-31/12.
Distance: 700m 150m.

Großalmerode 12B1

Panoramabad, Heinrich-Koch-Straße. **GPS**: n51,26603 e9,78452.
free. **Surface:** grassy. 01/01-31/12.
Distance: 500m 500m 500m.
Remarks: Next to swimming pool.

S Grünberg 12A2

Gallusplatz, Gerichtsstraße. **GPS**: n50,59517 e8,95593.

10 free € 0,50 Ch (10x)€ 0,50/10h. **Location:** Urban, simple, central. **Surface:** gravel. 01/01-31/12.
Distance: Old city centre 300m 100m Aldi 400m on the spot on the spot.

S Habichtswald 10A3

Am Erlebnisbad, Hasenbreite, Ehlen. **GPS**: n51,32291 e9,31961.

6 free € 2/24h WC.
Location: Rural, simple, isolated, quiet. **Surface:** grassy/metalled.
01/01-31/12 service: 01/10-31/03.
Distance: 400m 2,5km 400m 400m.
Remarks: Caution € 20, key electricity/toilet at swimming pool.

S Habichtswald 10A3

Am Kressenborn, Bergweg, Dörnberg. **GPS**: n51,34361 e9,34389.

DE

4 free (2x)€ 2/24h WC. **Location:** Simple, quiet. **Surface:** gravel. 01/01-31/12 service: 01/10-31/03.
Distance: 200m 5,5km 200m 500m.
Remarks: Caution € 20, key electricity/toilet at petrol station.

Hatzfeld 11H1

Edertalstrasse. **GPS**: n50,99144 e8,54817.

5 free. **Location:** Urban, simple, quiet. **Surface:** grassy/gravel. 01/01-31/12.
Distance: on the spot on the spot 200m on the spot.
Remarks: Behind fire-station.

Helsa 12B1

Sportplatzweg. **GPS**: n51,25444 e9,68638.

4 free. **Surface:** metalled. 01/01-31/12.
Distance: 800m 800m 700m 400m.

S **Herborn** 11H2

Herborner Schießplatz, Sinner Landstraße.
GPS: n50,67950 e8,30672.

6 free € 1/90liter Ch stay (6x)€ 1/kWh.
Location: Simple. **Surface:** metalled. 01/01-31/12.
Distance: 200m 1,8km.

S **Herbstein** 12A2

VulkanTherme Herbstein, Zum Thermalbad 1.
GPS: n50,56883 e9,34647.

11 € 6 + € 1,50/pp tourist tax € 1/100liter Ch (11x)€ 1/2kWh WC € 1,50. **Location:** Rural, comfortable, quiet.
Surface: metalled. 01/01-31/12.
Distance: 1,1km 800m 300m on the spot on the spot.
Remarks: Coins available at pay-desk of theTherme.

S **Hessisch Lichtenau** 12B1

Alter Bahnhof/Western Rail Station, Bahnhofstrasse 5, Warlburg.
GPS: n51,20055 e9,77833.

10 € 10 . **Location:** Rural, isolated, quiet.
Surface: asphalted. 01/01-31/12.
Distance: 5km 700m 1km on the spot.

S **Hessisch Lichtenau** 12B1

Sportcenter Fürstenhagen, Breslauer strasse 18.
GPS: n51,20672 e9,69443.

10 € 5/24h € 1/80liter Ch € 0,50/kWh .
Location: Rural, simple, quiet. **Surface:** metalled. 01/01-31/12.
Distance: 3km 1km 2km.
Remarks: Check in at sport centre.

Hessisch Lichtenau 12B1

Hopfelderstrasse. **GPS**: n51,19417 e9,72389.

14 free. **Location:** Urban, simple, isolated, quiet.
Surface: metalled. 01/01-31/12.
Distance: 500m 400m 500m.

Hessisch Lichtenau 12B1

Wohnmobilstellplatz am Hallenbad, Freiherr-vom-Stein-Straße 12.
GPS: n51,20445 e9,72655.

6 free. **Location:** Rural, simple, isolated, quiet.
Surface: metalled. 01/01-31/12.
Distance: 600m.
Remarks: Parking swimming pool.

S **Hessisch Lichtenau** 12B1

Berggasthof Hoher Meißner, Hoher Meissner 1.
GPS: n51,20376 e9,84852.

10 free WC. **Location:** Rural, simple, isolated, quiet.
Surface: metalled. 01/01-31/12.
Distance: 10km on the spot on the spot on the spot on the spot.

Hilders 12B2

Ulsterwelle, Heideweg 19. **GPS**: n50,56909 e9,99351.

5 free. **Location:** Rural. **Surface:** gravel. 01/01-31/12.
Distance: 750m 50m 800m.

S **Hirschhorn** 17A1

Beim Ätsche, Jahnstraße 2. **GPS**: n49,44214 e8,89804.

25 € 7 € 0,50/40liter Ch € 2,50/day.
Location: Rural, comfortable, quiet. **Surface:** grassy.
01/01-31/12 high water.
Distance: 500m on the spot train 400m on the spot.
Remarks: Along the Neckar river.

Hirzenhain 12A2

Festplatz Hirzenhain, Robert-Eichenauerweg.
GPS: n50,39259 e9,13593.

6 free. **Location:** Urban, simple, central.
Surface: metalled. 01/01-31/12.
Distance: 100m 100m on the spot on the spot.

S **Hirzenhain** 12A2

Müller-Mobil, Junkernwiese 2. **GPS**: n50,40004 e9,14744.

6 free € 1/130liter Ch (6x). **Location:** Rural, simple, quiet.
Surface: metalled. 01/01-31/12.
Distance: 1,5km on the spot on the spot on the spot.

S **Hofgeismar** 10A3

Am Sälber Tor. **GPS**: n51,49521 e9,37547.

100 free € 1/80liter Ch (18x)€ 1/2kWh.

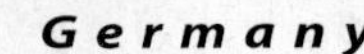

Location: Rural, comfortable, central, quiet. **Surface:** gravel. 01/01-31/12 31/05-14/06.
Distance: on the spot 300m on the spot on the spot.

S Homberg/Efze 12A1

Wassmuthshäuserstrasse, Dresdener Alee.
GPS: n51,02757 e9,41470.

7 free € 1/80liter Ch free. **Location:** Urban, simple.
Surface: gravel. 01/01-31/12.
Distance: on the spot 1km 500m.

S Homberg/Ohm 12A2

An der Stadthalle, Stadthallenweg 12.
GPS: n50,72626 e8,99439.

4 free € 1/80liter Ch (4x)€ 0,50/kWh.
Location: Rural, simple. **Surface:** metalled. 01/01-31/12.
Distance: 400m 350m 1km on the spot.

S Hünfeld 12B2

Hessisches Kegelspiel, Zu den Unaben.
GPS: n50,67626 e9,77622.

18 € 5 € 1/120liter Ch (12x)€ 1/2kWh.
Location: Urban, simple. 01/01-31/12.
Distance: 500m 250m 500m.

S Hünfeld 12B2

Knaus Campingplatz, Dr.-Detlev-Rudelsdorff-Allee.
GPS: n50,65299 e9,72409.
5 € 10 Chincluded € 3,50 WC € 3,50 .
Location: Rural. **Surface:** grassy. 01/01-31/12.
Distance: 4km 200m.

S Hungen 12A2

Inheiden, Am Köstgraben. **GPS:** n50,45509 e8,90049.

6 free € 1/100liter Ch € 2/6h WC.
Location: Rural, comfortable, quiet. **Surface:** grasstiles.
01/01-31/12 water: 01/11-31/03.
Distance: Trais-Horloffer See 3km 500m bike-bus 1km.

S Idstein 11H3

Wohnmobilhafen Idstein, Himmelsbornweg.
GPS: n50,21775 e8,27923.

12 € 10 € 1/80liter Ch € 1/8h. **Location:** Rural.
Surface: gravel/metalled. 01/01-31/12 water disconnected in winter. **Distance:** 500m Altstadt 3,3km.

S Kassel 12A1

Wohnmobilplatz Kassel, Am Sportzentrum/Giessenallee, Kassel-süd.
GPS: n51,29250 e9,48750.

12 € 12,50/day € 1/100liter € 0,50 Ch€ 0,50 (8x)€ 0,50/kWh. **Location:** Rural, simple, isolated, quiet.
01/01-31/12.
Distance: 1,4km 500m 50m
on the spot on the spot.
Remarks: With parking ticket free public transport, max. 3 nights.

Tourist information Kassel:
Treppenstrasse, shopping promenade, modern architecture.

S Kaufungen 12B1

Festplatz, Am Steckkopf. **GPS:** n51,28525 e9,61956.

4 free € 2/40liter Ch. **Location:** Rural, simple, quiet.
Surface: metalled. 01/01-31/12.
Distance: 800m Steinersee 300m 500m.

S Kirchheim 12B2

Campingplatz Seepark, Brunnenstrasse 20.
GPS: n50,81400 e9,52000.

50 € 13, dog € 2 € 1 Ch (30x)€ 3/day € 1,50.
Location: Rural, simple. **Surface:** metalled.
01/01-31/12.
Distance: 5km 4,9km 20m on the spot 20m.

S Kleinwallstadt 17A1

Fährstraße 14. **GPS:** n49,87571 e9,16378.
12 € 5 € 1/100liter Ch € 1/6h.
Surface: metalled. 01/01-31/12.
Distance: 500m 500m.

Korbach 12A1

Westring. **GPS:** n51,27260 e8,85509.

5 free. **Location:** Urban, quiet.
Surface: grasstiles/metalled. 01/01-31/12.
Distance: 1km Lidl 200m.
Remarks: Max. 3 nights.

S Laubach 12A2

Quick Camp Caravanpark Laubach, Kurze Hohl.
GPS: n50,55021 e9,00806.

30 € 6, 2 pers.incl € 2 € 2 ChWC € 2 .
Location: Rural, simple, isolated, quiet. **Surface:** grasstiles/grassy.
01/01-31/12.
Distance: 1,5km 1,5km 1,5km.

Lauterbach 12A2

Auf der Bleiche, Bleichstrasse. **GPS:** n50,63849 e9,40444.

5 free. **Location:** Rural, simple. **Surface:** metalled.
01/01-31/12.
Distance: 100m 150m on the spot.

Lauterbach 12A2

Freizeitzentrum Steinigsgrund, Am Sportfeld 9.
GPS: n50,62758 e9,39288.

8 free. **Location:** Urban. **Surface:** metalled. 01/01-31/12.
Distance: 800m 50m on the spot on the spot.

S Lauterbach 12A2

David-Eifertstrasse. **GPS:** n50,64288 e9,39393.
€ 1/80 Ch . **Location:** Urban. 01/01-31/12.

S Leun 11H2

Lahnwiese, Limburger Straße. **GPS:** n50,55089 e8,35346.

8 € 6 € 2 WC. **Location:** Rural, simple. **Surface:** grassy.
01/01-31/12.
Distance: 400m 400m 400m.

DE

Remarks: Along the Lahn river, max. 4 days.

Lich 12A2

P6, Ringstraße. **GPS**: n50,51816 e8,82257.

3 free. **Location:** Rural, simple, central, quiet. **Surface:** grassy/metalled. 01/01-31/12.
Distance: 300m 400m Lidl 50m 100m.
Remarks: Max. 3 days.

Limburg 11H2

Freizeitfalzeuge Singhof, Hoenbergstraße 2.
GPS: n50,40312 e8,07148.

3 free € 3 free. **Location:** Rural, simple. **Surface:** metalled. 01/01-31/12.

Limburg 11H2

Lahn Camping, Schleusenweg 16. **GPS**: n50,38902 e8,07387.

8 max. € 12-15/24h € 0,50/50liter Ch € 0,50/kWh € 2/day. **Location:** Rural, simple, quiet. **Surface:** gravel. 01/01-31/12.
Distance: 900m 1,5km Gaststätte.
Remarks: Along the Lahn river, summer: bread-service, biergarten.

Lindenfels 17A1

Kappstraße. **GPS**: n49,68077 e8,78304.

10 € 5 € 1/80liter Ch (4x)€ 0,50/6h WC.
Location: Rural, comfortable, quiet. **Surface:** grassy. 01/01-31/12.
Distance: on the spot on the spot on the spot.
Remarks: Max. 3 days.

Lorsch 16H1

Wohnmobilstellplatz Karolingerstadt Lorsch, Odenwaldallee.
GPS: n49,65206 e8,57855.

16 € 10 € 1/80liter Ch (16x)€ 1/2kWh.
Location: Rural, comfortable, quiet. **Surface:** metalled. 01/01-31/12.
Distance: 800m 4,5km 800m 800m on the spot.
Remarks: Max. 5 days.

Maintal 12A3

Wohmobilstellplatz Maintal, Uferpromenade, Dörnigheim.
GPS: n50,13067 e8,83920.

2 free. **Location:** Rural, simple, central. **Surface:** grasstiles. 01/01-31/12.
Distance: on the spot on the spot 1km on the spot on the spot.
Remarks: Along Main river.

Marburg 12A2

Jahnstraße. **GPS**: n50,80354 e8,77544.

8 € 10/24h € 1/100liter Ch (4x)€ 1/4h.
Location: Urban, simple. **Surface:** gravel. 01/01-31/12.
Distance: 300m 500m.
Remarks: Green zone: environmental badge obligatory.

Meineringhausen 12A1

Hobbywiese, Walmenstrasse 25. **GPS**: n51,25945 e8,93807.

17 € 7 Ch included € 0,50/kWh,or € 3/day WC € 1.
Location: Rural, comfortable. **Surface:** grassy/gravel. 01/01-31/12.
Distance: 2km Korbach 800m 2km on the spot on the spot.

Melsungen 12B1

Schloßbrücke, Sandstraße. **GPS**: n51,13280 e9,54502.

10 € 0,30/h, overnight stay free.
Location: Urban, central.
Surface: metalled. 01/01-31/12.
Distance: 200m 5km on the spot on the spot on the spot.
Remarks: Along the Fulda river, in front of police station.

Melsungen 12B1

Waldparkplatz, Dreuxallee. **GPS**: n51,12352 e9,55169.

5 free. **Location:** Urban, simple. **Surface:** grassy/gravel. 01/01-31/12.
Distance: centre 1,1km 5km on the spot.

Mernes 12B3

Wohnmobilstellplatz Mernes, Jossastraße, Mernes.
GPS: n50,24109 e9,47700.

6 € 5 € 0,50/80liter Ch € 0,50/kWh.
Location: Rural, comfortable, quiet. **Surface:** grasstiles. 01/01-31/12.
Distance: 200m 250m 200m on the spot.
Remarks: To be paid at Gasthaus Zum Jossatal, Salmünsterer Straße 15.

Michelstadt 17A1

Parkplatz Altstadt, Wiesenweg. **GPS**: n49,68038 e9,00143.

9 free € 1/90liter Ch € 1/2kWh WC.
Location: Urban, simple, central, noisy. **Surface:** gravel/metalled. 01/01-31/12.
Distance: 200m 200m 50m on the spot on the spot.

Münzenberg 12A2

Sporthallenparkplatz, Am Viehtrieb. **GPS**: n50,45712 e8,77171.

5 free. **Location:** Rural, simple, quiet. **Surface:** gravel. 01/01-31/12.
Distance: 800m 2,6km 500m.
Remarks: Max. 3 days.

Münzenberg 12A2

Sportplatz, Butzbacher Straße, Gambach. **GPS**: n50,45770 e8,73412.

15 free. **Location:** Rural, simple, noisy. **Surface:** asphalted. 01/01-31/12.
Distance: 2,4km 400m on the spot.
Remarks: Max. 3 days.

DE

Neuental 12A1

Neuenhainer See, Seeblick 14, Neuenhain.
GPS: n50,99533 e9,26652.

12 €4 €1 Ch €1/12h WC €0,50.
Location: Rural, simple. **Surface:** asphalted. 01/01-31/12.
Distance: Neuental 6km on the spot 250m.
Remarks: Use sanitary facilities at campsite.

Neukirchen 12A1

Reisemobilpark Urbachtal, Urbachweg 1.
GPS: n50,87139 e9,34861.

49 €10 + €1/pp tourist tax €1/100liter Ch (52x)€0,60/kWh WC €2,80 €1. **Location:** Rural, luxurious.
Surface: grassy/metalled. 01/01-31/12.
Distance: 300m 2km 300m 200m Rewe 300m 700m on the spot.

Neukirchen 12A1

Birkenallee, Knüllgebirge. **GPS**: n50,86567 e9,34478.

5 free free. **Surface:** asphalted. 01/01-31/12.
Distance: 500m 200m.

Niedenstein 12A1

Am Hallenbad, Am Schwimmbad 2. **GPS**: n51,22739 e9,31657.

2 free. **Location:** Rural, simple. **Surface:** gravel.
01/01-31/12.
Distance: 300m 300m.

Niestetal 10B3

Spiekershäuser Straße/Fuldablick. **GPS**: n51,32686 e9,55490.
3 free €1/100liter Ch €1/2kWh. **Surface:** asphalted.
01/01-31/12.
Distance: 1,1km on the spot on the spot.
Remarks: Along the Fulda river, Kassel centre 6km.

Oberaula 12B1

Sportplatz, Schwimbadstraße. **GPS**: n50,85421 e9,45908.

10 free Chfree. **Location:** Rural, simple.
Surface: asphalted. 01/01-31/12.
Distance: 800m Rewe 100m on the spot.

Oberaula 12B1

Golfplatz, Am Golfplatz 1. **GPS**: n50,83590 e9,46211.

3 free. **Location:** Rural, simple, isolated, quiet.
Surface: grassy.
01/01-31/12.
Distance: 2,5km 11km.
Remarks: Max. 4 days, follow the signs 'Golfplatz', 18-holes golf course.

Oberaula 12B1

Tennishalle, Teichstrasse. **GPS**: n50,86116 e9,47353.

10 free. **Location:** Rural, simple, isolated, quiet.
Surface: metalled. 01/01-31/12.
Distance: 500m 500m Edeka 500m.
Remarks: Parking tennis-court, max. 4 days.

Oberaula 12B1

Reiterhof Aumühle, Aumühle 1. **GPS**: n50,85235 e9,47794.
6 €10 Ch WC included. **Location:** Rural, comfortable. **Surface:** gravel/metalled. 01/01-31/12.
Distance: 1km 1km 1,5km.
Remarks: Use of sauna against payment.

Oberursel 11H3

Wanderparkplatz Taunus, Alfred-Lechler-Straße.
GPS: n50,21533 e8,53606.

5 €7. **Location:** Simple, quiet. **Surface:** metalled.
01/01-31/12.
Distance: 4km 100m metro 100m on the spot on the spot.

Oestrich-Winkel 11H3

Am Sportzentrum, Kirchstraße 125. **GPS**: n50,00470 e7,99904.

12 free. **Location:** Rural, simple, central.
Surface: metalled. 01/01-31/12.
Distance: 1km.
Remarks: Max. 2 days.

Ottrau 12A2

Am Schwimmbad 10. **GPS**: n50,80400 e9,38500.

4 €6 WC. **Location:** Rural, simple.
Surface: asphalted. 01/01-31/12.
Distance: on the spot.

Poppenhausen 12B2

Sport- und Freizeitgelände Lüttergrund, Sebastian-Kneippweg, Wasserkuppe. **GPS**: n50,49012 e9,87689.

10 €6 €1 Ch €1/6h. **Location:** Rural, simple.
Surface: metalled. 01/01-31/12.
Distance: 300m 300m 300m on the spot on the spot.

Rasdorf 12B2

Sport- und Freizeitgelände, Setzelbacher Straße.
GPS: n50,71422 e9,90306.

4 €4 €1/120liter Ch €1/10h.
Location: Rural, simple. **Surface:** metalled. 01/01-31/12.
Distance: 850m 500m.
Remarks: Max. 3 days.

Reichelsheim/Odenwald 17A1

Reichenbergschule, Beerfurhterstrasse.
GPS: n49,71507 e8,84234.

20 free €1/100liter Ch (8x)€0,50/kWh. **Location:** Urban, simple, central. **Surface:** asphalted. 01/01-31/12.
Distance: on the spot 100m on the spot on the spot.

DE

Reinhardshagen 10B3

Freibad, Klinkersweg. **GPS**: n51,48694 e9,59194.

4 free. **Location:** Rural, simple, isolated. **Surface:** asphalted. 01/01-31/12.
Distance: 2km on the spot 2km 2km on the spot on the spot on the spot.
Remarks: Parking swimming pool, OT Veckerhagen, max. 3 days.

Ringgau 12B1

Am Festplatz, In der Röste, Gandenborn. **GPS**: n51,08139 e10,04239.

20 free, service/electricity incl. € 7 Ch WC.
Location: Rural, simple, quiet. **Surface:** gravel. 01/01-31/12.
Distance: 100m 200m.

Rosenthal 12A1

Fischewosse, Willershäuser Straße 2. **GPS**: n50,97561 e8,86884.

5 free € 2/day. **Location:** Urban, comfortable.
Surface: metalled. 01/01-31/12 first 2 weeks of July.
Distance: 400m on the spot 800m.
Remarks: Max. 48h.

Rotenburg a/d Fulda 12B1

Wohnmobilpark Am Wittlich, Braacher Straße 14.
GPS: n51,00049 e9,72074.

50 € 6,50 € 1 Ch € 0,50/kWh.
Location: Simple, quiet. **Surface:** grassy. 01/01-31/12.
Distance: Old city centre 650m 200m on the spot on the spot. **Remarks:** Along the Fulda river.

Rotenburg a/d Fulda 12B1

Am Kuckucksmarktgelände, Braach. **GPS**: n51,00583 e9,69361.

15 free € 1/50liter Ch. **Location:** Rural. **Surface:** unpaved.
01/01-31/12.
Distance: 200m on the spot on the spot 200m.
Remarks: Max. 72h.

Rotenburg a/d Fulda 12B1

Im Heienbach. **GPS**: n51,00223 e9,74141.

5 free. **Location:** Simple. 01/01-31/12.
Remarks: Parking swimming pool.

Rotenburg a/d Fulda 12B1

Biergarten Hof Hafermas, Rotenburgerstrasse 13, Braach.
GPS: n51,00316 e9,69085.

3 free € 1 Ch. **Surface:** gravel. 01/01-31/12.
Distance: on the spot on the spot.

Tourist information Rotenburg a/d Fulda:
Kuckucksmarkt, Braach. Farmers market. 01/05-30/09 last weekend of the month10-18h.

Schlitz 12B2

Damenweg. **GPS**: n50,66909 e9,56908.

10 free € 1 Ch. **Location:** Rural, simple. **Surface:** gravel. 01/01-31/12.
Distance: 500m on the spot on the spot.
Remarks: At swimming pool.

Schlüchtern 12B2

Ludovica-von-Stumm-Straße. **GPS**: n50,34935 e9,53023.

5 free. **Location:** Urban, simple, noisy.
Surface: asphalted. 01/01-31/12.
Distance: 300m 4,3km on the spot.

Schwalmstadt 12A1

Altstad Schwalmstadt-Treysa, Zwalmstraße. **GPS**: n50,91447 e9,19327.

10 free Ch. 01/01-31/12.
Distance: 100m.
Remarks: Service nearby, indicated.

Schwalmstadt 12A1

Fünftenweg, Ziegenhain. **GPS**: n50,91753 e9,24633.

5 free Ch.
Location: Rural, simple. **Surface:** metalled. 01/01-31/12.
Distance: on the spot.
Remarks: Parking swimming pool, service nearby, indicated.

Schwalmtal 12A2

Reisemobilplatz, Friedenstrasse, Storndorf.
GPS: n50,65579 e9,26935.

15 € 3 € 1/80liter Ch (6x)€ 0,50/kWh.
Location: Rural, simple. **Surface:** asphalted. 01/01-31/12.
Distance: 300m on the spot on the spot.
Remarks: Nearby sports park.

Sinntal 12B3

Am Naturbad, Aspenweg, Altengronau.
GPS: n50,25453 e9,63316.

7 free € 0,50/50liter Ch (7x)€ 3/24h.
Location: Rural, simple, quiet.
Surface: metalled. 01/01-31/12.
Distance: 1,5km 1,5km 1,5km on the spot.

Sontra 12B1

Langhelle/Jahnstrasse. **GPS**: n51,07227 e9,94673.

5 free € 0,50/80liter Ch € 1/12h WC.
Location: Rural, simple, isolated, quiet.
Surface: asphalted/metalled. 01/01-31/12.
Distance: 600m on the spot.
Remarks: Parking behind swimming pool.

Sontra 12B1

Vimoutiersstrasse. **GPS**: n51,07139 e9,93306.
8 free € 1 € 1 Ch (3x)€ 1. **Location:** Urban, simple.
Surface: gravel/metalled. 01/01-31/12.
Distance: on the spot 300m 50m station 150m.

Steinau/Strasse 12B3

Am Steines. **GPS**: n50,31605 e9,46029.

5 free € 1 Ch € 1 (4x) € 1/kWh. **Location:** Rural, simple, quiet. **Surface:** asphalted. 01/01-31/12.
Distance: 1km 350m.
Remarks: Parking near sports centre, max. 2 days.

Tann/Rhön 12B2

Festplatz Tann, Am Unsbach. **GPS:** n50,64195 e10,01802.

8 € 5 € 1/120liter Ch (8x) € 1/6h.
Location: Rural, simple, isolated. **Surface:** gravel. 01/01-31/12.
Distance: 1km 1km 1km.
Remarks: Max. 3 days, tickets available at tourist office, petrol station or Schreib- und Spielwaren Krenzer.

Ulrichstein 12A2

Reisemobilstellplatz Panoramablick, Erlenweg.
GPS: n50,57588 e9,20619.

12 € 5 € 1/80liter Ch (6x) € 0,50/kWh.
Location: Rural, comfortable, quiet. **Surface:** asphalted.
01/01-31/12.
Distance: 1km 1km 1km on the spot on the spot on the spot.
Remarks: Beautiful view.

Villmar 11H2

P3, König-Konrad-Straße. **GPS:** n50,39102 e8,18625.

10 free. **Location:** Rural, simple. **Surface:** metalled.
01/01-31/12.
Distance: on the spot.
Remarks: Parking at the river.

Vöhl 12A1

Camping-und Ferienpark Teichmann, Herzhausen.
GPS: n51,17472 e8,89103.

10 € 10-14 , , Ch WC included € 3 € 4,50.
Location: Rural, comfortable. **Surface:** metalled.
01/01-31/12.
Distance: 1km on the spot fishing permit € 8/day on the spot.
Remarks: Max. 1 night.

Volkmarsen 10A3

Schulstraße. **GPS:** n51,41249 e9,11058.
4 free. **Surface:** asphalted. 01/01-31/12.
Distance: 200m 7,8km Aldi 650m.

Wahlsburg 10B3

Landhotel "Zum Anker", Weserstrasse 14.
GPS: n51,62447 e9,55212.

60 € 9 € 0,50/50liter Ch (60x) € 0,50/kWh WC .
Location: Rural, comfortable, quiet.
Surface: grassy. 01/01-31/12.
Distance: 200m on the spot on the spot 500m on the spot on the spot.
Remarks: Along the Weser river, bread-service.

Waldeck 12A1

Edersee Alm, Am Bettenhagen 2. **GPS:** n51,18861 e9,00944.

85 € 12 € 1/100liter Ch included € 0,50/kWh WC € 1/stay. **Location:** Rural, luxurious. **Surface:** gravel. 01/01-31/12.
Distance: on the spot fishing permit obligatory on the spot.
Remarks: Bread-service.

Waldeck 12A1

Seeblick Wohnmobil, Güldener Ort 12. **GPS:** n51,20309 e9,05004.

€ 11 2 pers.incl, dog € 1 Ch € 3 WC included.
Location: Rural, simple. **Surface:** grasstiles.
01/01-31/12.
Distance: 50m on the spot.
Remarks: At Edersee, waste dump € 2.

Waldkappel 12B1

Am Sportplatz. **GPS:** n51,14177 e9,87278.

4 free € 1/100liter. **Location:** Rural, simple, isolated, quiet.
Surface: gravel. 01/03-31/10.
Distance: 400m 400m 400m bakery Waldpark 500m.
Remarks: At sports park.

Wanfried 12B1

In der Werraaue, Eschweger Straße. **GPS:** n51,18722 e10,16528.

12 € 5 € 2/100liter Ch (12x) € 1/24h.
Location: Rural, simple, quiet. **Surface:** metalled.
01/01-31/12.
Distance: 50m 50m on the spot on the spot.

Weilburg 11H2

Wohnmobilstation, Hainallee. **GPS:** n50,48385 e8,25848.

80 € 6 included € 2 WC 10-17h. **Location:** Urban, simple. **Surface:** metalled. 01/01-31/12 events.
Distance: on the spot on the spot.
Remarks: Caution key € 15.

Weilmünster 11H2

In der Au, Am Froschgraben, L3054. **GPS:** n50,43345 e8,37343.

12 voluntary contribution Ch free € 2/16h.
Location: Rural, simple. **Surface:** metalled. 01/01-31/12.
Distance: on the spot 100m 100m.

Weilrod 11H3

Taunus Mobilcamp, Hochtaunussstrasse. **GPS:** n50,31138 e8,42581.

30 € 7 + € 1,50/pp, dog € 1 € 1/80liter Ch € 0,50/kWh WC included. **Location:** Rural, simple, isolated, noisy.
Surface: metalled. 01/01-31/12.
Distance: 500m 6km.

Weilrod 11H3

Golfclub Taunus, Merzhäuser Straße 29. **GPS:** n50,32082 e8,42694.
2 free, only guest players. **Location:** Noisy. **Surface:** asphalted.
01/05-30/09.
Distance: on the spot.

Wetzlar 11H2

An der Dill, Falkenstrasse. **GPS:** n50,55667 e8,49111.

DE

16 € 8 Ch (16x)included. **Location:** Urban, simple. **Surface:** gravel. 01/01-31/12.
Distance: 800m 3km 500m on the spot.

S Wetzlar 11H2

Parkplatz Lahninsel, Lahninsel. **GPS**: n50,55488 e8,49756.

4 € 8 (8-19h), overnight stay free Ch included WC.
Location: Urban. **Surface:** asphalted. 01/01-31/12.
Distance: 300m 1,5km 250m.

S Wiesbaden 11H3

Reisemobilhafen Wiesbaden, Wörther-See-Strasse/Saarstrasse.
GPS: n50,05583 e8,20972.

+40 € 7, overnight stay 21-9h € 3,50 € 1/60liter Ch (40x)€ 0,50/kWh WC € 1. **Location:** Urban, comfortable.
Surface: gravel. 01/01-31/12.
Distance: 150m 800m 800m 150m.
Remarks: Can be reached without environmental: A643 exit Wiesbaden Dotzheim.

S Willingen 11H1

Wohnmobilpark Willingen, Am Hagen.
GPS: n51,29050 e8,61278.

55 € 12, 2 pers.incl € 1/10minutes Ch € 1/2kWh WC € 1,50/30minutes,at swimming pool .
Location: Rural, comfortable. **Surface:** metalled. 01/01-31/12.
Distance: 1km 100m 1km 300m 300m.
Remarks: Discount at subtropical swimming pool and indoor skating rink.

S Witzenhausen 10B3

Reisemobilplatz Diebesturm, Oberburgstrasse.
GPS: n51,34110 e9,85435.

4 € 5 € 0,50/100liter Ch (4x)€ 0,50.
Location: Urban, simple, central, noisy. **Surface:** gravel.
01/01-31/12.
Distance: 500m on the spot 500m.

S Witzenhausen 10B3

Reisemobilplatz Josef-Pott-Platz, Laubenweg.
GPS: n51,34477 e9,85503.

10 € 5 € 1/100liter Ch (10x)€ 0,50/6h.
Location: Rural, simple, quiet. **Surface:** metalled.
01/01-31/12.
Distance: 800m 9km 800m Aldi 100m on the spot on the spot.

S Witzenhausen 10B3

Haus des Gastes, Ringkopfstrasse, Dohrenbach.
GPS: n51,31061 e9,83372.

8 € 4 Ch included € 2/24h WC.
Location: Rural, simple, isolated, quiet. **Surface:** metalled.
01/01-31/12.
Distance: on the spot on the spot 300m on the spot.

Tourist information Witzenhausen:
Kesperkirmes. Village fair. beginning Jul.

S Wolfhagen 10A3

Freizeitanlange Bruchwiesen, Siemensstrasse.
GPS: n51,32944 e9,17083.

35 € 3/24h € 1/80liter Ch (12x)€ 1/8h.
Location: Rural, simple, isolated, quiet. **Surface:** grassy/gravel.
01/01-31/12.
Distance: on the spot 500m 200m on the spot on the spot.

S Ziegenhagen 10B3

Erlebnispark Ziegenhagen, Ziegenberg 3.
GPS: n51,37191 e9,76472.

15 € 5 € 1 Ch.
Location: Simple, isolated, quiet. 01/03-31/10.
Distance: 6km.

Thuringia

S Asbach/Sickenberg 12B1

Grenzmuseum Schifflersgrund, Sickenberger Straße 1.
GPS: n51,28667 e10,01052.

6 € 4 € 1/20liter Ch € 1. **Surface:** gravel.
01/01-31/12.

S Bad Berka 12D1

P2, Bleichstrasse. **GPS**: n50,89969 e11,28528.

3 free € 1/3minutes € 1 Ch (3x)€ 1/3h.
Surface: asphalted. 01/01-31/12.
Distance: 200m on the spot 200m 200m.
Remarks: 10/7/10 during inspection service out of order.

S Bad Colberg/Heldburg 12C3

Am Rainbrünnlein. **GPS**: n50,27967 e10,73063.

5 free € 1/60liter Ch € 1/8h. **Location:** Simple.
Surface: grasstiles. 01/01-31/12.
Distance: 100m 200m 200m.
Remarks: At sports park.

S Bad Frankenhausen/Kyffhäuser 10D3

Bornstraße, B85. **GPS**: n51,35550 e11,10333.

15 € 14 included.
Location: Rural. **Surface:** metalled. 01/01-31/12.
Distance: 500m 200m 300m.
Remarks: Check in at pay-desk of the Therme.

S Bad Klosterlausnitz 12E1

Kristall Sauna-Wellnesspark/Soletherme, Köstritzerstrasse 16.
GPS: n50,91190 e11,87242.

15 € 10 + € 1,30/pp tourist tax € 1/80liter Ch € 1/2kWh WC. **Surface:** gravel. 01/01-31/12.
Distance: 800m 2,8km on the spot.

S Bad Langensalza 12C1

Friederiken Therme, Böhmenstrasse.
GPS: n51,11535 e10,64440.

DE

40 € 4, tourist tax € 1,20/pp € 1 Ch (8x)€ 1/10h.
Surface: metalled. 01/01-31/12.
Distance: 1km on the spot 200m.
Remarks: Parking spa resort, pay at pay-desk of theTherme.

Bad Liebenstein 12C1

Villa Georg, Friedensallee 12. **GPS**: n50,81876 e10,35517.

6 € 8 € 1/100liter Ch € 3 WC. **Location:** Comfortable, quiet. **Surface:** gravel. 01/01-31/12 Tuesday.
Distance: 500m on the spot 800m on the spot.

Bad Lobenstein 12E2

Ardesia Therme, Parkstrasse 8. **GPS**: n50,44981 e11,64294.

11 € 2,50 + € 1,50/pp tourist tax, free with use of spa € 2 Ch € 0,50/kWh WC € 3 . **Surface:** metalled.
01/01-31/12.
Distance: 200m on the spot 200m on the spot.

Bad Salzungen 12C1

ErlebisINSEL Flößrasen, Flössrasen 1. **GPS**: n50,81541 e10,23748.

88 € 10 + € 1,50/pp tourist tax € 1/60liter (88x)€ 1/2kWh € 2/30minutes. **Location:** Urban, comfortable.
Surface: metalled. 01/01-31/12.
Distance: 500m 400m 400m on the spot on the spot.
Remarks: Discount on access sauna/wellness.

Bad Tennstedt 12C1

Am Swimmbad, Zweifeldersporthalle. **GPS**: n51,15994 e10,83952.
5 free. **Location:** Urban, simple. **Surface:** metalled.
01/01-31/12.
Distance: 500m 500m 500m.

Breitungen 12C2

Hotel Jagdhaus Seeblick, Seeblick. **GPS**: n50,74250 e10,32306.

15 € 5 according consumption € 2/day WC.
Location: Rural, simple, quiet. **Surface:** grassy. 01/01-31/12
Mon. **Distance:** 2km 1km on the spot 2km on the spot.

Brotterode 12C1

Inselbergbad, Am Bad 1. **GPS**: n50,82290 e10,45302.

10 € 5. **Location:** Rural, simple. **Surface:** gravel.
01/01-31/12.
Distance: 500m on the spot Edeka 250m 50m.
Remarks: To be paid at swimming pool.

Dorndorf 12B1

Kultur- und Freizeitzentrum, Hardtstraße 3a.
GPS: n50,83453 e10,09087.

8 € 4 € 1/90liter € 1 Ch € 0,50/kWh.
Location: Urban, simple. **Surface:** grasstiles.
01/01-31/12.
Distance: 1km 50m.
Remarks: Next to Fahrradherberge.

Eisenach 12C1

Automobilmuseum, Heinrich-Erhardt-Platz.
GPS: n50,98122 e10,32342.

3 free. **Location:** Urban, simple. **Surface:** metalled.
01/01-31/12.
Distance: city centre 1km 400m 100m 500m.
Remarks: At museum.

Eisenach 12C1

Burg Wartburg, Auf der Wartburg 1. **GPS**: n50,96775 e10,30989.

5 € 6.
Location: Urban. **Surface:** metalled. 01/01-31/12.
Distance: on the spot.
Remarks: Nearby castle Wartburg.

Eisenach 12C1

Karl-Marx-Straße. **GPS**: n50,97861 e10,32083.

3 9-17h max. € 6, free overnight stay. **Surface:** gravel.
01/01-31/12.
Distance: 500m 100m 100m.

Eisenach 12C1

Landhotel Alte Fliegerschule, Am Weinberg 1.
GPS: n50,98737 e10,37180.
4 € 10 on demand WC included.
Surface: metalled.
01/01-31/12.
Distance: 3km on the spot 3km on the spot on the spot.
Remarks: Breakfest-service.

Eisenach 12C1

Wohnmobile A. Waldhelm, Ringstrasse 27.
GPS: n51,00194 e10,32667.

20 € 10 Ch included € 3/day WC € 0,50.
Location: Urban, simple. **Surface:** grasstiles.
01/01-31/12.
Distance: 1km 1km 1km Shuttle bus.
Remarks: Motorhome dealer, accessory shop, check in on arrival, bread-service.

Eisfeld 12D2

Festplatz, Am Volkshaus. **GPS**: n50,42615 e10,90992.

5 free. **Location:** Simple. **Surface:** grasstiles.
01/01-31/12 Whitsuntide.
Distance: 200m 200m 300m on the spot.

Eisfeld 12D2

Waldhotel Hubertus, Coburgerstrasse 501.
GPS: n50,39680 e10,92269.

20 free, use of a meal desired free € 5.
Location: Rural, simple. **Surface:** asphalted/grassy.
01/01-31/12.
Distance: 3km on the spot 2km on the spot.
Remarks: Bread-service + breakfast-service.

DE

Wohnmobilpark Trautmann, Rottenbacherweg 11, Melchendorf. **GPS**: n50,95404 e11,06654.
22 € 12,20 € 1,50/150liter Ch (22x)€ 1,50/5kWh,16Amp WC € 1,50 € 3,50/2,50 € 1.
Surface: gravel. 01/01-31/12.
Distance: on the spot 3km 400m 300m 200m 300m 900m.
Remarks: Discount on access sauna/wellness, video surveillance.

S **Erfurt** 12D1

P&R, Am Urbicher Kreuz. **GPS**: n50,94992 e11,09456.

15 free Ch.
Surface: asphalted. 01/01-31/12.
Distance: 7km Total-shop Tram till 24am.
Remarks: Service at petrol station.

Erfurt 12D1

Am kleinen Ring, Juri-Gagarin-Ring. **GPS**: n50,98111 e11,03472.

4 free. **Surface:** asphalted. 01/01-31/12.
Distance: Old city centre 1km 500m 500m.
Remarks: Max. 48h.

Erfurt 12D1

Eichenstrasse. **GPS**: n50,97327 e11,02737.

4 € 12. **Surface:** asphalted. 01/01-31/12.
Distance: 200m 200m 300m on the spot.
Remarks: Max. 48h.

Erfurt 12D1

P&R Parkplatz Messe, Gothaerstrasse. **GPS**: n50,95818 e10,98296.

4 free. **Surface:** asphalted. 01/01-31/12.
Distance: centre 4km Bus <23.00h.
Remarks: Parking exhibition ground.

Erfurt 12D1

P&R Parkplatz Thüringerhalle, Werner-Seelenbinderstrasse. **GPS**: n50,95771 e11,03605.

7 free. **Surface:** gravel. 01/01-31/12.
Distance: 2,6km Tram till 23am.
Remarks: Nearby B4, south edge of the city.

Tourist information Erfurt:
Erfurt-Card. Card gives for free entrance on among other things public transport and city museums, and discount on a lot of curiosities, guided tours, swimming pools, theater, souvenirs. € 14,90.
Stadtführung, Tourist Information, Benediktsplatz 1. Guided tour around the historic city center. 01/04-31/12 Mo-Fri 13h, Sa-Su 11h, 13h, 01/01-31/03 Sa-Su 11h, 13h. € 11.

Gotha 12C1

Parkallee 1. **GPS**: n50,94402 e10,70948.
3 free. **Location:** Urban, simple. **Surface:** metalled.
01/01-31/12.
Distance: 800m 800m.

S **Heiligenstadt** 10B3

Stadthalle, Aegidienstrasse 20. **GPS**: n51,37407 e10,13715.

6 free € 0,50 Ch € 1/3kWh WC.
Location: Comfortable. **Surface:** asphalted. 01/01-31/12.
Distance: 150m 200m.
Remarks: At swimming pool, in front of town hall.

Tourist information Heiligenstadt:
City of churches, health resort.
Literaturmuseum Theodor Storm. Museum of important German writer. Tue-Fri 9-12h, 13-16h, Sa-Su 14-16h.

S **Ichtershausen** 12D1

Autohof, Thöreyerstrasse. **GPS**: n50,88824 e10,93478.

20 € 6,50/24h, first hour free € 0,50 Ch € 0,50 WC.
Location: Motorway. **Surface:** asphalted. 01/01-31/12.
Distance: 4km on the spot Esso-shop.

S **Ichtershausen** 12D1

Freizeitfahrzeuge Mobilease, Feldstrasse 1.
GPS: n50,86907 e10,96563.

5 € 7,50 Ch (4x)included WC during opening hours.
Surface: gravel. 01/01-31/12.
Distance: 3km 500m bakery 500m.

S **Ilfeld** 10C3

Gasthof Brauner Hirsch, Dorfstrasse 42, Sophienhof. **GPS**: n51,63467 e10,79223.

15 € 5 Ch (3x)€ 0,35/kWh WC € 2.
Location: Rural. **Surface:** metalled. 01/01-31/12.
Distance: on the spot 3km on the spot on the spot.

S **Ilmenau** 12D2

Festhalle, Naumannstraße. **GPS**: n50,68139 e10,90472.

4 free € 2/80liter Ch. **Surface:** asphalted. 01/01-31/12.
Distance: 1km 100m 500m.
Remarks: Max. 24h.

S **Kühndorf** 12C2

Flugschule Dolmar, Am Flugplatz 1. **GPS**: n50,61198 e10,47079.

20 € 6 € 1 Ch € 1,50 € 2/day WC € 1,50.
Location: Rural, isolated. **Surface:** grassy/gravel.
01/01-31/12.
Distance: 2km on the spot on the spot.
Remarks: Bread-service, parking behind the hangar.

S **Lauscha** 12D2

Wanderparadies, Steinachtal 1. **GPS**: n50,47752 e11,13486.
4 € 14, 2 pers.incl Ch € 2 included . **Location:** Rural.
Surface: grassy. 01/04-30/09.
Distance: 2km 2,5km on the spot.
Remarks: Bread-service, playground.

Lauscha 12D2

Parkplatz P4, Obermühle. **GPS**: n50,48026 e11,16795.

DE

10 free. **Location:** Simple. **Surface:** asphalted.
01/01-31/12 1st and 2nd Sunday of advent.
Distance: 300m 100m 1km on the spot on the spot.
Remarks: Max. 24h.

Lauscha 12D2

Sommerrodelbahn, Lauschaer Straße, Ernstthal.
GPS: n50,48726 e11,17243.

10 free. **Location:** Simple. **Surface:** asphalted.
01/01-31/12.
Distance: 650m 1km 2km 50m 50m.

Linda 12E2

Knappmühle, Ortsstraße. **GPS**: n50,68473 e11,78324.

10 € 6 Ch (6x)€ 1/kWh. **Surface:** grassy/gravel.
01/03-31/10.
Distance: 300m 5km 3km 5km.

Meiningen 12C2

Rohrer Stirn, Frankental. **GPS**: n50,56976 e10,43477.

10 free € 5 Ch (6x)€ 0,50/kWh. **Location:** Urban, simple, quiet. **Surface:** asphalted. 01/01-31/12.
Distance: 2km 200m 1km.
Remarks: Parking at swimming pool, service on campsite.

Meiningen 12C2

Grossmutterwiesen, Werrastrasse. **GPS**: n50,56172 e10,41266.

5 free. **Location:** Simple. **Surface:** concrete. 01/01-31/12.
Distance: on the spot 200m 100m.
Remarks: Service possible at Kläranlage.

Meiningen 12C2

Volkshausplatz, Landsbergerstrasse. **GPS**: n50,57427 e10,41369.

5 free. **Location:** Urban, simple. **Surface:** metalled.
01/01-31/12.
Distance: 200m on the spot 200m 200m.
Remarks: Service possible at Kläranlage.

Mihla 12C1

Graues Schloss, Thomas-Münztzer-Straße 4.
GPS: n51,07854 e10,33166.

15 € 8, guests free € 5 € 5.
Location: Rural, simple, quiet. **Surface:** unpaved.
01/01-31/12 Whitsuntide.
Distance: on the spot fishing permit obligatory on the spot 500m on the spot on the spot.

Neustadt/Orla 12E1

Gaststätte & Pension Heinrichs-Ruhe, Heinrichsruhe 1, Rodaer Strasse. **GPS**: n50,75545 e11,75595.

20 guests free € 1/100liter Ch (6x)€ 0,50/kWh.
Location: Rural. **Surface:** grassy/gravel.
01/01-31/12 Restaurant: Mo.
Distance: 2,5km 12km on the spot 2km on the spot on the spot.
Remarks: Bread-service, bike and e-bike rental.

Nimritz 12E2

Wohnmobilstellplatz Nimritz, Ortsstrasse 29.
GPS: n50,70079 e11,64858.

10 voluntary contribution € 0,50 Ch (7x)€ 0,50/kWh.
Surface: grasstiles. 01/01-31/12.
Distance: 300m 300m.

Nordhausen 10C3

Am Badehaus, Grimmelallee 40. **GPS**: n51,50450 e10,78508.

2 € 5, € 10 service and swimming pool incl € 2 € 1 Ch € 1 € 1 € 3. **Location:** Urban, simple. **Surface:** metalled.
01/01-31/12.
Distance: 800m 500m 300m.
Remarks: At swimming pool.

Nordhausen 10C3

Am Kuhberg, Parkallee. **GPS**: n51,51502 e10,78492.

10 free. **Location:** Rural, isolated. **Surface:** asphalted.
01/01-31/12.
Distance: 2km on the spot 500m.

Oberhof 12C2

Wohnmobilstellplatz Oberhof, Jahnstrasse 7.
GPS: n50,70278 e10,72694.

DE

+60 € 10 + € 2/pp tourist tax € 1/80liter Ch (50x)€ 0,50/kWh . Location: Urban, simple. **Surface:** asphalted.
01/01-31/12.
Distance: 400m 200m 500m on the spot.
Remarks: Bread-service.

Tourist information Oberhof:
Rennsteiggarten Oberhof. Botanical garden. 01/05-30/09 9-18, 01/10-31/10 9-17h.

Reichenbach 12E1

Holzland Freizeitcenter, Rodaer Landstrasse.
GPS: n50,86118 e11,87607.

50 € 8, guests free € 1 Ch (15x)€ 2/day WC € 2/pp.
Surface: concrete. 01/01-31/12.
Distance: 2km on the spot bakery 500m.

Rudolstadt 12D2

Freizeit- und Erlebnisbad Saalemaxx, Hugo-Trinckler-Straße 6.
GPS: n50,70635 e11,31659.

9 € 7/24h € 1/80liter € 1 Ch € 0,50/kWh.
Surface: gravel. 01/01-31/12.
Distance: 2km 100m.
Remarks: Discount at swimming pool.

Saalfeld 12D2

Reschwitzerstrasse, B281. **GPS**: n50,63720 e11,36751.

10 free. **Surface:** gravel. 01/01-31/12.
Distance: 2,8km.
Remarks: Parking at swimming pool.

Saalfeld 12D2

Saalfelder Feengrotten, Feengrottenweg 2.
GPS: n50,63468 e11,33982.

10 € 10 € 3/5minutes € 3 Ch (6x)€ 0,50/kWh WC .
Surface: grassy. 01/01-31/12.
Distance: 2,3km on the spot bakery 500m 500m.

Schleiz 12E2

Spitzbergs Zollhaus, Burgkerstrasse 25.
GPS: n50,55507 e11,73438.

5 € 5, free with a meal Ch (7x)€ 2/24h.
Surface: gravel/metalled. 01/01-31/12 Mo.
Distance: 7km 5,4km on the spot 7km.

Schleiz 12E2

HEM-Großtankstelle, Saalburgerstrasse.
GPS: n50,55004 e11,78788.

8 € 2 € 1 € 1 ChWC.
Location: Motorway. **Surface:** asphalted. 01/01-31/12.
Distance: 5km on the spot shop.
Remarks: Industrial area, max. 24h.

Schmalkalden 12C2

Westendpark, Westendstrasse 4. **GPS**: n50,72118 e10,44071.
8 € 10 Chincluded € 1/8h,10Amp. **Location:** Urban.
Surface: asphalted. 01/01-31/12.
Distance: on the spot 250m 600m station 500m.
Remarks: On the Schmalkalde river.

Schmiedefeld 12C2

Sportplatz, Sportplatzstraße. **GPS**: n50,60324 e10,81491.

20 € 3 + € 1,80/pp tourist tax. **Location:** Rural, simple, quiet.
Surface: grasstiles/metalled. 01/01-31/12.
Distance: 500m 400m on the spot on the spot.
Remarks: Pay at tourist office or Gasthaus Thüringer Hof.

Sitzendorf 12D2

Sitzendorfer Porzellanmanufaktur, Hauptstrasse 26.
GPS: n50,63174 e11,16788.

5 free. **Surface:** asphalted. 01/01-31/12.
Distance: on the spot 200m 200m.

Sondershausen 10C3

P7 zur Windleite, Hospitalstrasse. **GPS**: n51,37824 e10,86234.

5 free € 1 Ch (4x)€ 1/2h.
Surface: metalled. 01/01-31/12.
Distance: 2,5km 500m 100m.

Sondershausen 10C3

Freizeitpark Possen, Possen 1. **GPS**: n51,33800 e10,86265.

10 € 4/stay. **Surface:** metalled. 01/01-31/12.
Distance: 5km on the spot.

Stadtlengsfeld 12B2

Am Schwimmbad, Eisenacher Straße. **GPS**: n50,79065 e10,11373.

6 free € 1/80liter € 1/kWh.
Location: Rural, simple. **Surface:** asphalted. 01/01-31/12.
Distance: 1,5km.

Steinheid 12D2

Am Rennsteig, Eisfelder Straße, Limbach.
GPS: n50,47568 e11,06937.

4 free. **Location:** Rural, simple, noisy. **Surface:** gravel.
01/01-31/12.
Distance: 150m 10km on the spot.

Steinheid 12D2

Thüringer Baumschmuck, Neuhäuser Strasse 8-10.
GPS: n50,47302 e11,08672.

8 € 5, free for clients € 2/90liter included.
Location: Simple. **Surface:** unpaved. 01/01-31/12.
Distance: 1,5km 3km, bakery 50m on the spot on the spot on the spot.
Remarks: At Christmas Balls manufacturer.

Tabarz 12C1

Karl-Kornhaß-Straße. **GPS**: n50,87782 e10,52038.

DE

8 free, tourist tax € 2/pp. **Location:** Rural, simple, quiet.
Surface: metalled. 01/01-31/12.
Distance: on the spot 200m Rewe 400m.
Remarks: To be paid at TABBS sports centre.

Tambach-Dietharz 12C1

Festplatz, Burgstallstraße. **GPS**: n50,78902 e10,60897.

4 free, tourist tax € 1/pp Ch service € 6.
Location: Urban, simple. **Surface:** gravel. 01/01-31/12.
Distance: on the spot on the spot.
Remarks: Key service at town hall.

Tambach-Dietharz 12C1

Freigelande Lohmühle, Lohmühle 1-5. **GPS**: n50,81056 e10,62778.

30 € 6 + € 4/pp Ch € 2 WC € 1 € 1.
Location: Rural, simple, quiet.
Surface: grassy.
01/01-31/12 Mon.
Distance: 2km on the spot 3km on the spot on the spot.
Remarks: Check in on arrival, barefoot park, museum.

Themar 12C2

Am Hexenturm, Mauerstrasse. **GPS**: n50,50512 e10,61194.

5 free € 1/50liter € 2 Ch € 1/kWh. **Location:** Urban, simple, quiet. **Surface:** grasstiles. 01/01-31/12.
Distance: 100m 300m 400m on the spot on the spot.
Remarks: Along the Werra river, 01/11-31/03 water disconnected.

Tiefenort 12B1

Freizeitanlage Heerstatt, Auf der Heerstatt.
GPS: n50,83444 e10,16306.

6 free € 2/day. **Location:** Rural, simple. **Surface:** concrete.
01/03-31/10.

Distance: on the spot 50m bakery 900m on the spot.
Remarks: On island in the Werra river.

Treffurt 12C1

Wohnmobilstellplatz Unter den Linden.
GPS: n51,13398 e10,23659.

20 free € 0,50/80liter Ch (8x)€ 1/kWh.
Location: Rural, simple, quiet. **Surface:** grasstiles/grassy.
01/01-31/12 15/07-31/07.
Distance: 300m on the spot 50m 500m on the spot on the spot.
Remarks: Along river, water closed during wintertime.

Tourist information Treffurt:
Small town with half-timbered houses and medival castle Normannstein.

Vacha 12B1

Frankfurter Strasse. **GPS**: n50,81856 e10,01327.
5 free. **Location:** Simple. **Surface:** gravel. 01/01-31/12.
Distance: 1km 1km.
Remarks: At swimming pool.

Weimar 12D1

Hermann Brill-Platz. **GPS**: n50,98501 e11,31701.

20 € 10/24h € 1 Ch (6x)€ 1/6h.
Surface: metalled. 01/01-31/12.
Distance: Weimar centre 1,2km on the spot 500m.

Zella-Mehlis 12C2

Toschis Station, An der Quelle 5. **GPS**: n50,64375 e10,68436.

10 € 5 Ch (20x) . **Location:** Simple, central.
Surface: grassy/gravel. 01/01-31/12.
Distance: on the spot 300m.
Remarks: Check in at reception.

Zeulenroda 12E2

Badewelt Waikiki, Am Birkenwege 1. **GPS**: n50,66543 e11,99355.

6 € 10 Ch included,water and electricity € 10/day.
Surface: metalled. 01/01-31/12.

Zeulenroda 12E2

Wohnmobilhafen Zeulenrodaer Meer, Bleichenweg 30.
GPS: n50,65778 e11,96556.
18 € 10 + € 2/pp Ch (28x)€ 0,50/kWh WC included.
Location: Rural. **Surface:** gravel. 01/01-31/12.
Distance: 1,5km on the spot on the spot 1km on the spot.
Remarks: At tourist office, use sanitary only during opening hours swimming pool, playground.

Baden Württemberg

Aalen 17C3

Hirschbach, Hirschbachstrasse 68. **GPS**: n48,84524 e10,10712.

12 free € 1/80liter Ch € 1/2kWh.
Location: Rural. **Surface:** asphalted. 01/01-31/12.
Distance: 800m 100m 200m.
Remarks: At swimming pool, max. 3 days.

Aalen 17C3

Limes-Thermen, P1, Osterbucher Steige.
GPS: n48,82047 e10,07918.

12 free. **Location:** Rural. **Surface:** grasstiles.
01/01-31/12.
Distance: 100m.

Achern 16H3

Wohnmobilstellplatz Achern, Kapellenstrasse/Badstrasse.
GPS: n48,62436 e8,07359.

14 € 8 € 1/100liter Ch (12x)€ 1/6h.
Location: Urban, simple, quiet. **Surface:** gravel/metalled.
01/01-31/12.
Distance: 500m 4,8km 650m on the spot on the spot.
Remarks: Next to swimming pool, tuesday and Saturday market.

Albstadt 20A1

Sonnencamping, Beibruck 54. **GPS**: n48,21438 e8,97879.

16 € 10 € 1/100liter Ch € 0,60/kWh WC € 2 .
Location: Rural. **Surface:** grassy/gravel. 01/01-31/12.
Distance: 5km 500m 2km on the spot on the spot 2km 2km.

Allensbach 20A2

Landgasthaus Mindelsee, Gemeinmärk 7.
GPS: n47,74279 e9,04411.

DE

15 € 8, guests free. **Surface:** metalled. 01/01-31/12 Tue.
Distance: 5km on the spot.
Remarks: Max. 1 night, max 3,5t.

S **Amtzell** 20B2

Wohnmobilstellplatz Büchelweisen, Büchel 3.
GPS: n47,70871 e9,76684.

36 € 10 € 1/90liter Ch (36x)€ 0,50/kWh WC € 1,50.
Surface: grasstiles. 01/01-31/12.
Distance: 1,5km 1km 1km on the spot 1,5km.
Remarks: Bread-service.

Aspach 17B2

Gemeindehallen, Rübengasse. **GPS**: n48,96437 e9,39706.
free. 01/01-31/12.
Distance: 100m.
Remarks: At gymnasium.

Aspach 17B2

Wanderparkplatz Fautenhau, Im Fautenhau, Hohrot.
GPS: n48,97823 e9,39483.

5 free. **Location:** Rural. **Surface:** metalled. 01/01-31/12.
Distance: on the spot.
Remarks: Max. 1 night, parking P0.

Aspach 17B2

Wanderparkplatz Heiligental, Heiligentalstrasse, Rietenau.
GPS: n48,99158 e9,40519.

5 free. **Location:** Rural, quiet. **Surface:** asphalted/grassy.
01/01-31/12.
Distance: on the spot.
Remarks: Max. 1 night.

S **Aspach** 17B2

Caravan-Service-Station, L1124. **GPS**: n48,96375 e9,37582.
Ch. 01/01-31/12.

Aulendorf 20B1

Schwaben-Therme, Ebisweilerstrasse 5. **GPS**: n47,95797 e9,63728.

20 (P3) free. **Location:** Rural. **Surface:** metalled.
01/01-31/12.
Distance: 500m on the spot 500m.
Remarks: Parking swimming pool, max. 2 nights.

S **Aulendorf** 20B1

Carthago-City, Carthago Ring 1. **GPS**: n47,93759 e9,65246.
100 free € 0,50 Ch € 0,50/kWh. **Surface:** metalled.
01/01-31/12.
Distance: 2,5km 950m.
Remarks: At motohome manufacturer.

S **Backnang** 17B2

Martin-Dietrich-Allee. **GPS**: n48,95041 e9,45281.

4 free € 1/90liter Ch. **Location:** Rural, simple.
Surface: gravel. 01/01-31/12.
Distance: 1km 400m on the spot on the spot.

S **Bad Bellingen** 19G2

Balinea Thermen, Badstrasse 14. **GPS**: n47,72963 e7,55233.

31 € 14 + € 1,45-2,25 tourist tax Ch included WC € 1,50.
Location: Urban, noisy. **Surface:** asphalted/metalled.
01/01-31/12.
Distance: 500m 5,5km on the spot on the spot.
Remarks: No trailers allowed.

S **Bad Buchau** 20B1

Adelindis Therme, Am Kurpark. **GPS**: n48,06865 e9,60653.

21 € 9,50 XL-pitch € 11 € 1/80liter Ch € 0,50/kWh WC € 1.
Surface: metalled. 01/01-31/12.
Distance: 500m.

S **Bad Buchau** 20B1

Seegasse. **GPS**: n48,06801 e9,60977.

17 € 9,50 € 1/80liter Ch (17x)€ 0,50/kWh.
Surface: metalled. 01/01-31/12.
Distance: 500m.
Remarks: Adelindis Therme 300m.

S **Bad Buchau** 20B1

Federseemuseum, Wellerstraße. **GPS**: n48,07051 e9,60949.

12 € 9 (12x)€ 0,50/kWh WC.
Location: Rural. **Surface:** asphalted. 01/01-31/12.
Distance: 800m.
Remarks: Adelindis Therme 500m.

Bad Buchau 20B1

Am Freibad, Friedhofstrasse. **GPS**: n48,06292 e9,61714.

10 € 9. **Surface:** asphalted. 01/01-31/12.
Distance: 700m.

S **Bad Ditzenbach** 17B3

Vinzenz Therme, Badstraße 20. **GPS**: n48,59003 e9,70553.

10 € 5, winter € 6 Ch.
Surface: asphalted. 01/01-31/12.
Remarks: Caution key € 50.

S **Bad Dürrheim** 20A1

Reisemobilhafen Bad Dürrheim, Huberstraße 34/2.
GPS: n48,01204 e8,53506.

300 € 8,50 + € 2,50/pp tourist tax € 1/100liter Ch € 2,50/night WC € 2. **Location:** Rural, comfortable.
Surface: gravel. 01/01-31/12.
Distance: on the spot.
Remarks: Pay at reception, bread-service, special health arrangement possible.

S **Bad Herrenalb** 16H3

Wohnmobilstation Siebentäler Therme, Schweizer Wiese.
GPS: n48,80334 e8,44067.

DE

9 € 5 + tourist tax € 2,50/pp € 1 € 1 Ch€ 1 (4x)€ 0,50/kWh.
Location: Rural, simple. **Surface:** asphalted.
01/01-31/12.
Distance: 500m 100m 200m 200m on the spot on the spot.
Remarks: Max. 2 nights, use sanitary only during opening hours, discount on access terme, friday market.

Tourist information Bad Herrenalb:
Quellenerlebnispfad, Kurpark Herrenalb. Hiking trails past 60 fountains.

Bad Krozingen 19G2

Wohnmobilstellplatz Vita Classica, Thürachstraße.
GPS: n47,91763 e7,68821.

80 € 12, from 7th night € 10,50 Ch € 3,50/day,16Amp WC € 3 included.
Location: Rural, comfortable. **Surface:** gravel.
01/01-31/12.
Distance: 600m 3km 50m 600m 800m on the spot on the spot on the spot.
Remarks: Bread-service, trailer € 2,50/night, bike and e-bike rental.

Bad Liebenzell 17A3

Campingpark Bad Liebenzell, Pforzheimer strasse 34.
GPS: n48,77850 e8,73120.

16 € 8, tourist tax € 2/pp Ch (16x)WC included € 3 . **Location:** Rural, simple, noisy. **Surface:** metalled/sand.
01/01-31/12.
Distance: on the spot 17km 500m 100m on the spot on the spot on the spot.

Bad Mergentheim 17B1

Wohnmobilstellplatz an der Solymar Therme, Erlenbachweg.
GPS: n49,49194 e9,79167.

20 € 5, tourist tax € 2,70/pp € 1/80liter Ch (8x)€ 1/8h.
Location: Rural, simple. **Surface:** gravel.
01/01-31/12.
Distance: Old city centre 1km 200m Lidl 800m 100m.
Remarks: Max. 3 nights.

Bad Niedernau 17A3

Wohnmobilparkplatz Bad Niedernau, Blaue Brücke.
GPS: n48,45931 e8,89959.

5 free. **Location:** Rural, simple. **Surface:** gravel.
01/01-31/12.
Distance: 500m 3km on the spot.
Remarks: Along the Neckar river, max. 3 nights.

Bad Rappenau 17A2

Salinenpark, Weinbrennerstrasse. **GPS**: n49,23517 e9,11396.

30 € 3/pp, child € 2 € 1/3minutes Ch (24x)€ 1/kWh.
Location: Rural, comfortable. **Surface:** metalled.
01/01-31/12.
Distance: 1km 50m 1km.
Remarks: Check in at pay-desk of the Therme, therme 400m.

Bad Rappenau 17A2

Autohof Bad Rappenau, A6, Wilhelm-Hauff-Straße 43, Fürfeld.
GPS: n49,21043 e9,06927.
15 € 12, free for clients ChWC .
Location: Motorway, simple. **Surface:** metalled. 01/01-31/12.
Distance: 300m on the spot on the spot.
Remarks: Breakfest-service.

Bad Säckingen 19H2

Reisemobilplatz Am Rheinufer, Ausstrasse.
GPS: n47,54903 e7,94765.

40 € 12/24h, >7,8m € 16/24h € 0,50/100liter € 0,20 Ch (39x) WC. **Location:** Urban, comfortable, quiet. **Surface:** gravel.
01/01-31/12 beginning Mar, end Oct.
Distance: 300m 6km 50m on the spot on the spot.
Remarks: Several offers, i.e. free public transport.

Tourist information Bad Säckingen:
Nachtwächterführungen. Evening tour guided by night watch in historical cloths and with lantern. Information and booking: Kurverwaltung. € 5.

Bad Saulgau 20B1

GolfPark Bad Saulgau, Koppelweg 103. **GPS**: n47,97928 e9,48623.

30 € 10, golfers free € 1/100liter Ch € 1/6h .
Location: Rural, quiet. **Surface:** metalled. 01/03-31/10.
Distance: 4km on the spot 4km.

Bad Saulgau 20B1

Wonhmobilstellplatz Sonnenhof-Therme, Am Schönen Moos.
GPS: n48,01703 e9,48838.

53 € 10 + € 1,50/pp tourist tax € 0,50/50liter Ch (69x)€ 0,50/kWh .
Location: Rural. **Surface:** metalled. 01/01-31/12.
Distance: on the spot on the spot on the spot.
Remarks: Bread-service, discount on access terme.

Bad Schönborn 17A2

Reisemobilhafen WellMobilPark, Kraichgaustraße 16.
GPS: n49,21839 e8,67144.

86 € 9, >10m € 13 € 1/100liter Ch (112x)€ 0,50/kWh € 2 € 1/h.
Location: Rural, luxurious. **Surface:** gravel. 01/01-31/12.
Distance: 800m on the spot 1km 200m.
Remarks: Bread-service, swimming pool available.

Bad Schussenried 20B1

Am Zellersee, Zellerseeweg. **GPS**: n48,00160 e9,64724.

10 € 5 + € 1,20/pp tourist tax Ch .
Surface: asphalted. 01/01-31/12.
Distance: 900m on the spot on the spot.

Bad Schussenried 20B1

Bierkrugmuseum, Wilhelm Schussenstrasse 12.
GPS: n48,00325 e9,65902.

30 free Ch € 5,reduction for guests WC.
Location: Quiet. **Surface:** metalled. 01/01-31/12.
Distance: on the spot 150m 250m.
Remarks: Brewery and brewery museum.

Tourist information Bad Schussenried:
Kloster Schussenried. History of the monastry. Easter-Oct 13.30-17.30h.

Bad Teinach 17A3

Untere talstasse 33. **GPS**: n48,68890 e8,69440.

DE

20 free. **Location:** Rural, simple. **Surface:** asphalted.
01/01-31/12.
Distance: 50m 100m 100m on the spot on the spot on the spot.
Remarks: Parking swimming pool, max. 24h.

Bad Teinach 17A3

Stellplatz am Wanderheim, Fronwaldstraße 48.
GPS: n48,69916 e8,69500.
5 free. 01/01-31/12.
Distance: centre 1,2km on the spot 1,3km 1km on the spot on the spot.
Remarks: Max. 8M.

Bad Urach 17B3

Wohnmobilstellplatz Bad Urach, Bäderstraße.
GPS: n48,50060 e9,37713.

26 € 8 € 0,50/60liter € 0,50 Ch included.
Location: Urban, simple. **Surface:** asphalted. 01/01-31/12.
Distance: on the spot 5km 200m 800m 200m 10km 10km.

Bad Waldsee 20B1

Bauernhof Lott, Mattenhaus 4. **GPS**: n47,95113 e9,75838.

10 € 10, 2 pers.incl, tourist tax € 2/pp Ch (10x)€ 0,50/kWh WC € 4. **Surface:** grassy. 01/04-31/10.
Distance: 3,5km 3km 3km 200m 3km.
Remarks: Bread-service.

Bad Waldsee 20B1

Waldsee-Therme, Unterurbacher weg. **GPS**: n47,91441 e9,76047.

39 € 6 + € 2/pp tourist tax € 1 € 1 Ch € 1/2kWh.
Surface: metalled. 01/01-31/12.
Distance: 1km 1km 1km 500m 1km 500m.
Remarks: Bread-service.

Bad Wildbad 16H3

Kernerstrasse. **GPS**: n48,74132 e8,54740.

11 € 10 € 1/3minutes Ch (16x)€ 2/8h.
Location: Rural, simple, noisy. **Surface:** asphalted.
01/01-31/12.
Distance: 500m 500m 300m on the spot on the spot on the spot.
Remarks: Max. 3 days, thursday market.

Bad Wimpfen 17A2

Wohnmobilstellplatz SRH Gesundheitszentrum, An der Alten Saline 2. **GPS**: n49,23383 e9,15069.

8 € 8 + € 1,80/pp tourist tax € 1/100liter Ch (8x)€ 1/12h WC. **Location:** Rural, comfortable, quiet. **Surface:** grasstiles.
01/01-31/12.
Distance: 800m on the spot.
Remarks: Parking at health resort.

Bad Wurzach 20C2

Wohnmobilstellplatz Vitalium, Riedhalde, An der Thermalquelle 1.
GPS: n47,91437 e9,90363.

17 € 5,50 + € 1,50/pp tourist tax € 0,50 € 0,50 Ch included WC. **Location:** Rural, quiet. **Surface:** asphalted.
01/01-31/12.
Distance: 500m 300m 500m.
Remarks: Check in at pay-desk of Vitalum.

Baden-Baden 16H3

Wohnmobilparkplatz, Hubertusstraße 2, Badenscheunern.
GPS: n48,78193 e8,20388.

28 € 12 € 1/100liter Ch (28x)€ 0,50/kWh.
Location: Urban, comfortable, noisy. **Surface:** metalled.
01/01-31/12.
Distance: Baden-Baden 4km 1km 100m 150m on the spot on the spot on the spot.
Remarks: Max. 4 days, video surveillance.

Baiersbronn 16H3

Schelklewiesen, Neumühleweg/Lochweg.
GPS: n48,51016 e8,37272.

15 € 10, tourist tax incl € 1/80liter Ch (12x)€ 0,50/kWh.
Location: Rural, simple, quiet. **Surface:** metalled.
01/01-31/12.
Distance: 300m on the spot 100m 200m on the spot on the spot.
Remarks: Max. 8M.

Balingen 20A1

Wohnmobilstellplatz an der Eyach, Heinzlerstrasse.
GPS: n48,27024 e8,85300.

10 free € 1 Ch (8x)€ 0,50/kWh.
Location: Urban, simple. **Surface:** asphalted. 01/01-31/12.
Distance: on the spot 500m 300m 300m.
Remarks: Max. 4 days.

Benningen am Neckar 17A2

Parkplatz Gemeindehalle, Max-Eyth Strasse.
GPS: n48,94574 e9,23363.

4 free. **Location:** Rural, simple. **Surface:** metalled.
01/01-31/12.
Distance: on the spot 50m 1km.

Bernau im Schwarzwald 19H2

Sportzentrum Spitzenberg, Sportplatzstraße.
GPS: n47,80614 e8,02803.

15 free, tourist tax € 2,20/pp € 1/100liter Ch € 1/8h. **Location:** Rural, simple, quiet. **Surface:** grassy/gravel.
16/04-30/09.
Distance: 500m 1km 500m.
Remarks: Pay at tourist office.

Besigheim 17A2

Wohnmobilstellplatz bei der Minigolfanlage, Auf dem Kies 32.
GPS: n48,99771 e9,14863.

DE

9 € 5 € 1/50liter Ch (6x)€ 0,50/kWh. **Location:** Rural, comfortable, quiet. **Surface:** metalled. 01/01-31/12.
Distance: 500m 10km 500m 200m 500m 200m on the spot on the spot.
Remarks: After 2 nights € 20/night.

S Beuren 17B3

Panorama Therme, Goethestraße. **GPS**: n48,56621 e9,39944.

4 € 6 € 1/3kWh. **Location:** Urban, simple.
Surface: metalled. 01/01-31/12.
Distance: 500m on the spot 500m 100m.

Beuron 20A1

Kloster Beuron, Abteistraße. **GPS**: n48,05306 e8,96704.

± 4 free. **Location:** Urban, simple.
Surface: gravel. 01/01-31/12.
Distance: on the spot.
Remarks: Parking monastery.

S Beuron 20A1

Besi-Kanu-Sport, Bahnhofstrasse 29. **GPS**: n48,08597 e9,09559.

10 € 5 Ch WC included. **Location:** Rural, simple.
Surface: gravel. 01/01-31/12.
Distance: 1km 200m 5km.
Remarks: Canoe rental.

S Biberach/Riss 20B1

Rißstraße. **GPS**: n48,10401 e9,79582.

18 € 5 Ch included € 0,50/kWh. **Surface:** gravel.
01/01-31/12 service: 01/11-28/02.
Distance: 700m 300m Donau-Bodensee-Radweg.
Remarks: Max. 3 days.

S Bietigheim-Bissingen 17A2

Wohnmobilstellplatz an der Enz, Mühlwiesenstrasse.
GPS: n48,96110 e9,13329.

9 € 5 € 0,50/80liter Ch (8x)€ 0,50/kWh.
Location: Urban. **Surface:** metalled.
01/01-31/12.
Distance: 200m 1km 1km 100m 100m 100m.
Remarks: Max. 4 days, max. 8M, check in at Lama Bar.

S Blaubeuren 17B3

Parkplatz P6, Dodelweg. **GPS**: n48,41351 e9,79102.

20 € 5 € 1/5minutes Ch € 1.
Surface: metalled. 01/01-31/12.
Distance: 1km 1km 1km 800m.
Remarks: Parking at swimming pool, max. 2 days.

Blaustein 17B3

Freizeitbad Bad Blau, Boschstraße. **GPS**: n48,41757 e9,91630.
3 free. **Location:** Simple. **Surface:** gravel. 01/01-31/12.
Distance: 6,5km 200m 500m.

S Blumberg 19H2

P1, Festplatz, Oberes Ried. **GPS**: n47,83943 e8,54226.

20 € 7,50, 01/11-30/04 € 6,50 € 1/50liter Ch (36x)€ 1/24h € 1,50. **Location:** Comfortable, quiet.
Surface: gravel/metalled. 01/01-31/12.
Distance: 800m 100m 80m.
Remarks: With payment: KONUS guest card with many advantages.

S Blumberg 19H2

P2, Parkplatz Bahnhof Zollhaus, Achdorf.
GPS: n47,83767 e8,55777.

5 € 7,50, 01/11-30/04 € 6,50 . **Location:** Urban, noisy.
Surface: gravel. 01/01-31/12.
Distance: 1,5km.

S Blumberg 19H2

P3, Achdorfer Tal. **GPS**: n47,83528 e8,49833.

10 € 7,50, 01/11-30/04 € 6,50 € 1 Ch (12x)€ 1/night,winter € 1,50. **Location:** Rural, simple, isolated, quiet. **Surface:** gravel.
01/01-31/12.
Distance: 4km.
Remarks: With payment: KONUS guest card with many advantages, caution key € 10 (connection electricity), service at Kläranlage 800m.

S Böblingen 17A3

Im Zimmerschlag. **GPS**: n48,67000 e9,03272.

4 free Ch free. **Location:** Urban, simple.
Surface: grasstiles/metalled. 01/01-31/10.
Distance: 3km 100m 1,5km on the spot.

S Bodman-Ludwigshafen 20A2

Wohnmobilhafen am Bodensee, Am Sportplatz.
GPS: n47,82369 e9,05153.

20 € 9 € 1/100liter Ch (4x)€ 2. **Location:** Simple.
Surface: grassy/metalled. 01/01-31/12.
Distance: 1km 3,2km 1,4km.

S Bonndorf 19H2

Schwimmbad, Ob dem Tal 1. **GPS**: n47,81644 e8,33969.
€ 7,50 + € 1/pp tourist tax WC on demand.
01/01-31/12.
Distance: 450m 500m.
Remarks: Check in at swimming pool.

S Bonndorf 19H2

Wohnmobilstellplatz Holzschlag, Schulstraße/Bonndorfer Straße, Bonndorf-Holzschlag. **GPS**: n47,84970 e8,26784.

€ 5, tourist tax € 0,80/pp Ch included.
Location: Simple, noisy. 01/01-31/12.
Distance: 100m.

S Bönnigheim 17A2

Mineralfreibad Bönnigheim, Bachstrasse 40.
GPS: n49,03910 e9,08439.

DE

6 free. Location: Rural, simple.
Surface: grasstiles/metalled. 01/01-31/12.
Distance: 500m 500m 1km.
Remarks: Max. 5 days, caution key € 10 (water).

Bönnigheim 17A2

Weinkellerei Heinz Kölle, Schmiedsberger Weg 38.
GPS: n49,04228 e9,10328.
2 € 5. **Surface:** grasstiles. 01/01-31/12.
Distance: 800m 800m.

Bopfingen 17C3

Gasthof zum Bären, Nördlinger Straße 3.
GPS: n48,85715 e10,35508.

6 € 6 € 1 € 1 Ch € 1.
Surface: asphalted. 01/01-31/12.
Distance: on the spot 16km on the spot 100m.
Remarks: Free with a meal.

Boxberg 17B1

Gasthof Hagenmühle, Uiffinger strasse 74.
GPS: n49,48710 e9,61299.

12 € 5 (12x) € 2,50. **Location:** Rural, simple.
Surface: grassy/gravel. 01/01-31/12 Restaurant: Thu.
Distance: 2km trout pond on the spot 1km 200m.

Brackenheim 17A2

Weingut und Besenwirtschaft 'Zum Alten Pflug', Seebergweg.
GPS: n49,10261 e9,04994.

3 € 6, free for clients Ch (3x) € 2 WC € 2.
Surface: metalled. 01/01-31/12.
Distance: 3km 3km.
Remarks: Sunday on demand.

Brackenheim 17A2

Weingut Winkler, Stockheimer strasse 13.
GPS: n49,08001 e9,06270.

3 € 5 Ch included.
Location: Rural, simple. **Surface:** grassy/metalled.
01/01-31/12.
Distance: on the spot 10km 10km 300m 1km 300m.
Remarks: When buying wine 1 night free.

Breisach/Rhein 19G1

Wohnmobil-Parkplatz, Josef-Buebstrasse.
GPS: n48,02944 e7,57576.

80 free 8-20h, € 6/night, 2 nights € 10, 3 nights € 13, winter free € 1/100liter € 1 Ch € 1.
Location: Urban, simple. **Surface:** asphalted.
01/01-31/12 Other parking in case of festivities.
Distance: 300m on the spot on the spot 300m 1,5km.
Remarks: Ground of wine festival, bread-service.

Breisach/Rhein 19G1

Restaurant Kläsles Gastronomie Am Rhein, Hafenstrasse 11.
GPS: n48,04292 e7,57378.

5 free.
Location: Simple. **Surface:** metalled. 01/01-31/12.
Distance: 2km on the spot 500m.
Remarks: Along the Rhine river, guests only.

Tourist information Breisach/Rhein:
Weinfest Kaiserstuhl Tuniberg. Wine festivals. end Aug.

Bretten 17A2

Reisemobil-Stellplatz Bretten, Willi-Hesselbacher-Weg.
GPS: n49,02980 e8,71914.

4 free € 1/100liter € 1/10h.
Location: Urban, comfortable. **Surface:** metalled. 01/01-31/12.
Distance: city centre 1,5km.
Remarks: Sports centre, max. 2 days.

Bruchsal 16H2

Stellplatz am Sportzentrum, Giesgrabenweg.
GPS: n49,13227 e8,58981.

2 free. **Location:** Urban, simple, central.
Surface: metalled. 01/01-31/12.
Distance: 1km 4km 100m 1km on the spot on the spot on the spot.
Remarks: At sports centre, max. 2 days.

Buchen/Odenwald 17A1

Wohnmobilhafen Morretal, Mühltalstraße 15.
GPS: n49,52888 e9,31020.

12 € 5/24h, 3 days € 20 € 1/100liter Ch (12x) € 0,50/kWh WC € 0,20 € 3/day. **Location:** Rural, comfortable, quiet.
Surface: grassy. 01/01-31/12. **Distance:** 800m on the spot.
Remarks: Parking Waldbad, use sanitary only during opening hours swimming pool.

Buchenbach 19H2

Wanglerhof, Vogtweg 1. **GPS:** n47,96820 e7,99269.

10 € 12 Ch (10x) includedstay € 2.
Location: Rural, simple, quiet. **Surface:** grassy.
01/01-31/12.
Distance: 1km 100m 1km.

Bühl 16H3

Wohnmobilstellplatz am SchwarzwaldbadS, Ludwig-Jahn-strasse 8.
GPS: n48,68862 e8,12995.

20 € 5 € 2/100liter Ch. **Location:** Urban, simple, noisy.
Surface: gravel/metalled. 01/01-31/12.
Distance: 1km 6km 500m 1km on the spot on the spot.
Remarks: Bread-service.

Burkheim 19G1

Am Kirchberg. **GPS:** n48,10226 e7,59656.

DE

14 free free. **Location:** Rural, simple, quiet. **Surface:** grasstiles.
01/01-31/12.
Distance: 500m on the spot on the spot.

S **Calw** 17A3

Wohnmobilstellplatz Am Alten Bahnhof, Bahnhofstrasse.
GPS: n48,70592 e8,73808.

6 free € 1/80liter € 1 Ch€ 1 (4x)€ 0,50/7kWh.
Location: Rural, simple, noisy.
Surface: asphalted. 01/01-31/12.
Distance: 1km 100m 200m on the spot on the spot.

Cleebronn/Tripsdrill 17A2

Erlebnispark Tripsdrill. **GPS:** n49,03102 e9,05096.

100 free. **Location:** Rural, isolated, quiet.
Surface: grassy.
07/04-06/11.
Distance: 1km on the spot 3km 400m.
Remarks: Max. 2 nights.

Tourist information Cleebronn/Tripsdrill:
Erlebnispark Tripsdrill. Amusement park.
19/03-06/11 9-18h.

S **Crailsheim** 17C2

Autohof Euro Rastpark, Marco-Polo-Straße 1, Satteldorf.
GPS: n49,18146 e10,06889.
10 € 10 . **Surface:** metalled. 01/01-31/12.
Distance: 600m on the spot.

S **Dettenheim** 16H2

Kartbahn Liedolsheim, Kartbahnring 1. **GPS:** n49,14326 e8,43118.

180 free Ch (10x)€ 5/day WC € 2,50.
Location: Rural, simple, isolated. **Surface:** grassy/metalled.
01/01-31/12.
Distance: 3km 2km 2km on the spot 5km.
Remarks: Parking at Karting.

S **Dietingen** 20A1

Reisemobilpark Turm und Kristalle, Fronstraße 7.
GPS: n48,20036 e8,64610.
48 € 10 Ch (48x),16Amp. **Location:** Rural.
Surface: gravel. 01/01-31/12.
Distance: 800m 100m 50m on the spot.
Remarks: At museum.

S **Donaueschingen** 20A2

Am Schlosspark, Prinz Fritz Allee. **GPS:** n47,94746 e8,51183.

20 free € 1/50liter (14x)€ 0,50/kWh. **Location:** Rural, simple, quiet. **Surface:** grassy. 01/01-31/12.
Distance: 1,5km Danube Bike Trail on the spot.
Remarks: Max. 2 days, service 300m.

S **Donaueschingen** 20A2

Kläranlage, Haberfeld. **GPS:** n47,94931 e8,52209.
€ 1/50liter Ch.
01/01-31/12.

Tourist information Donaueschingen:
Tourismus- und Sportamt, Karlstrasse 58, www.donaueschingen.de. Horse city, named after the source of the River danube.
Der Donau Radweg. Signposted cycle route along the Donau.

S **Durbach** 16H3

Grol/Festplatz, Almstrasse. **GPS:** n48,49407 e8,01105.

15 € 6 € 1/100liter (8x)€ 1/8h. **Location:** Rural, simple.
Surface: gravel. 01/01-31/12 festivities.
Distance: 500m 10km on the spot on the spot 50m on the spot.

S **Durbach** 16H3

Wohnmobilstellplatz Ebersweier, Wiesenstraße, Ebersweier.
GPS: n48,50122 e7,98940.

6 € 6 € 1/80liter Ch (6x)€ 1/4h.
Location: Rural, simple. **Surface:** grasstiles. 01/01-31/12.
Distance: 500m 10km 750m 200m on the spot.

S **Eberbach** 17A1

Wohnmobilstellplatz In der Au, In der Au.
GPS: n49,46162 e8,97812.

7 free (6x)€ 1/2kWh. **Location:** Rural, simple, isolated.
Surface: gravel. 01/01-31/12.
Distance: 1km on the spot.
Remarks: At swimming pool, max. 2 nights.

Eberbach 17A1

Wohnmobilstellplatz Neckarlauer, B37, Uferstrasse.
GPS: n49,46012 e8,98652.

8 free. **Location:** Rural, central. **Surface:** asphalted.
01/01-31/12 high water.
Distance: 300m 300m 500m.

S **Eberbach** 17A1

In der Au. **GPS:** n49,46217 e8,97351.
€ 1/60liter Ch. 01/01-31/12.

Ebringen 19G2

An der Schönberghalle, Schulstraße 8.
GPS: n47,95639 e7,77667.

3 free. **Location:** Rural, simple, quiet. **Surface:** grasstiles.
01/01-31/12.
Distance: 7,6km on the spot.
Remarks: Max. 2 days, max. 6,5m.

S **Ehingen** 20B1

Wohnmobilstellplatz Ehingen, Am Stadion.
GPS: n48,28053 e9,73571.

10 free € 1/50liter Ch (4x)€ 2/10h free.
Surface: metalled. 01/01-31/12.
Distance: 1km 1km on the spot 500m 10m Danube Bike Trail.

S **Eichstetten** 19G1

Weingut Köbelin, Altweg 131. **GPS:** n48,09510 e7,72057.

5 € 13 Ch included. **Location:** Rural, simple, isolated, quiet. **Surface:** gravel/sand. 01/01-31/12.
Distance: city centre 1,5km 1,5km 1,4km 900m on the spot on the spot.

S **Eigeltingen** 20A2

Landgasthof Mönchhof, Tannenbergstraße 16.
GPS: n47,88094 e8,95278.

DE

4 guests free Ch € 2. **Surface:** metalled.
01/01-31/12.
Distance: 6km on the spot 4km on the spot.

S Eisenbach 19H2

Reisemobilpark Höchstberg. GPS: n47,94938 e8,25441.

20 € 8, tourist tax € 1,60/pp € 1/100liter Ch (20x) included,only in summer. **Location:** Rural, comfortable, quiet. **Surface:** grassy/gravel. 01/01-31/12.
Distance: on the spot on the spot.
Remarks: Altitude 1033m, at sports park.

S Ellwangen 17C2

Maxi-Autohof Ellwangen, Max-Eyth-Strasse 1.
GPS: n48,95628 e10,18319.

15 € 5/night ChWC against payment.
Location: Motorway. **Surface:** asphalted. 01/01-31/12.
Distance: 3km on the spot 1km.

S Emmendingen 19H1

Wohnmobilstellplatz am Sportfeld, Am Sportfeld.
GPS: n48,11869 e7,84154.

30 free € 1/80liter Ch. **Location:** Urban, simple.
Surface: asphalted. 01/01-31/12.
Distance: 1km 400m 600m.
Remarks: In front of swimmingpool, max. 3 days.

Endingen am Kaiserstuhl 19G1

P2 Stadthalle, Freiburger Weg. **GPS:** n48,13830 e7,70321.

20 free. **Location:** Urban, simple, central.
Surface: concrete. 01/01-31/12.
Distance: 200m 200m.

S Eppingen 17A2

Wohnmobilhalt am Freibad, Am Altstadring.
GPS: n49,13793 e8,91402.

4 free € 1/80liter € 1 Ch€ 1 (4x)€ 1.
Location: Rural, comfortable. **Surface:** metalled.
01/01-31/12.
Distance: 500m on the spot 300m 500m on the spot on the spot.

Esslingen am Neckar 17B3

Äußerer Burgplatz, Mülbergerstraße. **GPS:** n48,74713 e9,31064.

2 free. **Location:** Urban, simple.
Surface: asphalted. 01/01-31/12.
Distance: 1km 1km on the spot 1km 300m.
Remarks: Max. 48h.

S Ettenheim 19G1

Ernst Caravan und Freizeit Center, Rudolf Hell Straße 32-44.
GPS: n48,27431 e7,78161.

30 free € 1 € 1 Ch€ 1 (12x)€ 0,50/kWh.
Location: Motorway, simple. **Surface:** concrete. 01/01-31/12.
Distance: 500m.
Remarks: Motorhome dealer, accessory shop, repairs.

S Ettlingen 16H3

Wohnmobilstellplatz Am Freibad, Schöllbronner strasse.
GPS: n48,93561 e8,41747.

14 free € 2/5minutes Ch (4x)€ 2/8h.
Location: Urban, simple. **Surface:** asphalted. 01/01-31/12.
Distance: 100m 3,3km 100m 700m on the spot on the spot on the spot.
Remarks: Parking swimming pool, max. 48h, market Wednesday and Saturday.

S Feldberg 19H2

Altglashütten, Dreiseenbahnweg. **GPS:** n47,85857 e8,11537.
16 € 10 + € 2,60/pp tourist tax € 1/100liter Ch (16x)€ 1/8h. **Location:** Urban. **Surface:** gravel.
01/01-31/12.
Distance: on the spot on the spot 2,5km Skibus.

S Filderstadt 17A3

Parkplatz P2, Tübinger Strasse 40. **GPS:** n48,67347 e9,21456.

8 € 7/24h € 1/80liter Ch (8x)€ 0,50/kWh,16Amp.
Location: Urban. **Surface:** gravel. 01/01-31/12.
Distance: 500m 500m 500m 500m.

S Freiburg 19H1

Reisemobilplatz Freiburg, Bissierstraße/Am Eschholzpark.
GPS: n47,99915 e7,82643.

60 € 1/100liter Ch (20x)€ 1/kWh € 1.
Location: Urban, comfortable.
Surface: asphalted/gravel.
01/01-31/12.
Distance: Old city centre 1,5km 4,3km 450m.
Remarks: Max. 72h, green zone: environmental badge obligatory.

S Freiburg 19H1

WV-Südcaravan, Hanferstrasse 30, Hochdorf.
GPS: n48,04146 e7,81473.

6 free € 1/80liter Ch€ 2 € 5/day. **Location:** Urban, simple.
Surface: asphalted/metalled. 01/01-31/12.
Distance: Old city centre 10km 3km 300m 3km.
Remarks: During opening hours.

S Freudenberg 17A1

P. Freudenberg-Süd, Hauptstrasse. **GPS:** n49,74001 e9,31938.

10 € 6/night € 1/15minutes Ch (6x)€ 2/8h,16Amp free.
Location: Rural, comfortable. **Surface:** metalled.
01/01-31/12.
Distance: 50m 20m 20m 300m 500m 200m on the spot.

S Friedrichshafen 20B2

Stellplatz Friedrichshafen, Lindauerstrasse 2.
GPS: n47,65025 e9,49597.

DE

20 free, 01/04-31/10 € 13,20 € 1/100liter Ch WC .
Location: Noisy. **Surface:** asphalted/metalled.
01/01-31/12. **Distance:** 200m 200m 450m 850m.
Remarks: Max. 3 nights, payment only with coins.

S Gaggenau 16H3

Badstrasze 15. **GPS**: n48,80786 e8,30275.

6 free Ch . **Location:** Rural, simple.
Surface: grasstiles/metalled. 01/01-31/12.
Distance: 1,5km 800m on the spot on the spot.
Remarks: Parking spa resort, market Saturday.

S Gaildorf 17B2

Bleichgärten. **GPS**: n49,00224 e9,76587.

7 free Ch (4x)free,16Amp. **Location:** Simple.
Surface: metalled. 01/01-31/12.
Distance: 500m 400m 500m 500m on the spot on the spot.
Remarks: Max. 3 days, service closed during wintertime.

S Gailingen am Hochrhein 20A2

Rheinuferpark, Strandweg. **GPS**: n47,69051 e8,75621.
20 € 15 Ch. 01/04-31/10.
Distance: 1km on the spot 900m.
Remarks: Service on demand.

S Gammertingen 20A1

Freizeitanlage an der Lauchert, Reutlingerstrasse.
GPS: n48,25611 e9,21056.

8 free (6x)€ 1/4h WC. **Location:** Simple.
Surface: grassy/gravel. 01/01-31/12.
Distance: 1km on the spot on the spot 1km 700m on the spot.

S Geisingen 20A2

Reisemobilstellplatz Geisingen, Am Espen 8.
GPS: n47,92016 e8,65153.

37 € 9 € 1/80liter Ch included (37x)€ 2/4kWh.
Surface: gravel. 01/01-31/12.
Distance: 200m 1,5km 200m 200m 500m 500m 200m 100m.

S Gengenbach 19H1

Kinzigdamm, Berghauptener Straße. **GPS**: n48,40174 e8,00776.
40 € 10/24h + € 1,50-2,20/pp tourist tax Ch included .
Surface: gravel. 01/01-31/12.
Distance: 1km 300m 700m 900m.

S Gengenbach 19H1

An der Brennerei, Streuobstgarten 1. **GPS**: n48,38750 e8,02000.
10 € 10 (8x) WC included. **Surface:** grassy. 01/01-31/12.
Distance: 2km 1km.
Remarks: Sale of wines.

S Gernsbach 16H3

Am Schwimmbad 1, Oberstrot. **GPS**: n48,74239 e8,34186.

10 free (4x)€ 1/8h. **Location:** Rural, simple, quiet.
Surface: grassy. 01/01-31/12.
Distance: 200m 200m on the spot on the spot.
Remarks: At swimming pool.

S Gernsbach 16H3

Parkplatz Murginsel, Schlossstrasse/Klingelstrasse.
GPS: n48,75934 e8,33900.

8 € 5 € 1/100liter Ch (8x)€ 1/12h WC.
Location: Rural, simple. **Surface:** asphalted. 01/01-31/12.
Distance: 500m on the spot 500m 1km on the spot

on the spot on the spot.
Remarks: Max. 7 days.

S Giengen 17C3

Reisemobilstation Charlottenhöhle, Lonetalstrasse 60, Hürben.
GPS: n48,58412 e10,21203.

15 € 7/night € 2 Ch (6x)€ 2/12h,16Amp WC € 2. **Location:** Rural, quiet. **Surface:** gravel. 01/01-31/12.
Remarks: At prehistoric cave, coins at Hölenhaus.

Giengen 17C3

Am Schießberg, Auf dem Schießberg. **GPS**: n48,62975 e10,25159.

8 free. **Location:** Simple. **Surface:** gravel. 01/01-31/12.
Distance: 1,5km 4,3km 1,5km 1,5km.

Tourist information Giengen:
Charlottenhöhle. Caves. 01/04-31/10 8.30-11.30 and 13.30-17h, Su/holidays 9-16.30h.

S Göppingen 17B3

Parkplatz P1, An der EWS-Arena, Lorcherstrasse.
GPS: n48,71176 e9,64816.

6 free € 1/60liter Ch. **Location:** Urban.
Surface: asphalted. 01/01-31/12.
Distance: 1km 1km 1km.
Remarks: Max. 2 nights.

S Grossbottwar 17B2

Winzerhäuser Tal, In den Frauengärten.
GPS: n49,00363 e9,28739.

5 € 10 Ch € 1/2kWh.
Surface: metalled. 01/01-31/12.
Distance: 400m 400m 200m.
Remarks: At sports park, max. 5 days.

Grünkraut 20B2

Bodnegger Straße. **GPS**: n47,74076 e9,65515.
3 free. **Surface:** metalled. 01/01-31/12.
Distance: 1km 1km 1km.
Remarks: Max. 3 nights.

Gschwend 17B2

Naturbadesee, Frickenhofer Strasse. **GPS**: n48,93603 e9,75143.

DE

3 free. **Location:** Rural. **Surface:** forest soil.
01/01-31/12.
Distance: 1,5km.

S Gschwend 17B2

Joosenhofer Sägmühle. **GPS:** n48,92312 e9,77393.
free € 1/80liter Ch. **Surface:** asphalted. 01/01-31/12.

S Güglingen 17A2

Kreuzgärten. **GPS:** n49,06492 e8,99489.

10 free € 1 Ch. **Location:** Rural, simple.
Surface: metalled. 01/01-31/12.
Distance: 700m 500m Aldi-Lidl 500m on the spot on the spot.
Remarks: At swimming pool, max. 5 nights.

S Haigerloch 20A1

Wohnmobilstellplatz Haigerloch, Weildorfer Kreuz 1.
GPS: n48,36875 e8,79384.

10 free € 1/60liter Ch (10x)€ 1/8h.
Location: Urban, simple. **Surface:** asphalted. 01/01-31/12.
Distance: 300m on the spot.
Remarks: Max. 4 days.

S Hardheim 17B1

Am Alten Bahnhof, Bretzinger Straße. **GPS:** n49,60245 e9,47126.

12 free € 1/80liter Ch (8x)€ 1/2kWh.
Location: Rural, comfortable, noisy. **Surface:** gravel.
01/01-31/12.
Distance: 1km 1km 1km.

Haslach/Kinzigtal 19H1

Eichenbachsporthalle, Strickerweg. **GPS:** n48,27854 e8,07968.

10 free. **Location:** Simple. **Surface:** metalled.
01/01-31/12.
Distance: 500m 300m.
Remarks: At gymnasium, at swimming pool.

Haslach/Kinzigtal 19H1

Waldseeparkplatz, Waldseeweg. **GPS:** n48,27161 e8,09148.

10 free. **Location:** Rural, simple. **Surface:** asphalted.
01/01-31/12.
Distance: 1km 200m 1km.

Haslach/Kinzigtal 19H1

Wanderparkplatz Klosterplatz, Klosterstraße 1.
GPS: n48,27572 e8,08509.

10 free. **Location:** Urban, simple.
Surface: concrete. 01/01-31/12.
Distance: 50m 150m 500m 100m on the spot.
Remarks: At tourist office.

S Hausach 19H1

Waldstadion, Waldstraße. **GPS:** n48,28058 e8,17829.

4 free WC. **Location:** Rural, simple, simple, quiet, noisy.
Surface: gravel/sand. 01/01-31/12.
Distance: 500m 100m on the spot.

Hausach 19H1

Badepark, Schanze 3. **GPS:** n48,28620 e8,16589.

6 free. **Location:** Rural, simple.
Surface: concrete. 01/01-31/12.
Distance: on the spot 500m on the spot on the spot.
Remarks: Nearby swimming pool.

S Hechingen 20A1

Freizeitanlage Domäne Areal, Brielhof 1.
GPS: n48,33773 e8,94966.

18 € 18 included. **Location:** Simple. **Surface:** metalled.
01/01-31/12.
Distance: 2km 200m on the spot.
Remarks: Discount at restaurants and Golf Park.

Hechingen 20A1

Burg Hohenzollern, K 7110. **GPS:** n48,32579 e8,96404.

3 € 4. **Location:** Rural, simple. **Surface:** asphalted.
01/01-31/12.
Distance: Imbiss on the spot.

S Hechingen 20A1

Zollernalbcamping, Niederhechingerstrasse.
GPS: n48,35797 e8,96093.

20 € 10 € 1 Ch€ 1 € 1/kWh WC€ 3 € 2,50.
Location: Simple. **Surface:** metalled.
01/01-31/12 sanitary building: 01/11-01/04.
Distance: 2km 500m on the spot on the spot.
Remarks: Waste dump € 2/day.

S Heidenheim 17C3

In den Seewiesen. **GPS:** n48,69455 e10,16410.

22 € 2/day € 1/70liter € 1 Ch (18x)€ 0,50/kWh,16Amp.
Location: Rural, simple. **Surface:** asphalted/gravel.
01/01-31/12.
Distance: city centre 3km 5km 1km.

S Heilbronn 17A2

Wertwiesenpark, Neckarhalde. **GPS:** n49,13047 e9,20469.

20 free € 1/100liter Ch (12x)€ 0,50/kWh.
Location: Comfortable. **Surface:** metalled. 01/01-31/12.
Distance: 2km 7km 100m 500m.

S Heiligenberg 20B2

Sennerei Schläge, Betenbrunner strasse.
GPS: n47,81892 e9,31445.

10 € 5/16-09h Ch.

Surface: grassy/metalled. 01/01-31/12.

Distance: 200m 300m 300m 200m bakery 200m on the spot.

Remarks: Max. 2 nights.

S Herbrechtingen 17C3

P7 Eselstalparkplatz, Baumschulenweg.
GPS: n48,61758 e10,17411.

15 € 7 € 2 Ch € 2/24h.

Location: Rural, quiet. **Surface:** asphalted. 01/01-31/12.

Remarks: Check in at Hölenhaus.

Herbrechtingen 17C3

Stellplatz an der Bibrishalle, Baumschulenweg.
GPS: n48,61944 e10,17111.

5 free. **Surface:** asphalted. 01/01-31/12.

Distance: on the spot 700m.

S Herrenberg 17A3

P Stadthalle, Stadthallenstrasse. **GPS**: n48,59832 e8,86943.

5 free € 1 € 1. **Location:** Simple, noisy. 01/01-31/12.

Distance: 300m 100m 50m.

S Hessigheim 17A2

Fasanenhof, Römerweg 1. **GPS**: n49,00939 e9,18877.

15 € 5 . **Location:** Rural, simple. 01/01-31/12.

Distance: 3,5km on the spot shop with farm products on the spot on the spot.

Remarks: Farm/restaurant/Biergarten/shop.

S Hessigheim 17A2

Felsengarten Kellerei Besigheim e.G., Am Felsengarten 1.
GPS: n48,99612 e9,18068.

5 guests free . **Surface:** asphalted. 01/01-31/12.

Distance: 1km on the spot 1km.

Remarks: Max. 2 nights.

S Heubach 17B3

Am Freibad, Mögglinger Strasse. **GPS**: n48,79726 e9,93763.

6 € 6 € 1/90liter Ch€ 0,50 (6x)€ 1/kWh.

Surface: grasstiles. 01/01-31/12.

Distance: 200m Lidl 400m.

Hinterzarten 19H2

Bahnhofstraße. **GPS**: n47,90441 e8,10996.

free. **Surface:** grassy. 01/01-31/12.

Distance: 300m 300m.

Remarks: At fire-station, max. 1 night.

S Höchenschwand 19H2

Natursportzentrum. **GPS**: n47,73652 e8,15990.

12 € 8 Ch (12x)€ 1/6h WC € 3.

Location: Rural, comfortable. **Surface:** gravel. 01/01-31/12.

Distance: 400m 100m 600m on the spot.

Holzmaden 17B3

Urwelt-Museum Hauff, Aichelbergerstrasse 75/90.
GPS: n48,63482 e9,52771.

6 free. **Surface:** metalled. 01/01-31/12.

Distance: 3km 2,2km.

Remarks: Max. 1 night.

S Hornberg 19H1

Hotel Schöne Aussicht, Schöne Aussicht 1, Niederwasser.
GPS: n48,19443 e8,18494.

4 € 8 included . 01/01-31/12.

Distance: on the spot.

S Hüfingen 19H2

Wohnmobil-Stellplatz an der Breg, Bräunlinger Straße.
GPS: n47,92361 e8,48707.

22 € 6, tourist tax € 1/pp € 1,20/100liter Ch € 1,20/10h WC € 1,20 € 3,50/3,50.

Location: Comfortable, noisy.

Surface: grassy. 01/01-31/12.

Distance: 300m 300m.

Remarks: Check in on arrival, bread-service, thursday market.

S Hülben 17B3

Phoenix Wohnmobihafen, Kaltentalstrasse.
GPS: n48,52620 e9,41227.

10 free € 0,50/80liter Ch (6x)€ 0,50/kWh.

Location: Rural, simple. **Surface:** gravel. 01/01-31/12.

Distance: 400m 400m 500m Vordere-Alb-Radweg on the spot on the spot.

Remarks: Max. 4 days.

S Ihringen 19G1

Kaiserstuhl Camping, Nachtwaid 5. **GPS**: n48,03083 e7,65778.

6 € 14,60 + tourist tax Ch € 1,80/3kWh WC included.

Location: Rural, comfortable. **Surface:** asphalted/metalled. 31/03-30/10.

Distance: 600m 200m on the spot.

S Isny 20C2

Parkplatz An der Untere Mühle, Seidenstrasse 43.
GPS: n47,69457 e10,03780.

16 € 7,50 + € 1,50/pp tourist tax Chincluded (8x)€ 0,50/kWh WC. **Location:** Urban. **Surface:** asphalted/gravel. 01/01-31/12.

Distance: 300m 100m 300m 200m.

Remarks: Max. 2 nights.

S Isny 20C2

Caravans Dethleffs, Rangenbergweg. **GPS**: n47,69938 e10,05490.

9 € 5 + € 1,50/pp tourist tax, clients Dethleffs free Ch (9x) included.

Surface: metalled. 01/01-31/12.

Distance: 1km 1km 1km 500m 300m 300m 300m.

Remarks: Max. 3 nights.

Kaisersbach 17B2

Schwaben-Park, Hofwiesen 11, Gmeinweiler.
GPS: n48,90304 e9,65484.

10 free. 01/04-31/10.

Remarks: Inclining pitches.

Tourist information Kaisersbach:

Schwaben-Park. Amusement park. 19/03-06/11 9-18.

S Kappelrodeck 16H3

Wohnmobileck am Heidenhof, Grüner Winkel.
GPS: n48,58370 e8,12650.

DE

17 € 5/day, 3 days € 10, 7 days € 20 € 1/100liter Ch (8x)€ 1/2kWh. **Location:** Rural, simple, quiet.
Surface: gravel/metalled. 01/01-31/12.
Distance: 800m 150m 500m on the spot on the spot.
Remarks: Max. 7 nights.

Karlsruhe 16H2

Am Yachthafen Maxau, Maxau am Rhein.
GPS: n49,03720 e8,30583.

12 free. **Surface:** gravel. 01/01-31/12.
Distance: Karlsruhe 9km on the spot 2km.
Remarks: Along the Rhine river, max. 24h.

Karlsruhe 16H2

Ettlinger Allee. **GPS**: n48,98761 e8,40412.

2 free. **Surface:** asphalted. 01/01-31/12.
Distance: centre 2,5km 400m metro 400m.
Remarks: Max. 24h, small pitches.

Kehl 16G3

Am Wasserturm, Schwimbadstrasse. **GPS**: n48,56350 e7,81400.

40 € 8 € 1/80liter Ch (40x)€ 0,50/kWh.
Location: Urban, comfortable, quiet. **Surface:** gravel.
01/01-31/12.
Distance: 1km 100m 500m on the spot on the spot on the spot.
Remarks: Max. 3 days, friday market.

Kehl 16G3

Reisemobilstellplatz Hurst, An den Sportanlagen 1, Kehl-Auenheim.
GPS: n48,60653 e7,83146.

18 € 7 € 1 Ch (12x)€ 3 WC € 0,50 € 1,50.
Location: Rural, simple, quiet. **Surface:** asphalted/grassy.
01/01-31/12.
Distance: 500m on the spot 500m on the spot on the spot.
Remarks: Check in on arrival.

Kehl 16G3

Bürstner-Service-Centrum, Elsässer strasse 80, Kehl-Neumühl.
GPS: n48,57010 e7,84042.

6 free € 1/100liter (6x)€ 1/kWh.
Location: Rural, simple. **Surface:** asphalted. 01/01-31/12.
Distance: 1km 100m 600m on the spot on the spot.
Remarks: Tuesday and Friday market.

Kenzingen 19G1

Ritter's Weingut, Rossleiteweg 1. **GPS**: n48,18739 e7,78343.

15 € 10, 2 pers.incl, € 2/pp € 2,50/day WC included.
Location: Rural, simple. **Surface:** grassy/gravel.
01/01-31/12.
Distance: 7,5km on the spot.

Kirchberg/Jagst 17B2

Wanderparkplatz Kirchberg-Tal, Hohen Loher Strasse.
GPS: n49,20367 e9,98344.

6 free . **Surface:** gravel. 01/01-31/12.
Distance: 300m.

Kirchheim unter Teck 17B3

Ziegelwasen, Schlierbacher Straße. **GPS**: n48,64998 e9,45919.

3 free. **Location:** Urban, simple.
Surface: asphalted/metalled.
01/01-31/12.
Distance: 500m Altstadt 500m 500m 100m on the spot.
Remarks: Max. 3 days.

Kisslegg 20C2

Wohnmobilhafen Kißlegg, Strandbadweg.
GPS: n47,79602 e9,87950.
24 € 5, 01/04-31/10 € 7 € 1/100liter Ch (24x)€ 0,50/kWh WC . **Surface:** metalled. 01/01-31/12.
Distance: 800m 100m 100m 100m 1km 400m.

Kisslegg 20C2

Familiefreizeitgelände St Anna, Le Pouliguenstrasse.
GPS: n47,79119 e9,87229.

3 free. **Surface:** grassy/metalled. 01/01-31/12.
Distance: 800m 500m 500m.
Remarks: Max. 2 nights.

Kisslegg 20C2

Hotel Sonnenstrahl, Sebastian Kneipp strasse 1.
GPS: n47,78269 e9,87964.
2 free. **Surface:** asphalted/metalled. 01/01-31/12.
Distance: 800m on the spot 1,2km.
Remarks: Max. 2 nights.

Königschaffhausen 19G1

Wohnmobilgarten im Kirschenhof Schmidt, Königsweg 5.
GPS: n48,14277 e7,66273.

28 € 15 Ch WC included € 1 . **Location:** Rural, comfortable. **Surface:** gravel/metalled. 01/01-31/12.
Distance: 500m on the spot on the spot.
Remarks: Wifi in café.

Königsfeld 19H1

Reisemobilpark Bregnitzhof, Buchenberger Strasse 34.
GPS: n48,14028 e8,40583.

21 € 10 € 0,10/10liter Ch € 1/2kWh.
Location: Rural, luxurious, quiet. **Surface:** gravel. 01/01-31/12.
Distance: 1km 10 min walking.
Remarks: Check in between 14-19h, 18-holes golf course, Saunalandschaft Bregnitzhof.

Konstanz 20B2

Parkplatz Döbele, Döbeleplatz. **GPS**: n47,65794 e9,16933.

12 € 1,40/h, € 14/24h Ch WC included.
Surface: asphalted/metalled. 01/01-31/12.
Distance: 1km 800m 800m 200m 800m 500m.
Remarks: Max. 24h.

Korb 17B3

Reisemobilstellplatz Unterm Korber Kopf, Brucknerstrasse 14.
GPS: n48,84597 e9,35544.

DE

6 € 3 € 0,50/80liter Ch (6x)€ 0,50/kWh.
Surface: metalled. 01/01-31/12.
Distance: 400m Gaststätte 300m 500m.
Remarks: Max. 3 nights, coins at restaurant.

Kraichtal 17A2

Gochsheim, Immenstrasse, Gochsheim. **GPS**: n49,10056 e8,74084.

2 free. **Location:** Simple. **Surface:** asphalted. 01/01-31/12.
Distance: 500m.
Remarks: At sports park, small pitches.

Krauchenwies 20B1

Seencamping Krauchenwies, Ablacher Str. 4.
GPS: n48,01851 e9,23590.

24 € 9 € 1/100liter Ch € 0,60 WC .
Location: Rural. **Surface:** gravel. 01/01-31/12.
Distance: 1km 100m 100m 700m 1km 500m 100m 2km.

Kressbronn 20B2

Wohnmobilstellplatz Tunau, Tunau 4.
GPS: n47,58999 e9,57512.

40 € 21 Ch (40x)WC € 1,50/pp included.
Surface: asphalted/grassy. 01/04-31/10.
Distance: 1km 1km 1km on the spot 1km.

Kressbronn 20B2

Gohren am See. **GPS**: n47,58818 e9,56256.
16 € 15 Ch € 3/12h WC € 1/day.
Surface: grassy/gravel. 01/04-15/10.
Distance: 250m.

Külsheim 17B1

Am Schloss Külsheim, Kirchbergweg. **GPS**: n49,67123 e9,52255.

12 free € 0,50/80liter Ch (12x)€ 0,50/kWh free.
Location: Rural, simple. **Surface:** grasstiles. 01/01-31/12
10/09-25/09.
Distance: 300m.

Ladenburg 17A1

Wohnmobilstellplatz Ladenburg, Heidelberger Straße.
GPS: n49,46596 e8,61460.

35 € 10/24h € 1/80liter Ch € 1/2kWh € 1/24h.
Location: Urban, comfortable, central, quiet. **Surface:** grassy.
01/01-31/12.
Distance: Altstadt 500m, Heidelberg 10km 3km 200m 200m.

Lahr/Scharzwald 19H1

Stellplatz Breitmatten, Breitmatten. **GPS**: n48,33954 e7,89885.

14 € 6 € 1/100liter Ch € 1/kWh.
Surface: metalled. 01/01-31/12.
Distance: city centre 1,5km 100m 1,2km on the spot on the spot.

Langenau 17C3

Wohnmobilstellplätze Langenau, Karlstraße 27.
GPS: n48,50193 e10,12203.
4 free € 0,50/65liter Ch € 0,50/kWh. **Location:** Simple.
Surface: metalled. 01/01-31/12.
Distance: 500m 3,2km 300m 1,2km.

Langenbrettach 17B2

Freibad Langenbeutingen, Schwabbacker Strasse 24, Langenbeutingen. **GPS**: n49,21227 e9,40767.

3 free. **Location:** Rural, simple. **Surface:** asphalted.
01/01-31/12.
Remarks: Parking swimming pool.

Langenburg 17B2

Am Freibad, In der Strut 5. **GPS**: n49,24973 e9,86681.
3 free . **Surface:** gravel. 01/01-31/12.
Distance: 1km 700m.
Remarks: Not accessible coming from the west.

Lauchringen 19H2

An der Wutach, Badstrasse. **GPS**: n47,62556 e8,31361.

19 € 8 Ch (16x)€ 2/24h included.
Location: Rural, comfortable, quiet. **Surface:** gravel.
01/01-31/12 service: 01/11-01/04.
Distance: on the spot on the spot on the spot.
Remarks: Pay at town hall or swimming pool, caution € 20, key electricity at pool.

Lauda-Königshofen 17B1

Badstrasse. **GPS**: n49,55886 e9,70099.

4 free. **Location:** Rural, simple. **Surface:** asphalted.
01/01-31/12.
Distance: 1km 1,5km 500m.
Remarks: Parking at swimming pool, service at Kläranlage ma-do 7-16 uur.

Lauda-Königshofen 17B1

Gasthaus Zur Lamm, St. Josefstrasse 30-32, Marbach.
GPS: n49,56568 e9,72834.

12 € 7/24h (12x)included WC free,at restaurant.
Location: Rural, simple, quiet. **Surface:** asphalted.
01/01-31/12 Restaurant: Mo.
Distance: on the spot on the spot.

Laufenburg 19H2

Laufenburg Baden P6, Andelsbachstraße.
GPS: n47,56585 e8,06677.

6 € 8 € 2/5minutes Ch€ 2 (6x)€ 0,50/kWh.
Location: Urban, quiet. **Surface:** concrete. 01/01-31/12.
Remarks: Along the Rhine river.

Laupheim 20B1

Schloß Grosslaupheim, Klaus-Graf-Stauffenberg-Strasse.
GPS: n48,23128 e9,88872.

7 € 8 € 0,50 € 0,50 Ch€ 0,50 included.
Location: Rural. **Surface:** grassy. 01/01-31/12.
Distance: on the spot.

Leonberg 17A3

Parkplatz Steinstrasse, Steinstrasse 19. **GPS**: n48,79705 e9,01751.

DE

5 free, Mo-Fr 8-18h € 2,50.
Surface: asphalted. 01/01-31/12 Sa 5-13h.
Distance: 400m 150m 300m on the spot.
Remarks: Max. 1 day.

S Leutkirch im Allgäu 20C2

Wohnmobilstellplatz Leutkirch, Kemptener Straße 62.
GPS: n47,82228 e10,03939.

14 € 6 € 1/100liter Ch (16x)€ 0,50/kWh.
Surface: grasstiles. 01/01-31/12.
Distance: 1km 300m.

S Löffingen 19H2

Waldbad Löffingen, Am Waldbad. **GPS**: n47,90017 e8,33287.

7 € 8, tourist tax € 2/pp (4x)included € 0,50,At swimming pool. **Location:** Comfortable. **Surface:** concrete.
01/01-31/12 service 01/10-01/05.
Distance: Swimming pool on the spot.
Remarks: Check in at pay-desk of swimming pool.

Tourist information Löffingen:

Schwarzwaldpark. Game preserve and summer toboggan slide (€ 1.02 a time). Easter-Oct 9-18h.

S Malsch 16H3

Gast Caravanning, Daimlerstr. 20b. **GPS**: n48,89079 e8,30747.

6 free € 1/80liter Ch. **Location:** Urban, simple.
Surface: asphalted/metalled. 01/01-31/12.
Distance: 7,6km.
Remarks: Motorhome dealer, accessory shop, friday market.

S Mannheim 16H1

Neuostheim, Hans-Thoma-Straße 3. **GPS**: n49,47446 e8,52522.

15 € 10/24h € 1/100liter Ch (15x)€ 1/kWh.
Location: Urban. **Surface:** grasstiles/metalled. 01/01-31/12.
Distance: 4km 900m 200m 500m 100m 400m 400m.

S Mannheim/Friedrichsfeld 16H1

Güma Reisemobile, Steinzeugstrasse 21. **GPS**: n49,44570 e8,56780.

4 free Ch WCfree.
Location: Rural, simple, noisy. **Surface:** metalled.
01/01-31/12.
Distance: 10km 1km 1km 300m.
Remarks: Max. 3 nights, sanitary use during shop opening hours.

S Marbach am Neckar 17A2

Parkplatz Bolzplatz, Poppenweiler/Weimarstrasse.
GPS: n48,93389 e9,26278.

5 € 5 Ch € 1/2kWh.
Location: Rural, simple. **Surface:** metalled. 01/01-31/12.
Distance: 1km 6,2km 100m 600m 500m.
Remarks: Max. 2 nights, service: Gruppenklärwerk Häldenmühle, L1100.

Markelsheim 17B1

Jahnstraße 6. **GPS**: n49,47629 e9,83278.

2 free. **Location:** Rural, simple. **Surface:** grasstiles.
01/01-31/12.
Distance: 100m 200m.
Remarks: Max. 2 days.

S Maulbronn 17A2

Am Kloster, Hilsenbeuerstrasse. **GPS**: n48,99872 e8,80501.
8 free € 1 Chfree € 0,50/kWh.
Location: Simple. **Surface:** metalled. 01/01-31/12.
Distance: on the spot 50m 250m.
Remarks: Motorhome max. 7m.

S Meckenbeuren 20B2

Wohnmobilplatz Besenwirtschaft Georgshof, Pfingstweiderstrasse 10-12/1, Reute. **GPS**: n47,68022 e9,55308.

9 € 9 Ch (9x)€ 0,50/kWh WC € 1.
Surface: grassy/gravel. 01/01-31/12.
Distance: on the spot Bodensee 5km 200m 100m.

S Meersburg/Bodensee 20B2

Wohnmobilparkplatz Ergeten, Daisendorfer Strasse.
GPS: n47,70160 e9,26898.

38 € 12/24h € 1/100liter € 1 Ch € 0,50/kWh WC.
Surface: metalled. 01/01-31/12.
Distance: 1km 100m 50m shuttle to centre.
Remarks: At edge of city, + 2x parking Allmendweg P1 n47.70211, o 9.26983, P2 n47,70159, o 9,27172.

S Meißenheim 19G1

Wohnmobilpark Ortenau, Winkelstrasse 36.
GPS: n48,41616 e7,77736.

24+30 € 8 € 1/100liter Ch (24x)€ 3,50/24h.
Location: Rural, comfortable.
Surface: gravel/metalled. 01/01-31/12.
Distance: 500m 200m 800m on the spot on the spot.

S Memmingen 20C1

Wohnmobil-stellplatz Memmingen, Colmarer Straße/Hemmerlesstraße. **GPS**: n47,99531 e10,18245.

20 € 1/2h, € 5/24h € 0,50/100liter Ch (18x)€ 0,50/kWh.
Location: Urban, simple. **Surface:** metalled.
01/01-31/12.
Distance: 900m 2,2km 700m Lidl 600m.
Remarks: Max. 2 nights.

S Mengen 20B1

Reisemobilstellplatz Zielfinger Seen, Uferweg 18.
GPS: n48,03117 e9,28265.

50 € 12 € 1/100liter Ch (16x)€ 0,60/kWh WC included. **Location:** Rural, comfortable, quiet. **Surface:** asphalted.
01/03-31/10.
Distance: 5000km on the spot on the spot 200m 25km on the spot on the spot.
Remarks: Incl. access Badesee.

S Messkirch 20A1

Messplatz P2, Am Stachus. **GPS**: n47,99381 e9,11514.

DE

4 free € 1/80liter ChWC. **Location:** Urban, simple.
Surface: metalled. 01/01-31/12, service 01/04-30/09.
Distance: 500m 400m 200m 500m.

Metzingen 17B3

Reisemobilplatz Outletcity Metzingen, Stetterstrasse 4.
GPS: n48,53241 e9,27574.

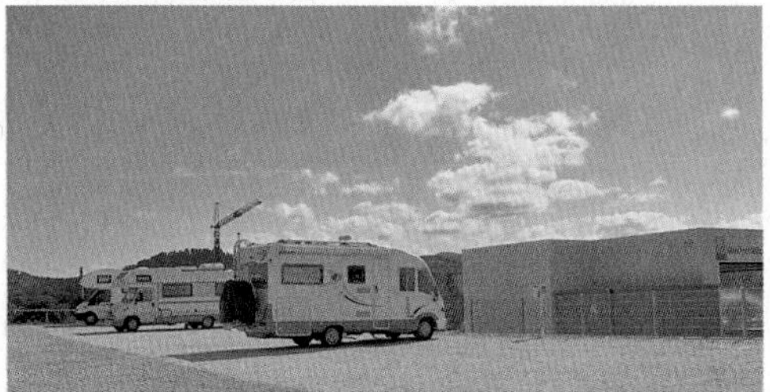

20 € 10 Chincluded (6x)€ 3,16Amp.
Location: Urban, simple. **Surface:** gravel. 01/01-31/12.
Distance: 800m 800m 800m 800m shuttle every 15 min.
Remarks: Money in envelope in mail box.

Michelbach an der Blitz 17B2

Hagenhofweg 8. **GPS**: n49,07133 e9,76993.
2 free € 1/100liter € 3/24h.
Location: Rural, quiet. **Surface:** metalled. 01/01-31/12.
Distance: 300m 400m 600m 300m on the spot on the spot.

Molpertshaus 20B2

Gasthof Zum Adler, Eintürner Straße 38. **GPS**: n47,87000 e9,80611.
4 € 4 Chincluded € 2. 01/01-31/12.
Distance: 200m.

Mosbach 17A2

Wasemweg. **GPS**: n49,36139 e9,14833.

10 free € 1/150liter Ch (8x)€ 1/12h.
Location: Rural, comfortable, quiet. **Surface:** concrete.
01/01-31/12.
Distance: 800m 300m 100m on the spot.
Remarks: Max. 3 nights.

Mössingen 20A1

Wohnmobilstellplatz Firstwald, Firstwaldstraße, Kernstadt.
GPS: n48,41348 e9,06915.

10 free € 1/50liter € 1 Ch (10x)€ 0,50/kWh,16Amp.
Location: Urban, simple. **Surface:** grasstiles.
01/01-31/12.
Distance: 1,5km 500m 1km 100m.

Mühlberg 20C1

Ferienhof Musch, Unterer weg 7. **GPS**: n47,98534 e9,98697.

4 € 15, 2 pers.incl Ch (3x)included WC € 3 € 2,50/day. **Surface:** grassy/metalled. 01/01-31/12.
Distance: 10km 100m 100m 10km 10km.
Remarks: Bread-service.

Müllheim 19G2

Am Friedhof, Am Engelberg, Hügelheim.
GPS: n47,83282 e7,62320.

2 free. **Location:** Rural, simple, isolated, quiet.
Surface: asphalted. 01/01-31/12.
Distance: 500m 300m 1,5km 400m.
Remarks: At cemetery.

Müllheim 19G2

Am Nüsslegarten, Am Nüsslegarten, Britzingen.
GPS: n47,82891 e7,67336.

2 free. **Location:** Rural, simple, quiet.
Surface: asphalted. 01/01-31/12.
Distance: centre 700m 250m 250m on the spot on the spot.
Remarks: Next to swimming pool, max. 2 nights.

Müllheim 19G2

Freibad Müllheim, Ziegleweg 7. **GPS**: n47,80237 e7,63403.

3 free. **Location:** Urban, simple.
Surface: asphalted. 01/01-31/12.
Distance: city centre 1km 200m 500m 600m.
Remarks: Next to swimming pool, max. 2 nights.

Müllheim 19G2

Parkplatz Nußbaumallee, Nußbaumallee.
GPS: n47,80942 e7,62985.

3 free. **Location:** Urban, simple. **Surface:** asphalted.
01/01-31/12.
Remarks: Max. 2 days.

Müllheim 19G2

Restaurant Kreuz, Bundesstrasse 3 Nr. 7. **GPS**: n47,80934 e7,60778.
5 free on demand € 5. **Surface:** gravel. 01/01-31/12.
Distance: on the spot on the spot.
Remarks: Breakfast-service.

Müllheim 19G2

Markgräfler Kräuterhof, Im Käppeleacker 3, Hügelheim.
GPS: n47,83237 e7,62045.

4 free. **Location:** Urban, simple.
Surface: grasstiles. 01/01-31/12.
Distance: 500m 50m 1km 300m.
Remarks: Herbery, herb-Stube.

Münsingen 20B1

Wiesentalstadion, Grafenecker Straße. **GPS**: n48,40939 e9,48580.

18 € 5/24h, 3 days € 12 € 1/100liter Ch € 1/6h.
Location: Urban, simple. **Surface:** gravel. 01/01-31/12.
Distance: 1km 200m within walking distance on the spot on the spot on the spot.

Murg 19H2

Am Freibad. **GPS**: n47,55196 e8,02403.

15 € 10 € 1/100liter € 0,50/kWh . **Location:** Rural, comfortable, quiet. **Surface:** gravel. 01/01-31/12.
Distance: 500m on the spot 650m 1km on the spot.

Murrhardt 17B2

Parkplatz Festhalle, Kaiser-Ludwig-Straße 25.
GPS: n48,97960 e9,57461.

3 free € 1/90liter Ch. **Location:** Rural, simple.
Surface: asphalted. 01/01-31/12.
Distance: 400m 100m.

Nagold 17A3

Wohnmobilhafen am Nagoldtal-Radweg, Am Glockenrain.
GPS: n48,56389 e8,72306.

DE

22 € 3 € 1/80liter € 1 Ch€ 1 (12x)€ 1/kWh.
Location: Rural, simple, quiet. **Surface:** gravel/metalled.
01/01-31/12.
Distance: 1km 25m 900m 400m on the spot on the spot.
Remarks: Market Wednesday and Saturday.

Nagold 17A3

Am Bahnhof, Bahnhofstraße. **GPS**: n48,55791 e8,72748.

4 free. **Location:** Rural, simple, noisy.
Surface: asphalted. 01/01-31/12.
Distance: 700m 100m on the spot on the spot on the spot.
Remarks: Max. 4 nights, market Wednesday and Saturday.

Nattheim 17C3

Ramensteinbad, Dieselstrasse 22. **GPS**: n48,70261 e10,23745.

4 free Chfree € 1/2kWh. **Location:** Urban, quiet.
Surface: metalled. 01/01-31/12 25/04-07/05.
Distance: 500m 300m 200m Lidl.
Remarks: Parking swimming pool, max. 3 days.

Neckarsulm 17A2

Freizeitbad Aquatoll, Reisachmühlweg. **GPS**: n49,18802 e9,24302.

25 free € 1/60liter Ch. **Location:** Rural, simple.
Surface: asphalted/gravel. 01/01-31/12.
Distance: 1km 4km 450m 400m.
Remarks: Parking swimming pool, max. 24h.

Neckarwestheim 17A2

Wohnmobilstellplätze Im Bühl, Liebensteiner Strasse.
GPS: n49,04186 e9,18797.

2 free € 2 Ch (4x)€ 2/8h. **Surface:** metalled.
01/01-31/12.
Distance: 500m 200m 500m.
Remarks: From 4th night € 25/night.

Nehren 17A3

Steinlach. **GPS**: n48,43795 e9,05384.
10 free (8x)€ 1/kWh. **Surface:** grassy. 01/01-31/12.
Distance: centre 500m 1km on the spot on the spot.

Neresheim 17C3

Stellplatz Alter Bahnhof, Dischinger Straße 11.
GPS: n48,75102 e10,33957.

5 free € 1 Ch (4x)€ 1/4h.
Location: Noisy. **Surface:** metalled. 01/01-31/12.
Distance: on the spot 12km on the spot 300m.
Remarks: Service during opening hours.

Neuffen 17B3

Am Schützenhaus, Schützenhausweg. **GPS**: n48,54726 e9,37057.

8 free € 2/8minutes Ch (7x)€ 2/8h. **Location:** Simple.
Surface: asphalted. 01/01-31/12.
Distance: 500m 500m 500m on the spot.

Neuhausen ob Eck 20A1

Wohnmobilstellplatz Auf der Eck, Beim Friedhof.
GPS: n47,97473 e8,92397.

8 voluntary contribution € 1 € 1 Ch€ 1 (9x).
Location: Urban, simple. **Surface:** metalled. 01/01-31/12.
Distance: 300m 500m 1km 300m 2km 2km.
Remarks: Max. 4 days.

Neunkirchen 17A2

Festplatz, Zwingenbergerstrasse. **GPS**: n49,38818 e9,01531.

8 free € 1/90liter Ch. **Location:** Rural, simple, quiet.
Surface: asphalted. 01/01-31/12.
Distance: 300m 500m.
Remarks: Service next to: Autohaus Weishaupt, Industriestrasse 3 (200m).

Nordheim 17A2

Lauffener Straße. **GPS**: n49,10461 e9,13552.

2 € 5/3 days Ch included. **Location:** Simple.
Surface: asphalted. 01/01-31/12.
Distance: on the spot on the spot.
Remarks: In front of swimmingpool, max. 3 days.

Nordheim 17A2

Müllers Weingut und Weinstube, Im Auerberg 3.
GPS: n49,10236 e9,13810.

2 € 5,with electricity and water € 8 Ch .
Location: Rural. 01/01-31/12.
Distance: 800m on the spot on the spot on the spot on the spot.

Nordheim 17A2

Rolf Willy Privatkellerei, Schafhohle 26. **GPS**: n49,11212 e9,12845.
4 € 10, guests free (2x). 01/01-31/12.
Distance: 350m.

Nordrach 19H1

Schwarzwald-Panorama Wohnmobilstellplatz, Im Dorf 29.
GPS: n48,39873 e8,07927.

8 free € 1/10liter Ch (8x)€ 1/6h .
Location: Rural, simple, central. **Surface:** metalled.
01/01-31/12.
Distance: 100m 100m.

Nürtingen 17B3

Stellplatz Plätschwiesen, B313, Plätschwiesen, Oberensingen.
GPS: n48,63645 e9,33051.

12 € 5/24h € 1 Ch (8x)€ 1.
Location: Urban. **Surface:** metalled. 01/01-31/12.
Distance: 1km 4,4km on the spot 500m on the spot.
Remarks: Max. 7 days.

Oberkirch 16H3

Am Renchtalstadion, Renchallee. **GPS**: n48,52972 e8,07250.

38 € 5, € 7/2 days + € 2 tourist tax € 1/80liter € 1 Ch (30x)€ 1/2kWh.
Location: Rural, simple, quiet. **Surface:** grassy/gravel.
01/01-31/12 week before and week after 1st weekend Sep.
Distance: 100m 100m 100m on the spot on the spot.

Oberkirch 16H3

Waldparkplatz Schauenburg, Burgstraße 29.
GPS: n48,53812 e8,09452.

4 € 8 (4x)€ 2. **Location:** Simple, isolated, quiet.
Surface: grassy/sand. 01/01-31/12.
Distance: 500m.
Remarks: Max. 4 days, € 8 voucher restaurant.

Oberndorf/Neckar 20A1

Neckarhalle, Austrasse 12. **GPS**: n48,28222 e8,58472.

8 free € 1/70liter Ch (4x)€ 1/8h.
Location: Rural, simple, noisy. **Surface:** asphalted. 01/01-31/12.
Distance: 1,5km 300m 200m 50m on the spot on the spot.
Remarks: Max. 3 days.

Oberstenfeld 17B2

Mineralfreibad, Beilsteiner Strasse 100. **GPS**: n49,03160 e9,31890.

4 free. **Surface:** asphalted. 01/01-31/12.

Oberteuringen 20B2

Ferienhof Kramer, St. Georg strasse 8. **GPS**: n47,73948 e9,47278.

6 € 18, 2 pers.incl Ch (8x)€ 2,50 WC € 4.
Surface: gravel/metalled. 01/05-15/09.
Distance: 2km on the spot 300m 300m.

Offenburg 16H3

Strandbad & Tiki Bar Gifizsee, Platanenallee 15.
GPS: n48,45785 e7,93663.

11 € 22, 2 pers.incl € 1/5minutes Ch (11x)€ 1/kWh WC included.
Location: Rural, simple. **Surface:** grasstiles. 01/04-31/10.
Distance: 2,5km 3,8km 100m on the spot 150m.
Remarks: Bread-service.

Offenburg 16H3

Bürgerpark, Stegermattstraße 26a. **GPS**: n48,46565 e7,94566.

2 € 2. **Location:** Urban, simple, quiet.
Surface: asphalted/metalled. 01/01-31/12.
Distance: 500m 300m.
Remarks: In front of swimmingpool, small pitches.

Offenburg 16H3

Camping + Freizeit Kuhn, Im Drachenacker 4.
GPS: n48,48039 e7,92776.

10 free € 0,50/50liter Ch (8x)free.
Location: Urban, simple. **Surface:** metalled. 01/01-31/12.
Distance: 2km 3,7km 500m.
Remarks: Service during opening hours.

Öhringen 17B2

Am Rendelbad, Rendelstr. 31. **GPS**: n49,19811 e9,51209.
14 € 8 Ch included. **Surface:** gravel. 01/01-31/12.
Distance: on the spot 300m 600m.
Remarks: At swimming pool, max. 3 days.

Öhringen 17B2

An der Reithalle, Hornbergstraße 2, Cappel.
GPS: n49,19918 e9,52610.

15 € 8 included. **Location:** Urban, simple.
Surface: metalled. 01/01-31/12.
Distance: 100m 100m.
Remarks: At manege, max. 3 days.

Tourist information Öhringen:
RADius. Cycle route, 18km.

Öllingen 17C3

Parking Rathaus, Hauptstrasse. **GPS**: n48,52816 e10,14813.

4 free Chfree. **Surface:** grasstiles. 01/01-31/12.
Distance: 100m 100m on the spot.

Oppenau 16H3

Wohnmobilstellplatz Oppenau, Hauptstrasse.
GPS: n48,47639 e8,16972.

6 € 7 € 1/100liter Ch (6x)€ 1/8h.
Location: Rural, simple, quiet. **Surface:** gravel.
01/01-31/12.
Distance: 300m 150m bakery 300m on the spot on the spot.
Remarks: Use sanitary only during opening hours swimming pool.

Oppenweiler 17B2

Caravanstation, Murrwiesenstraße 15.
GPS: n48,97999 e9,45898.

2 free € 1/80liter Ch. **Surface:** asphalted. 01/01-31/12.
Distance: 600m.
Remarks: Max. 2 days.

Ostrach 20B2

Wohnmobilstellplatz Weites Ried, Burgweiler.
GPS: n47,91722 e9,35438.
€ 4 (4x)€ 1/8h. **Surface:** gravel. 01/01-31/12.
Distance: 5km.

Pforzheim 17A3

Reisemobilplatz Oststadt am Enzauenpark, Wildersinnstraße.
GPS: n48,89784 e8,72232.

15 free (6x)€ 1/kWh. **Location:** Urban, simple, noisy.
Surface: metalled. 01/01-31/12.
Distance: 1,5km 200m 100m on the spot on the spot on the spot.
Remarks: Max. 2 days, service 200m.

Pforzheim 17A3

Parkplatz 2&3 Wildpark, Tiefenbronnerstraße.
GPS: n48,87651 e8,71749.
€ 3-5. **Location:** Urban. 01/01-31/12.
Remarks: Max. 1 night.

Pforzheim 17A3

Hohwiesenweg. **GPS**: n48,89750 e8,72674.
€ 1/80liter Ch. 01/01-31/12.

DE

Pfullendorf 20B2

Seepark Linzgau, P-Ost, Bannholzerweg 18. **GPS**: n47,93097 e9,23728.

20 € 4/24h € 0,50/kWh.
Surface: unpaved. 01/01-31/12.
Distance: 2km on the spot 50m 450m.

Pfullingen 17A3

Wohnmobilplatz Schönbergbad, Klosterstraße.
GPS: n48,45537 e9,22812.

8 free € 1/50liter € 1 Ch € 1/2kWh.
Location: Urban, simple. **Surface:** grassy. 01/01-31/12.
Distance: 1,5km nearby on the spot.
Remarks: Max. 4 days.

Radolfzell 20A2

Wohmobilstellplatz in den Herzen, Zeppelinstraße.
GPS: n47,73888 e8,95331.

15 € 10/24h € 1/80liter Ch (6x)€ 0,50/kWh.
Surface: metalled. 01/01-31/12.
Distance: 1km 500m 1km BodenseeRadweg Bodensee-Rundwanderweg.
Remarks: Max. 3 days.

Radolfzell 20A2

Wohnmobilstellplatz Halbinsel Mettnau, Strandbadstrasse.
GPS: n47,73784 e8,98007.

12 € 10/24h € 1/50liter Ch (6x)€ 0,50/kWh.
Surface: asphalted. 01/01-31/12.
Distance: 500m 700m 700m 500m 700m 100m.
Remarks: Max. 3 days.

Radolfzell 20A2

Campingplatz Böhringer See, Hindenburgstrasse 64.
GPS: n47,76176 e8,93488.

5 € 10 Ch € 3 WC € 1.
Surface: metalled. 01/01-31/12.
Distance: 1km on the spot 1km.

Rastatt 16H3

Stellplatz am Familienbad Alohra, Leopoldring 8.
GPS: n48,85409 e8,19970.

5 € 5 € 1/10minutes Ch (8x)€ 1/6h.
Location: Urban, simple. **Surface:** metalled. 01/01-31/12.
Distance: 500m 3,8km.
Remarks: Check in at pay-desk of swimming pool, discount at swimming pool and sauna, tuesday, thursday and saturday market 7-13h.

Ratzenried 20C2

Parkplatz Turnhalle. **GPS**: n47,72199 e9,90430.
3 free. **Location:** Urban. **Surface:** asphalted. 01/01-31/12.
Distance: on the spot 200m 200m on the spot on the spot.

Ravensburg 20B2

Wohnmobilstellplatz Ravensburg, Mühlbruckstrasse.
GPS: n47,78196 e9,60001.

19 € 8,50 € 1/80liter Ch € 0,50/kWh.
Surface: metalled. 01/01-31/12.
Distance: centre 800m 500m 200m 250m Donau-Bodensee Radweg.
Remarks: Max. 3 nights.

Ravensburg 20B2

Am Gasthaus Anker, Schlegel 22. **GPS**: n47,78378 e9,53787.
10 free. 01/01-31/12.

Tourist information Ravensburg:

Bodensee-Erlebniskarte. Card gives free access to all boats, telpher carriers, beaches etc. Around the Lake Constance in Germany, Switzerland and Austria. € 72/3 days.

Tourist Information, Kirchstrasse 16. City of the Tore und Turme, gates and towers.

Rechberghausen 17B3

Sportpark Lindach, Am Desenbach. **GPS**: n48,72405 e9,63594.

6 free € 0,50/80liter Ch (6x)€ 0,50/kWh.
Location: Rural, simple. **Surface:** grassy. 01/04-01/11.
Distance: 1km 500m 1km 1km 500m on the spot.

Reichenau 20A2

Zum Sandseele. **GPS**: n47,69887 e9,04711.

12 € 12/24h € 1/80liter Ch (8x)€ 1/2kWh.
Surface: asphalted/metalled. 01/01-31/12.
Distance: 1,5km on the spot on the spot 100m 2km.
Remarks: Max. 1 night.

Reichental 16H3

Auwiesenstraze. **GPS**: n48,73166 e8,39616.

10 free Ch. **Location:** Simple, isolated, quiet. **Surface:** gravel. 01/01-31/12.
Distance: 1km on the spot.

Renchen 16H3

Wohnmobilstellplatz Renchen-Ulm, Ullenburgstrasse, Ulm.
GPS: n48,58088 e8,04556.

12 € 6 € 1/100liter Ch € 1/2kWh.
Location: Rural, comfortable, quiet. 01/01-31/12.
Distance: 300m 300m on the spot on the spot.
Remarks: Friday market.

Reutlingen 17A3

P&R Parkplatz, Am Südbahnhof/Marktstrasse.
GPS: n48,48280 e9,22982.

3 free Ch. **Location:** Urban, simple, noisy.
Surface: gravel. 01/01-31/12.
Distance: 3km on the spot on the spot.
Remarks: In front of motorhome dealer Berger, max. 48h.

Reutlingen 17A3

Sportpark Markwasen, Hermann-Hesse-Straße.
GPS: n48,47536 e9,19377.

10 € 8 € 1/80liter Ch (8x)€ 0,50/kWh.

Location: Urban, simple. **Surface:** gravel. 01/01-31/12.
Distance: 3km.
Remarks: Public transport included.

S Rheinmünster 16H3

Freizeit Center Oberrhein, Am Campingpark 1.
GPS: n48,77250 e8,04240.

20 € 8/24h € 1/80liter Ch (20x)€ 0,50/kWh.
Location: Rural, comfortable, quiet. **Surface:** grassy.
01/01-31/12.
Distance: on the spot 200m on the spot on the spot.

S Riedlingen 20B1

Stadthalle, Hindenburgstraße. **GPS**: n48,15189 e9,47766.

3 free € 1/100liter Ch € 1/4h.
Location: Urban. **Surface:** asphalted. 01/01-31/12.
Distance: 300m 200m 100m.
Remarks: Max. 3 days.

S Rielasingen-Worblingen 20A2

Naturbad Aachtal, Herdweg. **GPS**: n47,72127 e8,86332.
6 free, May-Sep € 4,50/day € 1/100liter Ch € 0,50/kWh 01/05-30/09. **Location:** Rural. **Surface:** gravel. 01/01-31/12.
Distance: 600m.

S Rottenburg/Neckar 17A3

Wohnmobilhafen Neckarufer, Ulmenweg 4.
GPS: n48,47213 e8,95010.

12 € 5 € 1/80liter Ch (8x)€ 0,50/kWh.
Location: Urban, simple. **Surface:** asphalted. 01/01-31/12.
Distance: 800m 800m 800m 800m on the spot.
Remarks: Max. 3 days.

S Rottweil 20A1

Parkplatz, Stadionstrasse. **GPS**: n48,15556 e8,62861.

16 € 5 € 1 Ch (16x)€ 1/8h.
Location: Urban, simple, quiet. **Surface:** gravel. 01/01-31/12.
Distance: 1km 1km 1km 500m.
Remarks: Parking stadium.

S Rust 19G1

Europapark Rust, Europa-Parkstrasse. **GPS**: n48,27189 e7,71745.

200 8-20h € 2/h (max. € 6), 20-8h € 2,50/h (max. € 25) Ch WC included.
Location: Simple. **Surface:** grasstiles.
19/03-06/11, 26/11-08/01 9-18.
Distance: on the spot on the spot.

Tourist information Rust:
Europa-park, Europa-Park-Straße 2. Large amusement and theme park with Europe as theme. 19/03-06/11 9-18, 26/11-08/01 11-19.

S Sankt Blasien 19H2

Rehbach Skilift, Rehbachweg, Menzenschwand.
GPS: n47,81306 e8,06933.

20 € 7 Ch (16x)€ 3/24h. **Location:** Rural, simple, quiet.
Surface: grassy/gravel. 01/04-31/10.
Distance: 8km bakery 500m on the spot on the spot on the spot.
Remarks: At ski-lift Rehbach.

Sankt Blasien 19H2

Am Dom, Fürstabt-Gerbert-Straße. **GPS**: n47,76039 e8,12923.
5 free. **Surface:** metalled. 01/01-31/12.
Distance: on the spot 200m.

S Sasbachwalden 16H3

Wohnmobilstellplatz Alde Gott, Talstraße 2.
GPS: n48,61945 e8,12147.

30 € 7/night € 1/100liter Ch (20x)€ 2/24h.
Location: Rural, comfortable, quiet. **Surface:** gravel/metalled.
01/01-31/12.
Distance: centre 300m 9km 9km 100m 250m 250m 100m on the spot on the spot.
Remarks: Waterfall 1km, swimming pool 800m.

S Schiltach 19H1

Stellplatz P1 Lehwiese, Am Hirschen. **GPS**: n48,29111 e8,34250.

10 free (3x).
Location: Urban, simple, quiet. **Surface:** gravel. 01/01-31/12.
Distance: 200m 50m 50m on the spot on the spot on the spot.
Remarks: Busy parking during the day.

S Schluchsee 19H2

P Aqua Fun, Faulenfürster Straße 18. **GPS**: n47,81569 e8,18113.

22 € 10 + € 2,60/pp tourist tax € 1/100liter Ch € 1/8h.
Location: Rural, comfortable, central, quiet. **Surface:** asphalted.
01/01-31/12.
Distance: 200m.
Remarks: Max. 1 night.

S Schonach im Schwarzwald 19H1

Parkplatz Obertal, Schwimmbadweg. **GPS**: n48,14573 e8,18872.

10 € 7 € 1 € 1 Ch (8x)€ 1/8h.
Location: Rural, comfortable. **Surface:** grasstiles. 01/01-31/12.
Distance: 1km 650m on the spot on the spot on the spot on the spot.
Remarks: Max. 3 nights, coins at tourist info, free entrance swimming pool, ski-lift and public transport.

Schönwald im Schwarzwald 19H1

Skilift Dobel, Franz-Schubert-Straße. **GPS**: n48,09728 e8,19588.
free. 01/01-31/12.
Distance: 600m on the spot on the spot on the spot.

S Schorndorf 17B3

Gmünder Straße 84/1. **GPS**: n48,80539 e9,54187.

7 € 5 + € 4/pp € 2 Ch€ 2 € 0,50/kWh,+ € 1 WC € 2 € 2/2 € 1.
Location: Simple. **Surface:** metalled. 01/01-31/12.
Distance: 10min.

S Schorndorf 17B3

Oskar Frech SeeBad, Lortzingstraße 56. **GPS**: n48,79645 e9,51410.
5 free € 1 € 1 Ch€ 1 € 0,50/kWh. **Location:** Urban.
Surface: metalled. 01/01-31/12.
Distance: on the spot.
Remarks: At swimming pool.

S Schramberg 19H1

Bahnhofstraße, B462. **GPS**: n48,23017 e8,38323.

2 free € 1/80liter Ch. **Location:** Rural, simple, noisy.
Surface: concrete. 01/01-31/12.
Distance: on the spot 100m 50m 10m on the spot on the spot.
Remarks: Max. 7 days.

S Schwäbisch Gmünd 17B3

Schießtalplatz, Schiesstalstraße. **GPS**: n48,80543 e9,81308.

DE

8 free € 1/50liter Ch (8x)€ 0,50/kWh.
Location: Rural, simple. **Surface:** gravel. 01/01-31/12.
Distance: 1km 50m 500m.
Remarks: Motorhome < 7m, max. 5 days a month.

Schwäbisch Hall 17B2

Wohnmobilstellplatz Auwiese, Spitalmühlenstraße.
GPS: n49,12218 e9,73473.

7 free. **Surface:** gravel. 01/01-31/12.
Distance: 1,5km 100m.
Remarks: Max. 48h.

Schwaigern 17A2

Wohnmobilstellplatz Schaigern, Gemminger Straße 91.
GPS: n49,14576 e9,04529.

2 free € 1/90liter Ch free.
Surface: asphalted. 01/01-31/12.
Distance: 1km 300m on the spot on the spot.

Schwetzingen 16H2

Ketscher Landstrasse. **GPS**: n49,37803 e8,55820.

12 free € 3/80liter Ch. **Location:** Rural, simple, noisy.
Surface: grasstiles/metalled. 01/01-31/12.
Distance: 500m on the spot on the spot 100m on the spot on the spot.
Remarks: Max. 3 nights.

Seelbach 19H1

Reisemobil-Wellness-Stellplatz Schwarzwälder Hof, Am Tretenbach.
GPS: n48,30042 e7,94497.

14 € 20 € 1/90liter Ch (14x)kWh WC .
Location: Rural, comfortable, noisy. **Surface:** grassy.
01/01-31/12.
Distance: 600m 100m.
Remarks: Including access to swimming pool, use sanitary facilities, entrance 1p wellness/sauna.

Seewald 16H3

P4, L362. **GPS**: n48,55131 e8,49522.

17 free WC free. **Location:** Rural, simple, quiet. **Surface:** asphalted.
01/01-31/12 service 01/11-31/03.
Distance: 1,5km 25m 600m.

Siggen 20C2

Siggener Höhe. **GPS**: n47,70676 e9,92568.
2 free. **Location:** Rural. **Surface:** asphalted. 01/01-31/12.
Distance: 1km 1km.
Remarks: Max. 2 nights.

Sigmaringen 20B1

Wohnmobilplatz Sigmaringen, Georg Zimmerer Straße 4.
GPS: n48,08545 e9,21029.

20 € 8 € 1/80liter Ch (20x)€ 1/4h.
Location: Simple. **Surface:** metalled. 01/01-31/12.
Distance: 500m 500m 200m on the spot.

Sindelfingen 17A3

Badezentrum Sindelfingen, Hohenzollernstrasse.
GPS: n48,71993 e9,01779.

10 free. **Location:** Urban, simple. **Surface:** asphalted.
01/01-31/12.
Distance: on the spot on the spot on the spot on the spot.

Singen 20A2

P Landesgartenschau, Schaffhauserstrasse.
GPS: n47,75992 e8,82766.

20 free Ch free (16x)€ 1/6h.
Surface: grassy/gravel. 01/01-31/12, service 15/03-15/11.
Distance: 1km on the spot 200m.
Remarks: Max. 72h.

Singen 20A2

Hallenbad, Waldeckstraße 4. **GPS**: n47,76472 e8,84781.
3 free. **Surface:** asphalted. 01/01-31/12.
Distance: 500m 500m 400m.
Remarks: At swimming pool.

Sinsheim 17A2

Wohnmobilpark Sinsheim, Am Ilvesbach.
GPS: n49,25022 e8,88002.

32 € 6 € 1/100liter Ch € 0,50/kWh included.
Location: Rural, simple, quiet. **Surface:** metalled.
01/01-31/12.
Distance: 500m 500m 300m.
Remarks: Discount at swimming pool.

Sternenfels 17A2

Diefenbach, Burrainstrasse, Diefenbach. **GPS**: n49,02440 e8,85535.
3 free. **Location:** Urban, simple. **Surface:** asphalted.
01/01-31/12.
Distance: 100m on the spot.

Stetten 20B2

Alte Brennerei, Riedetsweilerstrasse 5. **GPS**: n47,69326 e9,29788.

15 € 9 € 1 € 1 Ch (6x)€ 0,50/kWh WC.
Surface: grassy/gravel. 01/01-31/12.
Distance: 300m 2km 2km 300m 300m 300m.

Stockach/Bodensee 20A2

WoMo-Park Papiermühle, Johann-Glatt-strasse 3.
GPS: n47,84169 e8,99945.

85 € 12, 2 pers.incl € 0,50/50liter Ch (118x) WC included.
Surface: gravel/metalled. 01/01-31/12.
Distance: 1,5km on the spot 700m.
Remarks: Bread-service in summer period.

Sulz am Neckar 20A1

Stellplatz Wöhrd, Ludwigstraße. **GPS**: n48,36427 e8,63681.

6 free € 1/80liter € 1 Ch € 1 (6x)€ 0,50/kWh.
Location: Rural, simple, quiet. **Surface:** concrete.
01/01-31/12.
Distance: 300m 10km 100m 100m on the spot on the spot on the spot.

Sulzburg 19G2

Camping Sulzbachtal, Sonnmatt 4. **GPS**: n47,84773 e7,69868.

DE

10 € 15 + tourist and eco tax Ch (10x)€ 0,70/kWh WC included.
Location: Comfortable. **Surface:** grassy/gravel. 01/01-31/12.
Distance: 500m on the spot.

Tauberbischofsheim 17B1

P Freibad, Vittryallee. **GPS**: n49,62155 e9,66632.

3 free ChWCfree € 0,50,during opening hours.
Location: Rural, simple. **Surface:** asphalted. 01/01-31/12.
Distance: 500m 300m 100m 500m.
Remarks: Service at Kläranlage ma-do 7-16 uur.

Tettnang 20B2

Loretostrasse. **GPS**: n47,66425 e9,59175.

14 € 5 € 1 € 1 Ch€ 1 (8x)€ 1/8h.
Surface: grassy/metalled. 01/01-31/12.
Distance: 800m 200m 200m 200m.
Remarks: Max. 72h.

Tettnang 20B2

Gutshof Camping Badhütten, Badhütten, Laimnau. **GPS**: n47,63370 e9,64668.

70 € 20 € 1 Ch € 1/3kWh WC € 1. **Surface:** grassy. 01/01-31/12.

Titisee 19H2

Camping Bankenhof, Bruderhalde 31a, Hinterzarten. **GPS**: n47,88643 e8,13046.

8 € 14, 2 pers incl Ch WC included € 3/3 € 0,50/h.
Location: Rural, comfortable, quiet.
Surface: gravel/sand.
01/01-31/12.
Distance: 3km Titisee 600m on the spot on the spot 3km.

Remarks: Pay at reception.

Todtmoos 19H2

Jägermatt, Vordertodtmoos. **GPS**: n47,73390 e8,00285.

20 € 5 Chincluded. **Location:** Rural, simple, noisy.
Surface: gravel/metalled. 01/01-31/12.
Distance: 1km 50m.

Triberg im Schwarzwald 19H1

Sommerauer Strasse, Nußberg. **GPS**: n48,13161 e8,25294.

20 free. **Location:** Rural, simple. **Surface:** gravel. 01/01-31/12.
Distance: 2km on the spot.

Trochtelfingen 20B1

Eberhard-von Werderberg-Halle, Siemensstrasse. **GPS**: n48,30811 e9,23546.

20 € 3 € 1/80liter Ch (4x)free,16Amp.
Location: Urban, simple. **Surface:** gravel. 01/01-31/12.
Distance: Old city centre 500m 500m on the spot.
Remarks: To be paid at town hall.

Trochtelfingen 20B1

Kräuter- und Erlebnisgarten Alb-Gold Nudelfabrik, Grindel 1. **GPS**: n48,32838 e9,24001.

4 free. **Location:** Rural, simple, noisy. **Surface:** metalled. 01/01-31/12.
Distance: 3km on the spot on the spot on the spot.

Tuttlingen 20A1

Stellplatz Donaupark, Stuttgarter strasse. **GPS**: n47,98490 e8,81316.

12 free € 1/5minutes € 1 Ch. **Location:** Urban, simple.
Surface: metalled. 01/01-31/12.
Distance: 500m 500m 500m 500m Donauradweg.
Remarks: Max. 3 nights.

Überlingen 20A2

Reisemobilhafen Überlingen, Kurt-Hahn-strasse. **GPS**: n47,77617 e9,15046.

20 € 6-10 € 0,50/70liter € 0,50 Ch (30x)€ 0,50/2kWh WC.
Surface: asphalted/gravel. 01/01-31/12.
Distance: 1km 1km 1km 200m 1,5km 200m.
Remarks: Max. 3 days, price incl. bus transport (max. 5 pers) to the city centre.

Uhldingen-Mühlhofen 20B2

Stellplatz zum See, Ehbachstrasse 1. **GPS**: n47,72535 e9,23649.

21 8-18h € 1,50/h, max. € 6, night € 10 WC.
Surface: grasstiles/metalled. 01/03-31/10.
Distance: 1km 800m 2km kiosk on the spot 300m.
Remarks: Max. 24h.

Ulm 17C3

P+R Friedrichsau, Wielandstraße 74. **GPS**: n48,40774 e10,00929.

50 free € 1 Ch. **Location:** Urban, simple, central.
Surface: metalled. 01/01-31/12.
Distance: 200m on the spot.
Remarks: Max. 3 days, green zone: environmental badge obligatory.

Ummendorf 20B1

Bräuhaus Ummendorf, Bachstrasse 10. **GPS**: n48,06340 e9,83252.

5 free (5x)€ 3/day WC € 3.
Surface: metalled. 01/01-31/12.
Distance: 300m on the spot 800m 100m.
Remarks: 3 days free stay.

Unterkirnach 19H1

Reisemobilhafen Am Rathaus, Rathausplatz. **GPS**: n48,07719 e8,36707.

DE

17 € 11 included,6Amp.
Location: Urban, luxurious, quiet. **Surface:** gravel.
01/01-31/12.
Distance: on the spot 400m 500m 200m 300m 200m 150m 400m.
Remarks: Pay at tourist office, alternative arrangement if full.

S Unterkirnach 19H1

Ackerloch-Grillschopf, Unteres Ackerloch 2.
GPS: n48,08473 e8,36573.

20 € 5, tourist tax € 2,10/pp Ch WC included.
Location: Rural, simple. **Surface:** unpaved.
01/01-31/12 Nov.
Distance: 1,5km on the spot on the spot on the spot on the spot.

S Untermünkheim 17B2

Wohnmobilpark Ostertag, Kupfer Straße 20, Übrigshausen.
GPS: n49,17603 e9,71321.

10 € 8 € 0,50 Ch € 0,50 € 1. **Location:** Rural, comfortable. **Surface:** grassy/gravel. 01/03-30/11.
Distance: 50m.
Remarks: At manege.

Unteröwisheim 17A2

Muhlweg. **GPS**: n49,14306 e8,67250.

2 free. **Location:** Simple, quiet. **Surface:** gravel.
01/01-31/12.
Distance: 500m on the spot.

S Uttenweiler 20B1

Naturfreibad, Weiherstrasse. **GPS**: n48,13814 e9,61962.
6 € 6 Ch free € 0,50/kWh. **Location:** Rural.
Surface: grassy/gravel. 01/05-01/11.
Distance: 600m on the spot 600m.

S Villingen/Schwenningen 20A1

Messegelände, Waldeckweg. **GPS**: n48,04771 e8,53869.

4 free € 1 Ch. **Location:** Urban, simple, noisy.
Surface: asphalted. 01/01-31/12.
Distance: 1km 500m.

Vogt 20B2

Sirgensteinhalle, Schützenweg. **GPS**: n47,77601 e9,77001.
3 free. **Surface:** unpaved. 01/01-31/12.
Distance: on the spot 200m 300m.
Remarks: Max. 3 days.

Vogtsburg im Kaiserstuhl 19G1

Hauptstraße/L115, Oberrotweil. **GPS**: n48,09000 e7,64361.

8 free. **Location:** Rural, simple, isolated, quiet.
01/01-31/12.
Distance: 800m 50m on the spot on the spot.
Remarks: At swimming pool.

S Waiblingen 17B3

Parkplatz Hallenbad, An der Talaue. **GPS**: n48,83029 e9,32540.

20 € 8/24h € 1/80liter Ch (6x)€ 1/8h WC.
Location: Urban. **Surface:** gravel. 01/01-31/12.
Distance: 500m 500m 50m 300m 600m.
Remarks: Parking swimming pool, max. 3 nights, during congresses special tariff.

Waldburg 20B2

Am Waldburger, Amtzeller Straße. **GPS**: n47,75800 e9,71672.
3 free. **Surface:** unpaved. 01/01-31/12.
Distance: 200m 300m 300m.
Remarks: Next to sports fields, max. 3 nights.

S Waldkirch 19H1

Wohnmobilstellplatz Waldkirch, Am Stadtrain.
GPS: n48,09023 e7,95833.

10 free € 1/80liter Ch. **Location:** Urban, simple, central.
Surface: concrete. 01/01-31/12.
Distance: 500m on the spot.
Remarks: Max. 2 days.

S Waldshut-Tiengen 19H2

Wohnmobil-Park Waldshut-Tiengen, Jahnweg 22, Waldshut.
GPS: n47,61121 e8,22513.

44 € 12 € 1/100liter Ch € 1/kWh € 0,50.
Location: Urban, luxurious, quiet. **Surface:** metalled.
01/01-31/12.
Distance: on the spot.
Remarks: Along the Rhine river, bread-service.

S Walldürn 17B1

Basilikaplatz, Hauptstrasse. **GPS**: n49,58637 e9,36726.

8 free € 1/80liter Ch (4x)€ 0,50/kWh.
Location: Rural, simple. **Surface:** gravel. 01/01-31/12.
Distance: 250m 400m.
Remarks: Pilgrimage site.

S Walldürn 17B1

Goldschmitt Technik-Center, Industrieparkstrasse.
GPS: n49,58977 e9,39339.

30 free € 1/80liter Ch (18x)€ 0,50/kWh.
Location: Rural, comfortable. **Surface:** asphalted/gravel.
01/01-31/12.
Distance: 2,6km 100m.
Remarks: Baker every morning.

S Wangen im Allgäu 20B2

P17, Am Klösterle. **GPS**: n47,68160 e9,83401.

40 € 7 + € 1,60/pp tourist tax € 0,50/120liter € 0,50 Ch € 0,50 (46x) WC. **Surface:** metalled. 01/01-31/12.
Distance: on the spot 500m 500m on the spot on the spot on the spot.

Tourist information Wangen im Allgäu:

Tourist Information, Parkplatz 1, Rathaus. Traditional small Bavarian town. Every Thursday city walk through historical city centre, 10.30-12h. € 5.
Wed.

S Wehr 19H2

Ludingarten. **GPS**: n47,62515 e7,90582.

DE

7 € 10/24h € 1/100liter Ch (8x)€ 1/8h WC.
Location: Simple, quiet. **Surface:** metalled. 01/01-31/12.
Distance: nearby.
Remarks: Pay at tourist office, Hauptstr. 14 or Bistro Gleis 13, Bahnhofplatz.

S Weikersheim 17B1

Campingplatz Schwabenmühle, Weikersheimer Strasse 21, Laudenbach. **GPS**: n49,45795 e9,92691.

6 € 7 € 1/80liter Ch (6x)€ 1/6h .
Location: Rural, simple. **Surface:** gravel. Easter-15/10.
Distance: 300m 200m.

S Weil der Stadt 17A3

Festplatz, Jahnstrasse. **GPS**: n48,75268 e8,87453.

4 free € 1 € 1 Ch (4x)€ 1/4h. **Location:** Urban, simple, noisy. **Surface:** asphalted. 01/01-31/12.
Distance: 300m 300m 250m on the spot on the spot.
Remarks: Max. 3 days.

S Weilheim 19H2

Gret-Stube, Fohrenbachstraße 5, Nöggenschwiel.
GPS: n47,69252 e8,21349.

4 € 12 Ch included.
Location: Rural. **Surface:** gravel. 01/01-31/12.
Distance: on the spot on the spot.
Remarks: Breakfast-service.

S Weingarten 20B2

Festplatz, Abt Hyller Strasse 55. **GPS**: n47,81009 e9,63041.
8 € 5 € 1 € 1 Ch € 2.
Surface: metalled. 01/01-31/12.
Distance: 1km 500m on the spot on the spot.
Remarks: Max. 3 nights.

Weinheim 17A1

Am Miramar, Waidallee. **GPS**: n49,53378 e8,64473.
5 free. **Location:** Rural, simple, noisy. **Surface:** asphalted.
01/01-31/12.
Distance: 350m.
Remarks: At paradise pool.

S Weinsberg 17A2

Eugen-Diez-Straße 2. **GPS**: n49,14846 e9,28464.

13 free € 1/100liter Ch (6x)€ 0,50/kWh free.
Location: Rural, quiet. **Surface:** grasstiles. 01/01-31/12.
Distance: 500m 2km 50m on the spot on the spot.

S Welzheim 17B2

Aichstruter Stausee, Seiboldsweiler, Aichstrut.
GPS: n48,90020 e9,63719.

9 € 5 € 1/80liter ChWC.
Surface: gravel. 01/01-31/12.
Distance: 5km on the spot on the spot on the spot.
Remarks: At artificial lake, max. 1 week.

S Welzheim 17B2

Am Bahnhof, Bahnhofstraße. **GPS**: n48,87256 e9,63053.
3 free. 01/01-31/12.
Distance: 400m 400m.
Remarks: Max. 3 days.

Welzheim 17B2

Am Stadtpark, Tannwaldweg. **GPS**: n48,86780 e9,63183.
2 free. 01/01-31/12.
Distance: 700m on the spot.

S Wertheim 17B1

Wohnmobilstellplatz An der Taubermündung, Linke Tauberstrasse.
GPS: n49,76501 e9,51213.

54 € 7/24h € 1/90liter Ch.
Location: Rural, simple, noisy. **Surface:** gravel.
01/01-31/12 2nd sa of the month + high water.
Distance: 500m on the spot.
Remarks: Along the Tauber river, max. 3 days.

S Wertheim 17B1

Erwin Hymer World, Hymerring 1. **GPS**: n49,77368 e9,58034.

90 free € 1/90liter Ch € 1/3h WC during opening hours.
Location: Rural, comfortable. **Surface:** asphalted.
01/01-31/12.
Distance: 400m 3,7km.
Remarks: Baker at 8am, Wertheim Outletcentrum 100m.

Tourist information Wertheim:
Wertheim Village, Almosenberg. Outlet-shopping.

S Wildberg 17A3

Wohnmobilstellplatz Wildberg, Klosterhof 4.
GPS: n48,62055 e8,74485.

4 free € 1/50liter Ch € 1/kWh.
Location: Quiet. **Surface:** asphalted/metalled.
01/01-31/12 service: 01/11-01/03.
Distance: historical centre 500m 700m 1km on the spot.
Remarks: Along river, nearby monastery.

S Wolfach 19H1

Ferienhof Bartleshof, Ippichen 6, Ippichen.
GPS: n48,30183 e8,26264.

3 € 15 Ch (3x) € 2. **Location:** Rural, simple, quiet.
Surface: grassy/gravel. 01/01-31/12.
Distance: on the spot on the spot.

S Wolfach 19H1

Trendcamping Schwarzwald, Schiltacher Straße 80, Halbmeil.
GPS: n48,29053 e8,27763.

6 € 18, 2 pers.incl ChWC included € 3 € 2
Location: Rural, simple, quiet. **Surface:** grassy/sand.
10/04-15/10.
Distance: on the spot.

S Wolfegg/Allgäu 20B2

Reisemobilhafen Loretopark, Rötenbacher Straße.
GPS: n47,81489 e9,79802.
12 € 5 € 1/80liter Ch € 0,50/kWh. 01/01-31/12.
Distance: 500m 700m.
Remarks: Max. 5 days.

Wolfegg/Allgäu 20B2

Hofgarten, Alttaner strasse. **GPS**: n47,82105 e9,79487.

2 € 5. **Surface:** gravel/metalled. 01/01-31/12.
Distance: on the spot.
Remarks: Max. 2 nights.

Wolfegg/Allgäu 20B2

Gasthof Post, Röthenbacher Straße 5. **GPS**: n47,81994 e9,79420.
4 free.
01/01-31/12.
Distance: 400m 50m.

Tourist information Wolfegg/Allgäu:
M Automobilmuseum. 200 oldtimers. 01/04-31/10 9.30-18h, 01/11-31/03 Su 10-17h.
M Bauernhaus-museum. Open air museum. 01/04-31/10 Tue-Su 10-18/17h Mo Apr Oct.

DE

S Wutöschingen 19H2

Wohnmobilplatz Degernau, Ofteringer Strasse 1, Degernau. **GPS**: n47,66639 e8,37917.

9 € 8/day, 2 pers.incl € 1/100liter Ch € 2/kWh,16Amp WC € 1 € 3/3. **Location:** Rural, comfortable, quiet. **Surface:** grassy/gravel. 01/04-31/10.
Distance: on the spot 200m 1km 500m on the spot on the spot on the spot.
Remarks: Arrival <20h, sauna, solarium.

S Zaberfeld 17A2

An der Ehmetsklinge, Seestrasse. **GPS**: n49,05607 e8,91646.
3 free against payment Ch € 0,50/kWh. **Location:** Rural. **Surface:** metalled. 01/01-31/12.
Distance: 250m on the spot on the spot on the spot 250m on the spot on the spot.

S Zell am Harmersbach 19H1

Stellplatz Zell am Harmersbach, Nordracher Strasse. **GPS**: n48,35146 e8,05942.

14 € 5 € 1/10minutes Ch (8x)€ 2/12h. **Location:** Rural, simple, quiet. **Surface:** gravel. 01/01-31/12.
Distance: 2km 2km.

Bavaria

S Absberg 17D2

Badehalbinsel Brombachsee, Gunzenhausen-Pleinfeld Ausfart Absberg. **GPS**: n49,13770 e10,87389.

240 € 12/24h € 0,20/60liter Ch (80x)€ 0,50/kWh WC € 0,50. **Location:** Rural, comfortable, quiet. **Surface:** grassy. 01/04-01/10.
Distance: 1km on the spot on the spot 1km on the spot on the spot.
Remarks: Bread-service.

Ahorn 12D3

Freizeitzentrum Wittmannsberg, Badstrasse 20, Eicha. **GPS**: n50,22537 e10,90252.

4 free. **Location:** Rural, simple. **Surface:** metalled. 01/01-31/12.
Distance: on the spot 600m 5km.

S Aichach 17D3

Reisemobilplatz, Franz-Beck-Strasse. **GPS**: n48,45889 e11,12611.

4 € 5 Ch free. **Location:** Urban, simple, quiet. **Surface:** grassy/gravel. 01/01-31/12.
Distance: 500m 500m 100m.

S Albertshofen 17C1

An der Fähre Mainstockheim-Albertshofen, Mainstraße. **GPS**: n49,77254 e10,15749.

10 € 5 Ch included. **Location:** Rural, simple, quiet. **Surface:** gravel. 01/01-31/12.
Distance: on the spot on the spot on the spot 50m on the spot.
Remarks: Along Main river, closed when high water.

S Altmannstein 17E2

Gasthof Forster, Schulstrasse 9. **GPS**: n48,90125 e11,69559.

20 guests free (4x)€ 2/night. **Surface:** asphalted. 01/01-31/12.
Distance: on the spot on the spot 3km.
Remarks: Bread-service, check in before 19h (Mo-Tue 16h).

S Altötting 20G1

P2 Dultplatz, Traunsteinerstrasse. **GPS**: n48,22287 e12,67921.

8 free € 1/10liter (8x)€ 1/4h. **Location:** Urban, simple, central. **Surface:** gravel. 01/01-31/12.
Distance: 700m 300m 300m 250m.
Remarks: Max. 3 days.

S Altötting 20G1

Wohnmobilstellplatz am Parkplatz, Griesstraße. **GPS**: n48,22946 e12,67493.

8 free € 1/80liter Ch (8x)€ 1/4h WC.

Location: Urban, simple, noisy. **Surface:** grasstiles. 01/01-31/12.
Distance: 600m 200m on the spot.
Remarks: Max. 3 days.

S Altusried 20C2

Am Freibad, Im Tal 4. **GPS**: n47,79915 e10,21934.

10 € 10-5 € 1 Ch € 0,50/kWh. **Location:** Rural, simple, quiet. **Surface:** grassy/gravel. 01/01-31/12.
Distance: 500m 700m.
Remarks: Parking at swimming pool, max. 3 days.

S Amberg 17E1

Gasfabrikstraße. **GPS**: n49,44043 e11,86198.

10 free (12x)€ 1/12h. **Location:** Urban, simple, central, quiet. **Surface:** asphalted. 01/01-31/12.
Distance: 500m 50m 1km 1km 50m 50m.

Amorbach 17A1

P Altstadt, Dr.F.A.Freundt-Straße. **GPS**: n49,64683 e9,22115.

5 free. **Location:** Urban, simple. **Surface:** asphalted. 01/01-31/12.
Distance: 500m 400m Lidl 300m on the spot on the spot.

S Andechs 20D1

Wohnmobilstellplatz Kloster Andechs, Seefelder Straße. **GPS**: n47,97530 e11,18551.

40 € 12 Ch included € 3. **Surface:** metalled. 01/01-31/12.
Distance: on the spot on the spot.
Remarks: Nearby monastery, bread-service.

S Ansbach 17C2

Freizeitbad Aquella, Am Stadion 2. **GPS**: n49,30459 e10,55852.

DE

12 free € 0,50/50liter Ch (12x)€ 0,50/kWh.
Location: Simple, central. **Surface:** metalled.
01/01-31/12.
Distance: 1km 7,7km on the spot 1km on the spot.
Remarks: At swimming pool, max. 3 days.

Ansbach 17C2

Freizeitwelt Nagel, Faunstraße 7. **GPS:** n49,25444 e10,59306.
8 free . **Surface:** gravel. 01/01-31/12.
Distance: 500m 2km.
Remarks: At motorhome dealer.

Arnbruck 17G2

Landhotel Rappenhof, Rappendorf 5. **GPS:** n49,13517 e12,95069.

5 € 10 Ch € 5 WC included. **Location:** Simple.
Surface: grassy. 01/01-31/12 15/11-15/12.
Distance: 2km on the spot 2km 10km 8km.
Remarks: Use of sauna against payment.

Arnstein 12B3

Badesee, Am Alten Schwimmbad. **GPS:** n49,97667 e9,95917.

12 free € 1/80liter Ch (4x)€ 1/2kWh.
Location: Rural, simple, quiet. **Surface:** grassy/metalled.
01/01-31/12, service 01/04-31/10.
Distance: 500m 100m 100m snack 100m 500m on the spot.
Remarks: At the old swimming pool.

Arnstein 12B3

Cancale Platz. **GPS:** n49,97637 e9,96725.

5 free. **Location:** Urban. **Surface:** metalled. 01/01-31/12.
Distance: 100m 100m 100m.
Remarks: Max. 1 night.

Arzberg 12E3

Am Rathausplatz. **GPS:** n50,05528 e12,18870.
2 free WC. **Surface:** metalled. 01/01-31/12.
Distance: 250m 300m 250m.

Aschaffenburg 12A3

Willigesbrücke, Grossostheimerstrasse. **GPS:** n49,97139 e9,13722.

25 € 3/24h (18x)€ 0,50/kWh. **Location:** Urban, simple, quiet.
Surface: grassy/gravel. 01/01-31/12.
Distance: historical centre 500m 8km on the spot on the spot.
Remarks: Parking along the Main, near Altstadt, being indicated with small signs, max. 3 days.

Aschheim 20E1

Gasthof Zur Post, Ismaningerstrasse 11. **GPS:** n48,17433 e11,71490.

2 € 10. **Surface:** asphalted. 01/01-31/12.
Distance: on the spot on the spot 300m.

Auerbach 17E1

Franz-Josef-Strauß-Platz, Hopfenoher Straße.
GPS: n49,69171 e11,63768.

3 free. **Location:** Simple. **Surface:** grassy. 01/01-31/12.
Distance: 500m 500m 500m.

Aufseß 12D3

Brauerei-Gasthof Reichold, Hochstahl 24.
GPS: n49,88389 e11,26855.

38 € 7 € 1/90liter Ch (38x)€ 1,50 WC € 1.
Location: Rural, comfortable, quiet. **Surface:** grassy/metalled.
01/01-31/12.
Distance: on the spot on the spot on the spot on the spot Brauereienweg.
Remarks: Bread-service, breakfast buffet € 8/pp.

Aufseß 12D3

Brauerei Rothenbach, Im Tal 70. **GPS:** n49,88413 e11,22781.

3 € 5 . **Location:** Urban, simple. **Surface:** metalled.
01/03-30/10.
Distance: on the spot on the spot on the spot on the spot on the spot.

Augsburg 17D3

Schillstraße 109, Lechhausen. **GPS:** n48,38914 e10,90435.

4 € 7 € 1/4minutes Ch € 1/2kWh WC .
Location: Urban, simple, central. **Surface:** gravel.
01/01-31/12.
Distance: 3,2km Sportgaststätte 250m 200m on the spot on the spot.
Remarks: At sports centre.

Augsburg 17D3

Wohnmobilstellplatz Wertach, Bürgemeister Ackermann strasse 1.
GPS: n48,36944 e10,87750.

15 € 8 € 1/90liter Ch (6x)€ 2/kWh.
Location: Urban, simple, noisy. **Surface:** gravel. 01/01-31/12.
Distance: on the spot 4,5km on the spot on the spot 500m 500m on the spot on the spot.

Bad Abbach 17E2

Kaiser-Therme, Kurallee 4. **GPS:** n48,92712 e12,04044.

34 € 10 + € 1,80/pp € 1/4minutes Ch (16x) WC .
Surface: grasstiles/grassy. 01/01-31/12.
Distance: 2km.
Remarks: Check in at pay-desk of the Therme.

Bad Aibling 20F1

Stellplatz an der Therme P13, Lindenstrasse/Heubergstrasse.
GPS: n47,85639 e12,00583.

31 € 10 € 0,50/80liter Ch (20x)included.
Location: Rural, comfortable. **Surface:** grasstiles/metalled.
01/01-31/12.
Distance: 500m 400m 500m 600m 100m.
Remarks: Use sanitary only during opening hours.

Bad Bayersoien 20D2

Wohnmobilstellplatz Bad Bayersoien, Am Bahnhof 6.
GPS: n47,68798 e10,99820.

DE

8 € 9/24h € 1/90liter Ch (12x)€ 1/2kWh.
Location: Rural, simple, quiet. **Surface:** gravel.
01/01-31/12.
Distance: 400m 300m 300m 400m 400m.

Bad Birnbach 17G3

Camping Arterhof, Hauptstraße 3, Lengham.
GPS: n48,43512 e13,10939.

10 € 10 ChWC included.
Location: Rural, simple, quiet. **Surface:** gravel. 01/01-31/12.
Distance: on the spot.

Bad Bocklet 12B3

Kurgarten, Aschacherstrasse. **GPS**: n50,26490 e10,07486.

13 € 8, tourist tax incl € 1/80liter Ch (13x)€ 0,50/kWh . **Location:** Rural, comfortable, quiet. **Surface:** metalled.
01/01-31/12.
Distance: 500m Free bus to Bad Kissingen.
Remarks: Pay at midgetgolf.

Bad Brückenau 12B3

Schlosspark König Ludwig I, Schlüchterner Straße.
GPS: n50,30556 e9,74861.

10 € 8 + € 2,80/pp tourist tax € 1/100liter Ch (10x)€ 0,50/kWh. **Location:** Urban, comfortable, quiet. **Surface:** asphalted.
01/01-31/12.
Distance: 4km 50m.

Bad Brückenau 12B3

Sinnflut, Industriestrasse P5. **GPS**: n50,31212 e9,79607.

10 € 3 + tourist tax € 2,50/pp € 1/100liter Ch (8x)€ 1/8h.
Location: Urban, simple, noisy. **Surface:** gravel.
01/01-31/12.
Distance: 250m 250m 250m.
Remarks: Nearby swimming pool.

Bad Brückenau 12B3

Stellplatz Bahnhofstrasse, Buchwaldstrasse.
GPS: n50,30667 e9,78556.

20 € 3 + tourist tax € 2,50/pp (10x)€ 1/8h.
Location: Urban, simple, noisy. **Surface:** metalled.
01/01-31/12.
Distance: 300m on the spot on the spot on the spot on the spot on the spot.

Bad Feilnbach 20F2

Gasthof Tiroler Hof, Aiblinger strasse 95.
GPS: n47,76476 e12,03857.

3 guests free. **Location:** Simple. **Surface:** gravel.
01/01-31/12.
Distance: on the spot on the spot 1km.

Bad Füssing 17G3

Campingplatz Holmerhof, Am Tennispark 10.
GPS: n48,35798 e13,30658.

9 € 12 + € 2,90/pp tourist tax € 1/80liter Ch (12x)€ 1/2kWh WC € 2.
Location: Rural, simple. **Surface:** metalled. 01/01-31/12.
Distance: 1km on the spot 1km.
Remarks: Max. 3 days, use sanitary € 5/motorhome, swimming pool available.

Bad Gögging 17E2

Limes-Therme, Am Brunnenforum 1. **GPS**: n48,81857 e11,78868.

+20 € 6, tourist tax € 1,80/pp € 0,50/50liter Ch .
Location: Simple. **Surface:** asphalted. 01/01-31/12.
Distance: 150m 150m 150m.
Remarks: Check in at pay-desk of the Therme.

Bad Griesbach 17G3

Mobilhafen Dreiquellenbad, Singham 40.
GPS: n48,42023 e13,19261.

29 € 17,50, tourist tax incl € 1/80liter Ch (29x)€ 0,60/kWh € 5. **Location:** Rural, simple, quiet. **Surface:** metalled.
01/01-31/12.
Distance: 2km on the spot.
Remarks: Max. 3 days, thermal-Vital-Oase incl.

Bad Hindelang 20C2

Wiesengrund Wohnmobilpark, Parkplatz Wiesengrund 1.
GPS: n47,49931 e10,37218.

30 € 10-16, tourist tax € 2,10/pp, child 7><16 € 0,90 € 1/100liter Ch € 0,50/kWh WC € 1 . **Location:** Rural, luxurious, quiet. **Surface:** grassy/gravel. 01/01-31/12.
Distance: centre 500m on the spot 1km on the spot 3km 3km.

Bad Hindelang 20C2

Wohnmobilplatz Bergheimat, Passstraße 60, Oberjoch.
GPS: n47,51791 e10,42142.

10 € 15, dog € 3,50 Ch € 0,80/kWh WC € 1 .
Location: Rural, simple, noisy. **Surface:** grassy/gravel.
01/01-31/12.
Distance: on the spot on the spot.

Bad Kissingen 12B3

KissSalis Therme, Heiligenfelder Allee 16.
GPS: n50,18861 e10,06139.

18 € 4 + € 3,50/pp tourist tax € 1/10minutes Ch (18x)€ 1/8h. **Location:** Rural, comfortable, quiet.
Surface: asphalted. 01/01-31/12.
Distance: 500m on the spot on the spot on the spot on the spot.
Remarks: Pay at pay-desk of theTherme.

Bad Kohlgrub 20D2

Kurhotel Lauter im Park, Kurhausstrasse 81.
GPS: n47,66412 e11,04315.

DE

4 € 15. **Location:** Rural, simple, quiet. **Surface:** gravel.
01/01-31/12.
Distance: 1,5km on the spot 1,5km 1km 1km.

Bad Kohlgrub 20D2

Campingoase Reindl, Sonnen 93. **GPS**: n47,65789 e11,04393.

16 € 16,40, 2 pers. incl., dog € 1 Ch € 0,40/kWh WC € 2,50. **Surface:** gravel. 01/01-31/12.
Distance: 1,5km 1,5km.

Bad Königshofen 12C3

Frankentherme, Am Kurzentrum 1. **GPS**: n50,30174 e10,47654.

77 € 11 € 1/80liter Ch (77x)€ 0,50/kWh WC € 0,50 € 3 € 3/2h.
Location: Urban, luxurious. **Surface:** grasstiles/metalled.
01/01-31/12.
Distance: on the spot on the spot 500m on the spot 500m 500m.
Remarks: Caution key sanitary € 20, if full 2 alternatives will be given, special health arrangement possible.

Tourist information Bad Königshofen:
Kurverwaltung Königshofen, Am Kurzentrum 1, www.bad-koenig-shofen.de. Traditional small town with half-timbered houses, cycle and hiking routes in the surroundings.

Bad Kötztingen 17G2

Aqacur, Bgm. Seidl Platz. **GPS**: n49,17539 e12,86196.

54 € 8 € 1/80liter Ch (48x)included.
Location: Rural, comfortable, quiet. **Surface:** grasstiles.
01/01-31/12.
Distance: 500m on the spot on the spot.

Bad Reichenhall 20G2

Wohnmobilpark an der RupertusTherme, Hammerschmiedweg.
GPS: n47,73466 e12,87536.

25 € 14, 2 pers incl € 1/80liter Ch included.
Location: Comfortable. **Surface:** asphalted. 01/01-31/12.
Distance: 500m 5km 600m 800m on the spot on the spot on the spot.
Remarks: Bicycle rental.

Bad Rodach 12C2

ThermeNatur Bad Rodach, Thermalbadstrasse.
GPS: n50,33452 e10,77499.

70 € 10 € 1/100liter Ch (70x)€ 0,60/kWh WC € 2/30minutes. **Location:** Urban, comfortable.
Surface: gravel/metalled. 01/01-31/12, water: 01/04-30/09.
Distance: 1km on the spot 500m on the spot.
Remarks: Bread-service, key service at swimming pool.

Bad Staffelstein 12D3

Stellplatz Obermain-Therme, Seestraße 3.
GPS: n50,10766 e10,99202.

27 € 11 € 0,50/40liter Ch (8x)€ 0,50/kWh WC included.
Location: Comfortable, quiet. **Surface:** metalled.
01/01-31/12.
Distance: 1km 1,5km on the spot 1,5km on the spot on the spot on the spot.
Remarks: Max. 4 nights, bread-service.

Bad Steben 12E2

An der Therme, P3, Steinbacher Straße. **GPS**: n50,36250 e11,63239.

3 free € 1 Ch € 1/8h. **Location:** Urban, simple.
Surface: metalled. 01/01-31/12.
Distance: 50m.

Bad Neustadt 12C2

Parkplatz An der Saale, Mühlbacher Straße.
GPS: n50,31637 e10,22205.

24 € 6 + € 2,90/pp tourist tax € 0,10/10liter Ch € 0,60/kWh WC € 3. **Surface:** metalled. 01/01-31/12.
Distance: 500m 200m 500m.
Remarks: Bread-service.

Bad Tölz 20E2

Bürgermeister Stohlreiterpromenade. **GPS**: n47,76252 e11,55142.

30 € 8/24h € 1/50liter Ch.
Location: Rural, simple. **Surface:** asphalted. 01/01-31/12.
Distance: 1km on the spot on the spot 500m 500m 500m.
Remarks: Max. 48h, incl. Kurkarte.

Tourist information Bad Tölz:
Alpamare. Large swimming pool complex with wave machine, Alpa, slides, sauna etc. Su-Thu 8-21h, Fri-Sa 8-22h, 24/12-01/01 8-16h.

Bad Windsheim 17C1

Phoenix Reisemobilhafen, Bad Windsheimer Strasse 7.
GPS: n49,51361 e10,41722.

100 € 10 + € 2,60/pp tourist tax € 1/80liter Ch (80x)€ 0,50/kWh WC € 0,50/4minutes € 2,50/2,50.
Location: Comfortable, quiet. **Surface:** gravel. 01/01-31/12.
Distance: 1km 100m 500m 1km.
Remarks: Bread-service.

Bad Windsheim 17C1

Fränkisches Freilandmuseum, Eisweiherweg.
GPS: n49,49705 e10,41667.

40 € 5 + € 2/pp tourist tax.
Location: Simple. **Surface:** grassy. 01/01-31/12.
Distance: 1km 500m 500m.
Remarks: Open air museum.

Bad Wörishofen 20D1

Therme Bad Wörishofen, Thermenallee 1.
GPS: n48,02120 e10,59100.

DE

25 € 9 € 1/100liter Ch WC included.
Location: Urban, simple. **Surface:** asphalted. 01/01-31/12.
Distance: 1,5km 4,3km on the spot 500m on the spot.
Remarks: Check in at pay-desk of the Therme, max. 3 nights, max. 8M, bread-service.

Balderschwang 20C2

Wohnmobilplatz Schwabenhof, Schwabenhof 23.
GPS: n47,45745 e10,12963.

56 € 12-17 + € 1,10/pp tourist tax € 0,50 Ch € 4/day WC € 0,50/5minutes.
Location: Rural, comfortable. **Surface:** grassy/gravel.
01/01-31/12.
Distance: 3km on the spot 3km 100m 100m 100m.
Remarks: Bread-service, drying room for skis.

Bamberg 12D3

Wohnmobilplatz, Am Heinrichsdamm. **GPS**: n49,88626 e10,90296.

25 € 12 € 1/100liter Ch € 0,50/kWh.
Location: Urban, simple. **Surface:** gravel. 01/01-31/12.
Distance: 10 min walking on the spot on the spot on the spot.
Remarks: Max. 24h.

Bärnau 12F3

Gasthof und Wald-Pension Blei, Altglashütte 4.
GPS: n49,77222 e12,38880.

30 € 10, guests free Ch WC included.
Surface: asphalted/grassy. 01/01-31/12.
Distance: 6km on the spot 6km 100m.

Baunach 12D3

Sportplatz-Festplatz, Bahnhofstrasse 14-4.
GPS: n49,98750 e10,85444.

12 free € 1/80liter Ch € 1/6h. **Location:** Rural, central, quiet. **Surface:** grassy/metalled. 01/01-31/12.
Distance: 200m 1km 200m 200m 200m on the spot on the spot.
Remarks: Parking at the edge of nature reserve Haßberge, in the old part of the city, max. 2 nights.

Bayerbach 17G3

Wohnmobilhafen Vital, Huckenham 11.
GPS: n48,41537 e13,13010.

10 € 12,50 2 pers.incl, dog € 2,50 Ch (8x)€ 0,60/kWh WC included € 1. **Location:** Rural, simple, quiet.
Surface: metalled. 01/01-31/12.
Distance: 500m on the spot.
Remarks: Max. 3 nights, use sanitary facilities at campsite.

Bayreuth 12E3

P6 Stadthalle, Jean-Paul strasse. **GPS**: n49,94028 e11,57639.

3 € 0,60/30min, max € 10. **Location:** Urban, simple, noisy.
Surface: metalled. 01/01-31/12.
Distance: on the spot 200m 200m.

Bayreuth 12E3

Lohengrin Therme Bayreuth, Kurpormenade 5.
GPS: n49,94204 e11,63493.

24 € 6 € 1/50liter € 1 Ch € 1 € 1/6h WC € 1,50.
Location: Rural, simple, central, quiet. **Surface:** asphalted.
01/01-31/12.
Distance: 1,5km 3,5km 500m 1km on the spot on the spot on the spot.
Remarks: Bread-service.

Bayrischzell 20F2

Wohnmobilstellplatz Bayrischzell, Seebergstraße.
GPS: n47,67189 e12,01023.

20 € 10 € 0,50/80liter Ch (12x)€ 0,50/kWh.
Location: Comfortable, central. **Surface:** gravel.
01/01-31/12.
Distance: 400m 400m 400m 400m bus 5min on the spot.

Beilngries 17E2

Landgasthof Euringer, Dorfstrasse 23. **GPS**: n49,01054 e11,50261.

6 guests free Ch. **Location:** Urban, simple, central.
Surface: metalled. 01/01-31/12.
Distance: 4km on the spot 4km.

Beilngries 17E2

An der Altmühl, An der Altmühl 24. **GPS**: n49,02649 e11,47079.

20 € 14 Ch WC included. **Location:** Urban, comfortable, central, quiet. **Surface:** grassy. 01/03-31/10.
Remarks: Check in at reception campsite.

Benediktbeuern 20E2

Wohnmobilstellplatz am Sportzentrum, Schwimmbadstraße 37.
GPS: n47,69920 e11,41556.

16 € 7 € 1 € 1 Ch € 2/12h. **Location:** Rural, comfortable, quiet. **Surface:** asphalted. 01/04-31/10.
Distance: 1km. **Remarks:** Max. 3 nights, Alpenwarmbad 01/05-01/09 (swimming pool).

Beratzhausen 17E2

Landgasthof Friesenmühle, Friesenmühle 1.
GPS: n49,08534 e11,81176.

10 free, use of a meal desired (2x) WC.
Surface: grassy/gravel. 01/01-31/12 Wed.
Distance: 1km on the spot 1km.
Remarks: Motorhome service: volutary contribution, apply< 22h.

DE

Berching 17E2

Wohnmobilstellplatz an der Schiffsanlegestelle, Uferpromenade.
GPS: n49,10972 e11,43910.
15 free, 01/04-31/10 € 5 € 1 Ch € 1/8h.
Surface: grasstiles/metalled. 01/01-31/12.
Distance: 200m 50m on the spot 300m 100m.

Berchtesgaden 20G2

Reisemobilplatz Rasp, Renothenweg 15, Oberau.
GPS: n47,65026 e13,07037.

20 € 8 + € 2,10/pp tourist tax € 2 Ch € 2 WC.
Location: Rural, central, quiet. **Surface:** gravel.
Easter-30/11.
Distance: 500m 500m on the spot.

Bergen/Chiemgau 20F1

Parkplatz Hochfelln-Seilbahn, Maria-Eck-Straße 8.
GPS: n47,79710 e12,59079.

10 € 4. **Location:** Simple. **Surface:** metalled.
01/01-31/12.
Distance: 1,2km on the spot 500m on the spot.
Remarks: Parking ski-lift, max. 1 night.

Bergrheinfeld 12C3

GPS: n49,97096 e10,17449.

15 free. **Location:** Rural, simple, quiet. **Surface:** gravel.
01/01-31/12.
Distance: 200m on the spot on the spot 200m on the spot on the spot.

Bernau am Chiemsee 20F1

Am Tenniszentrum, Buchenstrasse 17.
GPS: n47,80944 e12,38222.

30 € 13 + € 1/pp tourist tax Ch € 1,50/day WC € 4 included. **Location:** Urban, comfortable. **Surface:** metalled.
01/01-31/12.
Distance: 800m 2km Chiemsee 3km on the spot 400m 350m on the spot on the spot 5km 5km.
Remarks: Pay at reception.

Bernau am Chiemsee 20F1

Wohnmobilstellplatz im Chiemseepark Bernau-Felden, Rasthausstraße 11. **GPS**: n47,83111 e12,38528.

16 € 6 Ch WC € 0,50 € 1. **Location:** Noisy.
Surface: gravel/metalled. 01/04-31/10.
Distance: 2,5km 600m on the spot on the spot on the spot on the spot on the spot.
Remarks: Canoe and bicycle rental, charging point for electric bicycles.

Bernau am Chiemsee 20F1

Seiseralm & Hof, Reit 4. **GPS**: n47,79722 e12,35972.

10 € 10 Ch € 5 € 2 included.
Location: Simple. **Surface:** asphalted.
01/01-31/12.
Distance: 3,5km 5km on the spot on the spot on the spot.
Remarks: Sauna € 10.

Bernried 17G2

Altes Gasthaus Artmeier, Innenstetten 45.
GPS: n48,89675 e12,90262.

10 € 5 € 1/100liter (4x)€ 1/day.
Location: Rural, simple, quiet. **Surface:** gravel/sand.
01/01-31/12 Tue, water: 01/11-31/03.
Distance: 3km on the spot on the spot.

Biberach 20C1

Brauerei Biberach, Weißenhorner Straße 24, Roggenburg.
GPS: n48,28808 e10,22047.

8 € 9 € 1/80liter Ch € 1/2kWh.
Location: Simple, quiet. **Surface:** gravel/metalled.
01/01-31/12.
Distance: 400m 8km on the spot 400m 250m on the spot on the spot.
Remarks: Bike and e-bike rental.

Biesenhofen 20D2

Gasthof Stegmühle, Stegmühle 2. **GPS**: n47,82437 e10,64428.

4 € 5, guests free Ch WC included.
Location: Simple. **Surface:** gravel/metalled.
01/01-31/12 Wed-Thu (market).
Distance: 1km 1km on the spot 1km.

Bischofsgrün 12E3

Rangenweg. **GPS**: n50,05407 e11,79292.

6 free, tourist tax € 1,50 to be paid at tourist office € 1/40liter Ch (6x)€ 1/12h. **Surface:** metalled. 01/01-31/12.
Distance: 250m 500m nearby.

Bischofsheim an der Rhön 12B2

Hallenbad Haselbach, Viehweg 1. **GPS**: n50,39506 e9,99593.

5 € 5 € 1/100liter Ch kWh. **Location:** Urban, simple, quiet.
Surface: asphalted. 01/01-31/12.
Distance: 1km 1km 2km on the spot on the spot on the spot.
Remarks: Parking swimming pool in Haselbach, money in envelope in mail box.

Bischofsheim an der Rhön 12B2

Gasthof Roth, Kreuzberg 10. **GPS**: n50,38222 e9,97806.

20 € 6 WC. **Location:** Rural, simple. **Surface:** grassy.
01/01-31/12.
Distance: on the spot on the spot on the spot.

Bischofswiesen 20G2

Götschen Alm, Kollertradte 21, Loipl. **GPS**: n47,64817 e12,93631.

20 € 5, tourist tax excl WC € 3. **Location:** Rural, simple.
Surface: gravel. 01/05-30/10.
Distance: 2km on the spot 2km on the spot on the spot on the spot on the spot on the spot.
Remarks: Guests free.

DE

Blaichach 20C2

Alpen-Rundblick Mobil Camping, Am Eichbichl 1.
GPS: n47,54615 e10,25917.

60 € 11,50-13,50 + tourist tax € 1,70/pp € 1/80liter Ch (54x)€ 0,60/kWh WC € 1,60/pp € 2,50. **Location:** Luxurious.
Surface: grassy/gravel. 01/01-31/12.
Distance: 300m 3,3km on the spot on the spot 500m 500m 5km 1km.
Remarks: Playground.

Bodenmais 17G2

Concorde-Reisemobil-Stellplatz, Kötztinger Straße.
GPS: n49,07147 e13,09273.

12 € 7 + tourist tax € 0,50/100liter Ch € 0,50/kWh.
Surface: asphalted.
01/01-31/12.
Distance: 800m 200m 200m.
Remarks: Use swimming pool, sauna, fitness-studio incl.

Bodenwöhr 17F1

Gasthof zum Troidlwirt, Bodenwöhrer strasse 6.
GPS: n49,28305 e12,26272.

40 € 10 Ch (12x)€ 1 WC € 1. **Surface:** grassy/metalled.
01/01-31/12 Restaurant: Sa.
Distance: on the spot on the spot bakery 300m.

Bogen 17F2

Wohnmobilstellplätze am Volksfestplatz, Kotaustraße 12.
GPS: n48,90744 e12,68877.

5 € 10/24h € 1 Ch (4x)€ 1/6h. **Surface:** grassy/metalled.
01/01-31/12 03/07-12/07.
Distance: 300m Edeka 100m.
Remarks: Check in at pay-desk of swiming pool.

Burgbernheim 17C1

Wohnmobilstellplatz im Gründlein, Freibadstrasse.
GPS: n49,44627 e10,31869.

12 free € 1/80liter Ch (10x)€ 0,50/kWh € 1,50.
Location: Rural, simple, quiet. **Surface:** grasstiles. 01/01-31/12.
Distance: 500m 500m 500m on the spot on the spot.
Remarks: Entrance swimming pool € 2, at swimming pool, max. 7 nights.

Burghaslach 17C1

Hotel-Restaurant Steigerwaldhaus, Oberrimbach 2.
GPS: n49,72890 e10,54078.

10 € 10 € 4 WC . **Location:** Rural, simple. **Surface:** grassy.
01/01-31/12.
Distance: 500m on the spot 5km.
Remarks: Breakfast-service.

Burghausen 20G1

Waldpark Lindach, Berghamer Strasse 1.
GPS: n48,15443 e12,80859.

18 € 8/24h € 1/70liter Ch (14x)€ 0,50/kWh WC .
Location: Rural, comfortable, quiet. **Surface:** gravel.
01/01-31/12 sanitary 01/11-31/03.
Distance: 1,5km 500m 1,5km 800m.
Remarks: Check in at Bürgerhaus Marktlerstr. 15a, max. 7 days, caution key sanitary € 20.

Burgkirchen 20G1

Glöcklhofer, Peterhof 24. **GPS**: n48,15096 e12,75025.

3 € 15, 2 pers.incl € 0,50/kWh WC included.
Location: Rural, simple, quiet. **Surface:** grassy.
01/01-31/12.
Distance: 2km 2km 2km.

Burgkunstadt 12D3

Alter Postweg. **GPS**: n50,13965 e11,25017.

4 free € 1 Ch. **Location:** Rural, simple. **Surface:** gravel.
01/01-31/12.
Distance: 100m 15km 100m 100m 300m 300m on the spot on the spot.
Remarks: Max. 48h.

Bürgstadt 17A1

Winzerfestplatz, Josef-Ullrich-Straße. **GPS**: n49,71356 e9,26405.

25 free € 1/80liter Ch (12x)€ 1/6h.
Location: Rural, comfortable, quiet. **Surface:** asphalted.
01/01-31/12.
Distance: 500m 200m 200m on the spot on the spot.

Cadolzburg 17D1

Stellplatz Am Höhbuck. **GPS**: n49,46123 e10,85188.
8 free Ch . **Surface:** metalled. 01/01-31/12.
Distance: on the spot.

Coburg 12D3

Ketschenanger, Schutzenstrasse. **GPS**: n50,25306 e10,96417.

14 free. **Location:** Urban, noisy. **Surface:** asphalted.
01/01-31/12.
Distance: on the spot on the spot.
Remarks: Parking next to gymnasium, max. 48h.

Coburg 12D3

Aral-station, Bambergerstrasse. **GPS**: n50,24833 e10,96639.

9 free € 1/20liter Ch.
Surface: metalled.
01/01-31/12.
Distance: on the spot.

Tourist information Coburg:
Die Veste Coburg. Medieval fortress.
Schloß Ehrenburg.
guided tour Tue-Su.

Dachau 20E1

Wohnmobilstellplatz Dachau, Ostenstrasse 10.
GPS: n48,26260 e11,44167.
6 free. **Location:** Noisy. **Surface:** asphalted. 01/01-31/12.
Distance: 500m 300m 350m 300m on the spot on the spot.

Deggendorf 17G2

Konstantin-Bader-Straße. **GPS**: n48,82656 e12,96367.

DE

3 free. **Location:** Simple. **Surface:** asphalted. 01/01-31/12.
Distance: centre 500m 250m.

S Deggendorf 17G2

Elypso, Sandnerhofweg 4-6. **GPS**: n48,82029 e12,91098.
4 € 6,50 € 0,50/60liter € 0,50/kWh.
Surface: metalled. 01/01-31/12.
Distance: 5,3km 4km.

S Deiningen 17C2

Cowabanga, Am Sportpark. **GPS**: n48,86292 e10,58042.

10 free € 2,50 WC. **Location:** Urban, simple.
Surface: asphalted. 01/01-31/12.
Distance: 2km on the spot.
Remarks: Parking sports centre.

S Denkendorf 17E2

Gasthof Lindenwirt, Hauptstrasse 43. **GPS**: n48,92806 e11,45568.

10 € 5 included. **Location:** Urban.
Surface: gravel/sand. 01/01-31/12.
Distance: on the spot 700m on the spot 200m on the spot on the spot.

S Dettelbach 17C1

Zur Mainfähre, An der Mainlände. **GPS**: n49,80076 e10,16751.

35 € 5 € 1/60liter Ch (24x)€ 0,50/kWh.
Location: Rural, comfortable, quiet. **Surface:** grassy.
01/01-31/12 Service: winter.
Distance: 100m on the spot 100m 100m on the spot on the spot.

S Dettelbach 17C1

Am Weingut Mangold, Köhlerstaße 12. **GPS**: n49,82917 e10,17583.

4 € 5 € 1 (4x)€ 1 € 1/time.
Location: Rural, simple, quiet. **Surface:** grassy. 01/01-31/12.
Distance: 300m 300m on the spot on the spot.
Remarks: Free of charge when buying 12 bottles of wine.

S Dießen 20D1

Seestraße. **GPS**: n47,95220 e11,10598.
12 € 8/24h € 1 € 1 Ch (12x)€ 1/4h.
Surface: gravel. 01/01-31/12.
Distance: 200m 200m 150m 150m.
Remarks: Max. 3 days.

S Dingolfing 17F3

Wohnmobilstellplatz Dingolfing, Wollanger/Prasserweg.
GPS: n48,62827 e12,50206.

12 free € 1/80liter Ch (12x)€ 1/12h.
Location: Rural, comfortable, quiet. **Surface:** gravel.
01/01-31/12 01/10-31/10.
Distance: 400m 4,6km 250m.
Remarks: Nearby swimming pool.

S Dinkelsbühl 17C2

Mönchsrother Straße. **GPS**: n49,06377 e10,32721.
15 € 6/24h Ch. **Surface:** grasstiles.
01/01-31/12.
Distance: on the spot 300m 300m.
Remarks: Max. 7 days.

S Dinkelsbühl 17C2

Park- & Campanlage, Dürrwanger Straße.
GPS: n49,07812 e10,32906.

12 € 12 Ch included € 1,50.
Surface: metalled. 01/01-31/12.
Distance: 1,5km 100m 500m.
Remarks: To be paid at campsite (500m).

Dittelbrunn 12C3

Gasthaus Goldene Flasche, Strohgasse 1, Hambach.
GPS: n50,09787 e10,20763.

3 € 1. **Location:** Urban, simple. **Surface:** metalled.
01/01-31/12.
Distance: on the spot on the spot 200m.

S Donauwörth 17D3

Wohnmobilstellplatz am Festplatz, Neue Obermayerstraße 2.
GPS: n48,71490 e10,77874.

20 free € 1/95liter Ch € 1/kWh. **Location:** Urban, simple.
Surface: asphalted. 01/01-31/12.
Distance: on the spot on the spot 500m on the spot.
Remarks: Max. 5 days.

Ebermannstadt 17D1

P2, Oberes Tor. **GPS**: n49,78222 e11,18946.

10 free. **Location:** Urban, simple. **Surface:** metalled.
01/01-31/12.
Distance: 750m 450m 100m.
Remarks: Max. 1 night.

S Ebern 12C3

Wohnmobilhafen Ebern, Walk-Strasser-Anlage.
GPS: n50,09312 e10,79496.

20 € 6 Ch (26x)€ 1/2kWh WC included € 2.
Location: Comfortable. **Surface:** metalled.
01/01-31/12.
Distance: on the spot 1km 2km 100m 200m 100m.

S Ebern 12C3

Dietz, Bahnhofstrasse. **GPS**: n50,10167 e10,78917.

10 € 5 € 1/100liter Ch WC. **Location:** Urban, simple.
Surface: asphalted/grassy. 01/01-31/12.
Distance: 1km 400m 400m.

S Ebrach 12C3

Naturbad, Schwimmbadweg. **GPS**: n49,84639 e10,48306.

5 free € 1/80liter Ch. **Location:** Rural, simple.
Surface: metalled. 01/01-31/12.
Distance: 2km 2km 2km 500m.
Remarks: Parking swimming pool.

Eggenfelden 17G3

P2, Birkenallee. **GPS**: n48,40185 e12,77579.

5 free. **Location:** Simple, quiet. **Surface:** grasstiles.
01/01-31/12.
Distance: 1km.
Remarks: Max. 3 days.

DE

Eging am See 17G2

Bavaria Kur-Sport Camping Park, Grafenauer Str. 31.
GPS: n48,72120 e13,26519.

10 € 15, 2 pers.incl Ch (10x)included. **Location:** Rural, simple, quiet. **Surface:** asphalted. 01/01-31/12.
Remarks: Max. 2 days, check in at reception campsite, use sanitary facilities at campsite.

Eibelstadt 17B1

Wassersportclub Eibelstadt, Mainparkring.
GPS: n49,73146 e9,98701.

90 € 10 € 1/5minutes Ch (90x)included,6Amp WC € 1 € 5/5. **Location:** Rural, comfortable, quiet.
Surface: grassy/gravel. 01/01-31/12.
Distance: 2km 50m 50m 500m 1km on the spot.
Remarks: Along Main river, bread-service (weekend).

Eichstätt 17D2

Schottenwiese/Volkfestplatz, Schottenau.
GPS: n48,88400 e11,19816.

50 € 8 € 1/100liter Ch (30x)€ 0,50/kWh WC € 0,50.
Location: Urban, simple, central, quiet. **Surface:** metalled.
01/01-31/12 Eichstätter Volksfest.
Distance: 500m 500m on the spot on the spot.
Remarks: Baker at 8am.

Tourist information Eichstätt:
Volksfestplatz. Flea market. 10/05, 14/06, 12/07, 13/09, 04/10.
Altstadtfest, Innenstad. City celebration. 28/08-06/09.
Eichstätter Volksfest, Volksfestplatz. Folk festival. 02/09-11/09.
Informationszentrum Naturpark Altmühltal, Notre Dame 1. Information centre nature reserve. 01/04-31/10 Mo-Sa 9-17h, Su 10-17h, 01/11-31/03 Mo-Fr 9-12h. free.

Einsiedl 20E2

Wohnmobilstellplatz, B11. **GPS**: n47,57000 e11,30389.

80 € 6 € 1/70liter € 1/kWh. **Location:** Rural, comfortable, quiet. **Surface:** asphalted/gravel. 01/01-31/12.
Distance: 500m on the spot on the spot 500m 3,5km 1,5km 1,5km.
Remarks: Max. 3 nights.

Eisenheim 12C3

Weingut Herbert Schuler, An der Mainaue, Obereisenheim.
GPS: n49,88883 e10,17942.

60 € 5 € 1/80liter Ch (48x)€ 0,50. **Location:** Rural, comfortable, quiet. **Surface:** grassy/metalled. 01/01-31/12.
Distance: on the spot on the spot on the spot on the spot.
Remarks: Along Main river, bread-service.

Eltmann am Main 12C3

Parkplatz, Mainlände. **GPS**: n49,97306 e10,66250.

30 free € 1/80liter Ch € 1/6h WC. **Location:** Rural, simple.
Surface: metalled. 01/01-31/12.
Distance: 500m on the spot on the spot 100m 300m on the spot on the spot.

Enderndorf 17D2

Wohnmobilstellplatz Panorama, Kreisstraße, Spalt-Enderndorf.
GPS: n49,15028 e10,91083.

60 € 8 € 0,20/10liter Ch (60x)€ 1/kWh.
Surface: grassy. 01/04-31/10.
Distance: 400m 400m 400m 400m 3km 150m.

Enderndorf 17D2

Reisemobilstellplatz Enderndorf-West, Zum Hafen.
GPS: n49,14777 e10,91126.

25 € 12/24h € 0,20/20liter Ch € 0,50/kWh.
Location: Rural, simple, isolated, quiet. **Surface:** grasstiles.
01/01-31/12.
Distance: 200m 150m 200m 200m on the spot on the spot.

Erbendorf 12E3

Am Stadtpark, Bahnhofstraße 21. **GPS**: n49,84144 e12,04769.

10 free € 1 Ch. **Surface:** gravel. 01/01-31/12.
Distance: 100m 200m 200m.
Remarks: Max. 3 days.

Erding 20E1

Wohnmobilpark Erding, Thermenallee 1.
GPS: n48,29332 e11,88707.

55 € 10/day € 1/80liter Ch € 1/2kWh WC.
Surface: grasstiles/metalled. 01/01-31/12.
Distance: 2km 2km 2km 50m.
Remarks: Max. 7 nights.

Escherndorf 12C3

Campingplatz Escherndorf, An der Güß 9a.
GPS: n49,85996 e10,17632.

22 € 9 Ch (22x)€ 0,50 WC sanitary € 4/pp € 2.
Location: Rural, comfortable, quiet. **Surface:** grassy.
01/04-31/10.
Distance: 300m 300m on the spot on the spot.
Remarks: Max. 7 days, sanitary at campsite.

Ettenbeuren 20C1

Wohnmobilpark Kammelaue, Zum Sportplatz 12.
GPS: n48,37565 e10,36021.

40 € 8-9, € 14-15 service incl Ch € 3,50 WC included € 2/24h. **Location:** Rural, comfortable, quiet.
Surface: grasstiles/metalled. 01/04-31/10.
Distance: 500m on the spot 500m on the spot on the spot.

Feucht 17D1

Am Freibad Feuchtasia, Chormantelweg. **GPS**: n49,37848 e11,22495.

9 € 7-9 € 1/80liter Ch (8x)€ 1/2kWh.
Surface: grasstiles. 01/01-31/12.
Distance: 1km 900m.

Fichtelberg 12E3

Automobilmuseum, Eckert Naglerweg 9.
GPS: n49,99760 e11,85820.

DE

16 free. **Surface:** asphalted/metalled. 01/01-31/12.
Distance: 700m 100m 1km.
Remarks: Parking museum.

Fischen 20C2

Wohnmobil-Stellplatz Fischen, Mühlenstraße.
GPS: n47,44950 e10,26946.

11 € 8 + tourist tax € 2,50/pp € 1 € 1 Ch (12x)€ 1/12h.
Location: Rural, simple. **Surface:** asphalted.
01/01-31/12.
Distance: 1,2km on the spot on the spot on the spot.
Remarks: Pay at Sportpark, Mühlenstraße 55, incl. access swimming pool.

Forchheim 17D1

Sportinsel, An der Regnitzbrücke. **GPS**: n49,72120 e11,04939.

20 € 9 € 1/100liter Ch € 0,50/2kWh WC € 1,50.
Location: Rural, comfortable, noisy. **Surface:** grasstiles.
01/01-31/12 sanitary building: 01/11-28/02.
Distance: 600m 5km on the spot on the spot on the spot on the spot.

Freyung 17H2

Freizeitpark Solla, Solla. **GPS**: n48,80104 e13,54125.

12 € 5 € 1/50liter Ch (12x)€ 0,50/kWh.
Location: Rural, simple, quiet. **Surface:** grasstiles.
01/01-31/12.
Distance: 2km 500m on the spot on the spot.

Freyung 17H2

Am Freibad, Zuppingerstraße 1. **GPS**: n48,80515 e13,54102.

12 free. **Location:** Urban, simple, quiet. **Surface:** metalled.
01/01-31/12.

Distance: 1km 1km 1km.

Friedberg 17D3

Herrgottsruhstrasse. **GPS**: n48,35765 e10,99095.

4 free. **Location:** Simple. **Surface:** gravel. 01/01-31/12.
Distance: 600m 600m 600m.

Friedberg 17D3

Seestraße. **GPS**: n48,36540 e10,96529.

4 free. **Location:** Rural, simple, quiet.
Surface: asphalted. 01/01-31/12.
Distance: 1,8km 5km on the spot on the spot 400m 800m on the spot on the spot.
Remarks: Small pitches.

Friedberg 17D3

Marquardtstrasse 2/A. **GPS**: n48,34825 e10,99757.
Chfree. 01/01-31/12.
Distance: on the spot.

Friedenfels 12E3

Freibad, Badstrasse. **GPS**: n49,88639 e12,10417.

15 € 3,50 € 1/2kWh,Max. 2h WC € 1.
Surface: metalled. 01/01-31/12.
Distance: 1,5km.
Remarks: Max. 3 days, service during opening hours.

Friedenfels 12E3

Zentral, Gemmingenstraße. **GPS**: n49,88102 e12,10297.

15 € 3,50 € 1/2kWh. **Surface:** metalled. 01/01-31/12.
Distance: on the spot 25m.
Remarks: Max. 3 days, pay at tourist office, Café Am Steinwald, Gemmingenstr. 19.

Friedenfels 12E3

Stellplatz 'Ruhig', Weißensteiner Weg, Frauenreuth.
GPS: n49,89278 e12,08556.

5 € 3,50. **Surface:** metalled. 01/01-31/12.
Distance: 1,5km Frauenreuther Weiher.
Remarks: Max. 3 days.

Fürstenzell 17G3

Wohnmobilstellplatz bei der Waldschänke, Altenmarkt 1.
GPS: n48,55136 e13,34118.
€ 6 € 1/100liter Ch € 1,50. **Surface:** grassy.
01/01-31/12.
Distance: on the spot.

Füssen 20D2

Camper's Stop, Abt Hafnerstrasse 9. **GPS**: n47,58186 e10,70080.

120 € 14, trailer € 5 € 0,50/150liter Ch € 1/kWh WC € 1 € 2. **Location:** Urban, comfortable, noisy. **Surface:** gravel/metalled.
01/01-31/12.
Distance: 1,5km 600m 600m terrace 50m 250m 4km 400m.

Füssen 20D2

Wohnmobilstellplatz Füssen, Abt Hafnerstrasse 1.
GPS: n47,58224 e10,70355.

30 € 14 Chincluded (6x)€ 2,50 WC € 0,50 € 2.
Location: Noisy. **Surface:** metalled. 01/01-31/12.
Distance: 1,8km 1km 200m 300m 500m on the spot on the spot on the spot on the spot.
Remarks: Sauna, solarium.

Garmisch-Partenkirchen 20D2

Alpencamp am Wank, Wankbahnstraße 2.
GPS: n47,50573 e11,10802.

110 € 12, tourist tax > 16 € 2/pp, € 1 Umwelttaxe € 1/50liter Ch (110x)€ 0,75/kWh WC € 1 .
Location: Rural, comfortable. **Surface:** asphalted. 01/01-31/12.
Distance: 1km 2km 50m 700m 50m 2,5km 1,5km.
Remarks: Check in on arrival.

Gerolzhofen 12C3

P3 Zur Volkach, Schallfelderstrasse. **GPS**: n49,89841 e10,35104.

DE

4 free € 1/80liter Ch (4x)€ 0,50/kWh WC.
Location: Urban, simple. **Surface:** metalled. 01/01-31/12.
Distance: 100m 500m 300m 200m on the spot.
Remarks: Max. 3 days.

Gerolzhofen 12C3

P1 Geomaris, Dingolshäuser Straße 2. **GPS**: n49,89980 e10,36035.

6 free. **Location:** Urban, simple. **Surface:** asphalted.
01/01-31/12.
Distance: 750m 200m.
Remarks: Parking swimming pool.

Geslau 17C2

Bauernhof Mohrenhof, Lauterbach 3.
GPS: n49,34630 e10,32500.

14 € 13,50 Ch € 0,60/kWh WC € 0,50 € 4 € 2,50/2h.
Location: Rural, simple. **Surface:** gravel.
Easter-31/10.
Distance: 500m on the spot on the spot 2km on the spot on the spot.
Remarks: Bread-service.

Goldkronach 12E3

Festplatz, Schulstrasse. **GPS**: n50,01265 e11,68276.

4 free € 1/80liter Ch (4x)€ 1/10h. **Surface:** gravel.
01/01-31/12.
Distance: 50m 500m 2km.

Gößweinstein 17D1

Alte Jugendherberge, Etzdorfer Straße 6.
GPS: n49,76556 e11,33028.

6 € 7 € 1/80liter Ch € 1/2kWh. **Location:** Urban, simple. **Surface:** metalled. 01/01-31/12.
Distance: 600m 600m 600m 300m 600m.

Grafenau 17G2

Grafenauer Kurpark, Freyunger Straße.
GPS: n48,85605 e13,40456.

18 € 10 + € 1,95/pp tourist tax € 1/80liter Ch € 0,50 free. **Location:** Urban, simple, quiet. **Surface:** gravel.
01/01-31/12.
Distance: 500m 600m 550m ReWe on the spot.
Remarks: Wifi in Touristinformation + 1/2h free internet in Stadtbücherei.

Gräfendorf 12B3

Volkert an der Roßmühle, Roßmühle, Weickersgrüben.
GPS: n50,10660 e9,78309.

5 € 5 € 2/100liter Ch (5x) included. **Location:** Rural. **Surface:** asphalted. 01/04-31/10.
Distance: on the spot on the spot on the spot on the spot.
Remarks: At motorhome dealer, accessory shop, max. 24h, check in at shop.

Grafenrheinfeld 12C3

Wohnmobilstellplatz am Naturbadesee, Hermasweg 2.
GPS: n50,00831 e10,20325.

12 € 6 € 1/100liter Ch € 0,50/kWh.
Location: Rural, comfortable. **Surface:** gravel. 01/01-31/12.
Distance: on the spot on the spot 500m 500m on the spot.
Remarks: At gymnasium.

Grainau 20D2

Wohnmobilhafen Zugspitzblick, Griesener Strasse.
GPS: n47,47982 e11,05380.
80 € 21 Ch € 0,80 WC . **Location:** Rural.
Surface: grassy/gravel. 01/01-31/12.
Distance: 2km 50m 100m 100m.

Greding 17D2

Am Hallenbad. **GPS**: n49,04409 e11,35551.

20 free. **Location:** Urban.
Surface: metalled.
01/01-31/12.
Distance: Old city centre 300m 500m 250m 250m on the spot on the spot.
Remarks: Parking at city wall in front of swimming pool.
Tourist information Greding:
City wall and towers.

Großheubach 17A1

Weingut Gasthaus Zur Bretzel, Kirchstraße 1.
GPS: n49,72620 e9,22083.

25 € 17 Ch (25x) WC included € 1.
Location: Rural, comfortable, quiet. **Surface:** grassy/gravel.
01/01-31/12 Mo, 01/11-15/11.
Distance: 100m on the spot on the spot on the spot.
Remarks: To be paid at Gasthaus, € 10 euro discount coupon (restaurant, wine).

Großweil 20E2

Berggasthof Kreut-Alm, Kreut 1. **GPS**: n47,66184 e11,28286.

40 customers free . **Location:** Rural, simple, isolated, quiet.
Surface: asphalted. 01/03-31/10.
Distance: 3,2km on the spot.

Großweil 20E2

Freilichtmuseum Glentleiten, An der Glentleiten 4.
GPS: n47,66495 e11,28506.

10 free. **Surface:** gravel. 15/11-15/03.
Distance: 2km 3,5km Gaststätte - Biergarten 1km.
Remarks: Open air museum, only overnight stays.

Günzburg 17C3

Waldbad, Heidenheimer Straße. **GPS**: n48,46287 e10,26944.

24 € 5, 01/05-30/09 € 8 € 1/100liter (24x)€ 0,50/kWh. **Location:** Rural, simple. **Surface:** gravel.
01/01-31/12.
Distance: 2km 2km Danube Bike Trail.
Remarks: Parking swimming pool.

Gunzenhausen 17D2

Surfzentrum Schlungenhof. **GPS**: n49,12790 e10,74559.

DE

80 € 11/24h € 1 Ch included WC € 1 .
Location: Rural, comfortable, quiet. **Surface:** grassy/gravel.
01/04-30/10.
Distance: 100m on the spot 1,8km.

S Gunzenhausen 17D2

Altmühlsee, Seezentrum Mühr. GPS: n49,13145 e10,73534.

40 € 9/24h WC . **Location:** Rural, comfortable, isolated, quiet.
Surface: grassy. 01/01-31/12.
Distance: on the spot 200m on the spot on the spot.
Remarks: Max. 3 days.

S Hammelburg 12B3

Am Bleichrasen, P2, Am Weiher. **GPS**: n50,11390 e9,88820.

24 € 6/24h Ch included (24x)€ 0,50/kWh WC.
Location: Urban, simple, quiet. **Surface:** asphalted.
01/01-31/12.
Distance: on the spot on the spot 200m 300m.

S Hammelburg 12B3

Forellenhof Reuss, Am Erlich 30, Diebach.
GPS: n50,13310 e9,81917.

64 € 10 Ch included (64x)€ 3/24h WC € 2 € 2.
Location: Rural, comfortable, quiet. **Surface:** gravel.
01/01-31/12 service: 31/10-01/03.
Distance: Hammelburg 7km on the spot on the spot on the spot on the spot.
Remarks: Bread-service, weekend: Gaststätte/Biergarten.

S Hammelburg 12B3

Hotel Kaiser, An der Walkmühle 11. **GPS**: n50,11563 e9,90159.

4 free € 1/100liter Ch € 2/day . **Location:** Urban, simple, quiet. **Surface:** grassy/gravel. 01/01-31/12.
Distance: 800m on the spot on the spot on the spot.
Remarks: Bread-service.

Hammelburg 12B3

Restaurant Nöth, Morlesauer Strasse 3. **GPS**: n50,11707 e9,80313.

5 free. **Location:** Rural, simple, quiet. **Surface:** gravel.
01/01-31/12.
Distance: on the spot on the spot on the spot on the spot on the spot.
Remarks: Check in at restaurant, use of a meal desired.

S Hassfurt 12C3

Festplatz am Gries, Untere Fischergasse 9.
GPS: n50,03068 e10,50094.

22 € 8/24h € 1 Ch € 2/day WC € 1. **Location:** Urban, simple. **Surface:** asphalted. 01/01-31/12.
Distance: 200m 10m 200m 200m 200m on the spot on the spot.
Remarks: Along Main river.

S Hassfurt 12C3

Naturfreunde, Am Hafen 4. **GPS**: n50,02622 e10,51664.

23 € 8 € 1/100liter Ch € 2/24h € 0,50.
Location: Rural, comfortable. **Surface:** grassy. 01/01-31/12.
Distance: 1,5km on the spot on the spot on the spot 1,5km.

Herrieden 17C2

Volksfestplatz an der Altmühl, Staatsstrasse 2248.
GPS: n49,23191 e10,49588.

10 free. **Surface:** asphalted. 01/01-31/12.
Distance: 100m 200m 200m.
Remarks: Parking at the old mill bridge.

S Hersbruck 17D1

Fackelmann Therme Hersbruck, Badestraße.
GPS: n49,51142 e11,44267.

6 € 6 € 1/50liter Ch € 1/8h.
Surface: gravel. 01/01-31/12.
Distance: on the spot 200m 200m.
Remarks: Check in at pay-desk of the Therme.

S Herzogenaurach 17D1

Freizeitbad Atlantis, Würzburger Straße 35.
GPS: n49,57315 e10,86543.

12 € 6/24h € 1 Ch (12x)€ 0,50/kWh.
Location: Rural, simple. **Surface:** gravel. 01/01-31/12.
Distance: on the spot.
Remarks: € 2 reduction swimming pool.

S Hilpoltstein 17D2

Seezentrum Heuberg am Rothsee, Heuberg.
GPS: n49,20954 e11,18595.

50 € 8/24h Ch.
Surface: metalled. 01/01-31/12 Service: winter.
Distance: 200m 200m.

Hilpoltstein 17D2

Am Main-Donau-Kanal. **GPS**: n49,20455 e11,18813.

40 € 6. **Surface:** grassy. 15/04-15/10.
Distance: 1,9km Canal 1,9km 1km on the spot on the spot.

Tourist information Hilpoltstein:
Burgfeste. Festival with events. beginning Aug.

Hof/Saale 12E2

Park Theresienstein, Plauener Straße. **GPS**: n50,32956 e11,92041.

10 free. **Surface:** metalled. 01/01-31/12.
Distance: 2,5km on the spot 1km.
Remarks: Max. 24h.

DE

Hof/Saale 12E2

Utreusee, Schaumberggrund. **GPS**: n50,28296 e11,91849.

10 free. **Surface:** asphalted/metalled. 01/01-31/12.
Distance: 6km 350m 50m 500m.
Remarks: Max. 96h.

Hof/Saale 12E2

Clean Park, Ernst Reuterstrasse. **GPS**: n50,32641 e11,89248.

8 € 5 € 1 Ch € 2 WC. **Surface:** metalled.
01/01-31/12.
Distance: 2km 800m 300m 50m.
Remarks: Max. 72h.

Tourist information Hof/Saale:
Bürgerpark Theresienstein. Landscape park according English example. 9-18h, winter 9-16h.
Untreusee. Lake with water sports.

Hofheim in Unterfranken 12C3

Wohnmobilplatz Hofheim, Johannisstraße 28.
GPS: n50,14185 e10,51957.

30 € 8 € 1/80liter Ch € 0,50/kWh WC € 2,50.
Location: Urban, comfortable. **Surface:** grasstiles.
01/01-31/12.
Distance: 750m 750m on the spot.
Remarks: At swimming pool, bread-service.

Hohenberg/Eger 12E3

Wiesenfestplatz, Selberstrasse. **GPS**: n50,09762 e12,22085.

10-20 voluntary contribution Ch free WC.
Surface: metalled. 01/01-31/12.
Distance: 200m 50m.
Remarks: Beautiful view, porcelain museum.

Hohenburg 17E1

Sportplatz, Sportplatzweg 1. **GPS**: n49,29194 e11,80917.

6 € 8 € 2 WC. **Surface:** metalled. 01/01-31/12.
Distance: 1km 1km.
Remarks: Parking at sports park.

Immenstadt 20C2

P 3 Viehmarktplatz, Badeweg. **GPS**: n47,56192 e10,20857.

6 € 8/24h Ch WC included. **Location:** Urban, simple, comfortable. **Surface:** asphalted. 01/01-31/12.
Distance: 700m.

Ingolstadt 17E3

Parkplatz Hallenbad, Jahnstrasse. **GPS**: n48,76025 e11,42038.

13 € 5/24h € 1/80liter € 1 Ch included .
Location: Urban, comfortable. **Surface:** metalled.
01/01-31/12.
Distance: on the spot 1,6km on the spot on the spot on the spot on the spot.
Remarks: Parking at sports park, max. 3 days.

Ingolstadt 17E3

Ingolstadt Village, Marie-Curie-Straße 1. **GPS**: n48,78556 e11,47750.
20 free. **Surface:** gravel. 01/01-31/12.
Distance: 6km 300m.
Remarks: Motorhome parking at Outlet.

Inzell 20G1

Camping Lindlbauer, Kreuzfeldstraße 44.
GPS: n47,76717 e12,75417.

12 € 16 Ch € 2 WC included.
Location: Rural, simple, quiet. **Surface:** metalled. 01/01-31/12.
Distance: 1km on the spot on the spot.
Remarks: Max. 1 night, health resort 500m.

Iphofen 17C1

Einesheimer Tor, Ecke Einersheimer Straße/Stadtgraben Ost.
GPS: n49,70260 e10,26459.

9 free € 1 Ch (6x)€ 1/12h WC. **Location:** Urban, simple.
Surface: gravel. 01/01-31/12.
Distance: 200m 200m 700m.
Remarks: Parking at city wall.

Ippesheim 17C1

Kempe's Autohof Gollhofen, Industriestraße 1.
GPS: n49,58546 e10,17579.

25 free WC € 0,50 . **Location:** Motorway, simple.
Surface: asphalted. 01/01-31/12.
Distance: 1km on the spot.

Kastl/Oberpfalz 17E1

Wanderparkplatz Am Alten Bahnhof, Amberger Straße.
GPS: n49,36657 e11,68388.

5 free Ch WC free. **Surface:** gravel. 01/01-31/12.
Distance: 200m 200m 100m 50m on the spot on the spot.

Kaufbeuren 20D1

Wohnmobilplatz Kaufbeuren, Buronstraße.
GPS: n47,89885 e10,61650.

8 free Ch free (6x)€ 1/kWh.
Location: Urban. **Surface:** gravel. 01/01-31/12.
Distance: historical centre 3km 1km.
Remarks: Max. 3 days.

Kelheim 17E2

Volksfestplatz, Am Pflegerspitz. **GPS**: n48,91331 e11,87657.

50 € 6 Ch (18x)€ 1/2kWh WC.
Surface: metalled. 01/01-31/12 service 01/11-31/03.
Distance: 500m 500m.
Remarks: Max. 3 nights, hindmost part.

DE

Kemnath 12E3

Wohnmobilstellplatz Kemnath, Am Eisweier 8.
GPS: n49,87219 e11,88774.

5 free € 1 Ch (6x)€ 1/6h WC.
Surface: grasstiles. 01/01-31/12.
Distance: 650m 650m 650m.
Remarks: Max. 3 days.

Kempten 20C2

Illerstadion, Illerdamm/Jahnstrasse. **GPS**: n47,72915 e10,31940.

9 € 5 € 1/10minutes Ch.
Location: Urban, simple, noisy. **Surface:** metalled. 01/01-31/12.
Distance: 500m 2,7km.
Remarks: Max. 3 days.

Kiefersfelden 20F2

Hödenauer See, Guggenauerweg 2. **GPS**: n47,62881 e12,18949.

10 € 8 WC € 0,50.
Location: Simple. **Surface:** gravel/sand. 01/01-31/12.
Distance: 2km 3km on the spot on the spot 50m 300m.
Remarks: Max. 3 days, pay at Wasserskilift Hödenauersee.

Kiefersfelden 20F2

Rathausplatz. **GPS**: n47,61303 e12,18981.

20 € 10. **Location:** Simple. **Surface:** asphalted. 01/01-31/12.
Distance: on the spot 2km 100m.
Remarks: Max. 3 days.

Kirchenlamitz 12E3

Anfahrtsskizze, Weißenstädter Straße.
GPS: n50,14905 e11,94055.

12 free Chfree voluntary contribution.
Location: Comfortable. **Surface:** asphalted. 01/01-31/12.
Distance: 500m 10m.

Kirchham 17G3

Erlebnispark Haslinger Hof, Ed 1. **GPS**: n48,34947 e13,29115.

25-30 Overnight stay € 17 (incl. € 9 voucher) € 1 Ch.
Location: Rural, simple, quiet. **Surface:** gravel.
01/01-31/12.
Distance: on the spot.

Kitzingen 17C1

Wohnmobilpark Am Main, Bleichwasen, Etwashausen.
GPS: n49,74274 e10,16491.

70 € 7/24h € 1/80liter Ch € 0,50/kWh WC.
Location: Simple. **Surface:** asphalted. 01/01-31/12.
Distance: 300m on the spot on the spot 300m 300m on the spot.
Remarks: Between Alter Mainbrücke and Nordbrücke, bread-service.

Klingenberg 17A1

Sonja's Wohnmobilhafen, Zur Einladung.
GPS: n49,78370 e9,17805.

55 € 7,50 € 1/80liter Ch (50x)€ 2/day.
Location: Rural, comfortable, quiet. **Surface:** grassy/gravel.
01/03-29/10.
Distance: 500m on the spot 500m 2km on the spot on the spot.
Remarks: Check in on arrival, service passerby € 2.

Königsberg 12C3

Buchweg. **GPS**: n50,08472 e10,57028.

6 free . **Location:** Rural, simple, quiet. **Surface:** metalled.
01/01-31/12.
Distance: 300m 300m 300m 400m on the spot on the spot.
Remarks: Parking sports park.

Königsbrunn 20D1

Königsallee. **GPS**: n48,27243 e10,88283.

12 € 6/24h € 1/100liter Ch (12x)€ 0,50/kWh.
Location: Urban, noisy. **Surface:** metalled. 01/01-31/12.
Distance: 1km 1km.

Kreuth 20E2

Wildbad Kreuth, Bremerweg. **GPS**: n47,62597 e11,74681.

8 € 5. **Location:** Rural, simple. **Surface:** gravel/sand.
01/01-31/12.
Distance: 50m on the spot on the spot.

Kreuzwertheim 17B1

Am Mainufer, Fährgasse. **GPS**: n49,76251 e9,51840.

15 € 8 € 2/160liter ChWC.
Location: Urban, simple, quiet. **Surface:** gravel. 01/01-31/12.
Distance: Wertheim centre 1,2km on the spot 600m on the spot.
Remarks: Along Main river, max. 1 night.

Kronach 12D3

Hammermühle, Am Sand. **GPS**: n50,23195 e11,32735.

10 € 5/24h € 1 Ch (12x)€ 0,50/kWh.
Location: Rural, simple. **Surface:** asphalted. 01/01-31/12.
Distance: 10min on the spot 200m 300m.

Kronach 12D3

Lucky Stable Ranch, Mostrach 1. **GPS**: n50,21840 e11,34012.

5 € 5, 2 pers.incl WCincluded € 1,50 € 1,50 .
Location: Rural, simple, isolated, quiet. **Surface:** grassy/metalled.
01/01-31/12.
Distance: 2km on the spot on the spot 2km.
Remarks: At manege.

DE

S Krün 20E2

Tennsee Reisemobilhafen, Am Tennsee 1.
GPS: n47,49083 e11,25444.

37 € 14,50-17 + tourist tax € 1,50/pp, Umwelttaxe € 0,70/pp Ch € 0,75/kWh WC included € 3 € 3/h.
Location: Rural, comfortable, quiet. **Surface:** grassy/gravel.
01/01-31/12 07/11-15/12.
Distance: 2,5km 800m 3km on the spot on the spot 100m on the spot on the spot 5km 300m.
Remarks: Dog € 4.

S Kulmbach 12D3

Wohnmobilstellplatz Kulmbach, Am Schwedensteg.
GPS: n50,11130 e11,46118.

25 € 3 € 1/100liter Ch (25x)€ 1/2kWh.
Location: Urban, simple. **Surface:** gravel.
01/01-31/12 water disconnected in winter.
Distance: on the spot 50m 200m 500m on the spot on the spot 200m.

Kümmersbruck 17E1

Wohnmobilstellplatz Kümmersbruck, Am Butzenweg.
GPS: n49,41978 e11,89651.

8 free. **Location:** Rural, simple, quiet. **Surface:** metalled.
01/01-31/12.
Distance: 1km 1km.
Remarks: At sports centre.

S Lalling 17G2

Wohnmobilstellplatz Weber, Euschertsfurth 34.
GPS: n48,83222 e13,14444.

8 € 10 Ch included (10x)€ 0,30/kWh WC € 1,50.
Location: Rural, comfortable, quiet. **Surface:** grassy/metalled.
01/04-30/11.
Distance: 1,5km 100m.
Remarks: Swimming pool incl.

S Lalling 17G2

Lalling-Freizeitgelände, Waldstrasse. **GPS**: n48,84139 e13,13778.

2 free € 1/80liter Ch € 3/day. **Location:** Rural, simple, quiet. **Surface:** metalled/sand. 01/01-31/12.
Distance: 2km.
Remarks: At tennis-courts.

S Lalling 17G2

Ferienbauernhof Sieglinde, Obstgarten 13, Hunding.
GPS: n48,84502 e13,14939.

3 € 5 Ch included (2x)€ 2/day WC .
Location: Rural, simple, quiet. **Surface:** grassy. 01/04-31/12.
Distance: 700m.

S Lalling 17G2

Lallinger Hof, Hauptstrasse 23. **GPS**: n48,84560 e13,13851.

4 guests free against payment.
Location: Rural, simple, quiet. 01/04-31/10.
Distance: 250m 250m.
Remarks: Check in at restaurant.

Lalling 17G2

Gasthof zur Post, Pfarrweg. **GPS**: n48,84405 e13,14064.

15 free. **Location:** Rural, simple, quiet. **Surface:** metalled.
01/01-31/12 winter.
Distance: 200m 200m.

Lalling 17G2

Feng Shui Kurpark, Euschertsfurther Straße.
GPS: n48,84137 e13,13952.

10 € 1. **Surface:** gravel. 01/01-31/12.
Remarks: Not indicated.

Lalling 17G2

Erikas Wohlfühlplatz, Kleinfeld 6, Hunding.
GPS: n48,84333 e13,17944.

10 € 5 + € 0,50/pp (10x)€ 1/day WC € 4.
Location: Rural, simple, quiet. **Surface:** grassy/sand.
01/04-31/10.
Distance: on the spot on the spot 3km 200m on the spot on the spot.
Remarks: Check in at Kleinfeld 6.

S Landau/Isar 17F3

Am Festplatz, Harburger Straße 20/B20.
GPS: n48,67712 e12,68323.

± 20 free € 0,50/100liter Ch (6x)€ 0,50/kWh.
Surface: grassy/gravel. 01/01-31/12.
Distance: 1,5km 2,3km McDonalds 200m bakery 200m.

S Landau/Isar 17F3

Vilstaler Hof, Andreasstraße 2. **GPS**: n48,60972 e12,69528.
15 € 10, dog € 7 € 1/100liter Ch € 5 included WC € 3 .
Location: Rural. **Surface:** gravel/metalled. 01/01-31/12.
Distance: 7km on the spot.
Remarks: Breakfast-service.

S Landsberg am Lech 20D1

Waitzinger Wiese, Gottesackerangerweg.
GPS: n48,05534 e10,87371.

8 € 7/24h € 1/50liter Ch (8x)€ 1/6h WC € 0,50.
Location: Urban, simple. **Surface:** metalled. 01/01-31/12.
Distance: 400m 300m.

S Lauingen 17C3

E-Park-Eisenbahn-Erlebnispark, Riedhauser Straße 60.
GPS: n48,57237 e10,42187.

29 € 5/24h € 1/5minutes € 1 Ch (8x)€ 0,50/kWh WC free.
Location: Simple. **Surface:** metalled. 01/01-31/12.
Distance: 750m.
Remarks: Railroad theme park.

S Lechbruck am See 20D2

Wohnmobilpark via Claudia, Via Claudia 6.
GPS: n47,71556 e10,82139.

DE

52 € 11,50, 2 pers. incl., dog € 3-3,50 Ch included WC € 1,50 € 2,50 € 3/24h.
Location: Rural, comfortable. **Surface:** gravel. 01/01-31/12.
Distance: 5km on the spot on the spot on the spot on the spot on the spot 10km on the spot.

Lenggries 20E2

Dürrachstrasse, Fall. **GPS**: n47,57039 e11,53380.

25 € 0,50/h, € 4/24h € 2 WC.
Location: Rural, isolated, quiet. **Surface:** metalled.
01/01-31/12 service: 01/11-01/04.
Distance: 250m 250m 150m 8km on the spot on the spot.
Remarks: Max. 7 days.

Leupoldsgrün 12E2

Am Anger, Hauptstraße 48. **GPS**: n50,29389 e11,79961.
2 free € 0,50/50liter Ch € 0,50/kWh free.
Location: Urban. **Surface:** metalled. 01/01-31/12.
Distance: 100m 150m bakery 50m.
Remarks: Charging point for electric bicycles.

Lindau 20B2

Blauwiese, P1. GPS: n47,55869 e9,70130.

30 € 1/h, € 20/24h € 0,50 € 0,50 Ch WC.
Surface: metalled. 01/01-31/12.
Distance: on the spot 1km 1km 500m 500m on the spot.
Remarks: Max. 24h.

Lindau 20B2

Gitzenweiler Hof, Gitzenweiler 88. **GPS**: n47,58475 e9,70673.
17 € 17,50 + tourist tax Ch WC included.
Surface: asphalted/metalled. 01/01-31/12.
Distance: 150m.
Remarks: Max. 1 night, free entrance swimming pool.

Lindau 20B2

Park Camping, Frauenhoferstrasse 20. **GPS**: n47,53764 e9,73148.

12 € 12/24h Ch WC included,on camp site .
Surface: gravel. 15/03-31/10.
Distance: 600m 2km on the spot.
Remarks: Max. 24h.

Tourist information Lindau:

Lindau Insel. Promenade along the lake with Mangturm, 700 years old lighthouse.

Litzendorf 12D3

ASV Naisa, Am Wetterkreuz. **GPS**: n49,91559 e11,00261.

8 free. **Location:** Rural, simple, quiet. **Surface:** gravel.
01/01-31/12.
Distance: 200m on the spot on the spot.

Litzendorf 12D3

Tiefenellern, Ellerbergstrasse. **GPS**: n49,91927 e11,07006.

3 free. **Location:** Rural, simple, isolated.
Surface: gravel. 01/01-31/12.
Distance: on the spot on the spot.

Lohr/Main 12B3

Lohr am Main, Osttangente. **GPS**: n49,99429 e9,58053.

21 free, night € 5 € 1/100liter Ch (22x)€ 2/8h WC € 2/h.
Location: Urban, simple, noisy.
Surface: metalled. 01/04-31/10.
Distance: 300m on the spot Aldi 800m.
Remarks: Along Main river, max. 3 days.

Mainbernheim 17C1

Goldgrubenweg. **GPS**: n49,71153 e10,22045.

10 free. **Location:** Urban, simple, quiet. **Surface:** metalled.
01/01-31/12.
Distance: on the spot 200m 200m 100m.

Mainstockheim 17C1

Wohnmobilhafen Mainstockheim, Albertshöfer straße.
GPS: n49,77173 e10,15595.

37 € 7 Ch included. **Location:** Rural, simple, quiet.
Surface: gravel. 01/01-31/12.

Distance: on the spot 5km on the spot 100m 100m on the spot.
Remarks: Along Main river.

Manching 17E3

Am Braunweiher. GPS: n48,71078 e11,49602.

50 free € 1/80liter Ch. **Location:** Simple.
Surface: grasstiles/metalled. 01/01-31/12.
Distance: 1,5km 1,3km Edeka 1km.

Markt Wald 20C1

Wohnmobilpark Markt Wald, Bürgle 1a.
GPS: n48,14602 e10,57517.

20 € 8 € 1/100liter Ch € 0,50/kWh WC € 2/pppd.
Location: Rural, comfortable, quiet. **Surface:** grassy/gravel.
01/01-31/12.
Distance: 1km on the spot on the spot on the spot 1km on the spot on the spot on the spot. **Remarks:** At small lake, bread-service, use sanitary facilities at campsite.

Marktbreit 17C1

Am Kranen, Staatstraße. **GPS**: n49,66878 e10,14241.

3 free. **Location:** Simple. **Surface:** metalled.
01/01-31/12.
Distance: on the spot on the spot on the spot on the spot 500m on the spot.
Remarks: Max. 1 day.

Marktheidenfeld 17B1

Martinswiese, Georg-Mayr-Straße. **GPS**: n49,84918 e9,59887.

30 € 5/24h € 1/100liter Ch (18x)€ 1/4h WC included.
Location: Rural, comfortable, quiet. **Surface:** gravel.
01/01-31/12 during event.
Distance: 600m on the spot on the spot 200m Lidl 650m on the spot on the spot.
Remarks: Along Main river, max. 2 nights.

Marktheidenfeld 17B1

Georg-Mayr-Straße. **GPS**: n49,85364 e9,60025.

DE

20 free. **Location:** Rural, simple, noisy. **Surface:** gravel.
01/01-31/12.
Distance: 1km 50m Lidl 50m.
Remarks: Max. 3 days.

S Marktheidenfeld 17B1

Landgasthof Baumhof-Tenne, Baumhofstraße 147.
GPS: n49,84401 e9,63104.

10 € 5, free with a meal € 1/100liter € 3/day WC free.
Location: Rural, comfortable, quiet. **Surface:** gravel.
01/01-31/12 Mon, Tue.
Distance: on the spot on the spot on the spot.
Remarks: Max. 3 days, bread-service + breakfast-service.

S Marktleuthen 12E3

Am Angerparkplatz. **GPS:** n50,12946 e11,99483.

10 free Ch (10x)free WC € 0,50. **Surface:** metalled.
01/01-31/12.
Distance: 250m 150m 200m.
Remarks: Max. 7 days, bread-service.

S Marktoberdorf 20D2

Parkplatz der Bayerischen Musikakademie, Kurfürstenstraße 19.
GPS: n47,78013 e10,62284.

4 free € 1/50liter Ch € 0,50/kWh. **Surface:** grasstiles.
01/01-31/12.
Distance: on the spot 100m.

S Marktredwitz 12E3

Wohnmobilstellplatz am Auenpark, Dörflaser Platz, Fabrikstraße.
GPS: n49,99710 e12,08640.

20 free € 0,50/150liter € 0,50 Ch€ 0,50 (6x)€ 0,50/kWh.
Surface: asphalted/gravel. 01/01-31/12.

Distance: 300m 50m 150m.

Marktredwitz 12E3

Angerplatz, Egerland-Kulturhaus, Fikentscherstrasse.
GPS: n50,00379 e12,09506.

6 free. **Surface:** asphalted. 01/01-31/12.
Distance: 1km 500m 1km.

S Massing 17F3

Am Freilichtmuseum, Spirknerstraße. **GPS:** n48,39528 e12,60056.
10 free on demand.
Surface: grassy/metalled.
01/01-31/12.
Distance: Museumstüberl.
Remarks: Open air museum, busy parking during the day.

Mehlmeisel 12E3

Parkplatz Am Park, Am Park. **GPS:** n49,97615 e11,85471.

5 free. **Surface:** metalled. 01/01-31/12.
Distance: 250m bakery 100m.
Remarks: Max. 3 nights.

S Mellrichstadt 12C2

Malbachweg. **GPS:** n50,43139 e10,30972.

7 free € 1/80liter Ch (7x)€ 0,50/kWh.
Location: Urban, simple, quiet. **Surface:** asphalted.
01/01-31/12.
Distance: 500m 750m 750m on the spot on the spot.
Remarks: Max. 3 days.

S Memmelsdorf 12D3

Seehofblick, Pödeldorferstrasse 20-A. **GPS:** n49,92906 e10,95594.
4 € 5 € 1/80liter Ch € 1/8h. **Location:** Urban, simple.
Surface: asphalted. 01/04-31/10.
Distance: on the spot 250m.

S Memmelsdorf 12D3

Stocksee, Stockseestrasse. **GPS:** n49,92556 e10,93417.

5 € 5 € 1/80liter Chfree (4x)€ 1/8h.
Location: Urban. **Surface:** asphalted. 01/01-31/12.
Distance: 1,2km 500m 100m.

Miltenberg 17A1

Busparkplatz Ecke, Jahnstrasse/Luitpoldstrasse.
GPS: n49,70464 e9,25860.

10 free. **Location:** Urban, simple, central. **Surface:** asphalted.
01/01-31/12.
Distance: 200m 200m 200m.
Remarks: Only overnight stays 17-10h.

Miltenberg 17A1

Hallenfreibad Miltenberg, Jahnstraße 1.
GPS: n49,70694 e9,26027.

20 free. **Location:** Urban, simple, noisy.
Surface: metalled. 01/01-31/12.
Distance: 500m 200m 200m on the spot on the spot.
Remarks: At swimming pool.

Miltenberg 17A1

Am Yachthafen, Steingässerstrasse. **GPS:** n49,70446 e9,25435.

20 free. **Location:** Rural, simple. **Surface:** grassy/gravel.
01/01-31/12.
Distance: 800m on the spot 800m 500m on the spot on the spot.
Remarks: Along Main river.

S Mistelgau 12D3

Therme Obernsees, An der Therme 1, Obernsees.
GPS: n49,91630 e11,37831.

40 € 10 € 1/50liter Ch € 1/12h WC .
Location: Luxurious, quiet. **Surface:** grasstiles/metalled.
01/01-31/12.
Distance: 1km Therme-Bistro on the spot on the spot on the spot on the spot.
Remarks: Bread-service, discount on access terme.

S Mittenwald 20E2

Wohnmobil-Stellplatz Karwendel, Albert-Schott-Straße.
GPS: n47,43792 e11,26411.

DE

30 € 8/24h + € 4 tourist tax € 1/80liter Ch (30x)€ 0,80/kWh. **Location:** Simple, noisy. **Surface:** asphalted/gravel.
01/01-31/12.
Distance: 250m on the spot.
Remarks: Along railwayline.

S Mittenwald 20E2

Hotel Jägerhof, Partenkirchner Straße 35. **GPS**: n47,44652 e11,26440.
3 € 5/night . **Surface:** asphalted. 01/01-31/12.
Distance: 600m 500m.
Remarks: Free with a meal in hotel.

S Mitterteich 12E3

Freizeithugl Großbüchlberg, Großbüchlberg 32.
GPS: n49,97286 e12,22496.

24 € 12, 2 pers. incl., dog € 1,50 Ch (16x)€ 0,50 WC against payment € 2,50/2,50 € 1/24h.
Surface: metalled. 01/01-31/12.
Distance: 200m.
Remarks: Bread-service.

S Monheim 17D2

An der Stadthalle, Schulstraße. **GPS**: n48,84503 e10,85329.

7 free € 1/100liter Ch € 1/10h. **Location:** Simple, central, quiet. **Surface:** grasstiles. 01/01-31/12.
Distance: 400m 500m 500m.

S Moosbach 17F1

Am Natur-Waldbad Tröbes, Tröbes. **GPS**: n49,55851 e12,44074.
9 € 10 Ch WC. 01/03-31/10.
Distance: on the spot.

S Moosbach 17F1

Bei der Wieskirche, Am Badeweiher Tröbes, Friedhofgasse.
GPS: n49,59076 e12,41193.

6 € 5 Ch included. **Surface:** gravel. 01/03-31/10.
Distance: 250m 250m 250m.
Remarks: Check in at Gästeinformation.

S Mörnsheim 17D2

Wohnmobilstellplatz Hammermühle, Altendorf.
GPS: n48,87455 e11,02948.

21 € 10, dog € 1 Chincluded € 0,60/kWh WC € 2.
Location: Rural. **Surface:** unpaved. 01/04-31/10.
Distance: Altendorf 2km Imbiss, Biergarten on the spot on the spot.
Remarks: Nature reserve Altmühltal, bread-service.

S München 20E1

Allianz-Arena Wohnmobilstellplätze, Werner-Heisenberg-Allee 25, Munich (München). **GPS**: n48,22089 e11,62505.

110 € 15 € 0,20/20liter (10x)€ 1/kWh.
Surface: asphalted. 01/01-31/12 during event.
Distance: Bistro-Biergarten on the spot on the spot.
Remarks: FC Bayern Erlebniswelt (Fanmuseum).

S München 20E1

Oktoberfest-Camping, De-Gasperi-Bogen, München-Riem, Munich (München).
GPS: n48,13342 e11,70746.
1000 € 35, 2 pers.incl, extra pers € 15 Ch WC included.
Surface: metalled.
Oktoberfest.
Distance: on the spot on the spot metro 300m.
Remarks: Opened 2 days before Oktoberfest.

Tourist information Munich (München):
München CityTourCard. Card gives for free entrance on among other things public transport and 50% discounts on curiosities. € 10,90/day, € 20,90/3 days.
Agustinerbräu, Neuhauserstrasse 16. Brewery from 1644.
Schloß Nymphenburg. Former summer residence of the Witelbacher monarchs.
Tue-Su 9-12.30h, 13.30-17h. € 6.
Neumarkt. Ruins of citadel dominating the city.
Oktoberfest. Beer festival, special motorhome parking.

S Münnerstadt 12C3

An der Lache, P1, Seminarstrasse. **GPS**: n50,25188 e10,19348.

4 free € 1/90liter Ch (4x)€ 0,50/kWh,16Amp WC.
Location: Urban, simple, quiet. **Surface:** metalled.
01/01-31/12.
Distance: 350m.
Remarks: Max. 3 days.

Münnerstadt 12C3

Am Oberen Tor, P2, Dr. Engelhardt Weg. **GPS**: n50,24914 e10,19145.

2 free. **Location:** Urban, simple, noisy. **Surface:** metalled.
01/01-31/12.
Distance: on the spot on the spot.

S Murnau am Staffelsee 20D2

Am P&R Bahnof, Am Bahnhof. **GPS**: n47,68005 e11,19447.

6 € 1/day € 1/100liter Ch (6x)€ 1/2kWh.
Location: Rural, comfortable, central, quiet.
Surface: grasstiles/metalled. 01/01-31/12.
Distance: 500m 10km 400m 300m on the spot.
Remarks: Max. 72h.

S Naila 12E2

Christian-Schlicht-strasse. **GPS**: n50,33071 e11,71127.

4 free Ch. **Location:** Urban, simple.
Surface: metalled. 01/01-31/12.
Distance: 100m 50m 300m 300m on the spot on the spot.
Remarks: Parking left side of the station, thursday market.

Naila 12E2

Badstraße. **GPS**: n50,32965 e11,70108.

10 free. **Location:** Urban, simple, isolated. **Surface:** asphalted.
01/01-31/12.
Distance: 650m.
Remarks: Thursday market.

S Nesselwang 20C2

An der Riese, Altspitzbahn. **GPS**: n47,61995 e10,49830.

70 € 10 Ch (62x)€ 1/kWh included.
Location: Rural, comfortable.
Surface: gravel/metalled.
01/01-31/12.
Distance: 500m 3,8km 1km 3km 200m 500m 500m on the spot 200m 200m.
Remarks: Baker every morning, code internet at tourist office.

S Neualbenreuth 12F3

Reisemobilhafen Sibyllenbad, Parkplatz P2, Kurallee.
GPS: n49,98099 e12,42406.

DE

21 € 10 + € 1/pp tourist tax Ch (20x)€ 0,50/kWh WC.
Surface: metalled. 01/01-31/12.
Distance: 1,5km 1,5km.
Remarks: Bread-service.

Neubeuern 20F2

P2, Am Sportplatz. **GPS**: n47,77573 e12,14298.

6 free. **Location:** Rural, simple, quiet. **Surface:** gravel.
01/01-31/12.
Distance: 500m 500m.
Remarks: Max. 48h.

Neuburg/Donau 17D3

Parkplatz P1, Schlösslwiese, Zur Ringmeierbucht.
GPS: n48,74022 e11,18434.

30 free € 1/100liter Ch. **Location:** Urban, simple, central, quiet. **Surface:** gravel/sand. 01/01-31/12.
Distance: 100m 400m on the spot on the spot.
Remarks: On the Danube river.

Neumarkt/Oberpfalz 17E1

Volksfestplatz, Woffenbacherstrasse. **GPS**: n49,28118 e11,44528.

25 free. **Surface:** grassy. 01/01-31/12 Jura-Volksfest.
Distance: 600m.
Remarks: At sports centre.

Neumarkt/Oberpfalz 17E1

Fritz Berger, Fritz-Berger-Str. 1. **GPS**: n49,30500 e11,48444.

free Ch free. **Surface:** grassy. 01/01-31/12.
Distance: 2km 2km.

Neuötting 20G1

Landshuter Straße. **GPS**: n48,24023 e12,67521.
4 free Ch. **Location:** Rural. **Surface:** grassy/gravel.

01/01-31/12.
Distance: 800m 700m 100m.
Remarks: Playground.

Neusäß 17D3

Titania-Therme, Birkenallee 1. **GPS**: n48,40089 e10,82508.

5 free. **Location:** Urban, simple, central, quiet.
Surface: metalled. 01/01-31/12.
Distance: 1,2km 3km 1,2km on the spot on the spot.

Neustadt/Aisch 17C1

Am Festplatz, Bei den Sommerkellern. **GPS**: n49,58187 e10,60271.

16 free € 1 Ch € 1. **Surface:** gravel.
01/01-31/12.
Distance: 500m 500m 500m 500m on the spot on the spot.

Neustadt/Aisch 17C1

Am Sportzentrum, Eilersweg 1. **GPS**: n49,57630 e10,63250.

8 € 8/night € 1/100liter Ch € 0,50 (12x)€ 2/night € 1
Location: Rural, simple, quiet. **Surface:** gravel/metalled.
01/04-15/10.
Distance: 500m 700m 750m 1km on the spot.
Remarks: Nearby sports complex.

Neustadt/Aisch 17C1

Am Waldwad, Eilersweg 5. **GPS**: n49,57462 e10,62993.

6 free. **Location:** Rural. **Surface:** grasstiles.
01/01-31/12.
Distance: 3,5km 4km 4km 1km on the spot.
Remarks: At sports centre, at swimming pool.

Niederwerrn 12C3

Jahnstrasse. **GPS**: n50,06073 e10,17526.

35 voluntary contribution € 3 Ch WC. **Location:** Urban, simple. **Surface:** asphalted. 01/01-31/12.
Distance: on the spot on the spot on the spot.
Remarks: Near sports fields, max. 3 nights.

Nordheim am Main 12C3

Zehnthofstrasse. **GPS**: n49,85952 e10,17909.

50 € 8/24h Ch included (24x)€ 0,50.
Location: Rural, simple, quiet. **Surface:** metalled.
01/04-31/10.
Distance: 200m on the spot on the spot on the spot.
Remarks: Along Main river, max. 3 days.

Nördlingen 17C3

Wohnmobilstellpatz Innerer Ring, Kaiserwiese.
GPS: n48,85488 e10,48445.

30 € 3/24h € 2/75liter € 2 Ch € 2/24h WC.
Location: Urban, simple, quiet. **Surface:** asphalted.
01/01-31/12.
Distance: on the spot McDonalds.
Remarks: Max. 48h.

Nürnberg 17D1

Volkspark Dutzendteich, Munchener Strasse.
GPS: n49,42403 e11,10586.

8 free. **Location:** Urban. **Surface:** asphalted. 01/01-31/12.
Distance: 4km 700m on the spot.
Remarks: Max. 3 nights.

Nürnberg 17D1

Volkspark Marienburg, Kilianstrasse.
GPS: n49,47495 e11,09606.

8 free. **Location:** Urban. **Surface:** grasstiles/metalled.
01/01-31/12.
Distance: centre 4km 800m 800m on the spot.
Remarks: Max. 3 nights.

Nürnberg 17D1

Wöhrder See, Rechenberganlage, Dr Gustav Heinemannstrasse.
GPS: n49,46041 e11,11548.

8 free. **Location:** Urban. **Surface:** metalled. 01/01-31/12.
Distance: 3km 500m.
Remarks: Max. 3 nights.

Tourist information Nürnberg:

City walk through old city centre, daily from Tourist Information, Hauptmarkt. 14.30h.

Nürnberg Card. Card gives for free entrance on among other things public transport and museums, discounts on purchases, boat trips, city walks etc.

Spielzeugmuseum, Karlstrasse 13-15. Toy museum. Tue-Su 10-17h.

Kaiserburg Nürnberg, Burg 13. Palace. 01/04-30/09 9-18h, 01/10-31/03 10-16h. € 7.

Tiergarten. Zoo. 8-19.30.

Oberammergau — 20D2

Reisemobilhafen Oberammergau, Ettalerstrasse 56B.
GPS: n47,59040 e11,07157.

20 € 12, 2 pers.incl Ch € 0,70/kWh against payment.
Location: Simple. **Surface:** gravel. 01/01-31/12.
Distance: 1,2km 400m 100m 1,2km 1km.

Oberaudorf — 20F2

Pechler Hof, Tatzlwurmstrasse 5. **GPS**: n47,66132 e12,16890.

5 € 9 included. **Location:** Rural, simple, quiet.
Surface: grassy. 01/01-31/12.
Distance: 1km 500m 200m 100m.

Oberaudorf — 20F2

Hotel Feuriger Tatzlwurm, Tatzlwurm, B307.
GPS: n47,67223 e12,08448.

10 guests free . **Location:** Rural, simple.
Surface: gravel/metalled. 01/01-31/12.
Distance: on the spot on the spot on the spot.

Oberelsbach — 12B2

Wohnmobilstellplatz Oberelsbach, Gangolfstrasse.
GPS: n50,44234 e10,11412.

6 € 5 € 1/80liter Ch (6x)€ 0,50/kWh. **Location:** Rural, simple, quiet. **Surface:** metalled. 01/01-31/12.
Distance: 500m 500m on the spot on the spot.
Remarks: Max. 3 days, to be paid at town hall.

Oberkotzau — 12E2

Wohnmobilstellplatz Am Summa-Park, Fabrikstraße.
GPS: n50,26344 e11,93849.
9 € 12 € 1/100liter Ch WC included .
Surface: metalled. 01/01-31/12.
Distance: 450m.
Remarks: Max. 5 days.

Obermaiselstein — 20C2

Wohnmobilplatz Allgäu, Am Goldbach 3, Niederdorf.
GPS: n47,44422 e10,24288.

30 € 11-12 + € 1,80/pp tourist tax € 0,50/50liter Ch (25x)€ 4/day WC € 1 . **Location:** Rural, comfortable.
Surface: asphalted/gravel. 01/01-31/12.
Distance: 700m on the spot.

Obernbreit — 17C1

Wohnmobilstellplatz Obernbreit an der Pröschelwiese, Marktbreiter Straße. **GPS**: n49,65910 e10,16570.
10 € 3 WC. **Surface:** gravel. 01/01-31/12.
Distance: on the spot 200m.

Oberstdorf — 20C3

Rubi-Camp, Rubinger Straße 34. **GPS**: n47,42340 e10,27772.

80 € 23-27, tourist tax € 2,60/pp, dog € 3,50 Ch € 0,70/kWh WC € 3/time € 5/day.
Surface: grassy. 01/01-31/12.
Distance: 1km bistro mini market 150m (skibus) on the spot on the spot.
Remarks: Bread-service.

Oberstdorf — 20C3

Wohnmobilstellplatz Oberstdorf, Hermann-von-Barth-Straße 9.
GPS: n47,40856 e10,28625.

150 € 12 + € 2,60/pp tourist tax Chincluded € 2,50/24h WC free.
Location: Rural, luxurious. **Surface:** grassy/metalled. 01/01-31/12.
Distance: on the spot 250m 100m on the spot 500m 800m.

Oberthulba — 12B3

Reisemobilstellplatz Thulbatal. **GPS**: n50,17419 e9,92499.

25 € 10, 2 pers.incl Chincluded (20x)€ 2 WC € 1 € 2,50. **Location:** Rural, simple. **Surface:** grasstiles.
15/03-31/10.
Distance: 1km on the spot 150m.

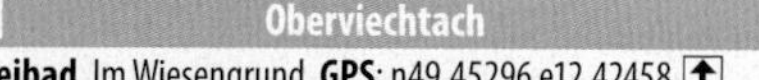

Oberviechtach — 17F1

Am Freibad, Im Wiesengrund. **GPS**: n49,45296 e12,42458.

+5 free Ch (3x)free. **Location:** Simple, isolated.
Surface: asphalted. 01/01-31/12.
Distance: 1km 600m.
Remarks: Max. 3 days.

Oettingen — 17C2

Schießwasen. **GPS**: n48,95690 e10,60894.

4 free € 1/10minutes Ch (4x)€ 1/8h.
Location: Simple, quiet. **Surface:** metalled.
01/01-31/12 last weekend Jul, 1st weekend Aug.
Distance: 10 min walking 500m.

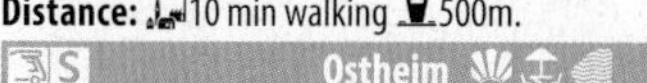

Ostheim — 12C2

Streuwiesenparkplatz, Nordheimer Straße/Alexander Straße.
GPS: n50,45820 e10,22656.

6 € 3 € 1/80liter Ch (6x)€ 0,50 WCincluded.
Location: Urban, simple, quiet. **Surface:** metalled.
01/01-31/12.
Distance: 300m 300m 300m on the spot on the spot.
Remarks: To be paid at AVIA petrol station, 200m.

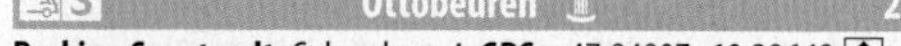

Ottobeuren — 20C1

Parking Sportwelt, Galgenberg 4. **GPS**: n47,94907 e10,29649.

10 free € 1/100liter Ch (6x)€ 0,50/kWh. **Location:** Urban,

DE

comfortable. **Surface:** metalled.
01/01-31/12.
Distance: 1km.
Remarks: Coins at Sportwelt (9-23h), village with noteworthy cathedral.

S Parkstein 17E1

Basaltkegel von Parkstein, Basaltstrasse 16.
GPS: n49,73179 e12,07127.

15 free. **Surface:** metalled. 01/01-31/12.
Distance: 200m 50m.
Remarks: Nearbij Gasthof Bergstüberl, beautiful view.

S Passau 17H3

Am Parkdeck Ilzbrücke, Halser Straße. **GPS**: n48,57895 e13,47437.

13 € 1/h, max. € 8/day € 1/50liter Ch € 0,50/kWh.
Location: Urban, comfortable, central. **Surface:** metalled.
01/01-31/12 high water.
Distance: centre 500m 500m 500m on the spot.
Remarks: Max. 24h.

S Passau 17H3

Am Parkhaus, Bahnhofstraße. **GPS**: n48,57406 e13,44495.

15 € 3/h, max. € 13/day Chincluded. **Location:** Urban, simple, noisy. **Surface:** metalled. 01/01-31/12.
Distance: 500m 500m 500m 100m.
Remarks: Price incl. bus transport to the city centre.

Passau 17H3

Winterhafen Racklau, Regensburgerstrasse/Racklau.
GPS: n48,57412 e13,42690.

30 free. **Surface:** gravel. 01/01-31/12 high water.
Distance: 2km On the Danube river on the spot 500m 500m 300m.

Peiting 20D2

Wellenfreibad, Ammergauer Strasse 22/A. **GPS**: n47,79317 e10,92227.

3 free. 01/01-31/12.
Distance: 100m 500m 1km.
Remarks: Parking at swimming pool, max. 48h, use sanitary only during opening hours swimming pool.

S Petting 20G1

Ferienhof Stubern, Stubern 1. **GPS**: n47,88988 e12,78455.

3 € 15, 2 pers.incl € 2/100liter Ch € 0,50/kWh WC.
Location: Rural, simple, quiet. **Surface:** grassy.
01/05-30/10.
Distance: 4km 5km 5km 3km 2km on the spot on the spot.

S Petting 20G1

Stellplatz Schneiderhof, Seestrasse 11a.
GPS: n47,91375 e12,81120.

4 € 15, 2 pers.incl Ch € 0,50/kWh WC included.
Location: Rural, comfortable. **Surface:** grassy. 01/05-30/10.
Distance: 300m 1km 300m 300m 500m.
Remarks: Dog € 4.

S Pfronten 20D2

Wohnmobilstellplatz Wohlfahrt, Am Wiesele 7, Weißbach.
GPS: n47,59829 e10,55240.

44 € 12, 2 pers.incl € 1/100liter Ch (44x)€ 0,50/kWh WC € 0,50/3minutes € 3/3 .
Location: Rural, comfortable, quiet.
Surface: gravel. 01/01-31/12.
Distance: 400m 100m 400m Skibus 5km on the spot.

S Plattling 17G2

Freizeit- und Sportzentrum Plattling, Georg-Ecklstrasse.
GPS: n48,77226 e12,87331.

20 free € 1/35liter Ch (6x)€ 0,50/kWh. **Location:** Rural, simple. **Surface:** grassy/metalled.
01/01-31/12.
Distance: 500m 500m.

S Pleinfeld 17D2

Freizeitanlage Ramsberg, Leitenbuckstraße.
GPS: n49,12103 e10,93275.
28 € 12/24h € 0,50/kWh WC. **Surface:** grassy.
01/01-31/12.
Distance: 800m on the spot on the spot 100m 5km.

S Pleystein 17F1

Reisemobilplatz Pleystein, Vohenstraußer Straße/Galgenbergweg.
GPS: n49,64429 e12,40548.

8 free WC free. **Surface:** gravel. 01/01-31/12.
Distance: 350m 200m.

Poppenricht 17E1

Wohnmobilstellplatz an der Vils, Vilsstrasse.
GPS: n49,48184 e11,83119.

20 free. **Location:** Rural, simple, quiet. **Surface:** gravel.
01/01-31/12.
Distance: 1km on the spot 2km 1km on the spot.
Remarks: Along the historic "Goldenen Straße" from Nürnberg to Prague, at sports centre.

S Pottenstein 17D1

Wohnmobilpark Pottenstein, Am langen Berg.
GPS: n49,76294 e11,40826.

25 € 7 € 1/80liter Ch € 1 (6x)€ 1/kWh.
Location: Rural, simple. **Surface:** grassy/metalled.
01/01-31/12 Service: winter.
Distance: 1km Aldi 200m.

S Pottenstein 17D1

Bernerhof, Prüllsbirkig 1. **GPS**: n49,77936 e11,44498.
8 € 10 € 1/80liter (2x)€ 1/2kWh.
Location: Rural. **Surface:** gravel.
01/01-31/12.
Distance: 3km 800m.
Remarks: Breakfast buffet € 8/pp.

Tourist information Pottenstein:

Teufelshöhle. Caves, constant temperature 9ºC and atmospheric humidity 98%. 19/03-06/11 9-17.
Burg Pottenstein. 1000 Jaar oude burcht. Tue-Su 10-17h.
Sommerrodelbahn. Toboggan slide 1km. 01/04-31/10 10-17h.

S Prichsenstadt 17C1

Wohnmobilstellplatz Schützengesellschaft 1752, Wiesentheider Straße 3. **GPS**: n49,81701 e10,35175.

DE

5 € 5 € 1 € 2,50. **Location:** Rural, simple. **Surface:** gravel.
01/01-31/12.
Distance: 300m 1,5km on the spot bakery 200m on the spot on the spot.
Remarks: Charging point for electric bicycles.

S Prien am Chiemsee 20F1

Wohnmobilstellplatz Strandbad Schraml, Harrasser Strasse 39.
GPS: n47,85400 e12,36679.

20 € 10 Ch € 3/day WC. **Location:** Rural, simple, isolated.
Surface: unpaved. 01/04-15/10.
Distance: 1,5km 6km on the spot 500m on the spot on the spot on the spot.
Remarks: Arrival >18h, departure <10h, pay at reception, nights closed with barrier, steep ramp.

S Rain/Lech 17D3

Wohnmobilstellplatz Rain, Fasanenweg.
GPS: n48,69195 e10,90699.

8 free € 1 Ch € 1/6h. **Location:** Rural, simple.
Surface: metalled. 01/01-31/12.
Distance: 1km on the spot on the spot.

S Ramsthal 12B3

Festplatz, Hauptstrasse, K6-4. **GPS:** n50,13750 e10,06111.

12 free € 1/80liter Ch (12x)€ 0,50/kWh.
Location: Rural, simple, quiet. **Surface:** grassy/metalled.
01/01-31/12.
Distance: 400m Gasthof Wahler, Gaststätte zum Beck on the spot.

S Reit im Winkl 20F2

Wohnmobilpark Reit im Winkl, Am Waldbahnhof 7, Groissenbach.
GPS: n47,67013 e12,48358.

250 € 12, 15/12-03/04 € 14 € 0,20/10liter Ch € 0,75/kWh WC use sanitary € 4,50. **Location:** Rural, quiet.
Surface: grassy/metalled. 01/01-31/12.
Distance: 1km 1,5km 200m on the spot on the spot on the spot on the spot.
Remarks: Shuttle bus to ski-piste.

S Reit im Winkl 20F2

Wohnmobilpark Seegatterl, Seegatterl 7.
GPS: n47,65898 e12,54213.

50 € 9, 05/12-03/04 € 13 + tourist tax € 0,20/10liter Ch € 0,75/kWh WC. **Location:** Rural, simple, quiet.
Surface: grassy/gravel. 05/12-10/04, 01/06-15/10.
Distance: 4km 1,5km 500m on the spot on the spot on the spot 150m on the spot.

S Reit im Winkl 20F2

Gasthof Stoaner, Birnbacher Straße 34.
GPS: n47,67900 e12,44930.

15 € 10, 2 pers.incl., winter € 12 Ch (12x)WC included.
Location: Rural, quiet. **Surface:** unpaved.
01/01-31/10 Easter-30/04.
Distance: 2km on the spot on the spot on the spot on the spot.
Remarks: At golf court.

S Riedenburg 17E2

Volksfestplatz, Austraße. **GPS:** n48,96446 e11,68181.

40 € 6 Ch included € 1/8h.
Location: Central. **Surface:** gravel/metalled.
01/01-31/12 last week of Aug.
Distance: 450m on the spot 300m 20m.
Remarks: At the Main-Danube Canal.

S Roding 17F2

Volksfestplatz, Jahnstraße 21. **GPS:** n49,19806 e12,51722.
4 free € 1/70liter € 1 Ch € 0,50/kWh. **Location:** Urban, simple. **Surface:** asphalted/metalled.
01/01-31/12.
Distance: 150m 150m 500m.
Remarks: Max. 1 day.

S Roßhaupten 20D2

Wohnmobilstellplatz Miller, Augsburger Strasse 23.
GPS: n47,65889 e10,71944.

25 € 9, 4 pers.incl € 1,50 Ch € 2 (3x)€ 2/day WC € 1,50.
Location: Simple. **Surface:** metalled. 01/01-31/12.
Distance: 50m 1,2km 1,2km 200m 150m 150m 1km 500m.
Remarks: Next to Camping- und Freizeitmarkt, reparation work.

S Roth 17D2

Steinerne Eiche, Hilpoltsteiner Strasse. **GPS:** n49,24089 e11,10637.
50 free Ch free. **Surface:** metalled. 01/01-31/12.
Distance: 1km 100m 200m.

S Rothenbuch 12B3

Freizeitanlage, Heigenbrücker Weg. **GPS:** n49,97460 e9,39475.

10 € 7 € 1/80liter Ch (10x)€ 0,50/kWh.
Location: Rural, simple, quiet. **Surface:** grasstiles.
01/01-31/12.
Distance: 250m on the spot.

S Rothenburg ob der Tauber 17C1

Parkplatz P2, Nördlinger Strasse. **GPS:** n49,37048 e10,18324.

25 € 10/24h, € 2/h € 1/80liter Ch € 0,50/kWh WC.
Location: Central. **Surface:** metalled. 01/01-31/12.
Distance: 700m 200m 200m 200m.

S Rothenburg ob der Tauber 17C1

Parkplatz P3, Schweinsdorfer Strasse. **GPS:** n49,38222 e10,18889.

30 € 10/24h, € 2/h € 1/45liter Ch WC.
Location: Urban, noisy.
Surface: metalled.
01/01-31/12.
Distance: on the spot.

Tourist information Rothenburg ob der Tauber:
M Mittelalterliches Kriminalmuseum, Burggasse 3. History of 1000 years of jurisdiction. 01/04-31/10 10-18h, 01/11-31/03 13-16h.
Schäfertanz. Traditional celebration.
27/03, 15/05, 04/09.

S Rothenkirchen 12D2

Waldschwimmbad, Badstraße 69. **GPS:** n50,37389 e11,31583.

DE

40 € 6 € 0,50 Ch€ 1 (16x)WC included.
Surface: metalled. 01/04-31/10.
Distance: 1,5km 900m.
Remarks: Parking swimming pool.

Röthlein 12C3

Sportanlage TSV/Bundeskegelbahn, Friedhofstrasse.
GPS: n49,98694 e10,21583.

6 free. **Location:** Urban, simple, quiet. **Surface:** unpaved.
01/01-31/12.
Distance: on the spot on the spot.

Röttingen 17B1

Wohnmobilplatz an der Tauber, Neubronner Straße.
GPS: n49,50724 e9,96995.

20 € 5 € 1/70liter Ch € 2/24h WC € 0,20 € 1,20.
Location: Rural, comfortable. **Surface:** gravel.
01/04-31/10 last 2 weeks of August.
Distance: 300m on the spot on the spot 500m 500m on the spot on the spot.
Remarks: Along the Tauber river.

Röttingen 17B1

Bach, KlingerStrabe 1. **GPS**: n49,50731 e9,97368.

10 free € 2,50/day WC € 2,50/day.
Location: Rural, simple, quiet. **Surface:** gravel. 01/01-31/12.
Distance: 500m on the spot on the spot on the spot 2km.
Remarks: Fishing permit available at town hall.

Ruhpolding 20G2

Campingplatz Ortnerhof, Ortsstraße 5.
GPS: n47,74260 e12,66303.

16 € 9 Ch € 0,70/kWh WC included € 3 € 3/24h.
Location: Rural, simple. **Surface:** gravel. 01/01-31/12.
Distance: 3km on the spot 2km on the spot on the spot on the spot on the spot.
Remarks: At golf court, max. 1 night.

Saulgrub 20D2

Ammertaler Hof, Alte Römerstraße 10. **GPS**: n47,64416 e11,02779.
3 € 15 WC. **Surface:** gravel. 01/01-31/12.
Distance: on the spot.

Scheidegg 20C2

Wohnmobilpark am Kurhaus, Am Hammerweiher 1.
GPS: n47,57351 e9,84545.
20 € 13,50 Ch (16x)included € 2.
Surface: gravel/metalled. 01/01-31/12.
Distance: Minishop.
Remarks: Bread-service.

Scheinfeld 17C1

Freibad Scheinfeld, Badstrasse 5. **GPS**: n49,67434 e10,46173.

14 € 7 Ch € 1/2kWh WC. **Location:** Rural, comfortable. **Surface:** gravel. 01/01-31/12.
Distance: on the spot on the spot.
Remarks: At swimming pool, picnic tables available.

Schliersee 20E2

Am Spitzingsee, Spitzingstraße. **GPS**: n47,66648 e11,88851.

+10 summer € 12, winter € 9 (no service) Ch.
Location: Rural, simple, isolated, quiet. **Surface:** gravel.
01/01-31/12 Service: winter.
Distance: 5,4km on the spot 500m on the spot on the spot on the spot.
Remarks: Altitude 1085m, at lake.

Schlüsselfeld 17C1

Bambergerstrasse. **GPS**: n49,75572 e10,62267.

5 free € 1/80liter Ch. **Location:** Urban, simple, central.
Surface: asphalted. 01/01-31/12.
Distance: on the spot on the spot on the spot 50m 50m.

Schlüsselfeld 17C1

Concorde, Concorde-Straße 2–4. **GPS**: n49,76745 e10,56478.

20 free € 1/100liter Ch € 0,50/kWh. **Location:** Rural, simple, quiet. **Surface:** metalled.
01/01-31/12.
Distance: 1km 1km 1km.
Remarks: At motohome manufacturer.

Schnelldorf 17C2

BP-Truckstop Feuchtwangen, Rudolph Dieselstrasse 1.
GPS: n49,17149 e10,24124.

15 € 7 € 1/80liter Ch (3x) WC € 2.
Surface: metalled. 01/01-31/12.
Distance: 300m on the spot on the spot.
Remarks: Discount at restaurant € 5, special part for motor homes.

Schöllkrippen 12A3

Naturerlebnisbad, Häfner-Ohnhaus-Straße.
GPS: n50,08484 e9,25247.

35 € 9/24h € 1/80liter Ch (24x)€ 0,50/kWh free1h.
Location: Rural, comfortable, quiet.
Surface: grassy. 01/01-31/12.
Distance: 500m on the spot on the spot on the spot.
Remarks: Bread-service.

Schongau 20D2

Festplatz, Lechuferstrasse. **GPS**: n47,80906 e10,89815.

70 € 5/24h € 1/50liter Ch WC.
Location: Urban, simple.
Surface: asphalted.
service: 20/03-05/11 during event.
Distance: 400m 100m 400m on the spot.
Remarks: Caution key sanitary € 30, guests free.

Schönsee 17F1

Moorbad, Böhmerwaldstrasse. **GPS**: n49,51091 e12,55321.
5 free. **Location:** Simple. 01/01-31/12.
Distance: 300m.
Remarks: Max. 3 days.

Schönwald 12E3

Freizeitland Schönwald, Grünhaid 4. **GPS**: n50,20958 e12,09570.
€ 10 € 2,50. 01/01-31/12.
Distance: on the spot.
Remarks: Breakfast-service.

Schrobenhausen 17D3

Am Klostergarten, Rot-Kreuz-Straße.
GPS: n48,55835 e11,26234.

4 free. **Location:** Simple, quiet. **Surface:** metalled.
01/01-31/12.
Distance: 400m 400m 400m.

S Schrobenhausen 17D3

Stadtwerke-Kläranlage, Köningslachenerweg 12.
GPS: n48,57374 e11,27519.
Ch Service € 5. 01/01-31/12.
Remarks: Mo-Thu 7-12h, 13-16h, Fr 7-12h.

S Schwandorf 17E1

Festplatz, Angerring, Krondorf. **GPS:** n49,33230 e12,10247.

30 free Ch free.
Location: Simple. **Surface:** asphalted/grassy.
01/01-31/12 week before/after Whitsuntide.
Distance: 500m 200m 500m.
Remarks: Along the Naab river.

S Schwangau 20D2

Wohnmobilpark Schwangau, Münchenerstrasse 151.
GPS: n47,59167 e10,77250.

24 € 14-19, tourist tax € 1,90/pp, dog € 2 Ch (24x) € 2,50 WC included. **Location:** Urban, comfortable.
Surface: grassy/gravel. 01/01-31/12.
Distance: 2km on the spot on the spot on the spot on the spot on the spot 1km on the spot.
Remarks: Dog € 2/day.

S Schwarzenbach an der Saale 12E3

Fleischgasse. **GPS:** n50,22324 e11,93311.
2 free € 1 Ch € 1. **Location:** Central. **Surface:** metalled.
01/01-31/12.
Distance: on the spot on the spot on the spot.

S Schweinfurt 12C3

Wohnmobilpark Saumain, Am Hutrasen.
GPS: n50,03868 e10,23499.

20 € 10 € 1/80liter Ch € 0,50/kWh.
Location: Rural, comfortable, quiet. **Surface:** grassy/gravel.
01/01-31/12.
Distance: 1,5km 1km on the spot on the spot 100m 100m on the spot on the spot.

Segnitz 17C1

Mainstraße 20. **GPS:** n49,67012 e10,14242.

4 free. **Location:** Urban, simple. **Surface:** metalled.
01/01-31/12.
Distance: on the spot on the spot on the spot 200m.
Remarks: Max. 1 day.

S Segnitz 17C1

Gasthaus zum Goldenen Anker, Mainstraße 8.
GPS: n49,67063 e10,14344.

9 € 5 € 0,50/50liter Ch (18x) € 0,50.
Location: Urban, simple. **Surface:** grassy/gravel.
01/01-31/12 Restaurant: Thu.
Distance: 850m on the spot on the spot on the spot 1km on the spot.
Remarks: Along Main river.

S Selb 12E3

Papiermühlweg 2. **GPS:** n50,16952 e12,12512.
10 € 6 € 0,50/100liter Ch € 0,50/kWh WC.
Surface: metalled. 01/01-31/12.
Distance: 200m 400m.

Selb 12E3

Eissporthalle, Hanns-Braun-Straße 27. **GPS:** n50,15601 e12,13489.

10 free. **Surface:** gravel. 01/01-31/12.
Distance: 1km 200m 1km on the spot.
Remarks: Hiking trails.

S Siegsdorf 20G1

Gasthof Hörterer der Hammerwirt, Schmiedstrasse, B306, Hammer.
GPS: n47,80096 e12,70392.

10 guests free WC. **Location:** Rural, simple. **Surface:** metalled.
01/01-31/12 Wed.
Distance: 6km on the spot on the spot 100m 100m on the spot on the spot 2,5km 300m.
Remarks: Max. 3 nights.

Sonthofen 20C2

Erlebnisbad Wonnemar, Stadionweg 5.
GPS: n47,50344 e10,27883.

10 € 3,50/night. **Location:** Urban, simple. **Surface:** gravel.
01/01-31/12.
Distance: 1,5km 2,5km on the spot on the spot on the spot.
Remarks: Max. 1 night.

S Spalt 17D2

Wohnmobilpark Rezattal, Obeltshauserstraße 3.
GPS: n49,17512 e10,92937.
12 € 9,50 + € 1,50/pp tourist tax Ch € 2,50 WC.
Surface: gravel. 01/01-31/12.
Distance: on the spot 500m 200m on the spot on the spot.

S Steinach/Straubing 17F2

Firma Hubert Brandl Caravantastic, Gewerbering 11.
GPS: n48,95639 e12,62250.

3 free € 1 . **Location:** Simple. **Surface:** grassy.
01/01-31/12.
Distance: 1,5km 2km 1km.
Remarks: Connection electricity < 18h.

S Steinberg am See 17F1

Movin'G'round, Am Steinberger See. **GPS:** n49,28247 e12,17357.

25 € 7 service € 2 Ch . **Location:** Rural, simple.
Surface: grassy. 01/04-31/10.
Distance: 500m on the spot on the spot.
Remarks: Check in at pay-desk.

S Sulzbach-Rosenberg 17E1

Großparkplatz, Bayreuther Straße. **GPS:** n49,50583 e11,74500.

4 free € 1/80liter Ch (4x) € 0,50/kWh.
Location: Urban, simple. **Surface:** gravel. 01/01-31/12.
Distance: 300m 500m 500m on the spot.

S Sulzemoos 20D1

Der Freistaat Caravaning, Ohmstrasse. **GPS:** n48,28267 e11,26084.

40 free € 1/80liter Ch (20x) € 1/kWh WC.
Location: Simple. **Surface:** gravel.
01/01-31/12.
Distance: 800m 800m McDonalds 800m 800m 600m.
Remarks: Motorhome dealer.

Tauberrettersheim 17B1

Brunnenstrasse. **GPS:** n49,49635 e9,93720.

DE

6 free. **Location:** Rural, simple, quiet. **Surface:** grassy.
01/01-31/12.
Distance: on the spot on the spot on the spot 50m bakery 200m on the spot on the spot.
Remarks: Swimming pool 100m.

S Thierstein 12E3

Kaiserstein, Hirtweg. **GPS**: n50,10610 e12,10490.

10 € 5/24h included voluntary contribution.
Surface: metalled. 01/01-31/12 01/10-31/03 water disconnected. **Distance:** 500m 500m 500m.
Remarks: Max. 2 nights, beautiful view.

S Thüngersheim 12B3

Parkplatz Main-Aue, Am Schwimbad. **GPS**: n49,88084 e9,83717.

20 free Chfree (16x)€ 0,50/kWh. **Location:** Rural, comfortable, noisy. **Surface:** grassy. 01/04-31/10.
Distance: 500m on the spot on the spot.
Remarks: Along Main river.

S Traunstein 20F1

Gasthaus Jobst, Balthasar Permoserstrasse 64, Rettenbach.
GPS: n47,91188 e12,64899.

10 € 3, guests free € 2 € 2,50 WC. **Location:** Rural, simple.
Surface: metalled. 01/01-31/12 Wed.
Distance: on the spot on the spot on the spot on the spot on the spot on the spot.

S Traunstein 20F1

Firma Grüaugl, Schmidhamerstrasse 31. **GPS**: n47,88227 e12,59941.

12 € 5 € 1/100liter Ch € 0,50/kWh. **Location:** Isolated.
Surface: metalled. 01/01-31/12.
Distance: 2,5km.

Remarks: Camping equipment store.

S Treuchtlingen 17D2

Reisemobilstellplatz am Kurpark, Kästleinmühlenstrasse 20.
GPS: n48,96028 e10,91778.

56 € 9,50 € 1/80liter Ch (56x)€ 1/8h WC included . **Location:** Urban, comfortable, quiet. **Surface:** grasstiles.
01/01-31/12.
Distance: 800m on the spot.
Remarks: Bread-service.

S Trostberg 20F1

Jahnstraße. **GPS**: n48,02194 e12,54607.

8 free € 1/50liter (2x)€ 1. **Surface:** gravel. 01/01-31/12
01/09-10/09.
Distance: 800m 300m 300m station 1km.

S Übersee/Chiemsee 20F1

Bauernhof Steiner, Almfischer 11, Stegen.
GPS: n47,80963 e12,49136.

25 € 12 Ch € 0,50/kWh WC € 0,50/2minutes.
Location: Rural, simple, quiet. **Surface:** gravel.
01/01-31/12.
Distance: Übersee 2km 4,6km Chiemsee 6km 1km.

S Übersee/Chiemsee 20F1

Wohmobilstellplatz Schmid, Stegen 4. **GPS**: n47,81237 e12,48843.

28 € 11,50 2p incl., excl. tourist tax Ch € 0,50/kWh
€ 1,50. **Location:** Rural, simple. **Surface:** grassy/gravel.
01/01-31/12.
Distance: Übersee 2km 4km Chiemsee 5km 2km 2km
1,5km on the spot.
Remarks: Bread-service.

Veitshöchheim 17B1

Parkplatz am Fußgängersteg, Am Güßgraben.
GPS: n49,83623 e9,86916.

5 free. **Location:** Rural, simple, quiet. **Surface:** metalled.
01/01-31/12.
Distance: 500m on the spot on the spot.
Remarks: Along Main river, max. 24h.

Viechtach 17G2

P1, Stadtmitte, Bierfeldstraße. **GPS**: n49,07876 e12,88235.

6 free. **Surface:** metalled. 01/01-31/12.
Distance: 400m 150m 50m.
Remarks: In front of supermarket Edeka, max. 3 nights.

Viechtach 17G2

P2, Stadthalle, Friedhofstrasse. **GPS**: n49,07722 e12,88528.

3 free. **Location:** Simple. **Surface:** metalled.
01/01-31/12.
Remarks: Max. 3 nights.

Viechtach 17G2

P5, TÜV, Karl-Gareis-Straße. **GPS**: n49,08222 e12,88306.

free. **Surface:** asphalted. 01/01-31/12.
Distance: 500m 500m.
Remarks: Max. 3 nights, small pitches.

S Viechtach 17G2

Berghütte 'Zum Pröller', Hinterviechtach 3, Kollnburg.
GPS: n49,02939 e12,83892.

3 € 5 included. **Surface:** gravel. 01/01-31/12.
Distance: Viechtach 7km 20m.
Remarks: Parking at skipistes.

S Viechtach 17G2

Am Regenufer 1. **GPS**: n49,08303 e12,88824.
€ 1 € 1 Ch. 01/01-31/12.

DE

Tourist information Viechtach:
Stadtplatz. Week market. Wed 7-17h.

Vilseck 17E1

Ziegelanger. **GPS**: n49,61145 e11,80068.

20 free. **Location:** Simple, central, quiet. **Surface:** asphalted/gravel.
01/01-31/12.
Distance: 200m on the spot on the spot on the spot 200m 200m.

Vilshofen 17G3

Schiffanleger, Donaukade. **GPS**: n48,63833 e13,18000.

12 free. **Location:** Simple, noisy. **Surface:** asphalted.
01/01-31/12.
Distance: 500m On the Danube river on the spot 500m 500m.
Remarks: Max. 1 night.

Vilshofen 17G3

Yachthafen Vilshofen, Am Bootshafen.
GPS: n48,63870 e13,18785.

10 € 12 Ch (10x)€ 3/day WC € 1. **Location:** Comfortable, quiet. **Surface:** gravel. 01/04-30/11.
Distance: 500m On the Danube river.

Vohenstrauß 17F1

Stadthalle, Neuwirtshauser Weg 11. **GPS**: n49,61872 e12,34523.

15 free Ch free WC.
Surface: gravel. 01/01-31/12.
Distance: 100m 800m 50m 100m.
Remarks: Caution key sanitary € 50.

Volkach 12C3

Am Mainufer, Am Gries. **GPS**: n49,87457 e10,16418.

10 € 5,50. **Location:** Rural, simple, quiet. **Surface:** metalled.
01/04-31/10.
Distance: on the spot on the spot 300m 200m on the spot.
Remarks: Max. 3 days.

Volkach 12C3

An der Mainbrücke. **GPS**: n49,86389 e10,22139.

30 € 5,50. **Location:** Urban, simple, noisy. **Surface:** gravel.
01/04-31/10.
Distance: 500m on the spot on the spot 500m 500m on the spot.
Remarks: Along Main river, max. 3 days.

Volkach 12C3

Unter der Mainbrücke, Mainufer. **GPS**: n49,86455 e10,21874.

8 € 5,50. **Location:** Urban, simple, noisy. **Surface:** gravel.
01/04-31/10.
Distance: 1km on the spot 900m 1km on the spot.
Remarks: Max. 3 days.

Waidhaus 17F1

Barbara Sonneschein, Pfrentsch 20. **GPS**: n49,61823 e12,49040.

10 € 5 Chincluded € 0,35/kWh. **Location:** Rural, simple, quiet. **Surface:** grassy. 01/01-31/12.
Distance: on the spot on the spot.

Wald 20D2

Walder Badeweiher, Am Sportplatz. **GPS**: n47,72294 e10,56348.

10 € 5 Ch. **Location:** Rural, simple, quiet.
Surface: gravel. 01/01-31/12.
Distance: 500m on the spot 250m on the spot on the spot.
Remarks: Service at fire-station, 200m.

Waldkirchen 17H2

Karoli-Badepark, VDK Heimstrasse 1. **GPS**: n48,72222 e13,60278.

16 free € 1/50liter Ch (10x)€ 0,50/kWh WC.
Location: Rural, simple, quiet. **Surface:** gravel.
01/01-31/12.
Distance: 1km 25m 2km on the spot on the spot.
Remarks: Parking skating rink-swimming pool, bread-service, use sanitary only during opening hours swimming pool, against payment.

Waldsassen 12F3

P2 Schwanenwiese, Schwanengasse. **GPS**: n50,00526 e12,30739.

4 € 5 (4x)€ 2/10h WC. **Surface:** metalled.
01/01-31/12.
Distance: 500m 500m 500m.
Remarks: Max. 3 days, pay at tourist office.

Waldsassen 12F3

P1, Joseph-Wiesnetstrasse. **GPS**: n50,00250 e12,30361.

2 free. **Surface:** metalled. 01/01-31/12.
Distance: 100m 100m 100m.
Remarks: Max. 3 days.

Wassertrüdingen 17C2

An der Wörnitz, Entengraben. **GPS**: n49,03926 e10,59494.

12 free € 1/80liter Ch (6x)€ 2/8h € 1.
Location: Urban, simple, quiet. **Surface:** metalled.
01/01-31/12.
Distance: on the spot on the spot on the spot 1km.

Weidenberg 12E3

Am Sportpark, In der Au. **GPS**: n49,93781 e11,73068.

2-3 free. **Surface:** gravel. 01/01-31/12.
Distance: 750m Chinese restaurant 100m 1,5km.

Weilheim in Oberbayern 20D2

Lohgasse. **GPS**: n47,84012 e11,13583.

DE

8 € 6 € 0,50/50liter Ch € 0,50/kWh WC.
Location: Urban, simple, central. **Surface:** asphalted.
01/01-31/12.
Distance: Old city centre 500m 100m 200m.
Remarks: Along the Ammer river, max. 5 days.

S **Weismain** 12D3

Bauhof, Burgkunstadterstrasse. **GPS**: n50,08639 e11,23872.

4 free € 1 € 0,50 Ch€ 0,50 (6x)€ 0,50. **Location:** Urban, simple. **Surface:** asphalted. 01/01-31/12.
Distance: on the spot on the spot 200m 200m 200m.
Remarks: Parking in centre.

S **Weissenburg** 17D2

Kirchweihplatz, Limesbad, Badstrasse 5.
GPS: n49,02476 e10,97180.

free € 1/80liter Ch. **Location:** Urban. **Surface:** metalled.
01/04-31/10.
Distance: Old city centre 300m La Fattoria, Frauentorstrasse 11; Mai Tai, Bismarckanlage 16; Wittelsbacher Hof, Fr.Ebertstrasse 21 on the spot.

S **Weissenburg** 17D2

Vino y Tapa Restaurant, Silbermühle 4. **GPS**: n49,04521 e10,96679.
9 free against payment. **Surface:** grassy/metalled.
01/01-31/12.
Distance: city centre 2km on the spot.

S **Wertach** 20C2

Camping Grüntensee, Grüntenseestraße 41.
GPS: n47,61003 e10,44704.

10 € 15 + € 1,50/pp tourist tax Ch (12x)€ 0,60/kWh.
Location: Rural, luxurious, quiet. **Surface:** gravel.
01/01-31/12.
Distance: 2,5km 600m on the spot on the spot on the spot 1,5km 1,5km on the spot on the spot on the spot on the spot.

S **Wertach** 20C2

Buron-Kinderpark, Grüntenseestraße 44. **GPS**: n47,61028 e10,44972.

36 € 5 € 1/100liter Ch (24x)€ 1,50/24h.
Surface: gravel. 01/01-31/12.
Distance: 3km 200m on the spot on the spot.

S **Wertingen** 17D3

Wohnmobilpark Wertingen, Am Bahnhof 4.
GPS: n48,55948 e10,69065.

12 € 7 € 0,50/50liter Ch (12x)€ 2/day.
Location: Urban, comfortable, central, quiet. **Surface:** grassy/gravel.
01/01-31/12.
Distance: 800m 100m.
Remarks: Money in envelope in mail box.

S **Wiesenttal** 12D3

Wohnmobilstellplatz Streitberg, Bahnhofstrasse, B470.
GPS: n49,80782 e11,21636.

7 € 2 Chfree. **Location:** Rural, simple, quiet. **Surface:** gravel.
01/01-31/12.
Distance: 500m 500m 500m 500m 300m.
Remarks: Along railwayline.

S **Wipfeld** 12C3

An der Mainlände, Follinaplatz. **GPS**: n49,91954 e10,17899.

20 € 5 € 1/100liter ChWC.
Location: Rural, comfortable. **Surface:** asphalted. 01/01-31/12.
Distance: on the spot on the spot on the spot 50m 50m on the spot on the spot.

S **Wolnzach** 17E3

Schwimm- & Erlebnisbad Wolnzach, Hanslmühlweg 6.
GPS: n48,59718 e11,62792.

4 free € 1/80liter Ch (4x)€ 0,50/kWh. **Location:** Simple.
Surface: metalled. 01/01-31/12.

Distance: 600m 500m 600m.
Remarks: Service 100m.

S **Wonneberg** 20G1

Gasthof Alpenblick, Traunsteiner Straße 21, Weibhausen.
GPS: n47,89880 e12,69123.

5 free, use of a meal desired WC against payment.
Location: Simple. **Surface:** gravel. 01/01-31/12.
Distance: 5km 10km 5km on the spot on the spot on the spot.

S **Wunsiedel** 12E3

Ferienhof, Sinatengrün 9. **GPS**: n50,05837 e12,04150.
3 € 20 Ch WC included. 01/01-31/12.
Distance: 5km.
Remarks: Bread-service + breakfast-service.

S **Wunsiedel** 12E3

Wohnmobilstellplatz Festspielstadt Wunsiedel, Ludwigstraße.
GPS: n50,03638 e11,99351.

6 € 5/24h Ch included.
Surface: gravel. 01/01-31/12 water: Nov-March.
Distance: 600m 300m 1km.
Remarks: Pay at tourist office.

Würzburg 17B1

Viehmarktplatz, Dreikronenstraße. **GPS**: n49,79782 e9,92319.

25 € 12/24h.
Location: Urban, simple, noisy. **Surface:** asphalted. 01/01-31/12.
Distance: 800m on the spot 50m. **Remarks:** Max. 2 days.

Tourist information Würzburg:

Würzburger Residenz, Residenzplatz. Baroque castle, Unesco World Heritage Site. 01/04-31/10 9-18h, 01/11-31/03 10-16.30h. € 7,50.

Zeil am Main 12C3

Altstadtparkplatz, Mittelweg. **GPS**: n50,00667 e10,59583.

10 free. **Location:** Urban, simple, noisy.
Surface: metalled.
01/01-31/12.
Distance: on the spot 350m 550m 400m 400m 400m.

Zeil am Main 12C3

Parkplatz Tuchanger, Oskar Winkler strasse.
GPS: n50,01083 e10,59056.

20 free. **Location:** Urban, simple. **Surface:** metalled.
01/01-31/12.
Distance: 1km 1km 1km 1km 1km 1km.
Remarks: Parking gymnasium.

Tourist information Zeil am Main:
Brauereigasthof Göller "Zum alten Freyung". Brewery restaurant with regional specialities and Göller-beer. Mo-Su 9.30-01h.
Altstadt Weinfest. Wine festivals. 06/08-08/08.
Wein-Wander-Weg. Hiking trail through wine region.

Zellingen 12B3

Am Freibad, Badstraße. **GPS**: n49,89476 e9,82680.

6 free. **Location:** Rural, simple, quiet. **Surface:** grassy.
01/01-31/12.
Distance: on the spot.

Zirndorf 17D1

Playmobil Funpark, Brandstätterstrasse. **GPS**: n49,43087 e10,93935.
40 € 5-10. **Surface:** metalled. 01/01-31/12.
Distance: on the spot on the spot.

DE

Denmark

Capital: Copenhagen
Government: Constitutional monarchy
Official Language: Danish
Population: 5,593,785 (2016)
Area: 44,000 km^2

General information
Dialling code: 0045
General emergency: 112
Currency: Danish Krone (DKK), 1 DKK= 100 øre,
DKK 1 = € 0,13, € 1 = DKK 7,44
DKK 1 = £0.12, £1 = DKK 8,45 (October 2017)
Payments by credit card are accepted at almost every shop and restaurant.

Regulations for overnight stays/campsites
Overnight parking is allowed: for 1 night, if there is no local prohibition, but no "camping" activities are allowed.

Camping Key Europe is obligatory when using Danish campsites: the card can be purchased at any campsite for DKK 110 (± € 14,80/£13), valid for one year.

Additional public holidays 2018
April 27 Great Prayer Day
June 5 Danisch Constitution Day
June 23 Sankt Hans Eve

Time Zone
Winter (Standard Time) GMT+1
Summer (DST) GMT+2

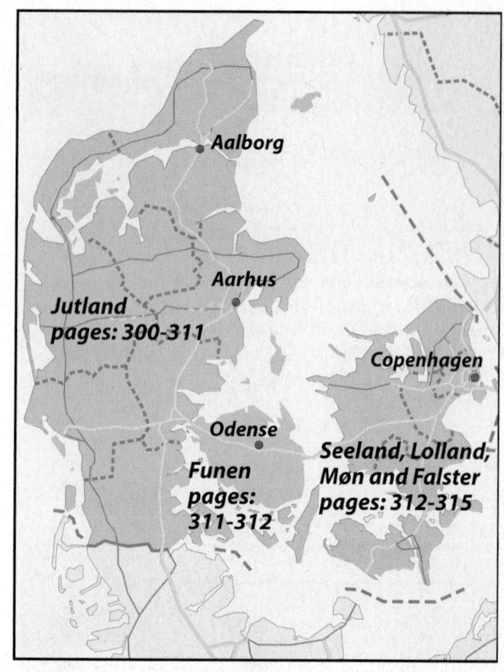

DK

Jutland

Aabybro 5C3
Birthe&Leif Brinkmann, Kanalvej 164. **GPS**: n57,11947 e9,73156.

3 DKK 50. **Location:** Simple, isolated. **Surface:** grassy.
01/05-30/09.
Distance: 5km.

Aalborg 5C3
Aalborg, Skydebanevej 50. **GPS**: n57,05379 e9,87233.
DKK 126 Ch against payment. 01/01-31/12.
Distance: on the spot.
Remarks: Quick-Stop: >20h - <10h.

Aalborg 5C3
Strandparken, Skydebanevej 20. **GPS**: n57,05502 e9,88499.
DKK 110 Ch against payment. 24/03-18/09.
Remarks: Quick-Stop: >20h - <10h.

Tourist information Aalborg:
Aalborg Tourist & Convention Bureau, østeraagade 8, www.visitaalborg.com.
Søfarts - og Marinemuseum, Vestre Fjordvej 81. Maritime museum. 01/05-31/12.
Aalborg Zoo, Mølleparkvej 63. Zoo. 01/05-30/12.

Aalbæk 5C2
Galleri & Selskabslokal Gyllegaard, Hirtshalsvej 48.
GPS: n57,60619 e10,41757.

5 DKK 100. **Location:** Simple, isolated, quiet. **Surface:** grassy.
01/01-31/12.
Distance: 4km 1km 4km 4km.

Aalbæk 5C2
Aalbæk Havn, Sønder Havnevej 69. **GPS**: n57,59306 e10,42686.

6 DKK 200 Ch (6x) WC DKK 20/20 included.
Location: Simple, quiet. **Surface:** gravel. 01/01-31/12.
Distance: 800m on the spot on the spot 800m 800m 250m.
Remarks: Pay at harbourmaster.

Aalbæk 5C2
Skiveren Camping, Niels Skiverens Vej 5-7. **GPS**: n57,61616 e10,27891.
DKK 130. 18/03-30/09.
Distance: on the spot.
Remarks: Quick-Stop: >20h - <10h.

Aarhus 6D1
Aarhus centrum parkerinsplads, Kalkværksvej 2.
GPS: n56,14815 e10,21015.

6 free. **Location:** Urban, simple, central. **Surface:** asphalted.
01/01-31/12.
Distance: 500m on the spot on the spot.
Remarks: Behind petrol station, max. 24h.

Aarhus 6D1
Marselisborg Havn, Marselisborg Havnevej 54.
GPS: n56,13927 e10,21916.
DKK 140 Ch WC against payment.
Surface: grassy. 01/05-30/09.
Distance: on the spot on the spot on the spot on the spot.

Aarhus 6D1
Aarhus Camping, Randersvej 400. **GPS**: n56,22672 e10,16335.
DKK 100 Chagainst payment DKK 3,75/kWh DKK 5.
Surface: grassy. 01/01-31/12.
Remarks: Quick-Stop: >20h - <10h.

Åbenrå 6D2
Camperstop Aabenraa, Sønderskovvej 104.
GPS: n55,02513 e9,41471.

34 DKK 100 DKK 20/120liter Ch DKK 4,50/kWh WC DKK 10/5minutes DKK 25 . **Location:** Simple, central, quiet.
Surface: grassy/gravel. 01/01-31/12.
Distance: 2km 8km 400m 400m 700m 600m.
Remarks: Chip-card available at campsite.

Åbenrå 6D2
Lystbådehavn, Kystvej 55. **GPS**: n55,03434 e9,42352.

48 € 17 Ch DKK 1/24 WCincluded DKK 20 DKK 30 .
Location: Simple, comfortable, central. **Surface:** gravel.
01/01-31/12.
Distance: 1km on the spot on the spot on the spot 300m 200m on the spot on the spot.
Remarks: Harbour Åbenrå.

Åbenrå 6D2
Fjordlyst Camping, Sønderskovvej 100. **GPS**: n55,02466 e9,41469.
DKK 100. 19/03-23/10.
Remarks: Quick-Stop: >20h - <10h.

Åbenrå 6D2
Sandskaer Strandcamping, Sandskaervej 592.
GPS: n55,10460 e9,48481.
DKK 100. 18/03-18/09.
Distance: 100m.
Remarks: Quick-Stop: >20h - <10h.

Aså 5C3
Asaa Camping og Hytteferie, Vodbindervej 13.
GPS: n57,14560 e10,40264.
4 DKK 145 DKK 35 WCfree DKK 5/5minutes.
Surface: grassy/gravel. 09/04-24/09.
Distance: 300m 300m 250m on the spot on the spot.
Remarks: Quick-Stop: >20h - <10h.

Augustenborg 6D2
Augustenborg Slot, Ny Stavensbøl 1. **GPS**: n54,94703 e9,85427.

70 DKK 130 Ch included.
Location: Rural, comfortable. **Surface:** grassy. 01/01-31/12.
Distance: 1,5km on the spot on the spot.

Augustenborg 6D2

Augustenborg Yachthavn, Langdel 6. **GPS**: n54,94074 e9,86942.

19 DKK 130 Ch DKK 25 WC. **Location:** Luxurious, central. **Surface:** grassy/gravel. 01/04-31/10.
Distance: 700m 1km on the spot.

Billund 6C1

Camperpark Billund, Grenevej 5. **GPS**: n55,70480 e9,12406.

10 € 16 Chincluded DKK 22. **Location:** Rural, comfortable. **Surface:** grassy. 01/01-31/12.
Distance: 3,5km 3,5km 3,5km.

Bindslev 5C3

Tannisbugt Hallen, Stadion alle 7. **GPS**: n57,54559 e10,19943.
20 DKK 75 ChWC. **Location:** Urban. **Surface:** metalled.
01/01-31/12 15/07-07/08.

Bjert 6D2

Stensager Strand, Oluf Ravnsvej 16. **GPS**: n55,42076 e9,58785.
DKK 180 Ch against payment. 24/03-15/09.
Remarks: Quick-Stop: >20h - <10h.

Bredsten 6C1

Naturstedet Gårdbutik, Hærvejen 96. **GPS**: n55,73927 e9,32001.
DKK 50 . **Surface:** gravel. 01/01-31/12.
Distance: 6km.

Bredsten 6C1

B&B Klingsbjerggaard, Vejlevej 50. **GPS**: n55,70077 e9,40296.
DKK 100. 01/01-31/12.
Distance: 1km 1km.

Broager 6D3

Broager Strand Camping, Skeldebro 32. **GPS**: n54,86780 e9,74419.
DKK 99. 01/01-31/12.
Distance: 100m.
Remarks: Quick-Stop: >20h - <10h.

Broager 6D3

Gammelmark Strand Camping, Gammelmark 20.
GPS: n54,88586 e9,72926.
DKK 150. 23/03-02/10.
Distance: 100m.
Remarks: Quick-Stop: >20h - <10h.

Brovst 5C3

Vilsbæk Ridecenter, Kanalvej 34. **GPS**: n57,11895 e9,53640.

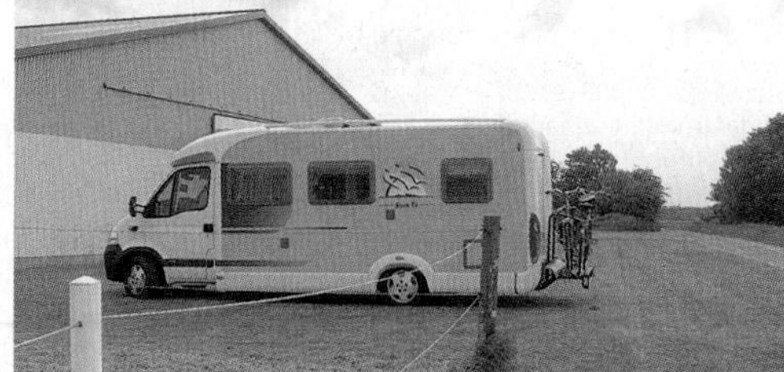

10 DKK 75 Ch WCincluded. **Location:** Rural, simple, isolated, quiet. **Surface:** grassy. 01/01-31/12.
Distance: 2km.
Remarks: At manege.

Brovst 5C3

Tranum Klit Camping, Sandmosevej 525. **GPS**: n57,17097 e9,46312.
DKK 120. 19/03-02/10.
Remarks: Quick-Stop: >20h - <10h.

Brædstrup 6D1

Hunos Museum & Samlinger, Hallevej 7.
GPS: n55,98548 e9,50352.
DKK 100 DKK 20. **Location:** Rural. **Surface:** grassy/gravel.
Distance: 8,5km.
Remarks: At museum.

Brønderslev 5C3

Ny Vestermark, Hollenstedvej 247. **GPS**: n57,21578 e10,04992.
DKK 100 ChWC included against payment.
Location: Rural, isolated, quiet.
Surface: grassy. 01/01-31/12.
Distance: 5km.

Brønderslev 5C3

Serritslev Fiskepark, Agårdsvej 35. **GPS**: n57,29750 e9,99597.

20 DKK 50 free WC. **Location:** Rural, simple, isolated, quiet.
Surface: grassy. 01/01-31/12.
Distance: on the spot.
Remarks: Fishpond.

Bylderup-Bov 6C2

Boskov, Kvænholtvej 15. **GPS**: n54,94488 e9,06078.

10 DKK 60 Ch included. **Location:** Rural, simple, isolated, quiet. **Surface:** grassy/gravel. 01/01-31/12.
Distance: 4km 200m.

Bylderup-Bov 6C2

B&B Bredevad, Bredevadvej 5. **GPS**: n54,96885 e9,12138.

2 € 14, 2 pers incl Ch WC included.
Location: Rural, comfortable, isolated. **Surface:** grassy.
01/01-31/12.
Distance: 15km 9km 4km on the spot on the spot.

Bylderup-Bov 6C2

Kristianshåb Autocamper Park, Kristianshåbvej 5.
GPS: n54,96189 e9,06950.
25 DKK 110, 2 pers.incl Ch DKK 3/kWh WC.
Location: Comfortable, isolated.
01/01-31/12.
Distance: 6km 1km 5km.

Tourist information Bylderup-Bov:
Schackenborg Slot, Schackenborg 2, Tønder. Visit the castle garden.

Bækmarksbro 6C1

Staudehaven-Granly, Kræmmergårdvej 5.
GPS: n56,41032 e8,31595.

3 DKK 50 included. **Location:** Simple, quiet.
Surface: grassy/gravel. 01/01-31/12.

Bælum 5C3

Bakgaarden, Hælskovvej 2. **GPS**: n56,83815 e10,12007.

4 DKK 75 Ch included.
Surface: grassy. 01/01-31/12.
Distance: 1km 1km.

Bønnerup 5D3

Bønnerup Lystbådehavn, Vestre Mole 2, Glesborg.
GPS: n56,53139 e10,71139.

20 DKK 150 Ch (12x)included WC against payment.
Location: Rural, comfortable, quiet. **Surface:** gravel.
01/01-31/12.
Distance: 500m on the spot on the spot 250m 400m.
Remarks: Parking at marina.

Børkop 6D1

Brejning Lystbådehavn, Brejning Strand.
GPS: n55,67431 e9,68920.

12 DKK 140 (12x)WC included .
Location: Rural, simple, isolated, quiet. **Surface:** gravel/metalled.
01/05-30/10.
Distance: Børkop 5km 4,1km 10m 10m.
Remarks: Restaurant only in summer.

Ebeltoft 6D1

Skøvgarde, Havmøllevej 5. **GPS**: n56,24475 e10,77902.

DK

2 DKK 50 DKK 20. Location: Rural, simple, isolated, quiet.
Surface: grassy. 01/01-31/12.
Distance: on the spot on the spot.
Remarks: Pay at Havmøllevej 5 or 20.

Ebeltoft 6D1

Kvickly, Østeralle 16. **GPS:** n56,19675 e10,68055.
overnight stay free. **Location:** Urban. **Surface:** grasstiles.
Distance: 500m 500m on the spot.

Ebeltoft 6D1

Ebeltoft Skudehavn, Skudehavnen 61. **GPS:** n56,19025 e10,66999.
7 DKK 150 Ch included DKK 2,50/day WC against payment . **Surface:** gravel. 01/05-15/09.
Distance: 1,2km on the spot 500m.

Ebeltoft 6D1

Blushøj, Elsegårdevej 53. **GPS:** n56,16795 e10,72943.
DKK 140 Ch against payment. 01/04-14/09.
Remarks: Quick-Stop: >20h - <10h.

Ebeltoft 6D1

Dråby Strand, Dråby Strandvej 13. **GPS:** n56,22172 e10,73778.
DKK 125 Ch against payment. 19/03-14/09.
Remarks: Quick-Stop: >20h - <10h.

Ebeltoft 6D1

Elsegårde, Kristoffenvejen 1. **GPS:** n56,16843 e10,72278.
DKK 140 Ch against payment. 01/01-31/12.
Remarks: Quick-Stop: >20h - <10h.

Ebeltoft 6D1

Krakær, Gl. Kærvej 18. **GPS:** n56,19730 e10,67426.
DKK 125 Ch against payment. 20/03-23/10.
Remarks: Quick-Stop: >20h - <10h.

Ebeltoft 6D1

Ebeltoft Strand Camping, Ndr. Strandvej 23.
GPS: n56,20983 e10,67852.
DKK 130. 01/01-31/12.
Distance: 100m.
Remarks: Quick-Stop: >20h - <10h.

Egå 6D1

Egå Marina, Egå Havvej 35. **GPS:** n56,20960 e10,28659.

7 DKK 150 Ch (7x) WC included DKK 5 DKK 40/10 . **Location:** Comfortable. **Surface:** asphalted. 01/01-31/12.
Distance: 2km 400m on the spot on the spot 600m 600m.
Remarks: Tallycard: service, electricity, sanitary building, caution DKK 50.

Ejerslev 5C3

Ejerslev Havn, Utkærvej 11. **GPS:** n56,91855 e8,92096.

10 DKK 100 Ch (10x) DKK 20 WC included DKK 20/20. **Location:** Rural, isolated, quiet. **Surface:** gravel.
01/01-31/12.
Distance: 4km on the spot on the spot 4km on the spot.

Remarks: Bread-service, last 2km gravel road, borrow cycles for free.

Engesvan 6C1

Pårup Autocamperplads, Silkeborgvej 8. **GPS:** n56,13694 e9,35028.
4 DKK 50 Ch included. **Location:** Urban, simple, central. **Surface:** gravel. 01/04-01/11.
Distance: on the spot.

Erslev 5C3

Sundby Mors Havn, Sundbyvej 236. **GPS:** n56,88440 e8,63886.

15 DKK 60 DKK 20 WC free.
Location: Simple. **Surface:** gravel.
Distance: on the spot on the spot 800m.

Erslev 5C3

Inger-Marie og Knud Erik Nielsen, Bindeleddet 4.
GPS: n56,83881 e8,68060.

4 DKK 40 . **Location:** Rural, simple, isolated, quiet.
Surface: gravel. 01/01-31/12.
Distance: 1km.

Esbjerg 6C2

Nebel Sø, Vestervadsvej 17, Vester Nebel.
GPS: n55,55000 e8,54361.

25 DKK 60, 2 pers.incl DKK 10 DKK 25.
Location: Rural, simple, isolated, quiet.
Surface: grassy/gravel.
01/04-01/11.
Distance: 15km on the spot.
Remarks: Fishpond, fishing license DKK90 www.nebelsoe.dk.

Esbjerg 6C2

Esbjerg Camping, Gudenåvej 20. **GPS:** n55,51293 e8,38942.
DKK 184. 01/01-31/12.
Remarks: Quick-Stop: >20h - <10h.

Fanø 6C2

Fanø Fiskesø, Storetoft 30. **GPS:** n55,43401 e8,39294.
4 DKK 100 Ch WC against payment. **Surface:** gravel.
Distance: on the spot.
Remarks: At fish pond.

Fanø 6C2

Feldberg Familie Camping, Kirkevejen 3-5, Rindby.
GPS: n55,42894 e8,39211.
DKK 100. 18/03-23/10.
Remarks: Quick-Stop: >20h - <10h.

Farsø 5C3

Hvalpsund Autocamperplads, Fjordvej 1, Hvalpsund.
GPS: n56,70584 e9,20565.
DKK 115 Ch WC .
Surface: grassy. 01/01-31/12.
Distance: on the spot on the spot on the spot.

Fjerritslev 5C3

Erna K Nielsen, Holmsøvej 31, Haverslev. **GPS:** n57,04102 e9,39252.

6 DKK 50 included. **Location:** Rural, simple, quiet.
Surface: grassy. 01/01-31/12.
Distance: on the spot Limfjord 1,7km.

Fjerritslev 5C3

Niels Balle, Hedegardsvey 19, Hjortdal. **GPS:** n57,12505 e9,33422.

4 DKK 75 (1x)included. **Location:** Rural, simple, isolated.
Surface: grassy. 01/01-31/12.
Distance: 7km 4km.

Fjerritslev 5C3

Haverslev Havn, Havegade 72. **GPS:** n57,02956 e9,39971.
15 DKK 100 WC . **Surface:** grassy/gravel.
Distance: on the spot on the spot.

Flauenskjold 5C3

Flauenskjold Autocamping, Agertoften 4, Dronninglund.
GPS: n57,24854 e10,28477.

10 DKK 50 DKK 25 WC included.
Location: Rural, simple, quiet. **Surface:** grassy/gravel.
01/01-31/12.
Distance: 5km.
Remarks: Money in envelope in mail box, festival and market place.

Fredericia 6D2

Lystbådehavnen, Strandvejen 115, Sanddalbakke.
GPS: n55,55246 e9,72805.

8 DKK 100 Ch (8x) WC included. .
Location: Rural, simple, quiet. **Surface:** metalled.
01/01-31/12.
Distance: 1km on the spot on the spot on the spot 1km 200m.
Remarks: Tallycard: service, electricity, sanitary building, caution DKK 50.

Fredericia 6D2

Trelde Næs, Trelde Næsvej 297. **GPS:** n55,62461 e9,83342.
DKK 135 Ch . 18/03-23/10.
Remarks: Quick-Stop: >20h - <10h.

Frederikshavn 5C3

Frederikshavn Marina, Søsportsvej 8. **GPS:** n57,42375 e10,52709.

DK

20 DKK 150 Ch (10x) WC included.
Location: Urban, comfortable, central, quiet. **Surface:** grassy/gravel.
01/01-31/12.
Distance: 800m on the spot on the spot on the spot 700m.
Remarks: Pay at harbourmaster.

Frederikshavn 5C3
Svalereden, Frederikshavnsvej 112B. **GPS**: n57,36001 e10,50927.
DKK 100 Ch . 01/01-31/12.
Remarks: Quick-Stop: >20h - <10h.

Fur 5C3
Fur Camping, Råkildevej 6. **GPS**: n56,83352 e8,97739.
€ 1/h Chservice € 6 DKK 0,50/kWh DKK 3,50.
Location: Isolated, quiet. 18/03-05/09.
Distance: 650m.
Remarks: Max. 1 night.

Gistrup 5C3
Kirsten og Karl Age, Gunderupvej 164. **GPS**: n56,93476 e9,95844.

4 DKK 100 included DKK 50.
Location: Rural, simple, isolated. **Surface:** gravel.

Give 6C1
Give Camping, Skovbakken 34. **GPS**: n55,85051 e9,22953.
DKK 125. 19/03-25/09.
Remarks: Quick-Stop: >20h - <10h.

Glejbjerg 6C2
Betina & Klaus Jørgensen, Gammelgårdsvej 3, Bolding.
GPS: n55,55052 e8,78705.
4 free Chfree against payment WC . **Location:** Comfortable. **Surface:** grassy/metalled. 01/01-31/12.

Grenaa 5D3
Fornæs, Stensmarkvej 36. **GPS**: n56,45398 e10,94009.
DKK 125 Ch against payment. 19/03-21/09.
Remarks: Quick-Stop: >20h - <10h.

Grenaa 5D3
Grenaa Strand Camping, Fuglsangvej 58. **GPS**: n56,38976 e10,91171.
DKK 130. 23/03-04/09.
Distance: 300m.
Remarks: Quick-Stop: >20h - <10h.

Tourist information Grenaa:
Kattegatcentret, Færgevej 4. The underwater world and shark centre. 10-16/17h 13/12-26/12.

Haderslev 6D2
Fam. Nowak, Felstrupvej 37. **GPS**: n55,25488 e9,52556.

2 free Service DKK 30 .
Location: Rural. **Surface:** gravel. 01/01-31/12.
Distance: 3km 100m on the spot.

Haderslev 6D2
Haderslev Sejl Club, Sydhavnsvej 1F. **GPS**: n55,24806 e9,50028.

10 DKK 110 ChWC included.
Surface: gravel. 15/05-30/09.
Distance: on the spot.

Haderslev 6D2
Gåsevig Strand, Gåsevig 19. **GPS**: n55,14222 e9,49903.
DKK 109 Ch against payment. 19/03-18/09.
Remarks: Quick-Stop: >20h - <10h.

Haderslev 6D2
Halk, Brunbjerg 105. **GPS**: n55,18599 e9,65374.
DKK 75 Ch against payment. 24/03-18/09.
Remarks: Quick-Stop: >20h - <10h.

Haderslev 6D2
Årø Camping, Årø 260. **GPS**: n55,25942 e9,75240.
DKK 100. 01/01-31/12.

Haderslev 6D2
Danhostel Haderslev, Erlevvej 34. **GPS**: n55,24431 e9,47710.
DKK 110. 18/03-23/10.
Distance: on the spot.
Remarks: Quick-Stop: >20h - <10h.

Haderslev 6D2
Sønderballe Strand Camping, Diernæsvej 218.
GPS: n55,13243 e9,47610.
DKK 130. 18/03-18/09.
Distance: on the spot.
Remarks: Quick-Stop: >20h - <10h.

Haderslev 6D2
Vikær Strand Camping, Dundelum 29. **GPS**: n55,15008 e9,49444.
DKK 125. 19/03-02/10.
Distance: on the spot.
Remarks: Quick-Stop: >20h - <10h.

Tourist information Haderslev:
Sillerup Mølle, Sillerup Møllevej 35. Mill, bake bread yourself. 01/07-31/08 Su 13-17h.
Wachman's Tour. Excursion with the night watch in the old part of the city. 01/07-31/08 Thu 21h.

Hadsund 5C3
Hadsund Havn, Thygeslundvej 3. **GPS**: n56,70988 e10,10428.

10 DKK 130 WC included. **Location:** Rural, comfortable, quiet. **Surface:** grassy. 01/01-31/12.
Distance: 2km on the spot on the spot 2km 2km.

Hadsund 5C3
Hvirvelkærgård, Kystvejen 202, Als. **GPS**: n56,76414 e10,28565.

10 DKK 90 DKK 30 WC included. **Location:** Rural, simple, quiet. **Surface:** grassy. 01/01-31/12.
Distance: 1km 1km.

Hadsund 5C3
Øster Hurup Havn, Havnen 46. **GPS**: n56,80405 e10,27851.
DKK 140 Ch . **Surface:** gravel.
Distance: 500m on the spot 500m 500m.

Remarks: Tuesday market.

Hadsund 5C3
Højvang Ferie, Hobrovej 62-64. **GPS**: n56,70773 e10,07975.

4 DKK 100 (2x) WC included.
Location: Rural, simple. **Surface:** grassy. 01/01-31/12.

Hadsund 5C3
Øster Hurup, Kystvejen 70. **GPS**: n56,79990 e10,27324.
DKK 130 Ch against payment. 19/03-25/09.
Remarks: Quick-Stop: >20h - <10h.

Hadsund 5C3
Hadsund Camping og Vandrerhjem, Stadionvej 33.
GPS: n56,72108 e10,13362.
DKK 90. 18/03-15/10.
Remarks: Quick-Stop: >20h - <10h.

Hals 5C3
Lagunen, Lagunen 8. **GPS**: n57,04025 e10,36053.
DKK 150 Ch against payment. 23/03-13/09.
Remarks: Quick-Stop: >20h - <10h.

Hanstholm 5C3
THY Minicamping (Rær Autocamperplads), Bybakken 1a.
GPS: n57,08945 e8,67104.

20 DKK 100 Ch DKK 30 WC included DKK 10 .
Location: Rural, comfortable. **Surface:** grassy. 01/01-31/12.
Distance: Hanstholm 4km 5km on the spot.

Hanstholm 5C3
Hanstholm, Hamborgvej 95. **GPS**: n57,10909 e8,66724.
DKK 120 Ch against payment. 01/01-31/12.
Remarks: Quick-Stop: >20h - <10h.

Tourist information Hanstholm:
Frøstrup mini-village, Søndergade 36, Frøstrup. Miniature village. 01/05-15/10 Wed-Thu 10-12h, 01/07-31/08 daily 13.30-16.30h.

Havndal 5C3
Udbyhøj Havn, Havnevej 62 Udbyhøj. **GPS**: n56,61111 e10,30583.

30 DKK 150 Chincluded against payment WC .
Location: Rural, comfortable. **Surface:** asphalted. 01/01-31/12
Distance: on the spot on the spot 500m.

Havndal 5C3
Rethe og Hans Jørn Mogensen, Klattrupgade 36, Klattrup.
GPS: n56,66397 e10,21208.

DK

4 DKK 50 Ch included. **Location:** Rural, simple, quiet. **Surface:** grassy/gravel. 01/01-31/12.
Distance: 2km 2km.

Havndal 5C3

Randers Fjord, Midtvasen 21. **GPS:** n56,60997 e10,29334.
2 DKK 125 Ch against payment. 01/01-31/12.
Remarks: Quick-Stop: >20h - <10h.

Hejls 6D2

Hejlsminde Strand, Gendarmvej 3. **GPS:** n55,36851 e9,60095.
DKK 160 Ch against payment. 19/03-14/09.
Remarks: Quick-Stop: >20h - <10h.

Hemmet 6C1

Bork Havn, Kirkehøjvej 9A. **GPS:** n55,84850 e8,28257.
DKK 120 Ch against payment. 18/03-24/10.
Remarks: Quick-Stop: >20h - <10h.

Herning 6C1

Møllegade. **GPS:** n56,13741 e8,96660.
4 free. 01/01-31/12.
Distance: on the spot 100m 200m.

Hirtshals 5C3

Banegårdspladse, Banegårdspladsen 1.
GPS: n57,59119 e9,96308.

30 DKK 75. **Location:** Simple, central. **Surface:** gravel.
01/01-31/12.
Distance: 600m 4,8km 600m on the spot.
Remarks: At station and ferry terminal.

Hirtshals 5C3

Hirtshals Autocamperplads, Doggerbanke.
GPS: n57,59027 e9,96449.
20 DKK 75. **Surface:** grassy. 01/01-31/12.
Distance: 500m 850m 500m 200m.

Hirtshals 5C3

Willemoesvej. **GPS:** n57,59097 e9,98601.

40 free. **Location:** Simple, quiet. **Surface:** unpaved.
01/01-31/12.
Distance: 1km Sandy beach 1km.
Remarks: Parking ferry to Norway.

Hirtshals 5C3

Hirtshals Transport Center, Dalsagervej 1.
GPS: n57,57645 e9,98480.
5 DKK 75 Ch. **Surface:** asphalted. 01/01-31/12.
Distance: on the spot.
Remarks: Video surveillance.

Hirtshals 5C3

Tornby Strand, Strandvejen 13. **GPS:** n57,55540 e9,93264.
10 DKK 120-170, 2 pers incl. Ch against payment DKK 40.
Surface: grassy/gravel. 01/01-31/12.
Remarks: Quick-Stop: >20h - <10h.

Hirtshals 5C3

Kjul Camping, Kjulvej 12. **GPS:** n57,58279 e10,03132.
DKK 130. 18/03-30/09.
Remarks: Quick-Stop: >20h - <10h.

Tourist information Hirtshals:
M Nordsømuseet, Willemoesvej 2. Oceanarium, large aquarium.
11/01-01/12 10-17.

Hjallerup 5C3

Peter Bastholm Galleri Retro, Alborgvej 715.
GPS: n57,17919 e10,15856.

5 DKK 75 DKK 25.
Location: Rural, isolated, quiet. **Surface:** gravel. 01/01-31/12.
Distance: fish pond.

Hjørring 5C2

Martin Urban, Tverstedvej 41, Uggerby.
GPS: n57,57523 e10,12868.
6 DKK 120 Ch included.
Location: Rural, quiet. **Surface:** grassy. 01/04-20/10.
Distance: 3km 3km 3km.

Hjørring 5C2

Thomas Lindrup, Tverstedvej 31. **GPS:** n57,57484 e10,12842.

6 DKK 120 Ch (6x) WC included. **Location:** Rural, comfortable, isolated, quiet. **Surface:** grassy. 01/01-31/12.

Hobro 5C3

Hobro Sejlklub, Nedre Strandvej 75. **GPS:** n56,64382 e9,81092.
3 DKK 130 WC included.
Surface: metalled. 01/04-31/10.
Distance: city centre 1km on the spot on the spot.
Remarks: Money in envelope in mail box.

Hobro 5C3

Hobro City Camping Gattenborg, Skivevej 35.
GPS: n56,64015 e9,78265.
3 DKK 160 Ch against payment. 01/01-31/12.
Distance: on the spot on the spot.
Remarks: Quick-Stop: >20h - <10h.

Holstebro 6C1

Viborgvej. **GPS:** n56,35851 e8,63041.

4 free. **Location:** Urban, simple. **Surface:** asphalted.
Distance: 800m 800m 800m.

Holsted 6C2

Holsted Golfbanen, Bergardsvej 4, Vejen-Esberg.
GPS: n55,52353 e8,93228.

15 € 10 WC. **Surface:** gravel. 01/04-30/10.
Distance: 1km.

Horsens 6D1

Lystbådehavn, Jens Hjernøes Vej 35. **GPS:** n55,85764 e9,87417.

5 DKK 160 Ch WC included.
Location: Rural, comfortable, quiet. **Surface:** gravel.
01/01-31/12.
Distance: 3km on the spot on the spot on the spot.
Remarks: Harbour Horsen, special motorhome parking, Tallycard: service, electricity, sanitary building, caution DKK 50.

Horsens 6D1

Husodde, Husoddevej 85. **GPS:** n55,86035 e9,91537.
DKK 135 Ch against payment.
01/01-31/12.
Remarks: Quick-Stop: >20h - <10h.

Tourist information Horsens:
Dolmen "Jættestuen", åbjerg Skov. Dolmen. 01/01-31/12.

Hovborg 6C2

Holme Å Camping, Torpet 6. **GPS:** n55,60919 e8,93281.
DKK 138. 01/01-31/12.
Remarks: Quick-Stop: >20h - <10h.

Hoven 6C1

Kvindehojskole, Bredgade 10, Tarm. **GPS:** n55,85065 e8,75938.

6 free WC free.
Location: Urban, simple. **Surface:** gravel. 01/01-31/12.
Distance: on the spot.
Remarks: Parking and stay overnight possible at several places; Brugsen 2/3 campers; sport hall.

Hurup Thy 5B3

Nordisk Folkecenter, Kammersgaardsvej 16.
GPS: n56,69358 e8,41306.

8 DKK 70 WC included. **Location:** Rural, simple, isolated, quiet. **Surface:** gravel. 01/01-31/12.
Distance: on the spot 4km.
Remarks: Check in at reception, access energy-park incl.

DK

Husum-Ballum 6C2

Ballum Camping, Kystvej 37, Ballum. **GPS**: n55,06873 e8,66128.
16 DKK 110 or € 15 Ch (16x)DKK 3,50/kWh WC DKK 1,50/1minutes DKK 25/25 included.
Location: Rural. **Surface:** grassy/gravel.
01/01-31/12.
Distance: 500m 1,5km 5km 500m 500m 500m on the spot on the spot.
Remarks: Payment also in euros.

Hvide Sande 6B1

Autocamper Fabriksvej 31, Fabriksvej 31.
GPS: n56,00245 e8,11979.
45 DKK 90. **Location:** Rural, simple. **Surface:** gravel/sand.
01/01-31/12.
Distance: 800m 500m 500m.
Remarks: Quick-Stop: >20h - <9h.

Hvide Sande 6B1

Autocamper Fabriksvej 42. **GPS**: n56,00475 e8,11754.
20 DKK 90. **Location:** Rural, simple.
Surface: gravel/sand.
Distance: 200m on the spot 200m.
Remarks: Quick-Stop: >20h - <9h.

Hvide Sande 6B1

Autocamper P, Tungevej 6. **GPS**: n55,99722 e8,12222.

40 DKK 90. **Location:** Rural, simple, quiet.
Surface: gravel/metalled. 01/01-31/12.
Distance: 200m on the spot 200m 300m on the spot.
Remarks: Quick-Stop: >20h - <9h, beach parking, service Hvide Sande Camping, 1km, DKK 37,50.

Hvide Sande 6B1

Bjerregaard, Sdr. Klitvej 185. **GPS**: n55,90620 e8,16565.
DKK 100 Ch against payment. 15/04-01/10.
Remarks: Quick-Stop: >20h - <10h.

Hvide Sande 6B1

Hvide Sande (Beltana), Karen Brands Vej 70. **GPS**: n55,98689 e8,13478.
DKK 120 Ch against payment. 03/04-26/10.
Remarks: Quick-Stop: >20h - <10h.

Højslev 5C3

Virksund Lystbådehavn, Sandkrogen 10. **GPS**: n56,61014 e9,29139.

12 DKK 125 WC included. **Location:** Rural, simple.
Surface: gravel. 15/05-15/10.
Distance: on the spot.

Højslev 5C3

Lund Forsamlingshus, Ørslevklostervej 229.
GPS: n56,60402 e9,24250.

10 DKK 50 Ch WC included. **Location:** Rural, simple.
Surface: gravel.
Distance: 3km.

Højslev 5C3

Virksund, Sundvej 14. **GPS**: n56,60785 e9,28917.
DKK 75 Ch against payment. 24/03-02/10.
Remarks: Quick-Stop: >20h - <10h.

Jelling 6C1

Fårup Sø Camping, Fårupvej 58. **GPS**: n55,73616 e9,41772.
DKK 130. 21/03-18/09.
Distance: on the spot.
Remarks: Quick-Stop: >20h - <10h.

Juelsminde 6D1

Havn & Marina, Havnegade 15. **GPS**: n55,71457 e10,01509.

12 DKK 150 Ch (12x) WC included.
Location: Rural, comfortable, central, quiet. **Surface:** gravel.
01/05-30/09.
Distance: 200m on the spot on the spot on the spot 200m.
Remarks: Tallycard: service, electricity, sanitary building, caution DKK 50.

Juelsminde 6D1

Strand Camping og Vandrerhjem, Rousthøj Allé 1a.
GPS: n55,71243 e10,01444.
DKK 125, 2 pers.incl Ch DKK 3,50/kWh included.
Location: Urban. **Surface:** metalled. 01/01-31/12.
Distance: on the spot on the spot 200m 550m on the spot.

Karup 6C1

2B Pack, Ulvedalsvej 43. **GPS**: n56,31528 e9,27361.

4 DKK 100 Ch included.
Location: Isolated, quiet. 01/05-31/10.
Distance: on the spot.

Karup 6C1

Hessellund Sø, Hessellundvej 12. **GPS**: n56,32308 e9,11501.
DKK 171 Ch against payment. 27/03-29/09.
Remarks: Quick-Stop: >20h - <10h.

Karup 6C1

Hessellund Sø Camping, Hessellundvej 12. **GPS**: n56,32309 e9,11511.
DKK 171. 19/03-25/09.
Remarks: Quick-Stop: >20h - <10h.

Knebel 6D1

Sølyst Gaard Strand Camping, Dragsmurvej 15, Fuglsø.
GPS: n56,17546 e10,53394.
DKK 140. 19/03-18/09.
Distance: 200m.
Remarks: Quick-Stop: >20h - <10h.

Kolding 6D2

Kolding Marina, Skamlingvejen 5. **GPS**: n55,48746 e9,50051.

15 DKK 125 Ch WC against payment.
Location: Rural, comfortable, quiet. **Surface:** grassy/gravel.
01/05-01/10.
Distance: 2,6km on the spot on the spot.
Remarks: Near marina, Tallycard: service, electricity, sanitary building, caution DKK 50.

Kvissel 5C3

Bondegård Hansen, Mejlingvej 65. **GPS**: n57,46753 e10,39556.

10 DKK 75 Ch WC included DKK 10.
Location: Rural, comfortable, quiet. **Surface:** grassy.
01/01-31/12.
Distance: 1km 5km.

Langå 5C3

Langå, Skov Alle 16. **GPS**: n56,38780 e9,90439.
DKK 130 Ch against payment. 01/01-31/12.
Remarks: Quick-Stop: >20h - <10h.

Lemvig 5B3

Aa Mølle, Remmerstrandvej 188. **GPS**: n56,54199 e8,50310.

15 DKK 75 WC included.
Location: Rural, simple. **Surface:** grassy.
Distance: 100m 100m.
Remarks: Near mill.

Lemvig 5B3

Lemvig Havn, Havnen 11. **GPS**: n56,55395 e8,30956.

10 free. **Location:** Urban, simple, central. **Surface:** gravel.
01/01-31/12.
Distance: 250m 250m.
Remarks: Max. 12h.

Lemvig 5B3

Bovbjerg, Juelsgårdvej 13. **GPS**: n56,52800 e8,12629.
DKK 110 Ch. 20/03-19/10.
Remarks: Quick-Stop: >20h - <10h.

Lemvig 5B3

Lemvig Strand Camping, Vinkelhagevej 6. **GPS**: n56,56726 e8,29426.

DK

DKK 100 DKK 35.
Distance: on the spot on the spot ⊗800m.
Tourist information Lemvig:
Bovbjerg Fyr, Fyrvej 27. Lighthouse.

Løgstrup 5C3

Hjarbæk Fjord Camping, Hulager 2. **GPS**: n56,53416 e9,33118.
DKK 125. 01/01-31/12.
Remarks: Quick-Stop: >20h - <10h.

Løgstør 5C3

Løgstør Golfklub, Viborgvej 13, Ravnstrup.
GPS: n56,94689 e9,25390.

5 DKK 100 (4x)included WC.
Location: Simple, isolated, quiet. **Surface:** gravel.
Distance: 2km ⊗2km 2km.
Remarks: At golf court.

Løgstør 5C3

Løgstør Lysbadehavn, Kanalvejen 19. **GPS**: n56,96728 e9,24528.

15 DKK 135 (12x)WC included.
Location: Comfortable, central. **Surface:** grassy/metalled.
01/01-31/12.
Distance: 200m on the spot on the spot ⊗on the spot 200m.
Remarks: Pay at harbourmaster.

Løgstør 5C3

Café Bondestuen, Over Aggersund 49. **GPS**: n57,00835 e9,28776.

6 free. **Location:** Rural, simple. **Surface:** gravel.
01/01-31/12.
Distance: ⊗on the spot.

Løgumkloster 6C2

Møllegade. **GPS**: n55,06090 e8,94896.
3 free DKK 20/100liter Ch. **Surface:** asphalted.
01/01-31/12.
Distance: 300m ⊗on the spot 300m.
Remarks: Max 3,5t.

Løkken 5C3

Galleri Munkens Klit, Munkensvej 11, Ingstrup.
GPS: n57,33871 e9,70522.

10 DKK 100 DKK 5 WC included. **Location:** Rural, comfortable, isolated, quiet. **Surface:** grassy. 01/01-31/12.
Distance: 3km.

Løkken 5C3

Løkkensvej 875. **GPS**: n57,38972 e9,77385.
DKK 75 DKK 40 DKK 25. **Surface:** grassy. 01/01-31/12.
Distance: 4,5km.

Løkken 5C3

Hugo Ottesen, Kettrupvej 80. **GPS**: n57,31135 e9,67861.

5 DKK 100. **Location:** Rural, simple, isolated.
Surface: grassy. 01/01-31/12.

Løkken 5C3

Camping Rolighed, Grønhoj Strandvej 35. **GPS**: n57,32143 e9,67818.
DKK 75 Ch against payment. 01/01-31/12.
Remarks: Quick-Stop: >18h - <10h.

Løkken 5C3

Gl.Klitgaard, Lyngbyvej 331. **GPS**: n57,41784 e9,76017.
DKK 169 Ch against payment. 15/04-23/10.
Remarks: Quick-Stop: >20h - <10h.

Løkken 5C3

Grønhøj Strand, Kettrupvej 125. **GPS**: n57,32127 e9,67293.
DKK 100 Ch against payment. 18/03-18/09.
Remarks: Quick-Stop: >20h - <10h.

Løkken 5C3

Løkken By Camping, Søndergarde 69. **GPS**: n57,36480 e9,70940.
DKK 125 Ch. 01/01-31/12.
Remarks: Quick-Stop: >20h - <10h.

Løkken 5C3

Løkken Strand, Furreby Kirkevej 97. **GPS**: n57,38533 e9,72571.

DKK 100 Ch against payment. 29/04-04/09.
Remarks: Quick-Stop: >20h - <10h.

Tourist information Løkken:
Løkken Turistbureau, Jyllandsgade 15, www.loekken.dk. Bathing resort.
Vendsyssel historiske museum "Jens Thomsens Gård", Strandfogedgården i Rubjerg, Langelinie 2. Cultural past of the coast area. Hiking-trails. 25/06-30/08 Thu-Su 11-17h.
Familiy Farm Fun Park, Lyngbyvej 86, Vittrup. Animal park.
14/05-24/10 10-18.

Mariager 5C3

Kongsdl Bådelaug, Kongsdal Havn 8. **GPS**: n56,68383 e10,07023.

24 DKK 120 Ch (24x)WC DKK 5/3minutes included.
Location: Rural, comfortable, isolated, quiet. **Surface:** gravel.
01/01-31/12 service 01/11-31/03.
Distance: 7km on the spot on the spot.
Remarks: Tallycard.

Mariager 5C3

Mariager, Ny Havnevej 5A. **GPS**: n56,65399 e9,97640.
2 DKK 100 Ch against payment. 23/03-25/09.
Remarks: Quick-Stop: >20h - <10h.

Nibe 5C3

Sølyst, Løgstørvej 2. **GPS**: n56,97248 e9,62460.
DKK 140 Ch against payment. 01/01-31/12.
Remarks: Quick-Stop: >20h - <10h.

Nordborg 6D2

Autocamperplads Als, Købingsmarksvej 53. **GPS**: n55,07887 e9,72912.

25 DKK 73 DKK 15/80liter Ch DKK 38 DKK 15/24h.
Surface: metalled. 01/04-25/10.
Distance: 3km on the spot on the spot ⊗3km 3km on the spot on the spot on the spot.

Nordborg 6D2

Kvickly, Gartnervænget. **GPS**: n55,05611 e9,74150.
10 free. **Surface:** asphalted. 01/01-31/12.
Remarks: At supermarket.

Nordborg 6D2

Lone & Henning Carlsson, Kådnervej 7. **GPS**: n55,03194 e9,73111.

5 DKK 100 DKK 20 WC. **Location:** Rural, comfortable, quiet. **Surface:** gravel. 01/01-31/12.
Distance: 5km.
Remarks: Narrow entrance.

Nykøbing Mors 5C3

Morsø Sejlklub & Marina, Jernbanevej 3A.
GPS: n56,79282 e8,86370.

18 DKK 130 Ch WC against payment included.
Location: Comfortable, quiet. **Surface:** gravel.
01/01-31/12.
Distance: 150m on the spot on the spot ⊗on the spot 200m.
Remarks: Tallycard: service, electricity, sanitary building, caution DKK 25.

Nykøbing Mors 5C3

Morsø Traktormuseum, Kjeldgårdsvej 49, Outrup.
GPS: n56,78038 e8,66547.

4 DKK 100 WC included.
Location: Rural, simple. **Surface:** metalled. 01/01-31/12.
Remarks: Use sanitary only during opening hours, 20% reduction museum.

Nørager 5C3

Stellplads E45 Autocamper, Fyrkildevej 39, Ladelund.
GPS: n56,77505 e9,70986.

15 DKK 50 included DKK 25. **Location:** Rural, simple, isolated, quiet. **Surface:** grassy. 01/01-31/12.
Distance: E45 5km.

Nørre Nebel 6B1

Nymindegab, Lyngtoften 12. **GPS**: n55,81368 e8,19992.
DKK 75 Ch against payment. 17/03-27/09.
Remarks: Quick-Stop: >20h - <10h.

Odder 6D1

Norsminde havn, Gl Krovej. **GPS**: n56,02253 e10,26262.
8 DKK 150 WC included. 15/04-01/10.
Distance: Odder 11km on the spot on the spot on the spot 4km 500m.

Odder 6D1

Jørgen Petersen, Aarhusvej 354. **GPS**: n56,01650 e10,18157.

3 DKK 75 Ch WC included. **Location:** Rural, luxurious, isolated, quiet. **Surface:** grassy/gravel. 01/01-31/12.
Distance: 5km on the spot.

Odder 6D1

Odder strand Camping, Toldvejen 50. **GPS**: n55,93891 e10,25054.
DKK 150 Ch against payment. 24/03-21/09.
Remarks: Quick-Stop: >20h - <10h.

Outrup 6C1

Autocamperplads Outrup, Gartnervænget 18.
GPS: n55,71551 e8,34654.

15 DKK 100 Ch DKK 22 WC included.
Surface: grassy/gravel. 01/01-31/12.
Distance: 500m 300m 500m on the spot.

Pandrup 5C3

Blokhus Klit Camping, Kystvejen 52. **GPS**: n57,22048 e9,58479.
DKK 100. 23/03-18/09.
Remarks: Quick-Stop: >20h - <10h.

Randers 5C3

Mellerup Bådelaug, Amtsvejen 153, Mellerup.
GPS: n56,52431 e10,22213.

3 DKK 100 WC included. **Location:** Rural, simple, quiet. **Surface:** gravel. 01/05-30/09.
Distance: Mellerup 1,2km on the spot on the spot.
Remarks: Pay at harbourmaster.

Randers 5C3

Randers havn, Kulholmsvej 1. **GPS**: n56,46280 e10,05262.

10 DKK 150. **Location:** Urban, simple. **Surface:** gravel. 01/01-31/12.
Distance: 500m on the spot.
Remarks: Max. 24h.

Redsted M. 5C3

Thissinghus Havn, Thissingvej. **GPS**: n56,71822 e8,62818.

10 DKK 60 WC included. **Location:** Simple.
Surface: grassy. 01/01-31/12.
Distance: 3km on the spot on the spot 3km.
Remarks: Money in envelope in mail box.

Ribe 6C2

Fabelbo, Hølleskovvej 48. **GPS**: n55,24076 e8,86077.
free WC free. **Location:** Isolated, quiet. **Surface:** grassy.
01/01-31/12.
Distance: Ribe 15km.

Ribe 6C2

Stampemøllevej. **GPS**: n55,32480 e8,75740.

25 free WC free. **Location:** Urban, simple.
Surface: asphalted.
01/01-31/12.
Distance: 500m 100m 400m.
Remarks: Parking south of centre, max. 48h.

Ribe 6C2

Storkesøen, Haulundvej 164. **GPS**: n55,31703 e8,76022.

24 DKK 140 Ch WC included DKK 5. **Location:** Rural, comfortable, quiet. **Surface:** grassy. 01/01-31/12.
Distance: 1km on the spot.
Remarks: At fish pond.

Ribe 6C2

Saltgade. **GPS**: n55,33258 e8,76830.
15 free. **Surface:** asphalted. 01/01-31/12.
Distance: 200m 200m.
Remarks: Max. 48h.

Ribe 6C2

Maglegaard, Toftlundvej 6. **GPS**: n55,31067 e8,79151.

3 DKK 100 DKK 20. **Location:** Rural, simple, quiet.
Surface: grassy.
Distance: 3km.

Ribe 6C2

Ribe, Farupvej 2. **GPS**: n55,33907 e8,76940.
DKK 75 Ch.
01/01-31/12.
Remarks: Quick-Stop: >20h - <10h.

Tourist information Ribe:

Ribe Tourism Office, Torvet 3, http://www.visitribe.com/. Oldest city of Denmark to Ribeå River.
Vadehavscentret, Okholmvej 5. Wadden Sea centre. 10-16/17h 01/12-31/01.
Museet Ribes Vikinger, Odins Plads 1. Viking period in Denmark. daily 10-16h, summer 10-18h 01/11-31/03 Mo.
Ribe Vikingecenter. Open air museum. 01/05-30/06, 01/09-15/10 Mo-Fri 10-15.30h, 01/07-31/08 daily 11-17h.
Weis Stue, Torvet 2. Oldest inn of Denmark with traditional Danish kitchen.

Ringkøbing 6B1

Lystbadenhavn, Fiskerstraede 60. **GPS**: n56,08611 e8,24056.

10 DKK 120 Ch (6x)DKK 2,30/kWh WC included DKK 10/3minutes. **Location:** Urban, comfortable, quiet.
Surface: gravel. 01/01-31/12.
Distance: on the spot on the spot on the spot 500m 500m.
Remarks: Parking at pier.

Ringkøbing 6B1

Autocamperplads, Vesterled 11. **GPS**: n56,09338 e8,23740.

20 DKK 70. **Location:** Urban, simple. **Surface:** gravel.
01/01-31/12.
Distance: 700m 400m 400m 700m 700m.
Remarks: Pay with Danish coins.

Ringkøbing 6B1

Annemette & Svend Erik Jensen, Birkmosevej 6.
GPS: n56,08806 e8,26722.

15 free. **Location:** Simple. **Surface:** grassy. 01/01-31/12.
Distance: 1km 500m 200m.

DK

Ringkøbing 6B1

Ringkøbing Camping, Herningverj 105. **GPS**: n56,08699 e8,31642.
DKK 130 Ch against payment. 31/03-01/10.
Distance: 5km.
Remarks: Quick-Stop: >20h - <10h.

Ringkøbing 6B1

Søndervig, Solvej 2. **GPS**: n56,11186 e8,11760.
DKK 100 Ch included DKK 2,75/kWh,+ DKK 20 DKK 6.
07/04-01/10.
Distance: 600m.

Tourist information Ringkøbing:
Fishing and Family Park West, Hovervej 56. Recreation park with swimming pool. 10h-sunset.

Roslev 5C3

Sallingsund Sejlklub, Færgevej 7. **GPS**: n56,76333 e8,86667.

12 DKK 120 Ch WC included.
Location: Comfortable. **Surface:** grassy. 01/05-30/09.
Distance: on the spot on the spot 200m 200m.

Roslev 5C3

Sundsøre Lystbådehavn, Sundsørevej 2B.
GPS: n56,70991 e9,17324.

8 DKK 130 WC included. **Location:** Rural, isolated, quiet. **Surface:** grassy/gravel. 01/01-31/12.
Distance: on the spot on the spot on the spot.
Remarks: At marina and ferry-boat.

Ry 6D1

Birkhede, Lyngvej 14. **GPS**: n56,10428 e9,74089.
DKK 150 Ch against payment. 18/03-15/09.
Remarks: Quick-Stop: >20h - <10h. **Tourist information Ry:**
Ry Turistbureau, Klostervej 3.
Labyrinthia, Gamle Ryvej 2. Wooden labyrinth.
23/04-25/09 11-16.

Rødding 6C2

JH ståldesign, Timekær 11. **GPS**: n55,33044 e9,05417.
DKK 75 Ch . **Surface:** grassy. 01/01-31/12.
Distance: 500m.

Rødding 6C2

Inga & Ejnar Gejl, Skodborgskovvej 25, Skodborgskov.
GPS: n55,40056 e9,15722.
4 free against payment WC free. **Location:** Rural, simple.
Surface: grassy. 01/01-31/12.
Distance: 5km.

Rødding 6C2

Brændekilde, Haderslevvej 59. **GPS**: n55,35750 e9,18833.

13 free DKK 25 Ch DKK 25 WC. **Location:** Rural, simple, noisy.
Surface: gravel. 01/01-31/12.
Distance: 1km.
Remarks: Max. 1 week.

Rødding 6C2

FB Camping Service, Industriparken 13. **GPS**: n55,42556 e9,16083.
15 free DKK 10 Ch DKK 40. **Location:** Urban, simple.
Surface: gravel. 01/01-31/12.

Rødekro 6C2

Rødekro Fiskepark, østermarkvej 3-7. **GPS**: n55,08806 e9,30889.

50 DKK 100/pp Ch DKK 35/24kWh WC included .
Location: Rural, simple, quiet. **Surface:** grassy.
01/01-31/12.
Distance: 2km on the spot on the spot on the spot 2km 100m.
Remarks: At fish lake.

Rømø 6C2

Autocamperplads Oasen Rømø, Rømersvej 9.
GPS: n55,09408 e8,54118.
180 DKK 110 DKK 7/80liter Ch DKK 2,50/kWh WC DKK 7 free. **Surface:** grassy/gravel. 01/03-01/11.
Distance: 1km 500m 500m on the spot.

Rømø 6C2

Kommandørgården Camping, Havnebyvej 201.
GPS: n55,09854 e8,54292.
DKK 125. 01/01-31/12.
Remarks: Quick-Stop: >20h - <10h.

Rømø 6C2

Rømø Familie Camping, Vestervej 13. **GPS**: n55,16254 e8,54518.
DKK 110. 18/03-23/10.
Remarks: Quick-Stop: >20h - <10h.

Rønde 6D1

Nappedam Bådelaug, Molsvej 33. **GPS**: n56,27755 e10,49529.
DKK 125 Ch WC .
Distance: 3,5km on the spot 3,5km.
Remarks: Max 3,5t.

Rønde 6D1

Kaløvig Strandgård, Strandvejen 150. **GPS**: n56,29330 e10,40399.
DKK 140 Ch . 01/01-31/12.
Remarks: Quick-Stop: >20h - <10h.

Rønde 6D1

Kaløvig Camping, Strandvejen 150. **GPS**: n56,29338 e10,40417.
DKK 140. 01/01-31/12.
Remarks: Quick-Stop: >20h - <10h.

Saltum 5C3

Saltum Strand, Saltum Strandvej 141. **GPS**: n57,28560 e9,65228.
DKK 140 Ch against payment. 19/03-23/10.
Remarks: Quick-Stop: >20h - <10h.

Samsø 6D1

Camping & Feriecenter Samsø, Stensbjergvej 6, Kolby.
GPS: n55,79669 e10,55146.
DKK 60. 15/03-20/12.
Remarks: Quick-Stop: >20h - <10h.

Sdr. Omme 6C1

Omme Å Camping, Sønderbro 10. **GPS**: n55,83837 e8,88872.
DKK 140. 18/03-01/10.
Remarks: Quick-Stop: >20h - <10h.

Silkeborg 6D1

Anne & Gert Lassen, Ellinglund, Ellingvej 16, Funder Kirkeby.
GPS: n56,16546 e9,40954.
3 DKK 100 Ch WC . **Location:** Rural, comfortable.
Surface: grassy. 01/01-31/12.
Distance: 2km.

Silkeborg 6D1

Jørgen Engebjerg, Lemmingvej 12. **GPS**: n56,22124 e9,53991.
3 DKK 75 included. **Location:** Rural. **Surface:** grassy.
01/01-31/12.
Distance: 5km.

Silkeborg 6D1

Sø-Camping, Århusvej 51. **GPS**: n56,16984 e9,57657.
DKK 94/pp Ch against payment.
18/03-23/10.
Remarks: Quick-Stop: >20h - <10h.

Tourist information Silkeborg:
AQUA, Vejlsøvej 55. Aquarium.
01/09-31/05 Mo-Fri 10-16h, Sa-Su 10-17h, 01/06-31/08 10-18h.

Sindal 5C3

Sindal, Hjørringvej 125. **GPS**: n57,46849 e10,17945.

3 DKK 110 Ch against payment DKK 30 WC included.
01/01-31/12.
Remarks: Quick-Stop: >20h - <10h.

Sjølund 6D2

Grønninghoved strand, Mosvigvej 21. **GPS**: n55,41105 e9,59220.
DKK 140 Ch against payment. 19/03-15/09.
Remarks: Quick-Stop: >20h - <10h.

Skagen 5C2

P-plads på Grenen i Skagen, Akandevej.
GPS: n57,73895 e10,63283.

20 DKK 13/h, overnight stay DKK 150.
Location: Rural, simple, isolated. **Surface:** asphalted. 01/01-31/12.
Distance: 2km on the spot on the spot 100m 3km on the spot.

Skagen 5C2

Råbjerg Mile, Kandestedvej 55. **GPS**: n57,65636 e10,45081.
DKK 130 Ch against payment. 20/03-30/09.
Remarks: Quick-Stop: >20h - <10h.

Skagen 5C2

Skagen Camping, Flagbakkevej 55. **GPS**: n57,71989 e10,53991.
DKK 120. 18/03-01/09.
Remarks: Quick-Stop: >20h - <10h.

Skals 5C3

Ulbjerg, Skråhedevej 6. **GPS**: n56,64495 e9,33915.
€ 10,50 Ch against payment. 01/01-31/12.
Remarks: Quick-Stop: >20h - <10h.

Skjern 6C1

Stauning Havn, Strandvejen, Stauning. **GPS**: n55,95488 e8,37352.

6 DKK 150 Ch WC included .
Location: Rural, simple. **Surface:** grasstiles. 01/01-31/12.
Distance: Skjern 8km on the spot on the spot on the spot.

Skjern 6C1

Skjern å Camping, Birkvej 37. **GPS**: n55,93316 e8,49291.
DKK 100 Ch against payment. 01/01-31/12.
Remarks: Quick-Stop: >20h - <10h.

Skærbæk 6C2

Skærbæk, Ullerupvej 76. **GPS**: n55,16584 e8,77909.
DKK 100 Ch against payment. 01/01-31/12.
Remarks: Quick-Stop: >20h - <10h.

Snedsted 5B3

Krohavens Familiecamping, Stenbjerg Kirkevej 21.
GPS: n56,91827 e8,36527.
DKK 135. 01/04-01/10.

DK

Remarks: Quick-Stop: >20h - <10h.

S Spøttrup 5C3

Gyldendal hav, Vester Hærup Strandvej 34.
GPS: n56,58107 e8,71066.

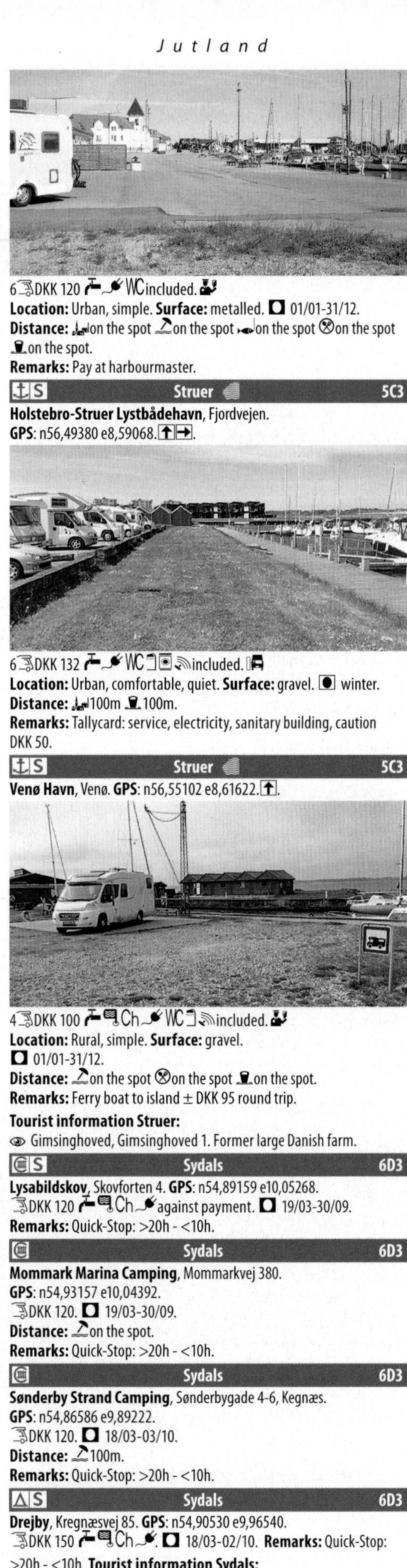

15 DKK 120 Ch (4x) WC included.
Location: Rural, simple, quiet. **Surface:** gravel/sand.
01/01-31/12.
Distance: Sandy beach on the spot on the spot.

S Storvorde 5C3

Egense Lystbådehavan, Kystvej 1. **GPS**: n56,98270 e10,30451.

6 DKK 110 (6x) WC. **Location:** Rural, simple, quiet.
Surface: metalled. 01/01-31/12.
Distance: on the spot on the spot 1km.
Remarks: Pay at harbourmaster.

Storvorde 5C3

Nørkærvej ved Limfjorden, Nørkærsvej 34. **GPS**: n57,02564 e10,11224.
5 free. **Location:** Isolated, quiet. **Surface:** grassy/gravel.
01/01-31/12.
Distance: 2,5km on the spot on the spot 2,5km.

S Storvorde 5C3

Dokkedal, Kystvej 118. **GPS**: n56,93305 e10,26225.
DKK 150 Ch against payment. 01/01-31/12.
Remarks: Quick-Stop: >20h - <10h.

S Storvorde 5C3

Egense, Kystvej 6. **GPS**: n56,98071 e10,30086.
DKK 100 Ch against payment. 24/03-17/09.
Remarks: Quick-Stop: >20h - <10h.

S Stouby 6D1

Løgballe Autocamperplads, Løgballevej 12.
GPS: n55,70765 e9,84359.

7 DKK 75 DKK 15 Ch (7x)DKK 30 WC. **Location:** Rural, simple, isolated, quiet. **Surface:** gravel. 01/04-01/10.

Stouby 6D1

Løgballe Camping, Løgballevej 12. **GPS**: n55,70786 e9,84423.
DKK 75. 18/03-25/09.
Remarks: Quick-Stop: >20h - <10h.

Stouby 6D1

Rosenvold Strand Camping, Rosenvoldvej 19.
GPS: n55,67691 e9,81356.
DKK 100-120. 18/03-25/09.
Remarks: Quick-Stop: >20h - <10h.

S Strandby 5C3

Strandby havn, Søndre Havnevej 27. **GPS**: n57,49249 e10,50245.

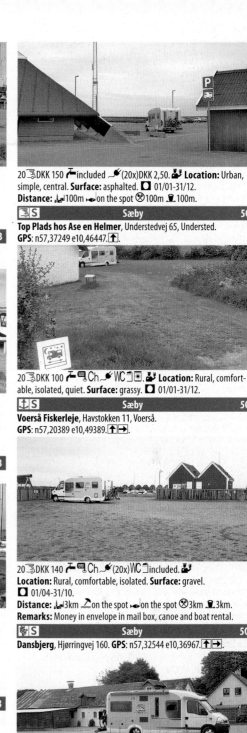

6 DKK 120 WC included.
Location: Urban, simple. **Surface:** metalled. 01/01-31/12.
Distance: on the spot on the spot on the spot on the spot on the spot.
Remarks: Pay at harbourmaster.

S Struer 5C3

Holstebro-Struer Lystbådehavn, Fjordvejen.
GPS: n56,49380 e8,59068.

6 DKK 132 WC included.
Location: Urban, comfortable, quiet. **Surface:** gravel. winter.
Distance: 100m 100m.
Remarks: Tallycard: service, electricity, sanitary building, caution DKK 50.

S Struer 5C3

Venø Havn, Venø. **GPS**: n56,55102 e8,61622.

4 DKK 100 Ch WC included.
Location: Rural, simple. **Surface:** gravel.
01/01-31/12.
Distance: on the spot on the spot on the spot.
Remarks: Ferry boat to island ± DKK 95 round trip.

Tourist information Struer:
Gimsinghoved, Gimsinghoved 1. Former large Danish farm.

S Sydals 6D3

Lysabildskov, Skovforten 4. **GPS**: n54,89159 e10,05268.
DKK 120 Ch against payment. 19/03-30/09.
Remarks: Quick-Stop: >20h - <10h.

Sydals 6D3

Mommark Marina Camping, Mommarkvej 380.
GPS: n54,93157 e10,04392.
DKK 120. 19/03-30/09.
Distance: on the spot.
Remarks: Quick-Stop: >20h - <10h.

Sydals 6D3

Sønderby Strand Camping, Sønderbygade 4-6, Kegnæs.
GPS: n54,86586 e9,89222.
DKK 120. 18/03-03/10.
Distance: 100m.
Remarks: Quick-Stop: >20h - <10h.

S Sydals 6D3

Drejby, Kregnæsvej 85. **GPS**: n54,90530 e9,96540.
DKK 150 Ch. 18/03-02/10. **Remarks:** Quick-Stop: >20h - <10h. **Tourist information Sydals:**
Sydals Turistbureau, Kegnæsvej 52.
Kegnæs Fyr, Nørre Landevej 7. Lighthouse. 01/06-30/09 Mo-Su 9-19h.

S Sæby 5C3

Sæby Havn, Havnen 20. **GPS**: n57,33218 e10,53373.

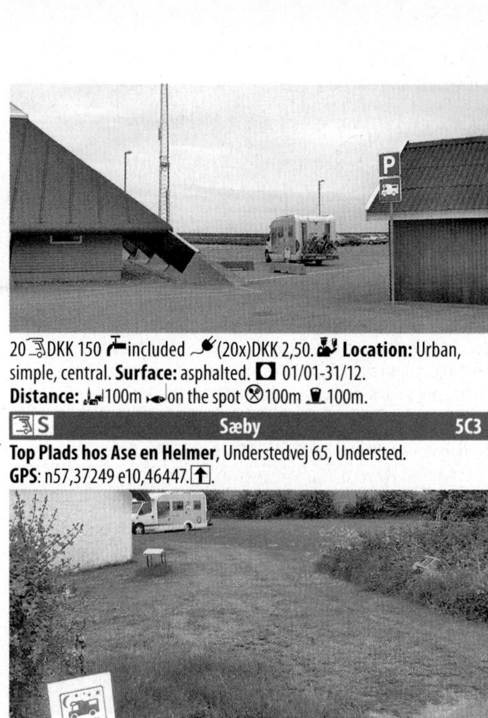

20 DKK 150 included (20x)DKK 2,50. **Location:** Urban, simple, central. **Surface:** asphalted. 01/01-31/12.
Distance: 100m on the spot 100m 100m.

S Sæby 5C3

Top Plads hos Ase en Helmer, Understedvej 65, Understed.
GPS: n57,37249 e10,46447.

20 DKK 100 Ch WC. **Location:** Rural, comfortable, isolated, quiet. **Surface:** grassy. 01/01-31/12.

S Sæby 5C3

Voerså Fiskerleje, Havstokken 11, Voerså.
GPS: n57,20389 e10,49389.

20 DKK 140 Ch (20x) WC included.
Location: Rural, comfortable, isolated. **Surface:** gravel.
01/04-31/10.
Distance: 3km on the spot on the spot 3km 3km.
Remarks: Money in envelope in mail box, canoe and boat rental.

S Sæby 5C3

Dansbjerg, Hjørringvej 160. **GPS**: n57,32544 e10,36967.

6 DKK 50. **Location:** Rural, simple, isolated, quiet.
Surface: grassy/gravel. 01/01-31/12.
Distance: 1km 1km.
Remarks: At manege.

S Sæby 5C3

Lene en Knut Holdensgård, Holdenggårdvej 16, Sønder.
GPS: n57,21616 e10,45253.

3 DKK 50. **Location:** Rural, simple, isolated, quiet.
Surface: grassy. 01/01-31/12.

S Tarm 6C1

Erik Andersen, Blåkildevej 41. **GPS**: n55,89825 e8,48057.

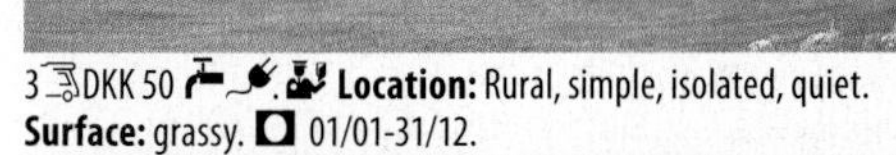

DK

3 DKK 50 included. **Location:** Rural, simple, quiet. **Surface:** grassy. 01/01-31/12.
Distance: 3km 500m 500m 3km 3km.

Tarm 6C1

Par3Golf, Grimlundvej 2. **GPS**: n55,83819 e8,71321.

free. **Location:** Rural, simple, isolated, quiet. **Surface:** gravel/sand. 01/01-31/12.
Distance: Tarm 19km.
Remarks: At golf court.

Tårs (Hjørring) 5C3

Vendelbo Vans Autocampere, Damhusvej 23.
GPS: n57,38972 e10,11500.

8 DKK 100 Ch (8x) WC included.
Location: Urban, comfortable, central, quiet. **Surface:** grassy/gravel. 01/01-31/12.
Distance: 100m 500m 500m 300m 300m 200m.
Remarks: At motorhome dealer, max. 48h, sanitary 9-17h.

Thisted 5C3

Vilsund Havn, Gamle Færgevej 30. **GPS**: n56,88232 e8,62848.

6 DKK 120 WC included DKK 10.
Location: Rural, simple. **Surface:** gravel. 01/01-31/12.
Distance: Thisted 11km 100m.
Remarks: To be paid at petrol station.

Thisted 5C3

Silstrupgård B&B, Åsvej 5B, Silstrup. **GPS**: n56,93047 e8,64754.

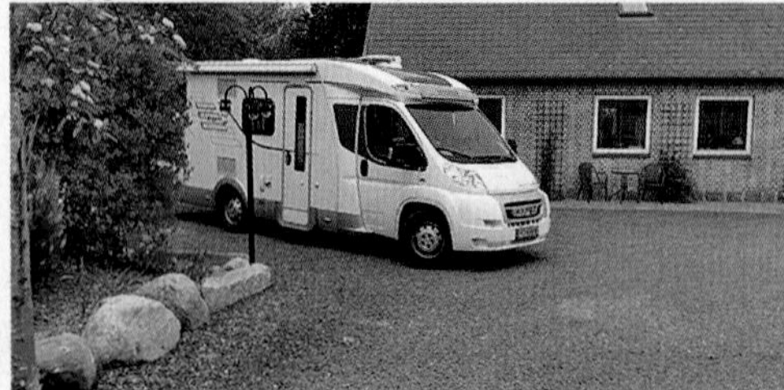

4 DKK 100 Ch WC included.
Location: Rural, simple. **Surface:** gravel. 01/01-31/12.
Distance: Thisted 5km.

Thisted 5C3

Thisted Camping, Iversensvej 3. **GPS**: n56,95309 e8,71249.
DKK 135 Ch against payment. 01/01-31/12.
Remarks: Quick-Stop: >20h - <10h.

Thisted 5C3

Nystrup Camping Klitmøller, Trøjborgvej 22, Klitmøller.
GPS: n57,03302 e8,47927.
DKK 100. 01/03-30/10. **Remarks:** Quick-Stop: >20h - <10h.

Tourist information Thisted:
Thy Turistbureau i Thisted, Store Torv 6, www.visitthy.dk. Bathing resort.
Thisted Bryghus, Bryggerivej 10. Brewery, information at Turistbureau. summer Wed 11h. DKK 50.

Thorsager 6D1

Dagli Brugsen, Thorsgade 26. **GPS**: n56,34305 e10,46286.

4 free. **Location:** Urban, simple. **Surface:** gravel/metalled. 01/01-31/12.
Distance: on the spot on the spot.
Remarks: Behind supermarket Brugsen, max. 24h.

Thyborøn 5B3

Thyborøn, Idrætsvej 3. **GPS**: n56,69456 e8,20456.
DKK 50 Ch. 01/01-31/12.
Remarks: Quick-Stop: >20h - <10h.

Thyholm 5C3

Jegindø Havn, Havnegade. **GPS**: n56,65219 e8,63575.

DKK 120 (2x) WC included.
Location: Simple. **Surface:** grassy. 01/01-31/12.
Distance: on the spot on the spot 100m.
Remarks: At harbour.

Tinglev 6C2

Stefan Christiansen, Uge Green 2. **GPS**: n54,97365 e9,34601.

8 € 10 Ch (6x) DKK 27/24h WC DKK 10 included.
Location: Rural, luxurious, isolated, quiet. **Surface:** grassy. 01/01-31/12.
Distance: 8km 2km on the spot on the spot 800m on the spot on the spot.
Remarks: Golf court 1km.

Toftlund 6C2

Dahl, Lebækvej 2. **GPS**: n55,17839 e9,07768.
5 DKK 45 Ch DKK 45 included.
Surface: grassy.

Tønder 6C3

Autocamperplads Tønder, Sønderlandevej. **GPS**: n54,93558 e8,87754.
40 DKK 110-125 Ch WC included.
Surface: gravel. 04/01-19/12.
Distance: 1km 300m.
Remarks: Incl. access swimming pool.

Tønder 6C3

Kennel Roager, Flensborg Landevej 25. **GPS**: n54,93190 e8,99793.

5 DKK 100 DKK 20/24h WC included DKK 20 DKK 30.
Location: Rural, simple, isolated, noisy. **Surface:** grassy. 01/01-31/12.
Distance: 10km 4km.

Ulfborg 6C1

Tingvej. **GPS**: n56,27297 e8,32253.

4 free. **Location:** Simple. **Surface:** gravel. 01/01-31/12.
Distance: on the spot 300m.
Remarks: Nearby town hall.

Ulfborg 6C1

Thorsminde Havn, Vesterhavsgade 1a. **GPS**: n56,36578 e8,12163.

DKK 100. **Location:** Simple.
Distance: on the spot on the spot 200m.

Ulfborg 6C1

Vestergaard, Hugvej 5, Vedersø. **GPS**: n56,24961 e8,16796.

15 DKK 50 included. **Location:** Rural, simple, isolated.
Surface: grassy. 01/01-31/12.
Distance: Ulfborg 14km North Sea 1,5km on the spot.
Remarks: Max. 48h, breakfast-service.

Ulfborg 6C1

Tvind Skolecenter, Skorkærvej 8. **GPS**: n56,25636 e8,28110.

15 free. **Location:** Rural, simple, isolated. 01/01-31/12.
Distance: 8km 8km 8km.

Ulfborg 6C1

Rejkjær, Ringkobingvej 24. **GPS**: n56,23319 e8,30966.
DKK 100 Ch against payment. 03/04-18/10.
Remarks: Quick-Stop: >20h - <10h.

DK

Ulfborg 6C1

Vedersø Klit Camping, Øhusevej 23. **GPS**: n56,25829 e8,14130.
DKK 70-130 Ch DKK 35 against payment DKK 25.
07/04-22/10.

Vandel 6C1

Dagli' Brugsen, Hans Thomsens Vej 103. **GPS**: n55,71285 e9,21800.
free. **Surface:** metalled.
01/01-31/12.
Distance: on the spot on the spot.
Remarks: At petrol station and supermarket, max. 24h, Legoland 6km.

Vandel 6C1

Rastplads, Billundvej. **GPS**: n55,70687 e9,26709.
free WC free. **Surface:** forest soil.
01/01-31/12.
Distance: on the spot 4km.
Remarks: Parking in the forest with place for campfire, Legoland 10km.

Vejers Strand 6B2

Vejers Familicamping, Vejers Havvej 15. **GPS**: n55,61950 e8,13594.
DKK 110 Ch against payment.
01/01-31/12.
Remarks: Quick-Stop: >20h - <10h.

Tourist information Vejers Strand:
Tirpitz. German bunker.

Vemb 6C1

Flamingo Naturpark, Skalstrupvej 10. **GPS**: n56,35396 e8,31230.
50 DKK 50 WC.
Location: Rural, simple, isolated. **Surface:** grassy.
Distance: 4,5km 2km 2km 4,5km.
Remarks: Including access park.

Vesløs 5C3

Amtoft Havn, Gårdbækvej 12. **GPS**: n57,00647 e8,94068.

5 DKK 100 Ch (10x) WC included free.
Location: Rural, comfortable, quiet. **Surface:** grassy/gravel.
01/01-31/12.
Distance: on the spot on the spot on the spot on the spot.
Remarks: To be paid at supermarket.

Vesløs 5C3

Vejlernes Grill & Kiosk, Aalborgvej 219B. **GPS**: n57,02518 e9,01585.

free. **Surface:** gravel. 01/01-31/12.

Vestervig 5B3

Krik-Vig, Krikvej 112. **GPS**: n56,77800 e8,26210.
DKK 100 Ch against payment. 19/03-23/10.
Remarks: Quick-Stop: >20h - <10h.

Viborg 5C3

Hanne Mølgaard, Jegstrupvej Vest 114. **GPS**: n56,46269 e9,34118.

6 DKK 75 included.
Location: Rural, simple. **Surface:** grassy.
Distance: 5km.

Viborg 5C3

Kjellerupvej 16. **GPS**: n56,38420 e9,44058.
5 DKK 100 Ch (2x),16Amp WC included.
Location: Rural, isolated, quiet. **Surface:** grassy.
01/01-31/12.
Distance: 1,5km.

Vinderup 5C3

Sportsplads, Nørgårdsvej. **GPS**: n56,48181 e8,78636.

12 free. **Location:** Urban, simple. **Surface:** asphalted/metalled.
01/01-31/12.
Distance: 500m 500m 450m.

Vinderup 5C3

Handbjerg Marina, Strandvejen. **GPS**: n56,47568 e8,71337.

24 DKK 125 against payment.
Location: Rural, quiet. **Surface:** gravel. 01/01-31/12.
Distance: on the spot on the spot on the spot.

Vinderup 5C3

Sevel Camping, Halallé 6, Sevel. **GPS**: n56,45889 e8,86950.
DKK 50.
01/01-31/12.
Remarks: Quick-Stop: >20h - <10h.

Tourist information Vinderup:
Hjerl Hedes Frilandsmuseum, Hjerl Hedevej 14. Open air museum.
01/05-30/09 10-16h, 01/07-31/07 10-17h.
Stubber Kloster, Stubbergård Sø. Ruins of former Benedictine monastery.
01/01-31/12. free.

Østbirk 6D1

Elite Camp Vestbirk, Møllehøjvej 4. **GPS**: n55,96840 e9,75000.
DKK 140 Ch against payment. 19/03-28/09.
Remarks: Quick-Stop: >20h - <10h.

Øster Assels 5C3

Sillerslev Havn, Havnevej 75. **GPS**: n56,68116 e8,72774.

16 DKK 120 Ch WC included.
Location: Comfortable. **Surface:** gravel/sand. 01/01-31/12.
Distance: on the spot on the spot on the spot.

Funen

Aarup 6D2

Aalsbogaard Lystfiskersøer, Store Landevej 125, Billesbølle.
GPS: n55,42686 e10,01935.
DKK 50/pp DKK 20 DKK 10.
Surface: grassy. 01/01-31/12.
Distance: on the spot on the spot.
Remarks: At fish lake.

Aarup 6D2

Annemette & Lars Mogensen, Frøbjerg Vænge 31.
GPS: n55,34907 e10,08323.
3 free free. **Surface:** gravel. 01/01-31/12.

Asperup 6D2

Skovlund Camping, Kystvejen 1. **GPS**: n55,50647 e9,89967.
DKK 99. 23/03-18/09.
Remarks: Quick-Stop: >20h - <10h.

Assens 6D2

Assens Havn, Nordre Havnevej 10. **GPS**: n55,27345 e9,88961.
40 DKK 100 WC. **Surface:** grassy. 01/01-31/12.
Distance: 350m on the spot on the spot 350m.
Remarks: Max. 24h.

Assens 6D2

Assens Marina, Næsvej 29. **GPS**: n55,26875 e9,00000.
20 DKK 140 WC. **Surface:** grassy. 01/01-31/12.
Distance: 1,5km on the spot on the spot 150m.

Assens 6D2

Britta Bang, Lilletoftevej 7, Gamtofte. **GPS**: n55,28165 e9,98850.
3 DKK 100 Ch included WC. **Location:** Rural.
Surface: metalled. 01/01-31/12.
Distance: 7,5km 7km 7km.

Tourist information Assens:
Vestfyns Hjemstavnsgård, Klaregade 23, Gummerup, Glamsbjerg. Open air museum. 01/04-31/10 10-16h Mo.

Bagenkop 6E3

Bagenkop Lystbådehavn, Færgevej. **GPS**: n54,75173 e10,67512.
20 DKK 130 WC.
Surface: asphalted. 01/01-31/12.
Distance: on the spot on the spot on the spot.

Bagenkop 6E3

Koldkrigsmuseum Langelandsfor, Vognsbjergvej 4A.
GPS: n54,75306 e10,71583.
DKK 95. **Surface:** metalled. 01/04-31/10.
Remarks: Check in at museum.

Bogense 6D2

Bogense Havn, Vestre Havnevej 29. **GPS**: n55,56806 e10,07833.

8 € 14 WC included.
Surface: gravel. 01/01-31/12.
Distance: 200m 300m 300m on the spot 200m.

Bogense 6D2

Kyst, Østre Havnevej 1. **GPS**: n55,56626 e10,08395.
DKK 210 Ch. 20/03-18/09.
Remarks: Quick-Stop: >20h - <10h.

Broby 6D2

Bakkelyet, Præsteskovvej 7. **GPS**: n55,25707 e10,19292.
DKK 50. **Location:** Isolated, quiet.
Distance: 3km on the spot 3km.

Faaborg 6D2

Faaborg Havn, Kanalvej 19. **GPS**: n55,09658 e10,23429.
6 DKK 130 DKK 5 Ch DKK 3/kWh WC.
Surface: unpaved. 01/06-30/09.
Distance: 200m on the spot on the spot on the spot 500m 200m.
Remarks: Check in at harbourmaster.

Faaborg 6D2

Havnen Fjellebroen, Fjellebrovejen 81. **GPS**: n55,06009 e10,38140.
10 DKK 100 WC DKK 5.
Surface: gravel. 01/01-31/12.
Distance: on the spot on the spot on the spot.

Faaborg 6D2

Faaborg Camping, Odensevej 140. **GPS**: n55,11667 e10,24477.
DKK 150 Ch against payment. 01/01-31/12.
Remarks: Quick-Stop: >20h - <10h.

Faaborg 6D2

Nab Strand Camping, Kildegaardsvej 8. **GPS**: n55,06428 e10,31390.
DKK 160. 29/04-28/08.
Remarks: Quick-Stop: >20h - <10h.

Ferritslev 6D2

Jørgen Christensen, Rolfvej 45. **GPS**: n55,32111 e10,56806.
47 free. **Location:** Urban, simple. **Surface:** gravel. 01/01-31/12.

DK

S Frørup 6E2
Kongshøj, Kongshøjvej 5. **GPS**: n55,22122 e10,80628.
DKK 105 Ch. 01/01-31/12.
Remarks: Quick-Stop: >20h - <10h.

S Gram 6C2
Anholm Fiskesø, Folevej 11. **GPS**: n55,30564 e8,99888.

15 DKK 150, dog DKK 10 Chincluded DKK 35.
Location: Rural, simple, isolated, quiet. 01/04-30/11.
Distance: 5km on the spot 1km 5km.
Remarks: At fish pond.

S Gram 6C2
Gram Slot, Slotsvej 54. **GPS**: n55,29722 e9,05946.
50 DKK 75 WC included. **Surface:** grassy.
Distance: 1km.

S Gram 6C2
Annemettes bondegård, Ribelandevej 18.
GPS: n55,28647 e9,00098.

3 DKK 100 Ch DKK 25. **Location:** Rural, simple, isolated, quiet. **Surface:** grassy/gravel. 03/01-01/11.

S Humble 6E3
Ristinge, Ristingevej 104. **GPS**: n54,81944 e10,63988.
DKK 150 Ch against payment. 03/06-28/08.
Remarks: Quick-Stop: >20h - <10h.

S Kerteminde 6E2
Kerteminde Marina, Nordre Havnekaj. **GPS**: n55,45210 e10,66427.
12 DKK 140 Ch included DKK 2 according consumption. **Surface:** gravel. 01/01-31/12.
Distance: 500m on the spot on the spot 250m 150m.

S Kerteminde 6E2
Color Camp Kerteminde, Hindsholmvej 80. **GPS**: n55,46409 e10,67183.
DKK 125 Ch. 21/03-18/09.
Remarks: Quick-Stop: >20h - <10h.

S Middelfart 6D2
Lystbådehavn, Østre Hougvej 112. **GPS**: n55,49250 e9,73028.

13 € 17 Ch (12x) WC included.
Location: Rural, luxurious, isolated, quiet.
Surface: asphalted/metalled. 01/01-31/12.
Distance: 2km on the spot on the spot on the spot on the spot.
Remarks: Harbour Middelfahrt, Tallycard: service, electricity, sanitary building, caution DKK 50.

S Middelfart 6D2
Strib Bådehavn, Strandvejen 271, Strib. **GPS**: n55,53829 e9,76387.
DKK 120 WC. **Surface:** gravel.
Distance: on the spot 350m 1km.

S Middelfart 6D2
Vejlby Fed Camping, Rigelvej 1. **GPS**: n55,51949 e9,84975.
DKK 120 Ch against payment. 19/03-11/09.
Remarks: Quick-Stop: >20h - <10h.

S Millinge 6D2
Fasled Havn, Fiskerstræde 1. **GPS**: n55,15347 e10,14431.
DKK 110 included. **Surface:** grassy/gravel.
Distance: on the spot 200m.
Remarks: Check in at harbourmaster, wifi code: havnen2.

S Nr. Åby 6D2
Ronæs strand, Ronæsvej 10. **GPS**: n55,43975 e9,82692.
30 DKK 130 Ch against payment. 01/04-24/09.
Remarks: Quick-Stop: >20h - <10h.

S Nyborg 6E2
Hjejlevej 107. **GPS**: n55,29734 e10,83963.

free Chfree. **Surface:** metalled.

S Nyborg 6E2
Sulkendrup Mølle, Sulkendrupvej 1. **GPS**: n55,29384 e10,71334.
3 DKK 75 DKK 25 Ch DKK 25 WC DKK 15.
Location: Rural, comfortable. **Surface:** grassy. 01/01-31/12.
Distance: 5km.

S Nyborg 6E2
Grønnehave strand, Rejstrupvej 83. **GPS**: n55,35646 e10,78767.
DKK 140 Ch against payment. 24/03-25/09.
Remarks: Quick-Stop: >20h - <10h.

Tourist information Nyborg:
Borgmestergården, Slotsgade 11. Local history. 01/05-31/10 10-15/16h.
Nyborg Fæstning, Slotsgade 1. Fortress.
Nyborg Slot / Danehofslottet, Slotsgade 34. Castle, end 12th century. 01/04-31/10 10-15/16h.

Odense 6D2
Tarup Campingcenter, Agerhatten 31. **GPS**: n55,36110 e10,46722.
20 free. **Surface:** grassy. 01/01-31/12.
Distance: 6km 2km.

S Rudkøbing 6E2
Færgegårdens, Spodsbjergvej 335. **GPS**: n54,93219 e10,82945.
DKK 130 Ch against payment. 01/01-31/12.
Remarks: Quick-Stop: >20h - <10h.

S Stenstrup 6D2
Tronbjerggård Strandhave, Højbjergvej 13.
GPS: n55,12944 e10,58306.
3 against payment WC.

S Svendborg 6D2
Svendborg Golfbane, Tordensgårdevej 3. **GPS**: n55,08750 e10,55389.
10 DKK 150 WC included. **Location:** Rural, comfortable.
Surface: grassy/metalled. 01/01-31/12.
Distance: 5km 5km on the spot.
Remarks: At golf court.

S Svendborg 6D2
Carlsberg, Sundbrovej 19. **GPS**: n55,03344 e10,61332.
DKK 130 Ch against payment. 17/03-02/10.
Remarks: Quick-Stop: >20h - <10h.

S Svendborg 6D2
Idrætshallen, Ryttervej 70. **GPS**: n55,05668 e10,57613.
DKK 100 Ch.

Tourist information Svendborg:
Egeskov Slot, Kværndrup. Citadel with park and 6 museums. 01/05-31/10 10-17/20h.
Valdemars Slot, Slotsalléen 100, Troense, Tåsinge. Castle on the island Tåsinge, fully furnished. 01/05-31/10 10-17h May, Sep, Oct: Mo.

Tranekær 6E2
Emmerbølle Strand Camping, Emmerbøllevej 24.
GPS: n55,03351 e10,84853.
DKK 170. 18/03-18/09.
Distance: on the spot.
Remarks: Quick-Stop: >20h - <10h.

S Varde 6C2
Fritidscenter, Lerpøtvej 55. **GPS**: n55,63294 e8,47447.
20 DKK 100 WC against payment.
Surface: grassy. 01/05-31/10.
Remarks: At sports centre.

S Varde 6C2
Jensen, Ringkøbingvej 143. **GPS**: n55,65762 e8,48942.

4 DKK 75 WC. **Location:** Rural, comfortable, isolated, quiet. **Surface:** grassy/metalled.
Distance: 5km.

S Varde 6C2
Joan & Preben Christensen, Ringkøbingvej 259, Hindsig.
GPS: n55,72077 e8,49345.

5 DKK 50 Ch. **Location:** Rural, comfortable, quiet.
Surface: grassy. 01/01-31/12.
Distance: 12km 3km.

Ærøskøbing 6D2
Ærøskøbing Camping, Sygehusvejen 40. **GPS**: n54,89408 e10,40118.
DKK 100. 01/04-23/10.
Distance: on the spot.
Remarks: Quick-Stop: >20h - <10h.

Seeland, Møn, Lolland and Falster

S Boeslunde 6E2
Campinggaarden Boelunde, Rennebjergvej 110.
GPS: n55,28463 e11,26837.
DKK 140 Ch against payment. 01/04-30/09.
Remarks: Quick-Stop: >20h - <10h.

S Bogø By 6F2
Farø Parkplatz, Grøsundvej. **GPS**: n54,94876 e11,98696.

25 free ChWCfree.
Location: Rural, noisy. **Surface:** gravel. 01/01-31/12.
Distance: 200m on the spot on the spot 100m.

S Bogø By 6F2
Café-Restaurant Stalden, Hougårdsbanke 5.
GPS: n54,93000 e12,02806.
4 free for clients Ch WC against payment.
Location: Rural. **Surface:** grassy. 01/01-31/12.
Distance: 1km on the spot.

S Borre 6F2
Klintholm Havn, Klintholm Havneby 24. **GPS**: n54,95418 e12,46695.
DKK 140 WC included. 01/01-31/12.
Distance: on the spot on the spot on the spot.

S Copenhagen 6F1
Copenhagen City Camp, Elvaerksvej 7-9.
GPS: n55,66064 e12,55896.

DK

60 DKK 225, 2 pers incl. Ch WC included.
Location: Urban, simple, quiet. **Surface:** asphalted.
Whitsuntide-03/09.
Distance: 2km 500m 200m 200m on the spot on the spot.

Tourist information Copenhagen:
Copenhagen Card. Card gives free entrance to public transport, 73 museums and attractions. Available at Tourist Offices, hotels, campsites.
Dyrehavsbakken, Dyrehavevej 62, Klampenborg (ten n. van Kopenhagen). Popular amusement park, oldest park of Denmark, with among other things 100 attractions and 35 restaurants.
Tivoli, Vesterbrogade 3. Large amusement park in the centre of the city with among other things 32 restaurants, 26 attractions, shows, concerts etc. DKK 110-120.

Dalby 6E2
Camp Hverringe, Blæsenborgvej 200. **GPS**: n55,50937 e10,71233.
DKK 75. 18/03-23/10.
Distance: on the spot.
Remarks: Quick-Stop: >20h - <10h.

Dannemare 6E3
Hummingen, Pumpehusvej 1. **GPS**: n54,71317 e11,24606.
DKK 140 Ch against payment. 18/03-23/10.
Remarks: Quick-Stop: >20h - <10h.

Dronningsmølle 6F1
Dronningmølle, Strandkrogen 2b. **GPS**: n56,08393 e12,39112.
DKK 160 Ch. 15/03-14/09.
Remarks: Quick-Stop: >20h - <10h.

Fakse 6F2
Feddet, Feddet 12. **GPS**: n55,17366 e12,10118.
DKK 75, dog DKK 30 Chagainst payment included.
01/01-31/12.
Remarks: Quick-Stop: >20h - <10h.

Tourist information Fakse:
Faksekystens Turistinformation, Hovedgaden 29, Fakse Ladeplads, www.faksekysten.dk. The municipality Fakse has 30 kilometres coastline, marked cycle and hiking routes.
Fortællerfestival, Fakse Lime Beach. Festival for story tellers.
last weekend Jun.
Rivierafest, Fakse Ladeplads. Festival with free herring-table on Sunday. Thu-Su of week 29.

Farum 6F1
Hovedgade 32. **GPS**: n55,81222 e12,36917.

3 free. **Location:** Urban, simple, noisy. **Surface:** asphalted.
01/01-31/12.
Distance: 500m 100m on the spot 500m on the spot on the spot.

Farum 6F1
Stavnsholt Renseanlæg. **GPS**: n55,81278 e12,40556.
Chfree. Mo-Thu 7-15.30h, Fr 7-11.30h.

Frederikssund 6F1
Marbæk Lystbådehavn, Strandlystvej 26 D.
GPS: n55,82778 e12,06389.

6 125 DKK Ch WCincluded against payment
DKK 20/20. **Location:** Rural, comfortable, quiet.
Surface: gravel. 01/01-31/12.
Distance: 1,5km on the spot on the spot 1,5km 1,5km on the spot on the spot.

Frederikssund 6F1
B&B Bybjerggaard, Sundbylillevej 42. **GPS**: n55,83579 e12,11622.
DKK 50/pp.
Distance: on the spot.

Frederiksværk 6F1
Frederiksværk Havn, Havnelinien 23. **GPS**: n55,96673 e11,99986.
4 DKK 140 included.
Distance: 2km on the spot on the spot.

Føllenslev 6E1
Vesterlyng, Ravnholtvej 3. **GPS**: n55,74278 e11,30883.
DKK 130 Ch against payment. 31/03-22/10.
Remarks: Quick-Stop: >20h - <10h.

Gedser 6F3
Gedser Lystbådehavn, Vestre Strand 3. **GPS**: n54,58194 e11,92361.
5 DKK 125 included. **Surface:** gravel. 01/01-31/12.
Distance: 200m.

Gilleleje 6F1
Smidstrup Farmen, Jydebjergvej 32. **GPS**: n56,10346 e12,22722.
DKK 100. **Location:** Rural. **Surface:** grassy/gravel.
01/01-31/12.
Distance: 1,5km 2km 1,5km.
Remarks: Max. 3 days.

Greve 6F1
Copenhagen Motorhome Camp, Hundige Strandvej 72.
GPS: n55,59399 e12,34247.

42 DKK 205, 15/06-31/08 DKK 215 Ch DKK 52 included.
Surface: grassy. 01/04-31/10.
Distance: Copenhagen 19km 1km 3km 800m.

Gørlev 6E2
Reersø Havn, Strandvejen 101, Reersø. **GPS**: n55,51750 e11,11833.

5 DKK 100 WC included. **Location:** Rural, simple, quiet.
Surface: gravel. 01/04-01/11.
Distance: 300m on the spot on the spot on the spot on the spot on the spot.
Remarks: Money in envelope in mail box.

Helsinge 6F1
Anisse Vingård, Præstevej 89, Annisse. **GPS**: n55,98114 e12,17474.
DKK 75. 01/01-31/12.

Hillerød 6F1
JOHS, Hestehavevej 24. **GPS**: n55,90221 e12,31155.
DKK 150. **Surface:** grassy/gravel.
Distance: on the spot on the spot.

Hundested 6E1
Hundested Havn, Havnegade 8. **GPS**: n55,96557 e11,84845.

5 DKK 150 Ch WC against payment.
Location: Urban, comfortable. **Surface:** metalled.
01/01-31/12.
Distance: 500m on the spot on the spot on the spot 200m 200m on the spot.

Hundested 6E1
Lynæs Havn, Lynæs Havnevej 15 B, Lynæs.
GPS: n55,94407 e11,86507.

10 DKK 160 Ch WC included free.
Location: Rural, simple, quiet. **Surface:** metalled.
01/01-31/12.
Distance: 2km 500m on the spot 2km on the spot on the spot.

Kalundborg 6E1
Debbies Bed & Breakfast, Hovvejen 114. **GPS**: n55,67564 e11,14552.
DKK 100.
Remarks: Breakfast-service.

Kalvehave 6F2
Lystbådehavn, Kalvehave Havnevej 26. **GPS**: n54,99584 e12,16641.
2 DKK 140 WC included.
Surface: grassy/gravel. 01/01-31/12.
Distance: 150m on the spot on the spot 100m 150m.

Karise 6F2
Lægårdens, Vemmetoftevej 2A. **GPS**: n55,27260 e12,22306.
DKK 105 Ch. 01/01-31/12.
Remarks: Quick-Stop: >20h - <10h.

Karrebæksminde 6E2
Naestved Sjelklub, Ved Broen 29. **GPS**: n55,17706 e11,65018.

6 € 18 Ch WC DKK 50/50 included.
Location: Rural, simple, quiet. **Surface:** gravel.
15/04-15/09.
Distance: on the spot on the spot on the spot on the spot on the spot.

Kirke Hyllinge 6F1
Gershøj Havn, Gershøj Havnevej 5, Gershøj.
GPS: n55,71667 e11,98000.

10 € 8 Ch against payment WC included.

DK

Location: Rural, simple, quiet. **Surface:** gravel. 01/01-31/12.
Distance: 1,5km on the spot on the spot.

Korsør 6E2

Pit-Stop Storebælt, Halskov Havn 2. **GPS:** n55,34769 e11,11463.

40 DKK 75 Ch included.
Location: Rural, simple. **Surface:** grassy. 01/01-31/12.
Distance: 1km 500m on the spot on the spot 500m on the spot on the spot on the spot.
Remarks: Along busy through road, use camp-site facilities allowed, closed at night.

Korsør 6E2

Lystbådehavn, Sylowsvej 10. **GPS:** n55,32664 e11,13190.

20 DKK 130 included WC against payment.
Location: Rural, simple, quiet. **Surface:** gravel.
01/01-31/12.
Distance: 300m 4km on the spot on the spot on the spot 300m on the spot on the spot.

Korsør 6E2

Lystskov, Korsør Lystskov 2. **GPS:** n55,32219 e11,18505.
DKK 90. 19/03-25/09.
Remarks: Quick-Stop: >20h - <10h.

Tourist information Korsør:
Korsør Fæstning, Korsør Coastal Battery, The Fortress, Søbatteriet 7. Fortress. 01/05-30/09 Wed-Su 11-16h.

Lynge 6F1

Irene & Aage Andersen, Stengårdsvej 12.
GPS: n55,81972 e12,27376.

3 free DKK 10/50liter. **Location:** Rural, simple, quiet.
Surface: grassy. 01/01-31/12.
Distance: 1km on the spot on the spot.

Maribo 6E3

Skelstrupgåren Bed and Breakfast, Skelstupvej 32.
GPS: n54,78774 e11,52095.
5 DKK 50 against payment. **Surface:** grassy.
Distance: 2,2km 4km.

Munke Bjergby 6E2

Dojringevej 40a. **GPS:** n55,49637 e11,55065.

10 free DKK 10/20liter DKK 10 DKK 30.
Location: Rural, comfortable, quiet. **Surface:** grassy.

01/01-31/12.
Distance: 8km on the spot on the spot.
Remarks: Max. 48h.

Nykøbing 6E1

Lystbådehavn, Snekkevej 9. **GPS:** n55,91610 e11,67287.

10 DKK 110 Ch WC included DKK 25/20.
Location: Urban, simple, quiet. **Surface:** grassy.
01/01-31/12.
Distance: 500m 100m 100m on the spot on the spot.

Nykøbing F. 6F3

Toreby Sejlklub, Dæmningen 2, Sundby Lolland.
GPS: n54,76051 e11,86041.
5 DKK 120 WC included.
Surface: gravel. 01/05-30/09.
Distance: on the spot on the spot on the spot.
Remarks: Money in envelope in mail box.

Nykøbing F. 6F3

Falster City Camping, Østre Alle 112. **GPS:** n54,76243 e11,89479.
DKK 120 Ch against payment. 01/04-01/12.
Remarks: Quick-Stop: >20h - <10h.

Næstved 6E2

Rådmandshaven. **GPS:** n55,23166 e11,75344.

14 free. **Location:** Urban, simple, noisy. **Surface:** concrete.
01/01-31/12.
Distance: 500m 500m 500m on the spot.
Remarks: Parking in front of town hall, special part for motor homes.

Præstø 6F2

Præstø Havn, Fjordstien 1. **GPS:** n55,12444 e12,04333.

5 DKK 115 Ch WC DKK 25/25 included.
Location: Urban, simple, quiet. **Surface:** asphalted.
01/01-31/12.
Distance: 500m 7km on the spot on the spot on the spot on the spot.

Ringsted 6E2

Autocamper P-plads Ringsted, Delingen.
GPS: n55,45029 e11,80077.

6 free free. **Location:** Urban, simple. **Surface:** grasstiles.
01/01-31/12.
Distance: 1km 900m 900m.

Remarks: Max. 48h.

Ringsted 6E2

Mogens Madsen, Vibevej 34. **GPS:** n55,44222 e11,80667.

3 free against payment. **Location:** Urban, simple, noisy.
Surface: metalled. 01/01-31/12.
Distance: 4 km 800m.

Ringsted 6E2

Skovly Camping, Nebs Møllevej 65. **GPS:** n55,49615 e11,85768.
DKK 150. 01/01-31/12.
Remarks: Quick-Stop: >20h - <10h.

Roskilde 6F1

Camp Roskilde, Baunehøjvej 7. **GPS:** n55,67374 e12,08209.
DKK 150 DKK 45. 18/03-02/10.
Remarks: Quick-Stop: >20h - <10h.

Rødvig 6F2

Rødvig Fiskerihavn, Fiskerihavnen 8. **GPS:** n55,25417 e12,37500.

4 € 12 WC included DKK 5/4minutes.
Location: Rural, simple, quiet.
Surface: metalled. 01/01-31/12.
Distance: 200m on the spot on the spot on the spot.
Remarks: Check in at harbourmaster.

Rødvig 6F2

Rødvig Camping, Højstrupvej 2 A. **GPS:** n55,25059 e12,34970.

5 DKK 100. **Location:** Rural, simple, quiet.
Surface: grassy. 01/04-28/09.
Distance: 2km on the spot.
Remarks: Quick-Stop: >20h - <10h.

Sakskøbing 6E3

Sakskøbing Lystbådehavn, Maltrup Vænge 38.
GPS: n54,81078 e11,61957.
5 DKK 100 WC against payment included.
Surface: gravel. 01/05-15/10.
Distance: 500m.

Sjællands Odde 6F1

Sjællands Odde Havn, Østre Havnevej 42.
GPS: n55,97139 e11,36956.

2 € 16 WC included DKK 5/5minutes.
Location: Rural, simple, quiet. **Surface:** gravel.
01/01-31/12.

DK

Distance: on the spot on the spot ⊗300m on the spot.

Skælskør 6E2

Skælskør Havn, Havnevej 20. **GPS**: n55,25223 e11,28992.

15 € 14 Ch (15x)DKK 25/kWh WC included DKK 5/5minutes DKK 25/25 free.
Location: Urban, simple, central. **Surface:** metalled. 01/01-31/12.
Distance: on the spot on the spot on the spot ⊗on the spot on the spot on the spot.
Remarks: Free bicycles available.

Skælskør 6E2

Skælskør Nor, Kildehusvej 1. **GPS**: n55,25818 e11,28395.
DKK 150 Ch . 01/01-31/12.
Remarks: Quick-Stop: >20h - <10h.

Store Fuglede 6E2

Bjerge Sydstrand Camping, Osvejen 30. **GPS**: n55,56298 e11,16489.
DKK 150. 01/01-31/12.
Distance: on the spot.
Remarks: Quick-Stop: >20h - <10h.

Taastrup 6F1

Park Hotel, Brorsonsvej 3. **GPS**: n55,65389 e12,30000.

10 DKK 200 (3x)DKK 25/day WC included on demand .
Location: Simple, quiet. **Surface:** metalled.
01/01-31/12.
Distance: 300m 1,5km ⊗on the spot 300m on the spot on the spot.
Remarks: Breakfast buffet DKK 75, code wifi in restaurant.

Tårs (Harpelunde) 6E2

Tårs Havn Lolland, Tårsvej 215, Harpelund Lolland.
GPS: n54,87811 e11,02381.
2 DKK 125 WC included. 01/01-31/12.
Remarks: Harbour Tårs.

Torrig 6E2

Kragenæs Havn, Kragenæsvej 84. **GPS**: n54,91565 e11,35730.
DKK 135 Ch against payment. 18/03-23/10.
Remarks: Quick-Stop: >20h - <10h.

Ugerløse 6E1

Minnislyst, Tølløsevej 294. **GPS**: n55,59730 e11,68250.

€ 10 Ch included.
Location: Rural. 01/01-31/12.
Distance: 2,2km 2,2km 2km.

Vejby 6F1

Åmosevejen 18. **GPS**: n56,00000 e12,00000.
DKK 100 . **Location:** Rural. 01/01-31/12.
Distance: 2km.
Remarks: Max. 3 days.

Vig 6E1

Kongsøre Camping, Egebjergvej 342. **GPS**: n55,82390 e11,66743.
DKK 120. 01/04-30/09.
Distance: ⊗on the spot.

Remarks: Quick-Stop: >20h - <10h.

Væggerløse 6F3

Marielyst Feriepark & Camping, Godthåbs Allé 7, Marielyst.
GPS: n54,67357 e11,94427.
DKK 100.
Remarks: Quick-Stop: >20h - <10h.

Værløse 6F1

Furesø Museer, Skovgårds alle 37. **GPS**: n55,78528 e12,37722.

4 free. **Location:** Urban, simple, noisy. **Surface:** metalled.
01/01-31/12.
Distance: on the spot ⊗250m 250m on the spot on the spot.

Værløse 6F1

Bryggeri Skovlyst, Skovlystvej 2. **GPS**: n55,76317 e12,38365.

3 free WC.
Location: Rural, simple, quiet. **Surface:** gravel.
01/01-31/12.
Distance: 5km ⊗on the spot on the spot on the spot.

DK

Spain

Capital: Madrid
Government: Constitutional monarchy
Official Language: Spanish
Population: 48,563,476 (2016)
Area: 505,992 km²

General information
Dialling code: 0034
General emergency: 112
Currency: Euro

Regulations for overnight stays
Wild camping is allowed having gained permission from the municipality, olice or property owner. Along the Mediterranean coast wild camping is almost always forbidden. Parking places (P) mentioned here can be considered as tolerated places to stay overnight.

Additional public holidays 2018
January 6 Epiphany
March 30 Good Friday
May 1 Labor Day
May 31 Corpus Christi
August 15 Assumption of the Virgin Mary
October 12 National Holiday
November 1 All Saints' Day
December 6 Constitution Day
December 8 Immaculate Conception

Time Zone
Winter (Standard Time) GMT+1
Summer (DST) GMT+2

ES

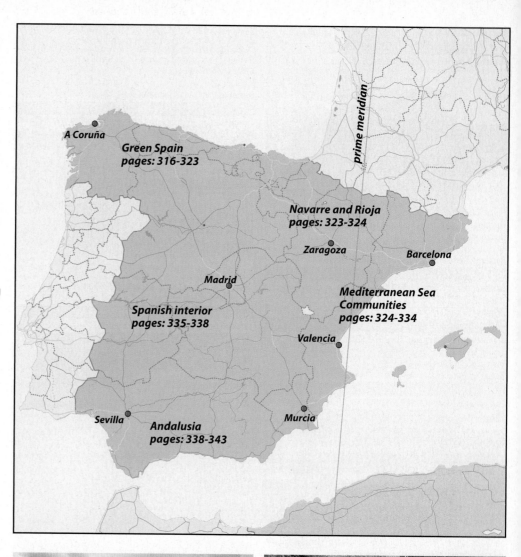

A Coruña
Green Spain
pages: 316-323
prime meridian
Navarre and Rioja
pages: 323-324
Zaragoza
Barcelona
Madrid
Mediterranean Sea
Communities
pages: 324-334
Spanish interior
pages: 335-338
Valencia
Sevilla
Murcia
Andalusia
pages: 338-343

Green Spain

S A Coruña 29C1
Puerto de San Pedro de Visma, Zona de O Portiño.
GPS: n43,37167 w8,44472.

12 free Chfree. **Surface:** metalled.
Distance: 3km on the spot 50m 1km Carrefour 1km.
Remarks: Max. 48h.

A Coruña 29C1
Tore de Hercules. **GPS**: n43,38378 w8,40228.
free. **Surface:** asphalted.
Distance: on the spot 50m 50m.

S A Coruña 29C1
Parking Marina Coruña, Paseo Marítimo Francisco Vázquez s/n.
GPS: n43,36976 w8,38786.
15 € 1,50/h, € 22/24h Ch WC included.
Location: Urban. **Surface:** metalled. 01/01-31/12.
Distance: centre 800m on the spot.
Remarks: Parking marina.

S A Coruña 29C1
Yakart, Carretera de mesoiro, 63. **GPS**: n43,33228 w8,425.
15 € 10/24h Ch included. **Location:** Urban.
Surface: metalled. 01/01-31/12.
Distance: centre 4,5km 500m 70m.
Remarks: At motorhome dealer, monitored parking.

A Guarda 29B2
GPS: n41,89892 w8,87825.

5. **Location:** Urban, simple, central.
Surface: asphalted.
Distance: 1km 300m 500m.
Remarks: Parking harbour.

S A Laracha 29C1
Area de O Regado, AC-552. **GPS**: n43,24972 w8,61694.
3 free Chfree. **Surface:** asphalted.

S A Laracha 29C1
Av. Laracha, 39. **GPS**: n43,31616 w8,59483.
free Chfree. **Surface:** asphalted. 01/01-31/12.
Distance: A Laracha 11km 1,3km.
Remarks: Max. 48h.

S A Pontenova 29D1
Camiño do Antigo Ferrocarril. **GPS**: n43,35578 w7,18939.
6 free Chfree. **Surface:** asphalted. 01/01-31/12.
Distance: 800m 800m on the spot on the spot.
Remarks: Next to swimming pool, max. 48h.

S A Pontenova 29D1
Rua de la Estación. **GPS**: n43,34739 w7,19171.

8 free Chfree. **Surface:** asphalted. 01/01-31/12.
Distance: 200m 100m.
Remarks: Max. 48h.

S A Rúa 29D2
Área Recreativa O Aguillón. GPS: n42,38800 w7,11459.
10 free Chfree. **Surface:** asphalted/grassy.
01/01-31/12.
Distance: 500m on the spot 500m 500m on the spot on the spot.
Remarks: Next to football ground.

S Agurain 29H2
Bizkaia Kalea. **GPS**: n42,85324 w2,38495.
7 free Chfree. **Surface:** asphalted. 01/01-31/12.
Distance: 500m 500m 350m.

S Amurrio 29H2
Araba Kalea. **GPS**: n43,05528 w2,99806.
3 free Chfree. 01/01-31/12.
Distance: 500m 500m.
Remarks: Max. 48h.

Añana 29G2
Mercado Kalea. **GPS**: n42,80344 w2,98437.
2 free. **Surface:** metalled. 01/01-31/12.
Distance: 300M.

S Arcade 29C2
Rúa do Peirao. **GPS**: n42,33946 w8,61329.
5 free Chfree. **Surface:** metalled. 01/01-31/12.
Distance: on the spot on the spot 100m 200m.

Arrigorriaga 29H2

Carretera Buia Etorbidea. **GPS**: n43,23772 w2,91938.

. **Location:** Urban, simple. **Surface:** asphalted.
01/01-31/12.

As Neves 29C2

Camino del Emenjeric. **GPS**: n42,08726 w8,41374.

1 free Chfree. **Location:** Rural. 01/01-31/12.
Distance: 200m 200m.
Remarks: Max. 48h.

As Nogais 29D2

Calle Rosalía de Castro. **GPS**: n42,81066 w7,1069.
3 free Chfree. **Surface:** asphalted. 01/01-31/12.
Distance: 500m 500m 500m on the spot.
Remarks: Max. 48h, swimming pool and picnic area available.

As Pontes de García Rodríguez 29D1

Rúa Juan Antonio Suanzes. **GPS**: n43,45103 w7,85445.
5 free Chfree. 01/01-31/12.
Distance: 200m 200m.
Remarks: Well situated for visiting Parque Natural de las Fragas do Eume.

Bakio 29H2

Parking, BI 3101. **GPS**: n43,42783 w2,80442.

20 free, weekend and 01/08-30/09 € 6 WCfree.
Location: Urban, simple.
Surface: grasstiles. 01/01-31/12.
Distance: 100m 200m 100m on the spot.
Remarks: Behind tourist info.

Barrio Cosío 29F2

Área de Autocaravanas del Valle del Nansa.
GPS: n43,23349 w4,39892.

6 first day free, then € 5 € 3 Ch. **Location:** Rural, simple, quiet. **Surface:** metalled.
Distance: on the spot on the spot 100m.
Remarks: Max. 24h.

Bárzana 29E1

Area de Bárzana-Quirós, El Felguere. **GPS**: n43,15611 w5,97306.

15 free Chfree. **Location:** Rural, simple, quiet.
Surface: asphalted. 01/01-31/12 holidays.
Distance: 100m 100m 100m.
Remarks: Max. 48h.

Beasain 29H2

Igartza Oleta Kalea. **GPS**: n43,04682 w2,21228.
13 free Ch service € 3. **Surface:** asphalted.
01/01-31/12.
Distance: city centre 1km 500m.

Becerreá 29D2

Parque Empresarial. **GPS**: n42,85283 w7,15179.
16 free Chfree. **Surface:** asphalted. 01/01-31/12.
Distance: 1km 400m.
Remarks: Max. 48h.

Beche 29C1

Lugar Beche, 6. **GPS**: n43,18318 w8,3067.
free Chfree. **Location:** Isolated, quiet. **Surface:** gravel.
01/01-31/12.
Distance: on the spot on the spot on the spot on the spot.
Remarks: Along river, max. 48h.

Behobia 27A2

N10, Calle de Aria Juncal. **GPS**: n43,34310 w1,7598.

6 € 3/2h < 19.30, overnight stay free. **Location:** Urban, simple, noisy.
Surface: asphalted. 01/01-31/12.
Distance: on the spot 500m 200m 500m on the spot.

Bergara 29H2

Telleria Kalea, Labegaraieta. **GPS**: n43,10481 w2,42265.
free Chfree. **Surface:** asphalted. 01/01-31/12.
Distance: 2km on the spot on the spot on the spot.
Remarks: Max. 48h.

Bermeo 29H2

Área de la Pérgola, Itsasoan Galdurakoen Lamera.
GPS: n43,42306 w2,72556.

10 free Chfree. **Location:** Urban, simple. **Surface:** asphalted.
01/01-31/12.
Distance: 500m 500m 500m 300m.
Remarks: Nearby football ground, max. 48h.

Bertamirans 29C1

Paseo Fluvial. **GPS**: n42,86009 w8,64838.

15 free Chfree. **Surface:** asphalted. 01/01-31/12.
Distance: 100m 50m Carrefour dir. Santiago every 30 min.
Remarks: Max. 48h.

Bilbao 29H2

Kobetamendi, Monte Kobeta, 31. **GPS**: n43,25961 w2,96355.

72 € 15/day Ch included WC.
Location: Urban, comfortable, quiet.
Surface: grasstiles.
01/01-31/12.
Distance: centre 4,5km 2,8km
Bilbao-bus 58.
Remarks: 16/10-14/05 free parking, asphalt, max. 72h, service pas-serby € 6.

Tourist information Bilbao:
Bilbao. Capital of the Basque Country and previously centre of the iron industry.
Basilica de Begoña, Virgen de Begoña, 38, Bilbao-Vizcaya. Basilica.

Boiro 29C2

Playa Mañons, S/n 15930 Chancelas–Abanqueiro.
GPS: n42,63138 w8,85311.
8 free free. **Surface:** metalled. 01/01-31/12.
Distance: on the spot.

Boiro 29C2

Praia Xardín de Barraña, La, Av. de Compostela, 54.
GPS: n42,64183 w8,89481.

10 € 3-6 Chfree. **Surface:** asphalted. 01/01-31/12.
Distance: 500m 20m 200m Bistro Prima 400m.
Remarks: Max. 48h.

Bueu 29C2

P0315 dir Cabo Udra. **GPS**: n42,33460 w8,8248.
10 free. **Location:** Isolated, quiet. **Surface:** sand.
01/01-31/12.
Distance: 200m.
Remarks: Max. 48h.

Bueu 29C2

Puerto, Avda. de Montero Rios. **GPS**: n42,32732 w8,7838.

. 01/01-31/12.

Burela 29D1

Area de Burela, Parque de O Campón, parking Hospital de Burela.
GPS: n43,65216 w7,35891.

ES

4 free Chfree. **Surface:** asphalted.
Distance: 200m 300m 200m.
Remarks: Max. 48h.

S Cabárceno 29G2

Área Lago del Acebo, N634> dir Parque de la naturaleze de Cabárceno.
GPS: n43,35802 w3,81959.

30 free Chfree. **Location:** Rural, quiet.
Surface: asphalted.
Distance: 100m 50m 50m 200m 200m.
Remarks: Max. 48h.

Camariñas 29B1

Puerto Club Nautico, Rúa Castelo. **GPS**: n43,12694 w9,18333.
5 free. **Surface:** asphalted. 01/01-31/12.
Distance: city centre 1km 100m.

S Candás 29E1

Area de La Fuente de los Angeles, Calle Estacion.
GPS: n43,58495 w5,77197.

6 free ChWCfree. **Location:** Urban, simple.
Surface: asphalted. 01/01-31/12.
Distance: 500m 1km 500m 500m.
Remarks: Along railwayline.

S Cangas de Morrazo 29C2

Camping Car Area Playa Arneles, Ctra Viso- Vilanova s/n.
GPS: n42,27618 w8,83399.
30 € 12 Ch € 3/day WC € 3 € 1/day.
Surface: grassy. 01/04-01/11.
Distance: 350m 300m 300m.

S Cangas de Morrazo 29C2

Ruá Campo Morelo, Gatañal. **GPS**: n42,25546 w8,79758.
5 free Chfree. **Surface:** asphalted. 01/01-31/12.
Distance: 2km.
Remarks: Behind gymnasium.

S Cangas de Onís 29F1

Parking Lanzadera Picos de Europa, Calle del Llreau.
GPS: n43,35211 w5,12536.

4 free Chfree. **Location:** Urban. **Surface:** asphalted.
Distance: 100m.
Remarks: Max. 48h.

S Cangas del Narcea 29E1

Av. de Oviedo,. **GPS**: n43,18068 w6,54848.
2 free Chfree. **Surface:** asphalted. 01/01-31/12.
Distance: 500m 400m.
Remarks: Max. 72h, no camping activities.

S Carnota 29B1

Area de Mar de Lira, Calle Miñarzo s/n. **GPS**: n42,80306 w9,12944.

4 free Chfree. **Surface:** sand.
Distance: Carnota 5km 10m on the spot.
Remarks: Parking next to hatchery.

S Carnota 29B1

Playa de Lombans. **GPS**: n42,84092 w9,09667.
5 free Chfree. **Location:** Isolated, quiet.
01/01-31/12.
Distance: 400m.
Remarks: At football ground.

S Cartelle 29C2

Camperpark O Mundil, Antigua Carretera OU-659.
GPS: n42,21444 w8,03306.

22 € 10 Ch WC free. **Surface:** gravel.
01/01-31/12.
Distance: 1km zona fluvial Río Arnoia 10m on the spot.

S Castro Caldelas 29D2

Travesía da Devesa. **GPS**: n42,37479 w7,41832.
8 free Chfree. 01/01-31/12.
Distance: 850m 850m 850m.
Remarks: Max. 48h.

S Castro de Rei 29D1

Castro de Ribeiras de Lea. **GPS**: n43,14663 w7,49211.
2 free Chfree. **Surface:** metalled. 01/01-31/12.
Distance: 250m.
Remarks: Max. 48h.

S Cenlle 29C2

Lugar Barbantes. **GPS**: n42,33252 w8,01296.
50 free Ch WC. **Location:** Isolated, quiet.
01/01-31/12.
Distance: Cenlle 10km on the spot on the spot on the spot.
Remarks: Max. 48h, free entrance swimming pool, picnic area.

S Chantada 29C2

Champ de Sangoñedo, Ctra. De Barrela o Seixo.
GPS: n42,60598 w7,77989.
5 free ChWCfree. **Surface:** gravel. 01/01-31/12.
Distance: 500m.
Remarks: At footballstadium, max. 48h.

S Coaña 29D1

Area de Ortiguera, Barrio Nueva Rasa. **GPS**: n43,56082 w6,73352.
2 free Chfree. **Location:** Rural, simple.
Surface: asphalted. 01/01-31/12.
Distance: on the spot on the spot.
Remarks: Max. 48h.

S Colombres 29F1

Area de Casa Junco, N-634. **GPS**: n43,38056 w4,55472.

15 free Chfree. **Surface:** asphalted.
Distance: on the spot.

S Colunga 29F1

Area de Los Llanos, Avda de Asturias N-632.
GPS: n43,48472 w5,26491.

23 € 4 € 3 € 1. **Location:** Simple. **Surface:** asphalted.
01/01-31/12.
Distance: 500m 2km 200m.
Remarks: Max. 48h, thursday market.

S Cospeito 29D1

Rosalia de Castro. **GPS**: n43,23984 w7,55579.
5 free Ch free. **Surface:** asphalted. 01/01-31/12.
Distance: 300m 300m 300m.
Remarks: Bird watching, max. 48h.

Cudillero 29E1

Puerto. **GPS**: n43,56568 w6,1517.

5. **Location:** Simple. **Surface:** asphalted.
Remarks: Parking in harbour.

S Cudillero 29E1

Hotel Rest. Casa Fernando II, N-632. **GPS**: n43,56028 w6,17722.

5 free Ch€ 3. **Location:** Simple, quiet. **Surface:** asphalted.
01/01-31/12.
Distance: on the spot.

S Elorrio 29H2

San Jose Kalea. **GPS**: n43,12834 w2.
11 free Ch. **Surface:** asphalted. 01/01-31/12.
Distance: 500m 500m.

S Eltziego 29H3

Área de Barrihuelo, Carr. de Laguardia. **GPS**: n42,51496 w2,61546.
14 free Chfree € 2/12h.
Surface: metalled. 01/01-31/12.
Distance: 300m 100m.
Remarks: Max. 72h.

S Ferrol 29C1

Ctra. de la Malata. **GPS**: n43,49333 w8,23972.

ES

15 free Ch free. **Surface:** asphalted. 01/01-31/12.
Distance: 700m 300m on the spot.
Remarks: Max. 48h.

S Finisterre 29B1

Area El Campo, Calle de La Coruña, 53. **GPS**: n42,91110 w9,2636.
30 € 5, € 8 service incl Ch .
Surface: sand. 01/01-31/12.
Distance: on the spot 500m 50m.
Remarks: Private beach.

S Finisterre 29B1

Praia de Langosteira. **GPS**: n42,92320 w9,26149.

5 free . 01/01-31/12.
Distance: on the spot 1km 1km.
Remarks: Beach parking, max. 48h.

S Foz 29D1

Atalaia Camper Park, Crta general Forxán. **GPS**: n43,57945 w7,27392.
20 € 10 Ch € 3 WC € 1 . **Location:** Rural.
Surface: sand. 01/04-30/11.
Distance: 700m 600m 1km 750m.

Fuente Dé 29F2

Picos de Europa, C621. **GPS**: n43,14433 w4,81274.
free. **Location:** Isolated, quiet. **Surface:** grasstiles.
01/01-31/12.
Remarks: Parking funicular railway.

S Gedrez 29D2

Área de Casa Funsiquín, CN-9, 42. **GPS**: n43,01344 w6,6081.
8 guests free Ch . **Location:** Rural. **Surface:** grassy.
01/01-31/12.
Distance: on the spot.

S Gijón 29E1

Área de El Arbeyal, Polígono Puerto Musel.
GPS: n43,54467 w5,69562.

18 free free. **Location:** Urban, simple, noisy.
Surface: asphalted. 01/01-31/12.
Distance: 3km on the spot on the spot.
Remarks: Max. 48h.

Gijón 29E1

Camino de las Mimosas, El Rinconin. **GPS**: n43,54708 w5,63648.

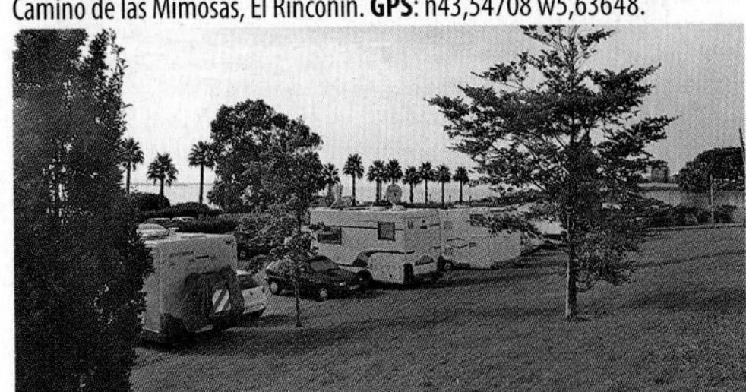

20 free. **Location:** Urban, simple, central. **Surface:** asphalted.
01/01-31/12.
Distance: 300m.
Remarks: Baker every morning (Jul/Aug).

Gorliz 29H2

Paseo de Astondo. **GPS**: n43,41220 w2,94194.

free. **Location:** Urban, simple. **Surface:** asphalted.
01/01-31/12.
Distance: 500m 50m on the spot.
Remarks: Parking beach.

S Gozon 29E1

Area Autocaravanas El Molino, Ctr. Luanco-Cabo Peñas.
GPS: n43,62541 w5,81125.

25 € 10 Ch included € 4,60. **Location:** Rural, comfortable, quiet. **Surface:** grassy. 01/01-31/12.
Distance: 500m on the spot on the spot on the spot.
Remarks: To be paid at campsite.

S Grado 29E1

Avenida de los Deportes. **GPS**: n43,38323 w6.
8 free Ch free. **Surface:** asphalted. 01/01-31/12.
Distance: 800m 100m 300m 50m.
Remarks: At sports grounds.

S Grandas de Salime 29D1

Calle Pedro de Pedre. **GPS**: n43,21592 w6,87576.
2 free Ch free. **Surface:** asphalted. 01/01-31/12.
Distance: 200m 100m 200m.
Remarks: At swimming pool, max. 48h.

S Guitiriz 29C1

Rua do Voluntariado. **GPS**: n43,17727 w7,88062.
5 free Ch free. **Surface:** gravel. 01/01-31/12.
Distance: 800m 100m.
Remarks: Max. 48h.

S Hernani 29H2

Ibaiondo Industrialdea. **GPS**: n43,26922 w1,96242.
free Ch free. **Surface:** asphalted.
Distance: 1,2km 1,5km 1,2km.
Remarks: Max. 5 nights, no camping activities.

S Illa de Arousa 29C2

Área de Surf Camp, Playa de Xestelas. **GPS**: n42,53565 w8,86929.
€ 10 € 3. 01/06-30/09.
Distance: on the spot on the spot on the spot.
Remarks: Surf spot.

S Illano 29D1

Area de Folgueirou, Area recreativa de Folgueirou.
GPS: n43,34252 w6,85433.
30 free Ch free. **Location:** Rural, simple.
Surface: grassy/gravel. 01/01-31/12.
Distance: on the spot.

S Labastida 29H3

Fray Domingo Salazar Kalea. **GPS**: n42,00000 w2,79446.
4 free Ch free € 1/30minutes. **Surface:** asphalted.
01/01-31/12.
Distance: 300m 300m.

S Lanestosa 29G2

Area de Lanestosa, Calle Mirabueno. **GPS**: n43,21789 w3,43878.

22 free, service € 8/24h Ch WC included.
Location: Rural, simple. **Surface:** gravel. 01/01-31/12.
Distance: 200m 400m 6km on the spot on the spot.

S Langreo 29E1

Ecomuseo Minero Valle de Samuño, Calle Puente Carbón.
GPS: n43,27835 w5,67433.

11 free Ch free. **Location:** Rural, simple, quiet.
Surface: asphalted/metalled. 01/01-31/12.
Distance: on the spot.
Remarks: At Ecomuseum.

S Legazpi 29H2

Parque Mirandaola de Legazpi, Carretera Legazpia, GI 2630.
GPS: n43,03678 w2,33758.

5 free Ch free. **Location:** Urban, simple, noisy.
Surface: asphalted. 01/01-31/12.
Distance: 1,5km on the spot on the spot.
Remarks: Max. 48h.

S Lekeitio 29H2

Iñigo Artieta Etorbidea. **GPS**: n43,35849 w2,50743.

14 free € 3/100liter Ch. **Location:** Urban, comfortable, quiet.
Surface: asphalted. 01/01-31/12.
Distance: 500m 500m 500m 300m.
Remarks: Coins at tourist info.

S Liérganes 29G2

Calle de Puente Romano. **GPS**: n43,34479 w3,74183.

10 free free. **Location:** Urban, simple, central.
Surface: asphalted. 01/01-31/12.
Distance: 200m 250m 350m.
Remarks: Parking nearby train station, max. 48h.

ES

Llanes 29F1

La Talá, Avenida la Paz. **GPS**: n43,42367 w4,76768.
16 € 3/24h Ch. **Surface:** asphalted.
01/04-31/12.
Distance: 1km 1,3km 1km 300m.
Remarks: Video surveillance.

Lugo 29D1

Pabellón Municipal de Deportes, Avda. de Santiago.
GPS: n43,00452 w7,56144.

15 free Chfree. **Surface:** asphalted. 01/01-31/12.
Distance: 5 min 5,2km 10min.
Remarks: Parking gymnasium, max. 48h.

Lugo 29D1

Plaza de Asturias, Rúa Ánxel Fole. **GPS**: n43,01203 w7,55496.
15 € 14/24h free. **Surface:** asphalted. 01/01-31/12.

Lugones 29E1

Area de Lugones, Calle Conde de Santa Bárbara.
GPS: n43,40694 w5,81139.

4 free Chfree. **Location:** Urban, simple.
Surface: asphalted/metalled. 01/01-31/12.
Distance: 9km Oviedo on the spot on the spot 200m.
Remarks: Next to sports centre.

Mazaricos 29B1

Calle Picota. **GPS**: n42,93458 w8,9906.
4 free Chfree. **Surface:** metalled. 01/01-31/12.
Distance: on the spot on the spot.
Remarks: Max. 72h.

Mazaricos 29B1

NaturMaZ, Aeródromo da Fervenza. **GPS**: n42,98398 w9,00771.
€ 8 Chincluded. **Location:** Isolated, quiet.
Surface: grassy/gravel. 01/01-31/12.
Distance: 10km on the spot on the spot on the spot on the spot.
Remarks: At airfield.

Melide 29C2

Rúa Ines de Castro. **GPS**: n42,91089 w8,01182.
5 free. **Location:** Urban. **Surface:** asphalted. 01/01-31/12.
Distance: centre 300m 400m 800m bus > Santiago
Route of Santiago de Compostela.

Melide 29C2

Casa Familia, N-547, 43. **GPS**: n42,88685 w7,962.
3 € 10 Ch included. **Location:** Rural. **Surface:** grassy.
01/01-31/12.
Distance: Melide 5km 2km bus 400m.

Mieres 29E1

Area de Mieres, Calle Asturias. **GPS**: n43,25194 w5,78083.

6 free Chfree. **Location:** Urban, simple.
Surface: asphalted. 01/01-31/12.
Distance: 100m 500m on the spot on the spot.

Remarks: Along railwayline.

Milladoiro 29C1

Traversia do Porto, Ames. **GPS**: n42,84512 w8,58079.

15 free Chfree.
Surface: asphalted.
01/01-31/12 1st week Aug.
Distance: 200m 200m dir. Santiago every 15 min.
Remarks: At swimming pool, max. 48h, monday market.

Miño 29C1

AP-9 Coruña-Ferrol ><, km 15,5. **GPS**: n43,37404 w8,18736.
12 free ChWC free. **Location:** Motorway.
Surface: asphalted. 01/01-31/12.
Distance: on the spot on the spot.
Remarks: Parking nearby motorway.

Miranda de Ebro 29G2

Calle de Burgos. **GPS**: n42,68880 w2,95403.

7 free Chfree. **Location:** Urban, simple, noisy.
Surface: metalled. 01/01-31/12.
Distance: 1km 3km river.

Tourist information Miranda de Ebro:
Medieval annual fair. around May 1.
Week market. Sa.

Mondariz 29C2

Área recreativa da Praia do Val. **GPS**: n42,23727 w8,45943.
free free. 01/01-31/12.
Distance: 1,2km 750m on the spot.

Mondoñedo 29D1

Calle de Vicedo. **GPS**: n43,42778 w7,37028.
10 free Chfree. **Location:** Urban. **Surface:** grasstiles.
01/01-31/12.
Distance: 500m 500m.
Remarks: Max. 48h.

Monfero 29C1

Área de Fragas do Eume, Lugar Vilafail Nº 2.
GPS: n43,39643 w8,07621.
12 € 8 Chincluded € 2 WC. **Location:** Isolated, quiet.
Surface: gravel. 01/01-31/12.
Distance: 8km 2,5km on the spot on the spot.
Remarks: In nature reserve, baker every morning.

Monforte de Lemos 29D2

Auditorio Multiusos de Monforte, Calle de la Circuvalación / Calle de Santa Clara. **GPS**: n42,52750 w7,5119.

20 free Chfree. **Surface:** asphalted. 01/01-31/12.
Distance: 500m 550m 300m.
Remarks: Beside river, max. 48h.

Nava 29E1

Area de Nava, Avda. de la Constitución. **GPS**: n43,35722 w5,49917.

4 free Chfree.
Surface: asphalted/metalled.
01/01-31/12.
Distance: 900m 10km.
Remarks: At sports centre, max. 72h, no camping activities.

Navelgas 29E1

Area de Navelgas, Recinto Ferial. **GPS**: n43,40402 w6,54167.
15 free Chfree. **Location:** Urban.
Surface: asphalted/metalled. 01/01-31/12.
Distance: 100m.

Navia 29D1

Area de la Granja, C/ Travesía de la Granja.
GPS: n43,54528 w6,72028.
10 free Chfree. **Location:** Urban.
Surface: gravel/metalled.
Distance: 1,5km on the spot on the spot.

Nogueira de Ramuín 29C2

Lugar Luintra. **GPS**: n42,41003 w7,72161.
8 free Chfree. **Surface:** metalled. 01/01-31/12.
Distance: 400m 400m on the spot.
Remarks: At swimming pool, max. 48h.

Noia 29C2

Rúa de Pedra Marques. **GPS**: n42,78783 w8,8906.

free. **Surface:** asphalted.
Distance: on the spot 50m 50m Bus 20m.

Noia 29C2

Hipermercado Eroski, Carretera Puerto Abarquiña.
GPS: n42,79799 w8,88836.
+10 free Chfree. **Location:** Urban. **Surface:** asphalted.
01/01-31/12.
Distance: city centre 1,7km on the spot.
Remarks: At supermarket.

Tourist information Noia:
El Pendo, 5km S. Santander. Cave with petroglyphs.

O Barco 29D2

Malecón Campiño. **GPS**: n42,41063 w6,97493.

10 free Chfree. **Surface:** unpaved. 01/01-31/12.
Distance: 400m 250m 250m.
Remarks: Max. 48h.

Oleiros 29C1

Rúa Marcial del Adalid, Muíño do Vento. **GPS**: n43,33936 w8,35474.
3 free Chfree. **Surface:** asphalted. 01/01-31/12.
Distance: 650m.
Remarks: Max. 48h.

Oñati 29H2

Area Autocaravanas Oñate, Martzelino Zelaia Kalea.
GPS: n43,02743 w2,40531.
17 free Chfree. **Location:** Rural. **Surface:** grasstiles.
01/01-31/12.

ES

Distance: 900m.
Remarks: Max. 72h.

Ourol 29D1

Rúa Ourol. **GPS**: n43,56485 w7,64348.
8 free Ch free. **Surface:** metalled. 01/01-31/12.
Remarks: Max. 48h.

Oviedo 29E1

Calle Daniel Moyano. **GPS**: n43,38266 w5,82396.
16 free Ch free. **Location:** Rural. **Surface:** asphalted.
01/01-31/12.
Distance: Oviedo 10km 150m 50m 200m.

Pajares 29E2

Valgrande-Pajares, Brañillín. **GPS**: n42,97889 w5,77194.

12 free Ch free. **Location:** Rural. **Surface:** asphalted.
01/01-31/12.

Parada do Sil 29D2

Rural Pepe, Campo da Feira 17. **GPS**: n42,38287 w7,57106.
4 guests free Ch € 2. 01/01-31/12.
Distance: on the spot on the spot.

Pobra do Brollòn 29D2

Campo Municipal de Fut. **GPS**: n42,56944 w7,39417.
8 free Ch free. **Location:** Isolated, quiet. **Surface:** metalled.
01/01-31/12.
Distance: 1,3km 1,3km.
Remarks: At football ground, max. 48h.

Poio 29C2

Parque de Seca, 4ª Travesia Seara. **GPS**: n42,43867 w8,69219.
20 free Ch free. **Location:** Urban. **Surface:** grasstiles.
01/01-31/12.
Distance: 2km 300m 200m.
Remarks: Max. 72h.

Pola de Laviana 29E1

Area de Pola de Laviana, Av. Real Titánico.
GPS: n43,25478 w5,56836.

8 free Ch free. **Location:** Rural, simple. **Surface:** grasstiles.
01/01-31/12.
Distance: 1,5km 1,5km 1,5km.

Pontedeva 29C2

Aldea Valiño, Trado. **GPS**: n42,17646 w8,15477.
5 free Ch free. **Surface:** unpaved. 01/01-31/12.
Remarks: Max. 48h.

Pontevedra 29C2

Rua Vial 2. **GPS**: n42,43347 w8,63471.
20 free Ch free. **Location:** Urban. **Surface:** metalled.
01/01-31/12.
Distance: centre 700m 500m 800m.
Remarks: Max. 72h.

Posada de Valdeón 29F2

Calle del General Mola. **GPS**: n43,15285 w4,91747.

18 € 10 Ch . **Location:** Rural.
Surface: grassy. 01/01-31/12.
Distance: on the spot on the spot.
Remarks: Max. 96h, in Parque Nacional de Los Picos de Europa.

Potes 29F2

Poblado Mijares. **GPS**: n43,15531 w4,61894.
+5 free. **Surface:** grassy. 01/01-31/12.
Distance: 200m 150m 50m.

Potes 29F2

Santo Toribio de Liébana, CA885. **GPS**: n43,15028 w4,65389.

free. **Location:** Isolated, quiet.
Surface: asphalted.
01/01-31/12.
Distance: Potes 3km on the spot.
Remarks: Parking monastery.

Tourist information Potes:
Local products. Mo.
Historical cattle market, since 1379. 01/08-15/08.

Redondela 29C2

Avda. de Mendiño. **GPS**: n42,28972 w8,61055.
15 free Ch. **Surface:** asphalted. 01/01-31/12.
Distance: 600m 500m 600m 600m.
Remarks: Nearby police station.

Rentería 29H2

Área Rural de Listorreta-Barrengoloia.
GPS: n43,26800 w1,90135.

2 free Ch free. **Location:** Rural, simple, isolated, quiet.
Surface: asphalted. 01/01-31/12.
Distance: Renteria 7km on the spot.
Remarks: Parking nature reserve.

Ribadavia 29C2

Rua Álvaro Cunqueiro. **GPS**: n42,28606 w8,14374.
80 free Ch free. **Location:** Rural. **Surface:** sand.
01/01-31/12.
Distance: 500m 300m 300m.

Ribadeo 29D1

Eroski, Camino de Vilar. **GPS**: n43,54000 w7,06055.
10 free Ch free. **Surface:** asphalted. 01/01-31/12.
Distance: 500m 1km on the spot.
Remarks: At supermarket.

Ribadeo 29D1

Rúa Daniel Cortezón. **GPS**: n43,53556 w7,04528.
5 free. **Location:** Urban, central, noisy. **Surface:** asphalted.
01/01-31/12.
Distance: 300m 300m 300m.
Remarks: No camping activities.

Ribamontán al Monte 29G1

A8 Bilbao > Santander. **GPS**: n43,40282 w3,62877.
10 free Ch free. **Location:** Motorway. 01/01-31/12.
Remarks: Parking nearby motorway.

Ribamontán al Monte 29G1

A8 Santander > Bilbao. **GPS**: n43,40446 w3,62476.
10 free Ch free. **Location:** Motorway. **Surface:** asphalted.
01/01-31/12.
Remarks: Parking nearby motorway.

Ríos 29D3

Repsol. **GPS**: n41,98297 w7,28602.
10 free Ch WC . 01/01-31/12.
Distance: 500m.
Remarks: At petrol station.

Riosa 29E1

Area de El Angliru, Viapará s/n. **GPS**: n43,24806 w5,90667.

15 € 5 Ch included . **Location:** Rural, simple, isolated, quiet. **Surface:** metalled. 01/01-31/12.
Distance: on the spot.
Remarks: No camping activities.

Salinas 29E1

Calle el Agüil. **GPS**: n43,57038 w5,95904.
12 free. **Surface:** asphalted. 01/01-31/12.
Distance: 1km 500m.

San Antolín de Ibias 29D2

Barrio Torgoal. **GPS**: n43,04389 w6,86931.
5 free. **Location:** Rural. **Surface:** unpaved.
01/01-31/12.
Distance: 1km.
Remarks: Max. 72h.

San Antolín de Ibias 29D2

Barrio el Fojo. **GPS**: n43,03887 w6,87202.
free Ch. 01/01-31/12.

San Clodio 29D2

Parque de Pena da Mula, Calle del Troque.
GPS: n42,46750 w7,28583.

3 free Ch free. **Surface:** asphalted. 01/01-31/12.
Distance: 200m Playa Fluvial 25m cafetaria.

San Martín del Rey Aurelio 29E1

Área del Pozo Entrego, Avenida de la Vega, AS17.
GPS: n43,28639 w5,63889.

3 free Ch free. **Location:** Urban, simple. **Surface:** asphalted.
01/01-31/12.
Distance: on the spot on the spot Alcampo 1km.
Remarks: Max. 48h.

San Sebastian 29H2

Paseo de Berio nº 2. **GPS**: n43,30797 w2,01426.

ES

44 € 7,60, 01/10-31/05 € 4 Chincluded.
Location: Urban, noisy.
Surface: grasstiles.
01/01-31/12.
Distance: city centre 3km 2km 50m 100m bus city centre 33 and 5.
Remarks: Max. 48h, marked pitches, registration with licence plate number.

Tourist information San Sebastian:
Centro de Atracción y Turismo (CAT), Boulevard Alameda, 8, www.donostia.org. Old city with, Parte Vieja, historical city centre with numerous cafés, restaurants and tapa bars.
Aquarium, Plaza de Carlos Blasco Imaz, 1. Museum for oceanografics. 10-19h, Sa/Su/holidays 10-20h, 01/07-31/12 10-21h.
Su-morning.

S Santa Eulalia de Oscos 29D1
Calle Teresa de Francisco. **GPS:** n43,25770 w7,01861.

17 free Chfree. **Surface:** metalled. 01/01-31/12.
Distance: on the spot on the spot 100m on the spot on the spot.

S Santander 29G1
Área de Las Llamas, Calle Marino Fernández-Fontecha.
GPS: n43,47318 w3,79771.
25 free Ch. **Location:** Urban. **Surface:** metalled.
01/01-31/12.
Distance: 1km 550m 1km on the spot.
Remarks: Max. 48h.

Santander 29G1
Calle César Llamazares, Nueva Montaña. **GPS:** n43,44336 w3,83747.
10 free. **Location:** Simple, isolated. **Surface:** asphalted.
01/01-31/12.
Distance: 3,5km.
Remarks: Max. 48h.

S Santander 29G1
Marina de Santander, Calle Tramo de Unión, Camargo.
GPS: n43,42736 w3,80537.

6 € 6 Chincluded (2x)€ 3/24h € 5 € 4/30minutes.
Location: Simple. **Surface:** metalled.
01/01-31/12.
Distance: 100m 3km.
Remarks: Service at marina.

P S Santiago de Compostela 29C1
Rúa Manuel María. **GPS:** n42,89560 w8,5317.
100 € 3,50/8-20h € 3 Ch.
Surface: asphalted.
01/01-31/12.
Distance: centre 2,5km 3km 50m line 1 > centre.
Remarks: Ticket for overnight stay € 12.

Tourist information Santiago de Compostela:
Oficina de Turismo, Rúa del Villar, 43, www.santiagoturismo.com. City known for the termination of the pilgrime route.
Plaza de la Quintana. Impressive square.
Fiesta del Apóstol Santiago.
Most important festival of Galicia.
15/07-31/07.

Santillana del Mar 29G1
Ctra. C6316. **GPS:** n43,38895 w4,10721.

€ 2/24h. **Surface:** asphalted.

S Sanxenxo 29B2
Playa Pragueira. **GPS:** n42,40967 w8,86157.

15 € 8-10 Ch included € 3. **Surface:** grassy.
01/01-31/12.
Distance: on the spot 200m 1km.

S Sanxenxo 29B2
Área de Cachadelos, PO-308. **GPS:** n42,41751 w8,86952.
65 € 10 Ch included . **Surface:** grassy.
Distance: 200m 2km on the spot.
Remarks: Service passerby € 3.

S Sarria 29D2
Rúa Castelao. **GPS:** n42,77194 w7,41028.

12 free Chfree. **Surface:** gravel. 01/01-31/12.
Distance: 800m on the spot 800m.

S Saturrarán 29H2
GPS: n43,31968 w2,41165.

5 free WC. **Location:** Rural, simple. **Surface:** grasstiles.
01/01-31/12.
Distance: 500m on the spot 700m.
Remarks: Parking beach.

S Sopela 29H2
Polideportivo de Urko, Urgitxieta kalea. **GPS:** n43,37370 w2,9898.
24 free € 1/100liter Ch.
Surface: asphalted.
01/01-31/12 service 01/10-31/05.
Distance: 300m 450m metro > Bilbao.
Remarks: Max. 48h, coins at tourist info, no camping activities.

S Suesa 29G1
Area de Autocaravanas Suesa, Mojante 25.
GPS: n43,44736 w3,72788.

66 € 9 Chincluded (10x)€ 3 WC.
Location: Comfortable. **Surface:** grasstiles. 01/01-31/12.
Distance: 1km 1,8km 1,5km 1km 1km.
Remarks: Max. 96h, pay at reception campsite.

S Tapia de Casariego 29D1
Area de Playa Grande, Av. San Esteban. **GPS:** n43,56667 w6,94639.

15 € 4 Chfree. **Location:** Rural. **Surface:** grasstiles.
01/01-31/12.
Distance: 500m 500m 500m.

S Taramundi 29D1
Barrio los Castros. **GPS:** n43,35955 w7,10698.
20 free Chfree. **Surface:** asphalted. 01/01-31/12.
Distance: 150m 150m 150m.
Remarks: Beautiful view.

S Teverga 29E1
La Plaza, AS265. **GPS:** n43,15945 w6,10075.
10 free Chfree. **Surface:** grasstiles. 01/01-31/12.
Distance: 300m, Teverga 1,5km 300m.

S Teverga 29E1
Parking Senda del Oso, Entrago. **GPS:** n43,16954 w6,09755.

20 free Chfree € 3. **Location:** Simple, noisy.
Surface: asphalted. 01/01-31/12.
Distance: on the spot on the spot.
Remarks: Max. 48h.

S Tolosa 29H2
San Esteban Auzoa Auzoa. **GPS:** n43,13348 w2,08315.
€ 1/day Chincluded. **Location:** Noisy. **Surface:** asphalted.
01/01-31/12.
Distance: 700m 700m 500m.
Remarks: Along railwayline, max. 72h.

S Touro 29C2
Praza do Luar, Rúa de Castelao, Fonte Díaz. **GPS:** n42,87061 w8,31277.
5 free Chfree. **Location:** Rural. **Surface:** asphalted.
01/01-31/12.
Distance: 600m 900m 900m on the spot.
Remarks: At sports park, max. 48h.

Tui 29C2
Puente Tripes, Avenida de Portual. **GPS:** n42,04333 w8,64656.

3 free. **Location:** Urban, simple. **Surface:** asphalted.
01/01-31/12.
Distance: 1,3km 500m Lidl 1,5km.
Remarks: Max. 48h.

S Vegadeo 29D1
Area de Vegadeo, Calle Emilio Cotarelo, s/n.
GPS: n43,46667 w7,05167.
8 free Chfree. **Location:** Urban.
Surface: asphalted/metalled. 01/01-31/12.
Distance: on the spot on the spot.
Remarks: Max. 72h.

S Vila de Cruces 29C2
A Carixa, Estrada Merza-Bodaño. **GPS**: n42,76199 w8,25602.
30 free WCfree . **Surface:** asphalted. 01/01-31/12.
Distance: Vila de Cruces 10km on the spot.
Remarks: Picnic area, recreation area.

S Vila de Cruces 29C2
Travesía Besexos. **GPS**: n42,79153 w8,16479.
30 free Chfree. **Surface:** asphalted. 01/01-31/12.
Distance: 1km 400m 1,2km.
Remarks: Max. 48h.

S Vilalba 29D1
Rua da Feira. **GPS**: n43,29556 w7,67694.
15 free Chfree. **Location:** Urban, central, noisy.
Surface: asphalted. 01/01-31/12.
Distance: 500m 300m 300m.

S Villanueva de Oscos 29D1
Area de Villanueva, Lugar de Villanueva. **GPS**: n43,31056 w6,98583.
2 free Chfree. **Surface:** gravel. 01/01-31/12.
Remarks: Max. 48h.

S Vitoria Gasteiz 29H2
Área de Lakua, Portal de Foronde. **GPS**: n42,86684 w2,68539.

10 free Chfree. **Location:** Urban, comfortable, central, quiet.
Surface: asphalted. 01/01-31/12.
Distance: 2km 5km 100m bakery 50m 50m.
Remarks: Max. 72h, market Wednesday.

S Xinzo de Limia 29C2
Camiño da Cerámica. **GPS**: n42,06168 w7,71941.
20 free Chfree. **Location:** Urban. **Surface:** asphalted.
01/01-31/12.
Distance: 200m 200m 200m.

S Zegama 29H2
San Bartolome. **GPS**: n42,97524 w2,29233.
8 free Chfree € 3/2h. **Surface:** asphalted.
01/01-31/12.
Distance: 300m 300m 300m on the spot.

S Zumaia 29H2
Calle de la Estación. **GPS**: n43,29279 w2,24684.

25 free Chfree. **Location:** Simple, noisy. **Surface:** asphalted.
01/01-31/12.
Distance: 2km 4,4km on the spot on the spot.

Navarre and Rioja

Aínsa 32C1
Plaza del Castillo. **GPS**: n42,41916 e0,13515.
20 € 0,50/h, € 5/day.
Surface: asphalted/grassy.
01/01-31/12.
Distance: 600m 350m 1,2km.
Remarks: Max. 24h.

Tourist information Aínsa:
The capital of a medieval kingdom by surrounded fortress walls.
Tue.

Albarracín 33A1
Quesería Sierra de Albarracín, Pol. Los Rubiales, 1.
GPS: n40,43286 w1,4405.

6 free. 01/01-31/12.
Distance: 1km 200m 1km 1km.

S Alquézar 32C1
Alquézar, Ctra.Barbastro,. **GPS**: n42,16456 e0,01499.
€ 16,50-19,50 Ch € 5. 01/01-31/12.

Tourist information Alquézar:
Historical city.

S Aoiz 27A3
Hotel Ekai. **GPS**: n42,77624 w1,38536.

10 free free. **Location:** Rural, simple.
Surface: gravel/metalled. 01/01-31/12.
Distance: 3km on the spot.

S Arguedas 32A1
Aparcamiento Municipal de Autocaravanas de Arguedas, Calle Val.
GPS: n42,17370 w1,59159.

9 free € 2/100liter Ch. **Location:** Rural, simple, quiet.
Surface: gravel. 01/01-31/12.
Distance: 800m 800m 800m.
Remarks: At Parque de Bardenas Reales, max. 48h.

Arguedas 32A1
Parking Entorno Virgen del Yugo, Camino a la Hermita de la Virgen del Yugo. **GPS**: n42,20550 w1,58591.
30 free. **Location:** Isolated, quiet. **Surface:** asphalted.
01/01-31/12.
Distance: 4km 4km.

Arguedas 32A1
Parking Senda Viva. **GPS**: n42,19018 w1,58494.
14 free. **Location:** Isolated, quiet. **Surface:** asphalted.
01/01-31/12.
Distance: 3km 3km 3km.

Ariza 30H1
Area de Servicios La Cadiera, A2 Madrid > Zaragoza.
GPS: n41,31210 w2,00329.
5 .

S Arnedillo 29H3
Calle Miguel del Pozo. **GPS**: n42,21361 w2,23972.

30 € 10 Ch (40x)€ 1/4h WC ,cold shower included.
Location: Rural, comfortable. **Surface:** asphalted.
01/01-31/12.
Distance: 200m 200m 200m on the spot.
Remarks: Follow the signs in the village.

S Arróniz 29H2
Carretera Barbarin 38. **GPS**: n42,58911 w2,09575.
6 free Chfree. **Surface:** asphalted. 01/01-31/12.
Distance: 300m 3km 250m.
Remarks: Max. 48h, no camping activities.

S Ayegui 29H2
Plaza San Pelayo. **GPS**: n42,65436 w2,0451.
20 € 4 Chincluded. **Surface:** grasstiles.
Distance: 700m 700m 700m.
Remarks: Next to swimming pool.

S Berriozar 27A3
Av. Berriozar. **GPS**: n42,84043 w1,66557.

30 free € 2/100liter Ch. **Location:** Urban, simple.
Surface: concrete. 01/01-31/12.
Distance: 4km Pamplona 500m.
Remarks: Max. 72h, coins at sports centre (9-21h).

S Cascante 29H3
Av. Fuentes Dutor Parking Termolúdico. **GPS**: n41,99372 w1,68669.

40 free free. **Location:** Urban, simple. **Surface:** asphalted.
01/01-31/12.
Distance: 750m 800m.

S Falces 29H3
Calle la Mota. **GPS**: n42,39295 w1,79574.
6 free Chfree. **Location:** Simple. **Surface:** metalled.
01/01-31/12.
Distance: 700m 300m.

S Fontellas 32A2
Aceite Artajo, Autovía A-68, Km 102, Finca Los Llanos.
GPS: n42,00068 w1,56067.

ES

10 free Chfree. **Location:** Rural. **Surface:** grassy.
01/01-31/12.
Distance: 3,5km 3,5km 5,5km 5,5km on the spot.
Remarks: Max. 72h.

Haro 29H2

LR111. **GPS**: n42,57253 w2,86739.

10 free free. **Location:** Rural, simple, quiet.
Surface: gravel. 01/01-31/12.
Distance: 1,5km 1,3km 1,5km.

Haro 29H2

Parking centro deportivo, Av de los Ingenieros del Ministerio Obras Públicas, LR-111. **GPS**: n42,57734 w2,85154.

4 free free.
Location: Urban, simple.
Surface: asphalted.
01/01-31/12.
Distance: 500m 14km on the spot.
Remarks: At sports park, Haro, Rioja Wine Capital, wine museum, wine cellars.

Tourist information Haro:
Capital of Rioja wine.

Irura 29H2

Area del Frontón, Calle Zilar. **GPS**: n43,16778 w2,0652.

4 free Chfree. **Location:** Urban, simple, noisy.
Surface: asphalted. 01/01-31/12.
Distance: 100m.

Jaca 32B1

Membrilleras, Calle San Indalecio. **GPS**: n42,56806 w0,54503.
15 free . **Surface:** asphalted. 01/01-31/12.
Distance: 300m 300m.

Logroño 29H3

Avenue de la Sonsierra, LR132. **GPS**: n42,47916 w2,4571.

3 free Chfree. **Location:** Urban, simple, noisy.
Surface: asphalted. 01/01-31/12.
Distance: 700m 100m 400m 300m 20m.
Remarks: Max. 48h.

Logroño 29H3

Emblase de la Grajera, Pontano de la Grajera.
GPS: n42,44909 w2,50189.

15 free. **Location:** Rural, simple. **Surface:** concrete.
01/01-31/12.
Distance: 7km 1km on the spot.
Remarks: Parking at lake, golf court and park La Grajera.

Maya 27A2

Otsondo, NA 4453. **GPS**: n43,23304 w1,49885.
6 free WCfree. **Location:** Rural, isolated, noisy. **Surface:** gravel.
01/01-31/12.
Distance: 3km.

Navarrete 29H3

Calle de la Carretera. **GPS**: n42,42458 w2,55584.

free. **Location:** Urban, simple. **Surface:** asphalted.
01/01-31/12.
Distance: 1km 3km 600m 800m.
Remarks: Parking at sports park.

Roncesvalles 27A3

Calle Roncesvalles. **GPS**: n43,00901 w1,31888.
10 free. **Location:** Rural, isolated, quiet. **Surface:** asphalted.
01/01-31/12.
Distance: 100m.

Roncesvalles 27A3

Paseo Ibaneta. **GPS**: n43,02018 w1,32401.

5 free. **Location:** Rural, simple. **Surface:** asphalted.
01/01-31/12.
Distance: 1,5km.
Remarks: Beautiful view.

Tudela 32A1

Avenida de la Argentina 20. **GPS**: n42,05853 w1,61197.
10 free Chfree. **Location:** Urban. **Surface:** metalled.
01/01-31/12.
Distance: 500m 500m on the spot.
Remarks: Max. 48h.

Zaragoza 32B2

Parque de Atracciones de Zaragoza. **GPS**: n41,61994 w0,90122.
10.
Distance: 4,5km.
Remarks: Parking amusement park.

Mediterranean Sea Communities

Águilas 31H2

Autocaravanas Anibal, Ctra. Nacional 332, KM 3,37.
GPS: n37,38893 w1,61554.
60 € 7 € 3 WC € 2 € 1. **Location:** Isolated, quiet.
Surface: gravel/metalled. 01/01-31/12.
Distance: 1km 1km 1km on the spot on the spot.

Águilas 31H2

Playa de la Carolina. **GPS**: n37,37614 w1,62903.
free. **Location:** Isolated. 01/01-31/12.
Remarks: Beach parking.

Albalate del Arzobispo 33A1

Ronda del Pintor Gárate. **GPS**: n41,12125 w0,50854.
10 free Ch. **Location:** Central, quiet.
Surface: gravel/metalled. 01/01-31/12.
Distance: 300m on the spot.
Remarks: Max. 48h.

Alcossebre 33B1

Las Moreras AC, Calle Na Violante de Hungría, 18.
GPS: n40,24530 e0,27162.
€ 9, Aug € 15 Chincluded € 3 WC.
Surface: gravel. 01/01-31/12.
Distance: 400m 600m 400m 300m on the spot on the spot.

Tourist information Alcossebre:
Xivert Castillo. Castle, 13-14th century.

Alcover 32E3

Avinguda Catalunya 2. **GPS**: n41,26315 e1,17324.

5 € 5/24h Chincluded. **Location:** Rural, simple, central, quiet.
Surface: concrete. 01/01-31/12.
Distance: on the spot 700m 350m 100m 300m.
Remarks: Max. 48h.

Alicante 33A3

Playa de San Juan, Avinguda de Costa Blanca 168.
GPS: n38,37868 w0,41134.
41 € 8-10 Ch WC included. **Location:** Urban.
Surface: metalled. 01/01-31/12.
Distance: on the spot on the spot on the spot 300m 100m.
Remarks: Max. 2 days.

Alicante 33A3

Vía Pista. **GPS**: n38,28923 w0,52072.
50 free. **Surface:** unpaved. 01/01-31/12.
Distance: Alicante 7km on the spot on the spot 600m.
Remarks: Beach parking, max 3,5t.

Alicante 33A3

Villafranqueza, Av. Pintor Gastón Castelló 41.
GPS: n38,37808 w0,48822.

25 € 7 Ch WC included. **Location:** Noisy.
01/01-31/12.
Distance: 1km 50m 50m.
Remarks: Next to petrol station.

S Altafulla 33B1

Área de Servicio Mèdol, AP-7 km 237, Barcelona > Taragona.
GPS: n41,14157 e1,34590.
10 free Chfree. **Location:** Motorway. **Surface:** asphalted.
01/01-31/12.
Distance: on the spot on the spot.

S Altafulla 33B1

Área de Servicio Mèdol, AP-7 km 237, Taragona > Barcelona.
GPS: n41,14054 e1,34746.
10 free Chfree. **Location:** Motorway. **Surface:** asphalted.
01/01-31/12.
Distance: on the spot on the spot.

S Altea 33A3

San Antonio Camperpark, Ctra. del Albir 5/6, CV7651.
GPS: n38,58544 w0,05989.

50 € 15, 2 pers.incl Ch € 0,45/kWh,10Amp WC € 3 included. **Location:** Comfortable. **Surface:** gravel.
30/09-30/04.
Distance: Altea > 1km < Albir 100m 500m 500m 200m, tram 1km.
Remarks: Bread-service, discount longer stays.

S Amposta 33B1

Casa de Fusta, Partida L'Encanyissada. **GPS**: n40,65851 e0,67475.

70 free € 3 Ch . **Location:** Rural, comfortable, isolated, quiet. **Surface:** gravel/sand. 01/01-31/12.
Distance: on the spot on the spot on the spot on the spot on the spot.
Remarks: Bread-service.

S Arbúcies 32G2

Área de Arbúcies, Camí del Molí. **GPS**: n41,81437 e2,52076.

free Chfree. **Location:** Urban, simple, central, quiet.
Surface: asphalted. 01/01-31/12.
Distance: 500m 700m 700m 250m.
Remarks: Max. 48h.

S Archena 31H1

Avendia del Río Segura. **GPS**: n38,12214 w1,29427.
30 free Chfree. **Surface:** gravel. 01/01-31/12.
Distance: 150m Mercadona 1,5km.

S Ascó 32D3

C/ Alcalde Tomas Biarnes Radua. **GPS**: n41,18673 e0,56802.

25 free Chfree. **Location:** Simple, central, noisy.
Surface: asphalted. 01/01-31/12.
Distance: 100m 200m 200m 500m 500m.

S Avinyo 32F2

Area Municipal de Avinyó, Calle Industria.
GPS: n41,86556 e1,97472.

10 free € 1/50liter Ch. **Location:** Rural, simple, quiet.
Surface: gravel/sand. 01/01-31/12.
Distance: 300m 3km 300m 300m 250m.
Remarks: Nearby swimming pool, video surveillance.

S Avinyonet del Penedès 32F3

Area Cellar Can Battle - Artcava, Masia Can Batlle s/n, BV2411.
GPS: n41,36790 e1,77306.

10 free Chfree. **Location:** Rural, simple, isolated, quiet.
Surface: gravel. 01/01-31/12.
Distance: 1km 6km 1km 1km.
Remarks: Wine tasting.

S Ayora 33A2

El Nogal, Romeral 5. **GPS**: n39,05870 w1,0324.

20 € 10 Chincluded € 2/day . **Location:** Rural, comfortable, isolated, quiet. **Surface:** grassy.
Distance: 2km 2km on the spot on the spot.

S Ayora 33A2

Calle Manuel Reig, N-330. **GPS**: n39,05605 w1,0526.
free Chfree. **Surface:** unpaved. 01/01-31/12.
Distance: 700m.

S Balsicas 33A3

Calle Laguna de Cifuentes, Torre-Pacheco. **GPS**: n37,82074 w0,97462.
20 € 7 € 3 Ch € 2 WC € 5 . **Location:** Motorway.
Surface: asphalted. 01/01-31/12.
Distance: 300m.
Remarks: Industrial area, motorhome washing place.

S Barberà de la Conca 32E3

Area de la Cooperativa Barberá, Calle Comercio 40.
GPS: n41,41025 e1,22734.

10 free Chfree. **Location:** Rural, simple, central, quiet.
Surface: gravel. 01/11-31/08.
Distance: on the spot 500m.

S Barcelona 32G3

CityStop, Rambla Guipúzcoa. **GPS**: n41,42433 e2,20748.

80 € 30 Ch € 4/24h WC . **Location:** Urban, comfortable. **Surface:** asphalted. 01/01-31/12.
Distance: 1km 2km 1km 400m 500m 200m.

S Barcelona 32G3

Park & Ride del Besòs, Carrer del Taulat, B10 > salida 24 / 25, Sant Adrià del Besos. **GPS**: n41,41565 e2,22363.

30 € 3/h, € 30/24h Ch WC included .
Location: Urban. **Surface:** metalled. 01/01-31/12.
Distance: 1km 300m 300m Tram 100m, metro 500m.
Remarks: Max. 72h, monitored parking.

Barcelona 32G3

Almogàvers, Carrer de la Llacuna. **GPS**: n41,40301 e2,19604.

7 € 2,55/h, night € 18,30. **Location:** Urban, simple.
Surface: asphalted. 01/05-31/08.
Distance: 800m 200m 400m on the spot.
Remarks: Video surveillance.

Barcelona 32G3

Garcia Fària, Carrer de Josep Pla. **GPS**: n41,40662 e2,21829.

10 € 20. **Location:** Urban, simple, noisy.
Surface: asphalted.
Distance: 1km 2km 100m 150m 400m on the spot on the spot on the spot.
Remarks: Max. ^4.50m.

ES

Barruera 32E1

Carrer de riu. **GPS**: n42,50127 e0,79614.
free. **Location:** Rural, isolated. **Surface:** unpaved.
01/01-31/12.
Distance: 800m 800m on the spot on the spot.
Remarks: Along river.

Bellcaire d'Empordà 32H2

Àrea Massís del Montgrí, Camí Vell d'Ullà, 21.
GPS: n42,07521 e3,09748.
36 € 9, 23/06-11/09 € 11-13 Ch (14x)€ 4 WC € 2/5minutes € 4 included. **Location:** Rural, comfortable. **Surface:** grassy.
01/01-31/12.
Distance: 500m 5km 500m 250m 100m on the spot on the spot.
Remarks: Swimming pool (summer).

Bellvei 32F3

Bellvei del Penedès, Camino Plains. **GPS**: n41,24613 e1,56992.

30 € 6 Ch included € 3 € 1/day.
Location: Comfortable, isolated, quiet. **Surface:** grassy/gravel.
01/01-31/12.
Distance: 1km 6,5km 5km 1,2km 1km on the spot.

Benagéber 33A2

Ctra. CV-3930. **GPS**: n39,70913 w1,10136.

70 free Ch free. **Location:** Rural, simple, isolated, quiet.
Surface: gravel/sand. 01/01-31/12.
Distance: 100m 400m on the spot on the spot.
Remarks: Max. 72h, picnic and barbecue place.

Bicorp 33A2

Junto al Polideportivo. **GPS**: n39,13278 w0,79056.

20 € 5 Ch included WC. **Location:** Rural, isolated.
Surface: gravel.
Distance: 200m.

Bigastro 33A3

Camper Area La Pedrera, Calle Cañada de Andrea, 100.
GPS: n38,05116 w0,89863.
20 € 12 Ch WC included. **Location:** Rural.
Surface: gravel. 01/01-31/12.
Distance: on the spot on the spot.

Blanes 32H3

Carrer d'Antoni Gaudí. **GPS**: n41,66873 e2,78440.

free, 15/06-15/09 € 10.
01/01-31/12.
Distance: on the spot 350m 250m 450m.

Tourist information Blanes:

Oficina de Turismo, Paseo de Catalunya, 2, www.blanes.net. Bathing resort.
Jardín Botànic Mar i Murtra. Botanical garden.
Mas Enlaire. Local products.
Mo-Fri 8-14h.
Passeig de Mar. Clothing, souvenirs etc.
Mo-morning.

Bordils 32H2

Can Carreras del Mas, Carrer Creu 34. **GPS**: n42,04580 e2,91320.

5 € 12 € 2 € 4 included.
Location: Rural, quiet. **Surface:** grassy.
Distance: 400m 100m.
Remarks: Narrow entrance.

Bovera 32D3

Carrer del Esport. **GPS**: n41,32496 e0,63774.
10 free Ch. **Surface:** gravel/metalled. 01/01-31/12.
Distance: on the spot 450m.
Remarks: At swimming pool.

Cabanes 32H1

El Noguer, Camí de la Creu. **GPS**: n42,30594 e2,97592.

30 € 10 Ch (16x)WC included.
Location: Rural, simple, quiet. **Surface:** grassy. 01/01-31/12.
Distance: Figueres 4km 400m 450m 300m on the spot on the spot.
Remarks: Video surveillance.

Cadaqués 32H1

Parking SABA, Riera de Sant Vicenç. **GPS**: n42,28964 e3,27260.

€ 20,20/24h WC. **Surface:** asphalted.
Distance: 100m 1km 1,5km 100m 100m.

Tourist information Cadaqués:

La Riera. Week market. Mo 8-14h.

Calaf 32F2

Area Calaf Barcelona, Calle Doctor Fleming, 6.
GPS: n41,72940 e1,52610.
10 € 10 Ch included free. **Location:** Rural, simple.
Surface: asphalted. 01/01-31/12.
Distance: 500m 300m.

Calaf 32F2

Area Municipal de Calaf, Carrer Berlin. **GPS**: n41,73500 e1,51389.

4 free Ch free. **Location:** Urban, comfortable, quiet.
Surface: gravel/metalled. 01/01-31/12.
Distance: 300m 400m 300m 400m.
Remarks: Max. 48h, market Saturday.

Calaf 32F2

Calle de Leida-Girona. **GPS**: n41,73306 e1,52667.

5 free Ch free. **Location:** Urban, simple.
Surface: gravel. 01/01-31/12.
Distance: 800m 1km 800m 700m 600m.
Remarks: At petrol station, inclining pitches, video surveillance.

Caldes de Malavella 32H2

Carrer Solei. **GPS**: n41,83873 e2,81080.

5 free Ch free. **Location:** Urban, comfortable, noisy.
Surface: gravel. 01/01-31/12.
Distance: 500m 200m 300m 100m.
Remarks: Max. 3 days.

Callosa d'en Sarrià 33A3

Fonts de l'Algar, Partida Segarra s/n. **GPS**: n38,65430 w0,09289.

40 € 14 Ch € 4 WC € 2 included.
Location: Comfortable, isolated. 01/01-31/12.
Distance: 700m 700m.

S Calnegre 31H2

Camperpark Taray, RM-D21, Puntas de Calnegre.
GPS: n37,51520 w1,3985.

50 € 6 € 1/100liter Ch € 4. **Location:** Simple.
Surface: sand. 01/01-31/12.
Distance: 100m 500m 500m.

S Calnegre 31H2

Puntas Calnegre, Ctra. Puntas de Calnegre, nº 42.
GPS: n37,51179 w1,41198.

17 € 6,50, 01/06-30/09 € 8 Ch included.
Surface: metalled. 01/01-31/12.
Distance: 600m.

S Calpe 33A3

Camperpark Sol de Calpe Austral, Calle Estonia 3-5.
GPS: n38,64444 e0,05999.
160 € 20 Ch WCincluded . **Location:** Luxurious.
Surface: metalled. 01/01-31/12.
Distance: on the spot 200m on the spot on the spot 100m.

S Calpe 33A3

Camperpark Sol de Calpe Boreal, Avenida Bulgaria 4.
GPS: n38,64969 e0,06792.
89 € 20 Chincluded WC . **Location:** Luxurious.
Surface: metalled. 01/01-31/12.
Distance: on the spot 700m on the spot on the spot.

S Calpe 33A3

Mediterráneo Camper, Calle Partida Colari 7E.
GPS: n38,65126 e0,06942.

75 € 9-12, Jul/Aug € 14 Ch WC included € 3/3 € 2/day. **Surface:** gravel. 01/01-31/12.
Distance: beach 750m 75m Mercadona 300m.
Remarks: Discount longer stays.

S Calpe 33A3

Paraiso Camper, Urbanización Los Almendros, 9A.
GPS: n38,64893 e0,06665.

58 € 12-15 (discount longer stays) Ch (58x)€ 0,25/kWh WCincluded € 0,20 € 3/3 € 2/day.
Location: Comfortable, luxurious, central.
Surface: gravel.
01/01-31/12.
Distance: 1,8km 7km 800m 800m 400m 250m 400m 1km.

S Calpe 33A3

Nautica caravanning, Ctra. N233. **GPS:** n38,65578 e0,03660.

20 € 10 Ch € 2 . **Location:** Simple, central.
Surface: asphalted. 01/01-31/12 Sa-Su.
Distance: 500m 400m.
Remarks: Motorhome dealer, arrival during opening hours.

S Cambrils 33B1

Camperpark Las Moreras, Carretera N-340, Km. 1.139,1.
GPS: n41,04471 e0,99437.

120 € 11,45, Jul € 11,25 + € 6,15/pp, Aug € 11,25 + € 8,60/pp Ch WC € 4/3 € 1/h.
Location: Comfortable, isolated, quiet. 01/01-31/12.
Distance: 4km on the spot on the spot on the spot 4km on the spot on the spot.

S Cambrils 33B1

Area de Cambrils, A7. **GPS:** n41,08542 e1,03777.

10 free, 20-8h € 16 Ch WC included € 4.
Location: Motorway, simple, central, noisy. **Surface:** asphalted.
01/01-31/12.
Distance: on the spot.

Tourist information Cambrils:
Oficina de Turismo, Paseo les Palmeres, nº 1, www.turcambrils.info. Bathing resort in traditional Mediterranean style.

Cañada de Callego 31H2

Loma de St.Antonio, Camino de Perchèles. **GPS:** n37,53542 w1,37226.

free. **Location:** Simple, isolated. **Surface:** sand.
Remarks: Parking at sea.

S Cantallops 32H1

Restaurant Can Pau, Carretera de Cantallops s/n.
GPS: n42,41863 e2,91386.
50 guests free Chfree. **Surface:** asphalted.
Distance: 1km 100m.
Remarks: Swimming pool.

S Cantonigròs 32G2

Carrer de Màrius Anglada. **GPS:** n42,04263 e2,40467.
8 free Ch (4x) . **Location:** Rural. **Surface:** unpaved.
01/01-31/12.
Distance: 500m 50m 550m.

S Carcaixent 33A2

Hort de Soriano, Font de la Parra. **GPS:** n39,07045 w0,40918.

15 free Ch free. **Location:** Rural, comfortable, quiet.
Surface: sand. 01/01-31/12 Mo, Aug.
Distance: 7km on the spot.
Remarks: Max. 48h, picnic and barbecue place. At recreation area, first drive into Carrer Julián Ribera (39°7'19'N 00°27'04'W) ± 5km, than follow Hort de Soriano.

S Cartagena 33A3

Area Autocaravanas Cartagena. **GPS:** n37,65373 w1,00345.

ES

30 € 10 Ch WC € 4 included.
Surface: gravel. 01/01-31/12.
Distance: centre 5km, port 8km 400m 400m 400m on the spot on the spot.
Remarks: Bread-service, sunday market Bohio 500m, Thursday market Dolores 1km.

S Cartagena 33A3

Área Belmonte Plus, Ctra. de Tentegorra, 1.
GPS: n37,61500 w1,00555.

15 € 10 Ch included.
Location: Noisy. **Surface:** asphalted.
Distance: 500m on the spot.

S Cassà de la Selva 32H2

Passeig del Ferrocarril 119. **GPS**: n41,88216 e2,87758.
9 free Ch WC .
Location: Urban. **Surface:** metalled/sand. 01/01-31/12.
Distance: 700m.
Remarks: Max. 48h, discount at swimming pool.

S Cervera 32E3

Centre d'Accolida Turistica, Av. Francesc Macià.
GPS: n41,67815 e1,28385.

20 free Ch free.
Location: Urban, quiet. **Surface:** sand. 01/01-31/12.
Distance: 500m 500m 500m.
Remarks: Near office de tourisme, friday market.

S Ceutí 31H2

Ceutí, Pz José Virgili 1. **GPS**: n38,08099 w1,26717.

20 free Ch WC free. **Location:** Simple.
Surface: asphalted. 01/01-31/12.
Distance: 300m 4,5km 170m 200m.

S Creixell 33C1

Area 340, Carrer Aneto. **GPS**: n41,16663 e1,45707.
25 € 10-20 Ch included. **Location:** Comfortable, noisy.
Surface: unpaved. 01/01-31/12.
Distance: 650m 300m.

S Daimús 33A2

Area Camper Dunes, Carrer Garbi 2a. **GPS**: n38,96981 w0,14509.

65 € 9, 01/07-31/08 + Semana Santa € 10, trailer € 1 Ch € 4,50 WC € 3 included. **Location:** Comfortable.
Surface: gravel/metalled.
Distance: 350m 50m 100m on the spot.
Remarks: Discount longer stays.

S Deltebre 33B1

Agrobotiga del Delta, Avda. Les Goles de l'Ebre, 2.
GPS: n40,72605 e0,72261.

50 free Ch free. **Location:** Rural, simple, central.
Surface: concrete. 01/01-31/12.
Distance: 800m 19km 1,5km 600m on the spot.

S El Campello 33A3

Camper Area 7, Avenida Fabraquer 14, Alicante.
GPS: n38,40500 w0,40968.

30 € 10-15, 2 pers.incl Ch € 3/24h,6Amp WC € 3/3 included. **Surface:** gravel.
01/01-31/12.
Distance: 1km 5km 500m 300m 250m on the spot.

S El Campello 33A3

Camper Area Campello Beach, Calle Juan de la Cierva.
GPS: n38,39479 w0,40985.

45 € 12, Jul-Aug € 14 Ch € 2/day WC included € 3 € 3/3 € 2. **Location:** Luxurious.
Surface: gravel/sand.
01/01-31/12.
Distance: 1km 5km 400m 500m 500m on the spot.

S El Campello 33A3

Camper Park Alicante, Carrer Llauradors 113.
GPS: n38,42599 w0,40914.

35 € 7,50 € 3 Ch € 2,50/day WC € 2 free.
Location: Comfortable. **Surface:** gravel. 01/01-31/12.
Distance: 500m 5km 1,8km 500m 1km.

S El Campello 33A3

Bar-Restaurant, N332 km124. **GPS**: n38,45746 w0,36129.

5 € 5 WC included. **Surface:** sand.
Distance: on the spot.
Remarks: 3 days free.

El Campello 33A3

Disaminado Afueras 459. **GPS**: n38,41863 w0,39478.
20 free. **Surface:** metalled. 01/01-31/12.

S El Catllar 33B1

Area de El Catllar, Cami de la Foni. **GPS**: n41,17658 e1,32685.

10 free Ch free. **Location:** Simple, central, quiet.
Surface: metalled. 01/01-31/12.
Distance: 200m 200m on the spot on the spot.

S El Masroig 33B1

Celler El Masroig, Passeig de Arbre 3. **GPS**: n41,12658 e0,73385.

10 free Ch WC. **Location:** Rural, simple. **Surface:** gravel.
01/01-31/12.
Distance: on the spot 200m 200m.
Remarks: Sale of wines.

S El Palomar 33A2

Font de Sis, Avenida Riuet. **GPS**: n38,85749 w0,5032.

17 € 5 Ch € 3/day € 2/day.
Location: Isolated. 01/01-31/12.
Distance: 200m on the spot 200m.
Remarks: Picnic and barbecue place.

S Els Muntells 33B1

Carrer Major. **GPS**: n40,66852 e0,75903.

ES

10 € 6 Chincluded. **Location:** Rural, simple, isolated, quiet. **Surface:** asphalted/gravel. 01/01-31/12.
Distance: 500m 1,2km 400m 600m on the spot on the spot.

Figueres 32H1

Parking Supermercado Esclat, Avda. de los Paisos Catalans, N260. **GPS:** n42,26042 e2,95096.

5 free. **Surface:** asphalted.
Distance: on the spot 500m on the spot 50m.
Remarks: Max. 48h.

Tourist information Figueres:
Rambla. Antiques market. 3rd Sa of the month.
Plaza Catalunya en Plaza del Gra. Tue-Thu-Sa 9-14h.

Garrigàs 32H2

Área del Empordà Norte, A7 km-35. **GPS:** n42,17333 e2,93194.
10 free WCfree. **Location:** Motorway. **Surface:** metalled. 01/01-31/12.

Garrigàs 32H2

Área del Empordà Sur, A7 km-35. **GPS:** n42,17456 e2,93074.

10 free WCfree. **Location:** Motorway. **Surface:** metalled. 01/01-31/12.

Girona 32H2

Vayreda la Devesa, Placa de Mela Mutermilch. **GPS:** n41,98392 e2,81384.

20 € 10 Ch € 1/40minutes WC included.
Location: Urban, simple, central.
Surface: metalled. 01/01-31/12.
Distance: 1km 100m 100m 200m 100m.
Remarks: Registration via intercom or phone, arrival <20h.

Granollers 32G3

Passeig Fluvial. **GPS:** n41,59857 e2,27833.
13 free Chfree. **Surface:** asphalted. 01/01-31/12.
Distance: city centre 1,5km 500m 500m.

Gualta 32H2

Camping Car Park de Torroella, C-31. **GPS:** n42,02456 e3,13490.
60 € 12,45 Ch (50x)included
Surface: gravel.
01/01-31/12.
Distance: 8km 400m 400m.

Remarks: Mandatory, one-time fee Pass'Etapes € 4, bicycle rental.

Ibi 33A3

Área Chambit, Calle Pedro Valdivia. **GPS:** n38,62222 w0,56694.

25 free Chfree. **Location:** Simple.
Surface: sand. 01/01-31/12.
Distance: 2,3km.

Jalance 33A2

N330. **GPS:** n39,18740 w1,0761.

10 free Chfree. **Location:** Isolated.
Surface: asphalted. 01/01-31/12.
Distance: 300m.
Remarks: Parking next to swimming pool, max. 48h.

Jávea 33B3

Avda.de Nancy. **GPS:** n38,77024 e0,18945.

10. **Surface:** unpaved.
Distance: 100m 100m.

L'Alqueria de la Comtessa 33A2

Camperpark KM Zero, Metge Panella nº 1. **GPS:** n38,93878 w0,15276.

35 € 10 Ch (35x)€ 3,50/day,6Amp WC € 3/3 included. **Location:** Comfortable. **Surface:** asphalted.
01/09-31/05.
Distance: 100m 1,5km 4km 200m 200m 150m 300m 500m.
Remarks: Car rental, discount longer stays.

L'Olleria 33A2

Carrer J Bautista Ferrere. **GPS:** n38,91572 w0,55402.

5 free Ch. **Location:** Urban. **Surface:** asphalted.
Distance: 300m 2km 250m.

Remarks: Max. 48h.

La Azohia 33A3

Carretera a La Azohía. **GPS:** n37,56332 w1,17393.

50 free. **Location:** Simple. **Surface:** unpaved.
Distance: 50m 100m 100m.

La Guàrdia dels Prats 32E3

Heretat Masia Poblet, Carretera d'Artesa.s/C-14. **GPS:** n41,41468 e1,17487.

14 € 10, guests free (14x)€ 3/night included.
Location: Rural, simple, isolated, quiet. **Surface:** grassy/gravel.
01/01-31/12 Tue.
Distance: on the spot 5km 5km on the spot on the spot.

La Marina 33A3

Finca La Escuera, Escuera 300. **GPS:** n38,14360 w0,66939.

11 € 14 Ch € 0,26/kWh WC € 4.
Surface: sand.
01/01-31/12.
Distance: 300m 3km 300m 300m 300m on the spot.

La Marina 33A3

La Marina Elche, Cami del Molar o Pinet. **GPS:** n38,15628 w0,63791.

20 € 8 Chincluded € 0,50/kWh,16Amp.
winter.

La Pobla de Segur 32E1

Avenida Camp de la Sala. **GPS:** n42,24029 e0,96635.
12 free Ch free. **Location:** Noisy. **Surface:** asphalted.
01/01-31/12.
Distance: 1km 250m 550m.

La Roca del Vallès 32F3

Área de l'Alba, C251, km3,5. **GPS:** n41,62470 e2,00000.
10 € 10-15 Ch included. **Surface:** grassy.
01/01-31/12.
Remarks: At motorhome dealer.

La Salzadella 33B1

Av. Tomas Molins. **GPS:** n40,41611 e0,17305.

ES

6 free Chfree. **Location:** Rural, simple, quiet.
Surface: asphalted.
Distance: 250m 250m 250m.
Remarks: Village of cherries: cherry soap, cherry jam.

S La Sénia 33B1

Carrer dels Domenges. **GPS:** n40,63897 e0,28502.

10 free € 2 Ch. **Location:** Rural, simple, quiet.
Surface: gravel. 01/01-31/12.
Distance: 800m 200m 200m.

S La Seu d'Urgell 32F1

Parking Doctor Peiró, Avinguda del Camí Ral de Cerdanya.
GPS: n42,35871 e1,46476.

10 free € 2/100liter € 2/2h.
Surface: unpaved. 01/01-31/12 during event.
Distance: 500m 350m.
Remarks: Max. 2 nights.

S La Tallada d'Empordà 32H2

L'Empordanet, Carretera de Marenyà, 6. **GPS:** n42,08335 e3,05734.

€ 12 € 3 Ch included.
Surface: gravel/metalled. 01/01-31/12.
Distance: 1km on the spot on the spot.
Remarks: Max. 48h, swimming pool.

S La Vilella Baixa 32D3

Carrer Catalunya. **GPS:** n41,21718 e0,76383.
4 free ChWCfree. **Location:** Rural. **Surface:** gravel.
01/01-31/12.
Distance: 250m 250m.
Remarks: Max. 48h, barbecue place, picnic area.

Lavern 32F3

Cava Guilera, Masia Ca l'Artigas. **GPS:** n41,39848 e1,77038.

4 free. **Location:** Rural, simple, isolated, quiet.
Surface: grassy. 01/01-31/12.
Distance: 1,5km 5km on the spot on the spot.
Remarks: Max. 2-3 days.

S Lleida 32D3

Autocaravanas Miguel, Ctra. N-IIa 456. **GPS:** n41,58945 e0,57591.

40 € 8 Ch (4x)€ 2/night WC included.
Location: Rural, simple, isolated. **Surface:** grassy/gravel.
01/01-31/12.
Distance: on the spot 4,5km 750m 2km on the spot.

S Lorca 31H2

Caravanas Lorca, P.I. Saprelorca Buzón 233. **GPS:** n37,61205 w1,75993.
20 free € 2 € 2 Ch. **Surface:** gravel. Su.
Distance: 7km 300m 20km 50m.
Remarks: At motorhome dealer.

S Lorquí 31H2

Parque de la Constitución. **GPS:** n38,07909 w1,25918.

15 free Chfree. **Location:** Simple, central.
Surface: asphalted/metalled. Mo 07-15h, market.
Distance: 500m 5km 300m.

S Los Alcázares 33A3

Camping Car Área Narejos, Calle Bergantín 6.
GPS: n37,76298 w0,83069.
90 €7,90-12,90 Ch €3 WC included € 3/3.
Surface: asphalted.
Distance: 700m on the spot.

S L'Arboç 32F3

Área del Penedés Norte, AP7 dir Barcelona. **GPS:** n41,28794 e1,59117.
10 free Chfree. **Location:** Motorway. **Surface:** metalled.
01/01-31/12.
Distance: on the spot on the spot.

S L'Arboç 32F3

Área del Penedés Sur, AP7 dir Taragona. **GPS:** n41,29029 e1,59235.

10 free Chfree. **Location:** Motorway. **Surface:** asphalted.
01/01-31/12.
Distance: on the spot on the spot.

S Mas de Barberans 33B1

Finca Poc A Poc. GPS: n40,71817 e0,37035.

5 € 8-10 ChWC included. **Location:** Rural, comfortable, isolated, quiet. **Surface:** grassy/gravel.
01/01-31/12.
Distance: 2km 2km 2km on the spot on the spot.
Remarks: Beautiful view.

S Moncófar 33A2

Carrer Guipuzkoa. **GPS:** n39,79668 w0,14033.

100 free Chfree. **Location:** Urban.
Surface: metalled. 01/01-31/12.
Distance: on the spot 900m 1km.

S Mont-roig del Camp 33B1

Camping Els Prats Village, Crrt N-340 Km 1137.
GPS: n41,04069 e0,98208.
391 € 19 Ch WC included € 5/5 € 5/10h.
Location: Comfortable, luxurious, quiet. **Surface:** grassy.
16/03-03/11.
Distance: 3km 1km on the spot on the spot on the spot on the spot on the spot.
Remarks: Swimming pool available.

Montanejos 33A1

Parquing Montanejos. GPS: n40,07319 w0,52634.

7 free. **Location:** Rural, simple, quiet. **Surface:** asphalted.
01/01-31/12.
Distance: 600m on the spot on the spot 600m on the spot.
Remarks: Along river.

S Montblanc 32E3

Restaurant Masia Poblet, C14, La Guardia dels Prats.
GPS: n41,41464 e1,17479.

10 € 10, guests free Chincluded € 3,10Amp.
Location: Rural, comfortable, isolated, quiet.
Surface: grassy/metalled. 01/01-31/12.
Distance: 5km on the spot 5km.

S Montblanc 32E3

Area de Autocaravanas Sam, Avda. Lluis Companys.
GPS: n41,36933 e1,17180.

10 € 10 Ch WC included. **Location:** Simple.
Surface: asphalted. 01/01-31/12.
Distance: 800m 350m 800m 400m.
Remarks: At motorhome dealer.

S Montseny 32G3

Área de Montseny, AP7-Nord km-117 > Francia.
GPS: n41,64700 e2,42586.

20 free free. **Location:** Motorway, simple, noisy.
Surface: metalled. 01/01-31/12.
Distance: on the spot on the spot.
Remarks: Parking nearby motorway.

S Montseny 32G3

Área de Montseny, AP7-Sur>Barcelona. **GPS**: n41,64803 e2,42661.

20 free free. **Surface:** metalled. 01/01-31/12.
Distance: on the spot on the spot.

S Morella 33A1

N232. **GPS**: n40,62398 w0,09141.

30 free Chfree. **Location:** Rural, simple, isolated, quiet.
Surface: grassy/metalled. 01/01-31/12.
Distance: 1,5km 1,5km 1,5km on the spot.
Remarks: Max. 72h.

S Mula 31H2

Camino de las Curtis. **GPS**: n38,03972 w1,48139.

5 free Chfree. **Location:** Simple. **Surface:** asphalted.
01/01-31/12.
Distance: 500m 500m.

S Murcia 33A3

Camperpark Casablanca, F16. **GPS**: n38,00189 w1,01939.

120 € 12 Ch WC € 3/3 included.
Location: Comfortable, central. **Surface:** gravel.
01/01-31/12.
Distance: Murcia 11km 500m 15km 500m on the spot on the spot on the spot.
Remarks: 24/24 surveillance.

S Murcia 33A3

Camperpark Huerta de Murcia, Carril los Cánovas, Rincón de Almodóvar, Los Ramos. **GPS**: n38,00520 w1,04229.

45 € 13 Ch WC € 3/3 included.
Location: Comfortable. **Surface:** gravel. 01/01-31/12.
Distance: Alquerías 1,7km 500m 500m on the spot.
Remarks: Bread-service.

S Navarcles 32F2

Area Municipal d'Autocaravanas, Calle de la Font de la Cura.
GPS: n41,75661 e1,90833.

6 free Chfree . **Location:** Urban, isolated, quiet.
Surface: gravel. 01/01-31/12.
Distance: 500m 3km 100m 600m 200m 700m 50m.

S Navata 32H2

Restaurante Can Janot, Ctra. de Olot nº 2.
GPS: n42,22600 e2,86325.

20 guests free € 5 ChWC at restaurant.
Location: Rural, simple, quiet.
Surface: grassy. 01/01-31/12.
Distance: 100m on the spot 100m 150m on the spot on the spot.

S Nules 33A2

Parking Autocaravanas L' Alquería, Camí la Serratella 25.
GPS: n39,83580 w0,10442.

free Ch free. **Surface:** grassy/sand.
01/01-31/12.
Distance: 150m on the spot on the spot.

S Oliva 33A2

Area Camper Kikopark, C/ Assagador de Carro.
GPS: n38,93282 w0,09742.

15 € 18-26,50 Ch WCincluded. 01/01-31/12.
Distance: on the spot on the spot.
Remarks: Stop & Go arrival >15h, departure <15h.

S Palamós 32H2

Autocaravanning Palamós, Camí Vell de la Fosca, 18.
GPS: n41,85592 e3,13535.
96 € 12, 15/07-31/08 € 17 Ch WC € 3 included.
Location: Comfortable. **Surface:** gravel. 01/01-31/12.
Distance: 500m 500m.
Remarks: Motorhome washing place.

ES

Palamós 32H2

EmpordArea, C/ Pui Gorgoll s/n - C/ Pla del Llop s/n.
GPS: n41,85740 e3,11467.

40 € 12, 15/07-28/08 € 17 Ch (40x),8Amp WC € 1 € 4 included. **Location:** Urban, comfortable, quiet.
Surface: gravel/metalled. 01/01-31/12.
Distance: 1km 1,3km 1km 1km 700m 350m 500m 1,2km 1,2km.
Remarks: Bread-service, video surveillance, rental of electric scooters and bicycles.

Peñíscola 33B1

Area camper Vizmar, Cami de la Volta.
GPS: n40,39357 e0,40778.

25 € 7 Ch € 4/day WC included € 3,95/day.
Location: Rural, comfortable, quiet. **Surface:** gravel.
15/09-15/06 Semana Santa.
Distance: 3km 500m 300m 300m 300m.
Remarks: Discount longer stays.

Peñíscola 33B1

Camper Park Los Pinos, C/ Abellers, 2.
GPS: n40,37912 e0,38827.

30 15/09-15/06 € 10, 16/06-14/09 tariff camp site Ch ,10Amp WC € 4,50/4,50 included. **Location:** Rural, luxurious, quiet. **Surface:** gravel/metalled. 01/01-31/12.
Distance: 1,5km 2km 1,5km 800m.

Peñíscola 33B1

Stop&Go La Volta, Camino de la Volta 20.
GPS: n40,39793 e0,40316.

70 € 7, 01/07-31/08 € 10, 2 pers incl., 1 pers + € 1-2 Ch € 3,6Amp WC € 4/4 included. **Location:** Rural, comfortable, isolated, quiet. **Surface:** grassy/gravel. 01/01-31/12.
Distance: 4km, Peñíscola 5km 1km 2km 4km 1km.

Peñíscola 33B1

Parking Els Daus, Avenida Valencia, 93. **GPS**: n40,37831 e0,40640.
130 € 6,30-12,60 ChWCincluded. **Surface:** grassy.
01/01-31/12.
Distance: 2km 100m 100m 30m.
Remarks: Beach parking.

Peralada 32H1

C-252, 206. **GPS**: n42,30597 e3,00845.
6 free Chfree. **Location:** Urban. **Surface:** metalled.
01/01-31/12.
Distance: 200m 200m 300m.
Remarks: Max. 48h.

Pineda de Mar 32G3

Àrea Pineda de Mar, Carrer Tarragona, 24.
GPS: n41,62199 e2,68941.

30 € 10-12 Ch € 3 WC € 1 included.
01/01-31/12 9-21h.
Distance: on the spot 100m 100m.

Platja d'Aro 32H2

Calle Roma. **GPS**: n41,81028 e3,05767.

30 free Chfree. **Surface:** asphalted. 01/10-31/03.
Distance: 750m.
Remarks: Max. 2 days.

Ponts 32E2

Carr. de la Seu d'Urgell 95. **GPS**: n41,92069 e1,19076.

30 € 7 € 3 Ch € 3. **Location:** Rural. **Surface:** gravel.
01/01-31/12.
Distance: 600m 500m 600m 800m.
Remarks: At petrol station.

Prats de Lluçanès 32F2

Zona Autocaravanes, B-432 2. **GPS**: n42,00442 e2,03410.
12 free Ch € 1/2h WC. **Surface:** gravel.
01/01-31/12.
Distance: 700m 900m 700m 850m.
Remarks: Max. 48h, picnic area.

Quart 32H2

Avinguda de la Bóbila. **GPS**: n41,93944 e2,83917.

4 free Chfree. **Surface:** metalled. 01/01-31/12.
Distance: on the spot 6,5km on the spot on the spot.
Remarks: Max. 48h, max. 8M.

Ramonete 31H2

Wo-Mo Puerto Villa Brisa, Los Curas, D21, Puntas de Calnegre.
GPS: n37,52589 w1,4336.

50 € 7 € 0,10/10liter Ch € 0,50 € 2 € 4/4 .
Location: Simple, isolated. **Surface:** gravel. 19/09-30/05.
Distance: 5km 5km 5km 5km.
Remarks: Bread-service.

Rialp 32E1

Paseig del Pallars. **GPS**: n42,43925 e1,13384.
5 free Ch . **Surface:** gravel.
Distance: 200m 200m 200m 100m.
Remarks: Next to football ground.

Ricote 31H1

Huerta de Rivote, Calle Alharbona. **GPS**: n38,15098 w1,36674.
30 free Chfree. **Surface:** gravel. 01/01-31/12.

Ripoll 32G2

Can Guetes, Carretera C-26 Km.126. **GPS**: n42,20267 e2,19390.

5 free Chfree. **Location:** Urban, simple, central.
Surface: asphalted. 01/01-31/12.
Distance: on the spot 500m 150m on the spot on the spot.
Remarks: Max. 24h.

Ripoll 32G2

Calle Pla D'Ordina, Raval de Barcelona. **GPS**: n42,20008 e2,18695.

ES

5 free. **Location:** Urban, simple, noisy.
Surface: asphalted. 01/01-31/12.
Distance: 300m 500m 500m.
Remarks: Parking next to police station, max. 24h.

Tourist information Ripoll:
Centrum. Week market. Sa-morning.

S San Fulgencio 33A3

Camper Park San Fulgencio, Mar Cartabrico 7, Centro Comercial las Dunas. **GPS**: n38,12080 w0,66005.

40 first day € 14, then € 12 Ch WC € 3 included.
Location: Comfortable. **Surface:** gravel.
01/01-31/12.
Distance: 1,5km 200m 150m 150m.

S San Fulgencio 33A3

Ghol, Calle Mar Cantabrico. **GPS**: n38,11896 w0,65614.
14 6m € 11, 9m € 12, 11m € 13 ,2kWh/day WC included. **Surface:** gravel. 01/01-31/12.
Distance: 2km 400m Lidl 120m.
Remarks: Next to petrol station.

S San Fulgencio 33A3

Oasis, Caminal del Convenio. **GPS**: n38,11972 w0,66194.

14 € 10, 15/06-15/09 € 14 Ch € 0,40/kWh,16Amp WC € 3/2 included. **Location:** Comfortable.
Surface: gravel. 01/01-31/12.
Distance: San Fulgencio 7km beach 1,5km 200m 200m 300m.

S San Rafael del Río 33B1

Restaurante Spätzle-Fritz, Planes del Reine, San Jorge, CV-11.
GPS: n40,57507 e0,39333.

50 € 8, guests free € 2 € 2 Ch € 4 WC € 2 .
Location: Rural, comfortable, isolated, quiet.
Surface: gravel. 01/01-31/12.
Distance: 3,5km 7km 9km on the spot.

S Sant Feliu de Guíxols 32H2

Carrer de la Via del Tren. **GPS**: n41,79036 e3,04414.
15 € 10 Ch . **Surface:** sand. 01/01-31/12.
Distance: 2km 1km 800m.
Remarks: Video surveillance.

S Sant Feliu de Guíxols 32H2

Parking Narcis Massanas, Ronda Narcis Massanas.
GPS: n41,78020 e3,02303.

15 free Chfree. **Location:** Simple, quiet.
Surface: unpaved. 01/01-31/12.
Distance: 200m 1,5km 200m 500m 50m.
Remarks: Max. 5 days.

S Sant Hilari Sacalm 32G2

Area Autocaravana, Carretera de la Font Picant.
GPS: n41,88417 e2,50778.

79 free Chfree (2x)€ 1/8h WC € 2.
Location: Rural, simple, quiet. **Surface:** gravel/sand.
01/01-31/12.
Distance: 300m 200m 200m 700m 10m 10m.
Remarks: Nearby swimming pool, max. 48h, key service at swimming pool, no camping activities.

S Sant Joan de les Abadesses 32G1

Area Sant Joan de les Abadesses, Passeig de l'Estació.
GPS: n42,23535 e2,28412.

15 free Chfree.
Location: Urban, simple, central, quiet. **Surface:** unpaved.
01/01-31/12.
Distance: 500m 500m 200m on the spot on the spot.
Remarks: 5 special pitches, all parking places permitted.

S Sant Llorenç de Morunys 32F2

Plaça del Mur. **GPS**: n42,13675 e1,59253.

6 € 4 Ch included.
Location: Rural. **Surface:** metalled. 01/01-31/12.
Distance: on the spot 150m.
Remarks: Max. 48h, pay at tourist office.

S Santa Coloma de Cervelló 32F3

Santa Coloma de Cervelló, Can Julià, s/n.
GPS: n41,36495 e2,02512.

6 free Chfree. **Location:** Simple, isolated, quiet.
Surface: asphalted. 01/01-31/12.
Distance: 500m 5km 400m 500m.

S Santa Coloma de Queralt 32E3

Carrer Llorac. **GPS**: n41,53686 e1,38181.
10 free Chfree € 2. **Location:** Rural. **Surface:** unpaved.
01/01-31/12.
Distance: 100m 500m 600m.
Remarks: Max. 48h.

S Segorbe 33A2

Area de Segorbe, Escalera de la Estación.
GPS: n39,84805 w0,48166.

12 free Chfree. **Location:** Simple, central, quiet.
Surface: asphalted/metalled. 01/01-31/12.
Distance: 1km 2km 800m 800m on the spot.
Remarks: Max. 48h.

S Sils 32H2

Area de Sils, Carrer de l'Estany. **GPS**: n41,80751 e2,74572.

10 free Chfree. **Location:** Urban, simple, central.
Surface: gravel/sand. 01/01-31/12.
Distance: 700m on the spot on the spot 50m.
Remarks: Max. 48h.

S Simat de la Valldigna 33A2

Carrer dels Brolls. **GPS**: n39,04120 w0,308.

20 free Chfree. **Surface:** sand. 01/01-31/12.
Distance: 500m 450m 500m.

S Sitges 32F3

Avda. del Cami Pla. **GPS**: n41,25083 e1,81838.

10 € 5, 01/04-31/10 € 8 Ch. **Location:** Simple.

ES

Surface: asphalted. 01/01-31/12.
Distance: 800m 2,5km 50m.
Remarks: Industrial area, max. 7 days, Barcelona 40km.

S Sta.Pola 33A3

Europa-Area, Carrer dels Electricistas. **GPS**: n38,20805 w0,57416.

33 € 9 Ch € 3 WC € 4 . **Location:** Comfortable.
Surface: gravel/metalled. 01/01-31/12.
Distance: 1,7km 1,8km 1,7km.

S Tavernes de la Valldigna 33A2

Area Camper La Finca, Carrer del Carbi. **GPS**: n39,08178 w0,21245.
50 € 8 Ch € 3 WC € 3 included. 01/01-31/12.
Distance: 750m 50m 600m.
Remarks: Bread-service, video surveillance.

S Tavertet 32G2

Carrer Jaume Balmes. **GPS**: n41,99462 e2,41572.
10 € 10 Ch included. **Surface:** gravel/sand.
01/01-31/12.
Distance: 100m 450m.

S Tortosa 33B1

Área de Tortosa, Cami de la Toia. **GPS**: n40,80277 e0,51388.

30 free Chfree. **Location:** Simple, central, quiet.
Surface: asphalted. 01/01-31/12.
Distance: 1,1km 10km 900m 1km.

S Totana 31H2

Camperstop Sierra Espuña, Morti s/n Camino del Polideportivo.
GPS: n37,79380 w1,51139.

25 € 7 Ch € 3/day WC € 1 € 3 included.
Location: Comfortable. **Surface:** gravel.
Distance: 2,5km 5km 450m.

S Tremp 32E2

Passeig de Conca de Tremp. **GPS**: n42,16312 e0,89043.

10 free free € 1/2h. **Surface:** asphalted.
01/01-31/12.
Distance: 200m 200m.
Remarks: Max. 48h, no camping activities.

S Turis 33A2

Carretera de Silla Tunis. **GPS**: n39,38944 w0,69777.

10 free Chfree. **Location:** Simple. **Surface:** unpaved.
01/01-31/12.
Distance: 500m.

S Ulldecona 33B1

Finca Mola de la Torre, Partida Llacuna. **GPS**: n40,61786 e0,46010.
3 € 8,50, 2 pers.incl included. **Location:** Rural.
Surface: grassy. 01/01-31/12.
Distance: 2,5km 2,5km 2,5km on the spot on the spot.
Remarks: At swimming pool.

S Valencia 33A2

Valencia Camper Park, Calle Universo, Bétera.
GPS: n39,57958 w0,44494.
78 € 12 € 0,50/40liter Ch (52x)€ 3/24h,4Amp, 6Amp € 5
WC € 3 included
Location: Urban, luxurious. **Surface:** gravel. 01/01-31/12.
Distance: Valencia 12km 1,5km train 300m.
Remarks: Discount longer stays, swimming pool (summer).

S Valencia 33A2

Area Camping-car La Marina, Carrer del Rio 556B, El Saler.
GPS: n39,38666 w0,3321.

70 € 11 ChWC . **Surface:** gravel.
Distance: Valencia 6km beach 150m 600m 500m
on the spot on the spot on the spot.
Remarks: Discount longer stays.

S Vallirana 32F3

Carrer Major, N340. **GPS**: n41,38239 e1,92719.

6 free Ch. **Location:** Simple, noisy.
Surface: asphalted. 01/01-31/12.
Distance: 800m 300m 800m.

S Vic 32G2

Area Municipal de Vic, Carrer de la Fura.
GPS: n41,93444 e2,24000.

10 € 5 € 2/100liter Ch € 6/3h.
Location: Rural. **Surface:** grassy.
Distance: 1,8km 2km 300m 500m 400m.
Remarks: Max. 48h.

S Vic 32G2

Área de pernocta ASM, Carrer del Blat. **GPS**: n41,95688 e2,24765.

6 free Chfree. **Location:** Rural, simple.
Surface: asphalted. 01/01-31/12.
Distance: 3,5km 500m 3,5km 3,5km.
Remarks: Video surveillance.

S Viladrau 32G2

Area de Viladrau, Carrer Montseny s/n. **GPS**: n41,84544 e2,38732.

16 free Ch free. **Location:** Rural, simple, quiet.
Surface: gravel/sand. 01/01-31/12.
Distance: 500m 500m 500m.
Remarks: Max. 48h.

S Vilafranca del Penedès 32F3

Vilafranca del Penedès, Avda. Tarragona, N-340a.
GPS: n41,34001 e1,69147.

10 free Ch. **Location:** Rural, simple, central, quiet.
Surface: gravel/sand. 01/01-31/12.
Distance: 500m 1,2km 900m 850m Lidl on the spot
on the spot.

S Yecla 33A2

Finca Caravana, Paraje Fuente del Pinar A-14.
GPS: n38,71443 w1,11948.

ES

10 € 8 Chincluded. **Location:** Rural, simple, isolated. **Surface:** gravel/sand. 05/06-30/06.

Spanish interior

S Aguilar de Campoo 29F2

N611, Ctra Palencia-Aguillar de Campoo.
GPS: n42,78631 w4,25757.

10 free Chfree. **Location:** Urban, simple. **Surface:** asphalted. 01/01-31/12.
Distance: 1km 3,1km 1km 1km.
Remarks: Max. 48h.

Alcuéscar 30D3

Hostal Los Olivos. **GPS**: n39,16461 w6,26425.
5 guests free. **Surface:** gravel. 01/01-31/12.
Distance: on the spot.

S Aldeadávila de la Ribera 30D1

GPS: n41,22028 w6,61333.

5 free Chfree. **Surface:** asphalted. 01/01-31/12.
Distance: 400m on the spot 200m.
Remarks: Max. 48h.

S Aldeanueva de Barbarroya 30E2

Calle Aldeanueva. **GPS**: n39,75843 w5,01482.
5 free Chfree. 01/01-31/12.
Distance: 700m 700m.
Remarks: Max. 72h.

S Algora 30H1

Area 112, Autovía A2 km 112. **GPS**: n40,95669 w2,66403.
1free Ch free. **Surface:** gravel/metalled.
01/01-31/12.
Remarks: At petrol station and supermarket, playground.

Almazán 30H1

Camino Viejo del Cubo de la Solana. **GPS**: n41,49259 w2,53385.
10 free. **Surface:** asphalted.
Remarks: Parking at swimming pool.

S Ampudia 29F3

Area de San Martín, Glorieta. S. Martín.
GPS: n41,91130 w4,78082.

6 free Chfree. **Location:** Rural, simple.
Surface: gravel/metalled. 01/01-31/12.
Distance: 400m.
Remarks: Max. 72h, no camping activities.

S Andorra 33A1

Area en Andorra. **GPS**: n40,98384 w0,44724.

3 free € 0,20/130liter Ch. **Surface:** asphalted.
01/01-31/12.
Distance: 1km 13km 1,2km.
Remarks: Coins at petrol station.

S Astorga 29E2

Parking plaza de Toros. **GPS**: n42,45138 w6,06593.

15 free Chfree. **Surface:** metalled.
Distance: 500m 1,4km 500m 500m.
Remarks: Max. 48h.

S Astudillo 29F3

Area de la Joya, Urbanizacion de don Bosco. **GPS**: n42,18944 w4,3.

10 free Chfree. **Location:** Rural, simple. **Surface:** gravel.
01/01-31/12.
Distance: 1km 300m.
Remarks: No camping activities.

Avila 30F1

Parking del Palacio de Congresos, Calle Molino dell Carril.
GPS: n40,66111 w4,70472.

10 free.
Surface: asphalted.
01/01-31/12.
Distance: centre 800m 2,2km
250m.
Remarks: Monitored parking.

Tourist information Avila:
Small medieval town surround by ramparts.
The San Vicenta basilica is a Roman building.

S Badajoz 30C3

La Codosera, Ctra. de Alburquerque, BA 053. **GPS**: n39,23870 w7,20297.
free Chfree. **Location:** Rural. **Surface:** unpaved.
01/01-31/12.
Distance: 2km on the spot.
Remarks: Swimming pool.

S Badajoz 30C3

Parque del Guadiana, Camino Viejo de San Vicente.
GPS: n38,88481 w6,97845.

8 free Chfree. **Surface:** asphalted. 01/01-31/12.
Distance: 600m on the spot.

S Baltanàs 29F3

Area de la Ermita de Revilla, Plaza Arrañales de Revilla.
GPS: n41,93472 w4,2475.

5 free Chfree. **Location:** Rural, simple.
Surface: concrete. 01/01-31/12.
Distance: on the spot 500m.
Remarks: No camping activities.

S Becerril de Campos 29F3

Carretera de Monzón. **GPS**: n42,10997 w4,64315.
free Chfree. **Surface:** metalled. 01/01-31/12.
Distance: on the spot 14km 500m 500m.
Remarks: No camping activities.

S Bretocino 29E3

Area para Autocaravanes, Cuesta de los Nogales.
GPS: n41,88654 w5,75517.

5 +25 € 7 Chincluded € 3,10Amp WC.
Location: Rural, comfortable, quiet. **Surface:** concrete.
20/03-20/10.
Distance: 300m 300m.
Remarks: Service passerby € 3, swimming pool.

S Burgo de Osma 30G1

Calle de Santos Iruela. **GPS**: n41,58662 w3,07338.

10 free . **Location:** Rural, simple. **Surface:** metalled.
01/01-31/12.
Distance: 500m 200m 500m.

S Burgos 29G3

Calle Farmacéutico Obdulio Fernández. **GPS**: n42,35012 w3,68068.
20 free Chfree. **Location:** Urban. **Surface:** asphalted.
01/01-31/12.
Distance: city centre 1km 100m 100m on the spot on the spot on the spot.

Burgos 29G3

N120, Calle de Cartuja de Miraflores. **GPS**: n42,34037 w3,69361.

ES

5 € 0,60/h, max. € 2,60, 20-10h free. **Location:** Central, quiet.
Surface: asphalted.
Distance: 2,6km.
Remarks: Parking beside river.

Tourist information Burgos:
City, 8th century, with a lot of curiosities such as the cathedral, the castle and Monasterio de las Huelgas.

Cabrerizos 30E1

Don Quijote, Ctra. Aldealengua km 4. **GPS**: n40,97500 w5,60306.
€ 17 Ch. 01/03-31/10.
Remarks: Formula Camper.

Cáceres 30D2

Valhondo, Calle Lope de Vega. **GPS**: n39,48041 w6,36649.

15 free Ch free. **Surface:** asphalted.
Distance: 600m 6,7km.
Remarks: Max. 24h, monitored parking.

Tourist information Cáceres:
Oficina de Turismo, Plaza Mayor, nº 3, www.inedito.com/caceres/. City with historical centre.
PeroPalo. Traditional celebration. 21/02-24/02.

Calaceite 33B1

Calle Font de la Vila 10. **GPS**: n41,01866 e0,19027.
10 free Chfree. **Surface:** gravel. 01/01-31/12.
Distance: 400m 650m 350m.
Remarks: Max. 72h.

Carrión de los Condes 29F3

Calle de Las Huertas. **GPS**: n42,33875 w4,60808.

10 free Chfree. **Location:** Rural, simple.
Surface: metalled.
Distance: 200m 200m 200m.
Remarks: Max. 48h.

Cervera de Pisuerga 29F2

C/ El Maderao. **GPS**: n42,87139 w4,49972.

10 free Chfree. **Location:** Rural, simple, isolated.
Surface: sand. 01/01-31/12.
Distance: 500m 500m 500m.
Remarks: Along river, max. 48h.

Coca 30F1

GPS: n41,21348 w4,52733.

5 free. **Location:** Urban, simple. **Surface:** metalled.
01/01-31/12.
Remarks: Parking castle.

Consuegra 30G3

Calle Fuentecilla. **GPS**: n39,45339 w3,6106.
free. **Location:** Isolated, quiet. **Surface:** sand.
01/01-31/12.
Remarks: Isolated parking at foot of hill with windmills.

Cuellar 30F1

Área El Castillo, Calle del Alamillo, 40. **GPS**: n41,40083 w4,32028.

6 free Chfree. **Location:** Rural, simple.
Surface: metalled.
Distance: 2km.
Remarks: At castle.

Cuenca 30H2

Parking del Auditorio, Paseo del Huecar.
GPS: n40,07639 w2,12917.
5 € 15/24h. **Location:** Urban.
Surface: metalled.
01/01-31/12.
Distance: 500m on the spot 350m station 1km.

Tourist information Cuenca:
Historical centre with casas colgadas (hanging houses).
Processions of guilds with much pomp and splendour.
Easter.
Ciudad Encantada. Nature reserve.

Cumbres Mayores 31D1

Calle Sevilla. **GPS**: n38,05937 w6,63797.
8 free Chfree. **Location:** Rural. **Surface:** metalled.
01/01-31/12.
Distance: 500m 500m 500m on the spot.

Daimiel 30F3

Parque Nacional Las Tablas de Daimiel, Carr. a las Tablas de Daimiel.
GPS: n39,13754 w3,69678.

10 free WC. **Location:** Rural. **Surface:** grassy/metalled.
01/01-31/12.
Distance: on the spot.

Deleitosa 30E2

Área PLA Deleitosa, Calle Eras. **GPS**: n39,64041 w5,64599.
3 free € 3 Ch € 1/h. **Surface:** metalled.
01/01-31/12.
Distance: 500m 500m.

Don Benito 30D3

Avda. de los Deportes. **GPS**: n38,96250 w5,86305.
3 free Chfree. **Location:** Central, noisy. **Surface:** metalled.
01/01-31/12.
Distance: on the spot on the spot on the spot.

Duruelo de la Sierra 29G3

Avenida del Duero. **GPS**: n41,95242 w2,92725.
16 € 4 Ch. **Surface:** metalled. 01/01-31/12.
Distance: 400m 250m.

Espinosa de los Monteros 29G2

Parking Las Cocinas, BU-570 > Bárcenas. **GPS**: n43,08556 w3,5575.

10 free Chfree. **Location:** Simple, isolated.
Surface: asphalted. 01/01-31/12.
Distance: 1km 1km 1km on the spot.
Remarks: Max. 48h, tuesday market.

Foncastín 29F3

Estación de Servicios La Loba, A6, salida 175.
GPS: n41,44131 w4,97957.

5 free Chfree. **Location:** Rural, simple. **Surface:** unpaved.
01/01-31/12.
Distance: 250m on the spot.

Frómista 29F3

Paseo de Julio Senador, P-980. **GPS**: n42,26494 w4,41198.

6 free Chfree. **Location:** Urban, simple.
Surface: metalled. 01/01-31/12.
Distance: 600m 200m 500m 500m.
Remarks: At sports park, max. 48h, weigh bridge nearby € 0,50.

Fuente de Cantos 31D1

Calle Real. **GPS**: n38,24900 w6,30079.
3 free € 3 Ch. **Surface:** metalled. 01/01-31/12.
Distance: on the spot on the spot.
Remarks: Max. 72h.

Herrera de Pisuerga 29F2

Fuente Los Caños. **GPS**: n42,59011 w4,33225.
7 free Chfree. **Location:** Rural. **Surface:** gravel.
01/01-31/12.
Remarks: No camping activities.

Hontoria del Pinar 29G3

Cañon de Río Lobos, C/ De la Cuesta Herrera.
GPS: n41,84379 w3,16514.
9+24 free Chfree. **Surface:** gravel. 01/01-31/12.
Distance: 500m 450m.

Huergas de Babia 29E2

El Moriscal, CL-626. **GPS**: n42,95651 w6,09335.
10 € 5 Ch included. **Location:** Rural. **Surface:** gravel.
01/01-31/12.
Distance: on the spot on the spot.

Jerez de los Caballeros 31D1

Calle Miguel Hermandez, Plaza de Toros. **GPS**: n38,32639 w6,7625.
8 free Ch free. **Location:** Urban. **Surface:** unpaved.
01/01-31/12.
Distance: on the spot.
Remarks: Video surveillance.

Jerte 30E2

Area de Jerte. **GPS**: n40,20976 w5,77284.
15 free € 3/150liter Ch (4x). **Location:** Rural.
Surface: asphalted/metalled. 01/01-31/12.
Distance: city centre 2km 400m on the spot on the spot.
Remarks: Max. 72h, monitored parking.

La Alberca 30D1

Casa del Parque. **GPS**: n40,48833 w6,11583.
10 free Chfree. **Surface:** metalled. 01/01-31/12.
Distance: 300m.
Remarks: Max. 48h, no camping activities.

La Joyosa 32A2

Área de Marlofa, Calle Sobradiel. **GPS**: n41,73744 w1,06664.
21 free Ch € 3 WC € 3 . **Surface:** asphalted/grassy.
Distance: 9km.

Lagartera 30E2

Camino de la Estacion. **GPS**: n39,91151 w5,19978.

3 free free. **Surface:** asphalted. 01/01-31/12.
Distance: on the spot 1,4km 100m.
Remarks: Max. 48h.

León 29E2

Avenida los Peregrinos. **GPS**: n42,60471 w5,58525.

6 free Chfree. **Surface:** metalled.
Distance: 300m 300m.
Remarks: Max. 48h.

Logrosán 30E3

El Palomar, Carretera Villanueva-Seré. **GPS**: n39,33188 w5,48044.
10 free Chfree. **Location:** Isolated. **Surface:** grassy.
01/01-31/12.
Remarks: Max. 48h.

Madrid 30G2

Valdebernando, Bulevar de Jose Prat.
GPS: n40,39671 w3,62.
15 free.
Location: Urban.
Surface: metalled.
01/01-31/12.
Distance: on the spot
200m 300m
on the spot on the spot.
Remarks: Monitored parking.

Tourist information Madrid:
Oficina de Turismo, C/Duque de Medinaceli, 2, Madrid. Capital of the country with a lot of curiosities.
Palacio Real, Madrid. Royal palace.
Museo de América, Madrid, Av de los Reyes Católicos.
Museo del Ejercito, Calle Mendez Nuñez 1, Madrid. Army museum.
Museo del Prado, Madrid. The largest art gallery of the world.
Museo Romántico, Calle de San Mateo 13, Madrid.
Collection of the romanticism.
Basílica de San Francisco el Grande, Madrid. Basilica.

Mérida 30D3

Área Teatro Romano de Mérida, C/ Cabo Verde, s/n.
GPS: n38,91903 w6,33611.
<8m € 12/24h, >8m € 15/24h, trailer € 3 Ch € 3
included.
Location: Urban.
Surface: asphalted.
01/01-31/12.
Distance: 700m.
Remarks: Video surveillance.

Tourist information Mérida:
Oficina de Turismo, Calle Santa Eulalia, 64. Also called Spanish Rome. Former stopover on the old silver trail.

Olmedo 30F1

Parque del Mudejar, N601, km 148,1. **GPS**: n41,29167 w4,68194.

9 free Chfree. **Location:** Rural, simple. **Surface:** metalled.
01/01-31/12.
Distance: 100m 200m.

Oropesa 30E2

Camino de Torralba. **GPS**: n39,92124 w5,16738.
4 free Chfree. **Surface:** metalled. 01/01-31/12.
Distance: 600m.
Remarks: Max. 48h, no camping activities.

Osorno 29F2

Los Chopos, N611 Osorno > Herrera de Pisuerga.
GPS: n42,41694 w4,35111.

30 free Chfree. **Surface:** asphalted. 01/01-31/12.
Distance: 700m 2,2km on the spot.
Remarks: Max. 48h, monitored parking.

Palazuelos de Eresma 30F1

Calle Cordel. **GPS**: n40,92848 w4,05529.
€ 1 Chfree. 01/01-31/12.
Distance: 4km.

Palencia 29F3

Parque Isla Dos Aguas, Avda. Ponce de León, 12.
GPS: n42,00389 w4,53333.

23 free Chfree. **Surface:** asphalted. 01/01-31/12.
Distance: on the spot 4km on the spot El Arbol 50m
100m.
Remarks: Max. 48h.

Peñafiel 29F3

Calle de Los Destiladeros. **GPS**: n41,59440 w4,11582.

5 free. **Location:** Rural, simple. **Surface:** asphalted.
01/01-31/12.
Distance: 150m.
Remarks: Parking castle.

Peñaflor 32B2

Parking Surrecreo, Urbanizacion Los Rosales Peñaflor.
GPS: n41,72777 w0,79194.
150 € 15 Ch WC included.
Distance: 8km.

Pollos 29E3

Estación de Servicios La Loba 2000, A62, salida 169.
GPS: n41,41004 w5,13396.

10 free Chfree. **Location:** Motorway, simple.
Surface: metalled. 01/01-31/12.
Distance: 200m on the spot on the spot.
Remarks: At petrol station.

Ponferrada 29D2

Calle Obispo Camilo Lorenzo 2. **GPS**: n42,54388 w6,58623.

40 free Ch. **Location:** Urban.
Surface: asphalted. 01/01-31/12.
Distance: centre 500m on the spot on the spot 600m.
Remarks: Monitored parking.

Tourist information Ponferrada:
Oficina de Turismo, C/ Gil Y Carrasco 4.

Ribaseca 29E2

Area de Léon, Carretera la Bañeza. **GPS**: n42,54439 w5,5882.
€ 15-25 Ch WC included. **Surface:** asphalted.
01/01-31/12.
Distance: 8km 2,3km 800m.
Remarks: At motorhome dealer, car rental, motorhome washing place.

Salamanca 30E1

Antiguo Campo De Rugbi. **GPS**: n40,95917 w5,67464.
+10 free. **Location:** Noisy. 01/01-31/12.
Distance: 1km 100m Lidl/Mercadona.
Remarks: Next to sports fields.

Saldaña 29F2

Calle de los Sauces. **GPS**: n42,51882 w4,74125.

6 free Chfree. **Location:** Rural, simple.
Surface: concrete. 01/01-31/12.
Distance: 1km 1km.
Remarks: Next to sports fields, max. 48h.

San Agustín 33A1

Alto Mijares, TE-V-2001. **GPS**: n40,12680 w0,67667.

ES

10 € 3/pp WC included. **Location:** Rural, isolated, quiet.
Surface: unpaved. 01/01-31/12.
Remarks: Max. 6m.

Sancti-Spiritus 30D1

Hostal-Restaurante La Ponderosa, Carretera nacional 620 km303.
GPS: n40,73481 w6,36093.

guests free . **Location:** Isolated, quiet.
Surface: unpaved. 01/01-31/12.
Distance: 3km on the spot.

Santelices 29G2

Diseminado Santelices 12A. **GPS**: n43,00397 w3,73891.
32 free € 3 Ch (32x) WC . **Location:** Urban.
Surface: metalled. 01/01-31/12.
Distance: 800m 800m 700m on the spot on the spot.

Segovia 30F1

Plaza de Toros. **GPS**: n40,94083 w4,10778.
10 free Chfree.
Location: Urban.
Surface: metalled.
01/01-31/12 Sa (market).
Distance: on the spot 600m 500m.
Remarks: Near arena, max. 72h.

Tourist information Segovia:
Oficina de Turismo, Plaza Mayor, 10. Old city, 800 years before Christ.
Castillo Alcazar. Medieval castle, museum. 01/04-30/09 10-19h, 01/10-31/03 10-18h.

Sepúlveda 30G1

Calle de el Postiguillo. **GPS**: n41,29897 w3,74479.

10 free. **Surface:** asphalted. 01/01-31/12.
Distance: 300m 12km 100m.

Soria 29H3

Monte de las Animas. **GPS**: n41,76769 w2,45391.

free. **Surface:** gravel. 01/01-31/12.

Soria 29H3

Hypermercado E. Leclerc, Calle J, P 290. **GPS**: n41,77249 w2,48497.
6 free € 2 Ch € 2 . **Surface:** asphalted.
01/01-31/12.
Distance: 1,8km on the spot on the spot on the spot.
Remarks: Coins at petrol station.

Terradillos 30E1

Area del Encinar, Paseo de Poniente. **GPS**: n40,88000 w5,58194.
10 free. **Location:** Simple, quiet. **Surface:** asphalted.
Distance: 200m.

Teruel 33A1

Parking Cuartel, Calle Tarazona de Aragon. **GPS**: n40,33170 w1,09243.
20 free. **Surface:** asphalted. 01/01-31/12.
Distance: 110m 300m 50m on the spot.
Remarks: In front of police station.

Toro 29E3

Area de Rumbeolas, Calle Santa María de la Vega.
GPS: n41,51489 w5,39301.
10 € 4 Chincluded € 3. **Location:** Rural. **Surface:** sand.
01/01-31/12.
Distance: 1,5km 5,5km on the spot.

Trujillo 30E3

Ronda de le Plaza de Toros. **GPS**: n39,45696 w5,87303.
10 free. **Surface:** asphalted. 01/01-31/12.
Distance: centre 800m 100m.

Turégano 30F1

CL603. **GPS**: n41,15209 w4,0082.

10 free Chfree. **Location:** Rural, simple. **Surface:** asphalted.
01/01-31/12.
Distance: 200m.
Remarks: Behind former grain factory, max. 48h.

Valencia de Alcántara 30C2

Area de Puerto Roque, N-521. **GPS**: n39,34104 w7,2775.
10 free € 3 Ch. **Location:** Rural. **Surface:** metalled.
01/01-31/12.
Distance: 9km on the spot.

Valencia de Don Juan 29E2

Area de Coyanza, Calle Tres de Abril. **GPS**: n42,28750 w5,51333.

12 free Chfree. **Location:** Urban, simple. **Surface:** concrete.
01/01-31/12.
Distance: 500m 300m.
Remarks: Max. 48h.

Valladolid 29F3

San Lorenzo, Av. Ramón Pradera. **GPS**: n41,65583 w4,73722.

15 € 2,50/24h included. **Location:** Urban.
Surface: asphalted.
Distance: city centre 1km 3,2km 400m.
Remarks: Max. 48h.

Villacañas 30G3

Calle Juan Pablo II. **GPS**: n39,62101 w3,33188.
2 free. **Surface:** asphalted.
Distance: on the spot 350m.
Remarks: Max. 48h.

Villada 29F3

C/ San Fructuoso, Calle del Ferial Nuevo 10.
GPS: n42,25533 w4,9649.

5 free Chfree. **Location:** Rural, simple, quiet.
Surface: gravel. 01/01-31/12.
Distance: 200m 200m 200m on the spot on the spot.
Remarks: Max. 48h, no camping activities.

Villalpando 29E3

Area de Servicios Villalpando, A6, salida 236.
GPS: n41,85906 w5,41993.
5 free. **Location:** Motorway, simple, isolated, noisy.
Surface: asphalted. 01/01-31/12.
Distance: 200m on the spot on the spot.
Remarks: At petrol station.

Villanueva del Fresno 31C1

Travesia Huertas 4. **GPS**: n38,37889 w7,16417.
10 free Ch free. **Location:** Urban. **Surface:** metalled.
01/01-31/12.
Distance: on the spot 200m 600m.
Remarks: Max. 48h.

Viso del Marqués 31F1

Calle Feria. **GPS**: n38,52709 w3,56287.
30 free Ch . **Location:** Urban. **Surface:** asphalted.
01/01-31/12.
Distance: 400m 650m.
Remarks: At sports grounds, max. 48h.

Zafra 31D1

Ctra. de los Santos de Maimona, Ex101. **GPS**: n38,42527 w6,41083.

30 free Chfree. **Location:** Urban, central, noisy.
Surface: asphalted. 01/01-31/12.
Distance: on the spot on the spot on the spot.

Zamora 29E3

Estadio Barrio 3 Arboles, Calle de los Pisones.
GPS: n41,50337 w5,75585.

18 free. **Location:** Urban, simple, central. **Surface:** asphalted.
01/01-31/12.
Distance: 1km 1km.
Remarks: Playground.

Andalusia

Abla 31G2

Area de Abla, A-92A. **GPS**: n37,14455 w2,77347.
7 free Chfree. **Surface:** asphalted. 01/01-31/12.
Distance: on the spot 1,5km 100m.

Abla 31G2

Area de Montagón, Carretera ALP-503.
GPS: n37,15415 w2,77716.

ES

13 free Chfree. **Location:** Rural, simple, quiet.
Surface: asphalted. 01/01-31/12.
Distance: 1,5km 2km 1,5km 1,5km.
Remarks: Next to football ground.

Alanís 31D1

Area de Alanís de la Sierra, Alameda del Parral.
GPS: n38,03729 w5,71057.
5 free Chfree. **Location:** Simple. **Surface:** metalled.
01/01-31/12.
Distance: on the spot 200m.

Alcalá de Guadaíra 31D2

Autocaravanas Hidalgo, A92 Sevilla><Malaga km 7.
GPS: n37,32856 w5,8056.

18 € 10 € 0,50 Ch included .
Distance: 170m exit 15.
Remarks: Motorhome dealer, max. 2 nights.

Alcázar de San Juan 30G3

Area de Alcazar de San Juan. GPS: n39,38972 w3,21944.
10 free Ch. **Surface:** asphalted. 01/01-31/12.
Distance: on the spot 150m 300m.

Algar 31D3

Complejo Tajo del Aguila. GPS: n36,65111 w5,66555.
€ 20 Ch WC included. 01/01-31/12.
Distance: 1km on the spot on the spot.
Remarks: Max. 7 nights.

Alicún de las Torres 31G2

GR6104. **GPS:** n37,50836 w3,10802.

3 free. **Surface:** metalled. 01/01-31/12.
Distance: 100m 100m.
Remarks: Next to the spa resort.

Almayate 31F3

Area AMB, Carretera Nacional 340, km 266,5.
GPS: n36,72372 w4,13999.

40 € 7, 01/06-30/09 € 10 Ch included.
Location: Rural, simple. **Surface:** gravel.
Distance: 700m 100m 100m 2km 200m.
Remarks: At motorhome dealer.

Almensilla 31D2

San Diego, A-8054. **GPS:** n37,31354 w6,09317.
15 free Chfree. 01/01-31/12.
Distance: on the spot.
Remarks: At petrol station BP and restaurant, restaurant visit appreciated.

Almería 31H3

Cabo de Gata Camperpark, Paraje El Nazareno Ctra. de San José.
GPS: n36,81603 w2,14878.
50 € 7 Ch € 3/24h WC € 3,50 included.
Surface: gravel/metalled. 01/01-31/12.
Distance: 100m 2km on the spot on the spot.

Almerimar 31G3

Parking Almerimar, Avenida del Mar. **GPS:** n36,70803 w2,80895.
136 € 7 Ch € 3/24h WC . **Location:** Urban.
Surface: metalled. 01/01-31/12.
Distance: city centre ± 1km 100m 50m 1km.

Almerimar 31G3

Area del Puerto Deportivo Almerimar, Torre del puerto.
GPS: n36,69612 w2,79425.

20 € 12,69 Ch WC included € 3,50/24h.
Location: Urban, simple. **Surface:** asphalted. 01/01-31/12.
Distance: on the spot 100m 300m 100m 100m.
Remarks: Check in at harbourmaster 9-14h, 16-21h.

Antequera 31E2

Area de Antequera, Calle Miguel de Cervantes.
GPS: n37,02139 w4,57191.

12 free Chfree. **Location:** Urban, simple, noisy.
Surface: asphalted. 01/01-31/12.
Distance: on the spot 6,5km 50m 500m.
Remarks: Next to football ground.

Archidona 31E2

A7200. **GPS:** n37,09097 w4,38879.

12 free Chfree. **Location:** Rural, simple, noisy.
Surface: concrete. 01/01-31/12.
Distance: 250m 1km 500m 1km on the spot.

Ayamonte 31C2

Autocaravanas Puerto de Ayamonte, Calle Madrid.
GPS: n37,21082 w7,40541.
27 € 12,50 € 3 Ch € 0,50 WC . **Surface:** asphalted.
01/01-31/12.
Distance: on the spot on the spot 200m 400m on the spot on the spot.

Baena 31F2

Área de Baena, Camino del Juncal. **GPS:** n37,62486 w4,32198.
8 free Chfree. **Surface:** unpaved. 01/01-31/12.
Distance: historical centre 600m.
Remarks: No camping activities.

Baeza 31F1

Calle Manuel Acero. **GPS:** n37,99679 w3,45923.
30 free Chfree. **Surface:** sand. 01/01-31/12.
Distance: 1km 500m bakery.
Remarks: Max. 96h, no camping activities.

Barbate 31D3

Autocaravanas Puerto de Barbate, Avenida del Mar, s/n..
GPS: n36,18355 w5,93533.
36 € 12,50 € 3 Ch € 0,50 WC . **Surface:** asphalted.
01/01-31/12.
Distance: 1,5km 1,5km on the spot on the spot.

Benarrabá 31E3

Area Autocaravanas Benarrabá, Carretera Comarcal MA-538.
GPS: n36,54935 w5,27901.
5 free Chfree. **Surface:** concrete. 01/01-31/12.
Distance: 500m 600m.

Cabo de Gata 31H3

Cabo de Gata Camper Park, Carrertera de San José.
GPS: n36,81639 w2,14918.

50 € 7-10 Ch (50x)€ 3 WC € 3,50/3,50 included.
Surface: gravel. 01/01-31/12.
Distance: 5km 7km 7km on the spot 5km on the spot on the spot on the spot.
Remarks: Service passerby € 3, bicycle rental.

Cabra 31F2

Area de Cabra II, Calle de la Libertad. **GPS:** n37,47602 w4,44271.

free Chfree. **Location:** Urban. **Surface:** asphalted.
01/01-31/12 Mo 07-13h.
Distance: 600m 200m.

Cabra 31F2

Auditorio Municipal Alcalde Juan Muños, Juanita la Larga.
GPS: n37,46608 w4,42361.

4 free Chfree. **Location:** Urban, simple, quiet.
Surface: asphalted. 01/01-31/12.
Distance: 500m 300m 500m.
Remarks: Max. 48h.

Cala de Mijas 31E3

Av. del Mediterraneo. **GPS:** n36,50496 w4,68344.

50 free. **Location:** Urban, simple. **Surface:** sand.
01/01-31/12.
Distance: 500m 500m 800m 50m 100m 50m.
Remarks: Market Wednesday and Saturday.

ES

Caleta de Vélez 31F3

Autocaravanas Puerto de Caleta de Vélez, Calle Miguel Ariza.
GPS: n36,74852 w4,06549.
33 € 12,50 € 3 Ch € 0,50. **Surface:** asphalted.
01/01-31/12.
Distance: on the spot on the spot 200m Aldi 1km.
Remarks: Golf court 2km.

Canjáyar 31G3

Paraje de la Alcoholera, A-348. **GPS**: n37,01400 w2,74523.

7 free Ch free. **Location:** Rural, simple, quiet.
Surface: asphalted/metalled.
Distance: 1km 450m.
Remarks: At tennis-courts.

Carboneras 31H3

El Rancho, ALP-711. **GPS**: n37,00371 w1,91127.
45 € 10 Ch WC € 3,50 included. **Location:** Rural.
Surface: sand. 01/01-31/12.
Distance: 2km 2,4km Mercadona 2km.

Casares 31E3

Carretera M528. **GPS**: n36,44611 w5,27833.
10 free Ch free. **Location:** Rural.
Surface: gravel/metalled. 01/01-31/12.
Distance: 1,5km 1,5km 1km.
Remarks: Max. 48h.

Castell de Ferro 31F3

2 carretera de Malaga. **GPS**: n36,72005 w3,36465.
60 € 10 Ch included. **Location:** Urban.
Surface: unpaved.
01/01-31/12.
Distance: sea 1,5km 700m 300m.

Tourist information Castell de Ferro:
Coastal town with former Arab fortress in the centre.
Week market. Sa.

Chipiona 31D2

Autocaravanas Puerto de Chipiona, Av. Rocío Jurado, s/n..
GPS: n36,74404 w6,42635.
63 € 12,50 € 3 Ch € 0,50 WC. **Surface:** gravel/sand.
01/01-31/12.
Distance: on the spot on the spot 300m 800m on the spot on the spot.

Conil de la Frontera 31D3

Avda. del Rio. **GPS**: n36,27282 w6,08994.

20 free. **Surface:** asphalted. 01/01-31/12.
Distance: on the spot 500m 500m.
Remarks: Parking along coast road.

Córdoba 31E1

Área del Centro Histórico, Avda. de los Custodios.
GPS: n37,87528 w4,78778.
30 € 11 Ch. **Surface:** asphalted/gravel. 01/01-31/12.
Distance: historical centre 300m 2,3km.
Remarks: In front of police station.

Tourist information Córdoba:
Museo Municipal Taurino, Plaza de las Bulas. Museum about bull-fighting. Tue-Fri 8.30-20.45h, Sa 8.30-16.30h, Su 8.30-14.30h Mo. € 4.
Torre de la Calahorra. Urban museum. 10-14, 16.30-20.30. € 4,50.
Oficina de Turismo, Torrijos, 10 (Plaza del Triunfo), www.cordoba-turismo.es. Historical and culturally rich city, city of the flamenco and bull-fighting.
Palacio del Marqués de Viana. Palace with collections of leather, silverware, porcelain etc. Mo-Sa 10-19h, Su 10-15h. € 8.
Mezquita. World-famous Moorish mosque. 10-18/19u.

Cuevas de San Marcos 31F2

GPS: n37,26059 w4,40237.

15 free free. **Location:** Rural, simple, isolated.
Surface: asphalted.
Distance: 1km 500m 1km.
Remarks: Parking at swimming pool.

Cullar 31G2

Venta de Peral. **GPS**: n37,55351 w2,60862.

20 free Ch WC free. **Location:** Motorway.
Surface: asphalted. 01/01-31/12.
Distance: 3km 250.
Remarks: Video surveillance.

Dólar 31G2

Area de Venta de Dólar, A92. **GPS**: n37,19521 w2,98397.

30 free Ch free. **Location:** Motorway, simple.
Surface: metalled. 01/01-31/12.
Distance: 2km 50m on the spot.
Remarks: At petrol station.

Doña Mencía 31F2

Area de Esparcimiento Dona Mencia. **GPS**: n37,54656 w4,35237.

7 free free. **Location:** Rural, comfortable, quiet.
Surface: gravel. 01/01-31/12.
Distance: 500m La Cantina on the spot.

Dos Hermanas 31D2

Multiparking La Jabega, Carretera SE 9024. **GPS**: n37,21278 w5,96389.

50 € 10 Ch € 3 WC included. **Surface:** concrete.
01/01-31/12.
Distance: city centre Sevilla 18km.
Remarks: Video surveillance.

Dos Hermanas 31D2

Rubiales, Calle Pasadilla de Barranco. **GPS**: n37,31030 w5,9584.
20 € 12 Ch included € 3.
Surface: gravel. 01/01-31/12.
Distance: Sevilla 10km > Sevilla 100m.

El Bosque 31D3

Calle de Juan Ramón Jiménez. **GPS**: n36,75670 w5,51056.

5 free Ch free. **Surface:** metalled. 01/01-31/12.
Distance: on the spot 100m 300m.

El Higuerón 31E1

Peter Pan, Avenida Principal. **GPS**: n37,87107 w4,85465.
10 € 6 Ch. **Surface:** concrete. 01/01-31/12.
Distance: Córdoba 7km 450m, Mercadona 2km line 54 > Córdoba.

El Puerto de Santa Maria 31D3

Parking Pasarela, Av. de Europa. **GPS**: n36,59840 w6,2212.

50 € 6. **Location:** Urban, simple. **Surface:** asphalted.
01/01-31/12.
Distance: 500m 200m Burgerking 300m 200m.

El Real de la Jara 31D1

Avenida Aguablanca. **GPS**: n37,95089 w6.
8 free Ch. **Surface:** asphalted. 01/01-31/12.
Distance: on the spot 300m.
Remarks: Max. 48h.

Frailes 31F2

Calle Mecedero. **GPS**: n37,48848 w3,8308.
10 free Ch. **Surface:** metalled. 01/01-31/12.
Distance: 500m 500m.
Remarks: Max. 48h.

Fuengirola 31E3

Calle Receinto Ferial. **GPS**: n36,54843 w4,61998.
+20 free. 01/01-31/12.
Distance: on the spot 300m 100m 100m.

Fuengirola 31E3

Ristorante El Rengo, Calle Tramo de Unión.
GPS: n36,53229 w4,63844.
15 € 4,50 Ch included € 5.
Surface: gravel/sand.
01/01-31/12.
Distance: 2,5km 1,6km on the spot Centro comercial 1km.

Gelves 31D2

Puerto Gelves, Calle de Puerto Gelves. **GPS**: n37,33934 w6,02405.

20 € 12-16 Ch € 2,80 WC.
Surface: asphalted. 01/01-31/12.
Distance: on the spot 4,3km on the spot on the spot on the spot.

ES

Remarks: Sevilla 10km, good bus connection.

Granada 31F2

Área de Geysepark-Cármenes, Torre de Comares.
GPS: n37,15136 w3,59533.

100 € 16/day ChService € 5 € 2/48h.
Location: Urban, simple. **Surface:** asphalted.
01/01-31/12.
Distance: 200m 2km 200m 200m 200m.
Remarks: Covered parking, entrance motorhomes 2nd ramp, max. ^3.10m, advice: pre-order entrance tickets Alhambra.

Granada 31F2

Alhambra, P5. **GPS**: n37,17168 w3,57974.

50 € 53/24h, 01/10-01/05 € 29/24h.
Location: Rural, simple. **Surface:** gravel.
01/01-31/12.
Distance: 1,5km 200m 200m 100m.

Tourist information Granada:

Alhambra. Most important curiosity of the city, the best kept Arab palace. 9-20h, winter, Sa 20-22h, Su 9-18h, summer Tue,Thu, Sa 22-24h.

Cuevas del Sacromonte. Caves in Sacromonte mountain, gypsies previously lived here. Now important tourist attraction and stage of flamenco shows.

El Albaicín. Moorish district facing the Alhambra.

Grazalema 31E3

Calle Juan de la Rosa. **GPS**: n36,75807 w5,36365.

4 free. **Surface:** asphalted. 01/01-31/12.
Distance: 300m 200m 500m.

Huelva 31C2

Monumento a Colón, Avenida Francesco Montenegro.
GPS: n37,21333 w6,93972.

15 free. **Surface:** asphalted. 01/01-31/12.
Distance: 6km 50m on the spot 6km 500m.

Huércal-Overa 31H2

Travesía de la Alameda. **GPS**: n37,39823 w1,94672.

10 free € 0,50/100liter Ch. **Location:** Urban, simple.
Surface: metalled. 01/01-31/12 Mo 09-14h, market.
Distance: 200m 200m 200m on the spot on the spot.
Remarks: Max. 72h, coins at El Pabellon Municipal.

Jerez de la Frontera 31D3

La Morada del Sur, Avda. Tío Pepe, 21. **GPS**: n36,71298 w6,10965.
20 € 15 Ch included WC. **Location:** Urban.
Surface: metalled. 01/01-31/12.
Distance: on the spot on the spot 1km.

Júzcar 31E3

Av. Havaral. **GPS**: n36,62823 w5,172.
4 free free. **Location:** Rural. **Surface:** grassy/metalled.
01/01-31/12.
Distance: 300m 400m 400m.

La Isleta 31H3

Playa del Pénom blanca, Carreta Noria. **GPS**: n36,81670 w2,05146.

15 free. **Location:** Rural, simple. **Surface:** gravel.
Distance: 100m sandy beach 20m 150m 300m.
Remarks: Parking at sea.

La Línea de Concepción 31D3

Av. Principe de Asturias. **GPS**: n36,15583 w5,34553.

50 € 1/h, € 15/24h. **Surface:** metalled. 01/01-31/12.
Distance: 500m 1km 200m 1km.
Remarks: Market Wednesday.

La Línea de Concepción 31D3

Area de Alcaidesa Marina, Av. Principe de Asturias.
GPS: n36,15528 w5,35389.
60 € 12 Ch included.
Surface: metalled. 01/01-31/12.
Distance: on the spot on the spot.
Remarks: Video surveillance.

Lora del Río 31E2

Calle Olivo 2. **GPS**: n37,65858 w5,51909.
20 free Chfree. **Surface:** asphalted. 01/01-31/12.
Distance: 700m 200m.
Remarks: Max. 48h, playground.

Málaga 31F3

Area Malaga Beach, Crta.MA-24 Diseminado R 10,44 entrada Cala del Moral. **GPS**: n36,71320 w4,31691.

90 € 10 Chincluded (46x)€ 3/24h WC € 3/stay € 1 free. **Surface:** grassy/gravel. 01/01-31/12.
Distance: on the spot 50m 50m on the spot 400m on the spot on the spot.
Remarks: 24/24 surveillance.

Tourist information Málaga:

Oficina de Turismo, Pasaje de Chinitas, 1, www.andalucia.org. Old sparkling port city with fine beaches.

Alcazaba. Moorish castle complex with archeological museum.

Museo casa natal de Pablo Picasso, Plaza de la Merced. House where the painter was born. Mo-Sa 10-20h Su-afternoon.

Palacio de los Condes de Buena Vista, Calle San Agustin, 6. Art-historical museum.
Su.

Marchena 31E2

Calle Sevilla s/n. **GPS**: n37,33083 w5,42416.
20 free Chfree. **Location:** Rural. **Surface:** metalled.
01/01-31/12.
Distance: 1km 450m 350m station 600m.

Montilla 31E2

Área de El Coto, Paseo de Cervantes, 8. **GPS**: n37,58763 w4,63432.
7 free Chfree. **Surface:** asphalted. 01/01-31/12.
Distance: 500m 450m.
Remarks: Max. 48h, no camping activities, beautiful view.

Olvera 31E2

Vía Verde de la Sierra. **GPS**: n36,94138 w5,25305.
4 € 7 Ch included. **Location:** Rural, isolated, quiet.
Surface: asphalted. 01/01-31/12.
Distance: 1km.

Palma del Río 31E2

Calle de la Bombilla s/n. **GPS**: n37,69222 w5,28361.
10 free Chfree. **Location:** Urban. **Surface:** unpaved.
01/01-31/12.
Distance: 500m.
Remarks: Max. 48h.

Peñarroya-Pueblonuevo 31E1

El Pantano. **GPS**: n38,27694 w5,27722.

20 € 7 ChService € 1,50 € 2 included.
Location: Comfortable, isolated, quiet.
01/01-31/12.
Distance: 4km lake on the spot on the spot on the spot.
Remarks: Direct access to the lake, motorhome washing place € 1, swimming pool.

Priego de Córdoba 31F2

Parque Niceto Alcalá - Zamora, Calle del Carrusel s/n.
GPS: n37,44361 w4,21186.

10 free Chfree. **Location:** Urban, simple.
Surface: concrete. 01/01-31/12.
Distance: 500m 500m 500m.

Tourist information Priego de Córdoba:

Iglesia de la Aurora.

Rute 31F2

Calle de Jésus Obrero. **GPS**: n37,33113 w4,37323.

ES

6 free Ch free. **Location:** Rural, simple.
Surface: asphalted.
Distance: 500m 500m 300m.
Remarks: Parking next to police station, max. 48h.

S San Juan de los Terreros 31H2

Playa de Entrevista, A332. **GPS**: n37,35083 w1,67972.

>20 free . **Surface:** gravel/sand. 01/01-31/12.
Distance: 500m 100m 2km 2,5km.
Remarks: Parking beach.

Sancti Petri La Barrosa 31D3

Carretera de la Barossa. **GPS**: n36,38612 w6,2053.

20 free. **Surface:** metalled. 01/01-31/12.
Distance: 2km 200m 1km 5km.
Remarks: Parking beach.

S Sanlúcar de Barrameda 31D2

Sanlúcar AC Parking, Camino de la Reyerta, s/n.
GPS: n36,76195 w6,39617.

58 01/07-30/09 € 12, 01/04-30/06 € 10, 01/10-31/03 € 8 Ch (30x)€ 3/day,5Amp WC € 3/3 included.
Surface: grassy. 01/01-31/12.
Distance: 4km 100m 100m 300m 350m 400m 500m.

S Sanlúcar de Guadiana 31C2

HU4401. **GPS**: n37,47009 w7,464.
15 free Ch. **Location:** Rural. **Surface:** metalled.
01/01-31/12.
Distance: 300m 600m 300m 500m on the spot on the spot.

S Sevilla 31D2

Area Ac Sevilla Centro, Carretera de la Esclusa, Seville (Sevilla).
GPS: n37,36239 w5,99452.

100 € 12 Ch (40x)€ 3 WC included.
Surface: asphalted.
01/01-31/12.
Distance: 200m 200m 300m on the spot 200m 200m.

S Sevilla 31D2

Parking Caravane, Calle Aeropuerto de San Pablo, Seville (Sevilla).
GPS: n37,41050 w5,94072.
50 € 12 Ch included € 3 € 1 .
Surface: unpaved. 01/01-31/12.
Distance: city centre 8km 2km.

S Sevilla 31D2

Parking Las Razas, Avenida de Las Razas, 41, Seville (Sevilla).
GPS: n37,36336 w5,98921.
30 € 10 Ch included € 5 . **Location:** Urban, central, noisy. **Surface:** asphalted. 01/01-31/12.
Distance: city centre 3km 100m.

P S Sevilla 31D2

Parking Puente de los Remedios, Avenida Presidente Adolfo Suarez, Seville (Sevilla). **GPS**: n37,37235 w5,99444.
+10 € 10 € 5. **Location:** Urban. **Surface:** asphalted.
01/01-31/12.
Distance: on the spot 300m 400m 400m.

P Sevilla 31D2

Parking Santa Justa, Avda. de Kansas City, Seville (Sevilla).
GPS: n37,39194 w5,97333.
30 € 22/24h. **Surface:** asphalted.
01/01-31/12.

Tourist information Seville (Sevilla):

Alcazar, Plaza del Triumfo.
Italica. Roman ruins, 9 km at north of Sevilla on N630.
Almeda de Hercules. Su-morning.
Parque de los Descubrimientos. Theme park science, in pavilion of Expo 1992. Fri-Su, summer Tue-Thu from 18h 10/01-28/02.
Calle de las Sierpes. Famous shopping street.

S Taberno 31H2

Área El Rancho, Los Llanos (La Carrasquilla), Santopetar.
GPS: n37,46028 w2,03833.

8 € 8 Ch (4x) WC included. **Location:** Rural, simple, quiet. **Surface:** gravel. Mo.
Distance: 600m 13km on the spot.
Remarks: Entrance swimming pool € 2.

S Tarifa 31D3

Área de Tarifa, El Lentiscal 29. **GPS**: n36,08776 w5,76566.
50 € 12 Ch included € 5/day . **Surface:** grassy.
01/01-31/12.
Distance: 500m 500m 150m.
Remarks: Video surveillance.

S Tarifa 31D3

Av. Pintor Guillermo Pérez Villalta. **GPS**: n36,01798 w5,61064.
40 € 8/24h Ch included. **Location:** Simple, central.
Surface: sand. 01/01-31/12.
Distance: 1km 300m 300m 200m.

Tarifa 31D3

GPS: n36,06804 w5,6856.

20 free. **Surface:** sand. 01/01-31/12.
Distance: 10km on the spot 50m 100m.
Remarks: Parking beach.

Tourist information Tarifa:

Tourist Office, Duke of Kent House, Cathedral Square, Gibraltar, www.gibraltar.gi. British colony at the northwest end of the Rock of Gibraltar.
Siege Tunnels, Gibraltar. Labyrinth of tunnels, ingenious defence system.

S Torre de Benagalbón 31F3

Camper Areas M&H El Rincón, Cortijo Casillas De Los Rubios.
GPS: n36,71658 w4,23799.

35 € 10, Jul/Aug € 12 Ch included € 3/24h WC € 1 € 7,50 € 1/24h. **Location:** Rural, comfortable, quiet.
Surface: gravel. 01/01-31/12.
Distance: 1km 3km 700m 100m 700m 750m.
Remarks: Car rental.

S Úbeda 31G1

Travesia Commendador Messias. **GPS**: n38,00649 w3,37953.
10 free Ch free. **Surface:** asphalted. 01/01-31/12.
Distance: centre 1km 1,8km 250m on the spot on the spot.
Remarks: Max. 48h.

S Ubrique 31D3

Calle La Harana 27, Plaza de las Palmeras. **GPS**: n36,67056 w5,44972.
10 free Ch free. **Location:** Urban. **Surface:** metalled/sand.
01/01-31/12.
Distance: centre 300m on the spot 400m.
Remarks: At swimming pool, max. 72h.

S Valverde del Camino 31C1

Ctra. de Zalamea. **GPS**: n37,58111 w6,75138.

10 free Ch free.
Surface: asphalted/sand. 01/01-31/12.
Distance: 500m.

S Vejer de la Frontera 31D3

Área El Palmar, Carril del pino. **GPS**: n36,23613 w6,06866.
100 <8m € 12/24h, >8m € 15/24h, trailer € 3 Ch € 3 WC . **Location:** Rural. **Surface:** unpaved.
01/01-31/12.
Distance: 500m 250m.

S Vélez-Rubio 31H2

Área Puerta Oriental de Andalucía, Calle Granada.
GPS: n37,65194 w2,07555.

10 free Chfree. **Location:** Rural, simple, quiet.
Surface: metalled. 01/01-31/12 1st week Aug.
Distance: 500m 2,2km 500m 500m.

S Vera 31H2

Acvera Motorhome Park & Aire, Camino de Los Pescadores s/n.
GPS: n37,26030 w1,85347.
160 € 9 Ch (160x)€ 2 WC included.
Location: Rural, comfortable.
Surface: metalled. 01/01-31/12.
Distance: Vera 2km 4,7km beach 10km on the spot.
Remarks: Tennis & padel lessons, 11 tennis courts.

S Vera 31H2

Oasis al Mar, Avenida del Salar. **GPS**: n37,22731 w1,82819.
50 € 10, trailer € 1/day Ch € 3/day € 3 included.
Location: Rural, comfortable. **Surface:** gravel.
01/11-01/05. **Distance:** centre Vera 4,4km 2km.
Remarks: Motorhome washing place € 4.

S Villanueva de Algaidas 31E2

Calle de la Archidona, A-7201. **GPS**: n37,17810 w4,45021.
20 free Chfree.
Location: Rural, simple. **Surface:** asphalted.
Distance: 500m 50m.
Remarks: Max. 48h.

ES

Finland

Capital: Helsinki
Government: parliamentary constitutional republic
Official Language: Finnish and Swedish
Population: 5,498,211 (2016)
Area: 336,855 km²

General information
Dialling code: 0358
General emergency: 112
Currency: Euro
Credit cards are accepted almost everywhere.

Regulations for overnight stays
Wild camping is in general allowed in the National Parks, on private land with permission of the owner.

Camping Key Europe is obligatory when using campsites: the card can be purchased at any campsite for € 16 (± £14), valid for one year.

Additional public holidays 2018
January 6 Epiphany
March 30 Good Friday
April 2 Easter Monday
May 1 Labour Day
June 22 Midsummer Eve
June 23 Midsummer
November 1 All Saints'Day
December 6 Independence Day

Time Zone
Winter (Standard Time) GMT+2
Summer (DST) GMT+3

Lapland
page: 347
Rovaniemi
Oulu
page: 347
Oulu
Eastern Finland
page: 346
Western Finland
pages: 345-346
Southern Finland
pages: 344-345
Helsinki

FI

Southern Finland

Hamina 4F2
Aallokko Caravan, Helsingintie. **GPS**: n60,56039 e27,18280.

20 € 10 + € 2,50/pp Chincluded € 3/24h freeh.
Location: Rural, simple, quiet. **Surface:** gravel.
01/04-31/10.
Distance: 1km on the spot on the spot 1km.
Remarks: Use of sauna against payment.

Helsinki 4F3
Mustikkanaantie / Blåbärslandsvägen. **GPS**: n60,18240 e24,99173.

10 free. **Location:** Rural, simple.
Surface: asphalted. 01/01-31/12.
Distance: 5,5km 1km on the spot on the spot on the spot 100m.

Imatra 4F2
ABC Imatra, Tiedonkatu 2. **GPS**: n61,18466 e28,73800.

20 € 5 Ch included at restaurant.
Location: Simple, noisy. **Surface:** asphalted. 01/01-31/12.
Distance: 3km on the spot on the spot on the spot.

Jyväskylä 4E2
Vespuolentie 674. **GPS**: n61,99235 e25,67093.
10 free.
Location: Rural, simple, quiet. **Surface:** asphalted.
01/01-31/12.
Distance: 10km on the spot on the spot.

Jyväskylä 4E2
Vespuolentie 674.
GPS: n61,99235 e25,67093.

10 free. **Location:** Rural, simple, quiet.
Surface: asphalted. 01/01-31/12.
Distance: 10km on the spot on the spot.

Karjaa 4E3
ABC Karjaa, Lepinpellonkatu 2. **GPS**: n60,05489 e23,64809.

4 € 5 Ch included WC free.
Location: Rural, simple. **Surface:** asphalted. 01/01-31/12.
Distance: 2km on the spot on the spot on the spot 10km.

Kortela 4E3
ABC Rauma Kortela, Unajantie 2. **GPS**: n61,09888 e21,50387.

10 € 5 Chincluded € 5/24h. **Location:** Motorway, simple, noisy. **Surface:** asphalted. 01/01-31/12.
Distance: 3,5km on the spot on the spot.

Lepaa 4E2
Kyläkauppa Pikkuakka, Tyrvännöntie 576.
GPS: n61,11587 e24,34537.

12 € 20 Ch WCincluded. **Location:** Rural, simple, quiet.
Surface: grassy. 01/01-31/12.

Distance: 7km 1km 1km on the spot on the spot.

Liikkala 4F2

Onnelan Tila, Hakalantie 37. **GPS**: n60,70986 e27,01708.

2 € 20 included. **Location:** Rural, simple, isolated, quiet.
Surface: grassy. 01/01-31/12.
Distance: 2km 2km.

Parikkala 4F2

Tukkikuja. **GPS**: n61,55592 e29,49803.

6 free € 10. **Location:** Urban, simple, quiet.
Surface: asphalted. 01/01-31/12.
Distance: 300m on the spot on the spot 300m 300m.
Remarks: At harbour.

Särkisalmi 4F2

Oronmyllyn Toimintakeskus, Oronmyllyntie 250.
GPS: n61,62059 e29,37868.

12 € 10 (4x)€ 10/24h WC. **Location:** Rural, simple, isolated, quiet. **Surface:** grassy. 01/01-31/12.
Distance: 7km 100m 100m.

Ylämaa 4F2

Korupirtti Oy Ravintola, Kikikylantie 7. **GPS**: n60,79054 e28,01026.

5 free € 1/time. **Location:** Rural, simple, quiet. **Surface:** gravel.
01/01-31/12.
Distance: 1km on the spot on the spot.
Remarks: At museum.

Western Finland

Björköby 4D2

Svedjehamn, Björköntie 1014. **GPS**: n63,35974 e21,29995.
15 € 4 WC included. **Location:** Rural, isolated, quiet.
Surface: unpaved. 01/05-31/10.
Distance: 3km on the spot on the spot on the spot.

Hanhikoski 4E2

Maatilamatkailu Koivusalo, Vanhatie 386.
GPS: n62,96175 e22,77427.

3 € 20 WC included. **Location:** Rural, simple, quiet.
Surface: grassy/gravel. 01/01-31/12.
Distance: 4km 200m.
Remarks: Sauna € 10.

Hattu 4G1

Arhipan Pirtti. **GPS**: n62,92948 e31,28065.
€ 14 € 4 WC.
Distance: 300m on the spot.

Huittinen 4E2

ABC Huittinen, Loimijoentie 89. **GPS**: n61,16713 e22,68061.

7 € 5 Ch included. **Location:** Urban, simple.
Surface: asphalted. 01/01-31/12.
Distance: 1km 1km on the spot on the spot.

Ikaalinen 4E2

Ikaalisten Kylpylä Rantasipi, Hämyläntie 2.
GPS: n61,77586 e23,01928.

20 € 12 included WC. **Location:** Rural, simple, quiet.
Surface: asphalted. 01/01-31/12.
Distance: 3km on the spot on the spot on the spot.

Ilmarinen 4E3

Ilmaristen Matkailutila, Väänteläntie 45.
GPS: n60,49801 e22,37492.

6 € 15 (4x)€ 5/24h WC € 2 included.
Location: Rural, simple, quiet. **Surface:** gravel.
01/01-31/12.
Distance: 2km 2km 1,5km 700m.

Kangasala 4E2

Mobilan Auto Kylä, Kustaa Kolmannen tie 75.
GPS: n61,44124 e24,12997.

5 free. **Location:** Rural, simple, quiet.
Surface: asphalted. 01/01-31/12.
Distance: 6km 100m 100m.
Remarks: At museum.

Keitele 4E1

Matkailukeskus Lossisaari, Sininentie 205.
GPS: n63,18941 e26,34270.

5 € 23 Ch WC included at restaurant.
Location: Rural, comfortable, quiet.
Surface: grassy/gravel. 01/01-31/12.
Distance: 1,5km on the spot on the spot on the spot 1,5km.
Remarks: Behind petrol station, bread-service.

Killinkoski 4E2

Killinkosken Kyläyhdistys, Inkantie 60. **GPS**: n62,40382 e23,89105.

5 free free. **Location:** Rural, simple, quiet.
Surface: grassy. 01/01-31/12.
Distance: on the spot on the spot 400m.

Lempäälä 4E2

Kärppälän Rustholli, Kärppäläntie 50. **GPS**: n61,33448 e23,67716.

8 € 25 WC included. **Location:** Rural.
Surface: grassy. 01/01-31/12.
Distance: 6km 100m 100m.

Mieto 4E2

Hakunin kotieläintila, Hakunintie 193.
GPS: n62,57169 e22,26394.

2 € 10 included. **Location:** Rural, simple, isolated, quiet. **Surface:** grassy/gravel. 01/01-31/12.
Distance: 2km.
Remarks: Sauna € 10.

Nokia 4E2

ABC Nokia Kolmenkulma, Rounionkatu 140.
GPS: n61,50143 e23,56800.

FI

10 € 5 Chincluded (10x)€ 5/24h
Location: Motorway, simple, noisy. **Surface:** asphalted.
01/01-31/12.
Distance: 2km on the spot on the spot on the spot.

Pyhäjärvi 4E1

Vaskikello Klokkenmuseum, Vaskikellontie 420.
GPS: n63,71402 e25,91985.

5 free free WC. **Location:** Motorway, simple, quiet.
Surface: asphalted.
Distance: 4km on the spot 200m.

Tuuri 4E2

Kyläkaupan Onnela Karavaanarialue, Onnelantie 45.
GPS: n62,60595 e23,71426.

243 € 20 Ch € 5 WC included. **Location:** Rural, luxurious, quiet. **Surface:** asphalted. 01/01-31/12.
Distance: 300m 300m.
Remarks: Swimming pool and sauna on site.

Vaajakoski 4E2

ABC Vaajakoski, Vaajakoskentie 850. **GPS**: n62,22871 e25,90290.

10 € 5 Chincluded € 5/24h at restaurant
Location: Motorway, noisy. **Surface:** asphalted. 01/01-31/12.
Distance: on the spot on the spot on the spot.

Vaasa 4D2

ABC Kiitokaari Vaasa, Kiitokaari 2. **GPS**: n63,05239 e21,71773.

20 € 5 Chincluded € 5/24h at restaurant.
Location: Motorway, simple, noisy. **Surface:** asphalted.
01/01-31/12.
Distance: 8km on the spot on the spot on the spot.

Viitasaari 4E1

ABC Viitasaari, Kokkosalmentie 78. **GPS**: n63,07527 e25,86618.

4 € 10 Ch (4x)included. **Location:** Motorway, simple. **Surface:** asphalted. 01/01-31/12.
Distance: 1km on the spot on the spot on the spot on the spot on the spot.

Ylönkylä 4E3

Katiskanmäki, Särkisalontie 2. **GPS**: n60,16479 e22,99639.

30 € 6 + € 5/pp Ch€ 5 WC included.
Location: Rural, simple, quiet. **Surface:** gravel.
01/01-31/12.
Distance: 8km 5km 5km on the spot 8km.

Eastern Finland

Heinävesi 4F2

Heinäveden satama, Kermarannantie 48.
GPS: n62,43835 e28,63796.

4 € 10 included WC. **Location:** Rural, simple, quiet.
Surface: asphalted. 01/01-31/12.
Distance: 2km on the spot.

Iisalmi 4F1

Untamonkatu 6. **GPS**: n63,56465 e27,19025.

10 free. **Location:** Urban. **Surface:** asphalted. 01/01-31/12.
Distance: on the spot 800m 250m 250m.
Remarks: At gymnasium.

Iisalmi 4F1

Luuniemenkatu 11. **GPS**: n63,55102 e27,18841.

10 free. **Location:** Urban, simple, quiet. **Surface:** gravel.
01/01-31/12.

Distance: 2km 100m 100m 500m 500m.

Ilomantsi 4F1

Hyvinvointikeskus Toivonlahti, Henrikintie 4.
GPS: n62,67684 e30,91145.
12 € 10.
Distance: on the spot on the spot 200m.

Jongunjoki 4F1

Eräkeskus Wilderness Lodge Oy, Alakylä 15.
GPS: n63,52483 e30,03822.

5 € 8 + € 4/pp Chincluded € 4/24h.
Location: Rural, simple, isolated, quiet. **Surface:** grassy/sand.
01/01-31/12.
Distance: 3km on the spot on the spot on the spot on the spot.

Karhunpää 4F1

Laitalan Lomat, Laitalantie 85. **GPS**: n63,61440 e28,86089.

10 € 12 stay WC included.
Location: Rural, quiet. **Surface:** grassy/gravel.
Distance: 9km on the spot on the spot on the spot.
Remarks: Sauna € 10.

Lieksa 4F1

ABC Lieksa, Kalliokatu 8. **GPS**: n63,32240 e30,00854.
guests free Ch. **Surface:** asphalted.
01/01-31/12.
Distance: on the spot.

Rantasalmi 4F2

Hotelli Rinssi-Eversti, Ohitustie 5. **GPS**: n62,06390 e28,30890.

6 € 10 Chincluded (6x)€ 5/24h WCat restaurant at restaurant at restaurant. **Location:** Rural, simple, quiet.
Surface: asphalted. 01/01-31/12.
Distance: 300m 100m 100m on the spot 500m.
Remarks: Use of sauna against payment.

Sulkava 4F2

Alanteentie. **GPS**: n61,78528 e28,37769.

5 € 14 Ch WC included.
Location: Urban, quiet. **Surface:** asphalted. 01/01-31/12.
Distance: 500m on the spot on the spot 100m 500m.

FI

Oulu

Kontiomäki 4F1

Shell, Viitostie 2. **GPS**: n64,31988 e28,04344.
20 € 6 WC included . **Location:** Motorway.
Distance: on the spot.
Remarks: At petrol station.

Puolanka 3D3

Pororajan Majoitus, Pudasjärventie 1. **GPS**: n64,87494 e27,64344.
8 € 12 € 3 WC . **Surface:** asphalted. 01/01-31/12.
Distance: 1km 1km 1km on the spot.

Sanginkylä 4E1

Valkeisen virkistysalueella, Puolangantie 207.
GPS: n64,86477 e26,74733.
€ 10 € 2 .
Distance: on the spot on the spot.

Siikajoki 4E1

Ruokolahden lava, Limingantie 197, Paavola.
GPS: n64,61267 e25,23947.
8 free Ch € 5 WC € 15. **Location:** Rural.
Surface: gravel. 23/05-06/09.
Distance: 2km on the spot on the spot.
Remarks: Key at kiosk.

Ylivieska 4E1

Hotelli Käenpesä, Lintutie 1. **GPS**: n64,06782 e24,52621.
4 € 20 WC .
Distance: 800m on the spot.
Remarks: Check in at hotel.

Lapland

Anetjärvi 3D3

Aneen Loma, Anetjärventie 72A. **GPS**: n65,91851 e27,98786.
10 € 25 WC included. **Location:** Rural.
Distance: on the spot on the spot.
Remarks: At the beach, sauna incl..

Tanhua 3C2

Tanhuan Erämajat, Pessijoentie 2. **GPS**: n67,52802 e27,53691.
10 € 5 Ch WC . **Surface:** grassy.
Distance: 300m.
Remarks: Use of sauna against payment.

FI

France

Capital: Paris
Government: Unitary republic
Official Language: French
Population: 62,814,000 (2016)
Area: 551,500 km²

General information
Dialling code: 0033
General emergency: 112
Currency: Euro
Payments by credit card are accepted almost everywhere, however chip and pin systems are non-compatible with British cards and fuel for example can only be bought at supermarkets during opening hours.

Regulations for overnight stays
Wild camping is accepted almost everywhere throughout inland France. Special regulations for motor homes you can find on signs by entering the town. It is permitted to stopover at motorway services, be aware that toll roads often issue time-constrained tickets.

Additional public holidays 2018
March 30 Good Friday
May 1 Labor Day
May 8 Liberation Day
July 14 National Holiday
August 15 Assumption of the Virgin Mary
November 1 All Saints Day
November 11 Armistice Day 1918

Time Zone
Winter (Standard Time) GMT+1
Summer (DST) GMT+2

FR

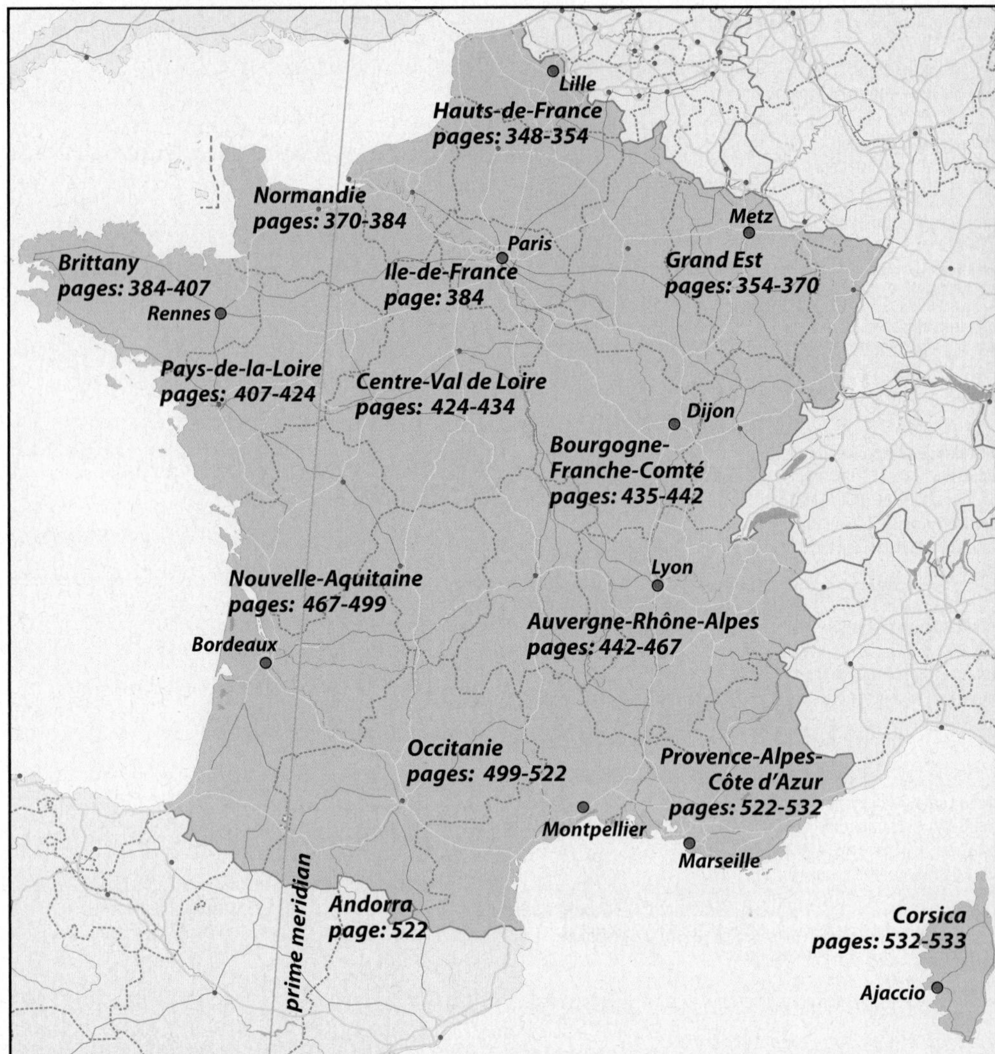

Hauts-de-France

Ambleteuse 13C2

D940 > Wimereux. **GPS**: n50,80638 e1,61484.

15 € 5. **Location:** Rural, simple, quiet. **Surface:** grassy.
01/01-29/12.
Distance: 750m 1,2km.

Amiens 15H1

Boulevard Faidherbe. **GPS**: n49,89430 e2,28675.
free. **Location:** Urban, central. **Surface:** asphalted.
01/01-31/12.
Distance: centre 800m 300m 300m.

Amiens 15H1

Parc Moulin Saint-Pierre, Rue Massey. **GPS**: n49,90001 e2,31072.
20 free.
Location: Central. **Surface:** asphalted. 01/01-31/12.
Distance: city centre 2km.

Amiens 15H1

Parc des Cygnes, 111, Avenue des Cygnes. **GPS**: n49,92086 e2,25971.
5 € 12,30 Ch included WC .
Surface: asphalted. 01/04-15/10.
Distance: city centre 5km 3km bus 50m.
Remarks: Max. 24h.

Tourist information Amiens:
Office de Tourisme, 23 Place Notre Dame, www.amiens-tourisme.com. Capital of the department Somme.
St.Leu. Picturesque district.
Musée Picardie, 48, rue de la République. Archeology, Middle Ages, Fine art. Tue-Su 10-12h, 14-18h.
Zoo d'Amiens, 101, rue du Faubourg de Hem. City-zoo. 10-17h, 01/04-30/09 10-18h 16/11-31/01.

Arques 13D2

Rue Michelet. **GPS**: n50,74551 e2,30459.

30 € 3,50 € 1,50 Ch € 1,50.
Location: Simple. **Surface:** gravel. 01/04-31/10.
Distance: 2km 100m.
Remarks: Behind camp site Beauséjour.

Arras 13D3

Rue des Rosati. **GPS**: n50,29463 e2,78812.

10 free € 2/100liter Ch € 2/h. **Surface:** asphalted.
01/01-31/12.
Distance: 700m 500m.
Remarks: Max. 48h.

Tourist information Arras:
Hôtel de Ville. Town hall in Gothic style. Also guided tours of the subterranean passages of Arras.
Wed, Sa.

Bailleul 13D2

Rue du collège. **GPS**: n50,74010 e2,73170.

20 free WC. **Surface:** asphalted. 01/01-31/12.
Distance: 700m 2,8km.
Remarks: At commemorative monument.

Banteux 11A3

Rue du port. **GPS**: n50,06259 e3,20106.

6 € 5 Ch (8x)included.

Location: Rural, simple, quiet. **Surface:** grassy/gravel.
01/01-31/12 service 01/11-31/03.
Distance: 500m 2,5km 20m on the spot on the spot.
Remarks: Baker every morning.

Bapaume 13D3

Avenue Abel Guidet. **GPS**: n50,10133 e2,85045.

2 free € 2 Ch WC. 01/01-31/12.
Distance: 300m 300m.
Remarks: Coins at tourist info, town hall and bakery.

Bavay 11B3

Chemin de Ronde. **GPS**: n50,30004 e3,79551.
10 free Ch free. **Surface:** gravel. 01/01-31/12.
Distance: 200m 200m 100m.
Remarks: Max. 72h.

Beautor 16A1

Rue du Port. **GPS**: n49,66083 e3,34927.

3 free € 2 Ch € 2/h WC. **Location:** Urban, simple.
Surface: asphalted. 01/01-31/12.
Distance: 500m 50m 200m.

Beauvais 15G2

Parking St. Quentin, Avenue Nelson Mandela.
GPS: n49,43160 e2,07038.

20 free WC. **Location:** Urban. **Surface:** asphalted.
01/01-31/12.
Distance: 1km 200m 100m.
Remarks: Max. 72h, video surveillance.

Bellicourt 11A3

Hameau de Riqueval, D1044. **GPS**: n49,95156 e3,23519.

2 free € 4 Ch € 4. **Location:** Rural, comfortable.
Surface: asphalted. 01/01-31/12 service: 01/10-31/03.
Distance: 300m on the spot on the spot.
Remarks: At museum, coins at tourist info.

Berck-sur-Mer 13C3

Les Sternes, Chemin aux Raisins. **GPS**: n50,39701 e1,56431.

80 € 10 Ch included. **Surface:** gravel. 01/01-31/12.
Distance: 1,5km 100m.
Remarks: Baker every morning.

Berck-sur-Mer 13C3

Parking Terminus, Rue Dr. Calot, Berck-Nord.
GPS: n50,42361 e1,56750.

40 € 10 Ch included. **Location:** Simple. **Surface:** gravel.
01/01-31/12.
Distance: beach 200m.
Remarks: Beach parking.

Berck-sur-Mer 13C3

Chez Mireille, Chemin Genty. **GPS**: n50,41654 e1,57696.

80 € 7 € 1 Ch (4x)€ 2 WC free.
Surface: grassy. 01/04-31/10.
Distance: 600m 800m on the spot.
Remarks: To be paid at bar.

Tourist information Berck-sur-Mer:
Bagatelle, CD 940. Amusement park. Easter-Sep 10.30-18.30h.

Bergues 13D2

Rue Maurice Cornette. **GPS**: n50,96543 e2,43596.

50 free.
Location: Simple, quiet. **Surface:** gravel. 01/01-31/12.
Distance: 500m 2,2km.
Remarks: Behind football ground, max. 48h.

Bertry 11A3

Rue Victor Hugo. **GPS**: n50,09092 e3,44829.

3 free Ch. **Location:** Rural, simple, noisy. **Surface:** gravel.
01/01-31/12.
Distance: on the spot 500m 700m.

Remarks: At station, max. 72h.

Blérancourt 16A1

Avenue de la Libération. **GPS**: n49,51285 e3,14996.

6 free Ch free. **Location:** Rural, simple, quiet.
Surface: gravel. 01/01-31/12.
Distance: 500m 750m.

Boulogne-sur-Mer 13C2

Parking Moulin Wibert, Boulevard Sainte Beuve, D940.
GPS: n50,74308 e1,59688.

40 first 48h € 7, € 9/24h € 4/10minutes Ch.
Surface: metalled. 01/01-31/12.
Distance: centre 2,5km 5,5km on the spot on the spot.

Boulogne-sur-Mer 13C2

Boulevard Chanzy. **GPS**: n50,72194 e1,60027.

free. **Location:** Simple. **Surface:** asphalted.
Distance: 500m 4,5km 300m 300m.
Remarks: Nearby casino.

Tourist information Boulogne-sur-Mer:
Boulevard Clocheville. Wed-morning.
place Dalton, centre. Wed + Sa morning.
place Vignon. Su-morning.

Bourseville 13C3

Lotissement le Village. **GPS**: n50,10350 e1,52702.

35 € 5 € 2 Ch € 3 WC. **Location:** Isolated, quiet.
Surface: asphalted. 01/01-31/12.
Distance: 500m 3km 500m 500m.

Boussois 11B3

Rue du Rivage. **GPS**: n50,28845 e4,04544.

FR

4 free free 2h. **Location:** Rural, simple. **Surface:** gravel.
01/01-31/12.
Distance: 1km 50m 50m 500m on the spot.
Remarks: Along Sambre River.

S Bray-Dunes 13D2

Carrefour Market Bray Dunes, Rue Pierre Decock.
GPS: n51,06275 e2,52162.

6 free € 2/10minutes Ch € 2/h WC.
Location: Simple, noisy. **Surface:** grasstiles.
01/01-31/12.
Distance: on the spot.
Remarks: At supermarket Carrefour, only overnight stays 20-8.30h.

Bruyères-et-Montberault 16A1

Avenue de Verdun. **GPS**: n49,52538 e3,66080.

4 free. **Location:** Urban, simple. **Surface:** asphalted.
01/01-31/12.
Distance: 100m 100m 200m.

S Calais 13C2

Flot Bleu Park, Rue d'Asfeld. **GPS**: n50,95961 e1,83277.

100 € 10/24h € 2 Ch. **Surface:** asphalted. 01/01-31/12.
Distance: 1,5km.

S Calais 13C2

Quai Edmond Pagniez. **GPS**: n50,96050 e1,84466.

100 free, 01/04-31/10 € 7/24h Ch included.
Location: Simple, noisy. **Surface:** asphalted. 01/01-31/12.
Distance: 300m 350m.
Remarks: Service: Digue Gaston Berthe.

Tourist information Calais:
Centre d'Information Eurotunnel. Exhibition about the Channel tunnel.
Wed, Thu, Sa.

S Cassel 13D2

Route d'Oxelaere, C301. **GPS**: n50,79328 e2,48852.

5 free € 2 Ch € 2. **Location:** Isolated, quiet.
Surface: gravel. 01/01-31/12.
Distance: 1km.
Remarks: At sports park, coins at tourist info.

S Catillon-sur-Sambre 11A3

Avenue de la Groise, N43. **GPS**: n50,07624 e3,64615.

4 € 5 Ch included.
Surface: asphalted. 01/01-31/12.
Distance: 200m on the spot.
Remarks: At the canal, max. 72h.

Catillon-sur-Sambre 11A3

Rue de la Gare. **GPS**: n50,07699 e3,64404.

20 free. **Location:** Simple. **Surface:** gravel. 01/01-31/12.
Distance: 500m on the spot.
Remarks: At the canal, baker every morning.

S Cayeux-sur-Mer 13C3

Aire de camping-cars Les Galets de la Mollière, Rue Faidherbe.
GPS: n50,20300 e1,52612.

30 € 8, 01/11-31/03 gratis € 3 Ch € 3 .
Surface: gravel. 01/05-01/11 service 01/11-31/03.
Distance: 2km At the sea, no beach 2km 2km.
Remarks: Max. 24h, to be paid at campsite.

Cayeux-sur-Mer 13C3

Route blanche, Le Hourdel, D102. **GPS**: n50,21448 e1,55208.

30 free. **Location:** Simple, isolated, quiet. **Surface:** gravel.
01/01-31/12.
Distance: 500m, Cayeux 6km sea 50m 500m 3km.

S Château-Thierry 16A2

Aire de Château, Avenue d'Essômes. **GPS**: n49,03657 e3,38365.

13 € 7,50 + € 0,22/pp tourist tax Ch € 4/24h WC included . **Location:** Urban, comfortable. **Surface:** asphalted.
01/01-31/12.
Distance: city centre 2km on the spot on the spot on the spot on the spot on the spot on the spot.
Remarks: Along the Marne river.

S Chavignon 16A1

Le domaine de ZAZA, La Fontaine Dubois.
GPS: n49,47941 e3,53396.

5 € 6 Ch included € 3/48h. **Location:** Simple.
Surface: gravel. 01/01-31/12.
Distance: 2km 2km on the spot.
Remarks: Check in at museum.

S Comines 11A2

Ferme Hélicicole, Chemin de l'Apothicaire. **GPS**: n50,74190 e3,02322.

6 € 5 € 2/10minutes Ch € 3/24h.
Surface: gravel. 01/01-31/12.
Distance: 3,5km on the spot on the spot.
Remarks: Max. 48h.

S Conty 15G1

Rue du Marais. **GPS**: n49,74333 e2,15583.

70 free € 3/100liter Ch WC .
Surface: grassy. 01/01-31/12.
Distance: 200m 6,5km 300m 300m 300m.
Remarks: Coins at tourist info, town hall and bakery.

S Coucy-le-Château-Auffrique 16A1

Chemin du Val Serain. **GPS**: n49,52037 e3,31150.

6 € 5 Ch WC included. **Location:** Rural, comfortable.
Surface: gravel. 01/01-31/12.

Distance: 500m on the spot 500m.
Remarks: Castle 1km.

S Crespin 11B3

Rue du Vivier. **GPS**: n50,41950 e3,66274.

3 free € 2 Ch € 2. **Location:** Urban, simple.
Surface: asphalted. 01/01-31/12.
Distance: 2km.
Remarks: At cemetery, coins at town hall.

S Doullens 13D3

Rue du Pont à l'Avoine, N25-Arras-Amiens. **GPS**: n50,15390 e2,34260.

4 free € 2 Ch. **Surface:** asphalted. 01/01-31/12.

S Embry 13C2

Les Salons de l'Embryenne, D108. **GPS**: n50,49534 e1,96610.

8 € 7 € 3 Ch € 3/1h WC € 3/12minutes
Location: Isolated, quiet. **Surface:** gravel.
01/01-31/12.
Remarks: Bread-service, video surveillance, picnic and barbecue place.

S Enquin-les-Mines 13D2

La Ferme des Templiers de Flechinelle, 2 Rue des Templiers, Fléchinelle. **GPS**: n50,58175 e2,30505.
4 € 7 € 2 Ch included. **Surface:** gravel.
01/01-31/12.
Distance: on the spot.

S Equihen-Plage 13C2

Plage de la Crevasse, Rue du Beurre Fondu.
GPS: n50,67993 e1,56830.

20 € 8 € 3/10minutes Ch (6x)€ 3/4h
Location: Comfortable, quiet. **Surface:** grassy/gravel.
01/01-31/12.
Distance: 100m 100m 100m 100m.

Esquelbecq 13D2

Parking de la Chenaie, Rue d'Arneke. **GPS**: n50,88395 e2,43119.
free. **Surface:** asphalted.
Distance: 200m 200m.

S Estaires 13D2

Rue Aimé Coupet. **GPS**: n50,64273 e2,72009.

3 free € 2/10minutes Ch € 2/1h (3x)€ 4/12h.
Surface: grasstiles. 01/01-31/12.
Distance: 200m 150m.
Remarks: Cash payment.

S Fort Mahon Plage 13C3

Plage Parking de la Dune, Rue de la Bistouille.
GPS: n50,33833 e1,55611.

60 € 10 Ch WC free.
Surface: gravel. 01/01-31/12.
Distance: 200m 600m 200m.

S Grand-Fort-Philippe 13D2

Rue Maréchal Foch. **GPS**: n51,00249 e2,09718.
free Ch.
Location: Rural. **Surface:** gravel. 01/01-31/12.
Distance: 200m 400m.
Remarks: In front of campsite, max. 72h.

S Grandvilliers 15G1

Place de la Censé. **GPS**: n49,66536 e1,93576.
3 free Ch WC free. **Surface:** asphalted. 01/01-31/12.
Distance: 100m 100m 400m.

S Gravelines 13D2

Parking des Miaules, Rue des Islandais/Rue du Port.
GPS: n50,98766 e2,12232.

20 € 7 **Location:** Rural, simple, quiet. **Surface:** gravel.
01/01-31/12.
Distance: 500m on the spot 300m.

S Gravelines 13D2

Rue de la Gendarmerie. **GPS**: n50,99342 e2,13177.
€ 2/100liter Ch.

Hardelot 13C2

Place R.L. Peeters. **GPS**: n50,63500 e1,59888.

15 free. **Location:** Simple. **Surface:** asphalted. 01/01-31/12.
Distance: 1,7km.

S Hautmont 11B3

Yacht Club Hautmont, Boulevard de l'Ecluse.
GPS: n50,25114 e3,91599.

5 € 7 Ch WC included. **Location:** Urban, comfortable, quiet. **Surface:** grassy. 01/01-31/12.
Distance: 600m 2km on the spot 600m 600m 200m on the spot.
Remarks: Along Sambre River, check in at harbourmaster, caution key € 20.

S Hondschoote 13D2

Impasse Spinnewyn. **GPS**: n50,97628 e2,58033.

8 free € 2/100liter Ch € 2/1h.
Location: Simple. **Surface:** asphalted.
Distance: 800m 800m 800m 300m on the spot on the spot.
Remarks: Behind Moulin de la Victoire, coins available, addresses indicated on the spot.

La Chapelle-Monthodon 16A2

Rue du Chemin de Chézy. **GPS**: n49,02904 e3,63616.

5 free. **Location:** Rural, simple, isolated, quiet.
Surface: grassy/metalled. 01/01-31/12.

Landrecies 11B3

Avenue Dumey. **GPS**: n50,12772 e3,69085.

4 free. **Location:** Rural, simple. **Surface:** asphalted/grassy.
01/01-31/12.
Distance: 500m on the spot 200m 100m.
Remarks: At the canal.

Laôn 16A1

Promenade de la Couloire. **GPS**: n49,56313 e3,62967.

6 free. **Location:** Urban, simple. **Surface:** asphalted.
01/01-31/12.
Distance: 300m 500m.

FR

Remarks: Near city wall.

Laôn — 16A1

Rue du Maréchal Alphonse Juin. **GPS**: n49,55665 e3,61411.

6 free. **Location:** Urban, simple. **Surface:** asphalted.
01/01-31/12.
Distance: 2km on the spot.
Remarks: Medieval village.

Le Crotoy — 13C3

Camping-Car Park le Tarteron, Route de Rue.
GPS: n50,22972 e1,64128.

25 € 8,80 Ch (4x) included.
Location: Noisy. **Surface:** gravel. 01/01-31/12.
Distance: 2km 2km 2km.
Remarks: Mandatory, one-time fee Pass'Etapes € 4.

Le Crotoy — 13C3

Aire Camping-car, Bassin des Chasses. **GPS**: n50,21800 e1,63300.

100 € 7 € 2/100liter Ch € 2/1h.
Surface: sand. 01/01-31/12.
Distance: 5 min walking 15 min walking Laverie Crotelloise, 20, avenue du Gal de Gaulle.

Le Crotoy — 13C3

Aire du Marais, Chemin du Marais. **GPS**: n50,22855 e1,61222.

35 € 7/24h € 2/10minutes Ch € 2/1h.
Surface: grassy/gravel. 01/01-31/12.
Distance: 1,5km on the spot 1,5km Laverie Crotelloise, 20, avenue du Gal de Gaulle on the spot on the spot.
Remarks: Max. 24h.

Le Nouvion-en-Thiérache — 11B3

Allée du S/I François d'Orléans. **GPS**: n50,00542 e3,78078.

5 free € 3 Ch € 3/h. **Location:** Rural, simple.
Surface: asphalted. 01/01-31/12.
Distance: 2km on the spot on the spot 1km on the spot on the spot.
Remarks: Max. 72h, coins at campsite.

Le Portel — 13C2

Rue des Champs. **GPS**: n50,71188 e1,57485.

40 € 3, 01/06-30/09 € 4 € 2/10minutes Ch € 2/4h .
Surface: metalled. 01/01-31/12.
Distance: 200m 300m 300m 300m.
Remarks: Next to sports fields, 300m from beach (stairs), friday market.

Le Touquet-Paris Plage — 13C2

Parc International de la Canoke, Boulevard de la Canche.
GPS: n50,52648 e1,59869.

200 € 10/24h € 2/100liter Ch € 2/55minutes.
Surface: grassy/gravel. 01/01-31/12.
Distance: on the spot on the spot on the spot on the spot on the spot.

Le Touquet-Paris Plage — 13C2

Centre Nautique du Touquet Base Nord, Avenue Jean Ruet.
GPS: n50,53588 e1,59285.

60 € 15/24h € 2/100liter Ch € 2/55minutes.
Surface: asphalted. 01/01-31/12.
Distance: on the spot on the spot on the spot on the spot on the spot.

Tourist information Le Touquet-Paris Plage:
Aqualud. Leisure pool park. 15/02-30/11 10-18h.

Le-Cateau-Cambrésis — 11A3

Avenue du Maréchal Leclerc, N43. **GPS**: n50,10197 e3,55491.

5 free Ch (4x)free. **Location:** Urban, simple, noisy.
Surface: asphalted. 01/01-31/12.
Distance: 1km 250m.

Lens — 13D3

Stade Bollaert-Delelis P6, Rue Maurice Fréchet.
GPS: n50,43192 e2,82057.

6 € 3 Ch included . **Location:** Simple.
Surface: asphalted. 01/01-31/12.
Distance: 500m on the spot 1km on the spot.
Remarks: Max. 24h.

Long — 13C3

Camping Municipal La Peupleraie, Rue de la Chasse à Vaches.
GPS: n50,03457 e1,98313.

8 € 5 € 2/150liter Ch € 2/h WC .
Surface: grassy/gravel. 01/01-31/12 service: 16/10-30/04.
Distance: on the spot on the spot.

Longfossé — 13C2

Ferme du Louvet, 5, Route de Wierre, D52 Desvres > Samer.
GPS: n50,64667 e1,79062.

8 € 14 Ch included. **Location:** Rural, isolated, quiet.
Surface: gravel. 01/01-31/12.
Remarks: Narrow entrance.

Longpont — 16A2

Rue Saint-Louis, D17. **GPS**: n49,27395 e3,22129.

3 free.
Location: Rural, simple. **Surface:** gravel. 01/01-31/12.
Distance: 100m.
Remarks: Max. 3 days, abbey 150m.

Luzoir — 16B1

Triperie de Luzoir, Place de l'Église. **GPS**: n49,92520 e3,96261.

2 free.
Location: Urban, simple. **Surface:** grassy. 01/01-31/12.
Distance: 100m 8km Axe vert.
Remarks: At cemetery, max. 48h.

Maisnil-lès-Ruitz 13D3

Parc d'Olhain, Rue de Rebreuve. **GPS**: n50,43926 e2,57826.

25 € 11,50 Ch included. **Location:** Comfortable, isolated, quiet. **Surface:** gravel. 01/01-31/12.
Remarks: Recreation park.

Malzy 16B1

Étangs des Sources, 16 rue des Marichoux.
GPS: n49,90602 e3,72153.

4 € 5 € 2 € 2 Ch € 2 € 2 WC free.
Location: Rural, comfortable, isolated, quiet. **Surface:** gravel.
15/03-01/11 Tue, Wed, Thu.
Distance: 8km on the spot 800m on the spot.
Remarks: Fishing lake (trout).

Marck 13C2

La Ferme des Aigrettes, Allée de la Découverte.
GPS: n50,95626 e1,92830.

5 € 8 Ch included. **Location:** Comfortable, quiet.
Surface: asphalted. 01/01-31/12.
Distance: 250m on the spot.
Remarks: Max. 48h, call for entrance code.

Marcoing 11A3

Place de la Gare. **GPS**: n50,12126 e3,18204.

6 free Ch (4x). **Location:** Rural, simple.
Surface: asphalted. 01/01-31/12.
Distance: 1km 1km.

Merlimont 13C3

Place de la Gare. **GPS**: n50,46026 e1,58053.

12 free Ch free.
Location: Simple. **Surface:** gravel. 01/01-31/12.
Distance: on the spot.

Mers-les-Bains 13C3

Chemin de la Petite Allée. **GPS**: n50,06175 e1,40150.

50 € 7,50 € 2 Ch included. **Location:** Comfortable.
Surface: gravel. 01/01-31/12.
Distance: 1,3km sandy beach 1,5km Auchan 600m.

Montreuil-sur-Mer 13C3

Avenue des Garennes. **GPS**: n50,45944 e1,75939.

8 free € 2/100liter Ch (2x)€ 2 WC free.
Location: Comfortable. **Surface:** asphalted. 01/01-31/12.
Distance: 500m 300m 450m on the spot on the spot.
Remarks: Max. 48h, market Saturday.

Morienval 15H2

Route de Pierrefonds 32. **GPS**: n49,30352 e2,92309.

25 € 8 € 2/100liter Ch (21x)€ 2/day.
Location: Rural, comfortable, quiet. **Surface:** grassy/gravel.
05/04-15/11.
Distance: 500m 500m 500m on the spot on the spot.
Remarks: In case of absence, money in an envelope in mail box.

Neuilly-Saint-Front 16A2

Chemin de la Chantraine. **GPS**: n49,16713 e3,26003.

20 free € 3 Ch € 3/55minutes. **Location:** Rural, simple.
Surface: grassy.
Distance: 600m.

Nuncq-Hautecôte 13D3

La Pommeraie, 13, route nationale. **GPS**: n50,30516 e2,29375.

5 € 5 € 2 Ch € 5 free. **Location:** Rural, comfortable, quiet. **Surface:** gravel. 01/01-31/12.
Distance: 50m.

Remarks: Covered pool € 3.

Oye-plage 13D2

Route du Pont d'Oye. **GPS**: n50,97703 e2,03915.
5 free € 2 Ch.
Location: Urban. **Surface:** metalled. 01/01-31/12.
Distance: on the spot 3km 200m 500m.
Remarks: At cemetery.

Picquigny 13D3

Rue de la Cavée d'Airaines. **GPS**: n49,94388 e2,13496.

20 € 5 Ch € 2 WC included.
Location: Rural. **Surface:** grassy.
Distance: 500m 500m on the spot.

Quend 13C3

Ferme de la Grande Retz. **GPS**: n50,32893 e1,61811.

10 € 8 Ch € 4 included.
Surface: grassy. 01/01-31/12.
Distance: 3km 9km 9km 2km.

Quend-plage-les-Pins 13C3

Plage des Pins. **GPS**: n50,32410 e1,55545.

50 € 7/24h € 2/10minutes Ch € 2/1h.
Surface: gravel. 01/01-31/12.
Distance: 800m beach 900m on the spot on the spot.

Richebourg 13D2

Rue de la Briqueterie. **GPS**: n50,58028 e2,74639.

6 free € 2/100liter € 2/55minutes included.
Location: Rural, comfortable. **Surface:** grassy. 01/01-31/12.
Distance: 500m on the spot on the spot.
Remarks: Max. 48h.

Rozoy-sur-Serre 16B1

Portes de la Thiérache, Rue de la Praille.
GPS: n49,71367 e4,12202.

FR

5 free € 2/120liter Ch . **Location:** Rural, comfortable, quiet. **Surface:** gravel. 01/01-31/12.
Distance: 1km 1km on the spot on the spot.

S Saint-Omer 13D2

De Haut Pont, Rue de la Gaieté. **GPS**: n50,75654 e2,25943.

13 € 5 € 2 Ch **Location:** Simple, noisy.
Surface: asphalted/gravel. 01/01-31/12.
Distance: 900m 900m.
Remarks: Max. 72h.

S Saint-Simon 21D3

Rue du Puits. **GPS**: n45,65289 w0,08517.

6 free € 2,50/100liter Ch € 2,50/10minutes .
Location: Rural, simple, quiet. **Surface:** asphalted.
01/01-31/12.
Distance: 1km.

S Saint-Valery-sur-Somme 13C3

Rue de la Croix l'Abbé. **GPS**: n50,18220 e1,62881.

180 € 10 Chincluded. **Location:** Rural.
Surface: gravel. 01/01-31/12.
Distance: 1km on the spot on the spot.
Remarks: Market on Sunday.

Stella-plage 13C3

Cours des Champs Elysées. **GPS**: n50,47470 e1,57726.

20 free. **Location:** Rural, simple, isolated. **Surface:** asphalted.
01/01-31/12.
Distance: 1km on the spot 650m on the spot on the spot.
Remarks: Parking at dune.

S Tardinghen 13C2

Le site des 2 caps, La Ferme d'Horloge, 1615 Route d'Ausques, D249.
GPS: n50,86250 e1,64890.

30 € 6/24h € 4 Ch € 4/24h .
Location: Comfortable, isolated, quiet. **Surface:** metalled.
01/01-31/12.
Distance: 1,6km.
Remarks: Swin-golf € 5.

Tardinghen 13C2

Le site des 2 caps, Le Fond de Sombre, Hervelinghen > Wissant.
GPS: n50,89361 e1,68972.

10 € 6/24h. **Location:** Simple, isolated, quiet. **Surface:** grassy.
01/01-31/12.
Distance: 1km.

S Tergnier 16A1

Base de loisirs de La Frette, Rue de la Prairie.
GPS: n49,64891 e3,31200.

20 € 0,50, 01/05-30/09 € 10 € 3/100liter Ch € 3/30minutes € 3. **Location:** Rural, comfortable. **Surface:** gravel.
01/01-31/12.
Distance: 1,5km on the spot on the spot on the spot.

S Villers-Côtterets 16A2

Rue Alfred Juneaux. **GPS**: n49,26052 e3,08713.

6 free € 3 Ch € 3/h . **Location:** Urban, simple, comfortable, quiet. **Surface:** asphalted. 01/01-31/12.
Distance: on the spot 600m 600m.
Remarks: Max. 72h, service 50m.

S Watten 13D2

3 Rue Paul Mortier. **GPS**: n50,83101 e2,20887.

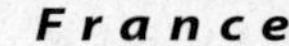

3 free € 4 Ch € 4/55minutes.
Location: Simple, quiet. **Surface:** metalled.
01/01-31/12.
Distance: 500m 500m 500m on the spot.
Remarks: Coins at tourist info, supermarket, tabac-press and cafe.

S Wissant 13C2

Parking Wissant, Avenue Georges Clémenceau.
GPS: n50,88684 e1,67064.

15 free Chfree. **Surface:** metalled. 01/01-31/12.
Distance: 700m 1,1km.
Remarks: Max. 48h, bread-service.

Grand Est

S Aix-en-Othe 19B1

Aire du Moulin à Tan. **GPS**: n48,22901 e3,72500.

10 € 7 Ch € 2,50 WC included € 3,50/1,50.
Location: Urban, comfortable, central. **Surface:** grassy.
01/04-15/10.
Distance: 1km 1km 1,5km 1km 1km.

S Allarmont 19F1

Le Meix du Haut Regard, 21, rue du Haut Regard.
GPS: n48,48070 e7,01381.

2 € 5 included Ch € 5/24h € 4 free.
Location: Simple. **Surface:** gravel. 01/01-31/12.
Distance: 400m 400m 400m.
Remarks: Steep ramp.

S Amnéville 16E2

Rue de l'Europe. **GPS**: n49,24780 e6,13842.

10 € 9-12 Ch included. **Location:** Rural, simple, quiet.
Surface: grassy. 01/01-31/12.
Distance: 1,8km.
Remarks: Max. 48h, pay at tourist office.

Ancerville 16C3

Impasse des Pransons. **GPS**: n48,63641 e5,01582.

FR

2 free. **Location:** Urban, simple, quiet. **Surface:** grasstiles.
01/01-31/12.
Distance: on the spot 400m 400m.

Arc-en-Barrois 19C2

Camping municipal, D3/D159. **GPS:** n47,95056 e5,00528.

25 € 5 Ch WC included,on camp site. **Location:** Simple.
Surface: gravel. 01/01-31/12 Whitsuntide.
Distance: 500m 500m 500m.

Avioth 16D1

Rue de l'Hôpital. **GPS:** n49,56561 e5,39067.

2 free.
Location: Simple, central, quiet. 01/01-31/12.
Distance: on the spot on the spot on the spot.

Avize 16B3

Place du Bourg Joli. **GPS:** n48,97175 e4,00999.

5 free Ch free. **Location:** Urban, simple, central, quiet.
Surface: asphalted. 01/01-31/12.
Distance: on the spot 200m bakery 50m.
Remarks: Next to town hall.

Avocourt 16D2

Restaurant La Terrasse, Rue du Moulin. **GPS:** n49,20417 e5,14227.

4 free.
Location: Rural, simple. **Surface:** grassy. 01/01-31/12.
Distance: on the spot on the spot.

Azannes-et-Soumazannes 16D2

Les Vieux Métiers, Domaine des Roises. **GPS:** n49,31096 e5,47714.

2 free. **Location:** Rural, simple, isolated, quiet. **Surface:** gravel.
01/01-31/12.
Remarks: At museum.

Baccarat 19F1

Place du General Le'Clerc. **GPS:** n48,44667 e6,74000.

15 € 4 Ch € 2/3minutes WC. **Location:** Simple.
Surface: asphalted. 01/01-31/12 Fri-morning market.
Distance: 300m on the spot on the spot 300m 300m.
Remarks: Along river, max. 24h.

Tourist information Baccarat:
Musée du Cristal. Crystal museum. Mo-Sa 10-18h.

Bar-le-Duc 16D3

Halte du port Fluvial, Rue du Débarcadère.
GPS: n48,77536 e5,16654.

7 free € 2,10/100liter Ch € 2,10/55minutes.
Location: Urban, simple, noisy.
Surface: asphalted.
01/01-31/12.
Distance: on the spot 150m 150m 150m on the spot.
Remarks: At the canal, coins at tourist info, 7 rue Jeanne d'Arc.

Bar-sur-Aube 19C1

7, Rue des Varennes. **GPS:** n48,23451 e4,70115.

2 free € 3,50/100liter Ch € 3,50/1h.
Location: Urban, simple. **Surface:** asphalted. 01/01-31/12.
Distance: 300m 500m 500m on the spot on the spot.
Remarks: Coins at tourist info.

Beaulieu-en-Argonne 16C2

Parking Mairie, Grande Rue, D2B. **GPS:** n49,03183 e5,06665.

6 free. **Location:** Urban, simple, central, quiet. **Surface:** grassy.
01/01-31/12.
Distance: on the spot 50m on the spot on the spot.
Remarks: In front of town hall.

Beaulieu-en-Argonne 16C2

Parking St. Rouin, D2. **GPS:** n49,03554 e5,02975.

4 free.
Location: Rural, simple, isolated. **Surface:** grassy/gravel.
Distance: Beaulieu 6km.
Remarks: Isolated parking.

Beaunay 16B3

Ferme Du Bel Air, Rue Principale. **GPS:** n48,88177 e3,87475.

12 € 8 Ch (6x)included. **Location:** Rural, simple, isolated, quiet. **Surface:** gravel. 01/01-31/12.
Distance: 2km 2km 2km.

Benfeld 19G1

Concessionnaire CLC Alsace, 9, Rue de Hollande, RN83 dir Strasbourg-Colmar. **GPS:** n48,37772 e7,59778.

5 free Ch free. **Location:** Motorway, simple, noisy.
Surface: asphalted. 01/01-31/12.
Distance: 2km 2km 2km.
Remarks: At motorhome dealer.

Biesheim 19G1

Camping-Car Park Ile du Rhin, Ile du Rhin. **GPS:** n48,02964 e7,56937.
20 € 7 + € 1,50/pp tourist tax Ch (20x)included,6Amp.
Surface: asphalted. 01/01-31/12.
Distance: centre 2,5km 2km.

Bitche 16G2

La Citadelle, Rue Bombelles. **GPS:** n49,05431 e7,43446.
5 free € 2 Ch € 2. **Location:** Comfortable, isolated, quiet.
Surface: asphalted. 01/01-31/12.
Distance: 750m 750m 750m.

Bogny-sur-Meuse 16C1

Rue de la Meuse. **GPS:** n49,85780 e4,74225.

6 free € 2/100liter Ch € 2/2h,only 2-euro coins.
Location: Rural, simple, quiet. **Surface:** asphalted. 01/01-31/12.
Distance: on the spot on the spot 250m 400m 500m on the spot on the spot.
Remarks: Along the Meuse river, service 75m.

FR

Bonzée 16D2

Parking de la Base de Loisirs du Colvert, D21.
GPS: n49,09806 e5,61551.

6 € 6,20 € 4 Ch **Location:** Rural, comfortable, isolated, quiet. **Surface:** gravel. 01/01-31/12.
Distance: 1km on the spot on the spot.

Bourbach-le-Haut 19F2

Route Joffre. **GPS**: n47,79463 e7,02868.

10 € 6 Ch included. **Location:** Rural, simple, quiet.
Surface: asphalted. 15/03-15/11.
Distance: 50m 100m 5km.
Remarks: In front of fire-station.

Brienne-le-Château 19C1

Rue de la Gare. **GPS**: n48,39617 e4,53130.

5 free € 3/10minutes Ch € 3/55minutes.
Location: Urban, simple, noisy. **Surface:** asphalted.
01/01-31/12 water disconnected in winter.
Distance: 300m 400m 300m.
Remarks: At former station, coins at tourist info, supermarket Champion.

Bruley 16E3

D118, rue Saint-Martin. **GPS**: n48,70640 e5,85554.

10 free € 3/10minutes Ch (2x)€ 3/8h.
Location: Comfortable, quiet. **Surface:** gravel. 01/01-31/12.
Distance: 200m 300m 300m.
Remarks: Max. 48h.

Bulgnéville 19E1

Étang des Récollets, Rue des Récollets.
GPS: n48,20733 e5,83899.

10 € 3/24h Ch WC included. **Location:** Rural, luxurious, quiet.
Surface: asphalted. 15/04-31/12.
Distance: 700m 1,8km on the spot on the spot 100m 700m.

Cerisières 19C1

D186, Froideau. **GPS**: n48,29921 e5,06339.

20 free Ch free. **Location:** Rural, simple, isolated, quiet.
Surface: gravel. 01/01-31/12.
Distance: 2km.

Certilleux 19D1

Rue de l'Église. **GPS**: n48,31193 e5,72679.

8 free free. **Location:** Urban, simple. **Surface:** asphalted.
01/01-31/12.
Distance: on the spot.
Remarks: Beautiful view.

Chamery 16B2

Salle Polyvalente, Rue du Château Rouge.
GPS: n49,17475 e3,95446.

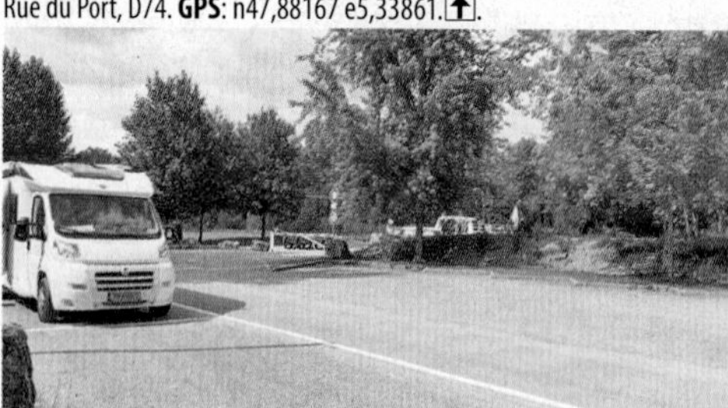

3 free € 2/100liter Ch € 2/2h. **Location:** Rural, simple, quiet. **Surface:** gravel. 01/01-31/12.
Distance: 300m 400m.
Remarks: In front of community centre, max. 48h.

Champigny-lès-Langres 19D2

Rue du Port, D74. **GPS**: n47,88167 e5,33861.

5 free WC. **Location:** Simple, noisy. **Surface:** gravel.
01/01-31/12.
Distance: 400m 800m.

Champougny 16D3

D145f. **GPS**: n48,54410 e5,69277.

3 free. **Location:** Rural, simple, quiet. **Surface:** grassy.
01/01-31/12.
Distance: 200m 25m.

Chaource 19B1

Chemin de Ronde/Rue des Roises. **GPS**: n48,05944 e4,13861.

10 € 2 € 2/100liter Ch € 2/1h.
Location: Comfortable, quiet. **Surface:** grassy.
01/01-31/12.
Distance: 100m on the spot on the spot on the spot on the spot.
Remarks: Coins at tourist info, 2, Grande rue, monday-morning market.

Charleville-Mézières 16C1

Rue des Pâquis. **GPS**: n49,78056 e4,72056.

8 free € 2/100liter Ch € 2/55minutes € 5,40 free.
Surface: asphalted.
01/01-31/12 electricity: 01/11-31/03.
Distance: 800m on the spot 500m 2km 600m on the spot on the spot.
Remarks: Service only with 2-euro coins, ask for electricity at campsite.

Tourist information Charleville-Mézières:

- Musée Ardennes, Place Ducale. Regional museum. 10-12, 14-18 Mo.
- place Ducale. Regional products. Tue, Thu, Sa.

Charmes 19E1

Port de Plaisance. **GPS**: n48,37334 e6,29542.

80 € 7 included Ch (80x)€ 2 WC € 1,50 € 3/day.
Location: Urban, central. **Surface:** grassy/metalled.
01/01-31/12.
Distance: 1km 1,5km on the spot on the spot.

Tourist information Charmes:

Fri-morning.

Châtenois 19G1

Allee des Bains 10. **GPS**: n48,27476 e7,39853.

7 free € 2 Ch WC free.
Location: Urban, simple, quiet. **Surface:** asphalted/grassy.
01/04-15/11.
Distance: 400m 250m.
Remarks: Max. 24h.

FR

Chaumont 19D1

Port de la Maladière, RN74 Neufchâteau > Chaumont.
GPS: n48,11815 e5,15437.

12 € 6,95, tourist tax € 0,20/pp Ch WC € 2,40 € 2,35/3,35 included. **Location:** Quiet. **Surface:** metalled.
02/04-31/10.
Distance: 4km Canal de la Marne 100m nearby.
Remarks: Baker every morning.

Chavanges 16C3

Ruelle du Fief Berthaux. **GPS**: n48,50691 e4,57627.

8 free € 3 Ch. **Location:** Simple, quiet.
Surface: asphalted/gravel. 01/01-31/12.
Distance: 300m 400m.
Remarks: Coins at the shops.

Chavannes-sur-l'Etang 19F2

Aire pique-nique La Porte d'Alsace, RD419, Rue d'Alsace.
GPS: n47,63325 e7,01858.

15 € 8 Ch WC included. **Location:** Rural, comfortable, quiet. **Surface:** asphalted. 01/01-31/12.
Distance: 900m on the spot 900m 1km on the spot on the spot.
Remarks: Parking picnic area.

Colmar 19G1

Port de Plaisance de Colmar, 6 rue du Canal.
GPS: n48,08054 e7,37599.

25 € 11-15 + € 0,22/pp tourist tax Ch WC € 3/2 included. **Location:** Rural, comfortable, quiet.
Surface: asphalted/grassy. 01/01-31/12.
Distance: 1,3km 200m on the spot on the spot on the spot.
Remarks: Baker 8.30-09.00.

Colmar 19G1

Rue de la Cavalerie. **GPS**: n48,08218 e7,35990.
20 € 3/h. **Location:** Urban, simple, central, noisy.
Surface: asphalted.
Distance: 200m on the spot on the spot on the spot.
Remarks: Max. 4h.

Colmar 19G1

Rue Henry Wilhelm. **GPS**: n48,08366 e7,35527.
16 € 3/h. **Location:** Urban, simple, central.
Surface: asphalted. 01/01-31/12.
Distance: 400m 400m 400m.
Remarks: Max. 4h.

Colombey-les-deux-Eglises 19C1

Rue de Général de Gaulle. **GPS**: n48,22316 e4,88619.

10 free Ch WC free. **Location:** Simple, quiet.
Surface: asphalted/gravel. 01/01-31/12.
Distance: on the spot 50m 50m.
Remarks: Museum and Memorial Général De Gaulle 800m.

Commercy 16D3

Parking de la Boîte à Madeleines, Rue de la Louvière.
GPS: n48,75378 e5,59928.

3 free Ch free. **Location:** Comfortable, isolated, quiet.
Surface: asphalted. 01/01-31/12.
Distance: 1km on the spot on the spot.

Commercy 16D3

Rue du Docteur Boyer. **GPS**: n48,76374 e5,59616.

4 free € 3/15minutes Ch (4x)€ 3/4h free.
Location: Urban, comfortable, central, quiet. **Surface:** asphalted.
01/01-31/12.
Distance: 800m on the spot on the spot 600m 100m on the spot on the spot.
Remarks: On the canal.

Consenvoye 16D2

Gr la Grande Rue. **GPS**: n49,28547 e5,28403.

5 free free.
Location: Urban, simple, quiet. **Surface:** asphalted.
Distance: 100m on the spot 50m.

Contrisson 16C3

Ballastière. **GPS**: n48,80530 e4,94714.

10 free WC. **Location:** Rural, simple, isolated, quiet.
Surface: grassy/sand. 01/01-31/12.
Distance: 800m on the spot on the spot 1km 1km.
Remarks: At small lake.

Corgirnon 19D2

Allée du Parc. **GPS**: n47,80681 e5,50308.

8 € 5 Ch included.
Location: Rural, comfortable, isolated, quiet. **Surface:** gravel.
01/01-31/12 water disconnected in winter.
Distance: 500m 10km 500m, baker on site (Tue-Su).
Remarks: Bread-service.

Damvillers 16D2

Rue de l'Isle d'Envie, D905. **GPS**: n49,33790 e5,39752.

3 free € 2/100liter Ch € 2/60minutes.
Location: Urban, simple, central, noisy. **Surface:** asphalted.
01/01-31/12.
Distance: on the spot on the spot on the spot on the spot on the spot 400m.
Remarks: Max. 6,5m.

Damvillers 16D2

Etang, D905. **GPS**: n49,34978 e5,39970.

10 free. **Location:** Rural, simple, isolated, quiet. **Surface:** grassy.
01/01-31/12.
Distance: Damvillers 1km on the spot 500m 700m.

Darney 19E1

Route de Vittel 6. **GPS**: n48,09395 e6,04324.
€ 12/24h € 2 Ch € 2/4h WC. **Location:** Urban.
Surface: asphalted. 01/01-31/12.
Distance: on the spot.
Remarks: Picnic tables available.

Dienville 19C1

Parking Autobus, Rue de Dienville. **GPS**: n48,34735 e4,52779.

FR

6 free. **Location:** Urban, simple, isolated, quiet. **Surface:** asphalted. 01/01-31/12.
Distance: 700m 300m 300m on the spot.

Dieue-sur-Meuse 16D2

Port de plaisance, Route des Dames. **GPS**: n49,07110 e5,42634.

15 free Chfree. **Location:** Rural, simple, quiet.
Surface: grassy. 01/01-31/12.
Distance: 200m on the spot 200m 200m.
Remarks: At the canal.

Dolancourt 19C1

Nigloland, RN19. **GPS**: n48,26086 e4,60945.

28 € 6/24h, free with a meal Ch included.
Location: Simple, isolated. **Surface:** asphalted. 03/04-03/11.
Distance: on the spot.
Remarks: Parking amusement park, max. 24h.

Dommartin-lès-Remiremont 19F2

Place de l'Église. **GPS**: n47,99959 e6,64401.

8 free € 3/10minutes Ch € 3/h.
Location: Simple, quiet. **Surface:** asphalted.
Distance: on the spot 200m.

Donjeux 19D1

Halte Nautique, D67a. **GPS**: n48,36586 e5,14891.

4 free Ch (4x)free. **Location:** Comfortable, quiet.
Surface: gravel/metalled. 01/01-31/12.
Distance: 1km Canal de la Marne on the spot 1km 800m on the spot.
Remarks: Baker every morning.

Dun-sur-Meuse 16D2

Rue du Vieux Port. **GPS**: n49,38919 e5,17787.

16 € 7 Ch WC included.
Location: Rural, comfortable, central, quiet. **Surface:** gravel.
01/01-31/12 sanitary building: 01/11-01/04.
Distance: 600m on the spot on the spot 400m 600m.

Eguisheim 19G1

Bannwarth, Rue de Bruxelles 3. **GPS**: n48,04456 e7,30478.

8 free Ch WCfree. **Location:** Urban, comfortable, central, quiet. **Surface:** metalled. 01/01-31/12.
Distance: 100m 100m on the spot on the spot.
Remarks: Sale of wines.

Épernay 16B2

Rue Dom Pérignon. **GPS**: n49,03602 e3,95130.

3 free € 2/100liter Ch € 2/1h WC € 0,50.
Location: Urban, simple, central, noisy.
Surface: asphalted.
01/01-31/12.
Distance: within walking distance Avenue Jean Jaurès.
Remarks: Behind church St.Pierre-St.Paul, coins at tourist info.

Tourist information Épernay:
Cave de Catellane, 154, avenue de Verdun.
Mercier, 70, avenue de Champagne. Mo-Sa 9.30-11.30h, 14-16.30h, Su/holidays 9.30-11.30h, 14-17.30h.

Épinal 19E1

Camping-Car Park, Chemin du Petit Chaperon Rouge.
GPS: n48,17969 e6,46865.

50 € 10,70 Ch (20x) included.
Location: Comfortable, quiet. 01/01-31/12.
Distance: 1,5km.
Remarks: Mandatory, one-time fee Pass'Etapes € 4.

Épinal 19E1

Port d'Épinal, Quai de Dogneville, D12. **GPS**: n48,18671 e6,44493.

5 summer € 5,50, winter € 8,50 Ch Service € 3/15min.
Surface: asphalted.
Distance: 1km 3,5km on the spot.
Remarks: Max. 48h.

Essoyes 19C1

Impasse de la Gare. **GPS**: n48,06067 e4,53444.

3 free € 2/10minutes Ch € 2/1h.
Location: Urban, comfortable, central, quiet. **Surface:** asphalted.
01/01-31/12.
Distance: 600m 600m 200m 300m 300m.
Remarks: Coins at tourist info.

Esternay 16A3

Place des Tilleuls, D48, Rue de la Paix. **GPS**: n48,73245 e3,55698.

8 free free.
Location: Urban, simple, central, quiet. **Surface:** gravel.
01/01-31/12 water: 15/11-15/03.
Distance: within walking distance 200m 400m.
Remarks: Behind church, Wifi code: wifi-la-champagne.

Etival-Clairefontaine 19F1

Rue du Vivier. **GPS**: n48,36355 e6,86504.

20 free Chfree. **Location:** Simple, quiet. **Surface:** gravel.
01/01-31/12 water disconnected in winter.
Distance: on the spot.
Remarks: Behind town hall.

Fains-Veel 16D3

Halte Fluviale, Rue du Stade. **GPS**: n48,79276 e5,12552.
6 free free.
Location: Simple, quiet. **Surface:** asphalted.
01/01-31/12.
Distance: 300m Canal on the spot 1,5km bakery 20m.

Favières 19E1

Base de Loisirs. **GPS**: n48,46660 e5,96124.

FR

8 free Ch WC. **Location:** Rural, comfortable, central, quiet. **Surface:** gravel/metalled.
Distance: 200m 13km on the spot on the spot on the spot bakery 300m on the spot on the spot.

S Fénétrange 16F3

Wally Services, Route de Sarre Union. **GPS:** n48,85365 e7,02723.
5 free € 2 Ch € 2. **Surface:** grassy/metalled.
Remarks: Max. 48h.

S Ferrette 19G3

Rue de Lucelle. **GPS:** n47,48882 e7,31118.

5 free € 2/10minutes Ch € 2/55minutes. **Location:** Rural, simple, isolated, quiet. **Surface:** asphalted.
Distance: 700m 700m 2km on the spot on the spot.

S Fessenheim 19G2

Allée de la Guyane. **GPS:** n47,91833 e7,53139.

40 free € 2 Ch € 2. **Location:** Rural, simple, quiet. **Surface:** asphalted/gravel. 01/01-31/12.
Distance: 700m 700m 200m on the spot on the spot.
Remarks: Coins available at swimming pool, supermarket.

S Forbach 16F2

Avenue Saint-Rémy. **GPS:** n49,18519 e6,89252.
5 free € 2/100liter Ch.
Surface: asphalted. 01/01-31/12.
Distance: 350m 200m.

S Fraize 19F1

Impasse de la Gare/ Place Jean Sonrel. **GPS:** n48,18188 e7,00360.

6 free € 3 Ch € 3 WC.
Surface: asphalted. 01/01-31/12.
Distance: 100m 100m 100m.
Remarks: Behind tourist info.

S Froncles 19D1

Halte Nautique. GPS: n48,29954 e5,15246.

10 € 3 € 3/day Ch (8x)€ 3/day € 2,50 € 3/3.
Location: Comfortable. **Surface:** gravel. 01/01-31/12.
Distance: 500m river-beach on the spot on the spot 1km on the spot.
Remarks: Baker on site (Tue-Su).

Fumay 11C3

Quai des Carmélites. **GPS:** n49,99736 e4,70986.

+10 free. **Surface:** unpaved. 01/01-31/12.
Distance: 400m.
Remarks: Along the Meuse river.

S Gérardmer 19F1

Chemin de la Rayée, La Mauselaine. **GPS:** n48,05846 e6,88862.

100 € 5,70/24h € 2/100liter Ch.
Surface: asphalted. 01/01-31/12.
Distance: Gérardmer 1,7km.
Remarks: Parking at skipistes.

S Gérardmer 19F1

Parking de la Prairie, Boulevard d' Alsace.
GPS: n48,07199 e6,87333.

100 € 6 € 2/100liter Ch WC. **Location:** Simple, central, noisy. **Surface:** asphalted/gravel. 01/01-31/12.
Distance: on the spot.
Remarks: Coins at tourist info.

Tourist information Gérardmer:
Thu, Sa.

S Giffaumont-Champaubert 16C3

Site de Chantecoq, Rue du Grand Der. **GPS:** n48,56809 e4,70096.

58 € 4 20-8h, parking free € 3,80/80liter Ch € 3,80/45minutes WC.
Location: Rural, simple. **Surface:** grassy.
01/01-31/12.
Distance: on the spot 900m.
Remarks: At lake Der de Chantecoq, coins at tourist info.

S Giffaumont-Champaubert 16C3

Station Nautique, P1, Rue du Port. **GPS:** n48,55358 e4,76434.

48 € 6 20-8h, parking free € 2,50/8minutes Ch € 2,50/45minutes included. **Location:** Rural, quiet.
01/01-31/12.
Distance: on the spot on the spot 200m 8km Montier-en-Der on the spot on the spot.

S Giffaumont-Champaubert 16C3

Station Nautique, P5, La Cachotte. **GPS:** n48,55071 e4,76829.

72 € 6 20-8h, parking free € 2,50/8minutes Ch € 2,50/45minutes. **Location:** Urban, comfortable, central, quiet. **Surface:** grassy. 01/01-31/12.
Distance: on the spot 650m 70m 1km on the spot on the spot.

Givet 11C3

Rue Jean Jaurès. **GPS:** n50,13593 e4,82138.

12 free. **Location:** Urban, simple, central, quiet. **Surface:** asphalted.
01/01-31/12.
Distance: on the spot on the spot on the spot on the spot on the spot on the spot.

S Givet 11C3

Camping Municipal, Rue Berthelot. **GPS:** n50,14291 e4,82611.

5 free € 3/100liter Ch € 3/h. **Location:** Rural, simple.
Surface: asphalted. 01/01-31/12.
Distance: 750m 750m 1km.
Remarks: Coins at campsite.

S Goncourt 19D1

Rue des Lottes, D74. **GPS:** n48,23685 e5,60998.

FR

30 € 3 € 3 Ch. **Location:** Rural, comfortable.
Surface: asphalted/gravel. 01/01-31/12.
Distance: 100m on the spot 100m 100m.
Remarks: Along the Meuse river, max. 48h, baker at 8am.

Gondrecourt-le-Château 16D3

Parking Musée du Cheval, Rue Saint Blaise.
GPS: n48,51390 e5,50975.

2 free. **Location:** Simple, quiet. **Surface:** gravel/metalled.
Distance: on the spot 50m 50m.

Gondrecourt-le-Château 16D3

Rue du Général Leclerc. **GPS**: n48,51373 e5,50386.

3 free Ch. **Location:** Urban. **Surface:** concrete.
01/01-31/12.
Distance: on the spot on the spot on the spot.
Remarks: Coins at town hall.

Guebwiller 19G2

Avenue Maréchal Foch. **GPS**: n47,90554 e7,21869.

20 free. **Location:** Urban, simple, central, noisy. **Surface:** gravel.
01/01-31/12.
Distance: 300m on the spot on the spot 300m 300m 300m on the spot 5km.

Haironville 16D3

GPS: n48,68438 e5,08586.

5 free € 2/10minutes Ch € 2/50minutes.
Location: Rural, simple, central, quiet.
Surface: gravel.
01/01-31/12.
Distance: 200m 200m.
Remarks: Coins at the shops in the village.

Harskirchen 16F3

Port de Plaisance, Rue de Bissert. **GPS**: n48,93930 e7,02759.
3 € 10 Ch included. **Surface:** gravel.
15/03-11/11.
Distance: on the spot.
Remarks: At canal Houillères de la Sarre, max. 24h.

Hartmannswiller 19G2

Grand Rue. **GPS**: n47,86311 e7,21494.

4 free Ch free. **Location:** Rural, simple, quiet.
Surface: asphalted. 01/01-31/12.
Distance: 200m.

Haybes 11C3

Halte Fluviale, Quai du Docteur Adolphe Hamai.
GPS: n50,01093 e4,70762.

4 free Ch € 2,05 € 3,30/3,30.
Surface: metalled. 01/01-31/12.
Distance: 200m 50m bakery 200m on the spot.
Remarks: Along the Meuse river, max. 2 nights, service at camping municipal.

Heiligenstein 19G1

Lieu-dit Lindel, D35. **GPS**: n48,42780 e7,45147.

3 free.
Location: Rural, simple. **Surface:** gravel. 01/01-31/12.
Distance: 800m 300m 500m on the spot.
Remarks: Hiking trails and wine tasting.

Heudicourt sous les Côtes 16D3

Entrée 2, D133. **GPS**: n48,94035 e5,71741.

50 € 5 € 3 Ch € 4 WC. **Location:** Rural, simple, quiet. **Surface:** grassy. 01/04-31/10.
Distance: 3km 100m 100m on the spot 200m.
Remarks: Next to campsite.

Heudicourt sous les Côtes 16D3

Ste Nautique de Madine. **GPS**: n48,93549 e5,71548.

60 € 12 Ch (20x) WC € 3/15minutes included.
Location: Rural, comfortable, quiet. **Surface:** grassy/gravel.
01/04-31/10.
Distance: 3km on the spot on the spot on the spot on the spot on the spot.
Remarks: Service passerby € 5, view on Lac de Madine.

Hirtzbach 19G2

Place de la Gare. **GPS**: n47,60061 e7,22542.

10 free Ch free. **Location:** Simple, quiet. **Surface:** asphalted.
01/01-31/12.
Distance: 300m 200m on the spot on the spot.

Hombourg-Haut 16F2

Rue des Suédois. **GPS**: n49,12448 e6,77888.

7 free € 2/100liter Ch € 2/4h.
Surface: asphalted. 01/01-31/12.
Distance: 400m 200m on the spot.
Remarks: Max. 48h.

Issoncourt 16D3

Parking Relais de la Voie Sacrée, Rue de la Voie Sacrée 1.
GPS: n48,97070 e5,28776.

6 free. **Location:** Rural, simple, quiet. **Surface:** gravel.
Distance: 50m on the spot.

Javernant 19B1

Le Cheminot, N77. **GPS**: n48,14789 e4,01046.

5 free. **Location:** Simple. **Surface:** asphalted. 01/01-31/12.

Joinville 19D1

Halte Nautique, Rue des Jardins. **GPS**: n48,44583 e5,15000.

FR

16 free € 2/10minutes Ch € 2/55minutes.
Location: Simple, quiet. **Surface:** gravel/metalled.
01/01-31/12.
Distance: 500m on the spot on the spot 800m 100m on the spot.

Juzennecourt 19C1

Place de la Mairie. **GPS**: n48,18429 e4,97890.

4 free Ch WC. **Location:** Simple, quiet. **Surface:** metalled.
15/04-15/11.
Distance: on the spot bakery in the village on the spot.
Remarks: Parking townhall.

Kaysersberg 19G1

Aire Camping-car P1, Place de l'Erlenbad.
GPS: n48,13565 e7,26325.

80 € 8/24h ChWC included.
Location: Urban, simple, quiet. **Surface:** asphalted. 01/01-31/12.
Distance: 300m 300m 300m.
Remarks: Wifi at Office de Tourisme.

Tourist information Kaysersberg:
Musée Albert Schweitzer. The life of Albert Schweitzer.

Kilstett 16G3

Place de la Mairie, Rue du Lieut de Bettignies.
GPS: n48,67501 e7,85691.

7 free. **Location:** Urban, simple, quiet. **Surface:** asphalted.
01/01-31/12.
Distance: on the spot on the spot.

Kilstett 16G3

Rue de l'Industrie. **GPS**: n48,67914 e7,84178.
Ch.

La Bresse 19F2

Camping du Haut des Bluches, 5, route des Planches.
GPS: n47,99889 e6,91762.
17 € 11,80 Ch WCincluded € 3,80 € 5.
Location: Quiet. **Surface:** asphalted.
01/01-31/12 12/11-15/12.
Distance: 4km on camp site on the spot on the spot on the spot on the spot.
Remarks: Zone camping-car, bread-service.

La Bresse 19F2

Route de Niachamp. **GPS**: n47,99430 e6,85431.
€ 2/100liter Ch. 01/01-31/12.

La Cheppe 16C2

Champ d'Attila, Rue de Champo d'Attila. **GPS**: n49,04892 e4,49377.

4 free € 2/100liter Ch € 2/2h WC.
Location: Rural, simple, quiet. **Surface:** asphalted.
01/01-31/12.
Distance: 500m.

La Croix-sur-Meuse 16D3

Auberge de la Truite, Route de Seuzey. **GPS**: n48,98267 e5,53393.

4 € 3 (4x)€ 5/24h WC. **Location:** Rural, comfortable, quiet.
Surface: grassy. 01/01-31/12.
Distance: 2km on the spot on the spot.

La Gault-Soigny 16A3

Rue de la Liberté, D373. **GPS**: n48,81758 e3,59072.

8 free Chfree. **Location:** Rural, simple, quiet.
Surface: asphalted. 01/01-31/12.
Distance: on the spot.
Remarks: Near Salle des Fêtes, service 50m.

Lachaussée 16E2

Domaine du Vieux Moulin, Grande Rue. **GPS**: n49,03564 e5,81755.

4 free free. **Location:** Rural, simple, isolated. **Surface:** grassy.
01/01-31/12.
Distance: 100m 50m on the spot on the spot.
Remarks: Along Étang de Lachaussée, regional products.

Laheycourt 16C3

Rue de la Gare. **GPS**: n48,88903 e5,02165.

4 free. **Location:** Rural, simple, quiet. **Surface:** grassy.
01/01-31/12.
Distance: on the spot 50m 50m.
Remarks: Along the Chée river.

Langres 19D2

Place de Bel Air. **GPS**: n47,85885 e5,33225.

free WC. **Location:** Urban, simple, noisy. **Surface:** asphalted.
01/01-31/12.
Distance: on the spot on the spot.
Remarks: Video surveillance.

Langres 19D2

Ruelle de la Poterne. **GPS**: n47,85795 e5,32989.

6 free Chfree. **Location:** Simple, quiet. **Surface:** asphalted.
01/01-31/12.
Distance: 800m.
Remarks: Max. 24h.

Langres 19D2

Parking Sous-Bie, Allée des Marronniers. **GPS**: n47,86104 e5,33674.

20 free. **Location:** Simple, quiet. **Surface:** asphalted.
01/01-31/12.
Distance: on the spot on the spot.

FR

Remarks: Inclining pitches, video surveillance, free elevator to old town.

Tourist information Langres:
Fri.

Launois-sur-Vence 16C1

Avenue Louis Jolly. **GPS**: n49,65467 e4,54005.

10 free. **Location:** Rural, simple, quiet. **Surface:** unpaved.
01/01-31/12.
Distance: on the spot 50m.
Remarks: In front of tourist office, max. 48h.

S Launois-sur-Vence 16C1

Rue du Thin. **GPS**: n49,65810 e4,53987.
€ 2/100liter Ch € 2/1h. water: frost.
Distance: 150m.
Remarks: Coins at tourist info and restaurant.

Tourist information Launois-sur-Vence:
Relais de Poste. Monthly antiques and flea market. 3rd Su of the month 9-18h.

Le Bonhomme 19F1

Col du Bonhomme, D148, route des Crêtes.
GPS: n48,16495 e7,07971.

free. **Location:** Rural, simple, quiet. **Surface:** gravel.
01/01-31/12.
Distance: on the spot on the spot on the spot.

S Les Islettes 16C2

Route du Lochères. **GPS**: n49,12122 e5,03684.

16 € 7 Ch WC included. **Location:** Rural, comfortable, quiet. **Surface:** gravel. 01/01-31/12.
Distance: 3km 10,5km 3km 3km.

S Les Riceys 19B2

D452. **GPS**: n47,99222 e4,36458.

40 free € 2 Ch € 2 . **Location:** Simple, isolated, quiet.
Surface: asphalted. 01/01-31/12.
Distance: 500m 500m 500m.

Ligny-en-Barrois 16D3

Aire de Pilvetus, Chemin des Pains de Seigle.
GPS: n48,69262 e5,33621.

10 free. **Location:** Simple, isolated. **Surface:** gravel.
01/01-31/12.
Distance: 1,2km.

S Ligny-en-Barrois 16D3

Relais Nautique, Rue Jean Willemert. **GPS**: n48,68787 e5,31943.

12 € 2 + € 0,20/pp tourist tax € 2/10minutes Ch € 2/55minutes WC € 2 € 4 free. **Location:** Urban, comfortable, central, quiet. **Surface:** asphalted.
Distance: 200m on the spot 200m 200m on the spot on the spot.
Remarks: Along Canal de la Marne au Rhin, small pitches.

S Linthal 19F2

Rue du Markstein, D430. **GPS**: n47,94495 e7,12783.

4 free Ch free. **Location:** Simple, quiet.
Surface: asphalted. 01/01-31/12.
Distance: 200m on the spot 200m 200m on the spot.

Longeville-en-Barrois 16D3

Gr Grande Rue. **GPS**: n48,74201 e5,20645.

6 free. **Location:** Urban, simple, quiet. **Surface:** asphalted.
Distance: on the spot on the spot 100m 100m on the spot on the spot.
Remarks: Along the Ornain river.

S Longuyon 16D2

Parking Salvador Allende, N18. **GPS**: n49,44802 e5,59973.

2 free € 2 Ch € 2 WC .
Location: Urban, simple, central, noisy. **Surface:** asphalted.
Distance: on the spot on the spot 100m.
Remarks: Parking next to tourist info, not suitable for big motorhomes.

S Longwy 16D1

Stade Municipal, Avenue du 8 Mai 1945.
GPS: n49,52656 e5,76559.

7 free € 2,50/20minutes Ch € 2,50/4h.
Location: Urban, simple, central, noisy. **Surface:** asphalted.
01/01-31/12.
Distance: on the spot 400m 350m.
Remarks: At football ground.

S Lunéville 16F3

Les Bosquets, Quai des Petits Bosquets. **GPS**: n48,59652 e6,49865.

23 € 8 Ch included free.
Location: Comfortable, central, noisy. 01/01-31/12.
Distance: 700m 50m 600m 600m.

Tourist information Lunéville:
Château Petit Versailles. Castle, 18th century and museum.
10-12h, 14-18h Tue. € 8.

Lusigny-sur-Barse 19B1

Route du Lac. **GPS**: n48,26451 e4,29735.

10 free. **Location:** Rural. **Surface:** asphalted. 01/01-31/12.
Distance: 2,5km on the spot on the spot.
Remarks: At the lake, max 3,5t.

S Mailly-le-Camp 16B3

Rue Victor Hugo. **GPS**: n48,66820 e4,19494.
8 free Ch . **Location:** Urban. **Surface:** gravel.
01/01-31/12.
Distance: 400m.
Remarks: At tennis-courts.

Marbotte 16D3

Parking de la Mairie, Rue Principale, D12.
GPS: n48,83445 e5,58142.

2 free. **Location:** Simple, quiet. **Surface:** unpaved.
Distance: on the spot.

S Mareuil-sur-Ay 16B2

Relais nautique, Place Charles de Gaulle. **GPS**: n49,04522 e4,03490.

FR

8 free 150liter Ch 3h,Service € 5.
Location: Urban, comfortable, central, quiet. **Surface:** asphalted.
01/01-31/12 water disconnected in winter.
Distance: on the spot on the spot on the spot on the spot on the spot.
Remarks: On the canal, in village, coins at supermarket.

S Maxey-sur-Meuse 19D1

Sous la Voie, D19A. **GPS**: n48,44861 e5,69500.

4 free (4x)WC free. **Location:** Simple. **Surface:** gravel.
14/05-31/12.
Distance: 2km 2km 500m.

Maxey-sur-Vaise 16D3

Grande Rue. **GPS**: n48,53836 e5,66705.

6 free.
Location: Simple, central, quiet. 01/01-31/12.
Distance: on the spot.

Mesnil-Saint-Père 19B1

Rue du Lac. **GPS**: n48,25524 e4,34090.

50 free.
Location: Simple. **Surface:** asphalted. 01/01-31/12.
Distance: beach 400m.
Remarks: Nearby lake Orient.

S Metz 16E2

Allée Metz Plage. **GPS**: n49,12371 e6,16887.

8 free Ch free.
Surface: asphalted.
Distance: 350m 1,5km 300m.
Remarks: At entrance campsite, max. 48h, inclining pitches.
Tourist information Metz:

Place St Louis. Square surrounded by houses from the 14th century.
Cathédrale St Etienne. Cathedral.

S Millery 16E3

Avenue de la Moselle, D40. **GPS**: n48,81507 e6,12716.

5 free Ch free.
Surface: asphalted. 01/04-31/10 water: 01/11-31/03.
Distance: on the spot 3,5km.
Remarks: Along Mosel.

S Mirecourt 19E1

Place Thierry. **GPS**: n48,29945 e6,13591.

20 € 6 10minutes Ch 35minutes WC included.
Location: Comfortable, central. **Surface:** gravel.
01/01-31/12.
Distance: on the spot.

Mittelbergheim 19G1

Parking Zotzenberg, Rue Ziegelscheuer. **GPS**: n48,39869 e7,44194.

4 free. **Location:** Rural, simple, quiet. **Surface:** asphalted.
01/01-31/12.
Distance: 300m 3km 300m 300m on the spot.
Remarks: At cemetery, wine tasting.

S Monthermé 16C1

Rue du Général de Gaulle. **GPS**: n49,88136 e4,73015.
3 free € 3 Ch. **Location:** Rural. **Surface:** metalled.
01/01-31/12.
Distance: 750m.

S Monthermé 16C1

Etape fluviale, Quai A. Briand. **GPS**: n49,88608 e4,73593.

± 20 € 3 + € 0,20/pp tourist tax € 2,80/day € 1,50
€ 3,50/3,50. **Surface:** grasstiles. 01/01-31/12.
Distance: 300m.
Remarks: Along the Meuse river, check in at harbourmaster.

S Monthureux-sur Saône 19E1

D460. **GPS**: n48,03199 e5,97390.

8 free Ch WC free € 3/48h,Wifi-Stop.
Location: Comfortable, quiet. 01/01-31/12.
Distance: on the spot on the spot 200m 75m.
Remarks: At football ground.

S Montier-en-Der 19C1

Rue de l'Isle. **GPS**: n48,47861 e4,76861.

6 free € 2/8minutes Ch € 2,80/55minutes WC.
Location: Simple, central, noisy. **Surface:** gravel.
01/01-31/12.
Distance: on the spot 50m 500m 200m.
Remarks: Coins at tourist info.

Montigny-lès-Vaucouleurs 16D3

Rue de la Côte. **GPS**: n48,58875 e5,63007.

10 free. **Location:** Rural, simple, quiet. **Surface:** gravel.
01/01-31/12.
Distance: 200m 200m on the spot 100m.

Montplonne 16D3

Rue du Four. **GPS**: n48,68630 e5,16934.

4 free. **Location:** Rural, simple. **Surface:** gravel.
Distance: on the spot.
Remarks: Next to cemetery.

Morley 16D3

Parking Lavoir, D5A. **GPS**: n48,57848 e5,24878.

5 free.
Location: Rural, simple, central, quiet. **Surface:** grassy.
Distance: on the spot.

S Mouzon 16C1

Halte fluviale, Rue du Moulin Lavigne. **GPS**: n49,60689 e5,07695.

FR

8 € 8, 01/11-31/03 gratis Ch (6x) WC included.
Location: Comfortable, central, quiet. **Surface:** asphalted.
01/01-31/12 Service: winter.
Distance: 100m on the spot 300m on the spot on the spot.
Remarks: Along the Meuse river, sanitary and wifi code at harbour master, felt museum 100m (May-Sep).

S Munster 19F1

Aire de camping-cars Munster, Rue du Dr Heid.
GPS: n48,03779 e7,13471.

54 € 6 € 3 Ch € 3 WC € 1,50 included
Location: Rural, comfortable, quiet. **Surface:** gravel.
01/01-31/12.
Distance: on the spot on the spot on the spot on the spot.

S Murbach 19G2

Abbaye de Murbach, Rue de Guebwiller.
GPS: n47,92321 e7,16059.

20 free Ch free. **Location:** Rural, isolated, quiet.
Surface: gravel/metalled. 01/01-31/12.
Distance: 350m on the spot on the spot 5km on the spot 5km.

S Mutigny 16B2

Aire de l'étang, Route de Montflambert.
GPS: n49,06894 e4,02669.

8 free 150liter Ch 3h, Service € 5.
Location: Rural, simple, isolated, quiet. **Surface:** asphalted.
01/01-31/12.
Distance: 1km 3km 3km.

Nancy 16E3

Parking Faubourg Des III Maisons, Rue Charles Keller.
GPS: n48,70403 e6,17598.

10 € 4,50. **Location:** Central. **Surface:** asphalted.
01/01-31/12.
Distance: city centre ± 1km.

S Nancy 16E3

Port Saint Georges, N57, boulevard du 21ème Régiment d'Aviation.
GPS: n48,69221 e6,19318.

15 € 15,50 + € 1,50/pp Ch included WC.
Location: Central. **Surface:** asphalted.
01/05-01/11.
Distance: 500m on the spot on the spot 100m 100m 100m.
Remarks: Max. 5 nights, check in at harbourmaster.

Tourist information Nancy:
M Musée Historique Lorraine, Palais Ducal. Regional museum.
15/06-15/09 Tue.
Zoo Haye, Velaine-en-Haye. Zoo with centre for wild birds.

Nant-le-Grand 16D3

Grand Rue, D169A. **GPS:** n48,67530 e5,22382.

4 free.
Location: Rural, simple, quiet. **Surface:** grassy/gravel.
Distance: on the spot.

Neuf-Brisach 19G1

Place de la Porte de Bâle. **GPS:** n48,01688 e7,53187.

free. **Surface:** asphalted. 01/01-31/12.
Distance: 300m 300m 300m.

Tourist information Neuf-Brisach:
Point I Neuf-Brisach, 6, place d'Armes, www.tourisme-rhin.com/. City worth a visit with defences of Vauban.

S Niderviller 16F3

Marina Niderviller, Avenue de Lorraine. **GPS:** n48,71748 e7,09901.

12 € 12 € 2/stay Ch € 3/day WC.
Location: Simple, quiet. 01/03-30/10.
Distance: 200m.

S Nixéville-Blercourt 16D2

Rue de la Grand. **GPS:** n49,11118 e5,24007.

4 € 6 Ch included. **Location:** Rural, simple, quiet.
Surface: concrete.
Distance: 100m.

S Nogent-sur-Seine 16A3

Parking Camping/Piscine, Rue du Camping.
GPS: n48,50388 e3,50888.

5 € 6,58/night, € 2,99/3h Chfree (2x)included3h.
Location: Urban, simple, quiet. **Surface:** asphalted.
01/01-31/12.
Distance: 1,5km 2km 1,5km 1,5km 2km.
Remarks: Max. 48h.

S Nomexy 19E1

Rue de l'Estrey. **GPS:** n48,31131 e6,38535.
10 € 7/24h, tourist tax € 0,55/pp € 1 Ch € 2.
Surface: asphalted. 01/01-31/12.
Distance: on the spot 750m 800m on the spot.
Remarks: Max. 72h.

S Nonsard Lamarche 16D3

Base de Loisirs, Base de Loisirs de Madine.
GPS: n48,93064 e5,74873.

30 € 12 € 3/15minutes Ch € 3/15minutes.
Location: Rural, simple, comfortable, isolated, quiet.
Surface: grassy/metalled. 01/04-31/10.
Distance: 700m on the spot on the spot on the spot on the spot on the spot.
Remarks: At lake Madine, coins at campsite.

Nubécourt 16D2

D151, Rue Raymond Poincaré. **GPS:** n48,99704 e5,17256.

FR

8 free. **Location:** Rural, simple, central, quiet. **Surface:** gravel.
01/01-31/12.
Distance: on the spot 200m on the spot on the spot.

Obernai 19G1

Parking de l'Altau, Route d'Ottrott. **GPS:** n48,46239 e7,47369.

10 free. **Location:** Urban, simple, central. **Surface:** asphalted.
01/01-31/12.
Distance: 600m 600m 600m.
Remarks: Video surveillance.

Obernai 19G1

Parking des Remparts, Rue Poincaré. **GPS:** n48,45972 e7,48667.

50 free free. **Location:** Urban, simple. **Surface:** gravel.
01/01-31/12.
Distance: 300m 2,7km 300m 300m 200m.
Remarks: Large parking in centre, video surveillance.

Oltingue 19G3

Place Saint Martin. **GPS:** n47,49158 e7,39068.

3 free € 2/10minutes Ch € 2/55minutes WC free.
Location: Urban. **Surface:** asphalted. 01/01-31/12.
Distance: 100m on the spot 100m 200m on the spot on the spot on the spot.

Orbey 19F1

Hôtel Restaurant Les Terrasses du Lac Blanc, Lac Blanc.
GPS: n48,13540 e7,08957.

8 € 7 included Ch (8x)€ 2,50.
Location: Comfortable, quiet. **Surface:** grassy/gravel.
Distance: 500m 500m on the spot.
Remarks: Guests free.

Orschwihr 19G2

Rue de la Source. **GPS:** n47,93722 e7,23083.

5 free Service € 4,30 Ch. **Location:** Rural, simple, quiet.
Surface: asphalted. 01/01-31/12.
Distance: 200m 200m 5km on the spot on the spot.
Remarks: Max. 48h.

Orschwiller 19G1

Aire de service du Haut-Koenigsbourg, A35.
GPS: n48,23278 e7,40477.
30 free Ch WC . **Location:** Motorway, noisy.
Surface: asphalted. 01/01-31/12.
Distance: on the spot on the spot.

Peigney 19D2

Lac de la Liez, D284, rue Côté de Recey.
GPS: n47,87272 e5,38077.

8 € 10,50 Ch € 2. **Location:** Simple.
Surface: asphalted. 01/01-31/12.
Distance: 500m on the spot on the spot on the spot on the spot.

Pfaffenheim 19G2

Aire du Winzerhof, Rue de la Tuilerie. **GPS:** n47,98639 e7,29167.

5 € 5 Ch (5x) WC included. **Location:** Urban, simple, quiet. **Surface:** gravel/metalled. 01/01-31/12.
Distance: 400m 400m 3km on the spot on the spot.
Remarks: Guests free, sale of wines.

Phalsbourg 16G3

Rue du commandant Taillant. **GPS:** n48,76545 e7,25950.
4 free € 2/10minutes Ch € 4/12h. **Surface:** metalled.
01/01-31/12.
Distance: 100m 100m 300m.
Remarks: Max. 48h.

Phalsbourg 16G3

TOTAL tankstation, ZAC Louvois, Route du Luxembourg.
GPS: n48,76899 e7,24182.

free € 2 Ch € 2. **Surface:** asphalted. 01/01-31/12.
Distance: on the spot.
Remarks: Max. 1 night.

Pierre-Percée 19F1

D182A. **GPS:** n48,46723 e6,92911.

± 8 free.
Location: Simple, isolated, quiet. **Surface:** asphalted.
Distance: on the spot on the spot.
Remarks: Picnic area at artificial lake.

Piney 19B1

Place des Anciens Combattants, Rue du Général de Gaulle.
GPS: n48,35878 e4,33442.

5 free € 3/10minutes Ch € 3/1h. **Location:** Simple.
Surface: metalled. 01/01-31/12 water: frost.
Distance: 500m 500m 500m.
Remarks: Coins at town hall and restaurant.

Plombières-les-Bains 19E2

Allée Eugene Delacroix. **GPS:** n47,95822 e6,44966.

15 free (5x). **Location:** Simple, quiet. **Surface:** asphalted.
01/01-31/12.

Pompierre 19D1

Chemin de la Corvée. **GPS:** n48,25691 e5,67188.

3 free free. **Location:** Urban, simple, noisy.
Surface: asphalted. 01/01-31/12.
Distance: 1km 500m 500m.

Pont-à-Mousson 16E3

Port de plaisance, Avenue des Etas Unis, D910.
GPS: n48,90296 e6,06088.

45 € 9,50 Ch WC included.
Location: Luxurious. **Surface:** asphalted. 01/04-31/10.
Distance: 400m 3,4km on the spot 400m 400m on the spot.
Remarks: Max. 15 days, check in at reception, bread-service.

FR

Rebeuville 19D1

Rue du Cougnot. **GPS**: n48,33530 e5,70128.

3 free Ch free. **Location:** Rural, comfortable, isolated. **Surface:** asphalted. 01/01-31/12.
Distance: 5km on the spot on the spot 5km 5km 500m.

Reims 16B2

Parc du CIS de la Comédie, Esplanade André Malraux, chaussée Bocquaine. **GPS**: n49,24881 e4,02110.

9 free Ch free. **Location:** Urban, simple, central, noisy. **Surface:** metalled.
Distance: 15 min walking 1,4km 350m 100m.
Remarks: Max. 48h, call for entrance code, noisy place.

Remiremont 19F1

Rue du Lit d'Eau. **GPS**: n48,01540 e6,60208.
31 € 6 Ch € 3/24h. **Location:** Comfortable. **Surface:** gravel.
Distance: 1km on the spot on the spot on the spot on the spot.
Remarks: At small lake, at station, video surveillance.

Rennepont 19C1

Domaine Rennepont, 31 Rue Principale. **GPS**: n48,14927 e4,85430.

4 € 10 € 3 € 2 WC € 3.
Location: Rural, simple, isolated, quiet. **Surface:** grassy/gravel. 15/03-31/10.
Distance: on the spot 200m on the spot on the spot.
Remarks: Baker every morning.

Revigny-sur-Ornain 16C3

Stade/Office de Tourisme, Rue de l'Abattoir. **GPS**: n48,82642 e4,98330.

2 free Ch free. **Location:** Urban, simple, central, quiet. **Surface:** asphalted. 01/01-31/12.
Distance: on the spot 100m on the spot on the spot on the spot.
Remarks: Coins at tourist info.

Revin 16C1

Rue du Port. **GPS**: n49,93962 e4,63843.
10 free € 2/100liter Ch € 2/1h. **Surface:** metalled. 01/01-31/12.
Distance: on the spot on the spot on the spot.
Remarks: Max. 8M.

Rhodes 16F3

Port Municipal, Rue Principale. **GPS**: n48,75784 e6,90053.

30 € 18/24h Ch WC included. **Location:** Luxurious, quiet. **Surface:** grassy. 01/04-30/09.
Distance: on the spot on the spot.
Remarks: Along Etang du Stock.

Ribeauvillé 19G1

Route de Guémar. **GPS**: n48,19231 e7,32867.

15 € 1,50/5h, € 1,50/night € 2 Ch.
Location: Urban, simple, noisy. **Surface:** gravel. 01/01-31/12.
Distance: 400m on the spot on the spot.
Remarks: Next to Cave de Ribeauvillé.

Tourist information Ribeauvillé:
Sa.

Richardmenil 16E3

Chemin de la Maize. **GPS**: n48,59457 e6,16078.

5 free Ch (4x)free. **Location:** Isolated, quiet. **Surface:** asphalted. 01/01-31/12.
Distance: 1km on the spot on the spot 500m 1km 1km.

Riquewihr 19G1

Avenue Jacques Preiss. **GPS**: n48,16608 e7,30175.

6 € 2/5h, € 4/night € 2 Ch € 2. **Location:** Simple, noisy. **Surface:** asphalted. 01/01-31/12.
Distance: 200m 200m 200m.
Remarks: Motorhomes <7m, video surveillance.

Tourist information Riquewihr:
Office de Tourisme, Rue de 1ère Armée. Picturesque street with houses of the 16th century.

Rollainville 19D1

Rue de la Cure. **GPS**: n48,36185 e5,73842.

1 free € 2/30minutes € 2/6h. **Location:** Urban, simple, central. **Surface:** asphalted. 01/01-31/12.
Distance: on the spot.
Remarks: Baker at 8am.

Rupt-sur-Moselle 19F2

Quai de la Parelle. **GPS**: n47,92061 e6,66194.

6 free € 3/10minutes Ch (4x)€ 3/3h WC.
Location: Simple, quiet. **Surface:** asphalted.
Distance: 350m 250m on the spot Voie Verte.
Remarks: Coins at the shops and town hall.

Saint-Dizier 16C3

Centre Loisirs Caravanning, Route de Villiers en Lieu. **GPS**: n48,64255 e4,91035.

6 free Ch (4x)WC free. **Location:** Rural, comfortable, noisy. **Surface:** asphalted. 01/01-31/12.
Distance: 1,5km 400m.
Remarks: At motorhome dealer, coins during opening hours.

Saint-Hippolyte 19G1

Rue de la 5E Division Blindée. **GPS**: n48,23084 e7,37681.

3 free € 4 Ch. **Location:** Urban, simple, quiet. 01/01-31/12.
Distance: on the spot 300m.
Remarks: Service 100m, 3 parking spaces Allée des Cygnes n48.23242, o7.37239, 3 parking spaces Rue Windmuehl n48.23172, e.36443.

Saint-Imoges 16B2

Rue de la Briquetrie. **GPS**: n49,10689 e3,97903.
8 free 150liter Ch 1h,service € 2. **Location:** Isolated, quiet. 01/01-31/12.

Saint-Mihiel 16D3

Chemin Gué Rapeau. **GPS**: n48,90227 e5,53960.

FR

4 €3 €3 Chfree €3/24h. **Location:** Rural, simple, isolated, quiet. **Surface:** asphalted. 01/01-31/12.
Distance: 1,5km 1km 1,5km.
Remarks: Directly at the river, nearby sluices, next to camping municipal, max. 24h.

Saint-Nabord 19F1

Rue de la Croix Saint Jacques. **GPS**: n48,04527 e6,58175.

10 free €3/80liter Ch €3. **Location:** Simple, quiet.
Surface: asphalted. 01/01-31/12.
Distance: 300m 200m 50m.

Saint-Nicolas-de-Port 16E3

Rue du Jeu de Paume. **GPS**: n48,63515 e6,30048.

10 free €4 Ch. **Location:** Urban, simple, central, quiet.
Surface: gravel. 01/01-31/12.
Distance: on the spot 150m 200m 100m.

Sainte-Livière 16C3

1 rue Sainte Libaire. **GPS**: n48,60133 e4,82139.

19 €8 Ch (19x) WC included.
Location: Urban, comfortable, central, quiet. **Surface:** gravel.
01/01-31/12.
Distance: on the spot 2km Lake Der-Chantecoq 2km 200m 200m.
Remarks: Bread-service, service passerby €3.

Sainte-Marie-aux-Mines 19G1

Place des Tisserands. **GPS**: n48,24700 e7,18322.

10 free. **Location:** Urban, simple, quiet. **Surface:** asphalted.
01/01-31/12.
Distance: 100m 100m 300m.
Remarks: Max. 24h.

Tourist information Sainte-Marie-aux-Mines:
Office de Tourisme, 86, rue Wilson, www.tourisme.fr/office-de-tourisme/sainte-marie-aux-mines-68.htm. Mineral city with silvermine, Mine d'Argent Sainte-Barthélemy.

Sainte-Marie-du-Lac-Nuisement 16C3

Port de Nuisement, D13A. **GPS**: n48,60285 e4,74922.

6 free €3/8minutes Ch €3/55minutes.
Location: Rural, comfortable, central, quiet. **Surface:** asphalted.
01/01-31/12.
Distance: 4km on the spot 800m 1km on the spot.
Remarks: Coins at tourist info.

Sapignicourt 16C3

Rue Deperthes à Larzicourt. **GPS**: n48,65111 e4,80583.

4 free €2,50/10minutes Ch €2,50/55minutes.
Location: Rural, simple, isolated, quiet. **Surface:** grassy.
01/01-31/12.
Distance: 500m.
Remarks: Coins at town hall and Mr. Bauer, 14, grande rue.

Sarralbe 16F2

Parc François Mitterand, Rue de la Sarre. **GPS**: n49,00171 e7,03240.
4 free. **Surface:** asphalted. 01/01-31/12.
Distance: 350m 350m.
Remarks: At sports centre.

Saverne 16G3

Rue des Emouleurs. **GPS**: n48,74512 e7,36854.

€7 €2 €2/6h. **Location:** Simple, central.
Surface: gravel/sand. 01/01-31/12.
Distance: centre 650m.

Saverne 16G3

Camping Les Portes d'Alsace, Rue du Père Liebermann.
GPS: n48,73131 e7,35504.

12 €10-12 Ch WC included €2,50 €2,50.
Location: Comfortable, quiet. **Surface:** gravel. 01/04-30/09.

Tourist information Saverne:
Château de Rohan. Museum, former summer residence of the bishops of Strasbourg.

Sedan 16C1

Château Fort, Rue Hue Tanton. **GPS**: n49,70145 e4,95092.
4 free. 01/01-31/12.
Distance: 400m 400m.
Remarks: Parking places around the castle of Sedan.

Seuil-d'Argonne 16C3

Rue du Commandant Laflotte, D2/D20. **GPS**: n48,98294 e5,06215.

5 free. **Location:** Rural, simple, quiet. **Surface:** gravel.
01/01-31/12.
Distance: 650m 650m 650m 650m.
Remarks: In fron of sports fields.

Sézanne 16B3

Place du Champ Benoist. **GPS**: n48,72222 e3,72125.

7 free Ch free WC.
Location: Urban, simple, central, noisy. **Surface:** asphalted.
01/01-31/12 Fri-Sa market.
Distance: on the spot 50m 300m 50m.

Sierck-les-Bains 16E2

Place de la Gro. **GPS**: n49,44424 e6,36217.

8 free. **Location:** Simple. **Surface:** asphalted. 01/01-31/12.
Distance: 200m 200m 350m on the spot.
Remarks: Along the Moselle river, nearby police station.

Soufflenheim 16H3

Rue des Hirondelle. **GPS**: n48,83233 e7,96045.

13 free €2 Ch €2. **Location:** Urban, simple, quiet.
Surface: asphalted. 01/01-31/12.
Distance: 300m 200m 300m 200m.

Souilly 16D2

Route de St.André-en-Barrois, D159. **GPS**: n49,02730 e5,27985.

6 free. **Location:** Rural, simple. **Surface:** gravel. 01/01-31/12.
Distance: 600m.

FR

Soultz 19G2
Rue de la Marne. **GPS**: n47,88806 e7,23139.

3 free Ch free. **Location:** Urban, simple, quiet.
Surface: asphalted. 01/01-31/12.
Distance: 200m 200m 500m 500m on the spot.

Stenay 16D1
Aire Camping-car, D947. **GPS**: n49,48979 e5,18323.

49 € 8, 01/11-31/03 € 9 Ch WC € 4/4 included.
Location: Rural, comfortable, quiet. **Surface:** metalled.
01/01-31/12.
Distance: 150m 150m 800m, bakery 300m.
Remarks: Pay and entrance code at harbourmaster, musée Européen de la Bière, beer museum.

Stenay 16D1
Port de plaisance, Rue du Port. **GPS**: n49,49096 e5,18312.

6 € 8, 01/11-31/03 € 9 Ch WC € 4/4 included.
Location: Comfortable, quiet. **Surface:** asphalted. 01/01-31/12.
Distance: on the spot 200m 500m.
Remarks: Pay at harbourmaster.

Tourist information Stenay:
Musée de la Bière. Beer museum.
Château, Louppy-sur-Loison. Renaissance castle, 17th century.

Strasbourg 16G3
Parking Auberge de Jeunesse des Deux Rives (Parc du Rhin), Rue des Cavaliers. **GPS**: n48,56659 e7,79975.

40 free € 2,50/100liter Ch € 2,50/1h.
Location: Rural, simple. **Surface:** asphalted/sand.
01/01-31/12.
Distance: Strasbourg centre 5km bus 21 + tram.
Remarks: Max. 7 days.

Tourist information Strasbourg:
Maison Kammerzell. Restaurant, 1467-1589, one of the most beautyfull half-timbered houses in the Alsace region.
Musée Alsacien. Folk art and handycrafts.
Cathédrale de Nôtre-Dame.

Suippes 16C2
Rue de l'Abreuvoir. **GPS**: n49,13074 e4,53419.

10 free € 2 Ch € 2. **Location:** Urban, simple.
Surface: asphalted. 01/01-31/12.
Distance: on the spot 200m 200m.

Tannois 16D3
Parking du Belvédère, D169. **GPS**: n48,71977 e5,22967.

10 free. **Location:** Rural, simple, isolated, quiet. **Surface:** gravel.
01/01-31/12.
Distance: 1,3km 1,5km on the spot on the spot.

Thann 19F2
Parking du Centre, Rue du Général de Gaulle. N66.
GPS: n47,80889 e7,10460.

30 free Ch Service € 4. **Location:** Urban, simple, noisy.
Surface: asphalted. 01/01-31/12.
Distance: 250m 50m 50m.

Thann 19F2
Place du Bungert, Rue des Pélerins. **GPS**: n47,81159 e7,10450.

10 free WC free.
Location: Urban, simple, central, quiet. **Surface:** asphalted.
01/01-31/12 Sa-morning market.
Distance: 200m on the spot 200m 500m on the spot on the spot.

Thaon-les-Vosges 19E1
Aire du Coignot, Rue du Coignot. **GPS**: n48,24920 e6,42520.

10 free Ch free. **Location:** Simple, quiet.
Surface: asphalted/gravel. 01/03-01/10.
Distance: 1,5km 400m.
Remarks: Next to port fluvial.

Thiaucourt-Regniéville 16E3
Rue du Stade. **GPS**: n48,95220 e5,86090.

8 free € 2/20minutes Ch (4x)€ 3/6h.
Location: Rural, comfortable, isolated, quiet. **Surface:** grassy/gravel.
01/01-31/12.
Distance: 700m 700m 500m.
Remarks: At tennis-courts.

Thierville-sur-Meuse 16D2
Thierville sur-meuse, Avenue de l,etangbleu.
GPS: n49,17499 e5,36357.

20 free. **Location:** Rural, simple. **Surface:** asphalted.
01/01-31/12.
Distance: 100m 50m 50m on the spot on the spot.
Remarks: Along the Meuse river.

Tilleux 19D1
Grande Rue. **GPS**: n48,29300 e5,72250.

8 free free.
Location: Simple. **Surface:** gravel. 01/01-31/12.
Distance: 100m.
Remarks: Inclining pitches, entrance road max. 3,5t.

Tonnoy 16E3
Aire de d' accueil Camping Car du Grand Vanné, RD 74.
GPS: n48,54934 e6,24337.
32 € 8/24h Ch 01/05-30/09.
Distance: 1km on the spot on the spot on the spot.
Remarks: Along the Moselle river.

Toul 16E3
Avenue du Colonel Péchot. **GPS**: n48,67670 e5,88549.

12 € 7/24h Ch (8x)included. **Location:** Urban, comfortable, quiet. **Surface:** asphalted. 01/01-31/12.
Distance: 4km.
Remarks: Max. 72h.

Trois Épis 19G1
Place des Antonins. **GPS**: n48,10101 e7,22948.

25 free € 2 Ch € 3/55minutes WC € 0,50 € 1.
Location: Urban, simple, quiet. **Surface:** asphalted.
01/01-31/12.
Distance: 150m 150m 150m on the spot.

Turckheim 19G1

Quai de la gare. **GPS:** n48,08555 e7,27739.

6 € 5.
Location: Urban, simple, noisy. **Surface:** metalled.
01/01-31/12.
Distance: historical centre 250m 250m 300m on the spot.

Ungersheim 19G2

Ecomusée. GPS: n47,85200 e7,28400.

20 € 6 included. **Location:** Rural, simple, quiet.
Surface: gravel/metalled. 01/01-31/12.
Distance: 6km 200m.
Remarks: Check in at hotel.

Val-d'Ornain 16C3

D2. **GPS:** n48,80327 e5,07284.

6 free. **Location:** Rural, simple, isolated, noisy. **Surface:** gravel.
01/01-31/12.
Distance: 400m on the spot on the spot.

Val-et-Châtillon 16F3

Grande Rue / D993a. **GPS:** n48,56039 e6,96525.

6 free € 3 Ch € 3/55minutes.
Location: Comfortable, quiet. **Surface:** gravel. 01/01-31/12.
Distance: 100m 3,5km on the spot.
Remarks: Max. 4 days, bread-service.

Vaucouleurs 16D3

Rue du Cardinal Lépicier. **GPS:** n48,60187 e5,66814.

3 € 5 € 2/100liter Ch € 2.
Location: Urban, simple, central, quiet. **Surface:** asphalted.
01/01-31/12.
Distance: on the spot 500m 500m 100m.
Remarks: Check in at town hall.

Vauquois 16C2

Parking municipal, D212. **GPS:** n49,20405 e5,07398.

8 free. **Location:** Rural, simple. **Surface:** gravel.
Distance: on the spot.

Velaines 16D3

D120A. **GPS:** n48,70589 e5,29804.

4 free.
Location: Urban, simple, central. **Surface:** gravel.
Distance: on the spot 300m.

Vendeuvre-sur-Barse 19C1

Place du 8 mai 1945, Rue du Pont Chevalier.
GPS: n48,23727 e4,46646.

5 free € 3 Ch € 3. **Location:** Urban, simple.
Surface: asphalted. tue-evening, wed-morning (market).
Distance: 100m on the spot ATAC on the spot.

Ventron 19F2

Chemin du Plain. **GPS:** n47,93906 e6,86900.

10 free € 2/100liter Ch € 2/55minutes. **Location:** Simple, central, quiet. **Surface:** asphalted. 01/01-31/12.
Remarks: Coins at tourist info.

Ventron 19F2

Route de Frère Joseph. **GPS:** n47,92514 e6,86223.

free. **Surface:** asphalted. 01/01-31/12.
Distance: Ventron 3,2km on the spot.
Remarks: Parking at skipistes.

Verdun 16D2

Dragées Braquir, Rue du Fort de Vaux, D112.
GPS: n49,15955 e5,39989.

10 free.
Location: Urban, simple, central. **Surface:** metalled.
Distance: on the spot.
Remarks: Max. 1 night.

Viéville 19D1

Halte Nautique La Licorne. GPS: n48,23825 e5,12988.

6 € 1,50 € 1,50/day (6x)€ 1,50/day.
Location: Rural, simple, quiet. **Surface:** gravel.
01/01-31/12.
Distance: on the spot 3km 500m on the spot on the spot.

Vigneulles-lès-Hattonchâtel 16D2

Rue Miss Skinner. **GPS:** n48,99200 e5,70122.

2 free. **Location:** Rural, isolated, quiet. **Surface:** gravel/metalled.
01/01-31/12.
Distance: 2km on the spot on the spot.
Remarks: At castle.

Villeneuve-Renneville-Chevigny 16B3

Champagne Leclère-Massard, 12, rue du Plessis.
GPS: n48,91488 e4,05959.

6 € 5 Ch included € 2/day.
Location: Comfortable. **Surface:** asphalted.
Distance: 3km 2km 3km 3km on the spot.
Remarks: Tu-Su fresh bread, champagne tastery.

FR

Villers-sous-Châtillon 16B2

Halte camping-cars, Rue du Parc. **GPS**: n49,09642 e3,80078.

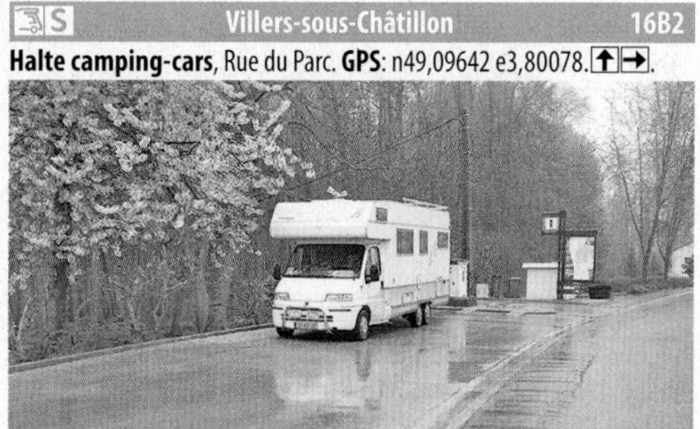

5 free € 3/100liter Ch € 3/1h. **Location:** Rural, simple, quiet. **Surface:** asphalted. 01/01-31/12.
Distance: 1,2km 50m 1,2km 2km.
Remarks: Coins at town hall and restaurant du Commerce.

Void-Vacon 16D3

Rue de la Gare. **GPS**: n48,68240 e5,61960.

12 free € 2/20minutes Ch € 2/20minutes.
Location: Rural, simple, isolated, quiet. **Surface:** grassy/gravel. 01/01-31/12.
Distance: 700m 10m 10m 300m 100m.
Remarks: Coins at shop/town hall.

Vouziers 16C2

Aire du Champ de Foire, Rue de Condé 33. **GPS**: n49,40030 e4,70197.
9 free € 2/100liter Ch € 2/20minutes.
Location: Urban. **Surface:** grassy/metalled. 01/01-31/12.
Distance: 200m 350m.
Remarks: Max. 48h.

Wadelincourt 16C1

Ferme du Chemin de Noyers, Rue Hubert Desrousseaux.
GPS: n49,68075 e4,93553.

1 free free. **Location:** Rural, simple, isolated, quiet. 01/01-31/12.
Distance: 2km 4km 2km 2km.
Remarks: Inclining pitches, regional products.

Wassy 19C1

Lac des Leschères, Réservoir Leschères Centre.
GPS: n48,48991 e4,94924.

2 free. **Location:** Rural, simple, quiet. **Surface:** asphalted. 01/01-31/12.
Distance: 1,5km on the spot on the spot 1,5km 1km on the spot.

Westhalten 19G2

Rue St Blaise, D18, Vallée Noble, dir Soultzmatt..
GPS: n47,95626 e7,25135.

10 free € 2 Ch. **Location:** Rural, simple, noisy.
Surface: asphalted. 01/03-30/11.
Remarks: Max. 48h.

Westhalten 19G2

Domaine du Bollenberg. GPS: n47,94459 e7,25652.
5 free . 01/01-31/12.
Distance: on the spot.
Remarks: Max 3,5t.

Willer-sur-Thur 19F2

Place de l'Eglise. **GPS**: n47,84315 e7,07292.

3 free Ch WC free. **Location:** Urban. **Surface:** asphalted. 01/01-31/12.
Distance: 250m 500m 500m, bakery 50m 500m on the spot 500m.

Normandie

Agon-Coutainville 15B2

Flot Bleu Park, Boulevard Louis Lebel-Jéhenne.
GPS: n49,05176 w1,59123.

25 € 6,80/24h Ch included
Location: Comfortable. **Surface:** grassy. 01/01-31/12.
Distance: 500m 800m.
Remarks: Service passerby € 2,70.

Allouville-Bellefosse 15E1

Place des Tilleuls. **GPS**: n49,60440 e0,63036.
6 free € 4 Ch € 4. **Surface:** asphalted. 01/01-31/12.
Distance: on the spot.

Allouville-Bellefosse 15E1

Place Paul Levieux, Rue Bourvil. **GPS**: n49,59659 e0,67725.
4 free Ch. **Surface:** asphalted. 01/01-31/12.
Distance: on the spot on the spot on the spot.
Remarks: At townhall.

Ardevon 15B3

La Bidonnière, 5 route de la Rive. **GPS**: n48,60352 w1,47612.
60 € 10,90 € 3 Ch (40x)€ 3/24h,10Amp WC € 3 included.
Location: Rural, comfortable, luxurious, quiet. **Surface:** grassy/gravel. 01/01-31/12.
Distance: on the spot 3km 1km 3km 1,5km on the spot on the spot.
Remarks: Bread-service, free bicycles available, view on Mt.St.Michel.

Argentan 15D3

De La Dentelle, Rue Charlotte Corday. **GPS**: n48,73984 w0,01664.
4 free free. **Surface:** asphalted. 01/01-31/12.
Distance: 500m on the spot on the spot 550m.

Arromanches-les-Bains 15C1

Arromanches 360, Cinéma Circulaire, Chemin du Calvaire / D514.
GPS: n49,33924 w0,61419.

20 € 6 € 2 Ch. **Location:** Rural, comfortable. 01/01-31/12.
Distance: 400m 300m.
Remarks: Beautiful view.

Arromanches-les-Bains 15C1

Rue François Carpentier. **GPS**: n49,33904 w0,62553.

14 free € 2/10minutes Ch € 2/1h free15minutes.
Surface: asphalted. 01/01-31/12.
Distance: 150m 100m 100m 250m.
Remarks: Next to camping municipal, max. 1 night.

Auderville 15B1

D901. **GPS**: n49,71431 w1,93481.

15 free. **Location:** Rural, simple. **Surface:** grassy/gravel. 01/01-31/12.

FR

Distance: 300m 700m 600m.

Auffay 15F1

Parking de la Gare. **GPS**: n49,71339 e1,09890.

4 free € 3/100liter Ch € 3/1h.
Location: Urban, simple, quiet. **Surface:** gravel. 01/01-31/12.
Distance: 800m 17km 700m 700m on the spot on the spot.

Auffay 15F1

Rue de la Libération. **GPS**: n49,71502 e1,09805.
4 free € 3 Ch € 3. **Surface:** asphalted. 01/01-31/12.
Distance: 600m 600m.

Avranches 15B3

Centre Culturel, Boulevard Jozeau Marigné.
GPS: n48,68585 w1,367.

8 free € 2/10minutes Ch. **Location:** Urban, simple.
Surface: gravel/metalled. 01/01-31/12.
Distance: 200m 1,9km 200m 200m.
Remarks: Behind community centre, max. 1 night, attractive medieval centre.

Tourist information Avranches:
Jardins des Plantes. Garden with exotic plants.
Basilique St Germain. 9-12h, 14-16h.
place des Halles. Sa + Tue-morning.

Bagnoles-de-l'Orne 15D3

Avenue du Dr Paul Lemuet. **GPS**: n48,55558 w0,40973.

6 free. **Location:** Simple, noisy. **Surface:** asphalted.
01/01-31/12.
Distance: 400m 400m 900m on the spot.
Remarks: Max. 48h.

Bagnoles-de-l'Orne 15D3

D235. **GPS**: n48,55821 w0,4129.

6 free.
Location: Urban, simple. **Surface:** gravel. 01/01-31/12.
Distance: on the spot 400m 400m on the spot.
Remarks: Behind tourist info, Place du Marché.

Bagnoles-de-l'Orne 15D3

D916. **GPS**: n48,55034 w0,40202.

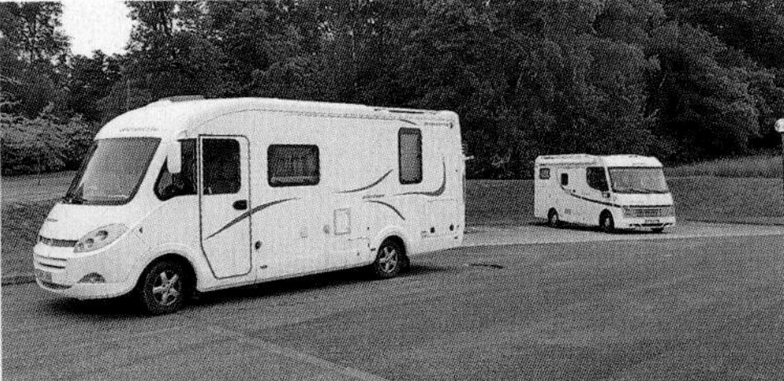

4 free Ch. **Location:** Simple. **Surface:** asphalted.
01/01-31/12.
Distance: 900m on the spot on the spot on the spot.

Bardouville 15F1

Le Grand Bois. **GPS**: n49,43027 e0,92362.

3 free Ch. **Location:** Rural, comfortable, central, quiet.
Surface: asphalted. 01/01-31/12.
Distance: 300m 500m 500m.

Barfleur 15C1

Chemin de la Masse. **GPS**: n49,67368 w1,2641.

20 free ChWC. **Location:** Urban, simple. **Surface:** grassy/gravel.
01/01-31/12.
Distance: 200m.

Barneville-Carteret 15B1

Quai Émile Valmy, Rue du Port. **GPS**: n49,37223 w1,79042.

12 free. **Location:** Urban, simple. **Surface:** asphalted.
01/01-31/12.
Distance: 600m on the spot on the spot 600m.
Remarks: In front of the Gare Maritime.

Barneville-Carteret 15B1

Carrefour Market, Route du Pont Rose. **GPS**: n49,38553 w1,75239.
€ 2 Ch € 2/1h. **Location:** Simple. 01/01-31/12.

Bayeux 15C2

Place Gauquelin-Despallières. **GPS**: n49,28044 w0,70775.

5 free ChWCfree.
Location: Urban. **Surface:** asphalted. 01/01-31/12.
Distance: on the spot 100m 100m on the spot.
Remarks: Max. 12h.

Bayeux 15C2

Voie de la Rivière. **GPS**: n49,28168 w0,69604.
free Ch. 01/01-31/12.
Distance: 850m.

Bayeux 15C2

Boulevard Fabian Ware. **GPS**: n49,27242 w0,71053.
10 overnight stay € 4. 01/01-31/12.
Distance: 900m.

Bayeux 15C2

Rue Pierre Trébucien. **GPS**: n49,27585 w0,71273.
28 € 4. **Surface:** asphalted. 01/01-31/12.
Distance: on the spot 750m.

Tourist information Bayeux:
M Musée Mémorial de la Bataille de Normandie, Boulevard Fabian Ware. Battle of Normandy, June 6 till August 22, 1944. 9.30-17h, 01/05-30/09 9-19h.
Cathédrale Nôtre Dame. Gothic cathedral.

Beauvoir 15B3

Aire de camping-car du mont St Michel, Route de Mont St Michel.
GPS: n48,59426 w1,5122.

122 € 12,50 Ch (122x) included.
Location: Rural, comfortable, quiet. **Surface:** grassy/gravel.
01/01-31/12.
Distance: 500m 500m.
Remarks: Service passerby € 4,50, le Mont Saint Michel 5km.

Beauvoir 15B3

Le Mont-St-Michel, Rue Au Bis. **GPS**: n48,60841 w1,50681.

220 € 17/24h.
Surface: asphalted. 01/01-31/12.
Distance: on the spot on the spot.
Remarks: Free shuttle to Le Mont-Saint-Michel 07.30-00.30h.

Bernières-sur-Mer 15D2

Rue Victor Tesnière. **GPS**: n49,33472 w0,41984.

35 free. **Location:** Urban, simple. **Surface:** gravel.
Distance: on the spot 100m 100m on the spot 100m on the spot on the spot on the spot.

Beuvron-en-Auge 15D2

Parking de la Gare, Avenue de la Gare. **GPS**: n49,18560 w0,0495.

16 € 6 Chincluded. **Location:** Rural, comfortable, quiet.

FR

Surface: gravel.
01/01-31/12.
Distance: 200m on the spot on the spot.
Remarks: Max. 24h, pay and coins at Tabac-Presse 200m.

Blangy-Sur-Bresle 13C3

Zone de Loisirs. **GPS**: n49,92338 e1,65535.
6 € 4 € 2 Ch. **Surface:** grassy. 01/04-31/10.
Distance: on the spot on the spot.

Bretteville-sur-Odon 15D2

Auto Camping Car Service, 4-6 Avenue des Carrières.
GPS: n49,18449 w0,41465.

6 free Chfree. **Location:** Urban, simple. **Surface:** metalled.
01/01-31/12.
Distance: 1km 500m.

Bréville-les-Monts 15D2

Rue des Dentellières. **GPS**: n49,24167 w0,228.

4 free € 2/10minutes Ch. **Location:** Simple.
Surface: asphalted. 01/03-15/11.
Distance: on the spot.
Remarks: Max. 72h, (may-july-aug) 48h, coins at tourist info Merville and harbour.

Bricquebec 15B1

Bas de Cattigny, D900, route de Cherbourg.
GPS: n49,47402 w1,64674.

6 free Ch (2x)free. **Location:** Comfortable, quiet.
Surface: gravel.
Distance: 1km on the spot.

Broglie 15E2

Parc de la bibliothèque. **GPS**: n49,00563 e0,52948.

8 € 5/night € 2,50/100liter Ch € 2,50/1h.
Surface: grassy/metalled. 01/03-31/10.
Distance: 200m 200m 200m, 7.30-19h.
Tourist information Broglie:
Fri 7-13h.

Buchy 15F1

D919, Route de Forges. **GPS**: n49,58538 e1,36417.

8 free € 2/100liter Ch € 2/h.
Location: Urban. **Surface:** gravel.
01/01-31/12.
Distance: 500m 500m 500m on the spot.
Remarks: Coins at the shops in the village, monday-morning market.

Cabourg 15D2

Avenue Michel d'Ornano. **GPS**: n49,28225 w0,11994.

6 free € 2/10minutes Ch. **Location:** Rural, comfortable, quiet. **Surface:** asphalted. 01/01-31/12.
Distance: centre 900m 7,5km 1,6km on the spot.
Remarks: Nearby Hippodrome.

Cabourg 15D2

Station Service Carrefour Market, Avenue de la Divette.
GPS: n49,27774 w0,13469.
free € 2 Ch. **Surface:** asphalted. 01/01-31/12.
Distance: 1km on the spot.

Cambremer 15D2

Place de l'Europe/Avenue des Tilleuls. **GPS**: n49,14991 e0,04729.

7 free € 2/100liter Ch € 2/1h.
Location: Rural, simple, central, quiet. **Surface:** gravel.
01/01-31/12 Service: winter.
Distance: 50m 100m bakery 100m.
Remarks: Coins at the shops and town hall.

Campigny 15E2

Chemin de la Motte. **GPS**: n49,31139 e0,55223.

4 free Chfree. **Surface:** grassy. 01/01-31/12.
Remarks: On inner court of old presbytery, max. 24h.

Canisy 15C2

Rue Jean Follain. **GPS**: n49,07615 w1,1753.
3 free ChWC. **Surface:** asphalted. 01/01-31/12.
Distance: on the spot.
Remarks: Coins at the shops.

Carentan 15C1

Camping-Car Park de Carentan, Chemin du Grand Bas Pays.
GPS: n49,30937 w1,2392.

12 € 10,80 Ch included. **Location:** Comfortable, quiet. **Surface:** gravel/metalled. 01/01-31/12.
Distance: 500m 500m.
Remarks: Mandatory, one-time fee Pass'Etapes € 4.

Carolles 15B3

Rue du Mont Dol. **GPS**: n48,75931 w1,57062.

15 € 8 € 3/100liter Ch € 3/55minutes.
Location: Comfortable. **Surface:** grassy/gravel. 01/01-31/12.
Distance: 150m on the spot on the spot.
Remarks: Only exact change.

Carolles 15B3

La Guériniére, Residence les Jaunets. **GPS**: n48,74989 w1,55695.
5 € 11, Jul/Aug € 17 € 2 Ch included. **Surface:** asphalted.
01/04-02/11.
Distance: on the spot 2km.
Remarks: In front of town hall.

Caumont-l'Éventé 15C2

Souterroscope des Ardoisières, Route de Saint Lô, D71.
GPS: n49,08868 w0,81645.

3 free € 2/10minutes Ch € 2/55minutes WC.
Location: Simple, isolated. **Surface:** asphalted.
01/01-31/12, service 15/02-15/11.
Distance: on the spot 500m on the spot.

Cerisy-la-Forêt 15C2

GPS: n49,19788 w0,93209.

10 free € 2 Ch € 2. **Location:** Rural, simple.
Surface: gravel. 01/01-31/12.
Distance: 500m 500m.
Remarks: Near abbey.

Cherbourg 15B1

Musée Cité de la Mer, Llée du President Menut.
GPS: n49,64740 w1,61782.

FR

40 free. **Location:** Urban, simple. **Surface:** asphalted.
Distance: 1km on the spot 1km on the spot.
Remarks: Max. 1 night.

Tourist information Cherbourg:
Musée Fort du Roule. War museum. 9.30-12h, 14-17.30h.

S Clecy 15D2

Rue du Stade. **GPS**: n48,91886 w0,48114.

5 free € 2/20minutes Ch. **Location:** Simple, quiet.
Surface: gravel. 01/01-31/12.
Distance: 100m 100m 300m 200m.
Remarks: Coins at the shops in the village.

S Clères 15F1

Rue Edmond Spalikowski. **GPS**: n49,60228 e1,11667.

15 free € 5/120liter Ch € 5/6h. **Location:** Comfortable, quiet. **Surface:** gravel. 01/01-31/12 service: 01/11-28/02.
Distance: 500m 500m 500m on the spot.
Remarks: Nearby football ground, max. 72h, coins at shops and tourist office.

S Colleville-Montgomery 15D2

Rue de Saint-Aubin/Rue les Petites Rues.
GPS: n49,27166 w0,29891.

9 € 5 Chfree.
Location: Rural, simple, quiet. **Surface:** grassy. 15/03-15/11.
Distance: 200m 450m.

Tourist information Colleville-Montgomery:
Musée Omaha Beach, St.Laurent-sur-Mer. Collection of military vehicles, weapons and costumes.

S Cormeilles 15E2

Route du Château de Malou, D810. **GPS**: n49,24926 e0,37371.

8 free Chfree. **Surface:** asphalted. 01/01-31/12.
Distance: 400m river 400m.

S Coudeville-sur-Mer 15B2

Avenue de la Mer D351. **GPS**: n48,88707 w1,56607.

30 € 7 Chincluded. **Location:** Rural.
Surface: grassy/gravel. 01/01-31/12.
Distance: 500m 200m 200m 500m 500m.

S Courcy 15B2

Ferme de la Pommeraie, La Pommeraie. **GPS**: n49,05861 w1,4092.
3 € 6 Ch included WC € 1/day € 1/day.
Surface: gravel/metalled. 01/01-31/12.
Remarks: Service passerby € 2.

S Courseulles-sur-Mer 15D2

Avenue de la Libération. **GPS**: n49,33440 w0,44551.

12 € 6,50 € 2 Ch. **Location:** Urban, comfortable, central.
Surface: asphalted. 01/04-02/10.
Distance: 50m 200m pizzeria 50m.
Remarks: Nearby entrance campsite, max. 24h.

Courseulles-sur-Mer 15D2

Juno Beach, Voie des Français Libres. **GPS**: n49,33694 w0,46502.

25 free. **Location:** Central, quiet. **Surface:** metalled.
01/01-31/12.
Distance: 100m 50m.

S Couterne 15D3

Place de la Mairie. **GPS**: n48,51223 w0,41417.

10 free ChWCfree. **Location:** Urban, simple.
Surface: asphalted. 01/01-31/12.
Distance: on the spot nearby nearby on the spot.
Remarks: Max. 1 night, closed when frosty.

S Criel-sur-Mer 13C3

Le Mont Joli-Bois, 29 Rue de la Plage. **GPS**: n50,02566 e1,30860.
19 € 9,90 € 5,40 Ch € 5,40. **Surface:** asphalted.
01/02-30/11.
Distance: 650m 650m.

S Deauville 15D2

Boulevard des Sports. **GPS**: n49,35727 e0,08417.

8 free Ch (6x)free. **Location:** Urban, simple, quiet.
Surface: gravel. 01/01-31/12.
Distance: on the spot 800m 500m.
Remarks: Behind stadium, max. 24h.

S Dieppe 13B3

Aire d'accueil Front de Mer, Boulevard Maréchal-Foch.
GPS: n49,93188 e1,08433.

40 € 12/24h Ch (8x)included.
Location: Urban, comfortable, central, quiet. **Surface:** asphalted.
01/01-31/12.
Distance: on the spot 100m 500m 500m 100m.
Remarks: Max. 48h.

S Dieppe 13B3

Quai de la Marne, Neuville-lès-Dieppe. **GPS**: n49,93014 e1,08667.

48 € 12/24h Ch (8x)free.
Location: Urban, comfortable, quiet. **Surface:** asphalted.
01/01-31/12.
Distance: 500m on the spot on the spot 500m 500m on the spot.
Remarks: Max. 48h, wifi card available at harbour master.

Tourist information Dieppe:
Château Dieppe. Castle, 15th century, with maritime museum.
10-12h, 14-18h 01/10-31/05 Tue.
Tue, Thu 8-14h.
Normandic market. Sa 8-14h.

S Dives-sur-Mer 15D2

Rue de l'Avenir. **GPS**: n49,29028 w0,10345.

10 free € 2/10minutes Ch. **Location:** Rural, comfortable, quiet. **Surface:** asphalted. 01/01-31/12.
Distance: 500m 900m.
Remarks: Nearby Port Guillaume.

S Doudeville 15E1

Place du Mont Criquet, centre-ville. **GPS**: n49,72000 e0,78750.

FR

12 free € 3,50/100liter Ch. **Location:** Urban, simple, central, quiet. **Surface:** asphalted. 01/01-31/12.
Distance: 100m 100m 100m on the spot on the spot on the spot.
Remarks: Coins at town hall, market Saturday.

Douvres-la-Délivrande 15D2

Parking Hyper U, Rue des Alliés. **GPS:** n49,30146 w0,3816.
free Ch. **Surface:** asphalted. 01/01-31/12.
Distance: on the spot on the spot.

Dragey-Ronthon 15B3

Route de la Plage. **GPS:** n48,70945 w1,5139.

9 free. **Location:** Simple, isolated. **Surface:** grassy/sand. 01/01-31/12.
Distance: 2km on the spot on the spot on the spot.
Remarks: Max. 24h.

Ducey 15B3

P du Domaine, Rue St Quentin. **GPS:** n48,62513 w1,294.

30 free € 2/100liter Ch € 2 WC. **Location:** Simple, noisy. **Surface:** gravel/metalled. 01/01-31/12.
Distance: 500m 500m 500m on the spot.
Remarks: Only exact change.

Ecouché 15D3

Rue Racinet. **GPS:** n48,71527 w0,12775.
3 free € 2 Ch 16Amp. **Location:** Rural. **Surface:** grassy/gravel. 01/01-31/12.
Distance: 500m 250m bakery.
Remarks: Picnic tables available.

Elbeuf 15F2

Allée du Front de Seine. **GPS:** n49,29262 e1,00807.
2 free. **Location:** Urban, central, noisy. **Surface:** asphalted. 01/01-31/12.
Distance: centre 500m 200m.

Englesqueville-la-Percée 15C1

Ferme de la Rouge Fossé, D514. **GPS:** n49,38781 w0,94829.

6 € 5 Ch € 3 (6x)included. **Location:** Comfortable, isolated, quiet. **Surface:** grassy/gravel. 01/01-31/12.
Distance: 500m.

Equeurdreville 15B1

Rue Jean Bart. **GPS:** n49,65465 w1,65044.

6 free Chfree. **Location:** Urban, simple. **Surface:** gravel/sand.
Distance: 1km 1km on the spot.

Étoutteville 15E1

Espace du Beau Soleil, Rue du Prieuré. **GPS:** n49,67609 e0,79073.

6 free € 2/140liter Ch € 2/1h. **Location:** Rural, comfortable, isolated, quiet. **Surface:** concrete. 01/01-31/12.
Distance: 500m 400m.

Etretat 15E1

Aire de stationnement Maupassant, Rue Guy de Maupassant. **GPS:** n49,70009 e0,21579.

30 € 8/24h € 2/100liter Ch € 3/55minutes. **Location:** Comfortable, central, quiet. **Surface:** grassy/metalled. 01/10-31/12.
Distance: 1km 1,2km 1km 1km 350m.
Remarks: Next to camping municipal, max. 24h.

Etretat 15E1

Pl. de la Gare. **GPS:** n49,70843 e0,21524.

10 free. **Surface:** metalled. 01/01-31/12.
Distance: 900m 1km.

Etretat 15E1

Route du Havre. **GPS:** n49,70101 e0,19973.
€ 3-5, overnight stay free.
Surface: unpaved. 01/01-31/12.
Distance: centre 750m 900m 700m.

Tourist information Etretat:
Office de Tourisme, Place Maurice Guillard, www.etretat.net. The cliffs which have the shape of an arch are a well-known tourist attraction.

Evreux 15F2

Camping-Car Park Evreux le Cadran, 64 boulevard de Normandie. **GPS:** n49,02302 e1,13839.
6 € 9,20 Ch (6x)included. **Surface:** asphalted. 01/01-31/12.
Distance: 500m.
Remarks: Mandatory, one-time fee Pass'Etapes € 4.

Falaise 15D2

Parking Carrefour, Rue Georges Clémenceau. **GPS:** n48,89670 w0,1905.
free € 2 Ch. **Surface:** asphalted. 01/01-31/12.
Distance: on the spot on the spot.
Remarks: Coins at campsite, coins at supermarket.

Fécamp 15E1

Parking de la Mâture, Chaussée Gayant. **GPS:** n49,76024 e0,37412.
+10 free € 3/100liter Ch. **Location:** Urban, simple, central. **Surface:** asphalted.
Distance: on the spot 200m 200m 200m.

Fécamp 15E1

Quai Sadi Carnot. **GPS:** n49,76087 e0,37157.

10 free. **Location:** Urban, simple, isolated. **Surface:** asphalted. 01/01-31/12.
Distance: 200m on the spot on the spot 200m 500m 200m.
Remarks: Between pier and marina, max. 7m.

Tourist information Fécamp:
Office de Tourisme, Quai Sadi Carnot, www.fecamptourisme.com. City against the chalk-cliff of the Côte d'Albâtre, fishing-port is now mainly a marina.
Palais Bénédictine, 110 rue Alexandre Le Grand. Museum with Bénédictine distillery and tasting-pub. 01/07-31/08 10-18.45h, 01/09-30/06 10.30-12.30h, 14.30-17.30h.

Fermanville 15B1

Le Cap Lévi, 17 route du Phare. **GPS:** n49,69002 w1,4673.

6 € 5. **Location:** Rural, simple, quiet. **Surface:** grassy. 01/01-31/12.

Fervaches 15C2

La Vallée. **GPS:** n48,99550 w1,0826.
8 free € 3 ChWC free. **Location:** Rural, comfortable. **Surface:** grassy/gravel. 01/01-31/12.
Distance: 150m 150m.
Remarks: Wifi code at grocery.

Forges-les-Eaux 15G1

Aire de camping car de la Minière, Boulevard Nicolas Thiessé. **GPS:** n49,60569 e1,54288.

38 free, 15/03-15/10 € 8 Ch (38x)included WC € 2. **Location:** Urban, comfortable, central, quiet. **Surface:** asphalted. 01/01-31/12.
Distance: 2km 1km 900m 300m 2km.
Remarks: Max. 48h, to be paid at campsite, sanitary at campsite, water closed during wintertime.

Formigny 15C1

La Ferme du Lavoir, D517. **GPS:** n49,34041 w0,89654.

FR

6 € 10/night Ch WC included. **Location:** Rural, comfortable, quiet. **Surface:** grassy/gravel. 01/01-31/12.
Distance: 300m 3km.
Remarks: Organic orchards, cider production.

S Gacé 15E3

Rue du Marché aux Bestiaux. **GPS**: n48,79500 e0,29583.

30 free € 2 Ch. **Surface:** asphalted. 01/01-31/12.
Distance: on the spot 2,5km 50m.
Remarks: In front of tourist office, max. 24h.

S Gaillon 15F2

Zone d'activités de la Bergerie, Rue de la Bergerie.
GPS: n49,16567 e1,35048.
free Chfree.
Surface: asphalted. 01/05-15/11 frost.

S Gavray 15B2

D38. **GPS**: n48,91113 w1,34641.

8 free € 4/10minutes Ch. **Location:** Urban, comfortable.
Surface: asphalted. 01/01-31/12.
Distance: 400m 200m 600m 100m.
Remarks: In front of police station.

Gerville 15E1

Salle du Clos Normand, Rue de la Liberté. **GPS**: n49,69594 e0,32852.
5 free. **Surface:** gravel. 01/01-31/12.
Distance: on the spot.

S Gisay-la-Coudre 15E2

D35. **GPS**: n48,95001 e0,62670.

6 free € 2/100liter Ch.
Surface: asphalted. 01/01-31/12.
Distance: on the spot 300m.
Remarks: Coins available at restaurant La Tortue.

S Gonzeville 15E1

La Ruette. **GPS**: n49,76590 e0,80738.

4 free WC. **Location:** Rural, simple, isolated, quiet.
Surface: asphalted/gravel. 01/01-31/12.
Distance: on the spot 7km 7km 100m on the spot on the spot.

S Gournay-en-Bray 15G1

Avenue Sadi Carnot. **GPS**: n49,48055 e1,72640.

8 free Chfree. **Location:** Urban, simple, central, quiet.
Surface: asphalted. 01/01-31/12 Thu-morning closed because of market + 2nd weekend Sep.
Distance: on the spot on the spot on the spot on the spot on the spot on the spot.
Remarks: Max. 48h.

S Gournay-en-Bray 15G1

Route du Vieux Saint-Clair. **GPS**: n49,50106 e1,72245.

10 € 6 € 1 € 2. **Location:** Rural, simple, isolated, quiet.
01/01-31/12.
Distance: 2,5km 3km 3km 2,5km on the spot on the spot.

S Gouvets 15C2

Le Bourg D454. **GPS**: n48,93133 w1,09492.

20 free WCfree. **Location:** Rural, simple, isolated, quiet.
Surface: grassy. 01/01-31/12.
Distance: on the spot 6km on the spot.

S Gouville-sur-Mer 15B2

Chemin du Beau Rivage. **GPS**: n49,09970 w1,60896.

40 € 5,50/19-10h Ch WCincluded.
Location: Urban. **Surface:** gravel. 01/01-31/12.
Distance: on the spot on the spot 50m.

S Grainville-Langannerie 15D2

Rue de Lapford. **GPS**: n49,01438 w0,26805.

6 free € 2/10minutes Ch € 2/55minutes.
Location: Rural, comfortable. **Surface:** metalled.
01/01-31/12.
Distance: 100m.
Remarks: Near Salle des Fêtes.

S Grandcamp-Maisy 15C1

Rue du Moulin Odo. **GPS**: n49,38620 w1,03782.

14 free € 2 Ch. **Location:** Rural, comfortable, quiet.
Surface: asphalted/gravel.
Distance: 500m 500m.
Remarks: Coins at tourist info, rue Aristide Briand.

S Granville 15B2

Haute Ville, Rue du Roc. **GPS**: n48,83530 w1,6095.

20 € 9 € 3/10minutes Ch € 3/55minutes.
Location: Simple. **Surface:** asphalted/gravel. 01/01-31/12.
Distance: 500m 500m 500m on the spot.
Remarks: Motorhome parking behind sea aquarium, upper city, Atlantic Wall 50m, max. 24h.

Tourist information Granville:
Office de Tourisme, 4, Cours Jonville, www.ville-granville.fr. The old centre, Haute-Ville, is surrounded by ramparts. The lower city is a bathing resort.
Wed, Sa.

S Gréville-Hague 15B1

D402. **GPS**: n49,67509 w1,80127.

10 free € 2 Ch € 2 WC. **Location:** Rural, comfortable.
Surface: metalled.
Distance: on the spot 100m.
Remarks: Next to sports fields.

S Grigneuseville 15F1

La Plaine d'Hermesnil, 7 rue de la Plaine. **GPS**: n49,64427 e1,19900.

FR

7 € 7 Ch (4x)included. **Location:** Rural, comfortable, isolated, quiet. **Surface:** gravel.
Distance: 2,5km 2,5km 2,5km.
Remarks: Service passerby € 3, barbecue place, picnic area.

S Grosville 15B1

Bar-Epicerie Caladjo, Rue des Touzés. **GPS**: n49,50659 w1,74311.

15 € 6 € 2 Ch € 2. **Location:** Rural, simple.
Surface: gravel. 01/01-31/12.
Distance: on the spot on the spot.

S Gruchet-Le-Valasse 15E1

Route de l'Abbaye. **GPS**: n49,53755 e0,50523.
12 € 2 Ch included. **Surface:** asphalted. 01/01-31/12.
Remarks: Service passerby € 2.

S Guilberville 15C2

D159. **GPS**: n48,98871 w0,94844.

8 free € 2/100liter Ch € 2/1h.
Location: Rural, simple, quiet. **Surface:** gravel.
01/01-31/12 service: 01/11-01/03.
Distance: 300m 1,5km 300m 300m.
Remarks: Coins at tourist info, Bistro and bakery.

S Hauteville-sur-Mer 15B2

Avenue du Sud. **GPS**: n48,97026 w1,55514.
22 € 8 Ch included,3Amp Nearby campsite.
Surface: gravel. 01/01-31/12.
Distance: 500m 500m 450m.

S Hermanville-sur-Mer 15D2

Rue Verte. **GPS**: n49,28592 w0,31243.

8 free Chfree. **Location:** Rural, comfortable.
Surface: asphalted. 01/01-31/12.
Distance: 250m 200m.

S Heurteauville 15E1

Les Cerisiers, Rue de Village. **GPS**: n49,44777 e0,81333.

12 € 8 + € 0,50/pp tourist tax Chincluded (12x)€ 2.
Location: Rural, comfortable, isolated, quiet.
Surface: grassy/gravel.
01/04-30/09.
Distance: 5km on the spot on the spot 5km 5km on the spot on the spot.
Remarks: Along the Seine river, max. 9m.

S Honfleur 15E1

Bassin de l'Est, Quai de la cale. **GPS**: n49,41916 e0,24166.

240 € 11/night Ch (60x)included.
Location: Urban, simple, central. **Surface:** gravel.
01/01-31/12 Service: winter.
Distance: 500m 2,7km 300m 500m.

S Incheville 13C3

Rue Mozart. **GPS**: n50,01397 e1,50441.
12 € 6,30 € 2,20 Ch. **Surface:** asphalted/grassy.
01/01-31/12.
Distance: on the spot on the spot on the spot.

S Isigny-sur-Mer 15C1

Quai Neuf. **GPS**: n49,32150 w1,10456.

6 free € 2/100liter Ch. **Location:** Rural. **Surface:** asphalted.
01/01-31/12.
Distance: 300m on the spot 200m.

S Jobourg 15B1

Nez de Jobourg, D202. **GPS**: n49,67722 w1,93806.

10 free WCfree. **Surface:** metalled. 01/01-31/12.
Distance: on the spot 500m 500m.

S Jumièges 15E1

Rue Alphonse Callais. **GPS**: n49,43106 e0,81452.

20 free € 3/100liter Ch. **Location:** Rural, simple, central.
Surface: grassy/gravel. 01/03-30/11.
Distance: 1km 500m 200m 200m on the spot on the spot on the spot.
Remarks: Coins at Tourist Info and bakery.

La Bouille 15F2

Parking du Bac. **GPS**: n49,35103 e0,93330.
free. **Location:** Noisy. **Surface:** asphalted. 01/01-31/12.
Distance: 300m on the spot on the spot 300m 300m.
Remarks: Along the Seine river, max. 24h.

S La Ferrière-aux-Etangs 15C3

Rue de l'Etang. **GPS**: n48,65931 w0,51706.

20 free € 2/10minutes Ch € 2/h.
Location: Simple, quiet. **Surface:** grassy/gravel.
01/01-31/12.
Distance: 400m 400m 400m on the spot.
Remarks: At lake, former campsite, only exact change.

S La Ferté-Macé 15D3

Ruelle des Fournelles, D916. **GPS**: n48,59018 w0,35528.

15 free ChWCfree. **Location:** Urban, simple.
Surface: asphalted. 01/01-31/12.
Distance: on the spot on the spot on the spot.
Remarks: Parking at church.

S La Haye-du-Puits 15B1

Place du Champ de Foire. **GPS**: n49,29353 w1,54386.
5 free Chfree. **Surface:** asphalted. 01/01-31/12.
Distance: 500m 400m 500m.

Tourist information La Haye-du-Puits:
Château, Pirou. Castle, 12th century.

S La Lucerne-d'Outremer 15B3

D35. **GPS**: n48,78437 w1,42727.

6 free Chfree. **Location:** Simple, central, quiet.
Surface: asphalted. 01/01-31/12.
Distance: on the spot 200m.
Remarks: Tuesday market.

Tourist information Hermanville-sur-Mer:
Tue morning.

S Hérouvillette 15D2

Place l'Aiguillon, Avenue de Caen, D 513A.
GPS: n49,21983 w0,24497.

6 free, voluntary contribution Ch WC free.
Location: Urban, simple. **Surface:** asphalted. 01/01-31/12.
Distance: on the spot 100m 100m.
Remarks: Next to castle, max. 2 days.

S La Mailleraye-sur-Seine 15E1

Quai Paul Girardeau. **GPS**: n49,48444 e0,77333.

34 € 5 + € 0,50/pp tourist taks, 01/11-31/03 free € 3/10minutes Ch € 3/1h.
Location: Urban, comfortable, central.
Surface: grassy.
01/01-31/12 2nd weekend April/May.
Distance: 200m on the spot on the spot on the spot 200m on the spot on the spot.
Remarks: Along the Seine river, coins at town hall and shops.

S La Mailleraye-sur-Seine 15E1

Quai Paul Girardeau. **GPS**: n49,48393 e0,77352.
34 free, 01/04-31/10 € 5 € 3 Ch € 3. **Surface:** grassy.
01/01-31/12.
Distance: 400m on the spot on the spot 150m.

La Poterie-Cap-d'Antifer 15E1

GPS: n49,68317 e0,16480.

4 free. **Location:** Rural, simple, quiet. **Surface:** grassy/gravel.
01/01-31/12.
Distance: 2km on the spot.

S La Vespière 15E2

Chemin de la Grand Mare/Campaugé. **GPS**: n49,02763 e0,42221.

2 free € 2/100liter Ch € 2/1h. **Location:** Simple.
Surface: asphalted. 01/01-31/12.
Distance: 300m A28 2,2km Carrefour 200m.

S La-Rivière-Saint-Sauveur 15E1

Parking de l'Orange, Chemin des Bancs, D580.
GPS: n49,40856 e0,26926.

20 free € 5/100liter Ch € 5/30minutes.
Location: Rural, simple, central, quiet. **Surface:** asphalted.
01/01-31/12.
Distance: on the spot 700m supermarket + bakery 100m.
Remarks: Coins at the shops in the village.

Langrune-sur-Mer 15D2

Rue du Colonel Pierre Harivel. **GPS**: n49,32474 w0,36814.

3 free. **Location:** Comfortable, central.
Surface: asphalted/metalled. 01/01-31/12.
Distance: on the spot beach 50m 50m.

S Le Billot 15D2

D39. **GPS**: n48,96948 e0,07217.

4 free € 2,50 Ch € 2,50 WC. **Location:** Rural, simple.
Surface: gravel/metalled. 01/01-31/12.
Distance: 200m on the spot.
Remarks: Coins at Relais du Billot 200m, beautiful view.

S Le Havre 15E1

Rue Andreï Sakharov. **GPS**: n49,50472 e0,17187.
13 € 6 Ch included. 01/01-31/12.
Distance: city centre 6km on the spot.
Remarks: Max. 3 days.

Tourist information Le Havre:
Musée de l'Ancienne Havre, rue Jerome Bellarmato. History of the city. Wed-Su 14-18h.
Canyon Parc, CD34, Epretot. Family park in western style.

S Le Mesnil-Jumièges 15E1

Base de loisirs, Route de Mesnil. **GPS**: n49,41172 e0,84494.

15 € 5, Jul/Aug € 10 € 3/100liter Ch WC
Location: Rural, comfortable, isolated. **Surface:** grassy/metalled.
01/01-31/12.
Distance: 1km 200m 200m 1km 1km on the spot on the spot on the spot.

S Le Mont-Saint-Michel 15B3

Aire Camping-car du Mont-Saint-Michel. **GPS**: n48,61401 w1,50773.

€ 15,50/24h Ch .
Surface: grassy. 23-06h.
Distance: La Rotisserie on the spot.

Le Mont-Saint-Michel 15B3

Parking Véolia, La Jacotière Ardevon. **GPS**: n48,61388 w1,5058.

50 € 17,20/24h. **Location:** Rural. **Surface:** metalled.
01/01-31/12.
Distance: 100m.
Remarks: Free shuttle to Le Mont-Saint-Michel.

Tourist information Le Mont-Saint-Michel:
Office de Tourisme, Corps de Garde des Bourgeois, www.mont-saint-michel.net. Town with abbey on a cliff in the sea.

S Le Noyer-en-Ouche 15E2

Ferme Lesur, La Godinière, D140. **GPS**: n49,01017 e0,72444.

5 € 7,50 € 3 € 3. **Surface:** grassy. 01/01-31/12.

S Le Sap 15E2

Les Terriers, Rue Nicolas Lesieur, D12. **GPS**: n48,89525 e0,33249.

4 free Ch free. **Surface:** gravel. 01/01-31/12.
Distance: 500m on the spot 500m 500m.
Remarks: Next to fire-station.

S Le Tréport 13C3

Du Funiculaire, Route Touristique, D126E. **GPS**: n50,05777 e1,36222.

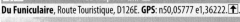

40 € 6,40, 2 pers.incl € 2,30/100liter Ch € 2,30/55minutes **Location:** Comfortable, isolated, quiet. **Surface:** grasstiles.
Distance: Le Tréport centre 2km 2km 100m.
Remarks: Free cableway to city centre, max. 48h.

FR

Le Tréport 13C3
Parc Sainte Croix, Rue Pierre Mendès France.
GPS: n50,05954 e1,38919.

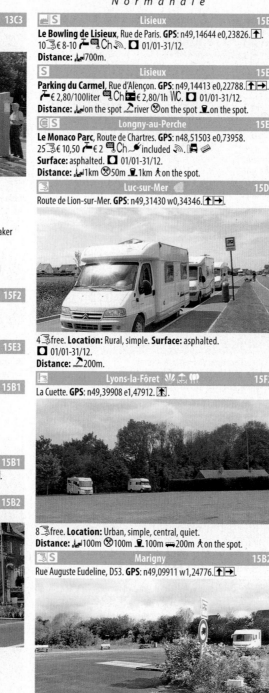

61 € 10 Ch included € 1,80.
Location: Comfortable, isolated, quiet. **Surface:** asphalted.
01/01-31/12.
Distance: 700m 700m 500m Mr.Ed.
Remarks: Industrial area, near camping municipal, max. 48h, baker every morning (Jul/Aug).

Tourist information Le Tréport:
Château d'Eu, Eu. Royal castle, 19th century. 15/03-01/11 Sa.

Léry 15F2
D110. **GPS**: n49,29718 e1,20822.
free Ch WC. **Surface:** metalled. 01/01-31/12.
Distance: on the spot on the spot.

Les Aspres 15E3
Place de l'Ilton. **GPS**: n48,68975 e0,59940.
free Ch WC free. **Surface:** asphalted. 01/01-31/12.

Les Pieux 15B1
Plage Sciotot. **GPS**: n49,50722 w1,84731.
6 free.
Location: Simple. **Surface:** metalled. 01/01-31/12.
Distance: beach 50m.
Remarks: Large parking, 50m from beach.

Les Pieux 15B1
Intermarché, Route de Cherbourg. **GPS**: n49,51736 w1,79797.
€ 2/100liter Ch.

Lessay 15B2
Place Saint Cloud. **GPS**: n49,21850 w1,53548.

6 free Ch WC free. **Location:** Urban, simple.
Surface: asphalted. 01/01-31/12.
Distance: on the spot 150m 200m.
Remarks: Check in at town hall (service).

Lion-sur-Mer 15D2
Rue du General Gallieni. **GPS**: n49,30174 w0,31316.

4 free.
Location: Urban, central, noisy. **Surface:** asphalted.
01/01-31/12.
Distance: on the spot on the spot 100m.
Remarks: At sea, parking townhall, only overnight stays 20-10h.

Lisieux 15E2
Avenue Jean XXIII. **GPS**: n49,14243 e0,24777.
15 free. **Surface:** asphalted. 01/01-31/12.
Distance: on the spot.

Lisieux 15E2
Basilique de Lisieux, Rue des Champs Rémouleux.
GPS: n49,14136 e0,23379.
free. **Surface:** asphalted. 01/01-31/12.

Lisieux 15E2
Le Bowling de Lisieux, Rue de Paris. **GPS**: n49,14644 e0,23826.
10 € 8-10 Ch. 01/01-31/12.
Distance: 700m.

Lisieux 15E2
Parking du Carmel, Rue d'Alençon. **GPS**: n49,14413 e0,22788.
€ 2,80/100liter Ch € 2,80/1h WC. 01/01-31/12.
Distance: on the spot river on the spot on the spot.

Longny-au-Perche 15E3
Le Monaco Parc, Route de Chartres. **GPS**: n48,51503 e0,73958.
25 € 10,50 € 2 Ch included.
Surface: asphalted. 01/01-31/12.
Distance: 1km 50m 1km on the spot.

Luc-sur-Mer 15D2
Route de Lion-sur-Mer. **GPS**: n49,31430 w0,34346.

4 free. **Location:** Rural, simple. **Surface:** asphalted.
01/01-31/12.
Distance: 200m.

Lyons-la-Fôret 15F2
La Cuette. **GPS**: n49,39908 e1,47912.

8 free. **Location:** Urban, simple, central, quiet.
Distance: 100m 100m 100m 200m on the spot.

Marigny 15B2
Rue Auguste Eudeline, D53. **GPS**: n49,09911 w1,24776.

10 free € 2/10minutes Ch € 2/55minutes.
Location: Urban, simple. **Surface:** metalled. 01/01-31/12.
Distance: 700m 200m 700m 700m on the spot.

Merville Franceville 15D2
Boulevard Wattier. **GPS**: n49,28483 w0,21071.

6 free € 2/10minutes Ch. **Location:** Comfortable, quiet.
Surface: asphalted. 01/03-15/11.
Distance: 75m.
Remarks: Max. 48h.

Mesnières-en-Bray 15F1
Grand'rue. **GPS**: n49,76627 e1,38088.
10 free € 2 Ch. **Surface:** gravel. 01/01-31/12.
Distance: 100m.

Montebourg 15B1
Parking Louis Lecacheux. **GPS**: n49,48486 w1,37449.

10 free Ch free. **Location:** Simple. **Surface:** metalled.
01/01-31/12.

Montfiquet 15C2
Hotel-Restaurant Relais de la Fôret, L'Embranchement, D572.
GPS: n49,19400 w0,863.

60 € 14 Ch included WC use sanitary € 2. **Surface:** asphalted.
01/01-31/12.
Distance: 1km 1km.
Remarks: Pay at reception, picnic tables available.

Montville 15F1
Place de l'Abbé Kerebel. **GPS**: n49,54710 e1,07304.

15 free € 4,50/100liter Ch € 4,50/1h free,(8-22.30).
Location: Urban, comfortable, central, quiet. **Surface:** gravel.
01/01-31/12.
Distance: 400m 500m 600m 400m 300m.
Remarks: Coins at mairie, restauration Hexagone, museum, market Saturday.

Tourist information Montville:
Mo-morning.

Mortain 15C3
Place du Château. **GPS**: n48,64887 w0,94489.

6 free Ch WC free. **Location:** Urban, simple.
Surface: asphalted. 01/01-31/12.
Distance: on the spot on the spot on the spot on the spot.
Remarks: Max. 48h.

Tourist information Mortain:
Office de Tourisme, Rue du Bourglopin, www.ville-mortain.fr. Hiking trail to the Grande and Petite Cascade, waterfalls.

Neufchâtel-en-Bray 15F1
Aire Camping Car Sainte Claire, Rue la Grande Flandre.
GPS: n49,73725 e1,42938.

FR

14 € 12 Ch on camp site included.
Location: Urban, comfortable, central, quiet. **Surface:** grassy/gravel.
01/01-31/12.
Distance: 1,5km 2,5km 500m 500m on camp site.
Remarks: Max. 8M.

Nonancourt 15F3

D53, Rue Hippolyte Lozier. **GPS**: n48,77269 e1,19261.

7 free Ch (2x)free.
Surface: asphalted. 01/01-31/12.
Distance: 200m 300m.

Norville 15E1

Clos Saint Martin. **GPS**: n49,47859 e0,64021.

3 free € 2/12minutes Ch € 2/3h.
Location: Urban, comfortable, central, noisy.
Surface: asphalted/grassy. 01/01-31/12.
Distance: on the spot 500m.

Notre-Dame-de-Courson 15E2

D4. **GPS**: n48,99021 e0,25922.

5 free € 2/20minutes Ch € 2/20minutes.
Location: Rural, comfortable, quiet. **Surface:** gravel.
01/01-31/12.
Distance: 200m Le Tournebroche 200m on the spot.
Remarks: Service only with 1-euro coins.

Oissel 15F2

Île du Bras Saint-Martin. **GPS**: n49,33783 e1,09183.

2 free € 2/10minutes Ch € 2/55minutes.
Location: Urban, comfortable, central, quiet.
Surface: gravel.
01/01-31/12.

Distance: 200m on the spot on the spot 200m 200m
200m on the spot.
Remarks: <7m, coins at the bakery: 1, Rue du Maréchal Foch.

Orbec 15E2

Parc de Loisirs, Rue St. Pierre, D915. **GPS**: n49,01758 e0,40506.

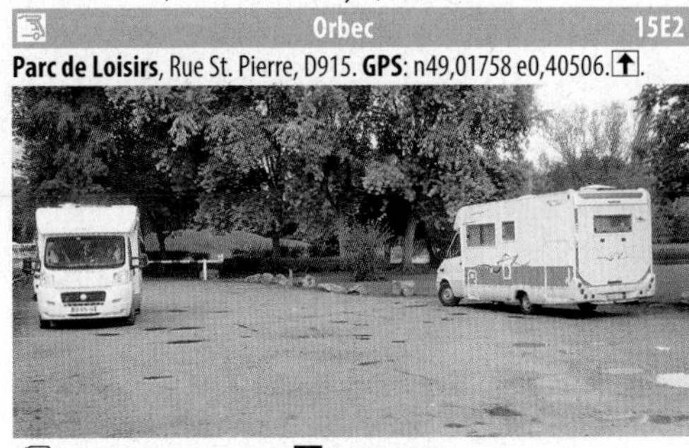

6 free. **Surface:** unpaved. 01/01-31/12.

Ouistreham 15D2

Rue des Dunes/Boulevard Maritime. **GPS**: n49,28716 w0,24968.

45 € 10 Ch included. **Location:** Urban, comfortable, noisy. **Surface:** asphalted/gravel. 01/01-31/12.
Distance: 650m 150m 2km.
Remarks: Near car ferry.

Pirou-Plage 15B2

Rue des Hublots. **GPS**: n49,16522 w1,58937.

6 free € 2/10minutes Ch € 2/55minutes. **Location:** Simple.
Surface: asphalted. 01/01-31/12.
Distance: 500m 500m 500m 500m.
Remarks: Coins at campsite Clos Marin and restaurant La Marée, market on Sunday.

Pommeréval 15F1

Centre équestre Lerat, Route des Essarts.
GPS: n49,73825 e1,29796.
2 € 7,50, 2 pers.incl. WC included. **Location:** Rural, isolated, quiet. **Surface:** grassy. 01/01-31/12.

Pont-d'Ouilly 15D2

Rue de la Libération. **GPS**: n48,87794 w0,41304.

43 € 11/24h € 2 Ch (43x)included.
Location: Rural, comfortable, quiet. **Surface:** gravel.
01/01-31/12.
Distance: 550m on the spot 550m 550m.
Remarks: Along the Orne river.

Pont-l'Évêque 15E2

Les Mouettes, Avenue de Verdun. **GPS**: n49,28563 e0,18769.

6 free. **Location:** Urban, simple, central. **Surface:** gravel.
01/01-31/12.
Distance: on the spot 6km 100m 150m.

Port-en-Bessin-Huppain 15C1

Super U, Avenue du Général de Gaulle. **GPS**: n49,34307 w0,75212.

12 free € 3 Ch € 3/24h. **Location:** Simple.
Surface: gravel/metalled. 01/01-31/12.
Distance: 200m 400m 400m on the spot.

Port-en-Bessin-Huppain 15C1

Rue du 11 Novembre. **GPS**: n49,34583 w0,75861.

17 € 4,50/night.
Location: Rural, simple. **Surface:** sand. 01/01-31/12.
Distance: 300m 400m 400m 500m.

Portbail 15B1

Rue Gilles Poerier. **GPS**: n49,33776 w1,69273.

4 free € 2 Ch € 2/1h. **Location:** Simple, quiet.
Surface: asphalted. 01/01-31/12.
Distance: 200m.
Remarks: At fire-station.

Portbail 15B1

Rue Lechevalier. **GPS**: n49,33689 w1,70084.
15 free. **Surface:** unpaved. 01/01-31/12.
Distance: 300m on the spot on the spot 300m.
Remarks: Beach parking.

Préaux-Saint-Sébastien 15E2

Le Bourg. **GPS**: n48,98679 e0,30732.

free. **Location:** Isolated, quiet. 01/01-31/12.
Distance: on the spot.

FR

Quiberville 13B3

Camping de la Plage de Quiberville, Rue de la Saâne.
GPS: n49,90504 e0,92725.

8 free € 3,80. **Location:** Urban, simple, central, quiet.
Surface: grassy/sand. 01/04-31/10.
Distance: 100m 100m 400m on the spot on the spot.
Remarks: Max. 48h, coins at campsite.

Rauville-la-Bigot 15B1

Résidence de la Moinerie, D900. **GPS**: n49,51622 w1,68371.

10 free Ch free. **Location:** Comfortable, quiet.
Surface: asphalted. 01/01-31/12.
Distance: 500m.

Réville 15C1

Ferme de la Froide Rue, 165, Rue des Monts.
GPS: n49,62583 w1,25278.

6 € 7,50 Ch . **Location:** Rural, comfortable.
Surface: grassy. 01/01-31/12.
Distance: 1km.

Rots 15D2

Centre Commercial Cora, Chemin de la Croix Vautier, RN13.
GPS: n49,19985 w0,46027.

free Ch free .
Location: Noisy. **Surface:** asphalted.
01/01-31/12.
Distance: 1km on the spot on the spot.
Remarks: Terrain with video surveillance.

Rouen 15F1

Quai Cours la Reine. **GPS**: n49,43305 e1,09659.
14 free.
Location: Central. **Surface:** asphalted.
01/01-31/12.
Distance: 700m 700m.
Remarks: Along the Seine river.

Tourist information Rouen:

Office de Tourisme, 25, Place de la Cathedrale, www.rouentourisme.com. Large city with historical centre on theseine river, city of Jeanne d'Arc.

Église St.Maclou.

Place du Vieux-Marché. The square of the stake of Jeanne d'Arc.

Musée de la Céramique. Collection of international ceramics.

Vieux Marché. daily 8-12h.

Rugles 15E3

Place de la Liberté. **GPS**: n48,82319 e0,71087.

20 free Ch free.
Surface: metalled. 01/01-31/12.
Distance: on the spot 200m 200m.
Remarks: Max. 48h.

Ry 15F1

Place Flaubert, Rue Grand' Rue. **GPS**: n49,47244 e1,34465.
2 free € 2 . **Surface:** asphalted. 01/01-31/12.
Distance: on the spot 250m 250m on the spot on the spot.
Remarks: Near office de tourisme, service during opening hours.

Saint Fromond 15C2

Rue des Gabariers, D8. **GPS**: n49,22202 w1,08956.

30 free € 2 Ch € 2. **Location:** Rural, simple.
Surface: asphalted/gravel. 01/01-31/12.
Distance: on the spot 50m on the spot.

Tourist information Saint Fromond:

Office de Tourisme, Bd de Verdun, Carentan, www.ot-carentan.fr. Old bishop city with Gothic cathedral.

Saint-André-de-l'Eure 15F3

Boulevard Verdun. **GPS**: n48,90644 e1,26927.

10 free Ch free. **Location:** Urban, comfortable, noisy.
Surface: metalled. 01/01-31/12.
Distance: 1km on the spot 1km on the spot.
Remarks: Along railwayline.

Saint-Aubin-sur-Mer 13B3

Parking de la plage. **GPS**: n49,89372 e0,87425.
15 € 4 € 2/100liter Ch. 01/04-31/10.
Distance: on the spot on the spot.
Remarks: Beach parking, to be paid at campsite.

Saint-Hilaire-du-Harcouët 15C3

Place de la Motte. **GPS**: n48,57602 w1,09086.

10 free € 2 Ch € 2. **Location:** Urban, simple.
Surface: asphalted/metalled. 01/01-31/12.
Distance: on the spot on the spot on the spot.
Remarks: Behind church.

Saint-Jean-le-Thomas 15B3

Boulevard Stanislas. **GPS**: n48,72567 w1,52296.

17 € 8, 15/11-15/03 free € 2 Ch € 2 WC € 1.
Location: Rural, comfortable. **Surface:** asphalted/grassy.
Distance: 500m 100m 100m 500m on the spot on the spot.

Saint-Jouin-Bruneval 15E1

Rue des Pruniers. **GPS**: n49,65099 e0,16322.

20 free € 2/100liter Ch € 2/1h. **Location:** Rural, simple, isolated, quiet. **Surface:** gravel. 01/01-31/12.
Distance: 1km 1km 1km.
Remarks: Coins at the shops and restaurant.

Saint-Jouin-Bruneval 15E1

Plage de Bruneval, Saint Jouin plage. **GPS**: n49,64970 e0,15349.

20 free. **Location:** Simple, quiet. **Surface:** gravel/metalled.
01/01-31/12.
Distance: 4km pebbled beach on the spot 100m 4km.

Saint-Lô 15C2

Place de la Vaucelle. **GPS**: n49,11351 w1,10309.

10 free € 2/10minutes Ch € 2/h . **Location:** Urban, comfortable. **Surface:** asphalted. 01/01-31/12.
Distance: 100m 100m 100m on the spot.
Remarks: Along river.

Tourist information Saint-Lô:

Haras National, Rue du Maréchal Juin. National Stud farm established by Napoleon in 1806. 01/06-30/09 14-18.

Musée de la Libération, Place du Champ de Mars. Invasion in 1944. 10-19h, winter 14-19h Tue. € 4.

Nôtre Dame. Renovated church 13th century.

Saint-Martin de Bréhal 15B2

Av. de l'Hippodrome. **GPS**: n48,89829 w1,56583.

FR

20 € 4/24h free. **Location:** Urban. **Surface:** asphalted.
01/01-31/12.
Distance: 300m beach 150m 300m 400m.

Saint-Nicolas-d'Aliermont 15F1

Place du 19 Mars 1962, Rue d'Arques 88. **GPS**: n49,88045 e1,22092.

2 free € 2/10minutes Ch € 2/1h.
Location: Urban, simple, central, quiet.
Surface: asphalted.
01/01-31/12.
Distance: 200m 12km 200m 200m on the spot.
Remarks: Behind town hall, max. 48h, coins at town hall and library.

Saint-Nicolas-de-Bliquetuit 15E1

Route du Bac. **GPS**: n49,52083 e0,72777.

12 free € 2/10minutes Ch € 2/1h.
Location: Simple, quiet. **Surface:** asphalted.
01/01-31/12.
Distance: 1,4km on the spot on the spot 2km 2km on the spot.
Remarks: Along the Seine river, coins at town hall, bar and restaurant.

Saint-Nicolas-de-la-Taille 15E1

Voie Grout. **GPS**: n49,51250 e0,47414.
7 free € 3,50 Ch € 350. **Surface:** asphalted.
01/01-31/12.
Distance: 200m 300m.
Remarks: Coins at townhall and bakery.

Saint-Pair-sur-Mer 15B2

Avenue Léon Jozeau-Marigné. **GPS**: n48,81711 w1,56988.

30 € 9,50 € 2,50/10minutes Ch € 2,50/55minutes .
Location: Urban, simple. **Surface:** asphalted/gravel.
01/01-31/12.
Distance: 500m beach 500m 500m on the spot.
Remarks: Parking at tennis-court, max. 48h.

Saint-Pierre-Église 15B1

Parking du 8 Mai 1945. **GPS**: n49,66897 w1,40387.

6 free € 3/100liter Ch € 3. **Location:** Urban.
Surface: metalled. 01/01-31/12.
Distance: 300m on the spot.
Remarks: Coins at supermarket.

Saint-Pierre-le-Vieux 15F1

Ferme du Moulin, Route de la Vallée du Dun.
GPS: n49,85816 e0,88000.

5 € 5 + € 1/pp € 2 Ch € 3. **Location:** Comfortable, isolated, quiet. **Surface:** grassy/gravel. 01/01-31/12.
Distance: 1km 1km 1km on the spot.

Saint-Pierre-lès-Elbeuf 15F2

Rue Galbois. **GPS**: n49,27121 e1,47634.
4 free. 01/01-31/12.
Distance: 300m.

Saint-Pierre-sur-Dives 15D2

Aire Camping-Cars de la Halle Médiévale, Place du Marché.
GPS: n49,01713 w0,03047.

12 € 5/24h € 3 Ch.
Location: Urban, simple, central. **Surface:** gravel.
01/01-31/12 Mo-morning market.
Distance: on the spot 50m 150m.
Remarks: Service passerby € 3.

Saint-Romain-de-Colbosc 15E1

Caux Estuaire, Route d'Oudalle, Parc Éco-Normandie.
GPS: n49,52108 e0,34658.
13 free Ch free. **Location:** Rural, isolated, quiet.
Surface: metalled. 01/01-31/12.
Distance: 1,5km 1,5km 1,5km on the spot.
Remarks: Next to castle, max. 3 days.

Saint-Saire 15F1

Rue de la Gare, D7. **GPS**: n49,69677 e1,49476.

8 free € 3/10minutes Ch € 3/1h. **Location:** Rural, simple, isolated, quiet. **Surface:** grassy. 01/01-31/12.
Distance: 300m on the spot on the spot on the spot.

Saint-Sauveur-le-Vicomte 15B1

Place Auguste Cousin. **GPS**: n49,38678 w1,52947.

free Ch free. **Surface:** asphalted.
Distance: on the spot.
Remarks: Next to town hall, max. 48h.

Saint-Sever-Calvados 15C2

Place de la Mairie. **GPS**: n48,84169 w1,04842.

15 free Ch free. **Location:** Urban, simple, noisy.
Surface: gravel. 01/01-31/12.
Distance: 100m 15km 100m.

Saint-Vaast-la-Hougue 15C1

Aire de la Gallouette, Rue Galouette. **GPS**: n49,58400 w1,267.

27 € 7/night € 2/10minutes Ch € 2/1h.
Location: Comfortable. **Surface:** metalled.
01/01-31/12.
Distance: 300m 300m.
Remarks: Near campsite Gallouette.

Tourist information Saint-Vaast-la-Hougue:
Office de Tourisme, 1, place Gen. de Gaulle, http://ot-pointedesaire.com. Important port for allied forces in 1944. Now large marina.
Île de Tatihou, Port. Island in front of the coast, maritime museum and bird hide. 01/04-30/09 10-18h.

Saint-Valery-en-Caux 13B3

Quai d'Aval. **GPS**: n49,87220 e0,70898.

40 free, weekend 01/03-31/10 € 6/day, 16/05-30/09 € 6/day + € 0,20/pp € 3 Ch. **Location:** Urban, comfortable, central, quiet.
Surface: asphalted. 01/01-31/12.
Distance: 600m on the spot on the spot 500m bakery 600m on the spot.
Remarks: Max. 48h, coins at tourist info.

Saint-Vigor-le-Grand 15C2

Les Peupliers, Rue de Magny. **GPS**: n49,29949 w0,67436.

FR

7 € 10, € 12 service incl Ch included.
Location: Rural, comfortable, isolated, quiet. **Surface:** gravel.
01/01-31/12.
Distance: 2km.
Remarks: Baker every morning, service passerby € 4, Bayeux centre 3,5km, Arromanches beaches 6,5km.

S Saint-Wandrille-Rançon 15E1

Ferme de la Mare. **GPS**: n49,54031 e0,76800.

3 € 5 Ch (3x)€ 2. **Location:** Rural, comfortable, isolated, quiet. **Surface:** gravel. 01/01-31/12.
Distance: 3km 3km.

S Sainte-Honorine-des-Pertes 15C1

Garage Vally, Route d'Omaha Beach, D514, dir Colleville-sur-Mer.
GPS: n49,34868 w0,81635.

32 € 6 € 1,50/100liter Ch (32x)included.
Location: Rural, comfortable, quiet. **Surface:** grassy.
01/01-31/12.
Distance: 200m 500m on the spot.
Remarks: Automatic bread distributor, service passerby € 2,50.

S Sainte-Marie-du-Mont 15C1

Camping-Car Park Utah Beach, La Madeleine, D913.
GPS: n49,41800 w1,18677.

49 € 10,80 Ch (12x) included.
Location: Simple, quiet. **Surface:** grassy/gravel. 01/01-31/12.
Distance: 500m.
Remarks: Mandatory, one-time fee Pass'Etapes € 4, code wifi: f2d1941a5c.

Tourist information Sainte-Marie-du-Mont:
M Musée du Débarquement, Utah-Beach. Landing museum.

S Sainte-Mère-Église 15B1

Super U, ZA les Crutelles. **GPS**: n49,40461 w1,32223.

10 free € 2 Ch.
Surface: asphalted.
Distance: 1km on the spot.
Remarks: Motorhome washing place max. ^3.80m.

Tourist information Sainte-Mère-Église:
i Borne 0 de la voie de la Liberté. Marker 0, start of the Libery Road.
i Office de Tourisme, 2, Rue Eisenhower, www.sainte-mere-eglise.info. Village well-known for the paratrooper who landed on the church-tower.
M Musée Airborne. Exhibition about the invasion at St.-Mère-Eglise.
10-12h, 14-18h.

S Sallenelles 15D2

Boulevard Maritime D514. **GPS**: n49,26474 w0,22694.

2 free € 2/10minutes Ch. **Location:** Rural, simple, quiet.
Surface: asphalted. 01/01-31/12.
Distance: 100m on the spot 300m.
Remarks: Behind town hall, max. 48h.

S Sassetot le Mauconduit 15E1

Château de Sissi, Rue Elisabeth d'Autriche.
GPS: n49,80522 e0,53091.
10 guests free Ch. 11/02-31/12.
Distance: on the spot.

S Sideville-Lorimier 15B1

Camping-car l'Orimier, Route du Pont Roger, D152.
GPS: n49,58722 w1,69222.

6 € 7/night Ch (6x)included. **Location:** Comfortable, quiet. **Surface:** asphalted/grassy. 01/01-31/12.
Remarks: Regional products.

S Siouville-Hague 15B1

Avenue des Peupliers. **GPS**: n49,56356 w1,8442.

40 € 7/24h € 4/100liter Ch € 4/1h.
Surface: grassy. 01/01-31/12.
Distance: 200m.

S Soligny-La-Trappe 15E3

Rue de Vaugelay. **GPS**: n48,61419 e0,53479.
€ 2 Ch € 2. **Surface:** metalled. 01/01-31/12.
Distance: on the spot 250m.

S Soumont-Saint-Quentin 15D2

Rue de la Mine. **GPS**: n48,97840 w0,25.

20 € 7, tourist tax € 0,20/pp € 1 € 2 Ch included.
Location: Simple. **Surface:** grassy. Easter-01/11.
Distance: 1km.
Remarks: Former iron mine.

S Sourdeval 15C3

Parc Saint-Lys, Rue Jean Baptiste Janin.
GPS: n48,72603 w0,92308.

8 free Ch free. **Location:** Urban, simple.
Surface: gravel/metalled. 01/01-31/12.
Distance: 100m 400m 400m.
Remarks: Max. 72h.

S Surtainville 15B1

Rue des mielles. **GPS**: n49,46373 w1,82871.

10 free € 4,30/10minutes Ch € 4,30/55minutes.
Location: Urban. **Surface:** metalled. 01/01-31/12.
Distance: on the spot 100m.
Remarks: Coins at camping municipal.

S Tinchebray 15C3

Rue André Breton, D911. **GPS**: n48,76302 w0,73753.

3 free Ch free. **Location:** Urban, simple.
Surface: asphalted. 01/01-31/12.
Distance: on the spot 300m.
Remarks: Max. 48h.

S Tourlaville 15B1

Espace Loisirs Collignon, Rue des Algues. **GPS**: n49,65398 w1,56606.

free € 2 Ch. **Location:** Simple. **Surface:** asphalted.
Remarks: Coins at campsite or swimming pool.

Tourlaville 15B1

Quai Amiral Kniskern/Boulevard Maritime. **GPS**: n49,64549 w1,59976.

FR

free.
Remarks: Parking at ferry-boat.

S **Tréauville** 15B1

1, La Chaussee, D65. **GPS:** n49,54444 w1,83472.

10 € 6,50 Ch included. **Surface:** grassy/metalled.
Distance: 2,5km.

S **Troarn** 15D2

Parking Super U, Route de Rouen. **GPS:** n49,17907 w0,1907.
free € 2 Ch WC. **Surface:** asphalted. 01/01-31/12.
Distance: on the spot 150m on the spot.

S **Val-de-Saâne** 15F1

Rue Moulin du Traversin. **GPS:** n49,70390 e0,96506.

6 free € 2/100liter Ch € 2/1h.
Location: Urban, comfortable, central, quiet.
Surface: asphalted.
01/01-31/12.
Distance: 300m 300m 300m on the spot on the spot.
Remarks: Coins at town hall, bakery and restaurant, market on Sunday.

S **Valognes** 15B1

Place Félix Buhot. **GPS:** n49,51159 w1,47813.

7 free € 2 Ch € 2. **Location:** Simple. **Surface:** asphalted.
01/01-31/12.
Distance: 1km on the spot.
Remarks: At supermarket Carrefour.

S **Valognes** 15B1

Zone Artisanale d'Armanville, Chemin de la Brique.
GPS: n49,51433 w1,50004.

€ 5/24h € 2 Ch € 2 WC. **Location:** Simple.
Surface: asphalted. 01/01-31/12.

Distance: 1km.
Remarks: Motorhome washing place.

Veules-les-Roses 13B3

Parking des Falaises, Sentier de Four. **GPS:** n49,87508 e0,79231.

40 free. **Location:** Rural, simple, isolated, quiet. **Surface:** grassy.
01/01-31/12.
Distance: 500m on the spot on the spot 500m 500m.

S **Veules-les-Roses** 13B3

Camping des Mouettes, Avenue Jean Moulin 7.
GPS: n49,87596 e0,80289.

15 € 10/24h + € 0,40/pp tourist tax Ch.
Location: Simple, isolated, quiet. **Surface:** gravel/metalled.
01/04-30/10.
Distance: 300m 500m 500m 300m 300m on the spot on the spot.
Remarks: Max. 48h, service on campsite.

S **Veulettes-sur-Mer** 15E1

Chemin des Courses. **GPS:** n49,85233 e0,60165.

15 € 5 € 3,50/100liter Ch € 3,50/1h (16x).
Location: Rural, simple, central, quiet. **Surface:** asphalted.
01/01-31/12.
Distance: 200m 100m 100m 400m 400m on the spot on the spot.
Remarks: Behind Syndicat d'Initiative, coins at tourist info, campsite and supermarket.

S **Veulettes-sur-Mer** 15E1

Parking de la Plage, D10. **GPS:** n49,85488 e0,60702.

20 € 7 € 3,50/10minutes Ch € 3,50/1h WC.
Location: Rural, simple, quiet. **Surface:** grassy.
01/01-31/12.
Distance: 500m pebbled beach 50m 50m 500m 400m 500m.
Remarks: Beach parking.

Villedieu-les-Poêles 15B2

Parc de la Commanderie, Rue Taillemarche.
GPS: n48,83682 w1,22436.

5 free. **Location:** Urban, simple. **Surface:** asphalted.
01/01-31/12.
Distance: on the spot 2,4km 100m 100m.

S **Villers-Bocage** 15C2

Rue du Canada. **GPS:** n49,07973 w0,6609.

5 free € 2/10minutes Ch € 2/55minutes.
Location: Urban, simple, quiet. **Surface:** asphalted.
01/01-31/12.
Distance: 1,5km on the spot 400m on the spot.
Remarks: Max. 48h.

S **Villers-sur-Mer** 15D2

Paleospace l'Odyssee, Rue des Martois.
GPS: n49,32910 e0,01273.

14 € 12 € 2 Ch included € 1
Location: Comfortable, quiet. **Surface:** gravel. 01/01-31/12.
Distance: 1km beach 250m bakery 1,5km.
Remarks: Max. 48h.

S **Villiers-en-Désœuvre** 15F2

Centre Equestre, La Harelle, D106. **GPS:** n48,97560 e1,50250.
4 € 10 WC included. **Location:** Isolated, quiet.
Surface: grassy.
Distance: 3,5km.
Remarks: At horse farm.

S **Vimoutiers** 15E2

D916, Avenue du Dr. Dentu. **GPS:** n48,93152 e0,19604.

6 free Ch (2x) WC free. **Location:** Urban, simple, central.
Surface: asphalted. 01/01-31/12.
Distance: 400m 500m Carrefour 200m.
Remarks: Major centre in the Camembert-region, Camembert museum.

S **Vire** 15C2

Place du champ de foire. **GPS:** n48,84084 w0,88862.

FR

25 free Chfree. **Location:** Urban, simple, noisy.
Surface: asphalted. 01/01-31/12 Fri-Sa.
Distance: on the spot on the spot on the spot.
Remarks: Water closed during wintertime, friday-Saturday market.

Yvetot 15E1

Parking du square Pierre Bobée, Rue de l'Étang.
GPS: n49,61617 e0,76216.
7 free € 3/10minutes Ch € 3/1h. **Location:** Urban.
Surface: asphalted. 01/01-31/12.
Distance: 600m 600m 600m.

Ile-de-France

Bray-sur-Seine 19A1

Quai de l'Ile. **GPS**: n48,41713 e3,23745.

30 free Chfree . **Surface:** asphalted.
Distance: 100m 100m.
Remarks: Along the Seine river, max. 72h, max. 7m.

Tourist information Bray-sur-Seine:
Fri 8-13h.

Coupvray 15H3

Parking Disneyland Paris, Boulevard du Parc.
GPS: n48,87500 e2,79700.

€ 35/day ChWC included. **Surface:** asphalted.
01/01-31/12. **Remarks:** Motorhome area at amusement park, water closed during wintertime, note: tariffs will be charged per day, even if you arrive in the evening.

Tourist information Coupvray:
Disneyland Paris, Marne-la-Vallée. Attractions and themepark.

Milly-la-Forêt 18H1

Route de Nemours. **GPS**: n48,39798 e2,48021.
6 free Chfree. **Location:** Rural. **Surface:** asphalted.
01/01-31/12.
Distance: 1km 9,4km A6.
Remarks: In front of Conservatoire Nationale des Plantes, gate opens automatically.

Milly-la-Forêt 18H1

Total, 49-51 Avenue de Ganay. **GPS**: n48,40720 e2,46782.

10 € 3,50 Ch. **Surface:** grassy. 01/01-31/12.
Distance: centre 500m 7,7km A6.

Remarks: Behind petrol station, gate open 6-21h.

Provins 16A3

Parking Office de Tourisme, Chemin de Villecran.
GPS: n48,56189 e3,27993.

30 € 8/24h € 3,50 Ch € 3,50. **Surface:** gravel.
01/01-31/12 service: frost.
Distance: 500m 500m.

Tourist information Provins:
Sa 8-14h.

Saint-Cyr-sur-Morin 16A3

Avenue Daniel Simon. **GPS**: n48,90627 e3,18516.
4 free Chfree. **Surface:** grassy. 01/01-31/12.
Distance: on the spot.
Remarks: Behind church.

Saint-Fargeau-Ponthierry 15H3

Base de loisirs Seine-Ecole, Avenue Max Pierrou.
GPS: n48,53610 e2,55065.
5 € 5,20 Chincluded. **Surface:** grassy.
Distance: 850m.
Remarks: Recreation park.

Souppes-sur-Loing 18H1

GPS: n48,18083 e2,72343.

5 € 5 € 2 Ch included. **Surface:** asphalted.
Remarks: Max. 72h.

Brittany

Antrain 15B3

Route de Pontorson. **GPS**: n48,46307 w1,47938.

2 free Ch WCfree. **Location:** Urban, simple, central, quiet.
Surface: asphalted.
Distance: 100m 100m 100m 100m 1km on the spot 2km.

Arzal 18A2

Barrage d'Arzal, D139. **GPS**: n47,50089 w2,38074.

15 free. **Location:** Rural, simple, quiet. **Surface:** asphalted.
01/01-31/12.
Distance: 1,5km 50m 50m 50m 50m.

Arzon 14D3

Aire d'accueil des Camping-cars de Kermor, Avenue de Kerlun, Kerjouanno. **GPS**: n47,53886 w2,88028.

49 € 7/24h € 2,50/10minutes Ch (16x) included.
Location: Rural, comfortable, quiet. **Surface:** asphalted.
01/01-31/12.
Remarks: Nearby Plage du Fageo, June/Sep max. 72h.

Audierne 14B2

Rue Lamartine. **GPS**: n48,02733 w4,53721.

15 € 7/24h Ch included. **Location:** Urban, simple.
Surface: unpaved. 01/01-31/12.
Distance: 1,5km on the spot 500m on the spot.

Auray 14D3

Chemin de Bellevue. **GPS**: n47,66365 w2,97393.

5 free ChWCfree.
Location: Simple. **Surface:** asphalted. 01/01-31/12.
Distance: 200m.
Remarks: Small pitches.

Auray 14D3

Place du Golheres. **GPS**: n47,66524 w2,99036.

3 free € 2 Ch.
Location: Urban, simple. **Surface:** asphalted. 01/01-31/12.
Distance: 500m on the spot.
Remarks: During inspection 2015 service out of order.

Tourist information Auray:
Mo.

Availles-sur-Seiche 18B1

D106. **GPS**: n47,96248 w1,19902.
6 free Chfree. **Surface:** unpaved. 01/01-31/12.
Distance: 100m 300m.
Remarks: Max. 24h.

Baud 14D2

Rue du Champ de Foire. **GPS**: n47,87375 w3,02008.

5 free.
Location: Central. **Surface:** metalled. 01/01-31/12.
Distance: on the spot 1,5km 200m on the spot.
Remarks: Max. 72h.

S Baud 14D2

Rue de Pont Augan. **GPS**: n47,87580 w3,02518.
Chfree. 01/01-31/12.

S Bazouges-la-Pérouse 15B3

Boulevard de Castel Marie. **GPS**: n48,42416 w1,57408.

7 free Ch free. **Location:** Urban, simple, central, quiet.
Surface: asphalted. 01/01-31/12.
Distance: 200m 150m 200m.
Remarks: Max. 48h.

Bécherel 15A3

La Feronière. **GPS**: n48,29769 w1,93971.

15 free.
Location: Rural, simple. **Surface:** gravel. 01/01-31/12.
Distance: 700m 700m on the spot 200m.
Remarks: Max. 48h.

S Bédée 18A1

Rue de Dinan. **GPS**: n48,18099 w1,94416.

6 free Chfree.
Location: Urban, simple. **Surface:** asphalted.
Distance: 1km 200m 50m.
Remarks: Nearby cemetery.

S Belle-Isle-en-Terre 14D1

Les Jardins du Guer, Rue Guerveur, D33.
GPS: n48,54425 w3,39472.

6 € 4,80, 15/06-15/09 € 5,20 Ch included.
Location: Comfortable, central, quiet. **Surface:** gravel.
01/01-31/12 service: 01/11-01/04.
Distance: 100m on the spot 350m mountainbike trail on the spot.
Remarks: Narrow entrance.

Belz 14D3

Parc de Loisirs, Rue des Sports. **GPS**: n47,66940 w3,17744.

10 free. **Location:** Simple. **Surface:** gravel/metalled.
01/01-31/12.

S Berric 14D3

Chemin de l'Étang. **GPS**: n47,63294 w2,52905.

5 € 5 € 2/10minutes Ch € 2/55minutes.
Location: Rural, comfortable, quiet. **Surface:** asphalted.
01/01-31/12.
Distance: 500m on the spot on the spot 500m 500m.
Remarks: Along river, coins at the shops in the village, access via Rue du Grand Pont.

S Berric 14D3

Rue du Grand Pont. **GPS**: n47,63304 w2,52888.

6 € 5 € 2/100liter ChWC. **Location:** Rural, simple, quiet.
Surface: asphalted/grassy. 01/01-31/12.
Distance: 300m on the spot on the spot 400m.
Remarks: Coins at the shops.

S Bignan 14D2

Salle des Sports. **GPS**: n47,87760 w2,77342.

3 free Ch. **Location:** Urban, simple. **Surface:** asphalted.
01/01-31/12.
Distance: 300m 250m.
Remarks: At gymnasium.

S Binic 14D1

Aire camping-car de l'Ic, Rue de l'Ic. **GPS**: n48,60059 w2,83573.

50 free Chfree. **Location:** Urban, simple, central, quiet.
Surface: gravel. 01/01-31/12.
Distance: 500m 700m 500m 500m.
Tourist information Binic:
Thu.

Bohal 18A1

Place de l'église. **GPS**: n47,78133 w2,43788.
free. **Location:** Simple. **Surface:** metalled. 01/01-31/12.
Distance: on the spot.
Remarks: Near church.

S Bourg-Blanc 14B1

Rue de Brest. **GPS**: n48,49188 w4,50312.

20 free Chfree. **Location:** Quiet. **Surface:** sand.
01/01-31/12.
Distance: 900m fish pond 100m on the spot on the spot.

S Bréal-sous-Montfort 18A1

Les Jardins de Brocéliande, Les Mesnils.
GPS: n48,05384 w1,88963.

12 € 6 Ch. **Location:** Rural, simple, quiet.
Surface: unpaved. 01/01-31/12.
Distance: 2,5km 3,5km on the spot on the spot on the spot.

S Brech 14D3

Rue de Pont Douar/Avenue des Pins, D768.
GPS: n47,71917 w3,00111.

6 free € 3 Ch.
Location: Simple. **Surface:** grassy. 01/01-31/12.
Distance: 100m 200m 200m.
Remarks: Parking nearby small lake, plan d'eau, coins at the bakery.

Brest 14B1

Parking Océanopolis, Rue du Cormoran. **GPS**: n48,38893 w4,43535.

FR

24 free. **Location:** Urban, simple. **Surface:** asphalted.
01/01-31/12.
Distance: on the spot on the spot 300m.
Remarks: Max. 1 night, 01/06-30/08 only overnight stays (18.30-9h), busy parking during the day, gate closes at 20h.

S Brest 14B1

Port du Moulin Blanc, Rue Eugène Berest.
GPS: n48,39174 w4,43612.
Ch free. 01/01-31/12.

Tourist information Brest:

Tour Tanguy. Diorama old Brest. daily, 01/10-31/05 Wed, Su afternoon.

Océanopolis. Sea-centre, penguin and seals. 01/04-31/08 9-18h, 01/09-31/03 10-17h Mo.

Brillac 14D3

Rue Saint-Maur. **GPS**: n47,54143 w2,81748.

7 free. **Location:** Urban, simple, quiet. **Surface:** asphalted.
01/01-31/12.
Distance: on the spot 400m 450m on the spot on the spot.

S Callac (22) 14C1

Av Ernest Renan. **GPS**: n48,40200 w3,43737.

6 free €2 Ch €2. **Location:** Simple, quiet.
Surface: gravel. 01/01-31/12.
Distance: 200m 200m on the spot.
Remarks: Lac Verte Vallée.

S Camaret-sur-Mer 14B1

Rue Georges Ancey. **GPS**: n48,27513 w4,60793.

75 free, 01/04-31/10 € 6 Ch € 2/55minutes.
Location: Rural, comfortable, quiet. **Surface:** gravel.
01/01-31/12.
Distance: 1km 500m 500m 500m on the spot on the spot.
Remarks: Max. 72h.

S Campénéac 18A1

Rue de l'Étang. **GPS**: n47,95736 w2,29039.

30 free €2 WC. **Location:** Rural. **Surface:** grassy.
01/01-31/12.
Distance: 250m on the spot 250m 250m.
Remarks: Coins at Fauchoux, rue nationale 32.

S Campénéac 18A1

Rue de la Fontaine. **GPS**: n47,95674 w2,29364.
€2 ChWC. 01/01-31/12.
Distance: on the spot on the spot on the spot.
Remarks: Coins at town hall and supermarket, overnight stay: 43.7911 12.4925.

S Cancale 15B3

Aire camping-car Ville Ballet, Rue des Français Libres.
GPS: n48,67004 w1,86583.

30 € 10, first hour free € 3,40/10minutes Ch € 3,40/h.
Location: Simple. **Surface:** grassy. 01/01-31/12.
Distance: 300m 1km 800m 100m.
Remarks: Max. 72h, bread-service.

Tourist information Cancale:

La Ferme Marine. Guided tour oyster farm. summer 11h,15h,17h Français, 14h English, 16h Deutsch.

S Carantec 14C1

Aire du Meneyer, Rue Castel an Dour. **GPS**: n48,65967 w3,9138.

20 free € 3/100liter Ch € 3/55minutes.
Location: Urban, comfortable, quiet. **Surface:** gravel/metalled.
01/01-31/12.
Distance: 500m.
Remarks: Max. 48h, service 50m.

Carantec 14C1

Chemin du Roch Glaz. **GPS**: n48,65235 w3,90308.

10 free. **Location:** Rural, simple, quiet. **Surface:** asphalted.
01/01-31/12.
Distance: beach 300m on the spot.
Remarks: Max. 24h, seaview.

Carantec 14C1

Rue Pen Al Lann. **GPS**: n48,66866 w3,89348.

15 free. **Location:** Rural, simple, quiet. **Surface:** gravel.
01/01-31/12.
Distance: 500m 150m 150m 1km 1km on the spot.
Remarks: At tennis-courts, max. 48h.

Carantec 14C1

Square du Grand Sacconex, Rue du Kélenn.
GPS: n48,66892 w3,91085.

10 free. **Location:** Rural, simple, quiet. **Surface:** grassy.
Distance: 300m on the spot on the spot on the spot 300m on the spot.
Remarks: At gymnasium.

Tourist information Carantec:

Musée Maritime. Navigation museum. 15/05-15-09 Thu.

S Carhaix-Plouguer 14C2

Rue de Bazeilles/Rue des Augustins. **GPS**: n48,27829 w3,57257.

10 free Ch free. **Location:** Urban, simple, central.
Surface: asphalted. 01/01-31/12.
Distance: 200m 200m 200m.

S Carnac 14D3

Square d'Illertissen. **GPS**: n47,58505 w3,08242.

20 free € 2/10minutes Ch € 2/2h. **Location:** Simple.
Surface: asphalted. 01/01-31/12.
Distance: 50m 1,5km 50m 50m.
Remarks: Max. 48h.

Tourist information Carnac:

Office de Tourisme, 74, avenue des Druides, http://www.ot-carnac.fr/. Seaside resort and important place of finding of 30.000 prehistoric menhirs.

Musée de Préhistoire. Prehistoric museum. 10-12.30h and 14-18h 01/12-01/04.

Caro 18A1

Parc des Sports. **GPS**: n47,86421 w2,32582.

FR

3 free. **Location:** Rural, simple, quiet. **Surface:** asphalted.
01/01-31/12.
Distance: 600m 600m.

Caulnes 15A3

Lavoir Fontaine, Rue de Dinan. **GPS**: n48,28655 w2,15517.

5 free € 2/10minutes Ch WC. **Location:** Urban, simple, quiet.
Surface: gravel. 01/01-31/12.
Distance: 500m 100m 100m 200m.
Remarks: Max. 7 days.

Cesson-Sévigné 18B1

Route de La Valette. **GPS**: n48,11802 w1,59121.

8 free € 2/10minutes Ch € 2/55minutes.
Location: Rural, simple, central, quiet. **Surface:** metalled.
01/01-31/12.
Distance: 500m on the spot on the spot 100m 100m 500m on the spot.

Châteauneuf-du-Faou 14C2

Penn ar Pont. **GPS**: n48,18286 w3,81576.

10 free.
Location: Simple, quiet. **Surface:** gravel. 01/01-31/12.
Distance: 1,3km on the spot on the spot.

Châtillon-en-Vendelais 18B1

D108. **GPS**: n48,23112 w1,17959.

10 free Ch free. **Location:** Rural, simple, quiet.
Surface: asphalted. 01/01-31/12.
Distance: 2km lake on the spot on the spot.
Remarks: At the lake, next to campsite.

Cléden-Cap-Sizun 14B2

Place du 19 mars 1962, Rue de la ville d'ys.
GPS: n48,04803 w4,65008.

20 free € 2/10minutes Ch. **Location:** Rural, simple, quiet.
Surface: asphalted/metalled. 01/01-31/12.
Distance: on the spot on the spot.

Cléden-Cap-Sizun 14B2

Pointe du Van, D7. **GPS**: n48,05936 w4,70727.

20 free.
Location: Simple, quiet. **Surface:** gravel. 01/01-31/12.
Distance: Cléden-Cap-Sizun ± 5km on the spot on the spot on the spot.

Cléden-Cap-Sizun 14B2

Route de Kastel Koz, Beuzec-Cap-Sizun. **GPS**: n48,08473 w4,51844.

20 free. **Location:** Rural, simple, isolated, quiet.
Surface: asphalted/gravel. 01/01-31/12.
Distance: on the spot on the spot.

Cléden-Poher 14C2

Route du Stade. **GPS**: n48,23686 w3,67165.

4 free Ch (4x)free. **Location:** Simple, quiet.
Surface: asphalted. 01/01-31/12.
Distance: 300m 50m bakery 200m 400m.
Remarks: Voluntary contribution.

Cléder 14C1

Camping-Car Park Cléder, Le Poulennou.
GPS: n48,69150 w4,12098.

20 € 11,24 Ch (20x)included. **Location:** Rural, comfortable, quiet. **Surface:** gravel. 01/01-31/12.
Distance: 3km on the spot.
Remarks: Mandatory, one-time fee Pass'Etapes € 4.

Cléder 14C1

Espace Nature des Palujous. **GPS**: n48,68636 w4,15212.
free. **Surface:** sand. 01/01-31/12.

Cléguérec 14D2

Etang du Portoir, St-Jean. **GPS**: n48,11670 w3,05534.

4 free. **Location:** Rural, simple, isolated, quiet. **Surface:** asphalted.
01/01-31/12.
Distance: 2km on the spot 2km 2km.

Clohars-Carnoët 14C2

Place de NAVA, Route de Quimperlé. **GPS**: n47,79790 w3,585.

10 free € 2/70liter Ch € 2/50minutes WC.
Location: Simple. **Surface:** asphalted. 01/01-31/12.
Distance: 200m 10km 4,5km bakery 200m.

Combrit 14B2

Place du 19 mars 1962, Hent Ty Plouz. **GPS**: n47,88755 w4,1546.

10 free € 2/10minutes Ch € 2/60minutes.
Location: Urban, simple, quiet. **Surface:** metalled.
01/01-31/12.
Distance: on the spot 5km 200m 1,3km on the spot.
Remarks: Coins at the shops in the village.

Commana 14C1

Place du salles de Sports, D11. **GPS**: n48,41611 w3,96139.

5 free free. **Location:** Rural, simple, isolated, quiet.
Surface: grassy. 01/01-31/12.
Distance: 200m 300m bakery 300m on the spot on the spot.

Concarneau 14C2

Le Porzou, Allée Jean Bouin. **GPS**: n47,86320 w3,9051.

FR

20 free, 01/04-30/09 20-8 uur € 6 € 4/10minutes Ch € 4/55minutes WC. Location: Urban, simple.
Surface: asphalted. 01/01-31/12.
Distance: city centre 2km on the spot on the spot on the spot.
Remarks: Foot ferry to centre.

Concarneau 14C2

Parking de la Gare, Avenue de la Gare. **GPS**: n47,87864 w3,9202.

47 € 6/20-8h € 4 Ch € 4/55minutes.
Location: Simple. **Surface:** asphalted.
01/01-31/12 01/11-30/11. **Distance:** 500m beach 1,4km on the spot on the spot. **Remarks:** Parking station.
Tourist information Concarneau:
Mo, Fri.

Crac'h 14D3

Intermarché, AC Les Alizés. **GPS**: n47,60421 w2,99669.

8 free € 2/10minutes Ch € 2 € 4,50.
Location: Rural, simple, quiet. **Surface:** asphalted.
01/01-31/12.
Distance: on the spot on the spot.

Crozon 14B1

Parking du Loc'h, Rue de l'Atlantique, Morgat.
GPS: n48,22523 w4,50851.

30 € 4,50/24h € 2,30/10minutes Ch € 2,30/55minutes WC.
Location: Urban, simple. **Surface:** asphalted.
01/01-31/12.
Distance: 300m on the spot on the spot 100m on the spot.
Remarks: Max. 48h, market Wednesday.

Crozon 14B1

Le Fret, Le Sillon, D55. **GPS**: n48,28457 w4,50934.

15 free € 2,20/10minutes Ch. **Location:** Rural, simple, quiet.
Surface: unpaved. 01/01-31/12.
Distance: 5,5km 50m 250m 5,5km on the spot.

Crozon 14B1

Parking Office de Tourisme, Boulevard de Pralognan, D887.
GPS: n48,24770 w4,4934.

20 free € 2,30/100liter. **Location:** Urban, simple.
Surface: asphalted. 01/01-31/12.
Distance: 50m on the spot on the spot.
Remarks: Nearby Office de Tourisme, max. 48h.

Crozon 14B1

E.Leclerc Express, Route de Brest. **GPS**: n48,24896 w4,4144.
5 free Ch. **Location:** Urban. **Surface:** asphalted.
01/01-31/12.
Distance: 6km 150m on the spot.

Damgan 14D3

Parking de Kervoyal. **GPS**: n47,51465 w2,56038.

70 € 7,50, 01/04-31/10 € 9,50 Ch included. **Location:** Rural, comfortable, quiet. **Surface:** metalled/sand. 01/01-31/12.
Distance: 600m Sandy beach.
Remarks: Parking at the beach, max. 48h.

Dinan 15A3

Rue du Port, D12. **GPS**: n48,45450 w2,0389.

10 € 5. **Location:** Urban, simple, central. **Surface:** asphalted.
01/01-31/12.
Distance: 800m 800m on the spot 500m on the spot.

Dol-de-Bretagne 15B3

Place Jean Hamelin. **GPS**: n48,54736 w1,75442.

30 free € 2 Ch € 2. **Location:** Urban, simple, noisy.
Surface: asphalted. 01/04-31/10.
Distance: on the spot 100m 100m 150m.

Douarnenez 14B2

Rue Jean Barre. **GPS**: n48,09192 w4,3328.

4 free.
Location: Urban, simple, noisy. **Surface:** asphalted.
01/01-31/12.
Distance: on the spot 200m 200m.
Remarks: Max. 24h, narrow road, not suitable for motorhomes +7m.

Elliant 19B2

Rue Saint Gilles. **GPS**: n47,99648 e3,89044.

15 free € 2,45 Ch € 2,45. **Location:** Simple. **Surface:** sand.
01/01-31/12.
Distance: on the spot 150m.
Remarks: Coins at the shops.

Elven 14D3

Avenue des Martyrs de la Résistance, Le Guého.
GPS: n47,73879 w2,58134.

26 free € 2 Ch (12x)€ 2/4h.
Location: Rural, simple, quiet. **Surface:** grassy/gravel.
parking 01/01-31/12 service 01/07-31/08.
Distance: 1,5km 800m 800m.

Erdeven 14D3

Chemin De Kerouriec. **GPS**: n47,62717 w3,17988.

10 € 7 € 2 Ch (10x)€ 2/night WC. **Location:** Rural, simple, isolated, quiet. **Surface:** grassy. 01/01-31/12.
Distance: 1,1km.

Erdeven 14D3

Parc Kerhillio, Boulevard d'Atlantique. **GPS**: n47,61429 w3,15958.

30 € 6,50/24h Chincluded. **Location:** Rural, simple.
Surface: grassy. 01/01-31/12.
Distance: 500m 200m 200m on the spot on the spot.

Erquy 15A3

Caroual Plage, Rue des Hirondelles. **GPS**: n48,62120 w2,4724.

44 € 6/24h € 2/100liter Ch € 2. **Location:** Urban, comfortable, central. **Surface:** asphalted/metalled.
Distance: 2,5km on the spot.
Remarks: Beach parking, max. 24h, baker at 8am.

Étel 14D3

Camping municipal, Rue de la Barre. **GPS**: n47,65100 w3,202.

25 € 7/night € 2/100liter Ch (16x)against payment .
Location: Rural, simple. **Surface:** grassy. 01/04-30/09.
Distance: 500m 200m on the spot on the spot.
Remarks: Baker every morning (Jul/Aug).

Fouesnant 14C2

Plage Mousterlin, Chemin de Kerneuc. **GPS**: n47,85144 w4,04662.

15 free. **Location:** Rural, simple, quiet. **Surface:** grassy/sand.
01/01-30/12 31/12.
Distance: beach 50m 400m 500m on the spot.
Remarks: Beach parking, max. 48h.

Fouesnant 14C2

Leclerc, D45, Route de Quimper. **GPS**: n47,90234 w4,02938.

12 free € 2/10minutes Ch € 2/55minutes.
Location: Simple, noisy. **Surface:** asphalted. 01/01-31/12.
Distance: on the spot.

Fougères 15B3

Allée des Fêtes. **GPS**: n48,35660 w1,20242.

25 free ChWCfree. **Location:** Urban, simple.
Surface: asphalted. 01/01-31/12.
Distance: 500m 200m 200m.

Fougères 15B3

Parking de la Poterne, Boulevard de Rennes.
GPS: n48,35524 w1,2113.

16 free Chfree. **Location:** Urban, simple, central.
Surface: metalled. 01/01-31/12.
Distance: on the spot 250m 300m on the spot.
Remarks: Castle of Fougères 500m.

Fréhel 15A3

La Ville Oie, Rue des Sports, D117, Pléhérel-plage.
GPS: n48,65032 w2,35241.

40 € 6 € 4/80liter Ch € 4/1h .
Location: Rural, simple, isolated. **Surface:** gravel/metalled.
01/01-31/12.
Distance: 1,1km beach 1,2km on the spot.

Gâvres 14C3

Les Joncs, Rue des Filets Bleus. **GPS**: n47,69515 w3,35097.
40 € 5-7,60, 16/06-31/08 tariff camp site € 2 Ch included.
Surface: grassy. 01/01-31/12.
Distance: 100m 100m.

Glomel 14C2

Etang du Coronc, Rue du Lac. **GPS**: n48,22052 w3,38972.

6 free € 2/100liter Ch € 2/1h . **Location:** Rural, simple, quiet. **Surface:** asphalted/gravel. 01/01-31/12.
Distance: 150m 400m.
Remarks: At lake.

Goulven 14B1

Aire Naturelle Ty Poas. **GPS**: n48,63109 w4,30833.

15 € 6 + tourist tax € 2 Ch € 2 WC included.
Location: Rural, comfortable, quiet. **Surface:** grassy/metalled.
15/06-30/09.
Distance: 500m beach 200m 500m.

Grand-Fougeray 18B2

Rue Camille de Jourdan. **GPS**: n47,72233 w1,7298.

5 free € 2/100liter Ch . **Location:** Urban, simple.
Surface: asphalted. 01/01-31/12.
Distance: 300m 300m.

Gueltas 14D2

Boju, Keriffe. **GPS**: n48,10406 w2,79064.

16 free WCfree. **Location:** Rural, simple, quiet. **Surface:** gravel.
01/01-31/12.
Distance: 1km on the spot.
Remarks: At the Nantes-Brest Canal.

Gueltas 14D2

Rue Maurice Maugain, D125. **GPS**: n48,09667 w2,80111.

10 free free. **Location:** Rural, simple, isolated, quiet.
Surface: gravel. 01/01-31/12.
Distance: 200m.
Remarks: Nearby sports park.

Guern 14D2

Kervazo, Rue de la Vallée, D1. **GPS**: n48,02815 w3,09215.

8 free Chfree. **Location:** Rural, simple, quiet.
Surface: asphalted. 01/01-31/12.
Distance: 250m on the spot bakery 300m.

Guern 14D2

Etang du Ponterre, D1. **GPS**: n48,03472 w3,0975.

6 free. **Location:** Rural, simple, quiet. **Surface:** gravel.
01/01-31/12.
Distance: 700m on the spot 700m bakery.
Remarks: Fishing permit available.

Guichen 18B1

Le Boel, Pont Réan. **GPS**: n48,00221 w1,77336.

5 € 5,40 ChWCfree. **Location:** Simple, quiet.
Surface: metalled. 01/01-31/12.
Distance: 500m on the spot on the spot on the spot bakery 150m.
Remarks: Max. 24h.

S Guidel 14C2

D152, Guidel-Plage > Fort-Bloqué. **GPS:** n47,75035 w3,50574.

15 free WC. **Location:** Rural, simple. **Surface:** gravel/sand.
01/01-31/12.
Distance: 1,5km 100m 1,5km on the spot on the spot.
Remarks: Behind Résidence Maéva, beach parking, max. 24h.

Guidel 14C2

La Falaise, Guidel plage. **GPS:** n47,76640 w3,5258.

7 free.
Location: Simple. **Surface:** metalled. 01/01-31/12.
Distance: on the spot.
Remarks: Behind yachting school, max. 24h.

Guidel 14C2

Plage du Loc'h, D152. **GPS:** n47,75650 w3,5159.

6 free. **Location:** Quiet. **Surface:** sand. 01/01-31/12.
Distance: 250m.

S Guidel 14C2

Arc-en-Ciel, ZA de Pen Mané. **GPS:** n47,80980 w3,4633.
service € 2, during opening hours ChWC. 01/01-31/12.

S Guimiliau 14C1

Parking Salle Polyvalente, Rue des Bruyeres.
GPS: n48,48676 w3,99665.

15 free free. **Location:** Simple, central, noisy.
Surface: metalled. 01/01-31/12.

Distance: on the spot 400m 400m on the spot on the spot.
Remarks: Max. 2 nights.

S Guingamp 14D1

Place du Vally. **GPS:** n48,56024 w3,1489.

free Chfree WC. **Location:** Simple, central.
Surface: asphalted. 01/01-31/12 Fri market.
Distance: on the spot.
Remarks: Max. 24h.

S Guiscriff 14C2

La Gare de Guiscriff, Rue de la Gare.
GPS: n48,05722 w3,65401.

4 free Ch (4x). **Location:** Rural. **Surface:** metalled.
01/01-31/12.
Distance: 1km bakery 1km on the spot on the spot.

S Guissény 14B1

Rue de Plouguerneau. **GPS:** n48,63299 w4,41127.

8 free Ch. **Location:** Urban, simple, central.
Surface: gravel. 01/01-31/12.
Distance: on the spot beach 550m 250m bakery.
Remarks: Coins at the shops and town hall.

Hédé-Bazouges 15B3

La Magdelaine. **GPS:** n48,30592 w1,79218.

50 free. **Location:** Rural, simple. **Surface:** grassy/gravel.
01/01-31/12.
Distance: 1km on the spot on the spot 50m on the spot on the spot.

S Hillion 14D1

Le Tertre Piquet, Lermot-plage. **GPS:** n48,53098 w2,66387.

20 free ChWCfree. **Location:** Simple, isolated. **Surface:** grassy.
01/01-31/12.
Distance: sandy beach 100m.
Remarks: Beach parking, max. 48h.

S Hillion 14D1

Rue Olivier Provost. **GPS:** n48,51743 w2,66772.

7 free Chfree. **Location:** Simple, central, quiet. **Surface:** gravel.
01/01-31/12.
Distance: 500m 100m on the spot.
Remarks: Max. 48h.

S Hirel 15B3

D155. **GPS:** n48,60841 w1,82032.

100 € 6/night € 2/100liter Ch € 2/50minutes.
Location: Rural, simple. **Surface:** grassy/gravel.
01/01-31/12.
Distance: 700m 200m 200m.

S Huelgoat 14C1

Place du Camping-cars, Route du Fao, D769a.
GPS: n48,36115 w3,75612.

30 free € 5/10minutes Ch 1h.
Location: Rural, simple, quiet. **Surface:** metalled. 01/01-31/12.
Distance: 500m on the spot on the spot 500m 500m 500m 500m 500m.
Remarks: In front of campsite municipal, service 100m.

S Janzé 18B1

Aire du Hardier, D41. **GPS:** n47,97258 w1,53825.

5 € 10 € 2 ChWCfree. **Location:** Motorway, simple.
Surface: asphalted.
Distance: on the spot.
Remarks: At petrol station.

S Josselin 14D2

Place St.Martin. **GPS:** n47,95639 w2,55056.

50 free € 2,50 ChWC . **Location:** Urban, central. **Surface:** metalled. 01/01-31/12 Sa 9-14h.
Distance: 300m N24 900m 300m bakery 300m 1km on the spot.
Remarks: Castle of Josselin 400m, market Saturday.

Tourist information Josselin:
Office de Tourisme, Place de la Congregation, www.paysdejosselin.com. City is dominated by the castle of Rohan.

S Kergrist-Moëlou 14D2
Lotissement Hélène Le Chevalier. GPS: n48,31016 w3,31876.

4 free Chfree. **Location:** Rural, isolated, quiet. **Surface:** gravel. 01/01-31/12.
Distance: 100m 500m on the spot.

S Kerlouan 14B1
Aire de Camping-Car de Ménéham, Lestonquet.
GPS: n48,66952 w4,36161.
50 € 7 Ch € 3,50/24h € 5/3 included.
Surface: grassy. 01/01-31/12.
Distance: on the spot on the spot 850m.
Remarks: Next to campsite, video surveillance.

S Kernascléden 14C2
Domaine du Scroff, Canquisquelen. **GPS**: n47,99785 w3,31845.

2 € 10 Ch WC included. **Location:** Rural, comfortable, quiet. **Surface:** grassy. 01/01-31/12.
Distance: 1km on the spot on the spot.
Remarks: Heated pool.

S La Chèze 14D2
Chemin d'Alénor, Allée du 19 mars 1962.
GPS: n48,13419 w2,65787.

10 € 4, weekend/holidays free Ch (6x)WCfree.
Location: Simple, quiet. **Surface:** asphalted. 01/01-31/12.
Distance: 200m on the spot 200m mountainbike trail.
Remarks: Parking at small lake.

S La Fontenelle 15B3
Rue de la Quintaine. **GPS**: n48,46575 w1,50495.

10 free € 2/10minutes Ch € 2/55minutes.
Location: Rural, simple, quiet. **Surface:** asphalted. 01/01-31/12.
Distance: on the spot 350m on the spot on the spot.
Remarks: Next to cemetery, adjacent walking and bicycle area.

S La Martyre 14C1
Route de Ploudiry, D35. **GPS**: n48,44861 w4,15694.

10 free Ch WCfree. **Location:** Rural, quiet. **Surface:** gravel. 01/01-31/12.
Distance: 100m 100m 100m on the spot on the spot.
Remarks: Nearby Maison du Plateau.

La Roche-Bernard 18A2
Place du Dôme. **GPS**: n47,51753 w2,29733.

10 free. **Location:** Urban, simple, central. **Surface:** asphalted. 01/01-31/12.
Distance: 50m 100m 50m.

S La Roche-Bernard 18A2
Halte Camping-car, Rue du Patis. **GPS**: n47,52012 w2,30466.

15 € 7, 01/07-25/08 € 11,10 Ch € 4,60 WC .
Location: Urban, comfortable, quiet. **Surface:** grassy. 02/04-16/09.
Distance: 100m 50m 50m 100m 100m.
Remarks: Next to campsite du Patis.

Tourist information La Roche-Bernard:
Small town especially known for the beautiful hanging bridge over the Vilaine river, 50m high and over 400m long.

S La Roche-Derrien 14D1
Rue du Jouet. **GPS**: n48,74696 w3,25976.

12 € 2 € 2 Ch (6x)€ 2 .

Location: Rural, simple, central, quiet. **Surface:** gravel. 01/01-31/12.
Distance: 100m 100m 100m.
Remarks: Coins at the shops and town hall.

S Lampaul-Guimiliau 14C1
Route du Saint-Jacques. **GPS**: n48,49408 w4,03857.

15 free Ch. **Location:** Rural, simple, quiet. **Surface:** grassy/sand. 01/01-31/12.
Distance: 250m 350m.

S Lampaul-Plouarzel 14B1
Aire de Porspaul, Rue de Beg ar Vir. **GPS**: n48,44667 w4,77722.

50 free, Easter-01/11 € 4 + € 0,60/pp touristt tax € 2/10minutes Ch € 2/55minutes WC € 2 € 3/3,50.
Location: Rural, comfortable. **Surface:** grassy. 01/04-05/11.
Distance: 150m 100m 200m 500m on the spot on the spot.
Remarks: Baker at 9am, shower and washing machine Jul/Aug.

S Landerneau 14B1
Rue du Calvaire. **GPS**: n48,44694 w4,25667.

25 € 6,50 € 2,55 Ch € 2,55 . **Location:** Rural, comfortable. **Surface:** grassy/gravel. 01/01-31/12.
Distance: 500m river 500m 500m on the spot.

S Landivisiau 14C1
P de Keravel, Rue du Manoir. **GPS**: n48,51015 w4,0758.

15 free Chfree. **Location:** Urban, simple, quiet. **Surface:** asphalted. 01/01-31/12.
Distance: on the spot on the spot 100m centre.

S Landudec 14B2
Super U, Rue des Écoles. **GPS**: n48,00143 w4,34088.

FR

5 free € 2/10minutes Ch € 2/55minutes. **Location:** Rural, simple. **Surface:** asphalted. 01/01-31/12.
Distance: 1km on the spot on the spot.
Remarks: Motorhome washing place.

S Lanfains 14D1

Étang du Pas, Le Pas, D7. **GPS**: n48,36466 w2,87938.

6 free Ch WC free. **Location:** Simple, quiet.
Surface: asphalted/grassy. 01/05-01/10.
Distance: on the spot on the spot.
Remarks: Parking at small lake.

S Languidic 14D2

Zone Lanveur, Place du Bouilleur de Cru.
GPS: n47,83722 w3,16188.

20 free Ch free. **Location:** Motorway, simple, noisy.
Surface: metalled. 01/01-31/12.
Distance: 700m N24 300m.

Lanloup 14D1

Rue de Saint-Roch. **GPS**: n48,71359 w2,96389.

2 free WC free. **Location:** Rural, simple, quiet. **Surface:** gravel.
01/01-31/12.
Distance: on the spot.

S Lannilis 14B1

Aire Fontaine Rouge. **GPS**: n48,55667 w4,50528.

20 free Ch WC free. **Location:** Rural, simple, noisy.
Surface: metalled. 01/01-31/12.
Distance: 1km 1,5km 1,5km.

S Lannilis 14B1

Rue Haie Blanche. **GPS**: n48,57125 w4,52151.

20 free Ch free. **Location:** Urban, simple, quiet.
Surface: asphalted. 01/01-31/12.
Distance: 100m bakery 150m.
Remarks: In front of cemetery.

S Lanvallay 15A3

Rue du terrain des sports. **GPS**: n48,45420 w2,03028.

5 free € 2/100liter Ch € 2/h. **Location:** Urban, simple.
Surface: asphalted. 01/01-31/12.
Distance: 50m 50m 50m.

S Larmor-Baden 14D3

Route d'Auray. **GPS**: n47,58816 w2,89868.

3 free free. **Location:** Simple. **Surface:** asphalted.
01/01-31/12.
Distance: 50m 100m 100m.
Remarks: Max. 6,5m.

S Larmor-Plage 14C3

Parking les Pins, Rue des Pins. **GPS**: n47,70970 w3,3791.

4 free Ch WC free. **Location:** Central. **Surface:** asphalted.
01/01-31/12.
Distance: on the spot 50m 100m 100m.
Remarks: Nearby plage de Toulhars, max. 72h.

S Le Conquet 14B1

Parking Parklec'H, Rue Général Leclerc. **GPS**: n48,36055 w4,7701.

+10 free € 2,50/100liter Ch € 2,50/1h.
Location: Urban, noisy. **Surface:** gravel. 01/01-31/12.
Distance: 200m beach 800m 400m bakery 300m on the spot.
Remarks: Coins at tourist info and town hall.

S Le Croisty 14C2

Aire de pique-nique, D132, Kergoff. **GPS**: n48,06720 w3,38196.

8 free € 2 Ch € 2/55minutes WC.
Location: Comfortable, isolated, quiet. **Surface:** asphalted.
01/01-31/12.
Distance: 1,5km on the spot.

S Le Faou 14C1

Camping-Car Park, Rue de la Grève. **GPS**: n48,29529 w4,18501.

20 € 10,92- 13,32 Ch (20x) included.
Location: Urban, simple. **Surface:** grassy/metalled.
01/01-31/12.
Distance: 500m 600m 1,5km.
Remarks: Mandatory, one-time fee Pass'Etapes € 4.

S Le Faouët 14C2

Restaurant Ty Blomen, Le Grand Pont. **GPS**: n48,03575 w3,48125.

15 free € 2 Ch. **Location:** Rural, simple. **Surface:** asphalted.
01/01-31/12.
Distance: on the spot.
Remarks: Inclining pitches.

S Le Folgoët 14B1

Parking Freppel, Route de Gorrékear. **GPS**: n48,56002 w4,33507.

30 free Ch free. **Location:** Rural, simple, central, quiet.
Surface: gravel/metalled. 01/01-31/12.
Distance: on the spot 100m 100m.
Remarks: Nearby basilica.

S Le Guilvinec 14B2

Parking de la Petite Sole, Rue Jean Baudry.
GPS: n47,79588 w4,27997.

16 € 4 € 2/100liter Ch € 2/10minutes.
Location: Urban, simple, noisy. **Surface:** asphalted.
01/01-31/12 Su market.
Distance: on the spot on the spot 100m 100m on the spot.
Remarks: Coins at tourist info.

Le Guilvinec 14B2

Le Malamok, Rue Mejou Bihan. **GPS**: n47,79827 w4,27665.
20 free. **Location:** Urban. **Surface:** asphalted. 01/01-31/12.
Distance: 500m 300m.

S Le Trévoux 14C2

Parking du Plan d'Eau, Rue des Sports. **GPS**: n47,89683 w3,64228.

FR

4 free Ch free. **Location:** Simple. **Surface:** gravel.
01/01-31/12.
Distance: on the spot.
Remarks: Nearby tennis-courts, max. 48h, crowdy during the day.

Le Trévoux 14C2

Plan d'Eau, Rue de Quimperlé. **GPS**: n47,89356 w3,6386.

10 free. **Location:** Simple. **Surface:** gravel. 01/01-31/12.
Distance: on the spot bakery.
Remarks: At lake.

Le Vivier-sur-Mer 15B3

Camping-Car Park, Rue de l'Abri des Flots.
GPS: n48,60291 w1,77255.

49 € 9,60 Ch (40x),4Amp included.
Location: Rural, comfortable, quiet. **Surface:** grassy/gravel.
01/01-31/12.
Distance: on the spot 100m 100m 150m 150m on the spot.
Remarks: Mandatory, one-time fee Pass'Etapes € 4.

Léhon 15A3

Parking Club de Tennis. **GPS**: n48,44177 w2,04233.

6 free Ch free. **Location:** Urban, simple. **Surface:** asphalted.
01/01-31/12.
Distance: on the spot bakery 100m.

Les Forges 14D2

Place de l'Église, D117. **GPS**: n48,01820 w2,6482.

5 free WC free. **Location:** Rural, simple.
Surface: metalled. 01/01-31/12.
Distance: 100m 100m.

Lézardrieux 14D1

Rue de l'Île à Bois. **GPS**: n48,83002 w3,08165.

5 free. **Location:** Simple, isolated, quiet. **Surface:** gravel/sand.
01/01-31/12.
Distance: Lézardrieux 6km 50m on the spot.
Remarks: Max. 24h.

Lézardrieux 14D1

Camping Municipal, Cité des Gardiens de Phare.
GPS: n48,78021 w3,1147.
Ch free. 01/01-31/12.
Distance: on the spot.

Liffré 18B1

Intermarché. **GPS**: n48,22459 w1,50165.

10 free Ch free. **Location:** Urban, simple.
Surface: asphalted. 01/01-31/12.
Distance: 300m on the spot.

Lizio 14D2

Rue du Souvenir. **GPS**: n47,86202 w2,5263.

10 free Ch free. **Location:** Rural, simple, quiet.
Surface: metalled. 01/01-31/12.
Distance: 150m.

Locmaria-Plouzané 14B1

Zône détente Ty Izella, Rue de la Fontaine.
GPS: n48,37343 w4,64386.

6 free Ch free. **Location:** Rural, quiet. **Surface:** gravel.
01/01-31/12.
Distance: 100m 250m 250m.

Locmaria-Plouzané 14B1

Plage de Portez, Rue de Portez, Porsmilin.
GPS: n48,35501 w4,67269.

8 € 5, tourist tax € 0,60/pp Ch included € 3.
Location: Rural, simple, quiet. **Surface:** gravel.
18/04-18/09.
Distance: 3,5km beach 50m on the spot on the spot.
Remarks: To be paid at campsite.

Locmariaquer 14D3

Aire de Pierres Plates, > Route des Plages.
GPS: n47,55720 w2,9486.

20 free.
Location: Simple. **Surface:** metalled. 01/01-31/12.
Distance: beach 50m on the spot.
Remarks: Max. 24h, 500m from 'Les Pierres Plates'.

Locmariaquer 14D3

Résidence de Cresidui. **GPS**: n47,57204 w2,95328.
€ 2/100liter Ch.

Tourist information Locmariaquer:
Office de Tourisme, Rue de la Victoire, www.ot-locmariaquer.com. Port city with many megalithics, signed dolmen.

Locminé 14D2

Rue Laennec / rue du Pont Person. **GPS**: n47,88788 w2,83174.

10 free Ch free. **Location:** Simple. **Surface:** gravel.
01/01-31/12.
Distance: 1km N24 1,4km 600m.
Remarks: Max. 48h.

Locmiquelic 14C3

Port de Ste. Catherine, Quai Rallier du Baty.
GPS: n47,72364 w3,34958.

free. **Location:** Simple. **Surface:** asphalted.
Distance: on the spot on the spot on the spot.
Remarks: Parking at marina, max. 1 night.

Locqueltas 14D3

Rue de la Fontaine. **GPS**: n47,75841 w2,76901.

FR

6 free Ch (4x)€ 3,50 WC free.
Location: Rural, simple, quiet. **Surface:** gravel.
01/01-31/12.
Distance: 100m 600m 100m 100m.
Remarks: Max. 24h, coins at Bar-Tabac, 18 Place de la Mairie, town hall.

S Locronan 14B2

Parking de la Croix de Mission, Rue du Prieuré.
GPS: n48,09811 w4,21245.

10 free, 01/06-15/10 € 6/24h € 2/10minutes Ch € 2/2h.
Location: Urban, simple, quiet. **Surface:** grassy/sand.
01/01-31/12.
Distance: 100m 50m on the spot on the spot.

S Loctudy 14B2

Camping-Car Park, Rue des Mésanges. **GPS:** n47,82813 w4,16563.
23 € 10,04-12,44 Ch (20x)included.
Surface: metalled. 01/01-31/12.
Remarks: Mandatory, one-time fee Pass'Etapes € 4.

Loctudy 14B2

Plage des Sables Blancs, Chemin de Toul Pesked.
GPS: n47,80110 w4,20044.

6 free. **Location:** Rural, simple. **Surface:** grassy/sand.
01/01-31/12.
Distance: 4km beach 80m on the spot on the spot.
Remarks: Beach parking.

S Loudéac 14D2

Parking de la Gare, Boulevard de la Gare.
GPS: n48,18058 w2,76277.

3 free Ch free. **Location:** Urban, simple. **Surface:** asphalted.
01/01-31/12.
Distance: 600m 50m 200m 200m on the spot.

S Maël-Carhaix 14C2

Place de l'école, Route de Rostrenen. **GPS:** n48,28344 w3,42148.

3 free € 2,25 Ch WC. **Location:** Urban, simple.
Surface: asphalted. 01/01-31/12.
Distance: 100m 100m 100m.
Remarks: Coins at town hall.

S Malansac 18A2

Rue Saint Fiacre. **GPS:** n47,67820 w2,29942.

5 free Ch free. **Location:** Rural, comfortable, quiet.
Surface: grassy. 01/01-31/12.
Distance: 100m 100m 100m.

S Malestroit 18A1

Chemin de l'Écluse. **GPS:** n47,81250 w2,38197.

12 free . **Location:** Rural, comfortable, quiet.
Surface: gravel/metalled. 01/01-31/12.
Distance: 100m on the spot on the spot 100m 100m 200m.
Remarks: Max. 48h.

S Malestroit 18A1

Chemin des Tanneurs. **GPS:** n47,80772 w2,37885.

12 free . **Location:** Comfortable, quiet. **Surface:** gravel/metalled.
01/01-31/12.
Distance: 500m on the spot 350m.
Remarks: Max. 48h.

S Malestroit 18A1

Rue de Narvik. **GPS:** n47,80896 w2,37591.
Ch free. **Surface:** asphalted. 01/01-31/12.
Distance: 1,5km 600m 600m 2km 1km.

S Marzan 18A2

Rue de la Source. **GPS:** n47,54023 w2,32383.

20 free Ch WC free. **Location:** Urban, simple, quiet.
Surface: asphalted. 01/01-31/12.
Distance: 50m 20m.
Remarks: Max. 72h.

S Maure-de-Bretagne 18A1

Rue de Campel, D65. **GPS:** n47,89230 w1,99031.

3 free Ch free. **Location:** Urban, simple, central, quiet.
Surface: gravel. 01/01-31/12.
Distance: 200m on the spot 200m 200m on the spot on the spot on the spot.

S Mauron 18A1

Route du Plan D'eau. **GPS:** n48,07883 w2,27573.

10 free Ch free. **Location:** Rural, simple, quiet.
Surface: gravel/metalled. 01/01-31/12.
Distance: 500m 500m.

S Mauron 18A1

Rue de la Libération. **GPS:** n48,08024 w2,27677.

12 free € 2,50/100liter Ch WC. **Location:** Rural, simple, quiet.
Surface: asphalted.
Distance: 150m on the spot on the spot 150m 150m on the spot on the spot.

S Mégrit 15A3

Parking du Stade, Rue des Granitiers. **GPS:** n48,37817 w2,24722.
free Ch free. **Surface:** asphalted/gravel. 01/01-31/12.
Distance: on the spot.

S Mellé 15B3

Rue Rouviel. **GPS:** n48,48919 w1,18814.

4 free Ch WC free. **Surface:** metalled. 01/01-31/12.
Distance: 200m 200m.
Remarks: Nearby football ground, max. 48h.

S Meslin 14D1

Allée des Loisirs, D28. **GPS:** n48,44363 w2,56994.

10 free Ch free. **Location:** Urban, simple, central.
Surface: metalled. 01/01-31/12.
Distance: 300m bar/crêperie 50m 50m.

S Moëlan-sur-Mer 14C2

Rue de Beg Tal Gward. **GPS**: n47,77749 w3,64404.

4 free . **Location:** Rural, isolated, quiet. **Surface:** asphalted.
01/01-31/12.
Distance: Moëlan 5km sea 50m.
Remarks: Along Mosel.

Moëlan-sur-Mer 14C2

Kerdoualen, Route de l'Île Percée. **GPS**: n47,79045 w3,70314.

4 free. **Location:** Rural. **Surface:** gravel. 01/01-31/12.
Distance: 200m.

Mohon 14D2

Route de Josselin, D793. **GPS**: n48,04903 w2,52838.

10 free . **Location:** Rural, simple. **Surface:** grassy.
01/01-31/12.
Distance: 1km 150m 250m.

S Moncontour 14D2

Camping la Tourelle, Rue François Lorant.
GPS: n48,35271 w2,63719.

3 €4 Ch included . **Location:** Rural, simple, quiet.
Surface: gravel. 01/01-31/12.
Distance: 1,5km 1,5km 1,5km.
Remarks: Max. 48h.

Monterrein 18A1

Parking de la Mairie, Rue de la Mairie. **GPS**: n47,88055 w2,35872.

2 free. **Location:** Simple, quiet. **Surface:** asphalted.
01/01-31/12.
Distance: on the spot 200m.

Montertelot 18A1

Rue du Casset. **GPS**: n47,88306 w2,4225.

20 free.
Location: Simple, quiet. **Surface:** grassy. 01/01-31/12.
Distance: 200m 100m 100m 300m.
Remarks: Near sports fields.

S Morlaix 14C1

Rue de Brest. **GPS**: n48,57422 w3,8316.

9 free Ch free. **Location:** Urban, simple, central, noisy.
Surface: asphalted. 01/01-31/12.
Distance: on the spot on the spot 200m 100m 200m
on the spot on the spot.

S Mûr-de-Bretagne 14D2

L'ancienne Gare, Place de la Gare. **GPS**: n48,19814 w2,98961.

4 free Ch free. **Location:** Urban, simple. **Surface:** metalled.
01/01-31/12.
Distance: 700m 500m on the spot.

Mûr-de-Bretagne 14D2

Anse de Leandroanec, Plage de Leandroanec.
GPS: n48,20969 w3,01309.

8 free. **Location:** Rural, simple, isolated, quiet. **Surface:** gravel.
01/01-31/12.
Distance: 2,5km on the spot.
Remarks: Inclining pitches.

Mûr-de-Bretagne 14D2

Chapelle Sainte-Suzanne, Place Ste Suzanne.
GPS: n48,20260 w2,98835.

4 free. **Location:** Urban, simple. **Surface:** metalled.
01/01-31/12.
Distance: 300m 100m.

S Neulliac 14D2

Rue des Deux Croix, D767. **GPS**: n48,12812 w2,98552.

4 free €2 Ch €2. **Location:** Urban, simple, isolated, quiet.
Surface: asphalted. 01/01-31/12.
Distance: 300m 300m.

S Névez 14C2

Parking du Stade, Rue de Port Manech, Impasse du Stade.
GPS: n47,81560 w3,7894.

20 free €2/10minutes Ch €2/55minutes WC free.
Location: Urban, simple. **Surface:** asphalted. 01/01-31/12.
Distance: 850m 300m 850m.
Remarks: Parking next to stadium, max. 24h, service only with 2-euro coins.

S Névez 14C2

Plage de Tahiti, Kerstalen. **GPS**: n47,79287 w3,79011.

± 11 free WC free. **Location:** Rural, simple, quiet.
Surface: grassy/sand. 01/01-31/12.
Distance: beach 150m.
Remarks: Beach parking, max. 24h.

Névez 14C2

Plage de Dourveil, Rue de Dourveil, D1. **GPS**: n47,79407 w3,8101.

5 free. **Location:** Simple. **Surface:** sand. 01/01-31/12.
Distance: on the spot on the spot.

FR

Remarks: Max. 24h, no camping activities.

Névez 14C2

Rue de la Plage. **GPS**: n47,80499 w3,74261.

5 free.
Location: Rural, simple. **Surface:** sand. 01/01-31/12.
Distance: 50m on the spot on the spot.
Remarks: Max. 24h.

Névez 14C2

Rue des Iles, Raguénez. **GPS**: n47,78908 w3,80174.

10 free. **Location:** Rural, simple. **Surface:** asphalted.
01/01-31/12.
Distance: sea 10m, beach 150m 100m.
Remarks: Max. 24h.

Noyal-Pontivy 14D2

Le Valvert, Caudan. **GPS**: n48,07833 w2,91583.

20 free WC free. **Location:** Rural, comfortable, isolated, quiet.
Surface: asphalted. 01/01-31/12.
Distance: Noyal-Pontivy 4,5km on the spot on the spot 50m.
Remarks: At small lake.

Noyal-Pontivy 14D2

Le Manoir, Avenue de la Liberation. **GPS**: n48,06689 w2,87937.

10 free.
Location: Rural, simple. **Surface:** gravel. 01/01-31/12.
Distance: 150m 250m 300m.

Paimpol 14D1

Parking de Goas Plat, Rue de Goas Plat. **GPS**: n48,77535 w3,04009.

37 € 8. **Location:** Urban, simple, central, quiet.
Surface: asphalted.
Distance: centre 500m 2km 500m 500m.
Remarks: Max. 24h.

Paimpol 14D1

Parking Pierre Loti, Rue Pierre Loti. **GPS**: n48,78404 w3,0463.

15 free, 01/06-30/09 € 5.
Surface: gravel/sand. 01/01-31/12.
Distance: on the spot 1km 400m 100m on the spot on the spot.
Remarks: Service 100m.

Paimpont 18A1

Rue de l'Enchanteur Merlin. **GPS**: n48,02286 w2,17128.

10 € 2,50, 01/06-30/09 € 4 € 3,70/10minutes ChWC.
Location: Simple. **Surface:** gravel.
Distance: 200m 200m 200m 200m 200m on the spot 100m.
Remarks: Coins at tourist info and supermarket.

Pénestin 14D3

Allée du Grand Pré. **GPS**: n47,48111 w2,47361.

7 free, € 6/night + € 0,20/pp € 2,50/100liter Ch € 2,50/1h.
Location: Urban. **Surface:** asphalted.
01/01-31/12.
Distance: 500m 1,5km 500m.
Remarks: Check in all aires in Pénestin: Office de tourisme; Bar-PMU Le Narval, Rue Calvaire; Café 0 20 100 0, Port de Tréhiguier, max. 48h, coins at tourist info.

Pénestin 14D3

Aire camping-car de la Pointe du Bile, Route de l'Espernel.
GPS: n47,44524 w2,48029.

free, € 6/night + € 0,20/pp. **Location:** Rural, simple, quiet.
Surface: grassy/sand. 01/01-31/12.
Distance: 100m.
Remarks: Max. 48h.

Pénestin 14D3

Allée de Poudrantais. **GPS**: n47,46681 w2,48716.

4 free, € 6/night + € 0,20/pp. **Location:** Urban, simple, quiet.
Surface: gravel/metalled. 01/01-31/12.
Distance: 50m.
Remarks: Max. 48h.

Pénestin 14D3

Chemin de Camaret. **GPS**: n47,49386 w2,49075.

4 free, € 6/night + € 0,20/pp. **Location:** Urban, simple, quiet.
Surface: gravel. 01/01-31/12.
Distance: 100m.
Remarks: Max. 48h.

Pénestin 14D3

Plage de la Source, Allée du Maro. **GPS**: n47,48158 w2,49005.

10 free, € 6/night + € 0,20/pp. **Location:** Rural, simple, quiet.
Surface: grassy/metalled. 01/01-31/12.
Distance: 300m.
Remarks: Max. 48h.

Pénestin 14D3

Plage du Palandrin, L'Isle du Clos Parc, Kerséguin.
GPS: n47,45000 w2,46417.

6 free, € 6/night + € 0,20/pp tourist tax.
Location: Rural, simple, isolated. **Surface:** grassy/sand.
01/01-31/12.
Distance: Sandy beach 1km.
Remarks: Pay at tourist office.

Pénestin 14D3

Route du Loguy. **GPS**: n47,49050 w2,49667.

20 free, € 6/night + € 0,20/pp. **Location:** Rural, simple, quiet.
Surface: grassy/metalled.
Distance: 150m.

FR

Remarks: Max. 48h.

Penmarch 14B2

Aire de Kérity, Rue Victor Hugo. **GPS**: n47,79981 w4,34794.

10 free, 01/04-31/10 € 4/19-9h. **Location:** Rural, simple, quiet.
Surface: grassy/gravel. 01/01-31/12.
Distance: 1,5km 50m 1km 5km on the spot on the spot.

Penmarch 14B2

Aire du Ster, Rue de la Grande Grève. **GPS**: n47,80042 w4,31807.

30 free, 01/04-31/10 € 4/19-9h.
Surface: sand. 01/01-31/12.
Distance: Sandy beach 2km on the spot on the spot.
Remarks: Beach parking.

Penmarch 14B2

Aire du Viben, Rue de la Plage. **GPS**: n47,82390 w4,3708.

30 free, 01/04-31/10 € 4/19-9h.
Location: Rural, simple, quiet. **Surface:** metalled. 01/01-31/12.
Distance: bakery 1km 50m 900m on the spot on the spot.
Remarks: Sandy beach.

Penmarch 14B2

Aire de Kerameil, Rue du Pont Nevez. **GPS**: n47,81369 w4,36077.
€ 2/10minutes Ch WC. 01/01-31/12.
Remarks: Only overnight stays 19-9h.

Penvins 14D3

Camping La Gree Penvins, Chemin du Marais 20.
GPS: n47,49746 w2,68606.

22 € 7. **Location:** Urban, comfortable, quiet. **Surface:** grassy.
01/01-31/12.
Distance: on the spot 350m.
Remarks: Max. 48h.

Penzé 14C1

Rue du Dossen. **GPS**: n48,59811 w3,93439.

5 free Ch WC free. **Location:** Urban, simple, quiet.
Surface: asphalted. 01/01-31/12.
Distance: 100m on the spot on the spot 50m 250m on the spot on the spot.
Remarks: Nearby port.

Piré-sur-Seiche 18B1

Rue de Boistrudan. **GPS**: n48,00719 w1,42871.

7 free Ch free. **Location:** Rural, simple. **Surface:** metalled.
01/01-31/12.
Distance: 300m on the spot 300m 500m.
Remarks: At fish lake.

Plabennec 14B1

Rue de l'Aber. **GPS**: n48,50155 w4,43374.

5 free Ch free. **Location:** Rural, simple. **Surface:** metalled.
01/01-31/12.
Distance: on the spot on the spot on the spot on the spot.
Remarks: Parking at small lake.

Planguenoual 15A3

Bien y Vient. **GPS**: n48,53447 w2,54506.

6 € 5 € 2/24h. **Location:** Rural, comfortable, isolated, quiet. **Surface:** grassy. 01/01-31/12.
Distance: on the spot.

Planguenoual 15A3

Ferme Gesbert, D786. **GPS**: n48,54883 w2,5556.

6 free € 2 Ch € 2 . **Location:** Rural.
Surface: grassy/gravel. 01/01-31/12.
Distance: 1km 1km 1km.
Remarks: Regional products.

Plelauff 14D2

Le Bout du Pont. **GPS**: n48,22434 w3,18048.

12 free Ch free WC. **Location:** Rural, comfortable.
Surface: asphalted. 01/01-31/12.
Distance: 500m on the spot 200m on the spot.

Plémet 14D2

Rue de l'Étang, D16. **GPS**: n48,17897 w2,58918.

15 free € 3/100liter Ch € 3/55minutes WC.
Location: Rural, simple, quiet. **Surface:** gravel.
01/01-31/12.
Distance: 500m.
Remarks: Parking at small lake, coins at town hall.

Pléneuf-Val-André 15A3

Avenue du Général Leclerc. **GPS**: n48,58355 w2,55669.

30 € 8 € 2 Ch. **Location:** Urban, simple, central, quiet.
Surface: grassy/gravel. 01/01-31/12.
Distance: 1km 450m.
Remarks: Max. 72h.

Plérin 14D1

Place François Guego. **GPS**: n48,53986 w2,7264.
9 free. **Location:** Urban. **Surface:** asphalted. 01/01-31/12.
Distance: 200m 200m 200m.

Plérin 14D1

Rue de Martin Plage. **GPS**: n48,55564 w2,72686.
3 free. **Surface:** asphalted. 01/01-31/12.
Distance: on the spot on the spot.

Plérin 14D1

Rue de Tournemine. **GPS**: n48,56835 w2,77075.
12 free. **Surface:** gravel. 01/01-31/12.
Distance: 300m 300m.

Pleslin-Trigavou 15A3

D28. **GPS**: n48,53631 w2,05009.

20 free Ch WC free. **Location:** Urban, simple.
Surface: asphalted. 01/01-31/12.
Distance: on the spot 400m on the spot on the spot.
Remarks: Cycle and hiking routes: voie verte, Circuit des Mégalithes.

Plessala 14D2

Rue de l'Étang. **GPS**: n48,27394 w2,62427.

FR

12 free Chfree. **Location:** Urban, simple, quiet.
Surface: gravel. 01/01-31/12.
Distance: 200m on the spot.
Remarks: At fish lake, max. 48h, fishing permit available.

Plestin-les-Grèves 14C1

Voie Communale de l'Armorique. **GPS**: n48,68157 w3,63411.

6 free. **Surface:** unpaved. 01/01-31/12.
Distance: 3km 50m 2km on the spot.
Remarks: Beach parking, max. 24h.

Plestin-les-Grèves 14C1

Du Grand Rocher, Avenue de la Lieue de Grève.
GPS: n48,66968 w3,5858.

free. **Location:** Simple, isolated, quiet.
Distance: 1,3km 100m 1,3km.

Plestin-les-Grèves 14C1

Route de la Corniche. **GPS**: n48,67235 w3,63602.

6 free. **Location:** Rural, simple, quiet. **Surface:** grassy/sand.
01/01-31/12.
Distance: 1km on the spot 300m Lidl 2km.
Remarks: Max. 24h.

S **Plestin-les-Grèves** 14C1

Avenue des Frères Le Gall. **GPS**: n48,66232 w3,62562.
€ 2/10minutes Ch € 2/1h.
Remarks: Motorhome washing place.

Pleubian 14D1

Port Béni. **GPS**: n48,84834 w3,17053.

4 free. **Location:** Rural, simple, isolated, quiet. **Surface:** asphalted.
01/01-31/12.
Distance: Pleubian 2,5km on the spot 2,5km on the spot.

Remarks: Max. 24h.

Pleubian 14D1

Rue de Kermagen, Kermagen. **GPS**: n48,85667 w3,14194.

4 free. **Surface:** grassy. 01/01-31/12.
Distance: Pleubian 1,6km beach 100m on the spot.
Remarks: Max. 24h.

Pleubian 14D1

Rue de Pen Lan, Lanéros. **GPS**: n48,85760 w3,07883.

4 free. **Surface:** asphalted. 01/01-31/12.
Distance: Pleubian 5,5km on the spot on the spot.
Remarks: Max. 24h.

S **Pleumeur-Bodou** 14C1

Parking de Toul ar Stang, Rue de Toul ar Stang, Ile Grande.
GPS: n48,79868 w3,58342.

6 € 6/night € 2/10minutes Ch € 2/1h.
Location: Rural, simple, quiet. **Surface:** grassy.
01/01-31/12.
Distance: Plemeur-Bodu 6km sandy beach 150m 150m on the spot.

S **Pleumeur-Bodou** 14C1

Cosmopolis-Parc Scientifique, Route du Radome.
GPS: n48,78297 w3,52587.

20 parking free, € 5/night Ch WCincluded.
Surface: gravel/sand. 01/01-31/12.
Distance: 1km 1km on the spot on the spot.

S **Plévenon** 15A3

Aire de la Roche aux Cygrons. **GPS**: n48,65595 w2,32843.
8 free € 2,30 Ch. **Surface:** grassy/gravel. 01/01-31/12.
Distance: 350m 450m.
Remarks: Max. 1 night, coins at shops and tourist office.

P **Plévenon** 15A3

Parking Cap Fréhel. **GPS**: n48,68174 w2,31811.

40 free, 01/06-30/09 8-22h € 5. **Surface:** metalled.
Distance: 50m.

S **Pleyben** 14C2

Pont Coblant. **GPS**: n48,19337 w3,98182.

80 free WC. **Location:** Rural, simple, quiet. **Surface:** grassy.
15/06-15/09.
Distance: 300m on the spot 300m 300m on the spot.
Remarks: On the canal, former campsite.

S **Ploemeur** 14C2

Aire de la Vraie Croix, Route de Larmor. **GPS**: n47,72784 w3,41423.

3 free Chfree. **Location:** Rural, simple, noisy.
Surface: concrete. 01/01-31/12.
Distance: 1km.
Remarks: Industrial area, max. 48h.

Ploemeur 14C2

Aire du Courégant, RD 152. **GPS**: n47,70850 w3,46552.
4 free. **Surface:** unpaved. 01/01-31/12.
Distance: Ploemeur 4,5km 450m.

Ploemeur 14C2

Aire du Fort-Bloqué, Allée des Korrigans. **GPS**: n47,73698 w3,49756.
6 free. **Location:** Urban. **Surface:** sand. 01/01-31/12.
Distance: Ploemeur 6km 550m 350m.

Ploemeur 14C2

Aire du Pérello, Chemin des Douves. **GPS**: n47,69891 w3,44684.
6 free. **Surface:** unpaved. 01/01-31/12.
Distance: Ploemeur 5km 180m.

Ploemeur 14C2

Centre-ville, Rue du Fort Bloqué, Rue Louis Lessart.
GPS: n47,73679 w3,42991.

7 free. **Surface:** asphalted. 01/01-31/12.
Distance: on the spot.
Remarks: Parking centre, max. 24h.

Ploemeur 14C2

Golf Ploemeur, D152, Boulevard de l'Atlantique.
GPS: n47,72316 w3,48156.

FR

9 free.
Location: Rural, quiet. **Surface:** gravel.
01/01-31/12.
Distance: Ploemeur 5km N165 10km beach 300m 1,8km.

Ploemeur 14C2

Kerroch, Place Louis Kermabon. **GPS**: n47,70331 w3,45477.
4 free. **Location:** Urban. **Surface:** asphalted. 01/01-31/12.
Distance: Ploemeur 4,5km 400m 140m.

S Plogoff 14B2

Aire Naturelle Kerguidy Izella, Rue Guillaume Pennamen.
GPS: n48,03694 w4,68139.

30 € 12 Ch WC included. **Location:** Rural, luxurious, quiet. **Surface:** grassy. 01/01-31/12.
Distance: 2km 4km 1km 2km on the spot.
Remarks: 9><20h.

S Plogoff 14B2

Parking de l'Eglise, Rue Cleder cap Sizum.
GPS: n48,03727 w4,6652.

3 free € 2/10minutes Ch . **Location:** Rural, simple.
Surface: asphalted. 01/01-31/12.
Distance: centre.

Plogoff 14B2

Aire de la Pointe du Raz, Route des Langoustiers.
GPS: n48,03651 w4,7173.

40 € 5. **Location:** Rural, simple, quiet. **Surface:** unpaved.
01/01-31/12.
Distance: 3km 50m on the spot on the spot.

Plogoff 14B2

Parking du Stade, Rue du 19 Mars 1962. **GPS**: n48,03245 w4,66316.

50 free. **Location:** Rural, simple, quiet. **Surface:** grassy/metalled.
01/01-31/12.
Distance: on the spot 450m 450m bakery.

S Plomelin 14B2

Rue Hent Keramer. **GPS**: n47,93410 w4,1515.

4 free € 2/10minutes Ch € 2/h. **Location:** Rural, simple, quiet. **Surface:** asphalted. 01/01-31/12.
Distance: on the spot 400m 200m.
Remarks: Parking sports park, max. 24h.

S Plonévez-Porzay 14B2

Rue des Eglantines. **GPS**: n48,12469 w4,22414.

15 free € 2/10minutes Ch € 2/55minutes.
Location: Rural, comfortable, quiet. **Surface:** grassy.
01/01-31/12.
Distance: 600m 450m 450m on the spot.

Plonévez-Porzay 14B2

Kervel Izella. **GPS**: n48,11570 w4,28065.

10 free. **Location:** Rural, simple. **Surface:** grassy/sand.
01/01-31/12.
Distance: 8km 50m on the spot on the spot.
Remarks: Beach parking, max. 48h.

S Plouarzel 14B1

Aire de camping-car de Ruscumunoc, Route de Ruscumunoc.
GPS: n48,42232 w4,78486.

40 free, 15/05-15/09 € 4,50 € 2/10minutes Ch € 2/55minutes € 1 . **Location:** Rural, comfortable, quiet. **Surface:** grassy. 01/01-31/12.
Distance: 3km 100m on the spot on the spot.

S Ploubalay 15A3

Rue des Ormelets. **GPS**: n48,58057 w2,14524.

3 free Ch free. **Location:** Simple. **Surface:** asphalted.
01/01-31/12.
Distance: 250m 100m 500m on the spot.

S Ploubalay 15A3

Rue du Chaffaud. **GPS**: n48,57800 w2,14166.
70 € 10 WC . **Surface:** asphalted. 01/01-31/12.
Distance: on the spot 450m 450m.

Ploubazlanec 14D1

Park Nevez, Cité de Lan ar Mendy. **GPS**: n48,80090 w3,0305.
3 free. **Location:** Simple. 01/01-31/12.
Distance: bakery.
Remarks: Max. 24h.

Ploubazlanec 14D1

Pointe de l'Arcouest, Route de l'Embarcadère.
GPS: n48,82102 w3,01948.

20 free, 30/06-30/09 € 6/24h. **Location:** Simple, isolated, quiet.
Surface: grassy. 01/01-31/12.
Distance: 2km 50m on the spot.

Ploubazlanec 14D1

Rue du Port Loguivy. **GPS**: n48,82011 w3,06279.

6 free. **Surface:** asphalted. 01/01-31/12.
Distance: 100m on the spot 100m 100m.

Plouescat 14C1

Rue de Pen an Théven. **GPS**: n48,65902 w4,21863.

6 free. **Location:** Rural, comfortable, quiet. **Surface:** metalled.
01/01-31/12.
Distance: 3,5km 100m on the spot.

S Plouescat 14C1

Intermarché, La Rocade-Kerchapalain.
GPS: n48,65083 w4,18444.

FR

4 free, € 2, Ch, € 2, € 5/4. **Location:** Rural, simple, noisy. **Surface:** asphalted. 01/01-31/12.
Distance: 500m, 600m, on the spot, on the spot.
Remarks: Parking supermarket.

Plouézec — 14D1

Parking A. Le Calvez, Route de Paimpol. **GPS**: n48,75041 w2,98651.

3 free. **Surface:** asphalted. 01/01-31/12.
Distance: 100m, 200m, 100m.

Plouézec — 14D1

Parking de la Corniche, Bréhec. **GPS**: n48,72875 w2,9455.

5 free. **Surface:** asphalted. 01/01-31/12.
Distance: on the spot.
Remarks: Beautiful view.

Plouézec — 14D1

Place du 19 mars 1962. **GPS**: n48,74788 w2,9853.

3 free. **Surface:** asphalted. 01/01-31/12.
Distance: on the spot.
Remarks: Service at camping municipal.

Plouézec — 14D1

Route de Paimpel. **GPS**: n48,75049 w2,98643.

3 free. **Location:** Urban, simple. **Surface:** asphalted. 01/01-31/12.
Distance: 100m, 100m.

Plougasnou — 14C1

Parking de la Métairie, Rue Charles de Gaulle. **GPS**: n48,69404 w3,79209.

7 free, € 2,50/10minutes, Ch, € 2,50/1h WC. **Location:** Rural. **Surface:** gravel. 01/01-31/12.
Distance: on the spot, sandy beach 1,4km, 200m, 250m bakery, on the spot, on the spot.
Remarks: Tuesday morning market.

Plougasnou — 14C1

Rue des Grands Viviers, Le Diben. **GPS**: n48,70811 w3,82731.

7 free, € 2, Ch. **Location:** Rural, simple, isolated, quiet. **Surface:** asphalted. 01/01-31/12.
Distance: 300m, on the spot, on the spot, 300m, on the spot.
Remarks: Max. 48h, coins at town hall.

Plougastel-Daoulas — 14B1

Rue de la Fontaine Blanche. **GPS**: n48,37111 w4,36428.

15 free, Ch, free. **Location:** Simple. **Surface:** asphalted. 15/05-15/10.
Distance: 450m, 450m, 450m.
Remarks: Parking at sports grounds.

Plougonvelin — 14B1

Rue de Bertheaume. **GPS**: n48,33792 w4,70742.

80 € 8/24h, Ch, WC included.
Location: Rural, comfortable, quiet. **Surface:** grassy/sand. 01/01-31/12.
Distance: 1km, beach 650m.

Plougonven — 14C1

Rond-Point de Kerivoas. **GPS**: n48,52633 w3,71836.

2 free, Ch free. **Location:** Rural, simple, quiet. **Surface:** asphalted. 01/01-31/12.
Distance: 400m.

Remarks: At sports centre.

Plouguerneau — 14B1

Lilia. **GPS**: n48,61891 w4,55341.

10 free, € 5/10minutes, Ch, € 5/55minutes.
Location: Urban, comfortable, quiet. **Surface:** asphalted. 01/01-31/12.
Distance: 400m, 850m, 450m.

Plouha — 14D1

Plage de Palus, Route du Palus. **GPS**: n48,67667 w2,88556.

10 free. **Location:** Rural, simple, isolated, quiet. **Surface:** grassy. 01/03-31/10.
Distance: 3km, sandy/pebbled beach 100m, 50m, on the spot.
Remarks: Max. 3 days.

Plouharnel — 14D3

Des Sables Blancs, Route de Quiberon. **GPS**: n47,56783 w3,12509.

40 € 12/24h, Ch, included. **Location:** Simple. **Surface:** grassy. 01/01-31/12.
Distance: 4km, 100m, 100m.
Remarks: Max. 72h, service passerby € 4,50.

Plouhinec — 14B2

Aire du Champion, Rue Brizeux. **GPS**: n48,01694 w4,50194.
5 free, € 2, Ch. **Surface:** asphalted. 01/01-31/12.
Distance: on the spot.
Remarks: At supermarket.

Ploumoguer — 14B1

Rue Huon de Kermadec, D28. **GPS**: n48,40507 w4,72492.

30 free, July-Aug € 4, € 2/80liter, Ch, € 2, € 4/2,30.
Location: Rural, quiet. **Surface:** metalled. 01/04-30/11.
Distance: 200m, 200m, 200m.
Remarks: Next to stadium, max. 48h, coins at town hall, supermarket, bakery and Tabac.

Plouneour — 14B1

Parking des Menhirs. **GPS**: n48,65090 w4,30573.

10 free. **Location:** Rural, simple, quiet. **Surface:** metalled.
01/01-31/12.
Distance: 1km 50m 50m.
Remarks: At sea.

Plouvorn 14C1

Plan d'Eau de Lanorgant. **GPS**: n48,57776 w4,03069.

19 € 5/24h € 2 Ch included WC .
Location: Rural, comfortable, quiet. **Surface:** metalled.
01/01-31/12.
Distance: 500m 100m 100m 500m 500m.
Remarks: Parking at small lake.

Pluméliau 14D2

Allée du vieux Blavet. **GPS**: n47,98229 w3,04209.

15 free Chfree. **Location:** Rural, simple. **Surface:** gravel.
01/01-31/12.
Distance: 500m on the spot 250m on the spot on the spot.
Remarks: Along the Blavet river, attention: max. ^3.1m.

Pont-Aven 14C2

Parking de Bel Air du Cimitière, Rue des Abbès Tanguy.
GPS: n47,85646 w3,75203.

5 free WCfree. **Location:** Urban, simple. **Surface:** asphalted.
01/01-31/12.
Distance: 400m.
Remarks: Inclining pitches.

Pont-Aven 14C2

Parking du Stade Henri Sinquin, Rue Louis Lomenech.
GPS: n47,85401 w3,74333.

30 free € 3,50/120liter Ch. **Location:** Urban, simple.
Surface: asphalted. 01/01-31/12.
Distance: 450m 450m.
Remarks: Parking near stadium Sinquin, coins at the shops.

Pont-Aven 14C2

Parking du Bois Amour, Rue de la Belle Angèle.
GPS: n47,85930 w3,74402.

20 free.
Location: Urban, simple. **Surface:** gravel. 01/01-31/12.
Distance: 550m 300m 700m.

Pont-Aven 14C2

Parking du Parcours Sportif, Rue de Rustéphan.
GPS: n47,85865 w3,75296.

30 free. **Location:** Comfortable. **Surface:** grassy/gravel.
01/01-31/12.
Distance: 900m 850m 150m on the spot.

Pont-l'Abbé 14B2

Parking de la Gare, Rue de la Gare. **GPS**: n47,86754 w4,22591.

30 free. **Location:** Urban, simple. **Surface:** unpaved.
01/01-31/12.
Distance: on the spot 50m 400m 1km.

Pont-l'Abbé 14B2

Leclerc, Route de Saint Jean Trolimont. **GPS**: n47,86414 w4,23646.

6 free € 1/100liter Ch € 1/2h . **Location:** Urban, simple.
Surface: asphalted. 01/01-31/12.
Distance: 1,5km on the spot on the spot on the spot.
Remarks: At supermarket.

Pontivy 14D2

Piscine Decouverte, Rue de Cascade. **GPS**: n48,07458 w2,97778.
10 free Chfree. **Location:** Rural, simple, isolated.
Surface: grassy. 01/01-31/12.
Distance: 1km.
Remarks: At swimming pool.

Pontivy 14D2

Rue de la Fontaine. **GPS**: n48,06758 w2,96941.

6 free. **Location:** Urban, simple. **Surface:** asphalted.
01/01-31/12.
Distance: 800m on the spot bakery 300m on the spot.
Remarks: Monday market.

Port-Louis 14C3

Aire de la Côte Rouge, D781 Port-Louis > Riantec.
GPS: n47,70873 w3,34295.

14 € 5/24h, 01/06-15/09 € 10/24h Ch (4x)included .
Surface: asphalted. 01/01-31/12.
Distance: on the spot on the spot.

Port-Louis 14C3

Aire des Remparts, Promenade Henri François Buffet.
GPS: n47,70496 w3,35602.

20 € 11/24h Ch included . **Location:** Urban.
01/01-31/12.
Distance: 100m 100m on the spot.
Remarks: In front of campsite.

Portsall 14B1

Aire camping-cars Kerros, Rue de Porsguen.
GPS: n48,56583 w4,69944.

37 € 7,11/24h Ch included. **Location:** Rural, comfortable, quiet. **Surface:** grassy. 01/01-31/12.
Distance: on the spot 350m 200m 200m.
Remarks: Max. 3 days.

Poullaouen 14C1

D236, Rue de Ty Meur. **GPS**: n48,33672 w3,64218.

5 free Chfree.
Location: Rural, comfortable, quiet. **Surface:** gravel.
01/01-31/12.

FR

Distance: 200m ⊗150m Véloroute Roscoff-Nantes on the spot.

Primelin 14B2

Camping Municipal de Kermaléro, Route de l'Océan.
GPS: n48,02550 w4,61821.

15 free, 13/06-13/09 € 3 € 2/100liter Ch € 3/h.
Location: Rural, simple, quiet. **Surface:** metalled.
01/01-31/12.
Distance: 1km 1km.

Priziac 14C2

Base de Loisirs du Lac du Bel Air, Rue du Bel Air.
GPS: n48,06237 w3,41079.

10 free € 3 Ch WC. **Location:** Rural. **Surface:** asphalted.
01/01-31/12.
Distance: ⊗300m.
Remarks: Service on campsite.

Questembert 14D3

Aire Communale, Célac. **GPS**: n47,66240 w2,46794.

10 free Ch free. **Location:** Rural, simple, quiet.
Surface: asphalted. 01/01-31/12.
Distance: 200m 200m.

Quiberon 14D3

Rue de Port Kerné. **GPS**: n47,49165 w3,13941.

140 € 6,40/24h € 1/60liter Ch.
Location: Rural, simple. **Surface:** gravel.
01/01-31/12 service: 15/10-01/04.
Distance: 2km sea 250m ⊗2km 2km on the spot on the spot on the spot.
Remarks: Next to camping municipal, max. 3 days, bread-service only in summer, seaview.

Quimper 14C2

Route de l'Innovation. **GPS**: n47,97399 w4,09319.

2 free € 2/100liter Ch € 2/10minutes.
Location: Urban, simple, noisy. **Surface:** asphalted.
01/01-31/12.
Distance: 1km ⊗on the spot on the spot on the spot on the spot.
Remarks: Parking at centre commercial, special part for motor homes.

Quimperlé 14C2

Aire Saint Nicolas, Rue du Viaduc. **GPS**: n47,86640 w3,54334.

3 free Ch free. **Location:** Simple. **Surface:** metalled.
01/01-31/12.

Quintin 14D1

Place du Champ de Foire. **GPS**: n48,40056 w2,90222.

7 free Ch free. **Location:** Urban, simple, quiet.
Surface: asphalted. 01/01-31/12 Service: winter.
Distance: on the spot on the spot.
Remarks: Next to swimming pool, near the lake, tuesday market.

Tourist information Quintin:
Tue-morning.

Quistinic 14D2

De Poul Fetan. **GPS**: n47,89311 w3,15166.

15 free WC. **Location:** Rural, simple. **Surface:** metalled/sand.
01/01-31/12.
Remarks: Max. 48h.

Radenac 14D2

Sente Verte, Les Gambris. **GPS**: n47,95778 w2,71333.

5 free. **Location:** Rural, simple, quiet. **Surface:** gravel.
01/01-31/12.
Distance: 700m on the spot on the spot on the spot.
Remarks: At small lake.

Redon 18A2

Quai Surcouf. **GPS**: n47,64510 w2,0897.

10 free Ch free. **Location:** Simple. **Surface:** asphalted.
01/01-31/12.
Distance: 500m on the spot 100m ⊗200m 200m.
Remarks: In front of Bureau du Port de Plaisance.

Tourist information Redon:
Manoir de l'Automobile de Loheac. Car collection: Ferrari, Lamborghini, Porsche, Maserati.

Réguiny 14D2

Base de Loisirs, Rue de la Piscine. **GPS**: n47,96843 w2,73828.

10 free Ch free WC. **Location:** Rural, simple, quiet.
Surface: unpaved. 01/01-31/12.
Distance: 1,3km bakery 1,3km on the spot on the spot.

Rennes 18B1

Rue du Professeur Maurice Audin. **GPS**: n48,13531 w1,64542.

5 free € 2/100liter Ch € 2/1h € 1/30minutes.
Location: Rural, simple. **Surface:** asphalted. 01/01-31/12.
Distance: 3km 100m ⊗100m 3km on the spot.
Remarks: In park, max. 48h.

Tourist information Rennes:
M Musée de Bretagne. Regional museum.
Tue-Sa.

Riantec 14C3

Camping-car Park de Kerdurand, Rue du stade.
GPS: n47,71735 w3,31778.
49 € 10 Ch (40x)included.
Location: Rural. **Surface:** grassy.
01/01-31/12.
Distance: 800m 1,5km.
Remarks: Mandatory, one-time fee Pass'Etapes € 4, video surveillance.

Riantec 14C3

Leclerc, Rond-point de Kersabiec. **GPS**: n47,72611 w3,32137.

10 free € 2 Ch € 2/55minutes. **Location:** Simple.
Surface: asphalted. 01/01-31/12.
Distance: on the spot.

Riantec 14C3

Route de Plouhinec. **GPS**: n47,71163 w3,29858.

4 free € 2/10minutes Ch € 2/55minutes.
Location: Rural, simple. **Surface:** metalled. 01/01-31/12.
Distance: 1,5km.
Remarks: Near old laundry place (still operational!), max. 24h.

Rochefort-en-Terre 18A2

Parking des Grées, Rue du Souvenir. **GPS**: n47,69975 w2,33384.

>100 € 2/24h. **Location:** Rural, simple, quiet. **Surface:** gravel. 01/01-31/12.
Distance: 200m.

Rohan 14D2

Port de Plaisance, Rue Saint-Gouvry. **GPS**: n48,07187 w2,75559.

20 free Ch WC free. **Location:** Rural, comfortable, quiet.
Surface: asphalted. 01/01-31/12.
Distance: 500m on the spot on the spot 500m on the spot.
Remarks: At the Nantes-Brest Canal.

Romagné 15B3

Allée des Prunus, D812. **GPS**: n48,34409 w1,27415.

5 free Ch WC free. **Location:** Urban, simple.
Surface: metalled. 01/01-31/12.
Distance: 100m 1,7km 200m 50m.

Roscoff 14C1

Route du Laber. **GPS**: n48,71215 w3,99918.

30 free Ch free. **Location:** Rural, simple, isolated, noisy.
Surface: asphalted. 01/01-31/12.
Distance: 2km on the spot on the spot on the spot on the spot.
Remarks: Service 200m.

Tourist information Roscoff:

Office de Tourisme, 46, rue Gambetta, www.roscoff-tourisme.com. Seaside resort and former pirates town.
Wed.

Rostrenen 14D2

Rue Rosa l'Hénaff, D23. **GPS**: n48,23318 w3,32019.

15 free € 2/100liter Ch € 2/1h.
Location: Urban, simple. **Surface:** gravel.
01/01-31/12.
Distance: 400m 100m.
Remarks: Coins at tourist info, town hall, maison de presse, tabac.

Ruffiac 18A1

Rue Biard. **GPS**: n47,81823 w2,28413.

3 free. **Surface:** metalled. 01/01-31/12.
Distance: on the spot.

Sains 15B3

Rue du Puits Rimoult. **GPS**: n48,55305 w1,58603.

10 € 5, tourist tax € 0,20/pp Ch free.
Location: Rural, simple, quiet. **Surface:** grassy/metalled.
01/01-31/12.
Distance: 100m 2km 150m 150m on the spot 100m on the spot.

Saint Aignan 14D2

Place de l'Église. **GPS**: n48,18306 w3,01361.

20 free Ch WC free. **Location:** Comfortable, quiet.
Surface: asphalted. 01/01-31/12.
Distance: 100m on the spot on the spot.
Remarks: Square behind the church.

Saint Aignan 14D2

Anse de Sordan, D15B. **GPS**: n48,19967 w3,07026.

10 free.
Location: Isolated, quiet. **Surface:** sand. 01/01-31/12.
Distance: 200m 200m 500m on the spot on the spot.

Saint Gérand 14D2

Keroret, D322. **GPS**: n48,11333 w2,89028.

12 free Ch WC free. **Location:** Rural, comfortable, quiet.
Surface: asphalted. 01/01-31/12.
Distance: 800m on the spot 150m on the spot on the spot.
Remarks: At the Nantes-Brest Canal.

Saint-Aubin-d'Aubigné 18B1

Rue de Rennes. **GPS**: n48,26147 w1,60621.

5 free Ch WC free. **Location:** Urban, simple.
Surface: asphalted. 01/01-31/12.
Distance: on the spot 100m on the spot on the spot on the spot.

Saint-Barnabé 14D2

Place du Vieux Chêne, Rue Pierre Loti. **GPS**: n48,13672 w2,70146.

10 free Ch free. **Location:** Urban, simple, central.
Surface: gravel. 01/01-31/12.
Distance: 200m bakery 50m.

Saint-Benoît-des-Ondes 15B3

Rue Bord de Mer. **GPS**: n48,61681 w1,84714.

10 free € 3/50liter Ch € 3/15minutes.
Location: Rural, simple. **Surface:** asphalted.
Distance: 100m on the spot on the spot 100m 200m on the spot on the spot.

Saint-Brice-en-Coglès 15B3

Espace Jules Verne, Rue de Normandie, D102.
GPS: n48,41126 w1,36252.

FR

8 free € 2/10minutes Ch € 2/55minutes WC.
Location: Urban, simple, central. **Surface:** asphalted/metalled.
01/01-31/12.
Distance: 300m 500m 400m 300m on the spot.

S Saint-Carreuc 14D1

Rue de la Lande, D27. **GPS**: n48,40219 w2,73917.

12 free € 2/10minutes Ch € 2/55minutes.
Location: Rural, simple, isolated, noisy. **Surface:** metalled.
01/01-31/12.
Distance: 300m on the spot on the spot.
Remarks: At Etang-du-Plessis, max. 24h.

S Saint-Connan 14D1

Etang Neuf. **GPS**: n48,41906 w3,10901.

2 free Ch free. **Location:** Isolated, quiet.
Surface: metalled. 01/01-31/12.
Distance: on the spot 50m 50m.

S Saint-Derrien 14C1

GPS: n48,54820 w4,1817.

20 free € 3 Ch € 3 WC free. **Location:** Rural, simple, quiet.
Surface: gravel/metalled. 01/05-31/10.
Distance: 100m on the spot on the spot 300m 300m.
Remarks: Nearby recreation area.

S Saint-Gelven 14D2

Rue de l'Ecole, D95. **GPS**: n48,22442 w3,09589.

10 free Ch free. **Location:** Urban, simple. **Surface:** gravel.
01/01-31/12.
Remarks: Service 100m.

Saint-Gelven 14D2

Tregnanton, D117. **GPS**: n48,21153 w3,08457.

free. **Location:** Rural, isolated, quiet. **Surface:** grassy/metalled.
01/01-31/12.
Distance: 2,5km on the spot on the spot on the spot.

S Saint-Gildas-de-Rhuys 14D3

Camping municipal de Kerver, Route du Rohu.
GPS: n47,52238 w2,85803.

35 € 6,70 € 2 Ch . **Location:** Rural, simple, quiet.
Surface: asphalted. 15/03-04/11.
Distance: 4km 50m 400m 4km.

S Saint-Guyomard 14D3

Route de Malestroit, D112. **GPS**: n47,78166 w2,51188.

5 € 5/night € 3 Ch € 3. **Location:** Rural, simple, quiet.
Surface: asphalted. 01/01-31/12.
Distance: 300m 100m.
Remarks: Behind church, check in at town hall.

S Saint-Jacut-de-la-Mer 15A3

Rue de la Manchette. **GPS**: n48,58969 w2,18947.

26 € 6/24h Ch included. **Location:** Comfortable.
Surface: grassy/gravel. 01/01-31/12.
Distance: 1km 500m.
Remarks: Baker at 8am.

S Saint-Malo 15A3

Aire des îlots, Avenue de la Guimorais.
GPS: n48,68109 w1,96348.

150 € 7, 25/06-04/09 € 12, 2 pers. incl € 3 Ch (40x) included. **Location:** Rural, comfortable. **Surface:** grassy.
01/01-31/12.
Distance: sandy beach 100m 100m 200m on the spot.

S Saint-Malo 15A3

Parking Paul Féval, Rue Paul Féval. **GPS**: n48,64341 w1,99385.

200 € 7,50, overnight stay 19-9h free € 3 Ch .
Location: Urban, simple. **Surface:** gravel. 01/01-31/12.
Distance: 800m 800m on the spot.
Remarks: Free bus to centre.

Saint-Malo 15A3

Parking du Grand Domaine. **GPS**: n48,61568 w2,0117.
free. **Surface:** grassy. 01/01-31/12.

Saint-Malo 15A3

Parking Le Davier, Avenue J. Kennedy. **GPS**: n48,67356 w1,98098.
free. 01/01-31/12.
Distance: 100m 400m.
Remarks: Max. 24h.

Saint-Malo 15A3

Parking Marville, Avenue de Marville. **GPS**: n48,64142 w2,00226.

free. **Surface:** asphalted. 01/01-31/12.
Distance: 300m 300m 100m.
Remarks: Max. 24h.

Saint-Malo 15A3

Rue Henri Lemairié. **GPS**: n48,65467 w1,97374.

free. **Surface:** metalled.
01/01-31/12.
Distance: on the spot 1km 1km.
Remarks: Max. 24h.

Tourist information Saint-Malo:
Château. Castle, 14/15th century, historical museum. 10-12h, 14-18h.
Fort National. Fort designed by Vauban. At ebb accessible by foot.

S Saint-Nicolas-du-Pélem 14D2

Parking des Associations. **GPS**: n48,31506 w3,16022.

10 free Ch free. **Location:** Urban. **Surface:** asphalted.
01/01-31/12.
Distance: 200m.
Remarks: Service 1km GPS N48,306605 W-3,164207.

Saint-Nicolas-du-Tertre 18A1

Terres du Bourg. **GPS**: n47,80047 w2,22383.
5 free. 01/01-31/12.
Distance: 300m on the spot on the spot on the spot.

S Saint-Pierre-Quiberon 14D3

Rue du Stade. **GPS**: n47,51160 w3,13903.

40 € 5/24h € 2/10minutes Ch € 2/45minutes.
Location: Simple. **Surface:** asphalted. 01/01-31/12.
Distance: 1km 1,5km on the spot on the spot.
Remarks: Max. 48h.

S Saint-Pol-de-Léon 14C1

Quai de Pempoul. **GPS**: n48,68361 w3,97083.

30 € 6 € 2 Ch € 2 WCfree. **Location:** Rural, comfortable, noisy. **Surface:** metalled. 01/01-31/12.
Distance: 800m on the spot on the spot 800m 800m.
Remarks: At sea.

S Saint-Renan 14B1

Route de l'Aber. **GPS**: n48,43878 w4,63063.

20 € 4/day Chfree. **Location:** Rural, quiet.
Surface: gravel. 01/01-31/12.
Distance: 1km on the spot.
Remarks: Nearby camp site, Jul/Aug max. 48h.

S Saint-Rivoal 14C1

Saint-Rivoal, D42. **GPS**: n48,34930 w3,99782.

6 free Ch free. **Location:** Rural, simple, isolated, quiet.
Surface: grassy/metalled. 01/01-31/12.
Distance: 300m 500m on the spot on the spot.

S Saint-Servais 14C1

Cité Yan d'Argent. **GPS**: n48,50984 w4,15434.

10 free Ch WCfree. **Location:** Rural, simple, quiet.
Surface: gravel/metalled. 01/01-31/12.
Distance: 200m 200m 200m.

S Saint-Thégonnec 14C1

Park an Iliz, D118. **GPS**: n48,52215 w3,94637.

25 free Ch free. **Location:** Urban, comfortable, central, quiet. **Surface:** gravel. 01/01-31/12.
Distance: on the spot 150m 150m on the spot on the spot.
Remarks: Free coins available at shops.

Tourist information Saint-Thégonnec:
Fri.
Crêperie Steredenn, Rue de la Gare 6.

S Santec 14C1

Le bistrot à Crèpes, Rue de Méchouroux.
GPS: n48,70102 w4,03868.

15 guests free € 2 Ch (14x)€ 2/24h WC free.
Location: Rural, simple, quiet. **Surface:** grassy.
01/01-31/12 Wed.
Distance: La plage du Staol 100m on the spot 800m on the spot on the spot.
Remarks: Max. 24h, bread-service.

S Sarzeau 14D3

Aire du Rohaliguen, Rue du Raker/Rue du Pont Neui.
GPS: n47,49769 w2,76748.

15 € 7/18-10h ChWCfree. **Location:** Rural, simple, quiet.
Surface: metalled. 01/01-31/12.
Distance: on the spot 200m.
Remarks: Max. 48h.

S Sarzeau 14D3

Rue de Brénudel. **GPS**: n47,52969 w2,7598.

20 € 5,50/24h € 2 Ch € 2. **Location:** Urban, simple, quiet.
Surface: asphalted. school holidays.
Distance: on the spot 750m.

S Sarzeau 14D3

Rue du Port St.Jacques, Kerbodo. **GPS**: n47,48906 w2,79297.

15 € 7/18-10h Ch WCfree € 2. **Location:** Urban, comfortable, quiet. **Surface:** asphalted. 01/01-31/12.
Distance: 200m 500m 100m 200m.
Remarks: Nearby port, max. 48h.

S Sarzeau 14D3

Rue du Stang, St.Colombier. **GPS**: n47,54665 w2,72151.

5 € 4,50 Chincluded. **Location:** Urban, simple, quiet.
Surface: asphalted.
Distance: St.Colombier 100m 50m 50m 50m.
Remarks: Max. 48h.

S Scaër 14C2

Rue Louis Pasteur. **GPS**: n48,02774 w3,6951.

60 free € 2/10minutes Ch € 2/55minutes WCfree.
Location: Rural, simple, quiet. **Surface:** asphalted.
01/01-31/12.
Distance: 500m bakery 200m on the spot on the spot.
Remarks: Max. 72h, coins at campsite and tourist info.

Sérent 14D2

Du Pont Salmon, Rue du Général De Gaule.
GPS: n47,82445 w2,50194.

10 free. **Location:** Urban, simple, quiet. **Surface:** asphalted.
01/01-31/12.
Distance: 400m 400m 400m on the spot.

S Silfiac 14D2

P Salle Polyvalente, Rue du Résistant P. le Bourlay.
GPS: n48,14816 w3,15668.

10 free Chfree. **Location:** Rural, simple, quiet.
Surface: asphalted. 01/01-31/12.
Distance: 150m 150m on the spot on the spot.

FR

Silfiac 14D2

Etang de Pont Samuel, Pont Samuel. **GPS**: n48,12847 w3,17109.

5 free. **Location:** Rural, simple, isolated. **Surface:** unpaved.
01/01-31/12.
Distance: 300m 200m on the spot 200m.

Sizun 14C1

Rue de Cornouaille. **GPS**: n48,40018 w4,07905.
€ 2 Ch. **Surface:** asphalted. 01/01-31/12.
Distance: 750m 700m.

Sougéal 15B3

Le Placis, D15. **GPS**: n48,50651 w1,52562.

30 free Ch WC free. **Location:** Rural, simple, quiet.
Surface: gravel/metalled. 01/01-31/12.
Distance: on the spot 300m bakery 300m.
Remarks: Bakery 500m.

Sulniac 14D3

Salle des Fêtes, Rue des Écoles. **GPS**: n47,67756 w2,56642.

20 free Ch free. **Location:** Rural, simple, quiet.
Surface: asphalted. 01/01-31/12.
Distance: 400m bakery 500m.

Theix 14D3

Allée de Noyalo. **GPS**: n47,62726 w2,66183.

4 free Ch free. **Location:** Urban, simple, quiet.
Surface: asphalted. Service: winter.
Distance: 500m 500m 500m 50m 50m.

Tinténiac 15B3

Quai de la Donac. **GPS**: n48,33168 w1,83202.

10 € 3 Ch free. **Location:** Rural, simple.

Surface: grassy/gravel. 01/04-31/10.
Distance: 500m on the spot on the spot 100m 550m.

Trébeurden 14C1

Route de Lannion, D65. **GPS**: n48,76711 w3,5514.

5 parking free, € 7/night € 4,30 Ch € 4,30.
Location: Rural, comfortable, central, quiet.
Surface: asphalted.
Distance: on the spot 1,4km 1,5km 1km bakery, Intermarché 1,5km.

Trébeurden 14C1

Corniche de Pors Mabo. **GPS**: n48,76886 w3,57794.

5 parking free, € 7/night. **Location:** Rural, simple, quiet.
Surface: gravel.
Distance: on the spot 800m 800m 300m 300m.

Trébeurden 14C1

Impasse du Vieux Puits. **GPS**: n48,76999 w3,56849.

5 parking free, € 7/night. **Location:** Urban, simple, quiet.
Surface: asphalted.
Distance: on the spot 1,5km on the spot on the spot.

Trébeurden 14C1

Route de Pors Mabo. **GPS**: n48,76194 w3,56537.

10 parking free, € 7/night. **Location:** Rural, simple, quiet.
Surface: metalled.
Distance: 1,5km 200m 200m.

Trébeurden 14C1

Rue Pierre Marzin. **GPS**: n48,76842 w3,56284.

20 parking free, € 7/night. **Location:** Urban, simple, quiet.
Surface: metalled. 01/01-31/12.
Distance: on the spot 1km 300m 600m on the spot on the spot.

Trégastel 14C1

Rue de Poul-Palud. **GPS**: n48,82437 w3,49874.

56 € 8 Ch included. **Location:** Rural, comfortable, isolated, quiet. **Surface:** asphalted. 01/01-31/12.
Distance: 1km 1km Super U on the spot.
Remarks: Aug max. 3 nights, max. 5 nights.

Tréguier 14D1

Bois du Poète, Boulevard Anatole le Braz. **GPS**: n48,78932 w3,23144.

20 free Ch free. **Surface:** asphalted. 01/01-31/12.
Distance: 100m 20m 20m 100m 100m.

Tréguier 14D1

Super U, Boulevard Jean Guehenno. **GPS**: n48,77892 w3,23346.
€ 1/10minutes Ch € 1/55minutes. 01/01-31/12.
Distance: 200m on the spot.

Trégunc 14C2

Parking Quentel, Place de la Mairie, Rue de Pont-Aven.
GPS: n47,85472 w3,85139.

5 free € 3/10minutes Ch € 3/55minutes WC.
Location: Urban, simple. **Surface:** asphalted. 01/01-31/12.
Distance: 100m.
Remarks: Behind town hall, max. 24h.

Trégunc 14C2

Parking de Pouldohan, Route de Pouldohan.
GPS: n47,84435 w3,88832.

5 free. **Location:** Rural, simple, isolated. **Surface:** grassy.
01/01-31/12.
Distance: 400m 400m.

Trégunc 14C2

Plage Ster Greich. **GPS**: n47,84918 w3,88656.

FR

10 free. **Location:** Rural, simple, isolated, quiet. **Surface:** sand.
01/01-31/12.
Distance: on the spot on the spot.
Remarks: Max. 24h.

Trégunc 14C2

Route de Kerlaëron. **GPS:** n47,82964 w3,8872.

6 free.
Location: Rural, simple. **Surface:** grassy. 01/01-31/12.
Distance: 200m.
Remarks: Max. 24h.

Trégunc 14C2

Rue de Porzh Breign. **GPS:** n47,84079 w3,89736.

5 free. **Location:** Rural, simple, quiet. **Surface:** grassy.
01/01-31/12.
Distance: 200m.
Remarks: Max. 24h.

Trégunc 14C2

Supermarché Casino, Route de Concarneau, D783.
GPS: n47,85633 w3,86343.

4 free € 2 Ch € 2/55minutes. **Location:** Simple.
Surface: asphalted. 01/01-31/12.
Distance: on the spot on the spot.

Tremblay 15B3

Route de Fougères. **GPS:** n48,42328 w1,47095.

6 free € 2/10minutes Ch € 2/55minutes. **Location:** Urban, simple. **Surface:** asphalted. 01/01-31/12.
Distance: 400m 200m on the spot.

Trémuson 14D1

Aire du Buchon, Rue de Brest, D712. **GPS:** n48,52250 w2,85278.

5 free Chfree. **Location:** Urban, simple. **Surface:** asphalted.
01/01-31/12 service: frost.
Distance: 500m 50m 200m.
Remarks: Max. 48h.

Trévou-Tréguignec 14D1

Rue de Trestel. **GPS:** n48,81902 w3,35432.
20 € 8/24h € 5 Ch.
Surface: metalled. 01/01-31/12.
Distance: 200m 50m 100m.

Val-d'Izé 18B1

Rue du Château. **GPS:** n48,17904 w1,30133.

3 free Ch WCfree. **Location:** Urban, simple, quiet.
Surface: asphalted. 01/01-31/12.
Distance: 100m on the spot 100m 100m on the spot.
Remarks: Next to sports fields.

Vannes 14D3

Camping-Car Park, Avenue du Maréchal Juin.
GPS: n47,63283 w2,77996.

34 € 11, Jul/Aug € 13,40 Ch (34x),10Amp WC included.
Location: Urban, comfortable, quiet. **Surface:** asphalted.
01/01-31/12.
Distance: Vannes 4km 200m 200m 1km on the spot on the spot on the spot.
Remarks: Mandatory, one-time fee Pass'Etapes € 4, free shuttle (summer).

Tourist information Vannes:
Office de Tourisme, 1, rue Thiers, www.tourisme-vannes.com. The old district is surrounded by ramparts with gates and parks with historical wash places.
Cathédrale St Pierre.

Vitré 18B1

Camping Municipal de Vitré, 109 Boulevard des Rochers.
GPS: n48,10974 w1,1986.
10 free. **Location:** Urban. **Surface:** metalled.
01/01-31/12.

Tourist information Vitré:
Office de Tourisme, Place du Général de Gaulle, www.ot-vitre.fr. Small medieval town with large castle and ramparts. Marked city walk, information OT.
Mo.

Pays de la Loire

Angers 18C2

Boulevard Olivier-Couffon. **GPS:** n47,46616 w0,56549.

30 € 14/24h Chfree. **Location:** Urban, noisy.
Surface: asphalted. 01/01-31/12.
Distance: centre 950m 3km.
Remarks: Max. 72h, monitored parking, Château d'Angers 600m.

Tourist information Angers:
Haras National du Lion d'Angers. National stud-farm. 10-18h. free.
Château d' Angers. Fortified castle, museum for contemporary art. 10-17.30h. € 8,50.

Angrie 18C2

Route du Vieux Bourg. **GPS:** n47,57176 w0,97312.

10 free ChWCfree. **Location:** Rural, simple, quiet.
Surface: gravel/metalled. 01/01-31/12 1st weekend Aug.
Distance: 400m on the spot.
Remarks: Max. 48h, picnic tables available, playground.

Arnage 18D1

Rue du Port. **GPS:** n47,93035 e0,18418.

2 free € 2 Ch € 2/15minutes. **Location:** Urban, simple, quiet. **Surface:** asphalted. 01/01-31/12.
Distance: 250m on the spot 250m 500m on the spot.
Remarks: Along Sarthe River.

Asnières-sur-Vègre 18D2

D190. **GPS:** n47,88950 w0,23716.

5 free WCfree.
Location: Rural, simple, quiet. **Surface:** gravel.
Distance: 200m 200m.

Assérac 14D3

Pen-Bé. **GPS:** n47,42556 w2,45528.

5 free WC.

FR

Location: Simple. **Surface:** grassy. 01/01-31/12.
Distance: 50m 100m 100m 200m 200m.

Assérac 14D3

Parking Marché aux Bœufs, Chemin de la Marché aux Bœufs.
GPS: n47,43111 w2,45194.

free. **Surface:** gravel/metalled. 01/01-31/12.
Distance: 1km 300m 300m 2km 2km.

Aubigné-sur-Layon 18C3

Rue de 17 mars 1962. **GPS:** n47,21167 w0,46383.

5 free Chfree. **Location:** Simple, quiet. **Surface:** metalled.
01/01-31/12.
Distance: 100m on the spot on the spot.

Auvers-le-Hamon 18D1

Chemin du tour. **GPS:** n47,90115 w0,34654.

10 free. **Location:** Rural, simple, quiet. **Surface:** gravel.
Distance: 500m on the spot 500m.
Remarks: At small lake.

Averton 18D1

Étang des Perles. **GPS:** n48,34744 w0,24468.

10 free € 2,50/80liter Ch € 2,50/2h WCfree.
Location: Rural, comfortable, quiet. **Surface:** gravel.
01/01-31/12.
Distance: lake on the spot on the spot on the spot.
Remarks: Playground.

Batz-sur-Mer 14D3

Route de la Govelle. **GPS:** n47,26747 w2,4537.

7 € 8 € 2 Ch € 2 WC. **Location:** Simple.
Surface: metalled. 01/01-31/12.
Distance: 1,5km 100m 100m 1,5km 50m.

Remarks: Max. 48h, coins at tourist info and town hall, no camping activities.

Baugé-en-Anjou 18D2

Rue du Pont des Fées. **GPS:** n47,53886 w0,09637.

10 free € 3/15minutes Ch € 3/15minutes.
Location: Rural, comfortable, quiet. **Surface:** gravel.
01/01-31/12.
Distance: 2km 400m on the spot on the spot.
Remarks: Max. 48h.

Baugé-en-Anjou 18D2

Super U, Avenue d'Angers. **GPS:** n47,54570 w0,11296.
15 free Ch. 01/01-31/12.
Distance: 300m on the spot.

Bazouges-sur-le-Loir 18D2

Camping-Car Park, Pré de la Boisardière. **GPS:** n47,68691 w0,16985.
27 € 8,40 Ch (36x)included. 01/01-31/12.
Remarks: Mandatory, one-time fee Pass'Etapes € 4.

Bazouges-sur-le-Loir 18D2

Voie de la Liberté. **GPS:** n47,68994 w0,16952.

6 free. **Location:** Rural, simple, quiet. **Surface:** gravel.
01/01-31/12.
Distance: 200m 200m on the spot on the spot.

Beauvoir-sur-Mer 18A3

Place des Paludier, Rue de Nantes. **GPS:** n46,91685 w2,0465.

24 free, night € 5 € 2,50/3minutes Ch € 2,50/15minutes WC. **Location:** Urban, simple. **Surface:** asphalted.
01/01-31/12.
Distance: 400m 800m 800m.
Remarks: Max. 48h.

Belleville-sur-Vie 21B1

Rue des Écoliers. **GPS:** n46,78160 w1,42875.
15 free. **Surface:** asphalted. 01/01-31/12.
Distance: 500m 500m 200m.
Remarks: Near Salle des Fêtes.

Benet 21C2

Rue de la Gare. **GPS:** n46,36896 w0,59482.

10 free ChWCfree. **Location:** Simple. **Surface:** asphalted.
01/01-31/12.
Distance: 300m 300m on the spot 50m.

Remarks: Monday market.

Blain 18A2

Place Jollan de Clerville, Rue Victor Schoelcher.
GPS: n47,47444 w1,76139.

30 free Chfree WC. **Location:** Simple, noisy. **Surface:** gravel.
01/01-31/12.
Distance: 100m 100m.

Blain 18A2

Rue de la Petite Arche. **GPS:** n47,46934 w1,76205.

12 free. **Location:** Comfortable, quiet. **Surface:** clay soil.
01/01-31/12.
Distance: 500m 500m on the spot.

Blaison-Gohier 18C3

Aire de Bajun, Rue Thibaut de Blaison. **GPS:** n47,39897 w0,37513.

4 free Ch WCfree. **Location:** Urban, simple, quiet.
Surface: asphalted. 01/01-31/12.
Distance: 400m on the spot 300m 1,5km on the spot on the spot.
Remarks: Automatic bread distributor.

Blaison-Gohier 18C3

Rue de Thibaut de Blaison. **GPS:** n47,39923 w0,37515.

5 free Chfree. **Surface:** asphalted. 01/01-31/12.
Distance: on the spot 200m 200m.

Bouchemaine 18C2

25 rue Chevrière. **GPS:** n47,41913 w0,61117.

45 € 13,50 € 0,50/50liter Ch WC € 1 included.
Surface: grassy/gravel. 01/01-31/12 service: 01/12-28/02.
Distance: 50m.
Remarks: Along the river Maine, former campsite, baker every morning

(Jul/Aug).

S Bouère 18C2

Rue des Sencies. **GPS**: n47,86320 w0,47661.

16 free € 2/80liter Ch € 2. **Location:** Rural, comfortable, quiet. **Surface:** grassy. 01/01-31/12.
Distance: on the spot 50m bakery 100m.

S Bouin 18A3

Port du Bec, Rue du Port du Bec. **GPS**: n46,93871 w2,07318.

33 € 5 € 2,50/10minutes Ch € 2,50/4h WC.
Surface: gravel. 01/01-31/12.
Distance: on the spot on the spot.

Bouin 18A3

GPS: n46,99821 w2,03314.

10 free.
Location: Simple. **Surface:** metalled. 01/01-31/12.
Distance: on the spot on the spot.

Bouin 18A3

Parking de La Coupelasse. **GPS**: n47,00918 w2,02782.

10 free. **Location:** Rural, simple. **Surface:** grassy/gravel.
01/01-31/12.
Distance: on the spot.

S Bourgneuf-en-Retz 18A3

D758. **GPS**: n47,04028 w1,95704.

12 free Ch WC free.
Location: Simple. **Surface:** asphalted.
01/01-31/12 Service: winter.
Distance: 300m 200m 300m 300m.
Remarks: Parking tourist info, max. 48h.

S Boussay 18B3

Place des Marronniers. **GPS**: n47,04240 w1,18648.

4 free € 2/100liter Ch € 2/60minutes. **Location:** Simple.
Surface: asphalted. 01/01-31/12.
Distance: 200m 200m 200m on the spot.
Remarks: Max. 48h, coins at town hall, poste.

Brétignolles-sur-Mer 21A1

Parking de la Normandelière, Rue de la Source.
GPS: n46,61664 w1,85974.

25 free. **Location:** Simple. **Surface:** metalled.
01/01-31/12.
Distance: 1,5km sandy beach 500m 1,5km on the spot on the spot.
Remarks: Service: Super U D38, GPS 46,62537 -1,85787.

Tourist information Brétignolles-sur-Mer:
Thu, Su.

S Briollay 18C2

Plage de Briollay. **GPS**: n47,56766 w0,50733.

20 free € 2/100liter Ch WC free. **Location:** Rural, comfortable, quiet. **Surface:** grassy/gravel. 01/01-31/12.
Distance: 450m.
Remarks: Along Sarthe River, coins at the shops, closed when frosty and high water.

S Brissac-Quincé 18C3

Aire Communale, Rue de l'Aubance. **GPS**: n47,35465 w0,4463.

10 € 4 Ch included. **Location:** Urban, simple, quiet.
Surface: asphalted. 01/01-31/12.
Distance: 300m 300m 300m on the spot on the spot.
Remarks: Max. 2 days.

S Brissac-Quincé 18C3

Domaine de la Belle Etoile, La Belle Étoile.
GPS: n47,33404 w0,43597.

8 € 12 Ch WC € 3 included. **Location:** Rural, comfortable, quiet. **Surface:** grassy. 31/10-01/04.

S Brissac-Quincé 18C3

Domaine de L'Etang, Route de Saint-Mathurin.
GPS: n47,36103 w0,43529.

6 € 12-15 Ch WC € 5 included.
Location: Rural, comfortable, quiet. **Surface:** grassy.
01/01-31/12.
Distance: 1,5km 500m 2km on the spot on the spot.
Remarks: To be paid at campsite.

S Chailland 18C1

Coccimarket. **GPS**: n48,22139 w0,86583.

4 free Ch free. **Location:** Rural, simple. **Surface:** asphalted.
01/01-31/12.
Distance: 300m 300m on the spot.
Remarks: Max. 24h.

S Chaille-les-Marais 21B2

Rue du 8 Mai 1945. **GPS**: n46,39228 w1,02127.

20 free € 3 WC free. **Location:** Simple, quiet. **Surface:** grassy.
01/01-31/12 Thu-morning.
Distance: 100m 100m 300m 50m.
Remarks: At fire-station and sports park.

S Challans 18A3

Parking du Viaud Marais. **GPS**: n46,85027 w1,8742.

20 free Ch free. **Location:** Urban. **Surface:** asphalted.
01/01-31/12.
Distance: 1km 500m 500m 100m.
Remarks: Max. 3 days.

FR

Chalonnes-sur-Loire 18C3

Le Champ du Bois, D751. **GPS**: n47,35105 w0,74466.

20 € 9 € 2 Ch included. **Location:** Rural, comfortable. **Surface:** grassy. 01/01-31/12.
Distance: 1km on the spot 1km on the spot.
Remarks: Nearby camp site.

Chambretaud 18C3

Aire des Diamants, Rue Notre Dame. **GPS**: n46,92300 w0,9717.

5 free € 2/150liter ChWC. **Location:** Rural, simple. **Surface:** asphalted. 27/03-01/10.
Distance: 1km 5km on the spot 1km.

Champ-Sur-Layon 18C3

Rue du Soleil Levant. **GPS**: n47,26369 w0,57289.

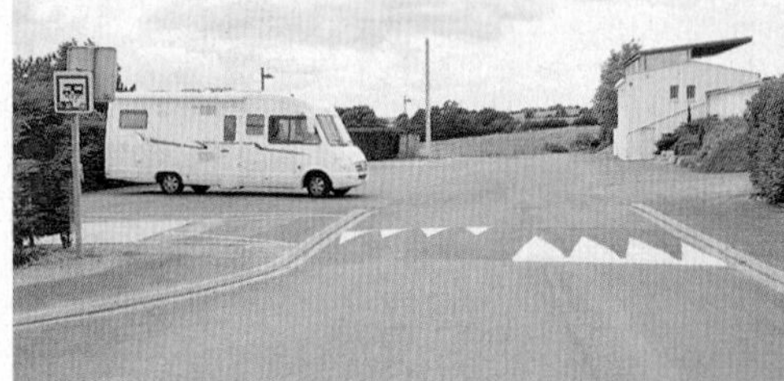

2 free Ch (1x) WC free. **Location:** Rural, simple, quiet. **Surface:** asphalted/metalled. 01/01-31/12.
Distance: 150m 6km 6km on the spot on the spot.

Champtocé-sur-Loire 18C2

Rue de la Hutte. **GPS**: n47,41143 w0,86958.

8 free Ch free. **Location:** Rural, simple. **Surface:** asphalted. 01/01-31/12.
Distance: 300m 5,7km 400m 400m.
Remarks: At stadium.

Champtoceaux 18B3

Parking Champalud, Place de Niederheimbach.
GPS: n47,33816 w1,2649.

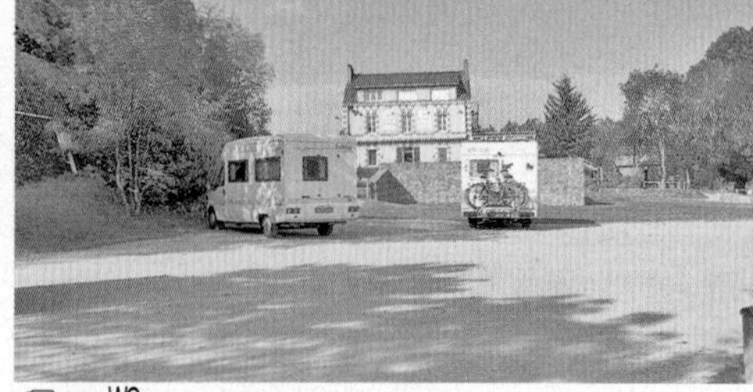

8 € 4 Ch h WC included. **Location:** Urban, simple, quiet. **Surface:** asphalted. 01/01-31/12.
Distance: 150m 100m 150m on the spot on the spot on the spot.
Remarks: Square behind the church, max. 48h, payment and wifi code at tourist office.

Champtoceaux 18B3

Le Port du Moulin, Le Cul du Moulin, D751.
GPS: n47,33913 w1,27445.

5 free WC free. **Location:** Rural, simple, quiet. **Surface:** gravel/metalled. 01/01-31/12.
Distance: 1,5km on the spot on the spot on the spot 1,5km.
Remarks: Along Loire river, max. 48h.

Changé 18C1

Parking du plan d'eau du Port, Rue du Bac.
GPS: n48,10047 w0,78584.

10 free ChWC free. **Location:** Urban, simple. **Surface:** gravel/sand. 01/01-31/12.
Distance: 5km 800m.
Remarks: Along the Mayenne river.

Chantenay-Villedieu 18D1

Route du Plan d'Eau. **GPS**: n47,91668 w0,16849.
5 free ChWC free. **Location:** Rural, comfortable, quiet. **Surface:** grassy/gravel. 01/04-31/10.
Distance: 150m 150m 650m.
Remarks: At lake, next to campsite.

Chantonnay 21B1

Rue de l'Arc en Ciel. **GPS**: n46,68754 w1,04104.

5 free € 2/100liter Ch € 2/60minutes. **Location:** Rural, simple, noisy. **Surface:** asphalted. 01/01-31/12.
Distance: 1km 500m 1km.
Remarks: Next to sports fields, coins at tourist info.

Chanzeaux 18C3

Aire de Ploizeau, Rue de Bel Air a Chanzeaux D121.
GPS: n47,25548 w0,63848.

6 free € 2/100liter ChWC. **Location:** Rural, simple, quiet. **Surface:** metalled. 01/01-31/12.
Distance: 1km on the spot 1km 1km on the spot on the spot.

Charcé-Saint-Ellier-sur-Aubance 18C3

Rue Saint Ellier. **GPS**: n47,35647 w0,41146.

free ChWC free. **Location:** Urban, simple, quiet. **Surface:** metalled/sand. 01/01-31/12.
Distance: 100m 3km 3km.

Château-d'Olonne 21A1

Les Plesses, Rue des Plesses. **GPS**: n46,49132 w1,74293.

20 € 7,30/night, € 12,30/2 nights € 2,07/6minutes Ch. **Location:** Simple. **Surface:** asphalted. 01/01-31/12.
Distance: 2km 500m.

Château-Gontier 18C2

Quai-du-Docteur Lefevre. **GPS**: n47,82450 w0,70206.

30 free. **Location:** Urban, simple, central. **Surface:** asphalted. 01/01-31/12.
Distance: 200m on the spot 50m.
Remarks: Along the Mayenne river.

Châteauneuf-sur-Sarthe 18C2

L'aire de repos, Rue de la Gare. **GPS**: n47,67774 w0,4866.

6 € 5,15 € 4 Ch. **Location:** Rural, comfortable, quiet. **Surface:** grassy/gravel. 01/01-31/12 service: 01/10-01/05.
Distance: 400m 400m 500m.
Remarks: Along Sarthe River.

Chauché 21B1

L'Oiselière. **GPS**: n46,84159 w1,30211.
11 € 8 Ch included. **Location:** Rural. **Surface:** unpaved. 01/01-31/12.
Distance: 3km 3km.
Remarks: Service on campsite.

Chavagne-en-Paillers 18B3

Place des Arcades. **GPS**: n46,89083 w1,24917.

FR

3 free € 2/10minutes Ch € 2/55minutes.
Location: Simple, central, quiet.
Surface: asphalted.
01/01-31/12.
Distance: 300m 50m 100m 300m.
Remarks: Coins at tourist office/Rest. Le petit Marmiton/Boulanger de Quartier, 8 rue G de Gaulle/ Carrefour Express, 197 rue G de Gaulle.

Chavagnes les Eaux 18C3

Rue de l'Église. **GPS**: n47,27024 w0,45437.

4 free Chfree. **Location:** Simple, quiet. **Surface:** metalled.
01/01-31/12.
Distance: on the spot 150m.
Remarks: Behind church.

Chemillé-Melay 18C3

La ferme Cabri d'Anjou, La Chaperonnière.
GPS: n47,22275 w0,7524.

2 free. **Location:** Rural, simple, isolated, quiet. **Surface:** grassy.
01/01-31/12.
Distance: 2km 3km 3km on the spot on the spot.
Remarks: Cheese farm.

Chênehutte-Trèves-Cunault 18D3

Rue Beauregard, D751, Cunault. **GPS**: n47,32685 w0,19459.

40 free € 3/100liter Ch € 3/6h.
Location: Rural, simple, quiet. **Surface:** grassy. 01/01-31/12.
Distance: 500m 500m 500m on the spot on the spot.
Remarks: Max. 72h.

Chenillé-Changé 18C2

Le Pin, D78. **GPS**: n47,69919 w0,66693.

8 € 5 Chincluded € 4. **Location:** Simple. **Surface:** gravel.
01/01-31/12.
Distance: on the spot 100m.
Remarks: Along the Mayenne river.

Clefs-Val d'Anjou 18D2

D938. **GPS**: n47,62442 w0,07698.

10 free. **Location:** Rural, simple, noisy. **Surface:** metalled.
01/01-31/12.
Distance: 500m 500m 500m.

Coëx 21A1

Rue des Goélettes. **GPS**: n46,69668 w1,76397.

4 free € 2/10minutes Ch € 2/55minutes.
Location: Rural. **Surface:** asphalted. 01/01-31/12.
Distance: 200m 500m 500m.
Remarks: Max. 48h, coins at town hall.

Combrée 18C2

Rue de Bretagne, Bel-Air. **GPS**: n47,71281 w0,9989.

3 free ChWCfree. **Location:** Rural, simple.
Surface: asphalted/grassy. 01/01-31/12.
Distance: 100m.
Remarks: Picnic tables available.

Combrée 18C2

Aire du Plan d'Eau, D203. **GPS**: n47,70321 w1,02755.

3 free. **Location:** Rural, simple, quiet. **Surface:** asphalted.
01/01-31/12.
Distance: 200m on the spot on the spot 50m.
Remarks: Behind tennis-court, picnic tables available.

Concourson-sur-Layon 18C3

Place du Prieuré. **GPS**: n47,17372 w0,34199.

10 free € 3/100liter ChWC. **Location:** Urban, simple, quiet.
Surface: asphalted. 01/01-31/12.
Distance: 400m 400m 400m on the spot on the spot on the spot.
Remarks: Coins at the bakery and auberge du Haut Layon, service 200m.

Dampierre-sur-Loire 18D3

L'aire d'accueil de Dampierre-sur-Loire, Route de Montsoreau.
GPS: n47,24157 w0,0232.

80 € 6 + € 0,50/pp tourist tax Chincluded WCfree.
Location: Urban, simple, central, quiet. **Surface:** forest soil.
01/04-31/10.
Distance: on the spot 100m on the spot 4,5km on the spot on the spot.
Remarks: On the river Loire, behind town hall.

Damvix 21C2

Camping-Car Park, Le Grand Port. **GPS**: n46,31159 w0,73249.
16 € 8,40-10,80 Ch (16x),10Amp included.
Location: Rural. **Surface:** metalled. 01/01-31/12.
Distance: on the spot.
Remarks: Mandatory, one-time fee Pass'Etapes € 4.

Deux-Evailles 18C1

Site de la Fenderie, Champ de Vigne, D129.
GPS: n48,20203 w0,52018.

6 free € 2 Ch € 2 WCfree.
Location: Rural, comfortable, quiet. **Surface:** grassy/gravel.
01/01-31/12.
Distance: 1km 20m 20m 20m 5km Montsurs on the spot.
Remarks: Coins at Auberge, playground, fishing permit available.

Doué-la-Fontaine 18D3

Domaine des Sablonnières, Rue Jean Gaschet.
GPS: n47,18280 w0,25742.

3 free Chfree. **Location:** Urban, simple, quiet.
Surface: gravel/metalled.
Distance: 500m 300m 500m on the spot on the spot.

Doué-la-Fontaine 18D3

Roseraie les Chemins, Route de Cholet. **GPS**: n47,18554 w0,31436.

8 free. **Location:** Rural, simple, quiet. **Surface:** gravel.
01/01-31/12.
Distance: 2km 2km 3km on the spot on the spot.
Remarks: Rose grower.

Durtal 18D2

Rue du Petit Port. **GPS**: n47,66842 w0,24172.

FR

5 free. **Location:** Rural, quiet. **Surface:** asphalted.
Distance: 300m 2,4km.

S Durtal 18D2

Rue Beausite. **GPS**: n47,67139 w0,2406.

2 free € 2/10minutes € 2 Ch € 2/60minutes.
Location: Urban, simple, noisy. **Surface:** asphalted.
01/01-31/12.
Distance: 300m 2,4km.
Remarks: Inclining pitches.

S Ernée 18C1

Plan d'eau d'Ernée, Plan d'eau d'Ernée. **GPS**: n48,29670 w0,93997.

2 free WC free. **Location:** Urban, simple, quiet.
Surface: asphalted. 01/01-31/12.
Distance: 500m on the spot 500m 500m.
Remarks: Parking at small lake.

S Faye d'Anjou 18C3

Chateau du Fresne, D55, Rue des Monts.
GPS: n47,29923 w0,53806.

10 free ChWC free. **Location:** Rural, simple, quiet.
Surface: gravel. 01/01-31/12.
Distance: 2km 3km.

S Feneu 18C2

Port Albert. **GPS**: n47,56560 w0,60994.

6 free € 2 Ch. **Location:** Rural, quiet. **Surface:** gravel.
01/01-31/12.
Distance: 1,5km.
Remarks: Along the Mayenne river, coins at the shops in the village.

S Fontaines 21C2

Place du Champ de Foire. **GPS**: n46,42291 w0,81952.

20 free ChWC free.
Location: Rural, simple. **Surface:** gravel.
Distance: 2km on the spot on the spot.

S Fontenay-le-Comte 21C1

Avenue du Général de Gaulle. **GPS**: n46,46203 w0,80544.

20 € 7 € 2/4minutes Ch included. **Location:** Simple, isolated, noisy. **Surface:** asphalted. 01/01-31/12.
Distance: 500m 500m 500m.
Remarks: In front of police station, max. 24h, centre.

S Fontevraud l'Abbaye 18D3

Allée des Jardins. **GPS**: n47,18444 e0,04917.

8 free ChWC free. **Location:** Urban, simple, central.
Surface: asphalted. 01/01-31/12.
Distance: 400m 400m 400m 300m.

S Foussais-Payré 21C1

Place du Prieuré. **GPS**: n46,53000 w0,68275.

20 free Ch free. **Location:** Rural, simple. **Surface:** gravel.
01/01-31/12 water: frost.
Distance: 500m 500m 200m.

Freigné 18B2

Aire du Plan d'Eau, D185. **GPS**: n47,55049 w1,12591.
free. **Surface:** grassy. 01/01-31/12.
Distance: on the spot 400m 400m.

S Fresnay-sur-Sarthe 18D1

Rue de la Gare. **GPS**: n48,28171 e0,02978.

8 free Ch free. **Location:** Rural, simple, quiet.
Surface: asphalted. 01/01-31/12.
Distance: 600m 600m 50m.

S Gené 18C2

Escale du Haut Anjou, La Petite Fenouillère.
GPS: n47,63770 w0,79641.

7 € 14 Ch included. **Location:** Rural, simple.
Surface: gravel. 01/01-31/12.
Distance: 1,2km fish pond.
Remarks: Cheese farm.

S Gorron 15C3

Route de Brecé, Rue du Maine. **GPS**: n48,40735 w0,80993.

6 free Ch (3x)free. **Location:** Simple, quiet.
Surface: gravel. 01/01-31/12.
Distance: on the spot 200m.
Remarks: Max. 2 nights.

S Grez-en-Bouère 18C2

Place A. Peigné. **GPS**: n47,87306 w0,52306.

6 free WC. **Location:** Rural, simple, quiet. **Surface:** asphalted.
01/01-31/12, service: 01/04-30/11.
Distance: 50m 50m 100m.
Remarks: Max. 48h.

S Grez-Neuville 18C2

Rue du Port, D291. **GPS**: n47,60119 w0,68504.

8 free Ch free. **Location:** Rural, simple. **Surface:** grassy.
01/01-31/12.
Remarks: Former campsite.

S Guenrouet 18A2

Rue des Hauts du Port. **GPS**: n47,52198 w1,94978.

2 free € 2 Ch € 2. **Location:** Simple, quiet.
Surface: asphalted/gravel. 01/04-31/10.
Distance: 200m 50m 200m 200m.

FR

Remarks: Along canal of Nantes/Brest, next to campsite Saint Clair, max. 24h.

S Guérande 14D3

Avenue de la Brière, D99E. **GPS:** n47,33389 w2,42083.

20 free € 6,50/100liter Ch € 5/1h.
Location: Simple, noisy. **Surface:** asphalted/grassy.
01/01-31/12.
Distance: 1km.

S Jans 18B2

Place de l'Église. **GPS:** n47,62222 w1,61222.

6 free ChWCfree. **Location:** Simple, quiet. **Surface:** gravel.
01/01-31/12.
Distance: on the spot 100m.
Remarks: Behind town hall.

S Jard-sur-Mer 21A1

Route des Goffineaux. **GPS:** n46,41074 w1,59358.

16 € 6,10/24h, € 10,20/48h € 2/10minutes Ch.
Location: Rural, simple. **Surface:** asphalted. 01/01-31/12.
Distance: 1km 50m 1,5km 1,5km.

S Juigne-sur-Loire 18C3

Domaine des 2 moulins, Route de Martigneau.
GPS: n47,40374 w0,47702.

5 € 5 Ch WC included. **Location:** Rural, comfortable, quiet. **Surface:** gravel. 01/01-31/12.
Distance: 1km 4km 2km 1km 500m on the spot on the spot.
Remarks: When buying wine 1 night free.

S Juvigné 18C1

Plan d'Eau de Saint Martin, Rue de la Croixille, D29.
GPS: n48,22806 w1,03806.

20 free ChWCfree. **Location:** Urban, simple. **Surface:** gravel.
01/01-31/12.
Distance: 200m 20m 200m 100m on the spot.
Remarks: Max. 72h.

S La Baconnière 18C1

Place de l'Eglise. **GPS:** n48,18361 w0,89139.

5 free Ch free.
Location: Urban, simple. **Surface:** asphalted.
01/01-31/12.
Distance: on the spot 100m.
Remarks: Inspection 2017: closed because of renovation, behind church, max. 1 night, service (winter) on demand (town hall).

S La Barre-de-Monts 18A3

Camping-Car Park La Grande Côte, Route de la Grande Côte.
GPS: n46,88528 w2,15196.
49 € 10,91-13,32 Ch (40x) included.
Surface: metalled/sand. 01/01-31/12.
Distance: 800m 200m 800m.
Remarks: Mandatory, one-time fee Pass'Etapes € 4.

S La Baule 14D3

Boulevard Guy de Champsavin, La Baule-Escoublac.
GPS: n47,28196 w2,42509.

12 free € 3 Ch (20x)€ 3/55minutes.
Location: Comfortable, quiet. **Surface:** metalled.
Distance: beach 700m.

S La Bernerie-en-Retz 18A3

Parking Wilson, Avenue de Jean d Arc. **GPS:** n47,07871 w2,03399.

30 € 7, 15/06-15/09 € 8 € 3,50/100liter Ch € 3,50/55minutes WC.
Surface: asphalted. 01/01-31/12.
Distance: 300m 100m 300m 300m on the spot.
Remarks: Max. 48h, coins at tourist info.

S La Chapelle-Saint-Florent 18B3

Aire du Stade, Rue de l'Evre. **GPS:** n47,33411 w1,05178.

6 free Chfree. **Location:** Rural, simple, quiet.
Surface: gravel/metalled. 01/01-31/12.
Distance: 300m 300m 50m.

S La Daguenière 18C2

Chemin de Beausse, Rue de Stade. **GPS:** n47,42222 w0,43936.

12 free € 2/100liter Ch. **Location:** Rural.
Surface: grassy/gravel. 01/01-31/12.
Distance: 200m 300m 300m.
Remarks: Next to sports fields.

S La Daguenière 18C2

Port Maillard. **GPS:** n47,41743 w0,43781.

10 free ChWC. **Location:** Rural. **Surface:** unpaved.
01/01-31/12 high water.
Remarks: Along Loire river.

S La Faute-sur-Mer 21B2

Camping-Car Park Les Amourettes, Route de la Point d'Arcay.
GPS: n46,31607 w1,30776.
32 € 10,44 Ch (32x) included.
Surface: asphalted. 01/01-31/12.
Remarks: Mandatory, one-time fee Pass'Etapes € 4.

S La Faute-sur-Mer 21B2

Camping-Car Park, Rond Point Fleuri. **GPS:** n46,33297 w1,32231.

31 € 10,44 Ch (31x) included.
Surface: asphalted.
01/01-31/12.
Distance: on the spot 850m 100m.
Remarks: At tourist office, mandatory, one-time fee Pass'Etapes € 4.

S La Flèche 18D2

Promenade du Maréchal Foch. **GPS:** n47,69767 w0,07875.

FR

10 free Chfree. **Location:** Urban, simple, noisy.
Surface: asphalted. 01/01-31/12 tue-evening, wed 06-16h (market).
Distance: 100m 100m 100m.

La Fresnaye-sur-Chédouet 15E3

La forêt de Perseigne, Les Ventes du Four, D236.
GPS: n48,43469 e0,25972.

20 free Chfree. **Location:** Rural, simple, quiet.
Surface: gravel. 01/01-31/12.
Distance: La Fresnaye 1,5km on the spot.

La Meilleraie-Tillay 21C1

Rue des Ombrages. **GPS**: n46,73923 w0,84578.

10 free € 2/5minutes ChWC € 1. **Location:** Simple, isolated, quiet. **Surface:** asphalted. 01/04-31/10.
Distance: 700m 700m 700m.

La Plaine-sur-Mer 18A3

Boulevard des Nations Unies. **GPS**: n47,13994 w2,19057.

8 free Chfree. **Location:** Simple, isolated.
Surface: asphalted. 01/01-31/12.
Distance: 300m 800m 500m.
Remarks: Max. 24h.

La Poitevinière 18C3

Aire de la Fontaine, Place de la Fontaine, D15.
GPS: n47,22750 w0,897.

5 free Ch WCfree. **Location:** Urban, comfortable, quiet.
Surface: asphalted. 01/01-31/12.
Distance: 50m on the spot 50m on the spot on the spot.
Remarks: Coins available at bar.

La Roche-sur-Yon 21B1

Boulevard Italie. **GPS**: n46,66833 w1,41861.

20 free Chfree. **Location:** Urban. **Surface:** metalled.
01/01-31/12.
Distance: 500m 500m 500m.
Remarks: Max. 36h.

La Roche-sur-Yon 21B1

Les crins au bord du lac, La brunetière. **GPS**: n46,71104 w1,40663.
7 € 5 included. **Location:** Rural, comfortable, isolated, quiet. **Surface:** grassy/gravel. 01/01-31/12.
Distance: 6km on the spot on the spot 2km 2km on the spot 1km on the spot.
Remarks: Bicycle rental, canoe rental.

La Séguinière 18C3

Avenue de Nantes. **GPS**: n47,06005 w0,93668.

10 free € 2/100liter Ch € 2/1h WC.
Location: Simple. **Surface:** asphalted.
Distance: 100m on the spot 50m.

La Selle-Craonnaise 18C1

Base de Loisirs, La Rincerie. **GPS**: n47,86330 w1,06843.

free € 2 Ch. **Location:** Simple, isolated, quiet.
01/01-31/12.
Distance: on the spot on the spot on the spot.
Remarks: At lake, playground.

La Suze-sur-Sarthe 18D2

Rue du Camping. **GPS**: n47,88904 e0,03305.

36 € 9, 01/04-15/05 € 6 + € 0,22/pp tourist tax € 2/100liter Ch (36x)included WC .
Location: Rural, comfortable, quiet. **Surface:** grassy/gravel.
01/01-31/12.
Distance: 300m 50m 50m 300m on the spot on the spot.

La Tranche-sur-Mer 21B2

Boulevard de la Petite Hollande. **GPS**: n46,34965 w1,44769.

16 € 4,50 € 3,50/10minutes Ch.
Location: Simple, quiet. 01/01-31/12.
Remarks: Max. 48h.

La Tranche-sur-Mer 21B2

Parking de la Baleine, Place des Baleines.
GPS: n46,34340 w1,46222.

23 € 4,50 + € 0,85/pp tourist tax . **Location:** Rural, quiet.
Surface: gravel. 01/01-31/12.
Distance: 200m on the spot on the spot.
Remarks: Max. 48h.

La Tranche-sur-Mer 21B2

Parking du Stade, Avenue du Général de Gaulle.
GPS: n46,35028 w1,43688.

80 free, 14/06-14/09 € 10 € 3,50 Ch.
Location: Rural. **Surface:** asphalted. 01/01-31/12.
Distance: 1km.
Remarks: Max. 15 days.

La Turballe 14D3

Boulevard de la Grande Falaise. **GPS**: n47,33106 w2,49919.

23 € 7,40/24h, tourist tax incl Chincluded.
Location: Comfortable. **Surface:** gravel. 01/01-31/12.
Distance: 2km 300m.
Remarks: Max. 72h.

La Turballe 14D3

Camping-Car Park, Rue du clos Mora. **GPS**: n47,35150 w2,50558.
23 € 10,40 Ch (23x) included.
Surface: metalled. 01/01-31/12.
Distance: 800m 800m 600m 400m on the spot.
Remarks: Mandatory, one-time fee Pass'Etapes € 4.

La Turballe 14D3

Rue Alphonse Daudet. **GPS**: n47,34870 w2,50804.

FR

15 free, June-Sep € 3 Chfree. **Location:** Simple, quiet. **Surface:** gravel. 01/01-31/12.
Distance: 800m 500m 100m 100m.
Remarks: Max. 5 days.

S Lassay-les-Châteaux 15C3

Allée du Haut Perrin. **GPS**: n48,43777 w0,49822.

8 free € 1/80liter Ch € 1/2h. **Location:** Urban, simple, central. **Surface:** asphalted. 01/01-31/12.
Distance: 100m 100m.
Remarks: Coins at Tourist Info and bakery.

S Laval 18C1

Parking de la Halte Fluviale, Rue du Vieux Saint-Louis. **GPS**: n48,07589 w0,77142.

10 free free WC. **Location:** Urban, simple, noisy. **Surface:** asphalted. 01/01-31/12.
Distance: 300m on the spot on the spot on the spot.
Remarks: Parking nearby viaduct.

Tourist information Laval:

Vieux Château. Medieval castle, museum with collection of naive art. 9.30-12h and 13.30-18.30h.

S Le Coudray Macouard 18D3

Route de Bron. **GPS**: n47,18806 w0,11722.

5 free Chfree. **Location:** Rural, simple, isolated, quiet. **Surface:** grassy/sand. 01/01-31/12.
Distance: 800m 800m.
Remarks: Near sports fields.

S Le Croisic 14D3

Le Lin Gorzé, Rue du Lin Gorzé. **GPS**: n47,29917 w2,52194.

9 € 6,30, € 0,75/pp tourist tax € 2 Ch. **Location:** Simple, quiet. **Surface:** asphalted. 01/01-31/12.
Distance: 500m 500m 500m 800m.
Remarks: Max. 48h, no camping activities.

S Le Croisic 14D3

Les Courlis, Rue des Courlis. **GPS**: n47,29000 w2,505.

15 € 6,30, € 0,75/pp tourist tax € 2 Ch. **Location:** Simple. **Surface:** gravel. 01/04-31/10.
Distance: 500m 500m 500m 500m.
Remarks: Max. 48h, no camping activities.

Le Croisic 14D3

La Vigie, Avenue de Pierre Longue, D45. **GPS**: n47,28917 w2,53667.

9 € 6,30, € 0,75/pp tourist tax. **Location:** Simple. **Surface:** asphalted. 01/01-31/12.
Distance: 3km 50m 3km 3km.
Remarks: Max. 48h, no camping activities.

Le Croisic 14D3

P1 Kerdavid, Rue Kerclavid 1. **GPS**: n47,29835 w2,51995.

8 € 6,30, € 0,75/pp tourist tax. **Location:** Urban, simple, quiet. **Surface:** asphalted. 01/01-31/12.
Distance: 500m 500m 500m 800m.
Remarks: Max. 48h, no camping activities.

Tourist information Le Croisic:

Océarium du Croisic. Sea aquarium. 01/06-31/08 10-20h, 01/05-31/05, 01/09-30/09 10-13h, 14-19h, 01/10-30/04 14-19h.

S Le Fenouiller 21A1

Camping-Car Park, 7 rue du Centre. **GPS**: n46,71491 w1,90777.
41 € 10,50-12,90 Ch (41x) included.
Surface: gravel/metalled. 01/01-31/12.
Remarks: Mandatory, one-time fee Pass'Etapes € 4.

S Le Guédéniau 18D2

Plan d'eau, Rue du Lavoir. **GPS**: n47,49405 w0,04488.

25 free ChWCfree. **Location:** Rural, comfortable, quiet. **Surface:** metalled. 01/01-31/12.
Distance: on the spot.
Remarks: Recreation area at lake.

Le Mans 18D1

Rue Denfert Rochereau. **GPS**: n48,01111 e0,19750.

free. **Location:** Urban, simple, noisy. **Surface:** asphalted. 01/01-31/12 Su-morning (market).
Distance: 500m 500m 500m.
Remarks: Max. 24h, sunday morning market.

Tourist information Le Mans:

Le Musée des 24 Heures - Circuit de la Sarthe, 9 Place Luigi Chinetti. Motorcar museum.

Place des Jacobins. Wed + Su-morning, Fri.

S Le Pallet 18B3

Rue Pierre Abelard. **GPS**: n47,13494 w1,3305.

20 free € 1 Ch. **Location:** Rural, simple. **Surface:** asphalted. 01/01-31/12.
Distance: 500m 500m 500m on the spot on the spot.
Remarks: Wine museum, coins at the shops in the village.

S Le Poiré-sur-Vie 21B1

Rue de Roc. **GPS**: n46,76773 w1,51162.

5 € 5/day, first 48h free Chfree.
Location: Central, quiet. **Surface:** gravel. 01/01-31/12.
Distance: 500m 500m 500m.

S Le Puy-Notre-Dame 18D3

Place du Gâte Argent, Rue du Parc. **GPS**: n47,12390 w0,23155.

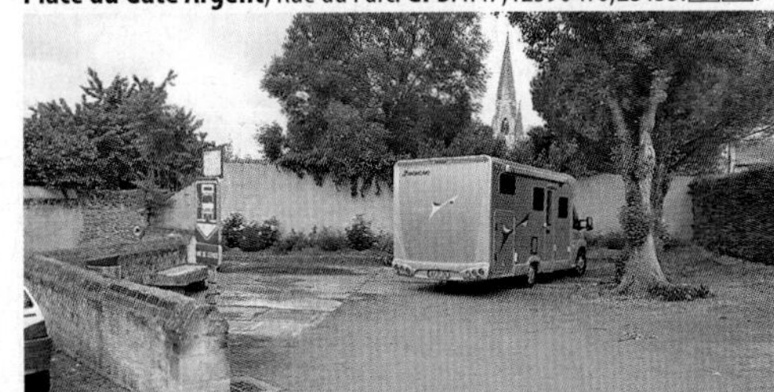

15 free Chfree. **Location:** Urban, simple, quiet. **Surface:** metalled. 01/01-31/12.
Distance: 100m 200m 200m.
Remarks: Next to cemetery.

S Le Puy-Notre-Dame 18D3

Cave-Champignonnière St.Maur, 1 Rue du Chateau, Sanziers. **GPS**: n47,11755 w0,20526.

FR

8 free (1x)on demand WC free. **Location:** Simple, quiet. **Surface:** metalled. 01/03-30/10.
Distance: 2km.
Remarks: At mushroom grower.

S Le Puy-Notre-Dame 18D3

Domaine de la Renière, Les Caves. **GPS**: n47,13429 w0,24256.

5 € 6 included € 5/24h. **Location:** Simple, quiet. **Surface:** metalled. 01/03-01/11.
Distance: 700m.
Remarks: When buying wine 1 night free.

S Le Puy-Notre-Dame 18D3

Domaine du Vieux Tuffeau, Les Caves. **GPS**: n47,13498 w0,24704.

6 free free € 5/night. **Location:** Rural, simple, quiet. **Surface:** metalled. 01/01-31/12.
Distance: 1km.

Le Puy-Notre-Dame 18D3

Domaine de la Girardrie, Rue Fontaine de Cix.
GPS: n47,11616 w0,24127.

5 free free. **Location:** Rural, simple, quiet. **Surface:** gravel. 01/01-31/12.
Distance: 1km 1km 1km.

Le Puy-Notre-Dame 18D3

Domaine des Hauts Buards, 17 Rue des Troglodytes.
GPS: n47,11149 w0,22544.

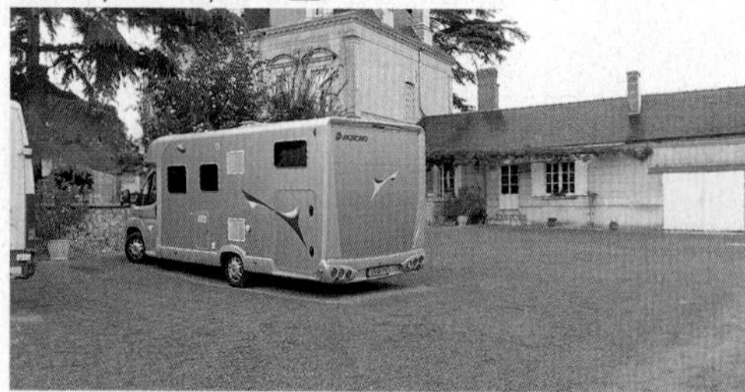

5 free. **Location:** Rural, simple, isolated, quiet. **Surface:** gravel. 01/01-31/12.
Distance: 7km 7km 7km on the spot on the spot.

Le Vaudelnay 18D3

Domaine du Vieux Pressoir, 235, Rue Château d'Oiré.
GPS: n47,14669 w0,25239.

4 free. **Location:** Rural, simple, quiet. **Surface:** metalled. 01/01-31/12.
Distance: 3km 3km 3km on the spot on the spot.
Remarks: No arrival on Sunday.

S Les Epesses 21C1

Le Puy du Fou, D27. **GPS**: n46,89425 w0,92506.
100 € 7 € 2/100liter Ch (36x)€ 2/12h WC.
Location: Simple, isolated, noisy.
Surface: grassy/gravel.
31/03-25/09.
Remarks: Baker at 8am, free shuttle to Puy du Fou.

S Les Essarts 21B1

Rue de la piscine. **GPS**: n46,77380 w1,23499.

10 free € 2/10minutes Ch (2x)€ 2/55minutes.
Location: Rural, simple. **Surface:** asphalted. 01/01-31/12.
Distance: 600m 5,6km 600m 600m.
Remarks: At swimmingpool and campsite.

S Les Herbiers 21B1

Rue Saint Exupéry. **GPS**: n46,87410 w1,01765.

8 free Ch free WC. **Location:** Simple.
Surface: asphalted/gravel. 01/01-31/12.
Distance: 600m 600m 600m.
Remarks: Max. 24h.

S Les Sables-d'Olonne 21A1

Aire camping-cars Port Olona, Rue des Bossis.
GPS: n46,50765 w1,78898.

38 € 8, tourist tax incl Ch .
Surface: asphalted. 01/01-31/12.
Distance: city centre 1,5km 1,6km 100m 2,6km 150m.
Remarks: Jul/Aug max. 48h, max. 72h.

S Les Sables-d'Olonne 21A1

Indigo Parking Plage, Rue Printanière. **GPS**: n46,49646 w1,77493.

150 € 15,10/24h, winter free Ch WC included.
Location: Urban, simple. **Surface:** gravel. 01/01-31/12 service: 06/11-31/03.
Distance: on the spot beach 600m 600m 400m.

S Les Sables-d'Olonne 21A1

Les Salines, 120 route de l'Aubraie. **GPS**: n46,51635 w1,80533.

20 € 5 Ch included € 4 free.
Location: Rural. **Surface:** sand.
01/04-30/09.
Distance: 600m on the spot.
Remarks: Baker every morning, july/Aug only overnight stays (18-11h).

Tourist information Les Sables-d'Olonne:
Cours Dupont. Wed + Sa morning.
Zoo d'Olonne. Zoo.

S Longeville-sur-Mer 21B1

Camping-Car Park, Avenue du Docteur Mathevet.
GPS: n46,40326 w1,50558.
33 € 9,50 Ch (34x) included. **Location:** Rural.
Surface: forest soil. 01/01-31/12.
Remarks: Mandatory, one-time fee Pass'Etapes € 4.

S Longeville-sur-Mer 21B1

Camping-Car Park, Boulevard du 8 mai. **GPS**: n46,42212 w1,49191.
15 € 9,50 Ch (15x) included. **Surface:** grassy.
01/01-31/12.
Remarks: Mandatory, one-time fee Pass'Etapes € 4.

S Longué-Jumelles 18D3

Boulevard Victor Hugo. **GPS**: n47,38097 w0,11236.

10 free Ch WC free. **Location:** Simple, quiet. **Surface:** gravel.
01/01-31/12.
Distance: 100m 3,3km on the spot on the spot.
Remarks: Service 300m: N 47,38046 W -0,11488, attention: follow the signs.

S Luçon 21B1

Domaine des Guifettes. **GPS**: n46,43339 w1,18189.

26 € 10,50 Ch included WC .
Location: Rural, comfortable, isolated, quiet.
Surface: gravel/metalled.
Distance: on the spot on the spot on the spot on the spot on the spot on the spot.

FR

Remarks: Free entrance swimming pool, jacuzzi, sauna, midget golf.

Tourist information Luçon:
Centre Ville. Wed + Sa morning.

L'Aiguillon-sur-Mer 21B2

Centre de Voile, Avenue Amiral Coubert.
GPS: n46,33238 w1,30726.

50 € 5 € 2/100liter Ch WC. **Location:** Rural, simple.
Surface: asphalted. 01/01-31/12.
Distance: 300m 300m on the spot 300m 300m.
Remarks: At lake, yachting school.

Maillé 21C2

La Petite Cabane. **GPS**: n46,34082 w0,79349.

€ 8 included € 3 Ch € 3 WC . **Location:** Rural, simple, quiet. **Surface:** grassy/gravel.
Distance: 500m 200m.
Remarks: Check in at harbourmaster, service passerby € 3, bicycle rental 500m.

Maillezais 21C2

Rue de l'Ecole. **GPS**: n46,37081 w0,74123.

20 free € 2/100liter Ch. **Location:** Simple.
Surface: asphalted. 01/01-31/12.
Distance: 500m 500m 200m.

Maisdon-sur-Sèvre 18B3

Domaine des Croix, Les Croix. **GPS**: n47,10710 w1,38757.

12 free Ch € 4/24h WC € 1. **Location:** Rural.
Surface: gravel. 01/01-31/12.
Distance: 1km.
Remarks: Max. 72h, wine tasting.

Mamers 18E1

Rue de la Piscine. **GPS**: n48,35523 e0,37187.

8 € 7/night, € 18/3 nights Ch included.
Location: Rural, comfortable, quiet. **Surface:** grassy/gravel.
01/01-31/12.
Distance: 1km 500m 500m 1km 1km.
Remarks: Entrance code available at campsite.

Mansigné 18D2

Camping de la Plage, Route du Plessis.
GPS: n47,75130 e0,13233.

10 € 5 € 2/80liter Ch € 2/2h € 5/4.
Location: Rural, comfortable, quiet. **Surface:** grassy/gravel.
Distance: 700m on the spot.

Martigné-Briand 18C3

Jardin des Vieux Pressoirs, Rue d'Anjou.
GPS: n47,23584 w0,42851.

4 free Ch free. **Surface:** metalled. 01/01-31/12.
Distance: 200m 200m 100m.
Remarks: Closed when frosty.

Martigné-Briand 18C3

Domaine de la Touche Blanche, La Touche Blanche.
GPS: n47,26977 w0,45274.

6 free € 3/day. **Location:** Rural, simple, quiet.
Surface: gravel. 01/01-31/12.
Distance: 3km 3km 3km on the spot on the spot.

Maulévrier 18C3

Route des Aubiers. **GPS**: n47,00652 w0,74014.
free Ch free. **Surface:** metalled.
Distance: 500m 500m 600m.

Mayenne 18C1

Quai Carnot. **GPS**: n48,30000 w0,62.

2 free € 2/100liter Ch. **Location:** Urban, simple, noisy.
Surface: asphalted. 01/01-31/12.
Distance: 1km 10m.
Remarks: Nearby basilica, max. 24h, coins at tourist info.

Mervent 21C1

Parking du Chêne Tord, Chemin du Chêne Tord.
GPS: n46,52385 w0,76432.

€ 5 Ch included. **Location:** Rural, simple, isolated, quiet.
Surface: gravel. 01/01-31/12.
Distance: 1km.
Remarks: At cemetery.

Mesnard-la-Barotière 21B1

Base de Loisirs de la Tricherie. **GPS**: n46,85280 w1,11764.

free € 3 Ch WC . **Location:** Rural, simple. **Surface:** grassy.
01/01-31/12.
Distance: 2km beach on the spot on the spot on the spot.
Remarks: At lake of Tricherie.

Mesquer 14D3

Aire du Parc de la Lande, Route de Campzillon.
GPS: n47,39309 w2,46549.
€ 5,50/night. 01/04-31/10.
Distance: 1,2km.
Remarks: Max. 72h.

Mesquer 14D3

Avenue de Praderoi, Quimiac. **GPS**: n47,40564 w2,48739.

10 free. **Surface:** forest soil. 01/01-31/12.
Distance: 400m sandy beach 300m.
Remarks: Tuesday morning market.

Mesquer 14D3

Route de la Bôle de Merquel. **GPS**: n47,41474 w2,46826.

15 free. **Surface:** gravel/metalled. 01/01-31/12.
Distance: 300m.
Remarks: Max. 48h.

Mesquer 14D3

Route de Kerlagadec. **GPS**: n47,39567 w2,46752.
Ch free. 01/01-31/12.

Mezeray 18D2

Rue de la Vezanne. **GPS**: n47,82300 w0,01485.

FR

4 free € 2/100liter Ch € 2/h. **Location:** Rural, simple.
Surface: gravel. 01/01-31/12 frost.
Distance: 500m.

Montfort-le-Gesnois 18E1

Parc des Sittelles. **GPS**: n48,03763 e0,41375.

16 € 10 Ch included. **Location:** Rural, simple, quiet.
Surface: forest soil. 01/01-31/12.
Distance: 50m.
Remarks: Inspection 2017: closed because of renovation.

Montreuil-Bellay 18D3

Place Dom Deschamps, Rue Georges Girouy.
GPS: n47,13272 w0,15835.

30 free € 2,20/10minutes ChWC.
Location: Urban, simple. **Surface:** gravel/metalled.
01/01-31/12 15/06-15/09 10-19h.
Distance: 150m on the spot 150m 150m on the spot on the spot on the spot.
Remarks: Along river, nearby campisite Les Nobis, coins at the shops and town hall.

Montreuil-Bellay 18D3

Caveau de la Prévoté, Rue du Cohu 55, Méron.
GPS: n47,13522 w0,11121.

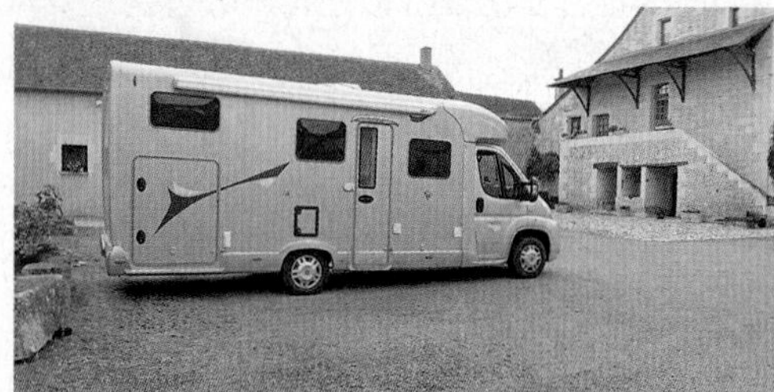

3 free Ch free. **Location:** Simple, quiet.
Surface: metalled. 01/01-31/12.
Distance: 50m 3km 3km.

Tourist information Montreuil-Bellay:
Office de Tourisme, Place du Concorde, www.ville-montreuil-bellay.fr. City with a fortress from 1025.

Montreuil-Juigné 18C2

Rue Saint Jean Baptiste. **GPS**: n47,54132 w0,61526.

8 free € 2/100liter Ch. **Location:** Rural, simple.
Surface: gravel/metalled. 01/01-31/12.
Distance: 1km 50m 800m.
Remarks: Along the Mayenne river, max. 72h, coins at camping municipal.

Moutiers-sur-le-Lay 21B1

Palias. **GPS**: n46,55375 w1,15483.

6 free Ch WC. **Location:** Simple.
Surface: grassy/metalled. 01/01-31/12.
Distance: 400m 400m 400m 200m.
Remarks: At gymnasium.

Mouzillon 18B3

Route de la Vendée. **GPS**: n47,13944 w1,28194.

12 free € 2 Ch. **Location:** Simple. **Surface:** asphalted.
Distance: 200m 200m 200m on the spot.

Mouzillon 18B3

En Vignoble Nantais, La Tucauderie. **GPS**: n47,12697 w1,23695.
6 € 5 WC included. **Surface:** gravel. 01/01-31/12.

Nantes 18B3

Camping-car park du Petit Port, Boulevard du Petit Port.
GPS: n47,24252 w1,5568.

15 € 13,30 Ch included.
Location: Urban, simple, central. **Surface:** grassy/metalled.
01/01-31/12.
Distance: on the spot 3,5km on the spot 300m tram 150m.
Remarks: Mandatory, one-time fee Pass'Etapes € 4, wifi code: 44-2207, entrance code: 2207A.

Tourist information Nantes:
Musée Jules Verne.

Noirmoutier-en-l'Ile 18A3

Aire de La Guérinière, Rue de la Tresson. **GPS**: n46,96591 w2,21482.

49 € 8-10, 02/07-27/08 € 13 Ch included.
Surface: gravel. 01/01-31/12.
Distance: sandy beach 450m 200m 100m.
Remarks: Max. 48h, video surveillance.

Noirmoutier-en-l'Ile 18A3

La Place de l'ancien moulin à eau, Noirmoutier-en-l'Ile.
GPS: n47,00139 w2,25167.

220 € 5, 01/04-30/10 € 8, parking free € 2/100liter Ch € 2/1h free. **Surface:** asphalted. 01/01-31/12.
Distance: 750m sandy beach 2,5km 750m.
Remarks: Max. 72h.

Noirmoutier-en-l'Ile 18A3

Place des Ormeaux, L'Epine. **GPS**: n46,98060 w2,26404.

51 € 8/24h, € 14/48h, € 20/72h 100liter Ch included50minutes WC.
Surface: metalled. 01/01-31/12.
Distance: 100m 1,3km on the spot 200m 3km on the spot.
Remarks: Max. 72h.

Noirmoutier-en-l'Ile 18A3

Place R. Ganachaud, l'Herbaudière. **GPS**: n47,02016 w2,30061.

18 € 5, 01/04-30/10 € 8, parking free € 2/100liter Ch € 2/1h. **Surface:** asphalted. 01/01-31/12.
Distance: on the spot 350m.
Remarks: Parking behind town hall, max. 72h.

Tourist information Noirmoutier-en-l'Ile:
Place de la République. Fri.
Sealand Aquarium, Le Vieux Port.

Nort-sur-Erdre 18B2

13 Place du Bassin. **GPS**: n47,43746 w1,49546.

6 free € 2 ChWC free. **Location:** Simple, quiet.
Surface: asphalted. 01/01-31/12.
Distance: 300m 100m 300m 300m.
Remarks: Max. 24h.

S Notre-Dame-de-Monts 18A3

10 Route de la Taillée. **GPS**: n46,83125 w2,12092.
12 € 10 Ch WC. **Location:** Urban. **Surface:** metalled.
01/01-31/12.
Distance: 800m beach 2km on the spot 750m.

S Notre-Dame-de-Monts 18A3

Aire de la Clairière, Rue de la Clairière.
GPS: n46,83460 w2,14282.

35 € 7/20-8h, 01/10-31/03 € 5/20-8h Chfree.
Location: Rural, simple. **Surface:** gravel.
01/01-31/12 service: 01/12-01/04.
Distance: 800m 200m 200m 800m 800m.
Remarks: Motorhome parking at the beach.

S Notre-Dame-de-Monts 18A3

Parking De Gaulle, Rue de La Barre. **GPS**: n46,83118 w2,13006.

20 € 7/20-8h, 01/10-31/03 € 5/20-8h ChWCfree.
Surface: asphalted. 01/01-31/12 service: 01/12-01/04.
Distance: 300m 500m 300m.

S Nozay 18B2

Étang de Nozay. **GPS**: n47,57500 w1,62528.

16 € 8 Ch (16x)WCincluded. **Location:** Simple.
Surface: gravel. 01/01-31/12 service: frost.
Distance: 1,5km 2km 10m 200m 400m.
Remarks: Playground.

S Olonne-sur-Mer 21A1

Aire camping-cars OlonnEscale, Rue des Anciens Combattants d'Afrique du Nord. **GPS**: n46,53814 w1,77517.

21 € 8/24h Ch included.
Location: Simple. 01/01-31/12.
Distance: 300m 6km 600m 300m.
Remarks: Jul/Aug max. 48h, max. 72h.

S Oudon 18B3

Aire de Camping-Car Oudon, Rue de la Vieille Cour.
GPS: n47,34567 w1,28415.

8 free Ch. **Location:** Rural, simple, quiet. **Surface:** gravel.
01/01-31/12.
Distance: 300m 500m 400m on the spot on the spot.
Remarks: Servicepoint at campsite 1km.

S Pellouailles-les-Vignes 18C2

Impasse de la Chapelle, D323. **GPS**: n47,52141 w0,43698.

3 free Chfree. **Location:** Rural. **Surface:** asphalted.
01/01-31/12.
Distance: on the spot 1,4km 100m bakery 50m.

S Piriac-sur-Mer 14D3

Parking de Brambel, Avenue du Général de Gaulle, D452.
GPS: n47,39647 w2,51292.

12 € 6,50 € 2/100liter ChWC.
Location: Comfortable. **Surface:** metalled. 01/01-31/12.
Distance: 2km sandy beach 50m 2km 2km.
Remarks: Parking to sea.

S Piriac-sur-Mer 14D3

Parking de Lérat, Route de Mesquêne, D99, Lieu-dit Lérat.
GPS: n47,36807 w2,53273.

25 € 6,50 € 2/100liter Ch. **Location:** Simple.
Surface: metalled. 01/01-31/12.
Distance: 2,5km 600m 600m 500m 500m.

S Piriac-sur-Mer 14D3

Port de Piriac, Rue de la Tranchée. **GPS**: n47,37861 w2,5422.

15 € 6,50 € 2/100liter Ch.
Surface: gravel. 01/01-31/12.
Distance: 500m 500m 500m.

Tourist information Piriac-sur-Mer:
01/06-30/09 Mo + Wed + Sa-morning, 01/10-30/05 Tue.
Arts market. 01/07-31/08 Thu-evening.

S Pontmain 15C3

Parking de la Mairie, Le Bourg. **GPS**: n48,43796 w1,06042.

50 free Chfree.
Location: Simple, quiet. 01/01-31/12.
Distance: on the spot.
Remarks: Max. 1 night, picnic tables available.

S Pornic 18A3

Le Val Saint-Martin. **GPS**: n47,12053 w2,09162.

7 free € 2/100liter Ch. **Location:** Comfortable, isolated.
Surface: asphalted. 01/01-31/12.
Distance: city centre 1,5km.
Remarks: Next to swimming pool.

S Pouancé 18B2

Rue de l'Hippodrome, Aubin. **GPS**: n47,75223 w1,18007.

5 € 4,40 Ch (4x)WCfree.
Location: Rural, simple, quiet. **Surface:** grassy. 01/01-31/12.
Distance: 500m small beach 20m 20m 1km 1km.
Remarks: Along étang de Saint-Aubin.

S Pouzauges 21C1

Parking de la Vallée, D49/D203. **GPS**: n46,77639 w0,82861.

20 free Chfree WC. **Location:** Simple. **Surface:** asphalted.

FR

01/01-31/12.
Distance: 1km ⊗1km 1km.

Préfailles 18A3

Camping-Car Park de La Pointe, Chemin du Port aux Anes.
GPS: n47,13872 w2,22213.

49 € 11,20 Ch (49x) included.
Location: Comfortable. **Surface:** asphalted/gravel. 01/01-31/12.
Remarks: Mandatory, one-time fee Pass'Etapes € 4.

Préfailles 18A3

Camping-Car Park Les Pinettes, D313, chemin des Pinettes.
GPS: n47,13663 w2,23843.

39 € 10 Ch included. **Location:** Rural, simple, quiet.
Surface: gravel/metalled. 01/01-31/12.
Distance: 3km 50m ⊗200m 3km.
Remarks: Mandatory, one-time fee Pass'Etapes € 4, baker every morning.

Préfailles 18A3

Aire de Biochon, Chemin de Levertrie. **GPS**: n47,12973 w2,19028.

75 € 3. **Location:** Rural, simple, quiet. **Surface:** gravel/sand.
01/01-31/12.
Distance: 3km 500m 500m ⊗3km 3km.
Remarks: Max. 48h, baker every morning.

Préfailles 18A3

Rue de la Prée. **GPS**: n47,13439 w2,2117.
€ 2,50/100liter Ch. **Location:** Simple. 01/01-31/12.
Remarks: Coins at tourist info.

Pruillé-l'Éguillé 18E2

Berce Loisirs, La Quellerie. **GPS**: n47,82509 e0,42632.

23 € 7 € 2 Ch (23x)€ 2/24h WC € 1.
Location: Rural, comfortable, quiet. **Surface:** grassy/gravel.
01/01-31/12.
Distance: 1,2km on the spot ⊗1,2km on the spot on the spot.
Remarks: At fish pond, barbecue place.

Rablay sur Layon 18C3

Parking les Lavandières, D54. **GPS**: n47,29772 w0,57767.

5 free Ch WC free. **Location:** Rural, simple, quiet.
Surface: gravel/sand. 01/01-31/12.
Distance: 300m.

Riaille 18B2

Rue de la Benate. **GPS**: n47,51412 w1,28803.

5 free Ch WC free. **Location:** Rural, simple, quiet.
Surface: gravel. 01/01-31/12.
Distance: 700m ⊗700m 700m.
Remarks: Max. 48h.

Rouans 18A3

Aire naturelle de Messan, Route des Marais.
GPS: n47,19272 w1,85419.

8 € 4, tourist tax € 0,60/pp Ch WC free.
Location: Rural, simple. **Surface:** grassy/metalled.
01/01-31/12.
Distance: 1km on the spot ⊗on the spot 1km.
Remarks: To be paid at town hall.

Saint-Aubin-de-Luigné 18C3

Domaine La Biquerie, Domaine viticole de la Biquerie D17.
GPS: n47,30843 w0,70211.

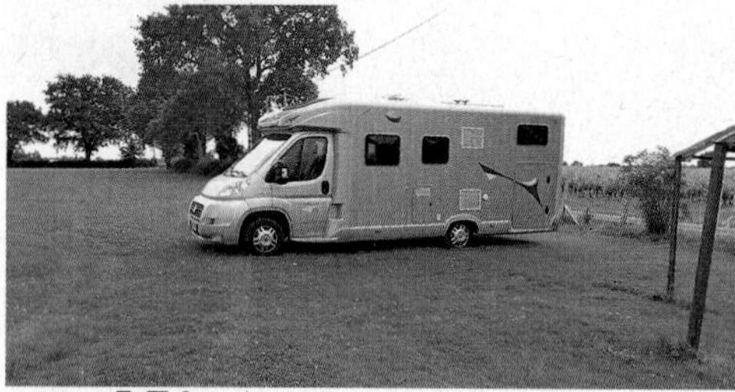

30 free Ch free.
Location: Rural, simple, quiet. **Surface:** grassy.
01/01-31/12.
Distance: 5km ⊗5km 5km 5km on the spot on the spot.

Saint-Aubin-de-Luigné 18C3

Camping du Layon, Rue Jean de Pontoise.
GPS: n47,32796 w0,67112.

10 € 4 Ch included. **Location:** Urban, central, quiet.
Surface: asphalted. 01/05-30/09.
Distance: 50m 100m ⊗250m 250m 250m on the spot on the spot.
Remarks: Pay at campsite or town hall.

Saint-Calais 18E2

Boulevard du Docteur Gigon. **GPS**: n47,92416 e0,74459.

7 free Ch (2x) WC free. **Location:** Rural, simple, quiet.
Surface: asphalted. 01/01-31/12.
Distance: 400m on the spot.

Saint-Calais 18E2

Le Champ Long, D249. **GPS**: n47,93375 e0,74568.

15 free WC. **Location:** Rural. **Surface:** asphalted.
01/01-31/12.
Distance: 1,6km lake on the spot on the spot.

Saint-Clément-des-Levées 18D3

Rue de la Laiterie. **GPS**: n47,33064 w0,18042.

10 free € 2 Ch. **Surface:** metalled. 01/01-31/12.
Distance: 300m.
Remarks: Coins at the shops and town hall.

Saint-Cyr-en-Bourg 18D3

Cave de Saumur, Route de Saumoussay.
GPS: n47,19642 w0,07266.

15 free Ch WC free. **Location:** Rural, simple, quiet.
Surface: asphalted. 15/03-15/09.
Distance: 3km.
Remarks: Max. 48h, wine tasting 300m.

Saint-Georges-sur-Loire 18C2

Rue de la Villette. **GPS**: n47,40610 w0,76301.

12 free Ch free. **Location:** Rural, simple, quiet.
Surface: asphalted. 01/01-31/12.

FR

Distance: 300m 100m 300m 300m.
Remarks: Next to the old abbey, max. 24h.

S Saint-Gervais 18A3

Route de St Urbain. **GPS**: n46,89999 w2,00134.
10 free € 3/10minutes Ch € 3/55minutes.
01/01-31/12.
Distance: 300m 300m.

S Saint-Gilles-Croix-de-Vie 21A1

La Rabalette, Rue de la Rabalette. **GPS**: n46,70302 w1,94728.

35 15/03-15/11 € 6/night € 2,60/10minutes Ch.
Location: Urban, simple. **Surface:** asphalted. 01/01-31/12.
Distance: 500m 1km 500m 500m.
Remarks: Nearby lake Soudinière, coins at tourist info.

S Saint-Gilles-Croix-de-Vie 21A1

Stade de la Chapelle, Rue du Bois. **GPS**: n46,69449 w1,92716.

€ 6 € 2,60 Ch. **Location:** Urban. **Surface:** unpaved.
01/04-30/09 weekend and school holidays.
Distance: centre 500m.
Remarks: Coins at tourist info.

Tourist information Saint-Gilles-Croix-de-Vie:
St.Gilles: Tue, Thu, Su; Croix de Vie; Wed, Sa.

S Saint-Hilaire-de-Chaléons 18A3

Rue Eloi Guitteny, D61. **GPS**: n47,10389 w1,86639.

2 free Ch WC free. **Surface:** asphalted. 01/01-31/12.
Distance: 100m 500m 100m.
Remarks: Next to campsite de l'Etoile, max. 24h.

S Saint-Hilaire-de-Riez 21A1

Base des vallées, Chemin des Vallées. **GPS**: n46,73154 w1,91132.

10 free € 2,60/10minutes Ch. **Location:** Rural, simple.
Surface: asphalted. 01/01-31/12.
Distance: St.Hilaire 3,7km 7km.

S Saint-Hilaire-de-Riez 21A1

Parking des Becs, Avenue des Becs. **GPS**: n46,76040 w2,02656.

25 € 6/24h € 2,60/10minutes Ch.
Surface: asphalted. 01/01-31/12.
Distance: 100m sandy beach 750m 200m.
Remarks: Max. 3 nights.

Saint-Hilaire-de-Riez 21A1

Allée de la Plage de la Parée Préneau. **GPS**: n46,72865 w1,99167.

48 free, night € 6. **Location:** Rural. **Surface:** metalled.
01/01-31/12.
Distance: on the spot.
Remarks: Beach parking.

Saint-Hilaire-de-Riez 21A1

Champ Gaillard, Avenue de Baisse. **GPS**: n46,76903 w2,03337.

28 free.
Location: Rural, isolated. **Surface:** gravel. 01/01-31/12.
Distance: sandy beach 1km.

S Saint-Jean-de-Monts 21A1

Le Repos des Tortues, Route de Notre Dame de Monts 38.
GPS: n46,79879 w2,07344.

98 € 8, 01/07-31/08 € 12 Ch (49x),4Amp WC € 5/stay
€ 4 included. **Location:** Rural, luxurious.
Surface: grassy/gravel. 01/01-31/12.
Distance: 800m 1,5km 50m 2km.
Remarks: Video surveillance.

S Saint-Jean-de-Monts 21A1

Aire de stationnement des Pimprenelles, Rue des Pimprenelles.
GPS: n46,78837 w2,07986.

20 € 8,50-12, tourist tax incl Ch included.
Location: Comfortable. **Surface:** asphalted. 01/04-01/11.
Distance: sandy beach 200m.

Tourist information Saint-Jean-de-Monts:
Wed, Sa.

S Saint-Jean-sur-Mayenne 18C1

Les Marchanderies. **GPS**: n48,12793 w0,75244.

25 € 9 Ch WC included. **Location:** Rural, luxurious, quiet. **Surface:** grassy/gravel. 01/03-30/11.
Distance: 500m on the spot 300m 400m bakery on the spot.
Remarks: Along the Mayenne river.

S Saint-Léonard-des-Bois 18D1

Aire Municipale, Le Gué Plard. **GPS**: n48,35318 w0,08127.

10 free Ch WC free. **Location:** Rural, simple, quiet.
Surface: asphalted. 01/01-31/12.
Distance: 500m on the spot on the spot 500m on the spot on the spot on the spot.

S Saint-Loup-du-Gast 15C3

Zone d'Activité du Creusot. **GPS**: n48,38750 w0,58548.

6 free Ch free.
Location: Rural, simple, quiet. **Surface:** asphalted/grassy.
01/01-31/12.
Distance: 350m.
Remarks: Max. 1 night, departure Vélorail, € 15 per bike for 4 pers.

S Saint-Mars-la-Jaille 18B2

Square de La Commune Libre du Bouffay, Rue Neuve.
GPS: n47,52327 w1,18357.

12 free Ch WC free. **Location:** Rural, comfortable, quiet.
Surface: asphalted. 01/01-31/12.
Distance: 200m on the spot on the spot.
Remarks: Parking at small lake, max. 48h, playground.

S Saint-Michel-Chef-Chef 18A3

Camping-Car Park Le Thar-Cor La Plaine sur Mer, Avenue Cormier.
GPS: n47,16017 w2,16881.

FR

24 € 9,60-12 Ch (4x) included.
Location: Simple, isolated, quiet. **Surface:** gravel/metalled.
01/01-31/12.
Distance: sandy beach 400m 400m 400m.
Remarks: Mandatory, one-time fee Pass'Etapes € 4.

S Saint-Michel-Chef-Chef 18A3

Mairie de Saint-Michel-Chef-Chef, Rue du Chevecier.
GPS: n47,18209 w2,14664.

30 € 3,30, 20-8h € 9,30 Chincluded.
Location: Simple. **Surface:** asphalted.
01/01-31/12.
Distance: 300m 300m 300m.
Remarks: Parking townhall, coins at tourist info and town hall.

Saint-Michel-Chef-Chef 18A3

Camping Clos Mer et Nature, Route de Tharon.
GPS: n47,17309 w2,15779.

€ 6 € 2/100liter Ch € 2. **Location:** Simple, quiet.
Surface: grassy. 01/01-31/12.
Distance: 500m sandy beach 400m 300m.
Remarks: Check in at reception campsite.

S Saint-Michel-en-l'Herm 21B2

Route de la Mer. **GPS**: n46,35161 w1,24821.

4 free € 2 Ch.
Location: Simple. **Surface:** asphalted/gravel.
Distance: 200m 200m 200m.
Remarks: Coins at the shops.

S Saint-Michel-et-Chanveaux 18B2

Aire de la Coulée Verte, Rue de Bretagne.
GPS: n47,68034 w1,13252.

4 free free. **Location:** Quiet. **Surface:** unpaved.
01/01-31/12.
Distance: on the spot 100m.

S Saint-Michel-Mont-Mercure 21C1

Place du Sommet. **GPS**: n46,83222 w0,88222.

20 free € 2/100liter Ch. **Location:** Simple, isolated.
Surface: gravel. 01/01-31/12.
Distance: 500m on the spot 500m.

S Saint-Nazaire 18A3

Parking du Théâtre, Boulevard Paul Leferme. **GPS**: n47,27895 w2.

28 € 7, tourist tax € 0,65/motorhome € 4/10minutes Ch included. **Location:** Urban, simple, isolated. **Surface:** metalled.
01/01-31/12.
Distance: on the spot 500m 50m.
Remarks: Free bus to centre.

S Saint-Nazaire 18A3

Route de l'Océan, D292, Saint-Marc-sur-Mer.
GPS: n47,23700 w2,30033.

15 free € 4/100liter Ch € 4/1h. **Location:** Rural, simple, quiet. **Surface:** gravel. 01/01-31/12.
Distance: 2km 100m 100m.

Saint-Nazaire 18A3

Quai du Port de Méan. **GPS**: n47,29937 w2,18333.
3 free. **Surface:** metalled. 01/01-31/12.
Distance: 4km 1km 150m.

Saint-Nazaire 18A3

Route du Bois Joalland. **GPS**: n47,27954 w2,26229.

5 free.
Location: Simple, central. **Surface:** gravel. 01/01-31/12.
Distance: 500m on the spot on the spot on the spot on the spot.

S Saint-Philbert-de-Grand-Lieu 18B3

Chemin de la Plage. **GPS**: n47,04500 w1,64172.

25 free Chfree WC. **Surface:** gravel. 01/01-31/12.
Distance: 1km on the spot on the spot 550m 1km.

S Saint-Rémy-la-Varenne 18D3

Rue St Aubin-D132. **GPS**: n47,39805 w0,31612.

3 free ChWCfree. **Location:** Urban, simple, quiet.
Surface: asphalted. 01/01-31/12.
Distance: on the spot 100m 100m 150m on the spot on the spot.

S Saint-Saturnin-sur-Loire 18C3

Route de Saumur, D751. **GPS**: n47,39267 w0,43285.

3 free Chfree. **Location:** Urban, simple, quiet.
Surface: metalled. 01/01-31/12.
Distance: on the spot 100m 100m 100m on the spot on the spot.

S Saint-Viaud 18A3

Rue du Parc des Sports. **GPS**: n47,25917 w2,015.

10 free Ch (2x) WC.
Location: Rural, comfortable, quiet. **Surface:** metalled.
01/01-31/12 service: 01/04-15/11.
Distance: 500m 100m 500m 500m.
Remarks: At recreational lake, max. 8 days.

S Saint-Vincent-sur-Jard 21B1

Chemin des Roulettes, Le Goulet. **GPS**: n46,41038 w1,5413.

30 € 9,20 € 2/10minutes Ch € 2/55minutes.
Location: Rural, simple. **Surface:** metalled.
01/01-31/12 Service: winter.
Distance: 1km 100m 400m.

S Sainte-Foy 21A1

Rue Maurice Raimbaud. **GPS**: n46,54568 w1,67306.

FR

3 free Ch free. **Surface:** asphalted. 01/04-31/10.
Distance: on the spot on the spot.

S Sainte-Suzanne 18D1
Camping-Car Park, 15 rue du Camp des Anglais.
GPS: n48,09933 w0,35044.
21 € 12,60 Ch (20x) included.
Surface: gravel/metalled. 01/01-31/12.
Remarks: Mandatory, one-time fee Pass'Etapes € 4.

S Sallertaine 18A3
Camping-Car Park, Route de Saint Urbain. **GPS:** n46,86032 w1,9607.
30 € 8,44-10,44 Chincluded. 01/01-31/12.
Remarks: Mandatory, one-time fee Pass'Etapes € 4.

S Saulgé l'Hôpital 18C3
Terrain de Loisirs, Chemin de la Planche.
GPS: n47,29853 w0,38344.

15 free Chfree. **Location:** Rural, simple, quiet.
Surface: gravel. 01/01-31/12.
Distance: 100m 100m 100m.
Remarks: Service 100m.

S Saumur 18D3
Camping-car park Ile D'offard, Rue de Verden.
GPS: n47,25993 w0,06489.
35 € 13,50 Ch (35x),6Amp included.
Location: Rural. **Surface:** gravel. 01/01-31/12.
Distance: 1km.
Remarks: Mandatory, one-time fee Pass'Etapes € 4.

Tourist information Saumur:
Office de Tourisme, Place de la Bilange, www.saumur-tourisme.com. Historical city on the Loire river.
Tuffeau. Wine-cellars in tuff.
Village Troglodyte, Rochemenier, Louresse. Cave dwelling village.
01/04-31/10 9.30-19h, 01/11-30/11, 01/02-31/03 Sa-Su 14-18h.
Château de Saumur. Castle, 13th century, with museum for decorative art and horse museum. 9.30-23h, 14-17.30h. € 6.

S Segré 18C2
Aire de l'Europe, D775. **GPS:** n47,68497 w0,85719.

free ChWCfree. **Location:** Rural, simple, noisy.
Surface: asphalted. 01/01-31/12.
Distance: 1km on the spot.

S Segré 18C2
Place du Moulin sous la Tour, Rue Emile Zola.
GPS: n47,68409 w0,87436.

10 free ChWCfree. **Location:** Urban, simple, quiet.
Surface: asphalted/gravel. 01/01-31/12 Service: winter.
Distance: 300m on the spot 100m on the spot.
Remarks: Steep entrance road.

S Segré 18C2
Place du Port. **GPS:** n47,68643 w0,86445.

10 free Chfree WC. **Location:** Urban, simple, noisy.
Surface: asphalted. 01/01-31/12.
Distance: on the spot on the spot 600m 500m.
Remarks: Picnic area.

S Sillé-le-Guillaume 18D1
2, Place de la Gare. **GPS:** n48,18167 w0,13111.

8 free € 3/80liter Ch € 3/2h. **Location:** Urban, simple, noisy. **Surface:** asphalted. 01/01-31/12.
Distance: 300m 300m 400m train 50m.
Remarks: Coins at tourist info.

Souvigné-sur-Sarthe 18D2
Le Val de Taude, Rue de la Vallée. **GPS:** n47,82782 w0,38896.

5 free. **Location:** Rural, simple, isolated, quiet. **Surface:** gravel.
01/01-31/12.
Distance: 200m.

S Talmont-Saint-Hilaire 21A1
Parking des Gâtines, Rue des Gâtines. **GPS:** n46,46761 w1,61718.

16 € 7,40/24h € 3/10minutes Ch € 3/50minutes.
Location: Rural, simple. **Surface:** asphalted. 01/01-31/12.
Distance: 500m Small lake (100m) 100m.

S Talmont-Saint-Hilaire 21A1
Parking du Château Guibert, Avenue de la Plage.
GPS: n46,44098 w1,66351.

16 € 7,40/24h € 3 Ch € 3 WC.
Location: Rural, simple. **Surface:** metalled. 01/01-31/12.
Distance: 1km.
Remarks: Max. 48h.

Tennie 18D1
Rue du Camping. **GPS:** n48,10636 w0,0786.

6 free. **Location:** Rural, simple, quiet. **Surface:** gravel.
01/01-31/12.
Distance: on the spot on the spot 250m on the spot.
Remarks: At lake.

S Thoiré-sur-Dinan 18E2
19 rue Gabriel Guyon. **GPS:** n47,75343 e0,44621.

4 € 5 Ch included. **Location:** Rural, comfortable, quiet. **Surface:** gravel. 01/01-31/12.
Remarks: Picnic and barbecue place.

S Turquant 18D3
Aire Municipal, Rue des Ducs d'Anjou. **GPS:** n47,22393 e0,02858.

20 free € 2,50 ChWC. **Location:** Simple, central.
Surface: metalled. 01/01-31/12.
Distance: 100m 50m 50m on the spot on the spot on the spot.
Remarks: Behind church, coins at the shops in the village.

S Vaiges 18C1
Rue Robert Gletron, D57. **GPS:** n48,04189 w0,48285.

5 free € 3 Ch. **Location:** Urban, simple, noisy.
Surface: gravel. 01/01-31/12.
Distance: 500m 1,7km 20m 700m bakery.

S Valanjou 18C3
Aire de Plaisance, Rue de la Mairie. **GPS:** n47,21658 w0,60326.

6 free ChWCfree. **Location:** Rural, simple, quiet.
Surface: metalled. 01/01-31/12.
Distance: 200m on the spot 300m 300m on the spot on the spot.
Remarks: Nearby town hall.

FR

Vauchrétien 18C3
Domaine Dittiére, Chemin de la Grouas Vauchrétien.
GPS: n47,33273 w0,47231.

5 free free. **Location:** Rural, simple, quiet. **Surface:** gravel.
01/01-31/12.
Distance: 500m 500m.

Venansault 21B1
Rue Pierre Nicolas Loué. **GPS**: n46,68250 w1,51472.

5 free. **Surface:** sand. 01/01-31/12.
Distance: 500m 100m 300m 500m.

Vendrennes 21B1
Route de l'Océan. **GPS**: n46,82690 w1,1217.

10 free € 3/150liter Ch WC. **Location:** Rural, simple, quiet.
Surface: metalled. 01/01-31/12.
Distance: 200m.
Remarks: Coins at the bakery.

Vihiers 18C3
Rue Champ de Foire des Champs. **GPS**: n47,14355 w0,5358.

5 free Ch WC free. **Location:** Urban, simple, quiet.
Surface: asphalted. 01/01-31/12.
Distance: 50m 100m 100m.

Villeveque 18C2
Rue du Port. **GPS**: n47,56222 w0,42257.

6 free € 1 Ch WC free. **Location:** Rural, comfortable, quiet.
Surface: gravel/metalled. 01/01-31/12.
Distance: 100m on the spot on the spot 50m bakery 200m on the spot on the spot.

Villiers-Charlemagne 18C1
Village Vacances et Pêche, Rue des Haies.
GPS: n47,92083 w0,68167.

25 € 5/night Ch included. **Location:** Rural, comfortable, quiet.
Surface: grassy. 01/01-31/12.
Distance: on the spot on the spot 500m on the spot.
Remarks: Fishing permit available.

Vouvant 21C1
Rue de Château Neuf. **GPS**: n46,57462 w0,77462.

20 € 5/night Ch free. **Surface:** gravel. 01/01-31/12.
Distance: 500m 500m 500m.

Centre-Val de Loire

Ainay-le-Vieil 21H1
La Tuilerie. **GPS**: n46,66159 e2,55582.

6 free Ch WC free. **Location:** Rural, simple, quiet.
Surface: grassy. 01/01-31/12.
Distance: 850m 800m.

Allogny 18G3
D944. **GPS**: n47,21913 e2,32329.

10 free Ch WC free. **Location:** Rural, simple, isolated, noisy.
Surface: asphalted. 01/01-31/12.
Distance: 800m 50m 50m.

Amboise 18E3
Vinci Park, Allée de la Chapelle Saint-Jean.
GPS: n47,41761 e0,98742.

20 € 12/24h Ch included (20x)€ 2
Location: Rural, comfortable, central, quiet.
Surface: asphalted/grassy. 01/01-31/12.
Distance: 200m 200m 200m 200m on the spot on the spot.
Remarks: Next to campsite, castle 500m.

Amboise 18E3
Parking St. Jean, Avenue Leonardo da Vinci 43, D61.
GPS: n47,40814 e0,98986.

11 free. **Location:** Urban, simple, isolated, quiet.
Surface: asphalted. 01/01-31/12.
Distance: on the spot 1,5km 1,5km on the spot.

Angé 18F3
Place de la Mairie. **GPS**: n47,33239 e1,24450.

20 free € 3/100liter Ch free. **Location:** Simple, quiet.
Surface: sand. 01/01-31/12.
Remarks: Coins at town hall and supermarket.

Ardentes 21G1
Avenue de Verdun. **GPS**: n46,74682 e1,82826.

5 free € 2,50/10minutes Ch (4x) WC
Location: Rural, noisy. **Surface:** gravel.
Distance: on the spot on the spot.

Argenton-sur-Creuse 21F1
Rue de la Grenouille. **GPS**: n46,58715 e1,52497.

50 free. **Location:** Simple. **Surface:** sand. 01/01-31/12.
Distance: 50m 3,4km.

Argenton-sur-Creuse 21F1
Allée du Champ de Foire. **GPS**: n46,58501 e1,52283.
Ch WC free. **Location:** Rural, simple. 01/01-31/12.
Distance: on the spot.

Athée-sur-Cher 18E3
Aire d'Athée-sur-Cher, D83, Rue de Cigogné.
GPS: n47,31439 e0,91756.

3 free Chfree. **Location:** Rural, simple, isolated, quiet. **Surface:** metalled. 01/01-31/12 service: frost.
Distance: 800m 11km 1,5km 1km on the spot.
Remarks: Max. 24h.

Aubigny-sur-Nère 18H3

Parc des Sports, D7. **GPS**: n47,48201 e2,44995.

9 free Chfree. **Location:** Rural, simple, isolated, quiet.
Surface: asphalted. 01/01-31/12.
Distance: 1km 1km 2km on the spot on the spot.
Remarks: Playground.

Aubigny-sur-Nère 18H3

Parking du Pré qui Danse, Mail Guichard.
GPS: n47,49140 e2,43830.

10 free Chfree. **Location:** Urban, simple. **Surface:** asphalted. 01/01-31/12.
Distance: 200m 200m 200m 100m.

Avoine 18D3

Avenue de la République. **GPS**: n47,21287 e0,17706.

11 € 4 € 2/10minutes Ch (11x)€ 2/24h
Location: Rural, comfortable, central, quiet.
Surface: asphalted/metalled. 01/01-31/12.
Distance: 1km Lac Mousseau 300m 300m 300m.
Remarks: Max. 3 nights.

Azay-le-Rideau 18E3

Camping-car Park, Rue du Stade. **GPS**: n47,25925 e0,46992.
48 € 11 Ch (40x) ,on camp site included.
Location: Urban, comfortable, central, quiet. **Surface:** asphalted.
01/01-31/12.
Distance: 200m 300m on the spot on the spot.
Remarks: Mandatory, one-time fee Pass'Etapes € 4.

Azé 18F2

M et Mme Hersant, Les Places, D957 Épuisay-Galette.
GPS: n47,86451 e0,97659.

6 € 10 Chincluded € 2.
Location: Rural, comfortable, isolated, quiet. **Surface:** grassy/gravel.
01/01-31/12.
Distance: 7km on the spot.

Barlieu 18H3

Base de loisirs de Badineau. **GPS**: n47,47918 e2,63168.

15 € 2, first night € 3,50 € 2/100liter Ch € 2/h WC.
Location: Rural, simple, quiet. **Surface:** grassy/gravel.
19/04-31/10.
Distance: 1km on the spot on the spot.
Remarks: At small lake.

Bauzy 18F2

L'étang communal, Route de Neuvy. **GPS**: n47,53734 e1,60982.
3 free. **Location:** Rural. **Surface:** metalled. 01/01-31/12.

Benais 18D3

Rue Saint-Vincent. **GPS**: n47,29875 e0,21598.

6 free. **Location:** Rural, simple, quiet. **Surface:** grassy.
01/01-31/12.
Distance: 350m 350m on the spot on the spot.

Bessais-le-Fromental 21H1

Base de loisirs de l'Étang de Goule, Champ de la Croix.
GPS: n46,73402 e2,80034.

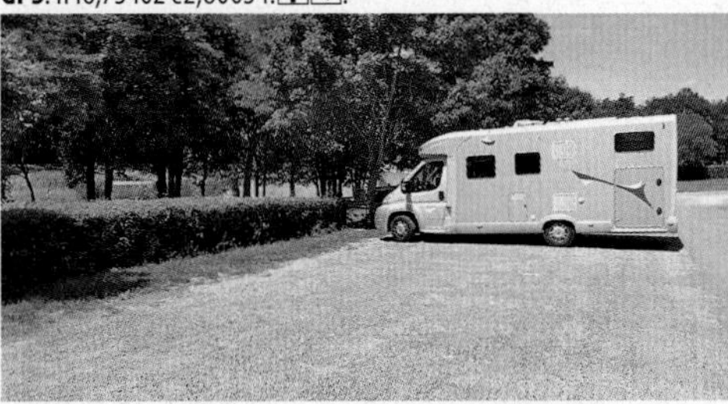

50 free € 2 Ch. **Location:** Simple, isolated, quiet.
Surface: asphalted/grassy. service: frost.
Distance: 4km on the spot on the spot on camp site on camp site.

Blois 18F2

P2, Rue Jean Moulin. **GPS**: n47,58653 e1,32641.

40 € 8/24h ChWC included. **Location:** Urban, simple, central. **Surface:** asphalted. 01/01-31/12.
Distance: on the spot 7km 100m 100m on the spot.

Tourist information Blois:
Château de Blois.
Cathédrale St Louis.
Quatier Coty. Wed 7-13h.

Bonneval 18F1

Rue de la Grève. **GPS**: n48,17980 e1,38840.

8 free ChWCfree. **Location:** Urban, simple, central.
Surface: asphalted. 01/01-31/12.
Distance: 200m 200m 350m.

Bonny-sur-Loire 18H2

Chemin de la Cheuille. **GPS**: n47,55925 e2,83967.

6 free € 2 Ch € 2/30minutes WC. **Location:** Rural, simple, central. **Surface:** gravel. 01/05-30/09.
Distance: 150m 50m 300m on the spot on the spot.
Remarks: Along La Cheuille river.

Boulleret 18H3

Place des Charmes. **GPS**: n47,42304 e2,87244.

4 free € 2/100liter Ch (1x)€ 2/6h WC free.
Location: Urban, simple, central. **Surface:** asphalted. 01/01-31/12.
Distance: on the spot on the spot on the spot on the spot on the spot.
Remarks: Coins at the shops and restaurant, sanitary building: 01/05-30/09.

Bourges 18G3

Rue du Pré Doulet. **GPS**: n47,08390 e2,38085.
15 free Chfree.
Surface: gravel/sand. 01/01-31/12.
Distance: 1,5km 700m on the spot on the spot.

Tourist information Bourges:
Ballades de Bourges. Festivities and market in the city centre. 01/07-31/08.

Bourgueil 18D3

Jardin de Tanneries, Rue des Tanneries. **GPS**: n47,28014 e0,17058.

6 free. **Location:** Simple, central, quiet. **Surface:** gravel/sand.
01/01-31/12.
Distance: 300m 150m.
Remarks: Max. 1 night.

FR

Bourré 18F3

Domaine Deniau, Route des Vaublins 18.
GPS: n47,35101 e1,24603.

6 free. **Location:** Rural, simple. **Surface:** forest soil.
01/01-31/12.
Distance: 2,5km 1km 1km.

Brézolles 15F3

Rue de Verneuil, D939. **GPS**: n48,69083 e1,06972.

10 free Chfree. **Surface:** gravel. 01/01-31/12.
Distance: 200m 200m.

Briare-le-Canal 18H2

Flot Bleu Park, Val du Martinet. **GPS**: n47,64304 e2,72270.

39 € 7/24h Chincluded. **Location:** Urban, comfortable, quiet. **Surface:** grassy. 01/01-31/12.
Distance: on the spot 4,5km on the spot on the spot 800m 800m 100m 500m.
Remarks: Max. 72h.

Briare-le-Canal 18H2

Rue des Vignes. **GPS**: n47,63215 e2,73981.

40 free € 2/100liter Ch . **Location:** Urban, simple.
Surface: gravel. 01/01-31/12.
Distance: 300m 4,5km 50m 500m 800m on the spot on the spot.

Céré-la-Ronde 18F3

Camping-Car Park, Rue du Stade. **GPS**: n47,25788 e1,18232.

10 € 8,40-10,80 Ch (10x) included.
Location: Rural, simple. **Surface:** gravel. 01/01-31/12.
Distance: 500m.
Remarks: Mandatory, one-time fee Pass'Etapes € 4.

Chabris 18F3

Place du Champ de Foire. **GPS**: n47,25317 e1,65211.

5 free € 2 Ch € 2.
Location: Rural, central, quiet. **Surface:** gravel/metalled.
01/01-31/12.
Distance: on the spot 250m 250m.
Remarks: Coins at Tourist Info and Maison de la Presse (250m).

Chaillac 21F2

Camping-Car Park, Les Vergnes. **GPS**: n46,43170 e1,28899.
15 € 9,40-11,80 Ch (15x) included.
Surface: gravel/metalled. 01/01-31/12.
Remarks: Mandatory, one-time fee Pass'Etapes € 4.

Chambord 18F2

Château de Chambord, Place St.Louis. **GPS**: n47,61608 e1,51057.

100 € 11/24h € 2/10minutes Ch € 5/8h WC .
Location: Rural, simple, quiet. **Surface:** asphalted.
01/01-31/12.
Distance: 7km 300m 300m.
Remarks: Parking castle, max. 1 night.

Champigny-sur-Veude 18D3

Place du Chapeau Rouge, Rue de la Bonne Dame.
GPS: n47,06499 e0,31773.

8 free Ch (2x)free. **Location:** Urban, simple, noisy.
Surface: asphalted. 01/01-31/12.
Distance: on the spot on the spot bakery 200m on the spot.
Remarks: At small lake.

Chaon 18G2

La Maison du Braconnage, Rue des Genêts, D129.
GPS: n47,60942 e2,16611.

10 free Chfree. **Location:** Rural, isolated, quiet.
Surface: grassy/metalled. 01/01-31/12.
Distance: 200m 200m bakery 50m.
Remarks: Video surveillance.

Châteaudun 18F1

Aire de Châteaudun, Rue des Fouleries.
GPS: n48,07172 e1,32421.

15 free € 2/100liter Ch € 2/20minutes WC.
Location: Urban, comfortable, central, quiet. **Surface:** asphalted.
01/01-31/12.
Distance: 400m Canoe rental on the spot on the spot on the spot.
Remarks: Along Loir river, castel of Châteaudun 300m.

Châteauroux 21F1

17, Avenue de Parc des Loisirs. **GPS**: n46,82278 e1,69507.

5 free € 2,50/100liter Ch € 2,50/h. **Location:** Simple.
Surface: asphalted. 01/05-31/10.
Distance: 3,6km 2km 2km.
Remarks: Coins at campsite.

Châtillon-Coligny 18H2

Rue du Loing. **GPS**: n47,81940 e2,84509.
free ChWCfree. **Surface:** gravel.
Distance: 250m 400m 450m.

Châtillon-sur-Loire 18H2

Rue du Port. **GPS**: n47,59128 e2,76044.

± 6 € 9 Ch WCincluded.
Location: Rural, comfortable, quiet. **Surface:** asphalted/gravel.
Distance: 800m 9km A77 400m bakery 500m.
Remarks: At the canal.

Chenonceaux 18F3

Aire de Chenonceaux, Chemin de la Varenne.
GPS: n47,33053 e1,06824.

10 free. **Location:** Rural, simple, isolated, noisy.
Surface: grassy. 01/01-31/12.
Distance: 500m 500m on the spot on the spot.
Remarks: Along railwayline.

Chenonceaux 18F3

Rue du Château. **GPS**: n47,33020 e1,06648.

FR

20 free. **Location:** Rural, simple, isolated. **Surface:** metalled.
01/01-31/12.
Distance: 500m 500m on the spot.
Remarks: Parking at castle of Chenonceaux, max. 24h.

Tourist information Chenonceaux:
Castle.

Cheverny 18F2

Château Cheverny P3, D102. **GPS:** n47,49762 e1,46097.

20 free. **Location:** Rural, simple, quiet. **Surface:** grassy/metalled.
01/01-31/12.
Distance: 250m 250m 250m bakery.

Tourist information Cheverny:
Château Cheverny. Castle. 9.30-12h, 14.15-17h, Apr-Sep 9.30-18.15h.

Chouzé-sur-Loire 18D3

Aire de Chouzé-sur-Loire, Rue de l'Eglise.
GPS: n47,23809 e0,12649.

6 free € 2 Ch. **Location:** Rural, comfortable, central, quiet.
Surface: gravel. 01/01-31/12.
Distance: on the spot 250m on the spot on the spot on the spot.
Remarks: Coins at the shops and town hall.

Civray-de-Touraine 18F3

Caves du Père Auguste, 14 rue des Caves. **GPS:** n47,33497 e1,04718.

5 free € 2/120liter (4x)€ 4/24h WC € 3 free.
Location: Rural, simple, quiet. **Surface:** asphalted.
01/01-31/12.
Distance: 500m 1,5km 4km on the spot.

Cloyes-sur-le-Loir 18F1

Rue du Colonel Boussa. **GPS:** n47,99171 e1,23216.

5 free € 2 Ch € 2/h. **Location:** Urban, simple.
Surface: asphalted. 01/01-31/12 water: frost.
Distance: 800m 450m 800m.

Coullons 18H2

Place du Monument. **GPS:** n47,62012 e2,49319.

10 free ChWCfree. **Location:** Urban, simple, quiet.
Surface: gravel. 01/01-31/12.
Distance: on the spot 500m 50m 50m on the spot.

Courmemin 18F3

Rue des Tisserands. **GPS:** n47,47115 e1,62685.
3 free. **Surface:** gravel. 01/01-31/12.
Distance: on the spot 100m 100m.
Remarks: Near church.

Courville-sur-Eure 15F3

Avenue Thiers. **GPS:** n48,44600 e1,24166.
16 free € 2,50/100liter Ch € 2,50/55minutes.
Surface: asphalted. 01/01-31/12.
Remarks: Coins at campsite and shops.

Culan 21G2

Place du Champ de Foire. **GPS:** n46,54727 e2,34630.

20 free € 1,50/10minutes Ch € 1,50/h WC.
Surface: asphalted. 01/01-31/12.
Distance: 50m 50m 50m.
Remarks: Near office de tourisme, coins available at the shops.

Cuzion 21F2

Base de Loisirs Pont des Piles, Rue des Petites Côtes.
GPS: n46,45639 e1,61167.

6 free. **Location:** Isolated, quiet. **Surface:** grassy/metalled.
01/01-31/12.
Remarks: At castle, max. 1 night.

Dampierre-en-Burly 18H2

Etang du Bourg, Rue nationale. **GPS:** n47,76250 e2,51413.

6 free ChWCfree. **Location:** Rural, simple, quiet.
Surface: gravel. 01/01-31/12.
Distance: 1km on the spot on the spot 1km 1,5km 500m on the spot.

Dreux 15F3

Camping-Car Park, Rue Jean-Louis Chanoine. **GPS:** n48,74029 e1,33227.
9 € 11,25 Ch (8x) included. 01/01-31/12.
Distance: 2,5km on the spot 2km.
Remarks: Mandatory, one-time fee Pass'Etapes € 4.

Dry 18G2

Rue de Meung. **GPS:** n47,79824 e1,71419.

10 free € 2/10minutes Ch € 2/1h WC. **Location:** Rural, simple. **Surface:** metalled. 01/01-31/12.
Distance: on the spot 1km 50m.
Remarks: Coins at town hall.

Épineuil-le-Fleuriel 21H1

Le Bourg. **GPS:** n46,55690 e2,58265.

5 free Chfree. **Location:** Rural, simple. **Surface:** gravel.
01/01-31/12.
Distance: 500m.

Esvres-sur-Indre 18E3

Salle des Fêtes, Impasse Auguste Noyant. **GPS:** n47,28291 e0,78418.

7 free Chfree.
Location: Urban, simple, central, quiet. **Surface:** gravel.
01/01-31/12 water disconnected in winter.
Distance: on the spot 100m 250m on the spot on the spot on the spot.

Fontaines-en-Sologne 18F2

Place du Champ de Foire, Route de Bracieux. **GPS:** n47,51039 e1,55078.
4 free. **Surface:** gravel. 01/01-31/12.
Distance: on the spot.
Remarks: Behind town hall.

Genillé 18F3

Rue de la Varenne. **GPS:** n47,18438 e1,09232.

FR

6 €5 €2/100liter Ch included. **Location:** Rural, simple. **Surface:** gravel. 01/01-31/12.
Distance: 500m 500m on the spot.

Germigny-des-Prés 18G2

21 Route de Saint-Benoît. **GPS**: n47,84430 e2,26798.

5 free Ch free. **Location:** Rural, simple, quiet.
Surface: gravel/metalled. 01/01-31/12 water disconnected in winter. **Distance:** 100m 1,5km, bakery 600m.

Gien 18H2

Quai de Nice. **GPS**: n47,67985 e2,64308.

8 free €2 Ch €2. **Location:** Urban, noisy.
Surface: asphalted. 01/01-31/12.
Distance: 2km on the spot.
Remarks: Max. 48h, coins at swimming pool.

Gizeux 18D3

Aire de Gizeux, Route du Lavoir. **GPS**: n47,39275 e0,19689.

10 free €3/100liter Ch stay.
Location: Rural, comfortable, central, quiet.
Surface: gravel.
01/01-31/12.
Distance: 200m 500m 200m on the spot on the spot on the spot.
Remarks: Coins at the shops and town hall, Château de Gizeux 400m.

Guilly 18G3

Le Prieuré Chambres d'Hôtes, Rue du Prieuré.
GPS: n47,07920 e1,72100.

10 €5 €3 Ch . **Location:** Rural, quiet.
Surface: grassy/metalled. 01/01-31/12.
Distance: 150m on the spot 150m.

Huisseau-sur-Cosson 18F2

Route de Chambord. **GPS**: n47,59375 e1,45974.
4 free Ch . **Location:** Urban. **Surface:** metalled.
01/01-31/12.
Distance: 500m.

Humbligny 18H3

Chemin des Faviots, D44. **GPS**: n47,25451 e2,65850.

8 free €2/100liter Ch €2/60minutes. **Location:** Rural, simple. **Surface:** gravel. 01/01-31/12.
Distance: on the spot 1km 3km 50m.
Remarks: Max. 24h, coins at town hall.

La Chapelle-Saint-Mesmin 18G2

Aire camping-cars, Chemin de Fourneaux.
GPS: n47,88550 e1,83990.

23 €12/72h Ch included . **Location:** Urban, comfortable, quiet. **Surface:** grassy. 01/04-31/12.
Distance: 500m 2,7km 50m 50m 500m 500m on the spot on the spot.
Remarks: Along Loire river, market Saturday.

La Châtre 21G1

Rue du Champ de Foire. **GPS**: n46,58250 e1,98250.

10 €2. **Location:** Urban, simple. **Surface:** asphalted.
Distance: 50m 50m 50m.

La Châtre 21G1

Supermarché Super U, Avenue d'Auvergne, D943.
GPS: n46,58278 e2,00139.
10 free €2/10minutes Ch €2/1h. **Location:** Simple.
Surface: asphalted. 01/01-31/12.
Distance: 800m 50m.

La Ferte-Beauharnais 18G2

D922. **GPS**: n47,54455 e1,84882.

12 free €2/10minutes Ch €2/55minutes WC.
Location: Simple, noisy. **Surface:** grassy/metalled.
01/01-31/12.
Distance: 300m on the spot on the spot 250m 100m.
Remarks: At small lake, max. 24h.

La Ferté-Saint-Cyr 18G2

D925, Rue Faubourg de Bretagne. **GPS**: n47,65623 e1,67249.

4 free €2,50/100liter Ch €2,50/1h. **Location:** Rural, simple, quiet. **Surface:** metalled. 01/01-31/12.
Distance: 200m 200m.
Remarks: Max. 48h, coins at townhall and bakery.

La Loupe 15F3

Place du 8 mai, Docteur Moenner St. **GPS**: n48,47262 e1,01768.
3 free €2,20 Ch €2,20. **Surface:** asphalted.
01/01-31/12.
Distance: 300m 100m 800m.
Remarks: Coins at tourist info.

La Pérouille 21F1

Étang de la Roche, Le Champ Perrot. **GPS**: n46,70507 e1,52259.

free €2/10minutes Ch WC.
Location: Rural, isolated, quiet. **Surface:** grassy/gravel.
01/01-31/12.
Distance: 750m 5km A20 750m.
Remarks: At small lake, coins at town hall and restaurant (750m).

Lailly-en-Val 18G2

Camping-Car Park, Place de l'Église. **GPS**: n47,77023 e1,68544.

21 €9,60/24h Ch (20x)WC included.
Location: Rural, comfortable, quiet. **Surface:** gravel.
01/01-31/12.
Distance: 100m 50m 300m 200m.
Remarks: Mandatory, one-time fee Pass'Etapes €4.

Lamotte-Beuvron 18G2

Aire municipale, Chemin de Maisonfort. **GPS**: n47,59795 e2,02524.

10 free Ch WC free.
Location: Urban, central. **Surface:** metalled.
01/01-31/12 Fri-morning, water disconnected in winter.
Distance: 200m 4,5km on the spot on the spot 200m 300m 100m on the spot on the spot.
Remarks: At the canal.

Tourist information Lamotte-Beuvron:
Avenue de la Republique. Market. Fri-morning.

Langon (Loir-et-Cher) 18G3

Parking Canal du Berry, D976. **GPS**: n47,28253 e1,82862.

7 free € 2/10minutes Ch € 2/1h. **Location:** Rural, quiet. **Surface:** asphalted. 01/01-31/12 Service: winter.
Distance: 50m on the spot 100m 100m.
Remarks: Coins at the shops and town hall.

Le Blanc 21E1

Place du Général de Gaulle. **GPS**: n46,63154 e1,06164.

free € 2/100liter Ch € 2/h.
Location: Central, noisy. **Surface:** asphalted.
01/01-31/12 service: 01/11-01/04.
Distance: on the spot 250m.
Remarks: Coins at tourist info.

Le Châtelet 21G1

Le Tivoli, Avenue de la Gare. **GPS**: n46,64502 e2,27863.

5 free € 2 Ch € 2/h. **Location:** Simple. **Surface:** asphalted.
01/01-31/12.
Distance: 50m 50m 300m.

Léré 18H3

Le Port, Rue du Champ des Noyers. **GPS**: n47,47485 e2,87477.

4 free € 2 Ch € 2/h. **Location:** Rural, simple, quiet.
Surface: asphalted. 01/01-31/12.
Distance: 400m on the spot on the spot.
Remarks: At the canal.

Les Bordes 18H2

Etang du Petit Moulin, Route de Gien.
GPS: n47,81041 e2,40729.

6 free Chfree.
Location: Rural, simple, quiet. 01/01-31/12.
Distance: 400m 100m 150m 2km 500m on the spot on the spot.

Les Choux 18H2

Route de Dampierre 13. **GPS**: n47,79716 e2,67276.
free Chfree. **Location:** Urban. **Surface:** metalled.
Remarks: At sports park.

Les Montils 18F2

Camping-Car Park des Montils, Route de Seur.
GPS: n47,49308 e1,30571.

45 € 10,15 Ch (24x) included.
Location: Rural, simple, quiet. **Surface:** grassy.
01/01-31/12.
Distance: 500m.
Remarks: Mandatory, one-time fee Pass'Etapes € 4.

Levet 21H1

Chemin du Crot A Thibault. **GPS**: n46,92306 e2,40639.

3 free (3x) WC. **Location:** Rural, simple, isolated, quiet.
Surface: gravel. 01/01-31/10.
Distance: 250m 250m 250m.
Remarks: Max. 24h.

Loches 18E3

Allée du Maquis Césario. **GPS**: n47,12656 e1,00221.

3 free. **Location:** Urban, simple, quiet. **Surface:** gravel.
01/01-31/12.
Distance: 700m 700m.
Remarks: Max. 24h.

Loches 18E3

Espace Agnes Sorel, Avenue de bas Clos. **GPS**: n47,12477 e0,99331.

10 free. **Location:** Urban, simple, noisy. **Surface:** asphalted.
01/01-31/12.
Distance: on the spot on the spot on the spot.
Remarks: Max. 24h.

Loches 18E3

P2, Avenue Louis XI. **GPS**: n47,13315 e1,00023.

5 free. **Location:** Urban, simple, quiet. **Surface:** asphalted.
01/01-31/12.
Distance: centre 500m 500m 500m.
Remarks: Max. 24h.

Loches 18E3

Rue de l'Amiral de Pointis. **GPS**: n47,13744 e1,00115.

4 free. **Location:** Urban, simple, noisy. **Surface:** asphalted.
01/01-31/12.
Distance: 1,4km 1,4km.

Loches 18E3

Avenue Aristide Briand. **GPS**: n47,12240 e1,00164.
Chfree. 01/01-31/12.
Remarks: At entrance campsite.

Louzouer 18H1

Cidre Chivet, 323 Les Mussereaux. **GPS**: n48,02833 e2,87062.

12 € 5 € 4 Ch € 5 WC € 5 . **Location:** Comfortable, quiet. **Surface:** asphalted/metalled. 01/01-31/12.
Distance: 4km 13km 13km on the spot on the spot.

Luant 21F1

L'Étang Duris. **GPS**: n46,72222 e1,57338.

10 free € 2 Ch € 2.
Location: Rural, isolated, quiet. **Surface:** gravel.
01/01-31/12.
Distance: 3km 3,3km A20 lake bar/brasserie on the spot.
Remarks: Coins at town hall and restaurant.

Marboué 18F1

L'Espace Loisirs des Fontaines, Rue du Croc Marbot.
GPS: n48,11240 e1,32870.

10 free € 2/10minutes Ch € 2/50minutes.

FR

Location: Rural, comfortable, central, quiet. **Surface:** grassy/metalled. 01/01-31/12.
Distance: on the spot 500m 150m on the spot on the spot.

Marcilly-en-Villette 18G2

Rue du Lavoir. **GPS**: n47,76197 e2,02448.

6 free Chfree. **Location:** Rural, simple, quiet.
Surface: gravel. 01/01-31/12.
Distance: 200m 400m 500m on the spot.
Remarks: At tennis-court.

Martizay 21E1

Aire de Loisirs, Rue des Afrique du Nord.
GPS: n46,80528 e1,03806.

6 free Ch (4x) WCfree. **Location:** Rural, quiet.
Surface: metalled/sand. 01/01-31/12.
Distance: on the spot bakery 500m.

Mehun-sur-Yèvre 18G3

Quai du Canal. **GPS**: n47,14409 e2,21010.

6 € 2,50 Chincluded. **Location:** Rural, quiet.
Surface: asphalted. 01/01-31/12.
Distance: 500m 400m.
Remarks: At the canal.

Menetou-Salon 18H3

Rue de la Liberté. **GPS**: n47,23162 e2,49002.

6 free Ch (6x)free. **Surface:** gravel/metalled.
01/01-31/12.
Distance: on the spot 50m 100m 100m.

Mennetou-sur-Cher 18G3

Place du 11 Novembre, N76. **GPS**: n47,26861 e1,86472.

8 free € 2/10minutes Ch € 2/h. **Location:** Rural, quiet.
Surface: sand. 01/01-31/12.
Distance: 150m 100m 150m 150m.
Remarks: Coins at shops and tourist office, small fortified town.

Méry-sur-Cher 18G3

Chemin Lucien Bonneau/N76. **GPS**: n47,24586 e1,98989.

6 € 7,55/24h € 1/12minutes Ch (7x) WCincluded.
Location: Rural, quiet. **Surface:** metalled. 01/01-31/12.
Distance: 150m 100m.
Remarks: Nights closed with barrier.

Meung-sur-Loire 18G2

Chemin des Grèves. **GPS**: n47,82327 e1,69814.

15 free € 2 Ch € 2. **Location:** Rural, comfortable.
Surface: gravel. 01/01-31/12.
Distance: 400m 300m 250m bakery.
Remarks: At castle, at swimming pool.

Monthou-sur-Cher 18F3

17 Route du Plan d'Eau. **GPS**: n47,34980 e1,29375.
5 € 10 Ch included. **Location:** Rural.
Surface: grassy/metalled. 01/01-31/12.
Distance: 600m on the spot on the spot 700m.
Remarks: Max. 48h.

Montigny 18H3

Le Vieux Château. **GPS**: n47,24283 e2,68627.

2 free € 2/100liter € 2/60minutes. **Location:** Rural, simple, isolated, quiet. **Surface:** gravel. 01/01-31/12.
Distance: 800m 850m.
Remarks: Coins at town hall, poste.

Montoire-sur-le-Loir 18E2

Aire de Montoire-sur-le-Loir, Boulevard des Alliés, Quartier Marescot.
GPS: n47,74990 e0,86317.

8 free. **Location:** Urban, simple, central, quiet. **Surface:** asphalted.
01/01-31/12.
Distance: 50m on the spot on the spot 500m 500m on the spot on the spot.

Montoire-sur-le-Loir 18E2

Avenue de la République. **GPS**: n47,75750 e0,86928.

15 free. **Location:** Urban, comfortable, quiet. **Surface:** asphalted.
01/01-31/12.
Distance: on the spot 500m 500m on the spot.
Remarks: At former station.

Montrésor 18F3

Rue du 8 Mai. **GPS**: n47,15750 e1,20169.

12 free Chfree. **Location:** Rural, simple. **Surface:** asphalted.
01/01-31/12 water: frost.
Distance: 500m 500m bakery 500m.
Remarks: At castle.

Montrichard 18F3

Camping-Car Park, Rue Frideloux 33. **GPS**: n47,34016 e1,17045.

40 € 9,60 Ch (40x) included. **Location:** Rural, comfortable. **Surface:** grassy/gravel. 01/01/-31/12.
Distance: 500m 500m 500m 400m.
Remarks: Mandatory, one-time fee Pass'Etapes € 4.

Morogues 18H3

Route des Aix, D46. **GPS**: n47,23990 e2,59857.

4 free € 2/100liter Ch € 2/60minutes.
Location: Rural, simple, quiet. **Surface:** gravel.
01/01-31/12.
Distance: on the spot 200m 1km 800m.
Remarks: Coins at tourist info Henrichemont (12km).

Neuillay-les-Bois 21F1

Route de Buzançais, D1. **GPS**: n46,76917 e1,47333.

5 free Ch (2x) WCfree. **Location:** Simple, quiet.
Surface: metalled. 01/05-31/10.
Distance: 50m 50m 50m 50m.
Remarks: Max. 24h.

FR

Neuvy-Le-Barrois 21H1

La Prairie, Le Pénisson, D45. **GPS**: n46,86159 e3,03930.

6 € 6 € 4/100liter Ch € 4/24h,16Amp € 2.
Location: Rural, comfortable, isolated, quiet.
Surface: gravel/metalled. 01/04-01/11.
Distance: 200m 200m.

Neuvy-Pailloux 21G1

Les Gloux, RN151. **GPS**: n46,88278 e1,83682.

15 free Ch WC free. **Location:** Rural, simple, isolated.
Surface: asphalted. 01/01-31/12.

Nogent-le-Roi 15F3

Rue du Pont des Demoiselles. **GPS**: n48,65059 e1,52894.
4 free Ch free.
Surface: asphalted. Service: winter.
Distance: 400m 400m 400m.
Remarks: Next to sports fields, max. 72h.

Nogent-sur-Vernisson 18H2

Rue du Gué Mulet. **GPS**: n47,84055 e2,73996.

6 free.
Location: Simple, quiet. **Surface:** gravel. 01/01-31/12.
Distance: 1km on the spot on the spot 1km.

Nogent-sur-Vernisson 18H2

Rue Georges Bannery. **GPS**: n47,85363 e2,74014.
€ 2 Ch € 2.
Remarks: Coins at tourist info, PMU Rue Bannery or bar in Rue A. Briand.

Nouan-le-Fuzelier 18G2

Rue des Peupliers. **GPS**: n47,53324 e2,03437.

6 free. **Location:** Urban, simple. **Surface:** asphalted/metalled.
01/01-31/12.
Distance: 300m 300m 300m.
Remarks: Max. 72h.

Orléans 18G2

Parc des expositions, Rue du Président Robert Schumann.
GPS: n47,87229 e1,91317.

40 free free. **Location:** Urban, simple, isolated.
Surface: asphalted. 01/01-31/12.
Distance: city centre 3km 200m 200m on the spot.

Tourist information Orléans:

- Office de Tourisme, 6, rue Albert 1er, www.ville-orleans.fr. City with many old bldg. And monuments.
- Maison Jeanne d'Arc. Museum about the life of Jeanne d'Arc. 01/04-31/10 Mo.
- Cathédrale Ste Croix. Gothic cathedral.
- Église Nôtre Dame de recouvrance. Church 16th century.
- Tour Saint Paul. Church 17th century.
- Allée Pierre Chevallier. Su morning.
- Quai du Roi. Sa-morning.
- Fête de Jeanne d'Arc. Historical celebration. 08/05.
- Parc Floral. Flowers and zoo. daily.

Oulches 21F1

Impasse de l'Étang. **GPS**: n46,61339 e1,29547.

5 free € 2 Ch € 2. **Location:** Rural, simple. **Surface:** gravel.
01/01-31/12.
Distance: on the spot 100m.
Remarks: Coins at town hall.

Ouzouer-sur-Trézée 18H2

Parking halte nautique, Rue Saint-Roche.
GPS: n47,67000 e2,80888.

5 free Ch WC free. **Location:** Urban, comfortable, quiet.
Surface: asphalted. 01/04-31/10.
Distance: 500m on the spot 500m 700m 50m.
Remarks: At canal 'de Briare', max. 48h.

Ouzouer-sur-Trézée 18H2

Camping municipal, Chemin du Rochoir.
GPS: n47,66819 e2,80611.

5 € 5,20 Ch € 2,60 WC included.
Surface: grassy/gravel. 01/04-31/10.

Paucourt 18H1

Rue de l'Église. **GPS**: n48,03441 e2,79179.

20 free Ch free. **Location:** Rural, simple. **Surface:** asphalted.
01/01-31/12 water: frost.
Distance: on the spot 4,5km 4,5km 4,5km on the spot on the spot.
Remarks: Behind church.

Pont-de-Ruan 18E3

D17. **GPS**: n47,26373 e0,57632.

6 free Ch. **Location:** Rural, simple, isolated.
Surface: gravel/sand. 01/01-31/12.
Distance: 300m 100m.

Pontlevoy 18F3

4 rue de Coutant. **GPS**: n47,38619 e1,25905.

10 free Ch free. **Location:** Rural, simple, quiet.
Surface: gravel. 01/01-31/12.
Distance: 500m.

Pouligny-Saint-Pierre 21E1

Route du Blanc, D950, Bénavent. **GPS**: n46,65591 e1,02054.

10 free € 2 € 2 Ch € 2 € 2. **Location:** Rural, simple, quiet.
Surface: gravel.
Distance: bakery 50m.
Remarks: Coins at the bakery.

Reignac-sur-Indre 18E3

Rue Louis de Barberin, D58. **GPS**: n47,22922 e0,91585.

5 free € 2/100liter Ch. **Location:** Rural, simple, central, noisy.
Surface: asphalted. 01/01-31/12.
Distance: 300m 20km on the spot on the spot on the spot.
Remarks: Max. 24h, coins at the shops in the village.

FR

Restigné 18D3

Rue Basse. **GPS**: n47,28041 e0,22614.

4 free € 2/100liter Ch. **Location:** Urban, simple, central, quiet. **Surface:** gravel. 01/01-31/12.
Distance: on the spot on the spot on the spot on the spot.
Remarks: Coins at town hall.

Richelieu 18D3

Avenue Pasteur. **GPS**: n47,01098 e0,32265.

10 free € 4 WC. **Location:** Urban, simple, central.
Surface: gravel. 01/01-31/12.
Distance: 300m 300m bakery 300m on the spot on the spot.
Remarks: Servicepoint at campsite 1km.

Saint-Amand-Montrond 21H1

Base de Loisirs Virlay, Etangs de Goule.
GPS: n46,73362 e2,48851.

21 free Chfree. **Location:** Rural, simple, quiet.
Surface: asphalted/grassy. 01/01-31/12.
Distance: 1km 5km 500m 500m on the spot on the spot.

Saint-Amand-Montrond 21H1

Quai Lutin, via Avenue Maréchal Foch. **GPS**: n46,71818 e2,50480.

4 free Chfree. **Location:** Urban, simple.
Surface: asphalted/gravel. 01/01-31/12.
Distance: 200m on the spot on the spot 200m 200m.
Remarks: On the canal.

Saint-Benoît-du-Sault 21F2

Place du Champ de Foire. **GPS**: n46,44117 e1,39249.

3 free € 2/120liter Ch € 2/4h . **Location:** Rural.
Surface: asphalted. 01/01-31/12.
Distance: 300m 300m.
Remarks: At tourist office.

Saint-Brisson-sur-Loire 18H2

Rue des Ruets, route d'Autry, D52. **GPS**: n47,64680 e2,68028.

6 free Ch. **Location:** Urban, simple, quiet.
Surface: asphalted. 01/01-31/12.
Distance: 100m 100m 100m 50m.
Remarks: Parking nearby town hall.

Saint-Claude-de-Diray 18F2

Rue du Moulin D98. **GPS**: n47,61356 e1,41402.

4 free. **Location:** Rural, simple, quiet. **Surface:** gravel.
01/01-31/12.
Distance: 500m.
Remarks: Next to cemetery.

Saint-Denis-les-Ponts 18F1

Aire de Saint Denis-les-Ponts, Rue Jean Moulin.
GPS: n48,06643 e1,28950.

12 free € 3/100liter Ch.
Location: Urban, comfortable, central, quiet. **Surface:** gravel.
01/01-31/12 Service: winter.
Distance: Châteaudun 3km on the spot on the spot 100m on the spot on the spot.
Remarks: Max. 48h, coins at the shops in the village, Châteaudun (city and castle) 4km.

Saint-Dyé-sur-Loire 18F2

Parking de la base nautique, val des chateaux.
GPS: n47,65454 e1,47852.

4 free. **Location:** Rural, simple, quiet. **Surface:** grassy.
01/01-31/12.
Distance: 800m on the spot on the spot 800m 800m on the spot on the spot.
Remarks: Along Loire river, max. 48h, canoe rental.

Saint-Épain 18E3

Plan d'eau. **GPS**: n47,14415 e0,53958.

6 € 5,10 Ch € 1,70 WC included. **Location:** Rural, comfortable, quiet. **Surface:** grassy. 01/01-31/12.
Distance: 300m on the spot 300m.
Remarks: Pay at town hall, key service at town hall, fishing permit available at Tabac and supermarket.

Saint-Genouph 18E3

Rue de l'Auberdière. **GPS**: n47,37702 e0,60200.

3 free Ch free. **Location:** Rural, simple. **Surface:** gravel.
01/01-31/12.
Distance: 350m 350m.

Saint-Georges-sur-Arnon 21G1

Allée de la Presle. **GPS**: n46,99999 e2,09884.

10 free Chfree. **Location:** Rural, isolated, quiet.
Surface: gravel. 01/01-31/12.
Distance: on the spot on the spot.
Remarks: At small lake, former campsite, max 3,5t.

Saint-Georges-sur-Arnon 21G1

N151. **GPS**: n46,97740 e2,06908.

10 free ChWCfree. **Location:** Simple, isolated.
Surface: asphalted.
Remarks: May 2016 during inspection service out of order.

Saint-Georges-sur-Moulon 18H3

Route de Ville. **GPS**: n47,18596 e2,41786.

2 free Chfree WC. **Location:** Simple, isolated, quiet.
Surface: gravel. 01/01-31/12.
Distance: 1,5km 1km 1,5km.

Saint-Gondon 18H2

Rue de Sully. **GPS**: n47,69808 e2,53876.

FR

2 free Chfree. **Location:** Rural, simple, quiet.
Surface: asphalted. 01/01-31/12.
Distance: 300m 300m 200m.
Remarks: Max. 48h.

S Saint-Gondon 18H2

Rue du Petit Clou. **GPS**: n47,69995 e2,54356.

5 free Chfree. **Location:** Rural, simple. **Surface:** metalled.
01/01-31/12.
Distance: 100m.
Remarks: In front of cemetery.

S Saint-Jean-le-Blanc 18G2

Base de loisirs de l'Ile Charlemagne, Levée de la Chevauchée.
GPS: n47,89437 e1,93870.

free € 2/100liter Ch. **Location:** Simple, isolated.
Surface: sand. 01/01-31/12.
Distance: Orléans 3km on the spot on the spot.

S Saint-Lubin-en-Vergonnois 18F2

Place Jacques Michaux. **GPS**: n47,61241 e1,23927.

4 free Ch. **Location:** Urban, simple, noisy. **Surface:** gravel.
01/01-31/12.
Distance: on the spot bakery 50m.

Saint-Nicolas-de-Bourgueil 18D3

Rue de la Treille. **GPS**: n47,28496 e0,12528.

5 free. **Location:** Rural, simple, quiet. **Surface:** gravel/sand.
01/01-31/12.
Distance: 150m 150m 250m.

S Saint-Saturnin 21G2

Route de Perassay. **GPS**: n46,50565 e2,23585.

free € 2 Ch. **Location:** Rural, simple, quiet.
Surface: gravel. 01/01-31/12.
Distance: 300m.

S Sainte-Maure-de-Touraine 18E3

Aire du Bois Chaudron, D910, Le Bois Caudron.
GPS: n47,09315 e0,61275.

40 € 4 € 2 € 2 Ch€ 3 (4x)€ 2/24h WC € 2 € 4/3
Location: Rural, comfortable, isolated, quiet. **Surface:** grassy.
01/01-31/12.
Distance: 1,5km 4,4km 1,5km 1,5km on the spot.
Remarks: Bread-service.

S Sainte-Maure-de-Touraine 18E3

Parking Ronsard, Rue de la Métairie. **GPS**: n47,11096 e0,61640.

15 free Chfree WC. **Location:** Urban, simple, central, quiet.
Surface: asphalted. 01/01-31/12.
Distance: 200m 3km 200m 200m on the spot.

S Sainte-Sévère-sur-Indre 21G2

Place du Champ de Foire, rue de Verdun. **GPS**: n46,48724 e2,07167.

free € 2 Ch.
Location: Rural, simple. **Surface:** gravel/sand.
Distance: 100m 200m.

S Sancoins 21H1

Quai du Canal. **GPS**: n46,83356 e2,91568.

20 free € 2/100liter ChWC. **Location:** Simple, quiet.
Surface: gravel/metalled. 01/01-31/12.
Distance: 200m on the spot on the spot 200m 150m
on the spot on the spot.

S Saran 18G2

Allée Claude Bernard. **GPS**: n47,95106 e1,87315.

10 free Chfree. **Location:** Simple, central. **Surface:** gravel.
01/01-31/12.
Distance: on the spot on the spot 1,5km 1km 800m
on the spot on the spot.

S Selles-sur-Cher 18F3

Avenue Kleber-Loustau, D856. **GPS**: n47,27639 e1,55889.

15 € 5 Ch. **Location:** Rural, comfortable, quiet.
Surface: asphalted. 01/04-30/09.
Distance: 500m 200m 500m 500m.
Remarks: To be paid at campsite, service on campsite.

S Sully-sur-Loire 18H2

Espace Loisirs Georges Blareau, Chemin de la Salle Verte.
GPS: n47,77139 e2,38451.

35 free Chfree. **Location:** Comfortable, quiet.
Surface: gravel/metalled. 01/01-31/12.
Distance: 800m on the spot on the spot 800m 800m.
Remarks: Nearby castle of Sully, not suitable for motorhomes +7m, narrow entrance.

S Sury-près-Léré 18H3

Route de Savigny. **GPS**: n47,48301 e2,86527.

6 free € 2/100liter Ch € 2/60minutes.
Location: Rural, simple, quiet. **Surface:** asphalted.
01/01-31/12.
Distance: 1,5km 50m 1,5km on the spot.
Remarks: Coins at town hall and restaurant.

S Theillay 18G3

Chemin du Ronaire. **GPS**: n47,31849 e2,03775.

10 free Chfree. **Location:** Rural, quiet.
Surface: gravel/metalled. 01/04-30/10.

FR

Distance: 250m 250m.
Remarks: At cemetery.

S Thenay 21F1

Rue de la Paix, D48. **GPS**: n46,63199 e1,43096.

5 free € 2 Ch € 2. **Location:** Rural, simple, quiet.
Surface: metalled. 01/01-31/12.
Distance: 200m.
Remarks: Coins at the shops and town hall.

S Thiron-Gardais 18F1

Aire de Thiron-Gardais, Avenue de la Gare.
GPS: n48,31194 e0,99583.

10 free Chfree.
Location: Urban, simple.
Surface: asphalted.
Distance: 100m 300m 300m 300m on the spot 100m.

S Tour-en-Sologne 18F2

Rue de la Mairie. **GPS**: n47,53786 e1,49973.

5 free € 2,50/100liter Ch € 2,50/h WC.
Location: Rural, comfortable, quiet. **Surface:** gravel.
01/01-31/12.
Distance: 100m 200m bakery 100m on the spot.
Remarks: Coins at townhall and bakery.

S Tours 18E3

Parking relais du Lac, Avenue du Général Niessel.
GPS: n47,36700 e0,70007.

6 free € 2/10minutes Ch . **Location:** Urban, simple, noisy.
Surface: asphalted. 01/01-31/12.
Distance: 2,5km 300m 500m on the spot.

S Vailly-sur-Sauldre 18H3

Rue du Pont. **GPS**: n47,45727 e2,64665.

10 € 7 € 2 ChWC € 0,80. **Location:** Comfortable, central.
Surface: gravel/metalled. 01/01-31/12.
Distance: 300m on the spot on the spot on the spot.
Remarks: Along the Sauldre river.

Tourist information Vailly-sur-Sauldre:
Fri.

S Valençay 18F3

Avenue de la Résistance. **GPS**: n47,16080 e1,56163.

10 free € 2 Ch € 4 . **Location:** Rural, quiet.
Surface: metalled. 01/01-31/12.
Distance: 100m 100m 100m.
Remarks: Nearby entrance castle.

Tourist information Valençay:
Château. Castle, 15th-18th century. 01/03-30/11.

Vendôme 18F2

Aire de Vendôme, Rue Geoffroy Martel. **GPS**: n47,79111 e1,07528.

5 free. **Location:** Urban, simple, central. **Surface:** asphalted.
01/01-31/12.
Distance: 500m.

S Véretz 18E3

Camping-car Park Véretz, Rue des Isles. **GPS**: n47,35810 e0,81466.

63 € 11,14 Ch (35x) included.
Location: Rural, comfortable. **Surface:** grassy/gravel.
01/01-31/12.
Distance: 800m 800m 750m.
Remarks: Mandatory, one-time fee Pass'Etapes € 4.

S Villaines les Rochers 18E3

Aire de Villaines-les-Rochers, Place de la Mairie/ Rue des Ecoles.
GPS: n47,22083 e0,49583.

7 free ChWCfree. **Location:** Urban, comfortable, central, quiet. **Surface:** asphalted. 01/01-31/12.
Distance: on the spot 100m 100m on the spot on the spot.
Remarks: Max. 24h.

S Villandry 18E3

Camping-Car Park, Rue Principale. **GPS**: n47,33930 e0,50762.
35 € 11,66-13,66 Ch included.
Surface: asphalted. 01/01-31/12.
Remarks: Mandatory, one-time fee Pass'Etapes € 4.

S Villedômer 18E2

Aire de Loisirs de Lavoir, Rue du Lavoir.
GPS: n47,54465 e0,88727.

6 free, 15/06-15/09 € 5 € 2/100liter Ch € 4/1h.
Location: Rural, simple, central, quiet. **Surface:** metalled.
01/01-31/12.
Distance: 100m 8,1km 100m 200m 200m on the spot on the spot.
Remarks: Max. 24h, coins at town hall (200m), bakery (200m) and supermarket (50m).

S Villefranche-sur-Cher 18G3

Avenue du Val de Cher. **GPS**: n47,29184 e1,76851.
5 free € 2 Ch. **Location:** Rural. **Surface:** gravel.
01/01-31/12.
Distance: 300m 200m.

S Villequiers 18H3

L'Étappe Berrichonne, Le Petit Azillon.
GPS: n47,08828 e2,77429.

6 € 6,50 € 3 Ch . **Location:** Isolated, quiet.
Surface: gravel/metalled. 01/01-31/12.
Distance: 3km.

S Vitry-aux-Loges 18G2

Rue des Érables. **GPS**: n47,93915 e2,27078.

5 free Chfree. **Location:** Rural, simple, quiet.
Surface: asphalted. 01/01-31/12.
Distance: 200m on the spot 200m on the spot on the spot.
Remarks: At canal of Orléans.

S Vouvray 18E3

Parking Bec de Cisse, Rue Bec de Cisse.
GPS: n47,40929 e0,79735.

FR

3 free € 3/100liter Ch € 3/1h WC.
Location: Rural, comfortable, central, quiet. **Surface:** asphalted.
01/01-31/12 Service: winter.
Distance: on the spot 8,5km 500m 150m 150m on the spot on the spot.
Remarks: Max. 48h, coins at campsite and tourist info.

Bourgogne-Franche-Comté

S Anost 19B3
Place Centrale. **GPS**: n47,07738 e4,09869.

10 free Chfree. **Location:** Rural, simple, quiet.
Surface: metalled. 01/01-31/12.
Distance: on the spot.

S Arc-et-Senans 22E1
Grande Rue. **GPS**: n47,03343 e5,78120.

6 free € 2 Ch. **Location:** Simple. **Surface:** gravel.
01/01-31/12.
Distance: 500m 500m.
Remarks: Coints at mairie, supermarket and campsite.

S Arinthod 22D2
Rue de la Prélette. **GPS**: n46,39654 e5,57013.

5 € 6 Ch included. **Location:** Rural. **Surface:** gravel.
01/01-31/12.
Distance: 100m.
Remarks: Near sports fields.

S Arsure-Arsurette 22E1
Châlet des Arches, Route de l'Aliance de vie blanc.
GPS: n46,72168 e6,08402.

10 free € 2 WC. **Location:** Isolated. **Surface:** asphalted.
01/01-31/12.

S Autun 22B1
Route de Chalon. **GPS**: n46,95548 e4,31667.

17 free € 3,50 ChWC.
Location: Urban, simple. **Surface:** asphalted.
01/01-31/12.
Distance: city centre 2km 100m 100m supermarket 900m on the spot on the spot.
Remarks: Parking at small lake Le Vallon at N80, in front of McDonalds.

Tourist information Autun:
Musée Rolin. Roman and Medieval excavations.
Wed, Fri, Su.

Auxerre 19A2
Quai de l'Ancienne Abbaye. **GPS**: n47,79742 e3,57738.

10 free. **Surface:** grassy/metalled. 01/01-31/12.
Distance: 300m 300m 300m.
Remarks: Along the Yonne river.

Tourist information Auxerre:
Tue, Fri.

S Baume-les-Dames 19E3
Quai du Canal. **GPS**: n47,34023 e6,35778.

30 € 9,30 + € 0,20/pp tourist tax € 2 Ch WCincluded € 1,70. **Location:** Rural, comfortable. **Surface:** asphalted/grassy.
01/01-31/12.
Distance: on the spot 5,3km on the spot on the spot on the spot.
Remarks: Bread-service.

Tourist information Baume-les-Dames:
Abbaye Nôtre Dame. Historical monument, 18th century.

Baume-les-Messieurs 22D1
Cascade des Tufs, Rue des Moulins. **GPS**: n46,69124 e5,63946.

10 free. **Location:** Simple, quiet. 01/01-31/12.
Distance: on the spot on the spot on the spot.

S Beaune 22C1
Avenue Charles de Gaulle. **GPS**: n47,01731 e4,83628.

5 free € 3 Ch € 3/2h.
Location: Urban, simple, central.
Surface: asphalted.
Distance: 500m 2,6km 200m centre commercial 300m.
Remarks: 5 special pitches, all parking places permitted.

Tourist information Beaune:
Hôtel Dieu et Musée. Former hospital, 15th century, museum.
Château de Meursault, Meursault. Castle with vineyard and wine tastery.

Belvoir 19F3
Chateaux Belvoir, Lieu-dit La Vierge. **GPS**: n47,32139 e6,61097.

3 free. **Location:** Rural, simple. **Surface:** asphalted/gravel.
01/01-31/12.

S Besançon 19E3
Parking du Crous, Cité Carnot, Quai Veil Picard.
GPS: n47,23702 e6,01644.

12 € 7 Chfree. **Location:** Urban, simple.
Surface: asphalted. 01/01-31/12. **Distance:** on the spot 500m 500m on the spot.

Tourist information Besançon:
Jardin Botanique, Avenue de la Paix. Botanical gardens. 7-19 Sa after11. free.
Château, Vaire-le-Grand. 15/08-18/09, 19/09-14/08 by agreement.
Tue, Fri, Su.

Blanot 22C2
Grottes de Blanot. **GPS**: n46,48476 e4,74417.
5 free. **Location:** Rural, simple, isolated, quiet.
Surface: grassy/gravel. 01/01-31/12.
Distance: 1,7km.

S Bois-d'Amont 22E2
Impasse de l'Eglantine. **GPS**: n46,53771 e6,13934.

FR

10 free € 2 Ch € 2. **Location:** Rural, comfortable, quiet. **Surface:** asphalted. 01/01-31/12.
Distance: on the spot on the spot on the spot on the spot.

Brognard 19F2

Base de Loisirs de la Savoureuse, Rue de Paquis.
GPS: n47,52834 e6,85652.

3 free Chfree. **Location:** Rural, noisy. **Surface:** asphalted. 01/01-31/12.
Distance: 50m 1,3km.
Remarks: Max. 48h.

Broindon 19C3

Aire Du Cerisier Chambertin, Rue du cerisier.
GPS: n47,19834 e5,04522.
free . 01/04-30/11.

Bucey-les-Gy 19E3

Chemin de Tranot 1. **GPS**: n47,42456 e5,83974.

5 free € 2/20minutes Chfree (5x)€ 2/4h.
01/01-31/12.
Remarks: Coins available at the shop.

Bussy-le-Grand 19C2

Château de Bussy, Rue du Château. **GPS**: n47,56069 e4,52544.
5 free. **Surface:** metalled. 01/01-31/12.
Distance: 200m.
Remarks: At castle.

Chablis 19B2

Route d'Auxerre, D235. **GPS**: n47,81711 e3,78425.

5 free free. **Location:** Simple, quiet. **Surface:** asphalted. 01/01-31/12.
Distance: centre 500m on the spot.

Chalon-sur-Saône 22C1

P Ville Historique, Promenade Sainte Marie.
GPS: n46,78365 e4,86046.

2 free Chfree. **Location:** Simple. **Surface:** asphalted/gravel. 01/01-31/12.
Distance: 500m 50m.
Remarks: Free shuttle to centre.

Champagnole 22E1

20, Rue Georges Vallerey. **GPS**: n46,74633 e5,89918.

5 € 6 € 4 Ch € 4 WC € 3. **Location:** Simple.
Surface: gravel/sand. 25/03-30/09.
Distance: 500m 250m.
Remarks: Max. 1 night, coins at campsite.

Charolles 22B2

Route de Viry. **GPS**: n46,43956 e4,28203.

8 € 3 € 2 Ch € 3. **Location:** Simple. **Surface:** gravel. 01/04-01/10.
Distance: 300m.
Remarks: Max. 48h.

Château-Chinon 19B3

Rue Jean Sallonnyer. **GPS**: n47,06304 e3,93627.

4 free Chfree WC. **Location:** Simple. **Surface:** metalled. 01/05-30/10.
Distance: 200m 250m 250m.
Remarks: Max. 24h.

Châtillon-en-Bazois 22A1

Place Pierre Saury. **GPS**: n47,05310 e3,65511.

5 free € 2 Ch. **Surface:** metalled. 01/04-31/10.
Distance: 50m.
Remarks: Coins at tourist info.

Chiddes 22B1

Le Bourg. **GPS**: n46,86108 e3,94091.

4 free Chfree WC. **Location:** Simple. **Surface:** gravel. 01/01-31/12.
Distance: on the spot on the spot.
Remarks: Max. 48h, free coins available at restaurant.

Chiddes 22B1

Augendre. **GPS**: n46,86781 e3,94364.
€ 3 + € 2,20/pp € 2 € 2,50. **Surface:** gravel.

Clairvaux-les-Lacs 22E1

Route de Lons-le-Saunier, D678. **GPS**: n46,58246 e5,74660.

6 free Chfree.
Location: Urban, simple. 01/01-31/12.
Distance: nearby.
Remarks: On entering village, nearby police station.

Clairvaux-les-Lacs 22E1

Chemin des Tilleuls. **GPS**: n46,57526 e5,74020.
5 free. **Surface:** grassy/gravel. 01/01-31/12.
Distance: 900m 900m.

Clairvaux-les-Lacs 22E1

Musée des Maquettes, Route de Lons. **GPS**: n46,58489 e5,73849.
20 free. **Location:** Isolated. 01/01-31/12.

Clamecy 19A3

Rue de l'Abattoir. **GPS**: n47,46222 e3,52250.

6 free. **Location:** Simple. **Surface:** gravel. 01/01-31/12.
Distance: 350m 150m.

Cluny 22C2

Chemin Georges Malère. **GPS**: n46,43479 e4,66621.
6 free. **Location:** Rural. **Surface:** asphalted. 01/01-31/12.
Distance: 800m 350m on the spot.

Cluny 22C2

Rue des Griottons. **GPS**: n46,43101 e4,66779.
free Ch. 01/01-31/12.

Conliège 22D1

Rue du Saugeois. **GPS**: n46,65270 e5,59981.

2 free ChWCfree. **Location:** Urban, simple.
Surface: asphalted. 01/01-31/12.
Distance: 100m.

FR

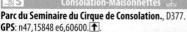

S Consolation-Maisonnettes 19F3

Parc du Seminaire du Cirque de Consolation., D377.
GPS: n47,15848 e6,60600.

10 € 10/24h Ch WCincluded. **Location:** Rural, simple.
Surface: asphalted. 01/01-31/12.
Distance: on the spot.
Remarks: Check in at shop.

S Corravillers 19F2

Rue de la Mairie. **GPS**: n47,89431 e6,62162.

2 free € 2/23minutes Ch € 2/23minutes.
Location: Rural, simple. **Surface:** grassy/gravel.
01/01-31/12.
Distance: 500m 500m.

S Corre 19E2

Fluvial Loisirs, Pré le Saônier. **GPS**: n47,91402 e5,99308.

32 € 10 Ch included € 4/3 € 3/day.
Location: Rural, comfortable, quiet. **Surface:** grassy.
01/01-31/12.
Distance: 200m 50m 50m bakery 300m, supermarket 500m 100m.

S Cousance 22D2

Grande Rue, Champs de foire. **GPS**: n46,52929 e5,39154.

4 free ChWCfree. **Surface:** asphalted. 01/01-31/12.
Distance: 100m 6,6km 100m.

Crosey-le-Petit 19F3

Rue de Begein. **GPS**: n47,35039 e6,48913.

free. **Location:** Rural, simple. **Surface:** asphalted/gravel.
01/01-31/12.
Distance: on the spot on the spot.

S Digoin 22B2

D982. **GPS**: n46,47300 e4,00344.
5 free € 3 Ch € 3. **Location:** Motorway.
Surface: metalled. 01/01-31/12.
Distance: 2km 100m 200m.

S Digoin 22B2

Place de la Grève, Route de Vichy. **GPS**: n46,48102 e3,97288.

10 free € 2 Ch € 2 (6x) WC. **Location:** Simple, central.
Surface: asphalted. 01/01-31/12.
Distance: on the spot on the spot on the spot on the spot.
Remarks: Next to office de tourisme, friday market.

S Dijon 19C3

Aire de Dijon, 3, Boulevard Chainoine Kir. **GPS**: n47,32125 e5,01090.

16 € 11,30-12,30 Ch (17x)included.
Location: Urban, comfortable, noisy. **Surface:** asphalted.
01/04-31/10 water: frost.
Distance: centre Dijon 1,5km 10km 300m 300m 500m 500m >Dijon 150m 10m.
Remarks: Attention: motorhomes ^3m take access road from southerly direction.

Tourist information Dijon:
Office de Tourisme, 11 Rue des Forges, Place Darcy, www.destinationdijon.com. City worth a visit with a number of large mansions and streets with half-timbered houses.

Dôle 19D3

Parking de Lahr, Avenue de Lahr. **GPS**: n47,08983 e5,49641.

20 free. **Location:** Simple, central, noisy. **Surface:** asphalted.
Village fair: mid-May.
Distance: on the spot on the spot.

Tourist information Dôle:
Maison natale de Louis Pasteur, 43 Rue Pasteur. Birth house Pasteur, museum. 1/4-31/10 10-12h, 14-18h, 01/11-31/03 Sa-Su 14-18h
Su-morning.

S Ecuisses 22C1

Place Marcel Pagnol, Route du Bourg. **GPS**: n46,76019 e4,52283.

20 free € 2 Ch € 2. **Location:** Simple. **Surface:** metalled.
01/01-31/12.
Remarks: At lake, max. 48h, coins at townhall and bakery.

Esmoulières 19F2

D236. **GPS**: n47,85243 e6,61502.

2 free. **Location:** Rural, simple. **Surface:** asphalted.
01/01-31/12.

S Étang-sur-Arroux 22B1

Place du Mousseau. **GPS**: n46,86631 e4,18946.

free Chfree. **Location:** Simple. **Surface:** asphalted.
01/01-31/12.
Distance: 100m 100m.

S Faucogney-et-la-Mer 19F2

Rue des Chars. **GPS**: n47,83735 e6,56003.

6 free € 2/23minutes Ch € 2/20minutes.
Location: Rural, simple. **Surface:** grassy/gravel.
01/01-31/12.
Distance: 800m.

S Fontaine-Française 19D3

Rue Berthault. **GPS**: n47,52487 e5,36768.

5 free € 3 Ch. **Location:** Rural, simple.
Surface: asphalted/grassy. 01/01-31/12.
Distance: 100m 16km on the spot 250m bakery.
Remarks: Along river and betwee 2 lakes, coins at shops in the village 08-21h.

S Fours 22A1

Rue des Saules, D981. **GPS**: n46,81720 e3,71806.

10 free Ch free. **Location:** Simple. **Surface:** gravel.
01/01-31/12.
Distance: 200m 200m 200m.

FR

Génelard 22B2

Place du Bassin, D974. **GPS**: n46,57750 e4,23500.

2 free Ch free. **Location:** Simple. **Surface:** asphalted. 01/01-31/12.
Distance: on the spot.

Gilly-sur-Loire 22B2

Le Gatefer. **GPS**: n46,53768 e3,78218.
10 free Chfree. **Surface:** metalled. 01/01-31/12.

Givry 22C1

Relais camping-car, Rue de la Gare. **GPS**: n46,78000 e4,74830.

15 free € 2/100liter Ch € 2/1h. **Location:** Comfortable.
Surface: asphalted. 01/01-31/12.
Distance: on the spot 300m bakery 300m on the spot on the spot.
Remarks: Coins at restaurant.

Givry 22C1

Moulin Madame, Rue du Moulin Madame. **GPS**: n46,79266 e4,77251.
€ 15 Ch . 01/01-31/12.
Remarks: Barbecue place.

Tourist information Givry:
Marché. Market. Thu.
La Voie Verte de Givry à Cluny. Cycle route on former railway,.

Gray 19D3

Rue de la Plage. **GPS**: n47,45253 e5,60259.

12 € 5 Ch included. **Location:** Rural, comfortable.
Surface: gravel. 01/01-31/12.
Distance: on the spot on the spot on the spot on the spot.
Remarks: Near camping municipal.

Gron 19A1

Rue des Petits Prés. **GPS**: n48,16011 e3,25636.
5 free ChWC. **Location:** Simple, quiet. **Surface:** asphalted.
01/01-31/12.

Gurgy 19A2

Quai des Fontaines. **GPS**: n47,86348 e3,55376.

20 € 7/24h Chincluded (12x).
Surface: grassy/gravel. 15/03-31/10.
Distance: 50m 7km on the spot 500m 300m.
Remarks: Along the Yonne river, coins at supermarket.

Heuilley-sur-Saône 19D3

Rue Condé. **GPS**: n47,32800 e5,45471.

20 free € 3 ChWC. **Location:** Rural, quiet.
Surface: gravel/sand. 01/01-31/12.
Distance: on the spot 100m 100m.
Remarks: Coins at town hall.

Jeurre 22D2

35, Rue Principale. **GPS**: n46,36662 e5,70769.

15 € 5-7 € 2 Ch € 2 € 3/day. **Location:** Rural, simple.
Surface: grassy. 01/04-31/10.

La Chapelle des Bois 22E1

Station de ski, Chemin du Marais Blanc. **GPS**: n46,60307 e6,11317.

free . **Surface:** unpaved. 01/01-31/12.
Distance: on the spot on the spot on the spot.

La Chapelle-de-Guinchay 22C2

Maison de Pays, Le Clos Meziat. **GPS**: n46,21017 e4,76720.

± 10 free ChWCfree. **Location:** Rural, comfortable, quiet.
Surface: gravel/metalled. 01/01-31/12.
Distance: centre 1,2km A6 10km 1,2km 1,2km.

La Charité-sur-Loire 18H3

Quai de la Tête de l'Ourth. **GPS**: n47,17577 e3,01254.
3 free. **Surface:** asphalted. 01/01-31/12.
Remarks: Parking at river.

La Charité-sur-Loire 18H3

Quai Romain Mollot. **GPS**: n47,17483 e3,01123.

5 free. **Surface:** asphalted. 01/01-31/12.
Distance: 250m on the spot on the spot on the spot on the spot on the spot.

Remarks: Parking at the river, max. 24h.

La Montagne 19F2

D136. **GPS**: n47,92581 e6,58710.

2 free. **Location:** Rural, simple. **Surface:** asphalted.
01/01-31/12.
Distance: on the spot.
Remarks: Parking at skipistes.

La Pesse 22E2

Rue de l'Epicéa, D25. **GPS**: n46,28400 e5,84764.

15 free € 2 ChWC. **Location:** Rural, simple, quiet.
Surface: unpaved. 01/01-31/12.
Distance: on the spot on the spot.
Remarks: At start of langlauf circuit.

La Pesse 22E2

Ferme Auberge de La Combe aux Bisons, Lieu-dit Pré Reverchon.
GPS: n46,29278 e5,86011.

3 guests free . **Location:** Simple, isolated.
01/01-31/12 Mon, Tue.
Distance: on the spot.

Laignes 19B2

Chemin du Moulin Neuf, D965. **GPS**: n47,84850 e4,36132.

7 free . **Location:** Simple, quiet. **Surface:** grassy.
01/01-31/12.
Distance: 1km on the spot.
Remarks: Parking at river, max. 24h.

Lamoura 22E2

Porte de la Serra, Route de Prémanon, D25.
GPS: n46,41107 e5,99458.

20 free Chfree WC. **Location:** Rural, simple.

FR

Surface: asphalted. 01/01-31/12.
Distance: winter on the spot on the spot.
Remarks: Service sportcentre La Serra, only in winter time.

S Lamoura 22E2

Route de Prémanon, D25. **GPS**: n46,40139 e5,98561.

6 free . 01/01-31/12.
Distance: on the spot on the spot.

S Larochemillay 22B1

Centre Bourg. **GPS**: n46,87793 e4,00155.
4 free Chfree. 01/01-31/12.
Distance: on the spot on the spot.
Remarks: Coins at town hall and restaurant, max. 48h.

S Le Vernois 22D1

Caveau des Byards. **GPS**: n46,73342 e5,59405.

2 free free.
Location: Urban, simple. **Surface:** grassy/gravel.

S Les Fourgs 22F1

D6. **GPS**: n46,83337 e6,42505.
12 free (12x)€ 3/10h. **Location:** Rural. 01/01-31/12.
Distance: 2km 2km.
Remarks: Parking at skipistes.

S Les Rousses 22E2

Parking du Balancier, Route Blanche, N5.
GPS: n46,44852 e6,07591.

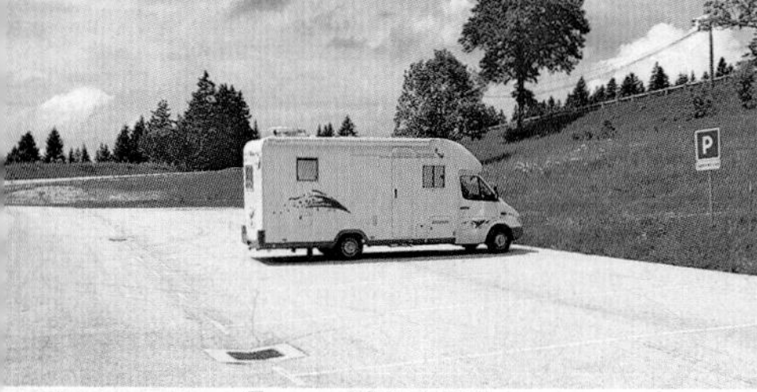

20 free, € 4/Winter € 3,50 Ch WC.
Surface: asphalted.
01/01-31/12.
Distance: Restaurant 5km.
Remarks: Coins at tourist info, ski station, ski rental, ski school.

S Les Rousses 22E2

Parking l'Aube, Route du Lac. **GPS**: n46,48779 e6,06690.

30 free, € 4/Winter € 5/100liter Ch € 5/1h .
Location: Simple. **Surface:** asphalted. 01/01-31/12.
Distance: 500m 500m 200m.

S Loisia 22D2

Rue du Pont. **GPS**: n46,48376 e5,46536.
3 free Chfree. **Location:** Simple, quiet.
Surface: grassy/gravel.
Distance: on the spot.

S Louhans 22D1

Halte nautique, Rue du Port. **GPS**: n46,62952 e5,21302.

22 free, 01/04-30/09 € 6 + € 0,20/pp tourist tax Ch WCincluded. **Location:** Comfortable, quiet. **Surface:** gravel.
Distance: 400m on the spot.
Remarks: To be paid at Halte Nautique, sanitary building: 01/05-30/09.

S Luxeuil-les-Bains 19E2

Place de l'Etang de la Poche, Rue Gambetta.
GPS: n47,81679 e6,38659.

20 free € 2/100liter Ch € 2/1h. **Location:** Simple, quiet.
Surface: gravel. 01/01-31/12 Service: winter.
Distance: 1km 100m 1km Auchan/Aldi 500m 1km.
Remarks: Max. 72h, coins at tourist info.

Tourist information Luxeuil-les-Bains:
Fougerolles. Since the 16th century the small town is the centre of distilleries (Kirsch and cherry brandy).

S Luzy 22B1

Place du champ De Foire. **GPS**: n46,79028 e3,96840.

4 free ChWCfree. **Location:** Simple. **Surface:** metalled.
01/01-31/12.
Distance: centre 300m 100m 200m 500m.
Remarks: Max. 48h, coins at the shops and restaurant.

S Mailly-le-Château 19A2

L'espace naturel du Beauvais, Rue du Beauvais.
GPS: n47,59308 e3,63059.
free € 3 Ch € 3 . **Location:** Isolated, quiet.
Surface: grassy. 01/01-31/12.
Distance: 650m.
Remarks: Coins at the shops.

S Maisod 22D2

La Mercantine. **GPS**: n46,46500 e5,68864.

40 € 9 € 2 Ch. **Location:** Rural, simple, isolated, quiet.
Surface: gravel. 01/01-31/12.
Distance: 100m 200m.
Remarks: At lake Vouglans, max. 24h.

Marigny-le-Cahouët 19C3

Chemin des Écluses. **GPS**: n47,46370 e4,45598.
free. **Surface:** gravel/metalled. 01/01-31/12.
Distance: 200m bakery 200m on the spot on the spot.

Remarks: At the canal, picnic area.

S Marsannay-la-Côte 19C3

Espace du Rocher, Rue du Rocher. **GPS**: n47,27099 e4,99224.

5 free Chfree. **Location:** Urban, simple, quiet.
Surface: asphalted. 01/01-31/12 service: 15/11-15/03.
Distance: 500m 3,5km 750m.
Remarks: Max. 48h.

S Marzy 22A1

Aire de camping-cars, Allée des Vignes du Clos.
GPS: n46,97982 e3,09357.
3 free € 2 Ch. **Location:** Simple, quiet. **Surface:** asphalted.
01/01-31/12.
Distance: 100m.
Remarks: Max. 72h.

S Mesnay 22E1

Rue Vermot. **GPS**: n46,89834 e5,80036.

20 free € 2/20minutes Ch € 2/20minutes .
Location: Simple. 01/01-31/12.
Distance: 500m, 2,5km Arbois.

Montbard 19B2

Place Gambetta, Rue Carnot. **GPS**: n47,62333 e4,33194.

5 free. **Location:** Simple. **Surface:** gravel. 01/01-31/12.
Distance: 300m on the spot on the spot.
Remarks: Bicycle rental.

S Montbéliard 19F3

Parking du Champ de Foire. **GPS**: n47,50663 e6,79128.

4 free € 2/100liter Ch € 2/1h. **Location:** Urban.
Surface: asphalted. 01/01-31/12.
Remarks: Max. 48h.

S Montreux-Château 19F2

D11. **GPS**: n47,60198 e7,00179.

FR

7 €5/24h €5/10minutes Ch (8x) WC included.
Location: Simple. **Surface:** gravel. 01/01-31/12.
Distance: on the spot on the spot on the spot.

Moussières 22E2

Combe au Prost. **GPS**: n46,32111 e5,89778.

6 free €2 Ch €2. **Location:** Rural, simple. **Surface:** gravel. 01/01-31/12.
Distance: on the spot.
Remarks: In front of cheese farm.

Mouthe 22E1

Place de l'Eglise. **GPS**: n46,71042 e6,19570.

20 free €3,50 Ch. **Location:** Rural, simple.
Surface: asphalted. 01/01-31/12.
Distance: 300m 300m.
Remarks: Coins at the bakery, supermarket, tourist office.

Nancray 19E3

Rue du Musée. **GPS**: n47,23933 e6,18588.
free €2 Ch. **Location:** Rural, isolated, quiet.
Surface: grassy. 01/03-31/10.
Distance: 1,3km 1,3km.

Nolay 22C1

Avenue de la Liberté. **GPS**: n46,95016 e4,62828.

± 10 free €3 Ch €3. **Location:** Urban, simple.
Surface: gravel. 01/01-31/12.
Distance: 100m 300m 300m.
Remarks: Coins at tourist info and town hall.

Tourist information Nolay:

Site Champetre du Bout du Monde, Vauchignon. Water falls.

Nozeroy 22E1

Rue des Remparts. **GPS**: n46,77249 e6,03516.

10 €6 Ch included, 2Amp. **Location:** Rural, isolated, quiet.
Surface: grassy/gravel. 01/01-31/12.
Distance: 200m.

Nuits-Saint-Georges 19C3

Rue de Cussigny. **GPS**: n47,13178 e4,95189.

10 free Ch free. **Location:** Urban, simple. **Surface:** asphalted. 01/01-31/12.
Distance: 400m 2,1km 500m Intermarché 300m.

Tourist information Nuits-Saint-Georges:

Fri.

Orgelet 22D2

Place Ancien Champ de Foire, Rue du Faubourg de l'Orme.
GPS: n46,52232 e5,60860.

10 free Ch WC free. **Location:** Simple.
Surface: grassy/metalled. 01/01-31/12.
Distance: 300m.
Remarks: Closed when frosty.

Pontigny 19B2

Rue Paul Desjardins, Pré Neuf. **GPS**: n47,91180 e3,71243.
13 €7 €3/10minutes Ch €2/2h
Location: Urban. **Surface:** gravel. 01/01-31/12.
Distance: on the spot on the spot.

Pougues-les-Eaux 19A3

D907. **GPS**: n47,08315 e3,09382.

5 free €2/10minutes Ch €2/10minutes.
Surface: asphalted. 01/01-31/12.
Distance: 250m 1,4km 100m.
Remarks: Coins at campsite and tourist info.

Prissé 22C2

Vignerons des Terres Secrètes, Les Grandes Vignes.
GPS: n46,32226 e4,75257.

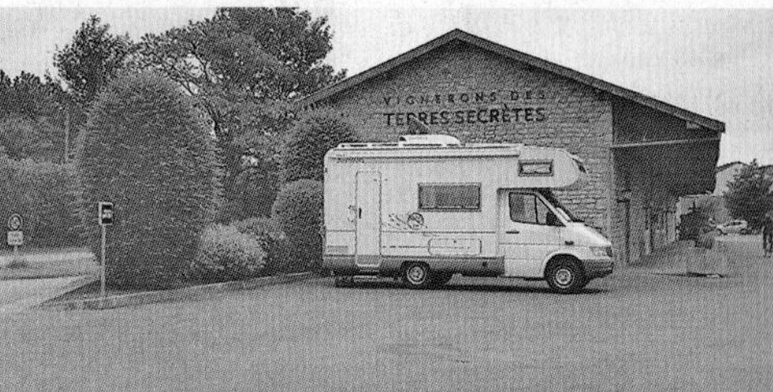

5 free €2 Ch WC. **Location:** Rural, simple. **Surface:** gravel. 01/01-31/12.
Distance: 500m 3km.
Remarks: Max. 24h.

Pruzilly 22C2

La Croix Blanche, salle des Fêtes. GPS: n46,25708 e4,69792.

6 free Ch WC free. **Location:** Rural, simple.
Surface: asphalted. 01/01-31/12.
Distance: on the spot on the spot.
Remarks: Max. 48h, vins de Côte de Beaujolais.

Quarre-les-Tombes 19B3

Rue des Ecoles. **GPS**: n47,36853 e3,99936.
6 free free. **Surface:** metalled. 01/04-31/10.
Distance: 100m 100m 100m.

Raddon-et-Chapendu 19F2

GPS: n47,84899 e6,47427.

6 free €2/23minutes €2/23minutes. **Location:** Rural, simple.
Surface: gravel. 01/01-31/12.
Remarks: Near sports fields.

Randevillers 19F3

Rue de la Cote. **GPS**: n47,30944 e6,52707.

3 free.
Location: Rural. **Surface:** asphalted/gravel. 01/01-31/12.

Rémilly 22B1

Le Bourg. **GPS**: n46,81995 e3,81171.
4 free Ch free. **Surface:** grassy. 01/01-31/12.
Distance: 200m 200m.
Remarks: Coins at town hall and restaurant, max. 48h.

Rogny-les-Sept-Écluses 18H2

Quai Sully. **GPS**: n47,74673 e2,88104.
4 free Ch free. **Location:** Simple, quiet. **Surface:** grassy. 01/01-31/12.
Distance: on the spot 350m.
Remarks: At the canal.

Rouvray 19B3

Place du Champs de Foire, D906. **GPS**: n47,42271 e4,10412.

FR

4 free Chfree. **Surface:** metalled. 01/01-31/12.
Distance: on the spot.
Remarks: Max. 48h.

Saint-Amour 22D2

Le Champ de Foire. **GPS:** n46,43303 e5,34207.
free. **Surface:** unpaved. 01/01-31/12.
Distance: 300m 300m.

S Saint-Benin-d'Azy 22A1

1 rue François Mitterrand. **GPS:** n47,00381 e3,40113.
3 free Ch free. 01/01-31/12.

Saint-Bresson 19F2

La Rue Saint Bresson. **GPS:** n47,86999 e6,50226.

2 free. **Location:** Rural, simple. **Surface:** asphalted.
01/01-31/12.

S Saint-Claude 22E2

Avenue de la Libération, D436. **GPS:** n46,38049 e5,85209.

3 free Ch free. **Location:** Urban, simple, noisy.
Surface: asphalted. 01/01-31/12.
Distance: 1km.

Tourist information Saint-Claude:
Tourist town, production of pipes.
Musée du Pipe et Diamant. Pipes and diamond exhibition.
01/06-30/09 9.30-12h, 14-18.30h, 01/10-31/05 14-18h Su.

S Saint-Fargeau 19A2

Rue de Laveau, D18. **GPS:** n47,63968 e3,06999.

10 free ChWCfree. 01/01-31/12.
Distance: 50m 50m.

S Saint-Gengoux-le-National 22C1

GPS: n46,60624 e4,66844.

16 free € 3/15minutes Ch € 3/50minutes WC.
Location: Simple, quiet. **Surface:** gravel. 01/01-31/12.
Distance: 500m.
Remarks: At former station.

Tourist information Saint-Gengoux-le-National:
La Voie Verte. Cycle route on former railway,.

Saint-Hippolyte 19F3

Esplanade des Fetes. **GPS:** n47,31874 e6,81543.

9 free. **Surface:** grassy/metalled. 01/01-31/12.
Distance: on the spot on the spot on the spot on the spot.

S Saint-Honoré-les-Bains 22B1

Allée de la Cressonnière. **GPS:** n46,90471 e3,84059.

4 free € 2 Ch € 2.
Location: Simple. **Surface:** gravel. 01/01-31/12.
Distance: 300m 300m 50m.
Remarks: Max. 48h, coins at town hall and supermarket.

S Saint-Julien-du-Sault 19A1

Stade Jean Sax, Rue du Stade. **GPS:** n48,02906 e3,30116.
13 free Chfree. **Surface:** gravel. 01/01-31/12.

S Saint-Léger-sur-Dheune 22C1

Route de Saint-Bérain. **GPS:** n46,84648 e4,63248.

12 € 7/24h Chincluded. 01/01-31/12.
Distance: on the spot.

S Saint-Loup-sur-Semouse 19E2

Rue de Champ de Tir. **GPS:** n47,88643 e6,27051.

4 free € 3 Ch. **Surface:** asphalted. 01/03-30/11.
Distance: on the spot 500m on the spot on the spot on the spot.

Remarks: Behind church, max. 24h.

S Saint-Pierre-le-Moûtier 22A1

Camping-Car Park, 13 rue de Beaudrillon. **GPS:** n46,78576 e3,11953.
48 € 10,04- 12,44 Ch (16x)included.
Location: Rural. **Surface:** grassy. 01/01-31/12.
Distance: 550m 550m 550m.
Remarks: Mandatory, one-time fee Pass'Etapes € 4.

S Saint-Point-Lac 22E1

Aire d'acceuil pour camping-cars, Rue du lac.
GPS: n46,81268 e6,30375.

40 € 6 10minutes Ch 55minutes WCfree.
Surface: gravel/sand. 01/03-30/11.
Distance: on the spot.
Remarks: Max. 3 nights, no camping activities.

Sainte-Marie-en-Chanois 19F2

Rue de la Lolonge. **GPS:** n47,83663 e6,51216.

5 free. **Location:** Rural, simple. **Surface:** asphalted.
01/01-31/12.

S Salins-les-Bains 22E1

Place Aubarède, Rue de la République, D472.
GPS: n46,93254 e5,87899.

6 free Ch free. **Location:** Simple. **Surface:** asphalted.
01/01-31/12.
Distance: 50m.
Remarks: Permitted to park/stay overnight on all parkings.

Sancey-le-Grand 19F3

D31. **GPS:** n47,29040 e6,57742.

2 free.
Location: Rural, simple. **Surface:** gravel. 01/01-31/12.
Distance: 500m.

S Sancey-le-Long 19F3

D31/D464. **GPS:** n47,30513 e6,59477.

FR

2 free € 2 Ch € 2. **Location:** Rural, simple. **Surface:** gravel. 01/01-31/12.
Distance: on the spot.
Remarks: Coins at supermarket, cafe, centre commercial.

S Saulx 19E2
Place de l'Eglise. **GPS:** n47,69620 e6,28030.
€ 2/100liter € 2/2h WC free. **Location:** Simple, quiet.

S Savigny-le-Sec 19C3
Rue de la Mare. **GPS:** n47,43365 e5,04607.

10 € 5 Ch included WC. **Location:** Rural, simple, isolated, quiet. **Surface:** asphalted/gravel. 01/01-31/12.
Distance: 1,3km bakery 1,3km.

S Savoyeux 19D2
Port de plaisance, Rue des Chênes. **GPS:** n47,56270 e5,73971.
4 € 5 Ch € 2 WC included € 2 € 1/12h.
01/01-31/12.
Distance: 1km.
Remarks: Pay at harbourmaster.

S Scey-sur-Saône-et-Saint-Albin 19E2
D3. **GPS:** n47,65366 e5,97379.
7 free € 1 Ch € 1 .
Location: Rural. 01/01-31/12.
Distance: 1km 1,5km.
Remarks: Picnic tables available.

S Semur-en-Auxois 19B3
Avenue Pasteur. **GPS:** n47,49506 e4,34945.

30 free Ch free. **Location:** Simple, quiet. **Surface:** asphalted. 01/01-31/12 water: Nov-March.
Distance: historical centre 1,3km 10km 800m 800m.
Remarks: At football ground.

Tourist information Semur-en-Auxois:
Alise-Ste-Reine. Findings of Gallo-Roman city. 01/04-31/10 daily.

Sermamagny 19F2
Rue Alfred Lallemand. **GPS:** n47,68351 e6,81416.

30 free. **Surface:** grassy.

S Seurre 22D1
Rue de la Perche à l'Oiseau. **GPS:** n47,00405 e5,14318.

15 free € 4,70/20minutes Ch Service € 4/20min .
Location: Rural, simple, quiet. **Surface:** asphalted.
01/01-31/12.
Distance: 800m 100m 100m 700m 700m.
Remarks: Camper service 8-20h.

S Thoirette 22D2
Grande Rue. **GPS:** n46,26924 e5,53529.

5 € 6 Ch included. **Location:** Simple. **Surface:** gravel.
01/01-31/12.
Distance: 25m 50m 25m on the spot.

S Tournus 22C2
Quai de la Marine. **GPS:** n46,56757 e4,91118.

8 free Ch . **Location:** Urban. **Surface:** metalled.
01/01-31/12.
Distance: 300m 300m 500m 300m.
Remarks: Market Saturday.

S Treigny 19A2
Rue du Champ de Foire. **GPS:** n47,54982 e3,18159.
2 free Ch. **Location:** Simple, quiet. **Surface:** asphalted.
01/01-31/12.
Distance: 200m 200m 200m.

S Vaivre-et-Montoille 19E2
20 avenue des Rives-du-Lac. **GPS:** n47,63718 e6,10752.

4 free € 2 Ch € 2. **Location:** Rural. **Surface:** asphalted.
01/01-31/12.
Distance: on the spot on the spot on the spot.
Remarks: Directly at lake, coins at campsite.

S Vaivre-et-Montoille 19E2
Avenue des Rives du Lac. **GPS:** n47,62938 e6,12701.

7 free € 2,50 Ch. **Location:** Rural, simple, quiet.
Surface: asphalted. 01/01-31/12.
Distance: 1,5km beach 100m 100m 25m on the spot on the spot.
Remarks: Swimming pool complex, lake.

Vellevans 19F3
D464. **GPS:** n47,31042 e6,49139.

2 free. **Location:** Rural. **Surface:** asphalted. 01/01-31/12.

S Villers-le-Lac 19F3
Vedettes Panoramiques, Rue du Clos Rondot.
GPS: n47,05948 e6,67195.

8 free € 2 Ch free . **Location:** Simple.
Surface: concrete. 01/01-31/12.
Distance: 50m.
Remarks: Small pitches.

S Villers-le-Lac 19F3
Bateaux du Saut du Doubs. GPS: n47,05611 e6,67034.

50 free € 3,50 Ch at office/shop.
Location: Simple, central. **Surface:** grassy/gravel.
01/04-31/10.
Distance: 100m.
Remarks: Check in at Bateaux.

S Vinzelles 22C2
Clos Bonin. **GPS:** n46,27145 e4,77008.

10 free Ch free. **Location:** Rural, simple. **Surface:** asphalted.
01/01-31/12.
Distance: 200m A6 2,8km on the spot on the spot on the spot.

Auvergne-Rhône-Alpes

S Aiguebelle 25E1
Pré de foire. **GPS:** n45,54289 e6,30635.

18 free € 2/100liter Ch. **Surface:** asphalted/grassy.
01/01-31/12 Thu-morning closed because of market.
Distance: on the spot 6,1km.

Tourist information Aiguebelle:
Tue-morning.

Aigueperse 22A3

Place du Foirail, Rue de la Porte aux Boeufs. **GPS**: n46,02634 e3,20313.

15 free € 2/10minutes Ch € 2/1h.
Location: Urban, simple, central, quiet. **Surface:** asphalted.
01/01-31/12 17/08-28/08.
Distance: on the spot 200m 300m.
Remarks: Market square.

Aiguilhe 25B2

Avenue de Bonneville. **GPS**: n45,05063 e3,88356.

6 free. **Location:** Urban, simple, central. **Surface:** asphalted.
01/01-31/12.
Distance: on the spot 350m.
Remarks: Max. 24h.

Aix-les-Bains 22E3

Camping-Car Park, Rue des Goélands. **GPS**: n45,69627 e5,88926.
85 € 13 Ch (52x) € 5/3 included.
Surface: grassy. 01/01-31/12.
Distance: 500m on the spot 200m 500m 200m.
Remarks: Mandatory, one-time fee Pass'Etapes € 4.

Alba-la-Romaine 25C3

Bragigous. **GPS**: n44,55329 e4,59741.

35 € 4 € 2 Ch. **Location:** Rural, quiet. **Surface:** grassy/gravel.
01/01-31/12.
Distance: on the spot 200m 200m.
Remarks: Service to be paid at retirement home.

Albertville 22F3

Parking Conflans, Montée Adolphe Hugues, Conflans.
GPS: n45,67389 e6,39694.
6 free € 3,50 Ch. **Surface:** asphalted.
Distance: 10 min walking.

Tourist information Albertville:
Quai des Allobroges. Thu 6-18h.

Allanche 24H1

Aire de la Gare, Chemin de la Roche Marchal.
GPS: n45,23000 e2,93139.

25 free € 2 Ch. **Location:** Rural, simple, quiet.
Surface: gravel/sand. 01/05-30/09, parking 01/01-31/12.
Distance: 300m 300m 300m.
Remarks: Altitude 1000m, coins at camping, tourist info and town hall, accessed via Allanche centre.

Allevard 25E1

Avenue des Bains. **GPS**: n45,38838 e6,07110.
10 € 4 Ch WC included. **Location:** Rural.
Surface: unpaved. 01/01-31/12.
Distance: 500m 300m.
Remarks: Max. 48h.

Alpe d'Huez 25E2

Parking de Brandes, Quartier des Bergers, chemin de font morelle.
GPS: n45,08654 e6,07916.

65 € 10/day + € 0,83/pp tourist tax Ch WC.
Surface: asphalted.
Distance: 1km 350m on the spot.
Remarks: First buy a parking ticket at Palais des Sports et des Congrès.

Alpe d'Huez 25E2

Parking l'Eclose, Rue du 93me Ram. **GPS**: n45,08796 e6,07019.
25 € 10/day + € 0,83/pp tourist tax Ch WC included.
Surface: asphalted.
01/12-01/04, 11/07-31/08.
Distance: 200m 200m 200m on the spot.
Remarks: First buy a parking ticket at Palais des Sports et des Congrès.

Ambierle 22B2

Complexe sportif, Rue Sainte Claude. **GPS**: n46,10663 e3,89384.

3 free Ch free. **Location:** Rural, simple, quiet.
Surface: asphalted. 01/01-31/12.
Distance: on the spot 200m 300m.
Remarks: At sports park.

Amplepuis 22B3

Rue Paul de la Goutte. **GPS**: n45,97027 e4,33085.
free Ch free. **Surface:** asphalted.
Distance: on the spot 50m 100m on the spot.
Remarks: Behind gymnasium.

Annecy 22E3

Parking de Colmyr, Rue des Marquisats, N1508.
GPS: n45,89070 e6,13915.

14 free Ch free.
Location: Urban, simple, central, quiet. **Surface:** asphalted.
01/01-31/12.
Distance: 700m 100m on the spot 700m 700m.
Remarks: Max. 24h, market days Tuesday, Friday, Sunday.

Tourist information Annecy:
Office de Tourisme, Bonlieu, 1 rue Jean Jaurès, www.lac-annecy.com. Located on lake of the same name and surrounded by mountain peaks. The old city centre exists of covered lanes, canals and bridges.
Place de Romains. Tue 7-19h.

Anse 22C3

Cave Saint Cyr, 31 chemin de Trechen - D70. **GPS**: n45,93169 e4,68623.

4 free, service € 5 Ch. **Location:** Rural.
Surface: gravel/metalled. 01/01-31/12.
Remarks: At wine-grower.

Anthy-sur-Léman 22F2

Rue du Lac. **GPS**: n46,35889 e6,42192.

5 free free. **Surface:** gravel. 01/01-31/12.
Distance: 700m 50m on the spot.
Remarks: Max. 48h, max. 7m.

Archignat 21H2

Rue des Chalets. **GPS**: n46,37336 e2,42408.

5 € 8 + € 0,20/pp tourist tax € 2 Ch € 2 WC included.
Location: Rural, comfortable, quiet. **Surface:** grassy.
01/01-31/12.
Distance: on the spot on the spot.

Arçon 22B3

Le Bourg. **GPS**: n46,00977 e3,88793.

3 free Ch free. **Location:** Rural, simple, quiet.

FR

01/01-31/12.
Distance: on the spot 50m.

Arlanc 25A1

Loumans. **GPS**: n45,41233 e3,71782.

+10 free € 2 Ch. **Location:** Rural, simple, quiet. **Surface:** asphalted/grassy. 01/04-31/10.
Distance: 500m on the spot 100m 1km on the spot.
Remarks: At swimming pool and small lake, coins at tourist info.

Arlebosc 25C2

Place du Marché aux Fruits. **GPS**: n45,03683 e4,65238.

10 free Chfree. **Location:** Rural, simple. **Surface:** gravel. 01/01-31/12.
Distance: on the spot bakery 150m on the spot.

Arnac (Cantal) 24G2

Aire camping-cars, Lacan. **GPS**: n45,06056 e2,23389.

2 free € 2/100liter Ch € 2/1h. **Location:** Rural, simple, quiet. **Surface:** grassy/gravel. 01/01-31/12.
Distance: 50m 150m 150m.

Aubignas 25C3

Aire camping-cars, Aubignas. **GPS**: n44,58732 e4,63177.

10 voluntary contribution € 5 € 2/100liter ChWC.
Surface: gravel. 01/01-31/12.
Distance: 350m.
Remarks: Beautiful view.

Aubusson-d'Auvergne 22A3

Base de Loisirs-lac d'Aubusson. **GPS**: n45,75377 e3,61079.

50 € 3, 01/04-31/10 € 6 ChWC included.
Location: Rural, simple, isolated, quiet.
Surface: metalled.

01/01-31/12.
Distance: on the spot on the spot 200m 8km on the spot.

Aurec-sur-Loire 25B1

Place de la Gare. **GPS**: n45,37164 e4,19919.

3 free Chfree. **Location:** Urban, simple, central, quiet. **Surface:** gravel/sand. 01/01-31/12.
Distance: 450m 450m 500m 50m.
Remarks: At station, max. 48h.

Aurillac 24G2

Place du Champ de Foire, Cours d'Angoulême.
GPS: n44,92944 e2,44963.

10 free € 3,50 Ch € 3,50.
Location: Urban, simple, noisy. **Surface:** asphalted.
01/01-31/12 service: 31/10-01/05.
Distance: on the spot 100m 100m.
Remarks: Max. 24h, coins at tourist info.

Tourist information Aurillac:
European street theatre and festival. 3rd week Aug.

Avermes 22A1

Avenue des Isles. **GPS**: n46,58587 e3,30509.

3 free € 2 ChWC. **Location:** Simple, quiet. **Surface:** metalled.
01/01-31/12.
Distance: 200m 20km.
Remarks: At sports centre.

Aydat 21H3

Aire camping-cars. **GPS**: n45,66025 e2,97778.

41 € 9,50/24h Ch (28x)WC included.
Location: Rural, comfortable, quiet. **Surface:** grassy.
01/01-31/12.
Distance: 200m on the spot on the spot on the spot 250m.
Remarks: Former campsite, max. 8,20m.

Balazuc 25B3

Parking Champsgelly, La Croisette. **GPS**: n44,50601 e4,37366.

free. **Location:** Rural. **Surface:** gravel. 01/01-31/12.
Distance: 280m 1km.

Banne 25B3

Quartier l'Eglise, D251. **GPS**: n44,36539 e4,15691.

25 free € 3/60liter Ch € 3/1h. **Surface:** gravel/metalled.
01/01-31/12.
Distance: 500m.
Remarks: Behind church, beautiful view.

Barjac 25B3

Rue Basse. **GPS**: n44,30589 e4,34343.

20 free Ch € 3,water 10 min + electricity 55min.
Location: Simple.
01/01-31/12.
Distance: 100m 100m on the spot.
Remarks: Coins at tourist info and town hall, friday market.

Beaulieu 25B2

Lous Saux. **GPS**: n45,12662 e3,94799.

5 free Ch (2x)free. **Location:** Rural, simple, quiet.
Surface: gravel. 01/04-31/10 service 01/11-31/03.
Distance: 800m 300m on the spot on the spot.
Remarks: Max. 48h.

Beaulon 22A1

Écluse de Beaulon, La Curesse. **GPS**: n46,60443 e3,65840.

+10 free Ch (10x)free.
Location: Rural, simple, isolated, quiet. **Surface:** gravel.
01/01-31/12.
Distance: 1,2km Canal on the spot 1,2km 1,2km on the spot on the spot.

FR

Beausemblant 25C1

Drôme des Collines, Rue des Glycines, D122.
GPS: n45,21826 e4,83282.

4 free Chfree. **Location:** Simple. **Surface:** gravel.
01/01-31/12.
Distance: 100m 100m on the spot.
Remarks: Max. 48h.

Beauzac 25B1

Espace La Dorlière, D42. **GPS**: n45,26161 e4,10170.

8 free Chfree. **Location:** Rural, simple, quiet.
Surface: gravel/sand. 15/04-31/10.
Distance: 250m 300m.

Bellerive-sur-Allier 22A2

Riv'Air Camp, Rue Claude Decloitre. **GPS**: n46,11514 e3,43114.

39 € 10 Ch (50x)WC included . **Location:** Urban, comfortable, isolated, quiet. **Surface:** metalled. 01/01-31/12.
Distance: 2,5km 17km on the spot on the spot on the spot 800m.
Remarks: Along the Allier river.

Belleville 22C2

Ancienne Avenue du Port. **GPS**: n46,10626 e4,75470.

8 free Chfree. **Surface:** asphalted. 01/01-31/12.
Distance: centre 500m A6 900m 500m 500m.

Belley 22D3

Route de Saint-Germain, D41. **GPS**: n45,75535 e5,67790.

20 free € 2 Ch € 2. **Location:** Urban, simple, central, quiet.
Surface: asphalted. 01/01-31/12.
Distance: city centre 1km 1km 1km 1km.
Remarks: Near sports park, service only with 1-euro coins.

Belleydoux 22E2

Relais Flot Bleu, Route Principale. **GPS**: n46,25556 e5,77994.
free € 2 Ch € 2/20minutes. 01/01-31/12.

Belmont-de-la-Loire 22B2

Place de l'Église. **GPS**: n46,16543 e4,34634.

2 free Ch WC. **Location:** Rural, simple, quiet.
Surface: metalled. 03/03-19/07, 01/08-31/10.
Distance: 50m 100m 100m on the spot.

Bibost 22C3

D91. **GPS**: n45,79500 e4,55144.
6 free Ch free. **Location:** Rural, quiet. **Surface:** gravel.
01/01-31/12.
Remarks: Beautiful view.

Billy 22A2

7 Rue de la Fontaine. **GPS**: n46,23586 e3,43044.

3 free Chfree. **Surface:** asphalted. 01/01-31/12.
Distance: on the spot 450m 150m.
Remarks: Max. 48h.

Blesle 25A1

Route du Babory, D8. **GPS**: n45,31733 e3,17424.

6 free. **Location:** Rural, simple, quiet. **Surface:** gravel/sand.
01/01-31/12.
Distance: 300m 300m 300m on the spot.
Remarks: Max. 2 nights, service at camping municipal.

Blesle 25A1

Hôtel-Restaurant Le Scorpion, Le Basbory, D909.
GPS: n45,31219 e3,18677.

25 € 12,50 Ch (8x)WC included. **Location:** Rural, comfortable, quiet. **Surface:** grassy. 01/01-31/12.
Distance: 5,8km on the spot on the spot.

Boën 22B3

Boulevard Moizieux. **GPS**: n45,74401 e4,00263.

8 free Chfree. **Location:** Simple, central, quiet.
Surface: gravel. 01/01-31/12.
Distance: 200m 900m 200m 300m.

Boulieu-lès-Annonay 25C1

Chemin du Lavoir. **GPS**: n45,26928 e4,66963.

6 free ChWCfree. **Location:** Rural, comfortable, quiet.
Surface: gravel.
Distance: 400m 400m 400m.
Remarks: Voluntary contribution, market on Sunday.

Bourg-en-Bresse 22D2

Allée du centre nautique 5. **GPS**: n46,20944 e5,24157.
1 free Chfree. **Location:** Urban. **Surface:** metalled.
01/01-31/12.
Distance: city centre 1km 550m 500m.

Bourg-en-Bresse 22D2

Parking V.L./Bus, Allée Loys Van Bòghem.
GPS: n46,19854 e5,23766.

10 free WC 100m. **Location:** Urban, simple, central, noisy.
Surface: asphalted. 01/01-31/12 Wed, Sa.
Distance: on the spot 6km 100m 200m on the spot on the spot.

Bourg-Saint-Andéol 25C3

Chemin de la Barrière. **GPS**: n44,37520 e4,64327.

30 free Ch free. **Surface:** asphalted. 01/01-31/12.
Distance: 750m 50m Lidl.
Remarks: Along railwayline, max. 48h.

Bourg-Saint-Maurice 22F3

Les Chapieux. **GPS**: n45,69532 e6,73364.
+20 free.
Location: Rural, isolated, quiet. **Surface:** grassy. winter.

Bourget-du-Lac 22E3

International au l'Lle de Cygnes. **GPS**: n45,65250 e5,86378.

FR

32 € 6,20-12,50 ChWC included.
Location: Rural, comfortable, quiet. **Surface:** metalled.
01/01-31/12 service: 01/12-01/03.
Distance: 500m 500m beach 300m 100m on the spot on the spot 100m on the spot on the spot.

S Bourgneuf 25E1

Aire camping-cars, D925. **GPS:** n45,55257 e6,21091.

30 free € 2 Ch. **Surface:** metalled. 01/01-31/12.
Distance: 5km Brasserie/Pizzeria bakery.
Remarks: Coins available at Pizzeria/Tabac.

S Bouvante 25D2

Village de Font d'Urle, Font d'Urle. **GPS:** n44,89789 e5,32195.

10 free € 2/100liter Ch (5x)€ 7/24h WC € 2.
Location: Simple, quiet. **Surface:** gravel. 15/05-30/09.
Distance: on the spot nordic walking on the spot.
Remarks: Altitude 1550m, coins at riding school.

S Brioude 25A1

Parking Centre Historique, Avenue de Lamothe, D588.
GPS: n45,29444 e3,38778.

30 free € 2 Ch € 2. **Location:** Urban, simple, central, quiet.
Surface: asphalted/gravel. 01/01-31/12.
Distance: 100m 100m 100m on the spot.
Remarks: Coins at tourist info(100m).

Tourist information Brioude:
L'aquarium-la Maison du Saumon et de la Rivière, Place de la Résistance. Museum about the salmon. 01/04-30/11.

S Calvinet 24G2

Aire de Calvinet, Le Puech D66. **GPS:** n44,71023 e2,35914.

6 free € 2 Ch € 2. **Location:** Rural, simple, quiet.
Surface: gravel. 01/01-31/12 service 01/11-31/03.
Distance: 1,5km 1,5km 1,5km.
Remarks: Nearby sports ground.

S Cassaniouze 24G2

Aire camping-cars, Le Bourg N. **GPS:** n44,69347 e2,38233.

6 free € 2/80liter Ch € 2/1h € 1.
Location: Rural, simple, quiet. **Surface:** gravel.
01/01-31/12 service 01/11-31/03.
Distance: 600m 600m 600m.

S Cayrols 24G2

Aire camping-cars, L'Étang, D51. **GPS:** n44,83000 e2,23278.

10 free € 3,80 Ch € 3,80 WC.
Location: Rural, comfortable, quiet. **Surface:** metalled.
01/01-31/12 service 01/11-31/03.
Distance: 100m 200m.
Remarks: Max. 1 week, coins at the shops in the village and petrol station.

S Chalmazel 22B3

Le Bourg, Le Pont Ouest. **GPS:** n45,70149 e3,85459.

8 free € 2 Ch € 2 € 2/4h. **Location:** Comfortable.
Surface: metalled. 01/01-31/12.
Distance: 50m on the spot 50m 50m on the spot on the spot 2km.
Remarks: Along river, coins at tourist info.

S Chambéry 25E1

Rue Costa de Beauregard. **GPS:** n45,56289 e5,93302.
6 free Chfree.
Location: Urban. **Surface:** asphalted.
01/01-31/12 water: 15/11-01/03.
Distance: 500m 1,2km 500m 500m.
Remarks: Water closed during wintertime.

Tourist information Chambéry:
Vieux Cité. Historical centre with old mansions.
Château des Ducs de Savoie. Complex of buildings, 13-14th century.

S Chambon-sur-Lac 24H1

Camping Les Bombes, La Vergne. **GPS:** n45,56991 e2,90176.

30 € 7 € 3 Ch. **Location:** Rural, simple, quiet.
Surface: grassy/gravel. 01/01-31/12 service: 15/09-01/05.
Distance: 500m 200m 1km 500m 500m bakery on the spot on the spot.
Remarks: Pay and coins at campsite.

S Chamonix-Mont-Blanc 22F3

Parking Grépon, Aiguille du Midi, D1506. **GPS:** n45,91578 e6,86970.

50 € 12,50/24h Chincluded WCfree. **Surface:** asphalted.
01/01-31/12, service only during summer period.
Distance: 1km 350m 600m.

Tourist information Chamonix-Mont-Blanc:
Aiguille du Midi. Telpher carrier from Chamonix (1036 m.) To Aiguille de Midi (3842m).
Montenvers et mer de Glace. Tramline from Montenvers to the ice lake, a glacier of 7 km long and 1.2 km broad.

S Champagnac 24G1

D12. **GPS:** n45,35806 e2,39929.

4 free ChWCfree. **Location:** Simple, quiet.
Surface: asphalted.
Distance: on the spot on the spot.

S Champeix 25A1

Champeix, Route de Montaigut, D996. **GPS:** n45,58845 e3,11568.

12 free € 2 Ch. **Location:** Rural, simple, isolated, quiet.
Surface: grassy/gravel. 01/04-31/10.
Distance: 1,3km 1,3km 500m.

S Champoly 22B3

La Péniche, Chemin de la salle des fêtes.
GPS: n45,85583 e3,83227.

2 free € 2 Ch € 2. **Location:** Rural, simple, quiet.
Surface: asphalted. 01/01-31/12.
Distance: 300m 400m.

S Chamrousse 25E2

Place des Niverolles, Rue de la Cembraie. **GPS:** n45,12666 e5,87356.

FR

12 €8 Ch included. **Surface:** asphalted. 01/01-31/12.
Distance: 400m 400m 400m.
Remarks: Max. 24h.

S Chanaleilles 25A2

Le Bourg. **GPS**: n44,85971 e3,49052.

5 free ChWCfree. **Location:** Rural, simple, isolated, quiet.
Surface: asphalted. 01/01-31/12.
Distance: 500m 400m on the spot.

S Chanteuges 25A2

Ancienne Gare. **GPS**: n45,07234 e3,53005.

6 free Chfree. **Location:** Rural, simple, isolated, quiet.
Surface: gravel. 01/01-31/12.
Distance: 200m.
Remarks: Max. 8M.

S Charbonnières-les-Varennes 21H3

Route de Saint-Georges, Paugnat. **GPS**: n45,88457 e2,97993.

9 free €2/10minutes Ch €2/55minutes.
Location: Rural, comfortable, quiet.
Surface: grassy.
01/01-31/12.
Distance: 500m 500m bakery 500m on the spot.
Remarks: Coins at the shops in the village, trail to volcano crater.

S Charix 22D2

Auberge du Lac Genin. **GPS**: n46,21981 e5,69556.

20 €5 + €0,20/pp tourist taks, guests free Chfree.
Location: Rural, simple, isolated, quiet. **Surface:** gravel.
01/05-30/09.
Distance: 4,7km lake on the spot on the spot on the spot on the spot.

S Charlieu 22B2

Place d'Eningen. **GPS**: n46,16031 e4,17813.

5 free ChWCfree. **Location:** Rural. **Surface:** gravel/metalled.
01/01-31/12.
Distance: historical centre 500m 500m 500m.
Remarks: In front of police station.

S Charols 25C3

Aire municipale, D9. **GPS**: n44,59160 e4,95441.

10 free free. **Surface:** asphalted. 01/01-31/12.
Distance: 200m 200m 50m.

S Chaspuzac 25A2

Aérodrome du Puy-en-Velay, Rue du Vol à Voile.
GPS: n45,07491 e3,76131.

4 free €2 Ch. **Location:** Rural, simple, quiet.
Surface: asphalted. 01/01-31/12 service: 01/11-28/02.
Distance: 50m on the spot.
Remarks: View on airport.

S Chastreix 24H1

Parking Station de Ski, Chastreix Sancy. **GPS**: n45,53507 e2,77695.

14 free Ch €9,(winter) WC €2,(winter).
Location: Rural, simple, quiet. **Surface:** metalled.
01/01-31/12.
Distance: Chastreix 6km on the spot.
Remarks: Check in between 9-17h.

S Château-sur-Allier 21H1

Domaine Fessebois. **GPS**: n46,76391 e3,03058.

4 free €3 Ch. **Location:** Rural, simple, isolated.
Surface: gravel. 01/01-31/12.
Distance: 200m 10km 1,5km 1,5km on the spot.

Remarks: Picnic area.

S Châtel-Guyon 21H3

Pré Morand, Avenue de Russie. **GPS**: n45,91707 e3,05779.

14 free, 01/04-31/10 €5 €2 Ch €2/2h .
Location: Simple. **Surface:** gravel. 01/01-31/12.
Distance: on the spot > Riom >Clermont-Ferrand.
Remarks: Next to spa resort.

Châtel-Guyon 21H3

Parking des Roches, Chemin de Bussane.
GPS: n45,91789 e3,06545.

10 free. **Location:** Urban, simple, quiet. **Surface:** asphalted.
01/01-31/12.
Distance: 500m 600m 600m.

S Chaudes-Aigues 24H2

Parking Beauredon, Avenue Georges Pompidou, D921.
GPS: n44,84972 e3,00306.

10 free €2 Ch €2/55minutes. **Location:** Urban, simple, quiet. **Surface:** gravel. 15/04-15/10.
Distance: 400m 400m 400m on the spot.

Tourist information Chaudes-Aigues:
Office de Tourisme, 1, avenue Georges Pompidou, www.chaude-saigues.com. Small town with warm thermal sources (82°C).

S Chevagnes 22A1

Route Nationale. **GPS**: n46,61028 e3,55219.

4 free Ch free. **Location:** Comfortable, isolated, quiet.
Surface: gravel. 01/01-31/12.
Distance: on the spot 200m.

S Chichilianne 25D2

Passière. **GPS**: n44,81226 e5,57532.

FR

4 free € 3 Ch. **Surface:** grassy.
01/01-31/12 water disconnected in winter.
Distance: on the spot on the spot 250m bakery.
Remarks: Coins at town hall or Maison du Parc.

Chomelix 25B1

Centre Multi Activités Chomelix, Route d'Estables, D135.
GPS: n45,26219 e3,82573.

5 free € 4 Ch. **Location:** Rural, simple, quiet. **Surface:** gravel.
01/01-31/12.
Distance: on the spot on the spot on the spot on the spot.

Clansayes 25C3

Aire de Toronne, Quartier Toronne RD133.
GPS: n44,36975 e4,79901.

25 € 10, 2 pers. incl., dog € 1,50 Ch € 4/day WC € 4.
Location: Rural, comfortable, isolated, quiet.
Surface: grassy/gravel.
01/01-31/12.
Distance: 2km 10km buvette-menu rapide-restauration 3km.
Remarks: Bread-service, regional products, swimming pool (summer).

Clermont Ferrand 22A3

P&R Les Pistes, Rue de la Fontaine de la Ratte.
GPS: n45,79810 e3,11222.

6 € 8 Ch included. **Location:** Urban, simple.
Surface: asphalted. 01/01-31/12.
Distance: historical centre 3km 900m 50m.
Remarks: Nearby Michelin museum, check in at parking attendant.

Colombier-le-Jeune 25C2

Le Village. **GPS:** n45,01106 e4,70132.

2 free Ch free. **Location:** Rural. **Surface:** metalled.
01/01-31/12 water disconnected in winter.
Distance: on the spot 150m 200m on the spot.

Coltines 24H2

D40. **GPS:** n45,09612 e2,98555.

5 free € 2/100liter Ch € 2/60minutes.
Location: Rural, simple, quiet.
Surface: gravel.
15/04-15/10.
Distance: 400m 400m 400m.
Remarks: Coins at Epicerie-Presse, Centre Chantarisa and town hall.

Combloux 22F3

Parking du Bouchet, Route du Bouchet. **GPS:** n45,89896 e6,63275.
6 free. **Surface:** asphalted. 01/01-31/12.
Distance: on the spot.
Remarks: At ski-lift.

Condat 24H1

Parking au Pont, D678. **GPS:** n45,33889 e2,76250.

4 free Service € 2,50 Ch. **Location:** Simple.
Surface: asphalted. 01/01-31/12 service: 01/10-01/05.
Distance: 50m 50m 50m.
Remarks: Coins at campsite La Borie Basse (500m).

Cornas 25C2

Impasse de Iris, Grande Rue, D86. **GPS:** n44,96024 e4,84722.

5 free Ch free. **Location:** Simple. **Surface:** gravel.
01/01-31/12.
Distance: 200m 200m bakery 200m.
Remarks: Max. 48h, several 'Caves' with wine tasting.

Coubon 25B2

Route du Plan d'Eau. **GPS:** n44,99735 e3,91742.

5 free € 3 Ch WC. **Surface:** asphalted.
01/01-31/12 water disconnected in winter.
Remarks: Along Loire river, key service at supermarket Vival and bar/tabac 75m.

Coucouron 25B2

Les Eygades. **GPS:** n44,80168 e3,96148.

33 01/05-30/09 € 8/day Ch included.
Location: Rural, simple. **Surface:** gravel. 01/01-31/12.
Distance: 1km on the spot on the spot 1km on the spot.
Remarks: At Lac de Coucouron, max. 7 days, outside season free stay on campsite municipal (no facilities).

Cournon d'Auvergne 22A3

Les Pres des Laveuses, Rue de Laveuses.
GPS: n45,73994 e3,22225.

10 € 4,20 € 2,50 Ch. **Location:** Rural, simple.
Surface: gravel. 01/01-31/12.
Distance: 2km on the spot on the spot on the spot.

Cours-la-Ville 22B2

La Rivière. **GPS:** n46,10399 e4,32315.

10 free Ch free. **Location:** Rural, simple.
Surface: grassy/gravel. 01/01-31/12.
Distance: 300m 700m on the spot on the spot.
Remarks: Along the river Trambouze, to be reached from northern direction, Boulevard Pierre de Coubertin.

Courtenay 22D3

Etang de Salette, Courtenay. **GPS:** n45,72417 e5,37124.

7 free. **Location:** Rural, isolated, quiet. **Surface:** gravel.
01/01-31/12.
Distance: 1km on the spot Pizzeria bread service 1,2km on the spot.

Crandelles 24G2

Aire camping-cars, Lac des Genevrières. **GPS:** n44,95877 e2,34289.

10 free € 3,50 Ch. **Location:** Comfortable, central, quiet.
Surface: gravel. 01/01-31/12 service: 01/11-01/04.
Distance: 300m 50m 50m 50m 300m.

Craponne-sur-Arzon 25B1

Place de la Gare. **GPS**: n45,33381 e3,84996.

+20 free € 2 Ch € 2/h.
Location: Urban, simple, quiet. **Surface:** asphalted/gravel.
01/01-31/12 service 01/11-31/03.
Distance: 150m 150m on the spot.

Crémieu 22D3

Rue du 19 mars 1962. **GPS**: n45,72549 e5,24670.

12 free Chfree. **Location:** Urban, simple, central.
Surface: asphalted. 01/01-31/12.
Distance: 300m 250m 300m 100m.

Crest 25C2

Place du Champ de Mars, Avenue Agirond. **GPS**: n44,72600 e5,02100.

17 € 5 € 3 Ch € 3 free. **Location:** Urban, simple.
Surface: asphalted. 01/01-31/12.
Distance: 200m pizzeria bakery 50m.

Cros-de-Géorand 25B2

Campng-Car Park Lac de la Palisse, D160.
GPS: n44,78041 e4,10356.
6 € 9,40 Ch (4x) included.
Location: Rural. **Surface:** gravel. 01/01-31/12.
Remarks: Mandatory, one-time fee Pass'Etapes € 4.

Die 25D2

Aire de Meyrosse, Avenue du Maréchal Leclerc, D238.
GPS: n44,75103 e5,37385.

30 € 5/24h ChWCfree.
Surface: grassy/gravel. 01/01-31/12.
Distance: 300m 300m 1km.
Remarks: Max. 1 night, pay at Police Municipale.

Diou 22B2

Camping du Gué de Loire, Chemin de la Procession.
GPS: n46,53523 e3,74401.

3 free Ch free. **Location:** Rural, simple. **Surface:** grassy.
01/01-31/12.
Distance: 900m.

Doizieux 25C1

Au bon air des chirats, Le Châtelard. **GPS**: n45,44239 e4,63307.
2 free € 2 € 5. **Location:** Rural. **Surface:** grassy.
01/01-31/12.
Distance: 5km 350m on the spot.

Dompierre-sur-Besbre 22A2

Les Gauffroux. **GPS**: n46,51822 e3,68469.

7 free Ch WCfree. **Location:** Simple. **Surface:** gravel.
01/01-31/12.
Distance: on the spot 300m 200m.

Donzère 25C3

Aire de respos de Combelonge, RN 7.
GPS: n44,44060 e4,71899.

15 free ChWCfree. **Surface:** asphalted. 01/01-31/12.
Distance: 500m 7km.
Remarks: Near RN7.

Drugeac 24G1

Aire de camping-cars, La Gare SNCF. **GPS**: n45,16694 e2,38667.

4 free € 2/100liter Ch € 2/1h.
Location: Rural, simple, quiet. **Surface:** asphalted.
01/01-31/12 service: 01/11-01/05.
Distance: 100m 100m 100m.
Remarks: At former station, now start Vélorail.

Ebreuil 21H2

Parking du Stade, D915. **GPS**: n46,10954 e3,07606.

10 free. **Location:** Simple. **Surface:** gravel. 01/01-31/12.
Distance: 6,5km 2km.
Remarks: In front of campsite municipal, service 500m.

Ebreuil 21H2

Chemin des Nières. **GPS**: n46,11083 e3,08111.
1 Chfree. 01/01-31/12.
Distance: 900.
Remarks: Overnight stay on Parking du Stade.

Estivareilles 21H2

Salle Polyvalente, Rue de la République.
GPS: n46,42471 e2,61529.

20 free Chfree. **Location:** Urban, simple. **Surface:** gravel.
01/01-31/12.
Distance: on the spot 9km 200m bakery 200m.

Eyzin-Pinet 25C1

Rue du Stade. **GPS**: n45,47463 e4,99965.

6 free Chfree. **Location:** Rural, simple, central, quiet.
Surface: gravel. 01/01-31/12.
Distance: 50m 50m 20m on the spot on the spot.

Faverges 22E3

Route d'Annecy, D2508. **GPS**: n45,74943 e6,28626.

20 free Chfree. **Location:** Rural, simple, noisy.
Surface: gravel. 01/01-31/12 Service: winter.
Distance: 800m 800m on the spot 100m 100m.
Remarks: Max. 48h, market Wednesday.

Faverolles 25A2

Place de la mairie, Le Bourg, D248. **GPS**: n44,93906 e3,14756.

4 free € 2/10minutes Ch € 2/55minutes.
Location: Urban, simple. **Surface:** gravel/metalled.
01/01-31/12.
Distance: 200m 200m on the spot.

Flaine 22F3

Parking P1, Flaine, 74300 Magland. **GPS**: n46,00377 e6,69083.

FR

25 € 5. **Surface:** gravel. 01/01-31/12.
Distance: 200m on the spot.
Remarks: Parking at skipistes.

S Fontanes 25C1

Fontanès, 42140. **GPS**: n45,54681 e4,44027.

3 free Chfree. **Location:** Rural, simple, quiet.
Surface: asphalted. 01/01-31/12.
Distance: 500m 13km 400m.
Remarks: At tennis-courts, inclining pitches.

S Gervans 25C2

Place des Amandiers, Rue de l'école. **GPS**: n45,10932 e4,83031.

4 free Chfree. **Location:** Simple. **Surface:** gravel.
Distance: on the spot on the spot on the spot.
Remarks: Max. 24h, no camping activities.

S Grane 25C2

Domaine Distaise, 95 Distaise, 26400 Grane.
GPS: n44,75564 e4,86768.

15 € 4 € 1 included. **Surface:** grassy. 01/01-31/12.
Distance: on the spot.

S Gresse-en-Vercors 25D2

Gresse-en-Vercors, 38650. **GPS**: n44,89184 e5,54766.

free Ch. **Surface:** gravel.
Distance: on the spot.
Remarks: Max. 24h, service on campsite.

S Hauteluce 22F3

Du Grand Tetras, Les Saisies, 1634, route du Mont Bisanne.
GPS: n45,74782 e6,53491.
50 € 16-19 + € 0,50/pp tourist tax Ch included,10Amp against payment. **Location:** Rural. **Surface:** metalled.
01/01-31/12.
Distance: Les Saisies 2km on the spot.

S Hauteluce 22F3

Parking de la Fôret, Tetras, D123. **GPS**: n45,74633 e6,53441.

5 free € 2 Ch € 2 .
Surface: gravel. 01/01-31/12.
Distance: 3km 3km 3km.

S Hauteluce 22F3

Parking Du Col des Saisies, Hauteluce 73620.
GPS: n45,76297 e6,53382.

40 € 8 € 2/10minutes Ch€ 2 € 2 WC.
Location: Rural. **Surface:** asphalted. 01/01-31/12.
Distance: 500m 400m 500m skibus (winter) 200m 200m.

S Hauterives 25C1

D538. **GPS**: n45,25497 e5,03022.

free, 01/04-31/10 € 5/24h € 3/50liter ChWC.
Location: Rural, simple. **Surface:** gravel.
Distance: 250m 250m.

Tourist information Hauterives:
Palais Idéal du Facteur Cheval.

S Hotonnes 22D3

Les Plans d'Hotonnes, D39B. **GPS**: n46,03857 e5,70023.
1 free € 1 ChWC. **Location:** Rural. **Surface:** asphalted.
01/01-31/12.
Distance: 200m.

S Illiat 22C2

Illiat 01140. **GPS**: n46,18495 e4,88802.

4 free ChWCfree. **Location:** Rural, simple, quiet.
Surface: gravel. 01/01-31/12.
Distance: 650m 200m 200m 350m on the spot on the spot.
Remarks: At small lake.

S Issoire 25A1

Boulevard André Malraux. **GPS**: n45,54521 e3,24107.

10 free € 2/100liter Ch. **Location:** Simple, quiet.
Surface: gravel/metalled. 01/01-31/12.
Distance: 300m 300m 100m on the spot.
Remarks: Max. 7 days.

S Izernore 22D2

Rue de l'Oignin. **GPS**: n46,21847 e5,55041.

8 free Chfree.
Location: Rural, simple, central, quiet.
Surface: gravel.
01/01-31/12 service 01/11-31/03.
Distance: on the spot 6km 500m 500m 500m 500m.
Remarks: On the foot of the Monts Berthiand.

S Jaligny-sur-Besbre 22A2

Rue de la Chaume. **GPS**: n46,38155 e3,59147.

5 free Ch (5x)free. **Location:** Rural, simple, quiet.
Surface: gravel. 01/01-31/12.
Distance: 200m on the spot on the spot 250m 250m.
Remarks: Along the Besbre river.

S Job 22A3

25 Route de Chansert, D255. **GPS**: n45,62019 e3,74502.

10 free Chfree. **Location:** Rural, simple, quiet.
Surface: gravel. 01/01-31/12.
Distance: 500m 500m on the spot on the spot.
Remarks: Playground.

S Joux 22B3

Salle des Fêtes, La Noirie, D79. **GPS**: n45,88869 e4,37587.

10 free Chfree. **Location:** Rural. **Surface:** asphalted.
01/01-31/12 water disconnected in winter.
Distance: 200m 3,2km 200m 200m.

Remarks: Nearby castle garden.

La Balme de Sillingy 22E3

Aire de Camping-cars Domaine du Tornet.
GPS: n45,97124 e6,03135.

20 €6 Ch included. **Location:** Rural, simple, central, noisy. **Surface:** gravel. 01/04-31/10.
Distance: 100m (fishing permit available) 100m on the spot.
Remarks: Recreation park, max. 48h.

La Bénisson-Dieu 22B2

Parking de l'école, Rue des Comtes du Forez.
GPS: n46,15094 e4,04708.

2 free. **Location:** Rural, simple, central, quiet. **Surface:** gravel.
01/01-31/12.
Distance: on the spot 200m.

La Bourboule 24H1

Chemin de la Suchére. **GPS**: n45,58572 e2,73489.

10 free €5 Ch. **Location:** Simple, quiet.
Surface: metalled. 01/01-31/12.
Distance: 500m 500m.
Remarks: Max. 48h.

La Bourboule 24H1

Plateau de Charlannes. **GPS**: n45,57811 e2,73513.

10 free. **Location:** Rural, simple, quiet. **Surface:** asphalted.
01/01-31/12.
Distance: 6,5km 350m on the spot on the spot.
Remarks: Parking at funicular railway.

La Chaise-Dieu 25A1

Esplanade de la Gare. **GPS**: n45,31682 e3,69694.

8 free €2 Ch. **Location:** Urban, simple, quiet.

Surface: gravel/sand. 01/04-31/10.
Distance: 500m on the spot.
Remarks: Coins at shops and tourist office.

La Chambre 25E1

Place du champ de foire. **GPS**: n45,36287 e6,29730.
9 free Ch . **Surface:** metalled. 01/01-31/12.
Distance: 300m 400m 100m on the spot on the spot.
Remarks: Max. 72h.

La Chapelle-Laurent 25A1

Aire camping-cars, D10. **GPS**: n45,18028 e3,24389.

20 free voluntary contribution Ch free.
Location: Rural, simple, quiet. **Surface:** grassy.
01/01-31/12 service: 15/11-31/03.
Distance: 50m nearby 100m 100m on the spot on the spot.

La Clusaz 22F3

Route des Confins. **GPS**: n45,92298 e6,48380.
free. **Surface:** asphalted. 01/01-31/12.
Distance: 800m on the spot.
Remarks: Parking at pistes.

La Féclaz 22E3

Aire Camping-cars de la Féclaz, Les Déserts.
GPS: n45,64210 e5,98411.

40 €4 €1,50 Ch €1,50. **Surface:** asphalted.
01/01-31/12.
Distance: on the spot 300m 600m 300m on the spot.

La Mure 25E2

Sur les bords de Jonche, Boulevard Fréjus-Michon.
GPS: n44,90617 e5,78301.
7 €8 Ch WC. **Location:** Urban. **Surface:** asphalted.
15/04-15/11.
Distance: on the spot 150m 400m.
Remarks: Max. 72h, picnic area.

La Roche-Blanche 22A3

Les Trolières, La Pigné Sud, Route des Fours à Chaux.
GPS: n45,71567 e3,14790.

100 €6 €2/100liter Ch (4x)€2/6h.
Location: Rural, simple, isolated, quiet. **Surface:** grassy.
01/03-30/11.
Distance: 1,1km.
Remarks: Max. 48h.

La Roche-de-Glun 25C2

Camping-Car Park, Rue de Crussol. **GPS**: n45,00921 e4,84583.
41 €10,60-11,80 Ch (20x) included.
Surface: grassy/gravel. 01/01-31/12.
Remarks: Mandatory, one-time fee Pass'Etapes €4.

La Tour-d'Auvergne 24H1

7 Route de Clermont. **GPS**: n45,53290 e2,68213.

25 free €2/100liter Ch €2. **Location:** Simple, quiet.
Surface: metalled. 01/01-31/12.
Distance: on the spot 650m 650m bakery.

Lablachère 25B3

La Ferme Théâtre, D104, Notre Dame. **GPS**: n44,45481 e4,22004.

20 €5/24h €2 €3/12h.
Location: Rural. **Surface:** gravel.
01/01-31/12.
Distance: 1km 150m.
Remarks: Max. 24h, theater, regional products.

Lacapelle-Viescamp 24G2

Aire camping-cars, D18. **GPS**: n44,92167 e2,26361.

5 free €3/100liter Ch €3/1h. **Location:** Rural, simple.
Surface: metalled. 01/01-31/12.
Distance: 100m 100m on the spot.
Remarks: Coins available at the shop.

Lachamp-Raphaël 25B2

D122, Le Village. **GPS**: n44,81133 e4,28860.

5 free €2 Ch.
Location: Rural, simple, quiet. **Surface:** gravel.
01/01-31/12.
Distance: 300m 300m Bread 300m departure Nordic.
Remarks: Altitude 1330m, coins at bar/hotel, beautiful view.

Lagorce 25B3

Le Sainte Anne, Leyris. **GPS**: n44,49581 e4,42190.
free. 01/01-31/12.

Lalouvesc 25C2

Vallon d'Or, Sainte Agathe. **GPS**: n45,11947 e4,53384.

3 free WC. **Location:** Simple, central. **Surface:** asphalted.

FR

01/01-31/12.
Distance: on the spot 100m 100m.

Lalouvesc — 25C2

La Fontaine. **GPS**: n45,12149 e4,53393.
€ 2/15minutes Ch € 2.
15/05-15/10.
Remarks: Coins at petrol station and camping municipal.

Lamastre — 25C2

Parking Pont de Tain, Place Pradon. **GPS**: n44,98672 e4,58001.

20 free € 4,40/100liter Ch € 2,50/1h. **Location:** Simple. **Surface:** asphalted. 01/01-31/12.
Distance: on the spot on the spot on the spot.
Remarks: Coins at tourist info.

Lamure-sur-Azergues — 22C3

Quartier Neuf. **GPS**: n46,06120 e4,49185.

10 free € 2 Ch € 2 WC.
Location: Rural, simple. **Surface:** asphalted.
01/01-31/12.
Distance: on the spot 100m 100m train/bus on the spot.
Remarks: Near train station.

Lanarce — 25B2

Camping Municipal. **GPS**: n44,72578 e4,00403.
free, 15/06-15/09 € 10 Ch € 3 WC included.
Surface: grassy. 01/01-31/12 Service: winter.
Distance: 700m on the spot on the spot 700m.
Remarks: Beside river.

Lans-en-Vercors — 25D2

La Sierre. **GPS**: n45,11628 e5,60966.
3 free € 4 Ch WC. **Location:** Rural. **Surface:** sand.
01/01-31/12.
Distance: 5km on the spot on the spot.
Remarks: At ski-lift.

Lans-en-Vercors — 25D2

Route de l'Aigle. **GPS**: n45,12418 e5,59125.

30 free Ch WC free. **Location:** Rural, simple. **Surface:** gravel.
01/01-31/12.
Distance: 500m on the spot.
Remarks: Large parking, tuesday and Saturday market.

Lapalisse — 22A2

Place Jean Moulin, RN7 dir Roanne. **GPS**: n46,25000 e3,63500.

50 free Ch WC. **Location:** Urban, simple, central, quiet.
Surface: asphalted. 01/01-31/12.
Distance: 300m on the spot on the spot on the spot.
Remarks: Coins at tourist info.

Laprugne — 22A3

Domaine La Bourbonnaise, D477. **GPS**: n45,98661 e3,74569.

free. **Surface:** asphalted. 01/01-31/12.
Distance: 200m on the spot.

Lapte — 25B1

Rue du Docteur Tassy, Chamdappe. **GPS**: n45,18419 e4,21363.
free € 2 Ch. **Surface:** gravel. 01/01-31/12.
Distance: 150m.
Remarks: Max. 48h.

Laqueuille — 21H3

Place de Foirail, Le Bourg. **GPS**: n45,65008 e2,73289.

2 free € 2/10minutes Ch € 4/8h. **Location:** Simple, quiet. **Surface:** asphalted. 01/01-31/12.
Distance: 100m 100m.

Lathuile — 22E3

Les Jardin du Tailleter, 190 route de la Porte, Bout du lac, N 508.
GPS: n45,79480 e6,20796.

24 € 8 Ch included (24x)€ 2. **Location:** Rural, simple. **Surface:** grassy. 01/06-31/08.
Distance: Lake of Annecy 750m.
Remarks: Max. 24h.

Lavaudieu — 25A1

Le Bourg. **GPS**: n45,26297 e3,45606.

+10 free. **Location:** Simple, isolated, quiet. **Surface:** grassy/gravel.
01/01-31/12.
Distance: 200m on the spot on the spot on the spot.

Le Bessat — 25C1

Croix de Chaubouret. **GPS**: n45,36812 e4,52768.

4 free € 2,50/20minutes Ch (4x)€ 2,50/6h.
Location: Rural. **Surface:** asphalted.
01/01-31/12.
Distance: 1km 100m mountainbike trail on the spot on the spot.
Remarks: Altitude 1200m, coins at Chalet des Alpes and the shops.

Le Breuil-sur-Couze — 25A1

Allée de Treize Vents. **GPS**: n45,46867 e3,26121.

8 free Ch free. **Location:** Urban, simple. **Surface:** gravel.
01/01-31/12.
Distance: 900m 800m.
Remarks: Along railwayline.

Le Cheix-sur-Morge — 22A3

D425. **GPS**: n45,95138 e3,17812.

6 free Ch free. **Location:** Rural, simple, isolated, quiet.
Surface: gravel. 01/01-31/12 water disconnected in winter.
Distance: 500m 950m on the spot.
Remarks: Max. 48h.

Le Cheylard — 25C2

Super U, Chemin du pre-jalla, ZI la Palisse.
GPS: n44,91143 e4,44162.

20 free € 2 Ch € 2. **Location:** Simple, noisy.
Surface: asphalted. 01/01-31/12.
Distance: on the spot on the spot.
Remarks: Max. 24h.

Le Cheylas — 25E1

Avenue de la Libération. **GPS**: n45,37170 e5,99014.
5 free Ch WC free. **Surface:** asphalted/metalled.
Distance: on the spot 50m.

Le Crozet — 22B2

Les Minières, Le Bourg. **GPS**: n46,16934 e3,85727.

FR

2 free € 2/30minutes € 2/4h. **Location:** Rural, simple.
Surface: metalled. 01/01-31/12.
Distance: 150m.

Le Grand Bornand 22F3

164 Route de La Broderie. **GPS:** n45,94144 e6,43636.

10 free. **Surface:** metalled. 01/01-31/12.
Distance: 600m 250m on the spot on the spot.
Remarks: Max. 48h.

Le Lac d'Issarlès 25B2

D16. **GPS:** n44,81948 e4,06156.

24 € 11 + € 0,25/pp tourist tax Ch WC included.
Location: Central. **Surface:** metalled.
15/04-01/11.
Distance: 100m 100m 100m.
Remarks: Attention: this town is not Issarlès!.

Le Monastier-sur-Gazeille 25B2

Rue Augustin Ollier. **GPS:** n44,93720 e3,99250.

10 free € 2/5minutes Ch. **Location:** Rural, simple, quiet.
Surface: gravel. 01/03-31/10.
Distance: 300m 300m 500m on the spot.

Le Monestier 25A1

D39. **GPS:** n45,56364 e3,66088.

10 free Chfree. **Location:** Rural, simple, quiet.
Surface: gravel. 01/01-31/12.
Distance: 300m 300m on the spot on the spot.

Le Puy-en-Velay 25B2

Camping-Car Park, Place Maréchal Leclerc.
GPS: n45,04489 e3,89498.

26 € 11,90-31,10 Ch (26x) included.
Location: Urban, comfortable, central, quiet. **Surface:** asphalted.
01/01-31/12.
Distance: 1km 1km 2km 300m.
Remarks: Mandatory, one-time fee Pass'Etapes € 4.

Le Puy-en-Velay 25B2

Boulevard de Cluny. **GPS:** n45,04963 e3,88976.
€ 2 Ch.

Le Reposoir 22F3

Route Departementale D204. **GPS:** n46,01010 e6,53648.

10 free Chfree WC.
Surface: metalled. 01/01-31/12.
Distance: 150m 250m on the spot.

Le Teil 25C3

Alleé Paul Avon. **GPS:** n44,55138 e4,68972.

6 free Chfree.
Location: Noisy. **Surface:** grassy/metalled.
Distance: on the spot on the spot 500m.
Remarks: Nearby D86.

Tourist information Le Teil:
Thu morning.

Le Vernet 25A2

Place de l'étang, D48. **GPS:** n45,03560 e3,66952.

14 € 3 Chincluded (14x)€ 3/night.
Location: Rural, simple, isolated, quiet. **Surface:** grassy/sand.
01/01-31/12 service: 01/11-30/04.
Distance: 50m on the spot on the spot.
Remarks: Max. 72h.

Lélex 22E2

Chemin Frênet. **GPS:** n46,29932 e5,93140.
8 free € 5 Ch € 8/24h. **Surface:** metalled.
01/01-31/12.
Distance: 650m 650m 650m on the spot on the spot 650m.
Remarks: At tennis-courts, max. 1 week.

Les Carroz-Arâches 22F3

Télécabine Les Cluses, 595 Route de la Télécabine.
GPS: n46,02500 e6,64361.

15 € 4,50 included Ch. 01/06-30/11.
Distance: 500m 500m.
Remarks: Parking funicular railway.

Les Deux-Alpes 25E2

Avenue de la Muzelle, D213. **GPS:** n45,02394 e6,12120.
20 € 12 Ch included. **Surface:** asphalted. winter.
Remarks: Beautiful view.

Les Estables 25B2

Foirail de la Mézine, Le Bourg. **GPS:** n44,90231 e4,15679.

8 free ChWC free.
Location: Rural, simple. **Surface:** asphalted.
01/01-31/12.
Distance: 50m 50m on the spot 500m on the spot.
Remarks: Service at petrol station, free wifi, code at tourist info.

Les Gets 22F2

Parking des Perrières, Route du Front de Neige.
GPS: n46,14952 e6,65719.

20 € 0,90/pp tourist tax, winter € 17 Ch.
Surface: gravel. 11/06-11/09 and 17/12-15/04.
Distance: 1km on the spot.
Remarks: Max. 7 days, bus to centre every 30 minutes.

Tourist information Les Gets:
Week market. Thu-morning.

Les Granges-Gontardes 25C3

Domaine de la Tour d'Elyssas, Quartier Combe d'Elissas.
GPS: n44,41811 e4,75465.

8 free Ch free. **Surface:** gravel. 01/01-31/12.
Distance: 9km.
Remarks: At wine-grower, max. 48h.

Les Houches 22F3

Aire d'accueil camping-car Mont Blanc, 556 route du Pont.
GPS: n45,89257 e6,81706.
22 € 16,50 + € 0,75 tourist tax Ch included.
Location: Comfortable, isolated, quiet. **Surface:** gravel.
01/04-30/11.
Distance: 2,5km 1km 1km 500m.

Les Karellis 25F1

D81B. **GPS:** n45,22756 e6,40907.
free. **Surface:** asphalted. 01/01-31/12.

FR

Distance: 600m 600m 600m.
Remarks: Mountain station nearby St.Jean-de-Maurienne.

S Les Menuires 25F1

Les Bruyères, Dir Val Thorens. **GPS**: n45,32557 e6,53414.
70 € 10/24h + € 0,20/pp tourist tax Ch (7x)€ 2/4h WC.
Surface: asphalted.
10/12-22/04 and 08/07-01/09.
Distance: on the spot on the spot on the spot on the spot.
Remarks: Near the pistes.

S Les Noës 22B3

Le Bourg, D47. **GPS**: n46,04083 e3,85206.

5 free ChWCfree. **Location:** Rural, simple, quiet.
Surface: gravel. 01/01-31/12.
Distance: on the spot 50m on the spot.

S Les Salles 22B3

Domaine de la Plagnette, La Plagnette. **GPS**: n45,84395 e3,81967.
free Ch. **Location:** Rural. **Surface:** gravel.
01/01-31/12.
Distance: on the spot.

S Les Sauvages 22B3

Les Sauvages, 69170. **GPS**: n45,92083 e4,37711.

5 free Chfree. **Location:** Rural, simple, quiet.
Surface: gravel. 01/01-31/12.
Distance: on the spot 100m 100m on the spot.

S Lezoux 22A3

Parking Musée départemental de la Céramique, Rue de la République. **GPS**: n45,82686 e3,38459.

25 free ChWCfree.
Location: Comfortable, central, quiet. **Surface:** gravel.
01/01-31/12 water: 01/11-31/03.
Distance: 500m 3,5km 500m 500m.

S Lurcy-Lévis 21H1

Plan d'eau des Sézeaux, Rue de Fontgroix.
GPS: n46,73797 e2,93863.

6 free € 3/100liter Ch € 3/55minutes WC.
Location: Rural, comfortable, quiet. **Surface:** grassy/gravel.
01/01-31/12.
Distance: 800m Small lake on the spot 800m 800m.
Remarks: Coins at cafe, in front of the church.

S Lus-la-Croix-Haute 25D2

D 505. **GPS**: n44,66712 e5,70800.
6 free ChWCfree. **Surface:** metalled. 01/01-31/12.
Distance: 500m on the spot on the spot.
Remarks: At fire-station, tenniscourt.

S Mâcot-la-Plagne 25F1

Caravaneige de Plagne Villages. **GPS**: n45,50510 e6,68870.
40 € 22 Ch included. **Surface:** asphalted.
01/01-31/12.
Distance: 300m on the spot.
Remarks: Video surveillance.

S Mandailles-Saint-Julien 24H2

Le Mas, D17. **GPS**: n45,06916 e2,65611.

5 free € 3,50 Ch. **Location:** Rural, simple, quiet.
Surface: metalled. 01/01-31/12 service: 30/09-01/05.
Distance: 200m 200m 200m on the spot.
Remarks: Max. 24h, coins at restaurants.

S Manzat 21H3

Place du 14 Juillet. **GPS**: n45,96180 e2,93883.

20 free Chfree. **Location:** Rural, simple, quiet.
Surface: unpaved. 01/01-31/12.
Distance: on the spot 5,6km 250m 200m.
Remarks: In front of police station.

S Marcolès 24G2

Aire camping-cars, 6 D66 15220 Marcolès.
GPS: n44,78028 e2,35389.

5 free Chfree. **Location:** Rural, simple, quiet.
Surface: gravel. 01/01-31/12 service 01/11-31/03.
Distance: 100m 100m 100m.
Remarks: Artists village.

S Marsanne 25C3

Avenue de Bailliencourt, D57. **GPS**: n44,64568 e4,87175.

5 free Chfree. **Location:** Rural, quiet. **Surface:** grassy.
01/01-31/12.
Distance: 300m 300m nearby.
Remarks: Max. 48h, medieval village.

S Massiac 25A1

Aire du Bouclier Arverne, Rue Jacques Chaban Delmas.
GPS: n45,25364 e3,19376.

8 free Chfree. **Location:** Urban, simple, quiet.
Surface: asphalted. 01/01-31/12.
Distance: 350m 400m 400m on the spot.

Massiac 25A1

Aire de Massiac, Rue Jacques Chaban Delmas.
GPS: n45,25267 e3,19433.

8 free. **Location:** Rural, simple, quiet. **Surface:** grassy.
01/01-31/12.
Distance: 400m 1,4km on the spot on the spot 400m 400m 200m on the spot.

S Mauriac 24G1

Aire camping-cars, Rue du Val Saint Jean.
GPS: n45,21863 e2,32183.

10 free € 2/100liter Ch € 2/1h.
Location: Rural, simple, quiet. **Surface:** metalled. 01/01-31/12.
Distance: 1km beach 300m 1,2km 1,2km.

S Maurs 24G2

Maurs La Jolie, Route de Quezac. **GPS**: n44,71442 e2,19615.

5 free € 2/100liter Chfree € 2/1h.
Location: Urban, simple, central, quiet. **Surface:** asphalted.
01/01-31/12.
Distance: 300m 300m 300m 300m.
Remarks: Coins at Papetterie and tourist office.

Megève 22F3

Chemin des Ânes. **GPS**: n45,86401 e6,62010.
free. 01/01-31/12.
Remarks: In front of parking Télécabine du Jaillet.

S Messeix 21H3

28 Rue des Lilas. **GPS**: n45,61576 e2,55621.

FR

6 free € 2/10minutes Ch € 2/55minutes.
Location: Urban, simple, quiet. **Surface:** asphalted.
01/01-31/12.
Distance: 500m 18km 1,7km on the spot.
Remarks: Coins at the shops.

S Meyras 25B2

Grande rue, D26. **GPS:** n44,67939 e4,26847.

15 € 4/48h € 4/100liter Ch € 4/5kWh.
Surface: asphalted. 01/04-31/10.
Distance: 200m 200m 200m.
Remarks: Max. 48h, coins at the shops in the village.

S Mijoux 22E2

D50, Route de la Combe-en-Haut. **GPS:** n46,36963 e6,00247.

20 free € 3,50 Ch € 3,50.
Surface: gravel. 01/01-31/12 Service: winter.
Distance: 500m 500m 500m on the spot on the spot.
Remarks: Coins at town hall and supermarket.

S Mirabel-aux-Baronnies 25D3

Aire camping-cars, Chemin des Grottes. **GPS:** n44,31260 e5,09968.

7+10 voluntary contribution Chfree.
Location: Rural. **Surface:** grassy/metalled. 01/01-31/12.
Distance: 200m.

S Molinet 22B2

Canal Lateral à la Loire, D779. **GPS:** n46,47190 e3,93960.

12 free € 2 Ch€ 2 € 6/h.
Surface: grasstiles. 01/01-31/12.
Distance: 1km on the spot.

S Montalieu-Vercieu 22D3

Chamboud. **GPS:** n45,82776 e5,42100.

6 free ChWCcampsite. **Location:** Rural, simple, isolated, quiet. **Surface:** asphalted.
Distance: 2km 2km 2km 1,5km.
Remarks: Next to campsite/Base de Loisirs de la Vallée Bleue, max. 2 nights.

S Montbrison-sur-Lez 25C3

Place Publique. **GPS:** n44,43663 e5,01779.

4 free free. **Surface:** metalled. 01/01-31/12.
Distance: 100m 100m 100m.

S Montbrison-sur-Lez 25C3

Quartier le Chatelard. **GPS:** n44,42751 e5,02438.

6 € 5 € 2/60liter Ch € 2. **Location:** Isolated.
Surface: gravel/metalled. 01/01-31/12.
Remarks: Coins at bar and garage.

Montbrun-les-Bains 28D1

Toscan. **GPS:** n44,17247 e5,43881.

10 free.
Location: Rural, quiet. **Surface:** grassy. 01/01-31/12.
Distance: 500m 300m 400m on the spot 400m Tour de la Citadelle.

S Montbrun-les-Bains 28D1

588 Condamine. **GPS:** n44,17413 e5,44071.
€ 2 Chfree € 2. 01/01-31/12.

S Montélimar 25C3

Domaine du Bois de Laud, Chemin du Bois de Laud.
GPS: n44,56522 e4,75691.

17 € 4,30 Chincluded. **Location:** Urban.
Surface: grassy/metalled. 01/01-31/12.
Distance: 500m 100m.
Remarks: Near centre commercial Leclerc, max. 48h.

S Montluçon 21H2

Route de l'Etang de Sault, Prémilhat. **GPS:** n46,33469 e2,55855.

8 free € 5/150liter Ch (6x)€ 2,50/10h.
Location: Rural, comfortable. **Surface:** gravel. 01/01-31/12.
Distance: 5km Montluçon 2,6km 150m 150m 500m on the spot.
Remarks: Max. 72h.

S Montluçon 21H2

Place de la Fraternité, 6 Place de la Fraternité.
GPS: n46,35535 e2,58686.

15 free € 5/150liter Chfree € 2,50/10minutes WC.
Location: Urban, simple, noisy.
Surface: asphalted.
01/01-31/12 water: Nov-March.
Distance: on the spot A71 16km 450m 150m on the spot.
Remarks: Thu-morning closed because of market (6-15h).

S Montmurat 24G2

Aire camping-cars, Le Bourg, D345. **GPS:** n44,62811 e2,19804.

10 free € 1 Ch. **Location:** Rural, simple, isolated, quiet.
Surface: gravel. 01/01-31/12.
Distance: on the spot.

S Montoldre 22A2

1851 D268, 03150 Montoldre. **GPS:** n46,33272 e3,44727.

7 free € 2/100liter Chfree. **Location:** Rural, simple, quiet.
Surface: asphalted. 01/01-31/12.
Distance: centre 300m.
Remarks: In front of town hall.

S Montpeyroux 22A3

D797C, Rue De l'Hume. **GPS:** n45,62373 e3,19911.

+10 free € 2,50 Ch € 2,50/1h. **Location:** Rural, simple,

FR

quiet. **Surface:** gravel. 01/01-31/12.
Distance: 100m 200m 200m on the spot.
Remarks: Coins at the shops in the village.

Tourist information Montpeyroux:
Small town with wine-cellar Cave de Montpeyroux. Mo/Sa 8.30-12.30h, 14-18/19h, Su 10.30-12h, 16-19h.

Montsalvy 24G2

Route de Junhac. **GPS**: n44,70778 e2,49667.

11 free € 2 Ch € 2 WC € 1. **Location:** Rural, comfortable, quiet. **Surface:** asphalted. 01/01-31/12.
Distance: 400m 400m 400m.

Morillon 22F3

GPS: n46,08291 e6,68124.
20 free Ch WC free. **Surface:** asphalted. 01/01-31/12.
Distance: 200m 100m 300m 100m.

Moulins 22A2

Flot Bleu Park, Chemin de Halage. **GPS**: n46,55852 e3,32491.

92 € 0,10/h € 2 Ch € 2 (12x) € 2/4h.
Location: Urban, comfortable, central, quiet.
Surface: grassy/metalled. 01/01-31/12.
Distance: city centre 1km 100m 300m on the spot.

Murat 24H2

Avenue du Dr Louis Mallet. **GPS**: n45,10912 e2,86728.

8 free € 2/10minutes Ch € 2/1h WC.
Location: Urban, simple, central, noisy. **Surface:** asphalted.
01/01-31/12.
Distance: 300m 100m 1,5km 100m on the spot.
Remarks: Coins at tourist info, marked pitches in the back of de parking.

Tourist information Murat:
Fri-morning.

Murat-le-Quaire 21H3

Camping-Car Park Les Rives du Lac, Route de la Banne d'Ordanche.
GPS: n45,60274 e2,73797.

37 € 10,70/24h Ch (32x) included.
Location: Rural, comfortable, quiet. **Surface:** grassy/metalled.
01/01-31/12.
Distance: 1,2km 12km 100m 100m day pass available on the spot on the spot 100m 5km.

Remarks: Mandatory, one-time fee Pass'Etapes € 4.

Murol 24H1

Domaine du lac Chambon, Plage Est. **GPS**: n45,57158 e2,92959.
15 € 10 Ch (15x)included. **Surface:** grassy.
20/04-01/09.
Distance: 100m.
Remarks: Entrance code available at campsite.

Nantua 22D2

Aire de service du Lac de Nantua, Route de Port, D74.
GPS: n46,15497 e5,59656.

13 € 8, tourist tax € 0,20/pp Ch WC included.
Location: Urban, comfortable, central. **Surface:** gravel.
01/04-30/10.
Distance: 700m 7km on the spot on the spot 150m 150m on the spot on the spot.
Remarks: At Nantua lake.

Naucelles 24G2

Aire camping-cars, Rue du Terrou. **GPS**: n44,95694 e2,41757.

5 free € 3,50/100liter Ch € 3,50/1h. **Location:** Urban, simple, quiet. **Surface:** asphalted. 01/01-31/12.
Distance: Spar 300m.
Remarks: Coins at supermarket in the village.

Néris-les-Bains 21H2

Camping du Lac, Avenue Marrx Dormoy, D155.
GPS: n46,28673 e2,65235.

6 € 8 Ch (6x)WC included € 1,50/h.
Location: Urban, comfortable. **Surface:** gravel. 01/03-31/10.
Distance: 500m 12km bakery 500m.
Remarks: Max. 3 nights, to be paid at campsite.

Neussargues-Moissac 24H1

Allée des Peupliers. **GPS**: n45,13438 e2,98130.

5 free € 2/100liter Ch € 2/2h WC.
Location: Rural, comfortable, quiet. **Surface:** gravel.
01/01-31/12 water disconnected in winter.
Distance: 300m 50m 300m on the spot on the spot.
Remarks: Coins at town hall and restaurant.

Neuvéglise 24H2

Le Bourg. **GPS**: n44,92924 e2,98344.
3 free Ch free. **Location:** Urban, simple, central.

Surface: asphalted. 01/01-31/12.
Distance: on the spot 100m 200m.

Noailly 22B2

Parking Maison du Temps Libre. **GPS**: n46,13656 e4,01157.

3 free. **Location:** Simple, quiet. **Surface:** asphalted.
01/01-31/12.
Distance: on the spot 200m.

Noirétable 21H3

Aire d'accueil de camping-cars, Lieu-dit La Roche.
GPS: n45,80739 e3,00000.

7 free € 3 Ch € 1/2h. **Location:** Simple, quiet.
Surface: metalled. 01/01-31/12.
Distance: 800m 100m 100m 100m 800m on the spot on the spot on the spot.
Remarks: Next to campsite (50m), coins at campsite.

Nyons 25D3

Promenade de la Digue. **GPS**: n44,35778 e5,13861.

20 € 10/24h Ch WC included. **Location:** Noisy.
Surface: gravel. 01/01-31/12.
Distance: 250m 250m 250m 250m.
Remarks: Next to Parc loisirs aquatique, max. 48h.

Nyons 25D3

Domaine Rocheville, Route de Montélimar, RD538.
GPS: n44,36850 e5,11775.

6 € 7, tourist tax € 0,20/pp € 4/100liter Ch € 4 WC € 1,summer included. **Surface:** grassy. 01/01-31/12.
Distance: city centre 2km on the spot.
Remarks: Regional products.

Tourist information Nyons:
Pavillon du Tourisme, Place de la Libération. Important Olive-city in the Provence.
Musée de l'Olivier, Espace Vignolis. Museum about the olive-tree and production of olive oil. daily 01/11-28/02 Su.
Centre-ville. Regional market. Thu-morning.

Orcines 21H3

Route de Limoges, D941B. **GPS**: n45,78838 e3,01114.
51 € 8, 01/10-30/04 € 6 € 2/100liter Ch € 2/4h.
Location: Simple, noisy. 01/01-31/12.
Distance: on the spot.

Remarks: Next to sports fields.

Orcines 21H3

Route du Puy de Dôme, D68. **GPS**: n45,76958 e2,98624.

10 free Ch WC free.
Location: Rural, simple, isolated, quiet. **Surface:** asphalted.
01/01-31/12 Service: winter.
Distance: on the spot.

Orcines 21H3

D941. **GPS**: n45,80394 e2,98726.

10 free. **Location:** Simple, noisy. **Surface:** metalled.
01/01-31/12.
Distance: on the spot.

Orgnac l'Aven 25B3

Le Fez, D217. **GPS**: n44,30419 e4,43240.

5 free Ch free. **Location:** Rural. **Surface:** gravel.
01/01-31/12.
Distance: 200m 50m 300m.
Remarks: Caves of Aven d'Orgnac 2km.

Panissières 22B3

Ferme Seigne, Rue des Lauriers. **GPS**: n45,78835 e4,34355.

4 € 7 Ch included4 WC use sanitary € 3,60/pp.
Location: Rural, simple, quiet. **Surface:** metalled.
01/01-31/12 Service: winter.
Distance: 300m 300m 300m.

Paray-le-Frésil 22A1

Le Bourg. **GPS**: n46,65472 e3,61294.

3 free Ch free € 2/55minutes.
Location: Rural, simple, quiet. **Surface:** gravel. 01/01-31/12.
Distance: on the spot 200m on the spot on the spot.

Paulhac 24H2

Place des Chausseurs. **GPS**: n45,00669 e2,90394.

3 free Ch free at townhall. **Location:** Rural, simple, isolated, quiet. **Surface:** grassy. 01/01-31/12.
Distance: on the spot on the spot.

Périgny 22A2

Rue de l'Église. **GPS**: n46,25208 e3,55422.

6 free Ch WC free. **Location:** Rural, simple, isolated, quiet.
Surface: gravel. 01/01-31/12.
Distance: on the spot 400m.

Pierrefort 24H2

Côte de Chabridet. **GPS**: n44,92172 e2,84199.

20 free € 2/100liter Ch € 2. **Location:** Rural, simple.
Surface: gravel. 01/01-31/12.
Distance: 200m 300m 300m on the spot.
Remarks: Coins at tourist info, service 100m.

Planfoy 25C1

Chemin du Vignolet. **GPS**: n45,37445 e4,44910.

10 free € 2,50/15minutes Ch (8x)€ 2,50/6h.
Location: Rural, comfortable, quiet. **Surface:** asphalted.
01/01-31/12.
Distance: 1,3km 7km 1,3km on the spot.
Remarks: Coins at the shops in the village.

Pleaux 24G1

Parc des Auzerals, Place d'Empeyssine.
GPS: n45,13556 e2,22833.

30 free Ch WC free. **Location:** Urban, simple, central, quiet. **Surface:** asphalted/gravel. 01/01-31/12.
Distance: on the spot 100m 100m.

Pont-de-Veyle 22C2

D933, Rue de la Poste. **GPS**: n46,26437 e4,88697.

20 free . **Location:** Urban, simple, central, noisy.
Surface: gravel.
Distance: on the spot 3,5km on the spot on the spot 50m 150m.
Remarks: Monday-morning market.

Pontcharra-sur-Turdine 22C3

Place A. Schweitzer. **GPS**: n45,87405 e4,49133.

4 free Ch WC free. **Location:** Urban. 01/01-31/12.
Distance: 50m on the spot 50m 50m on the spot.

Pouilly-sous-Charlieu 22B2

Place du Marché, Rue de la République.
GPS: n46,14335 e4,10832.

10 free Ch WC free. **Location:** Urban, simple.
Surface: asphalted. Su-morning (market).
Distance: on the spot on the spot on the spot.

Pouilly-sous-Charlieu 22B2

Rue de la Berge. **GPS**: n46,14699 e4,10075.
4 free. **Location:** Rural, simple. **Surface:** gravel.
01/01-31/12.
Distance: on the spot on the spot on the spot.
Remarks: Parking at the Loire river.

Pradelles 25B2

Aire de la Salaison, N88. **GPS**: n44,77540 e3,88752.

40 free Ch (8x)€ 2 free. **Location:** Rural, comfortable.
Surface: grassy/gravel. 01/01-31/12.
Distance: 1km on the spot on the spot on the spot.
Remarks: Max. 24h, regional products and bread.

Prapoutel-les-Sept-Laux 25E1

Les Adrets 38190. **GPS**: n45,25769 e5,99785.

FR

free WC. **Surface:** metalled. 01/01-31/12.
Distance: 50m.
Remarks: Parking at pistes.

S Privas 25C2

Avenue de la gare. **GPS**: n44,73134 e4,59309.

10 free Ch. **Location:** Urban. **Surface:** gravel/metalled.
01/01-31/12.
Distance: centre 750m.

S Prunet 24G2

Aire camping-cars, Le Bourg. **GPS**: n44,82049 e2,46398.

3 free Ch free. **Location:** Rural, simple, quiet.
Surface: gravel. 01/01-31/12 service 01/11-31/03.
Distance: 300m 300m.

S Puy-Saint-Martin 25C3

Aire de camping-car, Champ de Mars. **GPS**: n44,62753 e4,97492.

13 free Ch.
Location: Rural, comfortable. **Surface:** grassy.
Distance: on the spot 50m bakery 300m.
Remarks: Former campsite, max. 48h, voluntary contribution.

S Randan 22A3

Rue du Puy de Dôme. **GPS**: n46,01630 e3,35075.

6 free € 2/15minutes Ch € 2/15minutes.
Location: Urban, simple, quiet. **Surface:** gravel.
01/01-31/12.
Distance: 500m 500m 200m.
Remarks: Coins at Maison de la Presse, Rue de Commerce.

S Raucoules 25B1

Le Bourg. **GPS**: n45,18640 e4,29750.

4 free € 2/20minutes Ch (4x)€ 2/4h.
Location: Rural, simple, central, quiet. **Surface:** asphalted.
01/01-31/12.
Distance: 200m 300m on the spot on the spot.
Remarks: Coins available at the shops.

S Renaison 22B3

La Rivière. **GPS**: n46,04757 e3,92124.

10 free Ch free. **Location:** Rural, simple, quiet.
Surface: grassy/gravel. 01/01-31/12.
Distance: 400m on the spot 700m.
Remarks: Along river.

S Retournac 25B1

Aire de la Chaud, Rue de la Loire. **GPS**: n45,20328 e4,04501.

20 free Ch free. **Location:** Rural, simple, isolated, quiet.
Surface: gravel. 01/01-31/12 Service: winter.
Distance: city centre 1km on the spot on the spot 650m on the spot on the spot.
Remarks: Along Loire river.

S Reventin-Vaugris 25C1

Rue Mouret. **GPS**: n45,46821 e4,84239.

10 free WC. **Location:** Rural, simple, central, quiet.
Surface: gravel/metalled. 01/01-31/12.
Distance: on the spot 6km 100m bakery 100m.

S Riom 22A3

Route d'Ennezat, D224. **GPS**: n45,89455 e3,12477.

4 free € 2/15minutes Ch € 2/15minutes. **Location:** Urban, simple, central, noisy. **Surface:** gravel. 01/01-31/12.
Distance: 700m 2,5km nearby nearby.

S Riom-es-Montagnes 24H1

Rue du Champ de Foire. **GPS**: n45,28444 e2,65389.
€ 2/100liter Ch € 2/1h.
Location: Simple. 01/01-31/12.
Distance: on the spot 100m 100m.
Remarks: Overnight stay on Parking de la Piscine, GPS N 45,27902 E 2,66403.

S Roanne 22B3

Port de Plaisance, Quai Commandant de Fourcauld.
GPS: n46,03750 e4,08306.

10 € 6 € 2,50/15minutes € 2,50 Ch € 2,50 € 2,50/4h WC. **Location:** Urban, comfortable, quiet. **Surface:** gravel.
01/01-31/12.
Distance: 500m 500m 2km 2km on the spot on the spot on the spot.
Remarks: Max. 6 days.

Romans-sur-Isère 25C2

Avenue Gambetta. **GPS**: n45,04521 e5,05879.

4 free. **Location:** Urban, simple. **Surface:** metalled.
01/01-31/12.
Distance: centre 700m 50m 300m.
Remarks: Parking in front of Marques Avenue, max. 48h.

S Ruoms 25B3

Camping-Car Park La Grand Terre, La Grand Terre.
GPS: n44,42381 e4,33253.
15 € 11,40-13,60 Ch (12x) included.
Location: Rural. **Surface:** grassy/metalled. 01/01/-31/12.
Distance: 3km 200m on the spot on the spot.
Remarks: Mandatory, one-time fee Pass'Etapes € 4.

S Ruynes-en-Margeride 25A2

Le Bourg. **GPS**: n45,00111 e3,22389.

8 free € 2/10minutes Ch € 2/55minutes.
Location: Urban, simple, quiet. **Surface:** gravel/sand.
01/01-31/12.
Distance: 50m 6km 50m 50m.

S Sagnes-et-Goudoulet 25B2

Camping-Car Park, Les Sagnes. **GPS**: n44,79030 e4,22606.
6 € 9,80 Ch (12x)included. **Location:** Rural.
Surface: gravel. 01/01-31/12.
Remarks: Mandatory, one-time fee Pass'Etapes € 4.

S Saillans 25D2

La Roche, Quartier Tourtoiron, Montmartel.
GPS: n44,69549 e5,19350.

FR

20 € 3 € 2 Ch.
Location: Rural, simple. **Surface:** gravel.
01/01-31/12.
Distance: 300m.
Remarks: Along the Drôme river, max. 24h, closed when high water.

S Saint-Agrève 25B2

Coussac. **GPS**: n45,01042 e4,39339.

free € 3 Ch € 3,water 10 min + electricity 50min WC.
Location: Simple. **Surface:** asphalted. 01/01-31/12.
Distance: 500m 500m 500m.
Remarks: Coins at tourist info.

S Saint-Agrève 25B2

Le Lac de Véron, Pré de Gardy, D120. **GPS**: n44,99981 e4,40164.

5 € 5/24h on demand free. **Location:** Rural, comfortable, quiet. **Surface:** unpaved. 01/04-31/10.
Distance: village 1km 100m 200m on the spot on the spot on the spot.
Remarks: At fish lake.

S Saint-Alban-Auriolles 25B3

Rue Marius Perbost. **GPS**: n44,42693 e4,30096.

free € 3 Ch € 3. **Surface:** gravel. 01/01-31/12.
Distance: 300m 200m.

S Saint-André-d'Apchon 22B3

La Prébande. **GPS**: n46,03385 e3,92705.

3 free Chfree. **Location:** Rural, simple, quiet.
Surface: gravel. 01/01-31/12.
Distance: 300m 100m.

S Saint-André-de-Chalencon 25B1

Place des Droits de l'Homme. **GPS**: n45,27254 e3,97010.

2 free € 2/10minutes Ch € 2/1h.
Location: Urban, simple, central. **Surface:** gravel/sand.
01/01-31/12.
Distance: on the spot.

S Saint-Bonnet-le-Château 25B1

Esplanade de la Boule. **GPS**: n45,42514 e4,06436.

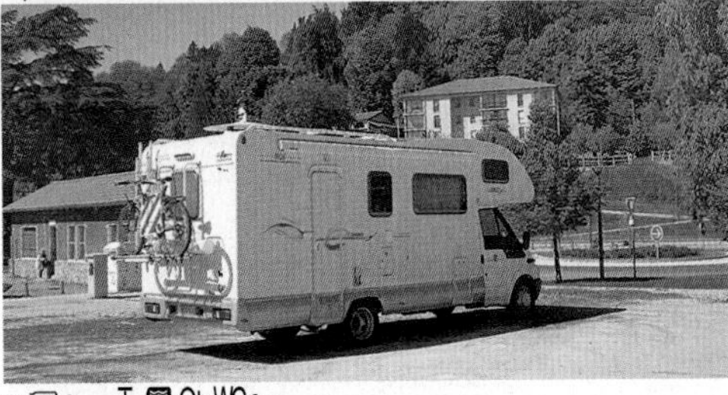

50 free ChWCfree.
Location: Simple. **Surface:** metalled. Fri.
Distance: 200m 1km 200m 200m.

Tourist information Saint-Bonnet-le-Château:
M Musée de la Pétanque et des Boules, Esplanade de la Boule. All about the beloved French national sport. 01/04-31/10.
M Musée International Pétanque et Boules, Boulevard des Chauchères. Fri.

S Saint-Bonnet-le-Froid 25C1

Chemin de Brard. **GPS**: n45,14136 e4,43454.

6 € 5 Ch included. **Location:** Urban, simple, central, quiet. **Surface:** gravel. 01/03-15/11.
Distance: 150m 150m 150m on the spot.
Remarks: Access via D105.

S Saint-Bonnet-Tronçais 21H1

Parking du Stade, Route de Tronçais, D39.
GPS: n46,66001 e2,69717.
10 free € 5 Ch. **Surface:** gravel.
01/01-31/12 water disconnected in winter.
Distance: 300m.
Remarks: Coins at the bakery and campsite.

S Saint-Bonnet-Tronçais 21H1

Rue de l'Étang. **GPS**: n46,65896 e2,69228.
10 free. **Location:** Simple, central. **Surface:** gravel.
01/01-31/12.
Distance: on the spot 27km Lake 450m bakery 200m.

S Saint-Christophe-sur-Dolaison 25B2

Place des Jardins, Le Bourg. **GPS**: n44,99802 e3,82158.

6 free € 2 Ch € 2. **Location:** Rural, simple, quiet.
Surface: asphalted. 01/01-31/12.
Distance: 100m 150m on the spot on the spot.
Remarks: Coins at town hall.

S Saint-Désirat 25C1

Musée de l'Alambic,Distillerie Jean Gauthier, D291.
GPS: n45,25856 e4,79261.

free WCfree. **Location:** Simple. **Surface:** asphalted.
Distance: 300m 300m.
Remarks: Max. 1 night.

S Saint-Donat-sur-l'Herbasse 25C2

Route de St.Bardoux. **GPS**: n45,11902 e4,98284.

free Chfree. **Location:** Simple. 01/01-31/12.
Distance: 400m 400m 1km.
Remarks: In front of gymnasium, max. 1 night.

S Saint-Éloy-les-Mines 21H2

Rue du Puy-de-Dôme, RN144. **GPS**: n46,15559 e2,83615.

30 free € 2 Ch € 2. **Location:** Rural, simple.
Surface: metalled. 01/01-31/12.
Distance: on the spot 700m 400m Carrefour Market.
Remarks: Max. 48h.

S Saint-Étienne-la-Varenne 22C3

Le Bourg. **GPS**: n46,07731 e4,63024.

4 free Ch free. **Location:** Rural, simple, quiet.
Surface: gravel/metalled. 01/01-31/12.
Distance: on the spot 50m on the spot on the spot.
Remarks: Next to church.

S Saint-Félicien 25C2

Place du Pré Lacour. **GPS**: n45,08453 e4,62848.

6 free € 2 Ch. **Location:** Urban, simple.
Surface: asphalted/gravel. 01/01-31/12.
Distance: on the spot on the spot on the spot.
Remarks: Behind police station, max. 2 nights.

S Saint-Ferréol-Trente-Pas 25D3

La Pisciculture l'Eau Claire, La Condamine. **GPS**: n44,43781 e5,23862.
WC. **Surface:** gravel. 01/01-31/12.

FR

Remarks: Trout pond, regional products.

Saint-Flour 24H2

Cours Chazerat. **GPS:** n45,03389 e3,08750.

20 free € 2 Ch € 2/55minutes. **Location:** Urban, simple. **Surface:** metalled. 01/01-31/12.
Distance: on the spot 4,6km 50m 50m on the spot on the spot.
Remarks: Higher part of the city.

Saint-Flour 24H2

Place de l'Ander, ville basse. **GPS:** n45,03556 e3,09750.

8 free € 2/100liter Ch € 2/55minutes.
Location: Urban, simple. **Surface:** asphalted. 01/01-31/12.
Distance: 300m 4km 300m 300m on the spot.
Remarks: Near campsite, lower part of the city.

Tourist information Saint-Flour:
Office de Tourisme, 17bis, place d'Armes, www.saint-flour.com. City with car-free historical centre, Vieux Saint Flour.

Saint-Forgeux 22C3

Le Tram. **GPS:** n45,85733 e4,47566.

free Ch free WC. **Location:** Rural, simple, quiet.
Surface: metalled. 01/01-31/12.
Distance: 300m 300m 300m on the spot.

Saint-Genest-de-Beauzon 25B3

Domaine la Pize, La Pize. **GPS:** n44,43759 e4,19431.

€ 10 Ch WC included. **Location:** Rural, isolated, quiet.
Surface: unpaved. 01/01-31/12.
Distance: 1,6km on the spot.

Saint-Georges 25A2

Aire du Cantal. **GPS:** n45,03167 e3,13500.

20 free € 2 Ch € 2 WC. **Location:** Motorway, simple, noisy.
Surface: asphalted. 01/01-31/12.
Distance: 3km 500m 200m 500m.
Remarks: At petrol station Esso.

Saint-Georges-d'Espéranche 25C1

Chemin des Platières. **GPS:** n45,55560 e5,07478.

14 free Ch free. **Location:** Rural, simple, central, quiet.
Surface: metalled. 01/01-31/12.
Distance: on the spot 100m 500m.
Remarks: Max. 48h.

Saint-Gérand-de-Vaux 22A2

Etang du Moulin, Les Gaillards. **GPS:** n46,38416 e3,39972.

30 free € 2/100liter Ch € 2/1h WC. **Location:** Rural, comfortable, isolated, quiet. **Surface:** grassy. 01/01-31/12.
Distance: 600m on the spot 600m.
Remarks: Coins at restaurant.

Saint-Germain-Lespinasse 22B2

Place du 8 mai 1945. **GPS:** n46,10510 e3,96229.

3 free Ch free. **Location:** Rural, simple, quiet.
Surface: gravel. 01/01-31/12.
Distance: 200m 50m 50m.

Saint-Gérons 24G2

Camping-Car Park Plage d'Espinet. **GPS:** n44,93257 e2,23190.
26 € 9,40-11,80 Ch included. 01/01-31/12.
Distance: 2km Snackbar.
Remarks: Mandatory, one-time fee Pass'Etapes € 4.

Saint-Gervais-les-Bains 22F3

77, impasse Cascade. **GPS:** n45,88864 e6,71287.

20 free € 2 Ch € 2. **Surface:** asphalted.

Distance: 200m 200m 200m 300m.
Remarks: Parking skating rink.

Saint-Haon-le-Châtel 22B3

Fondanges, Route de la Croix du Sud, D39.
GPS: n46,06362 e3,91313.

3 free Ch free. **Location:** Rural, quiet. **Surface:** metalled. 01/01-31/12.
Distance: 400m 400m 400m 400m.

Saint-Hilaire-sous-Charlieu 22B2

Le Grand Couvert, Les Perches. **GPS:** n46,11054 e4,18827.

2 free. **Location:** Rural, simple, isolated, quiet. **Surface:** gravel. 01/01-31/12.

Saint-Jean-d'Ardières 22C2

Domaine de Grande Ferrière, 831 route des Rochons.
GPS: n46,12954 e4,71581.

5 free Ch free € 5/4night WC. **Location:** Rural, simple.
Surface: gravel.
Distance: 3km 6km 5km 500m 3km 3km.

Saint-Jean-de-Bournay 25D1

Place du Marche. **GPS:** n45,50130 e5,13845.

10 free free Ch. **Location:** Rural, simple, central, quiet.
Surface: asphalted. 01/01-31/12.
Distance: on the spot 100m 100m.

Saint-Jean-de-Maurienne 25E1

Rue Louis Sibue. **GPS:** n45,27995 e6,34776.
10 free € 2 Ch € 2 WC. **Surface:** asphalted.
01/01-31/12.
Distance: 2,5km 100m.

Saint-Jean-en-Royans 25D2

Rue de la Gare. **GPS:** n45,02028 e5,29032.

3 free Chfree. **Location:** Simple. **Surface:** gravel.
01/01-31/12.
Distance: 200m 200m 200m.

S Saint-Julien-Chapteuil 25B2

L'Holme, La Croix Blanche. **GPS**: n45,03917 e4,06305.
€3 Ch. 01/01-31/12.
Remarks: Service in front of campsite.

S Saint-Just 25A2

Camping Municipal, Le Bourg. **GPS**: n44,88972 e3,20889.

10 €8 €2/100liter Ch €2/55minutes (4x)€3,50/night WC included. **Location:** Rural, comfortable, quiet.
Surface: grassy. 01/01-31/12.
Distance: 50m 6,2km 100m 100m on the spot.
Remarks: Incl. use camp-site facilities.

S Saint-Just-d'Ardèche 25C3

Domaine La Favette, D86, route des Gorges d'Ardèche.
GPS: n44,30134 e4,60649.

6 €5 €2 Ch €2. 01/01-31/12.
Remarks: At wine-grower, max. 24h.

Tourist information Saint-Just-d'Ardèche:
Good starting point to discover the Ardèche gorges.
Thu.

S Saint-Just-en-Chevalet 22B3

Boulevard de l'Astrée. **GPS**: n45,91411 e3,84727.

5 free ChWCfree. **Location:** Rural, simple.
01/01-31/12 Thu-morning.
Distance: on the spot on the spot on the spot on the spot.

S Saint-Mamet-la-Salvetat 24G2

Aire camping-cars, D20. **GPS**: n44,85714 e2,30981.

3 free €2/100liter Ch €2/1h WC.
Location: Rural, simple, quiet. **Surface:** asphalted. 01/01-31/12.
Distance: 500m 350m.
Remarks: Coins at the shops and town hall.

S Saint-Marcel-d'Urfé 22B3

Le Bourg. **GPS**: n45,87361 e3,88391.

3 free ChWCfree. **Location:** Simple, quiet. **Surface:** gravel.
01/01-31/12.
Distance: on the spot on the spot.
Remarks: At tennis-court.

S Saint-Marcel-en-Murat 21H2

D243. **GPS**: n46,32184 e3,00837.

10 free €2/100liter Ch €2/1h. **Location:** Rural, simple.
Surface: gravel. 01/01-31/12.
Distance: 3,5km exit 11 A71 nearby.
Remarks: Coins at town hall and restaurant.

Saint-Martin-d'Estréaux 22B2

Place des Gouttes. **GPS**: n46,20713 e3,79877.

3 free ChWCfree. **Location:** Simple, quiet.
Surface: asphalted. 01/01-31/12.
Distance: 200m 200m 200m.

S Saint-Martin-en-Haut 22C3

Etang du Kaiser, Lieu-dit-Jeangouttière. **GPS**: n45,64206 e4,53511.

4 €8 ChWC.
Location: Rural, comfortable, quiet. **Surface:** gravel.
01/01-31/12.
Distance: St.Martin 4km on the spot on the spot on the spot.
Remarks: At small lake, max. 72h.

S Saint-Ours-les Roches 21H3

Vulcania, 2 route de Mazayes. **GPS**: n45,81221 e2,94877.

65 €10 €2/100liter Ch (20x)€2/6h . **Location:** Rural, simple, quiet. **Surface:** asphalted/gravel. 15/03-13/11.
Remarks: Max. 2 nights.

S Saint-Paul-des-Landes 24G2

Aire camping-cars, Rue du Moinac. **GPS**: n44,94250 e2,31694.

3 free €3,50 Ch €3,50. **Location:** Rural, simple, central, quiet. **Surface:** asphalted. 01/01-31/12.
Distance: 50m 200m 50m.
Remarks: Coins at petrol station.

S Saint-Paul-le-Jeune 25B3

Rue Louis Roux, D901. **GPS**: n44,33999 e4,15322.

free €2 Ch €2. **Location:** Rural. **Surface:** grassy.
01/01-31/12.
Distance: on the spot 100m.
Remarks: Coins at the shops in the village.

S Saint-Paul-Trois-Châteaux 25C3

Parking Office de Tourisme, Le Courreau, Place Chausy.
GPS: n44,34786 e4,76995.

free Chfree WC. **Location:** Urban. **Surface:** asphalted.
Distance: 50m 50m.
Remarks: Max. 24h.

Tourist information Saint-Paul-Trois-Châteaux:
Marché. Tue-morning.
Marché aux truffes du Tricastin. Dec-Mar Su-morning.

S Saint-Pierre-en-Faucigny 22E3

Avenue de la Gare. **GPS**: n46,05884 e6,37450.

4 free Ch free. **Surface:** asphalted. 01/04-30/11.

FR

Distance: on the spot ⊗60m on the spot on the spot.
Remarks: Nearby railway station.

Saint-Pourçain-sur-Sioule 22A2

Aire Camping-car de la Moutte, Rue de la Moutte.
GPS: n46,31262 e3,29656.

73 free € 4 Ch (8x)€ 4/4h.
Location: Urban, comfortable, central, quiet. **Surface:** grassy.
01/01-31/12.
Distance: 800m on the spot ⊗on the spot on the spot.
Remarks: Along the Sioule river.

Saint-Rémèze 25C3

Les Chais du Vivarais, D362. **GPS:** n44,39536 e4,50576.

free Chfree. **Surface:** asphalted. 01/03-15/11.
Distance: 500m ⊗200m.
Remarks: Max. 48h.

Tourist information Saint-Rémèze:
Grotte Aven Marzal. Caves. Sa/Su/Holidays, 01/04-30/09 10.30-18h.
Grotte de la Madelaine. Caves. Apr-Oct 10-18h.
Musée de la lavande. Museum and distillery with lavender fields. 01/05-30/09 10-17h, Apr + Oct Sa-Su-holiday 10-17h.
Zoo préhistorique, Route des Gorges. Prehistoric park. 10.30-17.30h.

Saint-Rémy-de-Blot 21H3

Place du Bourg. **GPS:** n46,07722 e2,93139.

7 free WC. **Location:** Rural, simple, isolated, quiet.
Surface: grasstiles. 01/01-31/12.
Distance: ⊗on the spot.

Saint-Restitut 25C3

Le Village. **GPS:** n44,33144 e4,79093.

10 free Chfree. **Surface:** asphalted. 01/01-31/12.
Distance: on the spot.
Remarks: Max. 7 days.

Saint-Rirand 22B3

Le Bourg. **GPS:** n46,07501 e3,85016.

3 free Chfree. **Location:** Rural, simple, isolated, quiet.
Surface: gravel. 01/01-31/12.
Distance: on the spot on the spot.

Saint-Romain-d'Ay 25C1

Praperier, D6. **GPS:** n45,16430 e4,66339.

8 free € 2/20minutes Ch (4x)€ 2/4h WC.
Location: Simple. **Surface:** asphalted.
01/01-31/12 Service: winter.
Distance: 550m ⊗100m.
Remarks: Coins at town hall and superette.

Saint-Romain-de-Lerps 25C2

Le Village, D287. **GPS:** n44,98029 e4,79596.

10 free Ch € 4,100 liter water + 1h electricity WC.
Location: Rural, simple, quiet. **Surface:** gravel.
01/01-31/12 01/10 and 01/04.
Distance: 100m ⊗100m bakery 100m.
Remarks: Less suitable for motorhomes >6,5m, coins at bakery, bar/resto 3duPic and town hall, panoramic view over the Rhône-valley 200m.

Saint-Romain-Lachalm 25B1

Rulière. **GPS:** n45,26399 e4,33576.

4 free € 2/10minutes Ch (4x)€ 2/4h.
Location: Rural, simple, isolated. **Surface:** asphalted.
01/01-31/12.
Distance: 100m bakery 200m.
Remarks: Coins at the shops and town hall.

Saint-Sauves-d'Auvergne 21H3

Domaine de Lavaux, D82. **GPS:** n45,61688 e2,68975.

50 € 8 Ch (10x)€ 4/day WCincluded € 1,25 € 5.
Location: Rural, comfortable, isolated, quiet. **Surface:** grassy.
15/05-30/09.
Distance: 1km on the spot.

Saint-Symphorien-sur-Coise 22C3

Bois des Pinasses. **GPS:** n45,62578 e4,45837.

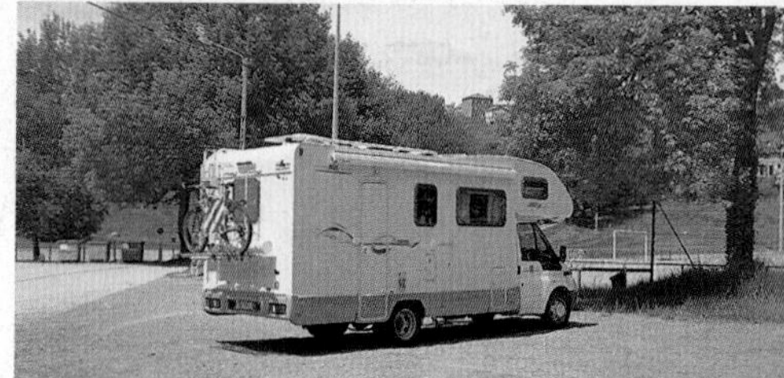

free.
Location: Rural, simple. **Surface:** gravel. 01/01-31/12.
Distance: 1km 50m.
Remarks: Next to sports fields.

Saint-Symphorien-sur-Coise 22C3

Rue des Rameaux. **GPS:** n45,63378 e4,45883.
Chfree. **Location:** Simple. 01/01-31/12.
Remarks: Free coins at Bar-Tabac and town hall.

Saint-Théoffrey 25E2

Camping Ser-Sirant, Chemin du Lavoir. **GPS:** n45,00034 e5,77819.
4 € 8-9,50 € 1,50 Ch. **Location:** Rural. **Surface:** grassy.
Distance: beach Saint Théoffrey.
Remarks: At lake Laffrey, pay at reception campsite.

Saint-Thomé 25C3

N107, Les Crottes. **GPS:** n44,50059 e4,63445.

1 free Chfree. **Surface:** asphalted.

Saint-Victor-sur-Loire 25B1

Base Nautique du lac de Grangent. **GPS:** n45,44787 e4,25626.

12 free Chfree (4x)€ 2,60/4h WC. **Location:** Rural, comfortable. **Surface:** asphalted. 01/01-31/12.
Distance: on the spot on the spot ⊗on the spot.
Remarks: Max. 72h, coins at the shops in the village.

Salers 24H1

Le Mouriol, Route du Puy Mary. **GPS:** n45,14718 e2,49900.

15 € 12/night + € 0,50/pp tourist tax € 3 ChWC included,on camp site. **Location:** Rural. **Surface:** asphalted.
01/04-31/10 service: frost.
Distance: 1,2km ⊗50m.
Remarks: Next to camping municipal, coins at campsite and tourist info.

Salers 24H1

D680. **GPS:** n45,14010 e2,49478.
12 € 3. **Location:** Rural. **Surface:** asphalted/metalled.
01/01-31/12.

Distance: 500m.

Salers 24H1

Rue Notre-Dame. **GPS**: n45,13898 e2,49583.
6 € 3. **Surface:** asphalted. 01/01-31/12.
Distance: 250m.
Remarks: Max. 7 days.

Sallanches 22F3

Parking de Charousse, 70 route du Fayet. **GPS**: n45,93210 e6,63337.
3 free € 2/20minutes Ch. **Location:** Urban, central, noisy.
Surface: asphalted. 01/01-31/12.
Distance: 400m 100m.
Remarks: Max. 24h.

Samoëns 22F3

Aire d'accueil camping-car de Vercland, Hameau de Vercland.
GPS: n46,07228 e6,70189.

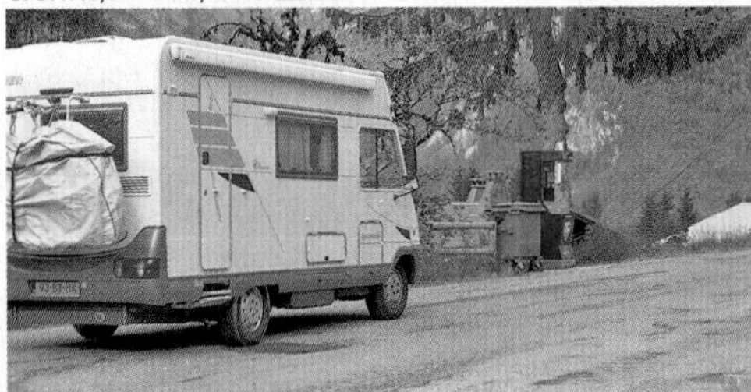

10 free € 6 Ch € 6.
Surface: metalled. 01/01-31/12 Service: winter.
Distance: 2km 100m 2km.

Samoëns 22F3

Parking du Giffre. **GPS**: n46,07666 e6,71899.

5 € 10 Ch.
Surface: asphalted. 01/01-31/12 Service: winter.
Distance: 100m 100m 100m Skibus to Samoëns 1600 100m on the spot.
Remarks: Near campsite du Giffre, parking 150m.

Sansac-de-Marmiesse 24G2

Aire camping-cars, Rue de la Vidalie. **GPS**: n44,88389 e2,34639.

3 free € 3,50 Ch € 3,50.
Location: Urban, simple, central. **Surface:** asphalted.
01/01-31/12 service: 01/10-30/04.
Distance: on the spot 200m on the spot.
Remarks: Coins at the bakery.

Sassenage 25D1

Rue Pierre de Coubertin. **GPS**: n45,21346 e5,66858.
9 free Chfree. **Surface:** asphalted. 01/01-31/12.
Distance: on the spot on the spot.
Remarks: At sports grounds, max. 48h.

Saugues 25A2

Place du Brieul. **GPS**: n44,95940 e3,54395.

10 free Chfree. **Location:** Simple. **Surface:** asphalted.
01/01-31/12.
Distance: on the spot bakery 200m.

Sauret-Besserve 21H3

D523. **GPS**: n45,99245 e2,80746.

4 free € 2 Ch. **Location:** Rural, simple, isolated.
01/01-31/12.
Remarks: Near church.

Ségur-les-Villas 24H1

Aire de camping-cars, Le Bourg. **GPS**: n45,22311 e2,81818.

10 free € 3/100liter Ch € 3/1h.
Location: Rural, simple, quiet. **Surface:** grassy. 01/05-30/10.
Distance: 200m 300m 200m.
Remarks: Nearby football ground, coins at the shops in the village.

Serrières-en-Chautagne 22E3

GPS: n45,87964 e5,84230.

15 free ChWCfree. **Location:** Rural, central, quiet.
Surface: metalled. 01/01-31/12 Service: winter.
Distance: on the spot 1km beach 50m on the spot 200m 100m 100m.
Remarks: At little mountain stream, max. 72h.

Seyssel 22E3

Parking Base de Loisirs, Quai du Rhône. **GPS**: n45,95146 e5,83343.

5 free Chfree.
Location: Rural, simple, central, quiet. **Surface:** gravel.
01/01-31/12 Service: winter.
Distance: 800m on the spot on the spot 500m 800m on the spot.
Remarks: At recreational lake and Rhone river.

Seyssel 22E3

Quai du Rhône. **GPS**: n45,95001 e5,83406.

5 free Chfree.
Location: Rural, simple, central, quiet. **Surface:** grassy.
01/01-31/12 Service: winter.
Distance: 400m on the spot on the spot 400m 400m 400m on the spot.
Remarks: Along the Rhone river.

Siaugues-Sainte-Marie 25A2

D590. **GPS**: n45,09303 e3,62784.

4 free € 2/10minutes Ch € 2/h. **Location:** Rural, simple.
Surface: grassy. 01/01-31/12.
Distance: 300m.

Sixt-Fer-à-Cheval 22F3

Route du Cirque du Fer à Cheval. **GPS**: n46,05698 e6,78048.

20 free Ch € 4/12h.
Surface: asphalted. 01/01-31/12.
Distance: 500m on the spot 500m.

Solignac-sur-Loire 25B2

Le Vis. **GPS**: n44,96471 e3,88001.

20 € 12 Ch WCincluded. **Location:** Rural, comfortable, isolated, quiet. **Surface:** grassy. 01/05-01/11.
Distance: 800m.

Solignat 25A1

Route des Dauphins d'Auvergne, D32. **GPS**: n45,51701 e3,17074.

5 free € 2/100liter Ch € 2/1h. **Location:** Rural, simple, quiet. **Surface:** grassy. 01/01-31/12.
Distance: 100m.
Remarks: Max. 48h.

Sorbier 22A2

Route de varennes sur Tèche. **GPS**: n46,36275 e3,65906.

FR

2 free Ch free. **Location:** Rural. **Surface:** gravel.
01/01-31/12.
Remarks: Picnic tables available, playground.

St Anthème 25B1

Rambaud. **GPS**: n45,52354 e3,91464.

30 € 5 Chincluded.
Location: Rural, simple, central, quiet. **Surface:** grassy/gravel.
01/01-31/12 water: frost.
Distance: 200m beach 250m 200m on the spot.
Remarks: Next to campsite Rambaud, water disconnected.

Super Besse 24H1

La Binche, Ronde de Vassivière. **GPS**: n45,50644 e2,85342.

172 € 5,60/24h, € 37,80/8 days € 1/20minutes Ch (100x) € 2,50/4h . **Location:** Comfortable, quiet.
Surface: asphalted. 01/01-31/12.
Distance: 300m 300m on the spot 300m.
Remarks: On ring-road around the lake, P5, P7 and P10, no camping activities.

Super Lioran 24H2

Aire de Laveissière, Parking Font d'Alagnon.
GPS: n45,08856 e2,73819.

25 free. **Location:** Rural, simple, quiet. **Surface:** asphalted.
01/01-31/12.
Distance: 200m 200m 50m 30m 30m.

Super Lioran 24H2

P5. **GPS**: n45,08705 e2,74793.
70 free. 01/01-31/12.
Distance: 400m 400m 400m.

Suze-la-Rousse 25C3

Route de Bollène, D94. **GPS**: n44,28598 e4,83185.

free free. **Surface:** grassy/gravel. 01/01-31/12.
Distance: 850m on the spot on the spot.
Remarks: At sports grounds.

Suze-la-Rousse 25C3

50 Impasse de la Zone Artisanale. **GPS**: n44,28965 e4,84783.
Chfree. 01/01-31/12.
Distance: 1,5km.

Talizat 24H2

Place du 19 mars 1962. **GPS**: n45,11417 e3,04583.

3 free € 2 Ch € 2.
Location: Rural, simple, quiet. **Surface:** asphalted.
01/01-31/12.
Distance: on the spot 100m 100m on the spot.
Remarks: Coins at town hall and restaurant, behind town hall.

Tence 25B2

Place du Fieu. **GPS**: n45,11580 e4,29220.

6 free € 2/10minutes Ch. **Location:** Urban, simple, quiet.
Surface: gravel/metalled. 01/01-31/12.
Distance: 200m 200m on the spot.

Thiel-sur-Acolin 22A2

Rue de la Motte. **GPS**: n46,52269 e3,58776.

11 free Ch free. **Location:** Rural, isolated, quiet.
Surface: gravel. 01/01-31/12.
Distance: 650m.

Thiel-sur-Acolin 22A2

Route Départementale 914. **GPS**: n42,63763 e2,93675.
6 € 12 Ch included.

Thiers 22A3

Base de loisirs Iloa, D44 > Dorat. **GPS**: n45,87070 e3,48311.

10 free free. **Location:** Rural, simple, isolated, quiet.
Surface: metalled. 01/01-31/12.
Distance: 2,6km.

Thiézac 24H2

Aire de camping-car La Sapinière, D59.
GPS: n45,01583 e2,66278.

8 free € 2 Ch € 2. **Location:** Rural, simple, quiet.
Surface: asphalted. 01/01-31/12.
Distance: 50m 100m 100m.

Remarks: Max. 24h, coins at petrol station.

Thueyts 25B2

Chemin d'Echelle du Roi, via N102. **GPS**: n44,67274 e4,21917.

10 free 5minutes Ch 10minutes,service € 2.
Location: Rural, simple, quiet. **Surface:** grassy/gravel.
15/03-15/11.
Distance: 200m 200m on the spot.
Remarks: Near the Ardèche river and Pont du Diable, next to sports fields, max. 24h.

Tiranges 25B1

Accueil Camping Car, La Nerceyre. **GPS**: n45,30702 e3,99107.

10 free € 2 Ch. **Location:** Rural, simple, quiet.
Surface: asphalted. 01/01-31/12.
Distance: 400m 400m 400m.

Tournon-sur-Rhône 25C2

Chemin de la Beaume/D86. **GPS**: n45,07337 e4,82150.

25 € 5 Chfree. **Location:** Urban, simple. **Surface:** asphalted.
01/01-31/12.
Distance: 1km 5km 1km 1km.
Remarks: Max. 24h.

Tourist information Tournon-sur-Rhône:
Wed, Sa.
Route Panoramique, place Jean Jaurès. Starting point touristic route.

Tourzel-Ronzières 25A1

Aire camping-car, Chemin du Clos, D23. **GPS**: n45,52989 e3,13504.

12 free Ch WCfree. **Location:** Rural, simple, isolated, quiet. **Surface:** grassy/gravel. 01/05-30/09.
Distance: 500m 500m.

Treffort 25D2

Plage de la Salette, D110b. **GPS**: n44,90732 e5,67208.

12 € 10/24h € 2 Ch € 2.
Surface: gravel. 01/05-30/09.
Distance: 3km lake lake on the spot on the spot on the spot.
Remarks: At lake Monteynard.

S Treteau 22A2

Rue du Rosier, D21. **GPS**: n46,36800 e3,51758.

+10 € 3,50/night € 2 Ch € 2 WC. **Location:** Rural, simple, quiet. **Surface:** grassy/metalled. 05/03-30/10.
Distance: 500m on the spot day pass available 100m on the spot.
Remarks: At small lake.

S Trévoux 22C3

Chemin du Camping. **GPS**: n45,94017 e4,76694.

4 € 5 € 3 Ch € 3 WC € 2.
Location: Urban, simple, central, quiet. **Surface:** grassy/gravel.
01/01-31/12.
Distance: on the spot 7km 100m 1km 1km 1km.
Remarks: Along river, at entrance campsite, pay at campsite or town hall.

S Ugine 22F3

Place du 8 Mai 1945. **GPS**: n45,74634 e6,41774.
free € 2 € 2 WC.
Surface: asphalted. 01/01-31/12.
Distance: 50m 50m 50m.

Tourist information Ugine:
Wed, Sa-morning.

S Val d'Isère 25F1

Le Pont Saint-Charles, Route du Col de l'Iseran, D902.
GPS: n45,45432 e6,97005.

50 free Chfree. **Surface:** gravel. 01/01-31/12.
Distance: on the spot.
Remarks: Parking at skipistes.

S Valette 24H1

Aire camping-cars, D678. **GPS**: n45,27000 e2,60222.

5 free € 2 Ch € 2. **Location:** Rural, comfortable, quiet.
Surface: gravel. 01/01-31/12 service: 01/11-01/05.
Distance: 50m 100m 150m.
Remarks: Max. 72h.

S Valloire 25F1

Camping-Car Park Les Verneys, Route du Galibier.
GPS: n45,14591 e6,42011.
30 € 9,40-13 Ch (28x) WC included.
Surface: asphalted.
01/01-31/12.
Distance: on the spot 250m.
Remarks: Mandatory, one-time fee Pass'Etapes € 4, free shuttle.

S Vallon-Pont-d'Arc 25B3

Chemin du Chastelas. **GPS**: n44,40537 e4,39683.

20 € 6/24h € 2 Ch € 2 WC. 01/01-31/12.
Distance: 100m 100m 100m.
Remarks: Free shuttle to the Pont d'Arc, 2x per hour.

S Vallon-Pont-d'Arc 25B3

Domaine de l'Esquiras, Chemin du Fez. **GPS**: n44,41583 e4,37738.

5 € 8, peak season € 10 + € 0,60/pp tourist tax Ch € 3 WC free. **Surface:** gravel. 12/04-21/09.
Distance: 800m.
Remarks: Use sanitary facilities + swimming pool € 4/pp.

Tourist information Vallon-Pont-d'Arc:
Office de Tourisme, 1 Place de l'Ancienne Gare, http://pontdarc-ardeche.fr. Small tourist town with the well-known Pont d'Arc, a natural arc over the Ardèche river.
Grotte des Huguenots. Former shelter of the Huguenots. 15/06-31/08.
Thu-morning.

S Valuéjols 24H2

Place de 19 Mars 1962. **GPS**: n45,05349 e2,92927.

15 € 3 Chincluded. **Location:** Rural, simple.
Surface: asphalted. 01/01-31/12.
Distance: 400m 400m 400m on the spot on the spot on the spot.

S Varennes-sur-Allier 22A2

Place Hôtel de Ville, Rue de Beaupuy. **GPS**: n46,31288 e3,40476.

100 free € 2/100liter Ch € 2/h WC.
Location: Urban, simple, central, noisy. **Surface:** metalled.
01/01-31/12.
Distance: on the spot on the spot on the spot.
Remarks: Coins at town hall, tuesday market.

S Vassieux-en-Vercors 25D2

Avenue du Mémorial, D76. **GPS**: n44,89703 e5,36927.

30 free Chfree. **Location:** Rural, simple. **Surface:** metalled.
01/01-31/12 Service: winter.
Distance: 200m 200m 200m on the spot 7km Font D'Urle on the spot.
Remarks: Next to football ground.

S Vaujany 25E1

Télécabine. **GPS**: n45,15694 e6,08011.

10 free Chfree € 10/24h. **Surface:** gravel.
01/01-31/12.
Distance: 300m 300m 300m 300m.
Remarks: Coins at tourist info (electricity).

S Védrines-Saint-Loup 25A2

Route du Plan d'Eau. **GPS**: n45,06758 e3,27565.

5 free € 2/10minutes Ch € 2/55minutes.
Location: Rural, simple, isolated, quiet. **Surface:** gravel/metalled.
01/01-31/12.
Distance: 400m on the spot on the spot on the spot.

S Velzic 24H2

Lavernière, Rue de Fracort. **GPS**: n45,00166 e2,54638.

5 free € 3,50 Ch. **Location:** Rural, simple, isolated.
Surface: asphalted. 01/01-31/12 service: 31/10-01/04.
Distance: 1km 1km 1km on the spot.

FR

Remarks: Coins at épicerie Pas de Peyrols.

Vernosc-lès-Annonay 25C1

Rue de la Lié. **GPS:** n45,21914 e4,71409.
6 free Ch. 01/01-31/12.
Distance: 200m 200m 200m.
Remarks: Next to town hall.

Vézac 24H2

Aire de camping-cars, Route de Cavanière.
GPS: n44,89059 e2,51779.

8 free € 3,50 Ch. **Location:** Rural, simple. **Surface:** asphalted.
01/01-31/12.
Distance: 100m 50m 700m.
Remarks: At golf court, coins at bar/tabac, 50m.

Vic-sur-Cère 24H2

Aire de camping-cars, Avenue des Tilleuls.
GPS: n44,98194 e2,63111.

10 free € 2 Ch € 2. **Location:** Rural, comfortable, quiet.
Surface: asphalted. 01/01-31/12.
Distance: 200m 200m 150m.
Remarks: Coins at tourist info, Avenue Mercier.

Vieille-Brioude 25A1

Rue de Combevignouse. **GPS:** n45,26540 e3,40557.

6 free € 2/10minutes Ch € 2/55minutes.
Location: Urban, simple, central, quiet. **Surface:** asphalted.
01/01-31/12.
Distance: 150m 200m.
Remarks: Service 200m.

Vieillevie 24G2

Aire de Vieillevie, Le Bourg. **GPS:** n44,64432 e2,41773.

5 free € 2/100liter Ch € 2/h. **Location:** Rural, comfortable, quiet. **Surface:** gravel. 01/01-31/12.
Distance: 50m 100m 50m 50m.

Vienne 25C1

Place Joseph Muray et Jean Tardy, N7. **GPS:** n45,53860 e4,87271.

6 free Chfree.
Location: Urban, simple, central, noisy. **Surface:** asphalted.
01/01-31/12 Fri market.
Distance: 50m 2km 50m 50m 50m.
Remarks: Max. 7 days, friday market.

Villards-de-Lans 25D2

Chemin des Bartavelles. **GPS:** n45,06619 e5,55609.

15 free. **Surface:** asphalted. 01/01-31/12.
Distance: 600m 600m 600m.
Remarks: Max. 48h.

Villars-les-Dombes 22C3

Parc des Oiseaux, RN83. **GPS:** n45,99126 e5,02582.

100 guests free. **Location:** Simple, quiet. **Surface:** asphalted/grassy.
01/01-31/12 sundays, holidays, winter.
Distance: 2km 1km 1km 2km 2km on the spot.
Remarks: Parking bird park, max. 1 night, gate closed from 21-8h.

Tourist information Villars-les-Dombes:
Parc des Oiseaux. Bird park, 23ha. 9.30-18.30h, winter 10-17.30h.

Villefranche-d'Allier 21H2

Avenue du 8 Mai 1945. **GPS:** n46,39565 e2,85672.

4 free € 2/10minutes Ch (4x)€ 2/2h WC.
Surface: asphalted. 01/01-31/12.
Distance: 150m 12km 150m 150m.
Remarks: Coins available at the shops.

Villefranche-sur-Saône 22C3

Camping-car Park, Route de Riottier. **GPS:** n45,97278 e4,75135.
128 € 13,30 Ch (128x)WC included.
Location: Urban, luxurious.
Surface: grassy.
01/01-31/12 sanitary 16/09-14/05.
Distance: A6 1,3km Station > Lyon 3,4km.
Remarks: Mandatory, one-time fee Pass'Etapes € 4, wifi code: 692712.

Villerest 22B3

Aire camping-car du Grezelon, D18, Route de Seigne.
GPS: n45,98610 e4,04300.

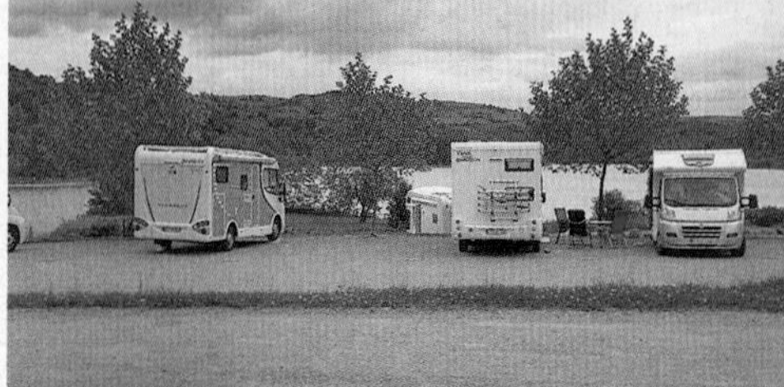

15 € 6, tourist tax € 0,25/pp € 4 Ch.
Surface: gravel. 01/01-31/12 service: 01/10-30/04.
Distance: on the spot 1km on the spot.
Remarks: At Lac du Villerest and barrage, max. 48h.

Violay 22B3

Place Giroud. **GPS:** n45,85268 e4,35564.

3 free € 2 Ch€ 2. **Location:** Rural, simple, quiet.
Surface: metalled. 01/01-31/12.
Distance: 100m A89 9km 200m 150m.
Remarks: Beautiful view.

Virieu 25D1

Rue du May, D17. **GPS:** n45,48166 e5,47746.

4 free ChWCfree. **Location:** Rural, simple, central, quiet.
Surface: gravel.
Distance: on the spot 200m 200m on the spot.
Remarks: Picnic area at edge of the village.

Viverols 25B1

Camping Le Pradoux, Le Ruisseau. **GPS:** n45,43123 e3,88279.

6 free € 2 Ch € 2. **Surface:** gravel. 01/04-31/10.

Vogüé 25B3

Chemin de Setras. **GPS:** n44,55163 e4,41308.

20 free. **Surface:** asphalted. 01/01-31/12.
Distance: 50m Ardèche 200m on the spot.
Remarks: At cemetery.

Vorey-sur-Arzon 25B1

Aire Les Moulettes, Chemin de Félines. **GPS:** n45,18667 e3,90489.

FR

5 €2 €3 Ch €4. **Location:** Rural, simple.
Surface: gravel. 01/01-31/12 service: 15/09-30/04.
Distance: 200m on the spot 200m 200m on the spot on the spot.
Remarks: Along river Arzon.

Ytrac 24G2

Aire camping-cars, Impasse Jean de la Fontaine.
GPS: n44,91510 e2,36368.

10 free €3,50 Ch €3,50. **Location:** Rural, simple, central.
Surface: asphalted. 01/01-31/12.
Distance: 150m 100m 150m.
Remarks: Max. 7 days, coins at shops and tourist office.

Nouvelle-Aquitaine

Accous 27B3

La Nabe, D339. **GPS:** n42,91028 w0,61939.

20 €12 Ch WC included.
Location: Rural, comfortable, isolated, quiet. **Surface:** grassy/gravel.
01/01-31/12.
Distance: 7km 100m on the spot.

Agris 21D3

Aire municipale, Le Pont d'Agris, D6. **GPS:** n45,78619 e0,33944.

2 free €2/100liter Ch €2/10minutes.
Location: Rural, simple, noisy. **Surface:** asphalted.
01/01-31/12.
Distance: 2km on the spot on the spot on the spot on the spot.

Aigre 21D3

Parc des Charmilles, Rue des Charrières. **GPS:** n45,89341 e0,00578.

5 €4 Ch (4x)WC included. **Surface:** metalled.
01/04-31/10.
Distance: 350m on the spot on the spot.
Remarks: 4th night free.

Aillas 24C3

À Bourg. **GPS:** n44,47514 w0,07318.

5 free Ch free. **Location:** Urban, simple, quiet.
Surface: gravel. 01/01-31/12.
Distance: 200m 100m.
Remarks: Next to sports fields.

Aire-sur-l'Adour 27C1

Rue des Graviers. **GPS:** n43,70333 w0,25535.

50 €3, 01/07-31/08 €4 €1 Ch.
Location: Rural, simple, quiet. **Surface:** gravel.
01/01-31/12 3rd week Jun.
Distance: 200m on the spot on the spot 200m.
Remarks: Near campsite, max. 72h.

Airvault 21D1

Rue Faubourg des Cyprès. **GPS:** n46,82516 w0,14219.

10 free Ch WC free. **Location:** Urban, simple, central.
Surface: asphalted. 01/01-31/12.
Distance: 250m 250m 250m.

Allassac 24F1

Avenue du Saillant. **GPS:** n45,25897 e1,47358.

4 free Ch (2x)free. **Location:** Urban, simple, noisy.
Surface: gravel/sand. 01/01-31/12.
Distance: 500m 5km 500m 500m.
Remarks: Parking station.

Andernos-les-Bains 24B2

Port Ostréicole, Avenue du Commandant Allègre.
GPS: n44,74477 w1,10969.

60 €12 €3/100liter Ch €2,10
Location: Urban, comfortable, quiet. **Surface:** grassy/metalled.
01/01-31/12.
Distance: 500m on the spot on the spot 50m.
Remarks: In harbour, max. 48h.

Anglet 27A1

Aire de camping-car de La Barre, Avenue de l'Adour, D405.
GPS: n43,52608 w1,51488.

50 free, Apr/June €6, July/Aug €10 €3 Ch.
Surface: grassy/metalled. 13/04-11/11.
Distance: 1km 300m 50m 500m 500m 100m.
Remarks: Private property.

Anglet 27A1

Parking "Haut" - Plage des Corsaires, Boulevard des Plages.
GPS: n43,50696 w1,53373.

80 €6, 01/07-31/08 €10, 06/11-01/04 free Ch included.
Surface: asphalted. 01/01-31/12.
Distance: 500m, Biarritz 2km 500m 500m 500m.
Remarks: Max. 24h, baker every morning.

Angliers 18D3

Aire de repos de la Briande, D347. **GPS:** n46,95861 e0,10472.

8 free Ch WC free. **Location:** Rural, comfortable, quiet.
Surface: asphalted. 01/01-31/12.
Distance: Angliers 1km 50m.

Angoisse 24E1

Le Pont du Jour, L'Hépital, D704. **GPS:** n45,43296 e1,44413.

8 €5 Ch included €3 €3. **Location:** Rural, simple.
Surface: grassy.
Distance: 500m 1km 4,5km.

FR

Angoulins 21B2
Rue du Chay. **GPS**: n46,10623 w1,13565.

17 € 3. **Location:** Rural, simple. **Surface:** asphalted.
Distance: 1km on the spot on the spot.

Angoulins 21B2
Chemin des Marais. **GPS**: n46,10602 e1,11710.
2€ 3/24h Chincluded. **Surface:** asphalted. 01/01-31/12.

Arcachon 24B2
Boulevard Mestrézat, D650. **GPS**: n44,65142 w1,14864.

20 free Chfree. **Location:** Urban, simple, noisy.
Surface: asphalted/gravel. 01/01-31/12.
Distance: 1km 50m.
Remarks: Max. 24h.

Arcachon 24B2
Avenue du Parc. **GPS**: n44,64868 w1,19672.

20 free.
Location: Simple, quiet. **Surface:** gravel.
01/01-31/12.
Distance: 500m 500m.
Tourist information Arcachon:
place du XI Novembre. Covered market. 01/06-31/08 daily 7-13h.

Arçais 21C2
Aire camping-cars du Coursault, Rue du Marais.
GPS: n46,29643 w0,68782.

20 € 8/24h Chincluded WCfree . **Location:** Simple, quiet.
Surface: grassy. 01/01-31/12 water disconnected in winter.
Distance: 400m on the spot 150m nearby on the spot.

Arette 27B2
Aire de camping car d'Arette, Place de la Mairie.
GPS: n43,09477 w0,71511.

10 free ChWC. **Location:** Simple. **Surface:** asphalted.
01/01-31/12.

Arzacq-Arraziguet 27C2
Aire de camping cars, Place du Marcadieu.
GPS: n43,53481 w0,41035.

10 free ChWCfree. **Location:** Urban. **Surface:** asphalted.
01/01-31/12.
Distance: on the spot 500m 500m 100m 100m.

Aubeterre-sur-Dronne 24D1
Base de Loisirs, D2, Route de Ribérac. **GPS**: n45,26934 e0,17586.

7 free Chfree. **Location:** Rural, simple, isolated, quiet.
Surface: gravel/metalled. 01/01-31/12.
Distance: 500m on the spot 300m 500m.
Remarks: At tennis-courts.
Tourist information Aubeterre-sur-Dronne:
Place de Village. Thu, Su.

Aubusson 21G3
Parking Champ de Foire, Rue des Fusilles, D988.
GPS: n45,95694 e2,17528.

70 free Ch WCfree.
Location: Urban. **Surface:** asphalted. 01/01-31/12.
Distance: 500m 500m 500m.

Aulnay 21C2
Place Charles de Gaulle, Rue Haute de l'Eglise.
GPS: n46,02306 w0,35444.

10 free WCfree. **Surface:** metalled. 01/01-31/12.
Distance: 200m 200m 200m.

Aulnay 21C2
Rue de Salles. **GPS**: n46,02239 w0,34528.

10 free. **Surface:** gravel.
Distance: 200m 200m 250m 200m.
Remarks: Max. 24h.

Auriat 21F3
Etang d'Auriat. **GPS**: n45,87790 e1,64277.

3 free Chfree. **Location:** Rural, isolated, quiet.
Surface: metalled. 01/01-31/12.
Distance: on the spot on the spot.
Remarks: At small lake.

Ayen 24F1
Route de la Noix, Ayen Bas. **GPS**: n45,24964 e1,32343.

20 free Chfree. **Location:** Rural, simple, quiet.
Surface: grassy/gravel. 01/01-31/12.
Distance: 300m.
Remarks: Nearby D39, campsite and sports grounds.

Azerat 24E1
Le Bourg. **GPS**: n45,14954 e1,12496.

6 € 2 € 3 Ch. **Location:** Urban, simple, quiet. **Surface:** gravel.
01/01-31/12.
Distance: 50m 150m.
Remarks: Pay at town hall.

Azur 27A1
Camping-Car Park, Route du Lac. **GPS**: n43,78842 w1,3119.

31 € 10,35 Ch included.
Location: Rural, quiet. **Surface:** gravel. 01/01-31/12.
Distance: 1,5km 150m 150m 200m on the spot on the spot.

Remarks: Mandatory, one-time fee Pass'Etapes € 4.

Badefols-sur-Dordogne 24E2

Le Bourg. **GPS**: n44,84254 e0,79160.

10 free € 2/100liter Ch WC free. **Location:** Rural, simple. **Surface:** asphalted. 01/01-31/12 Sa market.
Distance: on the spot bakery 50m.
Remarks: Coins at town hall.

Barbezieux-Saint-Hilaire 24C1

E.Leclerc, Rue du Commandant Foucaud. **GPS**: n45,47047 w0,16032.

8 free € 2/100liter Ch. **Location:** Urban, simple, central, noisy. **Surface:** asphalted. 01/01-31/12.
Distance: 500m on the spot on the spot.

Bazas 24C3

Rue de l'Eyrevieille. **GPS**: n44,43389 w0,21509.

5 free Ch WC free.
Surface: metalled. 01/01-31/12 Service: winter.
Distance: on the spot.

Beaumont du Périgord 24E2

Avenue Rhinau, D660. **GPS**: n44,77469 e0,76559.

20 free Ch free. **Surface:** asphalted. 01/01-31/12.
Distance: 800m.

Tourist information Beaumont du Périgord:
Bastide de Beaumont.

Bellac 21E2

Aire d'accueil camping-car rives du Vincou, Rue des Tanneries.
GPS: n46,11513 e1,05242.

4 free Ch free. **Location:** Rural, isolated, quiet. **Surface:** asphalted. 01/01-31/12.
Distance: 1km.
Remarks: Service 100m.

Bellac 21E2

Le Champ de foire, Rue des Doctrinaires.
GPS: n46,12085 e1,05018.

4 free. **Location:** Urban, simple. **Surface:** asphalted.
Distance: on the spot on the spot on the spot.
Remarks: >3,5t not allowed.

Bellac 21E2

Parking de la Mairie, Place de la République.
GPS: n46,12155 e1,04604.

2 free. **Location:** Urban, simple. **Surface:** asphalted. 01/01-31/12.
Distance: 300m.

Bénéjacq 27C2

L'Esplanade du Lagoin, Place de la Fontaine.
GPS: n43,19009 w0,20914.

6 free € 2/100liter Ch € 2/h. **Location:** Urban, comfortable, quiet. **Surface:** asphalted. 01/01-31/12.
Distance: 500m 50m 500m.
Remarks: Max. 48h, coins at the bakery, restaurant and pharmacy.

Bergerac 24D2

Parc Public de Pombonne, Avenue Marceau Feyry.
GPS: n44,87104 e0,50408.

6 free € 2/100liter Ch. **Location:** Simple.
Surface: metalled.
Distance: city centre 3km 1km.
Remarks: Max. 24h.

Tourist information Bergerac:
M Musée du Tabac, Maison Peyrarède, Place du Feu. History of tobacco. Mo-Fri 10-12h, 14-18, Sa 10-12h, 14-17h, Su 14.30-17.30h, Nov-Mar Mo-Fr.
Église Notre Dame, Rue Saint Esprit. Wed, Sa 7-13h.

Bernos-Beaulac 24C3

La Grande Route, N524. **GPS**: n44,36949 w0,24257.

10 € 4 € 2/10minutes Ch.
Location: Rural, simple, quiet. **Surface:** metalled. 01/01-31/12 water: frost.
Distance: river on the spot bakery 100m.
Remarks: Coins at petrol station.

Bessines-sur-Gartempe 21F2

Place du Champ de Foire, Rue d'Ingolsheim.
GPS: n46,10979 e1,37008.

4 free € 2 Ch € 2. **Location:** Urban, simple. **Surface:** asphalted. 01/01-31/12.
Distance: on the spot 900m 100m 50m.

Beynac-et-Cazenac 24E2

Le Parc, D703. **GPS**: n44,84466 e1,14560.

20 free.
Location: Rural, simple. **Surface:** gravel. 01/01-31/12.
Distance: historical centre 500m 500m.

Biarritz 27A2

Aire de camping-cars Gabrielle Dorziat, Allée Gabrielle Dorziat.
GPS: n43,45974 w1,56893.

19 € 12/24h Ch included. 01/01-31/12.
Remarks: Max. 48h.

Biarritz 27A2

Parking Milady, Avenue de la Milady. **GPS**: n43,46536 w1,57162.

50 € 12 Ch included. **Location:** Urban, simple.
Surface: asphalted. 01/01-31/12.
Distance: 500m 300m 500m 500m.
Remarks: Baker every morning.

Tourist information Biarritz:
Rue des Halles. daily.

FR

FR

S Biron 24E2

Route de Vergt de Biron. **GPS**: n44,63080 e0,87055.

10 free € 2/100liter Ch € 2/1h. **Location:** Simple.
Surface: grassy/metalled. 01/01-31/12 service 01/11-31/03.
Distance: 250m 250m on the spot.
Remarks: Coins at grocery.

S Biscarrosse 24B3

Port de Navarrosse, 710 chemin de Navarosse.
GPS: n44,43223 w1,16566.

80 € 12,50, 15/09-14/06 € 8, 15/07-31/08 € 16 Ch WC included.
Location: Simple. **Surface:** metalled. 01/01-31/12.
Distance: 4km 50m 100m 50m on the spot.
Remarks: Video surveillance.

S Biscarrosse 24B3

Rue des Viviers, Biscarrosse-plage. **GPS**: n44,46027 w1,24627.

180 € 12,50, 15/09-14/06 € 8, 15/07-31/08 € 16 Ch WC included. **Location:** Simple, quiet. **Surface:** forest soil.
01/05-31/10.
Distance: 2,5km 400m 100m 50m on the spot.
Remarks: Video surveillance.

S Blanquefort 24C2

Château Saint Ahon, Rue de Saint-Ahon.
GPS: n44,92663 w0,63217.

4 € 3 free.
Location: Urban, simple, central, quiet. **Surface:** gravel/metalled.
01/01-31/12 Su/holidays.
Distance: 300m 12km 300m on the spot.
Remarks: Arrival < 19h, max. 48h.

S Blasimon 24C2

Rue Abbé Greciet. **GPS**: n44,74836 w0,07537.

4 free Chfree. **Location:** Urban, simple, quiet.
Surface: gravel. 01/01-31/12.
Distance: 100m 100m 100m.

S Blasimon 24C2

Château la Peyraude, Bleurette. **GPS**: n44,73463 w0,09942.

15 € 5 Ch WC. **Location:** Rural, simple.
Surface: grassy. 01/01-31/12.
Distance: 3km.
Remarks: Arrival <22h, regional products.

Blaye 24C1

Parking de la Citadelle, Rue Pierre Semard.
GPS: n45,12549 w0,66535.

30 free. **Location:** Urban, simple, central, quiet.
Surface: gravel/metalled. 01/01-31/12.
Distance: 250m on the spot on the spot 300m 2km 300m.

S Blaye 24C1

Château le Cône, Route des Cônes. **GPS**: n45,13742 w0,66507.

12 free Ch (4x). **Location:** Rural, comfortable, quiet.
Surface: asphalted/gravel. 01/01-31/12.
Distance: 2km on the spot on the spot.

S Boismé 21C1

Rue des Essarts. **GPS**: n46,77765 w0,43347.

4 free ChWCfree. **Location:** Rural, isolated, quiet.
Surface: metalled. 01/01-31/12.
Distance: on the spot 500m 500m on the spot on the spot.
Remarks: At small lake, playground.

S Bort-les-Orgues 24H1

Rue de la Fontaine Grande. **GPS**: n45,39913 e2,49710.

6 free Chfree. **Location:** Urban, simple, central, quiet.
Surface: asphalted. 01/01-31/12.
Distance: 200m river 200m 200m.

S Bosmoreau-les-Mines 21F3

Le Bourg. **GPS**: n45,99936 e1,75194.

5 free Chfree. **Location:** Rural, simple, quiet.
Surface: gravel. 01/01-31/12.
Distance: 500m.

S Bouglon 24D3

Aire de Repos, Le Clavier. **GPS**: n44,38599 e0,10271.

4 free WCfree. **Location:** Rural, simple, quiet.
Surface: asphalted. 01/01-31/12.
Distance: 500m 500m 500m.
Remarks: Picnic area.

S Bougon 21D2

Musée des Tumulus, La Chapelle. **GPS**: n46,37845 w0,06825.

10 free free. **Location:** Rural, simple, isolated.
Surface: asphalted. 01/01-31/12.
Distance: 3km.
Remarks: Parking museum.

Bourcefranc-le-Chapus 21B3

Bois de Pin, Prise du Portail Rouge. **GPS**: n45,82611 w1,14278.

20 € 7,50.
Location: Isolated, quiet. **Surface:** gravel. 01/01-31/12.
Distance: 4km on the spot on the spot 3km.

Bourcefranc-le-Chapus 21B3

Rue du Président Kennedy. **GPS**: n45,84546 w1,14929.

10 free. **Location:** Urban, simple, central. **Surface:** asphalted.
01/01-31/12.
Distance: 250m 750m 250m 250m.
Remarks: Max. 24h.

Bourcefranc-le-Chapus 21B3

Camping de la Giroflée, Fief de Bonnemort.
GPS: n45,83112 w1,15073.
€ 3/100liter Ch. 01/05-31/10.
Distance: 2,5km on the spot.
Remarks: Coins at tourist info and town hall.

Bourdeilles 24E1

Plaine des Loisirs, Le Bourg. **GPS**: n45,32270 e0,58260.

40+ € 4,50 € 2/100liter Ch. **Location:** Comfortable, quiet.
Surface: grassy. 01/01-31/12.
Distance: 500m on the spot on the spot 200m 200m.
Remarks: Coins at the shops.

Bourg-sur-Gironde 24C1

Quai Jean Bart. **GPS**: n45,03794 w0,55699.

10 € 5 € 3. **Location:** Urban, simple, central. **Surface:** asphalted.
01/01-31/12.
Distance: on the spot On the river Gironde on the spot on the spot.

Bourganeuf 21F3

Place de l'Etang, Avenue du Dr Butaud. **GPS**: n45,95444 e1,75750.

10 free Ch free. **Location:** Urban. **Surface:** gravel.
01/01-31/12 tue-evening, wed-morning (market).
Distance: on the spot 300m on the spot.
Remarks: Max. 48h.

Branne 24C2

Route de Cabara. **GPS**: n44,83191 w0,18448.

3 free € 2/100liter Ch € 2/1h.
Location: Urban, simple, noisy.
Distance: on the spot on the spot 500m 500m.

Brantôme 24E1

Chemin de Vert Galant. **GPS**: n45,36134 e0,64842.

50 € 5,50 € 2/12minutes Ch. **Location:** Simple, quiet.
Surface: grassy. 01/01-31/12.
Distance: 200m 100m 300m.

Brantôme 24E1

Aire Camping-cars Font Vendôme, Route de Nontron.
GPS: n45,37924 e0,64588.

4 € 2 € 2 Ch € 1/night WC.
Location: Simple. **Surface:** asphalted. 01/01-31/12.
Distance: 3,5km 1km 1km.
Remarks: Money in envelope in mail box.

Tourist information Brantôme:
Fri-morning.

Bressuire 21C1

Place Labâte. **GPS**: n46,84417 w0,49086.

5 free Ch free. **Location:** Urban, simple, noisy. **Surface:** sand.
01/01-31/12.
Distance: 400m 400m 400m.

Brive-la-Gaillarde 24F1

Rue des 3 Provinces. **GPS**: n45,16486 e1,54170.

12 first night € 9, € 7 each additional night + tourist tax € 0,60/pp
Ch (12x)€ 3/6h. **Location:** Urban, simple.
Surface: asphalted.
Distance: 1km 150m 500m.
Remarks: Free bus to centre.

Bujaleuf 21F3

Route du Champ de Foire. **GPS**: n45,80418 e1,63696.

5 free Ch free. **Location:** Rural, simple, quiet.
Surface: gravel. 01/01-31/12.
Distance: 1,5km on the spot 1,5km.
Remarks: Max. 24h, service 1,5km GPS N45,79747 E1,63141.

Burie 21C3

Place du Champ de Foire, Avenue de la Republique.
GPS: n45,77185 w0,42487.

5 free Ch free. **Location:** Urban, simple, central, quiet.
Surface: grassy. 01/01-31/12.
Distance: on the spot 300m 300m.

Bussière-Poitevine 21E2

Croix de l'Hosanne, Rue du Quatriéme Zouave.
GPS: n46,23670 e0,90173.

10 free € 2/100liter Ch WC. **Location:** Rural.
Surface: gravel. 15/03-14/11.
Distance: 450m.
Remarks: Coins at the shops.

Buzet-sur-Baïse 24D3

Port de Buzet-Val d'Albret. **GPS**: n44,25799 e0,30569.

20 € 7 € 2 Ch € 2 WC € 2 € 2 € 2/24h.
Location: Rural, comfortable. **Surface:** grassy. 01/01-31/12.
Distance: 6,5km on the spot 350m 350m on the spot on the spot.

Cadillac 24C2

Avenue du Parc. **GPS**: n44,63871 w0,31721.

10 free Ch free. **Location:** Urban, simple. **Surface:** asphalted.
01/01-31/12.

FR

Distance: on the spot 100m 100m 100m.
Remarks: Max. 3 nights, closed when frosty.

S Cambo-les-Bains 27A2

Chemin Arroka. **GPS**: n43,35537 w1,41173.
44 € 10 Ch included. **Surface:** metalled.
01/01-31/12.
Distance: 500m 100m 500m 200m.

S Cancon 24E3

Rue des Écoles. **GPS**: n44,53638 e0,62562.

10 free Ch WC free. **Location:** Simple. **Surface:** metalled.
01/01-31/12.
Distance: 100m 100m 100m.

S Capbreton 27A1

Plage l'Océanide, Parking des Ortolans, Allée des Ortolans.
GPS: n43,63578 w1,44681.

135 € 10-18 Ch (120x) WC included.
Surface: asphalted. 15/11-31/03.
Distance: 1,5km on the spot on the spot 1,5km 1,5km.
Remarks: Beach parking, 14/07-20/08: max. 2 nights.

FR

S Capian 24C2

D13/Chemin de Lavergne. **GPS**: n44,71177 w0,33093.

25 free € 2/10minutes Ch € 2/55minutes.
Location: Rural, simple, quiet. **Surface:** gravel.
01/01-31/12.
Distance: 500m.

S Carcans 24B1

Route de Bombannes, Maubuisson. **GPS**: n45,08545 w1,14866.

20 € 6,10 Ch free € 2. **Location:** Rural, simple, isolated, quiet. **Surface:** asphalted/gravel. 01/07-31/08.
Distance: 2km 400m 2km 2km on the spot on the spot.

Tourist information Carcans:
Office de Tourisme, Maison de la Station, www.carcans-maubuisson.com. Touristic town between the ocean and a wine region, 120km signposted cycle routes.

S Casseneuil 24E3

Rue Grande, D225. **GPS**: n44,44667 e0,61861.

20 free Ch free. **Location:** Rural, simple. **Surface:** asphalted.
01/01-31/12.
Distance: 100m on the spot on the spot 100m 800m.

S Castelculier 24E3

GPS: n44,17475 e0,69452.

5 free € 2 Ch. **Location:** Urban, simple, quiet.
Surface: metalled. 01/01-31/12.
Distance: 200m.

S Casteljaloux 24D3

Ste Castel Chalets, D933. **GPS**: n44,29230 e0,07361.

11 € 10, Jul/Aug € 15, dog € 3 Ch WC included.
Location: Rural, comfortable, quiet. **Surface:** gravel/sand.
01/04-31/10.
Distance: 2km Lac de Clarens.

S Casteljaloux 24D3

Impasse de la Fôret. **GPS**: n44,31068 e0,07933.

4 free Ch free. **Location:** Rural, simple, quiet.
Surface: asphalted. 01/01-31/12.
Distance: 250m 250m.
Remarks: Parking at swimming pool, max. 48h.

S Casteljaloux 24D3

La Taillade, Route de la Forge, La Réunion.
GPS: n44,26998 e0,08004.

4 € 8 Ch included. **Location:** Rural, isolated, quiet.
Surface: forest soil. 01/04-31/10.

S Caumont-sur-Garonne 24D3

Bourg de Caumont. **GPS**: n44,44202 e0,17887.

14 free € 1 Ch € 1/2h. **Location:** Rural, simple, quiet.
Surface: gravel. 01/01-31/12.
Distance: 8km on the spot.

S Cellefrouin 21D3

D739. **GPS**: n45,89361 e0,38639.

20 free Ch WC free. **Location:** Rural, simple, quiet.
Surface: gravel. 01/01-31/12.
Distance: 300m.

S Celles-sur-Belle 21D2

Place de l'Aumônerie, Rue des Halles.
GPS: n46,26278 w0,20806.

10 free Ch free. **Location:** Urban, simple, quiet.
Surface: gravel. 01/01-31/12.
Distance: 100m 100m 100m.

Chabanais 21E3

Chemin des Tanneries, N141. **GPS**: n45,87447 e0,72008.

4 free. **Location:** Urban, simple, central, noisy. **Surface:** asphalted.
01/01-31/12 Thu.
Distance: on the spot on the spot 100m 100m.
Remarks: Along the river Vienne.

S Chalus 21E3

Aire des Energies, Avenue Jean Jaurès. **GPS**: n45,66095 e0,98798.

10 free € 2 Ch € 2.
Location: Simple. **Surface:** gravel.
Distance: 1,2km on the spot.
Remarks: Behind petrol station.

S Chamberet 21F3

Ris Combeix. **GPS**: n45,57926 e1,70843.

7 free (1x). **Location:** Rural, comfortable, isolated, quiet. **Surface:** grassy.
Distance: 1,3km 1,3km.

Chamberet 21F3

Route de St Dulcet. **GPS**: n45,57961 e1,72051.

4 free . **Location:** Urban, simple, quiet.
Surface: gravel. 01/01-31/12.
Distance: 900m.
Remarks: Next to football ground.

Chambon-sur-Voueize 21H2

Rue du Stade. **GPS**: n46,18579 e2,43426.

4 free € 2/10minutes € 2/1h. **Location:** Rural, quiet.
Surface: asphalted. 01/01-31/12 service 01/11-31/03.
Distance: 500m 500m 200m.
Remarks: Near camping municipal.

Chamboulive 24F1

GPS: n45,42255 e1,71639.
10 free € 2 € 2/h. 01/01-31/12.
Distance: 1,2km 1,2km 1,2km.

Chasseneuil-sur-Bonnieure 21D3

Rue de la Gare, Place du Champ de Mars.
GPS: n45,82493 e0,45172.

3 free € 2/100liter € 2/1h WCfree.
Location: Urban, simple, central, noisy. **Surface:** gravel.
01/01-31/12.
Distance: on the spot 3km on the spot on the spot 400m.
Remarks: At supermarket.

Château-Larcher 21D2

Val de Clouère. **GPS**: n46,41444 e0,31556.

10 € 5 WCincluded.
Location: Rural, comfortable, isolated, quiet. **Surface:** grassy/gravel.
01/03-30/11.
Distance: 300m 100m 300m 300m.
Remarks: At small lake, former campsite, baker every morning.

Château-l'Evêque 24E1

Place de la Fontaine. **GPS**: n45,24472 e0,68743.

8 free € 2 € 2. **Location:** Urban. **Surface:** gravel.
01/03-31/10 summer: Su (flea market).
Distance: 50m 100m on the spot.
Remarks: Max. 48h, coins at shops in the village 08-21h.

Châteauneuf-sur-Charente 21D3

Rue du Prieuré. **GPS**: n45,59876 w0,05655.

4 free € 2/10minutes € 2/10minutes .
Location: Urban, simple, central, quiet. **Surface:** asphalted.
01/01-31/12.
Distance: on the spot 100m 300m.

Châtelaillon-Plage 21B2

Camping-Car Park, Avenue de l'Hippodrome.
GPS: n46,07253 w1,07886.

51 € 12,46 (48x) included.
Location: Rural, simple. **Surface:** asphalted/grassy.
01/01-31/12.
Distance: 700m 800m 700m.
Remarks: Mandatory, one-time fee Pass'Etapes € 4.

Châtelaillon-Plage 21B2

Les Boucholeurs, Avenue de l'Abbé Guichard.
GPS: n46,05538 w1,08738.

7 free. **Surface:** asphalted. 01/01-31/12.

Distance: 150m 150m 150m.
Remarks: Max. 48h.

Châtelus-le-Marcheix 21F3

Rue du Tursaud. **GPS**: n45,99894 e1,60339.

8 free € 2 € 2. **Location:** Rural.
Surface: gravel/metalled. 01/01-31/12.
Distance: 300m 300m 300m.
Remarks: Next to camping municipal.

Chef-Boutonne 21D2

Aire camping-cars, Chemin du Parc. **GPS**: n46,10982 w0,07869.

20 free WCfree.
Surface: grassy/gravel. 01/04-31/10.
Distance: 800m 300m 800m on the spot.

Chénérailles 21G2

Route d'Aubusson, lotissement Marlaud, D990.
GPS: n46,11058 e2,17753.

5 free € 4 € 4. **Location:** Simple. **Surface:** asphalted.
01/01-31/12.
Distance: 200m 50m 100m.
Remarks: Coins available at restaurant le Coq d'Or (50m).

Cherves-Richemont 21C3

Allee des Coquelicots. **GPS**: n45,74030 w0,35607.

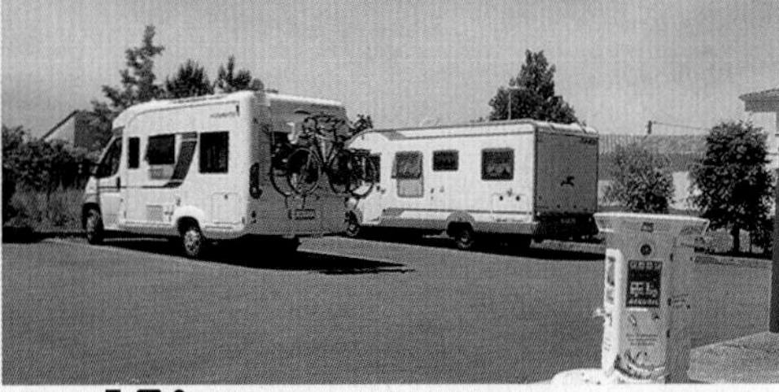

5 free free. **Location:** Rural, simple, quiet.
Surface: asphalted. 01/01-31/12 service: 01/11-15/04.
Distance: 500m 100m 500m.
Remarks: Bread-service.

Chey 21D2

Place de la Liberté. **GPS**: n46,30412 w0,05002.

4 free WCfree. **Location:** Rural, comfortable, quiet.

FR

Surface: asphalted. 01/01-31/12.
Distance: on the spot.

S Cieux 21E3

Avenue du Lac. **GPS:** n45,99173 e1,04939.

25 € 8 € 2 Ch € 1,50. **Location:** Simple.
Surface: grassy. 15/04-15/10.
Distance: 100m.

S Civrac-en-Médoc 24B1

Route de Montignac, Montignac. **GPS:** n45,33619 w0,922.

5 free. **Location:** Rural, simple, isolated, quiet. **Surface:** gravel.
01/01-31/12.
Distance: 2km.

S Clérac 24C1

Étang des Prés de Réaux, Route des Vignes.
GPS: n45,17906 w0,228.

8 free Ch free. **Location:** Rural, simple, isolated, quiet.
Surface: gravel. 01/01-31/12.
Distance: 200m on the spot 100m 100m on the spot on the spot.
Remarks: At small lake, max. 1 night.

S Cognac 21C3

Place de la Levade, Quartier Saint-Jacques. **GPS:** n45,69847 w0,33265.

7 free € 2/100liter Ch € 2/h.
Location: Urban, simple, central. **Surface:** asphalted.
01/01-31/12.
Distance: on the spot 100m 500m on the spot on the spot.
Remarks: Along the Charente river.

Tourist information Cognac:
Otard. Cognac distillery in 16th century castle. Guided tour and tasting. daily 01/10-31/03 weekend.
M Cognac-musée. Culture around the Cognac. 01/10-31/05 14-17.30h, 01/06-30/09 10-12h, 14-18h.

S Collonges-la-Rouge 24F2

Parking le Marchadial. GPS: n45,05833 e1,65889.

20 free, 01/03-31/10 € 8/24h Ch WC included.
Location: Rural, simple, quiet. **Surface:** gravel.
01/01-31/12.
Distance: 500m 500m 500m 1km.

S Concèze 24F1

D56E. **GPS:** n45,35472 e1,34583.

3 free Ch free. **Location:** Rural, simple, quiet.
Surface: gravel. 01/01-31/12.
Distance: on the spot.

S Confolens 21E2

Camping les Ribières, Avenue de Sainte-Germain.
GPS: n46,01894 e0,67570.

12 € 8, July-Aug € 10 Ch € 6 included.
Location: Rural, simple, central, noisy. **Surface:** metalled.
01/01-31/12 service: 30/09-01/04.
Distance: 750m on the spot 500m 500m on the spot on the spot on the spot.
Remarks: Canoe rental.

Tourist information Confolens:
Wed, Sa.

S Contis-Plage 24A3

Avenue du Phare. **GPS:** n44,09333 w1,31861.

70 € 9, 01/06-01/09 € 13/24h, 01/12-28/02 free € 2 Ch WC.
Location: Simple. **Surface:** gravel.
01/01-31/12.
Distance: 200m on the spot.
Remarks: Max. 72h.

S Couhé 21D2

Place du Marché. **GPS:** n46,29906 e0,17882.

25 free Ch WC free. **Location:** Urban, simple, central, quiet.
Surface: asphalted. 01/01-31/12.
Distance: 200m 200m 200m.

S Coulon 21C2

Parking d'Autremont, Rue André Cramois.
GPS: n46,32102 w0,59063.

80 € 8,50 Ch WC included. **Location:** Urban, comfortable. **Surface:** grassy/gravel. 01/04-30/11.
Distance: 350m 350m 350m on the spot on the spot.

S Coulonges-sur-l'Autize 21C1

Avenue de la Gare. **GPS:** n46,48011 w0,59393.

2 free Ch WC free. **Location:** Urban, simple, noisy.
Surface: asphalted. 01/01-31/12.
Distance: 450m 350m 350m.
Remarks: Max. 24h, picnic area.

S Coutras 24D1

Aux Petits Rois, Rue des Grands Champs 10.
GPS: n45,02509 w0,09662.

8 voluntary contribution Ch free.
Location: Rural, simple, isolated, quiet. 01/01-31/12.
Distance: 2km 2km 2km.
Remarks: Friday-Saturday market.

S Créon 24C2

Vélo-centre, Boulevard Victor Hugo, D20.
GPS: n44,77663 w0,34806.

5 free € 3 Ch € 3/4h.
Location: Urban, simple. **Surface:** asphalted.
01/01-31/12 tue-evening, wed-morning (market).
Distance: 500m 500m on the spot.

S Cressat 21G2

D990, Rue de la Prade. **GPS:** n46,13956 e2,11015.

FR

5 free € 3/100liter Ch € 3/h. **Location:** Rural. **Surface:** asphalted. 01/01-31/12.
Distance: 100m 500m.
Remarks: At fish lake, coins at superette 'la Montagne' (500m) and town hall.

S Criteuil la Magdeleine 21C3

Le Bourg. **GPS**: n45,53788 w0,21597.

3 free Ch WCfree. **Location:** Rural, simple, quiet. **Surface:** asphalted. 01/01-31/12.
Distance: on the spot.

S Cussac 21E3

Jardin de la Palène, Rue du 8 Mai 1945.
GPS: n45,70519 e0,84936.

4 free € 2 Ch (2x)€ 2. **Location:** Rural, comfortable, quiet. **Surface:** grassy/gravel. 01/04-31/10.
Distance: 200m 200m 100m.
Remarks: Coins at town hall, bar and restaurant.

S Damazan 24D3

Gites La Vignerai, Route Cap de Bosc. **GPS**: n44,28130 e0,26285.

6 € 9 € 1 Ch€ 1 € 1/day WC € 5 .
Location: Simple. 01/01-31/12.
Distance: 500m 1km.

S Dampniat 24F1

Stade, Le Mas. **GPS**: n45,16262 e1,63728.

4 free € 2/10minutes Ch (2x)€ 2/55minutes.
Location: Rural, simple, quiet. **Surface:** gravel.
Distance: 850m.
Remarks: At sports centre.

S Dax 27B1

Parking du Pont des Arènes, Boulevard des Sports.
GPS: n43,71427 w1,04931.

8 free free. **Location:** Urban, simple, noisy. **Surface:** asphalted. 01/01-31/12.
Distance: on the spot on the spot 1km.
Remarks: Max. 72h, saturday market in the halls.

Tourist information Dax:

Office de Tourisme, 11, cours Foch, www.dax.fr. Health resort with warm water sources and medicinal mud.

S Dolus-d'Oléron 21B3

Route du Stade. **GPS**: n45,91137 w1,25255.

40 € 6 € 4/100liter € 4/1h. **Location:** Rural, simple. **Surface:** grassy/metalled. 01/01-31/12.
Distance: 500m 1,2km Hypermarché.
Remarks: Coins at tourist info.

S Domme 24F2

Le Pradal. GPS: n44,80053 e1,22156.

20 € 9/24h € 2/100liter Ch € 2/1h.
Location: Simple, quiet. **Surface:** asphalted.
01/01-31/12 Service: winter.
Distance: 500m 500m.

Tourist information Domme:

Office de Tourisme, Place de la Halle, www.ot-domme.com. Fortified city worth seeing, parking for motorhomes outside of the town, being indicated.

S Dompierre-sur-Charente 21C3

Camping Municipal du Pré St Jean, Rue de Saintonge.
GPS: n45,70099 w0,49438.

5 € 2 water incl. € 4 Ch. **Location:** Rural, simple, isolated. **Surface:** gravel/metalled. 15/06-15/09.
Distance: on the spot 300m 100m 100m.
Remarks: Coins at the bakery and campsite.

S Donzenac 24F1

Village de Vacance La Rivière, Rue de la Riviere.
GPS: n45,21897 e1,51829.

10 free Ch € 4,20/night WCfree. **Location:** Rural, simple, quiet. **Surface:** gravel. 01/01-31/12.
Distance: 4km 1,3km 4km 400m.
Remarks: Max. 48h.

S Douchapt 24D1

Beauclair. **GPS**: n45,25145 e0,44335.

€ 5 € 2/100liter Ch € 2/1h. **Location:** Rural, simple, isolated. **Surface:** metalled. 01/01-31/12.
Distance: 1,5km Dronne river 1,5km.
Remarks: Pay and coins at Village Vacances Beauclair.

S Duras 24D2

Municipal du Château de Duras, Le Bourg.
GPS: n44,67755 e0,17854.

5 free, July-Aug € 2,60 + € 3,15/pp Chfree € 2,10 WC .
Location: Rural, simple, quiet. **Surface:** grassy.
01/01-31/12.
Distance: 350m 350m 350m.

S Eaux-Bonnes 27C3

Parking du Ley, D918, Gourette. **GPS**: n42,96304 w0,33933.

60 € 10 Ch € 5 WC included. **Location:** Rural, simple. **Surface:** asphalted. 01/01-31/12.
Distance: 1,4km 1,4km 1,4km 1,4km.

S Echillais 21B3

Place de la Carrière. **GPS**: n45,89753 w0,95545.

15 € 7,20 ChWCincluded. **Location:** Rural, simple. **Surface:** asphalted. 01/01-31/12.
Remarks: Access via rue de l'église.

FR

Egletons 24G1

Parking Espace Ventadour, Rue Henri Dignac.
GPS: n45,40406 e2,04791.

20 free € 2/100liter Ch.
Location: Urban, simple, quiet. **Surface:** gravel.
01/01-31/12 Service: winter.
Distance: 300m 3,5km 300m 300m.

Espés Undurein 27B2

Etche Gochoki, D11. **GPS**: n43,26388 w0,88083.

6 € 8 € 2 Ch € 2. **Surface:** grassy/metalled.
01/01-31/12.
Distance: 500m 500m 400m.

Excideuil 24E1

Rue Léon Barreau. **GPS**: n45,33614 e1,05269.

4 free Ch € 3. **Location:** Urban, simple, noisy.
Surface: asphalted. 01/01-31/12.
Distance: on the spot 100m 100m.

Felletin 21G3

Parking Lagrange, Avenue Joffre. **GPS**: n45,88308 e2,17667.

10 free ChWCfree. **Location:** Urban, quiet. **Surface:** gravel.
01/01-31/12.
Distance: on the spot.

Fontet 24D2

Base de Loisirs Fontet. **GPS**: n44,56118 w0,02282.

20 € 9 Ch WCincluded € 1. **Location:** Rural, comfortable, quiet. **Surface:** grassy/gravel. 01/01-31/12.
Distance: on the spot bakery 500m, supermarket 4km.
Remarks: At lake, near marina.

Forgès 24G1

Camping-Car Park, Rue Pierre et Marie Curie.
GPS: n45,15403 e1,87089.

33 € 9,15 Ch (12x) included. **Location:** Rural, comfortable, quiet. **Surface:** grassy. 01/01-31/12.
Distance: on the spot on the spot.
Remarks: Mandatory, one-time fee Pass'Etapes € 4.

Fouras 21B2

Plage Nord, Avenue du Cadoret. **GPS**: n45,99194 w1,08694.

20 € 8,20/24h € 1/50liter. **Location:** Urban, simple.
Surface: metalled. 01/01-31/12.
Distance: on the spot on the spot on the spot.
Remarks: In front of campsite Cadoret, Fun golf, max. 48h, coins at campsite and tourist info.

Fouras 21B2

Prairie du Casino, Avenue du Bois Vert. **GPS**: n45,99583 w1,10611.

30 € 8,20/24h. **Location:** Rural, simple. **Surface:** metalled.
01/01-31/12.
Distance: on the spot on the spot on the spot.
Remarks: Max. 48h.

Fourques-sur-Garonne 24D3

Halte Nautique d Pont des Sables, Pont des Sables, D933.
GPS: n44,46081 e0,13932.

4 free Chfree. **Location:** Urban, simple. **Surface:** metalled.
01/03-31/10.
Distance: Fourques 2,5km 3km on the spot.

Fromental 21F2

Place Jean Theillaud. **GPS**: n46,15950 e1,39643.

4 free Ch (4x) WCfree. **Location:** Rural, quiet.
Surface: gravel. 01/01-31/12.
Distance: on the spot on the spot.
Remarks: Near church.

Frontenac 24C2

D236. **GPS**: n44,73781 w0,16308.

10 free WC free. **Location:** Rural, simple.
Surface: grassy/gravel. 01/01-31/12.
Distance: 200m 200m bakery 200m on the spot.
Remarks: Behind town hall, max. 48h.

Fumel 24E3

Place Du Saulou, rue Massenet, D911. **GPS**: n44,49809 e0,97165.

10 free ChWCfree. **Location:** Urban, simple.
Surface: asphalted. 01/01-31/12.
Distance: 200m 200m.
Remarks: Château de Bonaguil 7km.

Gan 27C2

Cave de Gan Jurançon, Avenue Henri IV. **GPS**: n43,23670 w0,38979.

free € 2 Ch WC.
Location: Simple.
Surface: asphalted.
Distance: 900m on the spot bakery.
Remarks: Coins at Cave de Gan Jurançon, service accross the street.

Gan 27C2

Le Clos Husté, Chemin de Cours-Husté. **GPS**: n43,19703 w0,41247.
5 free. **Location:** Simple.
Distance: 5km.

Garlin 27C2

Place du Marcadieu. **GPS**: n43,55854 w0,27533.
free Chfree. **Location:** Urban. **Surface:** metalled.
01/01-31/12.
Distance: 450m 150m 400m.

Gastes 24B3

Port de Gastes, Avenue du Lac. **GPS**: n44,32880 w1,15068.

100 € 2-4,50, 01/06-30/09 € 8 ChWCincluded.
Location: Comfortable. **Surface:** grassy.
01/01-31/12 Service: winter.
Distance: Parentis-en-Born 7km on the spot on the spot 800m 800m.
Remarks: Along lake, baker every morning.

Gastes — 24B3

Camping Les Echasses, 193 rue de Bernadon.
GPS: n44,31871 w1,13879.

6 €7-9 € 3 Ch included. **Location:** Simple.
Surface: grassy. 01/01-31/12.
Distance: Gastes Lac 2km on the spot.
Remarks: Max. 1 night, no camping activities.

Gencay — 21D2

Place du Champs de Foire. **GPS**: n46,37315 e0,40638.

10 free € 2 Ch € 2 WC. **Location:** Urban, simple, noisy.
Surface: grassy/metalled. 01/01-31/12.
Distance: 200m 200m 200m.
Remarks: Coins at the shops.

Genté — 21C3

Rue de l'Eglise. **GPS**: n45,62861 w0,315.

6 free Ch (6x) WC free. **Location:** Rural, comfortable, quiet. **Surface:** asphalted. 01/01-31/12.
Distance: on the spot.

Gornac — 24C2

Aire Municipale, Esplanade Fongave. **GPS**: n44,66020 w0,18129.

30 free Ch free. **Location:** Rural, simple, quiet.
Surface: asphalted. 01/01-31/12.
Distance: 200m 200m.

Gouzon — 21G2

Place du Champ de Foire, Rue d'Alcantera.
GPS: n46,19139 e2,24028.

6 free Ch free. **Location:** Rural, simple, quiet.
Surface: metalled/sand. 01/01-31/12.
Distance: 300m 300m 300m.

Grayan-et-l'Hôpital — 24B1

Route de l'Océan. **GPS**: n45,43332 w1,1437.

30 free € 3,50 Ch € 3,50.
Location: Rural, simple, isolated, quiet. **Surface:** forest soil.
Distance: 5km 200m 100m on the spot on the spot on the spot.
Remarks: Near campsite, coins at campsite.

Grenade-sur-l'Adour — 27C1

Place du 19 mars 1962. **GPS**: n43,77500 w0,43472.

10 free Ch WC free. **Location:** Rural, simple.
Surface: asphalted/gravel.
Distance: 100m 100m 100m.
Remarks: Next to cemetery, max. 24h.

Grézillac — 24C2

D11. **GPS**: n44,81727 w0,21692.

10 free. **Location:** Rural, simple, quiet. **Surface:** gravel.
01/01-31/12.
Distance: 3km on the spot.

Guéret — 21G2

Aire des Monts de Guéret, RN145. **GPS**: n46,18189 e1,85837.
16 free € 2/100liter Ch free. **Surface:** asphalted.
01/01-31/12.
Distance: centre 4km 500m.

Hagetmau — 27C1

Rue de Piquette. **GPS**: n43,65398 w0,5983.

5 free Ch free.
Location: Rural, quiet. **Surface:** asphalted.
Distance: 500m 500m 1,5km.

Hautefort — 24E1

Route de Boisseuil. **GPS**: n45,26017 e1,14907.

3 free Ch € 2 WC free. **Location:** Simple.
Surface: asphalted. 01/01-31/12.
Distance: 50m 100m Intermarché 1km.

Tourist information Hautefort:
Château Hautefort. Classified castle. 01/04-30/09 daily, 01/10-31/03 afternoons 12/11-29/02.
Wed-morning.

Hendaye — 27A2

Gare des deux Jumeaux, Rue d'Ansoenia.
GPS: n43,37019 w1,7648.

25 € 10 € 2/100liter Ch € 2/1h. **Location:** Urban, simple. **Surface:** asphalted. 01/01-31/12.
Distance: on the spot 800m 450m 450m on the spot.
Remarks: Railway-station Hendaye-plage, max. 3 days, nights closed with barrier.

Hiers-Brouage — 21B3

D3. **GPS**: n45,86242 w1,07799.

20 free.
Location: Rural. **Surface:** grassy/gravel. 01/01-31/12.
Distance: 250m 250m 250m.
Remarks: Arrival >20h, departure <9h.

Hiers-Brouage — 21B3

Rue Palissy, D3. **GPS**: n45,85284 w1,07745.
€ 4 Ch . **Surface:** metalled. 01/01-31/12.

Hiersac — 21D3

Route de Chateauneuf. **GPS**: n45,66603 w0,00095.

3 free € 2/10minutes Ch € 2/h . **Location:** Rural, simple, quiet. **Surface:** asphalted. 01/01-31/12.
Distance: 500m 500m 500m.
Remarks: Picnic tables available.

Hostens — 24C3

Parking, La Hourcade. **GPS**: n44,49718 w0,64867.
5 free WC. **Surface:** metalled/sand.
Distance: 1,2km 1.2km on the spot on the spot.
Remarks: At lake, picnic area.

Houeillès — 24D3

Aire de Repos, Rue du 19 Mars 1962. **GPS**: n44,19611 e0,03250.

FR

15 free WCfree. **Location:** Rural, simple, quiet.
Surface: grassy/gravel. 01/01-31/12.
Distance: 100m 250m.
Remarks: Max. 24h.

S Hourtin 24B1

Aire de camping Car Hourtin, 108, Avenue du Lac.
GPS: n45,18083 w1,08056.

90 € 7,90, 01/04-30/09 € 10,50 Ch (40x)€ 2 WCincluded.
Location: Urban, comfortable, central, quiet.
Surface: gravel/metalled. 01/01-31/12.
Distance: 50m 50m 50m.

S Jarnages 21G2

Route des Promenctes, D65. **GPS**: n46,18417 e2,08098.

6 free € 2 Ch € 2. **Location:** Rural, simple, quiet.
Surface: asphalted. 01/01-31/12.
Distance: 500m on the spot 500m 500m.
Remarks: At tennis-courts.

S Javerdat 21E3

Le Bourg. **GPS**: n45,95249 e0,98582.

4 free € 2/100liter Ch € 2/55minutes WC. **Location:** Rural, quiet. **Surface:** gravel. 01/01-31/12.
Distance: 100m.
Remarks: Coins at Auberge Limousine (100m).

S Jonzac 24C1

Place du 8 Mai 1945. **GPS**: n45,44800 w0,433.

18 free € 4,20/100liter Ch € 4,20/h. **Location:** Urban, simple, central. **Surface:** asphalted. 01/01-31/12.
Distance: 500m 200m 200m on the spot.
Remarks: Max. 24h, coins at tourist info.

Jonzac 24C1

Chez M. Alex Beurg, Chez Marchand. **GPS**: n45,44121 w0,40427.
3 free. **Location:** Rural, simple, isolated, quiet. **Surface:** grassy.
01/01-31/12.
Remarks: Max. 24h.

S Jumilhac-le-Grand 24E1

Boulevard du Pigeonnier, D78. **GPS**: n45,49219 e1,06092.

2 free Chfree. **Location:** Urban, simple. **Surface:** asphalted.
01/01-31/12.
Distance: on the spot 200m bakery 200m.
Remarks: Near Château de Jumilhac.

S L'Hôpital-Saint-Blaise 27B2

Parking l'Église, D25. **GPS**: n43,25088 w0,76925.

5 free WCfree. **Location:** Rural, simple. **Surface:** asphalted.
01/01-31/12.
Distance: on the spot on the spot on the spot on the spot.

S La Brée-les-Bains 21B2

Rue de la Baudette. **GPS**: n46,00810 w1,35764.

50 free € 4,50 Ch. **Location:** Rural, simple, quiet.
Surface: asphalted. 01/01-31/12.
Distance: 200m.
Remarks: Coins at tourist info.

S La Coquille 24E1

N21, Place de l'église. **GPS**: n45,54245 e0,97702.

5 free ChWCfree. **Location:** Urban, simple, central.
Surface: asphalted. 01/01-31/12.
Distance: 100m 200m 200m.

S La Couronne 21D3

Rue du Champs de Foire. **GPS**: n45,60619 e0,10015.

10 free ChWCfree.
Location: Urban, simple, central. **Surface:** asphalted.
01/01-31/12 Wed-morning, Sa-morning market.
Distance: on the spot on the spot on the spot on the spot.

S La Courtine 21G3

Rue Impasse J Bayle. **GPS**: n45,70591 e2,25890.

5 free € 2/100liter Ch € 2/1h. **Location:** Simple, quiet.
Surface: asphalted. 01/01-31/12.
Distance: 1km 100m.

S La Mothe-Saint-Héray 21D2

Rue du Pont l'Abbé. **GPS**: n46,35971 w0,11775.

4 free € 1/50liter ChWC. **Location:** Rural, comfortable.
Surface: gravel. 01/01-31/12.
Distance: 500m 200m 200m.

S La Pierre-Saint-Martin 27B3

Aire de campingcar de la Pierre-Saint-Martin, Braça de Guilhers.
GPS: n42,97918 w0,7487.

40 € 10 Ch (winter). **Location:** Simple.
Surface: asphalted. 01/01-31/12.
Distance: 300m 300m 150m.

S La Réole 24D2

Les Justices, Avenue Gabriel-Chaigne. **GPS**: n44,58059 w0,03036.

10 € 4 Chfree. **Location:** Urban, simple, noisy.
Surface: grassy. 15/04-01/10.
Distance: 800m 700m.
Remarks: Nearby Musée Automobile et Militaire.

S La Roche-Chalais 24D1

Halte Nautique des bords de Dronne, D730.
GPS: n45,15701 e0,00419.

FR

4 free € 2/100liter Ch € 2/1h WC free.
Location: Rural, simple. **Surface:** metalled.
01/01-31/12.
Distance: 400m 100m 100m 400m 900m.
Remarks: Service at Intermarché, Av.d'Aquitaine, n45,14633 o0,00569.

S La Roche-Posay 21E1

Super U, ZA Les Chaumettes. **GPS**: n46,79361 e0,79750.

free Ch free. **Location:** Simple, noisy. **Surface:** asphalted.
01/01-31/12.
Distance: 1,5km on the spot.

S La Rochefoucauld 21D3

Aire camping-car, Rue des Flots, Rivières, Place du Champ de Foire. **GPS**: n45,74505 e0,38085.

5 free Ch . **Location:** Rural, simple. **Surface:** asphalted.
01/01-31/12.
Distance: 1km 10m 200m 200m.
Remarks: Beside river Tardoire, next to campsite, Château de La Rochefoucauld 1,3km.

S La Rochelle 21B2

Port Neuf, 6 Boulevard Aristide Rondeau. **GPS**: n46,16046 w1,18453.

171 € 12, tourist tax incl Ch included.
Location: Urban. **Surface:** gravel. 01/01-31/12.
Distance: centre 2,5km 1km on the spot.

S La Rochelle 21B2

Parking Jean Moulin, Avenue Jean Moulin. **GPS**: n46,15234 w1,13999.

50 € 13/24h, 01/04-30/09 € 15/24h Ch.
Surface: asphalted. 01/01-31/12.
Distance: 1,5km free.
Remarks: Shuttle bus to city centre.

Tourist information La Rochelle:

M La Maison Henri II, Rue de Augustins. Archeological museum. 15/5-30/9 Sa-Fr 10-19h Sa-Su 14-19h.

M Musée Maritime de la Rochelle, Bassin des Chautiers. Shipping museum. daily 10-18.30h.

Aquarium, Quai Louis Prunier. Sea aquarium. 01/07-31/08 9-23h, 01/09-30/06 10-20h.

S La Roque-Gageac 24E2

D703. **GPS**: n44,82428 e1,18376.

20 € 7 € 2/10minutes Ch € 2/1h WC. **Location:** Simple.
Surface: metalled. 01/01-31/12.
Distance: 200m 100m 100m 200m 200m.
Remarks: Along the Dordogne river, canoe rental.

Tourist information La Roque-Gageac:

www.cc-perigord-noir.fr. Small town worth seeing, in the Dordogne valley.

S La Teste-de-Buch 24B2

Aire de Camping Car du Lac de Cazaux, Rue Guynemer. **GPS**: n44,53158 w1,16025.

30 € 12/24h Ch included. **Location:** Comfortable, quiet. **Surface:** gravel/metalled. 01/01-31/12.
Distance: 450m 450m on the spot.

S La Teste-de-Buch 24B2

Centre LeClerc, Rue Pierre et Marie Curie. **GPS**: n44,61628 w1,11403.

15 free € 2/10minutes Ch € 2/30minutes.
Surface: asphalted.
Distance: on the spot on the spot.

S La Tremblade 21B3

85 Rue Marcel Gaillardon. **GPS**: n45,78268 w1,15228.

49 € 10/24h Ch ,16Amp included.
Location: Rural, comfortable, central, quiet. **Surface:** gravel/metalled.
01/01-31/12.
Distance: 2,2km on the spot 500m on the spot.
Remarks: Max. 72h, baker every morning.

S Labastide-d'Armagnac 27C1

Les Embarrats. **GPS**: n43,97205 w0,18602.

20 free Ch free. **Location:** Rural, simple, quiet.
Surface: grassy.
Distance: 300m.

S Labenne 27A1

Camping-Car Park, Route Océane. **GPS**: n43,59616 w1,45492.

80 € 9,60-13,64 Ch included.
Surface: metalled. 01/01-31/12.
Distance: 1km 2km 2km 1km 1km.
Remarks: Mandatory, one-time fee Pass'Etapes € 4.

S Lacanau 24B1

Le Huga, Alleé des Sauviels. **GPS**: n45,00583 w1,16528.

125 € 13,80/24h Ch included.
Location: Rural, comfortable, quiet. **Surface:** unpaved.
01/01-31/12.
Distance: 2km 2km 100m 2km on the spot on the spot.
Remarks: In front of heliport, max. 48h.

S Ladaux 24C2

Vignobles Lobre & Fils, Le Bos. **GPS**: n44,69677 w0,24393.

5 free Ch WC. **Location:** Rural, simple.
Surface: grassy/metalled. 01/01-31/12.
Distance: 300m.

S Lalinde 24E2

Avenue Général Leclerc. **GPS**: n44,83938 e0,74302.

2 free Ch free. **Location:** Simple. **Surface:** unpaved.
01/01-31/12.
Distance: 500m 500m 500m on the spot.
Remarks: Near train station.

FR

S Lanouaille 24E1

Rue du Chemin Neuf. **GPS**: n45,39248 e1,14002.

6 free Ch WC free. **Location:** Simple, central, quiet.
Surface: asphalted. 01/01-31/12.
Distance: 50m 100m 100m on the spot.
Remarks: Max. 48h.

S Lanton 24B2

Allée Albert Pitres, Taussat. **GPS**: n44,71710 w1,06991.

8 free Ch free. **Location:** Urban, simple, isolated.
Surface: asphalted. 01/01-31/12.
Distance: 2km sandy beach 100m 100m 4km.

S Lantueil 24F1

Route du Doux. **GPS**: n45,12900 e1,66138.

5 free Ch free. **Location:** Urban, simple, quiet.
Surface: gravel.
Distance: 100m 100m.

S Laruns 27C3

Artouste Fabrèges. **GPS**: n42,87914 w0,39693.

80 free € 5/100liter Ch € 5/1h WC. **Location:** Rural, simple. **Surface:** asphalted/grassy. 01/01-31/12.
Distance: 200m on the spot on the spot on the spot on the spot 1km.
Remarks: Coins at tourist info.

S Laruns 27C3

Parking du Cinéma, Avenue de la Gare. **GPS**: n42,98919 w0,42481.

30 € 6 Ch WC. **Location:** Urban, simple.
Surface: asphalted. 01/01-31/12.
Distance: 100m 100m 100m 400m.
Remarks: Max. 24h, coins at tourist info.

S Lauzun 24D2

Rue Saint-Colomb. **GPS**: n44,62762 e0,45979.

2 free WC free. **Surface:** gravel. 01/01-31/12.
Distance: 350m on the spot 350m 350m on the spot.
Remarks: At small lake, max. 48h.

S Lavardac 24D3

Rue de la Victoire - Place du Foirail. **GPS**: n44,17883 e0,29928.

3 free Ch free. **Location:** Rural, simple. **Surface:** asphalted.
01/01-31/12.
Distance: on the spot bakery 150m.

S Layrac 24E3

Aire de Layrac, Rue du 19 Mars 1962. **GPS**: n44,13233 e0,65946.

4 free Ch WC free. **Location:** Urban, simple.
Surface: asphalted. 01/01-31/12.
Distance: on the spot 150m 150m.

S Layrac 24E3

Le Moulin, D129. **GPS**: n44,13640 e0,66441.

max. 4 € 10/24h Ch WC included.
Location: Simple, noisy. **Surface:** gravel. 01/01-31/12.
Distance: on the spot.
Remarks: Call if no one is present, video surveillance.

Le Bois-Plage-en-Ré 21B2

Parking Municipal, Avenue du Pas des Boeufs.
GPS: n46,17708 w1,38613.
15 free. **Location:** Simple. **Surface:** gravel/sand.
Distance: 150m.

Le Bois-Plage-en-Ré 21B2

Route du Petit Sergent. **GPS**: n46,18264 w1,40417.
free. **Surface:** gravel. 01/01-31/12.
Distance: 200m 200m.
Remarks: Max. 48h.

S Le Bois-Plage-en-Ré 21B2

Aire Camping-Car Campéole, Avenue du Pas des Boeufs.
GPS: n46,17741 w1,38674.

35 € 16,95 € 3 Ch € 2/12h. **Location:** Rural, simple.
Surface: gravel/metalled. 01/01-31/12.
Distance: 150m.
Remarks: Payment also possible at campsite.

S Le Bugue 24E2

Place Léopold Salme. **GPS**: n44,91679 e0,92775.

50 € 7 Ch WC free. **Location:** Simple. **Surface:** grassy.
01/01-31/12 Service: winter.
Distance: 200m 20m 100m Intermarché 100m.
Remarks: Along the river Vézère, tuesday and Saturday market.

S Le Château d'Oléron 21B3

Boulevard Philippe Dastre. **GPS**: n45,89641 w1,20236.

90 € 12,50 Ch WC included. **Location:** Rural, comfortable. **Surface:** grassy.
Distance: on the spot.
Remarks: Former campsite.

S Le Grand Village Plage 21B3

Parking de l'épinette, Allée des Pins. **GPS**: n45,86222 w1,24111.

12 € 6 € 4/100liter Ch € 4. **Location:** Rural, simple.
Surface: asphalted. 01/01-31/12.
Distance: 1,5km.
Remarks: 01/04-30/09 max. 24h.

S Le Mas-d'Agenais 24D3

Grande Garesse. **GPS**: n44,40656 e0,22030.

8 free Ch (8x)free. **Location:** Urban, comfortable.
Surface: gravel. 01/01-31/12.
Distance: 600m 600m.

Le Porge 24B2

Avenue de l'Océan. **GPS**: n44,89437 w1,2131.

10 free. **Location:** Rural, simple, isolated. **Surface:** forest soil. 01/01-31/12.
Distance: Le Porge 10km on the spot on the spot on the spot on the spot.
Remarks: Max. 24h.

S Le Porge 24B2

Intermarché, D107. **GPS**: n44,87574 w1,07883.
€ 2/20minutes Ch. **Location:** Simple. 01/01-31/12.
Distance: on the spot on the spot.

S Le Teich 24B2

Parking de la Gare, Rue de l'Industrie. **GPS**: n44,63303 w1,02643.
free € 5/100liter Ch € 5/h. 01/01-31/12.
Distance: 700m 1km on the spot.

S Le Temple-sur-Lot 24D3

Avenue de Verdun. **GPS**: n44,38000 e0,52639.

4 free ChWCfree. **Location:** Urban, simple, quiet.
Surface: asphalted. 01/01-31/12.
Distance: 100m 100m.

S Le Temple-sur-Lot 24D3

Le Bosc, D911. **GPS**: n44,38144 e0,53649.
10 € 5 Chaccording consumption included.
Location: Rural. **Surface:** grassy. 01/01-31/12.
Distance: 800m 800m 800m on the spot.
Remarks: Picnic and barbecue place.

S Le Verdon-sur-Mer 21B3

Plage fluviale, Allée des Baïnes. **GPS**: n45,54633 w1,0541.

31+19 € 5/24h, 01/06-30/09 € 8/24h € 2/100liter Ch.
Location: Urban, comfortable, isolated, quiet.
Surface: gravel/metalled.
01/01-31/12.
Distance: 50m 500m 2km on the spot.
Remarks: Coins at town hall, tourist info and the shops at the beach.

S Lège-Cap-Ferret 24B2

Route des Pastourelles, Avenue Charles de Gaulle, D106, Claouey.
GPS: n44,75127 w1,18033.

10 free Ch (2x)free. **Location:** Urban, simple, noisy.
Surface: forest soil. 01/01-31/12.
Distance: on the spot 1km 600m 600m on the spot.
Remarks: Coins at camping municipal, day parking also allowed, overnight stay on motorhome stopovers.

Lège-Cap-Ferret 24B2

Avenue Edouard Branly. **GPS**: n44,75203 w1,18809.

15 free.
Location: Rural, simple. **Surface:** forest soil.
01/01-31/12.
Distance: 2km 600m 600m 600m 600m on the spot.
Remarks: Near campsite Les Embruns.

Lège-Cap-Ferret 24B2

D106, Avenue de Bordeaux, L'Herbe. **GPS**: n44,68655 w1,2451.

15 free. **Location:** Rural, simple, quiet. **Surface:** asphalted/metalled.
01/01-31/12.
Distance: 2km 1km 2km 2km.

S Léguillac-de-l'Auche 24E1

Glenon. **GPS**: n45,20319 e0,55876.
6 free € 2 € 3/24h. **Location:** Rural, isolated, quiet.
Surface: grassy.
Distance: 2km 2km 2km.

S Lembras 24D2

Aire de Caudeau, Impasse de l'Anguillère.
GPS: n44,88300 e0,52522.

10 free Chfree (10x)€ 6/12h. **Location:** Rural, comfortable, central. **Surface:** gravel. 01/01-31/12.
Distance: 200m 200m 200m 2,5km.

S Léon 27A1

Route de Puntaou. **GPS**: n43,88444 w1,31861.

80 € 11 Chincluded. **Location:** Simple.
Surface: grassy/gravel. 01/01-31/12.
Distance: 1km 250m 50m 50m 50m.
Remarks: Nearby lake.

S Les Eyzies 24E2

Parking de la Vézère, Promenade de la Vézère.
GPS: n44,93863 e1,00907.

25 € 5/night € 2/100liter Ch.
Location: Urban, comfortable, quiet. **Surface:** grassy/sand.
01/01-31/12.
Distance: 200m 200m 200m.
Remarks: Along the river Vézère, summer max. 48h, parking fee being collected at 9AM.

Tourist information Les Eyzies:
Village Troglodytique de la Madeleine, Tursac. Troglodyte-village.
M Le Village du Bournat, Le Bugue. Open air museum. 01/03-31/10 10-18/19h.

S Les Mathes/La Palmyre 21B3

Aire de la Garenne, Rue de la Garenne, Les Mathes.
GPS: n45,71433 w1,14752.

20 01/02-30/11 € 10/24h € 4/100liter ChWC.
Location: Rural, simple, isolated. **Surface:** metalled.
01/01-31/12.
Distance: 400m.
Remarks: Coins at town hall Mo-Fri 9-18h and tourist info La Palmyre daily 9-19h in July/Aug.

S Les Mathes/La Palmyre 21B3

Aire du Corsaire, Avenue de lAtlantique. **GPS**: n45,69193 w1,18896.

90 01/02-30/11 € 10/24h € 4/100liter Ch € 2/1h.
Location: Simple, central, quiet. **Surface:** asphalted.
01/01-31/12.
Distance: 1km 200m 200m on the spot.
Remarks: Max. 7 days.

Les Mathes/La Palmyre 21B3

Boulevard de la Plage, La Palmyre. **GPS**: n45,68287 w1,17942.

50 01/02-30/11 € 10/24h.
Location: Urban, simple, central, quiet. **Surface:** asphalted.
01/01-31/12 01/07-31/08.
Distance: 1,2km 100m 200m on the spot.

Tourist information Les Mathes/La Palmyre:
Zoo de la Palmyre. Zoo, 1600 animals, 14Ha. 01/04-30/09 9-20.30h, 01/10-31/03 9-12h, 14-18h.

S Les Portes-en-Ré 21B2

Parking de la Patache, Route du Fier. **GPS**: n46,22925 w1,48315.

FR

10 € 10/24h Ch WC included. Location: Rural, simple.
Surface: metalled. 01/01-31/12.
Distance: 150m on the spot 3,5km on the spot.
Remarks: Max. 24h, payment only with coins.

S Les Salles-Lavaugyon 21E3

Le Tilleul, Route de St Mathieu. **GPS**: n45,73998 e0,70100.

6 € 5 (3x)included. **Location:** Rural, simple, isolated.
Surface: gravel. 01/01-31/12.

Lescar 27C2

Parking Jacques Monod, Chemin de Beneharnum.
GPS: n43,33062 w0,43458.
5 free. **Surface:** asphalted. 01/01-31/12.
Distance: on the spot on the spot on the spot on the spot.
Remarks: Max. 48h.

Lescar 27C2

Place de l'Evêché. **GPS**: n43,33348 w0,43401.
3 free. **Surface:** metalled. 01/01-31/12.
Distance: on the spot 150m on the spot.
Remarks: Near office de tourisme, max. 48h.

S Lescar 27C2

Impasse du Vert Galant. **GPS**: n43,32669 w0,44373.
Ch free.

S Lesparre-Médoc 24B1

Rue Aristide Briand. **GPS**: n45,30539 w0,94012.
free Ch free. **Location:** Urban. **Surface:** asphalted.
01/01-31/12.
Distance: 250m 250m 200m.

Lestelle-Bétharram 27C2

D937. **GPS**: n43,12522 w0,2074.
10 free. **Location:** Urban, simple, noisy. **Surface:** asphalted.
01/01-31/12.
Distance: 500m 250m.

S Lezay 21D2

Rue de Gâte Bourse. **GPS**: n46,26500 w0,01139.

15 free Ch free. **Location:** Urban, simple. **Surface:** asphalted.
01/01-31/12.
Distance: 200m 200m.

S Liginiac 24G1

Le Maury-Liginiac. **GPS**: n45,39158 e2,30387.

2 free Ch (1x)free. **Location:** Rural, simple, isolated, quiet. **Surface:** gravel. 01/01-31/12.
Distance: 4,5km Sandy beach on the spot.
Remarks: At lake Neuvic. Follow restaurant Le Maury.

S Lignières-Sonneville 21C3

Parc de la Charmille, Le Bourg. **GPS**: n45,55666 w0,18276.

15 free Ch (1x)free. **Location:** Rural, simple, quiet.
Surface: metalled. 01/01-31/12.
Distance: 300m 300m 300m.
Remarks: Near sports fields and castle.

Limeuil 24E2

D31. **GPS**: n44,88564 e0,89151.

10 free. **Location:** Rural, simple, isolated. **Surface:** grassy/gravel.
01/01-31/12.
Distance: 400m 400m 750m.

S Lissac-sur-Couze 24F1

Parking du poste de secours. **GPS**: n45,09914 e1,46277.

15 € 4/stay € 4/100liter Ch (12x)€ 4/6h. **Location:** Rural, comfortable. **Surface:** gravel. 01/01-31/12.
Distance: on the spot on the spot.

S Lit-et-Mixe 24A3

Cap de l'Homy, 600, avenue Océan. **GPS**: n44,03730 w1,33419.

36 € 11,30-21,30 + € 0,61/pp tourist taks Ch WC.
Location: Simple, quiet. **Surface:** forest soil. 01/05-30/09.
Distance: 400m 200m 200m on the spot.
Remarks: Next to camping municipal.

S Lizant 21D2

Aire de Loisirs, Rue du Bourrelier. **GPS**: n46,08614 e0,27834.
8 free Ch WC. **Surface:** gravel. 01/01-31/12.
Distance: 100m on the spot.
Remarks: Playground.

S Londigny 21D2

Place de l'Eglise. **GPS**: n46,08333 e0,13472.

5 free Ch WC free. **Location:** Isolated, quiet.
Surface: gravel. 01/01-31/12.
Remarks: Max. 48h.

S Loudun 18D3

Place de la Porte Saint Nicolas. **GPS**: n47,01357 e0,07833.

3 free € 2/10minutes Ch € 2/55minutes.
Location: Urban, simple, noisy. **Surface:** asphalted.
01/01-31/12.
Distance: 500m 500m 100m, bakery 10m.
Remarks: Max 3,5t.

S Lussac 24D2

La Grange. **GPS**: n44,94628 w0,09541.

8 free Ch WC free. **Location:** Rural, simple, quiet.
Surface: gravel. 01/01-31/12.
Distance: 800m.

S Lussac-les-Châteaux 21E2

GPS: n46,40250 e0,72583.

20 free Ch WC free. **Location:** Urban, simple, central.
Surface: metalled. 01/01-31/12 Wed, market.
Distance: 200m 200m 200m.

Marennes 21B3

1 Avenue William Bertrand. **GPS**: n45,82140 w1,13828.

5 free.
Location: Rural, simple. **Surface:** metalled. 01/01-31/12.
Distance: on the spot.

FR

Remarks: Max. 6,5m.

S Marmande 24D3

La Filhole, Rue de la Filhole. **GPS**: n44,49667 e0,16412.

30 € 8 Ch included. **Location:** Rural, simple, quiet.
Surface: grassy. 01/04-01/11.
Distance: 500m 500m 1km.

S Marmande 24D3

Place du Moulin. **GPS**: n44,49833 e0,16028.

2 free Chfree. **Location:** Urban. **Surface:** asphalted.
01/11-01/04.
Distance: 150m on the spot.
Remarks: Max. 48h.

S Marquay 24E2

D6. **GPS**: n44,94401 e1,13529.
free Ch. **Surface:** gravel.
Distance: 100m.

S Mauléon 18C3

Rue de la Bachelette. **GPS**: n46,91904 w0,75267.

4 free Chfree. **Location:** Rural, simple, quiet.
Surface: asphalted. 01/01-31/12.
Distance: 500m 500m 500m.
Remarks: Next to swimming pool.

S Mauzé-sur-le-Mignon 21C2

Le Port, Rue du Port. **GPS**: n46,19989 w0,67952.

10 free € 4 Ch WC. **Location:** Rural. **Surface:** gravel.
01/01-31/12.
Distance: 1km on the spot on the spot on the spot.
Remarks: Coins at campsite and shops.

S Ménigoute 21D1

Rue des Vignes. **GPS**: n46,49790 w0,05795.

4 free Chfree. **Location:** Urban, simple, quiet.
Surface: gravel.
Distance: on the spot.

S Mensignac 24E1

Combecouyere-Sud. **GPS**: n45,22309 e0,56553.
4 free € 2 Ch. **Location:** Rural. **Surface:** metalled.
01/03-31/10.

S Meschers-sur-Gironde 21B3

Rue du 19 Mars 1961. **GPS**: n45,55698 w0,94741.
24 € 9 Ch included. **Surface:** unpaved.
01/01-31/12.
Distance: on the spot 500m.

S Meschers-sur-Gironde 21B3

Port de Plaisance, Route des Salines. **GPS**: n45,55614 w0,9451.

10 € 7/24h € 2/100liter Ch (8x) € 1,50 € 2/2.
Location: Rural, comfortable, isolated, quiet. **Surface:** asphalted.
01/01-31/12.
Distance: 1km 100m 100m 1km.

S Messanges 27A1

Camping-Car Park Plage Nord, Avenue de la Plage.
GPS: n43,81549 w1,40088.

55 € 8,40, 01/05-30/09 € 10,80 Ch WC included.
Location: Simple. **Surface:** metalled/sand. 01/01-31/12.
Distance: 1,5km 200m.
Remarks: Mandatory, one-time fee Pass'Etapes € 4.

S Messé 21D2

D114. **GPS**: n46,26306 e0,11203.

20 free Ch WC free. **Location:** Rural, isolated, quiet.
Surface: gravel. 01/01-31/12.
Distance: on the spot 10km.

S Meuzac 24F1

Étang de la Roche, D243. **GPS**: n45,54805 e1,44017.

15 free Chfree. **Location:** Rural, simple, quiet.
Surface: gravel. 01/01-31/12.
Distance: 100m 5km on the spot on the spot 100m 100m on the spot.
Remarks: Service 200m.

S Meymac 24G1

Parking Lac de Sechemailles, Le Montbazet.
GPS: n45,52500 e2,12761.

20 free € 2,60 Ch € 2,60. **Location:** Rural, comfortable, quiet. **Surface:** gravel. 01/01-31/12.
Distance: 2km 500m 500m.
Remarks: Coins available at Office du Tourisme and bar.

S Meymac 24G1

Boulevard de la Garenne. **GPS**: n45,53973 e2,15381.
30 free € 2 Ch (1x) € 2. **Location:** Rural, simple.
Surface: gravel. 20/04-02/11.
Remarks: Coins at campsite and tourist info.

S Mézières-sur-Issoire 21E2

Place de la République. **GPS**: n46,10726 e0,91014.

4 free Chfree. **Location:** Rural. **Surface:** asphalted.
01/01-31/12.
Distance: on the spot.

S Mimizan 24B3

Des Hournails, Route du CEL. **GPS**: n44,21375 w1,28239.

150 € 14,50 € 3/20minutes Ch. **Location:** Simple.
Surface: gravel/sand. 01/06-30/09.
Distance: 1,5km on the spot.

S Mimizan 24B3

Camping du Lac, Avenue de Woolsack, Mimizan-lac.
GPS: n44,21956 w1,22972.

FR

FR

21 € 11-18 + € 0,22/pp tourist tax, dog € 1,10-1,90 € 2/15minutes Ch WC € 3 . **Location:** Comfortable. **Surface:** gravel. 30/04-30/09.
Distance: 6km on the spot on the spot.

Mirambeau 24C1

Rue du parc de loisirs. **GPS**: n45,37816 w0,56872.

20 € 8 Ch included. **Location:** Urban, luxurious, central, quiet. **Surface:** grassy. 01/01-31/12.
Distance: 500m 3km 50m 150m.
Remarks: Former campsite.

Mirebeau 21D1

14 rue du Pas Martin. **GPS**: n46,78064 e0,19430.
€ 7 € 2 € 2 Ch € 5. 01/01-31/12.
Remarks: Barbecue place.

Moliets-et-Maa 27A1

Avenue de l'Océan, Moliets-Plage. **GPS**: n43,85091 w1,38188.

120 € 7, 01/04-31/08 € 13 Ch WC.
Location: Comfortable, noisy. **Surface:** forest soil.
Distance: 200m 750m 200m 200m.
Remarks: Shady.

Monbahus 24D3

Rue du Château d'Eau. **GPS**: n44,54738 e0,53517.

3 free Ch (2x)free. **Location:** Rural, simple.
Surface: asphalted. 01/01-31/12 Service: winter.
Distance: 300m 200m 300m.
Remarks: Beautiful view, steep entrance road.

Monbazillac 24D2

Château du Haut Pezaud, Les Pezauds. **GPS**: n44,78471 e0,48687.

10 € 5, first night free € 1,50 € 21/day WC free € 1/pppd € 1,50/day. **Location:** Rural, simple. **Surface:** grassy.
01/01-31/12.
Distance: table d'hôtes through the vineyards.
Remarks: Max. 7 nights, baker every morning, tasting of regional products.

Monbazillac 24D2

Domaine La Lande, Route de Ribagnac, D13.
GPS: n44,78822 e0,49587.

10 free Ch WC free. **Location:** Rural, simple. **Surface:** grassy.
01/01-31/12.
Distance: 800m 200m on the spot.
Remarks: Baker every morning, sale of wines.

Monflanquin 24E3

Chemin de la Source, 3, Allée des Érables.
GPS: n44,52812 e0,75537.

5 free Ch free.
Location: Simple. **Surface:** gravel.
01/03-01/11.
Distance: 1,5km Lac de Coulon 150m 1,3km 250m.
Remarks: Service 500m n44,52477 o0,75642.

Tourist information Monflanquin:
Office de Tourisme, Place des Arcades, www.monflanquin-tourisme.com. Medieval town.

Monpazier 24E2

La Duelle-Nord. **GPS**: n44,68499 e0,89362.

10 free Ch free. **Surface:** gravel. 01/01-31/12.
Distance: 300m 400m 500m.

Monségur 24D2

Place du 8 mai. **GPS**: n44,65060 e0,08363.

4 free WC free. **Location:** Simple, noisy. **Surface:** gravel.
01/01-31/12.
Distance: on the spot.
Remarks: Max. 48h. No access via La Bastide.

Mont-de-Marsan 27C1

Aire du Camping-Cars du Marsan, 541 Avenue de Villeneuve.
GPS: n43,88992 w0,47559.

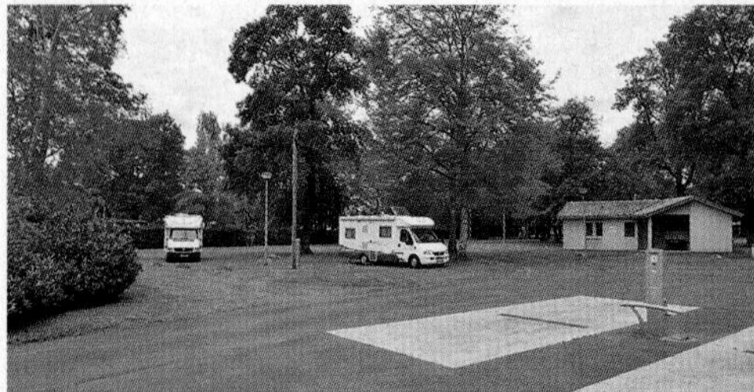

45 € 5,10-8,40, tourist tax € 0,33/pp € 1/5minutes Ch (3x) € 1/4h. **Location:** Rural, central. **Surface:** asphalted/grassy.
01/01-31/12.
Distance: 2,3km 500m.

Montalivet-les-Bains 24B1

Camping-Car Park, Boulevard de Lattre de Tassigny, Montalivet-sud.
GPS: n45,37625 w1,15664.

100 € 11,60 € 1 Ch included. **Location:** Urban, simple, quiet. **Surface:** grassy/metalled. 01/01-31/12.
Distance: on the spot 350m 400m 400m.
Remarks: Mandatory, one-time fee Pass'Etapes € 4.

Tourist information Montalivet-les-Bains:
Fri.

Montboucher 21F3

GPS: n45,95152 e1,68069.

10 free Ch WC free. **Location:** Rural, quiet.
Surface: grassy/gravel. 01/01-31/12.
Distance: 8km 8km 8km.

Montendre 24C1

Place de la Paix. **GPS**: n45,28627 w0,41116.

15 free Ch WC free. **Location:** Urban, simple, central, quiet.
Surface: asphalted. 01/01-31/12 Thu 6-14h.
Distance: 100m 100m 500m.

Monteton 24D2

D423. **GPS**: n44,62249 e0,25745.

25 free Ch free. **Location:** Rural, simple. **Surface:** grassy.
01/01-31/12.
Distance: on the spot 150m.
Remarks: Beautiful view.

Montguyon 24C1

Plaine des Sports, Rue de Vassiac. **GPS**: n45,21796 w0,18368.

15 free ChWC free. **Location:** Urban, simple, central, quiet. **Surface:** gravel. 01/01-31/12.
Distance: 500m 500m 500m on the spot.
Remarks: Max. 72h.

Montignac 24E1

P Vieux Quartiers, Rue des Sagnes. **GPS**: n45,06800 e1,16547.

35 € 5/night Ch included. **Location:** Comfortable, central. **Surface:** gravel. 01/01-31/12.
Distance: 200m 200m 200m.

Montignac 24E1

Ferme du Bois Bareirou, Les Baraques, Montignac-Lascaux. **GPS**: n45,09053 e1,11143.

20 free € 3 Ch € 3. **Location:** Rural, isolated, quiet. **Surface:** grassy. 01/01-31/12.
Distance: 5km.
Remarks: Max. 3 days.

Montils 21C3

Le Vignolet, D233. **GPS**: n45,65285 w0,50576.

20 free Ch free. **Location:** Rural, simple, isolated. **Surface:** gravel/metalled. 01/01-31/12.
Distance: 300m.

Montmorillon 21E2

Rue Léon Dardant. **GPS**: n46,42326 e0,86788.

10 free € 2/10minutes Ch € 2.
Location: Urban, simple, central, quiet. **Surface:** asphalted. 01/01-31/12.
Distance: 500m 500m 2km.
Remarks: Along the Gartempe river, max. 24h.

Morcenx 24B3

Chemin des Abattoirs. **GPS**: n44,03811 w0,90914.

free Ch free. **Location:** Simple. **Surface:** grassy.
Distance: 500m 8,8km.
Remarks: Along railwayline.

Mortagne-sur-Gironde 21C3

Le Port de Mortagne, Quai des Pêcheurs. **GPS**: n45,47472 w0,79778.

50 € 8 Ch WC against payment included.
Location: Rural, simple, isolated, quiet. **Surface:** grassy. 01/01-31/12.
Distance: 750m 200m 750m on the spot.
Remarks: In front of Capitainerie.

Moulismes 21E2

RN147. **GPS**: n46,33306 e0,81000.

50 free € 3 Ch WC. **Location:** Rural, simple, quiet. **Surface:** grassy/metalled. 01/01-31/12.
Distance: 400m on the spot on the spot 400m.
Remarks: At small lake (plan d'eau).

Mouthiers-sur-Boëme 21D3

Chemin de la Chauveterie. **GPS**: n45,55424 e0,12488.

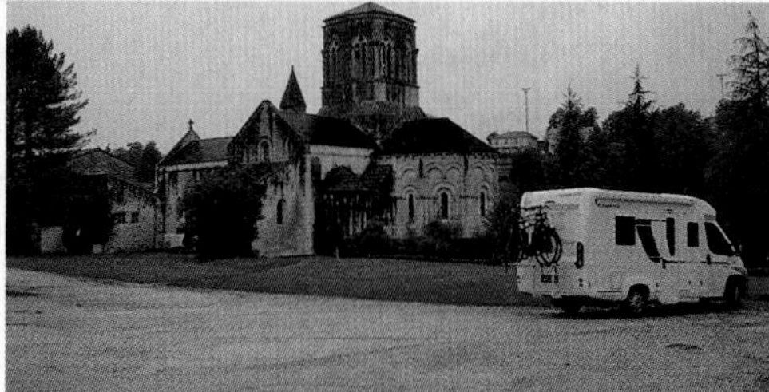

10 free Ch free. **Location:** Urban, simple, central, quiet. **Surface:** grassy/gravel. 01/01-31/12.
Distance: on the spot on the spot on the spot.
Remarks: Behind church.

Mugron 27B1

Avenue des Martyrs de la Résistance, D32e. **GPS**: n43,74846 w0,75063.

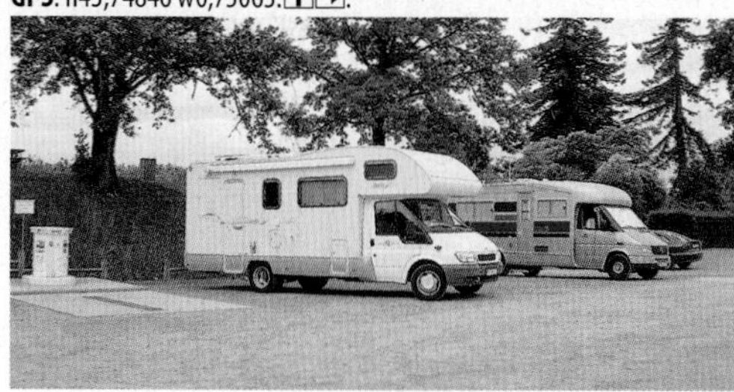

4 free Ch (4x)free. **Location:** Rural, simple. **Surface:** gravel. 01/01-31/12.
Distance: 300m on the spot.
Remarks: Max. 24h.

Nailhac 24E1

Lorserie, D62E3. **GPS**: n45,23276 e1,14214.

6 free Ch free € 3,50/24h. **Location:** Rural, simple. **Surface:** metalled.
Distance: 1,5km 1,5km.

Nantiat 21F3

L'Étang des Haches, Route de Chamboret. **GPS**: n46,00484 e1,15332.
free € 2/100liter Ch € 2/4h. 01/01-31/12.

Naujan-et-Postiac 24C2

Lafuge. **GPS**: n44,78715 w0,17928.

free.
Location: Rural, simple. **Surface:** gravel. 01/01-31/12.
Distance: 200m.

Nérac 24D3

Place du Foirail. **GPS**: n44,13435 e0,33655.

2 free ChWC. **Location:** Urban, simple. **Surface:** asphalted. 01/01-31/12.
Distance: 50m on the spot on the spot.

Nersac 21D3

Aire municipal, 5 Rue de la Foucaudie. **GPS**: n45,62599 e0,05015.

7 free Ch (4x)free. **Location:** Urban, simple, central, quiet. **Surface:** asphalted. 01/01-31/12.
Distance: on the spot 100m 100m 100m on the spot.
Remarks: Max. 48h, small pitches.

Nespouls 24F2

GPS: n45,05244 e1,49568.

FR

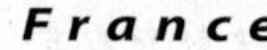

10 free Ch free. **Location:** Rural, comfortable.
Surface: gravel. 01/01-31/12.
Distance: 1km 500m on the spot on the spot.

S Nieuil-l'Espoir 21E2

Allée du champ de foire. **GPS**: n46,48505 e0,45417.

10 free € 2 Ch € 2. **Location:** Rural, comfortable, quiet.
Surface: grassy/metalled. 01/01-31/12.
Distance: 200m 150m on the spot on the spot.
Remarks: At Base de Loisirs, coins at the shops.

S Nieul 21F3

19 Mars 1962, D28. **GPS**: n45,92564 e1,17236.

15 free Ch WC free. **Location:** Rural, central, quiet.
Surface: grassy/gravel. 01/04-31/10.
Distance: 400m 400m 400m.
Remarks: Max. 72h.

S Nieulle-sur-Seudre 21B3

Place de la Mairie. **GPS**: n45,75275 w1,00209.

4 free € 4/100liter Ch against payment.
Location: Urban, simple, central, quiet. **Surface:** asphalted.
01/01-31/12.
Distance: on the spot.
Remarks: Coins at town hall.

S Niort 21C2

Aire des camping-cars du Pré Leroy, Rue de Bessac.
GPS: n46,32917 w0,46444.

14 € 7,70 Ch included.
Location: Urban, comfortable, quiet. **Surface:** metalled.
01/01-31/12.
Distance: 1,2km 150m 300m.

Tourist information Niort:
Tue, Sa.
Marais Poitevin. Swamp area, possibility of making boat trips.

S Nonaville 21D3

Pont à Brac. **GPS**: n45,52576 w0,09051.

4 free € 2/100liter Ch € 2/10minutes.
Location: Rural, simple, quiet. **Surface:** gravel.
01/01-31/12.
Distance: on the spot 500m.

S Objat 24F1

Parc Aquatique Espace Loisirs, Avenue Jules Ferry.
GPS: n45,27110 e1,41147.

20 € 6,60, 01/04-31/10 € 8,60 € 2/100liter Ch WC € 2 . **Location:** Rural, comfortable, quiet.
Surface: grassy/metalled.
01/01-31/12.
Distance: 500m 500m.
Remarks: Max. 7 days, baker on site: Tue-Sa, free electricity 72h, swimming pool 200m, entrance code available at tourist info.

S Ogeu-les-Bains 27C2

Avenue de Pau. **GPS**: n43,15349 w0,5022.

4 free Ch free. **Location:** Urban, simple.
Surface: asphalted/gravel. 01/01-31/12.
Distance: 100m 500m.
Remarks: Max. 48h.

S Oloron-Sainte-Marie 27B2

Parking Tivoli, Rue Adoue. **GPS**: n43,18399 w0,60854.

7 free € 4/55minutes Ch € 4/55minutes.
Surface: asphalted. 01/01-31/12.
Distance: 100m on the spot on the spot 400m 400m.
Remarks: Max. 48h, coins at tourist info.

S Ondres 27A1

P3, Avenue de la Plage, Ondres-Plage. **GPS**: n43,57611 w1,48611.

41 € 8, Jul/Aug € 10 Ch WC included.
Surface: asphalted. 15/04-01/11.
Distance: 3km on the spot on the spot on the spot on the spot on the spot.
Remarks: Max. 48h.

S Oradour-sur-Glane 21E3

Aire de camping-cars, Rue du Stade. **GPS**: n45,93570 e1,02471.

30 free € 2/100liter Ch € 2 WC.
Location: Rural. **Surface:** asphalted.
01/01-31/12 Service: winter.
Distance: 800m 800m 800m.
Remarks: Coins at tourist info, playground.

Tourist information Oradour-sur-Glane:
Office de Tourisme, Place du Champ de Foire. Martyre town, was attacked by 200 SS-soldiers on 10 June 1944. They assassinated the population. Afterwards the village was burned down. In commemoration a wall was built round the the city after the war. free.

S Oradour-sur-Vayres 21E3

Rue Jean Giraudoux. **GPS**: n45,73269 e0,86592.

10 free Ch free.
Location: Urban, simple. **Surface:** gravel.
Distance: 200m 200m.

S Orion 27B2

Labarraque, 223 route de Narp. **GPS**: n43,41350 w0,85217.
9 € 10 Ch included,20Amp . **Location:** Rural.
Surface: gravel. 01/01-31/12.
Distance: 1km on the spot.
Remarks: Max. 24h, picnic and barbecue place.

S Pageas 21E3

RN21. **GPS**: n45,67758 e1,00224.

20 free € 3 Ch € 3 WC. **Location:** Rural, comfortable.
Surface: grassy/gravel. 01/01-31/12.
Distance: 100m on the spot on the spot on the spot.
Remarks: Near N21, coins at town hall.

S Pamproux 21D2

Rue de la Cueille. **GPS**: n46,39625 w0,05874.

3 free € 2/20minutes Ch € 2/20minutes.
Location: Rural, simple, quiet. **Surface:** asphalted.
01/01-31/12.
Distance: 100m 5,2km 100m.

Parentis-en-Born 24B3

Site du Lac, Route des Campings. **GPS**: n44,34432 w1,09879.

25 €7 Ch (4x)included. **Location:** Comfortable.
Surface: gravel. 01/01-31/12 Service: winter.
Distance: 3km 50m 50m.

Parthenay 21D1

Aire base de loisirs Bois Vert, Rue de Boisseau 14.
GPS: n46,64088 w0,26689.

8 € 9-10 Ch included € 3 € 2 € 4/day.
Location: Urban. **Surface:** gravel.
05/04-31/10.
Distance: 2,5km on the spot nearby 2km 100m.
Remarks: Along the Thouet river, check in at campsite.

Tourist information Parthenay:
Les Halles. Weekly market in the halls and streets. Wed.

Pau 27C2

Place de Verdun, Rue Ambroise Bordelongue.
GPS: n43,29848 w0,37811.

20 free. **Location:** Urban. **Surface:** asphalted. 01/01-31/12.
Distance: on the spot on the spot 200m.
Remarks: Max. 48h, free shuttle.

Payzac 24F1

Le Bourg. **GPS**: n45,40008 e1,21950.

2 free Ch free. **Location:** Simple. **Surface:** asphalted.
01/01-31/12.

Distance: on the spot on the spot on the spot on the spot.

Pellegrue 24D2

Le Touran, Rue du Lavoir. **GPS**: n44,74514 e0,07416.

3 free Ch free. **Location:** Urban, simple.
Surface: metalled. 01/01-31/12.
Distance: 100m 200m 700m.

Pérignac 21C3

Pla de l'Église. **GPS**: n45,62532 w0,46309.

10 free free. **Location:** Simple, central, quiet.
Surface: asphalted. 01/01-31/12.
Distance: on the spot on the spot on the spot.
Remarks: Behind church.

Périgueux 24E1

Espace des Prés, Rue des Prés. **GPS**: n45,18770 e0,73081.

40 € 6 Chincluded.
Location: Urban, comfortable, central. **Surface:** asphalted.
01/01-31/12 water disconnected in winter.
Distance: 800m on the spot.
Remarks: Max. 48h.

Pérols-sur-Vézère 21G3

Le Bourg. **GPS**: n45,58665 e1,98460.

10 free € 2 Ch. **Location:** Rural, comfortable, quiet.
Surface: grassy.
Distance: 50m on the spot on the spot on the spot.
Remarks: Coins at tourist info.

Peyrat-le-Château 21F3

Auphelle. **GPS**: n45,80750 e1,84111.

100 € 4,20, Jul/Aug € 6 € 2,50/100liter € 6/4h.
Location: Rural, quiet. **Surface:** grassy. 12/04-07/11.

Distance: Lac de Vassivière 300m.
Remarks: In front of campsite, bread-service in summer period.

Peyrat-le-Château 21F3

Parking Pré de l'Age. **GPS**: n45,81468 e1,77085.
€ 2 Ch.
Remarks: Coins at tourist info and town hall.

Tourist information Peyrat-le-Château:
Office de Tourisme, 1, Rue du Lac, www.peyrat-tourisme.com.
Tourist town close water sports lake, Lac de Vassivière, marked cycle and hiking routes. Sa-Su 15-17h.

Peyrehorade 27B1

Des Gaves, Route de la Pêcherie. **GPS**: n43,54300 w1,1071.
16 € 9 Ch € 2,50 WC. **Surface:** grassy.
01/06-30/09.
Distance: 150m on the spot on the spot 150m 150m 200m.
Remarks: Bread-service.

Pomarez 27B1

Rue de la Mairie. **GPS**: n43,62853 w0,82895.
5 free Ch WC. **Location:** Urban, noisy.
Surface: asphalted. 01/01-31/12.
Distance: on the spot 200m 400m.
Remarks: At townhall, max. 72h.

Pons 21C3

Place de l'Europe. **GPS**: n45,58086 w0,5528.
10 free WC.
Location: Urban, simple, central. 01/01-31/12.
Distance: 400m 400m 400m.
Remarks: Max. 24h.

Pons 21C3

Chateau Renaud, D234E5, Bougneau. **GPS**: n45,60102 w0,5367.

6 free. **Location:** Rural, simple, isolated. **Surface:** gravel.
01/01-31/12.
Distance: on the spot 1km.
Remarks: Along river.

Pons 21C3

Camping municipal Le Paradis, Avenue du Poitou.
GPS: n45,57765 w0,55536.

5 free € 6 Ch € 6/h. **Location:** Urban, simple.
Surface: asphalted. 01/01-31/12.
Distance: 300m.

Port-des-Barques 21B2

Pré des Mays, Avenue des Sports. **GPS**: n45,94722 w1,09.

30 € 8/24h € 2/10minutes Chfree € 2/55minutes
Location: Rural, simple. **Surface:** grassy/gravel.
15/03-15/11.
Remarks: In front of stadium.

Port-Sainte-Foy-et-Ponchapt 24D2

Rue Jacques Jasmin. **GPS**: n44,84210 e0,20915.

FR

4 free Chfree. **Location:** Urban, simple, central, quiet.
Surface: asphalted. 01/01-31/12.
Distance: on the spot 600m 600m.
Remarks: Along the Dordogne river, service 200m.

Prats-de-Carlux 24F2

Les Oies du Périgord Noir, D47B. **GPS**: n44,89936 e1,31503.

4 free. **Location:** Rural, simple, quiet. 01/01-31/12.
Distance: 3km 3km 3km.
Remarks: Max. 24h.

S Rébénacq 27C2

Chemin de Montés. **GPS**: n43,15690 w0,39733.

4 free Ch free. **Location:** Rural, simple, quiet.
Surface: asphalted. 01/01-31/12.
Distance: 400m on the spot on the spot.
Remarks: At football ground, max. 48h.

S Ribérac 24D1

Camping de la Dronne, Route d'Angouleme, Aux Deux Ponts 0.
GPS: n45,25704 e0,34255.

10 free Chfree. **Location:** Urban, simple. **Surface:** metalled.
01/01-31/12 water: frost.
Distance: 1,3km 50m 900m.

S Rivedoux-Plage 21B2

Campéole Le Platin, 125, Av Gustave Perreau.
GPS: n46,15889 w1,27139.

17 € 14-17 € 3 Ch. **Location:** Urban, simple.
Surface: asphalted. 01/01-31/12.
Distance: 100m Plage Nord.
Remarks: Next to campsite Le Platin, to be paid at campsite.

S Rochefort 21B2

Rue de la Fosse aux Mâts. **GPS**: n45,92735 w0,95467.

30 € 4,10, tourist tax € 1,20/pp Chincluded.
Location: Urban, simple. **Surface:** asphalted. 01/01-31/12.

Rochefort 21B2

Avenue Marcel Dassault. **GPS**: n45,94661 w0,96002.

25 € 7,20 + € 1,20/pp tourist tax. **Location:** Urban, simple.
Surface: asphalted. 01/01-31/12.
Distance: 1km.

Rochefort 21B2

Pont Transbordeur, Chemin de Charente.
GPS: n45,91792 w0,96388.

5 free. **Location:** Urban, simple. **Surface:** grassy/gravel.
01/01-31/12.

Rochefort 21B2

Rue de la Vieille Forme. **GPS**: n45,94448 w0,95554.
12 € 7,20 + € 1,20/pp tourist tax. **Location:** Simple.
Surface: gravel. 01/01-31/12.
Distance: 300m 150m.
Remarks: Near marina.

S Rochefort 21B2

Port de Plaisance, Quai Lemoigne de Sérigny.
GPS: n45,94444 w0,95556.
Chfree WC € 2,50.
01/01-31/12.

Tourist information Rochefort:
Corderie Royale. Old royal rope-walk.
Tue, Thu, Sa.

S Romagne 21D2

Rue du Vigneau. **GPS**: n46,26884 e0,30373.

6 free ChWCfree. **Location:** Rural, comfortable, quiet.
Surface: gravel. 15/03-31/10.
Distance: 250m 250m.

S Roquefort 24C3

Allée de Nauton. **GPS**: n44,04754 w0,32255.

6 free Ch. **Location:** Rural. **Surface:** grassy/gravel.
01/01-31/12.
Distance: 1,7km 5km.
Remarks: Next to camping municipal.

S Rouillac 21D3

Super U, Rue de Genac. **GPS**: n45,77650 w0,06133.

4 free € 3/100liter Ch (2x)€ 3/24h. **Location:** Urban, simple, central. **Surface:** gravel. 01/01-31/12.
Distance: 500m 500m 50m.
Remarks: Coins available at supermarket.

S Roullet-Saint-Estèphe 21D3

Aire de camping-car Roullet, D210. **GPS**: n45,58086 e0,04461.

20 free Chfree. **Location:** Rural, simple, quiet.
Surface: asphalted. 01/01-31/12.
Distance: 300m 150m 350m.

S Roumazières-Loubert 21E3

Aire de Détente de Ronmatiéres, RN141.
GPS: n45,88275 e0,57287.

5 free Ch (2x)WCfree. **Location:** Urban, simple, noisy.
Surface: asphalted. 01/01-31/12.
Distance: 500m 100m 300m.

S Royan 21B3

Camping-Car Park Royan, Rue Bel-air. **GPS**: n45,62834 w1,01204.

40 € 9,60, 01/07-31/08 € 12 + € 1,65/pp tourist tax Ch (40x) included. **Location:** Urban, comfortable, central, quiet.
Surface: gravel/metalled. 01/01-31/12.
Distance: 500m 500m 500m.
Remarks: Mandatory, one-time fee Pass'Etapes € 4.

S Royère-de-Vassivière 21G3

Le Bourg. **GPS**: n45,84012 e1,91122.

6 free Ch WC free. **Location:** Rural, simple.
Surface: asphalted. 01/01-31/12 Thu>14h (market).
Distance: on the spot 200m on the spot.
Remarks: Max. 48h.

S Ruffec 21D2

SARL Remy Frères Camping-Cars, Route de Montjean.
GPS: n46,03316 e0,18366.

10 free Ch free. **Surface:** asphalted.
Distance: 1km.
Remarks: At motorhome dealer.

S Sadroc 24F1

Place du Château. **GPS**: n45,28325 e1,54854.

6 free Ch free. **Location:** Urban, simple, quiet.
Surface: asphalted. 01/01-31/12.
Distance: on the spot 5,2km 50m.
Remarks: Max. 24h.

S Saint Césaire 21C3

Parking Paléosite, Rue de Groies. **GPS**: n45,75406 w0,50751.

20 free Ch free. **Location:** Rural, simple, isolated, quiet.
Surface: asphalted/metalled. 01/01-31/12.
Distance: on the spot 500m 100m on the spot.

Tourist information Saint Césaire:
Paléosite, Route de la Montée Verte. Interactive park, in the footsteps of the Neanderthals. 10.30-18.30, Jul-Aug 10-20 January.

S Saint Estèphe 21E3

Etang de Saint Estèphe, Route du Grand Etang.
GPS: n45,59458 e0,67437.

10 € 5 Ch included. **Location:** Rural, comfortable.
Surface: forest soil. 01/01-31/12.
Distance: 700m lake on the spot on the spot 3km, bakery 800m.
Remarks: Max. 48h, summer: beach, bar, restaurant.

S Saint Laurent-de-la-Prée 21B2

La Cabane, Route de l'Océan. **GPS**: n45,99043 w1,04942.

10 € 6 Ch included. **Location:** Rural, simple.
Surface: gravel. 01/01-31/12.

S Saint-Agnant 21B3

Place de Verdun. **GPS**: n45,86635 w0,9641.

10 free free. **Location:** Rural, simple. **Surface:** asphalted.
01/01-31/12.
Distance: 1km.
Remarks: Next to town hall.

S Saint-Amand-sur-Sèvre 21C1

Boulevard de Maumusson. **GPS**: n46,86903 w0,8.

5 free Ch free. **Location:** Rural, simple, quiet.
Surface: grasstiles. 01/01-31/12.
Distance: 500m 500m 500m.

S Saint-Amand-sur-Sèvre 21C1

Le Moulin Chaligny. **GPS**: n46,88493 w0,82342.

10 € 10 Ch WC included. **Location:** Rural, isolated, quiet.
Surface: grassy. 01/01-31/12.
Distance: 3km 3km 3km on the spot on the spot.

S Saint-Antoine-Cumond 24D1

Salle de Fête, Le Bourg, D43. **GPS**: n45,25537 e0,19988.

10 free Ch WC free. **Location:** Rural, simple, quiet.
Surface: asphalted/gravel. 01/01-31/12.
Distance: on the spot on the spot bakery 100m.

S Saint-Antoine-de-Breuilh 24D2

Camping-Car Park, D936, Avenguda del Péirigord 89.
GPS: n44,84516 e0,15847.

26 € 8,84 Ch (24x) included. **Location:** Rural, comfortable, quiet. **Surface:** concrete. 01/01-31/12.
Distance: 200m 200m 300m 500m on the spot on the spot.
Remarks: Mandatory, one-time fee Pass'Etapes € 4.

S Saint-Caprais-de-Blaye 24C1

Aire de camping-car de Ferchaud, 169 Les Fermenteaux.
GPS: n45,29120 w0,5692.

8 € 7/24h ,service € 2 Ch WC included.
Location: Rural, simple, noisy. **Surface:** asphalted.
01/01-31/12.
Distance: 500m 6,4km 50m on the spot.
Remarks: Tourist information and picnic tables available.

S Saint-Clément-des-Baleines 21B2

Rue de la Forêt. **GPS**: n46,22756 w1,54644.

30 € 12,50/night Ch included. **Location:** Rural, simple. **Surface:** grassy. 01/01-31/12.
Distance: 250m 500m on the spot on the spot.
Remarks: Next to campsite, payment only with coins.

S Saint-Cyprien 24E2

Place Mackenheim, Rue du Priolat. **GPS**: n44,86828 e1,04435.

8 € 3,50 Ch.
Location: Simple. **Surface:** asphalted.
01/01-31/12.
Distance: 50m bakery 50m, supermarket 100m.
Remarks: Max. 24h, coins at tourist info and restaurant La Sivade.

Tourist information Saint-Cyprien:
Marché repas gourmand. summer Thu-evening.

S Saint-Cyr 21E1

Camping-Car Park, Rue de la Bourdillière. **GPS**: n46,72194 e0,45601.
36 € 10,80 Ch (36x) included. **Location:** Rural.
Surface: grassy. 01/01-31/12.
Remarks: Mandatory, one-time fee Pass'Etapes € 4.

S Saint-Denis-d'Oléron 21B2

Aire du Moulin, Route des Huttes. **GPS**: n46,02750 w1,38306.

FR

170 € 10/24h Ch WC included. **Location:** Rural, simple. **Surface:** grassy. 01/01-31/12.
Distance: 1km.
Remarks: Max. 4 nights.

S Saint-Dizant-du-Gua 24C1

Les berges du Taillon, 6 Rue du Pérat. **GPS**: n45,43062 w0,707.

25 free € 2/100liter Ch € 2/2h free.
Location: Rural, simple, quiet. **Surface:** grassy.
01/01-31/12.
Distance: 200m on the spot on the spot on the spot on the spot.
Remarks: Wifi code at shop.

S Saint-Estèphe 24C1

Rue du Littoral. **GPS**: n45,26544 w0,7582.

5 free Ch Service € 5. **Location:** Rural, simple, quiet.
Surface: gravel/metalled. 01/01-31/12.
Distance: 2km on the spot on the spot on the spot on the spot.
Remarks: Free, coins available at restaurant.

S Saint-Front-la-Rivière 24E1

Chez Boutau, D83. **GPS**: n45,46645 e0,72419.

10 free Ch (2x)free. **Location:** Rural, comfortable, isolated, quiet. **Surface:** metalled. 01/01-31/12.
Remarks: Max. 72h, picnic area.

S Saint-Genis-de-Saintonge 21C3

Rue Fanny. **GPS**: n45,48330 w0,56569.

20 € 6/24h 10minutes Ch (20x)included4h.
Location: Urban, comfortable, central, quiet. **Surface:** asphalted.
01/01-31/12.
Distance: 400m.
Remarks: Behind cinema, max. 72h.

S Saint-Georges-de-Didonne 21B3

Parking Maudet, Rue du Docteur Maudet.
GPS: n45,60408 w0,99964.

19 € 8/24h Ch included.
Location: Urban, simple, central, quiet. **Surface:** asphalted.
01/01-31/12.
Distance: 400m 500m.
Remarks: Max. 72h.

Saint-Georges-de-Didonne 21B3

Front de Mer, Boulevard de la Côte de Beauté.
GPS: n45,59557 w0,99163.

20 € 8/24h. **Location:** Urban, simple, quiet.
Surface: gravel/metalled. 01/01-31/12.
Distance: 500m on the spot 350m on the spot.
Remarks: Beach parking, max. 72h.

Saint-Georges-de-Didonne 21B3

Parking Gillet, Rue du Professeur Langevin.
GPS: n45,60324 w0,9921.

13 € 8/24h. **Location:** Urban, simple, central, quiet.
Surface: asphalted. 01/01-31/12.
Distance: on the spot 800m on the spot on the spot.
Remarks: Max. 72h.

Saint-Georges-de-Didonne 21B3

Parking Miramar, Rue du Port. **GPS**: n45,60031 w1,007.

18 € 8/24h. **Location:** Urban. **Surface:** gravel/metalled.
01/01-31/12.
Distance: 1km 100m on the spot 200m 1km.
Remarks: Max. 72h.

S Saint-Georges-Nigremont 21G3

Le Bourg. **GPS**: n45,83649 e2,26448.
5 free Ch free. **Location:** Rural. 01/01-31/12.
Distance: 650m.

S Saint-Germain-de-Marencennes 21C2

Rue du Moulin Neuf. **GPS**: n46,07882 w0,78283.
10 € 5 Ch WC included. **Location:** Simple, quiet.
Surface: asphalted. 01/01-31/12 service 01/11-31/03.
Distance: 500m 350m.

S Saint-Germain-et-Mons 24E2

D21. **GPS**: n44,84795 e0,59294.
20 € 8 Ch . **Surface:** gravel. 01/01-31/12.

S Saint-Hilaire-de-Lusignan 24D3

D813. **GPS**: n44,22491 e0,51364.

3 free € 3/10minutes Ch. **Location:** Urban, simple, noisy.
Surface: gravel. 01/01-31/12.
Distance: on the spot 1km 5km, bakery 500m.

Saint-Hilaire-la-Palud 21C2

Place de la Marie. **GPS**: n46,26444 w0,71306.

10 free. **Surface:** asphalted. 01/01-31/12.
Distance: on the spot on the spot on the spot.
Remarks: Parking in front of town hall, max. 2 nights.

S Saint-Jean-d'Angély 21C3

Base de Plein Air, Avenue de Marennes, D18.
GPS: n45,94537 w0,53735.

10 € 7/24h Ch WC included.
Surface: gravel. 01/01-31/12.
Distance: 1km 100m 100m 200m 1km on the spot.
Remarks: Max. 2 nights.

S Saint-Jean-de-Côle 24E1

Le Bourg. **GPS**: n45,41984 e0,84048.

3 free € 2 Ch € 2. **Location:** Urban, simple, quiet.
Surface: metalled. 01/01-31/12.
Distance: on the spot 200m 300m 200m.
Remarks: At tennis-court, coins at tourist info.

S Saint-Jean-de-Luz 27A2

Avenue Geneviève Antonios de Gaulle, D810.
GPS: n43,38527 w1,6629.

FR

17 € 4, 01-04/31-10 € 6 € 2/100liter € 2 Ch € 2 € 2/1h.
Surface: asphalted. 01/01-31/12.
Distance: 200m 2,2km 300m 300m 100m 100m.
Remarks: Max. 48h.

Tourist information Saint-Jean-de-Luz:
Office de Tourisme, Place du Maréchal Foch, www.saint-jean-de-luz.com. Tourist town with beautiful shops. The local speciality is chipirones, octopus cooked in its own ink.
Halles, Bd Victor Hugo. morning.

S Saint-Jean-Pied-de-Port 27A2

Parking du Jaï Alaï, 5 Chemin de la Nasse.
GPS: n43,16519 w1,23208.

50 € 7, tourist tax € 0,40/pp Ch WC.
Location: Urban. **Surface:** metalled.
01/01-31/12.
Distance: 350m 350m 350m 350m 350m on the spot.
Remarks: Nearby stadium, max. 48h.

Tourist information Saint-Jean-Pied-de-Port:
Office de Tourisme, 14, Place Charles de Gaulle, www.pyrenees-basques.com. Fortified city on the foot of the Roncesvallespass on the road to Santiago de Compostela.
Forêt d'Iraty. Nature reserve, hiking trails available at OT.

S Saint-Julien-le-Petit 21F3

Route de la Plage. **GPS**: n45,82142 e1,70531.

12 € 5, 2 pers.incl Ch WC. **Location:** Rural, quiet.
Surface: grassy. 01/01-31/12.

S Saint-Junien-la-Bregère 21F3

Rue du Chevalier de Châteauneuf. **GPS**: n45,88236 e1,75282.

3 free Ch free. **Location:** Rural, quiet. **Surface:** asphalted.
01/01-31/12.

S Saint-Laurent 21G2

Rue des Cerisiers. **GPS**: n46,16639 e1,96167.

4 free Ch free. **Location:** Rural. **Surface:** metalled.
01/01-31/12.
Distance: on the spot on the spot.

S Saint-Laurent-Médoc 24B1

Place du 8 mai 1945. **GPS**: n45,14903 w0,8215.

6 free Ch. **Location:** Urban, simple.
Surface: gravel/metalled. 01/01-31/12.
Distance: on the spot 300m 300m.

S Saint-Laurent-sur-Gorre 21E3

Les Chênes, Allée des Primevères. **GPS**: n45,76528 e0,95639.

20 € 6 € 2/100liter Ch (7x)€ 2/4h WC included.
Location: Rural, comfortable, quiet. **Surface:** grassy.
01/01-31/12.
Distance: 300m on the spot on the spot 300m 300m.

Saint-Leon-sur-l'Isle 24D1

Skate Park Bord de l'Isle, D41E2. **GPS**: n45,12002 e0,49628.

6 free. **Location:** Rural, simple. **Surface:** metalled/sand.
01/01-31/12.
Distance: 2km 5,3km on the spot 2km 2km.
Remarks: Service in village 750m, n45.11515 o0.5003400.

S Saint-Léon-sur-Vézère 24E2

Le Bourg, C201. **GPS**: n45,01230 e1,08978.

15 free, 01/04-15/11 € 6 € 2 WC. **Location:** Rural, simple, quiet. **Surface:** grassy/gravel. 01/01-31/12.
Distance: 100m 200m 150m.
Remarks: Coins at tourist info.

S Saint-Lon-les-Mines 27B1

D6. **GPS**: n43,61458 w1,12617.
10 free Ch WC. **Surface:** grassy. 01/01-31/12.

Distance: 200m 200m.
Remarks: Max. 48h, picnic tables available.

S Saint-Martial-d'Artenset 24D2

Le Gaec du Petit Clos, Lieu-dit Ferrachet. **GPS**: n44,99877 e0,22052.
€ 5, € 10 service incl Ch. **Location:** Comfortable, isolated, quiet. 01/01-31/12 Mo.
Distance: 2,5km 9km 2,5km.

S Saint-Martin-de-Ré 21B2

Rue de Rempart. **GPS**: n46,19925 w1,36514.

17 € 11 Ch included.
Location: Rural. **Surface:** gravel. 01/01-31/12.
Distance: 500m 700m 500m 500m.
Remarks: 01/04-30/09 max. 72h.

S Saint-Mathieu 21E3

Les Champs. **GPS**: n45,71465 e0,78720.

15 free € 2/100liter Ch. **Location:** Rural, simple, quiet.
Surface: asphalted. 01/01-31/12.
Distance: 2km on the spot on the spot.

S Saint-Médard-de-Guizières 24D2

Place du 14 Juillet. **GPS**: n45,01526 w0,0579.

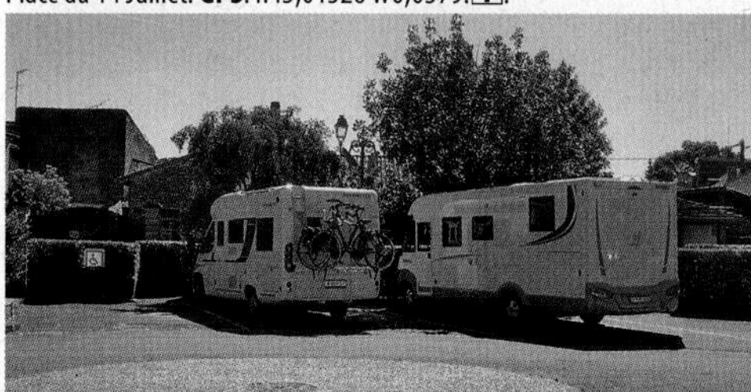

3 free Ch WC free. **Location:** Urban, simple, central.
Surface: asphalted. 01/01-31/12.
Distance: on the spot 200m 300m.

S Saint-Merd-les-Oussines 21G3

D109 > Tarnac. **GPS**: n45,63500 e2,03719.

6 free € 2 Ch. **Location:** Rural, simple, isolated, quiet.
Surface: grassy/gravel. 01/01-31/12.
Distance: 400m.
Remarks: Coins at Auberge du Mont-Chauvet.

S Saint-Palais-sur-Mer 27B2

Parking Place Ste. Elisabeth, Rue Gaztelu Zena.
GPS: n43,32944 w1,0325.

FR

10 free Ch WC free. **Location:** Simple. **Surface:** asphalted.
01/01-31/12.
Distance: 200m 250m 250m.

Saint-Paul-lès-Dax 27B1

Allée Salvador Allende. **GPS**: n43,73460 w1,07865.

8 free Ch free. **Location:** Simple. **Surface:** gravel/sand.
01/01-31/12.
Distance: 500m 500m.
Remarks: Max. 72h, shady.

Saint-Pée-sur-Nivelle 27A2

Flot bleu park St. Pée sur Nivelle, Promenade du Parlement de Navarre. **GPS**: n43,34945 w1,5215.

50 € 9,50/24h € 2,50/120liter Ch € 2,50/4h.
Surface: asphalted. 01/01-31/12.
Distance: 3km on the spot 500m Restaurant Aintzira Le Lac.
Remarks: Parking at lake, max. 48h, bread-service.

Saint-Pey-d'Armens 24C2

Château Gerbaud, Gerbaud. **GPS**: n44,85310 w0,10699.

40 € 5 Ch included (8x)€ 3. **Location:** Rural, simple.
Surface: grassy. 01/01-31/12.
Distance: 1km bakery 1km, supermarket 2km.
Remarks: Max. 48h.

Saint-Pierre-d'Oléron 21B2

La Fauchepрère, Avenue des Pins, La Cotinière.
GPS: n45,92393 w1,3427.

8 € 9 € 4 Ch € 4. **Location:** Rural, simple.
Surface: grassy/gravel. 01/01-31/12.
Remarks: In front of campsite municipal, pay at reception.

Saint-Porchaire 21C3

Place du Champ de Foire. **GPS**: n45,82063 w0,78215.

10 free Ch WC free. **Location:** Urban, simple, central, quiet.
Surface: gravel. 01/01-31/12.
Distance: 400m 200m 1km.
Remarks: Max. 48h.

Saint-Privat 24G1

Rue des Chanaux. **GPS**: n45,14037 e2,09765.

10 free € 2 Ch € 2. **Location:** Urban, simple, central, quiet.
Surface: grassy/metalled. 01/01-31/12.
Distance: 200m 200m 200m.

Saint-Quentin-sur-Charente 21E3

Barrage du Lavaud, Lieu-dit Versennes, D214.
GPS: n45,82714 e0,68813.

15 free Ch (4x) WC free.
Location: Rural, comfortable, isolated, quiet. **Surface:** gravel.
01/01-31/12 service: 01/10-30/04.
Distance: 4km no swimming 4km 4km on the spot on the spot.
Remarks: Max. 3 days.

Saint-Romain-la-Virvée 24C2

Rue des Milonis. **GPS**: n44,96449 w0,40139.

5 free Ch free. **Location:** Rural, comfortable, quiet.
Surface: asphalted. 01/01-31/12.
Distance: on the spot 10km 250m.
Remarks: Next to sports fields.

Saint-Saud-Lacoussière 21E3

Étang de la Gourgousse, Route du Grand Etang.
GPS: n45,55780 e0,82237.

free.
Location: Rural, isolated, quiet. **Surface:** forest soil.
Distance: Sandy beach on the spot on the spot.
Remarks: Max. 72h.

Saint-Saud-Lacoussière 21E3

Domaine Sous Chardonnièras, 4, Impasse Sous Chardonnièras.
GPS: n45,54053 e0,81909.

4 € 12,50 WC included. **Location:** Simple, quiet.
Surface: grassy. 01/01-31/12.
Distance: 500m 2km 2km 500m 500m.

Saint-Sauveur 24E2

Le Bourg, D21. **GPS**: n44,86850 e0,58834.

3 free Ch WC free. **Location:** Simple. **Surface:** asphalted.
01/01-31/12 service 01/11-31/03.
Distance: 100m 100m 100m.

Saint-Savin 24C1

Aire de Civrac-de-Blaye, Parc de la Mairie, D36, Civrac-de-Blaye.
GPS: n45,11222 w0,44444.

1 free WC free. **Surface:** grassy. 01/01-31/12.
Distance: 50m 100m.

Saint-Savin 24C1

Aire de St.Girons d'Aiguevives, St.Girons d'Aiguevives.
GPS: n45,13972 w0,5425.

2 free . **Surface:** grassy/gravel. 01/01-31/12.
Distance: on the spot 4km 10km.
Remarks: Parking in front of church.

Saint-Savin 24C1

Aire des Lacs du Moulin Blanc, St.Christoly-de-Blaye.
GPS: n45,15167 w0,47583.

FR

2 free WC free. **Surface:** gravel. 01/01-31/12.
Distance: 800m 50m on the spot on the spot 3km.
Remarks: Parking at lake.

Saint-Savin 24C1

Aire des Lagunes, St.Mariens. **GPS**: n45,11790 w0,40243.

2 free WC free. **Surface:** asphalted. 01/01-31/12.
Distance: on the spot 6km 6km 2km 3km.

Saint-Savin 24C1

Parking Centre Culturel. **GPS**: n45,13800 w0,4465.

2 free WC. **Surface:** gravel. 01/01-31/12.
Distance: on the spot 3km 3km 150m 800m, bakery 50m.
Remarks: Max. 48h.

Saint-Savin 24C1

Aire de l'Église, Générac. **GPS**: n45,18000 w0,54.
2 free. 01/01-31/12.
Distance: on the spot 6km 10km.

Saint-Savin 24C1

Aire de Marcenais, Marcenais. **GPS**: n45,05808 w0,33889.

2 free. 01/01-31/12.
Distance: on the spot 6km 6km.
Remarks: Next to community centre.

Saint-Savin 24C1

Aire de Saugon, Saugon. **GPS**: n45,17795 w0,50243.
2 free. 01/01-31/12.
Distance: on the spot 6km 6km 3km 6km.
Remarks: Behind town hall.

Saint-Savin 24C1

Aire de St. Vivien, RN137, St.Vivien-de-Blay. **GPS**: n45,09917 w0,51666.

2 free. 01/01-31/12.
Distance: on the spot 3km 3km 3km 3km.
Remarks: Parking at church.

Saint-Savin 24C1

Aire du Dojo, Cézac. **GPS**: n45,09000 w0,41.

1 free. 01/01-31/12.
Distance: on the spot 6km 6km 3km 3km.
Remarks: Nearby town hall.

Saint-Savin 24C1

Aire du Lac des Vergnes, Laruscade. **GPS**: n45,10000 w0,34.
2 free. 01/01-31/12.
Distance: 200m on the spot 500m 2km.
Remarks: Parking at lake.

Saint-Savin 24C1

Aire Maison de la Forêt, Donnezac. **GPS**: n45,24000 w0,44.

2 free. 01/01-31/12.
Distance: on the spot 6km 6km.
Remarks: Next to community centre.

Saint-Savin 24C1

Parking communal Aire de Cavignac, Rue de Paix, Cavignac. **GPS**: n45,10019 w0,39192.

2 free. 01/01-31/12.
Distance: on the spot 8km 50m 300m.

Saint-Savin 24C1

Parking communal Aire de Saint Yzan, Parking de la Gare, St.Yzan-de-Soudiac. **GPS**: n45,14006 w0,40996.
2 free. 01/01-31/12.
Distance: on the spot 12km 800m 3km 3km on the spot.

Saint-Savin 24C1

Parking de Marsas, Rue Chaignaud, Marsas. **GPS**: n45,06770 w0,3849.
2 free. 01/01-31/12.
Distance: on the spot 4km 4km.

Saint-Savin 24C1

Parking Maison des Jeunes, Cubnezais. **GPS**: n45,07500 w0,40861.

free. **Surface:** asphalted. 01/01-31/12.
Distance: 50m 3km 3km.

Saint-Séverin 24D1

Rue de la Pavancelle. **GPS**: n45,31269 e0,25527.

2 free Ch WC free. **Location:** Rural. **Surface:** asphalted. 01/01-31/12.
Distance: 200m 200m Spar 100m.

Saint-Sorlin-de-Conac 24C1

Pôle Nature de Vitrezay. **GPS**: n45,32780 w0,71053.

20 free. **Location:** Rural, simple, isolated, quiet. **Surface:** grassy. 01/01-31/12.
Distance: 6km 400m.
Remarks: Nature reserve.

Saint-Sulpice-le-Guérétois 21G2

Le Masgerot. **GPS**: n46,18265 e1,84714.

16 free € 3/100liter Ch . **Location:** Isolated, noisy. **Surface:** asphalted. 01/01-31/12.
Distance: on the spot on the spot.
Remarks: Next to petrol station.

Saint-Sylvestre-sur-Lot 24E3

Place du Lot, Avenue Jean Moulin. **GPS**: n44,39621 e0,80499.

12 free Ch free.
Location: Urban, simple. **Surface:** asphalted. 01/01-31/12.
Distance: 150m, Penne d'Agenais centre 1,8km 100m 50m.
Remarks: Service 100m.

Saint-Trojan-les-Bains 21B3

Parking de la Liberté, Rue Marie Curie. **GPS**: n45,84371 w1,20899.

9 free € 4. **Location:** Urban, simple. **Surface:** asphalted. 01/01-31/12.
Distance: 200m on the spot on the spot on the spot.
Remarks: Max. 72h.

FR

Saint-Trojan-les-Bains 21B3

Parking Patoizeau, 26 Boulevard de la plage.
GPS: n45,84100 w1,20491.

10 free. **Location:** Rural, simple. **Surface:** asphalted.
01/01-31/12.
Distance: 600m 100m.
Remarks: In front of fire-station, max. 72h.

Tourist information Saint-Trojan-les-Bains:
Bureau Municipal de Tourisme, Carrefour du Port, www.st-trojan-les-bains.fr. Seaside resort on the island of Oléron, well-known for the mimosa and oyster culture.
place de Filles de la Sagesse. Food and drugs market. Thu + Sa-morning, summer daily.
Marche Nocturne, rue de la République. Evening market. Thu from 17h.

Saint-Vincent-de-Cosse 24E2

Ferme d'Enveaux. **GPS**: n44,82669 e1,09822.

50 guests free Ch free.
Surface: unpaved. 01/01-31/12.
Distance: pebbled beach 50m on the spot on the spot on the spot.
Remarks: Along the Dordogne river, max. 48h, key service at canoe rental.

Saint-Vincent-Jalmoutiers 24D1

Le Bourg. **GPS**: n45,20055 e0,19091.

25 free Ch WC free. **Location:** Rural, simple, isolated, quiet.
Surface: grassy. 01/01-31/12.
Distance: 350m 350m.

Saint-Ybard 24F1

Foyer Rural, Rue des Fontaines. **GPS**: n45,44886 e1,52271.

2 free free.
Location: Urban, simple, central, quiet.
Distance: on the spot 200m on the spot on the spot.

Saint-Yrieix-la-Perche 24F1

Parking J.P Fabrègue, Avenue de Lattre de Tassigny, D901.
GPS: n45,51271 e1,20646.

5 free € 3,50 Ch. **Location:** Urban, simple.
Surface: asphalted. 01/01-31/12.
Distance: 300m 300m 300m.
Remarks: Coins at Tourist Info and Maison de la Presse.

Saint-Yrieix-la-Perche 24F1

Ferme du Poumier, Lieu-dit Poumier, Marcognac.
GPS: n45,52065 e1,26853.

4 € 6 Ch included. **Location:** Rural, isolated, quiet.
Surface: gravel. 01/01-31/12.
Distance: St.Yrieix 5km.

Sainte-Alvère 24E2

Rue de la Fontaine Saint Jean. **GPS**: n44,94500 e0,80499.

10 free € 2,50/100liter Ch € 2,50/h. **Location:** Rural, simple. **Surface:** gravel. 01/01-31/12.
Distance: 500m 500m 500m.
Remarks: At sports centre, coins at town hall.

Sainte-Colombe-en-Bruilhois 24D3

Lieu-dit Bécade. **GPS**: n44,17889 e0,51692.

4 free Ch WC free. **Location:** Rural, simple, quiet.
Surface: gravel. 01/01-31/12.
Distance: on the spot 200m 200m.

Sainte-Eulalie-en-Born 24B3

Route du Port, D652. **GPS**: n44,30634 w1,18206.

20 € 4,50-7, 01/11-31/03 gratis Ch WC included € 3.
Location: Comfortable, quiet. **Surface:** grassy.
01/01-31/12 service: 01/11-01/03.
Distance: 50m 50m on the spot on the spot on the spot.
Remarks: At marina, to be paid at campsite.

Sainte-Livrade-sur-Lot 24E3

Avenue René Bouchon. **GPS**: n44,39588 e0,59179.

8 free Ch free. **Location:** Urban, simple. **Surface:** asphalted.
01/01-31/12.
Distance: on the spot 850m.
Remarks: At fire-station.

Sainte-Nathalène 24F2

Les Ch'tis, Le Bourg, D47. **GPS**: n44,90409 e1,28765.

6 € 10 Ch included. **Location:** Rural, simple.
Surface: gravel. 01/01-31/12.
Distance: Sarlat 7km 50m bread service 50m.
Remarks: Market Wednesday (July-August).

Saintes 21C3

Aire camping-cars Avenue de Saintonge, Chemin de la Prairie.
GPS: n45,74047 w0,62696.

12 € 5/24h Ch Service € 5
Location: Urban, simple, central. **Surface:** asphalted.
01/01-31/12.
Distance: 1km 200m Leclerc 100m.
Remarks: Max. 7 days.

Tourist information Saintes:
Les Arènes. Roman anfiteatro.
Place 11 November. Tue + Fri morning.
Grande Foire. Large regional market. 1st Mon of the month.

Salies-de-Béarn 27B2

Aire Camping-car du Herre, Chemin du Herré.
GPS: n43,47270 w0,9339.

24 € 6,70 € 2,50 Ch
Location: Rural, simple, quiet. **Surface:** gravel. 01/01-31/12.
Distance: 300m on the spot on the spot 300m 300m 300m.

Salignac-Eyvigues 24F2

Rue des Ecoles. **GPS**: n44,97257 e1,32061.

FR

10 free Chfree. **Location:** Simple, quiet. **Surface:** grassy.
01/01-31/12.
Distance: 300m 300m 250m.

Salignac-Eyvigues 24F2

Les Jardins du Manoir d'Eyrignac, Rte des Jardins du Manoir.
GPS: n44,93875 e1,31609.

40 free. **Location:** Rural. **Surface:** grassy/gravel.
Distance: Sarlat 13km on the spot.

Sanguinet 24B2

Aire Des Bardets, 1131, Avenue de Losa. **GPS**: n44,48399 w1,09154.

15 free, 01/05-18/10 € 8 Chfree. **Location:** Simple, quiet.
Surface: metalled. 01/01-31/12.
Distance: 800m on the spot on the spot 50m on the spot.
Remarks: At lake, max. 48h.

Sanguinet 24B2

Parking du Pavillon, 459, Avenue de Losa.
GPS: n44,48579 w1,08479.

30 free, 01/05-15/09 € 9 ChWC. **Location:** Simple, quiet.
Surface: forest soil. 01/01-31/12.
Distance: on the spot Le Pavillon.
Remarks: Max. 48h.

Sare 27A2

Route des Platane. **GPS**: n43,31179 w1,5839.

23 free, night € 8 Ch. **Location:** Simple. **Surface:** asphalted.
01/01-31/12.
Distance: 400m 400m on the spot.
Remarks: Nearby swimming pool, cash payment.

Tourist information Sare:

Office de Tourisme, Bourg, www.sare.fr. Typical Basque village in Labourd-region.
Le petit train de la Rhune, Col de Saint Ignace. The little train runs through the mountains in the Basque Country on the Franco-Spanish border. 15/03-15/11 from 9h.
Les Grottes de Sare. Caves, prehistoric park and museum.
01/02-31/12.

Sarlat-la-Canéda 24F2

Place Flandres Dunkerque. **GPS**: n44,89530 e1,21266.

50 € 7/24h, € 15/48h € 2 Ch € 2
Location: Urban, simple, noisy. **Surface:** asphalted.
01/01-31/12.
Distance: 1km 100m bakery 50m.

Tourist information Sarlat-la-Canéda:
Centre ville. Centre of the French trade in foie grass.
Sa-morning.

Saujon 21B3

Route des Ecluses. **GPS**: n45,67503 w0,932.

14 € 4/24h € 2/100liter Ch € 2/1h.
Location: Urban, simple, central, quiet. **Surface:** asphalted.
01/01-31/12.
Distance: 900m.
Remarks: Max. 6 days, coins at town hall.

Sauvagnon 27C2

Champ de Foire, Rue du Béarn. **GPS**: n43,40361 w0,38635.

7 free ChWCfree. **Location:** Rural. **Surface:** asphalted.
01/01-31/12.
Distance: on the spot on the spot on the spot on the spot.
Remarks: Max. 48h.

Sauvagnon 27C2

Rue du Béarn. **GPS**: n43,40310 w0,3876.

5 free. **Location:** Rural, simple, quiet. **Surface:** grasstiles.
01/01-31/12.
Distance: on the spot.

Sauveterre de Guyenne 24C2

Boulevard de 11 Novembre. **GPS**: n44,69022 w0,08624.

4 free € 1,50/90minutes Ch € 1,50/90minutes.
Location: Urban, simple, noisy. **Surface:** metalled.
01/01-31/12.
Distance: 350m 1000m, bakery 100m.
Remarks: Coins at tourist info, supermarket.

Sauzé-Vaussais 21D2

Place des Halles. **GPS**: n46,13540 e0,10660.

free ChWCfree. **Surface:** asphalted.
01/01-31/12 water: Nov-March.
Distance: on the spot on the spot on the spot.

Savignac-Lédrier 24F1

Route de Juillac. **GPS**: n45,36401 e1,22066.

15 free Ch free. **Location:** Rural. **Surface:** gravel.
01/01-31/12.
Distance: on the spot 100m.
Remarks: Coins at restaurant des Forges.

Segonzac 21C3

Jardin Public, Rue Gourry. **GPS**: n45,61456 w0,22113.

4 free Ch (4x)WCfree. **Location:** Urban, comfortable, central, quiet. **Surface:** gravel. 01/01-31/12.
Distance: 500m, Cognac 8km 500m 500m.
Remarks: Wine tasting.

Segonzac 21C3

Cognac Forgeron, Chez Richon. **GPS**: n45,62545 w0,17514.

6 free.
Location: Rural, quiet. **Surface:** grassy. 01/01-31/12.
Distance: 500m.
Remarks: Check in on arrival, wine tasting.

FR

Seignosse 27A1

Camping-car Park, D79. **GPS**: n43,69089 w1,42539.

110 € 9,60- 11 Ch (48x) included.
Surface: grassy/gravel.
01/01-31/12.
Distance: 500m 500m 500m 500m 500m.
Remarks: Mandatory, one-time fee Pass'Etapes € 4, video surveillance.

Séreilhac 21E3

Allée Catherine Tabaraud. **GPS**: n45,76751 e1,07903.

10 free € 2/10minutes Ch € 2/h. **Location:** Rural, comfortable, quiet. **Surface:** gravel. 01/01-31/12.
Distance: 200m on the spot 400m on the spot.

Sers 21D3

Rue du Champ de Foire. **GPS**: n45,59653 e0,32177.

8 free € 1/100liter Ch € 1/1h. **Location:** Rural, comfortable, quiet. **Surface:** grassy. 01/01-31/12.
Distance: on the spot on the spot on the spot on the spot on the spot.
Remarks: Max. 48h.

Servières-le-Château 24G1

Centre touristique du lac de Feyt. **GPS**: n45,14415 e2,03665.

15 free, 29/03-27/09 € 5 € 2/100liter Ch € 2/1h.
Location: Rural, comfortable, isolated, quiet.
Surface: grassy/metalled. 01/01-31/12.
Distance: Sandy beach on the spot.

Sévignacq Méracq 27C2

Aire du gave d'Ossau, Quartier Raguette.
GPS: n43,10681 w0,42082.

20 € 10 € 3 Ch € 2 WC.

Location: Simple, quiet. **Surface:** grassy/gravel. 15/02-10/11.
Distance: 1km on the spot on the spot 1km 1km.

Soorts-Hossegor 27A1

Route des Lacs. **GPS**: n43,67279 w1,42087.

85 € 6/24h, 01/06-30/09 € 12 € 2/30weekend ChWC.
Location: Rural, quiet. **Surface:** gravel. 01/01-31/12.
Distance: 550m.
Remarks: Max. 5 days.

Sorges 24E1

Aire de repos Grangearias, Le Bourg, N21.
GPS: n45,30570 e0,87238.

4 free Chfree. **Location:** Urban, simple. **Surface:** metalled.
01/01-31/12.
Distance: 100m 200m 250m.
Remarks: Service 100m.

Soubise 21B3

Aire camping-car, Le Port/rue Colbert. **GPS**: n45,92833 w1,00666.

17 € 8/24h Ch WCincluded.
Location: Rural, simple. **Surface:** grassy/metalled.
01/01-31/12.
Distance: on the spot 50m.
Remarks: Along river, max. 24h, incl. showers and warm water.

Soubrebost 21G3

La Martinèche Maison Martin Nadaud Parking, D13.
GPS: n45,98489 e1,85317.

10 free Chfree. **Location:** Rural, isolated, quiet.
Surface: asphalted. 01/01-31/12.
Distance: 9km.

Soulac-sur-Mer 21B3

Boulevard de L'Amélie. **GPS**: n45,49938 w1,1373.

45 € 4, 15/06-15/09 € 8 € 3,70/10minutes Ch € 3,70/h.
Location: Urban, comfortable. **Surface:** gravel/metalled.
01/01-31/12.
Distance: 2km 50m 2,5km 2,5km on the spot on the spot.

Sourzac 24D1

D6089. **GPS**: n45,05147 e0,39518.

8 free € 2/100liter ChWC.
Location: Rural, central. **Surface:** gravel/metalled.
01/01-31/12 water disconnected in winter.
Distance: 600m 100m.
Remarks: Coins at petrol station.

Soustons 27A1

Parking du Lac Marin, Avenue de la Pêtre, Soustons Plage.
GPS: n43,77525 w1,41076.

82 € 7, 01/05-30/09 € 13 Ch WCincluded.
Location: Simple. **Surface:** gravel/metalled. 01/01-31/12.
Distance: city centre 3km lake 50m, ocean 300m 50m 50m on the spot.
Remarks: Max. 72h.

Taillebourg 21C3

Camping-Car Park, Rue des pres du Vivier. **GPS**: n45,83287 w0,64659.
16 € 10-13,60 Ch (12x)included,6Amp.
Location: Rural. **Surface:** grassy. 01/01-31/12.
Distance: 100m 350m 350m.
Remarks: Along river, mandatory, one-time fee Pass'Etapes € 4.

Talais 21B3

Rue du Bourg 6. **GPS**: n45,47218 w1,05718.
4 € 5 € 4 Ch. 01/01-31/12.
Distance: 100m.

Terrasson-Lavilledieu 24F1

MCD Camping-cars, Rue Alphonse Daudet.
GPS: n45,13389 e1,30832.

25 € 6 € 2 Ch € 3. **Location:** Rural, comfortable, quiet.
Surface: grassy. 01/03-30/11.
Distance: 1km 600m 600m.

Thouars 18D3

Rue Felix Gellusseau. **GPS**: n46,97614 w0,21151.

FR

10 free free. **Location:** Urban, simple, quiet.
Surface: sand. 01/01-31/12.
Distance: 200m 200m 200m.

Tourist information Thouars:
Tue, Fri.

Thurageau 21D1

Fam. Turpeau, Agressais. **GPS:** n46,78388 e0,25644.

5 free free. **Location:** Rural, simple, quiet.
Surface: gravel. 01/01-31/12.
Distance: 2,5km.
Remarks: Goat farm, farm products.

Tocane-Saint-Apre 24D1

Pré Sec, D103. **GPS:** n45,25712 e0,49471.

8 free € 2/100liter € 2/1h free.
Location: Rural, simple. **Surface:** metalled. 01/01-31/12.
Distance: 300m 100m 300m 300m.
Remarks: Coins at the shops in the village.

Tonnay-Charente 21B3

Quai des Capucins. **GPS:** n45,93921 w0,88171.

15 € 6 included. **Location:** Urban, simple. **Surface:** gravel.
01/01-31/12.
Distance: 1km 300m 500m on the spot.

Tournon-d'Agenais 24E3

Base de Loisirs Camp Beau, Pont Roumio, Route de Libos, D102.
GPS: n44,40444 e0,99833.
15 free free. **Location:** Rural, simple. **Surface:** metalled.
01/01-31/12.
Distance: 500m.

Tournon-d'Agenais 24E3

D656. **GPS:** n44,40178 e0,99959.
10 free free. **Location:** Urban. **Surface:** metalled.
01/01-31/12.
Distance: 300m 300m.
Remarks: Max. 48h.

Touvre 21D3

Place Hotel de Ville, Route de Pontil. **GPS:** n45,66085 e0,25834.

7 free free. **Location:** Rural, comfortable, quiet.
Surface: gravel. 01/01-31/12.
Distance: 1km 1km 1km on the spot.

Treignac 24F1

Les rivières, Route du lac, D940. **GPS:** n45,54341 e1,79950.

25 € 2 € 2,50 . **Location:** Rural, simple, quiet.
Surface: grassy/gravel. 01/04-01/10 service: frost.
Distance: 2km on the spot.
Remarks: Along river.

Tourist information Treignac:
Office de Tourisme, 1, Place de la République. Free itinerary city tour along all curiosities, available at OT.

Trémolat 24E2

D30. **GPS:** n44,87378 e0,83065.

5 free € 2/25minutes . **Location:** Rural, simple.
Surface: asphalted. 01/01-31/12.
Distance: 300m 300m 300m on the spot.
Remarks: Coins at town hall.

Turenne 24F2

Aire camping-cars, Avenue du Sénateur Labrousse, D8.
GPS: n45,05391 e1,57988.

10 free € 2 € 2 . **Location:** Rural, comfortable, central. **Surface:** gravel. 01/01-31/12.
Distance: on the spot 100m 100m.
Remarks: Behind tourist info, coins at tourist info and supermarket, narrow road, not suitable for motorhomes +7m.

Tourist information Turenne:
Tour de Cesar. Easter-Oct daily, winter Su.

Uhart-Mixe 27B2

Parking de la salle polyvalente d'Airetik, Route départementale 933.
GPS: n43,27780 w1,02245.

4 € 5 € 2 .
Location: Rural, simple, quiet. **Surface:** asphalted.
Distance: 1km.
Remarks: Max. 24h.

Ussel 24G1

Aire du lac de Ponty. **GPS:** n45,54762 e2,28330.

15 free € 2 € 2 . **Location:** Rural, simple, quiet.
Surface: grassy/gravel. 01/01-31/12.
Distance: Ussel 3km 8,5km on the spot on the spot.
Remarks: At lake, in front of campsite.

Uzerche 24F1

Place de la Petite Gare, Rue Paul Langevin.
GPS: n45,42477 e1,56696.

20 free free.
Location: Urban, simple, central, quiet. **Surface:** asphalted.
01/01-31/12 every twentieth day of the month.
Distance: 300m 4,4km little stream.

Valeyrac 24B1

Port de Goulée, Route Castillonaise. **GPS:** n45,40500 w0,91028.

5 free. **Location:** Rural, simple, isolated, quiet.
Surface: gravel/metalled. 01/01-31/12.
Distance: 50m on the spot on the spot 20m on the spot on the spot.
Remarks: At harbour.

Vanxains 24D1

Le Petit Verteillac, D708. **GPS:** n45,21204 e0,28399.

4 free free. **Location:** Rural, simple.
Surface: asphalted. 01/01-31/12.
Distance: 400m 700m.

FR

Varès 24D3

Place de l'Europe, As Picadis. **GPS**: n44,42838 e0,35544.
10 free Ch free. **Surface:** metalled. 01/01-31/12.
Distance: bakery.

Vasles 21D1

Mouton Village, Rue de la Cité. **GPS**: n46,57329 w0,02309.

10 free Ch WC free. **Location:** Rural, simple, quiet.
Surface: gravel. 01/01-31/12.
Distance: 400m 400m.

Verrières 21C3

Chez Coutard. **GPS**: n45,57092 w0,26714.

3 free Ch (2x)free. **Location:** Rural, simple, quiet.
Surface: asphalted. 01/01-31/12.
Distance: on the spot 200m.

Vertheuil 24B1

Château Ferré, 3 rue des Aubépines. **GPS**: n45,26225 w0,82798.

4 free Ch WC. **Location:** Rural, comfortable.
Surface: grassy/gravel. 01/01-31/12.
Distance: 2km 8km 2,5km.

Veyrines-de-Domme 24E2

Boutique des Bois d'Envaux, Route des Milandes, 6-102 Le Falgueyrat.
GPS: n44,82090 e1,10394.

30 free . **Location:** Simple, isolated. **Surface:** grassy.
Distance: on the spot.
Remarks: Sale of foie gras and wine, monday evening marché gourmand.

Vézac 24E2

Camping-Car Park, La Malartrie. **GPS**: n44,82440 e1,16950.

17 € 11,10-13,50 Ch (17x) included.
Surface: grassy/gravel. 01/01-31/12.
Remarks: Mandatory, one-time fee Pass'Etapes € 4.

Vicq-sur-Gartempe 21E1

25, Route de la Roche Posay. **GPS**: n46,72414 e0,86189.

10 free Ch WC free. **Location:** Rural, simple, quiet.
Surface: gravel. 01/01-31/12.
Distance: 500m.

Vielle-Saint-Girons 27A1

Lac de Léon, plage de Vielle. **GPS**: n43,90279 w1,30944.

30 € 8-14 + tourist tax € 0,61/pp, dog € 5,10 Ch (30x)€ 5 WC included. **Location:** Simple. **Surface:** gravel/metalled.
01/04-30/09.
Distance: 100m 300m 50m 100m.
Remarks: Max. 48h.

Vielle-Saint-Girons 27A1

Les Tourterelles, Saint Girons-Plage. **GPS**: n43,95278 w1,35778.

40 € 9,90 02/07-27/08 € 15,50 16/07-20/08 € 15,95
Ch € 4/24h WC . **Location:** Comfortable.
Surface: gravel/metalled. 01/04-30/09.
Distance: 300m 500m 500m.
Remarks: Sanitary at campsite.

Vieux-Boucau-les-Bains 27A1

Aire camping-cars Village, Avenue des Pêcheurs.
GPS: n43,77971 w1,40041.

150 € 6, 01/05-30/09 € 12 Ch included .
Location: Comfortable. **Surface:** gravel/sand. 01/01-31/12.
Distance: 500m 200m 500m 500m on the spot.
Remarks: >3,5t not allowed.

Vigeois 24F1

D7, route de Brive. **GPS**: n45,36717 e1,53392.

12 free € 3/150liter Ch € 3.
Location: Rural, simple, isolated, quiet. **Surface:** grassy/gravel.
01/04-31/10.
Distance: 2km 7,2km beach 150m.
Remarks: Coins at town hall and bars in the village.

Villars-les-Bois 21C3

Maison Bernard Begaud, La Barre. **GPS**: n45,80002 w0,44085.

3 free. **Location:** Rural, simple, quiet. **Surface:** grassy.
01/01-31/12.
Distance: 500m.
Remarks: Swimming pool.

Villefranche-du-Périgord 24E2

Plan d'eau, Le Bourg. **GPS**: n44,63104 e1,07728.

15 free € 2,50 Ch € 2,50 . **Location:** Rural, quiet.
Surface: metalled. 01/01-31/12.
Distance: 300m.

Villeneuve-de-Marsan 27C1

Avenue du Stade 40. **GPS**: n43,88737 w0,30595.

7 free Ch (2x)free,16Amp. **Location:** Rural, simple, quiet.
Surface: asphalted. 01/01-31/12.
Distance: 1km 1km 1km.
Remarks: Max. 48h.

Villeréal 24E2

Aire de Jeux, Boulevard Alphonse de Poitiers, D104.
GPS: n44,63798 e0,74065.
free Ch. **Surface:** asphalted. 01/01-31/12.
Distance: 300m 300m 300m.

Villeton 24D3

D120. **GPS**: n44,36386 e0,27279.

FR

4 € 4,60, 01/04-31/10 € 5,60 € 4 Ch € 2/4h WC.
Location: Rural, comfortable. **Surface:** gravel.
01/01-31/12 water disconnected in winter.
Distance: 10,5km on the spot on the spot on the spot 500m.

S Vitrac 24F2

Montfort, D703. **GPS**: n44,83558 e1,24852.

10 free € 3/100liter Ch € 3/h WC. **Location:** Rural, simple.
Surface: grassy/gravel. 01/01-31/12.
Distance: 50m 2km beach at Dordogne river 200m.
Remarks: Coins available at restaurant Le Point Vue (200m).

S Vœuil-et-Giget 21D3

Place du Lavoir. **GPS**: n45,58473 e0,15464.

4 free € 2/100liter Ch. **Location:** Urban, simple, central, quiet. **Surface:** gravel/sand. 01/01-31/12.
Distance: on the spot on the spot 6km.
Remarks: Not suitable for big motorhomes.

Occitanie

S Adé 27C2

Feerie-des-Eaux, 70 Avenue des Pyrénées, N21.
GPS: n43,12834 w0,0277.

27 € 10 Ch included. **Location:** Comfortable, noisy.
Surface: asphalted/grassy. Easter-31/10.
Distance: Lourdes 2km 1km 500m 200m.

S Agde 28A2

Les Canoës, Route de la Tamarissière. **GPS**: n43,29871 e3,45391.
€ 12-15 + € 0,83/pp tourist tax, dog € 3 Ch € 4/4. **Location:** Rural. **Surface:** grassy. 01/04-31/10.
Remarks: Former campsite.

Tourist information Agde:
Cathédrale Ste Étienne. Romanesque fortified cathedral, 12th century.

S Agos-Vidalos 27C3

Camping-Car Park Le Pibeste, Avenue du Lavedan.
GPS: n43,03552 w0,07069.

6 € 9,60, 01/07-31/08 €10,80 Ch included.
Location: Rural, comfortable. **Surface:** grassy/gravel.
01/01-31/12.
Distance: on the spot 10km on the spot 3km on the spot on the spot.
Remarks: Mandatory, one-time fee Pass'Etapes € 4.

S Aigues-Mortes 28B2

Les Poissons d'Argent, CD62. **GPS**: n43,56476 e4,16289.

120 € 10 Ch included (32x)€ 3/24h,5Amp.
Location: Simple. **Surface:** gravel.
01/03-31/10.
Distance: 3km 3km on the spot on the spot 1,5km Lidl 500m 500m.
Remarks: At fish lake, fishing permit incl, bread-service.

S Aigues-Mortes 28B2

Rue du Port. **GPS**: n43,56631 e4,18575.

50 € 16 Ch free. **Location:** Simple. **Surface:** metalled.
01/01-31/12.
Distance: 600m.
Remarks: Max. 24h.

Tourist information Aigues-Mortes:
Office de Tourisme, Place Saint Louis, ot-aiguesmortes.com.
Medieval fortress, 13th century, in the swamp of the Camargue, tourist attraction.
La Tour Carbonnière, Place Saint Louis. Tower, guard-post for the defence of the city.

Aiguèze 25C3

GPS: n44,30530 e4,55250.

+20 free. **Location:** Rural, simple, quiet. **Surface:** grassy/gravel.
01/01-31/12.
Distance: 300m 300m.

S Albas 24F3

Pech del Gal. **GPS**: n44,47480 e1,23275.

10 free Ch free. **Location:** Simple, isolated, noisy.
Surface: gravel. 01/01-31/12 water disconnected in winter.
Remarks: At weir.

S Albi 27G1

Base de Loisirs Pratgraussals, Rue de Lamothe.
GPS: n43,92951 e2,13480.

20 free Ch free. **Location:** Rural, simple, isolated, quiet.
Surface: asphalted. 01/01-31/12.
Distance: 1,5km.
Remarks: At cemetery, service 200m.

Albi 27G1

Parking Cathédrale. **GPS**: n43,92750 e2,14111.

10 free. **Location:** Urban, simple, noisy. **Surface:** asphalted.
01/01-31/12.
Distance: 50m 50m 100m.
Remarks: Parking nearby cathedral Sainte Cécile, max. 48h.

S Albi 27G1

Supermarkt Leclerc, Les portes d'Albi. **GPS**: n43,91846 e2,10968.

free € 2/10minutes Ch € 2/55minutes.
Location: Urban, simple, noisy. **Surface:** asphalted.
01/01-31/12.
Distance: 3km on the spot on the spot on the spot.
Remarks: Parking supermarket.

S Albi 27G1

Rue Michelet. **GPS**: n43,94583 e2,15111.
Ch free. 01/01-31/12.

S Alès 28B1

Place du camping-car, Avenue Jules Guesde.
GPS: n44,12013 e4,08207.

6 free Ch free. **Location:** Urban, comfortable, central, noisy.
Surface: asphalted. 01/01-31/12.
Distance: on the spot on the spot on the spot 400m 600m on the spot routes available at tourist office.

S Alvignac 24F2

Parc du Samayou, Route de Padirac. **GPS**: n44,82504 e1,69711.

FR

10 free ChWC. **Surface:** asphalted.
Distance: 100m 200m 200m.

S Alzon 28A1

D999. **GPS**: n43,96567 e3,43902.
20 free € 2/100liter Ch. **Surface:** gravel/metalled.
01/01-31/12.
Distance: 100m.
Remarks: Coins at restaurant.

S Amélie-les-Bains-Palalda 32G1

Carrer de l'Oreneta. **GPS**: n42,48063 e2,67951.

40 € 7 Chincluded. **Surface:** gravel. 01/01-31/12.
Distance: 2km 500m.
Remarks: Behind hotel du Lion D'Or, max. 7 days.

S Amélie-les-Bains-Palalda 32G1

Camping Amélie, Avenue Beau Soleil, D115.
GPS: n42,47894 e2,67414.

8 € 6 € 4. **Location:** Simple, noisy. **Surface:** grassy/gravel.
01/01-31/12.
Distance: on the spot 1km 1km.
Remarks: Max. 48h, coins at campsite.

S Anduze 28B1

Place de la Gare. **GPS**: n44,05000 e3,98444.

20 free € 2 Ch € 2/55minutes.
Location: Urban, simple, central, quiet. **Surface:** unpaved.
01/01-31/12.
Distance: on the spot 300m 400m on the spot on the spot.
Remarks: Max. 48h.

Tourist information Anduze:

Bambousserie de Prafrance, 552 rue de Montsauve. Bamboo garden laid out in 1835, with a large variety of bamboo species. 01/02-15/11.

Train Touristique, 38 Place de la Gare. Tourist train from Anduze to St. Jean-du-Gard. 26/03-31/10.

S Anglès 27H2

Route de Saint-Pons. **GPS**: n43,56553 e2,56544.
4 free Ch. **Surface:** metalled.
Distance: 500m.

S Aniane 28A2

Le Pont du Diable. **GPS**: n43,70270 e3,55988.

€ 5/day, € 18/24h € 3 Ch.
Location: Rural, isolated. **Surface:** gravel.
01/01-31/12.
Distance: 9km.
Remarks: Max. 48h, Pont du Diable 600m, St.Guilhem-le-Désert 4km, free shuttlebus Mai-Sept: weekend (11-19h), July-Aug daily (10-23h).

Aniane 28A2

Lotissement du Camp de Sauve. **GPS**: n43,68652 e3,58254.

15 free. **Surface:** gravel. 01/01-31/12.
Distance: 300m nearby 300m 300m.

S Aragnouet 27D3

Piau Engaly. **GPS**: n42,78599 e0,15800.

120 free, Winter € 15 Ch (120x) WC.
Location: Comfortable, isolated, quiet. **Surface:** asphalted.
01/12-31/08.
Distance: 300m 300m 300m.
Remarks: Service only during winter period.

S Arcambal 24F3

Aire Municipal, D911. **GPS**: n44,45685 e1,51605.

7 free Chfree. **Location:** Rural, simple. **Surface:** asphalted.
01/01-31/12.
Distance: on the spot.

S Arfons 27G2

Pierron-Les Escudiés. **GPS**: n43,43972 e2,19472.

4 € 5 Ch. **Surface:** grassy. 01/01-31/12.
Distance: 4km 1km 4km 4km.

S Argelès-Gazost 27C3

Carrefour Market, Route du Stade. **GPS**: n43,00455 w0,08636.

26 free Ch. **Location:** Rural, comfortable, quiet.
Surface: asphalted. 01/01-31/12.
Distance: 4km 350m on the spot on the spot.

S Argelès-sur-Mer 32H1

Camping-Car Park, Route du Littoral. **GPS**: n42,57542 e3,04244.
21 € 12,12-13,32 Ch (21x) included.
Surface: asphalted. 01/09-30/06.
Distance: Sandy beach.
Remarks: Mandatory, one-time fee Pass'Etapes € 4.

Tourist information Argelès-sur-Mer:

Office de Tourisme, Palais des Congrès, Place Armand Lanoux, Perpignan, www.perpignantourisme.com. In the old city of Perpignan the Spanish influence is well visible in the colours of the houses and the palm trees.

Office de Tourisme, Place de l'Europe, www.argeles-sur-mer.com. Big touristic seaside resort with boulevard, marina and a lot of campsites.

Palais du Rois de Majorque, Perpignan. Fortified palace of the kings of Mallorca.

Elne. Mo, Wed, Fri.

S Arre 28A1

D999. **GPS**: n43,96771 e3,52139.

6 free € 2/100liter Ch € 2/1h WC.
Location: Rural, simple, central, quiet. **Surface:** metalled.
01/01-31/12.
Distance: on the spot on the spot on the spot on the spot bakery 200m on the spot.

S Arreau 27D3

Chemin de Fregel. **GPS**: n42,90708 e0,35912.

25 free, July-Aug € 2 Chfree. **Location:** Urban, simple, central. **Surface:** metalled. 01/01-31/12.
Distance: 100m 100m 150m 300m 200m on the spot on the spot.

S Arrens-Marsous 27C3

D918. **GPS**: n42,95806 w0,20722.

10 free € 2/100liter Ch € 2.
Location: Rural, simple, isolated, quiet. **Surface:** asphalted.
01/01-31/12.
Distance: 650m 550m 500m on the spot on the spot.

FR

S Arvieu 24H3
GPS: n44,19246 e2,65916.

6 free €2/80liter Ch.
Location: Simple, quiet. **Surface:** gravel.
01/01-31/12.
Distance: 100m on the spot 100m 100m on the spot.
Remarks: At sports centre, max. 72h, coins at the shops and town hall.

S Aubrac 24H3
D533. **GPS**: n44,62026 e2,98705.
10 free ChWCfree. **Location:** Simple, quiet. **Surface:** gravel.
01/01-31/12.
Distance: 50m on the spot on the spot on the spot on the spot.

S Aubrac 24H3
GPS: n44,68193 e2,85431.
€2 Ch. **Surface:** gravel/metalled.
Distance: 1km.

S Auch 27D1
Camping municipal, Rue des Cormorans.
GPS: n43,63654 e0,58854.

3 €4 Chfree €1,50. **Surface:** asphalted. 01/01-31/12.
Distance: 15min 15min 15min.

S Auterive 27F2
Rue des Docteurs Basset. **GPS**: n43,35182 e1,47641.
10 free ChWC. **Surface:** asphalted. 01/01-31/12.
Distance: 200m 200m.
Remarks: Along river.

S Auterive 27F2
Grande Allée du Ramier. **GPS**: n43,35025 e1,47730.
Chfree. 01/01-31/12.
Remarks: At fire-station.

S Auzas 27E2
Base de Loisirs d'Auzas, La Grangère. **GPS**: n43,17016 e0,88690.

10 €4 Ch (4x)included. **Surface:** asphalted.
Distance: on the spot.
Remarks: At lake.

S Avèze 28A1
Aire de Loisirs du Pont Vieux, D999. **GPS**: n43,97517 e3,59899.

6 free €2 Ch €2/1h.
Surface: metalled. 01/01-31/12.
Distance: 500m on the spot on the spot 500m 1,3km on the spot.
Remarks: Next to campsite municipal, max. 48h.

S Ax-les-Thermes 27F3
A Bonascre, Rue des Chalets. **GPS**: n42,70340 e1,81657.
40 free €2/100liter Ch €6/24h. **Location:** Isolated, quiet. **Surface:** gravel. 01/01-31/12.

S Ax-les-Thermes 27F3
N20. **GPS**: n42,72565 e1,83154.
30 €8 100liter included1h. **Location:** Simple, noisy.
Surface: asphalted.
Distance: 1km.

Ax-les-Thermes 27F3
Parc d'Espagne. **GPS**: n42,71504 e1,84142.

35 €5. **Surface:** asphalted. 01/01-31/12.
Distance: 500m 500m 500m.

S Bagnères-de-Bigorre 27D3
Rue René Cassin. **GPS**: n43,07319 e0,15256.

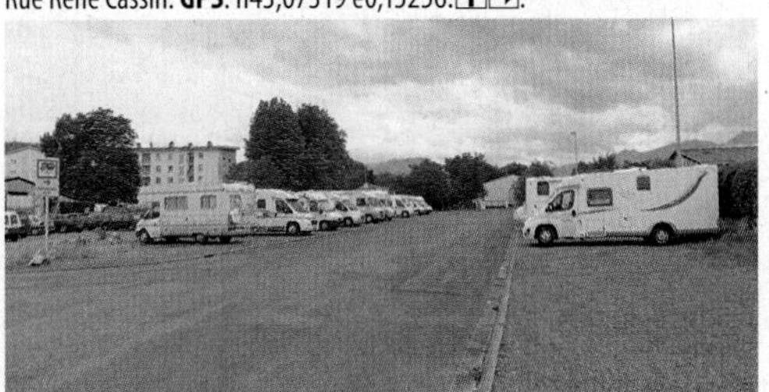

30 free ChWCfree. **Location:** Rural, simple, noisy.
Surface: gravel. 01/01-31/12.
Distance: 500m 15km 500m 650m.

Bagnères-de-Bigorre 27D3
Avenue de Belgique. **GPS**: n43,06917 e0,14889.

10 free. **Location:** Urban, simple, central, noisy. **Surface:** asphalted.
01/01-31/12.
Distance: 200m 15km 200m 200m on the spot on the spot on the spot.
Remarks: At station.

S Bagnères-de-Luchon 27D3
Lac de Badech, Rue Jean Mermoz. **GPS**: n42,79540 e0,59875.

50 €4/24h Service €4 Ch.
Location: Rural, simple, quiet. **Surface:** asphalted.
01/01-31/12 service: 01/12-01/04.
Distance: 1km 1km 500m on the spot on the spot.
Remarks: Coins at tourist info.

S Bagnols-sur-Cèze 28C1
Av. de l Europe, D8086. **GPS**: n44,16820 e4,61958.

20 free Chfree. **Surface:** gravel.
Distance: 200m 200m 200m.
Remarks: Max. 24h.

S Balaruc-les-Bains 28A2
Avenue des Hespérides 335. **GPS**: n43,44499 e3,67564.

6 €8,50 Ch. **Location:** Rural, quiet. **Surface:** unpaved.
01/01-31/12.
Distance: on the spot.

S Balaruc-les-Bains 28A2
Thermes Hespérides, Allée des Sources.
GPS: n43,44574 e3,67770.

6 €7 Ch 55minutes WCincluded.
Location: Simple, quiet. **Surface:** asphalted. 01/01-31/12.
Distance: 1km.
Remarks: Free bus to centre.

S Baraqueville 24G3
Rue du Val de Lenne. **GPS**: n44,27850 e2,43407.

10 free €3 Ch. **Location:** Simple, quiet.
Surface: asphalted. 01/01-31/12 service 01/11-31/03.
Distance: on the spot 50m on the spot on the spot.
Remarks: Coins at the shops in the village, inclining pitches.

Barbotan-les-Thermes 27C1
Avenue des Thermes. **GPS**: n43,94884 w0,04344.

6 €6. **Surface:** asphalted. 01/01-31/12.
Distance: 500m 50m 500m.

S Bardigues 27E1
GPS: n44,03869 e0,89271.

FR

4 free € 2/100liter Ch. **Location:** Simple. **Surface:** gravel.
01/01-31/12.
Distance: 150m 150m 150m.

Barèges 27D3

Le Tournabou, Route de Tourmalet, D918. **GPS:** n42,90329 e0,10151.

15 free. **Location:** Rural, isolated, quiet. **Surface:** asphalted.
01/01-31/12.
Distance: 2,5km on the spot 3km on the spot on the spot on the spot on the spot.

Beaucaire 28C1

Les Marguilliers, Chemin des Marguilliers.
GPS: n43,81667 e4,64107.

9 € 15/24h Ch included.
Surface: gravel. 01/01-31/12.
Distance: 500m 500m 500m 500m.

Beaucaire 28C1

Quai de la Paix. **GPS:** n43,80615 e4,63739.

10 free € 2/100liter Ch € 2/1h. **Location:** Urban, simple.
Surface: asphalted. 01/01-31/12 water disconnected in winter.
Distance: 300m 300m bakery 300m.
Remarks: Coins at tourist info.

Beaumont-de-Lomagne 27E1

Boulevard Georges Brassens. **GPS:** n43,88028 e0,99057.
free Chfree. **Surface:** gravel. 01/01-31/12.
Distance: 300m 300m.
Remarks: Max. 1 night.

Bédarieux 27H2

Avenue Jean Moulin. **GPS:** n43,61071 e3,15329.

10 free Chfree. **Location:** Urban, simple, central, quiet.
Surface: grassy. 01/01-31/12.
Distance: on the spot on the spot on the spot 800m.
Remarks: Along the Orb river.

Bélesta 27H3

Rue des Loisirs. **GPS:** n42,71560 e2,60786.

10 € 5 € 2/20minutes (8x)€ 2/4h.
Location: Rural, simple, quiet. **Surface:** grassy/gravel.
01/04-31/10.
Distance: 100m on the spot.

Bellas 24H3

D995. **GPS:** n44,31256 e3,12689.
10 € 5 free € 3. **Location:** Rural, quiet.
Surface: grassy/metalled. 01/01-31/12.
Distance: on the spot on the spot.

Bellegarde 28C1

Port de plaisance, Las Courrejos Est. **GPS:** n43,74422 e4,51890.

free € 2 Ch € 2/1h. **Location:** Rural, simple.
Surface: gravel/sand. 01/01-31/12.
Distance: city centre 1,5km.
Remarks: Max. 48h, coins at harbourmaster.

Belmont sur Rance 27H1

Parking de la Mairie, Route de Lacaune. **GPS:** n43,81630 e2,75269.

3 free Chfree. **Surface:** asphalted. 01/01-31/12.
Distance: on the spot.

Belpech 27F2

Stade municipal, Rue du Stade. **GPS:** n43,19864 e1,74472.

7 free Ch free WC. **Surface:** grassy. 01/01-31/12.
Distance: 1km 1km 1km.
Remarks: At football ground.

Boisse Penchot 24G3

Rue du Chateau Bas. **GPS:** n44,59201 e2,20567.

8 free € 3/100liter Ch € 3/1h.
Surface: asphalted. 01/01-31/12.
Distance: 100m on the spot on the spot on the spot on the spot.

Bonac Irazein 27E3

Lac Bonac. GPS: n42,87541 e0,97565.

10 € 8,60 Ch included.
Surface: grassy/gravel. 01/03-30/11.
Distance: 200m on the spot.
Remarks: At artificial lake of Bonac.

Bouillac 24G3

Aire de Bouillac, D840. **GPS:** n44,57333 e2,15750.

12 free € 3 ChWC. **Surface:** metalled. 01/03-30/11.
Distance: on the spot on the spot on the spot on the spot 600m.
Remarks: Max. 24h, coins at the shops.

Bourret 27E1

Cambonis. **GPS:** n43,93569 e1,14320.
2 € 10 Ch WC . **Location:** Rural. **Surface:** metalled.
01/01-31/12.
Distance: 2km.
Remarks: Barbecue place, swimming pool.

Bouzies 24F3

Le Bourg. **GPS:** n44,48401 e1,64423.
10 € 5,50 € 2/100liter Ch € 2/1h. **Surface:** gravel.
01/01-31/12.
Distance: 200m.

Bozouls 24H3

Parking de la Médiathèque. **GPS:** n44,47199 e2,72104.
15 free Ch. **Surface:** gravel. 01/01-31/12.
Distance: 500m 150m 350m.
Remarks: Service closed during wintertime.

Branoux-les-Taillades 25B3

Aire de la Placette, La placette. **GPS:** n44,22607 e4,01036.
4 free € 4/10minutes Ch . **Surface:** metalled.
01/01-31/12.
Distance: 100m.
Remarks: Picnic area.

Bréau-et-Salagosse 28A1

Le Rieumage, D272. **GPS:** n43,99338 e3,56716.
6 € 2 € 2 Ch. **Location:** Rural, isolated, quiet. **Surface:** gravel.
01/01-31/12.

Broquies 27H1

Route de Mazies. **GPS:** n44,00498 e2,69371.

FR

10 free Ch WC. **Surface:** gravel. 01/01-31/12.
Distance: 50m on the spot on the spot.
Remarks: Coins at supermarket.

Cadours 27E1

Rue Malakoff. **GPS:** n43,72320 e1,04861.

5 free Chfree. **Location:** Rural. **Surface:** grassy.
01/01-31/12 tue-evening, wed-morning.
Distance: 1km 1km.
Remarks: At football ground.

Cahors 24F3

Parking Chartreux, Rue de la Chartreuse.
GPS: n44,44016 e1,44119.

3 free Chfree. **Location:** Simple. **Surface:** gravel.
01/01-31/12.
Distance: 500m on the spot 250m 50m on the spot.
Remarks: Along river.

Cahors 24F3

Parking Saint George, Rue Saint George.
GPS: n44,43875 e1,44111.
20 free. **Location:** Simple. **Surface:** asphalted.
01/01-31/12.
Distance: 1,2km 100m on the spot.
Remarks: Max. 72h, shuttle bus to city centre.

Tourist information Cahors:
Wed, Sa.

Cahuzac-sur-Vère 27G1

Place du Mercadial. **GPS:** n43,98194 e1,91111.

5 free ChWCfree.
Location: Rural, simple. **Surface:** gravel.
Distance: 200m 200m 200m on the spot.
Remarks: At cemetery.

Cajarc 24F3

Place de la Gare. **GPS:** n44,48458 e1,84573.

8 free € 1/200liter Ch. **Location:** Simple. **Surface:** grassy.
01/01-31/12 water disconnected in winter.
Distance: 100m 200m 200m.

Camares 27H1

Base de loisirs des Zizines. **GPS:** n43,81654 e2,87988.

16 free, night € 5 ChWC free. **Surface:** gravel.
01/04-31/10.
Distance: 100m on the spot on the spot 1km 1km.
Remarks: Max. 72h.

Campagnac 24H3

La Sagne. **GPS:** n44,41885 e3,08875.

5 free, 13/06-13/09 € 3 Ch. **Surface:** metalled.
01/01-31/12.
Distance: 400m 400m 400m.
Remarks: Coins at campsite and town hall.

Campan 27D3

Le Bourg. **GPS:** n43,01817 e0,17828.

5 free ChWC. **Location:** Rural, simple, quiet. **Surface:** gravel.
01/01-31/12.
Distance: 100m on the spot 300m 200m.
Remarks: Max. 48h.

Campan 27D3

Serre Crampe, Payolle. **GPS:** n42,93711 e0,30259.

15 free ChWCfree. **Location:** Rural, isolated, quiet.
Surface: gravel. 01/01-31/12.
Distance: 5km 150m 150m 600m 6km on the spot on the spot on the spot on the spot.
Remarks: Max. 48h, service 100m.

Campuac 24H3

Les Crozes. **GPS:** n44,57027 e2,59162.
10 free ChWCfree. **Surface:** gravel. 01/01-31/12.
Distance: 100m on the spot.
Remarks: Max. 7 days.

Canet-de-Salars 24H3

Les Fontanelles. **GPS:** n44,23260 e2,74716.

6 € 6, tourist tax € 0,60/pp € 2/20minutes Ch WCincluded.
Location: Rural, simple, quiet. **Surface:** grassy/gravel.
01/04-30/10.
Distance: 750m 5km 750m on the spot.
Remarks: Coins at bar and garage.

Capdenac-Gare 24G3

Camping-Car Park, Boulevard Paul Ramadier.
GPS: n44,57302 e2,07292.
50 € 9,30 Ch (50x) included. 01/01-31/12.
Distance: on the spot.
Remarks: Mandatory, one-time fee Pass'Etapes € 4.

Carcassonne 27G2

Camping de la Cité, Route de Saint-Hilaire.
GPS: n43,19980 e2,35317.
38 € 12/24h + € 0,20/pp tourist tax € 2 Ch.
Surface: gravel. 01/01-31/12.
Distance: 3,5km.

Tourist information Carcassonne:
Office de Tourisme, 15, Boulevard Camille Pelletan, www.carcassonne-tourisme.com. Medieval fortified city, museum city with many curiosities.
The new city has a modern shopping centre.

Cardaillac 24G2

Le Pré del Prie. GPS: n44,67868 e1,99805.

12 free € 2/100liter Ch € 2/h. **Location:** Isolated, quiet.
Surface: gravel. 01/01-31/12.
Distance: 100m on the spot 100m.
Remarks: Behind church.

Carnon 28B2

Les Saladelles, Avenue Grassion Cibrand, Carnon-plage.
GPS: n43,55097 e3,99417.

18 € 11,50, 01/07-31/08 € 13 Ch WC included,on camp site € 5.
Location: Rural. **Surface:** asphalted. 01/04-15/10.
Distance: 1km 80m 50m.
Remarks: Next to campsite Les Saladelles.

Castanet 24G3

GPS: n44,27889 e2,28944.

FR

4 € 8 Ch included. **Location:** Rural, comfortable, quiet. **Surface:** gravel. 01/01-31/12.
Distance: on the spot on the spot.
Remarks: Money in envelope in mail box.

Casteil 32G1

D116. **GPS**: n42,53324 e2,39230.

5 free. **Location:** Rural, simple, isolated, quiet. **Surface:** forest soil. 01/04-31/10.
Distance: 1km on the spot on the spot.

Castelnau-de-Montmiral 27F1

Domaine Les Miquels. **GPS**: n43,96667 e1,80278.

6 € 10 Ch included. **Location:** Rural, comfortable, isolated, quiet. **Surface:** grassy. 01/01-31/12.
Distance: 2,5km on the spot 2,5km.

Castelnau-Durban 27F3

D117. **GPS**: n42,99994 e1,33976.

10 € 2 Ch included WC. **Surface:** metalled.
Remarks: Parking in front of church, max. 48h.

Castelnaudary 27G2

Camping-Car Park Castelnaudary, Passage des Lavandières.
GPS: n43,31427 e1,94899.

14 € 9,20 Ch (14x) included. **Location:** Urban, comfortable. **Surface:** grassy/gravel. 01/01-31/12.
Distance: on the spot on the spot on the spot.
Remarks: Mandatory, one-time fee Pass'Etapes € 4.

Castelsarrasin 27E1

Allée de la Source. **GPS**: n44,03861 e1,10221.

60 € 3/24h € 2,50/100liter Ch € 2,50/24h.
Location: Simple. **Surface:** gravel. 01/01-31/12.
Distance: 500m 500m 500m.

Castres 27G2

Place Gerard Philipe, Chemin des Porches. **GPS**: n43,60168 e2,24939.

free. **Location:** Urban. **Surface:** asphalted. 01/01-31/12.
Distance: 2km 2km 2km.
Remarks: Max 3,5t, free bus to centre.

Castres 27G2

Route de l'Industrie Z.I. de Melou. **GPS**: n43,59069 e2,20648.
Ch free. 01/01-31/12.

Tourist information Castres:
Palais Episcopal. Episcopal palace.
Tue, Thu-Su.

Catus 24F3

Place de la Vernière. **GPS**: n44,55576 e1,33829.
10 free Ch free. 01/01-31/12.
Distance: 200m.

Cauterets 27C3

Ancien Boulodrome, Avenue Charles Thierry.
GPS: n42,88628 w0,11522.

24 € 10 Ch included. **Location:** Rural, simple, quiet. **Surface:** asphalted. 01/01-31/12.
Distance: 300m 20km 300m 350m on the spot on the spot on the spot.

Cauterets 27C3

Place de la Patinoire, D920. **GPS**: n42,89361 w0,11256.

50 € 10/24h Ch included. **Location:** Rural, comfortable, quiet. **Surface:** asphalted. 01/01-31/12.
Distance: 300m 20km 300m 300m on the spot on the spot.
Remarks: Max. 21 nights.

Caylus 24F3

Base de loisirs Labarthe, D19. **GPS**: n44,23363 e1,77225.

6 free Ch free. **Location:** Rural, simple. **Surface:** grassy/gravel. 01/01-31/12.
Distance: 200m 200m 200m.

Tourist information Caylus:
St.Antonin. Small town with the oldest town hall of France.

Cazes-Mondenard 24E3

Musée du Corbillard, Lieu dit Minguet. **GPS**: n44,23047 e1,21157.
free. **Location:** Rural. 01/01-31/12.
Distance: on the spot.
Remarks: Regional products.

Chusclan 28C1

Cave Chusclan, Route d'Orsan, D138. **GPS**: n44,14552 e4,67762.

40 free Ch free. **Surface:** gravel. 01/01-31/12.
Distance: 500m 500m.

Clermont-l'Hérault 28A2

Aire de stationnement camping-car, Lac du Salagou.
GPS: n43,64677 e3,38915.

8 € 5-7 € 2/100liter Ch (6x). **Location:** Rural, simple, isolated, quiet. **Surface:** gravel. 01/01-31/12.
Distance: 7km on the spot on the spot on the spot 7km on the spot on the spot.
Remarks: Coins at campsite.

Collioure 32H1

Route de Madeloc/D914. **GPS**: n42,52315 e3,06741.
15 € 11/24h Ch WC included. **Location:** Comfortable, quiet. **Surface:** asphalted. 01/01-31/12.
Distance: 2,3km 2,5km 2km 2km.
Remarks: Monitored parking, may-Sep free shuttle to Collioure.

Comps 28C1

Place des Arènes. **GPS**: n43,85402 e4,60724.

50 € 6 Ch € 2/50minutes WC. **Location:** Rural. **Surface:** grassy/gravel. 01/01-31/12.
Distance: 50m on the spot on the spot 50m on the spot on the spot.

Comps 28C1

GPS: n43,85390 e4,60912.

30 € 5.
Location: Rural. **Surface:** unpaved. 01/01-31/12.
Distance: 500m on the spot 500m.
Remarks: Along river.

S Condom 27D1

Avenue des Mousquetaires. **GPS**: n43,94836 e0,36378.

12 free Ch. **Location:** Comfortable, isolated, quiet.
Surface: grassy/metalled. 01/01-31/12.
Distance: 500m 400m.
Remarks: Max. 3 days, market Wednesday.

S Condom 27D1

Ferme de Parette, Route de Nérac, RN930.
GPS: n43,98802 e0,35046.

8 € 12, 2 pers.incl Ch WC included € 4.
Location: Comfortable, isolated, quiet. **Surface:** grassy.
01/01-31/12.
Distance: 2km 2km 2km.

Tourist information Condom:
M Musée de l'Armagnac. All about Armagnac.

S Cordes-sur-Ciel 27G1

Parking les Tuileries. GPS: n44,06453 e1,95802.

40 € 6 60liter Ch included3h.
Location: Rural, simple, isolated, quiet. **Surface:** grassy/gravel.
01/01-31/12.
Distance: 500m 500m.

S Coupiac 27H1

Route de Martin. **GPS**: n43,95174 e2,58464.
15 free Ch free . **Surface:** grassy. 01/01-31/12.
Distance: 500m 450m.
Remarks: Max. 72h.

S Cransac 24G3

Aire de Camping-car Cransac, Route de la Gare.
GPS: n44,52278 e2,27444.

6 € 6,30, tourist tax € 0,40/pp Ch included. **Surface:** gravel.
01/03-23/11.
Distance: 500m 500m 500m.
Remarks: Max. 48h.

S Cuxac-Cabardès 27G2

La Cabasse. **GPS**: n43,36126 e2,30185.
20 € 9 Ch included . **Location:** Isolated, quiet.
Surface: metalled. 01/01-31/12.
Distance: on the spot on the spot on the spot on the spot.

S Donzac 24E3

Lac de Sources, D30. **GPS**: n44,11308 e0,82044.

10 free Ch free. **Location:** Rural, simple. **Surface:** gravel.
01/01-31/12.
Distance: 500m on the spot.
Remarks: Max. 48h.

S Douelle 24F3

Domaine Marcilhac, D8. **GPS**: n44,47927 e1,34947.

10 free € 2 Ch. **Location:** Rural, simple. **Surface:** gravel.
01/01-31/12.
Distance: 1km 1km 1km 1km.

S Duilhac-sous-Peyrepertuse 27G3

Route du château. **GPS**: n42,86160 e2,56527.

25 free Ch WC free. **Location:** Rural, simple, quiet.
Surface: asphalted. 01/04-31/10.
Distance: 200m 200m.

Entraygues-sur-Truyère 24H2

Route de Villecomtal, D904. **GPS**: n44,64020 e2,56925.

10 free. **Surface:** grassy. 01/04-31/12.
Distance: 50m on the spot on the spot 50m 50m.

S Entraygues-sur-Truyère 24H2

Rue du 16 Août 1944. **GPS**: n44,64269 e2,56577.
€ 3 Ch .
Remarks: Coins at tourist info.

S Espalion 24H3

Camping-Car Park, Avenue Pierre Monteil.
GPS: n44,52156 e2,76921.
25 € 9,60-10,80 Ch (8x) included.
Surface: gravel/metalled. 10/08-31/07.
Distance: 1km 1km 1km.
Remarks: Mandatory, one-time fee Pass'Etapes € 4.

S Espéraza 27G3

Promenade François Mitterand. **GPS**: n42,93370 e2,21589.

20 free Ch free. **Location:** Rural, simple, quiet.
Surface: grassy.
Distance: 500m on the spot on the spot 500m.

S Fanjeaux 27G2

Chemin des Fontanelles. **GPS**: n43,18611 e2,03222.

15 free Ch free. **Location:** Rural, simple.
Surface: grassy/gravel. 01/01-31/12.
Distance: 100m 100m 100m.
Remarks: Next to maison de retraite (home for the elderly), max. 48h.

S Félines-Termenès 27H3

Av. de Termenes, dir Mouthoumet. **GPS**: n42,98691 e2,61285.

3 free Ch free. **Location:** Rural, simple, quiet.
Surface: gravel. 01/01-31/12.
Distance: 50m.
Remarks: Closed when frosty.

Tourist information Félines-Termenès:
Cité Médiéval, Villerouge Termenes. Medieval village and castle from 12-14th century. 01/07-30/09.

S Figeac 24G3

Parking le Foiral, Boulevard Colonel Teulié.
GPS: n44,61089 e2,03674.

5 free € 2 Ch € 2. **Location:** Central, noisy.
Surface: asphalted. 01/01-31/12.
Distance: 100m 400m 100m 100m.

Tourist information Figeac:
Marché régional. Regional market. Sa-morning.

FR

Fitou 27H3

Aragon, Route Nationale 9, Les Cabanes de Fitou.
GPS: n42,89275 e2,99672.

15 € 5/12h, € 7/24h Ch € 2,50 included.
Location: Rural. **Surface:** gravel. 01/01-31/12.
Distance: A9 6,5km on the spot 500m.
Remarks: Video surveillance.

Fleurance 27E1

Route de Toulouse. **GPS**: n43,84769 e0,67165.

40 free € 2 Ch € 2/2h.
Surface: grassy/metalled. 01/01-31/12.
Distance: on the spot on the spot on the spot.
Remarks: Coins at tourist info.

Fleury-d'Aude 28A2

Base de Loisirs Étang de Pissevache, Saint-Pierre-la-Mer.
GPS: n43,18972 e3,19694.

100 € 5/24h, 01/04-31/10 € 8,75/24h Chincluded € 2/4h
Surface: unpaved. 01/01-31/12.
Distance: sandy beach 300m.
Remarks: Parking directly behind the beach, next to tennis park and small surf lake, follow Base de Loisirs.

Fleury-d'Aude 28A2

Les-Cabanes-de-Fleury. **GPS**: n43,21529 e3,23315.

100 € 7 € 2 Ch.
Surface: metalled/sand. 01/01-31/12.
Distance: on the spot on the spot 200m.
Remarks: Next to campsite municipal Rive d'Aude, coins at capitainerie (1km).

Florac 25A3

D16. **GPS**: n44,32582 e3,59032.

23 free € 2/100liter Ch € 2/1h WCfree.
Location: Rural, comfortable, central, quiet. **Surface:** asphalted.
01/01-31/12.
Distance: 150m 300m 300m 150m 150m mountain-bike trail on the spot.
Remarks: Nearby cemetery.

Florensac 28A2

Domaine de Veyrac, Route de Bessan, D28.
GPS: n43,36221 e3,47671.

10 € 7 .
Location: Simple, isolated, quiet. **Surface:** gravel.
Distance: 5km 3,6km.

Fraïsse-sur-Agout 27H2

Chemin de la Salvetat. **GPS**: n43,60446 e2,79560.

15 € 7 Ch (1x)included. **Surface:** asphalted/grassy.
01/04-30/11.
Distance: 400m 20m 20m 400m.
Remarks: At the edge of village, on the Agout river.

Frejairolles 27G1

Domaine du Grand Chêne, D81. **GPS**: n43,86043 e2,24799.
10 € 10 Ch WC € 5/3 included.
Surface: grassy/gravel.

Gaillac 27F1

Parking des Rives Thomas, Rue Claude Nougaro.
GPS: n43,89951 e1,89494.

4 free Chfree. **Location:** Urban, simple, noisy.
Surface: asphalted. 01/01-31/12.
Distance: 200m 200m 200m.

Gavarnie 27C3

Parking Holle, Route de la station des Espécières, D923.
GPS: n42,73857 w0,01959.

20 free, July-Aug € 7 Chincluded. **Location:** Rural, simple, isolated, quiet. **Surface:** metalled. 01/01-31/12.
Distance: 1,5km 100m 800m 800m 800m on the spot 100m 1,5km.

Gavarnie 27C3

Parking du Cirque, Baretge. **GPS**: n42,73549 w0,0116.

20 € 7.
Location: Rural, simple. **Surface:** asphalted. 01/07-31/08.
Distance: 200m 200m 200m 200m on the spot on the spot on the spot.

Tourist information Gavarnie:
Cirque de Gavarnie. Can be reached with a donkey, a horse or by foot. A giant waterfalll, snow pillars and mountain slopes.

Gèdre 27C3

Aire Naturelle Le Cairn, Harneau d'Heas. **GPS**: n42,74916 e0,08935.
5 € 12 . **Location:** Rural, simple, isolated, quiet. **Surface:** grassy.
winter.
Distance: 9km 600m.
Remarks: At Chapelle de Héas.

Gèdre 27C3

Place de la Bergère, Gedre Débat. **GPS**: n42,78860 e0,01967.

12 free. **Location:** Rural, simple. **Surface:** asphalted.
01/01-31/12.
Distance: on the spot 250m 50m.

Gèdre 27C3

Auberge de la Munia, Héas, D922. **GPS**: n42,73643 e0,08631.
5 € 12, 2 pers.incl.
Distance: on the spot.

Génolhac 25B3

Les Taillades, Place du 19 Mars 1962, D906.
GPS: n44,35388 e3,94844.

10 free Chfree. **Location:** Rural, simple, isolated, quiet.
Surface: metalled. 01/01-31/12.
Distance: 200m 800m on the spot.
Remarks: Max. 48h.

Gignac 24F2

Le Moulin, Place des Troubadours. **GPS**: n45,00624 e1,45687.

10 free Chfree. **Surface:** metalled. 01/01-31/12.
Distance: 50m 150m 150m.
Remarks: Festival and market place.

S Gimont 27E1

Avenue de Cahuzac, RN124. **GPS**: n43,62987 e0,87009.

12 free Ch free. **Location:** Simple, noisy. **Surface:** gravel.
01/01-31/12.
Distance: 100m on the spot on the spot 300m 300m 300m on the spot.
Remarks: At lake, max. 48h, market Wednesday and Sunday.

S Girac 24F2

Camping-Car Park, D803 Pont de Puybrun.
GPS: n44,91984 e1,80276.
18 € 9,40-13 Ch included.
Location: Rural. **Surface:** grassy. 01/01-31/12.
Distance: 2km 1km.
Remarks: Along the Dordogne river, mandatory, one-time fee Pass'Etapes € 4.

S Gourdon 24F2

Esplanade du foirail. **GPS**: n44,73423 e1,38523.

8 free € 1/100liter Ch (8x)€ 1/kWh. **Location:** Simple, quiet. **Surface:** gravel. 01/01-31/12 water disconnected in winter. **Distance:** 200m 100m 200m on the spot.

S Gramat 24F2

La Garenne, Avenue Paul Mezet. **GPS**: n44,77966 e1,72904.

10 free Ch free. **Surface:** gravel. 01/01-31/12.
Distance: 400m 400m 400m.
Remarks: Max. 48h.

Grenade-sur-Garonne 27F1

Parking de la salle des fêtes, Rue de l'Amiral Cabanié.
GPS: n43,76838 e1,29464.
10 free. **Location:** Urban. **Surface:** grassy/metalled.
01/01-31/12.
Distance: on the spot 500m 600m.
Remarks: Playground.

S Grenade-sur-Garonne 27F1

Quai de Garonne. **GPS**: n43,77201 e1,29673.

4free Ch. **Surface:** gravel. 01/01-31/12.
Distance: 100m 100m 100m 100m.
Remarks: Service: Allées Alsace Lorraine (100m).

S Gruissan 27H3

Aire des 4 Vents, Avenue des quatre vents.
GPS: n43,10444 e3,09944.

120 free, 12/02-30/11 € 9 ChWC included.
Surface: gravel. 01/01-31/12.
Distance: on the spot on the spot on the spot on the spot.

S Gruissan 27H3

Aire des Châlets, Avenue de la Jetée, Gruissan-plage.
GPS: n43,09583 e3,11111.

80 € 9 Chincluded. **Surface:** gravel. 01/04-30/09.
Distance: 2km on the spot on the spot 2km 2km.

S Gruissan 27H3

Étang de Mateille, Gruissan dir Narbonne-Plage, base de voile, D332.
GPS: n43,12083 e3,11417.

150 € 9 Ch (24x)€ 1,50 WC included.
Surface: grassy/metalled.
01/07-31/08.
Distance: 4km on the spot on the spot 800m Lidl 2km.

Tourist information Gruissan:
L'Hospitalet. Probably the largest wine-cellar of the world.
Vieux Port. Old fishing-port.

S Guzet-Neige 27E3

Station de ski de Guzet. **GPS**: n42,78007 e1,29979.
free WC. 01/01-31/12.
Distance: on the spot on the spot.

S La Bastide-de-Sérou 27F3

Bargnac, D15. **GPS**: n43,00194 e1,44556.

15 € 14,50, Jul/Aug € 17,50 Ch WC included.
Location: Rural, isolated, quiet. **Surface:** asphalted/gravel.
01/04-12/11.
Distance: 1km.

S La Canourgue 25A3

Avenue du Lot, D998. **GPS**: n44,43325 e3,20775.

20 free Chfree. **Location:** Rural, simple, isolated, quiet.
Surface: metalled. 01/01-31/12 Jul/Aug: tue.
Distance: 500m 1,3km 600m 600m 600m.
Remarks: Max. 24h.

S La Cavalerie 27H1

Camping-Car Park, Centre du village. **GPS**: n44,00876 e3,15228.
32 € 10,20 Ch (32x) included.
Surface: gravel. 01/01-31/12.
Distance: 200m 200m.
Remarks: Mandatory, one-time fee Pass'Etapes € 4.

S La Couvertoirade 28A1

GPS: n43,91012 e3,31276.

10 € 3 € 3/100liter WC. **Location:** Rural, isolated, quiet.
Surface: gravel. 01/01-31/12.
Distance: 50m 50m.
Remarks: Large parking on edge from village.

Tourist information La Couvertoirade:
Citadelle de l'Ordre de Tempeliers. Fortified city in original state. Now many old craft industries are exercised. There is a toll-house at the entrance of the village, entrance fee is charged.

S La Grande Motte 28B2

Aire camping-car Les Cigales, Avenue de la Petite Motte.
GPS: n43,56789 e4,07404.

50 € 11-13, Jul-Aug € 16 + € 1/pp tourist tax ChWC.
Location: Rural. **Surface:** gravel. 01/01-31/12.
Distance: 2km 1,2km 2km 2km.

S La Palme 27H3

Camping-Car Park Les Salins de La Palme, Route de Port la Nouvelle.
GPS: n42,98033 e3,01858.
49 € 9,60 Ch (48x) included. **Location:** Rural, comfortable, isolated, quiet. **Surface:** grassy. 01/01-31/12.
Distance: 2,5km 2km on the spot.
Remarks: Mandatory, one-time fee Pass'Etapes € 4.

FR

La Roque-sur-Cèze 25C3

Camping-Car Park, Route de St. Laurent de Carnols. **GPS**: n44,19567 e4,52320.
28 € 10,04-12,44 Ch (24x) included. **Location**: Rural. **Surface**: grassy. 01/01-31/12.
Remarks: Mandatory, one-time fee Pass'Etapes € 4.

La Salvetat-sur-Agout 27H2

Chemin du Redoundel. **GPS**: n43,60584 e2,69911.
6 free Chfree. **Location**: Rural. **Surface**: gravel. 01/01-31/12.
Distance: 600m 900m Spar 650m.
Remarks: Near sports fields.

Labastide-Marnhac 24F3

D7. **GPS**: n44,38595 e1,39771.
10 free Chfree. **Surface**: gravel. 01/01-31/12.
Distance: 100m.

Labastide-Murat 24F2

Route de Gramat. **GPS**: n44,64944 e1,57061.

10 free Ch € 8. **Location**: Rural, simple.
Surface: asphalted. 01/01-31/12.
Distance: 300m 10m 10m.
Remarks: At supermarket Carrefour.

Labruguiere 27G2

Domaine d'en Laure, Avenue Arthur Batut.
GPS: n43,53139 e2,25528.

10 € 6/24h € 2/10minutes Ch € 2/minutes.
Location: Rural, simple, isolated, quiet. **Surface**: grassy/metalled. 01/01-31/12.
Distance: 2km on the spot on the spot 1,3km 1,3km.

Lacapelle Marival 24G2

Place de Larroque. **GPS**: n44,72806 e1,92944.

50 free Ch.
Surface: asphalted. service 15/05-30/09.
Distance: on the spot 100m 50m.

Lacroix-Barrez 24H2

Aire de Camping Car Municipale, Le Ventoux.
GPS: n44,77793 e2,63086.
10 € 3 + € 0,30/pp tourist tax Chfree. **Surface**: grassy. 01/01-31/12 service: 01/11-17/04.
Distance: 400m.

Lagrasse 27H3

Parking de la Promenade, P2, Les Condamines.
GPS: n43,09273 e2,62004.

40 € 4, 01/06-30/09 € 6 ChWCfree. **Location**: Rural, simple, quiet. **Surface**: grassy/gravel. 01/01-31/12.
Distance: on the spot on the spot on the spot on the spot on the spot.

Laguepie 24G3

Chemin de Saint Cambraire. **GPS**: n44,14578 e1,97298.

6 free Chfree. **Location**: Rural, simple, quiet.
Surface: grassy/gravel. 01/01-31/12.
Distance: 600m 600m 500m.

Laguiole 24H2

Du Bouyssou, La Serre. **GPS**: n44,67199 e2,92451.
€ 8 € 3. **Surface**: asphalted. 01/01-31/12.
Distance: 7km on the spot on the spot.

Laguiole 24H2

Rue de Lavernhe. **GPS**: n44,68408 e2,85048.

10 free Chfree. **Surface**: gravel.
01/01-31/12, service: 17/04-15/10.
Distance: on the spot.

Laguiole 24H2

La Montagnettte, Les Clauzades. **GPS**: n44,70457 e2,84037.
5 free € 3. **Location**: Simple, isolated, quiet. **Surface**: gravel. 01/01-31/12.
Distance: 4km.

Laissac 24H3

Chemin d'Ampiac. **GPS**: n44,38590 e2,82160.

6 voluntary contribution Chfree WC. **Surface**: asphalted. 01/03-30/11 frost.
Distance: 500m 500m 500m.
Remarks: Max. 24h, tuesday morning market.

Langogne 25B2

Camping-Car Park, Route du lac. **GPS**: n44,73700 e3,83448.

40 € 10,30, 01/11-28/02 € 9,60 Ch (16x) included. **Location**: Rural, comfortable, quiet.
Surface: grassy.
01/01-31/12.
Distance: 2km beach 1km on the spot 2km 2km.
Remarks: At lake Naussac, mandatory, one-time fee Pass'Etapes € 4.

Langogne 25B2

Centre Polyvalent. **GPS**: n44,72281 e3,85419.

10 free € 2/100liter Ch. **Location**: Central, quiet.
Surface: asphalted. 01/01-31/12.
Distance: on the spot 300m 300m on the spot.
Remarks: Coins at tourist info.

Langogne 25B2

Rue de la Ponteyre. **GPS**: n44,72534 e3,83841.
5 free. **Surface**: gravel. 01/01-31/12.
Distance: city centre 1,5km on the spot on the spot.
Remarks: At lake.

Lannemezan 27D2

L'Espace du Nébouzan, Chemin du Carrérot de Blazy.
GPS: n43,12779 e0,38085.

20 free Ch free. **Location**: Rural, comfortable.
Surface: gravel. 01/01-31/12.
Distance: 450m 200m 250m.

Lanuéjouls 24G3

Aire Campingcar Lanuéjouls, Avenue du Rouergue, D1.
GPS: n44,42528 e2,16139.

14 € 5 Ch WC included. **Location**: Rural, comfortable.
Surface: gravel. 01/01-31/12.
Distance: 100m 100m 100m.
Remarks: Ticket for access at shops in the village.

Lapradelle Puilaurens 27G3

D117. **GPS**: n42,81003 e2,30854.

FR

6 free Chfree. **Location:** Rural, simple, quiet. **Surface:** metalled. 01/01-31/12.
Distance: on the spot on the spot on the spot.
Remarks: At fire-station.

S Latour-Bas-Elne 32H1

Aire de Latour Bas Elne, Route de la Mer.
GPS: n42,60017 e3,00667.

40 € 10, € 14 Jun-Aug, trailer € 4 Ch included € 3/48h. **Location:** Comfortable. **Surface:** grassy. 01/01-31/12.
Distance: 3km.
Remarks: Baker at 9am, monitored parking.

S Latour-de-Carol 32F1

Village Club Yravals, 2 Rue de Saneja. **GPS**: n42,45829 e1,89460.

5 € 10, 2 pers.incl, extra pers € 1 Ch WCincluded € 2/day. **Surface:** grassy. 01/04-31/10.
Distance: 2km.

S Latronquière 24G2

Place du Foirail. **GPS**: n44,79917 e2,07917.

4 free Ch WCfree.
Surface: asphalted. 01/01-31/12.
Distance: 300m 3km 3km 300m 300m.

S Laudun-l'Ardoise 28C1

Place des Arènes. **GPS**: n44,10791 e4,65556.

3 free € 4 Ch. **Location:** Simple, central, noisy.
Surface: asphalted. 01/01-31/12.
Distance: 300m 300m 300m.

S Laudun-l'Ardoise 28C1

Route d'Avignon, N580. **GPS**: n44,09527 e4,70164.

free Chfree. **Location:** Simple, central. **Surface:** asphalted. 01/01-31/12.
Distance: 5,5km.
Remarks: Behind police station, at tennis-court.

S Laudun-l'Ardoise 28C1

Vignerons de Laudun, Avenue du Général de Gaulle.
GPS: n44,10388 e4,66362.

10 free Ch. **Surface:** grassy/gravel.
Distance: 750m 300m 750m.
Remarks: Max. 3 days.

S Lauzerte 24E3

1, Place du Foirail. **GPS**: n44,25432 e1,13666.

10 free ChWCfree. **Surface:** asphalted.
01/01-31/12 tue-evening, wed-morning.
Distance: 500m on the spot on the spot.

S Lauzerte 24E3

D2, Vignals. **GPS**: n44,26750 e1,14083.

10 free ChWCfree. **Location:** Simple. **Surface:** grassy/gravel.
01/01-31/12.
Distance: Lauzerte 1km on the spot 2km.

Tourist information Lauzerte:
Wed-morning.

S Le Barcarès 27H3

Camping-Car Park Barcarès le Port, Quai des Tourettes.
GPS: n42,80165 e3,03277.
200 € 10,80-13 Ch (16x) included.
Surface: metalled. 01/01-31/12.
Distance: 1,5km 2km on the spot on the spot 1,5km.
Remarks: Mandatory, one-time fee Pass'Etapes € 4.

S Le Bosc 28A1

Parc Activités Méridienne. **GPS**: n43,68932 e3,35328.

10 free € 2/100liter Ch € 2/1h. **Location:** Motorway, simple, isolated. **Surface:** asphalted. 01/01-31/12.
Distance: 400m on the spot Intermarché 50m.

S Le Boulou 32H1

Chemin du Moulin Nou. **GPS**: n42,52719 e2,83704.

21 free € 2 ChWC. **Location:** Rural, simple, comfortable.
Surface: asphalted. 01/01-31/12.
Distance: 300m 1km 300m 300m.
Remarks: In front of cemetery, max. 24h.

S Le Cap d'Agde 28A2

Rue du Gouverneur. **GPS**: n43,28600 e3,51739.

30 € 5, 27/03-02/11 € 10 € 2 Ch included.
Location: Rural, comfortable, central. **Surface:** asphalted/metalled. 01/01-31/12.
Distance: on the spot 500m 500m 500m.
Remarks: Nearby Camping La Clape, video surveillance.

S Le Caylar 28A1

Domaine des Templiers, Route de la Couvertoirade, D609.
GPS: n43,86944 e3,31466.

30 € 10 Ch (9x)included12h WC € 4/pp.
Location: Comfortable, isolated, quiet. **Surface:** gravel. 01/04-31/10.
Distance: 600m 500m on the spot.

S Le Fossat 27F2

Aire des Lallières, Place de la Mairie. **GPS**: n43,17201 e1,41170.

21 € 12 Ch WC included. **Location:** Luxurious.
Surface: gravel. 01/03-30/11.

FR

S Le Grau du Roi 28B2

Parking de la plage, Rue du Commandant Marceau.
GPS: n43,54061 e4,13349.

40 € 11,60, June-Aug € 26,70 € 2/100liter Ch € 2/55minutes. **Surface:** asphalted. 01/01-31/12.
Distance: centre 550m sandy beach 20m on the spot on the spot.
Remarks: Beach parking, video surveillance.

S Le Houga 27D1

Ferme aux Cerfs, Route de Mont de Marsan, D6.
GPS: n43,78430 e0,20997.

15 € 5 Chfree . **Surface:** grassy. 01/01-31/12.
Distance: 2,5km on the spot.

S Le Malzieu-Ville 25A2

Place Foirail. **GPS**: n44,85506 e3,33385.

10 free ChWCfree . **Location:** Rural, simple, central, quiet.
Surface: asphalted. 01/01-31/12.
Distance: on the spot 10km on the spot 200m 200m on the spot.

S Le Monastier-Pin-Moriès 25A3

Place de la Gare. **GPS**: n44,50896 e3,25162.

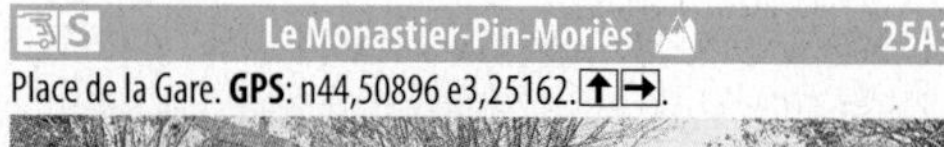

4 free ChWCfree. **Location:** Rural, simple, isolated, quiet.
Surface: asphalted. 01/01-31/12.
Distance: 1km 1,5km 1km.
Remarks: Coins at petrol station (200m), picnic area.

S Le Ségala 27F2

Esplanade du Canal. **GPS**: n43,34089 e1,83544.

5 free WC. **Location:** Rural, simple, noisy. **Surface:** gravel.
01/01-31/12.

Distance: on the spot 1km on the spot on the spot on the spot on the spot.
Remarks: No camping activities.

S Le Ségur 27G1

Place de Marie. **GPS**: n44,10889 e2,05861.

3 free ChWCfree. **Location:** Rural, simple, quiet.
Surface: metalled. 01/01-31/12.
Distance: 50m 100m 100m.
Remarks: At townhall.

S Les Angles 32G1

Pla del Mir. **GPS**: n42,56321 e2,06780.

100 free € 3,50 ChWC. **Location:** Rural, simple, quiet.
Surface: asphalted. 01/01-31/12.
Distance: 2,6km on the spot.

S Les Cabannes 27F3

Quartier la Bexane. **GPS**: n42,78493 e1,68301.

30 € 5 € 2/100liter ChWC. **Surface:** asphalted.
01/01-31/12.
Distance: 300m 300m.
Remarks: Max. 24h.

S Les Mages 25B3

Serre Marine, D904, St. Ambroix/Alés. **GPS**: n44,23442 e4,16967.

7 free Chfree. **Location:** Rural, simple, isolated, noisy.
Surface: metalled. 01/01-31/12.
Distance: 700m 700m 800m.
Remarks: Picnic area.

S Leucate 27H3

Chemin des Coussoules, La Franqui. **GPS**: n42,94329 e3,02917.

70 € 6 Ch € 7 on campsite. **Surface:** unpaved.
01/02-30/11.

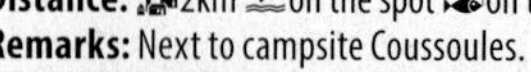

Distance: 2km on the spot on the spot 2km 2km.
Remarks: Next to campsite Coussoules.

S Leucate 27H3

Le Goulet, D627. **GPS**: n42,91145 e3,01946.

150 € 10,20-13,80 € 2 Ch € 2.
Location: Rural, simple. **Surface:** unpaved.
01/01-31/12.
Distance: centre Leucate 850m on the spot on the spot.
Remarks: Terraces, at lake of Leucate, baker on site (20/03-31/10).

S Leucate 27H3

Mouret, Chemin du Mouret, Leucate Plage.
GPS: n42,90022 e3,05272.

236 € 10,20-13,80/24h Chincluded .
Location: Rural, simple. **Surface:** asphalted/gravel.
01/01-31/12.
Distance: 300m on the spot on the spot.
Remarks: Beach parking, baker on site (20/03-31/10).

S Limoux 27G3

Parking, Rue Louis Braille. **GPS**: n43,05741 e2,21490.

30 free Chfree. **Location:** Urban, simple, quiet.
Surface: metalled. 01/01-31/12.
Distance: 200m on the spot 200m.

S Lisle sur Tarn 27F1

Aire de Bellevue, Rue des Aulnes. **GPS**: n43,86167 e1,81833.

12 free € 2/100liter Ch. **Location:** Rural, simple, isolated, quiet. **Surface:** sand. 01/01-31/12.
Distance: 1,5km on the spot on the spot 1,5km 1,5km.
Remarks: Coins at Tourist Info and Maison de la Presse.

Lodève 28A2

Baie des Vailhés, Celles. **GPS**: n43,67087 e3,35565.
€ 5, 01/07-31/08 € 8 + tourist tax € 0,20/pp.

Tourist information Lodève:
Maison de Tourisme, 7, Place de la République, www.lodeve.com. Old city to the gate of the Mediteranean.

S Lombez 27E2

Parking de la Gendarmerie, Route de Toulouse, D632.
GPS: n43,47417 e0,91592.

FR

20 free WCfree. **Surface:** gravel. 01/01-31/12.
Distance: 200m 150m 200m.

Loudenvielle 27D3

Aire de campingcar Les Seguettes, Chemin du Hourgade.
GPS: n42,80163 e0,41088.

30 free, 01/07-15/09 € 3 € 2/100liter Ch € 2/h.
Location: Rural, quiet. **Surface:** gravel.
01/01-31/12.
Distance: 700m 700m 800m.
Remarks: At lake, coins at Tourist Info and Maison de la Presse.

Loudenvielle 27D3

La Ribère, D25 Génos. **GPS**: n42,79963 e0,40813.
6 free, 01/07-15/09 € 3. **Location:** Rural, simple, quiet.
Surface: gravel. 01/01-31/12.
Distance: 500m on the spot on the spot 500m on the spot on the spot.

Lourdes 27C2

Le Vieux Berger, Route de Julos. **GPS**: n43,10451 w0,0332.

27 € 11, May-Jun € 13, Jul-Sep € 14 Ch WC € 3/3 included.
Location: Rural, luxurious, noisy.
Surface: grassy/gravel. 01/01-31/12.
Distance: 1km 2km 700m 700m 100m on the spot.
Remarks: Next to campsite.

Tourist information Lourdes:
Office de Tourisme, Place Peyramale, www.lourdes-infotourisme.com. Lively place of pilgrimage.
Basilique St.Pius X. Underground basilica, of the largest sanctuaries in the world, there is place for 25,000 people.

Lunas 28A1

Base de Loisirs Prade, D35. **GPS**: n43,70555 e3,18555.

75 free Chfree. **Location:** Simple, isolated, quiet.
Surface: grassy/metalled. 01/01-31/12.
Distance: 900m on the spot on the spot 200m 700m 200m.

Luzech 24F3

Les Berges de Caïx, D9. **GPS**: n44,49068 e1,29506.

15 € 8,50 + € 0,22/pp tourist tax Ch WCincluded € 2.
Location: Simple. **Surface:** gravel. 01/01-31/12.
Distance: 2km.
Remarks: Along Lot river.

L'Hospitalet-près-l'Andorre 32F1

N22. **GPS**: n42,58823 e1,79833.

5 free € 2 Ch € 6. **Surface:** asphalted. 01/01-31/12.
Distance: 100m on the spot.

Marbre 27D3

Lac de Payolle, D918, Campan > Col de Aspin.
GPS: n42,93528 e0,29222.

free.
Location: Rural, simple, isolated. **Surface:** grassy/gravel.
Distance: 5km 50m 50m 700m 5km on the spot on the spot.

Marseillan-Plage 28A2

Rue des Goélands. **GPS**: n43,31902 e3,54864.

122 € 4-6-12/24h € 2/10minutes Ch
Location: Comfortable, quiet. **Surface:** gravel. 01/01-31/12.
Distance: on the spot sandy beach 600m on the spot on the spot.
Remarks: Max. 48h.

Martel 24F2

La Fontanelle, Avenue de Nassogne. **GPS**: n44,93378 e1,60803.

12 free Ch. **Surface:** gravel. 01/01-31/12.
Distance: 250m 250m 250m.

Martel 24F2

Parking Monti. **GPS**: n44,93957 e1,60827.
12 free. **Surface:** asphalted. 01/01-31/12.

Distance: 400m 400m 400m.

Marvéjols 25A3

Le Pré de Suzon. **GPS**: n44,55406 e3,28753.

10 free ChWCfree. **Location:** Central. **Surface:** asphalted.
01/01-31/12.
Distance: on the spot 7,5km on the spot on the spot.

Tourist information Marvéjols:
Maison de Tourisme, Porte du Soubeyran, www.ville-marvejols.fr.
Old fortress city, gates with battlements and towers.

Matemale 32G1

GPS: n42,57964 e2,10227.

10 free € 1 ChWC. **Location:** Rural, simple, isolated, quiet.
Surface: asphalted. 01/01-31/12.
Distance: 3km on the spot on the spot 300m.
Remarks: Parking at lake.

Matemale 32G1

Rue de la Truite. **GPS**: n42,56559 e2,10433.

10 free. **Location:** Rural, simple, isolated, quiet. **Surface:** gravel.
01/01-31/12.
Distance: 1,5km 20m 1,5km 1,5km.
Remarks: Parking at lake.

Mauléon-Barousse 27D3

Air De Camping Car Flot Bleu, D925. **GPS**: n42,96112 e0,56848.
6 free € 3/20minutes Ch (4x)€ 3/3h
Location: Rural. **Surface:** asphalted/grassy.
Distance: 350m.

Maureillas-Las-Illas 32H1

GPS: n42,48711 e2,80748.
20 € 8-12,50 Ch € 4 WC € 4.
Surface: metalled. 01/01-31/12.
Distance: 500m 500m 500m on the spot.

Mazamet 27G2

D118. **GPS**: n43,46278 e2,34609.
9 free Chfree. **Location:** Rural, isolated, quiet.
Surface: grassy/gravel. 01/01-31/12 Service: autumn/winter.
Distance: 8km on the spot on the spot on the spot.
Remarks: Max. 48h.

Mazamet 27G2

Rue Galibert-Ferret, Champ de la Ville. **GPS**: n43,49089 e2,37918.

FR

10 free Chfree. **Location:** Urban. **Surface:** asphalted. 01/01-31/12 Fri-Sa market.
Distance: on the spot on the spot.
Remarks: At townhall, max. 24h.

S Mazères-sur-Salat 27E3

Rue de Vieux Ruisseau. **GPS**: n43,13457 e0,97633.

15 free Chfree. **Surface:** metalled. 01/01-31/12.
Distance: 4,5km river.

S Mende 25A3

Camping-car Park, Aérodrome Mende-Brenoux.
GPS: n44,52063 e3,49660.
38 € 9,60/24h Ch (24x) included.
Surface: grassy.
01/01-31/12.
Remarks: At airfield, mandatory, one-time fee Pass'Etapes € 4.

S Mende 25A3

Rue du Faubourg Montbel. **GPS**: n44,52063 e3,49660.

20 free € 2/10minutes Chfree € 2/55minutes.
Location: Urban, comfortable, central, quiet. **Surface:** asphalted.
01/01-31/12.
Distance: on the spot on the spot 200m 400m on the spot on the spot.
Remarks: Along Lot river, max. 96h.

S Mèze 28A2

Camping-Car Park Escale de Thau, Avenue du stade.
GPS: n43,44135 e3,59436.
44 € 12,46, 01/04-31/10 € 13,66 Ch (44x) included.
Location: Simple, noisy. **Surface:** gravel.
01/01-31/12.
Distance: 2,5km 10km.
Remarks: Mandatory, one-time fee Pass'Etapes € 4.

S Miélan 27D2

Rue du Cubet. **GPS**: n43,43319 e0,30900.

6 free Chfree. **Location:** Rural, simple. **Surface:** gravel.
01/01-31/12.
Distance: 350m 350m 350m.

S Millau 27H1

Camping-car Park, Rue de la Saunerie 19.
GPS: n44,09610 e3,08577.

41 € 10,50 Ch (30x) included.
Location: Comfortable. **Surface:** gravel. 01/01-31/12.
Distance: 500m.
Remarks: Mandatory, one-time fee Pass'Etapes € 4, motorhomes <7.5m.

Tourist information Millau:
Office de Tourisme, 1, Place du Beffroi, www.ot-millau.fr. City tourist in the Valley of the Tarn and the Dourbie. Important for the leather trade.
Vieux Millau. Historical hiking route, info at Office de Tourisme.

S Mirandol-Bourgnounce 24G3

Place de Foirail. **GPS**: n44,14167 e2,16667.

8 free ChWCfree. **Location:** Rural, simple, quiet.
Surface: asphalted. 01/01-31/12.
Distance: on the spot on the spot 50m on the spot.

S Mirepoix 27F3

Parking des Capitouls, Alée des Soupirs. **GPS**: n43,08491 e1,87399.

20 free ChWCfree. **Surface:** asphalted. 01/01-31/12.
Distance: centre 500m 200m 400m.
Remarks: Next to community centre.

Tourist information Mirepoix:
Cattle market. winter 2nd, 4th Mo of the month.
Thu, Sa.

S Moissac 27E1

Les Berges du Tarn, Chemin de la Rhode. **GPS**: n44,09803 e1,09304.

44 € 8, 01/10-31/03 € 6,50 Ch included.
01/01-31/12.
Distance: 900m 900m.
Remarks: Along the Tarn river.

S Monclar-de-Quercy 27F1

Lotissement les Terrasses du Lac. **GPS**: n43,96493 e1,59157.
6 free, June-Sep € 10 Ch.
Surface: gravel. 01/04-31/10.
Distance: on the spot on the spot.

S Mont Roc 27G1

Salle de Fêtes. **GPS**: n43,80330 e2,37192.

8 free € 2 Ch € 2 WC.
Surface: metalled. 01/01-31/12.
Distance: 50m on the spot on the spot.

S Mont-Louis 32G1

Parking des Remparts. **GPS**: n42,50765 e2,12273.

20 € 5 included. **Location:** Urban, simple, quiet.
Surface: asphalted.
Distance: 200m 200m 200m.
Remarks: Parking at city wall.

S Montagnac 28A2

D613. **GPS**: n43,47520 e3,49129.

5 free Chfree. **Surface:** gravel. 01/01-31/12.
Distance: 1km 1km 1km.

S Montauban 27F1

Mr. Lacaze, 225, route de Corbarieu, D21. **GPS**: n43,99188 e1,35196.

15 € 7 Ch included WC € 1. **Location:** Simple.
Surface: gravel. 01/01-31/12.
Distance: Montauban 3km 1km.
Remarks: Max 3,5t.

S Montauban 27F1

Port Canal, Rue des Oules 125. **GPS**: n44,00744 e1,34105.

10 € 8 Ch. **Location:** Comfortable, quiet.
Surface: grassy/gravel. 01/01-31/12.
Distance: 2,5km.
Remarks: At the canal.

S Montauban 27F1

La Ferme des Pibouls, Route de Saint-Antonin.
GPS: n44,03658 e1,40499.
12 free Chfree.

Location: Simple. **Surface:** grassy.
01/01-31/12.
Distance: 5km.

Tourist information Montauban:
Office de Tourisme, 2, rue du Collège, officetourisme.montauban.com. City of roses.
Sa.

Montcalm 28B2

Le Caveau du Chêne, Route d'Aigues Mortes, D58.
GPS: n43,57322 e4,30505.

40 free for clients. **Location:** Rural, isolated, quiet. **Surface:** grassy.
01/01-31/12.

Montcuq 24E3

Route de Cahors, D653. **GPS**: n44,34082 e1,20242.

15 free € 2/100liter Ch € 2/1h.
Location: Simple. **Surface:** gravel.
01/01-31/12.
Distance: 250m 250m 50m.
Remarks: Coins at Tourist Info and petrol station.

Montdardier 28A1

Rue de l'église. **GPS**: n43,92885 e3,59073.
5 free.
Distance: 350m.
Remarks: Max. 72h.

Monteils 24G3

D47. **GPS**: n44,26694 e1,99667.

4 free Chfree. **Location:** Rural, simple, quiet.
Surface: grassy/gravel. 01/01-31/12.
Distance: 100m 100m 50m.

Montézic 24H2

Les Prades Sud. **GPS**: n44,71054 e2,64413.

4 free Ch. **Surface:** asphalted. 01/03-31/10.
Distance: 500m on the spot on the spot.

Montferrand 27F2

Col de Naurouze, Route du Ségala, N113> D218.
GPS: n43,35238 e1,82390.

20 free. **Location:** Rural, simple, quiet. **Surface:** gravel.
01/01-31/12.
Distance: 2km on the spot 2km on the spot on the spot.

Montpellier 28B2

Parking Joffre, Rue d'Argencour. **GPS**: n43,61316 e3,88608.
€ 1/h. **Surface:** asphalted. 01/01-31/12.
Distance: 4km.
Remarks: Overnight stay possible. Via avenue Jean Mermoz.

Tourist information Montpellier:
Corum. Opera-complex.
Place de la Comédie. Square with many cafés.

Montréal (Gers) 27D1

Stade André Daubin, D29. **GPS**: n43,95375 e0,19730.

free Chfree WC. **Surface:** gravel. 01/01-31/12.
Distance: 200m 500m 500m.
Remarks: Parking at rugby ground.

Tourist information Montréal (Gers):
Office de Tourisme, place de l'Hôtel de Ville, www.montrealdugers.com/. Fortified city with ramparts, square with arcades and picturesque alleys.

Montréjeau 27D3

Grande Halle, Place de Verdun. **GPS**: n43,08448 e0,57112.

4 free. **Location:** Urban, simple, central, noisy. **Surface:** asphalted.
01/01-31/12.
Distance: 100m 400m on the spot.

Monze 27G3

La Bretonne. **GPS**: n43,15475 e2,45867.

2 free. **Location:** Rural, simple, isolated, quiet. **Surface:** asphalted.
01/01-31/12.
Distance: 50m 500m.
Remarks: Max. 48h.

Mourèze 28A2

D8. **GPS**: n43,61728 e3,36111.

6 € 6 ChWCincluded. **Location:** Simple, isolated, quiet.
Surface: gravel. 01/01-31/12.
Distance: on the spot 300m on the spot.

Mur de Barrez 24H2

Parc de la Corette, Place du Foirail. **GPS**: n44,84842 e2,65980.

6 free Ch. **Surface:** asphalted. 01/04-30/11.
Distance: 100m on the spot 50m.
Remarks: Max. 72h.

Murviel-lès-Béziers 27H2

Camping-Car Park, Route de Réals, D36. **GPS**: n43,43953 e3,13420.

25 € 11,90 Ch (20x)WC included.
Location: Rural, comfortable, isolated, quiet.
Surface: unpaved.
01/01-31/12.
Distance: 700m 10km 700m 1,7km on the spot.
Remarks: Mandatory, one-time fee Pass'Etapes € 4, historical centre.

Nages 27H2

Aire de camping car du Lac, Lac du Laouzas, D162.
GPS: n43,64694 e2,78194.

22 € 7,50, peak season € 8,50 Ch included.
Location: Isolated, quiet. **Surface:** grassy/gravel. 31/03-01/11.
Distance: on the spot.
Remarks: Nearby base nautique.

Najac 24G3

Le Pontet. **GPS**: n44,22167 e1,96778.

10 € 6, 01/04-30/09 € 8 Ch (12x)included.
Location: Comfortable, quiet. **Surface:** asphalted. 01/01-31/12.
Distance: 1,8km on the spot on the spot 1,8km on the spot on the spot.

FR

Remarks: Historical centre.

Narbonne 27H3

Parking du Parc des Sports, Avenue Maître Hubert Mouly.
GPS: n43,18017 e3,02294.

36 € 9/24h € 2/20minutes Ch € 2 .
Surface: asphalted.
01/01-31/12.
Distance: on the spot 2,3km Carrefour.
Remarks: Free bus to centre every 30 minutes.

Tourist information Narbonne:

Autorail Touristique du Minervois. Train tourist from Narbonne to Bize. 01/07-17/09.
Palais des Archevêques. Palace, 11th century, with cathedral.
Thu, Su.

Narbonne-Plage 27H3

Créneau Naturel, Route de Gruissan. **GPS**: n43,14725 e3,15408.
100 € 10 Ch WC included. 01/01-31/12.
Distance: Narbonne 16km on the spot on the spot 1km.

Naucelle 24G3

Place du Ségala. **GPS**: n44,19723 e2,34175.

4 free Ch free.
Location: Simple, noisy. **Surface:** asphalted. 01/01-31/12.
Distance: on the spot 500m 500m on the spot on the spot.

Nègrepelisse 27F1

Avenue Jean Fleury. **GPS**: n44,07408 e1,52664.
15 free Ch free. **Location:** Simple. **Surface:** grassy/gravel.
01/01-31/12 service: 01/12-01/04.
Distance: 500m 500m on the spot.
Remarks: Near sports fields.

Nîmes 28B1

Domaine de Fontbespierre, 3359, route d'Anduze.
GPS: n43,87142 e4,27746.

50 € 10 € 2 Ch € 2/day WC. **Location:** Rural.
Surface: grassy. 01/01-31/12.
Distance: 6km 6km 6km.
Remarks: Terrain with video surveillance.

Octon 28A2

Avenue de la Molière. **GPS**: n43,65390 e3,30378.

8 free.
Location: Simple, quiet. **Surface:** asphalted.
Distance: 50m 50m 50m Lac du Salagou Lac du Salagou.
Remarks: Parking behind 'Clamery', Lac du Salagou.

Olargues 27H2

Camping-Car Park, Chemin du Coulayro Bas.
GPS: n43,55655 e2,91879.
12 € 11,24 Ch (12x)included.
Surface: asphalted. 01/01-31/12.
Distance: 500m 500m 500m.
Remarks: Mandatory, one-time fee Pass'Etapes € 4.

Oust 27E3

Aire camping-car, Foute d'Aulus les Bains.
GPS: n42,87167 e1,21833.

10 € 15,50, Jul/Aug € 18, 2 pers. Incl Ch WC .
Surface: gravel.
01/01-31/12.
Remarks: Next to campsite Les 4 Saisons, arrival >14h departure <12h.

Ouveillan 27H2

Place Cave Coopératieve. **GPS**: n43,29204 e2,97080.

10 free Ch free.
Surface: gravel/metalled. 01/01-31/12.
Distance: 2km 2km 2km.

Palavas-les-Flots 28B2

Port Fluvial, Base Paul Riquet, Avenue de Lattre Tassigny.
GPS: n43,53091 e3,92316.

135 € 15, Jul-Aug € 18 + € 0,83/pp tourist tax, extra charge >8m and trailer € 3 Ch € 3 WC included .
Surface: asphalted. 01/01-31/12.
Distance: 1km 1km 1km.
Remarks: Bicycle rental.

Perville 24E3

Centre du village. **GPS**: n44,18065 e0,88143.
2 free Ch free. **Surface:** asphalted. 01/01-31/12.

Peyragudes 27D3

Parking de Balestas, Culas. **GPS**: n42,79629 e0,44015.

25 free € 2/100liter € 2/1h. **Location:** Rural, simple, isolated, quiet. **Surface:** gravel. 01/01-31/12.
Distance: 10km 150m 850m on the spot on the spot on the spot.
Remarks: Coins at Maison de Peyragudes.

Peyriac-de-Mer 27H3

Route des Bages. **GPS**: n43,09372 e2,96205.

20 € 5/24h Ch. **Location:** Rural, simple.
Surface: grassy/metalled. 01/01-31/12.
Distance: 1km on the spot 1km 1km on the spot on the spot.
Remarks: Next to rugby ground.

Peyrusse le Roc 24G3

D87. **GPS**: n44,49500 e2,13972.

12 free Ch free. **Surface:** grassy/sand. 01/01-31/12.
Distance: 500m 500m 500m.

Pierrefitte-Nestalas 27C3

Chemin de la Portere. **GPS**: n42,96048 w0,07638.

15 free € 1/50liter Ch WC. **Location:** Rural, isolated, quiet.
Surface: asphalted. 01/01-31/12.
Distance: 200m 10km 200m 200m on the spot on the spot.
Remarks: Max. 8 days.

Pinsac 24F2

Parking Salle des Fêtes, D43. **GPS**: n44,85500 e1,51222.

5 free € 2 Ch. **Surface:** gravel. 01/01-31/12.
Distance: on the spot 9,5km 700m.

Piquecos 27F1

Parking de la Salle des Fêtes. **GPS**: n44,10144 e1,32093.
free Ch. 01/01-31/12.

Pont-de-Salars 24H3

Place de la Rivière. **GPS**: n44,27822 e2,72853.

5 free € 5/80liter Ch. **Location:** Simple. **Surface:** asphalted.
01/05-31/10.
Distance: 100m 2km 2km on the spot 100m on the spot.
Remarks: Along river, max. 3 days, coins at the shops.

S Port Vendres 32H1

L'Anse des Tamarins, Route de la Jetée. **GPS**: n42,51778 e3,11375.

40 € 6, May/Okt € 10 € 2/100liter ChWC.
Location: Rural, simple. **Surface:** gravel. 01/01-31/12.
Distance: 1,3km 100m on the spot.

S Port-la-Nouvelle 27H3

Camping-Car Park, Chemin des Vignes.
GPS: n43,01366 e3,04077.

100 € 9,60-11,80 Ch on camp site included.
Location: Rural, simple. **Surface:** grassy/gravel.
01/01-31/12.
Distance: 2km 8,6km 2km 2km 1km Huit-à-huit, Passage de l'Abbé Gavanon.
Remarks: Mandatory, one-time fee Pass'Etapes € 4.

S Port-la-Nouvelle 27H3

Parking Super U, Avenue du Général de Gaulle.
GPS: n43,01609 e3,04933.
free € 2/10minutes Ch € 2/55minutes .
Surface: asphalted. 01/01-31/12, 19.30-08.30h.
Distance: 1km 1km 1km on the spot.

S Portiragnes 28A2

Avenue de la Grande Maïre. **GPS**: n43,27558 e3,35156.

30 € 5 Chincluded. **Location:** Rural, simple, quiet.
Surface: unpaved. 01/01-31/12.
Distance: sandy beach 200m.
Remarks: Max. 48h.

S Pradinas 24G3

Place de l'Eglise. **GPS**: n44,23855 e2,26583.

5 free Chfree. **Location:** Rural, simple, quiet.
Surface: grassy/sand.
Distance: on the spot.

S Prayssac 24E3

Avenue Maréchal Bessières. **GPS**: n44,50352 e1,19197.

10 free Chfree WC. **Location:** Simple. **Surface:** grassy/gravel.
01/01-31/12 Service: winter.
Distance: 200m 1,5km.

S Preignan 27D1

Rue Emile Zola. **GPS**: n43,71243 e0,63378.

5 free Chfree. **Surface:** gravel.
Distance: 1km.
Remarks: At sports park.

S Puy l'Eveque 24E3

Place de la Gendarmerie. **GPS**: n44,50699 e1,13560.

8 free ChWCfree. **Surface:** gravel.
01/01-31/12 01/08-11/08,,service: winter.
Distance: 250m 300m 300m.
Remarks: In front of town hall, max. 24h, upper city.

S Puylaurens 27G2

Rue Albert Thorel. **GPS**: n43,56861 e2,01194.

17 free Chfree . **Surface:** gravel. 01/01-31/12.
Distance: 700m 100m 700m 400m.
Remarks: Max. 48h, wifi at supermarket.

S Quillan 27G3

Camping-Car Park, Rue Baptiste Marcet. **GPS**: n42,85472 e2,18166.
29 € 9,60-10,80 Ch (28x)included.
Location: Rural. **Surface:** gravel. 01/01-31/12.
Remarks: Mandatory, one-time fee Pass'Etapes € 4.

S Remoulins 28C1

N86. **GPS**: n43,93789 e4,55851.

10 free € 5/20minutes Ch.
Location: Urban. **Surface:** asphalted.
Distance: 100m 100m 100m.
Remarks: Parking nearby river, service on the other side of the bridge: Route du Pont du Gare.

Tourist information Remoulins:
Pont du Gard. Roman aqueduct.

S Rennes-les-Bains 27G3

Plateau Sport Nature, Route des Corbières.
GPS: n42,91479 e2,31814.

7 € 5/24h Chfree. **Location:** Rural, simple, quiet.
Surface: asphalted. 01/01-31/12.
Distance: 500m 100m.

S Requista 27H1

Place François Fablé. **GPS**: n44,03465 e2,53599.

6 free free WC.
Surface: gravel. 01/01-31/12 service 01/11-30/04.
Distance: 200m.

S Revel 27G2

Roy des Eaux, Chemin de la Pergue. **GPS**: n43,45286 e2,01233.
28 € 7, 01/06-31/08 € 9, tourist tax excl Ch included.
Surface: gravel. 01/01-31/12.
Distance: 1km 1km 1km.
Remarks: Max. 7 nights.

S Rieupeyroux 24G3

15 Rue de la Calquière. **GPS**: n44,30861 e2,23194.

3 free Ch free. **Location:** Simple. **Surface:** asphalted.
01/04-01/11.
Distance: 500m 500m 1,5km.
Remarks: Next to school.

S Rieutort-de-Randon 25A3

Lac de Charpal. **GPS**: n44,62491 e3,56046.

FR

10 free WC. **Location:** Rural, isolated, quiet. **Surface:** unpaved.
01/01-31/12.
Distance: 8km 18km on the spot on the spot on the spot on the spot.
Remarks: At lake Charpal.

Rignac 24G3

Hameau du Lac, La Peyrade. **GPS:** n44,40456 e2,28958.

12 free, June-Aug € 5 Chfree. **Location:** Rural, simple, quiet. **Surface:** grassy. 01/01-31/12.
Distance: 1km on the spot 1km 1km on the spot.

Rivières 27G1

Aire de Salta, La Courtade Haute. **GPS:** n43,91072 e1,98889.

6 € 12 Ch (6x)included. **Location:** Rural, comfortable, quiet. **Surface:** gravel. 01/06-30/09.
Distance: 2km on the spot on the spot 3km.
Remarks: Along the Tarn river, bread-service in summer period.

Rocamadour 24F2

Le Château, D673. **GPS:** n44,80000 e1,61528.

30 free. **Surface:** gravel. 15/06-15/09.
Distance: 100m.

Rodés 32G1

Route Neuf de Conquille 8. **GPS:** n42,65560 e2,56263.
6 € 8 Chincluded € 3.
Surface: grassy/metalled. 01/01-31/12.
Distance: 1,5km 450m.

Rodez 24H3

Route du Gué de Salelles. **GPS:** n44,35731 e2,59374.

6 free Chfree. **Location:** Urban, simple, noisy.
Surface: gravel. 01/01-31/12.

Distance: 1km 1km.
Remarks: Max. 72h.

Roquecor 24E3

Place du Foirail, D82. **GPS:** n44,32346 e0,94496.

6 free Chfree. **Surface:** asphalted. 01/01-31/12.
Distance: 250m 300m 250m.
Remarks: Max. 48h.

Roquefort-sur-Soulzon 27H1

D23. **GPS:** n43,98120 e2,98163.

10 free ChWCfree.
Surface: asphalted.
01/01-31/12 Service: winter.
Distance: 100m.
Remarks: Parking behind tourist info, max. 7 days, inclining pitches.

Roques 27F2

Parking E.Leclerc, Allée de Fraixinet. **GPS:** n43,51192 e1,36920.

6 free Ch € 0,50/h. **Location:** Urban. **Surface:** asphalted.
01/01-31/12.
Distance: 1km 200m.

Routier 27G3

Sous la Serre. **GPS:** n43,10813 e2,12362.

7 free Chfree.
Location: Rural, simple, quiet. **Surface:** grassy/gravel.
01/01-31/12 water disconnected in winter.
Distance: on the spot.

Tourist information Routier:
Corbières. Region is known for its wines and the Cathar citadels, the castle of Queribus in Cucugan is one of the last bastions of the Cathars.

Saillagousse 32F1

Rue des Sports. **GPS:** n42,45764 e2,03766.

7 free € 4 Ch WC. **Location:** Urban, simple, quiet.
Surface: asphalted. 01/01-31/12.
Distance: on the spot on the spot on the spot.
Remarks: Coins at tourist info and town hall.

Saint-André 32H1

Parking de Taxo. GPS: n42,55248 e2,97303.

6 € 2,30 € 2 Ch € 2. **Surface:** asphalted. 01/01-31/12.
Distance: on the spot.
Remarks: Max. 3 nights, coins at tourist info.

Saint-Antoine 27E1

GPS: n44,03587 e0,84209.

10 free € 2 Ch. **Location:** Rural, simple, quiet.
Surface: asphalted. 01/01-31/12.
Distance: 200m 4,3km 200m 200m.

Saint-Antonin-Noble-Val 24F3

Chemin de Rouméqous. **GPS:** n44,15222 e1,75139.

15 free Chfree. **Location:** Rural, simple, quiet.
Surface: asphalted/gravel. 01/01-31/12.
Distance: 200m 300m 100m on the spot.

Saint-Bertrand-de-Comminges 27D3

Parking Cathédrale, D26a. **GPS:** n43,02944 e0,57221.

25 free WC. **Location:** Rural, quiet. **Surface:** asphalted/grassy.
01/01-31/12.
Distance: 200m 200m 3km on the spot on the spot.

Saint-Céré 24G2

Rue du Stade. **GPS:** n44,86139 e1,88583.

3 free Chfree. **Location:** Simple, central. **Surface:** asphalted.
01/01-31/12.
Distance: 200m 200m 150m.
Remarks: Behind stadium, nearby cemetery.

Saint-Chély-d'Apcher 25A2

Parking du Péchaud, Boulevard G. d'Apcher, N9.
GPS: n44,80084 e3,27296.

2 free € 2/100liter Ch € 2/10minutes.
Location: Simple, central, quiet. **Surface:** asphalted.
01/01-31/12.
Distance: 200m 2,5km 200m 200m on the spot.
Remarks: Coins at tourist info.

Saint-Cirq-Lapopie 24F3

Porte Roques, D8. **GPS:** n44,47024 e1,67887.

40 € 7,50 € 2/100liter Ch € 2 WC € 2.
Location: Isolated, quiet. **Surface:** grassy/gravel. 01/01-31/12.
Distance: 1,5km on the spot 50m.
Remarks: Along Lot river, near campsite, max. 48h.

Tourist information Saint-Cirq-Lapopie:
Village, entirely under preservation order, has been built on a rock above the river Lot.
Grotte de Pech-Merle, Cabrerets. Temple cave, monument from the Paleolithicum with images of mammoth, horses and bizons.

Saint-Clar 27E1

Aire de repos, Avenue de la Garlepe. **GPS:** n43,89111 e0,77250.

10 free ChWC free. **Location:** Simple, isolated, quiet.
Surface: grassy/gravel. 01/01-31/12.
Distance: 500m 250m.

Saint-Côme-d'Olt 24H3

Rue des Ginestes. **GPS:** n44,51647 e2,82072.
9 free Ch. **Location:** Rural. **Surface:** asphalted.
01/01-31/12.
Distance: 500m 500m 500m.
Remarks: At cemetery, coins at tourist info and supermarket.

Saint-Couat-d'Aude 27H2

La Bellevue. GPS: n43,21429 e2,63052.
€ 5 € 3 Ch € 3 WC. **Location:** Comfortable, isolated, quiet.

Saint-Cyprien 32H1

Aire du Théâtre de la Mer, Quai Arthur Rimbaud.
GPS: n42,61776 e3,03512.

49 € 8,20, Jul/Aug € 12 Ch included.
Location: Comfortable. **Surface:** asphalted.
01/01-31/12 service 15/10-31/03.
Distance: 450m marina 300m.

Saint-Cyprien-sur-Dourdou 24G3

La Citarelle. **GPS:** n44,54782 e2,40844.
13 € 5 Ch. **Surface:** grassy/gravel. 01/01-31/12.
Distance: on the spot 350m.

Saint-Félix-Lauragais 27F2

Lac de Lenclas, D622. **GPS:** n43,42667 e1,89806.

10 free ChWC. **Location:** Simple, isolated, quiet.
Surface: gravel. 01/01-31/12.
Distance: 100m 100m.
Remarks: Max. 24h.

Saint-Gaudens 27E3

Rue Chanteurs du Comminges. **GPS:** n43,10997 e0,70813.
60 € 8 Ch included. **Surface:** grassy.
01/01-31/12.
Distance: 1,5km.
Remarks: Former campsite, max. 7 days.

Saint-Geniez-d'Olt 24H3

Avenue de la gare. **GPS:** n44,46305 e2,97563.

10 free WC free. **Surface:** gravel. 01/01-31/12.
Distance: on the spot on the spot on the spot on the spot on the spot.
Remarks: Max. 24h.

Saint-Géry 24F3

Domaine du Porche, D662. **GPS:** n44,47818 e1,58091.

15 € 5,50 € 2/100liter Ch € 2/1h WC.
Location: Simple. **Surface:** gravel. 01/01-31/12.
Distance: 100m 100m.
Remarks: Market on Sunday.

Saint-Gilles 28B2

Quai du Canal. **GPS:** n43,67154 e4,43281.

free. **Location:** Rural. **Surface:** asphalted. 01/01-31/12.
Distance: 500m 200m 500m.

Tourist information Saint-Gilles:
Abbay St.Gilles. Abbey with underground church.

Saint-Girons 27E3

Rue Aristide Berges. **GPS:** n42,98865 e1,13852.

7 free € 2/150liter Ch € 2/15minutes.
Surface: asphalted.
Distance: 100m.
Remarks: Max. 48h.

Saint-Jean-du-Gard 28B1

Av. de la Résistance. **GPS:** n44,10210 e3,88347.

20 free ChWC free. **Location:** Urban, simple.
Surface: metalled. 01/01-31/12.
Distance: on the spot 100m 100m 50m 300m on the spot.
Remarks: Tourist train.

Saint-Jean-et-Saint-Paul 27H1

Saint Jean d'Alcas. **GPS:** n43,92646 e3,00887.
10 free ChWC free. **Surface:** gravel. 01/01-31/12.
Distance: on the spot.

Saint-Just-sur-Viaur 27G1

Parking La Fabrie, D532. **GPS:** n44,12402 e2,37588.

4 free Ch WC free. **Location:** Rural, isolated, quiet.
Surface: gravel. 01/01-31/12 service 01/11-31/03.
Distance: 10km on the spot on the spot.

Saint-Lary-Soulan 27D3

Parking du Stade, Route de Vieille Aure. **GPS:** n42,82248 e0,32329.

FR

44 € 6/night € 2/100liter Ch € 2/h.
Location: Rural, simple, noisy. **Surface:** asphalted.
01/01-31/12.
Distance: 500m 500m 500m on the spot on the spot.
Remarks: Parking behind stadium.

S Saint-Laurent-de-Carnols 25C3

Cave Coopérative Vinicole, Route de Bagnols D166.
GPS: n44,21002 e4,53132.
5 free Ch . 01/01-31/12.
Distance: 200m.

S Saint-Laurent-de-Cerdans 32G1

Parking Halle Polyvalente, Place du Syndicat.
GPS: n42,38336 e2,61572.

15 free ChWCfree. **Location:** Urban, simple, quiet.
Surface: gravel. 01/01-31/12.
Distance: 500m 100m 500m on the spot.
Remarks: Max. 48h.

Saint-Mamert-du-Gard 28B1

Rue des Fraisses. **GPS:** n43,88965 e4,19039.

6 free. **Location:** Simple. **Surface:** asphalted. 01/01-31/12.
Distance: 400m.

S Saint-Mamert-du-Gard 28B1

Route du Stade. **GPS:** n43,88491 e4,19054.
Chfree. 01/01-31/12.

S Saint-Mamet 27D3

Rue Pierre Baysse, D27. **GPS:** n42,78399 e0,60393.

7 € 5 Chfree. **Location:** Rural, quiet. **Surface:** asphalted.
01/01-31/12.
Distance: 200m 850m 150m.
Remarks: Next to cemetery, max. 3 nights, to be paid at town hall.

S Saint-Marsal 32G1

GPS: n42,53755 e2,62242.

25 € 3 free. **Location:** Rural, simple. **Surface:** asphalted.
01/01-31/12.
Distance: on the spot.

S Saint-Martin-de-Londres 28A1

Rue des Sapeurs. **GPS:** n43,79046 e3,73470.

6 € 4 included. **Location:** Simple. 01/01-31/12.
Distance: 150m on the spot.

S Saint-Martory 27E2

Place Nationale, D52E, D117. **GPS:** n43,14203 e0,92939.

7 € 3 ChWC. **Surface:** asphalted. Thu (market).
Distance: 3km.
Remarks: Along river, max. 1 night.

S Saint-Mathieu-de-Tréviers 28B1

D17. **GPS:** n43,76206 e3,86016.

8 € 5 Ch included. **Surface:** gravel. 01/01-31/12.
Distance: 1km.
Remarks: Check in at gymnasium.

Saint-Maurice-en-Quercy 24G2

Place de l'église. **GPS:** n44,74306 e1,94722.

10 free.
Location: Simple, quiet. **Surface:** gravel. 01/01-31/12.

S Saint-Médard-de-Presque 24G2

D30. **GPS:** n44,87114 e1,84434.

20 € 15 Ch included. **Location:** Rural.
Surface: gravel. 01/01-31/12.
Distance: 1km.

S Saint-Nicolas-de-la-Grave 27E1

Rue de la Calle, Rue Bouchotte. **GPS:** n44,06379 e1,02471.

10 free Chfree. **Location:** Simple. **Surface:** asphalted/gravel.
01/01-31/12.
Distance: 100m 50m 100m.

S Saint-Nicolas-de-la-Grave 27E1

Camping de la Base de Loisirs, Avenue du Plan d'Eau.
GPS: n44,08616 e1,02745.
12 free, 01/05-15/09 € 10 € 2/10minutes Ch € 4/2h.
01/01-31/12.
Distance: 2,8km 100m 100m.
Remarks: Summertime on campsite, wintertime in front of campsite.

S Saint-Puy 27D1

Grande Rue, D654. **GPS:** n43,87611 e0,46250.

3 free ChWCfree. **Surface:** gravel. 01/01-31/12.
Distance: 20m 50m 20m.

S Saint-Sauveur-Camprieu 28A1

D710 Maison du Bois. **GPS:** n44,10843 e3,48304.
6 free € 2/100liter Ch. **Location:** Rural, isolated.
01/01-31/12.
Distance: on the spot.
Remarks: Altitude 1000m.

S Saint-Thibéry 28A2

Domaine de la Vière, Chemin de la Vière.
GPS: n43,38301 e3,40137.

26 € 10 Ch WC included. **Location:** Rural, comfortable, isolated. **Surface:** unpaved. 01/01-31/12.
Distance: 2km A9 3km 14km 3km 4km.
Remarks: During the weekend possible inconvenience of motocross.

S Sainte-Croix-Volvestre 27E3

Lenclos. **GPS:** n43,12673 e1,17094.

free Chfree. **Location:** Simple, isolated, quiet.
Surface: grassy/gravel. 01/01-31/12.
Remarks: At football ground.

S Sainte-Eulalie-d'Olt 24H3

La Grave. **GPS:** n44,46466 e2,94974.

FR

10 € 7, 15/05-15/09 € 8 Ch WC included.
Location: Rural, quiet. **Surface:** gravel. 01/01-31/12.
Distance: 300m on the spot 250m 350m.
Remarks: Along Lot river, next to campsite.

Sainte-Eulalie-de-Cernon 27H1

Chemin de Millau. **GPS:** n43,98349 e3,13733.
€ 7/24h Ch WC included. **Location:** Rural.
Surface: gravel/metalled. 01/01-31/12.
Distance: 200m 150m.

Sainte-Geneviève-sur-Argence 24H2

Rue de l'Argence. **GPS:** n44,80194 e2,76222.

30 free € 2 Ch. **Surface:** gravel. 01/01-31/12.
Distance: 300m 500m 500m 300m 300m.

Sainte-Marie-de-Campan 27D3

Place du 19 Mars 1962, D918. **GPS:** n42,98234 e0,22821.

5 free Ch free. **Location:** Rural, simple, quiet.
Surface: asphalted. 01/01-31/12.
Distance: 100m 250m 200m on the spot on the spot.
Remarks: Max. 48h.

Salasc 28A2

Route de la Gloriette, D148. **GPS:** n43,61746 e3,31709.
2 free. 01/01-31/12.
Distance: 300m 300m.

Salles-Curan 24H3

Aire de camping-car des Vernhes, Lac de Pareloup.
GPS: n44,20002 e2,77573.

80 € 11/24h € 4 Ch (80x) WC included.
Location: Rural, comfortable, quiet. **Surface:** grassy/gravel.
01/04-31/10.
Distance: 4km on the spot on the spot 4km 4km on the spot.
Remarks: At lake, former campsite.

Salles-sur-l'Hers 27F2

Allée des Platanes. **GPS:** n43,29194 e1,78844.

10 free Ch free. **Location:** Rural, simple, isolated, quiet.
Surface: gravel. 01/01-31/12.
Distance: on the spot 100m 100m.
Remarks: At football ground.

Samatan 27E2

Les Rivages Base de Loisirs, Avenue de Lombez, D39.
GPS: n43,48791 e0,92616.

10 € 3 + € 0,20/pp tourist tax Ch WC included.
Surface: asphalted. 01/01-31/12.
Distance: 500m on the spot on the spot 250m 250m 250m.

Sarrant 27E1

Route de Solomiac. **GPS:** n43,77532 e0,92822.

20 free Ch free. **Surface:** grassy/gravel. 01/01-31/12.
Distance: 150m 150m.
Remarks: In front of football stadium.

Sauve 28B1

D999. **GPS:** n43,94017 e3,95218.

5 free Ch free. **Location:** Urban, simple, central, noisy.
Surface: metalled. 01/01-31/12.
Distance: 50m 50m on the spot.

Sauveterre-de-Comminges 27D3

Hameau de Bruncan, D9. **GPS:** n43,03391 e0,66711.

5 € 6 Ch WC included. **Location:** Rural, simple, quiet.
Surface: grassy/gravel. 01/01-31/12.
Distance: on the spot on the spot 10km on the spot on the spot.
Remarks: Check in at bar, service passerby € 3.

Sauveterre-de-Rouergue 24G3

Le Sardou, D997. **GPS:** n44,21613 e2,31700.

15 free Ch free € 2/day WC € 1,50/12minutes.
Location: Rural, comfortable, quiet. **Surface:** gravel.
01/05-31/10.
Distance: 500m 500m 500m.
Remarks: Coins at tourist info.

Ségur 24H3

Impasse du Pré Amat. **GPS:** n44,29087 e2,83503.

3 free Ch WC free € 2/6minutes. **Location:** Rural, simple.
Surface: asphalted. 01/05-31/10.
Distance: 500m 500m.
Remarks: Coins at town hall and supermarket, small pitches, covered picnic area with electricity.

Senergues 24G3

La Ferme des Autruches, La Besse. **GPS:** n44,58861 e2,48361.
5 € 5 Ch WC. **Surface:** grassy/gravel. 01/03-30/11.
Distance: 2km.

Sérignan-Plage 28A2

Camping-Car Park Serignan Plage, D37. **GPS:** n43,26909 e3,33149.
49 € 9,60, 01/07-31/08 € 12 Ch included.
Surface: grassy. 01/01-31/12.
Distance: 200m 200m.
Remarks: Mandatory, one-time fee Pass'Etapes € 4.

Sérignan-Plage 28A2

Mini Golf du Lion, Avenue de la Plage. **GPS:** n43,26892 e3,33629.

20 € 8, 01/05-30/09 € 13 + tourist tax € 2/pp Ch WC included € 4. **Location:** Rural, comfortable, quiet.
Surface: unpaved. 01/01-31/12.
Distance: 150m on the spot 150m.
Remarks: Behind restaurant, bread-service, swimming pool.

Serres-sur-Arget 27F3

D45. **GPS:** n42,96990 e1,51972.

€ 5 Ch included. **Location:** Isolated, quiet.
Surface: metalled. 01/01-31/12.
Remarks: Next to community centre.

Sète 28A2

Parking Les 3 Digues. **GPS:** n43,36663 e3,61523.

FR

70 € 6,66-9,66, Jul/Aug € 11,66 € 1/10minutes Ch
Location: Rural, simple. **Surface:** gravel. 01/01-31/12.
Distance: 50m on the spot on the spot.
Remarks: Beach parking, max. 72h, 01/06-30/09 no dogs allowed on the beach.

S Sommières 28B1

Chemin de la Princesse. **GPS**: n43,78701 e4,08717.

25 free € 3 Ch. **Location:** Simple. **Surface:** gravel.
01/01-31/12.
Distance: 500m 100m 300m.
Remarks: In front of campsite municipal.

Sommières 28B1

Chemin de la Royalette. **GPS**: n43,77989 e4,08437.
€ 5. 01/01-31/12.
Remarks: Next to sports fields.

S Souillac 24F2

Parking de Baillot, Chemin de Baillot. **GPS**: n44,89139 e1,47667.

20 free € 3 Ch € 3 . **Surface:** asphalted.
01/01-31/12.
Distance: 400m 4,5km 400m 500m.

Tourist information Souillac:
Bd Louis-Jean Malvy. Monastery-city, 12th century, between the regions Périgord and Quercy.

S Soulom 27C3

Place des Fêtes, D921. **GPS**: n42,95611 w0,0725.

15 free free. **Location:** Rural, simple, noisy. **Surface:** asphalted.
01/01-31/12.
Distance: 200m 500m 200m 200m.

S Sousceyrac 24G2

Place des Condamines. **GPS**: n44,87255 e2,03649.

10 free Ch WC free. **Location:** Simple, central, noisy.
Surface: asphalted. 01/04-30/10.
Distance: on the spot on the spot on the spot 100m.
Remarks: In front of town hall, max. 1 night.

S Tarbes 27D2

Aire de Service Camping-car Ambulance Didier, Avenue de la Libération. **GPS**: n43,24284 e0,06790.

30 € 10 Ch included € 2/night. **Location:** Quiet.
Surface: asphalted. 01/01-31/12.
Distance: 1km 1km 800m 1km.
Remarks: Service only: water € 2, water + electricity € 5, video surveillance.

S Thémines 24F2

Place de l'église. **GPS**: n44,74083 e1,82972.

3 free Ch free. **Surface:** asphalted. 01/01-31/12.
Distance: on the spot 100m 100m.
Remarks: Near church.

S Therondels 24H2

La Cazournie. **GPS**: n44,89833 e2,75937.
10 free Ch free WC.
Surface: grassy. 01/04-15/11.
Distance: 500m 100m 100m on the spot.

S Theza 32H1

Route Départementale 914. **GPS**: n42,63763 e2,93675.
6 € 12 Ch WC included. 01/01-31/12.
Remarks: Service passerby € 6.

S Thues-entre-Valls 32G1

Gorges de la Carança. **GPS**: n42,52346 e2,22517.

25 € 9/24h Ch included.
Location: Simple, isolated, quiet. **Surface:** grassy/gravel.
01/01-31/12 frost.
Distance: 2km on the spot on the spot on the spot.

S Thuir 32H1

Camping-Car Park Cité du Byrrh, Chemin du Salaou.
GPS: n42,63040 e2,76814.
24 € 11,80-13 Ch (24x) included.
Location: Rural. **Surface:** gravel. 01/01-31/12.
Distance: 500m on the spot on the spot.
Remarks: Mandatory, one-time fee Pass'Etapes € 4.

S Trouillas 32H1

Les Oliviers de la Canterrane, Solt de las Moles, D612.
GPS: n42,61399 e2,81599.

20 free Ch WC € 2 free. **Location:** Rural, isolated, quiet. **Surface:** gravel. 01/01-31/12.
Distance: 500m 4km on the spot.

S Vabre 27G1

Route de Castres. **GPS**: n43,69401 e2,42595.

free Ch free. **Surface:** asphalted.
Distance: 500m 500m on the spot on the spot.
Remarks: Tenniscourt, swimming pool (summer).

S Vabres-l'Abbaye 27H1

Le Coustel, Rue de la Vigne. **GPS**: n43,94575 e2,83957.
25 free Ch free. **Surface:** gravel. 01/01-31/12.
Distance: 50m on the spot on the spot.

S Vailhan 28A2

Parking de l'Eglise. **GPS**: n43,55527 e3,29882.

6 € 5 Ch included. **Surface:** gravel. 01/01-31/12.
Distance: 1km 200m 50m.

S Valderiés 27G1

Place de Mairie, D91. **GPS**: n44,01167 e2,23333.

5 free Ch WC free. **Location:** Simple. **Surface:** asphalted.
01/01-31/12.
Distance: on the spot on the spot on the spot on the spot.
Remarks: Service 100m, weighbridge.

S Valence (Tarn-et-Garonne) 24E3

Aire de camping-car à Valence d'Agen, Rue Garonne.
GPS: n44,10547 e0,88608.
€ 5 € 2/100liter Ch € 2/kWh WC included.
Location: Comfortable. **Surface:** asphalted. 01/01-31/12.
Distance: 600m.

S Valence (Tarn-et-Garonne) 24E3

M. Cadot, aire privée, 341, Route des Charretiers, Valence-sud.
GPS: n44,09803 e0,89043.
8 € 10 Ch included. **Location:** Rural, comfortable, isolated, quiet. **Surface:** gravel. 01/01-31/12.
Distance: 1,2km 1,2km 1,2km.

FR

Valence-sur-Baïse 27D1

Route d'Auch, D930. **GPS**: n43,87272 e0,38787.

7 free ChWCfree. **Location:** Simple, noisy. **Surface:** gravel.
01/01-31/12.
Distance: 500m 500m 500m on the spot.

Vallabrègues 28C1

Route d'Aramon, D183A. **GPS**: n43,85763 e4,62639.

5 free € 2 Ch € 2/h. **Location:** Rural. **Surface:** gravel.
01/01-31/12 high water.
Distance: 500m.
Remarks: At lake and along the Rhone river.

Valleraugue 28A1

Avenue de l'Aigoual, D986. **GPS**: n44,08054 e3,63613.
6 free € 2 Ch. **Surface:** asphalted. 01/01-31/12.
Distance: 450m.

Valras-Plage 28A2

Avenue du Casino. **GPS**: n43,24230 e3,28162.

30 free € 2 Ch. **Surface:** asphalted/metalled.
01/10-30/06 summer.
Distance: on the spot 200m on the spot on the spot on the spot.
Remarks: Behind casino/disco, service: Boulevard Pierre Giraud 200m, no camping activities.

Valras-Plage 28A2

Boulevard de la Recanette. **GPS**: n43,25310 e3,29623.
20 € 12 Ch (9x)included. **Surface:** gravel.
Distance: 800m 800m 800m.

Vayrac 24F2

Camping-Car Park la Palenquière, Route de la Dordogne.
GPS: n44,94467 e1,70307.
25 € 8,84-12,44 Ch (26x)included. **Surface:** gravel.
01/01-31/12.
Remarks: Mandatory, one-time fee Pass'Etapes € 4.

Vénerque 27F2

Allée du Duc de Ventadour. **GPS**: n43,43356 e1,44021.

10 free Ch free. **Surface:** gravel/metalled.
01/01-31/12.
Distance: on the spot.

Vernet-les-Bains 32G1

Chemin de la Laiterie. **GPS**: n42,54268 e2,39092.

7 free € 2,50/20minutes Ch € 2,50/20minutes.
Location: Rural, simple, quiet. **Surface:** gravel.
01/03-31/10.
Distance: 600m on the spot 600m.
Remarks: Coins at tourist info and town hall.

Vers 24F3

Halte Nautique, Le bourg. **GPS**: n44,48551 e1,55503.

20 € 5,50 ChWC included. **Location:** Simple.
Surface: grassy. 01/05-30/09.
Distance: 100m 100m 200m 100m on the spot on the spot.
Remarks: Service 100m.

Vézénobres 28B1

Parc Audibal. **GPS**: n44,03851 e4,14118.
3 € 7 Ch included. 01/01-31/12.

Vézins-de-Lévézou 24H3

La Ferme du Lévézou, Les Vialettes du Ram.
GPS: n44,26275 e2,92293.

6 free. **Location:** Rural, isolated, quiet. **Surface:** gravel.
Distance: 6km 25km.
Remarks: Max. 24h, regional products.

Vias 28A2

Aire de l'Espagnac, 2080 Chemin de Portiragnes.
GPS: n43,31013 e3,36226.
27 € 5-10,50 Ch € 3 included. **Location:** Rural.
Surface: grassy/gravel. 01/01-31/12.
Distance: 9km.

Vic-en-Bigorre 27D2

Rue du Stade, Avenue de Pau D6. **GPS**: n43,38472 e0,04917.

4 free Chfree. **Location:** Rural, noisy. **Surface:** gravel.
01/01-31/12.
Distance: 500m 300m 50m 50m.

Vicdessos 27F3

D8. **GPS**: n42,76891 e1,50257.

20 € 7 Ch included.
Surface: metalled. 01/01-31/12.
Distance: on the spot.
Remarks: Thursday market.

Villasavary 27G2

Camping-Car Park, D623 Lieu dit Pradel. **GPS**: n43,21881 e2,03242.

11 € 8,40, 01/07-31/08 € 9,60 Ch (8x) included.
Location: Rural, comfortable, isolated, quiet.
Surface: asphalted.
01/01-31/12.
Distance: 650m 10km on the spot.
Remarks: Mandatory, one-time fee Pass'Etapes € 4, video surveillance.

Villecomtal-sur-Arros 27D2

Rue de la Fontaine. **GPS**: n43,40286 e0,19852.

15 free € 1,50/100liter Ch € 1,50/h. **Location:** Rural, simple, quiet. **Surface:** gravel. 01/01-31/12.
Distance: on the spot 100m 200m 50m.
Remarks: Coins at townhall and bakery.

Villefranche-de-Rouergue 24G3

Parking des Ruelles, Traverse des Ruelles.
GPS: n44,35111 e2,03333.

3 free. **Location:** Urban, simple, noisy. **Surface:** asphalted.
01/01-31/12.
Distance: 100m 100m 100m.
Tourist information Villefranche-de-Rouergue:
place Notre Dame. Thu.

Villeneuve (Aveyron) 24G3

La Coustone. **GPS**: n44,44104 e2,03737.

10 € 7 Ch (4x)WCincluded. **Location:** Rural, simple,

FR

quiet. **Surface:** gravel. 12/04-01/11.
Distance: 200m 200m 200m.

Villeneuve-lès-Maguelone 28B2

Avenue René Poitevin. **GPS**: n43,52980 e3,86584.

26 € 9, 01/05-14/09 € 15/24h Ch included.
Location: Rural. **Surface:** asphalted. 01/01-31/12.
Distance: 500m 8km 2,5km 500m 250m 50m on the spot.
Remarks: 26/04-30/09: also cash payment at office de tourisme (200m).

Villeneuve-Minervois 27G2

Avenue du Jeu de Mail. **GPS**: n43,31516 e2,46432.

10 free ChWC. **Surface:** asphalted/metalled.
01/01-31/12.
Distance: on the spot on the spot on the spot.
Remarks: In front of town hall, max. 48h.

Vinça 32G1

Camping-Car Park Portes du Canigou, Lac des Escoumes.
GPS: n42,64939 e2,53184.
35 € 10,80-12 Ch (32x) included.
Surface: metalled. 01/01-31/12.
Distance: 650m on the spot on the spot 100m 650m 500m on the spot on the spot.
Remarks: Mandatory, one-time fee Pass'Etapes € 4.

Tourist information Vinça:

Office de Tourisme, Place Bernard Alart, www.ville-vinca.fr. Catalan city on a lake of 10ha.

Andorra

Pas de la Casa 32F1

Avinguda del Consell General. **GPS**: n42,54468 e1,73525.
20-8h € 2,10 . **Surface:** metalled. 01/01-31/12.
Distance: on the spot.

Sant-Julia-de-Lòria 32F1

Carretera de la Rabassa. **GPS**: n42,46573 e1,49462.

4 € 0,50/h, 20-8h free Ch (4x)included.
Surface: asphalted. 01/01-31/12.
Distance: 1km.

Provence-Alpes-Côte d'Azur

Allos 25F3

La Foux d'Allos, D908. **GPS**: n44,29583 e6,56944.

5 free ChWCfree. **Location:** Urban. **Surface:** asphalted.
01/01-31/12.
Distance: 1km 100m 100m Skibus 50m 50m.

Allos 25F3

Parking Val d'Allos, Les Prés. **GPS**: n44,24289 e6,62220.

30 € 6 € 2/20minutes Ch (16x)€ 2/4h WC.
Location: Rural, simple, quiet. **Surface:** asphalted.
01/01-31/12.
Distance: 500m 200m 500m 500m 200m 200m.
Remarks: Max. 72h, coins at ski-lifts.

Allos 25F3

Parking de la Cluite, D226. **GPS**: n44,24677 e6,66918.

5 free. **Location:** Rural, simple, isolated, quiet. **Surface:** gravel.
01/01-31/12.
Distance: Allos 6,5km on the spot.
Remarks: Jul/Aug shuttle bus to Lac d'Allos.

Annot 28F1

Chemin de la Colle Basse. **GPS**: n43,96351 e6,66386.

25 free Chfree.
Location: Rural, simple, quiet. **Surface:** grassy/gravel.
15/02-15/11 Snow, Tuesday before/after Whitsuntide.
Distance: 400m 400m 400m on the spot.
Remarks: Tuesday market.

Arles 28C2

Quai Kalymnos, Avenue de la Camargue. **GPS**: n43,67796 e4,61802.

€ 5, overnight stay free Ch. 01/01-31/12.
Distance: city centre ± 1km 300m.
Remarks: Along the Rhone river.

Tourist information Arles:

Office de Tourisme, Boulevard des Lices, www.tourisme.ville-arles.fr. City on the border of the nature reserve Camargue with Roman ruin. The painter Van Gogh lived in Arles, 1888-89.
Église St.Trophine. Romanesque and Gothic construction.
Palais Constantin. Large Roman imperial palace of which only the baths are left.

Aspres-sur-Buëch 25E3

Avenue de la Gare. **GPS**: n44,52060 e5,75349.
10 free Chfree. **Surface:** grassy/gravel. 01/01-31/12.
Distance: 200m.
Remarks: Behind tourist info.

Avignon 28C1

Aire de camping-car Pont d'Avignon, 10 chemin de la Barthelasse.
GPS: n43,95691 e4,80184.
35 € 11,50-18,50, tourist tax incl € 2,50 Ch € 2,50.
Surface: grassy. 01/03-01/11.
Distance: city centre 1,5km 200m 200m on the spot on the spot.

Tourist information Avignon:

Office de Tourisme, 41, cours Jean Jaurès, www.ot-avignon.fr. Roman city dominated by the Palais du Papes. 01/04-31/08, 01/10-31/10 9-17h, 01/09-30/09 9-20h, 01/11-31/03 9-12.45h, 14-18h.
Place d'Horloge. Cosy square in the old centre of the city.
Pont Saint Bénézet. Known as the Pont d'Avignon, bridge over the river Rhône.
Petit Palais. Former residence of the archbishop.

Bagnols-en-Fôret 28F2

Parc de Notre-Dame Les Merles, 1 chemin des Meules, D47.
GPS: n43,53590 e6,68893.

15 € 5 € 4 . **Location:** Rural, comfortable, isolated, quiet.
Surface: grassy. 01/01-31/12.
Distance: 1km 1km 1km on the spot.

Banon 28D1

Espace de la Grand Fontaine, Rue de la Grande Fontaine.
GPS: n44,03982 e5,63006.

15 € 4 Chincluded WC. **Location:** Rural, simple.
Surface: gravel/metalled. 01/01-31/12.
Distance: 250m 250m 100m on the spot on the spot.
Remarks: Max. 7 days, tuesday morning market.

Banon 28D1

Fontaine de Crême, Route de La Rochegiron D112.
GPS: n44,05960 e5,66880.

10 € 10 included € 3 . **Location:** Rural, simple, isolated.
Surface: grassy. 01/01-31/12.
Distance: 3km on the spot on the spot.
Remarks: Regional products.

Barcelonnette 25F3

Aire de Camping Car Jacques Villain, Chemin des Alpages.
GPS: n44,38222 e6,65778.

15 € 6 € 2/100liter Ch € 2/day. **Location:** Rural, simple, isolated, quiet. **Surface:** forest soil. 01/01-31/12.
Distance: 1km 200m 1km 1km on the spot on the spot.
Remarks: Next to sports fields.

Barcelonnette 25F3

Boulevard de l'Adroit. **GPS**: n44,39001 e6,65263.

5 free. **Location:** Rural, simple, quiet. **Surface:** asphalted.
01/01-31/12.
Distance: 500m 500m 600m on the spot.
Remarks: At swimming pool, max. 48h.

Bédoin 28D1

Camping-Car Park Bedoin, Chemin des Sablières.
GPS: n44,12472 e5,17167.

58 € 11 Ch (58x) included.
Location: Rural, simple, quiet. **Surface:** grassy/metalled.
01/01-31/12.
Distance: 600m 600m 600m Mont-Ventoux on the spot.
Remarks: Mandatory, one-time fee Pass'Etapes € 4.

Bollène 25C3

Centre Leclerc, Route de Saint Paul Trois Châteaux, D26.
GPS: n44,32222 e4,74306.

free Ch free. 01/01-31/12.
Distance: 4,3km.
Remarks: Service only during opening hours shop.

Tourist information Bollène:
Village Troglodyte. Cave dwelling village. 01/04-31/10 9.30-19h, 01/11-31/03 Sa-Su, holidays, vacation 14-18h 01/12-31/01.

Bormes-les-Mimosas 28F3

Route de Bénat. **GPS**: n43,13797 e6,35038.

30 free. **Location:** Urban. **Surface:** metalled.
01/01-31/12.
Distance: 2km 300m on the spot.

Briançon 25F2

Parc des Sports, Rue Jean Moulin. **GPS**: n44,89028 e6,62883.

30 free € 2/100liter Ch € 2.
Location: Urban, simple, quiet. **Surface:** asphalted.
01/01-31/12.
Distance: 2km 1km.
Remarks: At sports park, max. 24h.

Tourist information Briançon:
Office de Tourisme, 1, place du Temple, www.ot-briancon.fr. Highest city of Europe, fortress is now a tourist centre, in winter as winter sports resort and in summer parapente, rafting and biking.
Parc des Écrins. Nature reserve.

Caille 28F1

Aire de Caille, Chemin de la Plaine. **GPS**: n43,77893 e6,73331.

3 free € 4/15minutes Ch € 2/15minutes.
Location: Simple, quiet. **Surface:** asphalted.
01/01-31/12.
Distance: 50m 50m 100m on the spot 10km 150m.

Carpentras 28C1

Parking de Coubertin, Avenue de Coubertin.
GPS: n44,04398 e5,05372.

8 free Ch free. **Location:** Urban, simple. **Surface:** asphalted.
01/01-31/12.
Distance: 1,5km.
Remarks: At sports centre P.de Coubertin, max. 24h, market Friday-morning.

Tourist information Carpentras:
Hôtel Dieu. Former hospital, 18th century.
Centre-ville. Fri-morning.

Carro 28C2

Quai Jean Verandy. **GPS**: n43,32931 e5,04076.

70 € 6,30, 01/04-30/06 € 8,40, 01/07-31/08 € 10,50 Ch included. **Location:** Comfortable, central, quiet. **Surface:** gravel.
01/01-31/12.
Distance: on the spot on the spot on the spot 200m 200m.
Remarks: Max. 72h, fish sales from 08h.

Carry-le-Rouet 28D2

Avenue Pierre Sémard. **GPS**: n43,33829 e5,15921.

4 free. **Location:** Simple, noisy. **Surface:** asphalted.
01/01-31/12.
Distance: 1km 1km 500m.
Remarks: Nearby police station, max. 48h.

Castellane 28F1

Ancienne Route de Grasse. **GPS**: n43,84600 e6,51471.

30 € 6,50 Ch included WC. **Location:** Urban, simple.
Surface: asphalted. 01/01-31/12.
Distance: 100m 3km 100m 100m on the spot.
Remarks: Directly at the river, near Pont du Roc, max. 48h, water closed during wintertime.

Castellane 28F1

Castellane Camping-cars, Carrefour RD 955 et RD 402.
GPS: n43,87170 e6,51140.
35 € 7 Ch . **Location:** Rural, quiet. **Surface:** grassy/gravel.
01/03-31/10.
Distance: 3,5km 350m 3,5km on the spot.

Castellane 28F1

D402. **GPS**: n43,87173 e6,51152.

40 € 7 Ch included € 3/24h.
Location: Rural, simple, isolated, quiet. **Surface:** grassy.
01/01-31/12.
Distance: 3km 3km 3km 3km on the spot on the spot.
Remarks: Bread-service.

Castellane 28F1

La Halte Napoléon, Route de Digne. **GPS**: n43,85468 e6,50159.

FR

25 € 5,50 Ch included € 3 WC. **Location:** Simple, isolated. **Surface:** grassy/metalled. 01/01-31/12.
Distance: 800m 3km 800m 500m on the spot.
Remarks: At museum, video surveillance.

Castellane 28F1

Supermarché Casino. GPS: n43,85222 e6,50791.

6 free € 2 Ch. **Location:** Urban, simple. **Surface:** metalled.
01/01-31/12.
Distance: 400m 300m on the spot 400m.
Tourist information Castellane:
Sa-morning.

Cavalière 28F3

Avenue du Cap Nègre, D559. **GPS:** n43,15228 e6,43078.

50 € 20 Ch included.
Surface: sand. 01/01-31/12.
Distance: 50m 50m 50m 200m.

Château-Arnoux-Saint-Auban 28E1

Avenue Gén. de Gaulle, N85. **GPS:** n44,09543 e6,01022.

+10 free Ch free. **Location:** Urban, simple, central, noisy.
Surface: asphalted. 01/01-31/12.
Distance: on the spot 2,3km.
Remarks: Max. 48h, service 50m.

Chorges 25E3

Place du Champ de Foire. **GPS:** n44,54600 e6,28008.

10 € 5 Ch included. **Location:** Urban, simple, quiet.
Surface: gravel. 01/01-31/12.
Distance: 400m 400m 1km on the spot on the spot.
Remarks: Max. 48h.
Tourist information Chorges:
Lac de Serre Ponçon, Serre Ponçon. Clear blue artificial lake, many water sports.

Colmars-les-Alpes 25F3

Parking de la Lance, La Bourgade. **GPS:** n44,17943 e6,62695.

10 free € 2 Ch. **Location:** Rural, simple, quiet.
Surface: asphalted. 01/01-31/12.
Distance: 300m 50m 50m 300m 300m on the spot on the spot.
Remarks: Max. 24h, service closed during wintertime, tuesday market.

Comps-sur-Artuby 28F1

La Grange du Roux, D955. **GPS:** n43,70652 e6,50678.

10 free € 3 Ch WC.
Location: Rural, comfortable, quiet. **Surface:** gravel.
01/01-31/12.
Distance: 350m pizzeria/crêperie 50m 350m 350m.
Remarks: Coins at the shops, beautiful view, picnic tables available.

Crots 25F3

Camping-Car Park, Plage de Canterenne. **GPS:** n44,53830 e6,45489.

40 € 9,60-10,80 Ch (16x) included.
Location: Rural, simple, isolated, quiet.
Surface: asphalted.
01/01-31/12.
Distance: 1km 100m 100m 500m on the spot on the spot.
Remarks: Mandatory, one-time fee Pass'Etapes € 4, historical centre.

Cuges-les-Pins 28E2

Le Jardin de la Ville. GPS: n43,28150 e5,70558.

10 € 4,50 Ch included. **Location:** Rural, comfortable, isolated, quiet. **Surface:** grassy/gravel. 01/01-31/12.
Distance: 500m 500m 500m.
Remarks: Monitored parking.
Tourist information Cuges-les-Pins:
Musée Légion Etrangères, Aubagne. Museum about the French Foreign Legion.

Dauphin 28E1

Route de la Rencontre. **GPS:** n43,90028 e5,78417.

4 free. **Location:** Rural, simple, quiet. **Surface:** metalled.
01/01-31/12.
Distance: 300m 300m on the spot on the spot.
Remarks: Near Salle des Fêtes.

Digne-les-Bains 28E1

La Halle des Sports, Avenue René Cassin. **GPS:** n44,08280 e6,22170.

20 free € 2,50/10minutes Ch.
Location: Urban, simple, central. **Surface:** gravel.
01/01-31/12 during fair.
Distance: city centre 1,4km 300m on the spot 300m 300m on the spot.
Remarks: Natural swimming pool.

Digne-les-Bains 28E1

Le Vallon des Sources, Avenue des Thermes.
GPS: n44,07998 e6,26091.

25 free € 2 Ch. **Location:** Rural, simple.
Surface: asphalted/metalled. 01/03-1/11.
Distance: 2,5km 750m 2km 100m on the spot on the spot.
Remarks: Coins available at pay-desk of theTherme.

Esparron de Verdon 28E1

D82. **GPS:** n43,74233 e5,97366.

7 free. **Location:** Rural, simple.
Distance: 500m 500m 500m 500m on the spot.

Fayence 28F2

Allée des Jardins. **GPS:** n43,62308 e6,68982.

2 free € 4 Ch. **Location:** Simple, central, noisy.
Surface: asphalted.
Distance: 750m 750m 300m.

FR

Remarks: At tennis-court and swimming pool, max. 48h.

S Fontaine-de-Vaucluse 28D1

Camping-Car Park, Route de Cavaillon. **GPS:** n43,92024 e5,12452.

30 € 10,80 Ch (8x) included. **Location:** Rural, comfortable, quiet. **Surface:** gravel/metalled. 01/01-31/12.
Distance: 500m 500m on the spot on the spot.
Remarks: Mandatory, one-time fee Pass'Etapes € 4.

S Fontvieille 28C1

Parking du Moulin de Daudet, Allée des Pins.
GPS: n43,72000 e4,71200.

€ 6,50/24h € 2/100liter Ch. **Location:** Rural, comfortable, quiet. **Surface:** gravel. 01/01-31/12.
Distance: 800m 800m.
Remarks: Market Friday-morning.

S Gap 25E3

Avenue de Traunstein. **GPS:** n44,54176 e6,06101.
6 free Ch free. **Location:** Urban. **Surface:** asphalted. 01/01-31/12.
Distance: on the spot 600m 300m.
Remarks: Max. 48h.

S Gap 25E3

Parking Dumont, Avenue Commandant Dumont, N85.
GPS: n44,56544 e6,08447.

3 free € 3 Ch € 3.
Location: Urban, simple, noisy. **Surface:** asphalted. 01/01-31/12.
Distance: 300m on the spot on the spot 200m.
Remarks: Stay overnight allowed at other pitches, max. 7 days.

S Gap 25E3

Avenue d'Embrun 93. **GPS:** n44,56958 e6,10249.

6 free Ch free. **Location:** Urban, simple, noisy. **Surface:** asphalted. 01/01-31/12.
Distance: 800m 100m 100m 50m.
Remarks: Free bus to centre.

S Gémenos 28D2

Cours Sudre. **GPS:** n43,29772 e5,62953.

3 free Ch WC free. **Location:** Central, quiet. **Surface:** metalled. 01/01-31/12.
Distance: 100m 100m 100m 50m.
Remarks: Near office de tourisme, max. 24h.

S Gigondas 28C1

Domaine des Florets, Route des Dentelles, D80.
GPS: n44,16220 e5,01725.

3 free free. **Location:** Rural, simple, quiet. **Surface:** gravel. 01/01-31/12.
Distance: 1,7km 500m on the spot Des Dentelles.
Remarks: Check in at tasting room.

Gordes 28D1

Parking Village des Bories, D2. **GPS:** n43,90056 e5,19306.

20 free. **Location:** Rural, simple. **Surface:** gravel. 01/01-31/12.
Distance: 2km 2km 2km.
Remarks: Max. 7 days.

S Greasque 28D2

Musée de la Mine, Route de Puits Hely d'Oissel.
GPS: n43,43281 e5,53439.

30 € 5 Ch included. **Surface:** gravel. 16/01-20/12.
Distance: 600m.
Remarks: Max. 72h.

S Gréoux-les-Bains 28E1

Aire Camping-car, Chemin de la Barque.
GPS: n43,75562 e5,88862.

80 € 10/24h Ch WC included. **Location:** Urban, simple, noisy. **Surface:** gravel. 01/01-31/12.
Distance: 150m 150m 150m on the spot.

Remarks: Max 3,5t, max. 30 days.

S Grimaud 28F2

Saint Pons Les Mûres, D98. **GPS:** n43,28000 e6,57806.

12 € 15 Ch included € 2,50 . **Location:** Simple, noisy. **Surface:** asphalted. 01/01-31/12.
Distance: 800m 800m 200m 500m.
Remarks: Max. 72h.

S Guillaumes 28F1

Place de Provence, Avenue du Lieutenant Colonelli.
GPS: n44,08861 e6,85285.

10 free € 2/100liter Ch € 2/h.
Location: Rural, simple, quiet. **Surface:** grassy/gravel. 01/01-31/12.
Distance: 50m on the spot on the spot 50m 50m on the spot on the spot.
Remarks: Max. 7 days, coins at Bar-Tabac, tourist info, town hall.

Hyères 28E3

Parking des Îles, Avenue des Arbannais. **GPS:** n43,02864 e6,15438.
4. **Location:** Urban. 01/01-31/12.
Distance: 100m bakery 100m.
Remarks: At harbour.

S Isola 25G3

M2205. **GPS:** n44,18811 e7,04350.

15 free Ch free. **Location:** Urban, simple, quiet. **Surface:** asphalted. 01/01-31/12.
Distance: 500m 100m 100m 500m 500m on the spot on the spot.
Remarks: Next to sports fields.

S Istres 28C2

Parking du Castellan, Chemin du Castellan.
GPS: n43,51550 e4,99288.

12 € 8/24h Ch included. **Location:** Central, quiet. **Surface:** asphalted/gravel. 01/01-31/12.
Distance: 700m on the spot on the spot 200m.
Remarks: At lake, max. 48h.

S Jausiers 25F3

Route de Jausiers-Barcelonette, D900. **GPS:** n44,41266 e6,72936.

FR

6 free € 3 Ch. **Location:** Rural, simple, noisy.
Surface: metalled. 01/01-31/12.
Distance: 600m 50m 100m 400m on the spot on the spot.
Remarks: Max. 7 days.

Jausiers 25F3

Aire Municipale Pont de Barnuquel, Sainte-Anne, Route des Nites.
GPS: n44,41278 e6,72996.

20 free. **Location:** Rural, simple, quiet. **Surface:** grassy/gravel.
01/01-31/12.
Distance: 600m on the spot 100m 400m on the spot on the spot.
Remarks: Along river, service 200m.

Jausiers 25F3

Mazagrand, Les Esminjots, D900. **GPS**: n44,42445 e6,73679.
8 free. **Surface:** gravel. 01/01-31/12.

Jausiers 25F3

Parking d'Arnaudville, Rue Principale. **GPS**: n44,41967 e6,73515.
20 free. **Surface:** asphalted. 01/01-31/12.
Distance: on the spot.

Jausiers 25F3

Salle Polyvalente, Rue des Écoles. **GPS**: n44,41822 e6,73646.
10 free. **Surface:** asphalted. 01/01-31/12.
Distance: on the spot.

S **Jouques** 28D2

Parking Saint Honorat, D11. **GPS**: n43,63176 e5,64414.
5 free Ch. **Surface:** asphalted.
Distance: 750m 750m 750m.

L'Isle-sur-la-Sorgue 28C1

Parking de la Gare, Avenue Julien Guigue.
GPS: n43,91768 e5,04686.

free.
Location: Simple, noisy. **Surface:** gravel. 01/01-31/12.
Distance: 500m 150m 700m on the spot.
Remarks: At station.

S **La Bréole** 25E3

Bourg La Bréole, D707. **GPS**: n44,45777 e6,29194.

8 free Ch WC free. **Location:** Urban, simple, quiet.
Surface: asphalted. 01/01-31/12.

Distance: on the spot 2km 2km Lac de Serre Ponçon 100m 100m.
Remarks: At petrol station, max. 7 days.

S **La Crau** 28E3

Espace Lavage Auto Grand Bleu, La Moutonne.
GPS: n43,12417 e6,07444.

3 free € 4 Ch. **Location:** Simple, noisy. **Surface:** concrete.
01/01-31/12.

S **La Londe-les-Maures** 28E3

Rond-point Ducourneau, chemin du Pansard.
GPS: n43,13185 e6,23053.

4 free € 3 Ch.
Location: Simple, isolated, quiet. **Surface:** asphalted.
01/01-31/12.
Distance: 800m 3km 800m 800m.
Remarks: 03/07/2015 during inspection service out of order, max. 24h.

S **La Martre** 28F1

Chemin de Fontvieillle. **GPS**: n43,77233 e6,60255.

3 € 5 Ch included. **Location:** Comfortable, isolated, quiet.
Surface: grassy/gravel. 01/01-31/12.
Distance: 300m 300m 300m.

S **La Motte** 28F2

Chemin des Correns. **GPS**: n43,48860 e6,54212.

10 free € 2 Ch. **Location:** Rural, simple, isolated, quiet.
Surface: gravel. 01/01-31/12.
Distance: 800m 300m 800m.
Remarks: At tennis-courts, max. 24h, coins at the shops.

S **La Motte** 28F2

Moulin de Vallongues, Avenue Fréderique Mistral, D47.
GPS: n43,49630 e6,53134.

10 free € 2/100liter Ch € 2/h. **Location:** Urban, simple, isolated, quiet. **Surface:** gravel. 01/01-31/12.
Distance: 600m 600m 4km on the spot.
Remarks: Max. 24h.

La Roche-des-Arnauds 25E3

D994, Chemin des Digues. **GPS**: n44,56134 e5,95637.

5 free. **Location:** Urban, simple, noisy. **Surface:** asphalted.
01/01-31/12.
Distance: 100m 1km on the spot on the spot 100m 100m on the spot 100m.
Remarks: Max. 24h.

S **La Salle-les-Alpes** 25F2

Aire camping car Pontillas, Chemin des Charrières.
GPS: n44,94805 e6,55564.

20 € 8 Ch included. **Location:** Urban, simple.
Surface: metalled. 01/01-31/12.
Distance: 400m 400m 400m on the spot on the spot 20m.
Remarks: Pay at tourist office.

S **La Salle-les-Alpes** 25F2

Parking Camping Car Le Bez, Chemin de l'Oratoire, Villeneuve.
GPS: n44,94417 e6,55583.

15 € 9, winter € 18 Ch included € 9,50.
Location: Urban, simple, central. **Surface:** gravel.
01/01-31/12.
Distance: 200m 50m on the spot on the spot 20m.
Remarks: Parking at skipistes.

S **Laragne-Montéglin** 25E3

Parking de Véragne, Avenue de Provence, D1075.
GPS: n44,31212 e5,82543.

FR

15 free Ch free WC100m. **Location:** Urban, simple.
Surface: asphalted. 01/01-31/12.
Distance: 300m 300m 300m on the spot on the spot.

Laragne-Montéglin 25E3

Intermarché, D1075, Rue de Souvenir. **GPS:** n44,30300 e5,83700.

30 free € 2 Ch. 01/01-31/12.
Distance: 2km.

Le Lauzet-Ubay 25F3

D900. **GPS:** n44,42833 e6,43389.

6 free WC free. **Location:** Urban, simple, quiet. **Surface:** gravel.
01/01-31/12.
Distance: 50m 50m 50m on the spot.
Remarks: At small lake, max. 2 days.

Le Monêtier-les-Bains 25F2

Aire camping car les Charmettes, Route des Bains.
GPS: n44,97131 e6,51279.

40 € 4,80/day + tourist tax Ch free.
Location: Rural, simple, quiet. **Surface:** asphalted.
01/01-31/12.
Distance: 300m on the spot on the spot on the spot.
Remarks: Along river, parking at skipistes, discount longer stays.

Le Monêtier-les-Bains 25F2

Col du Lautaret, D1091. **GPS:** n45,03301 e6,40696.
35 free. **Surface:** metalled/sand. 01/01-31/12.
Distance: 200m 200m 200m on the spot.

Le Thoronet 28E2

D17, boulevard du 17 aout 1944. **GPS:** n43,45097 e6,30411.

2 free € 2 Ch. **Location:** Rural, simple, central, noisy.
Surface: asphalted. 01/01-31/12.

Distance: on the spot 50m.
Remarks: Max. 48h, coins at tourist info.

Les Issambres 28F2

Chez Marcel, Plage La Gaillarde, N98. **GPS:** n43,36559 e6,71202.

40 € 11, peak season € 16 Ch included € 3/day € 0,50
€ 5/5 . **Location:** Comfortable, isolated, quiet.
Surface: gravel/sand. 01/01-31/12.
Distance: 3km 50m 200m 200m 50m.

Les Salles-sur-Verdon 28E1

L'Ermitage, D957. **GPS:** n43,77434 e6,21773.

10 € 7, Jul/Aug € 9 Ch € 4 included.
Location: Rural, simple, isolated, quiet. **Surface:** gravel/sand.
01/01-31/12.
Distance: 700m Lac de Ste Croix 1km on the spot on the spot on the spot.
Remarks: Service passerby € 5, swimming pool incl.

Malaucène 25D3

Avenue Charles de Gaulle. **GPS:** n44,17792 e5,12970.

40 € 3,50 excl. tourist tax Ch free.
Location: Rural, simple, noisy.
Surface: unpaved.
01/01-31/12.
Distance: 150m 150m 150m Mont-Ventoux on the spot.
Remarks: Between sports fields and gendarmerie.

Tourist information Malaucène:
Marché Provencal. Wed-morning.

Malemort-du-Comtat 28D1

Avenue Docteur Tondut, D5. **GPS:** n44,02175 e5,15714.

5 free Ch free. **Location:** Rural, simple. **Surface:** gravel.
01/01-31/12 Service: winter.
Distance: 200m on the spot.
Remarks: Near Salle des Fêtes, max. 24h.

Malijai 28E1

Impasse des Bugadières. **GPS:** n44,04433 e6,02971.

10 free Ch free. **Location:** Rural, simple. **Surface:** asphalted.
01/01-31/12.
Distance: on the spot on the spot 50m 50m on the spot.
Remarks: Along river.

Marseille 28D2

Marlyparc, Chemin de Morgiou 120. **GPS:** n43,24085 e5,40693.

40 € 12 Ch included € 5 .
Location: Urban, simple, central, quiet. **Surface:** metalled.
01/01-31/12.
Distance: 7km Marseille 3km 1km on the spot.

Ménerbes 28D1

Parking Longue Durée, Rue de la Fontaine.
GPS: n43,83193 e5,20828.

20 free WC. **Location:** Rural, simple. **Surface:** gravel.
01/01-31/12.
Distance: 250m 100m on the spot.
Remarks: Max. 7 days.

Mison 25E3

Les Armands Sud. **GPS:** n44,26551 e5,85728.

4 free Ch WC free. **Location:** Rural, simple.
Surface: asphalted. 01/01-31/12.
Distance: 50m 200m 200m 200m.
Remarks: Playground.

Montclar 27H1

D60, route Montclar-Faveyrolles. **GPS:** n43,96756 e2,65137.
10 free Ch free. **Surface:** gravel. 01/01-31/12.
Distance: 500m.
Remarks: Picnic area, playground.

Montgenèvre 25F2

Aire de Camping Car Du Collet, Cros Lateron, N94.
GPS: n44,93417 e6,73317.

FR

220 € 13 Ch (80x)included . **Location:** Rural, simple, isolated, quiet. **Surface:** metalled. 01/01-31/12.
Distance: 500m 500m on the spot on the spot on the spot.
Remarks: Service passerby € 8.

S Moustiers-Sainte-Marie 28E1

P5, D952. **GPS:** n43,84361 e6,21874.

25 € 7,50, 31/10-31/03 free € 2/10minutes Ch € 2/10minutes. **Location:** Rural, simple. **Surface:** gravel. 01/01-31/12.
Distance: 10 min walking 200m 200m on the spot on the spot.
Remarks: Max. 2 nights, beautiful view.

S Névache 25F2

D994G. **GPS:** n45,01666 e6,64261.

€ 8,50 WC included. **Location:** Simple, isolated, quiet. **Surface:** grassy. 01/01-31/12.
Distance: 1km on the spot on the spot on the spot on the spot.

Névache 25F2

D994G, Rue de Roubion. **GPS:** n45,01698 e6,63062.

15 free. **Location:** Urban, simple, quiet. **Surface:** grassy. 01/01-31/12.
Distance: 200m on the spot on the spot 200m on the spot on the spot.

Ollioules 28E3

Route des Gorges, DN8. **GPS:** n43,13868 e5,85002.
8 € 3. 01/04-30/09.
Distance: 600m 600m 450m.
Remarks: Max. 48h.

S Oppède-le-Vieux 28D1

Parking Oppède-le-Vieux, Chemin de Sous Ville.
GPS: n43,83094 e5,15897.

5 € 5/day free WC.
Location: Rural, simple. **Surface:** gravel. 01/01-31/12.
Distance: 500m 500m.
Remarks: Max. 7 days.

Tourist information Oppède-le-Vieux:
Hiking route through medieval top-hill village.

S Orcières-Merlette 25E2

Camping-car Casse Blanche, Pra Palier, P2.
GPS: n44,69517 e6,32567.

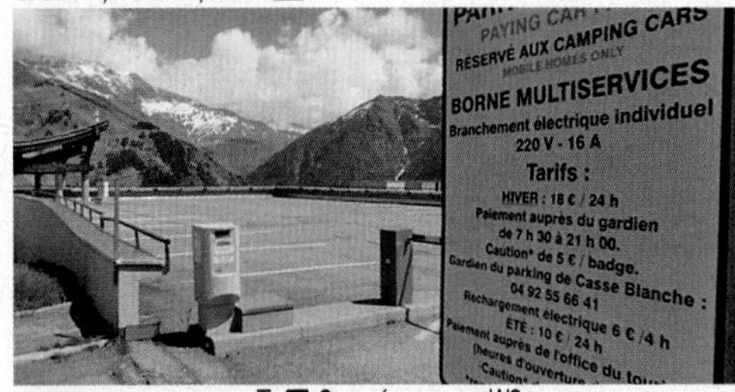

21 € 18, Jul/Aug € 10 Ch included WC € 9,50/24h.
Location: Rural, simple. **Surface:** asphalted.
17/12-17/04, 01/07-02/09.
Distance: on the spot on the spot.
Remarks: Summer: pay at tourist office, caution € 5.

S Pélissanne 28D2

Prouvenque, Chemin de la Prouvenque.
GPS: n43,62805 e5,15307.

15 free Ch free. **Location:** Urban, simple, quiet.
Surface: asphalted.
Distance: 500m 8km.
Remarks: Parking stadium, video surveillance.

Plan-de-la-Tour 28F2

Parking Foch. GPS: n43,33787 e6,54532.

free.
Location: Simple, central, quiet. **Surface:** gravel.
Distance: on the spot 100m 150m.
Remarks: Max. 48h.

Tourist information Plan-de-la-Tour:
Thu morning 6-12h.

S Port Saint-Louis-du-Rhône 28C2

Camping-car park, 1233 quai de la Suisse.
GPS: n43,38424 e4,81909.

100 € 9,60-12 Ch included. **Location:** Simple, isolated, quiet. **Surface:** asphalted/gravel. 01/01-31/12.
Distance: 1,5km 2km on the spot 1km 1,5km.
Remarks: Mandatory, one-time fee Pass'Etapes € 4.

S Pra-Loup 25F3

Parking des Choupettes, D109. **GPS:** n44,36806 e6,60611.

35 free € 3 Ch € 3 . **Location:** Urban, simple, quiet.
Surface: asphalted. 01/01-31/12.
Distance: 400m 400m 400m on the spot 50m.
Remarks: Parking at skipistes, max. 72h.

S Puget Theniers 28F1

Aire de la Condamine, Route des Grandes Alpes.
GPS: n43,95306 e6,89944.

10 € 4 Ch included. **Surface:** asphalted. 01/01-31/12.
Distance: 300m 20m 300m 300m.

S Puimoisson 28E1

Les Lavandins, Basses Touires. **GPS:** n43,87006 e6,12979.

40 € 5/24h € 1/100liter € 1,05/1h.
Location: Rural, simple, isolated. **Surface:** grassy.
01/04-31/10.
Distance: 650m 650m.

S Puy-Saint-Vincent 25F2

Les Sagnes-Station 1400, D404. **GPS:** n44,82478 e6,49839.

5 € 6, tourist tax € 0,60/pp Ch included.
Location: Rural, simple, quiet. **Surface:** asphalted.
01/01-31/12.
Distance: on the spot on the spot on the spot on the spot on the spot.

Puy-Saint-Vincent 25F2

Station 1600, Clôt de Saint-Romain, D4. **GPS**: n44,83245 e6,48331.

20 € 6 Ch included. **Location:** Rural, simple, quiet.
Surface: asphalted. 18/12-25/04.
Distance: 200m 200m 200m 200m.
Remarks: Altitude 1600m, at ski-lift, max. 15 days, information at cableway.

Puyvert 28D1

Super U, D118. **GPS**: n43,74763 e5,33727.

5 free Ch (2x)free € 4. **Location:** Rural.
Surface: asphalted. 01/01-31/12.
Distance: 1,5km on the spot.
Remarks: Parking near Super-U, max. 24h.

Quinson 28E1

Les Prés du Verdon, Allée des Prés du Verdon.
GPS: n43,69801 e6,03911.

5 free Chfree WC. **Location:** Rural, simple, quiet.
Surface: gravel/sand. 01/01-31/12.
Distance: 100m 100m 300m 500m on the spot.
Remarks: Near the prehistoric museum of the gorges du Verdon.

Ramatuelle 28F2

Parking de Tamaris, Plage de Pamplonne, Route des Tamaris.
GPS: n43,23893 e6,66149.

60 € 18 € 2 Ch (20x)€ 7/day WC. **Location:** Rural.
Surface: gravel. 01/01-31/12.
Distance: on the spot on the spot on the spot.
Remarks: Beach parking.

Ramatuelle 28F2

Parking Municipal, Plage de Pamplonne, Route de Bonne-Terrasse.
GPS: n43,21126 e6,66217.

130 € 8,20, 02/11-10/03 € 5,10 ChWC.
Location: Rural. **Surface:** gravel. 01/04-31/10.
Distance: 200m 200m 2km.
Remarks: Beach parking, max. 48h, bread-service.

Tourist information Ramatuelle:
La place de l'Ormeau. Provencal Market. Thu, Su.

Reillanne 28D1

Aire Camping Car Reillanne, Boulevard de la Tuilière.
GPS: n43,88020 e5,66404.
3 free Ch free. 01/01-31/12.
Distance: 500m.
Remarks: Service closed during wintertime.

Riez 28E1

P de l'Auvestre, Chemin du Relais. **GPS**: n43,82180 e6,09197.

30 € 5/24h Chincluded. **Location:** Rural, comfortable, quiet. **Surface:** gravel. 01/01-31/12.
Distance: 500m 500m 100m on the spot on the spot.
Remarks: Market Saturday.

Rosans 25D3

D25. **GPS**: n44,39307 e5,47395.
free. **Surface:** unpaved. 01/01-31/12.
Distance: 200m 650m.

Roubion 28G1

Les Buisses. **GPS**: n44,08397 e7,04287.

14 free Chfree. **Location:** Rural, simple, isolated, quiet.
Surface: asphalted. 01/01-31/12.
Distance: on the spot on the spot on the spot.
Remarks: At ski-lift, narrow entrance.

Roussillon 28D1

Parking Saint Joseph, D149. **GPS**: n43,89660 e5,29593.

20 € 7/night.
Location: Rural, comfortable. **Surface:** gravel.
Distance: 800m 800m on the spot on the spot.
Remarks: Max. 48h.

Tourist information Roussillon:
Sentier des Ocres. Hiking trail, 45 min.

Sablet 25C3

Domaine du Parandou, D977. **GPS**: n44,19325 e4,99522.

5 € 1,50 € 3 Ch (2x)€ 3 WC. **Location:** Rural, simple.
Surface: gravel. 01/01-31/12.
Distance: 2km.

Saint-André-les-Alpes 28F1

Chez Julo, Chemin de Neouille. **GPS**: n43,96394 e6,51185.

30 € 8 Chincluded € 2/24h. **Location:** Rural, simple, quiet. **Surface:** grassy. 01/01-31/12.
Distance: 800m 800m 800m on the spot on the spot.

Saint-André-les-Alpes 28F1

Grand Rue. **GPS**: n43,96525 e6,50735.

30 free Chfree. **Location:** Urban, comfortable, quiet.
Surface: asphalted. 01/01-31/12.
Distance: on the spot 2km 100m 250m on the spot.

Saint-Chamas 28C2

Avenue Marx Dormoy. **GPS**: n43,54636 e5,03246.

10 free Ch. **Location:** Urban, simple. **Surface:** gravel.
01/01-31/12.
Distance: on the spot on the spot.
Remarks: Near marina.

Saint-Crépin 25F2

D138. **GPS**: n44,70562 e6,60196.

24 € 8, tourist tax € 0,60/pp Ch € 3,80 WC included. . **Location:** Rural, simple, quiet. **Surface:** grassy.
01/05-30/09. **Distance:** 500m on the spot on the spot on the spot on the spot on the spot.
Remarks: Service on the other side of the bridge, swimming pool available.

Saint-Jean-Saint-Nicolas 25E2

Camping Car Park, Le Châtelard. **GPS**: n44,66782 e6,23484.

FR

49 € 10,20 Ch (60x) included.
Location: Rural, simple, isolated, quiet. **Surface:** forest soil.
01/04-15/11.
Distance: 600m on the spot on the spot 600m 600m on the spot.
Remarks: Mandatory, one-time fee Pass'Etapes € 4.

S Saint-Laurent-du-Var 28G1

Route des Pugets. **GPS**: n43,68584 e7,18459.

7 free Chfree. **Location:** Isolated, noisy. **Surface:** asphalted.
01/01-31/12.
Distance: 1,2km 4,5km 1,2km 1,2km.
Remarks: Max. 7 days.

Saint-Laurent-du-Var 28G1

Avenue Francis Teisseire. **GPS**: n43,66628 e7,19595.

5 free. **Location:** Simple, central, noisy. **Surface:** asphalted.
01/01-31/12.
Distance: city centre 2km 200m 600m 500m 500m 500m.
Remarks: Max. 8M.

S Saint-Mandrier-sur-Mer 28E3

Pin Roland, Impasse de la Mer. **GPS**: n43,07771 e5,90444.

6 free Chfree. **Surface:** asphalted. 01/01-31/12.
Distance: 500m 500m.
Remarks: Max. 48h.

S Saint-Martin-de-Crau 28C2

Place François Miterrand. **GPS**: n43,63859 e4,81454.
3 free ChWCfree. **Location:** Urban. **Surface:** metalled.
01/01-31/12.
Distance: 400m 400m 1,5km.
Remarks: In front of town hall, max. 48h.

Saint-Michel-l'Observatoire 28E1

Place du Serre. **GPS**: n43,90908 e5,71750.

10 free .
Location: Simple. **Surface:** gravel. 01/03-15/11.
Distance: 200m 200m on the spot.
Remarks: Beautiful panorama.

S Saint-Paul-lès-Durance 28E2

Rue du Camping le Retour. **GPS**: n43,68700 e5,70588.

6 free Chfree. **Location:** Rural, simple, quiet.
Surface: gravel. 01/01-31/12.
Distance: 500m 4km 500m 700m.
Remarks: Max. 48h.

S Saint-Pons 25F3

D900. **GPS**: n44,38571 e6,60912.
6 free Chfree. **Surface:** gravel. 01/04-31/10.
Distance: on the spot.

S Saint-Tropez 28F2

Aire camping-car, Chemin Fontaine du pin, Chemin de la Moutte.
GPS: n43,26468 e6,67227.

15 € 16 € 2 Ch € 2,50 WC € 1. **Location:** Isolated.
Surface: grassy/sand. 01/01-31/12.
Distance: 3km 800m.

Tourist information Saint-Tropez:
La Citadelle, musée de la Marine. Navy museum.
Place des Lices. Week market. Wed + Sa morning.

S Saint-Véran 25F2

Parking St. Marie Madeleine, D5. **GPS**: n44,70447 e6,86091.

20 € 5 ChWCincluded. **Location:** Rural, simple, isolated, quiet. **Surface:** metalled. 01/01-31/12.
Distance: 100m 100m 200m on the spot on the spot 200m.

S Sainte-Croix-du-Verdon 28E1

Route du Lac. **GPS**: n43,76077 e6,15102.

20 € 8/24h € 2/10minutes Ch € 2 WC.
Location: Rural, simple, quiet. **Surface:** asphalted.
01/01-31/12.
Distance: 100m Lac de Ste Croix 1km 100m 200m on the spot on the spot.
Remarks: Max. 3 nights, water closed during wintertime, beautiful view.

S Sainte-Maxime 28F2

D25, le Muy dir Ste.Maxime. **GPS**: n43,31730 e6,62999.

50 € 10/24h, 01/10-31/03 € 5 Chfree.
Location: Comfortable, quiet. **Surface:** metalled. 01/01-31/12.
Distance: city centre 1km 1,2km McDonalds 50m Lidl 200m. **Remarks:** Max. 48h.

Tourist information Sainte-Maxime:
Thu-morning.
Les Greniers du Golfe, Aire des Magnoti. Bric-a-brac. Wed 08-18h.

S Sainte-Tulle 28E1

Avenue Léo Lagrange. **GPS**: n43,78500 e5,76395.
20 € 5 Chincluded (3x) WC. 01/01-31/12.
Distance: 400m 350m.

S Saintes-Maries-de-la-Mer 28B2

Avenue d'Arles, D570. **GPS**: n43,45535 e4,42750.

60 € 12,30 + € 0,70 tourist tax ChWCincluded.
Location: Simple, central, quiet. **Surface:** asphalted.
01/01-31/12.
Distance: 200m beach 400m 100m 50m 100m.
Remarks: Max. 48h, service: 8.30-11.30h, 16-19.30h.

S Saintes-Maries-de-la-Mer 28B2

Plage Ouest, Route d'Aigues-Mortes, D38.
GPS: n43,44991 e4,40407.

50 € 12,30 + € 0,70 tourist tax Chincluded.
Location: Isolated, quiet. **Surface:** asphalted/gravel.
01/01-31/12.
Distance: 1,5km 50m.
Remarks: Beach parking.

S Saintes-Maries-de-la-Mer 28B2

Valée des Lys, Parking Plage Est, Avenue Cousteau.
GPS: n43,45364 e4,43695.

150 € 12,30 + € 0,70 tourist tax Chincluded.
Surface: asphalted. 01/01-31/12.
Distance: 250m beach 50m 100m 250m.

Saintes-Maries-de-la-Mer 28B2

Parking du Large, Avenue du Docteur Cambon.
GPS: n43,45430 e4,43326.

20 free.
Location: Simple, central. **Surface:** gravel.
Distance: 250m 700m 250m 250m.

Saintes-Maries-de-la-Mer 28B2

Route de Cacharel. **GPS**: n43,45684 e4,43305.

10 free. **Location:** Simple, isolated, quiet.
Distance: 700m 750m.

Salernes 28E2

Aire Municipal, Route des Quatre Chemins.
GPS: n43,55923 e6,23381.

35 free Chfree. **Location:** Rural, simple, quiet.
Surface: grassy/gravel. 01/01-31/12.
Distance: 300m Lac de Ste Croix 1km on the spot.
Remarks: Max. 24h.

Salin-de-Giraud 28C2

Rue de la Bouvine. **GPS**: n43,41222 e4,73056.

20 free € 2 Ch € 0,80.
Location: Simple, quiet. **Surface:** gravel.
01/04-31/10.
Distance: 500m 500m 500m.
Remarks: At fire-station, coins at town hall, showers only in july/aug.

Salin-de-Giraud 28C2

Rue Georges-Jo Maillis. **GPS**: n43,41236 e4,73621.

50 free. **Location:** Urban, simple. **Surface:** asphalted.
01/01-31/12.
Distance: on the spot 10km 200m 200m.

Sarrians 28C1

Avenue de la Camargue. **GPS**: n44,07943 e4,97788.

10 € 3/day Ch included. **Location:** Rural, simple.
Surface: gravel. 01/04-31/10.
Distance: 800m 500m.

Sault 28D1

P3, Route de Saint-Trinit. **GPS**: n44,09434 e5,41308.

15 free € 2 Ch € 2/h. **Location:** Rural, simple.
Surface: gravel. 01/01-31/12.
Distance: 500m 500m on the spot 4km chemin des Lavandes.

Sausset-les-Pins 28D2

Avenue Pierre Matraja. **GPS**: n43,33890 e5,10916.

15 free € 4/100liter Ch € 4/1h. **Location:** Simple, isolated, quiet. **Surface:** asphalted. 01/01-31/12.
Distance: 1,2km 800m 1,2km 1,2km 5m.
Remarks: At stadium, max. 72h.

Savines-le-Lac 25F3

Parking du Barnafret, Av. du Faubourg, D954.
GPS: n44,52495 e6,40090.

19 € 9,50 € 2/120liter Ch (20x)included.
Location: Rural, simple, central. **Surface:** asphalted.
01/01-31/12.
Distance: 300m 500m 100m on the spot on the spot.
Remarks: At lake Serre Ponçon.

Selonnet 25E3

Quartier de Boulangère. **GPS**: n44,36862 e6,31525.

7 free € 2/10minutes Ch € 2/55minutes.
Location: Rural, simple, quiet. **Surface:** gravel.
01/01-31/12.
Distance: 300m 300m 300m.
Remarks: Coins at town hall, supermarket, bakery and Tabac, free wifi at town hall.

Sénas 28D1

Rue du Moulin. **GPS**: n43,74403 e5,08020.

6 free € 2/100liter Ch € 2/30minutes.
Location: Urban, simple. **Surface:** asphalted.
01/01-31/12 last weekend of August.
Distance: 200m 1,5km 200m 200m.
Remarks: Coins at tourist info and maison de presse.

Sillans-la-Cascade 28E2

Route de Salernes. **GPS**: n43,56692 e6,18277.
10 free € 3 Ch € 3. 01/01-31/12.
Distance: 500m 500m.
Remarks: Free entrance swimming pool.

Sisteron 25E3

Aire camping-cars, Avenue de la Libération.
GPS: n44,19105 e5,94542.

12 € 4 € 2/20minutes Ch € 2/4h.
Location: Urban, simple. **Surface:** asphalted.
01/01-31/12 Service: winter.
Distance: 800m 800m 800m.
Remarks: Along railwayline.

Sisteron 25E3

Parking Melchior Donnet, D4085. **GPS**: n44,20028 e5,94389.

10 free € 2 Ch € 2/10minutes. **Location:** Urban, simple.
Surface: asphalted. 01/01-31/12.
Distance: on the spot 4,5km.

Six-Fours-les-Plages 28E3

Port de la Coudoulière. **GPS**: n43,09750 e5,81194.

FR

5 € 10 WCincluded € 2. **Location:** Central.
Surface: asphalted. 01/10-30/04.
Distance: 100m 100m 100m.

S Six-Fours-les-Plages 28E3

Promenade Gén. Charles de Gaulle. **GPS**: n43,11252 e5,81172.
€ 3 Ch. 01/01-31/12.
Remarks: Behind tourist info, 8-12, 14-19h.

S Sospel 28G1

Stade E. Donato, D2566. **GPS**: n43,87876 e7,44213.

4 € 5 Chincluded. **Surface:** asphalted. 01/01-31/12.
Distance: 300m 300m 300m.
Remarks: Pay at tourist office.

S Thorenc 28F1

Lac de Thorenc, D2. **GPS**: n43,79921 e6,80802.

10 free € 5 Ch WC. **Location:** Rural, simple, isolated, quiet.
Surface: metalled. 01/01-31/12.
Distance: 750m on the spot on the spot on the spot épicerie 750m on the spot.
Remarks: Along Lake Thorenc.

S Trigance 28F1

Quartier Saint Roch. **GPS**: n43,76060 e6,44255.

5 € 5, dog € 3,50 € 1 € 1 Ch € 1. **Location:** Rural, isolated, quiet. **Surface:** asphalted/gravel. 01/01-31/12.
Distance: on the spot on the spot 100m 100m.
Remarks: Max. 2 days, inclining pitches, beautiful view.

S Vaison-la-Romaine 25D3

Aire camping-car, Avenue André Coudray.
GPS: n44,24650 e5,07392.

30 € 8/24h, tourist tax € 0,55/pp Chfree.
Location: Urban, comfortable. **Surface:** gravel.
01/01-31/12 Tue-morning.
Distance: 800m.

Tourist information Vaison-la-Romaine:
Le Pont Romain. Bridge from the Roman Empire.
Le Château. Ruins of the castle of the Counts of Toulouse.
Tue.

S Valberg 28F1

Le Lagopède, Route de Rouya. **GPS**: n44,09615 e6,93675.

16 € 10 + € 0,20/pp tourist tax Ch (21x)WCincluded.
Location: Rural, comfortable, isolated, quiet. **Surface:** asphalted.
01/01-31/12.
Distance: 500m on the spot 500m 500m 600m.

Valréas 25C3

Aire camping-car. **GPS**: n44,38713 e4,99245.

5 free. **Location:** Simple. **Surface:** asphalted. 01/01-31/12.
Distance: 400m 250m.
Remarks: Behind tourist info, max 3,5t.

S Valréas 25C3

Domaine du Lumian, Route de Montélimar, D941.
GPS: n44,39384 e4,96325.

6 free Ch free. **Surface:** gravel. 01/01-31/12.
Distance: 2,5km.

S Vars 25F3

Parking P5, Allee Trub. **GPS**: n44,57510 e6,67789.

44 free Ch (6x)WCfree. **Location:** Rural, simple, isolated, quiet. **Surface:** gravel. 01/01-31/12.
Distance: 500m 500m 500m on the spot on the spot.
Remarks: Coins at tourist info.

Vauvenargues 28D2

Boulevard Moraliste. **GPS**: n43,55485 e5,59764.
3 free. **Surface:** asphalted. 01/01-31/12.
Distance: 300m on the spot 300m.
Remarks: At cemetery.

S Veynes 25E3

Base de Loisirs Les Iscles, Les Graviers, D994.
GPS: n44,51830 e5,79860.

30 free, June-Sep € 6 . **Location:** Rural, simple, quiet.
Surface: gravel. 01/01-31/12.
Distance: 2km on the spot on the spot 3km on the spot.
Remarks: Natural swimming pool, max. 48h, wifi at restaurant.

S Veynes 25E3

Place du 19 Mars, D994. **GPS**: n44,53332 e5,82346.
free ChWCfree. **Surface:** asphalted.
01/03-30/11 Thu-morning closed because of market.
Distance: 1,5km.

S Villeneuve 28E1

GPS: n43,89611 e5,86167.

12 free Chfree. **Location:** Rural, simple, quiet.
Surface: gravel. 01/01-31/12 service: 30/11-01/03.
Distance: 200m 5,5km on the spot on the spot.
Remarks: At cemetery, max. 48h.

S Vinon sur Verdon 28E1

Chemin du Plan. **GPS**: n43,72952 e5,80141.

20 free € 2/20minutes Ch. **Location:** Rural, simple.
Surface: asphalted. 01/01-31/12.
Distance: 3km on the spot on the spot.
Remarks: Parking Carrefour Market, coins at petrol station.

S Visan 25C3

Domaine de Lucena, 1600 chemin du Rastelet.
GPS: n44,31576 e4,98406.
5 € 5 Ch . **Location:** Isolated, quiet. **Surface:** gravel.
01/01-31/12.
Distance: 4km on the spot.

S Visan 25C3

Domaine des Lauribert, D976. **GPS**: n44,34833 e4,97276.

20 free Chfree (8x)€ 2 WC. **Surface:** unpaved.
01/01-31/12.
Remarks: At wine-grower, max. 72h.

Corsica

S Aléria 33G1

Le Banana's, Casaperta. **GPS**: n42,17353 e9,42103.

FR

16 € 15 Ch € 5 included. **Location:** Rural, comfortable. **Surface:** asphalted/grassy. 01/01-31/12.
Distance: river 200m 800m on the spot.
Remarks: Swimming pool available.

S Barretalli 33G1

Marine de Giottani. **GPS**: n42,86593 e9,34370.

10 € 10 Chincluded. **Location:** Rural, simple, isolated.
Surface: gravel/sand. 01/01-31/12.
Distance: 300m 300m.
Remarks: Narrow entrance.

P Col de Bavella 33G1

Parking du Col, D268. **GPS**: n41,79567 e9,22470.

15 € 4. **Location:** Simple, isolated. **Surface:** gravel/sand.
01/01-31/12.
Distance: 250m.
Remarks: Overnight stay allowed.

S Col de Vergio 33G1

D84. **GPS**: n42,28647 e8,89441.

20 € 12 Chincluded. **Location:** Rural, simple, isolated.
Surface: gravel/sand. 01/01-31/12.
Distance: 100m on the spot 1km.

Galéria 33G1

D351. **GPS**: n42,41661 e8,65660.

20 free, night € 20. **Location:** Rural, simple, isolated.
Surface: gravel.
Distance: 600m 400m on the spot.
Remarks: Canoe safari ± 1 hour, € 6/pp.

S Ogliastro 33G1

Parking de la Plage, Marine d'Albo D80. **GPS**: n42,81041 e9,33592.

10 free, July-Aug € 6 service € 2 Ch. **Location:** Simple.
Surface: unpaved. 01/01-31/12.
Distance: 100m 100m.
Remarks: Coins at the shops and restaurant.

S Porto Vecchio 33G2

Camperpark Guiseppe, Route de Palombaggia.
GPS: n41,55015 e9,30636.

25 € 25 Ch WCincluded € 0,50 at restaurant.
Location: Comfortable. **Surface:** unpaved.
Distance: Porto Vecchio 9km white sandy beach 150m 150m.

S Porto Vecchio 33G2

Parking de la Plage, Route de Palombaggia.
GPS: n41,56389 e9,33601.

50 € 14 € 2 Ch ,cold included.
Location: Comfortable. **Surface:** sand. 15/05-15/09.
Distance: Porto Vecchio 10km 500m 500m.
Remarks: Bread-service.

Rogliano 33G1

Parking de Tollare, D153, Ersa. **GPS**: n43,00733 e9,38831.

+10 free, July-Aug € 10. **Location:** Simple, isolated.
Surface: grassy/sand. 01/01-31/12.
Distance: on the spot on the spot on the spot.
Remarks: Attention: narrow road, 5,5km.

FR

United Kingdom

Capital: London
Government: Constitutional monarchy
Official Language: English
Population: 64,430,428 (2016)
Area: 242,495 km²

General information
Dialing code: 0044
General emergency: 112
Currency: Pound sterling (GBP)
£1 = € 1,13, € 1 = £0.88 (October 2017)

Regulations for overnight stays
Wild camping is forbidden in the UK. Motorway service stations allow overnight parking.

Additional public holidays 2018
March 17 St. Patricksday (Northern Ireland)
March 30 Good Friday
April 2 Easter monday
May 1 Labour Day
May 7 Early May Bank Holiday
May 28 Spring Bank Holiday
July 12 Orangemens' Day (Northern Ireland)
August 6 Summer Bank Holiday
October 31 Halloween
November 5 Guy Fawkes Day
December 26 Boxing Day

Time Zone
Winter (Standard Time) GMT+0
Summer (DST) GMT+1

GB

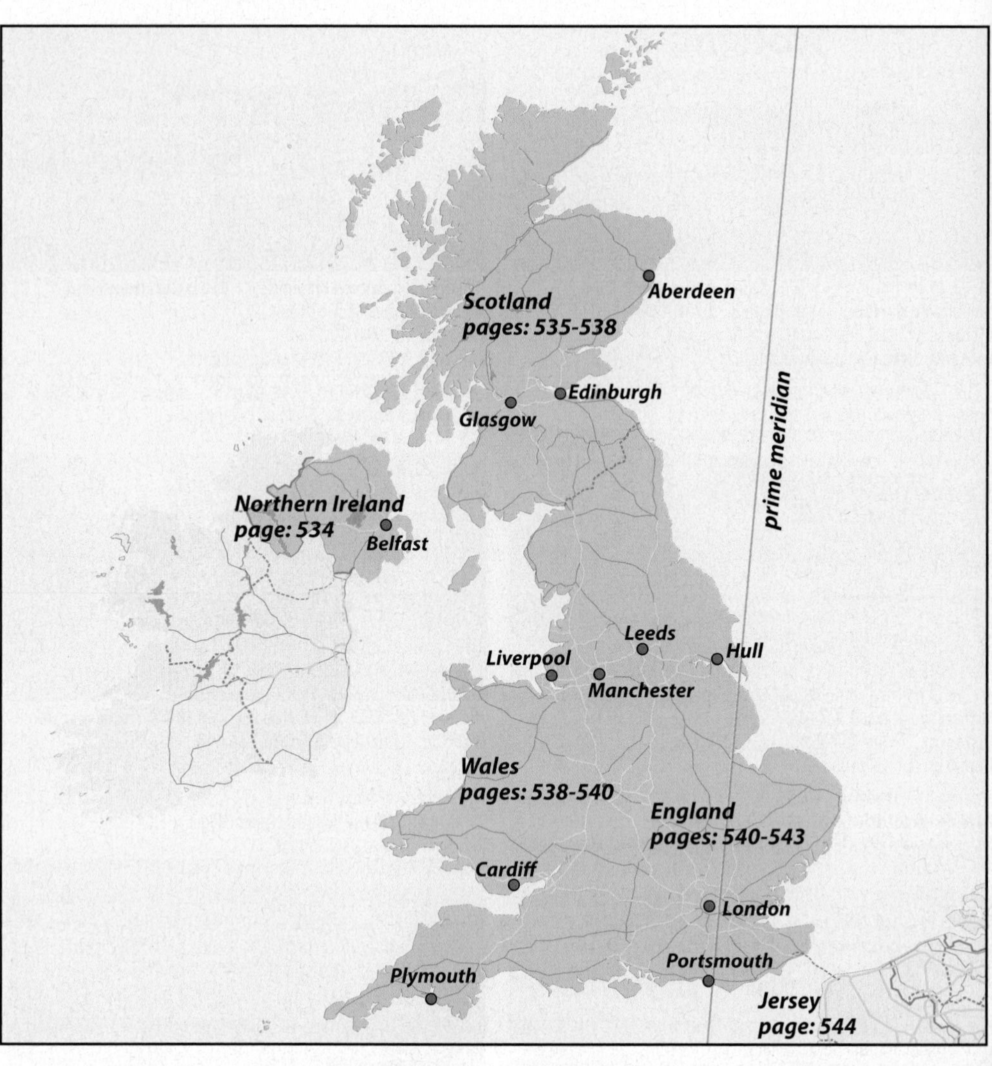

Northern Ireland

Aghadowey 1C1

Golf Car Park, Brown Trout Golf and Country Inn, 209 Agivey Road, A54. **GPS**: n55,02413 w6,59985.
free.
Remarks: Max. 48h.

Annalong 1D2

Glasdrumman Road. **GPS**: n54,10953 w5,8971.
4 free £ 2/100liter £ 2/10kWh. **Location:** Rural.
Surface: gravel. 01/01-31/12.
Distance: 800m on the spot 800m.
Remarks: Coins at restaurant.

Antrim 1D1

McLarnon's Ramble Inn, 236 Lisnevenagh Road.
GPS: n54,76198 w6,24265.
free.
Distance: Antrim 7km.

Ballinamallard 1C1

Ballinamallard Football Club, Ferney Park. **GPS**: n54,41474 w7,60092.

free. **Surface:** gravel. 01/01-31/12.
Distance: 1,5km.
Tourist information Ballinamallard:
Ballinamallard River, Kilgortnaleague Bridge, A35 Enniskillen > Irvinestown. Wild Salmon and Trout River.

Broughshane 1D1

Houston Mills, Buckna road. **GPS**: n54,89352 w6,20076.

£5 Ch (4x)£ 2/10h.
Location: Central, noisy. **Surface:** asphalted.
Distance: on the spot on the spot.
Remarks: Coins at supermarket.

Carrickfergus 1D1

Carrickfergus Harbour Car Park, Rodgers Quay.
GPS: n54,71330 w5,80902.
free £ 1 Ch £ 1. **Surface:** asphalted. 01/01-31/12.
Distance: on the spot on the spot on the spot.
Remarks: Coins at harbourmaster and tourist office.

Donaghadee 1D1

The Commons Parks, Millisle Road. **GPS**: n54,63475 w5,5312.
free £ 2/100liter £ 2/1h.
Surface: asphalted. 01/01-31/12.
Distance: on the spot on the spot on the spot on the spot on the spot.
Remarks: Coins at restaurant.

Larne 1D1

Carnfunnock Country Park, Coast Road. **GPS**: n54,89066 w5,84302.
31 £22.50-25.50 Ch WC. **Surface:** grassy/metalled.
10/03-26/11.
Distance: Larne 6km 500m 500m.

Larne 1D1

Curran Caravan Park, 131 Curran Rd. **GPS**: n54,85063 w5,80386.
£16 £ 4. **Surface:** grassy. 01/04-01/10.
Distance: 1km 1km.

Newtownards 1D1

Daft Eddys, Sketrick Island. **GPS**: n54,48812 w5,64807.

free.
Distance: Newtownards 17km.
Tourist information Newtownards:
Somme Heritage Centre, 233 Bangor Road, Conlig, A21. The centre examines Ireland's role in the 1st World War.
Castle Espie Wildfowl And Wetlands Centre, 78 Ballydrain Road, Comber. 01/01-31/12 10-17 23-25/12.

Portglenone 1C1

Portglenone Marina, Gortgole Road. **GPS**: n54,87432 w6,47979.
£10 WC.
Distance: on the spot on the spot on the spot 400m.

Portrush 1C1

Sandhill Drive Motorhome Parking. **GPS**: n55,20107 w6,65253.
10 £0.50/h £ 1,25/100liter Ch £ 1,25/kWh.
Location: Simple, central. **Surface:** asphalted.
01/01-31/12.
Distance: on the spot 600m.
Remarks: Max. 72h.

Whitehead 1D1

Bentra Golf Club, Slaughterford Road. **GPS**: n54,75908 w5,72012.
free £ 1 Ch. **Surface:** asphalted.
Distance: 1km 1,5km 150m.
Remarks: Coins at harbourmaster and tourist office.

Scotland

Aberdeen 2C2

Aberdeen Lighthouse, Greyhope Road. **GPS**: n57,14219 w2,05728.

8 free. **Location:** Rural, simple, quiet. **Surface:** asphalted.
01/01-31/12.
Distance: 3km on the spot 2,5km 1,5km on the spot.
Remarks: Whale and dolphin spotting.

Aberlour 2B1

GPS: n57,47020 w3,22929.

20 free. **Location:** Rural, simple, quiet.
Surface: asphalted. 01/01-31/12.
Distance: 500m 100m 100m 500m 500m 250m on the spot.

Appin 2A2

Creagan Station Tourers, Creaganlea. **GPS**: n56,55130 w5,30619.
7 £15-20, 4 pers.incl Ch included. **Surface:** grassy/gravel.
01/01-31/12.
Distance: Appin 3,5km on the spot on the spot 200m.

Ardfern 2A2

Ardfern Motorhome Park, Lochgilphead.
GPS: n56,17402 w5,54799.

10 £15, 01/06-15/08 £20 Ch WC included.
Location: Rural, comfortable, isolated, quiet. **Surface:** gravel.
01/01-31/12.
Distance: 1km on the spot on the spot 1km 1km.

Ardmair 2B1

Ardmair Point Campsite, A835. **GPS**: n58,03430 w5,07101.

8 free. **Location:** Rural, simple, quiet. **Surface:** asphalted.
01/01-31/12.
Distance: 2km.

Balchrick 2B1

Lairg. **GPS**: n58,48394 w5,11249.

5 free. **Location:** Rural, simple, quiet. **Surface:** asphalted.
01/01-31/12.
Distance: on the spot 1km.

Ballachulish 2B2

Glencoe Mountain Resort Campsite, Glencoe, A82 Ballachulish > Achallader. **GPS**: n56,63295 w4,82744.

9 £15 Ch WC included.
Location: Rural, comfortable, isolated, quiet.
Surface: asphalted/gravel. 01/01-31/12.
Distance: 15km on the spot on the spot on the spot.
Remarks: Parking ski-lifts.

Ballater 2B2

Balmoral Visitor Centre, Crathie. **GPS**: n57,04022 w3,2161.
overnight stay free. **Location:** Isolated, quiet. **Surface:** asphalted.
01/01-31/12.
Distance: 1,5km.
Remarks: At castle.

Balmacara 2A1

Reraig, Kyle Of Lochalsh. **GPS**: n57,28290 w5,62608.

40 £15.90 Ch £ 1,50/day WC £ 3/h.
Location: Rural, comfortable, quiet.
Surface: grassy/gravel.
01/05-30/09.
Distance: 8km on the spot on the spot 8km on the spot.

Banff 2C1

Gamrie Bay, Easter Cushnie, Gardenstown.
GPS: n57,65139 w2,33382.

6 £12, 01/04-30/09 £14 Ch included.
Location: Rural, luxurious, isolated, quiet. **Surface:** gravel.
01/01-31/12.
Distance: 2,5km 2,5km 2,5km 1km.

Banff 2C1

Quayside. **GPS**: n57,67092 w2,52462.

10 free WC free. **Location:** Urban, simple, quiet. **Surface:** concrete.
01/01-31/12.
Distance: 300m on the spot on the spot 700m 700m 400m.

Banff 2C1

Temple View. **GPS**: n57,66366 w2,51905.

25 free.
Location: Urban, simple, quiet. **Surface:** concrete. 01/01-31/12.
Distance: 1km 300m 300m 200m 200m 400m.
Remarks: At football ground.

Boat of Garten 2B2

Loch Garten Nature Reserve. **GPS**: n57,24382 w3,69541.
10 free. **Location:** Rural. **Surface:** metalled.
03/04-03/09.
Distance: on the spot on the spot on the spot on the spot.
Remarks: Max. 2 nights.

Callander 2B2

Loch Katrine, Trossachs Pier. **GPS**: n56,23368 w4,42897.

12 £18 Ch WC included.
Location: Rural, isolated, quiet. **Surface:** asphalted. 01/03-31/12.
Distance: on the spot on the spot on the spot on the spot.
Remarks: At lake.

Callander 2B2

The Cabin at Loch Lubnaig, A84. **GPS**: n56,27765 w4,2834.

Auchtertyre 2A1

A890. **GPS**: n57,28867 w5,57118.

GB

2 £7/pp Ch £ 2 £ 1. Location: Rural, simple, isolated, noisy.
Surface: asphalted. 01/01-31/12.
Distance: 7,5km on the spot on the spot 7,5km 7,5km on the spot 1km.
Remarks: Max. 3 nights, gate closes at 20h.

S Cruden Bay 2C1

Port Errol, Harbour Street. **GPS**: n57,41130 w1,84546.

voluntary contribution (£10) free.
Location: Rural, simple, quiet. **Surface:** metalled. 01/01-31/12.
Distance: on the spot on the spot on the spot 850m on the spot.
Remarks: Max. 3 days.

S Cullen 2B1

Port Long Road. **GPS**: n57,69408 w2,81992.

6 free WC free. **Location:** Rural, simple, quiet. **Surface:** gravel. 01/01-31/12.
Distance: 400m on the spot on the spot 400m 400m on the spot.

Dufftown 2B1

Castle Road. **GPS**: n57,45325 w3,12912.

20 free. **Surface:** asphalted. 01/01-31/12.
Distance: 400m 400m 400m.

Dumfries 2B3

P Long Stay, White Sands. **GPS**: n55,06722 w3,6125.

10 free. **Location:** Simple, noisy.
Surface: asphalted.
01/01-31/12.
Distance: 100m on the spot on the spot on the spot on the spot on the spot.

Dundonnell 2B1

A832. **GPS**: n57,75898 w5,03397.

8 free. **Location:** Rural, simple, quiet. **Surface:** asphalted. 01/01-31/12.
Distance: 5km 300m.

S Dunthulm 2A1

Camus More Campsite. **GPS**: n57,65020 w6,40459.

7 £8 WC included. **Location:** Rural, simple, isolated, quiet.
Surface: grassy. 15/05-07/09.
Distance: 10km on the spot 10km 10km.
Remarks: Nearby Dunthulm Castle.

S Durness 2B1

Sango Sands Oasis, A838, Sango Bay. **GPS**: n58,57013 w4,74269.

60 £20, 01/11-31/03 free Ch WC included £2/2 £ 5/day. **Location:** Rural, comfortable, quiet.
Surface: grassy/metalled. 01/01-31/12.
Distance: on the spot 100m 200m on the spot on the spot.

S Easdale 2A2

Highland Arts Exhibition. **GPS**: n56,29521 w5,64926.

10 £10 WC. **Location:** Rural, simple, quiet.
Surface: metalled. 01/01-31/12.
Distance: on the spot on the spot on the spot on the spot 4,5km on the spot on the spot.

S Falkirk 2B2

The Falkirk Wheel, Lime Road. **GPS**: n56,00031 w3,83982.

30 £15 WC. **Location:** Rural, simple, quiet.
Surface: asphalted. 01/01-31/12.
Distance: 4km on the spot on the spot 4km on the spot on the spot on the spot on the spot.
Remarks: Check in during opening hours or call: 01324676912, caution key sanitary £20.

Fettercairn 2B2

Car Park Bowling Club, Fettercairn, Laurencekirk.
GPS: n56,84971 w2,57306.

10 free.
Location: Rural, simple, noisy. **Surface:** asphalted. 01/01-31/12.
Distance: 100m 100m 250m 100m.

Tourist information Fettercairn:

Fettercairn Distillery Visitor Centre Information, Distillery Road. One of Scotland's oldest malt whiskey distilleries. 01/05-30/09, Mon-Sa 10-14.30h. £5.

Fort William 2A2

West End Car Park, Achintore Road. **GPS**: n56,81522 w5,11686.

10 £2.
Location: Urban, simple, noisy. **Surface:** asphalted. 01/01-31/12.
Distance: 200m 200m 200m 200m 200m 10km.

S Girvan 2A3

Harbour street- Henriettastreet. **GPS**: n55,24324 w4,85869.

50 free WC. **Location:** Rural, simple, quiet.
Surface: asphalted. 01/01-31/12.
Distance: 100m sandy beach 50m 50m 500m 600m 50m on the spot.

S Glenbrittle 2A1

Glenbrittle Campsite, Carbost. **GPS**: n57,20251 w6,29021.

33 £9/pp Ch £ 6 WC included £ 6,50.
Location: Rural, comfortable, isolated, quiet.
Surface: grassy/metalled. 01/04-01/10.
Distance: 10km on the spot on the spot on the spot on the spot.

S Hawick 2B3

Common Haugh, Victoria Road. **GPS**: n55,42310 w2,79114.

50 free WC. **Location:** Urban, simple, central.
Surface: asphalted. 01/01-31/12.
Distance: 800m 800m on the spot on the spot on the spot.
Remarks: Max. 24h, special part for motor homes.

S Helensburgh 2B2

W Clyde St. **GPS**: n56,00198 w4,73503.

20 £1.20/h 9-18h WC free. **Location:** Urban, simple, central, noisy. **Surface:** asphalted. 01/01-31/12.
Distance: 200m on the spot on the spot 200m 250m 300m on the spot on the spot.

Helmsdale 2B1

Helmsdale Harbour, Shore Street. **GPS**: n58,11522 w3,65113.

7 free. **Surface:** metalled. 01/01-31/12.
Distance: 200m on the spot 50m 200m on the spot on the spot on the spot.

S Irvine 2B3

Beach Drive. **GPS**: n55,60628 w4,69263.

100 free WC free.
Location: Rural, simple, quiet. **Surface:** asphalted. 01/01-31/12.
Distance: 1,5km 4km on the spot on the spot 1,2km 850m 400m on the spot.
Remarks: At sea, historical centre.

S Jedburgh 2B3

Canongate, 7 Queen Street. **GPS**: n55,47761 w2,55313.

15 free WC free. **Location:** Urban, simple, central, noisy.
Surface: concrete. 01/01-31/12.
Distance: on the spot on the spot 100m on the spot on the spot on the spot.

Remarks: At tourist office.

Kalnakill 2A1

GPS: n57,54182 w5,84807.

4 free. **Location:** Rural, simple, isolated, quiet. **Surface:** asphalted. 01/01-31/12.
Distance: 2,2km.

S Kilchoan 2A2

Far View Campsite, Pier Road. **GPS**: n56,69409 w6,09621.

2 £15 Ch included. **Location:** Rural, comfortable, isolated, quiet. **Surface:** grassy/gravel. 01/01-31/12.
Distance: 1,5km 500m 500m 500m on the spot on the spot.
Remarks: Ferry boat to Isle of Mull 400m.

Kilchoan 2A2

Kilchoan Ferry Terminal, Pier Road. **GPS**: n56,69008 w6,09603.

15 free. **Location:** Rural, simple, isolated, quiet. **Surface:** asphalted. 01/01-31/12.
Distance: 2km on the spot on the spot 1km.

S Kirkcudbright 2B3

Beaconsfield Place. **GPS**: n54,83707 w4,05045.

5 free WC free.
Location: Simple, central, noisy. **Surface:** asphalted. 01/01-31/12.
Distance: on the spot on the spot on the spot on the spot on the spot on the spot on the spot.

Kylesku 2B1

A894. **GPS**: n58,25756 w5,02726.

10 free. **Location:** Rural, simple, isolated, quiet. **Surface:** asphalted. 01/01-31/12.
Distance: 1Km on the spot on the spot 1km.

Lendalfoot 2A3

8 A77 Girvan. **GPS**: n55,16301 w4,94904.

4 free. **Location:** Rural, simple, noisy. **Surface:** concrete. 01/01-31/12.
Distance: 500m on the spot.

S Lochgelly 2B2

Lochore Meadows Country Park. **GPS**: n56,15061 w3,33675.
£10 Ch. **Location:** Isolated, quiet.
Distance: 1,6km on the spot on the spot 1,6km on the spot on the spot.
Remarks: Arrival <17h.

S Lochwinnoch 2B2

Castle Semple Country Park, Lochlip Road.
GPS: n55,79569 w4,62302.

10 free WC free. **Location:** Rural, simple, quiet.
Surface: asphalted. 01/01-31/12.
Distance: 500m on the spot on the spot on the spot 300m on the spot on the spot.

Luskentyre 2A1

A859. **GPS**: n57,86673 w6,91537.

3 £5. **Location:** Rural, simple, isolated, noisy.
Surface: asphalted/metalled. 01/01-31/12.
Distance: on the spot on the spot.
Remarks: Online payment with PayPal.

Moffat 2B3

Grey Mare's Tail Nature reserve, A708, Moffat Water Valley.
GPS: n55,41779 w3,28646.

10 £2. **Location:** Rural, simple, isolated, quiet.
Surface: gravel. 01/01-31/12.
Distance: on the spot on the spot.

New Abbey 2B3

Parking Sweetheart Abbey, A710, Main Street.
GPS: n54,98070 w3,61966.

GB

6 free WC. **Location:** Simple, quiet. **Surface:** asphalted/metalled.
01/01-31/12.
Distance: 200m on the spot 200m 200m on the spot.

Newton Steward 2B3

Galloway Forrest Park. **GPS**: n54,97358 w4,43804.

3 free. **Location:** Rural, simple, isolated, quiet.
Surface: asphalted/gravel. 01/01-31/12.
Distance: 6km 500m on the spot.

Oban 2A2

Lochavullin road. **GPS**: n56,40948 w5,47142.

4 £10. **Location:** Urban, simple, noisy.
Surface: asphalted. 01/01-31/12.
Distance: 400m 400m on the spot 400m.
Remarks: At tourist office.

Oban 2A2

The Wide Mouthed Frog, A85. **GPS**: n56,44856 w5,4319.

5 free. **Location:** Urban, simple, noisy.
Surface: gravel.
01/01-31/12.
Distance: 6km on the spot on the spot on the spot 5km.

Pairc Niseaboist 2A1

Talla na Mara, Island of Harris, A859. **GPS**: n57,85948 w6,99296.
3 £ 24 Ch WC. **Location:** Rural. **Surface:** unpaved.
01/04-31/10.
Distance: on the spot.
Remarks: Beautiful panorama.

Rhugarbh 2A2

Parking Scottish Sea Life Sanctuary, A828 Rhugharb - Barcaldine.
GPS: n56,51731 w5,34679.

10 free. **Surface:** metalled. 01/01-31/12.

Scourie 2B1

Scourie Campsite, A894. **GPS**: n58,35157 w5,15523.

50 £20 Ch WC included £2/1.
Location: Rural, comfortable, isolated, quiet.
Surface: grassy/metalled. 01/04-30/09.
Distance: 200m on the spot on the spot on the spot 200m on the spot.

Seilebost 2A1

Seilebost School, Isle of Harris, A859 11. **GPS**: n57,86873 w6,95357.
4 £ 21 . **Location:** Rural. **Surface:** metalled.
01/04-31/10.
Distance: 200m.
Remarks: Playground.

Seilebost 2A1

A859. **GPS**: n57,86615 w6,88152.

10 £5. **Location:** Rural, simple, quiet. **Surface:** gravel/metalled.
01/01-31/12.
Distance: 6km 2km.
Remarks: Online payment with PayPal.

Shawbost 2A1

Eilean Fraoich Camp Site. **GPS**: n58,31989 w6,68753.

25 £14-18 Ch £ 4 WC included £4/3 £ 5/day.
Location: Rural, comfortable, isolated, quiet.
Surface: gravel/metalled. Easter-01/10.
Distance: 500m 1km 500m on the spot.

Sligachan 2A1

Sligachan Campsite, A87. **GPS**: n57,29146 w6,17696.

100 £7.50/pp Ch £ 5 WC £ 3 included.
Location: Rural, simple, isolated, quiet. **Surface:** grassy/gravel.
01/04-15/10.
Distance: 10km on the spot 100m 10km on the spot 100m.

Tomintoul 2B2

Tomintoul Bowlingclub Campsite, 10 Tomnabat Lane.
GPS: n57,25073 w3,37636.

5 £7 WC included. **Location:** Urban, simple, central, quiet.
Surface: gravel. 01/01-31/12.
Distance: 300m 300m 300m 300m 300m 300m 12km.
Remarks: Money in envelope in mail box.

Tourist information Tomintoul:

Tourist Information Centre, The Square.
Tomintoul Museum, Tomnabat Lane. Historical regional museum.
Easter-31/10, mon-sa 9.30-12h, 14-16h.

Uig 2A1

Uig Bay Campsite, A87. **GPS**: n57,58559 w6,37971.

15 £7.50/pp Ch £ 4 WC £ 3 included.
Location: Rural, simple, isolated, quiet. **Surface:** gravel/metalled.
01/01-31/12.
Distance: 200m on the spot 100m 200m on the spot.

Wales

Abergynolwyn 1F2

Riverside Guest House, Llanegryn Street.
GPS: n52,64584 w3,95856.

5 £10/night Ch included £ 6/night.
Location: Rural, comfortable, central, quiet. **Surface:** grassy/metalled.
01/01-31/12.
Remarks: Arrival <18h, narrow entrance (2.6m), Snowdonia National Park.

Brecon 1F2

The Watton Car Park, Heol Gouesnou. **GPS**: n51,94609 w3,38531.

25 £0.70/h, max. £3.20 8-18h, overnight stay free WC free,150m.
Location: Urban, simple, quiet. **Surface:** asphalted.
01/01-31/12.
Distance: on the spot on the spot.
Remarks: 1 night per 7 nights.

Brecon 1F2

Canal Road Car/Coach-Lorry Park, Canal Road.
GPS: n51,94486 w3,38993.

GB

10 £0.70/h, max. £3.20 8-18h, overnight stay free.
Location: Urban, simple, central, quiet. **Surface:** asphalted.
01/01-31/12.
Distance: 100m 100m.
Remarks: 1 night per 7 nights.

Brecon 1F2

The Promenade Car Park, Fenni-Fach Rd. **GPS**: n51,95089 w3,4036.

25 £0.70/h, max. £3.20 8-18h, overnight stay free.
Location: Urban, simple, isolated, quiet. **Surface:** asphalted.
01/01-31/12.
Distance: 600m on the spot 700m.
Remarks: 1 night per 7 nights.

Builth Wells 1F2

The Groe Car Park, The Strand. **GPS**: n52,14969 w3,40252.

20 £0.70/h, max. £3.20 8-18h, overnight stay free WC.
Location: Urban, simple, quiet.
Surface: asphalted. 01/01-31/12.
Distance: on the spot on the spot on the spot.
Remarks: 1 night per 7 nights.

Builth Wells 1F2

Smithfield Car Park, Brecon Rd. **GPS**: n52,14714 w3,40261.

50 £0.70/h, max. £3.20 8-18h, overnight stay free.
Location: Urban, simple, central. **Surface:** asphalted.
01/01-31/12.
Distance: 200m.
Remarks: 1 night per 7 nights.

Crickhowell 1F2

Beaufort Street Car Park, Greenhill Way. **GPS**: n51,85838 w3,13557.

8 £0.70/h, max. £3.20 8-18h, overnight stay free.
Location: Urban, simple, central, quiet. **Surface:** asphalted.
01/01-31/12.
Distance: 50m.
Remarks: 1 night per 7 nights.

Hay-on-Wye 1F2

Oxford Road Car Park, Oxford Road. **GPS**: n52,07316 w3,12592.

25 £0.70/h, max. £3.20 8-18h, overnight stay free WC free.
Location: Urban, simple, central, quiet. **Surface:** asphalted.
01/01-31/12.
Distance: 150m 150m 150m on the spot.
Remarks: 1 night per 7 nights.

Knighton 1F2

Bowling Green Lane Car Park, Bowling Green Lane.
GPS: n52,34324 w3,04553.

30 £0.70/h, max. £3.20 8-18h, overnight stay free WC free.
Location: Rural, simple, central, quiet. **Surface:** asphalted.
01/01-31/12.
Distance: 200m 300m on the spot.
Remarks: 1 night per 7 nights.

Llandrindod Wells 1F2

High Street Car Park, High Street. **GPS**: n52,24151 w3,38042.

30 £0.70/h, max. £3.20 8-18h, overnight stay free.
Location: Urban, simple, central. **Surface:** asphalted.
01/01-31/12.
Distance: 150m on the spot.
Remarks: 1 night per 7 nights, max. 6m.

Llandudno Junction 1F1

Conwy Motorhome Stopover, 40 Conwy Rd.
GPS: n53,28441 w3,81271.
8 £10 Ch . **Location:** Urban, central, quiet.
01/01-31/12.
Distance: on the spot 500m on the spot.
Remarks: Arrival <17h, at motorhome dealer.

Llandysul 1E2

Penrhiwgaled Arms, Cross Inn. **GPS**: n52,18959 w4,35595.
5 £5.
Distance: on the spot.

Llanidloes 1F2

Mount Street Car Park, Mount Lane. **GPS**: n52,44750 w3,53938.

12 £0.70/h, max. £3.20 8-18h, night £5.
Location: Urban, simple, central, quiet. **Surface:** asphalted.
01/01-31/12.
Distance: on the spot 100m 100m 100m.
Remarks: 1 night per 7 nights.

Moelfre 1F1

Lligwy Bay. **GPS**: n53,35910 w4,26132.
£10/night.
Remarks: Beach parking.

Nantgaredig 1E2

Railway Hotel, B4310. **GPS**: n51,86533 w4,18976.
5 £5 WC. 01/01-31/12.

New Quay 1E2

Parking Far Field, Towyn Rd. **GPS**: n52,21181 w4,36087.

£6/day £8/night. **Surface:** unpaved. 01/01-31/12.
Distance: on the spot 300m 150m.

Newton 1F2

Back Lane Car Park, Back Lane. **GPS**: n52,51534 w3,31735.

40 £0.70/h, max. £3.20 8-18h, night £5 WC free.
Location: Urban, simple, central, quiet.
Surface: asphalted. 01/01-31/12.
Distance: 150m on the spot on the spot.
Remarks: 1 night per 7 nights.

Newton 1F2

The Gravel Car Park, Heol Les Herbiers. **GPS**: n52,51421 w3,31167.

25 £0.70/h, max. £3.20 8-18h, night £5.
Location: Urban, simple, central. **Surface:** asphalted.
01/01-31/12.
Distance: 250m 50m 250m.
Remarks: 1 night per 7 nights.

Presteigne 1F2

Hereford Street Car Park, Hereford Street.
GPS: n52,27245 w3,00488.

10 £0.70/h, max. £3.20 8-18h, overnight stay free WC free.
Location: Urban, simple, central, quiet. **Surface:** asphalted.
01/01-31/12.
Distance: 100m on the spot.
Remarks: 1 night per 7 nights, max. 6m.

GB

Welshpool 1F2

Berriew Street Car Park, Berriew Rd. **GPS**: n52,65875 w3,14806.

30 £0.70/h, max. £3.20 8-18h, night £5 WCfree.
Location: Urban, simple, central, quiet. **Surface:** asphalted.
01/01-31/12.
Distance: 200m 500m.
Remarks: 1 night per 7 nights.

Welshpool 1F2

Church Street Car Park, Church Street. **GPS**: n52,66031 w3,1438.

25 £0.70/h, max. £3.20 8-18h, night £5 WCfree. **Location:** Urban, simple, central, quiet. **Surface:** asphalted.
01/01-31/12.
Distance: 150m 300m.
Remarks: 1 night per 7 nights.

England

Abingdon 1G2

Rye Farm Pay & Display car park, Bridge Street, A415.
GPS: n51,66746 w1,27799.

8 £7.30/24h WC.
Location: Urban, simple. **Surface:** asphalted. 01/01-31/12.
Distance: 500m 500m 800m.
Remarks: Max. 24h, first call or mail, carparks.southandvale.uk@parkindigo.com, 01235 470118.

Aldershot 1G3

Parsons Barracks Car park, Ordnance Road.
GPS: n51,24979 w0,75731.

10 £0.50/h, night £1. **Location:** Urban, simple.
Surface: asphalted. 01/01-31/12.
Distance: 550m 550m.

Appledore 1E3

Churchfields Car Park, The Quay. **GPS**: n51,05464 w4,19135.

25 £5 18-10h, £3 day WCfree. **Location:** Urban, simple, quiet.
Surface: asphalted. 01/01-31/12.
Distance: 150m 50m 200m.
Remarks: Max. 2 nights, min. 6m space between motorhomes.

Arundel 1G3

Mill Road Car Park, Mill Road. **GPS**: n50,85392 w0,55067.

50 £10. **Location:** Simple, quiet.
Surface: grassy. Sa-Su.
Distance: 100m 100m 200m.
Remarks: At castle, arrival 8><16h.

Bideford 1E3

Riverbank (long stay) Car Park, Kingsley road.
GPS: n51,02086 w4,20386.

20 £5 18-10h, £3 day. **Location:** Urban, simple, quiet.
Surface: asphalted. 01/01-31/12.
Distance: 1,5km 50m 500m 1km 500m.
Remarks: Max. 2 nights, min. 6m space between motorhomes.

Bourton-on-the-Water 1G2

Bourton Rovers, Rissington Road. **GPS**: n51,87995 w1,7513.

5 £10 Ch WC free,Password at the bar.
Location: Rural, simple, central, quiet. **Surface:** grassy.
01/01-31/12.
Distance: 500m 500m 500m.

Bourton-on-the-Water 1G2

Bourton Vale Car & Coach Park, Station Rd.
GPS: n51,88512 w1,75471.

10 9-18h parking rate, overnight stay £8 WCfree.
Location: Urban, simple, central, quiet. **Surface:** asphalted.
01/01-31/12.
Distance: 200m on the spot on the spot.

Brampton 2B3

Blenkinsopp Castle Inn. **GPS**: n54,97334 w2,52267.
5 £10 . **Surface:** gravel.
Distance: on the spot.

Bude 1E3

Bude Town Football Club, Broadclose Hill.
GPS: n50,83000 w4,5359.

20 £8. **Location:** Simple. **Surface:** grassy. 01/01-31/12.
Distance: 500m.
Remarks: At football ground.

Bury St Edmunds 1H2

Ram Meadow Carpark Annexe, Cotton Lane.
GPS: n52,24775 e0,71893.

5 £2.20 8-18h, overnight stay free WCfree.
Location: Urban, simple, central, quiet. **Surface:** asphalted.
01/01-31/12.
Distance: 300m 300m 300m.
Remarks: Max. 1 night.

Canterbury 1H3

New Dover Road Park&Ride, New Dover Road.
GPS: n51,26199 e1,10258.

24 £3 Ch WCincluded.
Location: Rural, simple, isolated, quiet. **Surface:** asphalted.
Acces Mo-Sa 6.30-20.30h, exit 24/24.
Distance: Vintage Inn 100m on the spot.

Canterbury 1H3

Canterbury Coach Park, Kingsmead Road.
GPS: n51,28470 e1,08340.

10 £15/12h. **Location:** Urban. **Surface:** asphalted.
01/01-31/12.
Distance: 650m 650m 100m 150m.

Cheltenham 1F2

The Gloucester Old Spot, Tewkesbury Road, A4109.
GPS: n51,93325 w2,14881.

5 free, use of a meal obligated WC included, during opening hours. **Location:** Rural, simple, isolated. **Surface:** gravel/sand. 01/01-31/12.
Distance: 500m on the spot.

S Chester 1F1

Car Park, Little Roodee, Castle Road. **GPS:** n53,18447 w2,89245.
£5.80, overnight stay £1.50 WC. 01/01-31/12.
Distance: 3,5km.
Remarks: Along the Dee river, gate closed from 22.30-6h.

Cirencester 1F2

Old Cricklade Road lorry park, Cricklade Road.
GPS: n51,70760 w1,955.

20 £6.20. **Location:** Urban, simple. **Surface:** asphalted. 01/01-31/12.
Distance: 1,5km 50m 150m.
Remarks: Near McDonalds.

S Cirencester 1F2

The Crown Inn, High Street, Cerny Wick. **GPS:** n51,66264 w1,88933.

5 £10 Ch WC during opening hours.
Location: Rural, simple.
Surface: grassy/metalled. 01/01-31/12.
Distance: on the spot.

Clovelly 1E3

Clovelly Visitors Centre. **GPS:** n50,99867 w4,40386.
£7.25/pp, child £4.40. **Surface:** gravel.

S Crediton 1F3

Thelbridge Cross Inn, Thelbridge Hill. **GPS:** n50,89530 w3,72228.

6 £5 (2x)£ 3,50.
Location: Isolated, quiet. **Surface:** asphalted. 01/01-31/12.
Distance: 14km on the spot.
Remarks: Discount at restaurant.

Dover 1H3

Marine Parade. **GPS:** n51,12350 e1,31710.

10 £1.10/h, max. £8.25, overnight stay free. **Surface:** asphalted. 01/01-31/12.
Distance: on the spot 100m.
Remarks: Max. 24h, max 3,5t.

S Great Missenden 1G2

The Black Horse, Aylesbury Road. **GPS:** n51,71019 w0,71215.
5 guests free WC. **Surface:** metalled.
Distance: 800m on the spot.

S Hayling Island 1G3

West Beach Car Park, Sea Front. **GPS:** n50,78530 w1,0007.

40 8-22h parking rate, max. £6, overnight stay £10, 01/03-01/10 £15 Ch WC included £ 1,At TI, 7 Sea-Front (600m).
Location: Rural, simple, quiet. **Surface:** grassy/gravel. 01/01-31/12.
Distance: on the spot on the spot 600m.
Remarks: Max. 72h, key service at Touristinformation (900m).

Helmsley 1G1

Cleveland Way. **GPS:** n54,24619 w1,06617.
6 9-18.30h parking rate, overnight stay free. **Location:** Central. 01/01-31/12.
Distance: 500m 500m.

Holsworthy 1E3

The Manor Car Park, Western Road. **GPS:** n50,81133 w4,35282.

6 £5 18-10h, £3 day. **Location:** Urban, simple, quiet.
Surface: asphalted. 01/01-31/12.
Distance: on the spot 150m 150m.
Remarks: Max. 2 nights, min. 6m space between motorhomes.

S Huntingdon 1G2

Wellsbridge Motorhomes Sales, Ramsey Forty Foot, Ramsey.
GPS: n52,47540 w0,08834.

5 £5 WC. **Location:** Rural, simple, isolated, quiet.
Surface: asphalted. 02/01-23/12.
Distance: on the spot.

S Ipswich 1H2

Burnt House Farm, Wash Lane, Witnesham.
GPS: n52,11418 e1,20094.

5 £9 Ch WC included. **Location:** Rural, comfortable, isolated, quiet. **Surface:** grassy/metalled. 01/01-31/12.
Distance: 2km 2km.

Ipswich 1H2

Orwell Crossing Lorry Park, A14 Eastbound, Nacton.
GPS: n52,02473 e1,22678.

20 £18/18h. **Location:** Motorway, simple, noisy.
Surface: asphalted. 01/01-31/12.
Distance: on the spot.

S Ivybridge 1E3

Lee Mill Services, A38. **GPS:** n50,38493 w3,97041.

10 £17.50/night WC included. **Location:** Simple, noisy.
Surface: asphalted. 01/01-31/12.
Distance: on the spot 500m.
Remarks: Behind petrol station, discount at restaurant £5.

S Liverpool 1F1

Liverpool Marina, Coburg Wharf. **GPS:** n53,39051 w2,9864.
10 £18/24h WC .
Location: Urban. **Surface:** metalled. 01/01-31/12.
Distance: 1,5km on the spot 100m on the spot 400m.

Lydford 1E3

The Castle Inn. **GPS:** n50,64359 w4,10893.
4 guests free. **Location:** Simple, quiet. 01/01-31/12.
Distance: on the spot.

S Maidstone 1H3

Maidstone Services, M20. **GPS:** n51,26687 e0,61502.

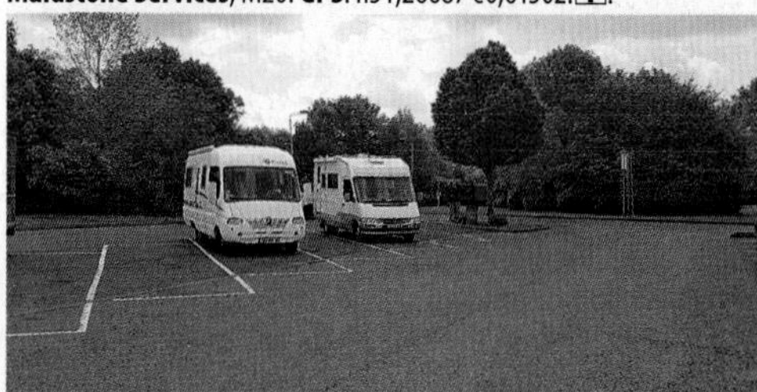

8 £20/24h, first 2 hours free WC against payment.
Location: Motorway, simple, noisy. **Surface:** asphalted. 01/01-31/12.
Distance: 200m on the spot 150m.
Remarks: Payment with mobile phone.

Tourist information Maidstone:

M Museum of Kent Life, Lock Lane, Sandling. History and traditions of Kent. 10-17h.

S Mevagissey 1E3

Willow Car & Coach Park, Valley Road. **GPS:** n50,27155 w4,79044.

GB

10 10-18h parking rate, overnight stay £7.50 on demand.
Location: Simple, central.
Surface: metalled. 01/01-31/12.
Distance: 150m 1km 300m.

New Milton 1F3

Orchard Lakes, New Lane, Bashley. **GPS**: n50,77182 w1,6645.

5 £15 Ch included. **Location:** Rural, comfortable, isolated, quiet. **Surface:** grassy/metalled. 01/01-31/12.
Distance: 400m 6,5km on the spot New Forest.
Remarks: Arrival >18h.

Newhaven 1G3

West Side Promenade. **GPS**: n50,78189 e0,05530.

30 £3. **Surface:** concrete. Easter-30/09.
Distance: 2km on the spot on the spot 400m 850m 2km.
Remarks: Arrival 8><17h.

Newnham on Severn 1F2

Elton Farm, Littledean Road, A4151. **GPS**: n51,82355 w2,44753.
5 £5 Ch. **Location:** Rural, simple, isolated.
Surface: grassy. 01/01-31/12.
Distance: on the spot on the spot.

Northcumberland 2C2

Hazlehead Park, Hazledene Road. **GPS**: n57,13987 w2,17956.

20 free. **Location:** Simple, noisy.
Surface: asphalted. 01/01-31/12.
Distance: 6km 2km 2km on the spot.

Northcumberland 2C2

The Barn at Beal. **GPS**: n55,67754 w1,89434.

9 £15 Ch £5 WC included. **Location:** Rural, comfortable, quiet. **Surface:** gravel/metalled. 01/01-31/12.
Distance: 2km on the spot on the spot on the spot.
Remarks: Possibility for reservation.

Oldham 1F1

The Hawthorn, Roundthorn Road. **GPS**: n53,53352 w2,08637.
5 £15 £ 2,50/night WC . 01/01-31/12.
Distance: 3km.

Pickering 1G1

Antiques Centre, Southgate. **GPS**: n54,24413 w0,78026.

5 £10 Ch. **Location:** Simple. **Surface:** asphalted. 01/01-31/12.
Distance: 500m.

Praa Sands 1E3

Sydney Cove Car Park, Castle Drive. **GPS**: n50,10440 w5,3919.

10 £8/24h. **Location:** Simple.
Distance: 100m 100m.

Rake 1G3

The Flying Bull, London Road. **GPS**: n51,04419 w0,85418.

5 £5 included WC at restaurant.
Location: Rural, isolated, quiet. **Surface:** grassy. 01/01-31/12.
Distance: 3km on the spot.
Remarks: Max. 1 night, check in at restaurant.

Rye 1H3

River Haven Hotel, Winchelsea Road. **GPS**: n50,94880 e0,72990.

5 £5. **Surface:** gravel. 01/01-31/12.
Distance: 400m on the spot 100m.
Remarks: Pay at hotel.

Scarborough 1G1

South Moor Farm, Dalby Forest Drive. **GPS**: n54,30049 w0,61169.
5 £10 Ch. **Location:** Rural, simple. **Surface:** grassy.
01/01-31/12.

Settle 1F1

Lower Greenfoot. **GPS**: n54,06644 w2,27563.
3 day: parking rate, overnight stay £5.
Surface: asphalted. 01/01-31/12.
Distance: 500m 500m 500m.

Settle 1F1

Helwith Bridge Inn, Austwick Road, Helwith Bridge.
GPS: n54,12127 w2,29113.
5 guests free. **Location:** Rural.
Surface: gravel. 01/01-31/12.
Distance: on the spot on the spot on the spot.

Sewerby 1G1

The Ship Inn, Cliff Road. **GPS**: n54,10167 w0,16411.
5 £15 Ch. **Surface:** unpaved.
Distance: on the spot.

Shrewsbury 1F2

Halfway House, Main Rd. **GPS**: n52,69799 w2,97851.
guests free . **Surface:** asphalted/metalled.
Remarks: Free, use of a meal obligated.

Shrewsbury 1F2

The Red Barn Inn, Longden Road. **GPS**: n52,69786 w2,76066.
3 guests free. **Surface:** asphalted/metalled. 01/01-31/12.
Distance: 1km.
Remarks: Free, use of a meal obligated.

Skipton 1G1

Coach Street car park. **GPS**: n53,96130 w2,01981.
3 10-18h parking rate, overnight stay £5. **Location:** Urban, central, noisy. **Surface:** asphalted. 01/01-31/12.
Distance: on the spot on the spot on the spot.

Southampton 1G3

Long Stay Car Park, West Quay Road. **GPS**: n50,90090 w1,4083.

day max. £7.50, night £2. 01/01-31/12.
Distance: 800m 800m 800m.
Remarks: Max 3,5t.

St Austell 1E3

Edgemoor, Enniscaven, St.Dennis. **GPS**: n50,39636 w4,8676.

5 £5/night WC included. **Location:** Comfortable, quiet.
Surface: grassy/metalled. 01/01-31/12.
Distance: St.Austell 14,5km on the spot on the spot.

St Ives 1G2

The Seven Wives, Ramsey road. **GPS**: n52,33193 w0,07634.

5 £5 Ch £ 6/night WC. **Location:** Urban, simple, central. **Surface:** metalled. 01/01-31/12.
Distance: 1,4km on the spot.

St Jidgey 1E3

Halfway House Inn. **GPS**: n50,48949 w4,89943.
4 £10, guests free. **Location:** Rural, isolated, quiet.
Surface: grassy.
Distance: on the spot.

Staple Fitzpaine 1F3

Home Mead, New Road. **GPS**: n50,95970 w3,0489.

GB

5 £5 included. **Location:** Rural, isolated, quiet.
Surface: grassy. 01/01-31/12.
Distance: on the spot.

Stoke St Gregory 1F3

The Royal Oak, The Square. **GPS**: n51,04050 w2,9318.

5 guests free Chfree £ 4. **Surface:** asphalted.
01/01-31/12.
Distance: on the spot 50m 50m.
Remarks: Parking in front of church.

Stratford-upon-Avon 1G2

Stratford Marina Car Park, Bridgeway. **GPS**: n52,19280 w1,70154.

10 9-18h £8, overnight stay £15. **Location:** Urban, simple, central. **Surface:** asphalted. 01/01-31/12.
Distance: 200m 200m 200m.

Stratford-upon-Avon 1G2

The New Inn Hotel, Clifford Chambers. **GPS**: n52,16929 w1,7168.

5 £8 £ 4,80.
Location: Rural, simple. **Surface:** grassy. 01/01-31/12.
Distance: on the spot on the spot.

Tourist information Stratford-upon-Avon:
Birthplace of William Shakespeare.

Tarrington 1F2

The Tarrington Arms, Ledbury road. **GPS**: n52,06473 w2,5604.

5 free WCfree. **Location:** Rural, simple.
Surface: metalled.
Distance: 200m on the spot.

Tenby 1E2

Carew Airfield & Pavilion, Sageston. **GPS**: n51,69362 w4,80973.

5 £15-20/night Ch WCincluded.
Location: Comfortable, quiet. **Surface:** concrete. 01/01-31/12.
Distance: 150m 8km 500m 1,5km 1,5km.

Thaxted 1G2

Margaret Street Car Park, Margaret Street.
GPS: n51,95530 e0,34328.

2 free WCfree. **Location:** Urban, simple, central, quiet.
Surface: concrete. 01/01-31/12.
Distance: 150m 150m.
Remarks: Max. 48h in fortnight.

Tintagel 1E3

King Arthur's Car Park, Fore Street. **GPS**: n50,66441 w4,75119.

50 £3.90 10-16h, £3 16-10h WC.
Location: Simple. **Surface:** asphalted.
Distance: on the spot on the spot 100m.
Remarks: Opposite Tintagel Old Post Office.

Tintagel 1E3

Mayfair Car Park, Fore Street. **GPS**: n50,66386 w4,75061.

30 £2 8.00-20h, £3.50 20-08h. **Location:** Urban, simple, central.
Surface: grassy. 01/01-31/12.
Distance: on the spot 100m on the spot.
Remarks: Next to King Arthur's Car Park.

Tintagel 1E3

Sword in Stone Car Park, Bossiney Road. **GPS**: n50,66257 w4,74763.

20 £5/24h.
Location: Urban, simple. **Surface:** asphalted. 01/01-31/12.
Distance: 150m 250m.

Tourist information Tintagel:
Tintagel Old Post Office, Fore Street. 600 year-old traditional Cornish Longhouse.
King Arthur's Castle, Castle Road. 25/03-30/10.

Torrington 1E3

Sydney House Car Park, South Street. **GPS**: n50,95121 w4,14438.

20 £5 18-10h, £3 day. **Location:** Urban, simple, quiet.
Surface: asphalted. 01/01-31/12.
Distance: 300m 250m 250m.
Remarks: Max. 2 nights, min. 6m space between motorhomes.

Westward Ho! 1E3

Main Car Park, Golf Links Rd. **GPS**: n51,04069 w4,23728.

8 £7, 01/11-14/03 £3, night £5.
Location: Urban, simple, central, quiet. **Surface:** asphalted.
01/01-31/12.
Distance: on the spot 200m 200m.
Remarks: Max. 5000kg, min. 6m space between motorhomes.

Whaplode St Catherines 1G2

The Bleu Bell Inn, Cranesgate S. **GPS**: n52,75956 w0,0155.
5 £5, free with a meal Ch (2x)£ 2,50/night.
Location: Simple. 01/01-31/12 Mo.
Distance: on the spot.

Winchester 1G3

Coach Park, Worthy Lane, B3044. **GPS**: n51,06931 w1,31628.

10 £7, overnight stay free.
Location: Urban, simple. **Surface:** asphalted.
Distance: 850m 500m 50m.
Remarks: Max. 24h.

Yeovil 1F3

Cartgate and Picnic Area, A303/A3088 roundabout.
GPS: n50,96926 w2,74087.

20 free WC Password at the restaurant. **Location:** Motorway, simple, noisy. **Surface:** asphalted. 01/01-31/12.
Distance: 15km on the spot.

York 1G1

Bleak House Farm, 138 Mitchel's Ln. **GPS**: n53,93928 w1,05883.

GB

5 £8 Ch included. **Location:** Rural. **Surface:** grassy.
01/01-31/12.
Distance: 3km 1km 200m on the spot on the spot.

Jersey

S Saint Peter 15A2

Hideaway Motorhome Stopover, Beaumont Hill.
GPS: n49,20084 w2,16652.
5 € 16 Ch (5x)included. **Surface:** gravel/sand.
01/01-31/12.
Distance: 900m 900m 800m 900m 800m 800m 800m.
Remarks: Adults only.

GB

Greece

Capital: Athens
Government: Parliamentary democracy
Official Language: Greek
Population: 10,773,253 (2016)
Area: 131,957 km²

General information
Dialling code: 0030
General emergency: 112
Currency: Euro

Regulations for overnight stays
Wild camping and overnight parking is not officially allowed. Overnight parking places mentioned here are not official motorhome stopovers but tolerated areas.

Additional public holidays 2018
January 6 Epiphany
February 19 Ash Monday, 41 days before Easter
March 25 Independence Day
April 8-9 Orthodox Easter
May 1 Labor Day
August 15 Assumption of the Virgin Mary
October 28 National Holiday, Ochi day

Time Zone
Winter (Standard Time) GMT+2
Summer (DST) GMT+3

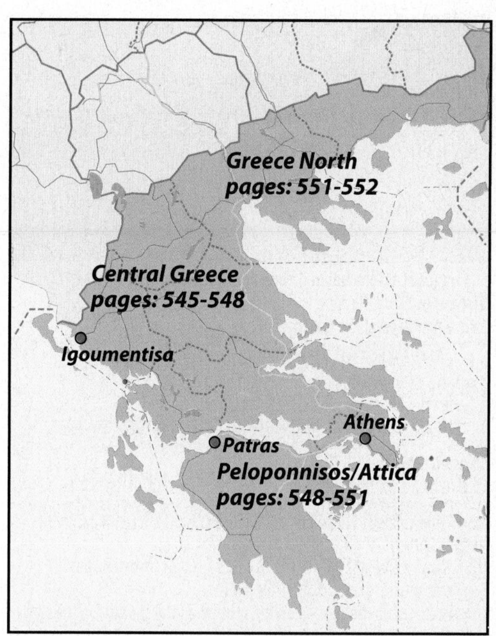

Central Greece

Achillio 35G2
Epar. Od. Archilliou-Glifas. **GPS**: n39,00943 e22,95758.
Distance: on the spot on the spot on the spot.

Agios Nikolaos 35F2
GPS: n38,34959 e22,15661.
01/10-30/04.
Remarks: Parking at harbour.

Ammoudia 35F2
GPS: n39,23989 e20,48116.
Surface: sand.
Distance: on the spot on the spot on the spot 200m 50m.
Remarks: Beach parking.

Ammoudia 35F2
GPS: n39,23636 e20,48073.

Surface: gravel/sand.
Distance: on the spot 50m on the spot 100m 250m.
Remarks: At harbour.

Arahova 35G2
GPS: n38,47948 e22,58164.
01/01-31/12.

Arillas 35E2
Restaurant Soukas, Aglias-Platarias. **GPS**: n39,35278 e20,28861.

€ 8, free for clients WC.
Location: Rural. **Surface:** grassy/sand. 01/05-01/10.
Distance: on the spot on the spot.

Armirichi Beach 35H2
GPS: n38,26129 e24,25115.
2 free. **Location:** Isolated.
Surface: gravel/sand. 01/01-31/12.
Distance: on the spot on the spot.
Remarks: Beach parking.

Boukka 35F2
GPS: n38,93125 e21,14200.

Surface: sand.
Distance: on the spot 100m.
Remarks: Next to sports fields, beach parking.

Chiliadou 35F2
GPS: n38,39408 e21,92096.

Surface: gravel. 01/01-31/12.
Distance: Nafpaktos 7km on the spot 200m.
Remarks: Beach parking.

Chorefto 35G1
GPS: n39,45168 e23,12364.

free. **Surface:** unpaved. 01/01-01/12.
Distance: Sandy beach.
Remarks: Parking at the beach.

Corfu 35E1
Dionysus, Dassia. **GPS**: n39,66472 e19,84440.
€ 18,20-21 Ch WC. 01/04-20/10.

Corfu 35E1
Dolphin Camping, Sidari. **GPS**: n39,78890 e19,72354.
€ 12-14,10 Ch WC. 01/07-10/09.

Corfu 35E1
Karda Beach, Dassia. **GPS**: n39,68611 e19,83861.
€ 22,30-23,60 Ch WC. 26/04-01/09.
Distance: on the spot.

Tourist information Corfu:
Esplanada, Kerkyra (Corfu). Meeting point for inhabitants and tourists.
Kerkyra (Corfu).
Frurion, Kerkyra (Corfu). Citadel, 1550.
Aqualand, Corfu Water Park, Ag.Ioannis. Leisure pool park.

Damasta 35G2
GPS: n38,80436 e22,49485.

GR

3 free. **Location:** Isolated. **Surface:** asphalted. 01/01-31/12.
Distance: on the spot.
Remarks: Natural hot spring pond.

Delphi 35G2

Apollon. GPS: n38,48388 e22,47550.
Ch. 01/01-31/12.

Delphi 35G2

Chrissa. GPS: n38,47267 e22,46206.
55 € 18,50-22,50 Ch WC. 01/01-31/12.

Delphi 35G2

Delphi Camping. GPS: n38,47833 e22,47450.
€ 21,50-22,40 Ch WC. **Location:** Rural.
Surface: grassy/gravel. 01/04-31/10.
Distance: on the spot on the spot on the spot on the spot on the spot.

Tourist information Delphi:
Site of Delphi. Archeological site. 7.30-17.30h holiday. € 9.

Dodoni 35F1

Amphitheater. GPS: n39,54606 e20,78466.
15 € 10. **Location:** Rural. **Surface:** grassy. 01/01-31/12.
Distance: 2,1km 500m on the spot.

Eratini 35F2

N48/E65 km 47. **GPS:** n38,33769 e22,19198.

. **Surface:** grassy/sand.
Distance: on the spot on the spot.
Remarks: Beach parking, max 3,5t.

Erétria 35G2

Milos Camping. GPS: n38,39139 e23,77556.
€ 25-32 ChWC. 15/04-30/09.

Tourist information Erétria:
Seaside resort and archological site Antique Eretria.

Gliki 35F2

Taverne Panorama. GPS: n39,32726 e20,61568.

guests free WC. **Surface:** grassy. 01/01-31/12.
Distance: 500m 500m.
Remarks: Along the Acheron river.

Igoumenítsa 35E2

GPS: n39,51540 e20,21087.

10. **Surface:** sand.
Distance: on the spot 100m.
Remarks: Beach parking.

Igoumenítsa 35E2

Grekou. **GPS:** n39,51278 e20,25741.
. 01/01-31/12.
Distance: on the spot 600m on the spot.
Remarks: Parking supermarket at the ring-road 6, dir Ioánnina.

Tourist information Igoumenítsa:
Goumani (titani). Archeological site.

Ioánnina 35F1

Sta Papagou 7. **GPS:** n39,67319 e20,85476.

10 € 12. **Surface:** metalled. 01/01-31/12.
Distance: 100m 100m 100m.
Remarks: Monitored parking.

Ioánnina 35F1

Limnopoula. GPS: n39,67770 e20,84280.
€ 24 Ch.
01/04-15/10.

Tourist information Ioánnina:
Capital of Epirus, important city in the Turkish time.
Perama. Caves.
daily.

Itea 35G2

Ayannis, Kirra. **GPS:** n38,42440 e22,45880.
€ 20-25 Ch. 01/05-30/09.

Tourist information Itea:
Nautical Museum, Mouseio, 4, Galaxídi.

Kalpaki 35E1

GPS: n39,88539 e20,62385.
10 free. **Location:** Rural. **Surface:** gravel. 01/01-31/12.
Distance: 200m 200m.
Remarks: Next to school.

Kanatadika 35G2

Bekatsas. GPS: n38,99389 e23,11551.

10 free for clients WC free,cold shower. **Location:** Comfortable, quiet. **Surface:** grassy.
Distance: 5km Sandy beach on the spot 5km.

Kato Polidendri 35G1

GPS: n39,65558 e22,89326.

10 free free. **Location:** Rural, isolated.
Surface: unpaved. 01/01-01/12.
Distance: 1,5km Sandy beach.

Kipi 35F1

GPS: n39,85738 e20,80483.
25 free. **Location:** Isolated, quiet.
Surface: grassy/gravel. 01/01-31/12.
Distance: 4km 350m 4km on the spot on the spot.

Konitsa 35E1

Kleidonia. **GPS:** n39,96934 e20,66126.
15 free. **Location:** Rural.
Surface: grassy. 01/01-31/12.
Distance: Konitsa 12km on the spot on the spot.

Konitsa 35E1

Epar.Od. Konitsas. **GPS:** n40,05042 e20,75031.
15 free. **Surface:** asphalted. 01/01-31/12.
Distance: on the spot 200m 200m on the spot.

Konitsa 35E1

Bourazani Wild Life Resort, Bourazani.
GPS: n40,05348 e20,62643.
5 € 10 WC included.
Location: Rural, isolated, quiet.
Surface: grassy/gravel. 01/01-31/12.
Distance: Konitsa 14km on the spot on the spot on the spot.
Remarks: At mountainbike trail, discount at restaurant € 5.

Krioneri 35F2

GPS: n38,34397 e21,58823.

. **Surface:** gravel. 01/01-31/12.
Distance: on the spot on the spot 300m.

Lazena 35F1

GPS: n39,51039 e20,97030.
5 free. **Location:** Isolated, quiet.
Surface: grassy/gravel. 01/01-31/12.
Distance: 2,5km.
Remarks: Less suitable for motorhomes >6,5m.

Levkas 35F2

L Camper Stop, Epar. Od. Lefkadas, Apolpainas 225, Lefkada (Levkas).
GPS: n38,82579 e20,70007.
€ 10-20 Ch WC. 01/01-31/12.
Distance: 1km 1,8km 1,5km.
Remarks: Monitored parking 24/24, scooter rental.

Levkas 35F2

Vlycho. **GPS:** n38,68318 e20,69819.
. 01/01-31/12.
Distance: on the spot.
Remarks: Parking on the quay.

Levkas 35F2

Dessimi Beach, Vlicho, Lefkada (Levkas). **GPS:** n38,67250 e20,71100.
€ 28-35 Ch WC. 01/04-30/11.

Levkas 35F2

Poros Beach, Poros, Lefkada (Levkas). **GPS:** n38,64094 e20,69698.
Ch WC. 01/05-30/09.

Ligkiades 35F1

GPS: n39,69080 e20,88842.
5 free. **Location:** Rural, isolated, quiet.
Surface: gravel. 01/01-31/12.
Distance: on the spot on the spot.
Remarks: Beautiful view.

GR

Limnionas Beach 35G2
GPS: n38,71253 e23,75319.

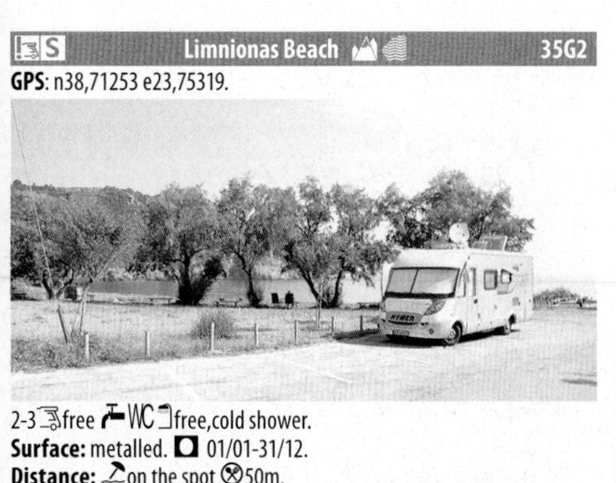

2-3 free WC free,cold shower.
Surface: metalled. 01/01-31/12.
Distance: on the spot 50m.

Loggades 35F1
GPS: n39,66989 e20,92092.
10 free. **Location:** Rural, isolated, quiet.
Surface: gravel. 01/01-31/12.
Distance: 2km on the spot on the spot on the spot.
Remarks: At lake.

Melani Beach 35G1
GPS: n39,25963 e23,29588.

3. **Location:** Isolated. **Surface:** unpaved. 01/01-01/12.
Distance: Sandy beach.
Remarks: Beach parking.

Mesolóngi 35F2
GPS: n38,36358 e21,42016.
. 01/01-31/12.
Remarks: Parking in harbour.

Mesopotamou Beach 35H2
GPS: n38,24347 e24,24729.

. **Surface:** metalled.
Distance: on the spot on the spot.
Remarks: Parking at the beach.

Metéora 35F1
Taverna Arsenis, East Street, Kalambaka. **GPS**: n39,70871 e21,65443.

20 guests free WC free. **Location:** Rural, isolated, quiet.
Surface: metalled. 01/01-31/12.

Metéora 35F1
Camping International Rizos, Kalambaka. **GPS**: n39,69010 e21,64564.
Ch. 01/01-31/12.

Metéora 35F1
Meteora Garden, Kalambaka. **GPS**: n39,70869 e21,60915.
Ch WC. 01/01-31/12.

Metéora 35F1
Vrachos Kastraki, Kastraki. **GPS**: n39,71338 e21,61588.
€ 18 Ch. 01/01-31/12.

Tourist information Metéora:
Important cultural inheritance, 24 monasteries built on enormous sandstone peaks, of which 6 can be visited.
9-13h, 15-17h.
against payment.

Metochou Beach 35G2
GPS: n38,66093 e23,95309.

2-3 free. **Location:** Isolated. **Surface:** asphalted/sand.
01/01-31/12.
Distance: pebbled beach 100m.

Métsovo 35F1
GPS: n39,83457 e21,06543.
10 free. **Location:** Rural, isolated, quiet. **Surface:** grassy/gravel.
01/01-31/12.
Distance: Métsovo 20km on the spot on the spot.
Remarks: Altitude 1350m, at lake.

Métsovo 35F1
Country Cafe. GPS: n39,78073 e21,16253.
4 guests free on demand.
Location: Isolated, quiet.
Surface: gravel.
01/01-31/12.
Distance: Métsovo 3km on the spot on the spot on the spot on the spot.

Tourist information Métsovo:
Traditional mountain village.
Archotiko Tositsa. Restored 18th century mansion, museum or folk art. 8.30-13h, 16-18h. € 3.

Molossi 35E1
O Lófos - Snack Bar Cafe Grill, Voutsaras, E92.
GPS: n39,66408 e20,58164.
5 guests free WC. **Surface:** grassy. 01/01-31/12.
Distance: on the spot.

Mourteri 35G2
GPS: n38,56406 e24,16295.

. **Surface:** asphalted/sand. 01/01-31/12.
Distance: pebbled beach.
Remarks: Parking along coast road.

Nafpaktos 35F2
Xiliadou, N48/E65 km 80,5.
GPS: n38,38186 e21,81809.
. **Surface:** gravel/sand.
01/01-31/12.
Distance: on the spot on the spot nearby.
Remarks: Parking at the beach.

Tourist information Nafpaktos:
Old city with Venetian Castle and circular walled harbor.

Pades 35F1
GPS: n40,04007 e20,91068.
5 free € 5 WC. **Location:** Rural. **Surface:** grassy/gravel.
01/01-31/12.
Distance: on the spot on the spot on the spot.
Remarks: Panoramic view.

Paltsi Beach 35G1
GPS: n39,23624 e23,31497.

± 12 free. **Location:** Isolated. **Surface:** unpaved.
01/01-01/12.
Distance: Sandy beach 100m.
Remarks: Beach parking.

Parga 35E2
Enjoy Lichnos. GPS: n39,28358 e20,43340.
€ 28-36 Ch WC. 01/05-15/10.

Parga 35E2
Valtos Camping.
GPS: n39,28556 e20,38972.
€ 20-21,50 Ch.
01/05-30/09.

Tourist information Parga:
Lively bathing resort.
Necromanteion of Ephyra. Oracle of death.

Perama 35F1
E0 Trikalon Ioanninon. **GPS**: n39,69069 e20,84734.
free. **Location:** Central, quiet.
Surface: asphalted. 01/01-31/12.
Distance: on the spot 200m 200m on the spot.
Remarks: At lake, at mountainbike trail.

Perdika 35E2
GPS: n39,38607 e20,27473.

free.
Distance: Perdika 7km on the spot.
Remarks: Beach parking.

Pilion 35G1
Olizon, Milina. **GPS**: n39,16472 e23,21666.
€ 24-32 Ch WC. 01/05-15/10.

Pilion 35G1
Sikia Fig Tree, Kato Gatzea. **GPS**: n39,31025 e23,10977.
€ 19-24,50 Ch WC. 01/04-31/10.

Tourist information Pilion:
Mythological peninsula, beautiful nature, authentic mountain villages and fishing towns.
Makrinitsa. Village worth seeing, car-free.
Miliés. Folk museum. 01/04-31/10 Tue-Su, 01/11-31/03 Wed-Su.
Archeological Museum, Athanasáki 1, Vólos. Tue-Su holiday.

Plataria 35E2
Nautilos. GPS: n39,44389 e20,25806.
€ 21-23,50 Ch. 01/04-20/10.

Potistika Beach 35G1
GPS: n39,26448 e23,29110.

5 free. **Location:** Isolated. **Surface:** unpaved. 01/01-01/12.
Distance: Sandy beach 100m.
Remarks: Beach parking.

GR

Pramanta 35F1

GPS: n39,51332 e21,08711.
10 € 10 WC included. **Surface:** gravel. 01/01-31/12.
Distance: Pramanta 4km on the spot on the spot on the spot.
Remarks: Parking at the caves.

Préveza 35F2

Mitikas. GPS: n39,01719 e20,71555.

. **Surface:** asphalted/gravel.
Distance: Preveza 7km on the spot on the spot 500m.
Remarks: Parking at the beach.

Préveza 35F2

GPS: n38,95008 e20,75498.

Tourist information Préveza:
Kassópi, Kassópi. Archeological site.
Nikopolis. Old Roman city.

Psaropouli 35G2

GPS: n38,96778 e23,37853.

free. **Surface:** asphalted/sand. 01/01-31/12.
Distance: on the spot pebbled beach.
Remarks: Parking along coast road.

Sistrouni 35F2

Lakka Souliou. **GPS**: n39,41586 e20,69796.
10 free. **Location:** Isolated, quiet. **Surface:** grassy.
01/01-31/12.
Distance: on the spot on the spot.
Remarks: Along the Acheron river, narrow road, picnic area.

Sivota 35E2

Parking. GPS: n39,40772 e20,24270.

± 4 free. **Surface:** unpaved.
Distance: 200m harbour 200m 200m 50m.
Remarks: No beach.

Sivota 35E2

Parking. GPS: n39,40924 e20,24061.
free. **Surface:** unpaved.
Distance: 200m harbour 200m 200m 200m.
Remarks: No beach.

Spothi 35F1

GPS: n39,67375 e20,93523.
15 free. **Location:** Rural, isolated, quiet. **Surface:** gravel.
01/01-31/12.
Distance: 2km 2km.
Remarks: Beautiful view.

Tyria 35F2

Epar.Od. Meliggon - Paramithias. **GPS**: n39,53351 e20,68794.
12 free. **Location:** Rural. **Surface:** gravel. 01/01-31/12.
Distance: 350m 500m 100m.

Tzoumerka 35F1

Petrouni. **GPS**: n39,57899 e21,03291.
15 free. **Location:** Isolated, quiet. **Surface:** grassy.
01/01-31/12.
Remarks: Narrow road.

Vagia 35G2

Restaurant Ynaiopio, Palaia Ethniki Odos Athinon-Lamias.
GPS: n38,34331 e23,19378.
free with a meal.

Vonitsa 35F2

Agio Sotiriou. GPS: n38,93302 e20,91937.

free . **Surface:** grassy. 01/01-31/12.
Distance: Vonitsa 3km lake on the spot taverne 3km.

Vonitsa 35F2

Marina. GPS: n38,92172 e20,88482.
5 free. **Location:** Simple. **Surface:** gravel.
Remarks: Near marina.

Zitsa 35F1

GPS: n39,75195 e20,65361.
15 free WC. **Surface:** grassy/gravel. 01/01-31/12.
Distance: 750m 750m 750m.
Remarks: Nearby monastery.

Zitsa 35F1

E92. **GPS**: n39,69516 e20,59853.
10 free. **Location:** Isolated, quiet. **Surface:** unpaved.
01/01-31/12.
Distance: Zitsa 20km on the spot on the spot.
Remarks: Along river.

Peloponnisos/Attica

Agia Kyriaki 35G3

GPS: n36,71883 e23,02305.

Remarks: At the beach.

Agios Andreas 35G3

GPS: n37,37120 e22,78262.

free. **Surface:** gravel.
Distance: 3km on the spot on the spot on the spot.
Remarks: At harbour.

Agios Andreas 35G3

Camping Agios Andreas. GPS: n36,86664 e21,92087.
. 20/04-30/09.
Distance: on the spot.

Agios Fokas 35G3

GPS: n36,59565 e23,06108.

5. **Surface:** sand.
Distance: Monemvasia 13km.
Remarks: Parking at pier.

Agios Kiriaki 35F3

Filiatra, Epar.Od.Filiatron. **GPS**: n37,11963 e21,57611.
. 01/01-31/12.

Aigio 35F2

En Plo Camperstop/beach cafe. GPS: n38,22365 e22,14709.

10 € 10, guests free Ch € 3 WC included.
Surface: unpaved. 01/01-01/12.
Distance: 1,5km on the spot mini market 100m.

Assini 35G2

Kastraki. GPS: n37,52861 e22,87556.
€ 24,50-26,50 Ch WC. 01/04-01/10.

Athens 35G2

Rovertou Galli. **GPS**: n37,96987 e23,72263.
. 01/01-31/12.
Remarks: Parking of the Acropolis, guarding after authorization Probably only outside the main season.

Athens 35G2

Athens camping, Leoforis Athinon.
GPS: n38,00889 e23,67222.
€ 29 Ch WC.
01/01-31/12.

Tourist information Athens:
Monasteraki. Old district with Athenian flea market.
Su 8-14h.
Panathenaic Stadium. Stadium of the first Olympic Games in 1896.
Plaka. Old district around the Acropolis.
Tomb of the Unknown Soldier, Plateía Syntágmatos. Sunday 11h changing of the guard.
Acropolis. Archeological site.
01/05-31/10 Mo-Fri 8-18.30h, Sa-Su 8.30-14.30h, 01/11-30/04 8.30-16.30h
01/05, 28/10, holiday.

Bozas 35G3

GPS: n36,70443 e22,82147.

20 free for clients Ch.
Location: Isolated. **Surface:** sand. 01/01-31/12.
Distance: on the spot on the spot.

Diakofto 35F2

GPS: n38,20176 e22,19282.

. **Surface:** asphalted. 01/01-31/12.
Distance: pebbled beach on the spot on the spot 500m.

Diakofto 35F2

Anapafseos. **GPS**: n38,19166 e22,19894.

GR

5 free.
Surface: metalled.
01/01-31/12.
Distance: on the spot 750m on the spot 300m on the spot.
Remarks: Nearby railway station, overnight stay allowed.

Tourist information Diakofto:
Rack railway, Kalavryta. Train journey with rack-railway.

Dimitsána 35G3
Kefalari tou Ai-Yanni. GPS: n37,59058 e22,04286.
4.
Remarks: Parking water museum.

Dimitsána 35G3
Taverna Koustenis, Eparchiaki Odos Kato Davias.
GPS: n37,58650 e22,04459.
5 free. **Location:** Rural, simple.
Surface: gravel.
01/01-31/12.
Distance: 9km on the spot on the spot.
Remarks: Beautiful view.

Tourist information Dimitsána:
Loúsios-kloof. 5km long and 300m deep, marked trails.

Elefsina 35G2
GPS: n38,04235 e23,53942.
free. **Location:** Urban, noisy. **Surface:** asphalted.
01/01-31/12.
Distance: on the spot 150m.
Remarks: Parking in front of the ruins in the city center.

Epidaurus 35G2
EO Isthmou Archaias Epidavrou. **GPS:** n37,59675 e23,07444.

WC free.
Surface: gravel. 01/01-31/12.
Distance: on the spot.
Remarks: Overnight stay on parking at the Ancient theater is generally tolerated.

Tourist information Epidaurus:
Ancient Epidaurus. Archeological site. 8-19h.

Ermioni 35G3
Eparchiaki Ermionis Kranidiou. **GPS:** n37,38833 e23,24776.

7 free. **Surface:** asphalted. 01/01-31/12.
Distance: on the spot on the spot 800m 200m on the spot on the spot.

Ermioni 35G3
Hydras Wave. GPS: n37,40583 e23,31556.
€ 18 Ch WC. 15/04-15/10.

Galatas 35G2
Epar.Odos Ermionis. **GPS:** n37,49491 e23,45546.
20. **Surface:** unpaved. 01/01-31/12.
Distance: on the spot on the spot on the spot on the spot.

Remarks: At the quay.

Gerolimenas 35G3
GPS: n36,48230 e22,39969.

3. **Surface:** asphalted.
Distance: on the spot on the spot 50m on the spot.
Remarks: Parking at the beach.

Gialova Pylou 35F3
Navarino Beach. GPS: n36,94770 e21,70620.
€ 20-23 Ch WC. 01/04-31/10.

Glifa Kyllini 35F2
Ionion. GPS: n37,83640 e21,13340.
€ 21-24,50 Ch. 01/01-31/12.

Gythion 35G3
Valtaki beach, Valtaki. **GPS:** n36,78883 e22,58225.

. **Surface:** sand.
Distance: on the spot on the spot.
Remarks: At the beach, ± 5km from Gythion dir Skala.

Gythion 35G3
Gythion Bay. GPS: n36,72942 e22,54535.
€ 20,50-22 Ch. 01/04-31/10.

Kakovatos 35F3
GPS: n37,45721 e21,63869.
. **Surface:** metalled.
Remarks: Parking at the beach.

Kalo Nero 35F3
GPS: n37,29786 e21,69525.

10 free. **Surface:** gravel.
Distance: 100m Sandy beach 100m.

Kalogria 35F2
Camper Stop Kalogria, Kalogria. **GPS:** n38,15986 e21,37162.

40 € 10, 16/07-31/08 € 12 Ch (20x)€ 3/day WC included.
Surface: unpaved.
01/05-31/10.
Distance: 5km 11km 500m 300m 50m on the spot on the spot on the spot on the spot.

Tourist information Kalogria:
Kotychi, Lapas. Visitors centre, swamp area.

Kamares 35G3
Anatoliki Mani. **GPS:** n36,68203 e22,52090.

. **Surface:** sand. 01/01-31/12.
Distance: 1km on the spot on the spot 350m.

Kameras Irion 35F1
Poseidon. GPS: n40,01305 e22,59039.
€ 30-38 Ch WC. 01/04-31/10.

Karathona 35G2
GPS: n37,54389 e22,82278.

50 free.
Distance: Sandy beach.

Karavastasi 35G3
Vasilis Taverne. GPS: n36,68839 e22,82765.

free.
Distance: Sandy beach on the spot.
Remarks: Free, use of a meal obligated.

Karavostasi 35G3

Taverna O Faros, Karavostasi. **GPS:** n36,69733 e22,38073.
15 free. **Location:** Rural, simple. **Surface:** gravel.
Distance: on the spot on the spot.
Remarks: No beach.

Kastro 35F2
Killinis Beach. **GPS:** n37,87413 e21,10748.

GR

free. **Surface:** grassy/sand.
Distance: 2km on the spot on the spot Beach taverne.
Remarks: Beach parking.

Tourist information Kastro:
Chlemoutsi. Medieval castle.

Kato Alissos 35F2

Kato Allissos. GPS: n38,14986 e21,57740.
€ 18,30-19 Ch WC . 30/06-01/09.

Kifisiá 35G2

Dionissiotis. GPS: n38,10535 e23,81355.
€ 19 Ch WC . 01/01-31/12.
Remarks: 18km north of Athens, route Athens dir Lamia.

Tourist information Kifisiá:
Holiday resort of the Athenian since the Roman time.
Goulándris, Levidou 13. History of nature.

Killini 35F2

Epar Od. Andravidas-Killinis. **GPS:** n37,92598 e21,16699.
Distance: 2km.
Remarks: Parking at the beach.

Kiveri 35G3

GPS: n37,52761 e22,73120.

10 free. **Surface:** gravel.
Distance: 200m pebbled beach 50m 100m.
Remarks: At harbour.

Kokkinia 35G3

GPS: n36,79762 e22,78485.

20 free . **Surface:** metalled.
Distance: Sandy beach 400m.
Remarks: Beach parking.

Korfos 35G2

GPS: n37,76361 e23,13302.

. **Surface:** gravel. 01/01-31/12.
Remarks: At fishing port.

Korinthos 35G2

Afrodites Waters, Ancient Corinth. **GPS:** n37,91139 e22,87861.

30 € 10 Ch WC included. 01/01-31/12.
Distance: 350m 350m 350m.
Remarks: Barbecue place.

Korinthos 35G2

Ancient Corinth. **GPS:** n37,90750 e22,87806.

. 01/01-31/12.

Tourist information Korinthos:
Important trade centre.
Korinth Canal. Canal, 23m wide.
Acrocorinth. Fortress.
8-19h, winter 8-17h.
free.
Ancient Korinthos. Archeological site.
01/04-31/10 8-19h, 01/11-31/03 8-17h 25/12-26/12, 01/01, 25/03, Easter, 01/05.

Koroni 35G3

GPS: n36,79729 e21,96002.

. 01/01-31/12.
Remarks: Parking at harbour.

Koroni 35G3

Camping Koroni. GPS: n36,79942 e21,95068.
€ 25 Ch WC . 01/01-31/12.
Distance: 600m on the spot on the spot.

Tourist information Koroni:
Port city with Venetian castle, 1206.

Kosmas 35G3

Epar.Od.Leonidiou-Kosma. **GPS:** n37,09180 e22,74043.

. **Surface:** metalled.
Distance: on the spot on the spot on the spot.
Remarks: Behind church.

Kotronas 35G3

Epar.Od. Chosiariou-Gerolimena. **GPS:** n36,61899 e22,49367.

free free. **Surface:** concrete. 01/01-31/12.
Distance: on the spot on the spot 50m.
Remarks: Parking at pier.

Lambiri 35F2

Tsolis, Old National Road. **GPS:** n38,32083 e21,97194.
€ 17-20 Ch WC . 01/01-31/12.

Legrena 35G2

GPS: n37,66206 e23,99772.
. 01/01-31/12.

Marathon 35G2

Ramnous.
GPS: n38,13139 e24,00722.
€ 27-35 Ch WC .
01/04-31/10.

Tourist information Marathon:
www.marathon.gr. The name marathon, course of 41 km, comes from this town.

Mayroyouni/Gythion 35G3

Meltemi.
GPS: n36,72986 e22,55360.
€ 19 Ch WC .

Tourist information Mayroyouni/Gythion:
Tourist Information Areópoli, Vasiléos Pávlou 21, Máni. Peninsula.
Pýrgos Diroú, Máni. Caves.

Monemvasía 35G3

GPS: n36,68875 e23,05076.
. **Surface:** asphalted.
Distance: on the spot on the spot shuttle to old town.

Monemvasía 35G3

GPS: n36,68240 e23,03821.
Remarks: Parking harbour.

Tourist information Monemvasía:
Fortified city, lower town have been restored.
Agía Sofia. Church 13th century.

Mycenae 35G2

Atreus. GPS: n37,71911 e22,74114.
€ 24-32 Ch WC .
01/01-31/12.

Tourist information Mycenae:
Archeological Museum, Argos. € 12.
Archeological site. 1/4-31/10 8-19h, 1/11-31/3 8-17h holiday.
Agora Argos, Argos. Archeological site. summer 8.30-15h.

Nafplio 35G2

GPS: n37,56823 e22,80170.

free. **Surface:** asphalted.
Distance: 500m 300m.
Remarks: Parking marina.

Tourist information Nafplio:
Tourist information, Ikostispémtis Martiou 2. First Greek capital.
Archeological Museum. Tue-Su 8.30-15h Mo.
Palamídi. Citadel 18th century.

Neo Itylo 35G3

Black Pirate. GPS: n36,69154 e22,38986.

10 free. **Surface:** grassy/gravel.
Distance: on the spot pebbled beach on the spot 50m.

Olympia 35F3

Alphios. GPS: n37,64360 e21,61930.
€ 24-33 Ch WC . 01/04-31/10.

Tourist information Olympia:
Archeological Museum. Important Greek archeological museum.
Mo 11-19h, Tue-Su 8-19h.

Paralia Platanou 35G2

GPS: n38,17104 e22,26828.

. **Surface:** gravel.
Distance: on the spot.
Remarks: At the beach.

Pátra 35F2

Golden Sunset, Old national Road km 19. **GPS**: n38,14389 e21,58778.
€ 32-39 Ch WC . 01/04-15/10.

Tourist information Pátra:
Archaïa Klauss. First commercial producer of wine of Greece.

Perahóra 35G2

Limni Vouliagmenis. **GPS**: n38,03188 e22,87293.

Distance: on the spot on the spot.
Remarks: At the lake.

Petalidi 35G3

GPS: n36,95871 e21,93418.
. **Surface:** asphalted.
Remarks: Nearby port.

Petalidi 35G3

GPS: n36,95915 e21,92870.

. **Surface:** asphalted.
Distance: on the spot.
Remarks: Parking in village, near the sea.

Piraeus 35G2

Parkopolis, Fokionos 3. **GPS**: n37,94759 e23,64595.

± 10 € 13 included.
Location: Urban. **Surface:** asphalted. 01/01-31/12.
Distance: on the spot metro > Athens 300m.

Pírgos Dhiroú 35G3

Diros. **GPS**: n36,64206 e22,38357.

20. **Location:** Isolated. **Surface:** unpaved.
Distance: on the spot.

Porto Kagio 35G3

Taverna Porto. GPS: n36,42811 e22,48697.
3 guests free. **Surface:** grassy.
Distance: on the spot on the spot on the spot mini market on the spot.

Rafina 35G2

GPS: n38,01835 e24,01227.
. 01/01-31/12.

Salandi 35G3

GPS: n37,44748 e23,12474.

. **Location:** Isolated. **Surface:** gravel.
Distance: Didyma 5km on the spot on the spot.
Remarks: At the beach.

Savalia 35F2

Savalia Beach. **GPS**: n37,79685 e21,25578.

. **Surface:** asphalted.
Distance: on the spot on the spot.

Skoutari 35G3

GPS: n36,65921 e22,49962.

max. 3. **Surface:** concrete.
Distance: on the spot on the spot within walking distance.

Remarks: Near fishing-port.

Sounion 35H2

Camping Bacchus.
GPS: n37,67694 e24,04750.
€ 23 Ch WC .
01/01-31/12.

Tourist information Sounion:
Mineralogical Museum, Lavrió. Old mine shaft of the silvermines.
Wed, Sa-Su.
Archeological site.

Tolo 35G2

GPS: n37,51469 e22,85662.

WC. **Surface:** asphalted.
Distance: 500m 100m on the spot 200m.
Remarks: Near fishing-port.

Tyrchu 35G3

Taverne Ostria. GPS: n37,31414 e22,82054.

3 guests free. **Surface:** gravel.
15/05-30/09.
Distance: Tyros 10km on the spot on the spot on the spot.
Remarks: At the beach, attention: via steep path.

Zacharo 35F3

GPS: n37,51917 e21,60248.

Distance: on the spot.

Zacharo 35F3

Tholo Beach. GPS: n37,41160 e21,66830.
€ 18,50 Ch WC . 01/04-31/10.

Greece North

Ag.Mamas Moudania 35G1

Ouzoni Beach. GPS: n40,21611 e23,31833.
€ 17,60-23 Ch WC . 01/05-30/09.

Akt Armenistis Sithonia 35G1

Armenistis. GPS: n40,15222 e23,91361.
€ 31-40 Ch WC . 01/05-15/09.

Alexandroúpoli 39D4

GPS: n40,84364 e25,87693.
Remarks: Parking harbour.

Alexandroúpoli 39D4

Apollonias.
GPS: n40,84342 e25,86477.
Surface: asphalted.
Remarks: Parking near stadium.

Tourist information Alexandroúpoli:
Tourist Information, Mákris. Large holiday resort, beautiful beach.

GR

Gerakani 35G1
Kouyoni. **GPS**: n40,26464 e23,46347.
€ 22,25-24,50 Ch. 01/05-30/09.

Kalamaria 35G1
Zampetaz, Tessaloniki-Perea. **GPS**: n40,50239 e22,97138.

10 free Ch WC free. **Location:** Urban, simple, noisy. **Surface:** gravel. 9-17/20h Su.
Distance: 10km 3km 500m > Thessaloniki.
Remarks: At motorhome dealer.

Kastoriá 35F1
GPS: n40,50461 e21,27977.
against payment. 01/01-31/12.
Remarks: Voluntary contribution.

Kastoriá 35F1
Meg. Alexandrou. **GPS**: n40,50461 e21,27970.
free. **Location:** Urban, central, noisy. **Surface:** asphalted. 01/01-31/12.
Distance: on the spot on the spot on the spot.

Metamorphosi 35G1
Sunny Bay. **GPS**: n40,22694 e23,58944.
€ 18,90-21,70 Ch WC. 01/05-31/10.

Moustheni 39C4
Moystheni Station. **GPS**: n40,84413 e24,11506.
10 free Ch WC. **Surface:** asphalted. 01/01-31/12.
Distance: 100m on the spot mini market.
Remarks: Special part for motor homes, shop, restaurant, station 24/24.

Ouranoupoli 35G1
Ouranoupoli. **GPS**: n40,33944 e23,97056.
€ 28-31 Ch. 01/04-31/10.

Porto Lagos 39D4
GPS: n41,00633 e25,12028.

5 free. **Surface:** asphalted.
Distance: on the spot.
Remarks: Parking at pier.

Thessaloníki 35G1
Camper Stop Sallonicco, Voulgari 74. **GPS**: n40,59741 e22,96979.

10 free. **Location:** Urban, simple, central, noisy. **Surface:** asphalted.
01/01-31/12.
Distance: on the spot 150m.

Tourist information Thessaloníki:
Tourist Information, Plateia Aristolélous 8. Second city of Greece, busy port and many places of interest.
Lefkos Pyrgos. White tower.
Modiano. Turkish fair.
Agios Dimitrios. Biggest church of Greece. Tue-Sa.

Vergina 35F1
Parking, Aristotelos 25. **GPS**: n40,48506 e22,31978.

22 € 4 € 3.
Location: Urban, simple. **Surface:** asphalted. 01/01-31/12.
Distance: on the spot 200m 450m.
Remarks: Near archeological site and museum.

GR

Croatia

Capital: Zagreb
Government: parliamentarian democracy
Official Language: Croatian
Population: 4,313,707 (2016)
Area: 56,594 km²

General information
Dialling code: 00385
General emergency: 112
Currency: Kuna, kn, 1 kuna = 100 lipa
1kn = € 0,13, € 1 = 7,52kn
10kn = £1.17, £1 = 8,54kn (October 2017)
Credit card are accepted almost everywhere.

Regulations for overnight stays
Wild camping is forbidden.

Additional public holidays 2018
January 6 Epiphany
May 1 Labor Day
May 31 Corpus Christi
June 22 Dan antifasisticke borbe, Anti-Fascist Resistance Day
June 25 Dan drzavnosti, National Holiday
August 5 Victorie Day and National Thanksgiving
August 15 Assumption of the Virgin Mary
October 8 Independence Day

Time Zone
Winter (Standard Time) GMT+1
Summer (DST) GMT+2

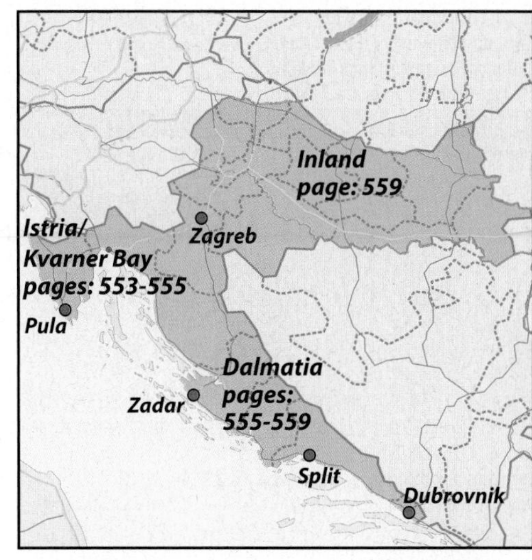

Istria/Kvarner Bay

Baderna 37A2

Farm Pino, Katun 1. **GPS**: n45,22020 e13,72908.

14 € 10 + € 3/pp Ch (23x) WC Service € 4 € 2
Location: Rural, isolated, quiet. **Surface:** grassy.
01/01-31/12.
Distance: 2km 6km 2km 400m on the spot on the spot.

Cres/Cres 37A2

Kovačine, Melin I, 20. **GPS**: n44,96278 e14,39694.
€ 19,20-41,10 Ch WC . 19/03-16/10.
Distance: on the spot.

Tourist information Cres/Cres:
Turisticka zajednica, Riva Creskih Kapetana, www.tzg-cres.hr. Island can be reached with ferry service from Brestova, south of Rijeka and Valbiska, west Krk.

Cres/Martinšćica 37A2

Slatina. **GPS**: n44,82091 e14,34238.
€ 16-28,20 Ch WC . 19/03-31/10.

Cres/Nerezine 37A2

Camping Lopari, Nerezine. **GPS**: n44,68092 e14,39561.
€ 8,50-17,50 Ch WC . **Surface:** gravel.
25/03-10/10.

Cres/Nerezine 37A2

Preko Mosta, Osor 76, Nerezine. **GPS**: n44,69250 e14,39167.
129-179 kn Ch WC . 01/04-30/09.

Cres/Nerezine 37A2

Rapoća, Rapoća, Nerezine. **GPS**: n44,66357 e14,39756.
€ 20-28 Ch WC . 22/04-10/10.

Crikvenica 37B2

Kacjak, Kacjak BB. **GPS**: n45,16703 e14,70511.
Ch WC . 15/05-15/09.

Dobrinj 37A2

Slamni Camping, Klimno 8a. **GPS**: n45,15360 e14,61758.
€ 20,27 Ch WC . 22/04-10/10.

Fažana 37A2

Ul.1.Maja. **GPS**: n44,92880 e13,80255.

200 kn/€ 30 WC. **Location:** Urban, simple, central.
Surface: grassy/sand. 01/01-31/12.
Distance: 100m on the spot 100m 100m on the spot on the spot.
Remarks: Max. 24h.

Fažana 37A2

Bi Village, Dragonja 115. **GPS**: n44,91750 e13,81111.
€ 21-46 Ch WC . 21/04-30/09.

Fažana 37A2

Pineta Fažana, Perojska cesta bb.
GPS: n44,93835 e13,79554.
€ 11,10-24,10 Ch WC .
27/04-30/09.

Tourist information Fažana:
Nationaal Park Brijuni, Brijuni. Nature reserve, boat connection from Fažana. daily.

Grožnjan 37A2

Parking bus. **GPS**: n45,38163 e13,72375.

20 free. **Location:** Rural, simple, isolated, quiet.
Surface: gravel. 01/01-31/12.
Distance: 200m 200m on the spot on the spot on the spot.
Remarks: Next to cemetery.

Ičići 37A2

Opatija. **GPS**: n45,31083 e14,28472.
Ch WC . 27/04-13/10.

Klenovica 37B2

Klenovica, Zidinice BB. **GPS**: n45,09788 e14,84393.
€ 19-26,60 Ch . 01/05-30/09.
Distance: on the spot on the spot.

Koromačno 37A2

Tunarica. **GPS**: n44,96917 e14,09889.
€ 20,50-24,10 Ch WC . 29/04-30/09.

Kraljevica 37A2

Ostro. **GPS**: n45,27109 e14,56402.
Ch . 01/05-30/09.

Krk/Baška 37B2

Kamp Mali, Put Zablace 100. **GPS**: n44,96609 e14,74710.

33 € 10-20 Ch (30x),10Amp WC € 5 included.
Location: Urban, comfortable, central, quiet. **Surface:** grasstiles.
01/03-30/10.
Distance: 300m 150m on the spot on the spot 50m on the spot on the spot.

Krk/Baška 37B2

Zablace, Emila Geitslicha 34, Baška. **GPS**: n44,96694 e14,74528.
€ 38,50-47,30 Ch WC . 01/05-01/10.

Krk/Klimno 37A2

Slamni, Klimno 8a. **GPS**: n45,15351 e14,61770.
€ 18-38 Ch . 22/04-10/10.
Remarks: Mini-camp.

Krk/Krk 37A2

Camperstop Krk, Sv. Petar bb. **GPS**: n45,03574 e14,56819.
16 € 12,90-23,10 + tourist tax Ch included WC .
Location: Urban. **Surface:** gravel. 01/01-31/12.
Distance: 1,2km 2km 100m Konzum.

Krk/Krk 37A2

Camper Stop Felix, Ulica Narodnog preporoda 51.
GPS: n45,02928 e14,58149.

12 € 25 Ch (12x),16Amp WC € 5 included.
Location: Urban, comfortable, central, quiet.
Surface: grassy/gravel. 01/01-31/12.
Distance: 300m 300m 300m 50m 50m on the spot on the spot on the spot.

Krk/Krk 37A2

Bor. **GPS**: n45,02250 e14,56194.
€ 20,40-29 Ch WC . 01/01-31/12.

Krk/Krk 37A2

Jezevac, Plavnička bb. **GPS**: n45,01963 e14,57000.
€ 26-38 Ch WC . 25/03-01/10.

Krk/Krk 37A2

Marta, Škrbcici 29. **GPS**: n45,04930 e14,48940.
€ 12,30-17,10 Ch WC . 01/05-30/09.
Remarks: Mini-camp.

HR

Tourist information Krk/Krk:
Tourist Information, Vela placa 1/1, www.krk.hr. Krk accessible via toll-bridge south-east from Rijeka.
Jazz-festival, Kamplin. Aug.

S Krk/Malinska 37A2
Camp Mali Raj, Brzac, Glavotok 10. **GPS**: n45,09080 e14,43720.
10 € 23-36, 15/07-19/08 € 50 Ch (10x) WC included.
Location: Rural. **Surface:** grassy/gravel. 01/05-31/10.
Distance: 2km 300m 300m 500m 2km on the spot on the spot.

S Krk/Malinska 37A2
Draga, Palih Boraca 4. **GPS**: n45,12052 e14,52494.
€ 12,90-17 Ch WC. 01/04-15/10.
Remarks: Mini-camp.

S Krk/Malinska 37A2
Glavotok, Glavokok 4. **GPS**: n45,09472 e14,44111.
€ 17,95-43,15 Ch WC. 22/04-02/10.
Distance: on the spot.

S Krk/Njivice 37A2
Njivice, Primorska bb. **GPS**: n45,16963 e14,54740.
€ 20,80-40,20 Ch WC. 09/04-30/10.

S Krk/Omišalj 37A2
Pusca, Pušča bb. **GPS**: n45,23613 e14,55108.
Ch WC. 01/06-30/09.

Krk/Pinezici 37A2
Amar, Njivine 8. **GPS**: n45,04351 e14,47985.
Remarks: Mini-camp.

S Krk/Punat 37A2
Maslinik, Nikole Tesle 1. **GPS**: n45,01809 e14,63478.
€ 13,33-21,99 Ch WC. 01/04-04/10.
Remarks: Mini-camp.

S Krk/Punat 37A2
Pila, Setalište Ivana Brusića. **GPS**: n45,01581 e14,62860.
250 € 15-20 Ch. 22/04-09/10.

S Krk/Punat 37A2
Škrila, Stara Baška. **GPS**: n44,96611 e14,67389.
350 € 20,60-33,20 Ch.
01/04-01/10.

Tourist information Krk/Punat:
Otočić Košljun. Monastery.

S Krk/Šilo 37A2
Tiha Šilo, Konjska bb. **GPS**: n45,14876 e14,67150.
€ 16,50-26 Ch WC. 01/04-15/10.
Remarks: Mini-camp.

S Labin 37A2
Kamp Tunarica, Koromačno. **GPS**: n44,96933 e14,09979.
50 € 15, 01/07-31/08 € 19 Ch (50x) € 4/night,16Amp WC € 5 included. **Location:** Rural, simple, isolated, quiet.
Surface: forest soil. 01/05-30/09.
Distance: 15km on the spot on the spot on the spot on the spot 2km on the spot.

S Labin 37A2
Camping Romantik, Kapelica 47b. **GPS**: n45,08167 e14,10188.
8 € 17-24 Ch WC € 5,30 included.
Distance: 2km on the spot on the spot.
Remarks: Mini-camp.

S Labin 37A2
Marina. **GPS**: n45,03333 e14,15806.
€ 27,80-42,10 Ch WC. 25/03-30/10.

S Labin 37A2
Marina, Sveta Marina. **GPS**: n45,03387 e14,15723.
€ 37-47 Ch WC.
25/03-30/10.
Remarks: Mini-camp.

Tourist information Labin:
Narodni muzej, N. Katunara 6. Ethnological museum. daily 10-13h, 17-19h.

S Lošinj/Mali Lošinj 37A2
Čikat. **GPS**: n44,53750 e14,45056.
940 € 22,50-36,60 Ch WC. 01/01-31/12.

S Lošinj/Mali Lošinj 37A2
Poljana. **GPS**: n44,55556 e14,44167.
€ 16,50-21 Ch WC. 17/03-17/10.

Tourist information Lošinj/Mali Lošinj:
Dolphins day, action day with possibility for adoption of a dolphin.
1st Sa Aug.

S Medulin 37A2
Indije, Banjole. **GPS**: n44,82398 e13,85090.
Ch WC. 01/05-01/10.

S Medulin 37A2
Kazela. **GPS**: n44,80695 e13,95015.
Ch WC. 01/04-15/10.

S Medulin 37A2
Kranjski Kamp, Runke 52, Premantura. **GPS**: n44,80694 e13,91616.
€ 19,80-27,10 Ch WC. 01/06-18/09.
Remarks: Mini-camp.

S Medulin 37A2
Medulin. **GPS**: n44,81417 e13,93194.
Ch WC. 03/04-09/10.

S Medulin 37A2
Piškera, Indie 49, Banjole. **GPS**: n44,82332 e13,84855.
170-200kn Ch WC.
Remarks: Mini-camp.

S Medulin 37A2
Pomer, Pomer. **GPS**: n44,82064 e13,90205.
Ch WC.
Remarks: Mini-camp.

S Medulin 37A2
Postolovic, Bumbište 10. **GPS**: n44,82037 e13,85749.
Ch.
Remarks: Mini-camp.

S Medulin 37A2
Runke, Premantura. **GPS**: n44,80742 e13,91632.
€ 28-37 Ch WC. 01/05-30/09.

S Medulin 37A2
Širola, Rupice Bd. **GPS**: n44,82113 e13,85872.
10 Ch.
Remarks: Mini-camp.

S Medulin 37A2
Stupice, Premantura. **GPS**: n44,79779 e13,91354.
Ch. 01/05-25/09.

S Medulin 37A2
Tasalera, Premantura. **GPS**: n44,81425 e13,91275.
€ 27-35 Ch WC.
01/04-30/09.

Tourist information Medulin:
Premantura. Most Southern place of Istria.
Banjole. Fisherman's village with natural harbour.

S Moščenička Draga 37A2
Draga. **GPS**: n45,24023 e14,25021.
131-186kn Ch. 15/04-01/10.
Remarks: Mini-camp.

Moščenička Draga 37A2
Draga. **GPS**: n45,24000 e14,25028.
165. 15/04-01/10.

S Motovun 37A2
Motovun Camping, Rizanske skupstine 1a.
GPS: n45,33446 e13,82523.

12 € 15-25 + tourist tax € 1/pp Ch WC included.
Location: Rural, comfortable.
Surface: gravel. 01/01-31/12.
Distance: 50m on the spot 50m 50m 100m on the spot on the spot.
Remarks: Free entrance swimming pool, discount longer stays.

S Novi Vinodolski 37B2
Autocamp Sibinje, Sibinj. **GPS**: n45,04405 e14,87751.
80 € 24 Ch WC. 01/04-30/09.
Distance: on the spot 50m 50m.
Remarks: Mini-camp.

S Novigrad (Istria) 37A2
Aminess Sirena camping, Terre 6. **GPS**: n45,31528 e13,57556.
€ 32-52 Ch WC. 01/04-30/09.

S Novigrad (Istria) 37A2
Mareda. **GPS**: n45,34149 e13,54610.
800 from € 17 Ch WC included. 15/04-30/09.

Tourist information Novigrad (Istria):
Hoofdstraat van de oude stad. Farmers market. daily.
Feest van de beschermheilige Pelegrinus, Umag. 23/05.

Poreč 37A2
30. Travinja/Karla Huguesa. **GPS**: n45,22104 e13,60742.
28 200kn, winter free. **Location:** Simple, central, noisy.
Surface: asphalted. 01/01-31/12.
Distance: 800m 2km 2km 400m 2km 500m on the spot on the spot.

S Poreč 37A2
Bijela Uvala. **GPS**: n45,19139 e13,59667.
2000 € 35-52 Ch WC. 01/04-15/10.

S Poreč 37A2
Laternacamp. **GPS**: n45,29639 e13,59444.
3000 from € 22,65 Ch WC. 01/04-15/10.
Distance: on the spot on the spot.

S Poreč 37A2
Puntica, Funtana. **GPS**: n45,17749 e13,60406.
250 Ch WC. 11/04-13/10.

S Poreč 37A2
Zelena Laguna. **GPS**: n45,19611 e13,58917.
1000 € 32,50-55 Ch WC. 01/04-15/10.

Poreč 37A2
Materada, Materada. **GPS**: n45,24628 e13,59600.
Remarks: Mini-camp.

Tourist information Poreč:
Turisticka zajednica, Zagrebacka 9, www.istra.com/porec. Old city, centre tourist and cultural.
Decumanus. Roman main street with palazzi from the Venetian time.
Zavicajnog muzeja poreštine. Native museum of Porec.
daily 10-13h, 18-22h.
Eufrazijeva bazilika. Basilica, 6th century, in the centre.
daily 7-19h.

S Pula 37A2
Puntižela. **GPS**: n44,89806 e13,80722.
480 Ch WC included. 01/05-31/10.

S Pula 37A2
Stoja. **GPS**: n44,86000 e13,81472.
750 € 32,50-45 Ch WC. 03/04-02/11.

HR

Tourist information Pula:
M Arheoloski Muzej Istre, Carrarina 3. Archeological museum.
winter Mo-Fri 9-14h, summer Mo-Sa 9-19h.
Amfiteatar. Large anfiteatro from Roman time. daily 8-21h.
Ljetni klasicni Festival, Amfitheatar. Opera festival.
Aug.

S Rab 37B2
Camperpark Lando Resort, Kampor 321. **GPS**: n44,78404 e14,70682.
12 € 23,50-55 Ch WC € 7 included.
Location: Comfortable. **Surface:** grassy/metalled. 01/01-31/12.
Distance: city centre 1,5km 50m 50m 1,5km on the spot on the spot.
Remarks: Heated pool.

Rab 37B2
Mel, Kampor 319. **GPS**: n44,79390 e14,70302.
Remarks: Mini-camp.

Rab 37B2
Planka, Kampor 326. **GPS**: n44,78049 e14,72048.
Remarks: Mini-camp.

S Rabac 37A2
Oliva. GPS: n45,07960 e14,14777.
300 Ch WC. 15/03-30/09.
Distance: on the spot.

S Ribnik 37B1
Srce Prirode/Heart of Nature Camp, Gorica Lipnička 8.
GPS: n45,56389 e15,39278.
30 € 29,40-35 Ch WC. 01/04-31/10.
Remarks: Mini-camp.

S Rijeka 37A2
Preluk Katalinic, Preluk 1.
GPS: n45,35340 e14,33235.
90 Ch WC.
Remarks: Mini-camp.

Tourist information Rijeka:
Tourist Information, Kastav 47, Kastav. Walled city with rich history.
M Pomorski i povijesni muzej, Muzejski trg 1. Navy museum.
Mo-Fri 10-13h, 18-21h.
Velika trznica. Market opposite to Modello palace.
Carnaval van Rijeka. Feb.

S Rovinj 37A2
Aleja Ruera Boskovica. **GPS**: n45,08898 e13,64537.

30 25kn/h 6-23h (± € 55), overnight stay free Ch WC included.
Location: Urban, simple, central, noisy. **Surface:** asphalted.
01/01-31/12.
Distance: 1km 300m 300m 300m 1km 300m on the spot on the spot.

S Rovinj 37A2
Camping Polari. GPS: n45,06300 e13,67480.

40 € 12-32 Ch WC included 25kn 100kn
Location: Rural, simple, quiet. **Surface:** grassy/metalled.
22/04-04/10.
Distance: 3km on the spot on the spot on the spot on the spot on the spot June/July/Aug on the spot on the spot.
Remarks: Camperstop max. 48h.

S Rovinj 37A2
Mon Paradiso, Uvala Veštar. **GPS**: n45,04947 e13,69000.
40 € 36-50 Ch WC. 01/06-30/09.

Remarks: Mini-camp.

S Rovinj 37A2
Polari. GPS: n45,06258 e13,67477.
2150 € 18-44,80 Ch WC. 22/04-02/10.

S Rovinj 37A2
Porton Biondi. GPS: n45,09410 e13,64232.
396 114-226kn Ch WC. 15/03-30/10.

S Rovinj 37A2
Vestar. GPS: n45,05389 e13,68639.
800 € 15-52,40 Ch WC. 22/04-25/09.

Rovinj 37A2
Ulika, Polari Bd. **GPS**: n45,06528 e13,67583.
01/04-01/10. **Remarks:** Mini-camp.

Tourist information Rovinj:
Turisticka zajednica, Budicin 12, www.istra.com/rovinj. City has been a cultural monument since 1963.
Aquarium, Obala G. Paliage 5. daily 9-21h.
Palazzo Califfi, Trg Marsala Tita 11. Tue-Su 10.30-14h, summer 18-20h.
Market.
Grisia, Grisia. Art festival. 2nd week Aug.

S Savudrija 23H3
Pineta. GPS: n45,48667 e13,49250.
460 € 15,70-36,70 Ch WC. 22/04-25/09.

S Savudrija 23H3
Veli Jože, Borozija. **GPS**: n45,49556 e13,50444.
Ch WC. 01/04-30/09.

Savudrija 23H3
Ravna Dolina. GPS: n45,49206 e13,50288.
01/05-30/09.

S Selce 37B2
Selce. GPS: n45,15408 e14,72533.
€ 17,50-31,10 Ch. 01/04-15/10.

S Selina 37A2
Camp Terre, 79. **GPS**: n45,15770 e13,76765.

10 100-125kn Ch (14x),16Amp WC € 5 included.
Location: Rural, luxurious, isolated, quiet.
Surface: gravel.
01/01-31/12.
Distance: 3km 5km 3km 3km on the spot on the spot.

S Umag 37A1
Finida. GPS: n45,39278 e13,54194.
204 € 15,70-36,30 Ch WC. 22/04-25/09.

S Umag 37A1
Stella Maris. GPS: n45,45056 e13,52278.
400 € 15,50-24,40 Ch WC. 24/04-25/09.

S Vižinada 37A2
Agroturizam Jadruhi, Jadruhi 11. **GPS**: n45,29978 e13,74819.

10 50kn Ch (6x)included,16Amp WC free.
Location: Rural, simple, isolated, quiet. **Surface:** gravel/metalled.
01/01-31/12.
Distance: 4km 6km on the spot 4km on the spot on the spot on the spot.
Remarks: Check in at restaurant.

S Vrsar 37A2
Camperstop Valkanela, Fontana. **GPS**: n45,16501 e13,60804.

20 € 12-32 Ch WC included 100kn/24h
Location: Urban, simple, central, quiet.
Surface: grassy.
22/04-03/10.
Distance: 500m on the spot on the spot on the spot 1km on the spot on the spot.
Remarks: Camperstop, max. 48h, use camp-site facilities incl.

Vrsar 37A2
Dalmatinska ulica. **GPS**: n45,14706 e13,60422.

30 50kn/day. **Location:** Urban, simple, central, noisy.
Surface: asphalted. 01/01-31/12.
Distance: 350m 350m 350m 350m 350m 350m on the spot on the spot.

S Vrsar 37A2
Porto Sole. GPS: n45,14139 e13,60222.
€ 15,40-38,60 Ch WC. 01/03-01/11.

Dalmatia

S Babino Polje 34H1
Mungos. GPS: n42,73885 e17,53441.
€ 25-35 Ch. 15/05-30/09.
Remarks: Mini-camp.

S Baška Voda 34H1
Basko Polje. GPS: n43,34561 e16,96272.
€ 29-37 Ch WC. 15/05-30/09.

S Bibinje 37B3
Anđela. GPS: n44,05557 e15,29263.
Ch.
Remarks: Mini-camp.

S Bibinje 37B3
Dido, Težački put. **GPS**: n44,05708 e15,29116.
€ 23, 2 pers.incl Ch WC.
Remarks: Mini-camp.

S Bibinje 37B3
Kero, Punta Bibinje. **GPS**: n44,05730 e15,28918.
€ 20 Ch WC.
Remarks: Mini-camp.

Bibinje 37B3
Kamp Punta, Težački put. **GPS**: n44,05680 e15,29162.
Remarks: Mini-camp.

S Biograd na Moru 37B3
Dijana & Josip, Put Solina 26. **GPS**: n43,93229 e15,45252.
€ 42-50 Ch WC. 01/05-30/09.
Remarks: Mini-camp.

S Biograd na Moru 37B3
Ljutic, Put Solina. **GPS**: n43,92654 e15,45353.
€ 26-36 Ch WC. 01/05-01/10.
Remarks: Mini-camp.

S Biograd na Moru 37B3
Mia, Put Solina 47. **GPS**: n43,93441 e15,44803.
€ 18-40 Ch. 01/01-31/12.
Remarks: Mini-camp.

S Biograd na Moru 37B3
Soline, Put Kumenta. **GPS**: n43,92756 e15,45595.
€ 21,90-39,20 Ch WC. 22/04-30/09.

S Bol 34G1
Kito, Ante Radića 1. **GPS**: n43,26407 e16,64820.

HR

110-180 kn Ch WC. 01/01-31/12.

Drace-Pelješac 34H1

Plaža, Janjina. **GPS**: n42,92477 e17,43079.

Remarks: Mini-camp.

Dubrovnik 39A4

Solitudo, Vatroslava Lisinskog 17. **GPS**: n42,66178 e18,07052.
€ 24,20-51,60 Ch WC. 01/04-31/10.

Tourist information Dubrovnik:

Akvarij Dubrovnik, D. Jude 2. Sea aquarium. Mo-Sa 9-13h.

City Walls, Gundulićeva poljana 2. City wall surround the entire Old City. 10-12h, 01/04-31/10 10-18.30h. 90kn.

Place Stradun. Main street with Onofrio-fountain and Sveti Frane monastery.

Dubrovacki Muzej, Pred Dvorom 3. History of the city. Mo-Sa 9-14h.

Pomorski Muzej, Sveti Ivan. Shipping museum. Tue-Sa 9-16h.

Zomerfestival. 10/07-25/08.

Dugi Rat 37C3

Ivo, Duce Rogac. **GPS**: n43,44111 e16,65778.
€ 11-20 WC. 15/04-15/11.
Remarks: Mini-camp.

Dugi Rat 37C3

Luka, Duce Rogac. **GPS**: n43,44164 e16,65347.
€ 12,50-21 Ch WC. 30/06-01/09.
Remarks: Mini-camp.

Dugi Rat 37C3

Orij, Orij, Duce Rogac. **GPS**: n43,44631 e16,63429.
Remarks: Mini-camp.

Grebaštica 37C3

Ante&Toni, Brodarica. **GPS**: n43,63833 e15,95833.
25 Ch WC. 01/05-01/10.
Distance: 100m on the spot.
Remarks: Mini-camp.

Grebaštica 37C3

Tomas, D8. **GPS**: n43,63003 e15,93764.
30 € 10,70 Ch WC. 01/05-01/11.
Distance: on the spot.
Remarks: Mini-camp.

Kaštel Kambelovac 37C3

U Dragama, A. Starcevica 39. **GPS**: n43,54951 e16,37778.
Remarks: Mini-camp.

Kaštel Štafilic 37C3

Koludrovac, Resnik Bb. **GPS**: n43,54373 e16,31753.
Remarks: Mini-camp.

Kaštel Stari 37C3

Kamp- Biluš Josip. **GPS**: n43,55162 e16,34978.
95-138kn Ch WC. 01/04-30/09.
Remarks: Mini-camp.

Kaštel Stari 37C3

Adria. **GPS**: n43,55143 e16,35349.
Remarks: Mini-camp.

Kolan 37B2

Sveti Duh. **GPS**: n44,51518 e14,95525.
120-150 kn Ch. 01/06-30/09.
Remarks: Mini-camp.

Korčula 34H1

Kalac. **GPS**: n42,95056 e17,14500.
€ 40-50 Ch WC. 01/06-01/10.

Korčula 34H1

Oskorušica, Oskorušica 27/ VI, Racišce. **GPS**: n42,96795 e17,07335.
Ch WC.
Remarks: Mini-camp.

Korčula 34H1

Vela Postrana, Lumbardra 142.
GPS: n42,92230 e17,17266.
Ch WC.
Remarks: Mini-camp.

Tourist information Korčula:

Turisticka zajednica, Obala Tudmana, www.korcula.net. City with historical centre, birth-place Marco Polo.

Marco Polo fest. 09/07-11/07.

Zwaarddansfestival. daily 04/07-23/08.

Korenica 37B2

Bistro Marina, Zagrebačka 6. **GPS**: n44,74702 e15,70464.

12 guests free € 2/night,10Amp WC.
Location: Urban, simple, central, quiet. **Surface:** asphalted.
01/01-31/12 06/01-30/01.
Distance: 100m on the spot 10m 100m on the spot on the spot.

Kornati/Murter 37B3

Jazina, Tisno. **GPS**: n43,80940 e15,62760.
92-155kn Ch WC. 01/04-15/10.

Kornati/Murter 37B3

Jezera-Lovišča, Jezera. **GPS**: n43,79370 e15,62867.
€ 16,55-36 Ch WC. 28/04-10/10.

Kornati/Murter 37B3

Kosirina, Betina. **GPS**: n43,79727 e15,61004.
Ch WC. 01/05-30/09.

Kornati/Murter 37B3

Plitka Vala, Betina. **GPS**: n43,80515 e15,61284.
€ 14,50-23,60 Ch WC. 01/04-31/10.

Kornati/Murter 37B3

Slanica, Jurija Dalmatinca 17. **GPS**: n43,81682 e15,57733.
109,40-173,40 kn Ch WC. 15/04-15/10.

Krvavica 34H1

Autocamp Krvavica. **GPS**: n43,32375 e16,98559.
Distance: 100m.

Kucište 34H1

Palme. **GPS**: n42,97639 e17,12917.
€ 16,50-26 Ch WC. 01/06-01/10.

Kucište 34H1

Camp Ponta, Viganj 5, Od Gaja. **GPS**: n42,97935 e17,10400.
01/05-15/10.
Remarks: Mini-camp.

Lokva Rogoznica 37C3

Danijel, Ruskamen bb. **GPS**: n43,40973 e16,74529.
Ch WC.
Remarks: Mini-camp.

Lokva Rogoznica 37C3

Linda. **GPS**: n43,40834 e16,75683.
Ch WC.
Remarks: Mini-camp.

Lovište 34H1

Lupiš. **GPS**: n43,02790 e17,03012.
€ 20-30 Ch WC. 01/03-01/11.
Remarks: Mini-camp.

Lukoran 37B3

Novi Kamp, Punta 28. **GPS**: n44,10538 e15,15518.
Remarks: Mini-camp.

Mlini 39A4

Kate, Tupina 1. **GPS**: n42,62472 e18,20806.
158-214kn Ch. 04/04-28/10.
Remarks: Mini-camp.

Mlini 39A4

Kupari, Kupari bb. **GPS**: n42,62462 e18,18833.
€ 11,50-15,20 Ch WC. 01/04-30/09.
Remarks: Mini-camp.

Mlini 39A4

Matkovica, Srebreno 8. **GPS**: n42,62450 e18,19295.
€ 20-24 Ch WC.
Remarks: Mini-camp.

Mlini 39A4

Paradiso Laguna, Za Gospom, Plat. **GPS**: n42,60759 e18,22838.
109-130kn Ch.
Remarks: Mini-camp.

Mlini 39A4

Porto, Srebreno. **GPS**: n42,62433 e18,19107.
Ch.
Remarks: Mini-camp.

Mljet 34H1

Marina, Marina Matana,Ropa 11. **GPS**: n42,75260 e17,46000.
€ 27,80-42,10 Ch WC. 25/03-30/10.
Remarks: Mini-camp.

Mokalo 34H1

Adriatic. **GPS**: n42,97694 e17,22500.
100-270kn. 01/04-31/10.

Molunat 39A4

Adriatic I, Višnjici 4, Đurinici. **GPS**: n42,45341 e18,43554.
Ch.
Remarks: Mini-camp.

Molunat 39A4

Monika, Molunat 10. **GPS**: n42,45284 e18,42871.
80-180kn Ch. 01/01-31/12.
Remarks: Mini-camp.

Molunat 39A4

Adriatic II. **GPS**: n42,45327 e18,43582.
Remarks: Mini-camp.

Murvica 37B3

Camper stop Marni, Kralja Tomislava 102.
GPS: n44,13305 e15,29338.

36 150-190kn Ch WC included.
Surface: gravel. 01/01-31/12.
Distance: 5km on the spot 1km 2km.
Remarks: Video surveillance.

Nin 37B3

Dišpet, Put Ždrijaca 13. **GPS**: n44,24618 e15,18971.
€ 26-35 Ch WC. 01/04-15/10.
Remarks: Mini-camp.

Nin 37B3

Nin, Put Venere Anzotike 41. **GPS**: n44,24541 e15,17401.
100-132kn Ch. 01/05-15/10.
Remarks: Mini-camp.

Nin 37B3

Ninska Laguna, Put blata 10. **GPS**: n44,24639 e15,17389.
€ 10-20 Ch WC. 01/01-31/12.
Remarks: Mini-camp.

Tourist information Nin:

Arheološka zbirka Nin, Trg Kraljevac 8. Archeological museum. 01/10-31/5 8-14h, 01/06-30/09 8-22h.

Novigrad (Dalmatia) 37B3

Adria-Sol Mulic. **GPS**: n44,19019 e15,54703.
€ 17,70-19,70 Ch WC. 01/05-30/09.
Remarks: Mini-camp.

Obrovac 37B3

Zrmanja Camping Village, Kruševo, Župani - Drage bb.
GPS: n44,18506 e15,69279.
Remarks: Mini-camp.

Omiš 37C3

Galeb. **GPS**: n43,44061 e16,68128.
125-250kn Ch WC. 13/05-01/11.

Omiš 37C3

Lisičina, Lisičina 2. **GPS**: n43,44737 e16,69038.
76-131kn Ch WC. 01/01-31/12.
Remarks: Mini-camp.

Opuzen 34H1

Rio, Put Zlatinovca 23. **GPS**: n43,01351 e17,46890.
€ 18-25 Ch WC. 01/04-30/10.

Orašac 39A4

Pod Maslinom, Put prema moru b.b.. **GPS**: n42,69907 e18,00592.
KN 96-138 Ch. 01/04-01/11.
Remarks: Mini-camp.

Pag 37B2

Košljun, Košljun B.B.. **GPS**: n44,39849 e15,07936.
131-156kn Ch WC. 01/06-01/10.
Remarks: Mini-camp.

Pag 37B2

Pere, Dinjiška. **GPS**: n44,35939 e15,18641.
€ 15 WC. 01/05-15/10.
Remarks: Mini-camp.

Pag 37B2

Porat, Stjepana Radića bb., Povljana. **GPS**: n44,34914 e15,10547.
60 € 12,66-20,94 Ch WC. 23/04-30/09.
Remarks: Mini-camp.

Pag 37B2

Simuni, V. Nazora b.b, Simuni. **GPS**: n44,45979 e14,97670.
94-379kn Ch WC. 01/01-31/12.

Pakoštane 37B3

Blaž. **GPS**: n43,90763 e15,50089.
Ch.
Remarks: Mini-camp.

Pakoštane 37B3

Kozarica. **GPS**: n43,90970 e15,49881.
€ 16,90-48,90 Ch WC. 15/04-15/10.

Pakoštane 37B3

Marin. **GPS**: n43,90442 e15,51866.
€ 13,50-32,50 Ch WC. 01/07-31/10.
Remarks: Mini-camp.

Pakoštane 37B3

Nordsee. **GPS**: n43,90525 e15,51617.
€ 14,40-27,50 Ch WC. 01/03-05/11.

Pakoštane 37B3

Oaza Mira, Dr. Franje Tuđmana bb, Drage. **GPS**: n43,88607 e15,53290.
150 € 23-56 Ch WC. 01/04-15/10.
Remarks: Mini-camp.

Pakoštane 37B3

Oaza, Drage. **GPS**: n43,87035 e15,55917.
€ 14-24 Ch WC. 01/04-15/10.
Remarks: Mini-camp.

Pakoštane 37B3

Pakoštane. **GPS**: n43,91120 e15,49983.
. 08/04-31/10.
Remarks: Mini-camp.

Pašman 37B3

Camp Arboretum, Barotul 8. **GPS**: n43,96283 e15,36082.
€ 20-22 Ch WC. 01/06-30/09.
Remarks: Mini-camp.

Pelješac/Orebić 34H1

Camping Ponta, Kvaternikova 3. **GPS**: n42,97722 e17,22444.
30 65-80kn WC.
Distance: on the spot on the spot.

Pelješac/Orebić 34H1

Ulica Bana Josipa Jelačića. **GPS**: n42,97499 e17,16929.
±10 70kn. **Surface:** grassy/gravel. 01/01-31/12.
Distance: pebbled beach 500m.

Pelješac/Orebić 34H1

Camping Adriatic, Mokalo 6. **GPS**: n42,97672 e17,22489.
€ 14-35,50 Ch WC. 01/04-31/10.
Remarks: Mini-camp.

Pelješac/Orebić 34H1

Glavna Plaža. **GPS**: n42,97583 e17,18917.
€ 12-20,20 Ch WC. 15/05-15/10.

Pelješac/Orebić 34H1

Paradiso. **GPS**: n42,96750 e17,24293.
Ch.
Remarks: Mini-camp.

Pelješac/Orebić 34H1

Perna. **GPS**: n42,97638 e17,13272.
€ 13,50- 18,80 Ch. 16/04-14/10.

Pelješac/Orebić 34H1

Trstenica, Šetalište Kneza Domagoja 50. **GPS**: n42,97725 e17,18995.
25 Ch WC.
Remarks: Mini-camp.

Pelješac/Orebić 34H1

Paradiso, Obala Pomoraca 70 A. **GPS**: n42,96693 e17,24230.
.
Remarks: Mini-camp.

Pelješac/Trpanj 34H1

Divna. **GPS**: n43,00944 e17,26806.
100 Ch. 01/06-30/09.
Remarks: Mini-camp.

Pelješac/Trpanj 34H1

Vrila. **GPS**: n43,00360 e17,28467.
Ch WC. 20/05-10/10.

Petrcane 37B3

Pineta, Punta Radman 21. **GPS**: n44,17805 e15,16161.
110-138kn Ch WC. 01/05-01/09.
Remarks: Mini-camp.

Podgora 34H1

Sutikla. **GPS**: n43,23455 e17,07759.
99-198kn Ch WC. 22/06-15/09.

Podstrana 37C3

Tamaris, Sv.Martin 114. **GPS**: n43,47551 e16,56383.
50 € 18,70-21,37 Ch WC. 15/06-15/09.
Distance: on the spot.
Remarks: Mini-camp.

Podstrana 37C3

Autocamp, Cesta Svetog Martina. **GPS**: n43,47408 e16,56754.
.
Remarks: Mini-camp.

Tourist information Podstrana:
Sinjska alka, Sinj. Knight celebration. 5th August.

Posedarje 37B3

Kristina. **GPS**: n44,21288 e15,49820.
€ 12,80-15,80 Ch. 01/05-30/09.
Remarks: Mini-camp.

Posedarje 37B3

Bristi. **GPS**: n44,21231 e15,48038.
.
Remarks: Mini-camp.

Povijana 37B3

Mali Dubrovnik, Kralja P. Svacica 1. **GPS**: n44,34931 e15,10060.
Ch WC.
Remarks: Mini-camp.

Povijana 37B3

Porat, Ante Starcevica Bb. **GPS**: n44,14466 e15,08569.
30 120-136kn Ch WC. 01/05-01/10.
Remarks: Mini-camp.

Primošten 37C3

Zagrebacka ul.. **GPS**: n43,58854 e15,92632.
10 € 7/24h.
Distance: 200m 200m 200m 200m.

Primošten 37C3

Adriatic, Huljerat b.b.. **GPS**: n43,60645 e15,92193.
€ 16,80-30,90 Ch WC. 07/04-31/10.

Privlaka 37B3

Dalmacija, Ivana Pavla II 40. **GPS**: n44,25613 e15,12557.
€ 15,70-40,40 Ch WC. 01/05-15/10.

Privlaka 37B3

Medanić, Put Brtalica 47. **GPS**: n44,24887 e15,13379.
Ch WC.
Remarks: Mini-camp.

Ražanac 37B3

Kamp Miočić, Rtina I 139, Rtina. **GPS**: n44,29219 e15,30179.
Ch WC.

Ražanac 37B3

Kamp Odmoree, Rtina Stošići bb. **GPS**: n44,30040 e15,28881.
13 345kn Ch.

Ražanac 37B3

Planik. **GPS**: n44,27778 e15,34472.
€ 14,94-19,33 Ch WC. 01/01-31/12.
Remarks: Mini-camp.

Ražanac 37B3

Puntica, Puntica 1. **GPS**: n44,28389 e15,34306.
€ 12-18,80 Ch WC. 01/05-15/10.
Remarks: Mini-camp.

Rovanjska 37B3

Tamaris. **GPS**: n44,25037 e15,53735.
30 112-142kn Ch WC. 01/05-01/10.
Remarks: Mini-camp.

Senj 37B2

Kamp Škver, Filipa Vukasovica 5. **GPS**: n44,99385 e14,90012.

50 69kn, Jun/Sep 89kn, Jul/Aug 106kn Ch night,20kn, 16Amp WC 35kn included **Location:** Urban, comfortable. **Surface:** gravel/metalled. 01/04-01/10.
Distance: 500m on the spot on the spot on the spot 150m 500m on the spot on the spot.
Remarks: Fishing permit available.

Senj 37B2

Bunica, Bunica 33. **GPS**: n45,02607 e14,88630.
Ch.
Remarks: Mini-camp.

Senj 37B2

Ujca, M. Cihlar Nehajeva, 4. **GPS**: n44,96833 e14,92167.
100-150kn Ch WC. 01/05-01/10.
Distance: on the spot.
Remarks: Mini-camp.

Šibenik 37C3

Cikada, Konjevodci 63. **GPS**: n43,78200 e15,99116.
10 € 9-12 + € 0,50-1/pp tourist tax Ch € 2,50 WC.
Location: Rural. **Surface:** gravel. 01/05-31/10.

Šibenik 37C3

Camperstop, Lozovac-Gradina. **GPS**: n43,79207 e15,97042.

40kn. **Surface:** unpaved. 01/01-31/12.
Remarks: 1km from Krka waterfalls.

Šibenik 37C3

Solaris. **GPS**: n43,69917 e15,87795.
€ 15-62 Ch WC. 24/03-20/10.

Šibenik 37C3

Solaris-Zablaće, Obala palih boraca 2a. **GPS**: n43,70524 e15,86850.
€ 30-32,50 Ch WC. 01/05-30/09.

Tourist information Šibenik:
Internationaal kinderfestival. 22/06-06/07.
Nacionalni Park Krka, Krka. Nature reserve.

Skradin 37C3

Robeko Camping, Piramatovci. Bilostanovi 12.
GPS: n43,89193 e15,82320.
Ch WC.
Remarks: Mini-camp.

Slano 39A4

Baldo. **GPS**: n42,79683 e17,84989.
€ 26-32 Ch. 19/04-09/10.
Remarks: Mini-camp.

Slano 39A4

Bambo. **GPS**: n42,77513 e17,88500.
Ch.
Remarks: Mini-camp.

Slano 39A4

Banja, Put Od Banje. **GPS**: n42,77414 e17,88405.
Ch.
Remarks: Mini-camp.

Slano 39A4

Rogac, Grgurici. **GPS**: n42,78229 e17,87536.
64-76kn Ch WC. 01/04-01/10.
Remarks: Mini-camp.

Slano 39A4

Sladenovici, Sladenovici 9. **GPS**: n42,78451 e17,85984.
€ 11 Ch.
Remarks: Mini-camp.

HR

Slatine 37C3

Domic, Put Porta 71, Ciove. **GPS**: n43,49784 e16,34060.
Remarks: Mini-camp.

Soline 37B3

Camping Mandarino. **GPS**: n44,14148 e14,86495.
€ 20-48 Ch WC. 14/05-30/09.
Remarks: Mini-camp.

Split 37C3

Stobreč. **GPS**: n43,50401 e16,52644.
€ 16,70-30,30 Ch WC.
01/01-31/12.
Distance: centre 7km on the spot.

Tourist information Split:
Arheoloski Muzej, Zrinjsko-Frankopanska 25. Findings from Roman time and Middle Ages. Tue-Fri 9-14h, Sa-Su 9-13h, 01/06-30/09 Tue-Fri 9-12, 13-20h, Sa-Su 9-13h.
Galerija Ivana Mestrovica, Setaliste I. Mestrovica 46. Gallery. Mo-Sa 10-18h, Su 10-14h.
Muzej Hrvatskih Arheoloskih Spomenika, S. Gunjace bb. Archeological findings. Mo-Sa 9-20h.
Dioklecijanova palača. Roman palace.

Starigrad/Paklenica 37B3

Camp National Park, Paklenica. **GPS**: n44,28832 e15,44573.
€ 35-50 Ch WC. 15/03-15/10.
Remarks: Mini-camp.

Starigrad/Paklenica 37B3

Marko, Paklenicka 7, Paklenica. **GPS**: n44,28643 e15,45247.
€ 16-19 Ch WC. 01/01-31/12.
Remarks: Mini-camp.

Starigrad/Paklenica 37B3

Pinus, Ive Senjanina 5, Paklenica. **GPS**: n44,32242 e15,39288.
€ 12,70-16,80 Ch WC. 01/05-01/09.
Remarks: Mini-camp.

Starigrad/Paklenica 37B3

Pisak, Paklenica. **GPS**: n44,27285 e15,47806.
124-146kn Ch WC. 01/05-01/10.
Remarks: Mini-camp.

Starigrad/Paklenica 37B3

Plantaža, Put Plantaže 2, Paklenica. **GPS**: n44,30056 e15,43211.
€ 27-33 Ch WC. 01/01-31/12.
Remarks: Mini-camp.

Starigrad/Paklenica 37B3

Vesna, Paklenicka 103, Paklenica. **GPS**: n44,28610 e15,45243.
Ch WC. 01/01-31/12.
Remarks: Mini-camp.

Starigrad/Paklenica 37B3

Jaz, Seline, Paklenica. **GPS**: n44,28323 e15,46028.
01/05-30/09.
Remarks: Mini-camp.

Tourist information Starigrad/Paklenica:
Nacionalni park "Paklenica". Nature reserve, 150 km biking ad hiking trails, bird observation, tunnels and caves.

Ston 34H1

Prapratno. **GPS**: n42,81778 e17,67611.
€ 35-50 Ch WC. 01/05-30/09.

Ston 34H1

Vrela, Brijesta 10. **GPS**: n42,90397 e17,53266.
€ 22-30 Ch WC. 01/04-30/10.
Remarks: Mini-camp.

Sukošan 37B3

Brajde. **GPS**: n44,04256 e15,30755.
Ch WC.
Remarks: Mini-camp.

Sukošan 37B3

Malenica, Vl. Milan Gašparović. **GPS**: n44,03658 e15,32790.
50 WC. 01/05-01/10.
Remarks: Mini-camp.

Sukošan 37B3

Oliva. **GPS**: n44,04247 e15,30805.
Ch WC. 01/01-31/12.
Remarks: Mini-camp.

Sukošan 37B3

Kamp Kaj, Punta 15. **GPS**: n44,04278 e15,30655.
7.
Remarks: Mini-camp.

Supetar 34G1

Waterman Beach. **GPS**: n43,38076 e16,56439.
Ch WC. 01/05-30/09.

Sutivan 34G1

Mlin, Brac. **GPS**: n43,38316 e16,47795.
Remarks: Mini-camp.

Sutivan 34G1

Sutivan, Gorana Pavlova 12. **GPS**: n43,38523 e16,48460.
01/01-31/12.

Sv. Filip I Jakov 37B3

Antonio, Turanj. **GPS**: n43,97488 e15,39990.
Ch WC.
Remarks: Mini-camp.

Sv. Filip I Jakov 37B3

Djardin, Sveti Filip i Jakov bb. **GPS**: n43,96139 e15,42750.
€ 14,60-26,20 Ch WC. 23/04-01/10.

Sv. Filip I Jakov 37B3

Filip, Put Primorja 10a. **GPS**: n43,96055 e15,42910.
€ 9,73-26,66 Ch WC. 01/04-01/10.
Remarks: Mini-camp.

Sv. Filip I Jakov 37B3

Maestral, Turanj 90. **GPS**: n43,96611 e15,41162.
122-152kn Ch WC. 01/05-31/10.
Remarks: Mini-camp.

Sv. Filip I Jakov 37B3

Moče, Put Primorja 8. **GPS**: n43,95968 e15,42915.
€ 14-27 Ch WC. 01/04-01/10.
Remarks: Mini-camp.

Sv. Filip I Jakov 37B3

R & B, Turanj. **GPS**: n43,96592 e15,41196.
6 WC.
Distance: on the spot on the spot.
Remarks: Mini-camp.

Sv. Filip I Jakov 37B3

Rio, Put Primorja. **GPS**: n43,95583 e15,43500.
€ 33-44 Ch WC.
Remarks: Mini-camp.

Sv. Filip I Jakov 37B3

Bepo, Turanj. **GPS**: n43,96562 e15,41254.
Distance: on the spot on the spot.
Remarks: Mini-camp.

Sv. Filip I Jakov 37B3

Milan, Sv. Petar. **GPS**: n44,00205 e15,36859.
3.
Remarks: Mini-camp.

Sveti Juraj 37B2

Camping Ujča, Ujča 146/A. **GPS**: n44,96853 e14,92223.
100-110kn Ch WC. 01/05-01/10.
Remarks: Mini-camp.

Sveti Petar na Moru 37B3

Autocamp Martin. **GPS**: n44,00003 e15,36880.
15 € 14 Ch € 3 WC. **Surface:** grassy/gravel.
01/01-31/12.
Distance: on the spot on the spot.

Sveti Petar na Moru 37B3

Ante, Turanj. **GPS**: n43,99637 e15,37915.
Remarks: Mini-camp.

Sveti Petar na Moru 37B3

Bozo. **GPS**: n43,99688 e15,37838.
Remarks: Mini-camp.

Tkon 37B3

Brist. **GPS**: n43,92312 e15,41493.
Ch.
Remarks: Mini-camp.

Tkon 37B3

Adriana. **GPS**: n43,91734 e15,42596.
Remarks: Mini-camp.

Tribanj 37B2

Camp CTT, D8. **GPS**: n44,34673 e15,32444.
7 € 20. **Surface:** grassy/gravel. 01/01-31/12.
Distance: 900m on the spot.
Remarks: Not suitable for motorhomes +7m.

Tribanj 37B2

Punta Šibuljina, Šibuljina. **GPS**: n44,33631 e15,34627.
150 € 13,95-22 Ch WC. 23/04-08/10.
Remarks: Mini-camp.

Tribanj 37B2

Ante, Kopovine 9. **GPS**: n44,34469 e15,32842.
Remarks: Mini-camp.

Trogir 37C3

Seget, Seget Donji. **GPS**: n43,51904 e16,22430.
50 from € 21 Ch WC. 01/03-31/10.
Distance: 800m on the spot.
Remarks: Mini-camp.

Trogir 37C3

Vranjica Belvedere, Seget Vranjica. **GPS**: n43,51196 e16,19159.
451 Ch WC. 15/04-15/10.

Tourist information Trogir:
Tourist Information, Ivana Pavla II Square, www.trogir-online.com. City with rich culture from Greek, Roman and Venetian time.
Town Museum, Fanfogna palace, Garagnin. History of the city. 16/09-14/06 by request 8-14h, 15/06-15/09 9-21h.
Zbirka Kairos. Ecclesiastical art collection. 15/6-15/9 8-13, 15-19h.
Fortress Kamerlengo. Fortress. 15/6-15/9 9-20h.
Katedrala St. Lawrence. Bell-tower of Cathedral of St. Lawrence, 47m. 15/6-15/9 9-12, 16-19h. 5kn.

Vela Luka 34H1

Mindel, Stani 193. **GPS**: n42,98369 e16,67060.
€ 14 Ch WC. 01/01-31/12.

Veli Rat 37B3

Camping Kargita, Veli Rat 67. **GPS**: n44,15402 e14,82221.
30 € 17,10- 31 Ch WC. 23/04-01/10.
Remarks: Mini-camp.

Viganj 34H1

Antony Boy. **GPS**: n42,97889 e17,10752.
134-170kn Ch WC. 01/01-31/12.

Vir 37B3

Sapavac, Put Bunara 101. **GPS**: n44,29432 e15,07640.
WC.
Distance: on the spot on the spot.
Remarks: Mini-camp.

Vir 37B3

Auto Camp Luka. **GPS**: n44,29721 e15,10256.
Remarks: Mini-camp.

Vodice 37C3

Imperial, Vatroslava Lisinskog 2/I. **GPS**: n43,75287 e15,78992.
145 € 23-41 Ch WC. 21/03-11/11.

Vransko Jezero 37B3

Crkvine. **GPS**: n43,93035 e15,51012.
€ 23-29 Ch WC. 15/04-15/10.

Vrsi 37B3

Mulic, Mulo. **GPS**: n44,26174 e15,21246.
Remarks: Mini-camp.

Zaboric 37C3

Jasenovo. **GPS**: n43,65116 e15,95025.
50 € 13-29 Ch WC. 01/05-01/10.
Distance: on the spot.
Remarks: Mini-camp.

Zadar 37B3

Borik, Radovana 7. **GPS**: n44,13528 e15,21528.
500 € 19,20-30,10 Ch WC. 01/05-01/10.

Tourist information Zadar:
Trg Pet Bunara. Square of the five fountains.
Arheoloski Muzej, Simuna Kozicica Benje bb. Archeological findings. Mo-Sa 9-13h, 18-20h.
Muziekavonden in de St. Donatius van Zadar. 01/07-15/08.

Zaostrog 34H1

Uvala Borova, Mkarska. **GPS**: n43,13123 e17,28750.
90 € 21,80-32,60 Ch WC. 01/05-30/09.

Zaton 37B3

Zaton. **GPS**: n44,23385 e15,16671.
€ 22,60-57,70 Ch WC. 30/04-30/09.

Ždrelac 37B3

Ruža. **GPS**: n44,00987 e15,27653.
40 WC.
Remarks: Mini-camp.

Živogošće 34H1

Dole. **GPS**: n43,17118 e17,19669.
€ 36-45 Ch WC. 01/05-30/09.

Žrnovo 34H1

Vrbovica, Vrbovica bb. **GPS**: n42,95882 e17,11394.
120-160kn Ch WC. 01/06-01/09.
Remarks: Mini-camp.

Žrnovo 34H1

Tri Žala, Uvala Tri Žala 808. **GPS**: n42,96407 e17,09104.
01/06-30/09.
Distance: on the spot on the spot 1km 1km.
Remarks: Mini-camp.

Žuljana 34H1

Vucine. **GPS**: n42,88257 e17,45135.
Ch WC.
Remarks: Mini-camp.

Inland

Kopačevo 39A2

Autokamp Family Kopačevo, Ferenca Kiša 7.
GPS: n45,59832 e18,78467.
20 € 18 . **Location:** Rural. **Surface:** grassy.
01/04-30/09.

Koprivnica 36C3

Cerine, Miroslava Krleze 81. **GPS**: n46,15361 e16,84250.

11 first night 110kn, 75kn each additional night, 2 pers incl. + 7kn tourist tax Ch WC included. **Location:** Comfortable.
Surface: grasstiles. 01/01-31/12.
Distance: 1,5km 300m 1km.
Remarks: Parking spa resort, wifi code at swimming pool.

Lipovac 39A3

Spacva. **GPS**: n45,04593 e18,99682.
6. 01/05-01/10.

Plitviča 37B2

Bear, Selište Drežničko 52. **GPS**: n44,94804 e15,63639.

30 130kn, 01/06-30/09 150kn, 01/07-31/08 170kn Ch (30x), 16Amp WC included. **Location:** Rural, comfortable, central, quiet. **Surface:** asphalted/gravel. 01/04-15/10.
Distance: 300m 700m 20km 150m 400m on the spot on the spot on the spot.
Remarks: Baker every morning, water falls Plitvica 5km.

Plitviča 37B2

Cvetkovic, Jezerce 28. **GPS**: n44,86338 e15,63967.

20 € 10/pp Ch WC included.
Location: Rural, comfortable, central, quiet. **Surface:** grassy/gravel.
01/01-31/12.
Distance: 800m 10km 800m 800m on the spot on the spot 800m 800m.
Remarks: Water falls Plitvica 2km.

Plitviča 37B2

Korana. **GPS**: n44,99260 e15,64916.
€ 20-24 Ch. 25/03-31/10.

Tourist information Plitviča:
Nacionalni Park Plitviča Jezera, www.np-plitvicka-jezera.hr. National park Plitvice lakes. 9-17h.

Racovica 37B2

Turist, Grabovac 102. **GPS**: n44,97222 e15,64750.
€ 20-26,40 Ch WC. 30/04-01/10.

Šimunčevec 37B1

Val-travel, Popovic Dure 9. **GPS**: n45,87839 e16,09302.
€ 17,50 + tourist tax WCincluded. **Location:** Rural.
Surface: gravel. 01/01-31/12.
Distance: Zagreb 18km 100m.
Remarks: Dutch owners.

Zagreb 37B1

Camp-Zagreb, Jezerska 6. **GPS**: n45,80253 e15,82622.

50 € 23-31 Ch WC included.
Location: Urban, luxurious. **Surface:** metalled.
Distance: on the spot on the spot on the spot on the spot on the spot.
Remarks: Bus to Zagreb € 8/round trip.

Zagreb 37B1

E Camper Zagreb, Josipa Ressela. **GPS**: n45,78197 e15,97774.
20 150kn Ch included. **Surface:** gravel/metalled.
01/01-31/12.
Distance: 2,5km 600m on the spot 400m on the spot on the spot.
Remarks: Max. 72h, water closed during wintertime.

Zagreb 37B1

Val-Travel Camp, Ulica Popovic Dure 9. **GPS**: n45,88131 e16,08861.
€ 14,50-17,50 WCincluded. 01/01-31/12.
Distance: 18km.
Remarks: Max. 7m.

Tourist information Zagreb:
http://www.infozagreb.hr/. Capital, surface 64133 km ^{2}, inhabitants 885,000, 11 theaters and 22 museums.
Archeological Museum, 19 Nikola Subic Zrinski Square. Tue-Fri 10-17h, Sa-Su 10-13h.
Atelje Mestrovic, Mletacka 8. Former dwellinghouse of sculptor Ivan Mestrovic. Tue-Fri 10-18h, Sa-Su 10-13h.
Ethnographic Museum, Mazuranicev trg 14.
Tue-Thu 10-18h, Fri-Su 10-13h.
Muzej Grada Zagreb, Opaticka 20. City museum.
Tue-Fri 10-18h, Sa 11-19h, Su 10-14h.
Tehnicki Muzej, Savska cesta 18. Technical museum.
Tue-Fri 9-17h, Sa-Su 9-13h.
Medjunarodna Smotra Folklora. International folk festival.
20/07/05-24/07/05.
Zomerfestival van Zagreb.
01/07-15/08.
Park Prirode Kopacki Rit. Nature reserve, boat rental.
daily 8-16h.

HR

Hungary

Capital: Budapest
Government: parliamentary constitutional republic
Official Language: Hungarian
Population: 9,874,784 (2016)
Area: 93,024 km²

General information
Dialling code: 0036
General emergency: 112
Currency: Forint (HUF)
€ 1 = 311 HUF, 100 HUF = € 0,32
£1 = 353 HUF, 100 HUF = £0.28 (October 2017)
Credit cards are accepted almost everywhere.

Regulations for overnight stays
Free overnight stay is not allowed.

Additional public holidays 2018
March 15 Revolution Memorial Day 1848
April 2 Easter Monday
August 20 Hungarian National Day
October 23 Revolution Memorial Day 1956
November 1 All Saints' Day

Time Zone
Winter (Standard Time) GMT+1
Summer (DST) GMT+2

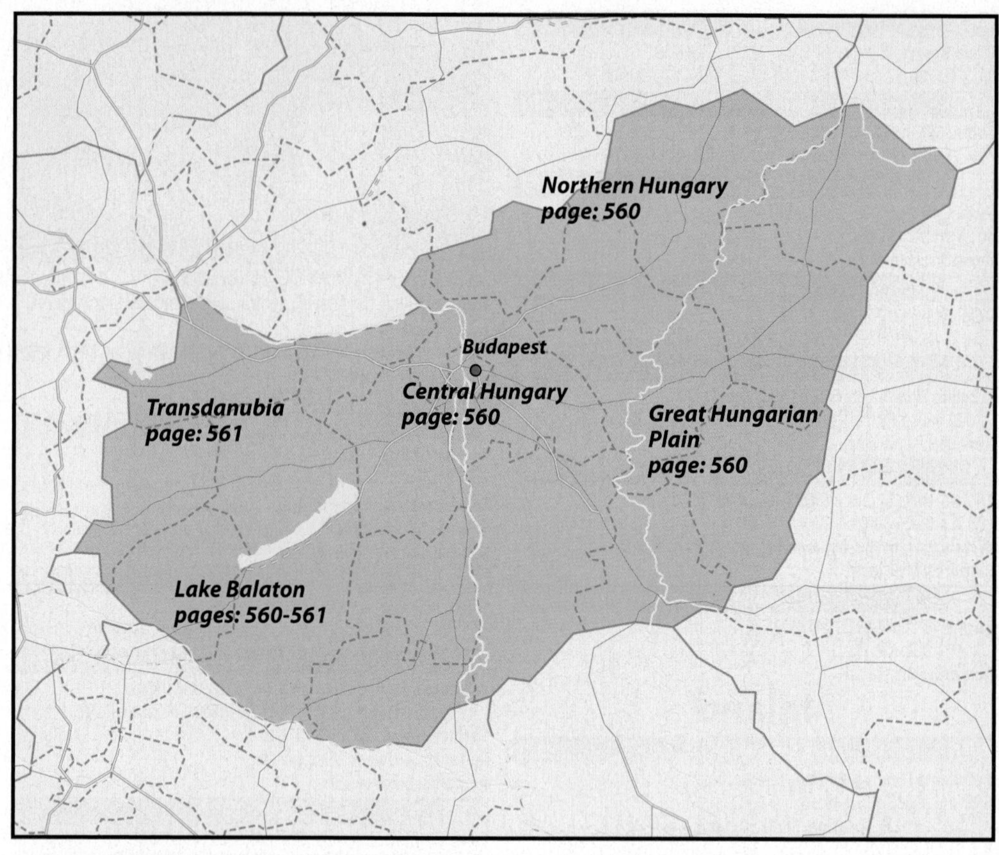

HU

Northern Hungary

Bekölce 39A1
Camping Bekölce, Béke út 252. **GPS**: n48,08260 e20,24904.
10 € 15 Ch included. 01/01-31/12.

Borsodbóta 39A1
Camping Amedi, Rákóczi út 181. **GPS**: n48,21329 e20,40569.
40 € 12,50, 01/07-31/08 € 16,50 Ch included € 4.
Surface: grassy. 01/05-30/09.

Budapest 39A1
Arena Camping Budapest, Pilisi straat 7.
GPS: n47,50424 e19,15839.
€ 21,35 Ch WC 01/01-31/12.

Budapest 39A1
Ave Natura, Csermely u 3.
GPS: n47,51416 e18,97300.

12 € 18,50 Ch (12x)€ 3,80 WC included.
Surface: grassy/sand. 01/04-10/11.
Distance: 5km 100m 2km on the spot on the spot on the spot.

Budapest 39A1
Zugligeti Niche, Zugligeti út 101. **GPS**: n47,51637 e18,97509.
25 € 27, 2 pers.incl Ch WC included.
Surface: grassy.
01/01-31/12.
Distance: 5km on the spot on the spot 200m on the spot on the spot.
Remarks: Breakfest-service.

Hernádvécse 38C4
Zonnebloempaleis, Rákóczi út 96. **GPS**: n48,43360 e21,17230.
1 € 10, 15/06-28/08 € 12 Ch included. **Location:** Rural.
Surface: grassy. 14/04-01/10.
Distance: 2km.

Pécs 36D3
Família Camping, Gyöngyösi utca 6. **GPS**: n46,08559 e18,26206.
15 € 15 Ch included. **Location:** Rural. **Surface:** metalled.
01/05-30/09.
Distance: 2,5km 200m 100m.

Great Hungarian Plain

Püspökladány 39A1
Árnyas Thermal Camping és Üdülőpark, Petőfi Sándor Ut 62.
GPS: n47,32192 e21,10273.
50 € 15 Ch included. **Location:** Rural.
Surface: grassy/metalled. 01/05-30/09.
Distance: on the spot.

Szentkirály 39A2
Fantazia Tanya, Felsö Tanya 165. **GPS**: n46,94087 e19,93109.

20 € 13 Ch included € 4.
Location: Rural. **Surface:** grassy. 01/04-01/11.
Distance: on the spot.

Zsana 39A2
Camping Oázis Tanya, 1. Körzet 15. **GPS**: n46,41438 e19,61111.

20 € 15,30, 01/07-31/08 € 18,30 Ch (20x)€ 3 WC € 3,75 included. **Location:** Rural. **Surface:** grassy. 15/04-30/09.
Distance: 12km on the spot 5km on the spot 12km 2km 2km on the spot.

Central Hungary

Csemő 39A2
Békés Föld, Bezzeg dülö. **GPS**: n47,13217 e19,73983.
4 € 12,50 Ch included. **Surface:** grassy/sand.
01/01-31/12.

Lake Balaton

Balatonkeresztúr 36C3
Bertalan, Ady Endre utca 51. **GPS**: n46,70333 e17,37047.

6 € 12 Ch WC included. **Location:** Urban, simple.
Surface: grassy. 01/01-31/12 service: Jul/Aug.
Distance: on the spot lake Balaton 300m 200m 150m 500m.

Cserszegtomaj 36C3
Camping Panorama, Panoráma köz 1. **GPS**: n46,80667 e17,21306.
15 € 14 excl. tourist tax Ch included .
Surface: grassy. 01/04-31/10.
Distance: 5km 5km 2km 2km.

Gyenesdiás 36C3
Wellnes-Park, Napfény utca 6. **GPS**: n46,76417 e17,30250.
€ 14-17 + € 1,40/pp tourist tax Ch included.
Surface: grassy. 01/04-15/10.
Distance: 2km lake Balaton 2km 200m 500m 2km.

Kisbárapáti 36D3
Camping Jó Napot, Ady Endre utca 46. **GPS**: n46,59827 e17,86750.

15 € 15,50 Chincluded € 3,50. **Location:** Rural. **Surface:** grassy. 15/04-15/09.

Koppányszántó 36D3

Tranquil Pines, Dózsa György utca 334. **GPS**: n46,59027 e18,10344.

10 € 11,50 Ch included € 5,50. **Location:** Rural. **Surface:** metalled. 01/01-31/12. **Distance:** 1,5km.

Somogyvár 36C3

Kimis Camp, Bartók Béla utca 58. **GPS**: n46,58275 e17,62398.

36 € 9 Ch (24x)WC included € 1. **Location:** Rural, comfortable. **Surface:** grassy. 01/05-30/09. **Distance:** 500m on the spot.

Transdanubia

Bozsok 36B2

Nagy Vendégház, Rákoczi út 105. **GPS**: n47,32059 e16,48590.

5 € 5 Ch WC. **Location:** Rural, comfortable. **Surface:** grassy. 01/01-31/12. **Distance:** 30m 400m. **Remarks:** Arrival >14h departure <12h.

Felsőszentmárton 37D1

Camping de-ommekeer, Szent Lhászló Utca 38. **GPS**: n45,85261 e17,69925. 10 € 15 Ch included. **Surface:** grassy. 01/04-30/09.

Győr 36C2

Camping Pihenö, Mártírok útja. **GPS**: n47,72515 e17,71406.

35 € 15,50 Ch included.

Surface: grassy. 01/01-31/12. **Distance:** 7km 9km.

Halászi 36C2

Party Csárda, Duna sétány. **GPS**: n47,88586 e17,32201.

5 € 15 + € 1,75/pp tourist tax Ch € 2 WC ,cold included. **Location:** Rural, simple. **Surface:** grasstiles. 01/01-31/12. **Distance:** 300m on the spot on the spot on the spot 200m. **Remarks:** Wifi at restaurant.

Lenti 36C3

Rudas, Béke utca 32. **GPS**: n46,62582 e16,53266.

6 € 10 Ch on demand WCincluded . **Location:** Rural, simple. **Surface:** grassy. 01/01-31/12. **Distance:** 200m 800m 800m 30m 300m 600m.

Magyaregregy 36D3

Camping Máré Vára, Várvölgyi utca 2. **GPS**: n46,23407 e18,30913.

36 € 17,50 Ch (36x)WC included . **Location:** Rural. **Surface:** grassy. 15/04-30/09. **Distance:** 500m on the spot 1km 1km on the spot on the spot. **Remarks:** Bread-service, swimming pool 200m.

Mosonmagyaróvár 36C2

AquaThermalcamp, Kigyo utca 1. **GPS**: n47,87715 e17,27948.

40 € 9 + 9/pp + € 1/pp tourist tax Ch € 3/24h WC included . **Location:** Urban, comfortable. **Surface:** grassy. 01/01-31/12. **Distance:** 100m on the spot on the spot 100m.

Mosonmagyaróvár 36C2

Kocisi Joseph, Vízpart utca 59. **GPS**: n47,87335 e17,27851.

8 € 15 Ch included. **Location:** Rural, comfortable. **Surface:** grassy/metalled. 01/01-31/12. **Distance:** 300m 200m 200m.

Nagysáp 36D2

Granárium Camper-port, Granárium domb 3. **GPS**: n47,68573 e18,60741.

7 € 15 Ch (4x),16Amp WC € 10 included . **Surface:** gravel. 01/01-31/12. **Distance:** 500m on the spot 500m 50m on the spot on the spot.

Pápa 36C2

Thermalcamping Pápa, Varkert Utca 7. **GPS**: n47,33781 e17,47359.

6 € 12 + € 1,60/pp tourist tax Ch WC included . **Location:** Urban, simple. **Surface:** gravel. 01/01-31/12. **Distance:** 500m on the spot 500m. **Remarks:** Use sanitary facilities at campsite.

Patosfa 36D3

Camping Farkas, Petőfi utca 52-56. **GPS**: n46,12545 e17,65788.

9 € 19 Ch WC included. **Location:** Rural. **Surface:** sand. 01/05-30/09. **Remarks:** Natural swimming pool, bread-service, regional products.

Sormás 36C3

István Parkhotel & Restaurant, Külterület 28. **GPS**: n46,46071 e16,90783.

16 € 7 Ch (16x)€ 3,50,10Amp WC € 3 included . **Location:** Rural, comfortable, luxurious. **Surface:** grassy/metalled. 01/01-31/12. **Distance:** 2km 1km on the spot.

HU

Ireland

Capital: Dublin
Government: parliamentary constitutional republic
Official Language: Irish and English
Population: 4,952,473 (2016)
Area: 69,825 km²

General information
Dialling code: 00353
General emergency: 112
Currency: Euro
Credit cards are accepted almost everywhere.

Regulations for overnight stays
Free overnight stay is allowed with consent of the landowner, and up to 24 hours on regular parking spaces.

Additional public holidays 2018
March 17 Saint Patrick's Day
March 30 Good Friday
April 2 Easter Monday
May 7 Early Bank Holiday
June 4 June Bank Holiday
August 6 First Moday in August
October 29 October Bank Holiday
November 1 All Saints'Day

Time Zone
Winter (Standard Time) GMT+0
Summer (DST) GMT+1

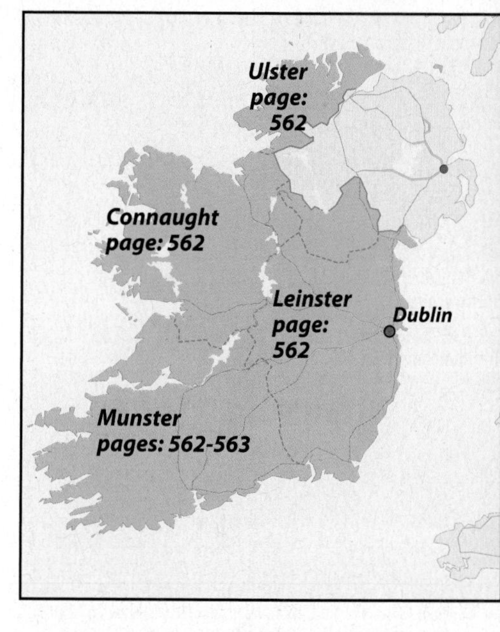

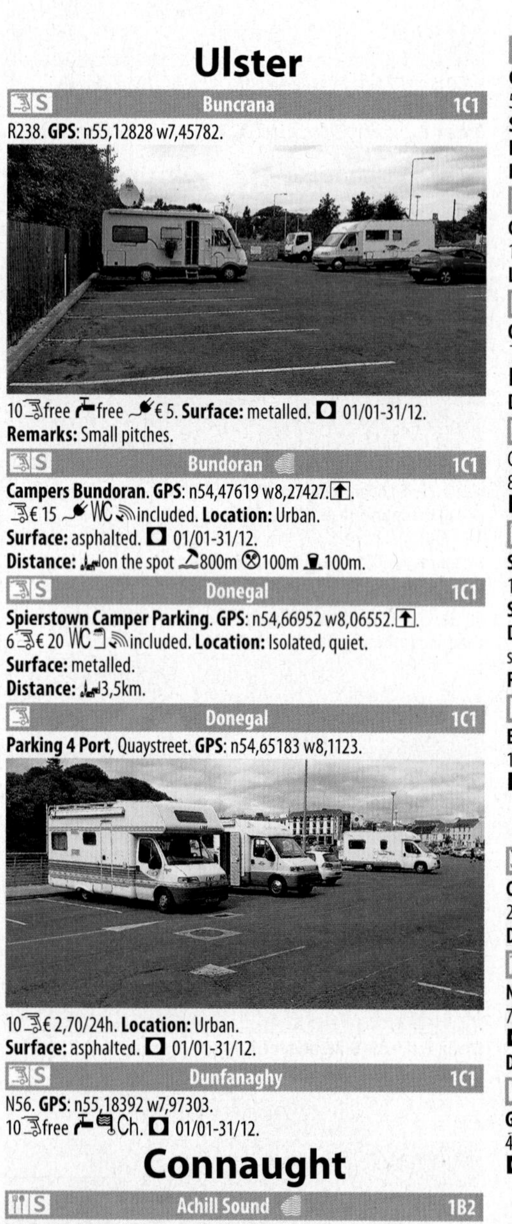

Ulster

Buncrana 1C1
R238. **GPS:** n55,12828 w7,45782.
10 free free € 5. **Surface:** metalled. 01/01-31/12.
Remarks: Small pitches.

Bundoran 1C1
Campers Bundoran. GPS: n54,47619 w8,27427.
€ 15 included. **Location:** Urban.
Surface: asphalted. 01/01-31/12.
Distance: on the spot 800m 100m 100m.

Donegal 1C1
Spierstown Camper Parking. GPS: n54,66952 w8,06552.
6 € 20 included. **Location:** Isolated, quiet.
Surface: metalled.
Distance: 3,5km.

Donegal 1C1
Parking 4 Port, Quaystreet. **GPS:** n54,65183 w8,1123.
10 € 2,70/24h. **Location:** Urban.
Surface: asphalted. 01/01-31/12.

Dunfanaghy 1C1
N56. **GPS:** n55,18392 w7,97303.
10 free Ch. 01/01-31/12.

Connaught

Achill Sound 1B2
Hy Breasal B&B, St. Fionans Road. **GPS:** n53,92836 w9,93123.
10 € 10, € 20 service incl Ch WC
Surface: gravel.
Distance: on the spot 500m 500m 500m 750m on the spot on the spot.

Corraguan 1B2
White Strand. GPS: n53,66904 w9,90211.
10 free. **Location:** Rural. 01/01-31/12.

Crossmolina 1B1
Gortnor Abbey Pier, Lake Rd. **GPS:** n54,09352 w9,2989.
5 free WC free. **Location:** Simple, isolated, quiet.
Surface: concrete. 01/01-31/12.
Distance: 2km on the spot on the spot 2km.
Remarks: Max. 2 nights, video surveillance.

Galway 1B2
Galway Harbour, Dockstreet. **GPS:** n53,27004 w9,04885.
15 8-19h € 2/h, 19-8h € 4 € 3/10kWh.
Location: Urban. **Surface:** asphalted. 01/01-31/12.

Oughterard 1B2
Camp Street Cafe. GPS: n53,42912 w9,31955.
guests free. **Location:** Central, noisy.
01/01-31/12.
Distance: on the spot on the spot on the spot.

Portumna 1B2
Castle Avenue. **GPS:** n53,08388 w8,22038.
8 free WC free. **Location:** Rural. **Surface:** asphalted.
01/01-31/12.

Roosky 1C2
Shannon River. GPS: n53,83192 w7,9197.
10 € 10 Ch € 2. **Location:** Simple, central.
Surface: grassy/gravel. 01/01-31/12.
Distance: on the spot 100m 100m on the spot on the spot.
Remarks: Along river.

Templeboy 1B1
Beach Bar, Aughris head. **GPS:** n54,26908 w8,75696.
10 € 20 Ch included. **Location:** Rural. **Surface:** grassy.
01/01-31/12.

Leinster

Carlingford 1C2
Carlingford Marina, North Commons. **GPS:** n54,05228 w6,19314.
20 € 10 Ch WC included. **Surface:** asphalted.
Distance: 2km on the spot on the spot on the spot.

Fethard-on-Sea 1C3
Norman View Motorhome Park. GPS: n52,18342 w6,83659.
7 € 12 included. **Location:** Rural. **Surface:** grassy/gravel.
01/01-31/12.
Distance: 1km 400m 1km.

Glenmalure 1C2
Glenmalure lodge, Wicklow Way. **GPS:** n52,95743 w6,35405.
4 guests free. **Location:** Rural. **Surface:** metalled.
01/01-31/12.

Munster

Ardmore 1C3
Ardmore Seaview Motorhome Park. GPS: n51,95639 w7,72578.
30 € 10 Ch. **Surface:** grassy. 01/01-31/12.
Distance: 500m on the spot on the spot 500m.
Remarks: Money in envelope in mail box.

Askeaton 1B2
Askeaton Leisurecenter, The Quay. **GPS:** n52,60273 w8,97511.

5 free. **Location:** Urban. **Surface:** asphalted. 01/01-31/12.

Ballinskellig 1A3
Cois Tra Lower. **GPS:** n51,82093 w10,27323.
10 free. **Location:** Rural. **Surface:** asphalted. 01/01-31/12.

Bandon 1B3
Cloghmacsimon. **GPS:** n51,74101 w8,74082.
15 € 7/24h Ch included. **Surface:** asphalted.
01/01-31/12.
Distance: 500m 300m 500m.
Remarks: Next to petrol station, max. 2 days.

Bantry 1B3
The West Lodge Hotel. GPS: n51,67222 w9,47543.
€ 10. **Location:** Rural, isolated, quiet. **Surface:** gravel.
Distance: 2km on the spot.
Remarks: Breakfast-service.

Castletownbere 1B3
Berehaven Golf Club, Filane West. **GPS:** n51,65417 w9,86125.
10 € 18, Jul/Aug € 20 Ch € 2 WC included.
Location: Rural. **Surface:** metalled. 01/01-31/12.
Distance: on the spot.

Cobh 1B3
Whitepoint Moorings. **GPS:** n51,84716 w8,30735.
30 € 10 Ch. **Location:** Urban, simple, quiet.
Surface: asphalted. 01/01-31/12.
Distance: 900m on the spot on the spot.
Remarks: Max. 48h.

Kilrush 1B2
Kilrush Marina, Merchants Quay. **GPS:** n52,63520 w9,49518.
5 € 20 WC € 3 **Location:** Urban.
Surface: metalled. 01/01-31/12.
Distance: 800m on the spot 600m 500m.

Kinsale 1B3
Lidl Kinsale, Barrack's Lane. **GPS:** n51,70796 w8,51726.
10 free. **Surface:** metalled. 01/01-31/12.
Distance: 750m 750m on the spot.
Remarks: Max. 1 night.

Kinsale 1B3
New Road Car Park. GPS: n51,70969 w8,51945.
free. **Surface:** asphalted. 01/01-31/12.
Distance: 500m 500m.
Remarks: At fire-station.

Liscanor 1B2
Cliffs of Moher. GPS: n52,97145 w9,42475.
€ 6/pp. **Location:** Rural. **Surface:** metalled. 01/01-31/12.

Midleton 1B3
Distillery Road Car Park. GPS: n51,91344 w8,16981.
6 free € 0,25 € 0,25 Ch € 0,25. **Location:** Urban.
Surface: asphalted. 01/01-31/12.
Remarks: Max. 48h.

Sneem 1B3
Goosey Island Motor Home Park, Inchinaleega East.
GPS: n51,83772 w9,89934.
26 € 10/24h Ch € 5. **Surface:** grassy/gravel.
01/01-31/12.

Distance: on the spot on the spot on the spot on the spot on the spot on the spot.
Remarks: Along river, max. 48h, check in at bar.

Sneem 1B3

Sneem Hotel. **GPS:** n51,83349 w9,89844.
€ 10. **Surface:** asphalted.
Distance: 500m 100m on the spot 500m.
Remarks: Max. 48h.

Italy

Capital: Rome
Government: parliamentarian republic
Official Language: Italian
Population: 61,007,540 (2016)
Area: 301,339 km²

General information
Dialling code: 0039
General emergency: 112
Currency: Euro
Credit cards are accepted almost everywhere.

Regulations for overnight stays
Wild camping is allowed with permission of municipality, police or property owner when no problems occur.

Additional public holidays 2018
January 6 Epiphany
April 25 Liberation Day
May 1 Labor Day
June 2 Festa della Republica, National Holiday
August 15 Assumption of the Virgin Mary
November 1 All Saints' Day
November 4 Armistice Day
December 8 Immaculate Conception

Time Zone
Winter (Standard Time) GMT+1
Summer (DST) GMT+2

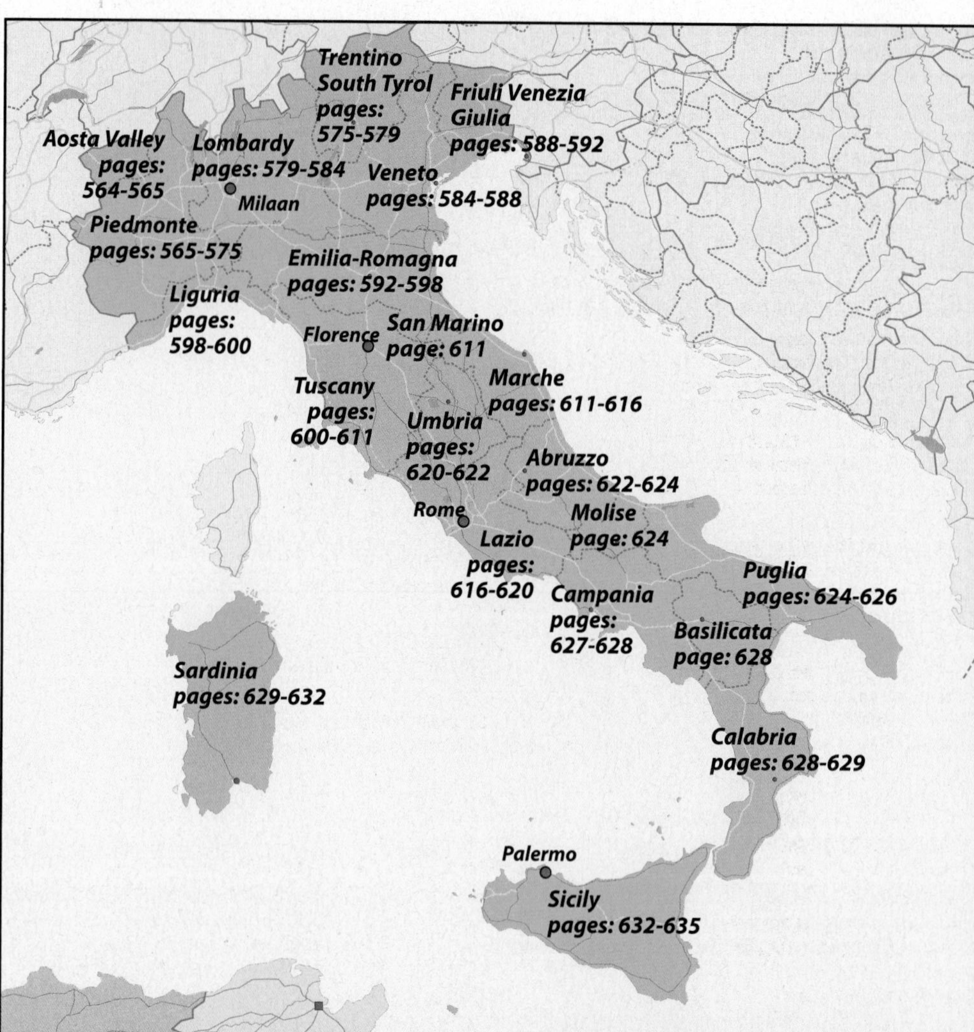

IT

Aosta Valley

Antey-Saint-André — 22G3

Località Filey, SR46. **GPS**: n45,81246 e7,58898.
15 € 8, tourist tax € 0,20/pp Ch included. **Surface:** metalled.
01/01-31/12.
Distance: 850m.
Remarks: To be paid at bar, service passerby € 5.

Aosta — 22G3

Via Cadutti del Lavoro. **GPS**: n45,73600 e7,33035.

30 € 12/24h Ch included € 1/kWh. **Location:** Urban, noisy.
Surface: asphalted. 01/01-31/12 Thu-morning closed because of market.
Distance: on the spot 4,5km 200m on the spot.
Remarks: Parking closes at 22h, video surveillance.

Aymavilles — 22G3

Strada Comunale del Moulins. **GPS**: n45,70125 e7,23960.

20 € 8/24h . **Surface:** metalled. 01/05-31/10.
Distance: on the spot 2km.

Bard — 22H3

SS 26 della Valle d'Aost. **GPS**: n45,61564 e7,74204.
free. **Surface:** metalled. 01/01-31/12.
Distance: on the spot.

Bionaz — 22G3

Area Attrezzata Bosco di Lexert. **GPS**: n45,87458 e7,42381.
€ 10/night Ch. **Surface:** grassy/gravel.
Remarks: Picnic area at small lake.

Brusson — 22H3

Foyer du Ski, Rue Vollon. **GPS**: n45,76617 e7,71117.

50 € 10,80/24h Ch included. **Surface:** grassy/metalled.
01/01-31/12.
Distance: on the spot.
Remarks: At lake.

Cervinia/Breuil — 22G3

Area Camper del Breuil. **GPS**: n45,92614 e7,62026.
50 € 7/24h Ch. **Surface:** asphalted. 01/01-31/12.
Distance: 1km Lago Blu 400m on the spot.
Remarks: Altitude 2000m, shuttle bus to city centre.

Champorcher — 22G3

Area pic-nic, Loc. Chardonney. **GPS**: n45,62141 e7,60992.
35 € 6 free. **Surface:** grassy.
Distance: 300m 300m.
Remarks: Nearby parking funicular railway.

Chatillon — 22G3

Area Camper attrezzata Chatillon, Frazione Perolle.
GPS: n45,74889 e7,62388.

16 € 6/12h Ch. **Surface:** metalled. 01/01-31/12.
Distance: historical centre 500m.

Cogne — 22G3

Fraz. Lillaz. **GPS**: n45,59602 e7,38815.

37 € 8,70, Jul-Aug and 24/12-6/1 € 10,70, tourist tax excl Ch € 2,50. **Surface:** asphalted. 01/01-31/12.
Distance: 100m on the spot 100m 100m on the spot 1km.
Remarks: Altitude 1650m.

Cogne — 22G3

Fraz. Revettaz. **GPS**: n45,60840 e7,35830.

130 € 8,70, Jul/Aug and 24/12-06/01 € 10,70 Ch € 2,50.
Surface: asphalted. 01/01-31/12 water disconnected in winter.

Tourist information Cogne:
Parco Nazionale Gran Paradiso, Vall d'Aosta. Nature reserve, information centres: Dégioz, Rhêmes-Notre-Dame and Cogne.

S Courmayeur 22F3

Funivia Val Veny. GPS: n45,81428 e6,95612.
free . **Surface:** metalled. 01/01-31/12.
Distance: 3km on the spot.

S Étroubles 22G3

Camping Tunnel, Rue des Chevrières, 4. **GPS:** n45,81874 e7,22922.
9 € 13, 22/07-27/08 € 18 Ch included.
Surface: grassy/metalled.
Remarks: Max. 48h.

Fénis 22G3

Località Chez Sapin. **GPS:** n45,73939 e7,48553.
free. **Surface:** asphalted.
Distance: 500m.
Remarks: At cemetery.

S Fontainemore 22H3

SR44. **GPS:** n45,64598 e7,85916.
2 € 6 Ch € 3 WC € 1,summer. 01/01-31/12.
Distance: 350m 350m.
Remarks: To be paid at bar.

S Gaby 22H3

Piazzale Vourry. GPS: n45,70157 e7,87295.
9 free . 01/01-31/12 Service: winter.
Distance: 1,5km.
Remarks: Altitude 1000m.

S Gressoney-Saint-Jean 22H3

P Weissmatten, Via Bildschocke, Saint Jean.
GPS: n45,76028 e7,83556.

€ 6/12h then € 0,50/h, 01/05-30/06 gratis Ch included.
Surface: asphalted. 01/01-31/12.
Remarks: Parking funicular railway.

S Gressoney-Saint-Jean 22H3

Tschaval, La Trinité. **GPS:** n45,85657 e7,81362.

36 € 12/24h + € 0,80/pp tourist tax Ch € 3 WC .
Surface: metalled. 01/01-31/12, 24/24h.
Distance: 2 restaurants 300m on the spot on the spot on the spot 200m.

S Hône 22H3

Via Raffort. **GPS:** n45,61169 e7,73262.
18 € 8 Chincluded € 1/4h. **Surface:** metalled.
01/01-31/12.
Distance: 350m 7km.
Remarks: Max. 48h.

S La Thuile 22F3

Azzurra Camper. GPS: n45,70823 e6,95335.

80 € 13-18 + € 0,80/pp tourist tax Ch (45x)€ 3 € 3
€ 5. **Surface:** metalled. 01/01-31/12.
Distance: 500m 500m 100m.
Remarks: Bread-service, video surveillance.

Pont-Saint-Martin 22H3

Piazzale Palazzetto dello Sport. GPS: n45,60025 e7,79338.
free. **Surface:** asphalted.
Distance: 1km.

S Rhemes Notre Dame 25G1

Gipeto, Loc. Chanavey. **GPS:** n45,57960 e7,12392.
30 € 6/12h, >1 hour € 0,50/h included. **Surface:** metalled.
01/01-31/12.
Distance: on the spot.

Rhemes Notre Dame 25G1

Frazione Bruil. **GPS:** n45,57148 e7,11848.
20 free. **Surface:** asphalted.

S Saint-Denis 22G3

Strada Regionale del Col Saint Pantaléon, Loc. Plaù.
GPS: n45,77129 e7,56092.

4 € 7/24h Ch WC. **Location:** Quiet.
Surface: grasstiles/grassy. 15/04-31/10.
Distance: 16km.

S Saint-Oyen 22G3

Rue de Flassin. **GPS:** n45,82133 e7,20822.
€ 15/24h Ch WCincluded € 1. 01/01-31/12.
Distance: 22km on the spot on the spot.

S Saint-Pierre 22G3

Place des Valdôtains à l'étranger, Località Pommier.
GPS: n45,70831 e7,22402.
8 free . 01/01-31/12.
Distance: 300m 300m on the spot.

S Torgnon 22G3

Plan Proriond. **GPS:** n45,80397 e7,55490.
25 € 8/24h Ch . **Surface:** grasstiles/metalled.
01/01-31/12.
Distance: 50m.

S Valgrisenche 22G3

Localita' Mondanges. **GPS:** n45,62638 e7,06252.
20 free . **Location:** Rural. **Surface:** asphalted.
01/01-31/12.
Distance: on the spot.

S Valsavarenche 25G1

Località Dégioz. **GPS:** n45,59404 e7,20721.
11 € 5/12h Ch. **Surface:** grasstiles/metalled.
01/04-31/10.
Distance: 100m.
Remarks: Check in at town hall Tabaccheria or Bar Lo Fourquin, with registration number motorhome.

S Verrès 22G3

Piazzale Grand Ronc, Via Stazione. **GPS:** n45,66226 e7,69392.

6 € 5 free. **Surface:** asphalted. 01/01-31/12.
Distance: 200m 1,5km.

Piedmont

Acceglio 25F3

SP422. **GPS:** n44,47526 e6,98530.

6 free Chfree. **Location:** Rural, simple, quiet.
Surface: grassy/gravel. 01/01-31/12.
Distance: 400m 400m 400m.
Remarks: At sports grounds, max. 24h.

S Acqui Terme 26A2

Area comunale, SS456, Viale Einaudi. **GPS:** n44,66533 e8,47228.

100 € 8 Ch (16x)WCincluded. **Location:** Urban, comfortable, central, noisy. **Surface:** grasstiles/metalled.
01/01-31/12.
Distance: 1,5km 25km on the spot 50m 250m 1,5km.
Remarks: Parking beside river.

S Agliè 25H1

Via della Gula. **GPS:** n45,36662 e7,76381.

40 free . **Location:** Urban, simple. **Surface:** metalled.
01/01-31/12.
Distance: on the spot 500m 1km 400m.

S Alba 25H2

Alba Village, Corso Piave 219, loc. San Cassiano.
GPS: n44,68553 e8,01095.

10 € 5 + € 0,50/pp tourist tax € 2/30liter Ch .
Location: Urban, simple, central.
Surface: grassy. 01/01-31/12.

IT

Distance: 2,5km 1km on the spot 100m on the spot.
Remarks: Nearby Hotel&Camping Alba Village, max. 48h, check in at reception, monitored parking.

S Alessandria 26A2

Area comunale, Viale Teresa Michel. **GPS**: n44,92075 e8,62722.

25 free Ch. **Location:** Urban, simple. **Surface:** asphalted.
01/01-31/12.
Distance: 2km 2km on the spot 500m on the spot.

Arona 23A3

Via Michelangelo Buonarrotti. **GPS**: n45,76879 e8,54495.
20 free WC free. **Location:** Rural, simple, quiet. **Surface:** metalled.
01/01-31/12.
Distance: 2km 200m 2km on the spot on the spot.

S Asti 25H2

Piazza Campo del Palio. **GPS**: n44,89712 e8,21057.

>50 free . **Location:** Urban, simple, central, noisy.
Surface: asphalted. 01/01-31/12 Wed-Sa.
Distance: on the spot 50m 100m 300m.

S Avigliana 25G2

Via Giovanni Suppo. **GPS**: n45,07304 e7,39004.

8 free Ch free. **Location:** Urban, simple, quiet.
Surface: asphalted.
Distance: 1km 4,6km.
Remarks: Nearby sports complex.

Tourist information Avigliana:
Thu.

S Barge 25G2

Via Carlo Alberto. **GPS**: n44,73108 e7,32000.

4 free Ch free. **Location:** Simple. **Surface:** asphalted.
01/01-31/12.
Distance: 800m 1km 700m on the spot.

S Battifollo 25H3

Cian del Mondo, Loc. Piano del Mondo.
GPS: n44,31994 e8,01858.

20 € 15 Ch (20x)€ 2,50/day WC included.
Location: Rural, comfortable. **Surface:** gravel. 01/03-08/12.
Distance: 700m 500m on the spot on the spot.

S Baveno 23A3

Area Comunale, Via Brera. **GPS**: n45,91187 e8,50101.

40 € 12/24h Ch WC included. **Location:** Urban, simple, noisy. **Surface:** metalled. 01/01-31/12.
Distance: 500m 2,8km Lago Maggiore 300m 300m on the spot on the spot on the spot.
Remarks: Behind railway station, max. 72h, no camping activities, weekend: noisy.

S Bibiana 25G2

Piazza 3° Alpini. **GPS**: n44,79581 e7,29366.

8 free Ch free. **Location:** Urban, simple. **Surface:** metalled.
01/03-01/11.
Distance: 500m 500m 600m.

S Biella 25H1

Area Comunale, Piazzale Sandro Pertini. **GPS**: n45,55559 e8,06760.

30 free free. **Location:** Urban. **Surface:** asphalted.
01/01-31/12.
Distance: on the spot 100m station 100m.
Remarks: Square next to station F.S San Paolo.

S Bielmonte 22H3

Piazzale 2, Strada Statale 232. **GPS**: n45,66250 e8,08472.
8 € 8/24h Ch included € 3,50 . **Location:** Rural.
01/01-31/12.
Distance: on the spot 1,5km.

S Borgo San Dalmazzo 25G3

P Area Camper, Strada Communale Del Cimitero.
GPS: n44,32889 e7,49167.

15 free Ch free. **Location:** Urban, simple, quiet.
Surface: asphalted. 01/01-31/12.
Distance: 100m 450m 900m 200m.
Remarks: At sports park.

S Borgosesia 22H3

Piazza Milanaccio, Via Varallo. **GPS**: n45,72005 e8,27408.

8 free Ch free. **Location:** Urban. **Surface:** asphalted.
01/01-31/12 Jun.
Distance: 300m.
Remarks: Market Saturday.

S Candelo 25H1

Area Comunale, Via Cesare Pavese. **GPS**: n45,54163 e8,11595.

2 free Ch free. **Location:** Urban, quiet. **Surface:** gravel.
01/01-31/12.
Distance: 400m 400m 100m.
Remarks: Nearby sports center.

S Candelo 25H1

Area Ricetto, Via Mulino. **GPS**: n45,54624 e8,11573.

25 free Ch free. **Location:** Comfortable.
Surface: metalled. 01/01-31/12.
Distance: 400m 400m.

S Canelli 25H2

Piazza Unione Europea. **GPS**: n44,72039 e8,29369.

15 free Ch free. **Location:** Urban, simple, noisy.
Surface: asphalted. 01/01-31/12.
Distance: 500m on the spot on the spot on the spot.

S Cannobio 23A2

Area Comunale, Via Al Fiume / Via San Rocco.
GPS: n46,06179 e8,69242.

IT

55 € 15/24h Ch WC included. Location: Rural, comfortable, quiet. **Surface:** grasstiles. 01/01-31/12.
Distance: 500m on the spot 500m 300m on the spot on the spot.
Remarks: Along river, max. 3 days.

Tourist information Cannobio:
Su.

S Carcoforo 22H3

Le Giare, SP11, Loc. Tetto Minocco. **GPS**: n45,90769 e8,05130.

100 € 10/day, € 15/weekend, € 40/week Chfree (16x)€ 1,50 WC € 1. **Surface:** grassy. 01/01-31/12.
Distance: on the spot 50m 300m on the spot.
Remarks: Along the Egua river.

S Casale Monferrato 26A1

Palazzetto dello Sport Paolo Ferraris, Via Visconti.
GPS: n45,12556 e8,46194.

15 free in shopping centre. **Location:** Rural.
Surface: asphalted. 01/01-31/12.
Distance: 1,5km 3,6km 200m 200m.
Remarks: At sports centre.

Casale Monferrato 26A1

Parcheggio Castello, Piazza Castello. **GPS**: n45,13722 e8,44806.

>10 free. **Location:** Urban, simple, central, noisy.
Surface: asphalted. Tue, Fri 6-16h (market).
Distance: 200m 4km 100m 250m on the spot on the spot.

S Casaleggio Boiro 26A2

Via Castello. **GPS**: n44,63354 e8,73254.

8 free Ch (6x)free. **Location:** Rural, comfortable, quiet.

Surface: gravel. 01/01-31/12.
Distance: 250m 10km 150m 250m 200m.
Remarks: At sports park.

S Castelletto Stura 25G3

Via Cuneo. **GPS**: n44,44194 e7,63444.

20 free free. **Location:** Rural, simple.
Surface: gravel.
Remarks: Nearby sports park.

S Castiglione Falletto 25H2

Area comunale, Piazzale Muntelier. **GPS**: n44,62379 e7,97486.

4 free Chfree. **Location:** Rural, comfortable, quiet.
Surface: metalled. 01/01-31/12.
Distance: 100m 100m 100m on the spot on the spot.
Remarks: Playground.

S Castiglione Tinella 25H2

Camperstop Ai Ciuvin, Agriturismo, Strada Manzotti 3.
GPS: n44,73357 e8,18140.

12 € 20 Ch WC included. **Location:** Rural, comfortable, isolated, quiet. **Surface:** grassy. 01/01-31/12.
Distance: 15km 20km on the spot 15km.
Remarks: Max. 48h.

S Cavour 25G2

Via Vigone 3. **GPS**: n44,78766 e7,37660.

18 € 5/24h Chincluded . **Location:** Urban.
Surface: metalled. 01/01-31/12.
Distance: 400m 100m 300m.

S Ceresole Reale 25G1

Area sosta Camper Lungolago, Strada Provinciale 50.
GPS: n45,43407 e7,22783.
€ 8 Ch € 3 WCincluded € 0,50/15minutes.
01/01-31/12.
Distance: 300m 300m 300m on the spot on the spot.

S Ceresole Reale 25G1

Borgata Chiapili Inferiore, SP50. **GPS**: n45,45049 e7,18765.
€ 8 € 4 Ch € 3. **Surface:** unpaved.
Distance: 4km Ristorante Lo Sciatore 2km.
Remarks: Along the Orco river, national Park 'Gran Paradiso'.

S Cesana Torinese 25F2

Area Sosta Camper Casa Cesana, Viale Sen. Bouvier.
GPS: n44,94782 e6,79516.

12 € 10/night Chincluded (12x)€ 3/day,6Amp WC.
Location: Rural, simple. **Surface:** asphalted. 01/01-31/12.
Distance: 300m 50m 100m.
Remarks: Check in at hotel.

S Cherasco 25H2

Parking Area Camper, Piazza Giovanni Paolo II.
GPS: n44,64946 e7,85529.

8 free Chfree (6x) WC. **Location:** Urban, simple, quiet.
Surface: asphalted. 01/01-31/12.
Distance: 400m 3,7km 200m 300m 300m.
Remarks: Max. 48h.

S Chianocco 25G1

Area Camper Giraude. **GPS**: n45,14110 e7,16592.

20 € 3-10 Ch WC included. **Location:** Rural, simple.
Surface: grassy/gravel. 01/04-31/10.
Distance: 1km.
Remarks: Max. 48h.

S Chiaverano 25H1

Area Camper Lago Sirio, Strada Provinciale 75.
GPS: n45,48585 e7,88815.

€ 10/24h Ch € 2 WC . **Location:** Rural. **Surface:** grassy.
01/01-31/12.
Distance: on the spot on the spot on the spot on the spot on the spot on the spot.
Remarks: At lake Sirio.

S Chieri 25H2

Strada San Silvestro. **GPS**: n45,01460 e7,83214.

IT

10 free Ch free. **Location:** Urban, simple. **Surface:** asphalted.
01/01-31/12.
Distance: on the spot 50m 50m 50m.

Chieri 25H2

Piazza Quarini, via Bernardo Vittone. **GPS**: n45,00391 e7,82744.

20 free. **Surface:** asphalted. 01/01-31/12.
Distance: on the spot 600m lidl 800m 200m > Turin.
Remarks: Behind Barracks, tuesday market.

S Chiusa di Pesio 25H3

Via Provinciale (SP42). **GPS**: n44,27233 e7,66361.

8 € 4 Ch.
Distance: on the spot 300m 700m on the spot on the spot.

S Chiusa di Pesio 25H3

Cascina Veja, Fraz. Vigna 4. **GPS**: n44,29307 e7,67244.
free WC. **Location:** Rural. **Surface:** grassy. 01/01-31/12.
Distance: 4km on the spot 200m.

S Chiusa di San Michele 25G2

Via Pragallo. **GPS**: n45,10294 e7,33034.

5 € 7 included. **Location:** Rural, simple.
Surface: gravel.
01/04-31/10.
Distance: 8km 600m 500m 2km.
Remarks: Max. 48h, to be paid at Uffici Comunali, Piazza Bauchiero 2.

S Chivasso 25H1

Piazza Libertini, Via Gerbido. **GPS**: n45,18514 e7,89296.

20 free € 2 . **Location:** Urban, simple. **Surface:** asphalted.
01/01-31/12.
Distance: 300m 3km 100m Carrefour 100m 500m.

Remarks: Parking swimming pool.

S Chivasso 25H1

Via Ceresa 4. **GPS**: n45,19479 e7,89001.

20 € 2,50 € 2 Ch. **Location:** Urban, simple.
Surface: metalled. 01/01-31/12.
Distance: 600m 2km 200m 800m 300m.

S Collegno 25G2

Collegno Area Sosta Camper, Corso Pastrengo angolo Viale Certosa.
GPS: n45,08070 e7,58313.

28 free € 0,50 € 0,50 Ch € 1 € 1/4h. **Location:** Urban, quiet. **Surface:** asphalted. 01/01-31/12.
Distance: 500m 4km 1km on the spot.
Remarks: Coins at Autolavaggio Il Draghetto, video surveillance.

S Cortemilia 25H3

Strada San Roco. **GPS**: n44,57848 e8,18567.

10 free Ch free. **Location:** Rural, simple. **Surface:** gravel.
01/01-31/12.
Distance: 500m 500m 500m.
Remarks: Max. 48h.

S Cravagliana 22H3

Pian delle Fate, Loc. Brugarolo, SP di Valle Mastallone.
GPS: n45,85223 e8,22473.

30 € 14 + € 1/pp Ch (4x) WC included. **Surface:** grassy.
15/03-15/10.
Distance: on the spot on the spot.

S Crevoladossola 22H2

Via Thomas Alva Edison. **GPS**: n46,15832 e8,30719.
8 free Ch free. **Location:** Rural. **Surface:** grasstiles.
01/01-31/12.
Distance: 1,5km.

S Crissolo 25G2

Baita della Polenta, Strada Provinciale 234.
GPS: n44,70075 e7,11686.

14 € 12/24h Ch included WC. **Location:** Rural.
Surface: grassy. 01/01-31/12.
Distance: on the spot on the spot.
Remarks: Not suitable for big motorhomes, narrow entrance, entrance road closed for motorhomes between 14-18h.

S Crissolo 25G2

Via Ruata. **GPS**: n44,69771 e7,15931.

20 free, 01/06-30/09 € 5 Ch WC included. **Location:** Urban, simple, quiet. **Surface:** asphalted. 01/01-31/12.
Distance: on the spot on the spot on the spot.
Remarks: Near the chair-lift.

S Cuceglio 25H1

Area Camper Erbaluce, Via Porta Pia 69/71. **GPS**: n45,34724 e7,81168.

10 € 12 Ch (10x) included. **Location:** Rural, comfortable. **Surface:** gravel. 01/01-31/12.
Distance: 2km on the spot 1km 500m.
Remarks: Wine tasting.

S Cuneo 25G3

Parco Fluviale, Piazzale Walther Cavallera.
GPS: n44,38563 e7,55154.

8 free Ch free. **Location:** Urban, comfortable, quiet.
Surface: gravel. 01/01-31/12.
Distance: 300m on the spot 850m 600m on the spot.
Remarks: Max. 72h, video surveillance, elevator (free) to centre.

Tourist information Cuneo:
Piazza Galimberti. Tue.

S Donato 25H1

Area Camper Fabrizio de André, Via S. Pertini, SP405.
GPS: n45,52774 e7,90944.

6 € 5 WCfree. **Location:** Rural. **Surface:** grasstiles.
01/01-31/12.
Distance: 300m 300m.
Remarks: Pay at Tabaccheria in the village.

S **Entracque** 25G3

Area C'era una Volta, SS22. **GPS**: n44,25151 e7,38975.

18 € 15 Ch (16x)WC € 5/day € 1 included.
Location: Rural. **Surface:** unpaved. 01/01-31/12.
Distance: 1km river-beach 500m 500m on the spot 1km > Cuneo on the spot on the spot 1km.
Remarks: Monitored parking.

S **Entracque** 25G3

Parcheggio Camper Real Park, Ponterosso.
GPS: n44,26111 e7,37750.

66 € 6 Ch included. **Location:** Rural.
Surface: grassy/gravel. 01/01-31/12.
Distance: 3km on the spot on the spot on the spot 400m 6km.
Remarks: Recreation park, max. 2 days.

S **Entracque** 25G3

Via del Mulino 1. **GPS**: n44,23389 e7,39723.

65 € 12/24h, € 20/48h Ch (50x)included € 2.
Location: Rural, simple. **Surface:** gravel. 01/01-31/12.
Distance: 300m 150m 500m on the spot on the spot.

S **Fenestrelle** 25G2

Le Casermette, Via Nazionale. **GPS**: n45,03671 e7,05090.

20 free, fri-su € 5-10, Jun-Aug € 10 Ch included.
Location: Rural. **Surface:** unpaved. 01/01-31/12.
Distance: 100m.

S **Fenestrelle** 25G2

Via Nazionale, SS23. **GPS**: n45,03889 e7,04583.

9 free Chfree. **Location:** Rural. **Surface:** asphalted.
01/01-31/12.
Distance: 500m 400m on the spot.
Remarks: Next to cemetery.

S **Frabosa Soprana** 25H3

Fontane. **GPS**: n44,23554 e7,83561.
free Chfree. **Location:** Rural, isolated, quiet.
01/01-31/12.

S **Frabosa Soprana** 25H3

Grotta di Bossea, Loc.Bossea 10. **GPS**: n44,24077 e7,83939.
5 free Chfree WC. **Location:** Rural, simple, isolated.
Surface: asphalted. 01/01-31/12.
Distance: 12km on the spot on the spot 12km on the spot.
Remarks: Parking at the caves.

S **Garessio** 25H3

Area Comunale, Str.Provinciale del Colle di San Bernardo (P582).
GPS: n44,19927 e8,02587.

30 free Chfree. **Location:** Rural, simple. **Surface:** asphalted.
01/01-31/12.
Distance: 1km 22km 1km 1km.

S **Genola** 25H3

Grosso Vacanze, Via Divisione Alpina Cuneense 2, SS20.
GPS: n44,59751 e7,65982.

4 free Ch. **Location:** Rural. **Surface:** metalled.
01/01-31/12.
Distance: 150m 500m 350m.
Remarks: Motorhome dealer, accessory shop.

S **Giaveno** 25G2

SP187, via Torino. **GPS**: n45,04154 e7,36096.

free free. **Surface:** asphalted. 01/01-31/12.
Distance: 500m 100m on the spot.

S **Grinzane Cavour** 25H2

Piazza Ugo Genta, Via Bricco 14. **GPS**: n44,65515 e7,98936.

3 free Chfree. **Location:** Rural, simple, isolated, noisy.
Surface: asphalted. 01/01-31/12.
Distance: 500m 500m 2km on the spot on the spot.

S **Ivrea** 25H1

La Dora d'Ivrea, Via Dora Baltea. **GPS**: n45,46334 e7,87621.

10 € 5 € 3 Chincluded. **Location:** Rural, comfortable.
Surface: asphalted. 01/01-31/12.
Distance: 500m 4,5km on the spot 300m Ipermercato 800m 350m.
Remarks: Beside river, playground.

S **Locana** 25G1

Via Nusiglie. **GPS**: n45,41361 e7,46278.
€ 8/24h € 4/24h WC.

S **Macugnaga** 22H3

Pecetto, Di Iacchine Pierluigi Loc. Pecetto. **GPS**: n45,97015 e7,95352.

28 € 10, 2 nights € 15 ChWCfree. **Location:** Rural, simple, quiet. **Surface:** concrete.
01/05-30/11.
Distance: 1km 100m 500m 100m on the spot.
Remarks: At ski-lift.

S **Madonna del Sasso** 23A3

Area Comunale, Via Santuario, Fraz. Boleto.
GPS: n45,78974 e8,37222.

8 free Chfree. **Location:** Rural, simple, isolated, quiet.
Surface: grasstiles. 01/01-31/12.
Distance: 200m Lago d'Orta 700m 100m 50m on the spot on the spot.
Remarks: Narrow entrance, view at Lago d'Orta.

S **Maglione** 25H1

SP78, Via Cigliano. **GPS**: n45,34338 e8,01456.

IT

20 free free. **Location:** Rural, simple, quiet. **Surface:** grassy. 01/01-31/12.
Distance: on the spot 50m 150m.
Remarks: Art city.

S Marsaglia 25H3

Agriturismo Cascina Zanot, Strada S. Rocco, 17.
GPS: n44,47120 e7,96010.

6 € 25 Ch WC included. **Location:** Rural, comfortable, isolated, quiet. **Surface:** gravel. 01/01-31/12.
Distance: 8km 10km.
Remarks: Beautiful view, playground, sale of wines.

S Melle 25G3

SP8. **GPS**: n44,56245 e7,31739.

22 € 3, 01/06-01/10 € 7 Ch WC included. **Location:** Rural, comfortable. **Surface:** metalled.
01/01-31/12.
Distance: 100m 200m 250m 300m 100m.

S Mergozzo 23A3

Parcheggio Area Camper, Via Sempione 49.
GPS: n45,96204 e8,44320.
6 € 10/24h Ch included € 5/day. **Location:** Rural, simple. **Surface:** asphalted. 01/01-31/12.
Distance: 300m Lake Mergozzo 500m 300m 100m on the spot on the spot.
Remarks: To be paid at bar.

S Mirabello Monferrato 26A2

SS31. **GPS**: n45,02976 e8,52939.

8 free € 2 Ch € 1. **Location:** Simple, isolated, quiet. **Surface:** asphalted. 01/01-31/12.
Distance: 900m 10km 800m 50m 50m.

S Mombarcaro 25H3

SP103. **GPS**: n44,46900 e8,08352.

8 € 5 Ch included. **Location:** Rural, comfortable, quiet. **Surface:** metalled. 01/01-31/12.
Distance: 200m 500m.
Remarks: Beautiful view.

S Mondovì 25H3

Piazza della Repubblica. **GPS**: n44,38964 e7,81930.
18 free WC . **Location:** Urban, simple, central. **Surface:** asphalted.
01/01-31/12.
Distance: 400m 5km 50m 100m on the spot.
Remarks: Nearby the old station.

S Mondovì 25H3

Piazza le Giardini. **GPS**: n44,39430 e7,82370.

10 free Ch free. **Location:** Urban, simple. **Surface:** asphalted.
01/01-31/12.
Distance: 500m 350m 300m.
Remarks: Nearby bus station, parking under railway bridge.

S Mondovì 25H3

Mondovicino Outlet Center, Via Tanaro.
GPS: n44,41889 e7,84966.

free € 1/100liter Ch. **Location:** Simple. **Surface:** asphalted.
01/01-31/12.
Distance: 4km 1,2km 100m on the spot 500m.
Remarks: Parking at Outlet Center and Centro Commercial.

S Mongrando 25H1

Area Comunale, Via dei Giovanni. **GPS**: n45,52543 e8,00595.

15 free Ch free . **Location:** Urban, quiet.
Surface: grasstiles. 01/01-31/12.
Distance: 900m.
Remarks: At sports centre.

S Montiglio Monferrato 25H2

Via Padre Carpignano. **GPS**: n45,06230 e8,10390.

6 free. **Location:** Rural, simple, quiet. **Surface:** asphalted.
01/01-31/12.
Distance: 200m 600m.
Remarks: At cemetery.

S Neive 25H2

Via Crocetta. **GPS**: n44,72753 e8,11332.

8 € 10/24h Ch (6x) WC included. **Location:** Rural, comfortable, quiet. **Surface:** grassy/gravel.
01/01-31/12.
Distance: 100m 100m.
Remarks: Check in at sport centre, playground.

Niella Belbo 25H3

Agriturismo Ca'd Tistu, Via Pian Lea, 2.
GPS: n44,49941 e8,07991.

6 € 5 Ch WC included. **Location:** Rural, isolated, quiet.
01/01-31/12.
Distance: 1,8km on the spot.
Remarks: Steep ramp.

S Niella Tanaro 25H3

Agriturismo I Fornelli, Via Fornello 1. **GPS**: n44,41418 e7,90988.

3 € 5 € 3,50 Ch € 2,50/24h WC . **Location:** Rural, simple, isolated, quiet. **Surface:** grassy/gravel.
01/01-31/12.
Distance: 4km 2km 1km 10km.
Remarks: Farm products.

S Nizza Monferrato 26A2

Parking Camper Piazzale S.Pertini, Piazzale Sandro Pertini.
GPS: n44,77140 e8,35346.

13 € 5 Ch Service, electricity incl. € 3.

Location: Urban, comfortable, central, quiet. **Surface:** grassy.
01/01-31/12.
Distance: 200m 500m 500m.
Remarks: Gate closed, first call Motorhome Club Nicese between 9-20h.

S Novi Ligure 26A2

Viale Pinan Cichero, zona stadio comunale. **GPS**: n44,77041 e8,78181.

25 free free. **Location:** Urban, simple, noisy.
Surface: asphalted. 01/01-31/12.
Distance: 1,5km 2km on the spot 600m.
Remarks: Parking gymnasium.

S Occimiano 26A2

Via Circonvallazione. **GPS**: n45,05834 e8,50940.

5 € 5 Ch included. **Location:** Rural, comfortable.
Surface: asphalted. 01/01-31/12.
Distance: 250m 15km 250m 400m.
Remarks: To be paid at bar Concordia.

S Oggebbio 23A3

Area Camper Oggebbio, Via Martiri Oggebbiesi 6.
GPS: n45,99680 e8,65304.

22 € 18/24h Ch WC included € 1 € 5/24h.
Location: Luxurious, isolated, quiet. **Surface:** gravel.
01/03-01/12.
Distance: 1,2km 700m on the spot on the spot.
Remarks: Attention: narrow road, view on Lago Maggiore, video surveillance.

S Omegna 23A3

Area Camper Lago d'Orta, Via Caduti di Bologna 1.
GPS: n45,86340 e8,39840.

25 € 8/12h, 01/06-30/09 € 10/12h Ch WC included.
Location: Urban, comfortable, quiet. **Surface:** metalled.
01/01-31/12.
Distance: 1,8km beach 800m 800m on the spot on the spot. **Remarks:** Caution key electricity € 30, cash payment, video surveillance.

S Ormea 25H3

Via Orti della Rana. **GPS**: n44,14532 e7,90751.

10 € 10 Ch. **Location:** Rural, comfortable, quiet.
Surface: grasstiles. 01/01-31/12.
Distance: 1km 500m 1km.
Remarks: Pay at tourist office.

S Ormea 25H3

Riserva la Regina, Via Martinetto. **GPS**: n44,15162 e7,90929.
€ 10/24h WC € 1,50 . **Surface:** gravel.
Easter-30/10.
Distance: 500m fishing permit obligatory on the spot 500m on the spot.
Remarks: Regional products.

S Oropa 22H3

Area di Santuari, Via Santuario di Oropa.
GPS: n45,62864 e7,97530.

31 € 10 Ch WC . **Location:** Rural. **Surface:** metalled.
01/05-31/10.
Distance: 200m.

S Orta San Giulio 23A3

Panoramic, Via Panoramica. **GPS**: n45,79729 e8,41527.

20 € 10/24h, 19/12-28/02 free. **Location:** Rural, simple, noisy.
Surface: asphalted. 01/01-31/12.
Distance: 500m Lago d'Orta 500m 100m on the spot on the spot on the spot.

S Orta San Giulio 23A3

Parco del Sacro Monte, Via Sacro Monte. **GPS**: n45,79732 e8,41204.

10 free WC free. **Location:** Rural, simple, quiet. **Surface:** gravel.
01/01-31/12.
Distance: 900m 1km 400m 1km on the spot on the spot.
Remarks: Nearby lake Orta, max. 48h.

S Ovada 26A2

Via Gramsci. **GPS**: n44,64084 e8,64920.

25 free free. **Location:** Simple, central. **Surface:** grasstiles.
01/01-31/12.
Distance: 300m 3km 100m 500m.

S Piatto 22H3

Area Comunale, Fraz. Malina. **GPS**: n45,58908 e8,13630.

10 free Ch. **Location:** Urban. **Surface:** asphalted.
01/01-31/12.
Remarks: At sports park.

S Pietraporzio 25G3

Area Camper Pontebernardo, Via Nazionale, SS21.
GPS: n44,34868 e7,01831.

21 € 5/24h Ch WC included. **Location:** Rural, comfortable.
Surface: gravel. 01/01-31/12.
Distance: 450m 450m 600m.
Remarks: 3rd night free.

S Pinerolo 25G2

Olimpico, Via Alpi Cozie. **GPS**: n44,88917 e7,35111.

10 free Ch (10x)against payment. **Location:** Urban, simple. **Surface:** metalled. 01/03-01/11.
Distance: 2km 1,5km 300m 300m 200m.
Remarks: Nearby sports park.

S Pinerolo 25G2

Via Vecchia di Buriasco. **GPS**: n44,88143 e7,34664.
Ch free. 01/01-31/12.

S Pollone 22H3

Burcina di Pollone, Via Felice Piacenza.
GPS: n45,58548 e8,00521.

21 € 16/24h Ch WC included € 2 .
Location: Rural, comfortable. **Surface:** grasstiles.

IT

01/01-31/12.
Distance: 600m on the spot.
Remarks: At parco Naturale Burcina, max. 48h.

S Pombia 23A3

Safari Park, Via Larino. **GPS**: n45,64167 e8,61740.
50 € 20 Ch WC included. **Location:** Rural, comfortable, quiet. **Surface:** grassy/gravel. 16/03-01/10.
Distance: on the spot 6km on the spot on the spot.
Remarks: Max. 2 days, check in at reception.

S Ponderano 25H1

Area Comunale, Strada Vicinale al Cimitero.
GPS: n45,53683 e8,04949.

10 free free. **Location:** Urban, simple. **Surface:** gravel.
01/01-31/12.
Distance: 400m.
Remarks: Nearby sports park.

S Pont Canavese 25G1

Feiteria, Via Soana. **GPS**: n45,42153 e7,60020.
12 € 7,50 € 2,50 Ch € 2,50. **Surface:** grassy.
01/01-31/12.
Distance: on the spot.
Remarks: Max. 48h, video surveillance.

Pontechianale 25G3

Chianale, SP 251. **GPS**: n44,65055 e6,99280.

15 free. **Location:** Rural, simple, isolated, noisy.
Surface: grassy/gravel. 01/01-31/12.
Distance: 400m 500m.

S Pontechianale 25G3

Area Camper, Fraz Maddalena. **GPS**: n44,62158 e7,02776.

30 € 7/24h Ch. **Location:** Rural, simple, central.
Surface: grassy. 01/05-30/09.
Distance: 200m 200m 200m 200m.

S Pragelato 25F2

Villagio GoFree, SS23. **GPS**: n45,02187 e6,94914.

18 € 16-21, 4 pers.incl Ch € 1,50 WC .
Location: Rural. **Surface:** grassy. 12/06-13/09.
Distance: on the spot on the spot on the spot on the spot on the spot.
Remarks: Spa, ski, tennis, golf.

S Prali 25G2

Fraz. Ghigo. **GPS**: n44,89176 e7,04956.

free Ch free. **Location:** Rural. **Surface:** grassy.
01/01-31/12.
Distance: 300m on the spot 400m.
Remarks: Altitude 1450m, along river, at sports park.

S Prali 25G2

Piazza Garrou Emanuele 17. **GPS**: n44,89150 e7,04982.
€ 5 Ch included. **Location:** Rural. **Surface:** grassy/gravel.
01/01-31/12.
Distance: on the spot 450m on the spot.
Remarks: Near the chair-lift, to be paid at Pro Loco.

S Prarostino 25G2

Porto di Montagne, Via Piani. **GPS**: n44,86488 e7,26970.

12 € 7/24h Ch WC included. **Location:** Rural, comfortable.
Surface: grassy/gravel. 01/01-31/12 With snow.
Distance: 300m 200m on the spot on the spot.
Remarks: To be paid at bar.

S Prato Nevoso 25H3

Area Stalle Lunghe, Via Corona Boreale. **GPS**: n44,25200 e7,78192.

€ 15-20 Ch included. **Surface:** asphalted.
01/01-31/12.
Distance: on the spot A6 33km on the spot 50m on the spot.

Prato Nevoso 25H3

Piazza G. Dodero. **GPS**: n44,25200 e7,78192.

10 free. **Location:** Rural, simple, central. **Surface:** asphalted.
01/01-31/12.
Distance: on the spot on the spot on the spot on the spot.

S Premia 22H2

AleSte Area Camper, Via Provinciale 33, Cadarese.
GPS: n46,29723 e8,36232.
15 € 15/24h Ch included € 1/kWh. **Surface:** metalled.
01/01-31/12.
Distance: on the spot on the spot on the spot.

S Rimasco 22H3

Il Laghetto, Strada del Lago. **GPS**: n45,86109 e8,06450.

20 € 10/24h Ch € 3/day WC included. **Surface:** grassy.
01/05-30/09 Restaurant: Tue.
Distance: on the spot on the spot.
Remarks: At lake.

S Riva Valdobbia 22H3

Area Lo Chalet, Via Circonvallazione. **GPS**: n45,83476 e7,95486.

48 € 13/24h Ch € 2 WC included .
Surface: grassy/metalled. 01/04-31/10.
Distance: on the spot on the spot on the spot.
Remarks: Along river.

S Roaschia 25G3

Area camper I Funtanil, Via Circonvallazione, SP 108.
GPS: n44,26758 e7,45860.

16 € 10/24h Ch (16x) WC included. **Location:** Rural, comfortable, quiet. **Surface:** gravel.
01/01-31/12.
Distance: 200m on the spot 350m on the spot.
Remarks: Grill and picknic area.

S Romano Canavese 25H1

Strada provinciale 56. **GPS**: n45,38644 e7,86177.

10 free . **Location:** Rural, simple.
Surface: grasstiles/metalled. 01/01-31/12.
Distance: 2,2km on the spot 1km 400m.

S Rosta 25G2

Via Buttigliera Alta 2, Via Piave. **GPS**: n45,07106 e7,46333.

5 free € 2 free Ch € 2. **Location:** Urban. **Surface:** asphalted.
01/01-31/12.
Distance: on the spot 12km 300m on the spot train > Turin 19min on the spot.

IT

Saluzzo 25G2

Area Bodoni, Via Olivero Matteo. **GPS**: n44,63886 e7,49192.

19 free € 0,50/60liter Ch€ 1 (12x)€ 0,50/kWh.
Location: Urban, simple. **Surface:** grasstiles.
01/01-31/12.
Distance: 700m 200m 550m 50m on the spot on the spot.
Remarks: Max. 72h, small pitches.

Saluzzo 25G2

Via Cuneo 16. **GPS**: n44,63739 e7,49740.

±10 free free. **Location:** Urban. **Surface:** asphalted.
01/01-31/12.
Distance: 1km 650m 100m 150m.

San Damiano d'Asti 25H2

Via Monsignor Franco. **GPS**: n44,82659 e8,05921.

50 free Ch. **Location:** Rural, simple. **Surface:** gravel.
01/01-31/12.
Distance: 1km 1km 1km.
Remarks: At cemetery.

San Damiano d'Asti 25H2

Agriturismo Gran Collina, Frazione Stizza 38.
GPS: n44,84044 e8,05026.
€ 10 Ch.
Distance: 1,5km.
Remarks: Bicycle rental, regional products.

San Damiano d'Asti 25H2

Azienda Agricola Cascina Piana, Fraz S.Grato.
GPS: n44,85136 e8,07417.

25 € 8 Ch (8x) WC included. **Location:** Rural, comfortable, isolated, quiet. **Surface:** grassy.
01/02-30/06 and 01/09-30/11.
Distance: 1,5km 1,5km 700m.

Sanfront 25G2

Via Montebracco, SP26. **GPS**: n44,64944 e7,32056.

15 free Chfree. **Location:** Urban, simple. **Surface:** unpaved.
01/01-31/12.
Distance: on the spot Po 650m 550m 750m 150m.
Remarks: At sports park, max. 24h.

Santa Maria Maggiore 23A2

Area Verde Attrezzata, Via Alfredo Belcastro/via Pineta.
GPS: n46,13219 e8,45500.

32 € 20/24h Ch. **Location:** Rural.
Surface: grassy/gravel. 01/01-31/12.
Distance: 200m on the spot.
Remarks: Max. 48h.

Santa Maria Maggiore 23A2

Agriturismo Al Piano delle Lutte, Via Domodossola 57.
GPS: n46,13569 e8,44753.

6 € 10/24h Ch according consumption WC.
Location: Rural, simple. **Surface:** grassy/gravel.
01/01-31/12.
Distance: on the spot.
Remarks: Regional products.

Sant'Antonino di Susa 25G2

Area Sosta Il Sentiero Dei Franchi, Borgo Cresto 16/1.
GPS: n45,09973 e7,27754.

20 € 10 Chincluded € 2. **Location:** Rural, simple, comfortable, quiet. **Surface:** grassy/gravel. 01/01-31/12.
Distance: 1km on the spot 3km 3km on the spot.
Remarks: Check in at restaurant.

Sestriere 25F2

Lago Losetta, Strada Azzurri d'Italia. **GPS**: n44,96465 e6,88141.

60 € 15/24h Ch WC included. **Location:** Rural.
Surface: unpaved. 01/01-31/12.
Distance: 800m on the spot on the spot 1km Shuttle bus to ski-piste.
Remarks: Altitude 2046m, monitored parking.

Sommariva Perno 25H2

Area comunale, Loc.Piano, SP0. **GPS**: n44,75126 e7,89667.

10 free Chfree. **Location:** Rural, simple, noisy.
Surface: gravel. 01/01-31/12.
Distance: 500m 13km 50m 250m on the spot on the spot.
Remarks: Max. 48h.

Susa 25G1

Piazza Repubblica. **GPS**: n45,13861 e7,05389.

12 € 7/24h Chincluded € 1/kWh. **Location:** Urban, simple, central. **Surface:** asphalted. 01/01-31/12.
Distance: 300m 500m 200m 150m.

Tagliolo Monferrato 26A2

Str. del Varo. **GPS**: n44,63960 e8,67126.
21 € 5/24h Ch.
Location: Rural, simple, quiet. **Surface:** grassy/gravel.
01/01-31/12.
Distance: 250m 2km 200m 400m.
Remarks: Max. 72h, keycard barrier at Bar/Tabac, caution € 10.

Torino 25H2

Corso Casale 327. **GPS**: n45,08084 e7,72993.

10 free Chfree. **Location:** Urban, noisy. **Surface:** asphalted.
01/01-31/12.
Distance: on the spot Po 700m 100m 150m.
Remarks: Parking funicular railway.

Torino 25H2

Parco Ruffini, Corso Lione/Corso Carlo Piaggia, Turin (Torino).
GPS: n45,05686 e7,63166.

20 free Chfree. **Location:** Urban, simple, noisy.
Surface: asphalted. 01/01-31/12.
Distance: city centre 5km on the spot 1km on the spot.

Torino 25H2

Parking Caio Mario, Corso Giovanni Agnelli, Turin (Torino).
GPS: n45,02888 e7,63924.

IT

57 € 18/24h € 0,75 € 0,75 Ch€ 0,75 € 3/24h WC € 0,60/minutes free. Location: Urban, comfortable. **Surface:** grasstiles. 01/01-31/12.
Distance: 4km 4km 100m 100m Tram 4 centre.
Remarks: Max. 5 days, monitored parking 24/24.

Tourist information Turin (Torino):
M Mole Antonelliana. National Film museum.
M Museo Nazionale dell'Automobile, Corso Unità d'Italia 40. Museum of motor-cars. Tue-Sa, 10-18.30h, Su 10-20.30h Mo.
M Palazzo Madame. Historical art.
Palazzo Reale. Royal palace.
Cathedral, 1498.
Basilica di Superga. Baroque basilica.

S Usseaux 25G2
Magic Forest, Strada Comunale dell'inverso 1.
GPS: n45,04170 e6,98518.

100 € 15 Ch WC € 1 € 5 included. **Location:** Rural, comfortable. **Surface:** grassy. 01/06-01/09.
Distance: 550m on the spot 1km on the spot.
Remarks: Grill and picknic area.

S Usseaux 25G2
Lago di Laux, Via Lago 7. **GPS**: n45,04166 e7,02222.

100 € 15/24h € 3 € 3 Ch (54x)€ 2,50/24h .
Location: Rural, simple, isolated, quiet. **Surface:** grassy.
01/06-30/09 with mucht snowfall.
Distance: 500m 200m on the spot 5km.
Remarks: Altitude 1450m, pay at restaurant, playground.

S Valdieri 25G3
Centro Alpino S.Anna, Loc. S. Anna. **GPS**: n44,24513 e7,32548.

40 € 12/24h Chincluded € 2. **Location:** Rural.
Surface: grassy/gravel. 01/05-30/09.
Distance: 100m on the spot 100m 350m.
Remarks: At sports park, narrow entrance (bridge).

S Valdieri 25G3
Parco Alpi Marittime, Terme di Valdieri. **GPS**: n44,20546 e7,26840.

€ 12/night Ch WC. **Location:** Rural. **Surface:** gravel.
01/01-31/12.
Distance: 700m on the spot.

S Valle Mosso 22H3
Piazza Alpini d'Italia. **GPS**: n45,63316 e8,14629.

3 free Chfree. **Location:** Urban. **Surface:** asphalted.
01/01-31/12.
Distance: on the spot Conad 20m 50m.

S Varallo 22H3
Area Comunale, Via Sant'Antonio. **GPS**: n45,81797 e8,24857.

8 € 10/24h Ch (4x)included. **Location:** Urban, quiet.
Surface: gravel/sand. 01/01-31/12.
Distance: 500m 500m.
Remarks: To be paid at town hall.

S Venaria Reale 25G1
Relax and Go, Via Scodeggio 15. **GPS**: n45,14108 e7,62404.

15 € 18/24h Ch included WC . **Location:** Rural, simple.
Surface: grassy. 01/01-31/12.
Distance: 1km 2km 500m 500m bus GTT, tram 72>Turin.
Remarks: Borrow cycles for free.

S Venasca 25G3
SP8, Via Provinciale. **GPS**: n44,56620 e7,39328.

20 free Chfree WC. **Location:** Rural, simple, noisy.
Surface: asphalted. 01/01-31/12.
Distance: 600m on the spot 750m 650m.

S Verbania 23A3
Punto Sosta Camper, Viale Giuseppe Azari, 97.
GPS: n45,93122 e8,55317.

34 € 6/12h, € 12/24h (18x)included. **Location:** Urban, simple, quiet. **Surface:** asphalted. 01/01-31/12.
Distance: 900m 1,2km 200m on the spot on the spot.
Remarks: Max. 48h.

Verbania 23A3
Via Brigata Cesare Battisti. **GPS**: n45,94027 e8,57676.
10 free. **Location:** Urban, simple, noisy. **Surface:** asphalted.
01/01-31/12.
Distance: 350m on the spot 350m.
Remarks: Along river.

S Verbania 23A3
Corso Europa 66. **GPS**: n45,92732 e8,56266.
Ch.

S Vercelli 26A1
Via Trento, c/o piazzale Pala-hockey. **GPS**: n45,33417 e8,41861.

10 free free. **Location:** Urban, simple. **Surface:** asphalted.
01/01-31/12.
Distance: 1,5km 6km 50m 1,5km on the spot.

Tourist information Vercelli:
Basilica di Sant'Andrea. Basilica, part of abbey.

S Vernante 25G3
Piazza Vermenagna, E74. **GPS**: n44,24489 e7,53219.

20 € 6,50 included. **Location:** Rural, simple. **Surface:** asphalted.
01/01-31/12.
Distance: 200m 200m 300m on the spot on the spot.

S Vialfrè 25H1
Via Luigi Emanuel, SP55. **GPS**: n45,38298 e7,81754.

7 free Chfree. **Location:** Rural, simple. **Surface:** grasstiles.
01/01-31/12.
Distance: on the spot 6km 300m 300m 200m.

S Vidracco 25H1
Damanhur Crea, Via Baldissero 21. **GPS**: n45,42884 e7,75327.

30 € 8/24h Ch (24x)WC included. **Location:** Urban, simple, quiet. **Surface:** asphalted. 01/01-31/12.
Distance: 200m 650m cafetaria on the spot 500m.
Remarks: Next to sports fields.

Tourist information Vidracco:
Damanhur Crea, Via Baldissero 21. Extraordinary Italian artistic and spritual community.

S Villar Focchiardo 25G2
Area Camper Villar Focchiardo, Via Fratta, SS24.
GPS: n45,11336 e7,22408.

54 € 5-10, weekend € 15 Chincluded. **Location:** Rural, comfortable, quiet. **Surface:** grassy. 01/04-30/09.
Distance: 500m 4,5km 450m 950m.
Remarks: Max. 72h.

S Villar Pellice 25G2
Parco Flissia, Via Cave del Fin. **GPS:** n44,80472 e7,15083.

20 € 8 ChWCincluded. **Location:** Rural, simple, isolated.
Surface: grassy. 01/04-01/10.
Distance: 500m on the spot fishing permit obligatory 650m agriturismo.
Remarks: Max. 48h, service passerby € 3.

S Vinadio 25G3
Area di Sosta Communale, Bagni di Vinadio, Fraz. Strapesi.
GPS: n44,28747 e7,07534.

30 € 11/24h Ch free. **Location:** Rural, simple.
Surface: grassy/gravel.
Distance: 300m, Vinadio 10km on the spot on the spot.
Remarks: Altitude 1350m, parking at the spa resort of Strapeis.

S Vinadio 25G3
Piazza d'Armi, SS21. **GPS:** n44,30667 e7,17083.

01/06-31/08 € 5 Chfree. **Surface:** asphalted.
Distance: 400m.

S Volpedo 26B2
Lungo Curone Matteotti. **GPS:** n44,88512 e8,98707.

6 free Chfree. **Location:** Rural. **Surface:** grassy/gravel.
01/01-31/12.
Distance: 600m on the spot 400m 500m.
Remarks: At sports park.

Trentino South Tyrol

S Andalo 23D2
Via Rindole, 6, Loc. Rindole. **GPS:** n46,16113 e11,00647.

80 € 15-20 Chincluded (20x)€ 5. **Location:** Rural, simple, quiet. **Surface:** asphalted. summer.
Distance: 200m on the spot on the spot.
Remarks: Service passerby € 10, beautiful view.

Arco 23D3
Piazzale Carmellini, Viale Paolina Caproni.
GPS: n45,92232 e10,89032.

14 € 1/4h, max. € 10/24h. **Location:** Urban, simple.
Surface: asphalted. 01/01-31/12.
Distance: 200m 200m on the spot.
Remarks: Max. 72h.

S Arco 23D3
Viale Rovereto. **GPS:** n45,91820 e10,89225.
Chfree. water disconnected in winter.

S Avio 23D3
Agriturismo Erta, Via Pozza, Località Erta 2.
GPS: n45,74292 e10,96807.

25 € 15 Ch (16x) included. **Location:** Rural.
Surface: grassy. 01/01-31/12.
Distance: 800m 200m 300m on the spot 800m on the spot on the spot on the spot 20km.

S Barbiano 23E1
Kollmann Stop, Frazione Colma, SS12. **GPS:** n46,58728 e11,52401.

15 € 12, in envelope in mail box € 5 Ch included.
Location: Simple, noisy. **Surface:** gravel. 01/01-31/12.
Distance: 300m 9km 300m 300m on the spot on the spot.
Remarks: Along through road, max. 48h.

Baselga di Pine 23E2
Ice Rink Piné, Via Dello Stadio. **GPS:** n46,12617 e11,25382.

10 free. **Location:** Rural, simple, quiet.
Surface: metalled.
Distance: 1km.
Remarks: >18.00h free.

S Bezzecca 23D3
Via Peluca. **GPS:** n45,89861 e10,71833.

22 € 10/24h Chincluded. **Location:** Rural, simple, isolated, quiet. **Surface:** grasstiles. 01/04-01/11.
Distance: 450m 2km 300m.

S Bolzano/Bozen 23E1
Parking Fiera Messe, Via Bruno Buozzi. **GPS:** n46,47417 e11,32617.

30 free Chfree. **Location:** Urban, simple, noisy.
Surface: asphalted. 01/01-31/12.
Distance: centre 4km 1,1km on the spot 4km on the spot.
Remarks: Along railwayline.

IT

Bolzano/Bozen 23E1

Via Maso della Pieve. **GPS**: n46,47327 e11,33693.

8 € 1/h 8-19h, Sa 8-13h, overnight stay free Ch.
Location: Urban, simple, noisy. **Surface:** asphalted.
01/01-31/12.
Distance: city centre 3km 100m on the spot.

Borgo Valsugana 23E2

Via Tommaso Temanza. **GPS**: n46,05444 e11,46361.

18 € 10/24h Ch included.
Location: Urban, simple.
Surface: grasstiles.
Distance: 100m 20m 20m 100m 100m on the spot.
Remarks: Max. 48h, service passerby € 5.

Braies 23F1

P2, Lago di Braies, Fraz. San Vito. **GPS**: n46,70265 e12,08520.

25 € 12 € 0,50. **Location:** Rural, simple, quiet. **Surface:** gravel.
30/05-31/10.
Distance: Braies 5km Lago di Braies 250m 250m 5km on the spot on the spot.

Braies 23F1

P1, Lago di Braies, Fraz. San Vito. **GPS**: n46,70577 e12,08698.
€ 9/day, € 7/night. **Surface:** gravel. 01/01-31/12.
Distance: Lake Prags 850m.

Brentonico 23D3

Via al Dosset. **GPS**: n45,81540 e10,95581.

11 € 7 € 2/100liter Ch € 3/24h. **Location:** Rural, comfortable, quiet. **Surface:** grasstiles. 01/01-31/12.
Distance: 400m 10km 250m 300m.

Brunico/Bruneck 23F1

P2, Piazza Mercato di Stegona. **GPS**: n46,79558 e11,93006.

>25 € 7. **Location:** Urban, simple, noisy. **Surface:** gravel.
01/01-31/12.
Distance: 800m 500m 500m on the spot on the spot on the spot.

Tourist information Brunico/Bruneck:
Associazione Turistica, Via Europa,24. Fortified city, 14th century.
Regional museum.
Annual fair. last week Oct.

Caldes 23D2

Rafting Val di Sole, Loc. Contrè. **GPS**: n46,36139 e10,94528.

30 € 10, Jul € 13, Aug € 15 (6x)€ 6 WC. **Location:** Rural.
Surface: asphalted. 01/04-30/09.
Distance: 2km 200m 2km 900m.
Remarks: At sports centre, to be paid at bar.

Caldonazzo 23E2

Via al Lago. **GPS**: n46,00501 e11,26307.

30 € 8/6-22h (01/04-30/9), € 10/night. **Location:** Simple.
Surface: grassy/sand. 01/01-31/12.
Distance: 2km 50m 300m.
Remarks: Payment only with coins.

Castelfondo 23E1

Belverde, Via Alfonso Lamarmora. **GPS**: n46,45831 e11,13163.

16 € 12/24h (16x) WC. **Surface:** gravel.
Distance: 800m 800m 300m on the spot.
Remarks: Max. 72h.

Cavalese 23E2

P Fondovalle, SP232. **GPS**: n46,28438 e11,47256.

50 € 12 . **Location:** Simple. **Surface:** grasstiles/metalled.
01/01-31/12.

Chiusa 23E1

Gamp, Via Gries 10. **GPS**: n46,64128 e11,57244.

20 € 14,50-16/24h 2 pers. + 2 children incl, dog € 2 Ch included. **Location:** Rural, simple. **Surface:** grassy.
01/01-31/12.
Distance: 300m 800m on the spot mini market 100m on the spot on the spot.
Remarks: Bread-service.

Corvara in Badia 23F1

P Corvara, Strada Planac SS244. **GPS**: n46,54105 e11,88388.

10 free. **Location:** Rural, simple, isolated. **Surface:** gravel.
01/01-31/12.
Distance: 3,5km on the spot 3,5km on the spot on the spot.

Dimaro 23D2

Camper Solander, Loc. Rovina. **GPS**: n46,32488 e10,86215.

10 € 20/24h, € 10/night Ch WC included € 1.
Location: Rural. **Surface:** gravel. 01/01-31/12.
Distance: 500m on the spot.
Remarks: Near campsite Dolomiti.

Dimaro 23D2

Dolomiti, Via Gole. **GPS**: n46,32507 e10,86267.
€ 20-31 Ch included. **Location:** Rural.
Surface: asphalted. 01/01-31/12.
Distance: on the spot on the spot.

Eppan 23E1

Camper Stop Eppan-Appiano, Sillnegg 2.
GPS: n46,44871 e11,26418.

27 first hour € 4, than € 0.70/h Ch WC included.
Location: Comfortable, quiet. **Surface:** metalled.
Distance: 800m pizzeria 200m 800m 200m on the spot on the spot.

Folgaria 23E3

Area Sosta Bucaneve, Via Negheli 87. **GPS**: n45,91849 e11,19255.

IT

25 € 8. **Location:** Simple.
Surface: grasstiles.
01/01-31/12.
Distance: 300m 100m.
Remarks: Check in and pay at reception, golf court, shuttle bus.

S Folgaria 23E3

SS3501. **GPS:** n45,91397 e11,17081.
€ 1 Ch.

S Folgarida 23D2

Hotel Belvedere, Piazzale Belvedere. **GPS:** n46,29716 e10,86741.
€ 15 € 5.
Distance: on the spot 200m 150m.

S Gargazzone 23E1

Weißhof-Keller, Landstrasse 65 SS38. **GPS:** n46,58500 e11,20528.

10 € 10 Ch € 2/24h WC € 1. **Location:** Rural, simple, quiet. **Surface:** grassy/gravel. 01/01-31/12.
Distance: 2km 1,5km 500m 2km on the spot on the spot on the spot.
Remarks: Reservation for Christmas holidays, tel.: +39 (0)473 292448.

Tourist information Gargazzone:
Consorzio Turistico, Via Maria Trost, 5, Merano, www.meranerland.com. Place with medicinal sources.
Castel Tirolo, 4km N. de Merano. Regional museum. 01/03-31/12.
Merano. Tue, Fri.
Festa della Città, Merano. 1st weekend Aug.

S Glorenza 23D1

Glurms Camping im Park, > SS41. **GPS:** n46,67067 e10,54520.

40 € 12-15 + € 0,70/pp tourist tax Ch included € 2 WC € 0,50. **Location:** Rural. **Surface:** grassy. 01/01-31/12.
Distance: 500m on the spot 600m 1km 650m.
Remarks: Along the Adige river, water closed during wintertime.

S Glorenza 23D1

Camping Gloria Vallis, Wiesenweg 5. **GPS:** n46,67322 e10,56942.
15 € 15, dog € 2 Ch included WC. **Location:** Rural.
Surface: grassy. 01/01-31/12.
Distance: 500m on the spot 700m 1km 1,5km on the spot.

S La Villa in Badia 23F1

Odlina, Strada Ninz, 49. **GPS:** n46,58889 e11,90028.

45 summer € 25, winter € 30 Ch WC included € 5 € 3. **Location:** Rural, luxurious, quiet. **Surface:** metalled.
01/01-31/12.
Distance: 400m 150m 150m on the spot on the spot on the spot 300m.
Remarks: Reservation for Christmas holidays: info@odina.it, use of sauna against payment.

S Lago 23E2

Via Tresselume, Tesero. **GPS:** n46,28291 e11,52557.

30 € 6 € 1 € 2 Ch € 1 (12x) € 2/8h. **Location:** Rural, simple. **Surface:** metalled. 01/01-31/12.
Distance: 200m 200m 300m on the spot on the spot.
Remarks: Max. 48h, bicycle rental.

S Lavarone 23E2

Prà Grando, Via Padova. **GPS:** n45,93602 e11,27099.

40 € 16,50 May/June/July, € 19 Aug, € 18 Dec-April Ch (3x) € 1/3minutes included. **Location:** Rural, simple, quiet.
Surface: grassy/gravel. 01/05-30/09, 01/12-31/03.
Distance: 300m 32km Lago di Lavarone 1km 1km 300m 300m 300m 1km 1km.

S Lavarone 23E2

SS 349, Loc Moar. **GPS:** n45,94575 e11,26397.

18 € 13/24h € 0,50 Ch. **Location:** Rural, simple, quiet.
Surface: metalled. 01/01-31/12.
Distance: 800m Lago di Lavarone 1,9km 500m.
Remarks: Next to sports fields, max. 72h.

S Levico Terme 23E2

Area Sosta Camper Valsugana, Loc Pleina.
GPS: n46,00691 e11,28706.

50 € 19/24h Ch WC € 4 included. **Location:** Rural, comfortable. **Surface:** grassy. 01/01-31/12.
Distance: 1,3km 200m, Lido di Levico 1,1km 50m 50m on the spot on the spot on the spot.
Remarks: Max. 3 nights, check in at reception campsite.

S Levico Terme 23E2

Area 47, SP1. **GPS:** n46,00415 e11,28880.

18 € 20, 01/06-30/09 € 25 Ch WC included.
Location: Rural, comfortable. **Surface:** asphalted.
Distance: 1,3km on the spot.
Remarks: Including access to swimming pool and private beach.

S Moena 23E2

Bar Il Giardino, SS 48 Forno di Moena. **GPS:** n46,35238 e11,63149.

40 € 12, 01/07-31/08 and 25/12-08/01 € 14 € 4 Ch € 4/24h WC. **Location:** Rural, comfortable, central. **Surface:** grassy/metalled.
01/01-31/12.
Distance: 3,5km 500m 2km 300m on the spot on the spot on the spot.
Remarks: Max. 48h, skibus comes at parking.

S Molveno 23D2

Area attrezzata per camper Lago di Molveno, Via Lungolago, 25, Loc. Ischia. **GPS:** n46,14122 e10,95819.

50 € 15-30 Ch included. **Location:** Rural, simple, quiet. **Surface:** metalled. 01/01-31/12.
Distance: 800m 200m 200m 100m.

S Pergine Valsugana 23E2

Soleando Camperparking, Via al lago 23/A.
GPS: n46,05121 e11,23593.

10 € 12 Ch included. **Location:** Urban, simple, noisy.
Surface: gravel. 01/01-31/12.
Distance: 600m Lago di Caldonazzo 1km 300m 300m 100m on the spot.

Tourist information Pergine Valsugana:
www.apt.trento.it. City at the foot of the Dolomites with historical centre.
Palazzo Pretorio, Trento. Ecclesiastical museum.

S Ponte Arche 23D2

Via Lungo Sarca. **GPS:** n46,03707 e10,86585.
15 € 5/24h Ch. **Location:** Rural.

IT

Surface: grassy. winter.
Distance: 1,5km on the spot 400m 800m 350m.
Remarks: Along river.

S Predazzo 23E2

Latemar 2200, SS48, dir Moena. **GPS**: n46,32582 e11,59970.

50 free, peak season € 7-10/24h Chincluded.
Location: Rural, simple, noisy. **Surface:** asphalted/gravel.
01/01-31/12.
Distance: 2,5km 2,5km on the spot on the spot on the spot on the spot on the spot.
Remarks: Parking ski-lifts.

S Rabbi 23D2

Al Plan, Loc. Plan, Bagni di Rabbi. **GPS**: n46,40768 e10,79559.

105 € 18-23, 2 pers. incl., dog € 1 Ch WCincluded against payment .
Location: Rural. **Surface:** metalled. 01/05-30/09.
Distance: 600m 600m on the spot on the spot on the spot.
Remarks: Max. 48h.

Racines 20E3

Sportzone Ratschings, Belprato, Stanghe.
GPS: n46,88254 e11,38383.

20 free. **Location:** Rural, simple. **Surface:** gravel.
01/01-31/12.
Distance: 400m 5km 400m 400m 400m Gilfenklam-mroute.

S Riva del Garda 23D3

Via Monte Brione. **GPS**: n45,87986 e10,85872.

41 € 0,50/h, max. € 24/48h Chincluded.
Location: Urban, simple. **Surface:** grasstiles.
01/11-07/12.
Distance: 1,5km 200m.
Remarks: Max. 48h.

Tourist information Riva del Garda:
M Museo Civico, Piazza Battisti.

S Rovereto 23E3

Area Camper Quercia, Via Palestrina. **GPS**: n45,90232 e11,03704.

15 € 8/12h, € 16/24h Ch WC included .
Location: Simple. **Surface:** grasstiles. 01/01-31/12.
Distance: 1,5km 2km.
Remarks: Caution € 5, bicycle rental, picnic tables available.

Tourist information Rovereto:
M Museo Storico Italiano della Guerra, Via Castelbarco, 7. War museum.
Mo-Fri 8.30-12.30h, 14-18h 01/01-28/02.
Castel Beseno, Besenello. Tue-Su.

S San Candido 23F1

Area di Sosta Camper, Via Prato alla Drava, 1/A.
GPS: n46,73924 e12,36559.

90 € 20 Ch WCincluded € 2. **Location:** Rural, comfortable, quiet. **Surface:** gravel. 01/01-31/12.
Distance: 6km on the spot 500m on the spot on the spot on the spot 2km 500m.
Remarks: Bicycle rental, shuttle bus San Candido and skipistes € 1/pp.

S San Guiseppe al Lago 23E2

Posteggio Camper Lago di Caldero, San Guiseppe 18.
GPS: n46,39038 e11,25663.

35 € 20/night Ch WC . **Location:** Rural, comfortable, quiet. **Surface:** gravel. 13/03-15/11.
Distance: 5km Caldero Private beach 50m Nearby campsite on the spot on the spot on the spot.
Remarks: Next to campsite, max. 4 days.

S San Martino di Castrozza 23F2

Area Sosta Tognola, Loc.Tognola. **GPS**: n46,25373 e11,80158.

90 € 15 included Ch € 1/80minutes.
Location: Rural, comfortable, quiet. **Surface:** gravel.
01/01-31/12.
Distance: 1,5km 500m on the spot on the spot on the spot.
Remarks: Next to ski-lift, free shuttle.

S San Vigilio di Marebbe 23F1

Restaurant Pizzeria Rittenkeller, Str. Ras Costa, 2.
GPS: n46,70630 e11,92920.

120 01/04-30/11 € 25, 01/12-31/03 € 30 Ch included.
Location: Rural, simple, quiet.
Surface: gravel. 01/01-31/12.
Distance: 600m 500m on the spot 600m 600m on the spot 600m.
Remarks: Next to ski-lift, breakfast-service, reservation for Christmas holidays: info@ritterkeller.it.

Santa Cristina Valgardena 23E1

P1 Monte Pana, Strada Pana. **GPS**: n46,55174 e11,71624.

50 € 15/24h.
Location: Simple, isolated, quiet. **Surface:** gravel. 01/01-31/12.
Distance: 2,5km on the spot 2,5km on the spot on the spot on the spot.
Remarks: Altitude 1650m, max. 7 days, narrow entrance.

Selva di Val Gardena 23F1

Piz Sella, Strada Plan de Gralba. **GPS**: n46,53204 e11,77230.

50 € 12/24h. **Location:** Rural, simple. **Surface:** gravel.
01/01-31/12.
Distance: 4km 150m on the spot on the spot.
Remarks: Inclining pitches.

S Sesto/Sexten 23F1

Caravanpark Sexten, SS52 St Josefstrasse 54.
GPS: n46,66741 e12,39996.

35 € 23-27 Ch ,4Amp WC included € 4 € 2.
Location: Rural, luxurious, quiet. **Surface:** grasstiles.
01/01-31/12.
Distance: 3km on the spot on the spot on the spot on the spot on the spot 900m on the spot.
Remarks: Max. 48h, sauna and spa.

S Smarano 23E2

Area Sosta Ostaria del Filò, Viale Merlonga 48/a.
GPS: n46,34962 e11,10956.

IT

43 € 10-13 Ch WC € 1 € 4.
Surface: grassy. 01/01-31/12.
Distance: 1km on the spot.
Remarks: Check in at restaurant.

Solda 23D1

Forststraße. **GPS**: n46,51448 e10,59578.
25 free. **Location:** Rural, simple.
Surface: gravel. 01/01-31/12.
Distance: 1km 100m on the spot on the spot.

Tirolo 23E1

Schneeburghof, Monte Benedetto 26. **GPS**: n46,67789 e11,16495.

20 € 23 Ch included.
Location: Comfortable. **Surface:** gravel.
Distance: on the spot.
Remarks: Bread-service, swimming pool (summer).

Tonadico 23F2

Lanterna Verde, Via Zocchet 10. **GPS**: n46,18216 e11,84318.

46 € 16 Ch WC included. **Location:** Rural, comfortable, quiet. **Surface:** grasstiles. 01/01-31/12.
Distance: 1km 100m 1km on the spot on the spot on the spot 15km 15km.
Remarks: Max. 48h, check in at restaurant.

Trento 23E2

P Zuffo, Loc. Vela. **GPS**: n46,07650 e11,11050.

20 € 5 € 1 Ch.
Location: Simple, noisy. **Surface:** asphalted. 01/01-31/12.
Distance: 1,8km 150m 200m.
Remarks: Max. 48h.

Trento 23E2

Camper Trento Park, Via Brennero, 181. **GPS**: n46,09438 e11,11335.
200 € 12/24h Ch included € 1.
Surface: asphalted. 01/01-31/12.
Distance: city centre 3km 2km 400m 400m bus 3-11-17 > centre.
Remarks: Inspection 2015: closed because of renovation.

Trento 23E2

Parking Trentino, Via Santi Cosma e Damiano 64.
GPS: n46,07674 e11,10411.

20 € 15 Ch included. **Location:** Urban, simple, noisy.
Surface: grasstiles. 01/01-31/12.
Distance: 1,8km 300m 300m bus > centre 15 min.
Remarks: Call for entrance code: 3389004343 Mr. Pisetta.

Trento 23E2

P3 Giardino Botanico Fondo Viote, SP85.
GPS: n46,02445 e11,03973.

100 € 4-10/10h, overnight stay free. **Location:** Rural, simple, isolated, quiet. **Surface:** asphalted. 01/01-31/12.
Distance: 18km Trento 150m on the spot on the spot on the spot on the spot.
Remarks: Altitude 1450m, max. 48h.

Tres 23E2

Batuda, SP della Predaia. **GPS**: n46,32040 e11,10202.

15 € 12/24h Ch WC included. **Location:** Rural.
Surface: grasstiles/metalled. 01/01-31/12.
Distance: 800m.

Vezzano 23D2

Vecchio Mulino, Naran 1. **GPS**: n46,07684 e11,01980.
10 € 15. **Location:** Rural, simple. **Surface:** grassy.
15/04-01/10.
Distance: on the spot.

Lombardy

Biassono 23B3

Via al Parco/Via della Sciavatera. **GPS**: n45,63102 e9,28865.

4 free Ch WC free. **Location:** Rural, simple, isolated.
Surface: asphalted. 01/01-31/12.
Distance: 500m 300m Centro Commerciale Vilasanta 4km train > Milan 500m.

Borgofranco sul Po 26E1

Via Filipo Turati. **GPS**: n45,04775 e11,20524.

4 free Ch free. **Location:** Rural, simple, quiet.
Surface: grassy. 01/01-31/12 water: frost.
Distance: 600m 1km 200m 300m 200m 200m.
Remarks: Playground.

Bormio 23C1

Bormio 2000, Via Battaglion Morbegno. **GPS**: n46,46260 e10,37190.

€ 8/24h Ch included. **Surface:** sand. 01/01-31/12.
Distance: 500m 500m on the spot.
Remarks: Parking funicular railway, service passerby € 5.

Tourist information Bormio:

Ufficio Informazioni e di Accoglienza Turistica, Via Roma, 131/b. Alps city, large winter sport area, also summer skiing.

Parco Nazionale dello Stelvio. Region with 50 glacier lakes and high mountain peaks. Access around Bormio.

Brescia 23C3

Agriturismo Cascina Maggi, Via della Maggia 3.
GPS: n45,51232 e10,23634.

16 € 15 Ch included.
Surface: metalled. 01/01-31/12.
Distance: 2,5km on the spot 500m on the spot.
Remarks: Check in at hotel, market Saturday.

Campione 23D3

Area Camper Campione del Garda, Via Verdi.
GPS: n45,75651 e10,74985.

30 € 15/24h included.
Location: Rural. **Surface:** unpaved. 01/04-31/10.
Distance: 500m on the spot 200m 100m.

Capo di Ponte 23C2

Concarena, Via Santo Stefano. **GPS**: n46,02447 e10,34325.

IT

12 € 10/24h, 01/10-28/02 free Ch (12x) WC included.
Location: Rural. **Surface:** asphalted. 01/01-31/12.
Distance: 300m on the spot 300m 300m 1km on the spot.

S Carenno 23B3

Via per il Colle. **GPS**: n45,79952 e9,46606.
8 € 5 Ch WC included. **Location:** Simple, isolated, quiet. **Surface:** asphalted. 01/01-31/12.
Distance: 250m on the spot on the spot on the spot.
Remarks: Next to sports fields, max. 72h, pay at restaurant, steep entrance road.

S Certosa di Pavia 26B1

Parking Certosa, Via di Vittorio, SP27. **GPS**: n45,25735 e9,14161.

20 € 15/24h Ch WC free. **Location:** Simple.
Surface: grassy/gravel. 01/01-31/12 water disconnected in winter. **Distance:** 1km 200m on the spot on the spot.
Remarks: Monastery Certosa di Pavia 450m.

S Chiavenna 23B2

Piazzale Leonardo da Vinci, Via A. Moro, SS36.
GPS: n46,31424 e9,39631.

20 free Ch free. **Location:** Rural. **Surface:** asphalted.
01/01-31/12.
Distance: 800m 500m 200m.
Remarks: At sports park.

S Chiesa in Valmalenco 23C2

Loc. Vassalini. **GPS**: n46,27020 e9,85670.

20 free € 3 Ch.
Location: Rural. **Surface:** gravel. 01/01-31/12.
Distance: 1km 250m 200m.
Remarks: Near sports fields.

S Clusone 23C3

Busgarina, Via Vago 6, loc Fiorine. **GPS**: n45,87312 e9,91642.

80 € 15/24h Ch included (33x) € 2 € 1/7minutes.
Location: Rural. **Surface:** unpaved. 01/01-31/12.
Distance: 3km on the spot on the spot on the spot on the spot.
Remarks: Barbecue place, picnic area, playground, swimming pool.

S Clusone 23C3

Viale Vittorio Emanuele. **GPS**: n45,88926 e9,95812.

5 free Ch free.
Location: Rural. **Surface:** asphalted. 01/01-31/12.
Distance: 600m 200m on the spot 200m.
Remarks: Max. 48h.

S Colico 23B2

L'Ontano, Via Montecchio Nord. **GPS**: n46,14213 e9,37452.

25 € 20/24h Ch WC € 1/3minutes included.
Location: Rural, simple, quiet. **Surface:** metalled.
01/02-31/12.
Distance: 500m on the spot on the spot on the spot 1km 1km on the spot on the spot.
Remarks: Canoe rental, view on Lake Como.

S Como 23B3

Area Camper Como, Via Brennero 7, Tavernola.
GPS: n45,83518 e9,06140.

10 € 0,50/h, € 12/24h € 1,50 Ch € 2,50 € 1/kWh.
Location: Comfortable. **Surface:** grasstiles. 01/01-31/12.
Distance: city centre Como 4,5km 800m 400m 200m on the spot on the spot.

S Como 23B3

Via Aldo Moro. **GPS**: n45,80286 e9,09155.

3 € 0,50/h € 1,50 Ch € 2,50 € 0,50/kWh.
Location: Urban, central, noisy.
Surface: asphalted. 01/01-31/12.
Distance: city centre 1km 150m 100m.

S Costa Volpino 23C3

Via Nazionale 24. **GPS**: n45,82298 e10,08680.
25 € 12/24h Ch included WC € 1.
Surface: metalled. 01/01-31/12.
Distance: 900m on the spot 100m on the spot on the spot.
Remarks: At lake, picnic and barbecue place, playground.

S Cremona 26C1

Piazzale della Croce Rossa, Via Mantova.
GPS: n45,13744 e10,03464.

20 free Ch free.
Location: Urban, simple. **Surface:** asphalted. 01/01-31/12.
Distance: on the spot 3km on the spot 200m on the spot.
Remarks: Nearby stadium.

S Desenzano del Garda 23D3

Area Sosta Camper La Spiaggia, Via Vò, 19.
GPS: n45,48747 e10,52180.

100 € 12/24h Ch included WC.
Surface: gravel.
01/01-31/12.
Distance: 200m Pizzeria Stella Del Garda 10m on the spot.
Remarks: Video surveillance, barbecue place.

S Esine 23C3

Fontanelle on the Road, Via Toroselle 12, SS42.
GPS: n45,90302 e10,21820.

15 guests free Ch. **Surface:** grassy. 01/01-31/12.
Distance: 4km on the spot.

S Gandino 23C3

Via Giovanni Pascoli. **GPS**: n45,81286 e9,90538.

2 free Ch free. **Surface:** grasstiles. 01/01-31/12.
Distance: historical centre 250m.
Remarks: Max. 48h.

S Gavirate 23A3

Via Cavour. **GPS**: n45,83913 e8,72105.

30 € 12/day € 1 € 2 Ch € 1 € 1/12h.
Location: Rural, simple, quiet.
Surface: grasstiles. 01/01-31/12.
Distance: 200m on the spot on the spot on the spot

IT

250m on the spot on the spot.
Remarks: At lake of Varese, friday market.

S **Germignaga** 23A3

Area Sosta Camper Germignaga, Via Bodmer, 41/A.
GPS: n45,99170 e8,71923.

10 € 23, 15/07-20/08 € 28 Ch € 1/kWh € 1/2minutes € 2,50. **Location:** Rural, simple, noisy. **Surface:** grassy. 01/01-31/12.
Distance: 1km on the spot on the spot 1km 500m 300m on the spot on the spot.
Remarks: Video surveillance.

S **Germignaga** 23A3

Via A. Bodmer. **GPS:** n45,99630 e8,72421.

5 € 1,50/h, € 15/24h € 1 € 1 Ch € 3/12h.
Location: Urban, simple, central, quiet. **Surface:** asphalted. 01/01-31/12.
Distance: 500m on the spot on the spot 500m 500m on the spot on the spot on the spot.
Remarks: Max. 48h, key electricity at pay-desk.

Iseo 23C3

Viale Europa. **GPS:** n45,65350 e10,04500.

5 free. **Location:** Urban. **Surface:** unpaved. 01/01-31/12.
Distance: 1km 250m 600m 300m.

Tourist information Iseo:

I.A.T. (Ufficio Informazioni e di Accoglienza Turistica), Lungolago Marconi, 2. Old fishermen's village.
Week market. Fri.

S **Lecco** 23B3

Via Arturo Toscanini, Loc. Bione di Lecco. **GPS:** n45,83136 e9,40779.

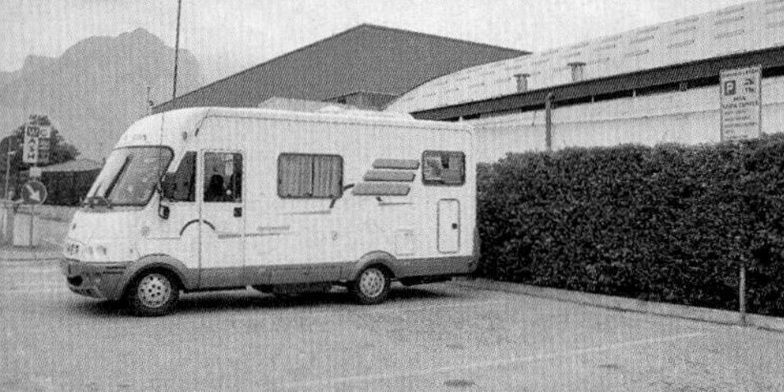

12 free Chfree. **Location:** Urban, simple, noisy.
Surface: asphalted. 01/01-31/12.
Distance: 2,8km on the spot 500m 1km 650m on the spot on the spot.
Remarks: At lake Garlate, at sports park, cycle routes.

Lecco 23B3

Via Prealpi 34. **GPS:** n45,86312 e9,42761.
20 free, weekend € 10. **Location:** Rural, simple, isolated, quiet.
Surface: gravel. 01/01-31/12.
Distance: 4,5km on the spot 4,5km on the spot on the spot on the spot on the spot.
Remarks: Pay at restaurant.

S **Livigno** 23C1

Aquafresca, Via Palipert 374. **GPS:** n46,50713 e10,11952.
€ 10-13 Ch WC .
Location: Rural. **Surface:** grassy. 01/01-31/12.
Distance: 100m on the spot on the spot on the spot.
Remarks: Free shuttle, playground.

S **Livigno** 23C1

Stella Alpina, Via Palipert 570. **GPS:** n46,50515 e10,11958.

28 € 15/24h, 2 pers.incl Ch € 3 WCincluded € 2 .
Location: Rural. **Surface:** gravel. 01/01-31/12.
Distance: 400m 500m Free bus on the spot.
Remarks: Free shuttle to ski-lifts.

S **Livigno** 23C1

Trepalle, SS301. **GPS:** n46,52655 e10,17578.

50 € 10 Chincluded.
Location: Rural. **Surface:** asphalted. 01/01-31/12.
Distance: Livigno 6,6km 200m 200m bus to Livigno every 40 minutes on the spot.
Remarks: Altitude 2000m.

Tourist information Livigno:

Latteria di Livigno, Via Pemonte 911. Discover the secrets of dairy products from Livigno. On Wednesday the possibility of preparing meals, costs € 7, from 14h. summer Mo-Fr 8-20h.

S **Lodrino** 23C3

Via Kennedy, Localité Dade. **GPS:** n45,71450 e10,28107.

3 free Ch free. **Surface:** asphalted. 01/01-31/12.
Distance: 500m.

S **Luino** 23A3

Via Gorizia. **GPS:** n45,97255 e8,75275.

16 € 9 Chincluded € 3. **Location:** Rural, isolated, quiet. **Surface:** grasstiles/grassy. 01/01-31/12.
Distance: Luino 5km on the spot 3km on the spot on the spot.
Remarks: At sports grounds, max. 72h, pay at restaurant.

S **Maccagno** 23A2

Via Virgilio Parisi. **GPS:** n46,04010 e8,73545.

18 free free. **Location:** Rural, simple, central, noisy.
Surface: gravel. 01/01-31/12.
Distance: 300m 200m 200m 300m 300m 300m on the spot on the spot.
Remarks: At sports centre, max. 72h, friday market.

Maccagno 23A2

Via Alberto Martinetti. **GPS:** n46,04130 e8,73857.
6 free. **Location:** Urban, simple, quiet. **Surface:** grasstiles. 01/01-31/12.
Distance: 500m 500m 300m 300m 400m.
Remarks: Along railwayline.

S **Magnacavallo** 26E1

Via Salvador Allende. **GPS:** n45,00587 e11,17906.

15 free Chfree. **Location:** Simple. **Surface:** asphalted. 01/01-31/12.
Distance: 200m 200m 200m 50m.
Remarks: At sports park.

S **Mandello del Lario** 23B3

Area Cima, Via Giulio Cesare. **GPS:** n45,91830 e9,31589.

12 € 10 Chincluded. **Location:** Urban, simple, central, noisy. **Surface:** concrete. 01/01-31/12.
Distance: 800m Lago di Lecco 400m on the spot 200m 200m on the spot on the spot.
Remarks: Check in at restaurant.

S **Mantova** 26D1

Parco Paganini, Via Fiera 11, Grazie di Curtatone.
GPS: n45,15333 e10,69111.

108 € 12 Ch WC included. **Location:** Simple, central.
Surface: asphalted/grassy. 01/03-13/11.
Distance: 300m, Mantova 6km 300m 4km, bakery 300m.

S **Mantova** 26D1

Sparafucile, Via Legnago 1/a. **GPS:** n45,16336 e10,81244.

IT

54 € 10/12-12h, € 15/24h Ch WC included.
Location: Comfortable, quiet. **Surface:** grassy/metalled.
01/01-31/12.
Distance: 1km 4km 500m 500m on the spot on the spot.
Remarks: Thursday market.

Mantova 26D1

Anconetta, Via Jacopo Daino. **GPS:** n45,15322 e10,79864.

free. **Location:** Urban, simple.
Surface: asphalted.
01/01-31/12.
Distance: centre 800m on the spot 300m 300m 300m.
Remarks: Marina.

Menaggio 23B2

Via Armando Diaz 12. **GPS:** n46,02454 e9,23900.
20 free free.
Location: Rural. **Surface:** asphalted. 01/01-31/12.
Distance: 550m on the spot 200m 200m on the spot.

Merate 23B3

Via Papa Giovanni Paolo I, loc. Sartirana. **GPS:** n45,71326 e9,41865.

10 € 15/24h Ch included.
Location: Rural, simple, quiet. **Surface:** grasstiles. 01/01-31/12.
Distance: 300m 400m 800m 200m on the spot.
Remarks: Max. 72h.

Milano 26B1

New Park, Via L. Tukory 6, Milan (Milano).
GPS: n45,51167 e9,16019.
50 € 25/24h Ch WC included.
Location: Urban, central, quiet.
Surface: asphalted. 01/01-31/12.
Distance: 7km 300m 50m.
Remarks: Monitored parking.

Milano 26B1

Ripamonti SNC, Via Ripamonti 481, Milan (Milano).
GPS: n45,40914 e9,20937.

30 € 20/24h Ch € 5 WC included.
Location: Urban, simple, quiet. **Surface:** asphalted.
01/01-31/12.
Distance: centre 7km 2km on the spot Milan 40min on the spot.
Remarks: Check in at reception, monitored parking.

Milano 26B1

Camper Village Linate Parking, Viale Enrico Forlanini, 123, Milan (Milano). **GPS:** n45,46245 e9,27024.
20 € 20/24h WC included.
Location: Urban, simple, noisy. **Surface:** grassy/metalled.
01/01-31/12.
Distance: centre 7km 300m N 74 > centre on the spot.
Remarks: Monitored parking.

Milano 26B1

Leone Automobili, Via Lainate 94, Rho, Milan (Milano).
GPS: n45,54232 e9,03328.
40 € 22-25 Ch included € 3/24h.
Location: Rural. **Surface:** grassy/gravel. 15/05-15/10.
Distance: Milan 16km 3km 650m.
Remarks: 24/24 surveillance.

Tourist information Milan (Milano):
Castello Sforzesco.
Duomo. History of Gothic architecture. Tue-Su.
Via Fauché. Tue, Sa.
Mercatone del Naviglio Grande, Naviglio Grande. Antiques market, 400 stalls. last Su of the month.
Galleria.

Moglia 26E2

Via Tazio Nuvolari. **GPS:** n44,93639 e10,91582.

14 free Ch free. **Surface:** asphalted. 01/01-31/12.
Distance: 300m A22 7km 300m.
Remarks: At swimming pool.

Monte Marenzo 23B3

Via Papa Gionvanni. **GPS:** n45,77639 e9,45222.

8 free Ch free € 6/24h.
Location: Rural, simple. **Surface:** gravel/metalled. 01/01-31/12.
Distance: 300m 300m 300m on the spot on the spot on the spot.
Remarks: Max. 72h, playground.

Monzambano 26D1

Area attrezzata camper Comunale di Monzambano, Via Degli Alpini n. 9. **GPS:** n45,38916 e10,69277.

130 € 13/24h (24x) € 0,50 included.
Surface: gravel. 01/01-31/12.
Distance: 200m 100m 300m, bakery 100m on the spot on the spot.
Remarks: Max. 48h, market on Sunday.

Morbegno 23B2

Area Sosta Camper Morbegno, Via del Foss.
GPS: n46,14419 e9,57500.
22 € 12 Ch included. **Location:** Rural, simple, quiet. **Surface:** asphalted/grassy. 01/01-31/12.
Distance: historical centre 500m 2km 50m 100m 2km Skibus on the spot on the spot.
Remarks: At tennis-courts, money in envelope in mail box, monitored parking 24/24, picnic and barbecue place.

Niardo 23C2

Area di sosta Mr. Sanders, Località Crist.
GPS: n45,97690 e10,31959.

20 € 10 Ch € 2 WC.
Surface: metalled. 01/01-31/12.
Distance: Niardo 1,3km on the spot on the spot.
Remarks: Bread-service.

Nova Milanese 23B3

Via G. Brodolini. **GPS:** n45,58298 e9,19668.

4 free Ch free. **Location:** Urban, simple.
Surface: asphalted. 01/01-31/12.
Distance: 500m 1,6km 200m 400m on the spot.
Remarks: At sports park, max. 48h, video surveillance.

Novate Mezzola 23B2

Via al Lido. **GPS:** n46,21083 e9,45000.

25 free. **Location:** Rural. **Surface:** grassy/gravel.
01/01-31/12.
Distance: 800m on the spot 400m 800m on the spot.
Remarks: At lake Mezzola, signposted cycle routes.

Olginate 23B3

Via Cesare Cantù. **GPS:** n45,79523 e9,41610.

46 € 10/24h Ch included.
Location: Simple, quiet. **Surface:** metalled.
01/01-31/12 Thu>16h-Fri<16h (market).
Distance: 200m on the spot 200m 200m 200m on the spot on the spot.
Remarks: At Olginate lake.

Pizzighettone 26C1

Via De Gasperi. **GPS:** n45,18538 e9,79402.

IT

4 free Ch free. **Location:** Urban, simple. **Surface:** gravel.
01/01-31/12.
Distance: 400m 300m Lidl 100m 350m.

S Ruino 26B2

Agriturismo Adriana Tarantani, Loc. Tre Venti.
GPS: n44,92833 e9,26311.

6 guests free Ch free € 2,50. **Location:** Rural, simple.
Surface: grassy/gravel. 01/01-31/12.
Distance: 1km on the spot 1km 100m.

S Sabbioneta 26D2

Via Piccola Atene. **GPS:** n44,99459 e10,48849.

15 free Ch free. **Location:** Urban, simple, quiet.
Surface: metalled. 01/01-31/12.
Distance: 200m 400m 500m on the spot.
Remarks: Max. 72h.

S San Benedetto Po 26E1

Via Cardinal Ruffini. **GPS:** n45,04292 e10,93432.
3 free Ch free. **Location:** Urban. **Surface:** asphalted.
01/01-31/12.
Distance: 500m 650m 800m 200m on the spot.
Remarks: Behind swimming pool, nearby monastery.

S Santa Caterina Valfurva 23D2

Agriturismo Zia Edda, Via Forni, loc. Nassegno.
GPS: n46,40917 e10,50833.

€ 12 Ch € 3. **Surface:** grassy.
Distance: 500m on the spot on the spot.

S Saronno 23B3

Via E.H.Griegh. **GPS:** n45,61265 e9,04274.

10 free € 0,20/100liter Ch. **Location:** Urban, simple.
Surface: asphalted. 01/01-31/12.
Distance: 1,5km 3,5km 500m 200m.

Saronno 23B3

Via Dalmazia 11. **GPS:** n45,62446 e9,02469.

3 free. **Location:** Urban, central.
Surface: concrete.
01/01-31/12.
Distance: on the spot 2km 300m Carrefour 200m 400m.
Remarks: Max. 24h.

S Sartirana Lomellina 26A1

Via Cavour. **GPS:** n45,11337 e8,66936.

3 free € 2/100liter Ch. **Location:** Simple. **Surface:** asphalted.
01/01-31/12 Sa-morning market.
Distance: 100m 200m 100m on the spot.

S Sirmione 23D3

Camper Park Sirmione, Via Cantarane. **GPS:** n45,46083 e10,63333.

100 € 20/24h, € 11/20.30-9.30h Ch € 3 included.
Surface: gravel. 15/03-31/10.
Distance: 1,5km Lake Garda 100m 1km 100m.

S Sirmione 23D3

Piazzale Montebaldo. **GPS:** n45,48694 e10,61028.

21 from € 2,50 1/2h till-€ 21/24h Ch WC.
Surface: asphalted. 01/01-31/12.
Distance: 200m on the spot 50m 200m.

S Sondrio 23C2

Area Sportiva, Via Vanoni. **GPS:** n46,16064 e9,86957.

6 free Ch free (2x).
Location: Urban. **Surface:** asphalted. 01/01-31/12.
Distance: 600m on the spot 200m 1km.

Remarks: Parking sports park.

S Songavazzo 23C3

Via Pineta 71. **GPS:** n45,88104 e9,98940.

3 free Ch free. **Location:** Urban. **Surface:** asphalted.
01/01-31/12.
Distance: on the spot 200m on the spot on the spot on the spot.

S Stezzano 23B3

Via Pietro Mascagni. **GPS:** n45,65594 e9,65301.

5 free Ch free.
Location: Urban. **Surface:** asphalted.
01/01-31/12.
Distance: 500m 6km 350m Carrefour 850m on the spot.

S Sulzano 23C3

Parking Gerolo, Via Tassano 14. **GPS:** n45,68830 e10,10341.

30 € 15/24h, € 10/night Ch WC.
Surface: grassy. 01/01-31/12.
Distance: 300m Lago Iseo 400m 500m 300m 400m.
Remarks: Picnic tables available.

S Ternate 23A3

Via Roma. **GPS:** n45,78006 e8,69780.

17 € 10 Ch (4x) included. **Location:** Simple, central, quiet. **Surface:** unpaved. 01/01-31/12.
Distance: 200m on the spot on the spot 100m 200m on the spot on the spot.
Remarks: At Comabbio lake, pay at hotel.

S Tirano 23C2

Area Camper Tirano, Via Polveriera/Via Sala Piero.
GPS: n46,21361 e10,15722.

IT

20 € 15/24h Ch included. Location: Comfortable.
Surface: grasstiles. 01/01-31/12.
Distance: 1km station 800m.

Tourist information Tirano:
Bernina Express. The highest-altitude trans-Alpine line in Europe, with one of the steepest gradients in the world between Tirano (It) and Chur (Ch). UNESCO's List of World Heritage. ± € 100/pp return ticket (Tirano-Chur), ± € 45/pp return ticket (Tirano-Pontresina).

S Torbole 23D3
Camperstop Torbole, Via Al Cor. **GPS:** n45,87264 e10,87260.

120 € 20-34 Ch WC included. **Location:** Rural.
Surface: grassy. 01/01-31/12.
Distance: on the spot on the spot on the spot on the spot.
Remarks: Along Lake Garda.

S Treviglio 23B3
Via al Malgari. **GPS:** n45,53142 e9,59710.

4 free Chfree. **Surface:** metalled. 01/01-31/12.
Distance: 700m 400m.
Remarks: At sports park.

Valcanale 23C3
Via Alpe Corte. **GPS:** n45,94968 e9,85020.

5 free. **Location:** Rural. **Surface:** gravel/sand.
01/01-31/12.
Distance: 500m 500m on the spot on the spot.

S Varzi 26B2
Strada Circonvallazione. **GPS:** n44,82172 e9,19727.

30 free, summer € 5 ChWCfree. **Location:** Rural, simple, central. **Surface:** asphalted/metalled.
01/01-31/12.
Distance: 200m 150m 300m on the spot 50m 50m.
Remarks: Along the Staffora river, friday market.

S Varzi 26B2
Via Generale Maretti 6. **GPS:** n44,81951 e9,19102.
5 guests free free . **Location:** Rural. **Surface:** metalled.
01/01-31/12.
Distance: 750m on the spot 1km 750m.

Veneto

S Arquà Polesine 26F1
Ostello Canalbianco, SS 16, n15. **GPS:** n44,99665 e11,76243.
12 € 10 Ch WC . **Surface:** metalled. 01/01-31/12.
Distance: city centre 3km on the spot station 3km.
Remarks: At youth hostel.

Asiago 23E3
P Verdi Mosele, SS349, Via Giuseppe Verdi.
GPS: n45,87129 e11,50026.

20 € 1/h, € 4/day. **Surface:** asphalted. 01/01-31/12.
Distance: 300m 500m.

S Asolo 23F3
Area Camper Communale, Via Forestuzzo.
GPS: n45,79637 e11,91283.

20 € 7/24h Ch (14x)included. **Location:** Rural, comfortable. **Surface:** grassy/sand.
01/01-31/12.
Distance: 400m 400m 400m.
Remarks: Access 8-19.30h, barbecue place, picnic area.

S Auronzo di Cadore 23F1
Taiarezze, SR48, Via Reaneloc. **GPS:** n46,56217 e12,41640.

30 € 12, 01/07-31/08 and 24/12-06/01 € 18 Chincluded.
Location: Rural, simple, quiet. **Surface:** asphalted.
01/01-31/12.
Distance: 1,5km on the spot on the spot on the spot on the spot on the spot on the spot 1,6km 1,6km.
Remarks: Max. 48h, payment only with coins.

S Barbarano Vicentino 26E1
Viale Vittorio Veneto 66. **GPS:** n45,40725 e11,54654.

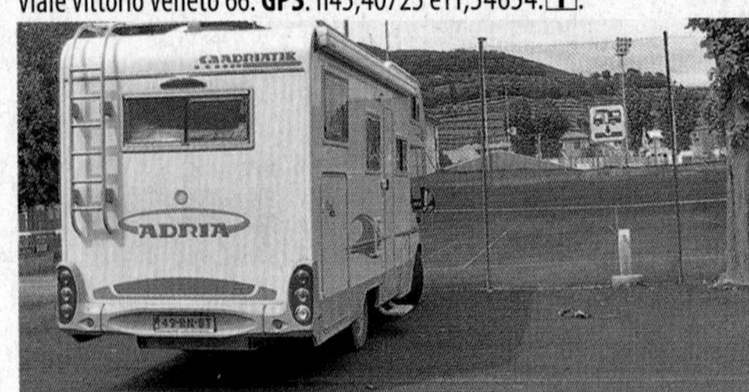

3 free free. **Location:** Urban. **Surface:** asphalted.
01/01-31/12.
Distance: 200m 200m 200m.
Remarks: Near sports fields.

S Bardolino 23D3
Parking Serenella, Via Gardesana dell'Acqua.
GPS: n45,56115 e10,71412.

10 € 17/24h Chincluded. **Location:** Rural, simple, quiet.
Surface: grasstiles. 01/01-31/12.
Distance: 2km on the spot on the spot on the spot Lidl 2km on the spot on the spot on the spot.

Tourist information Bardolino:
I.A.T. (Ufficio Informazioni e di Accoglienza Turistica), Piazzale Aldo Moro.

S Bassano del Grappa 23F3
Parcheggio Gerosa, Via Alcide de Gasperi.
GPS: n45,75831 e11,73091.

20 € 12/24h Ch included WC. **Location:** Urban.
Surface: asphalted. 01/01-31/12.
Distance: 300m 300m 300m on the spot.
Remarks: Max. 48h.

Bassano del Grappa 23F3
Prato Santo Caterina, Via Chini 6. **GPS:** n45,76009 e11,73413.
5 free. **Location:** Urban. **Surface:** metalled. 01/01-31/12.
Distance: on the spot 400m 300m on the spot.

S Bassano del Grappa 23F3
Fattoria Sociale Conca D'Oro, Via Rivoltella Bassa, 22.
GPS: n45,78437 e11,73248.
10 € 10 € 2 Ch € 2 WC € 2. **Location:** Rural.
Surface: grassy. 01/01-31/12.
Distance: 3km on the spot.
Remarks: Bread-service.

S Belluno 23F2
Rio Cavalli, Via Sagrogna 74. **GPS:** n46,15646 e12,26136.

20 € 15 € 5 WC . **Location:** Comfortable, central, quiet.
Surface: grassy/sand. 01/01-31/12.
Distance: 3km 6km on the spot on the spot 3km on the spot.
Remarks: Arrival < 19h.

S Belluno 23F2
Viale dei Dendrofori, loc. Lambioi. **GPS:** n46,13712 e12,21371.

12 8-18 € 0,80/h, overnight stay free Chfree.
Location: Simple, central, noisy. **Surface:** grasstiles/metalled.
01/01-31/12.
Distance: 100m 100m 100m.
Remarks: Nearby swimming pool and skating rink.

Bibione 23H3

Valle Vecchia, Strada Brussa. **GPS**: n45,62458 e12,95866.

100 € 10/08-18h, overnight stay free free WC .
Location: Rural, simple, isolated, quiet. **Surface:** grassy.
01/01-31/12.
Distance: 12km sandy beach 250m 12km 12km on the spot on the spot.
Remarks: Guarded during the day, shower during opening hours, dog permitted on the beach.

Borghetto di Valeggio sul Mincio 26D1

Camper Parking Visconteo, Strada provinciale 55.
GPS: n45,35537 e10,72017.
60 € 10/24h € 3 Ch € 2/24h . **Location:** Rural, comfortable. **Surface:** gravel. 01/01-31/12.
Distance: on the spot Lake Garda 13km 250m on the spot on the spot.
Remarks: Borghetto 200m.

Castelguglielmo 26E1

Via Alessandro Volta. **GPS**: n45,02246 e11,53518.

10 free Ch free. **Surface:** metalled.
Distance: 500m 500m.

Cavallino-Treporti 23G3

Spiaggia di Cà Ballarin, Via Gabrielle Berton.
GPS: n45,45998 e12,51659.

4 free. **Location:** Rural, simple, quiet. **Surface:** sand.
01/05-31/10.
Distance: 1km on the spot on the spot on the spot 1km 300m.
Remarks: Beach parking.

Tourist information Cavallino-Treporti:
Week market. Tue-Thu morning.

Chioggia 26G1

2 Palme, Lungomare Adriatica. **GPS**: n45,22122 e12,29624.

100 € 15, peak season € 20 Ch (100x),2Amp WC included € 1/3minutes. **Location:** Urban, simple, central.
Surface: grassy/gravel. 01/01-31/12.
Distance: city centre 1,5km 200m on the spot 1km on the spot.
Remarks: Chioggia: little Venice.

Cittadella 23F3

Stazione Q8, Via Cristofolo Colombo 1. **GPS**: n45,64377 e11,77432.
5 free € 1/60liter Ch € 2,50 € 1/h WC. **Location:** Urban.
Surface: metalled. 01/01-31/12.
Distance: on the spot.
Remarks: At petrol station.

Cittadella 23F3

Centro Sportivo, Viale dello Sport. **GPS**: n45,64403 e11,77995.
20 free. **Location:** Urban. **Surface:** asphalted. 01/01-31/12.
Distance: on the spot 600m 150m.
Remarks: At sports centre, swimming pool.

Cittadella 23F3

Villa Rina, Via Riva del Grappa. **GPS**: n45,65035 e11,78778.
20 free. **Location:** Urban. **Surface:** asphalted. 01/01-31/12.
Distance: on the spot 200m Lidl 1,5km 250m.

Colà di Lazise 23D3

Villa dei Cedri, Via Possoi. **GPS**: n45,46777 e10,74972.

200 € 1/h, 5 hours min Ch included. **Location:** Rural, comfortable, quiet. **Surface:** grasstiles. 01/01-31/12.
Remarks: Parco Termale 300m.

Conegliano 23F2

Area de Sosta Campeggio Club Conegliano, Via San Giovanni Bosco, SS13. **GPS**: n45,87799 e12,30111.

30 € 12/24h Ch (16x)included WC .
Location: Simple, central, quiet. **Surface:** grassy.
01/01-31/12.
Distance: 2km nearby on the spot.

Domegge di Cadore Belluno 23F1

Camping Cologna, Vallesella di Cadore. **GPS**: n46,44605 e12,40658.

30 € 10 Ch. **Location:** Rural, simple, quiet. **Surface:** grassy.
01/05-20/10.
Distance: 1km At the lake on the spot on the spot 1km 1km on the spot on the spot.
Remarks: Max. 24h, narrow entrance.

Feltre 23F2

Area Camper Vincheto, Via Casonetto 158C.
GPS: n46,03124 e11,95911.
12 € 15 Ch included € 3. **Surface:** grassy/metalled.
01/01-31/12.
Distance: 6km on the spot.

Feltre 23F2

Piazale Pra del Vescovo, Viale A. Gaggia.
GPS: n46,02013 e11,90792.

15 free Ch free . **Surface:** metalled.
01/01-31/12.
Distance: 500m 500m 500m 500m.
Remarks: Max. 48h.

Ferrara di Monte Baldo 23D3

Via Chiesa. **GPS**: n45,67794 e10,85491.

16 free Ch free (16x)€ 5/day. **Location:** Rural, simple, isolated, quiet. **Surface:** gravel. 01/01-31/12.
Distance: 300m 300m 300m 300m on the spot on the spot on the spot.
Remarks: To be paid at bar.

Garda 23D3

P Centro, SS249. **GPS**: n45,57501 e10,71019.

20 € 17/24h Ch WC included. **Location:** Simple.
Surface: metalled. 01/01-31/12.
Distance: 200m on the spot on the spot.

Garda 23D3

Via Preite. **GPS**: n45,57620 e10,71404.

30 € 17/24h Ch included. **Location:** Quiet.
Surface: grasstiles. Easter-31/10.
Distance: 300m Lake Garda 300m.

Grancona 26E1

Strada di Grancona. **GPS**: n45,42403 e11,45221.
30 free Ch (2x)free. **Location:** Rural. **Surface:** gravel.
01/01-31/12.
Distance: 500m 300m.

Lazise 23D3

Parking Lazise Dardo, Via San Martino, SP31.
GPS: n45,50623 e10,73584.

IT

15 € 17/24h. **Surface:** asphalted. 01/01-31/12.
Distance: 200m 5,8km 200m 200m 200m.

S Lido di Jesolo 23G3

Area camping Albatros, Via Correr 102/A.
GPS: n45,52477 e12,68995.

131 € 12-32 Ch WC included. **Location:** Rural, comfortable, isolated, quiet. **Surface:** grassy. 01/03-31/10.
Distance: 500m 700m 100m 100m 100m 100m.

S Lido di Jesolo 23G3

Boscopineta, Via Vettor Pisani. **GPS**: n45,52278 e12,69178.

250 € 11-20 Ch WC € 1 € 5 included.
Location: Rural, comfortable, central. **Surface:** grassy.
Easter-31/10.
Distance: 100m 400m 250m on the spot.

S Lido di Jesolo 23G3

Camping Park dei Dogi, Viale Oriente. **GPS**: n45,52146 e12,68828.

200 € 14-26, 4 pers.incl. Ch WCincluded € 0,50 € 5 € 1/week. **Location:** Rural, comfortable, central, quiet.
Surface: grassy. 01/01-31/12.
Distance: 200m sandy beach 200m 40m 150m 20m.

S Lido di Jesolo 23G3

Jesolo Camper Don Bosco, Via Oriente/via G.Don Bosco.
GPS: n45,52188 e12,68943.

250 € 11-20 Ch € 3 WC € 1 € 5 included.
Location: Rural, comfortable. **Surface:** grassy/gravel.
01/01-31/12.
Distance: 100m 100m on the spot 100m on the spot.
Remarks: Bus to Venice stops in front of motorhome parking.

S Livinallongo del Col di Lana 23F1

Sportbar del Ghiaccio, Via Piagn,6 Arabba.
GPS: n46,49678 e11,87692.

50 € 17 Ch (17x)€ 3/24h WC € 3. **Location:** Rural, comfortable, quiet. **Surface:** grassy/gravel. 01/01-31/12.
Distance: on the spot on the spot 200m 200m on the spot on the spot 200m.
Remarks: At the skating rink, check in at bar, service passerby € 6.

S Malcesine 23D3

Camping Lombardi, Via Navene 141, loc. Campagnola.
GPS: n45,78429 e10,82187.

20 € 18/24h, 28/06-01/09 € 21/24h Ch € 1/24h WCincluded € 1,50 according consumption.
Location: Rural, simple, quiet. **Surface:** grasstiles. 01/04-31/10.
Distance: 3km Lake Garda 500m 50m on the spot on the spot on the spot.
Remarks: Max. 48h.

P Marghera 23F3

Parcheggio Terminal Service, Via dei Petroli 1/3 angolo via della Libertà. **GPS**: n45,46806 e12,26589.

€ 20/24h. **Location:** Simple, central, quiet.
01/01-31/12.
Distance: > Venice.
Remarks: Monitored parking.

S Mirano 23F3

Camper Club Mirano, Via viasana, 4. **GPS**: n45,49322 e12,08968.

€ 15 Ch included.
Location: Rural, comfortable. **Surface:** grasstiles. 01/01-31/12.
Distance: historical centre 1,5km 8km 500m 600m 300m Padua-Venice.
Remarks: For entrance email: camperclubmirano@libero.it of phone 3479831010.

S Misurina 23F1

Piazzale Loita, Via Monte Piana. **GPS**: n46,58839 e12,25737.

50 € 2/h, € 18/day Chincluded. **Location:** Rural, simple, central, noisy. **Surface:** gravel.
01/01-31/12.
Distance: 300m 500m 50m 300m on the spot on the spot on the spot 3km.
Remarks: Max. 48h, cash payment.

Misurina 23F1

P camper Rifugio Auronzo, Rifugio Auronzo.
GPS: n46,61267 e12,29342.

40 € 40 toll road incl., extra night € 15.
Location: Rural, simple, isolated. **Surface:** gravel. 01/05-30/10.
Distance: Misurina 12km on the spot 12km on the spot Tre Cime di Lavadero 15km.
Remarks: Beautiful view.

S Molina 23D3

Camper el Crear, Via Bartolomeo Bacilieri 145.
GPS: n45,61229 e10,90855.

20 € 5 included. **Location:** Rural, simple, quiet.
Surface: grassy/gravel. 01/01-31/12.
Distance: on the spot on the spot.
Remarks: Max. 48h, pay at restaurant.

S Montagnana 26E1

Via Circonvallazione. **GPS**: n45,23528 e11,46639.

20 free ChWCfree. **Location:** Urban.
Surface: asphalted. 01/01-31/12.
Distance: 200m 200m 200m.
Remarks: At sports centre.

S Padova 26F1

Park Camper Pontevigordarzere, Via Telemaco Signorini, Padua (Padova). **GPS**: n45,44267 e11,88926.
17 € 8/24h Ch € 2/8h. 01/01-31/12.
Distance: centre 4,5km 300m 300m on the spot.

Padova 26F1

P1, Piazza della Pace Ytzhak Rabbin, Via cinquantottesimo Fanteria, Padua (Padova). **GPS**: n45,39686 e11,87673.
8-20h € 10, 20-8h € 10, 18-10h € 20.
Surface: asphalted.
01/01-31/12.
Distance: on the spot 6km on the spot on the spot

IT

on the spot.

Tourist information Padua (Padova):

Caffe Pedrocchi, Via Oberdan. Café, meeting point for students.

Capella degli Scrovegni. Chapel.

S Peschiera del Garda 26D1

Area Camper Frassino, Via Frassino 11. **GPS**: n45,43115 e10,67500.

80 € 15 Ch WC included.
Location: Rural, simple. **Surface:** gravel. 01/01-31/12.
Distance: 1,5km 300m.

S Peschiera del Garda 26D1

Area camper Peschiera, Via Milano. **GPS**: n45,43995 e10,68474.

100 € 18/24h Ch WC € 1 included.
Location: Simple. **Surface:** gravel. 01/01-31/12.
Distance: 200m 1km 400m 400m on the spot on the spot on the spot.
Remarks: Monday-morning market.

Tourist information Peschiera del Garda:

Tourist town at Lake Garda.

Mo-morning.

S Pianiga 23F3

Il Graticolato, Via Giulio Onesti. **GPS**: n45,45681 e12,03344.

15 € 6/24h Ch included. **Surface:** unpaved.
01/01-31/12.
Distance: 250m 8km 200m 150m 50m 250m 200m.

Porto Tolle 26G2

Via strada del Mare, loc. Barricata, SP38. **GPS**: n44,84997 e12,46342.

50 € 3,50. **Location:** Rural, quiet. **Surface:** grassy/sand.
Distance: 50m.
Remarks: Beach parking.

S Porto Tolle 26G2

Agriturismo La Ca' del Delta, Via Mazzini, 1.
GPS: n44,97798 e12,39785.
8 € 15 € 2/day. **Location:** Isolated, quiet.
Distance: on the spot.

S Punta Sabbioni 23G3

Parking Dante Alighieri, Dante Alighieri 26.
GPS: n45,44132 e12,42131.

36 € 17-20 + € 3/pp Ch € 3/24h WC included € 3 free. **Location:** Urban, simple, central, quiet.
Surface: grassy.
01/03-01/11.
Distance: 1,5km 1,5km 1,5km 500m.
Remarks: Arrival <22h, monitored parking, ferry boat to Venice 500m.

Punta Sabbioni 23G3

Lungomare Dante Alighieri. **GPS**: n45,44342 e12,42189.

5 € 1,60/h, € 9/12h, overnight stay free. **Location:** Simple, quiet.
Surface: gravel. 01/01-31/12.
Distance: 750m 500m.
Remarks: Max. 24h.

S Punta Sabbioni 23G3

Agricamping da Scarpa, Via Pealto 15.
GPS: n45,44279 e12,44055.

15 € 16-20 + € 6-7/pp Ch WC € 3 included.
Location: Rural, comfortable, quiet.
Surface: grassy.
01/01-31/12.
Distance: 500m on the spot 500m ferry Venice 1,5km.
Remarks: Breakfast-service.

S Recoaro Terme 23E3

Area Communale, Via Della Restistenza.
GPS: n45,70430 e11,22902.

16 € 5/24h € 0,10/10liter Ch (16x)€ 0,50/2h,6Amp.
Location: Rural. **Surface:** grassy/gravel. 01/01-31/12.
Distance: on the spot on the spot on the spot on the spot on the spot.

San Salvaro 26E1

Monastero di San Salvaro, Via Guglielmo Marconi.
GPS: n45,20485 e11,40877.
free Ch. 01/01-31/12.

S Santo Stefano di Cadore 23G1

Albergo Gasperina, Loc. Cima Canale, Val Visdende.
GPS: n46,60835 e12,63053.

49 € 12/24h, Aug € 14 Ch (49x)€ 2,50/day WC included € 2. **Surface:** gravel. 01/06-01/10.
Distance: 12km 300m on the spot 6km on the spot on the spot.
Remarks: Check in at restaurant, bread-service, 10% discount at restaurant.

S Sappada 23G1

Borgata Palù. **GPS**: n46,56254 e12,67991.

40 € 12/24h Ch (24x)included.
Location: Rural, simple, quiet. **Surface:** gravel. 01/01-31/12.
Distance: 1,1km 500m 1km on the spot on the spot 100m.
Remarks: Keycard at townhall, caution € 10.

S Schio 23E3

Camper Schio, Via Cardatori. **GPS**: n45,71518 e11,34607.
15 € 10 Ch. **Location:** Urban. **Surface:** metalled.
01/01-31/12.
Distance: 750m 200m 200m.
Remarks: On site of a former barracks complex, video surveillance.

S Schio 23E3

Parking Palasport, Viale dell'Industria. **GPS**: n45,71389 e11,37599.

4 free Ch free. **Location:** Urban. **Surface:** asphalted.
01/01-31/12.
Distance: 1km 250m 250m.

S Sernaglia della Battaglia 23F3

Area attrezzata Le Grave, Via Passo Barca, Falzè di Piave.
GPS: n45,85676 e12,16566.

24 € 5/12h Ch included € 2/24h.
Location: Rural, simple. **Surface:** grassy. 01/01-31/12.
Distance: 500m on the spot 100m 500m 300m.

S Soave 26E1

Via Invalidi del Lavoro. **GPS**: n45,42340 e11,24541.

IT

16 € 5/24h Ch (16x),16Amp WC included.
Surface: grasstiles.
01/01-31/12.
Distance: 200m 3km on the spot 200m 200m 300m.
Remarks: Nearby police station.

S Soave 26E1

Cantina Filippi, Via Liberta 55. **GPS**: n45,46373 e11,23798.
12 € 15 2 pers. incl., free for clients (>€ 30) Chincluded WC. **Location:** Rural. **Surface:** grassy. 01/01-31/12.
Distance: on the spot.
Remarks: Barbecue place, playground.

S Treviso 23F3

Parking ex Foro Boario, Via Castello d'Amore.
GPS: n45,67014 e12,25733.

13 free Chfree.
Location: Rural, simple. **Surface:** metalled. 01/01-31/12.
Distance: 500m 11,5km 500m 500m 200m.
Remarks: Max. 48h.

S Treviso 23F3

Via Giovanni Boccaccio. **GPS**: n45,66769 e12,26361.

24 free Chfree. **Location:** Urban, simple, central, noisy.
Surface: asphalted. 01/01-31/12.
Distance: 1km 500m 500m 300m.
Remarks: Along railwayline.

Tourist information Treviso:
Sile. Fish-market on island.

S Venezia 23G3

Parcheggio Al Tronchetto, Venice (Venezia).
GPS: n45,44146 e12,30514.

40 € 21/0-12h, 12-24h € 16 included .
Location: Urban, simple, central, quiet. **Surface:** asphalted.
01/01-31/12.
Distance: 2km on the spot 2km 2km ferry, train.

S Venezia 23G3

Parco di San Giuliano, Via San Giuliano 19, Venice (Venezia).
GPS: n45,46742 e12,27916.

100 € 18/24h Ch (30x)€ 4/24h WC included € 5.
Location: Urban, comfortable, central, quiet. **Surface:** grassy.
01/01-31/12.
Distance: 4km 5km 200m 1,5km 2,5KM ferry Venice 100m, bus on the spot on the spot.

Tourist information Venice (Venezia):
A.P.T. (Azienda di Promozione Turistica), www.turismovenezia.it. Historical city consits of 117 islands, 150 canals and 400 bridges.

S Verona 26E1

Area sosta camper Porta Palio, Via dalla Bona.
GPS: n45,43354 e10,97879.

37 € 5/4h, € 10/24h Chincluded. **Location:** Urban, simple, central.
Surface: asphalted. 01/01-31/12.
Distance: 500m Pizza (ordering service) bus 62 > centre.

S Verona 26E1

Agricamping Corte Finiletto, Strada Bresciana, 41.
GPS: n45,44651 e10,91917.

15 € 21, 2 pers.incl Ch € 2 WC included.
Location: Rural. **Surface:** grassy.
Distance: 6km 3km 3km on the spot 1,5km 1,5km.
Remarks: 10% discount on presentation of the most recent guide.

Tourist information Verona:
Arena. Large anfiteatro, in July/August opera performances.
Via Capella. Known for the love drama of Romeo and Juliet.
Piazza dellen Erbe. daily.

S Vicenza 23E3

Park Interscambio CentroBus, Via Bassano, Zona sud-est.
GPS: n45,54321 e11,55886.

40 € 10/24h WCincluded. **Location:** Urban.
Surface: asphalted. 01/01-31/12 during event.
Distance: 2km on the spot 2km Free bus to centre, every 15 min on the spot.
Remarks: At stadium, monitored parking 24/24, borrow cycles for free.

S Vicenza 23E3

Park Interscambio CentroBus, Viale Cricoli, Zona nord.
GPS: n45,56418 e11,54903.

18 € 8,40/24h ChWCincluded. **Location:** Urban.
Surface: asphalted.
01/01-31/12.
Distance: 1,6km on the spot on the spot Free bus to centre.

Tourist information Vicenza:
Quartiere delle Barche. District with palaces in Venetian style.

Friuli Venezia Giulia

S Ampezzo 23G1

Via Laucjit. **GPS**: n46,41170 e12,80073.

6 € 7/24h Ch WCincluded. **Location:** Rural, comfortable, quiet. **Surface:** gravel. 01/01-31/12.
Distance: 500m 650m on the spot.
Remarks: Next to sports fields.

S Andreis 23G2

SP20. **GPS**: n46,19912 e12,61315.

20 € 5/day . **Location:** Simple, quiet.
Surface: gravel.
Distance: 200m little stream on the spot.

S Aquileia 23H3

Via Achille Grandi. **GPS**: n45,76549 e13,36898.

20 € 10/day ChWCincluded. **Location:** Urban, quiet.
Surface: grasstiles. 01/01-31/12.
Distance: 500m 200m on the spot.
Remarks: Max. 48h.

S Arta Terme 23G1

Terme di Arta. **GPS**: n46,47554 e13,01677.

7 free Chfree . **Surface:** grasstiles.
01/01-31/12.

Distance: 1km ⊗300m.
Remarks: Narrow entrance.

Artegna 23H2

Via Vicenza. **GPS**: n46,23465 e13,14919.

2 free Chfree. **Location:** Urban, simple, noisy.
Surface: concrete. 01/01-31/12.
Distance: 800m ⊗800m.
Remarks: Along railwayline.

Barcis 23G2

Loc. Portuz, SS251. **GPS**: n46,19055 e12,56507.

20 € 12/24h Ch included. **Location:** Comfortable, isolated, quiet. **Surface:** grasstiles/metalled. 01/01-31/12.
Distance: 400m on the spot ⊗500m 500m on the spot on the spot.
Remarks: At the lake of Barcis.

Brugnera 23G2

Parco Di Villa Varda, Via Villa Varda di S. Cassiano.
GPS: n45,88861 e12,52980.

10 free Chfree. **Location:** Rural, quiet. **Surface:** gravel.
01/01-31/12.
Distance: ⊗on the spot.
Remarks: Recreation park.

Capriva del Friuli 23H2

Via degli Alpini. **GPS**: n45,94657 e13,51107.

free Ch free. **Location:** Rural, quiet. **Surface:** metalled.
01/01-31/12.
Distance: 600m on the spot on the spot.

Cavasso Nuovo 23G2

Via Dante Alighieri. **GPS**: n46,19514 e12,77467.

4 free Ch free. **Location:** Noisy. **Surface:** asphalted.
01/01-31/12.
Distance: 400m.

Cividale del Friuli 23H2

Via delle Mura. **GPS**: n46,09446 e13,43618.

4 free Chfree.
Location: Urban, quiet. **Surface:** asphalted.
Distance: 500m ⊗500m on the spot.
Remarks: Max. 72h.

Clauzetto 23G2

Ambito delle Grotte di Pradis, Via Pradis di sotto,76.
GPS: n46,24538 e12,88974.

10 free Chfree. **Location:** Rural, isolated, quiet.
Surface: gravel. 01/01-31/12.
Distance: Clauzetto 3km ⊗150m on the spot on the spot.
Remarks: Parking at the caves.

Codroipo 23H2

Strada vicinale molino della sega, Passariano.
GPS: n45,94649 e13,00836.

8 free € 3/1h Ch (8x)€ 3/6h. **Location:** Rural, quiet.
Surface: grasstiles. 01/01-31/12.
Distance: centre 3,5km ⊗300m on the spot.
Remarks: Coins at tourist info.

Colloredo di Monte Albano 23H2

Strada Provinciale 49. **GPS**: n46,16556 e13,13932.

8 free. **Location:** Rural, simple, quiet. **Surface:** metalled.
01/01-31/12.
Distance: 100m ⊗100m.
Remarks: Max. 7m.

Cormons 23H2

P.le Luciano Zani, Salita del Monte Quarin.
GPS: n45,96672 e13,47341.

3 free free. **Location:** Rural, isolated, quiet.
Surface: metalled. 01/01-31/12.
Distance: 3,5km ⊗2km 2,5km on the spot on the spot.

Corno di Rosazzo 23H2

Via dei Pini. **GPS**: n45,98955 e13,43917.

8 free Ch free. **Location:** Rural, simple, quiet.
Surface: asphalted. 01/01-31/12.
Distance: 300m ⊗1,5km 1km.
Remarks: Max. 48h.

Forni di Sopra 23G1

Santa Viela, SS52. **GPS**: n46,42500 e12,57036.

20 € 7-9 Chfree. **Location:** Rural, simple, noisy.
Surface: asphalted. 01/01-31/12.
Distance: 800m ⊗on the spot 800m 400m on the spot on the spot on the spot on the spot.
Remarks: No camping activities.

Gemona del Friuli 23H2

Piazzale Mons. Battista Monai. **GPS**: n46,27585 e13,13728.

15 free Chfree. **Location:** Rural, simple, central, noisy.
Surface: asphalted. 01/01-31/12.
Distance: on the spot 3,3km ⊗300m 500m on the spot.

Gorizia 37A1

Viale Oriani. **GPS**: n45,94554 e13,61603.

30 free Chfree. **Location:** Urban, simple, quiet.
Surface: asphalted. 01/01-31/12.
Distance: centre 500m on the spot.
Remarks: Max. 72h.

Gradisca d'Isonzo 23H2

Viale Trieste. **GPS**: n45,88577 e13,49582.

IT

3 free Chfree. **Location:** Urban, central. **Surface:** asphalted. 01/01-31/12.
Distance: on the spot 2,3km on the spot on the spot.
Remarks: Max. 48h.

Gradisca d'Isonzo 23H2

Agriturismo Ai Feudi di Marizza Monica e Villi, Via Venuti, 11.
GPS: n45,89214 e13,46782.
guests free.
Distance: on the spot.

Grado 23H3

Viala Italia. **GPS:** n45,68218 e13,41230.

41 € 16/24h Ch included. **Location:** Simple.
Surface: asphalted. 01/01-31/12.
Distance: 2km 600m on the spot.
Remarks: Video surveillance.

Latisana 23H3

Via Gasperi. **GPS:** n45,78163 e12,99325.

10 free Chfree. **Location:** Urban, simple. **Surface:** asphalted. 01/01-31/12.
Distance: 500m on the spot on the spot.
Remarks: At supermarket.

Malborghetto Valbruna 23H1

Malga Saisera. **GPS:** n46,45624 e13,46955.

10 € 0,60/h. **Location:** Rural, isolated, quiet.
Surface: gravel.
Distance: 5,5km 5,5km on the spot.

Maniago 23G2

Via Colvera. **GPS:** n46,17632 e12,71149.

5 free Ch free. **Location:** Urban, simple.

Surface: grasstiles. 01/01-31/12.
Distance: 400m 200m.

Monfalcone 23H2

Areacamper F.V.G, Via Consiglio d'Europa, 13.
GPS: n45,79754 e13,55867.

36 € 15/24h Ch WC included. **Location:** Quiet.
Surface: metalled. 01/01-31/12.
Distance: city centre 3km 100m.
Remarks: Nearby port, video surveillance.

Montereale Valcellina 23G2

Via dell'Omo. **GPS:** n46,15168 e12,66122.

15 € 5 Ch included. **Location:** Urban, simple.
Surface: asphalted. 01/01-31/12.
Distance: 500m 300m.
Remarks: Service passerby € 2, key at petrol station/bar.

Mossa 23H2

Via delle Fornaci. **GPS:** n45,94563 e13,54536.

4 free. **Location:** Rural, quiet. **Surface:** metalled. 01/01-31/12.
Distance: 1km on the spot on the spot on the spot.

Oleis 23H2

Via Rosazzo. **GPS:** n46,01634 e13,39311.

10 free Ch free. **Location:** Quiet. **Surface:** metalled. 01/01-31/12.
Distance: 100m.

Paluzza 23G1

Ponte di Sutrio, Via Nazionale. **GPS:** n46,51148 e13,00203.

5 free € 3,50 € 3,50 Ch. **Location:** Simple, noisy.
Surface: gravel. 01/01-31/12.

Distance: 150m 150m.
Remarks: At petrol station.

Piancavallo 23G2

Via Barcis. **GPS:** n46,11141 e12,51411.

70 € 13/24h Ch WC included. **Location:** Quiet.
Surface: metalled. 01/01-31/12.
Distance: 600m on the spot.
Remarks: Max. 7 days, check in at hotel.

Pordenone 23G2

SS13, Pordenone. **GPS:** n45,97236 e12,64332.

8 € 3 Ch. **Location:** Urban, simple, noisy. **Surface:** asphalted. 01/01-31/12.
Distance: 1km 3km 200m on the spot.
Remarks: Max. 48h, to be paid at petrol station.

Preone 23G1

Strada Provinciale 12. **GPS:** n46,39736 e12,86561.
10 € 13/24h Ch included. **Surface:** grasstiles. 01/01-31/12.
Distance: 500m 350m 350m.
Remarks: Inspection 2017: closed because of renovation.

Quinto di Trevisio 23F3

Camper Resort Quinto, Via Costamala 26.
GPS: n45,63901 e12,15728.

28 € 15 Ch WC included. **Location:** Luxurious.
Surface: gravel. 01/01-31/12.
Distance: 800m on the spot 500m 650m on the spot on the spot.
Remarks: Max. 5 days.

Ravascletto 23G1

Via Valcalda. **GPS:** n46,52348 e12,92790.

10 € 6 Ch (4x)included. **Location:** Simple.
Surface: asphalted. 01/01-31/12.
Distance: 500m 200m.
Remarks: Pay at tourist office.

Sacile 23G2

Viale Repubblica. **GPS:** n45,95662 e12,49667.

7 € 5/24h Chfree. **Location:** Urban. **Surface:** metalled.
01/01-31/12.
Distance: 600m 300m on the spot.
Remarks: Max. 48h, video surveillance.

S San Daniele del Friuli 23G2

Via Udine, SP16. **GPS**: n46,15610 e13,01368.

20 free Chfree. **Location:** Rural, central, quiet.
Surface: grasstiles. 01/01-31/12.
Distance: 300m 300m 300m 200m.
Remarks: Parking sports park.

S San Vito al Tagliamento 23G2

Area di sosta San Vito al Tagliamento, Via Pulet.
GPS: n45,91224 e12,86590.

12 € 5/12h, € 8/24h, € 15/48h € 1 Ch included.
Location: Rural, simple, isolated, quiet. **Surface:** asphalted.
01/01-31/12.
Distance: 500m 15km 500m 500m 500m.
Remarks: Max. 48h, gate can be opened manually.

S Sauris 23G1

Prosciuttificio Wolf Sauris, Sauris di Sotto 88.
GPS: n46,46756 e12,70833.
10 free WC free. **Location:** Rural, simple, quiet.
Surface: asphalted. 01/01-31/12.
Distance: on the spot 150m on the spot.
Remarks: Regional products.

S Sesto al Reghena 23G2

Viale degli Olmi. **GPS**: n45,84615 e12,81273.

6 € 5/day € 0,10/10liter € 3 Ch € 2 € 1/12h.
Surface: asphalted. 01/01-31/12.
Distance: 500m 500m.

S Spilimbergo 23G2

Via Udine. **GPS**: n46,10814 e12,90411.

10 free Ch free. **Location:** Urban, simple, central.
Surface: grasstiles. 01/01-31/12.
Distance: 300m 300m 400m.
Remarks: Max. 48h.

S Tarcento 23H2

Plein-air Torre, Via Sottocolleverzan. **GPS**: n46,21446 e13,22504.

10 free Chfree . **Location:** Urban, simple, quiet.
Surface: grasstiles.
01/01-31/12.
Distance: 200m 200m 200m.
Remarks: Nearby sports center, max. 72h, no camping activities.

S Tarvisio 23H1

Localita Plezzut. **GPS**: n46,49633 e13,68937.
€ 15/24h Ch. **Surface:** grasstiles.
01/01-31/12.
Distance: Tarvisio 10km on the spot on the spot.

S Tarvisio 23H1

Parcheggio P3, Via Armando Diaz. **GPS**: n46,50426 e13,57157.

16 € 0,60/h Chfree WC. **Location:** Urban, simple, central.
Surface: metalled. 01/01-31/12.
Distance: 300m 100m 200m 200m.
Remarks: Max. 2 days.

Tarvisio 23H1

Monte lussari. **GPS**: n46,50737 e13,53421.

20 free. **Surface:** asphalted/metalled. 01/01-31/12.
Distance: on the spot 600m on the spot 100m.

S Timau 23G1

Strada Statale 52bis. **GPS**: n46,58904 e12,97276.

5 € 5 Chincluded € 5/day. **Location:** Rural, isolated, quiet. **Surface:** grasstiles/grassy. 01/06-30/09.
Distance: 2,5km on the spot.
Remarks: At small lake, to be paid at bar.

S Tramonti di Sopra 23G2

Area picnic Sot Trivea, Strada Da Lis Fornas.
GPS: n46,30133 e12,77974.

4 € 7 Ch included. **Location:** Rural, isolated, quiet.
Surface: grassy/gravel. 01/01-31/12.
Distance: 1,5km 1,5km.
Remarks: Beside river.

S Trieste 37A1

Mamaca park, Via del Pane Bianco. **GPS**: n45,62539 e13,78707.

6 € 8 Ch included4h WC. **Location:** Urban.
Surface: gravel. 01/01-31/12.
Distance: 200m 100m.
Remarks: Call for entrance code, narrow entrance.

S Trieste 37A1

Via Karl Ludwig Von Bruck. **GPS**: n45,63710 e13,76990.

20 € 4 Chincluded. **Location:** Urban, simple, noisy.
Surface: asphalted. 01/01-31/12.
Distance: 3km shuttle to centre.
Remarks: Max. 72h, pitches under motorway.

P Trieste 37A1

Via Ottaviano Augusto. **GPS**: n45,64599 e13,75654.

€ 0,80/h 8-20h. **Location:** Urban, central, noisy.
Surface: asphalted. 01/01-31/12.
Distance: centre 500m 100m on the spot.

Tourist information Trieste:
Grotta del Giganta. Caves. Tue-Su, 01/07-31/08 Mo-Su.

S Udine 23H2

Via Chiusaforte. **GPS**: n46,08115 e13,22317.

IT

50 free Chfree. **Location:** Urban, simple, noisy. **Surface:** grasstiles. 01/01-31/12.
Distance: city centre 2km 3,5km 160m 400m line 1 > centre.

S Valvasone 23G2
Via Pier Pasolini. **GPS:** n45,99819 e12,86031.

8 free Ch free. **Location:** Rural, simple, quiet. **Surface:** asphalted. 01/01-31/12.
Distance: 350m 350m 400m.
Remarks: Max. 48h.

S Villa Vicentina 23H2
Via Duca d'Aosta. **GPS:** n45,81738 e13,39369.

5 free Chfree. **Location:** Simple. **Surface:** asphalted. 01/01-31/12.
Distance: 200m on the spot.

S Vito d'Asio 23G1
Via Gialinars, San Francesco. **GPS:** n46,31244 e12,93427.

5 free Ch free. **Location:** Rural, isolated, quiet. **Surface:** metalled. 01/01-31/12 With snow.
Distance: Vito d'Asio 15km 350m on the spot.
Remarks: Near sports fields.

S Zoppola 23G2
Via Manteghe. **GPS:** n45,96502 e12,78019.

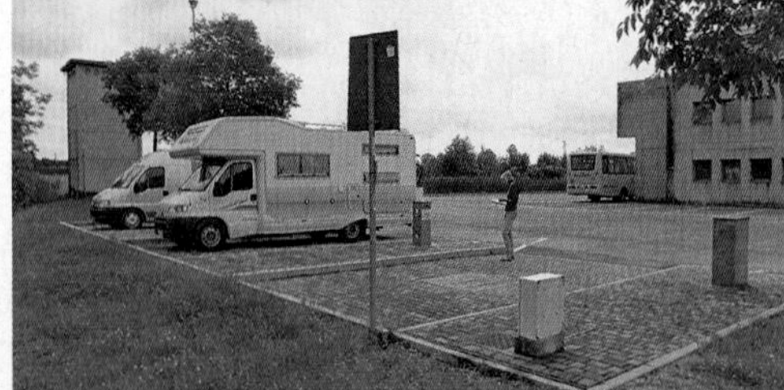

20 free Ch free. **Location:** Rural, isolated, quiet. **Surface:** metalled. 01/01-31/12.
Distance: centre 500m 850m 1,5km.
Remarks: At gymnasium, max. 48h.

Emilia-Romagna

S Anita 26F2
Agriturismo Prato Pozzo, Via Rotta Martinella 34/a.
GPS: n44,54892 e12,13322.

20 € 6 + € 6/pp, guests free Ch (12x)€ 2,60/day WC included. **Location:** Rural, comfortable, isolated, quiet.
Surface: grassy/metalled. 01/01-31/12.
Distance: 1km 500m 500m on the spot 1km 1km.

S Argenta 26F2
Area Golf Club, Via Poderi. **GPS:** n44,63027 e11,81112.
5 € 5 Ch included. **Location:** Rural.
Surface: gravel/metalled. 01/01-31/12.
Distance: 3km 1,5km 400m.
Remarks: Key at Golf Club.

S Argenta 26F2
Via Galassi. **GPS:** n44,61265 e11,83972.

10 free free. **Location:** Urban. **Surface:** metalled. 01/01-31/12.
Distance: 200m 200m 200m 200m.
Remarks: At tennis-courts, max. 24h.

S Bagno di Romagna 34C1
Area camper Diga di Ridracoli, SP112, Santa Sofia.
GPS: n43,88477 e11,83343.
13 € 21 Ch WC included. **Location:** Isolated.
Surface: grassy. 01/03-31/10.
Remarks: In nature reserve.

Bagno di Romagna 34C1
Via Lungo Savio 1. **GPS:** n43,84108 e11,96532.

10 free. **Surface:** metalled. 01/01-31/12.
Distance: 500m 1km 500m 500m on the spot.
Remarks: Parking swimming pool.

Tourist information Bagno di Romagna:
Week market. Fri 7.30-12.30h.

S Bellaria-Igea Marina 26G3
Parking delle Robinie, Via Pinzon 260, Igea Marina, Zona sud.
GPS: n44,12783 e12,48873.

106 € 10-19 Ch € 2,50/day € 1. **Location:** Rural, comfortable, central, quiet. **Surface:** grassy/gravel.
12/03-15/10, 8-23h.
Distance: 10m 200m 100m 50m.

S Bellaria-Igea Marina 26G3
Mare d'Inverno, Via Murri, 13. **GPS:** n44,11639 e12,49972.

45 € 11, 21/06-31/08 € 17,50, holidays + € 2 Ch € 2,50/day € 1. **Location:** Rural, comfortable, quiet. **Surface:** grassy. 15/03-30/09.
Distance: 800m 200m 800m 1,5km, bakery 800m 100m.

S Bellaria-Igea Marina 26G3
Area Sosta Rio Pircio, Via Benivieni 4, Igea Marina.
GPS: n44,12688 e12,48849.

68 € 14, 21/06-31/08 € 19 Ch € 2/day WC € 1 hot shower € 1. **Location:** Rural, comfortable, central, quiet. **Surface:** grassy. 01/03-31/10.
Distance: 100m 200m 250m.

S Bellaria-Igea Marina 26G3
L'Adriatico Parking, Via Benivieni, 12. **GPS:** n44,12644 e12,48740.

60 € 10, 21/06-31/08 € 19 Ch € 2,50/day € 1 against payment € 1/24h,€ 5/week. **Location:** Rural, comfortable, quiet. **Surface:** grassy. 15/03-31/12.
Distance: 250m.

S Bellaria-Igea Marina 26G3
Porto Mario Family Village, Viale A. Pinzon 310.
GPS: n44,12308 e12,49416.
77 € 13-18 Ch (77x)€ 2/24h WC included.
Surface: metalled. 01/03-30/09.
Distance: 1km 100m on the spot.
Remarks: Bicycle rental.

S Berceto 26C3
Via P. Salas. **GPS:** n44,51123 e9,98589.

20 € 7 Ch WCincluded.
Surface: asphalted. 01/01-31/12.
Distance: 200m 4km 200m 200m on the spot on the spot.
Remarks: Caution € 20, key at kiosk in front of restaurant Rina.

S Bertinoro 26G3
Via Superga, SP 83, Loc. Fratta Terme. **GPS:** n44,13749 e12,10313.

IT

free Chfree. **Location:** Rural. **Surface:** asphalted.
01/01-31/12.
Distance: 1km 1km 1km 300m.
Remarks: Near spa resort and sports centre.

S Bomporto 26E2

Piazza dello Sport, Via Verdi. **GPS:** n44,72886 e11,03585.

10 free free. **Location:** Urban, simple.
Surface: metalled.
Distance: 500m 500m.
Remarks: Parking at sports park.

S Brisighella 26F3

Piazzale Donatori di Sangue. **GPS:** n44,22168 e11,77883.

18 € 8 Chfree € 2/12h. **Surface:** asphalted.
01/01-31/12.
Distance: 1km 1km 1km 500m.
Remarks: Near spa resort.

S Carpi 26D2

Bruno Losi, Piazzale delle Piscine. **GPS:** n44,78444 e10,86817.

free Chfree. **Surface:** metalled. 01/01-31/12.
Distance: 300m 50m on the spot.
Remarks: Parking swimming pool, max. 72h.

S Casal Borsetti 26G2

Area Sosta Camper Mare e Parco, Via Ortolani.
GPS: n44,55000 e12,27997.

238 € 10, 01/06-01/09 € 12/24h, 01/11-28/02 free Chincluded € 3/24h WC. **Location:** Rural, comfortable, central, quiet.
Surface: grassy/metalled. 01/01-31/12.
Distance: 150m 150m.
Remarks: Dogs beach.

S Casola Valsenio 26F3

Via don Milani/Via Antonio Gramsci. **GPS:** n44,22597 e11,62953.

3 free free. **Location:** Urban. **Surface:** asphalted.
01/01-31/12.
Distance: 300m 500m 500m.
Remarks: At swimming pool.

S Casola Valsenio 26F3

Viale Domenico Neri. **GPS:** n44,22483 e11,62392.
4 free free. **Location:** Urban. **Surface:** asphalted.
01/01-31/12.
Distance: 100m 500m 100m 250m.

S Castel San Pietro Terme 26F3

Via Oriani. **GPS:** n44,39725 e11,59197.

8 free € 1 ChWC € 0,20. **Location:** Urban. **Surface:** asphalted.
01/01-31/12.
Distance: 300m 4,2km 200m 250m 250m 250m.
Remarks: Nearby hospital.

S Castellarano 26D2

Parco Don Reverberi, Via Don Reverberi.
GPS: n44,50777 e10,73419.

5 free Chfree. **Location:** Rural, simple. **Surface:** asphalted.
01/01-31/12.
Distance: 500m 500m 500m 500m 500m.

S Castelnovo ne' Monti 26D3

Impianti Sportivi, Zona PEP, Via Fratelli Cervi, SS63.
GPS: n44,43277 e10,41133.

4 free Chfree. **Location:** Rural, simple, quiet.
Surface: asphalted. 01/01-31/12.
Distance: 500m 100m on the spot 200m on the spot.

S Cervia 26G3

Via Aldo Ascione, Cervia-nord. **GPS:** n44,28151 e12,32459.

50 free Chfree. **Location:** Simple, isolated, noisy.
Surface: asphalted. 01/01-31/12.
Distance: 3km 3km 1,3km.
Remarks: No camping activities.

S Cervia 26G3

Viale Tritone, Fraz. Pinarella. **GPS:** n44,23984 e12,35883.

40 free Chfree. **Location:** Urban, simple, noisy.
Surface: asphalted/metalled. 01/01-31/12.
Distance: 750m 900m on the spot.
Remarks: No camping activities.

Cervia 26G3

Via Ravenna. **GPS:** n44,27597 e12,34107.
against payment. 01/01-31/12.
Distance: 500m 1km 500m 500m.
Remarks: No camping activities.

S Cervia 26G3

Terme di Cervia, Viale C. Forlanini, Cervia-nord.
GPS: n44,27335 e12,32964.

50 € 10/24h (6x)€ 2. **Location:** Rural, quiet.
Surface: grassy/gravel. 01/04-30/11.
Distance: 3km 3km 50m.
Remarks: Parking spa resort.

Tourist information Cervia:
Week market. Thu.

S Cesena 26G3

Zona Ippodromo, Via G. Ambrosini. **GPS:** n44,14549 e12,22865.
10 free € 1/100liter € 2 ChWC. **Location:** Urban.
Surface: grasstiles. 01/01-31/12.
Distance: 500m on the spot 1km 200m.
Remarks: At sports centre.

S Cesena 26G3

Agriturismo Macin, Via San Mauro 5280. **GPS:** n44,13592 e12,16953.

4 € 5, free for clients Ch WC included. **Location:** Rural.
Surface: grassy/metalled. 01/01-31/12.
Distance: 5km 8,4km 5km 5km.

S Cesenatico 26G3

Area Camper Cesenatico, Viale Camillo Benso Cavour 1/b.
GPS: n44,20620 e12,38875.
160 € 10, Apr/May € 14, Jun/Sep € 18, Jul/Aug € 23 Ch € 3

IT

WC included. **Surface:** grassy. 01/01-31/12.
Distance: 500m on the spot.
Remarks: Check in on arrival, monitored parking 24/24.

S Cesenatico 26G3

Piazzale della Rocca. **GPS**: n44,19855 e12,39086.

35 free € 0,50/25liter Ch. **Location:** Simple.
Surface: metalled. 01/01-31/12.
Distance: 500m 2km 200m 500m 200m.

S Cesenatico 26G3

Via Mazzini, zona Ponente. **GPS**: n44,21408 e12,38008.

21 € 12/24h Ch included. **Location:** Rural, simple.
Surface: grassy/gravel. 01/01-31/12.
Distance: centre 3,5km 800m.
Remarks: At entrance campsite Cesenatico, max. 48h.

S Civitella di Romagna 26F3

Agriturismo Acero Rosseo, Via Seggio.
GPS: n44,00200 e11,97539.

20 guests free free. **Location:** Rural. **Surface:** grassy.
01/01-31/12.
Distance: 5km on the spot 5km.

S Collecchio 26C2

Via Spezia. **GPS**: n44,75178 e10,22265.

8 free Ch. **Location:** Simple. **Surface:** asphalted.
01/01-31/12.
Distance: 500m.

S Comacchio 26F2

Area di sosta Cavallari, Via Villaggio San Carlo 9.
GPS: n44,70297 e12,16862.

80 € 18 Ch included WC € 2. **Location:** Rural, luxurious, quiet. **Surface:** grassy. 16/02-30/11.
Distance: 1km on the spot.
Remarks: Bicycle rental.

Comacchio 26F2

Via Fattibello. **GPS**: n44,69095 e12,18447.

13 free. **Location:** Rural, central, quiet. **Surface:** metalled.
01/01-31/12.
Distance: 300m 100m.

S Conselice 26F2

Agriturismo Massari, Via Coronella 110, Chiesanuova di Conselice.
GPS: n44,53167 e11,81856.

10 € 9/pp, guests free Ch WC included.
Location: Rural. **Surface:** metalled.
01/01-31/12.
Distance: 1,5km 200m on the spot 1,5km.

S Faenza 26F3

Via Proventa. **GPS**: n44,31272 e11,89289.

2 free Ch free. **Surface:** asphalted. 01/01-31/12.
Distance: 4km 2km.

S Faenza 26F3

Agriturismo Trerè, Via Casale 19. **GPS**: n44,29968 e11,80368.

5 € 8 + € 5/pp, guests free Ch included € 2 WC.
Surface: metalled. 01/01-31/12.
Distance: 7km on the spot 200m on the spot.
Remarks: Dog € 4, swimming pool € 5.

S Farini 26B2

Viale dei Sassi Neri. **GPS**: n44,70994 e9,56611.

50 free Ch free. **Surface:** grassy/gravel. 01/01-31/12.
Distance: 400m on the spot.

S Ferrara 26F2

Via Rampari di San Paolo. **GPS**: n44,83544 e11,61090.
30 € 6/24h € 1/100liter € 2 Ch € 1 € 5/2h.
Location: Central, noisy. **Surface:** metalled.
01/01-31/12.
Distance: 800m 6,5km 250m 500m 50m.

Tourist information Ferrara:
Museo della Cattedrale. € 6.
Castello Estence.
Palazzo Scifanoia.
Mo, Fri.

S Fontanellato 26C2

Via XXIV Maggio. **GPS**: n44,87797 e10,16987.

20 € 10/24h Ch (16x) WC free. **Surface:** asphalted.
01/01-31/12.
Distance: 300m 6km 200m 500m.
Remarks: Motorhome washing place.

Forlimpopoli 26G3

Via De Gasperi. **GPS**: n44,19044 e12,12608.

free. **Surface:** asphalted. 01/01-31/12.
Distance: 100m 100m 100m 100m.
Remarks: Nearby railway station.

S Forlimpopoli 26G3

Palazzetto dello Sport, Via del Tulipano. **GPS**: n44,18534 e12,11960.
Ch free. 01/01-31/12.

S Gropparello 26C2

Via D. Aligieri. **GPS**: n44,83521 e9,73051.

€ 10 free. **Location:** Rural, simple, quiet.
Surface: asphalted. 01/01-31/12.
Distance: 100m 500m.
Remarks: Castello di Gropparello 300m.

S Guastalla 26D2

Piazzale Ugo Foscolo. **GPS**: n44,92364 e10,65148.

6 free free (6x) € 5. **Surface:** asphalted.
01/01-31/12.
Distance: historical centre 300m 1,5km 600m 100m on the spot.
Remarks: Cycle route along the Po river.

Imola 26F3

Via Pirandello. **GPS**: n44,34628 e11,70922.

30 free Chfree. **Surface:** grassy/sand. 01/01-31/12.
Distance: 700m 50m 80m 50m supermercato Famila.
Remarks: In front of the Ferrari Circuit.

Tourist information Imola:
Piazza Gramsci. Mo-Thu, Sa 8-12.30h.

Lagosanto 26F2

Locanda Il Varano, Via Valle Oppio 6, Marozzo di Lagosanto.
GPS: n44,78167 e12,12533.

36 € 15, guests free Ch (36x) WC.
Location: Rural, comfortable, quiet.
Surface: gravel. 01/01-31/12.
Distance: 3km 12km on the spot 500m.

Langhirano 26D2

Salumificio La Perla, Quinzano. **GPS**: n44,58748 e10,23783.

10 free . **Location:** Rural, simple, quiet.
Surface: gravel.
01/01-31/12.
Distance: 3km on the spot 3km on the spot.
Remarks: Producer Parma ham.

Langhirano 26D2

La Fazenda, Cascinapiano di Langhirano.
GPS: n44,63322 e10,27410.

50 € 10, guests € 5 WCincluded. **Location:** Simple, quiet.
Surface: grassy/gravel. 01/01-31/12.
Distance: 1km on the spot on the spot 500m.

Lido di Dante 26G3

Via Marabina 208. **GPS**: n44,38867 e12,31364.

30 € 6-10 Chincluded. **Surface:** grassy. 01/04-30/09.
Distance: 250m 100m 50m 200m 50m.

Maranello 26E2

Area Camper Maranello, Via Fondo Val Tiepido 77, Torre Maina.
GPS: n44,50008 e10,87384.

10 € 7 € 2 Ch WC. **Location:** Rural, comfortable, quiet. **Surface:** unpaved.
01/01-31/12.
Distance: on the spot shuttle Bologna-Modena on the spot.
Remarks: Entrance code available at bar.

Marzaglia 26D2

Area di sosta Marzaglia, Strada Pomposiana 305.
GPS: n44,63514 e10,80733.

30 € 15, 2 pers.incl Ch € 1,50/day WC.
Location: Rural, comfortable, quiet. **Surface:** gravel.
01/01-31/12.
Distance: Modena 10km 7km.

Mesola 26G2

Oasi Park II, Via Cristina 84, SP27, Bosco Mesola.
GPS: n44,86822 e12,24898.

130 € 8-15 Ch (100x)€ 2/day WC against payment included. **Location:** Rural, comfortable, quiet. **Surface:** grassy.
01/03-01/11.
Distance: 400m 1km.
Remarks: Free bicycles available.

Mesola 26G2

Via Beatrice d'Este. **GPS**: n44,92331 e12,23469.

6 free Ch. **Location:** Rural, simple. **Surface:** asphalted.
01/01-31/12.
Distance: 400m 400m 150m.
Remarks: Parking sports park.

Mesola 26G2

Agriturismo Ca'Laura, SP 27, Bosco Mesola.
GPS: n44,87122 e12,24444.

6 € 15 Ch WC. **Location:** Luxurious, quiet.
Surface: metalled. 01/01-31/12.
Distance: 10km on the spot 1km 1km.
Remarks: Swimming pool, training golf course.

Mirandola 26E2

Via Luigi Galvani. **GPS**: n44,89812 e11,06199.
10 free Ch free. **Location:** Simple, quiet.
Surface: gravel.
Distance: 500m 1km 1km 500m.
Remarks: At cemetery.

Misano Adriatico 26G3

Centro Caravan Misano, Via Taveleto 53. **GPS**: n43,96694 e12,67306.

12 € 20 Ch (12x)€ 1,50,6Amp WC € 0,50 € 1 included. **Location:** Luxurious, quiet. **Surface:** grassy.
01/01-31/12.
Distance: 500m 5km 2km 500m 500m.
Remarks: Arrival < 19h, caution key € 10, video surveillance.

Modena 26E2

Camper Club Mutina, Strada Collegarola 76/A, zona Vaciglio.
GPS: n44,61361 e10,94444.

32 € 16/24h Ch WC included. **Location:** Rural, luxurious, quiet. **Surface:** asphalted. 01/01-31/12.
Distance: 600m 3km 600m on the spot.

Modena 26E2

Taverna Napoleone, Via San Lorenzo 44, Castelnuovo Rangone.
GPS: n44,57766 e10,96552.

10 free free. **Location:** Rural. **Surface:** metalled.
01/01-31/12.
Distance: 5km 2,8km pizzeria 5km.
Remarks: 10% discount at restaurant.

Tourist information Modena:
Galleria Ferrari, Via Dino Ferrari 43, Maranello. Museum of motor-cars.

Montese 26E3

Via Campo del Sole. **GPS**: n44,26637 e10,94456.
8 € 8 Ch (8x)free. **Surface:** grasstiles.
01/01-31/12.
Distance: 500m 550m 550m 400m.
Remarks: Max. 72h.

IT

Monticelli d'Ongina 26C1

Piazza Resistenza. **GPS**: n45,09050 e9,93537.

10 free Chfree.
Location: Simple, quiet. **Surface:** asphalted. 01/01-31/12.
Distance: centre 300m 6,2km 300m 300m.

Parma 26D2

Area Camper Parma, Largo XXIV Agosto 1942, n° 21/a.
GPS: n44,80931 e10,28495.

26 € 20 Ch included WC € 1.
Location: Comfortable. **Surface:** grasstiles. 01/01-31/12.
Distance: centre 3,5km 7km Lidl 100m 100m.
Remarks: Monitored parking, arrival <22h, service passerby € 4, motorhome washing place 50m.

Tourist information Parma:
Palazzo Pilotta. morning.
Via Verdi. Week market. Wed-Sa 7-14h.

Pavullo nel Frignano 26D3

Via Marchiani. **GPS**: n44,34294 e10,83309.

12 free Chfree. **Location:** Comfortable, noisy.
Surface: gravel/sand. 01/01-31/12.
Distance: 700m 600m 600m 600m.
Remarks: Picnic area.

Porto Corsini 26G2

Ancora Blu, Via G. Guizzetti. **GPS**: n44,49620 e12,27950.

163 € 9, 01/06-31/08 € 11 Ch (20x)€ 3/day WC.
Location: Rural, comfortable, quiet. **Surface:** grassy.
01/03-31/10.
Distance: 500m 200m 300m 300m 300m.
Remarks: Video surveillance.

Portomaggiore 26F2

Via Giuseppe Mazzini. **GPS**: n44,69584 e11,81389.

10 free Chfree.
Location: Urban. **Surface:** asphalted. 01/01-31/12.
Distance: 500m 500m 500m 300m.
Remarks: Nearby cemetery.

Tourist information Portomaggiore:
Valli di Comacchio. Nature reserve, in winter whereabouts birds.

Premilcuore 26F3

Via G. Matteotti 4. **GPS**: n43,97399 e11,77220.
5 € 10 Ch. **Location:** Rural. **Surface:** grassy.
15/05-15/09.
Distance: 500m 600m 600m.
Remarks: Near the Rabbi river.

Premilcuore 26F3

Parcheggio Fluviale, Loc. Fontanalba. **GPS**: n43,97618 e11,77615.

€ 1. **Surface:** metalled. 01/01-31/12.
Distance: 500m 20m 500m 50m.
Remarks: Along river.

Ravenna 26G3

Parking Bus-Camper, Via E.Ferrari. Loc.Classe.
GPS: n44,37849 e12,23461.

30 € 2,25/24h free. **Location:** Urban, simple.
Surface: grasstiles. 01/01-31/12.
Distance: Ravenna centre 6km.
Remarks: Nearby basilica.

Ravenna 26G3

Piazza della Resistenza. **GPS**: n44,41433 e12,18852.

10 € 0,50/h, € 2,50/24h Chfree.
Location: Urban, simple, central.
Surface: grasstiles.
01/01-31/12.
Distance: historical centre 500m 5km 150m 500m 50m.
Remarks: Max. 24h.

Ravenna 26G3

Via Pomposa. **GPS**: n44,43002 e12,20827.

40 free Chfree. **Surface:** asphalted. 01/01-31/12.
Distance: city centre 2km 100m on the spot.

Ravenna 26G3

Via Teodorico. **GPS**: n44,42317 e12,20981.

10 free Chfree. **Location:** Urban, simple, quiet.
Surface: asphalted. 01/01-31/12.
Distance: 500m on the spot.
Remarks: In front of the Mausoleum.

Ravenna 26G3

Via Brancaleone/circonvallazione S. Gaetanino.
GPS: n44,42339 e12,20478.

25 free. **Location:** Urban, simple, noisy. **Surface:** metalled.
01/01-31/12.
Distance: 200m 5km 100m 200m 200m 10m.
Remarks: Next to Rocca Brancaleone.

Ravenna 26G3

Area Camper Atrezzata, Eurolandia, SS16.
GPS: n44,33533 e12,26949.

72 € 10/day, € 15/2 days Chincluded € 0,50/30minutes.
Location: Rural, simple. **Surface:** gravel.
01/04-31/10.
Remarks: Video surveillance.

Ravenna 26G3

Parco Divertimenti Mirabilandia, SS16, via Romea Sud 463.
GPS: n44,33290 e12,26966.

400 € 15 included.
Location: Rural, simple, noisy. **Surface:** gravel.
Distance: Ravenna centre 10km McDonalds.
Remarks: Max. 48h.

IT

Tourist information Ravenna:

U.I.A.T. (Ufficio Informazioni e di Accoglienza Turistica), Piazza S. Francesco, 7, http://www.turismo.ra.it/. City of the mosaics, historical city with many curiosities.

Piazza Garibaldi. Antiques market. 3rd weekend of the month.

Parco Divertimenti Mirabilandia, SS16, via Romea Sud 463. Amusement park. 01/04-15/09.

S Reggio nell'Emilia 26D2

Parking Ex Foro Boario, Via XX Settembre.
GPS: n44,70941 e10,62463.

50 free Chfree. **Location:** Urban, simple.
Surface: grasstiles.
01/01-31/12.
Distance: 1km 3,7km 100m 500m Free bus to centre.

S Riccione 26G3

La Baita degli Ulivi, Via Ascoli Piceno. **GPS**: n43,98439 e12,64668.
€ 20 . **Location:** Noisy. **Surface:** gravel.
01/01-31/12.
Distance: 300m 3,5km on the spot.
Remarks: Video surveillance.

S Rimini 26G3

La Valletta Sosta Verde, Via Della Lama 47, SS 16.
GPS: n44,09889 e12,49867.

200 € 11, >7,3m € 18, dog € 1 Chincluded € 3 WC € 1.
Location: Rural, noisy. **Surface:** grassy/gravel.
01/04-30/09.
Distance: Rimini 11km 3,8km 2km 800m 800m.
Remarks: Shuttle bus to beach.

S Rimini 26G3

Parking Settebello, Via Roma 86. **GPS**: n44,05982 e12,57669.

300 € 10/24h € 2 Ch€ 2 (80x)€ 3/day.
Location: Urban, simple, central, noisy. **Surface:** metalled.
01/01-31/12.
Distance: 200m 500m.
Remarks: Next to cinema Settebello.

Rimini 26G3

P30 Chiabrera, Via Chiabrera. **GPS**: n44,04803 e12,59548.
01/05-30/09 € 12,10. **Location:** Urban, simple, central, noisy.
Surface: asphalted.

S Rimini 26G3

Camper Nautica, Via Ortigara 78/80. **GPS**: n44,07461 e12,57005.
20 € 20-30/24h € 1,50 . 01/01-31/12.
Distance: on the spot on the spot on the spot.
Remarks: Monitored parking 24/24.

Tourist information Rimini:

Casa Zanni, Via Casale, 205, Villa Verucchio. Restaurant with authentic Italian cuisine.

S Ro 26F1

Mulino sul Po. **GPS**: n44,95498 e11,75668.

4 free (4x)free WC .
Location: Rural, simple, noisy. **Surface:** metalled.
Distance: 1km on the spot on the spot.
Remarks: Along the Po river.

S Rocca San Casciano 26F3

Foro Boario, Viale Dante Alighieri, SP23, 17.
GPS: n44,06173 e11,84604.
4 free € 1/100liter Ch € 1/4h. **Location:** Rural.
Surface: metalled. 01/01-31/12.
Distance: 300m 100m 800m 150m.

S Sala Baganza 26C2

Via Vittorio Emanuele, 42. **GPS**: n44,70856 e10,23070.

4 free Ch (4x)free. **Location:** Rural, simple, quiet.
Surface: asphalted. 01/01-31/12.
Distance: 500m 15km 500m.

S Salsomaggiore Terme 26C2

Via Antonio Gramsci. **GPS**: n44,82005 e9,98981.

20 free free. **Location:** Urban, simple, quiet. **Surface:** gravel.
01/01-31/12.
Distance: 800m.
Remarks: Parking next to station.

S San Giuseppe 26G2

Ariaperta Sosta Camper, Via Delle Nazioni 39.
GPS: n44,72578 e12,22528.
99 € 15 Ch (32x)included WC. **Surface:** grassy.
Distance: 500m 1,5km 500m 500m.

S San Piero in Bagno 34C1

Via G.Mazzini, Via Battistini. **GPS**: n43,86353 e11,97692.

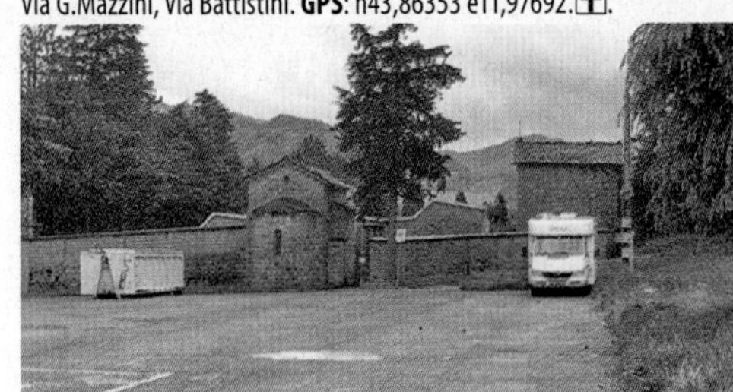

5 free Chfree.
Location: Rural. **Surface:** asphalted. 01/01-31/12.
Distance: 500m 1km 500m 500m 200m.

S Santa Sofia 34C1

Piazzale K. Marx. **GPS**: n43,94165 e11,90930.

10 free Chfree. **Surface:** asphalted. 01/01-31/12.
Distance: 200m 650m 650m on the spot.

Tourist information Santa Sofia:

Foreste Casentinesi. National nature reserve.

S Serramazzoni 26D3

Piazzale Largo Olimpico. **GPS**: n44,42223 e10,79402.

20 free Chfree.
Location: Urban. **Surface:** asphalted. 01/01-31/12.
Distance: 300m 100m 300m 300m 300m 800m.

S Serramazzoni 26D3

Ristorante La Roccia, Via Giardini Nord, Montagnana di Serramazzoni.
GPS: n44,47157 e10,82050.

15 free .
Location: Rural, simple, quiet. **Surface:** gravel. 01/01-31/12.
Distance: 8km Maranello on the spot 8km.
Remarks: Maranello: Ferrari factory and museum.

Sestola 26D3

Via Guidellina. **GPS**: n44,22591 e10,77374.
10 free. **Surface:** asphalted. 01/01-31/12.
Distance: 300m 800m 500m on the spot.

S Soragna 26C2

Via Matteotti / via Gramsci. **GPS**: n44,92988 e10,12566.

10 free Chfree. **Location:** Urban, simple, quiet.
Surface: asphalted. 01/01-31/12.
Distance: 120m 200m 200m.

Suviana 26E3

Via Lungo Lago. **GPS**: n44,12039 e11,04592.

60 Free, hollidays € 9. **Location:** Rural, simple, quiet.

IT

Surface: asphalted. 01/01-31/12.
Distance: on the spot on the spot on the spot.
Remarks: At lake Suviana, canoe rental.

S Terenzo 26C2
Loc. Bardone. **GPS:** n44,62528 e10,10083.

8 € 13 Ch WC included. **Location:** Rural, comfortable, quiet. **Surface:** metalled. 01/01-31/12.
Distance: 200m 12km 12km on the spot.
Remarks: Max. 2 nights.

S Tredozio 26F3
Area Le Volte, Via Salvo D'Acquisto. **GPS:** n44,07431 e11,73228.

40 € 5 Ch included € 2,50. **Surface:** metalled.
01/01-31/12.
Distance: 1,5km 200m camping 1,5km.
Remarks: Next to campsite Le Volte, max. 48h, discount at restaurant/ swimming-pool.

S Tresigallo 26F2
Fraz. Finale di Rero. **GPS:** n44,81643 e11,90050.
5 free Ch free. **Surface:** metalled. 01/01-31/12.
Distance: 600m 750m on the spot.
Remarks: Nearby sports park.

S Vergato 26E3
SS 64, Bologna-Pistoia. **GPS:** n44,28952 e11,11270.

25 free Ch free. **Location:** Rural, simple. **Surface:** asphalted.
01/01-31/12.
Distance: 400m 400m 500m 500m.

S Vezzano Sul Crostolo 26D2
Area Sosta Camper Matildica, SS63. **GPS:** n44,58960 e10,53608.
10 free Ch . **Surface:** asphalted. 01/01-31/12.
Distance: 1,5km on the spot on the spot on the spot.
Remarks: Eco Parco di Vezzano, keycard at Bar Sport, Via Roma, SS63, n44,59963, o10,54542.

Liguria

S Borghetto Santo Spirito 28H1
Area Camper Geoservizi, Via Po. **GPS:** n44,11548 e8,23758.

132 € 10/24h, Jul-Aug-Dec € 13 Ch (42x)€ 3/day,16Amp.
Location: Urban. **Surface:** gravel. 01/01-31/12.
Distance: 1,1km 2,5km 400m.

Remarks: Along the river Varatella.

S Borghetto Santo Spirito 28H1
Val Varatella, Via Tiziano. **GPS:** n44,11565 e8,23507.
24 € 18-27 WC . **Surface:** grassy. 01/01-31/12.
Distance: 500m 1km.

S Camporosso 28H1
Camper Park Nervia, Via Primo Maggio. **GPS:** n43,79339 e7,63088.
60 € 16 Ch € 4/day WC € 1 included.
Surface: metalled.
01/01-31/12.
Distance: 500m 500m on the spot on the spot on the spot.
Remarks: Dog € 2/day, video surveillance, bike/car rental, playground.

S Castelnuovo Magra 26C3
Agriturismo Cascina dei Peri, Via Montefrancio 71.
GPS: n44,10355 e10,00734.

3 € 10/pp, child € 3 Ch € 3 WC included € 5.
Surface: grassy/gravel. 01/01-31/12.
Distance: 2,4km.
Remarks: Dinner € 20/pp wine incl. (to order <16h), selling of wine and olive oil, swimming pool from june.

S Celle Ligure 26A3
Via Natta. **GPS:** n44,34888 e8,55674.

25 free Ch. **Surface:** asphalted. 01/01-31/12.
Distance: 300m 200m 500m 200m 300m 100m.

S Celle Ligure 26A3
Via Sanda 30. **GPS:** n44,35007 e8,53901.
10 € 15 Ch WC included. **Location:** Rural.
Surface: metalled. 01/01-31/12.
Distance: 1km 1,5km on the spot.
Remarks: Playground.

S Cengio 25H3
Area Attrezzata Cengio Isole, Via Isole.
GPS: n44,39083 e8,20194.

10 free Ch free. **Location:** Urban. **Surface:** asphalted.
01/01-31/12.
Distance: 600m on the spot on the spot 1km 800m.
Remarks: Nearby sports park.

S Cervo 28H1
Camper Cervo, Via Steria. **GPS:** n43,92833 e8,10527.

130 € 12-15/day Ch included € 3/24h WC .
Location: Urban. **Surface:** gravel.
01/01-31/12.
Distance: on the spot 2,5km 1km 900m 600m.
Remarks: At tennis-courts, monitored parking, free bicycles available.

S Deiva Marina 26B3
Via Aranella. **GPS:** n44,22543 e9,53288.
10 € 15/24h included. **Location:** Rural.
Surface: unpaved.
15/03-15/11.
Distance: 1,5km sea 2km on the spot 150m on the spot.

S Diano Marina 28H1
Oasi Camper, Via Sori 5. **GPS:** n43,90667 e8,07083.

300 € 12-20/day Ch included € 3 WC € 1 .
Surface: grassy/gravel. 01/01-31/12.
Distance: 600m 6,8km 800m 600m 600m 600m mountainbike trail.
Remarks: Max. 72h, beachshuttle with bar/restaurant.

S Diano Marina 28H1
Il bowling di Diano, Via Diano S. Pietro, 71 - Diano Castello.
GPS: n43,91683 e8,07576.

100 € 15-30/night Ch included . **Surface:** unpaved.
01/01-31/12.
Distance: 1km 5,5km 1,2km on the spot 50m.
Remarks: Narrow entrance, swimming pool, bar, bowling.

S Diano Marina 28H1
Agriturismo Solo Blu, Via Gombi San Siro, 5.
GPS: n43,91743 e8,08510.
24 € 14-30/24h, 2 pers.incl Ch (24x)included WC .
Surface: gravel. 01/01-31/12.
Distance: 1,2km 500m 750m on the spot.
Remarks: Swimming pool.

S Diano Marina 28H1
Al Roseto, Via Case Parse, San siro, Diano Castello.
GPS: n43,91983 e8,07733.

100 € 12-23 Ch ,6Amp WC € 2 included .
Location: Rural. **Surface:** grassy/sand. 01/01-31/12.
Distance: 1km 5,5km 1km 1km 400m.
Remarks: At Floriculturist, monitored parking 24/24, shuttle bus to

IT

beach.

Finale Ligure 26A3

Area Caprazoppa, Via Aurelia, SS1. **GPS**: n44,16549 e8,33750.

40 € 18/24h Ch included. **Location:** Rural. **Surface:** gravel/sand. 01/01-31/12.
Distance: 500m 4km on the spot 700m 500m 500m.
Remarks: At sea, max. 36h.

Giusvalla 26A3

Strada Comunale. **GPS**: n44,44885 e8,39329.

6 free Ch free. **Location:** Rural. **Surface:** grassy/sand.
01/01-31/12.
Distance: on the spot on the spot.

Imperia 28H1

Francy Park, Via dei Giardini. **GPS**: n43,86917 e8,00010.

32 € 10, 01/06-30/09 € 13 Ch included .
Surface: metalled. 01/01-31/12.
Distance: centre 4km sea 150m 150m 100m.

La Spezia 26C3

Viale San Bartolomeo. **GPS**: n44,10417 e9,85917.

100 € 6,50 € 5 WC. **Surface:** grassy. 01/01-31/12.
Distance: 4km on the spot on the spot.
Remarks: Monitored parking.

Tourist information La Spezia:
Lerici. Former fishing village, nowadays holiday resort.
Cinque Terre. Protected coast area.
Castello di Lerici, Lerici. 01/04-31/10.
Lerici. Sa-morning.

Levanto 26C3

SP556, Loc. Moltedi. **GPS**: n44,17476 e9,61836.

16 € 18/24h Ch included. 01/01-31/12.
Distance: 500m 1km train 100m.
Remarks: Behind railway station, well situated for visiting the Cinque Terre by train.

Loano 25H3

La Sosta, Via delle Fornaci, 31. **GPS**: n44,13115 e8,24111.
41 € 15 Ch WC included. **Surface:** gravel.
01/01-31/12.
Distance: 2km 400m.
Remarks: Shuttle bus.

Tourist information Loano:
Grotta di Santa Lucia, Toirano. Stalactites and stalagmites.
Grotta della Basura, Toirano. Man and beast from the stone age.

Pietra Ligure 26A3

Area Camper, Via Crispi 43. **GPS**: n44,15484 e8,28397.

53 € 13/24h, 01/06-30/09 € 16/24h Ch (53x)included WC € 0,70. **Surface:** gravel. 01/01-31/12.
Distance: 200m.

Pontinvrea 26A3

Via Roma 15. **GPS**: n44,44309 e8,43739.

10 € 5 Ch (10x)included. **Location:** Rural. **Surface:** gravel.
31/03-30/09.
Distance: 150m 150m 150m on the spot.

Portovenere 34A1

Via Olivo, Loc. Cavo. **GPS**: n44,05961 e9,84843.

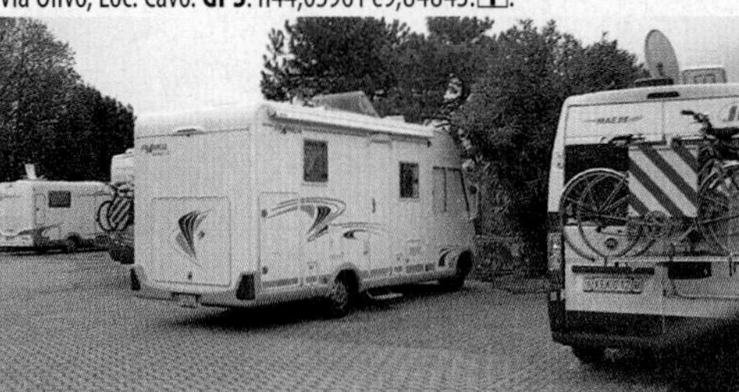

20 € 2,25/h 8-20h, overnight stay free Ch included.
Location: Rural. **Surface:** metalled. 01/01-31/12.
Distance: 2km 750m 600m 50m.
Remarks: Max. 36h, shuttle € 1/pp.

San Lorenzo al Mare 28H1

Area Camper Il Pozzo, Via Gaetano Salvemini.
GPS: n43,85512 e7,96083.

30 € 15-31 Ch WC € 4 included. **Location:** Urban, luxurious. **Surface:** gravel. 01/01-31/12.
Distance: 400m 600m 400m 200m on the spot.
Remarks: Max. 7m.

San Rocco 26B3

Viale Franco Molfino, Camogli. **GPS**: n44,33472 e9,16084.

9 € 15/24h. **Location:** Rural. **Surface:** asphalted.
01/01-31/12.
Distance: 300m 700m 150m 350m on the spot on the spot.
Remarks: Monitored parking, marked hiking trails in Parco di Portofino (45min-2h).

Santo Stefano al Mare 28H1

Camper Village, Strada Porsani. **GPS**: n43,84378 e7,90824.

60 € 12-30/24h Ch € 3 WC € 1. **Surface:** gravel.
Distance: 10km 800m on the spot.
Remarks: Free shuttle, swimming pool.

Santo Stefano al Mare 28H1

Marina degli Aregai, Via Gianni Cozzi. **GPS**: n43,83723 e7,90581.

± 30 € 1,50/h, € 5-10/day. **Location:** Urban. **Surface:** asphalted.
01/01-31/12.
Distance: on the spot Sandy beach on the spot 800m on the spot.

Sassello 26A3

Piazza San Rocco. **GPS**: n44,48060 e8,48229.

5 free WC. **Location:** Urban. **Surface:** metalled.
01/01-31/12.
Distance: on the spot 50m 50m on the spot on the spot on the spot.

IT

Sestri Levante 26B3

Levante Camper, Via Liguria 39. **GPS**: n44,27848 e9,40209.
25 € 18-28 Ch 6Amp WC € 0,50 included.
Location: Rural. **Surface:** grassy. 01/01-31/12.
Distance: 800m 800m 750m 500m 700m.

Toirano 28H1

Camper Paradise, Via Marici. **GPS**: n44,12491 e8,22498.
€ 14-20 Ch WC included. **Surface:** grassy/gravel.
01/01-31/12.
Distance: 500m 2km 700m on the spot.
Remarks: Arrival <20h, video surveillance, free shuttle.

Torriglia 26B3

Area Comunale Piscina, Via degli Alpini. **GPS**: n44,51667 e9,16000.

10 free Ch free. **Surface:** grasstiles. 01/01-31/12.
Distance: 200m 300m 250m 350m.
Remarks: Next to swimming pool, market Saturday.

Vado Ligure 26A3

Area Sosta Camper, Via Aurelia 16, SS1. **GPS**: n44,27797 e8,44171.

68 € 8/12h, € 16/24h Ch included. **Surface:** metalled.
01/01-31/12.
Distance: 600m 50m 50m.
Remarks: Ferry > Corsica 2km.

Tuscany

Alberese 34B2

Parco Naturale della Maremma, Via del Bersagliere.
GPS: n42,66944 e11,10416.

50 free free. **Location:** Rural. **Surface:** gravel/sand.
01/04-30/09.
Distance: 100m 7km on the spot 100m 200m on the spot on the spot.

Albinia 34B2

Ai Delfini, Via Aurelia km 153. **GPS**: n42,50882 e11,19552.

24 € 1/h, Aug € 1,50/h 4 pers incl. + tourist tax Ch WC included € 1 € 5 1h incl., € 10/15 days.
Location: Comfortable, quiet. **Surface:** grassy/sand.
24/04-31/10.
Distance: 2km 50m on the spot 2km.

Anghiari 34C1

Via Campo della Fiera. **GPS**: n43,53904 e12,05291.

8 free Ch WC free. **Location:** Urban, simple, quiet.
Surface: asphalted. 01/01-31/12.
Distance: on the spot on the spot on the spot 100m.

Anghiari 34C1

Agriturismo Val della Pieve, Via della Fossa 8.
GPS: n43,53657 e12,05131.

10 € 15/24h, Jul/Aug € 20 Ch WC € 3 included.
Location: Rural, comfortable, isolated, quiet. **Surface:** gravel.
01/01-31/12.
Distance: 300m 300m 300m 300m.
Remarks: Swimming pool € 3/pppd.

Anghiari 34C1

Agriturismo La Taverna dei Sorci, San Lorenzo.
GPS: n43,51467 e12,07799.

20 free free. **Location:** Rural, simple, quiet. **Surface:** metalled.
01/01-31/12.
Distance: 3km on the spot 350m.

Arcidosso 34B2

Parco Faunistico Monte Amiata, Località Poderi.
GPS: n42,83740 e11,52922.

15 free Ch. **Location:** Rural, isolated, quiet. **Surface:** grassy.
01/01-31/12.
Distance: 10km.
Remarks: Nature reserve.

Arezzo 34C1

Via Da Palestrina/Via Tarlati. **GPS**: n43,47213 e11,88773.

30 € 0,80/h, € 8/24h € 0,10/10liter Ch. **Location:** Urban, simple, quiet. **Surface:** asphalted.
01/01-31/12.
Distance: 1km 300m 300m 300m.
Remarks: Escalator to city centre.

Arezzo 34C1

P Tarlati, Via Guido Tarlati. **GPS**: n43,47237 e11,88362.

50 free. **Location:** Urban, simple, central. **Surface:** grasstiles.
01/01-31/12.
Distance: city centre 1km 500m 500m 300m on the spot.
Remarks: Escalator to city centre.

Tourist information Arezzo:
Week market.

Barberino di Mugello 26E3

Lago di Bilancino, Viale Antonio Gramsci.
GPS: n43,98911 e11,24145.

100 € 16/night Ch WC included. **Location:** Rural, comfortable, quiet. **Surface:** unpaved. 15/04-15/10.
Distance: 1km 100m on the spot 800m on the spot on the spot.
Remarks: At lake Bilancino.

Barberino di Mugello 26E3

SS65, Fraz. Monte di Fó. **GPS**: n44,07613 e11,28062.

10 free Ch free. **Location:** Rural, simple, quiet.
Surface: metalled. 01/01-31/12.
Distance: 4km 150m (camping) 150m (camping).
Remarks: In front of campsite Il Sergente.

Barga 26D3

Area San Cristoforo, Via Hayange. **GPS**: n44,07234 e10,48131.

30 € 10/24h Ch WC 200m. **Location:** Urban, simple, central, quiet. **Surface:** gravel.
01/01-31/12.
Distance: centro storico within walking distance 300m 300m 250m 100m.

Bibbiena 34C1

La Collina delle Stelle, Loc. Casanova 63.
GPS: n43,71669 e11,85173.

IT

8 € 15-20, 2 pers.incl, extra pers € 5 Ch € 2/24h WC € 5,ironing services € 5 included.
Location: Rural, comfortable, quiet. **Surface:** gravel.
15/03-01/11, Christmas.
Distance: 7km on the spot on the spot.
Remarks: Dog € 2/day, playground, swimming pool € 5/pp (free with a meal).

S Borgo a Mozzano 34A1

Via I° Maggio, SP2. **GPS**: n43,97612 e10,54113.

4 free Ch (4x)free. **Location:** Simple, noisy.
Surface: gravel. 01/01-31/12.
Distance: 200m Serchio river on the spot 700m on the spot.
Remarks: At tourist office, picnic tables available.

S Borgo San Lorenzo 34B1

Via Caduti di Montelungo. **GPS**: n43,95112 e11,38518.

10 free Chfree. **Location:** Urban, simple. **Surface:** asphalted.
01/01-31/12 Fri.
Distance: 500m 500m 300m 400m.
Remarks: Friday market.

Buonconvento 34B2

Viale della Liberta. **GPS**: n43,13854 e11,48109.

free. **Location:** Simple. **Surface:** unpaved.
Distance: 50m 50m.
Remarks: At the city walls.

S Buonconvento 34B2

Viale Ferruccio Parri. **GPS**: n43,13065 e11,48349.
€ 1 Ch. 01/01-31/12.

S Calci 34A1

Via Brogiotti 35. **GPS**: n43,72769 e10,51722.

8 € 8/24h, € 0,50/h Chincluded. **Location:** Urban, simple, noisy. **Surface:** asphalted. 01/01-31/12.
Distance: 100m 50m 200m 50m.
Remarks: At sports park, payment only with coins.

S Campiglia Marittima 34B2

Parcheggio La Pieve, Via di Venturina. **GPS**: n43,05672 e10,61439.

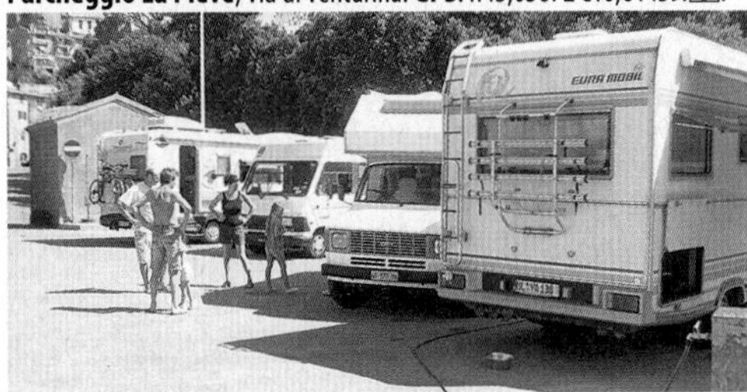

4 free Chfree. **Location:** Rural. **Surface:** asphalted.
01/01-31/12.
Distance: 350m 450m 500m.
Remarks: In front of cemetery, near gymnasium.

S Campiglia Marittima 34B2

Via di Caldana. **GPS**: n43,03662 e10,59969.
free € 1/100liter Ch. 01/01-31/12.
Distance: 800m 250m.

Capalbio 34B2

Via Giacomo Leopardi, SP75. **GPS**: n42,45363 e11,42401.
10 free. **Location:** Urban. **Surface:** metalled.
01/01-31/12.
Distance: 100m 200m 300m 200m.

S Capraia e Limite 34B1

Via delle Ginestre, zona industriale, loc. Capraia Fiorentina.
GPS: n43,73660 e11,00442.

20 free Chfree. **Location:** Urban, simple, noisy.
Surface: metalled. 01/01-31/12.
Distance: 500m 200m 100m.

S Castagneto Carducci 34A2

Camperesort, Via Aurelia 373/B. **GPS**: n43,15630 e10,56097.

50 € 10 + € 5/pp, 15/06-15/09 € 10/Pp Ch WC € 1 € 3 included. **Location:** Luxurious. **Surface:** grassy/gravel.
01/01-31/12. **Distance:** 1,2km on the spot.
Remarks: Video surveillance, swimming pool incl.

S Castagneto Carducci 34A2

Via del Seggio, Marina di Castagneto. **GPS**: n43,18401 e10,54841.

30 € 10/24h Chfree. **Surface:** unpaved.
01/01-31/12.
Distance: 2km 500m 2,5km 2,5km.

S Castagneto Carducci 34A2

Viale delle Palme, Marina di Castagneto. **GPS**: n43,19323 e10,54152.

20 € 20-30/24h Ch. **Surface:** unpaved.
Distance: 100m.
Remarks: Max. 48h, dogs beach.

S Castel del Piano 34B2

Via Po. **GPS**: n42,88872 e11,53733.

30 free Chfree. **Location:** Rural, simple. **Surface:** asphalted.
01/01-31/12.
Distance: 500m 300m 500m 200m.
Remarks: At footballstadium.

S Castelfiorentino 34B1

Via Che Guevara, circonvallazione Ovest. **GPS**: n43,60885 e10,96365.

5 free free. **Location:** Simple, isolated.
Surface: asphalted.
Distance: 1,5km 1,5km 1,5km.

S Castellina in Chianti 34B1

La Strada del Chianti, SR222. **GPS**: n43,47330 e11,28760.

15 € 12/24h € 0,20/10liter Ch (8x)included WC € 0,50.
Location: Rural, comfortable.
Surface: asphalted. 01/01-31/12.
Distance: 200m.

Tourist information Castellina in Chianti:
Via IV Novembre. Week market. Sa-morning.

IT

S Castelnuovo di Garfagnana 26D3

Via Valmaira. **GPS**: n44,11447 e10,40304.

50 free Chfree. **Location:** Urban, simple, noisy. **Surface:** metalled. 01/01-31/12.
Distance: 1km 100m 800m 200m.
Remarks: At sports park.

S Castiglion Fiorentino 34C1

Piazza Garibaldi, viale Marconi. **GPS**: n43,34465 e11,92278.

20 free Chfree WC. **Location:** Rural, simple. **Surface:** asphalted. 01/01-31/12 Fri-morning market.
Distance: on the spot on the spot.

S Castiglione della Pescaia 34B2

Rocchette Serignano, Via Rio Palma, Rocchette. **GPS**: n42,77970 e10,79955.

120 € 20/day € 3 Ch€ 5 (18x)included € 1.
Location: Rural, comfortable. **Surface:** gravel. 01/04-15/09.
Distance: Castiglione della Pescaia 7km 200m 200m 200m 100m on the spot.
Remarks: Beach parking, unguarded.

Castiglione della Pescaia 34B2

Via Andromeda. **GPS**: n42,76888 e10,89079.

11 free. **Location:** Urban, simple. **Surface:** asphalted. 01/01-31/12.
Distance: 1km 800m 300m.

Castiglione della Pescaia 34B2

Via Ponte Giorgini. **GPS**: n42,76515 e10,88545.

5 € 1,50h, € 10/24h. **Location:** Urban, simple. **Surface:** asphalted. 01/01-31/12 Sa.
Distance: on the spot 100m 500m on the spot.

Remarks: Market Saturday.

S Castiglione d'Orcia 34C2

Area Pro Loco, Viale Marconi. **GPS**: n43,00292 e11,61552.

5 free free. **Location:** Rural, simple. **Surface:** gravel/sand. 01/01-31/12.
Distance: 200m on the spot.

Tourist information Castiglione d'Orcia:
Rocco d'Orcia. Medieval citadel.

S Cecina 34A1

Agricamper Impalancati, Via Aurelia Nord, 108. **GPS**: n43,33682 e10,49946.
20 € 10, Jun/Sep € 15, Jul € 20, Aug € 25 Ch included WC. **Location:** Comfortable, isolated, quiet.
Surface: grassy/gravel.

S Cecina 34A1

Agricamper Gioia Selvaggia e Fabio, Via Paratino Alto, 53. **GPS**: n43,28780 e10,55314.
18 € 10, Jul/Aug € 15 Ch included.
Surface: grassy/gravel.
Distance: city centre 5km 6km.
Remarks: Swimming pool (summer).

S Certaldo 34B1

Area Comunale, Piazza dei Macelli. **GPS**: n43,54629 e11,04611.

10 free Chfree. **Location:** Rural. **Surface:** metalled. 01/01-31/12.
Distance: medieval centre 150m (elevator) 150m 250m.

S Chifenti 34A1

Area sosta Chifenti, SS12. **GPS**: n44,00492 e10,56337.

10 free Ch free. **Location:** Rural, comfortable, central, quiet. **Surface:** gravel. 01/01-31/12.
Distance: 500m 100m 100m 100m 600m 100m.

S Chiusdino 34B2

Abbazia San Galgano, SS441. **GPS**: n43,15283 e11,15137.

15 € 1,50/h, € 10/8-20h, overnight stay free (9x)free.
Location: Rural, isolated, quiet.
Surface: grasstiles. 01/01-31/12.
Distance: 12km 300m.
Remarks: Abbey of San Galgano 300m.

S Chiusi 34C2

Via Torri del Fornello. **GPS**: n43,01461 e11,94972.

5 free Chfree. **Location:** Urban. **Surface:** asphalted.
Distance: 100m 4,5km 350m 450m on the spot.
Remarks: Next to school.

Chiusi 34C2

Loc. Sbarchino. **GPS**: n43,05049 e11,95756.
10 free. **Location:** Rural.
Surface: unpaved. 01/01-31/12.
Distance: 6km on the spot Pesce d'Oro on the spot on the spot.
Remarks: At lake Chiusi.

S Cutigliano 26D3

Via di Risorgimento/Sp37. **GPS**: n44,09877 e10,75450.

14 € 1,50/h, € 15/24h Ch (14x)included.
Location: Rural, comfortable, quiet. **Surface:** metalled. 01/01-31/12.
Distance: 200m 300m 300m 350m 350m 100m.
Remarks: Max. 48h, picnic area.

S Dicomano 34B1

SS67, Tosco Romagnola. **GPS**: n43,89407 e11,53715.

4 free Chfree. **Location:** Rural, simple. **Surface:** asphalted. 01/01-31/12.
Distance: 1km 200m on the spot.

S Empoli 34B1

Via Montaioncino. **GPS**: n43,69103 e10,97624.

6 € 15 Ch WC included. **Surface:** grassy/gravel. 01/01-31/12.
Distance: 5km.

S Equi Terme 26C3

Via della Stazione. **GPS**: n44,17009 e10,15513.

IT

40 € 10/night Ch free. Location: Rural, simple.
Surface: gravel. 01/01-31/12.
Distance: 300m on the spot 300m 300m 300m.
Remarks: To be paid at caves, caves (500m) and marble quarry.

S Firenze 34B1

FiPark, Viale Europa, Fraz. Bagno a Ripoli, Florence (Firenze).
GPS: n43,75554 e11,30609.

40 7-19h € 2/h, 19-7h € 1/h, € 15/24h Ch included.
Location: Urban, simple.
Surface: metalled.
01/01-31/12.
Distance: centre 4km 350m 400m bus 23/33 > centre.

S Firenze 34B1

Parking Camper Stopgo, Via leopoldo Pellas 27, Florence (Firenze).
GPS: n43,80677 e11,23589.

26 € 15 Ch included free. **Location:** Urban, comfortable, central, quiet. **Surface:** gravel.
01/01-31/12.
Distance: centre 4km 300m 200m city centre: bus 20.
Remarks: Max. 72h, monitored parking.

S Firenze 34B1

Area sociale 'Flog', Via M Mercati 24/b, zona Careggi, Florence (Firenze).
GPS: n43,79491 e11,24835.

25 € 15/24h € 3 Ch. **Location:** Urban, simple.
Surface: gravel. 01/01-31/12.
Distance: city centre 2km Pizzeria Coop 650m centre : bus 4, 6-24h.

S Firenze 34B1

Florence Park Scandicci, Via di Scandicci 241, Florence (Firenze).
GPS: n43,76267 e11,20875.

25 € 15 included. **Location:** Urban, comfortable, central, quiet.
Surface: metalled. 01/01-31/12.
Distance: 4km 5km 150m.
Remarks: Video surveillance.

S Firenze 34B1

Gelsomino SCAF, Via del Gelsomino 11, Florence (Firenze).
GPS: n43,75173 e11,24388.

150 € 15/24h Ch included.
Surface: grasstiles.
01/01-31/12.
Distance: 2km bus 37 > centre.
Remarks: Max. 7m.

Tourist information Florence (Firenze):
U.I.A.T. (Ufficio Informazioni e di Accoglienza Turistica), Piazza Stazione, 4, www.firenze.turismo.toscana.it. Renaissance city with many curiosities.
Ponte Vechio. Famous bridge with jeweller's shops.
Cappella Brancacci, Santa Maria del Carmine. Renovated frescoes.
The Mall, le griffe, Via Europa 8, Leccio Reggello. Factory outlet.

S Firenzuola 26E3

Loc. Pieve di Camaggiore. **GPS:** n44,14594 e11,45361.

50 free ChWC. **Location:** Simple, quiet. **Surface:** grasstiles.
01/01-31/12.
Distance: Firenzuola 10km river 100m 1km.
Remarks: Playground.

Firenzuola 26E3

Area Picnic, Loc. Badia a Moscheta. **GPS:** n44,07586 e11,42030.

10 free. **Location:** Rural, simple, isolated, quiet.
Surface: gravel.
01/01-31/12.
Distance: Firenzuola 8km 500m agriturismo Badia di Moscheta.

Fivizzano 26C3

Piazza Libertà. **GPS:** n44,23914 e10,12735.

6 free. **Location:** Urban, simple, quiet. **Surface:** asphalted.
01/01-31/12.
Distance: on the spot 100m 100m on the spot.

S Fivizzano 26C3

Agriturismo Ristorante Al Vecchio Tino, Loc. Germalla 1, Monte dei Bianchi. **GPS:** n44,17380 e10,12603.

6 € 8/night Ch included. **Location:** Rural, luxurious.
Surface: gravel. 01/01-31/12.
Distance: on the spot 3km.
Remarks: Swimming pool available.

Foiano della Chiana 34C1

Outlet Village Valdichiana, Via Enzo Ferrari 5, loc. Farniole.
GPS: n43,22398 e11,80301.

10 free. **Location:** Simple. **Surface:** asphalted. 01/01-31/12.
Distance: on the spot on the spot.
Remarks: Motorhome parking at Outlet.

S Follonica 34B2

Eucalyptus Camper Park, Via Sanzio. **GPS:** n42,92804 e10,77569.

40 € 10 € 4 Ch included € 1. **Location:** Rural.
Surface: grassy. 01/06-30/09.
Distance: beach 1,8km 1km 1km.
Remarks: At paradise pool.

S Follonica 34B2

Agriturismo dal Pastore, Via Cassarello, 342.
GPS: n42,92835 e10,78912.
10 € 10 + € 1/pp tourist tax Ch. **Location:** Rural.
Surface: grassy.
Distance: city centre 3km 2,5km.
Remarks: Regional products.

Fonteblanda 34B2

Talamone Wind Beach Parking, Strada Provinciale Talamone.
GPS: n42,56334 e11,15659.

IT

150 free, June-Sep € 15. **Location:** Rural, simple, isolated.
Surface: gravel. 01/01-31/12.
Distance: 1,5km on the spot on the spot 1,5km 1,5km.
Remarks: Beach parking, shuttle bus to village.

S Gaiole in Chianti 34B1

Via Michelangelo Buonarroti. **GPS**: n43,46470 e11,43428.

free Chfree. **Location:** Rural, simple. **Surface:** metalled.
01/01-31/12.
Distance: 400m on the spot.
Remarks: At footballstadium.

S Gallicano 26D3

Via Maresciallo Guiliano Guazelli. **GPS**: n44,05827 e10,44565.

4 free Ch (2x)free. **Location:** Urban, simple, noisy.
Surface: metalled. 01/01-31/12.
Distance: 500m 450m 100m.
Remarks: Grotta del Vento.

S Greve in Chianti 34B1

Monte S. Michele, Via Montebeni. **GPS**: n43,59066 e11,31355.

17 free free. **Location:** Rural, comfortable, quiet.
Surface: metalled. 01/01-31/12.
Distance: 500m 500m.

Tourist information Greve in Chianti:
Sa-morning.

S Isola dElba 34A2

Area Camper Cavo, San Bennato, Cavo, Elba (Isle) (Isola dElba).
GPS: n42,85459 e10,42267.
30 € 15-35, 4 pers.incl Chincluded € 3/24h € 1.
Location: Rural. **Surface:** gravel. 01/04-30/10.
Distance: 600m 400m 650m.

S Isola dElba 34A2

Area Camper La Perla, Loc. Campo All'Aia, Procchio, Elba (Isle) (Isola dElba). **GPS**: n42,78893 e10,24877.
20 € 18, Jun/Sep € 24, Jul € 30, Aug € 39 € 3,50.
Surface: gravel. 01/01-31/12.
Distance: on the spot.

S Isola dElba 34A2

Loc. Bocchetto, Porto Azzurro. **GPS**: n42,77114 e10,39985.
60 free, peak season € 10/24h Chfree. **Location:** Rural.
Surface: asphalted. 01/04-01/10.

Distance: city centre 1km 350m Coop 850m on the spot.
Remarks: Nearby cemetery.

S Isola dElba 34A2

Sighello, area La Pila, Marina di Campo. **GPS**: n42,75357 e10,24228.
30 € 15 Ch € 3. **Surface:** unpaved. 01/05-30/09.
Distance: 400m 200m.
Remarks: At sports park.

S Larciano 34B1

Agriturismo Poggetto, Via Stradella 1489.
GPS: n43,83319 e10,88042.

25 € 15/24h, free with a meal Ch € 3/day WCincluded € 1. **Location:** Rural. **Surface:** grassy/gravel.
01/01-31/12.
Distance: 1km 1km 700m.
Remarks: Beautiful view.

S Livorno 34A1

Parco del Mulino, Via Voltolino Fontani. **GPS**: n43,51394 e10,32503.
25 € 10, May/Sep € 12 Ch included. **Surface:** grassy.
01/01-31/12.
Distance: city centre 3km 1km 350m.

S Livorno 34A1

Parco Marina del Boccale, Via del Littorale,238.
GPS: n43,47861 e10,33138.
€ 20 ChWC. **Surface:** grassy. 01/04-31/09.
Distance: Livorno 8km on the spot on the spot.

Livorno 34A1

Piazza Ordoardo Borrani, Viale d'Antignano.
GPS: n43,50465 e10,32144.

50 free. **Location:** Rural. **Surface:** asphalted.
Distance: 400m Antignano 100m 300m.

S Livorno 34A1

Calata Carrara. **GPS**: n43,55581 e10,30302.
30 free Chfree. **Location:** Urban.
Surface: asphalted.
01/01-31/12.
Distance: on the spot 400m 600m.

Tourist information Livorno:
Ufficio Informazioni, Piazza del Municipio. Medieval port city.

S Lucca 34A1

Il Serchio, Via del Tiro a Segno 704, loc. Sant'Anna.
GPS: n43,85000 e10,48583.

66 € 25/24h, dog € 1 Ch (66x)WC € 5 included.
Location: Comfortable, quiet. **Surface:** grasstiles.
01/03-31/01.
Distance: 1km 2km 200m 500m on the spot on the spot on the spot.
Remarks: Waste dump € 2/day, shuttle € 1/pp, swimming pool € 5/pp.

S Lucca 34A1

Area Sosta Lucca, Viale Gaetano Luporini.
GPS: n43,84028 e10,48878.

65 € 10/24h, peak season € 14/24h, € 3/h Ch included.
Location: Urban, simple, central, noisy. **Surface:** asphalted.
01/01-31/12.
Distance: 1km 2km 300m 500m 500m on the spot.

Tourist information Lucca:
Casa di Puccini, Via di Poggio. Birth place of the composer.
Tue-Su.
Wed, Sa, 3rd Su of the month antiques market.

S Lucignano 34C1

SP19. **GPS**: n43,27664 e11,74512.

20 free Ch (9x)free. **Location:** Rural, simple.
Surface: grassy. 01/01-31/12.
Distance: 500m.
Remarks: At the edge of village.

S Marina di Bibbona 34A2

Via dei Cipressi. **GPS**: n43,24825 e10,53389.
€ 10/24h Ch € 2 WCfree € 1. 01/04-31/10.
Distance: 1km 500m 500m.

S Marina di Cecina 34A1

Parcheggio Aqua Park, Via Tevere. **GPS**: n43,30070 e10,49948.

100 € 8 Ch. **Location:** Rural. **Surface:** metalled.
01/03-15/11.
Distance: 2km 1km 200m 200m.

S Marina di Cecina 34A1

Via della Cecinella. **GPS**: n43,29278 e10,50785.

30 € 8/24h Ch. **Location:** Rural, simple, quiet.
Surface: asphalted. 01/03-15/11.
Distance: 2km 300m 2km 2km.

S Marina di Cecina 34A1

New Camping Le Tamerici, Via della Cecinella, 5.
GPS: n43,29192 e10,51053.
€ 25-44 Ch WCincluded. 11/05-03/10.
Distance: 1,5km 1km on the spot on the spot.
Remarks: Swimming pool.

IT

Marina di Grosseto 34B2

Oasi di Maremma, SP158 delle Collacchie Km 34,4.
GPS: n42,72611 e10,99055.

50 € 16, peak season € 20, 4 pers.incl Ch (100x)€ 2 WC € 1 € 4. **Location:** Rural, comfortable, quiet. **Surface:** grassy.
01/04-30/09.
Distance: 1km 1km 1km 1km on the spot.
Remarks: Water at each pitch, barbecue place, picnic area, shuttle € 1/pp.

Marina di Grosseto 34B2

Area di sosta l'Oasi, S332 > dir San Vincenzo d'Elba.
GPS: n42,73466 e10,97483.

50 € 14, Jun € 18, Jul/Aug € 23 Ch € 2 WCincluded € 2 **Location:** Rural, comfortable. **Surface:** grassy.
Easter-30/09.
Distance: Marina 1,5km 1,1km 400m nearby on the spot on the spot.
Remarks: Monitored parking 24/24, grill and picknic area, playground.

Marina di Grosseto 34B2

Via Costiera, SP158. **GPS**: n42,73722 e10,96388.

50 free. **Location:** Rural, simple. **Surface:** gravel.
01/01-31/12.
Distance: 2km 400m.

Marina di Grosseto 34B2

Via della Trappola/SP40. **GPS**: n42,72150 e10,99864.
10 free. **Location:** Urban, noisy. **Surface:** metalled.
01/01-31/12.
Distance: 1,5km beach 2km 100m on the spot.

Marina di Grosseto 34B2

Via Grossetana. **GPS**: n42,71552 e10,98646.

8 free. **Location:** Urban. **Surface:** sand. 01/01-31/12.
Distance: on the spot 400m 400m on the spot on the spot.
Remarks: At harbour.

Tourist information Marina di Grosseto:
Parco Naturale della Maremma. Nature reserve. Wed, Sa, Su, holidays 9h 01/06-30/09 guided walk 7h, 16h.

Marina di Pisa 34A1

Parcheggio Camper Pisamo, Viale Gabriela d'Annunzio.
GPS: n43,67909 e10,27887.

130 € 1/h, night € 8 Ch € 2. **Location:** Rural, simple, noisy. **Surface:** gravel.
01/01-31/12.
Distance: 1km 8km sea 1km 1km 600m 1,5km 300m on the spot.

Marina di Pisa 34A1

Area Sosta Camper Marina Di Pisa, Via Litoranea, 1.
GPS: n43,65834 e10,28075.

50 € 1/h, night € 8. **Location:** Comfortable, noisy.
Surface: asphalted. 01/01-31/12.
Distance: on the spot on the spot 150m 1km.

Marradi 26F3

Area sosta Marradi, Via San Benedetto. **GPS**: n44,07347 e11,61166.

30 free 100liter Ch 8kWh,Service € 5. **Location:** Rural, simple, quiet. **Surface:** asphalted. 01/01-31/12.
Distance: 50m on the spot 100m 200m on the spot.
Remarks: Caution key service € 7.

Massa Marittima 34B2

Viale del Risorgimento. **GPS**: n43,04530 e10,89050.

10 free Chfree. **Location:** Urban.
Surface: asphalted.
01/01-31/12.
Distance: historical centre 650m 600m 500m on the spot.

Montalcino 34B2

Via Osticcio. **GPS**: n43,04913 e11,48749.

30 € 5/24h Chfree. **Location:** Rural, comfortable, quiet.
Surface: asphalted/metalled. 01/01-31/12.
Distance: 700m 700m 700m.

Montalcino 34B2

Agriturismo la Croce, La Croce 9. **GPS**: n43,03931 e11,50373.
15 € 20, guests free. **Location:** Rural, isolated, quiet.
Surface: grassy. 01/04-31/10.
Distance: 3,5km on the spot.
Remarks: Regional products and wine.

Monte San Savino 34C1

Via del Casalino. **GPS**: n43,33177 e11,72204.

20 free Chfree. **Location:** Rural, simple. **Surface:** gravel.
01/01-31/12.
Distance: on the spot 4,2km 200m 150m.
Remarks: Near sports fields, steep ramp.

Montecatini Terme 34B1

Piazza Pietro Leopoldo, SS 436. **GPS**: n43,88286 e10,76386.

40 free free. **Location:** Urban, simple, central, noisy.
Surface: asphalted. 01/01-31/12 Thu (market).
Distance: 100m 3km 200m 500m on the spot.
Remarks: In front of stadium, thursday market.

Montepulciano 34C2

P5, Piazza Pietro Nenni. **GPS**: n43,09577 e11,78684.

32 € 10/24h free. **Location:** Rural, simple.
Surface: asphalted. 01/01-31/12 Wed morning, market.
Distance: 200m 100m 400m.
Remarks: Cash payment.

Montepulciano 34C2

La Buca Vecchia, Strada per Pienza, 38. **GPS**: n43,09903 e11,73939.
7 € 20 + € 1/pp tourist tax Ch included.
Location: Comfortable, isolated, quiet. **Surface:** metalled.
01/01-31/12.
Distance: 5km.
Remarks: Check in on arrival, barbecue place.

Monteriggioni 34B1

Via Cassia Nord 142. **GPS**: n43,38560 e11,22784.
30 € 16/24h Ch included WC. **Surface:** metalled.
Distance: 400m 400m.
Remarks: Service passerby € 4.

Monteriggioni 34B1

Strada di Monteriggioni. **GPS**: n43,38801 e11,22511.

IT

12 € 2/h 8-20h, max. € 6, overnight stay free. **Location:** Rural, comfortable. **Surface:** gravel. 01/01-31/12.
Distance: 300m 1,4km 300m on the spot.

Monteriggioni 34B1

Agriturismo "Il Sambuco", Via Maestri del Lavoro 12, Uopini.
GPS: n43,35266 e11,29415.
8 € 15/24h free Ch included WC. **Surface:** gravel.
01/01-31/12.
Distance: 1km 350m 300m.
Remarks: Regional products, swimming pool € 5.

Monteroni d'Arbia 34B1

Via San Giusto. **GPS**: n43,23048 e11,42371.

free Chfree. **Location:** Rural, simple. **Surface:** sand.
01/01-31/12.
Distance: 50m.
Remarks: P centre.

Montespertoli 34B1

Molino del Ponte, Via Volterrana Nord. **GPS**: n43,65606 e11,08445.

5 free € 1/100liter € 2 Ch. **Location:** Rural.
Surface: metalled. 01/01-31/12.
Distance: Montespertoli 2,3km on the spot 400m.

Montevarchi 34B1

Via B. Latini. **GPS**: n43,53052 e11,56784.

free free. **Location:** Urban, simple. **Surface:** asphalted.
01/01-31/12.
Distance: 7km Coop.
Remarks: Nearby stadium.

Montopoli in Val d'Arno 34B1

Camper di Alessio e Irene, Piazza Amerigo Vespucci, Via di Masoria.
GPS: n43,67333 e10,75222.

31 free Chfree. **Location:** Urban, simple, central, quiet.
Surface: metalled. 01/01-31/12.
Distance: 500m 2km 600m 400m 600m.
Remarks: Barbecue place, picnic area.

Orbetello 34B3

Lanino Parco Sosta, Loc. Santa Liberata.
GPS: n42,43346 e11,15959.

50 € 10/motorhome, € 8/pp, € 5/child Ch (40x)included WC. **Location:** Rural. **Surface:** grassy/gravel.
01/01-31/12.
Distance: Orbetello 5km 50m 200m alimentari.
Remarks: Max. 72h.

Palazzuolo sul Senio 26F3

Parcheggio Casone, Via Casone. **GPS**: n44,11073 e11,54968.

50 free Chfree. **Location:** Rural, simple. **Surface:** asphalted.
01/01-31/12.
Distance: 100m 100m 100m 200m.
Remarks: Narrow entrance.

Palazzuolo sul Senio 26F3

Via Francesco Pagliazzi. **GPS**: n44,11551 e11,55000.

6 free. **Location:** Urban, isolated. **Surface:** metalled.
01/01-31/12.
Distance: on the spot 600m 350m 200m.
Remarks: At swimming pool, next to cemetery, upper part of the parking.

Pienza 34C2

Via Mencattelli e Foro Boario. **GPS**: n43,07799 e11,68087.

8-22h: € 1,50/1h, € 5/4h, € 10/8h, overnight stay free Chincluded WC. **Location:** Rural, simple. **Surface:** asphalted.
01/01-31/12 Fri-morning market.
Distance: 100m.

Pienza 34C2

Podere il Casale, Via Podere Il Casale 64. **GPS**: n43,08090 e11,71161.
8 € 26, 2 pers. incl € 3 WC. **Location:** Quiet.
Surface: gravel. 01/01-31/12.
Distance: on the spot.
Remarks: Regional products.

Pieve Santo Stefano 34C1

Grey camper, Via della Verna. **GPS**: n43,67058 e12,03729.

20 € 10 Ch WCincluded € 1. **Location:** Urban, simple, noisy. **Surface:** metalled. 01/01-31/12.
Distance: on the spot 1,7km 300m 350m 200m.
Remarks: Nearby viaduct E45.

Piombino 34A2

Camperoasi, Loc. Mortelliccio, Riotorto.
GPS: n42,95416 e10,66638.

93 € 20, Apr-Jun, Sep € 30, Jul/Aug € 40 Ch WC € 0,50 included. **Location:** Comfortable. **Surface:** grasstiles/grassy.
01/01-31/12 01/10-31/03 Mo-Thu.
Distance: 200m 50m 50m.
Remarks: Water/drainage at each pitch, 10% discount on presentation of the most recent guide, reception open: 9.30-12.30 14-19.30.

Piombino 34A2

Area Sosta Camper Isolotto, Loc. Mortelliccio, 7, Riotorto.
GPS: n42,95765 e10,67374.
23 € 20, Jul/Aug € 27 Ch included. **Surface:** gravel.
Distance: 200m.
Remarks: Fruit-vegetables-wine-regional products for sale, swimming pool available.

Piombino 34A2

Area Sosta l'OrtiCillo, Loc. Le Pinete, 3 Riotorto.
GPS: n42,98414 e10,68011.
12 € 8-10, 01/07-31/08 € 14 + tourist tax € 0,50/pp Ch included. **Surface:** gravel.
01/01-31/12.
Distance: 300m.
Remarks: Barbecue place, borrow cycles for free, regional products.

Piombino 34A2

Carbonifera 1, Loc. Torre Mozza. **GPS**: n42,94750 e10,69277.

± 75 € 2,20/h, € 18,70/24h Chincluded. **Surface:** gravel.
01/01-31/12.
Distance: 50m.
Remarks: Beach parking, no camping activities.

Piombino 34A2

Parcheggio Caldanelle, Loc. Caldanelle. **GPS**: n43,00216 e10,52816.

IT

150 € 2/h, € 17/8-20h, overnight stay free Ch.
Location: Isolated, quiet. **Surface:** grassy. 01/01-31/12.
Distance: Piombino 9km 1,5km.
Remarks: Beach parking, camper service 8-20h, no camping activities, shuttle bus.

S Piombino 34A2

Perelli 1-3, Loc. Perelli. **GPS**: n42,95527 e10,61944.

50 € 2,20/h, € 18,70/8-20h, overnight stay free Chfree.
Location: Quiet. **Surface:** grassy/sand. 01/06-30/09.
Distance: Sandy beach Perelli 1.
Remarks: Beach parking, service: Perelli 3, no camping activities, dogs beach.

S Piombino 34A2

Podere Mortelliccio, Loc. Mortelliccio 8, Riotorto.
GPS: n42,95700 e10,67884.
8 € 20-25, Jul/Aug € 32 Ch. included € 3,50.
Surface: gravel. 01/01-31/12.
Distance: 400m on the spot.
Remarks: Regional products and wine, barbecue place.

S Piombino 34A2

Via della Pace. **GPS**: n42,93777 e10,52194.

15 free € 0,10/10liter Ch. **Location:** Urban, noisy.
Surface: metalled. 01/01-31/12.
Distance: 500m 1km 700m 800m.

S Piombino 34A2

Parcheggio di Alvin, Piazzale Salvatore Allende.
GPS: n42,92578 e10,54219.
€ 15/24h Ch. 01/04-31/10.
Distance: 200m.

S Pisa 34A1

Parcheggio camper, Via di Pratale 78.
GPS: n43,72106 e10,42066.

100 € 12/night, € 1/h, € 5/6h € 3 Ch. € 3. **Location:** Urban, comfortable, quiet.
Surface: asphalted.
01/01-31/12.
Distance: 800m 7km 100m 500m 800m on the spot.
Remarks: Monitored parking.

S Pisa 34A1

Via A. Paparelli. **GPS**: n43,72433 e10,41178.

100 € 1/h, overnight stay free. **Location:** Urban, simple, noisy.
Surface: asphalted/metalled. 01/01-31/12
Wed, Sa market.
Distance: on the spot 100m 200m on the spot.
Remarks: Max. 5 days.

S Pistoia 34B1

Via Marino Marini/via della Quiete. **GPS**: n43,94389 e10,91556.

50 free Chfree. **Location:** Urban, simple, noisy.
Surface: asphalted. 01/01-31/12.
Distance: city centre 1km 6km 300m 500m on the spot.
Remarks: At sports park, max. 48h.

S Pistoia 34B1

Agricamper Podere Campofossato, Via Calabbiana 2.
GPS: n43,99595 e10,89544.

8 € 20 Ch. included. **Location:** Rural, comfortable, quiet. **Surface:** grassy. 01/01-31/12.
Distance: 10km on the spot on the spot 100m on the spot.
Remarks: Regional products.

S Poggibonsi 34B1

Via Fortezza Medicea, loc. Vallone. **GPS**: n43,46203 e11,14593.

± 15 free € 0,10/10liter Ch. (6x)€ 1/12h. **Location:** Rural.
Surface: gravel. 01/01-31/12.
Distance: centre 500m 400m 500m.

Tourist information Poggibonsi:
Monteriggioni. Walled small town.

S Pomarance 34B1

Area Sosta Camper Attrezzata, Viale della Costituzione.
GPS: n43,29966 e10,86974.
18 € 10/24h Ch. WC included. **Location:** Urban, comfortable. **Surface:** metalled. 01/01-31/12.
Remarks: Max. 72h, video surveillance.

S Pontassieve 34B1

Viale Hanoi/viale Lisbona. **GPS**: n43,77355 e11,42764.

free Chfree. **Location:** Urban, simple. **Surface:** asphalted.
01/01-31/12.
Distance: 500m.

S Poppi 34C1

La Crocina, Viale dei Pini. **GPS**: n43,71982 e11,76529.

12 free Chfree € 3/5h. **Location:** Urban, simple, quiet.
Surface: asphalted.
01/01-31/12.
Distance: historical centre 500m 300m 700m on the spot.

S Porto Ercole 34B3

Le Miniere, SP di Porto Ercole. **GPS**: n42,41749 e11,20386.

130 € 20-25 Ch. WC € 0,50 € 5 included.
Location: Rural, comfortable, noisy. **Surface:** grassy.
Easter-30/09.
Distance: Porto Ercole 2km 800m 800m 2km on the spot.
Remarks: Bread-service, borrow cycles for free, free shuttle to beach every 30 minutes.

S Porto Ercole 34B3

Parking Da Renzo, SC della Feniglia. **GPS**: n42,41527 e11,20777.

150 € 15-20/24h Ch. € 3 WC included.
Location: Rural, comfortable, quiet. **Surface:** grassy.
Easter-01/10.
Distance: Porto Ercole 3km beach 1km 800m 300m on the spot.
Remarks: Bike/car rental, picnic tables available, beach shuttle (August).

S Pratovecchio 34C1

Via Uffenheim. **GPS**: n43,78666 e11,71952.

IT

12 free Ch free. **Location:** Urban, simple, quiet.
Surface: asphalted.
01/01-31/12.
Distance: 50m on the spot 100m 100m 100m.
Remarks: Along river, near sports fields, follow signs instead of GPS.

S Radda in Chianti 34B1

Via Degli Ulivi. **GPS**: n43,48643 e11,37543.

6 € 12/24h WC free. **Location:** Rural, simple.
Surface: metalled. 01/01-31/12.
Distance: 200m (stairs).

S Radicofani 34C2

Via A. de Gasperi. **GPS**: n42,89471 e11,77506.

5 free Ch free. **Location:** Rural, simple.
Surface: grassy/gravel. 01/01-31/12.
Distance: 400m 800m.

S Radicondoli 34B1

Il Pianetto. GPS: n43,25888 e11,04250.

free Ch € 1/h. **Surface:** grassy/gravel.
01/01-31/12.
Distance: medieval centre 300m 300m 2km.

S Rapolano Terme 34C1

Area di sosta camper Il Pini, Via Vittorio Veneto.
GPS: n43,29601 e11,60312.
50 € 10/24h, € 8/12h, € 6/6h € 3 included.
Surface: gravel. 01/01-31/12.
Distance: on the spot 1km 300m.
Remarks: Terme Antica Querciolaia 200m.

S Rapolano Terme 34C1

Villa dei Boschi, Loc. Villa dei Boschi 50, Fraz San Gimignanello, SP10.
GPS: n43,22829 e11,65429.

20 € 20/24h, free with a meal WC included.
Location: Rural, simple, isolated. **Surface:** grassy. 01/01-31/12.
Distance: on the spot.

S Rapolano Terme 34C1

Area di sosta Le Terme, Via Trieste. **GPS**: n43,29268 e11,60781.

64 € 5/6h, € 8/12h, € 12/24h Ch WC included € 2.
Location: Rural, comfortable. **Surface:** gravel/metalled.
01/01-31/12.
Distance: 500m 50m 200m.
Remarks: Terme Antica Querciolaia 50m.

S Rosignano Marittimo 34A1

Molino a Fuoco, Via dei Cavalleggeri Antica, Vada.
GPS: n43,32816 e10,46005.

70 01/04-15/09 € 15 Ch included. **Surface:** grassy/gravel.
Distance: 400m 500m 400m 400m.
Remarks: Max. 72h.

S Rosignano Marittimo 34A1

Il Fortullino, Località il Fortullino. **GPS**: n43,43005 e10,39632.

150 € 18/night, Jul-Aug € 23 Ch included.
Surface: unpaved. 01/04-30/09.
Distance: Castiglioncello 4km, Livorno 20km, Pisa 40km 150m Pizzeria 100m 5km.

S Rosignano Marittimo 34A1

SP39, Via Aurelia, Loc Caletta. **GPS**: n43,39900 e10,42807.

18 € 10 free. **Surface:** metalled.
Distance: on the spot 300m 100m.
Remarks: Along busy road, max. 48h.

Rosignano Marittimo 34A1

Parcheggio del Lillatro, Via Fratelli Gigli, loc Lillatro.
GPS: n43,38380 e10,43206.

40 € 9. **Location:** Simple, isolated, quiet. **Surface:** sand.
Easter-31/10.
Distance: 50m 50m.

Rosignano Marittimo 34A1

Sportiva Vada, Via Mare Mediterraneo, Vada.
GPS: n43,35208 e10,45183.

75 € 10/day. **Location:** Rural, quiet. **Surface:** unpaved.
01/04-01/10.
Distance: 400m 200m 200m 400m.

San Casciano dei Bagni 34C2

Via Della Pineta. **GPS**: n42,86530 e11,87383.

15 free. **Location:** Rural, simple. **Surface:** gravel/sand.
01/01-31/12.
Distance: 500m.

S San Casciano dei Bagni 34C2

Piazzale del Ponte. **GPS**: n42,87024 e11,87742.

15 € 6/12h, € 12/24h Ch. **Surface:** asphalted.
01/01-31/12.
Distance: 100m.
Remarks: Near spa resort.

S San Casciano in Val di Pesa 34B1

Parco del Poggione, Piazza Dante Tacci. **GPS**: n43,65395 e11,18768.

10 € 8 Ch WC included. **Location:** Urban.
Surface: gravel. 16/09-14/06.
Distance: on the spot 700m 700m 300m.

S San Gimignano 34B1

Sosta Camper Santa Chiara, Via di Castel San Gimignano, Loc. Fornace.
GPS: n43,45572 e11,03476.

30 € 22/24h € 2 Ch WC included. **Location:** Rural, luxurious. **Surface:** gravel. 01/01-31/12.
Distance: 3km Osteria/bar 1,5km shuttle.
Remarks: Barbecue place, free shuttle bus to San Gimignano, ten-

niscourt.

San Gimignano 34B1

Park Santa Lucia, Loc. Santa Lucia. **GPS**: n43,45205 e11,05586.

50 € 1/h, € 15/24h Ch included (14x). **Location:** Rural, simple. **Surface:** gravel. 01/01-31/12.
Distance: 3km Citybus Linea 1.
Remarks: Next to swimming pool, 24/24 video surveillance, shuttle bus to city centre.

San Miniato Basso 34B1

Area Camper Il Salice, Via Pier delle Vigne 28/A, loc. La Catena. **GPS**: n43,68325 e10,82335.

20 € 20 Ch WC included . **Location:** Rural, comfortable, quiet. **Surface:** gravel. 01/01-31/12.
Distance: 2,5km 400m 300m 300m.
Remarks: Max. 3 days, monitored parking 24/24, shuttle bus to city centre.

San Miniato Basso 34B1

Piazza G. Impastato, Via Pestalozzi/Via G. Pizzigoni, zona industriale. **GPS**: n43,69403 e10,83604.

60 € 0,50/h, overnight stay free free. **Location:** Urban, simple, noisy. **Surface:** asphalted. 01/01-31/12.
Distance: 3km 800m 50m 100m 100m.

San Piero a Sieve 34B1

Via Giudici Falcone e Borsellino. **GPS**: n43,96260 e11,32732.

20 free € 2 Ch. **Location:** Urban, simple, quiet. **Surface:** metalled. 01/01-31/12.
Distance: 500m 250m 400m 400m.

San Quirico d'Orcia 34C2

Via delle Scuole. **GPS**: n43,05607 e11,60682.

30 € 10/24h free. **Location:** Rural, simple. **Surface:** asphalted. 01/01-31/12.
Distance: 200m.
Remarks: Picnic area, playground.

San Quirico d'Orcia 34C2

Strada di Bagno Vignoni, Bagno Vignoni. **GPS**: n43,02904 e11,62450.

± 20 free. **Location:** Rural, simple, quiet. **Surface:** unpaved. 01/01-31/12.
Distance: 500m 350m.
Remarks: Parco dei Mulini: natural hot springs, free entrance, 400m.

San Romano in Garfagnana 26D3

Via Campo Sportivo/via Prà di Lago. **GPS**: n44,17243 e10,34199.

15 free Ch free. **Location:** Rural. **Surface:** grassy. 01/01-31/12.
Distance: 400m 550m 650m 150m on the spot.
Remarks: At sports park, Parco Avventura Selva del Buffardello 100m.

San Vincenzo 34A2

Via Biserno. **GPS**: n43,08790 e10,54134.

50 01/04-30/09 € 10/24h free.
Surface: grassy/gravel. 01/01-31/12.
Distance: 1km beach 200m 50m 50m.
Remarks: Beach parking, no camping activities, bicycle rental.

San Vincenzo 34A2

SS. Annunziata, Via del Castelluccio, 142. **GPS**: n43,10086 e10,56001. € 16, Jul/Aug € 25-35 Ch included € 0,50 € 3 .
Distance: 1km 1km on the spot 50m.
Remarks: Playground, swimming pool.

Sansepolcro 34C1

Viale Alessandro Volta. **GPS**: n43,56976 e12,13727.

20 free Ch free. **Location:** Urban, simple. **Surface:** asphalted. 01/01-31/12.
Distance: 200m 200m 100m.

Sansepolcro 34C1

Podere Violino, Via del Tevere 1150, Gricignano. **GPS**: n43,55539 e12,12312.

8 € 6 + € 5/pp Ch WC included. **Location:** Rural, comfortable, isolated, quiet. **Surface:** grassy. 15/02-31/12.
Distance: 2km river on the spot 1km.
Remarks: Arrival < 19h, restaurant closed on Sunday, swimming pool available.

Santa Fiora 34C2

Via Martiri della Niccioleta. **GPS**: n42,83531 e11,58397.

20 free Ch free (6x) € 1/2h. **Location:** Rural, simple. **Surface:** gravel/sand. 01/01-31/12.
Distance: 450m.

Sasso Pisano 34B2

Buca San Rocco. **GPS**: n43,16748 e10,86586.

10 free € 2 Ch € 3/12h. **Location:** Rural. **Surface:** metalled. 01/01-31/12.
Distance: 100m 200m.

Saturnia 34B2

L'Alveare dei Pinzi, Strada della Peschiera, Saturnia. **GPS**: n42,65597 e11,50368.

400 € 14/24h Ch (120x) € 2 WC € 0,50 € 6 included. **Location:** Rural, comfortable, quiet. **Surface:** gravel. 01/01-31/12.
Distance: Saturnia 3km 1,5km.
Remarks: Panoramic view, free shuttle to spa resort and Saturnia, bar/snack/fruit, terme di Saturnia (sulfur baths) 1,7km, Cascate del Mulino (water fall, free entry) 2,5km, friday market.

Saturnia 34B2

La Quercia, Via Aurina 15. **GPS**: n42,66667 e11,50457.

30 € 16/24h Ch WC € 1 included.
Location: Rural, comfortable, central. **Surface:** gravel.

IT

01 15/03-01/10.
Distance: 200m 100m 100m on the spot.
Remarks: Shuttle bus, terme di Saturnia (sulfur baths) 1,7km, Cascate del Mulino (water fall, free entry) 2,5km.

S Scarperia 26E3

Toscana Ranch, Via di Galliano 21. **GPS**: n44,01189 e11,30681.

20 € 10 Ch WC included. **Location:** Rural, simple, quiet. **Surface:** grassy. 01/01-31/12.
Distance: 5km on the spot 5km.
Remarks: Western style ranch.

S Sestino 34C1

Via Travicello. **GPS**: n43,71223 e12,30356.

12 free free. **Surface:** grasstiles.
Distance: 2km.
Remarks: Nearby sports park.

S Sesto Fiorentino 34B1

Area Antica Etruria, Via Ferruccio Parri. **GPS**: n43,84150 e11,17667.

50 € 18/24h Ch WC included € 1,50/day.
Location: Rural, comfortable. **Surface:** grassy/gravel.
01/01-31/12.
Distance: 1,5km 400m 400m 50m > Florence.
Remarks: Monitored parking.

S Sesto Fiorentino 34B1

Viale Ariosto. **GPS**: n43,83238 e11,18997.

15 free. **Location:** Simple, quiet. **Surface:** asphalted.
01/01-31/12.
Distance: 500m 3km 200m 500m train 100m.
Remarks: In front of Lidl supermarket, 20 mins to Florence by train.

S Siena 34B1

P1, Palasport, Via Achille Sclavo. **GPS**: n43,33323 e11,31739.

35 € 20/motorhome (8.00-20.00h) Ch WC free.
Location: Urban, simple. **Surface:** metalled. 01/01-31/12.
Distance: on the spot.

S Siena 34B1

P2, Il Fagiolone, Via di Pescaia. **GPS**: n43,31456 e11,31760.

60 € 20/motorhome (8-20h), overnight stay free WC free.
Location: Urban, simple, noisy. **Surface:** metalled.
01/01-31/12.
Distance: on the spot.
Remarks: Along busy road.

Siena 34B1

Acqua Calda, Via Fausto Coppi. **GPS**: n43,33627 e11,29695.

free. **Location:** Urban, simple. **Surface:** grasstiles.
01/01-31/12.
Distance: 650m bus 10 centre Siena.

Siena 34B1

Via delle Province/via Napoli. **GPS**: n43,34168 e11,30512.

free. **Location:** Urban, simple, noisy. **Surface:** asphalted.
01/01-31/12.
Distance: 200m McDonalds 200m on the spot.

Tourist information Siena:
- Palazzo Publico. Gothic town hall from 1342.
- Torre del Mangia. Bell tower. daily.
- Duomo. Romanesque Gothic cathedral.
- La Lizza. Week market. Wed morning.
- Palio, Piazza del Campo. Famous historical horse race. 02/07, 16/08.

S Stia 34C1

Parco comunale del Canto della Rana, Via Londa, SP556.
GPS: n43,80417 e11,70326.

10 free Ch free. **Location:** Rural, simple, quiet.
Surface: gravel. 01/01-31/12.
Distance: 500m 600m 700m.

S Suvereto 34B2

Via dei Forni. **GPS**: n43,07572 e10,67802.

12 free free. **Location:** Rural, simple, quiet. **Surface:** grassy.
01/01-31/12.
Distance: medieval centre 200m 300m 300m.

S Torrita di Siena 34C2

Via di Ciliano. **GPS**: n43,16475 e11,77173.

6 free Ch free. **Location:** Rural, comfortable, quiet.
Surface: metalled. 01/01-31/12.
Distance: 400m 200m on the spot on the spot.

S Venturina 34B2

Parco Termale Calidario, Via di Caldana.
GPS: n43,03666 e10,60000.

20 free € 1/100liter Ch. **Location:** Urban, quiet.
Surface: metalled. 01/01-31/12.
Distance: 800m 50m 800m 300m.
Remarks: Thermal centre 50m.

S Viareggio 34A1

Via Martiri di Belfiore. **GPS**: n43,88120 e10,25080.

44 € 15/24h Ch included.
Surface: asphalted.
01/01-31/12.
Distance: 1km 2,5km.
Remarks: Check in at All Events Festival Puccini Viareggio, Viale Regina Margherita 1, 43,8673339 10,2431529, terrain with video surveillance.

IT

S Vinci 34B1

Via Girolamo Calvi. **GPS**: n43,78080 e10,92830.

12 free ChfFree. **Location:** Rural, simple, noisy. **Surface:** metalled. 01/01-31/12.
Distance: 300m 200m 650m on the spot 100m.
Remarks: At sports park, max. 24h.

S Volterra 34B1

Parking P3, Fonti Docciola, Viale Dei Filosofi. **GPS**: n43,40306 e10,86417.

15 € 10 8-20h, overnight stay free Chfree .
Location: Urban. **Surface:** gravel. 01/01-31/12.
Distance: historical center 100m 200m 300m.

San Marino

S San Marino 26G3

Camper Stop, Via del Serrone 94. **GPS**: n43,92057 e12,45056.
free free. **Surface:** grassy. 01/01-31/12.
Distance: city centre 3km on the spot.

S San Marino 26G3

Gualdicciolo, Via Fabrizio di Montebello. **GPS**: n43,94630 e12,40551.
20 free ChWCfree. **Surface:** metalled. 01/01-31/12.
Distance: 8km on the spot.

S San Marino 26G3

P10, Via Napoleone Boneparte. **GPS**: n43,93567 e12,44362.

20 € 8/24h € 2. **Location:** Urban. **Surface:** asphalted. 01/01-31/12.
Distance: 2km 1,5km 900m.
Remarks: Elevator to centre 50m.

S San Marino 26G3

P13, Baldasserona, Borgo Maggiore. **GPS**: n43,94054 e12,44289.

50 free ChWCfree. **Location:** Rural. **Surface:** asphalted. 01/01-31/12 Service: winter.
Distance: 300m 650m.
Remarks: Service 300m, picnic tables available.

S San Marino 26G3

Strada Genghe di Atto, Acquaviva. **GPS**: n43,94491 e12,42963.

5 free ChWCfree. **Surface:** asphalted. 01/01-31/12.
Distance: 6km.

Tourist information San Marino:
Borgo Maggiore. Week market. Thu.

Marche

S Amandola 34D2

Area Sosta Sibillini, Piazzale Sandro Pertini. **GPS:** n42,97085 e13,35488.
42 € 10 Ch € 2 WC included. **Surface:** asphalted. 01/01-31/12.
Distance: 850m.

S Ancona 34D1

Area di sosta Posatora, Via Sanzio Blasi, Loc. Posatore. **GPS:** n43,59964 e13,48530.

30 € 12 Ch (24x)included.
Location: Simple. **Surface:** metalled. 01/01-31/12.
Distance: 4,5km 10m.
Remarks: Max. 72h, only exact change, entrance between 8-22h.

S Ancona 34D1

Centro Commerciale Auchan, Via Scataglini, Zona Industriale Baraccola, SS16, Ancona-sud. **GPS:** n43,55133 e13,51506.

25 free Chfree. **Location:** Simple. **Surface:** grasstiles. 01/01-31/12.
Distance: 8km 3,6km on the spot on the spot.

Tourist information Ancona:
Riviera del Conera. Touristic peninsula with beaches and several bathing resorts.

S Apecchio 34C1

Via Isidoro Pazzaglia. **GPS:** n43,55938 e12,41969.
30 free Ch (6x)free. **Location:** Urban. **Surface:** metalled. 01/01-31/12.
Distance: 100m 100m 50m 100m.

Tourist information Apecchio:
Week market. Fri-morning.

S Ascoli Piceno 34E2

Ex Seminario, Viale Alcide Gasperi. **GPS:** n42,85222 e13,58222.

20 € 3/night,20/h, night € 3 included € 2. **Location:** Urban. **Surface:** asphalted. 01/01-31/12.
Distance: centre 500m 200m 200m.
Remarks: Guarded parking.

S Ascoli Piceno 34E2

Bed & Breakfast Chartaria, Via Adriatico. **GPS:** n42,84792 e13,57306.
7 € 15 included € 3. **Location:** Urban. **Surface:** grassy. 01/01-31/12.
Distance: city centre 1km 500m on the spot.
Remarks: Barbecue place.

Tourist information Ascoli Piceno:
City with many monumental bldg.
Wed, Sa.

S Camerino 34D1

Via Macario Muzio, Viale Betti. **GPS:** n43,13677 e13,06718.

8 free Chfree € 1/4h WC. **Location:** Rural. **Surface:** asphalted. 01/01-31/12.
Distance: centre 500m 350m.
Remarks: Beautiful view, picnic area, escalator to city centre.

S Carpegna 34C1

Via Aldo Moro. **GPS:** n43,78083 e12,34040.

10 free € 1 Ch € 0,60/h. **Location:** Urban. **Surface:** concrete. 01/01-31/12.
Distance: 300m 300m 300m 400m.

S Castelfidardo 34D1

Croce Verde, Via Lumumba/via Donato Bramonte. **GPS:** n43,46603 e13,55563.

3 free free. **Location:** Simple. **Surface:** asphalted. 01/01-31/12.
Distance: 200m.
Remarks: Max. 48h.

S Castelsantangelo sul Nera 34D2

Strada Provinciale 136. **GPS:** n42,89117 e13,15355.
8 free Chfree. **Location:** Isolated, quiet. **Surface:** asphalted. 01/01-31/12.
Distance: 200m.

S Cerreto D'Esi 34D1

Via Dante Alighieri. **GPS:** n43,32714 e12,99114.

10 free Ch free. **Location:** Urban, simple. **Surface:** metalled. 01/01-31/12.

IT

Distance: 1km 500m 200m.

S **Cingoli** 34D1

Area Balcone delle Marche, Via San Esuperanzio.
GPS: n43,37643 e13,20943.
€ 10 Ch included. **Location:** Rural.
Surface: asphalted/gravel. 01/01-31/12.
Distance: 200m 200m 100m on the spot.

S **Colmurano** 34D1

Via Piero della Francesca, Contrada Peschiera.
GPS: n43,16260 e13,35828.

8 free Ch WC free. **Location:** Rural. **Surface:** asphalted.
01/01-31/12.
Distance: 400m 550m 850m.
Remarks: Near sports park and historical centre.

S **Corinaldo** 34D1

CoriCamper, Via Pecciameglio. **GPS**: n43,64688 e13,04850.
14 free Ch free. **Surface:** metalled.
01/01-31/12.
Distance: 200m 300m 200m.
Remarks: Max. 48h.

S **Corinaldo** 34D1

Via Lepri 3. **GPS**: n43,64703 e13,04910.

8 free Ch free. **Location:** Simple. **Surface:** asphalted.
01/01-31/12.
Distance: 400m 50m.

S **Corinaldo** 34D1

Ristorante Camping Colverde, Via per Montalboddo 52.
GPS: n43,63504 e13,09743.

10 € 15, guests € 10 Ch WC, on camp site included, on camp site. **Location:** Rural, simple. **Surface:** grassy.
01/01-31/12.
Distance: 5km on the spot.
Remarks: Max. 48h.

S **Cossignano** 34E2

Via Gallo. **GPS**: n42,98050 e13,69213.
6 € 6 € 3 Ch included. **Location:** Urban, simple.
Surface: metalled. 01/01-31/12.
Distance: on the spot 500m 400m.
Remarks: Max. 72h.

S **Cupramontana** 34D1

Verdicchio, SP 11. **GPS**: n43,43934 e13,11837.

10 free Ch free (10x). **Location:** Simple, noisy.
Surface: metalled. 01/01-31/12.
Distance: 500m 100m 500m.
Remarks: Beautiful view of Monte San Vicino.

S **Fabriano** 34D1

Fraz. Poggio San Romualdo. **GPS**: n43,36473 e13,02534.

35 free free. **Location:** Rural, simple, quiet. **Surface:** grassy.
01/01-31/12.
Distance: 3,5km on the spot.

S **Fabriano** 34D1

Via Bruno Buozzi. **GPS**: n43,34650 e12,91645.

16 free € 2/100liter Ch (6x) € 3/12h. **Location:** Simple.
Surface: grassy. 01/01-31/12.
Distance: 3km.
Remarks: Next to sports centre.

S **Falerone** 34D1

Ex-stazione FS di Piane di Falerone, Via Togliatti.
GPS: n43,09944 e13,49944.

15 free Ch free. **Surface:** metalled. 1st Su of the month.
Distance: 100m 200m 200m 100m.
Remarks: Nearby the old station and theatre Romano.

S **Fano** 34D1

Lungomare Sassonia, Via Ruggeri. **GPS**: n43,84238 e13,03197.

60 € 5-8,50 (20x) € 2 . **Surface:** grassy/gravel.
01/01-31/12.
Distance: 1km 2km 50m 50m 600m.

S **Fano** 34D1

Area di Sosta Adriatico, SS16, Torrette di Fano.
GPS: n43,80789 e13,08198.

30 € 10-23, camperstop 18-9h € 8-10 Ch (12x) WC included € 0,50 € 3. **Location:** Comfortable. **Surface:** grassy/gravel.
22/04-11/09.
Distance: 4km 9km 200m 50m 500m.
Remarks: Service passerby € 5.

S **Fano** 34D1

Viale Kennedy. **GPS**: n43,84557 e13,01133.

16-20 free Ch free. **Location:** Simple. **Surface:** asphalted.
01/01-31/12.
Distance: 200m 2,7km 800m.
Remarks: Nearby cemetery.

S **Fano** 34D1

Campo Nunzia, SS Adriactica Sud-Loc. Torrette di Fano.
GPS: n43,80474 e13,08488.

28 € 10-15 Ch € 2,50/24h WC € 1.
Location: Comfortable. **Surface:** grassy/gravel. 24/04-01/09.
Distance: 7km 10km 150m.

Fano 34D1

Ristorante La Tratta Maria Angela, Via Fratelli Zuccari 37.
GPS: n43,83589 e13,04182.

14 € 7. **Location:** Simple, quiet. **Surface:** grassy.
01/04-01/10.
Distance: 2,5km 50m on the spot on the spot.
Remarks: P camper.

Tourist information Fano:
Wed, Sa.

S **Fermo** 34E1

Area Camper 2004, Lungomare Marina Palminese.
GPS: n43,15085 e13,81382.

IT

80 € 12 Ch (32x)included hot shower against payment . **Surface:** grassy. 01/04-30/09.
Distance: 10km 2,5km on the spot 450m 900m 450m.
Remarks: Swimming pool.

S **Fermo** 34E1

Baia dei Gabbiani, Viale A. de Gasperi, Lido S. Tomasso.
GPS: n43,22158 e13,78113.

50 € 13-20, Aug € 25 Ch included € 0,50 .
Surface: grassy/gravel. 01/04-30/09.
Distance: 6,6km Private beach.

S **Fermo** 34E1

Onda Verde, Via Usodimare, Lido di Fermo.
GPS: n43,20289 e13,78825.

100 € 10 to € 20 (Aug) Ch 2Amp WC included.
Surface: grassy. 01/04-30/09.
Distance: Fermo 10km 5,4km 10m 10-500m 200m.

S **Fermo** 34E1

Via di Crollanza. **GPS:** n43,16176 e13,72318.

8 free ChWC. **Surface:** asphalted. 01/01-31/12.
Distance: 100m 300m on the spot on the spot.

S **Fossombrone** 34D1

Via Oberdan. **GPS:** n43,69301 e12,81835.

8 free Chfree. **Location:** Urban. **Surface:** asphalted.
01/01-31/12.
Distance: 500m 1,4km 400m on the spot 100m.

Tourist information Fossombrone:
Week market. Mo.

S **Genga** 34D1

Frasassi, Fraz San Vittore. **GPS:** n43,40321 e12,97597.

50 free ChWC free. **Location:** Simple, quiet.
Surface: gravel. 01/01-31/12.
Distance: 7km on the spot.
Remarks: Nearby pay-desk Gole di Frasassi, free shuttle to the caves.

S **Gradara** 26H3

Parcheggio dei Cipressi, Via Mancini. **GPS:** n43,94163 e12,77461.
€ 5/6h, € 10/24h € 3/6h. **Surface:** grassy.
01/01-31/12.
Distance: on the spot on the spot.

S **Gradara** 26H3

Parking P1, Piazza Paolo e Francesca. **GPS:** n43,94083 e12,77083.

14 € 10/24h ChWCfree. **Location:** Simple, central.
Surface: asphalted.
01/01-31/12.
Distance: historical center 100m 7,3km on the spot 400m.
Remarks: Parking centre, castle 500m.

S **Grottammare** 34E2

Sosta Camper 43° Parallelo, Via Carlo Alberto dalla Chiesa.
GPS: n42,96673 e13,87694.
40 € 15 Ch WC . **Location:** Urban.
Surface: asphalted. 01/03-30/11.
Distance: on the spot 2,7km 500m 500m 100m on the spot.
Remarks: Behind centro commerciale Cityper, along railwayline, monitored parking.

S **Grottammare** 34E2

Briciola di Sole, Contr. Granaro 19. **GPS:** n42,99045 e13,82536.

14 € 15, guests free Ch included. **Location:** Rural.
Surface: gravel/metalled.
01/04-31/10.
Distance: 2,5km sea 5km on the spot 2km.
Remarks: Restaurant with traditional kitchen, located on estate.

S **Jesi** 34D1

Via Alfredo Zannoni. **GPS:** n43,51882 e13,24180.

10 free free. **Location:** Simple, quiet. **Surface:** asphalted.
01/01-31/12.
Distance: 500m centro storico.

Tourist information Jesi:
Area with many vineyards.
Grotte di Frasassi. Caves.

S **Loreto** 34D1

Area Camper Pro Loco, Via Maccari. **GPS:** n43,44125 e13,61491.

65 € 12/24h Chincluded (20x)€ 3/day WC € 1 € 2/8h.
Location: Comfortable. **Surface:** grasstiles.
01/01-31/12.
Distance: 150m 15km.
Remarks: Max. 48h.

S **Loreto** 34D1

Parking P1, Via Benedetto XXV. **GPS:** n43,44129 e13,60756.

6 € 6/day, overnight stay free WC. **Surface:** asphalted.
Distance: 300m 50m.
Remarks: Parking at city wall.

S **Macerata** 34D1

Sferisterio, Via Paladini. **GPS:** n43,29806 e13,45694.
8 € 5 Ch . **Surface:** asphalted. 01/01-31/12.
Distance: 200m 200m.

S **Macerata Feltria** 34C1

Loc. San Gasparre. **GPS:** n43,80098 e12,42886.

4 free ChWC free. **Location:** Rural. **Surface:** metalled.
01/01-31/12.
Distance: 1km on the spot Pizzeria 250m.
Remarks: Along Aspa river, at sports park.

Tourist information Macerata Feltria:
Week market. Tue.

S **Marina di Montemarciano** 34D1

Lungomare Alfredo Cappellini. **GPS:** n43,65936 e13,32780.

40 € 0,70/h Ch (32x)€ 2. **Location:** Simple, noisy.
Surface: grassy. 15/05-15/09.
Distance: 4km 9km 50m pebbled beach 100m.
Remarks: To coast road and railwayline.

S **Marotta** 34D1

Area di Sosta Marotta, Lungomare Colombo 157, Mondolfo.
GPS: n43,76067 e13,15312.

IT

80 € 6,50-14 Ch (80x)€ 2/24h WC included,cold.
Location: Simple. **Surface:** grassy. 01/04-30/09.
Distance: 500m 1,5km 50m on the spot.
Remarks: Between coast road and railwayline.

Matelica 34D1

Porte Capamante, Via Circonvallazione. **GPS**: n43,25917 e13,01083.

6-8 free free. **Location:** Simple. **Surface:** asphalted.
01/01-31/12.
Distance: 200m 200m 200m.

Matelica 34D1

Country House Salomone, Località Salomone 437.
GPS: n43,29635 e13,00031.

40 € 7, free with a meal (16x)included WC at restaurant.
Location: Rural, simple. **Surface:** grassy/gravel.
01/01-31/12.
Distance: on the spot.
Remarks: Beautiful view.

Mergo 34D1

Area Sosta Comunale, Via Colli. **GPS**: n43,47394 e13,03598.

10 free Ch free (8x). **Location:** Simple. **Surface:** concrete.
01/01-31/12.
Distance: 300m.
Remarks: Nearby sports park.

Mondavio 34D1

Via Cappuccini. **GPS**: n43,67744 e12,96165.
10 free Ch free. **Surface:** asphalted. 01/01-31/12.
Distance: 500m 700m.
Remarks: Nearby police station.

Tourist information Mondavio:
Week market. Mo.

Montalto delle Marche 34E2

Via Cuprense. **GPS**: n42,98726 e13,60870.

6 free free. **Surface:** metalled. 01/01-31/12.
Distance: 100m.

Monte San Giusto 34D1

Campo Sportivo, Via Magellano, Villa San Filippo.
GPS: n43,26343 e13,60070.

20 free Ch free. **Location:** Urban. **Surface:** asphalted.
01/01-31/12.
Distance: 1km.
Remarks: Near sports fields, outlet center leather and shoes.

Monte Vidon Corrado 34D1

Viale Trento e Trieste. **GPS**: n43,12205 e13,48381.

5 free Ch free. **Location:** Urban. **Surface:** metalled.
01/01-31/12.
Distance: 200m 200m 500m 450m.

Montecosaro 34E1

Via Martiri della Libertà Ungherese. **GPS**: n43,31779 e13,63653.

30 free Ch free. **Location:** Urban. **Surface:** concrete.
01/01-31/12.
Distance: 100m 100m 100m 50m.

Montefiore dell'Aso 34E1

Piazza Pietro Nenni. **GPS**: n43,04992 e13,75021.

10 free Ch free WC. **Location:** Urban. **Surface:** sand.
01/01-31/12.
Distance: 200m 350m 100m on the spot.

Montefiore dell'Aso 34E1

Agricamper Il Poggio del Belvedere, Contrada Aso no. 11.
GPS: n43,04611 e13,72500.

6 € 8/pp Ch WC included. **Location:** Rural.
Surface: metalled. 01/01-31/12.
Distance: 3,5km.

Montelupone 34D1

Loc. San Firmano. **GPS**: n43,36383 e13,54950.

20 free free. **Location:** Simple. **Surface:** asphalted.
Distance: 500m.
Remarks: Parking sports park.

Montelupone 34D1

Via Allesandro Manzoni. **GPS**: n43,34300 e13,57080.

10 free free. **Location:** Simple. **Surface:** asphalted.
01/01-31/12.
Remarks: Parking city park.

Morro d'Alba 34D1

Area Comunale, Via degli Orti. **GPS**: n43,60198 e13,21263.

30 free free. **Location:** Simple, quiet.
Surface: asphalted.
01/01-31/12.
Distance: 500m.
Remarks: Access with electronic card, Bar Pro Loco or town hall.

Offida 34E2

Via Tommaso Castelli. **GPS**: n42,93689 e13,69180.

3 free free. **Location:** Rural. **Surface:** unpaved.
01/01-31/12.
Distance: 400m 350m 350m.
Remarks: At the city walls.

Pedaso 34E1

Via Martiri della Libertà. **GPS**: n43,09985 e13,84272.
free. **Surface:** asphalted. 01/01-31/12.

Distance: on the spot on the spot 150m.
Remarks: Parking at the beach.

Pesaro 26H3

Via dell Aquedotto. GPS: n43,90842 e12,90097.

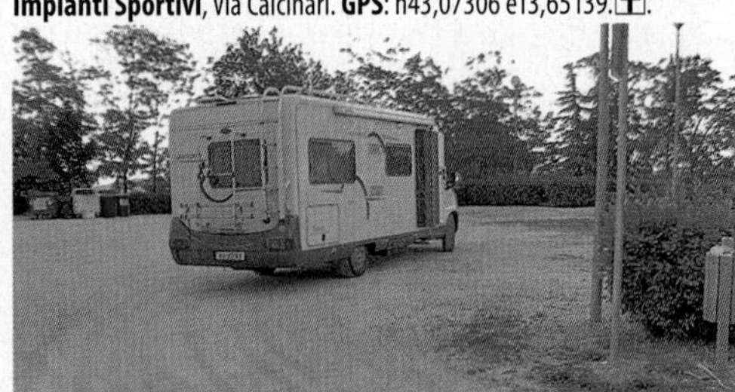

12 free Chfree (12x)€ 1. Location: Urban.
Surface: asphalted. 01/01-31/12.
Distance: 1km 7,5km 800m 1km 50m.

Pesaro 26H3

Waterfront Parking, Via Calata Caio Duilio.
GPS: n43,92244 e12,90657.
20 € 12. Location: Urban. Surface: grassy. 01/01-31/12.
Distance: 300m on the spot on the spot 1km 400m.

Pesaro 26H3

Vallugola Parking, Str. della Vallugola. GPS: n43,96227 e12,78689.
50 € 13,50 € 3 Ch € 3/24h. Location: Rural.
Surface: grassy. 01/01-31/12.
Distance: Pesaro 13,5km 50m 300m.
Remarks: Video surveillance.

Tourist information Pesaro:
Week market. Tue.

Petritoli 34E1

Impianti Sportivi, Via Calcinari. GPS: n43,07306 e13,65139.

10 free ChWCfree. Location: Rural. Surface: sand.
01/01-31/12.
Distance: 1km 900m 900m 900m.
Remarks: At sports park, picnic area, playground.

Piandimeleto 34C1

Via Giacomo Leopardi. GPS: n43,72541 e12,41328.

9 free Chfree. Location: Urban. Surface: grassy.
01/01-31/12.
Distance: 100m on the spot 200m.

Pietrarubbia 34C1

Vulcangas, Via Montefeltresca 107, Ponte Cappuccini.
GPS: n43,80278 e12,36667.

2 free WCfree. Location: Rural. Surface: metalled.
01/01-31/12.
Distance: 200m 350m 300m.

Pievebovigliana 34D2

Via Rancia. GPS: n43,06583 e13,08526.

10 free Chincluded free € 1. Location: Rural.
Surface: asphalted. 01/01-31/12.
Distance: 300m 350m 550m.

Pioraco 34D1

Loc. Buchetto, SS361 km77. GPS: n43,18010 e12,97422.

18 (+20) € 13 (16x) WC included. Location: Rural, comfortable, quiet. Surface: gravel. 01/01-31/12.
Distance: 700m on the spot summer on the spot.

Pollenza 34D1

Contrada Morazzano. GPS: n43,26482 e13,34614.

8 free free. Location: Simple. Surface: asphalted.
01/01-31/12.
Distance: 500m.
Remarks: Nearby elevator to centre, max. 48h.

Porto Recanati 34E1

Area sosta camper Porto Recanati, Viale Scarfiotti, loc. Scossicci.
GPS: n43,44605 e13,65639.

35 € 10-18 Chincluded (8x)€ 2 WC € 1.
Location: Simple. Surface: grassy. 01/01-31/12.
Distance: 500m 3km 50m 200m 1km.
Remarks: Max. 72h, video surveillance, dogs beach.

Porto Recanati 34E1

Karting Club Pista del Conero, Viale Scarfiotti, loc. Scossicci.
GPS: n43,47067 e13,64246.

80 € 25/24h Ch (80x) WCincluded € 1 free.
Location: Simple, noisy. Surface: gravel. 01/04-30/09.
Distance: 100m 200m.

Porto Recanati 34E1

Campeggio Club Adriatico, Via Scossicci, Scossicci.
GPS: n43,46393 e13,64642.
€ 17-30 Ch WC included. Surface: grassy.
09/04-29/09.
Distance: on the spot on the spot on the spot on the spot.

Porto San Giorgio 34E1

La Perla Adriatico, Via San Martino 13. GPS: n43,16400 e13,80836.
75 € 15/20 Ch WC included,cold . Surface: unpaved.
01/04-30/09.
Distance: beach 200m 300m.
Remarks: Shuttle bus.

Potenza Picena 34E1

Via Togliatti, Porto Potenza Picena. GPS: n43,36167 e13,69306.

45 € 7/24h, € 10/48h, € 15/72h € 2 Ch (12x)€ 2 WC against payment. Location: Urban. Surface: asphalted.
01/01-31/12.
Distance: 200m 600m 200m 200m.
Remarks: Thursday market.

Recanati 34D1

Camperclub Recanati, Viale Giovanni XXIII.
GPS: n43,40245 e13,55777.

25 free (22x)free. Location: Urban, simple.
Surface: asphalted. 01/01-31/12.
Distance: 500m.

San Benedetto del Tronto 34E2

Sosta Camper 43° Parallelo, Via Domenico Bruni.
GPS: n42,96677 e13,87670.
40 € 15 Ch € 3 . Surface: asphalted.
Distance: on the spot sandy beach 100m 80m.

San Benedetto del Tronto 34E2

Viale dello Sport. GPS: n42,92312 e13,89527.

70 € 7, Jul/Aug € 10 Chincluded € 2. Surface: asphalted.
Distance: 4,3km 500m on the spot.
Remarks: Along railwayline, under viaduct.

San Ginesio 34D1

Via Ciarlatini. GPS: n43,10945 e13,31801.

8 free Chfree. Surface: gravel. 01/01-31/12.
Distance: 200m 200m 200m 1km.

IT

Remarks: Swimming pool 100m.

S San Leo 34C1

Via Michele Rosa. **GPS:** n43,89871 e12,34950.

20 free Ch free. **Surface:** asphalted. 01/01-31/12
festivities.
Distance: 500m on the spot.

S San Severino Marche 34D1

P7, Viale Mazzini. **GPS:** n43,22757 e13,18836.

12 free free (12x)€ 0,50/4h. **Location:** Simple, quiet.
Surface: asphalted. 01/01-31/12.
Distance: 800m.
Remarks: Parking sports park.

S Sant'Agata Feltria 34C1

Piazzale Europa. **GPS:** n43,86386 e12,20549.

40 free, hollidays € 8/24h (6x)free. **Location:** Rural.
Surface: asphalted. 01/01-31/12.
Distance: 100m 300m 250m 300m.

S Sarnano 34D2

Via Corridoni. **GPS:** n43,03444 e13,29972.

15 free ChWCfree. **Surface:** asphalted. 01/01-31/12.
Distance: 100m 100m 100m 50m.
Remarks: Thursday market.

S Sassoferrato 34D1

Via Raffaello Sanzio. **GPS:** n43,43122 e12,85471.

7 free free (6x)€ 1/day. **Location:** Simple.
Surface: asphalted. 01/01-31/12.
Distance: 500m.

S Senigallia 34D1

Via F. Podesti 234, SS16, Senigallia-sud. **GPS:** n43,70483 e13,23764.

14 € 10 free. **Location:** Simple, noisy. **Surface:** asphalted.
01/01-31/12.
Distance: 3km 3,3km 150m.
Remarks: Along busy road, next to petrol station, max. 48h.

S Tolentino 34D1

Via Miguel Hernández Gilabert. **GPS:** n43,21046 e13,29613.
10 free Ch. **Location:** Urban. **Surface:** asphalted.
01/01-31/12.
Distance: 1km on the spot 550m 550m on the spot.

S Tolentino 34D1

Viale Foro Boario. **GPS:** n43,20773 e13,28784.

15 free Chfree. **Location:** Urban. **Surface:** asphalted.
01/01-31/12.
Distance: 200m 200m 300m on the spot.
Remarks: At swimming pool.

S Urbania 34C1

Area camper Barco, Loc. Barco Ducale Colonia.
GPS: n43,67916 e12,51277.
65 free Ch free. **Location:** Rural. **Surface:** gravel/sand.
01/01-31/12.
Distance: 1km 1km 1km 1km.
Remarks: Biking trail, behind former summer residence of dukes of Urbania.

S Urbania 34C1

Piazzale Fosso del Maltempo, Viale Michelangelo.
GPS: n43,66482 e12,52191.

50 free Ch free. **Location:** Urban, noisy.
Surface: asphalted. 01/01-31/12.
Distance: 500m 700m 850m 250m.
Remarks: At sports park.

Tourist information Urbania:
Week market. Thu.

S Urbino 34C1

Via Pablo Neruda. **GPS:** n43,73333 e12,62722.

10 free Chfree. **Location:** Rural. **Surface:** asphalted.
01/01-31/12.
Distance: historical centre 2,5km on the spot.

Remarks: At sports centre, shuttle bus to city centre.

S Urbino 34C1

Corte della Miniera, Via Miniera, 10. **GPS:** n43,78336 e12,59091.
5 guests free Ch WC. **Location:** Rural.
Surface: grassy/gravel. 01/01-31/12.
Distance: Urbino 11km on the spot.

Tourist information Urbino:
Week market. Sa.

S Urbisaglia 34D1

Abbadia di Fiastra, P4. **GPS:** n43,22111 e13,40722.

50 € 15/24h Ch free WC . **Location:** Rural.
Surface: metalled. 01/01-31/12.
Distance: 4km 50m.
Remarks: Parking monastery, monitored parking, archaeological park Urbs Salvia 3km, hiking area.

S Visso 34D2

Largo Gregorio XIII. **GPS:** n42,93139 e13,09141.

15 free Ch € 0,80/h. **Location:** Rural. **Surface:** asphalted.
01/01-31/12.
Distance: 800m 350m 350m.

Lazio

S Acquapendente 34C2

Agriturismo Buonomore, SS Cassia Km 130.
GPS: n42,73367 e11,88361.

8 € 15-20, Aug € 25 Ch WC included
Location: Rural, simple, quiet. **Surface:** grassy/gravel.
01/01-31/12.
Distance: 3km on the spot.
Remarks: Swimming pool incl.

S Acquapendente 34C2

Via Campo Boario. **GPS:** n42,74203 e11,86240.

20 free Chfree. **Location:** Urban.
Surface: asphalted/metalled. 01/01-31/12.
Distance: 250m 250m.
Remarks: At sports park.

S Albano Laziale 34D3

Piazza Guerucci, Via Riccardo Lombardi. **GPS:** n41,73206 e12,65213.

IT

8 free Chfree. **Location:** Simple, noisy.
Surface: asphalted.
Distance: 1km train > Rome 55min.
Remarks: Next to post office and sports park.

S Amatrice 34D2

AgriCamper Amatrice, Località Retrosi. **GPS**: n42,62349 e13,31788.
20 € 10 Ch included. **Location:** Isolated. **Surface:** gravel.
01/01-31/12.
Remarks: Located in national nature reserve Gran Sasso.

S Bolsena 34C2

Guadetto, Via della Chiusa. **GPS**: n42,63604 e11,98695.

60 € 15/24h Ch included WC . **Location:** Rural.
Surface: grassy/sand. 01/01-31/12.
Distance: 1km 10m 300m 1,5km on the spot on the spot.
Remarks: Bread-service, tuesday market.

Bolsena 34C2

Via Santa Maria. **GPS**: n42,63898 e11,98562.

50 € 5/12h, € 10/24h. **Location:** Urban, simple.
Surface: asphalted. 01/01-31/12.
Distance: 800m 100m on the spot 400m 400m 100m on the spot on the spot.

S Bolsena 34C2

Agricampeggio Le Calle, Via Cassia km 111,200.
GPS: n42,63029 e11,99716.
€ 15-19, incl. 2 pers, dog € 3 Ch WC included.
Location: Rural. **Surface:** grassy. 01/04-01/11.
Distance: 1km on the spot on the spot on the spot.
Remarks: Sale of wines.

Tourist information Bolsena:
Citadel and ramparts.

S Bracciano 34C3

Le Mimose, Via del Lago 25. **GPS**: n42,10856 e12,17893.

50 € 14/24h Chincluded (40x)€ 3/24h € 0,50.
Location: Rural, comfortable, quiet. **Surface:** gravel.
01/01-31/12.
Distance: 800m Lago di Bracciano 250m 150m 800m 200m.

S Capodimonte 34C2

Temporanea. **GPS**: n42,55979 e11,88714.

50 € 10/24h € 3 Ch. **Location:** Urban, simple, quiet.
Surface: grassy. 01/01-31/12.
Distance: 2km on the spot.
Remarks: At lake Bolsena, check in at bar.

S Cassino 35B1

Parking Europa, Via Agnone 5. **GPS**: n41,48289 e13,83750.

20 € 13,50-16,50, 2 pers.incl Service € 2,50 Ch € 3 WC € 1 € 4/day. **Location:** Rural. **Surface:** grassy/gravel.
01/01-31/12.
Distance: 800m 4km 1km 1km 1,5km.
Remarks: Service passerby € 7.

S Castel di Tora 34D3

Via Turano, SP34. **GPS**: n42,21362 e12,96888.
15 € 15/24h Ch WC included. **Surface:** gravel.
01/01-31/12.
Distance: 1km on the spot 250m.
Remarks: At Turano lake.

Castel Gandolfo 34D3

Parcheggio Bus Lago Albano, Via Spiaggia del Lago.
GPS: n41,75797 e12,65359.

17 € 10/24h. **Location:** Rural, simple, noisy. **Surface:** metalled.
01/01-31/12.
Distance: on the spot on the spot 800m > Rome.
Remarks: At lake Albano.

S Civita Castellana 34C3

Via Terni. **GPS**: n42,29905 e12,41520.

+50 free. **Location:** Simple. **Surface:** asphalted.
01/01-31/12.
Distance: 500m 50m.
Remarks: At cemetery.

Tourist information Civita Castellana:
Palazzo Farnese, Caprarola. Pentagonal country house, accessed by winding staircase.

S Colle di Tora 34D3

Via Maria Letizia Giuliani. **GPS**: n42,20898 e12,94915.

25 € 10/24h Ch WCincluded. **Location:** Rural, simple, quiet. **Surface:** gravel. 01/01-31/12.
Distance: on the spot on the spot on the spot.
Remarks: At Turano lake, pay at restaurant.

S Colleferro 34D3

Viale Europa. **GPS**: n41,72540 e13,00989.
5 free Chfree. **Location:** Urban. **Surface:** metalled.
01/01-31/12.
Distance: on the spot 5km on the spot 500m train > Rome.
Remarks: Next to swimming pool.

Tourist information Colleferro:
Anagni. Region with number of old settlements.

S Farfa in Sabina 34D3

Abbazia di Santa Maria, SP41A. **GPS**: n42,22166 e12,71603.

20 free Chfree. **Location:** Rural, simple, isolated.
Surface: gravel. 01/01-31/12.
Distance: 4,7km.

S Gaeta 35B1

Playa Colorada, Località S.Agostino, SS 213, Sperlonga>Gaeta.
GPS: n41,22812 e13,50281.

60 € 25-30, 2 pers.incl Ch WCincluded € 1 € 0,50/h.
Location: Rural, comfortable, central. **Surface:** gravel.
01/04-30/09.
Distance: 50m bar/restaurant 200m.
Remarks: Shuttle to Gaeta, market Wednesday.

S Gaeta 35B1

Sosta Camper Internationale, Via Flacca km 20.500.
GPS: n41,23598 e13,49045.

30 € 20-25 Ch WCincluded € 1. **Location:** Rural.
Surface: gravel. 01/01-31/12.
Distance: on the spot on the spot.
Remarks: Monitored parking.

S Gaeta 35B1

Copacabana Beach, Via flacca Km 20.350, S.agostino Gaeta.
GPS: n41,23743 e13,48781.

IT

18 € 25-30, 4 pers.incl € 0,50 Ch WC € 0,50 € 1.
Location: Rural, simple. **Surface:** gravel/sand.
01/04-30/09.
Distance: 6km on the spot on the spot.
Remarks: Shuttle to Gaeta.

S Gaeta 35B1

Loremar, Via Flacca, km 21,200. **GPS**: n41,23240 e13,49525.
6 € 20-30 Ch included WC . **Location:** Rural.
Surface: gravel. 01/01-31/12.
Distance: on the spot 200m.
Remarks: Monitored parking 24/24.

S Gaeta 35B1

Oasi Camper Service, Via Flacca km. 20,643, Loc. riviera di Ponente.
GPS: n41,23583 e13,49048.

22 € 25-35 Ch WC included € 1. **Location:** Simple.
Surface: gravel. 01/04-01/10.
Distance: 6km 50m 500m.

S Gradoli 34C2

Parcheggio camper San Magno, Strada di Gradoli, SP114 km 6+137.
GPS: n42,59925 e11,86547.

50 € 15 Ch included. **Location:** Comfortable, isolated, quiet. **Surface:** grassy. 01/01-31/12.
Distance: 7km on the spot 500m.
Remarks: At lake Bolsena, discount longer stays.

S Latina 35A1

Area Camper Alta Marea, Strada Lungomare 3253, SP39, Loc. Foce Verde. **GPS**: n41,41043 e12,86008.

91 € 15 Ch WC included € 0,50.
Location: Rural, comfortable, quiet. **Surface:** grassy.
01/04-30/09.
Distance: on the spot 50m on the spot 200m.

S Latina 35A1

Museo di Piana delle Orme, Strada Migliara 43 Mezza.
GPS: n41,44452 e12,98479.

25 free Ch. **Location:** Rural, simple, quiet. **Surface:** gravel.
01/01-31/12.
Distance: Latina 10km 2km.
Remarks: At museum.

S Leonessa 34D2

Via Amor della Patria 21. **GPS**: n42,56436 e12,96172.

50 free Ch free. **Location:** Urban. **Surface:** asphalted.
01/01-31/12 Market day.
Distance: 500m 500m 500m 300m.

S Lubriano 34C2

Parco Paime, Piazza Palme. **GPS**: n42,63500 e12,10512.

17 € 5/24h Ch (36x) WC included.
Location: Comfortable, quiet.
Surface: grasstiles. 01/01-31/12.
Distance: 1km on the spot.
Remarks: Nights closed with barrier.

S Lunghezza 34D3

Camper Club Antichi Casali, Via Lunghezzina 302/a.
GPS: n41,93039 e12,70454.

40 € 15/24h Ch WC included.
Location: Rural, comfortable, isolated, quiet. **Surface:** gravel.
01/01-31/12.
Distance: 3km 5km Rome 20min.
Remarks: Monitored parking 24/24, shuttle bus.

S Lunghezza 34D3

Camper Club Mira Lago Roma, Via Lunghezzina 75.
GPS: n41,93159 e12,67642.

60 € 18/24h Ch WC € 0,50 € 4 included.
Location: Rural, comfortable, isolated, quiet. **Surface:** grassy.
01/01-31/12.
Distance: 700m on the spot on the spot on the spot on the spot on the spot.
Remarks: At 2 small lakes, service passerby € 5.

S Montalto di Castro 34C3

Area di Sosta La Pineta. GPS: n42,36595 e11,49444.
€ 15-28/24h, dog € 1 Ch € 3 WC included € 1 .
Location: Rural. **Surface:** grassy. 01/04-30/09.
Distance: sea 100m 1km.
Remarks: Max. 72h, picnic and barbecue place, playground.

S Montalto di Castro 34C3

Il Pioppo, Strada delle Murelle. **GPS**: n42,31271 e11,60526.
€ 12/24h Ch € 2/24h WC included € 1. **Location:** Rural.
Surface: grassy. 01/01-31/12.
Distance: Montalto di Castro 5km 400m.

S Montalto di Castro 34C3

Via Arbea, Marina di Montalto di Castro.
GPS: n42,32981 e11,57699.

50 € 7,50/day, overnight stay free Ch free. **Location:** Rural, simple, quiet. **Surface:** grassy/gravel. 01/01-31/12.
Distance: 250m 200m 200m 200m.
Remarks: Shady, thursday market.

S Montalto di Castro 34C3

Via Torre Marina, Marina di Montalto di Castro.
GPS: n42,32137 e11,59015.

64 free, 01/06-15/09 8-20h € 7,50 Ch included.
Location: Rural, simple. **Surface:** gravel. 01/01-31/12.
Distance: 500m 200m 400m 300m.

S Montefiascone 34C2

Cantina di Montefiascone, Via Grilli 2. **GPS**: n42,53346 e12,04293.

30 free Ch free. **Location:** Urban, comfortable, noisy.
Surface: metalled. 01/01-31/12.
Distance: 1km.

S Montefiascone 34C2

Agricamper Bella Cima, Strada Limitone.
GPS: n42,52241 e12,00767.

18 € 15/24h Ch included. **Surface:** gravel.
01/01-31/12.
Distance: 4km 4km 4km.

IT

Remarks: Swimming pool.

S Nettuno 35A1

Area Sosta L'Ippocampo, Via Palestrina 9.
GPS: n41,47354 e12,68916.

50 € 15 Ch WC included. **Location:** Rural, simple, quiet. **Surface:** gravel. 01/01-31/12.
Distance: 3km 3km.

S Oriolo Romano 34C3

Viale degli Artigiani. **GPS:** n42,16699 e12,13902.

3 free free. **Location:** Simple. **Surface:** asphalted. 01/01-31/12.
Distance: 850m on the spot station 600m Roma-Viterbo.

S Pescia Romana 34B3

Area La Pineta, Loc. Marina di Pescia Romana.
GPS: n42,36552 e11,49389.

50 € 10-22 Ch included € 3 € 1. **Location:** Rural, comfortable, quiet. **Surface:** grassy. Easter-30/09.
Distance: Pescia Romana 5km 100m 100m.
Remarks: Bread-service, monday market.

S Rieti 34D2

Via Fonte Cottorella. **GPS:** n42,39548 e12,86463.

10 free . **Location:** Urban, noisy. **Surface:** asphalted. 01/01-31/12.
Distance: historical center 100m 700m.

S Roma 34D3

Area Attrezzata per Camper LGP Roma, Via Casilina 700, Rome (Roma). **GPS:** n41,87595 e12,55515.

200 € 18/<8m, € 25/8><10m, € 35/10><18m + tourist tax € 2/pp Ch against payment included. **Location:** Urban, luxurious, central, quiet.
Surface: grassy.
01/01-31/12.
Distance: 100m 100m bus service to city centre day and night.
Remarks: Accessory shop, trailer/additonal car € 15 on separate parking € 7, repairs. Exit 18 ring road (G.R.A.), follow Roma centro, ± 4km dir centre, company is on the left side of the road, turning after 2nd lights.

S Roma 34D3

Prato Smeraldo, Via Ardeatina/Via di Tor Pagnotta 424, Rome (Roma).
GPS: n41,80970 e12,52857.

16 € 14 Ch € 2/24h included.
Location: Motorway, simple, noisy. **Surface:** grassy/metalled.
01/01-31/12, 24/24h.
Distance: on the spot on the spot on the spot.
Remarks: Service passerby € 5. Exit 25 ring road (G.R.A.), second light to the right, Via di Tor Pagnotta.

S Roma 34D3

Le Terrazze, Via di Fioranello 170, Rome (Roma).
GPS: n41,79250 e12,54083.

40 € 20, max. 4 pers.incl Ch (40x)included.
Location: Simple, quiet. **Surface:** metalled. 01/01-31/12.
Distance: 750m 1km on the spot on the spot.
Remarks: Video surveillance, car rental, excursions. Exit 25 ring road (G.R.A.), dir Santuario Divino Amore.

S Roma 34D3

Parcheggio IAT, Air terminal Ostiense, Piazza G. da Verrazzano 9, Zone Mercati Generali, Rome (Roma). **GPS:** n41,86931 e12,48944.

€ 1,50, at least € 6, € 27/24h Chincluded € 3,65/24h.
Location: Urban, simple, central, noisy. **Surface:** asphalted.
01/01-31/12.
Distance: metro 1km.
Remarks: Motorhome and Coach Parking.

S Roma 34D3

Area Sosta Camper Park Colombo, Via C. Colombo 170, Rome (Roma).
GPS: n41,86236 e12,49713.
€ 20 Ch Service € 5. 01/01-31/12.
Distance: 100m.
Remarks: Monitored parking 24/24.

S Roma 34D3

Parkbus Roma, Piazzale 12 Ottobre 1492, Rome (Roma).
GPS: n41,86931 e12,48944.
€ 20 Chincluded € 3 WC. **Location:** Urban.
Surface: asphalted. 01/01-31/12.
Distance: on the spot 500m 300m 200m.
Remarks: Monitored parking, bicycle rental.

S Roma 34D3

Spazio Ardeatina, Via Ardeatina, 933, Rome (Roma).
GPS: n41,79808 e12,53556.
€ 20 Ch included. **Surface:** asphalted.
Distance: Rome 11km on the spot on the spot 450m on the spot.
Remarks: Monitored parking 24/24.

Tourist information Rome (Roma):

Città del Vaticano. Domicile of the pope. Independent state since 1929.

A.P.T. (Azienda di Promozione Turistica), Via Parigi, 11. Capital of the country, a lot of curiosities in the old town centre. Roma Archeologica Card: 7-days ticket € 27,50, free entrance to Roman National Museum, Colosseum, Palatine, Baths of Caracalla, Tomb of Cecilia Metella and Villa of the Quintili.

Piazza del Campidoglio.

Palatino, Via di S. Gregorio, 30. Archeological site. 9h-sunset. € 16, incl. Colosseum.

Subiaco.

Musei Vaticani, Città del Vaticano. Paintings and art objects.

Basilica di San Pietro. Basilica with Sistine Chapel.

Colosseo, Piazza del Colosseo. Colosseum, anfiteatro, the most important monument of ancient Rome. 9h-sunset. € 12, entrance Palatine Hill incl.

Forum Romanum, Via dei Fori Imperiali. Novel Forum, the political, economic, and religious centre of ancient Rome. 9h-sunset.

Pantheon, Piazza della Rotonda. Church of Santa Maria ad Martyres. 9-19.30h, Su 9-18h, holidays 9-13h, Mass Sa 17, Su 10.30h, 16.30h. free.

Città del Vaticano. Pope blesses the mob for the window of the library. Su 12h.

Piazza di Spagna.

S San Felice Circeo 35B1

Circeo Camper, Viale Europa 1. **GPS:** n41,24095 e13,10426.

50 € 23-33, 4 pers. incl Ch € 3/24h WC € 1 € 7 included. **Location:** Rural, luxurious, central. **Surface:** grassy. 01/04-20/09.
Distance: 100m 10m 10m 100m 100m.

S San Felice Circeo 35B1

CirceMed, Via Molella 2/A. **GPS:** n41,25684 e13,12089.

60 € 18-27 Ch (50x)WC € 1 € 1 € 3 included.
Location: Rural, comfortable, quiet. **Surface:** grassy.
01/04-30/09.
Distance: 500m 200m 200m on the spot.

Tourist information San Felice Circeo:

Tue-morning.

Terracina 35B1

Via Amerigo Vespucci. **GPS:** n41,28528 e13,25450.

20 € 12. **Location:** Urban, simple. **Surface:** asphalted.
Distance: on the spot 100m on the spot 200m 300m.

S Tivoli 34D3

Via Aquaregna. **GPS:** n41,95841 e12,80465.

IT

30 free Ch. **Location:** Urban, simple, central, quiet. **Surface:** asphalted. 01/01-31/12 Wed, market.
Distance: 400m.
Remarks: Along the Aniene river.

Tourist information Tivoli:
Villa d'Este. Country house with gardens and fountains, 16th century. Villa Adriana. Roman villa.

S Trevignano Romano 34C3

Blue Lake Camper, Via della Rena. **GPS**: n42,15877 e12,22411.
€ 15-20 Ch WC. **Surface:** gravel. 01/01-31/12.
Distance: on the spot on the spot.
Remarks: At the lake.

S Tuscania 34C2

Via Nazario Sauro. **GPS**: n42,42217 e11,87520.

12 free free. **Location:** Urban, simple.
Surface: grasstiles/metalled. 01/01-31/12.
Distance: 250m 250m 250m.

S Velletri 34D3

Via del Camelieto. **GPS**: n41,69314 e12,78264.
9 free Ch. **Location:** Urban. **Surface:** metalled. 01/01-31/12 Thursday.
Distance: 500m 800m.

S Villa San Giovanni in Tuscia 34C3

Viale Europa. **GPS**: n42,28160 e12,05282.

free. **Location:** Rural, simple, quiet. **Surface:** asphalted. 01/01-31/12.
Distance: 200m.

S Viterbo 34C2

Agricampeggio Paliano, Strada Pian di Tortora.
GPS: n42,39301 e12,08601.
100 € 15, 2 pers.incl, extra pers € 5 Ch WC.
Surface: grassy.
Distance: city centre 2km.
Remarks: Video surveillance.

S Viterbo 34C2

Piazza Mariano Romiti, loc. Belcolle. **GPS**: n42,40897 e12,11049.

50 free free. **Location:** Urban, simple. **Surface:** asphalted. 01/01-31/12.
Distance: Lazise centre 300m on the spot.

Remarks: At station.

S Viterbo 34C2

Bed&breakfast Axia, Strada Procoio 2/C.
GPS: n42,41157 e12,05061.

5 € 18 Ch € 3 included. **Location:** Rural.
Surface: grassy. 01/01-31/12.
Distance: Viterbo 4km.
Remarks: 10% discount at entrance Terme dei Papi (900m), bus to Viterbo € 5.

Viterbo 34C2

Agriturismo Monteparadiso, Loc. Monterazzano.
GPS: n42,44161 e12,03062.

5 guests free. **Location:** Simple, isolated. **Surface:** gravel. 01/01-31/12.
Distance: 7km.
Remarks: Near Termale Bullicame and Terme dei Papi.

Viterbo 34C2

Terme dei Papi, Strada Montarone. **GPS**: n42,41487 e12,06351.

100 guests free. **Surface:** grassy/gravel. 01/01-31/12.
Distance: 3km.
Remarks: At Terme dei Papi.

S Vitorchiano 34C2

SP23 Via della Teverina. **GPS**: n42,47152 e12,17212.

10 free Ch. **Surface:** asphalted. 01/01-31/12.
Distance: 500m.

Umbria

S Amelia 34C2

Piazzale del Mercato, Via Rimembranze.
GPS: n42,55200 e12,41880.
10 free Ch WC free. **Location:** Urban. **Surface:** asphalted. 01/01-31/12 Mo-morning (market).
Distance: 50m 50m 50m 300m.

S Assisi 34C2

Via Giosuè Borsi, loc. Santa Maria degli Angeli.
GPS: n43,05972 e12,58747.

€ 18/24h, € 1,80/h Ch. **Surface:** asphalted. 01/01-31/12.
Distance: 2km bus > Assisi 20min (retour € 1,80).

Assisi 34C2

Area San Vittorino, Via San vittorino. **GPS**: n43,07848 e12,60229.

30 € 14/24h, € 2/h. **Surface:** asphalted. 01/01-31/12.
Distance: 500m.
Remarks: Convento di San Francesco 1km.

Assisi 34C2

Viale Vittorio Emanuele II/SS147. **GPS**: n43,06864 e12,61420.

10 € 20/24h. **Surface:** gravel. 01/01-31/12.
Distance: city centre 100m.

S Bevagna 34D2

Piazza dell'Accoglienza, Via Raggiolo. **GPS**: n42,93417 e12,60639.

50 free Ch WC free. **Location:** Urban. **Surface:** gravel. 01/01-31/12.
Distance: 100m 100m 100m on the spot.

S Borghetto 34C1

Via Pontile. **GPS**: n43,18415 e12,02372.

4 free free. **Surface:** asphalted. 01/01-31/12.
Distance: 150m 100m.
Remarks: At lake Trasimeno.

S Cannara 34C2

Via Giaime Pintor, Loc. Casone. **GPS**: n42,99272 e12,57840.

20 free Chfree. **Location:** Urban. **Surface:** asphalted.
01/01-31/12.
Distance: 300m 600m 300m 500m on the spot.
Remarks: At sports park XXV Aprile, cycle routes.

Tourist information Cannara:
Assisi. Historical city.

S Cascia 34D2

Piazzale Papa Leone XIII, Via della Molinella.
GPS: n42,71968 e13,01605.

14 € 8/24h Chincluded (8x)€ 0,50/2h. **Surface:** asphalted.
01/01-31/12 Service: winter.
Distance: 300m 300m 300m 100m 100m.
Remarks: Escalator to city centre.

S Cascia 34D2

SS Discascia. **GPS**: n42,72139 e13,01778.
20 free . **Surface:** gravel. 01/01-31/12.
Distance: 1km.
Remarks: Next to petrol station.

Castelluccio di Norcia 34D2

Pian Grande, SP477. **GPS**: n42,80045 e13,18947.

25 free. **Location:** Rural. **Surface:** grassy. 01/01-31/12.
Distance: Castelluccio 5km.
Remarks: Parco Nazionale dei Monti Sibilini.

S Castiglione del Lago 34C2

Viale Divisione Partigiani Garibaldi. **GPS**: n43,12389 e12,05054.

50 € 12 Ch included.
Location: Rural. **Surface:** grassy. 01/01-31/12.
Distance: 800m on the spot 500m 800m 500m.
Remarks: At lake Trasimeno.

S Città di Castello 34C1

Piazzale E. Ferri, Viale Nazario Sauro. **GPS**: n43,45892 e12,23465.
25 free € 1/100liter Ch. **Location:** Urban.
Surface: asphalted. 01/01-31/12.
Distance: 300m 1,5km on the spot 1km 200m.
Remarks: Escalator to city centre.

S Città di Castello 34C1

La Fontana del Boschetto, Via Aretina 38. **GPS**: n43,45737 e12,22882.
20 € 15/24h Ch included WC.
Location: Motorway. **Surface:** unpaved.
01/01-31/12.
Distance: 2km on the spot on the spot 2km on the spot.
Remarks: Free shuttle.

S Ferentillo 34D2

Loc. Precetto, Via delle Macchie. **GPS**: n42,61802 e12,79347.
5 free Chfree. **Location:** Urban. **Surface:** asphalted.
01/01-31/12.
Distance: 200m 350m 700m on the spot.

S Ficulle 34C2

Parco Cittadino, Via Orvieto SR 71. **GPS**: n42,83044 e12,06828.

25 free Chfree WC. **Surface:** gravel.
01/01-31/12 events (01/07-31/08).
Distance: 500m 10km 1km 500m 200m.

S Gualdo Cattaneo 34C2

Parco Acquarossa, Via Bonifacio 6. **GPS**: n42,89168 e12,53591.
50 € 8 Ch WC included.
Location: Rural. **Surface:** gravel. 01/01-31/12.
Distance: on the spot on the spot 1km.
Remarks: Excursions, regional products.

S Gualdo Tadino 34D1

Via Lucatonii. **GPS**: n43,23193 e12,78019.

20 free Chfree. **Location:** Urban. **Surface:** asphalted.
01/01-31/12 Thu (market).
Distance: 500m on the spot 600m 200m.
Remarks: Free shuttle.

S Gubbio 34C1

Camperclub Gubbio, Via del Bottagnone.
GPS: n43,35000 e12,56389.

80 € 5 Chincluded (8x)€ 1/2h.
Surface: asphalted. 01/01-31/12.
Distance: historical centre 1,5km 100m 200m shuttle to centre 500m.
Remarks: Video surveillance, Teatro Romano 500m.

S Monte Castello di Vibio 34C2

Via Bartolomeo Jacopo della Rovere. **GPS**: n42,84168 e12,35055.

10 free Chfree. **Surface:** gravel. 01/01-31/12.
Distance: 350m 50m.

S Montefalco 34D2

Via G. Pascoli. **GPS**: n42,89230 e12,64791.

25 € 5,50/24h Ch WC. **Location:** Rural, simple, quiet.
Surface: grasstiles. 01/01-31/12.
Distance: 100m 400m 300m.

S Montone 34C1

Via Aldo Bologni. **GPS**: n43,36346 e12,32499.
€ 10/24h Ch . **Surface:** asphalted. 01/01-31/12.
Distance: 200m 250m.
Remarks: At sports park.

S Orvieto 34C2

Area Sosta Camper Battistelli Renzo, Strada della Direttissima, Piazza delle Pace. **GPS**: n42,72562 e12,12736.

50 € 18/day Ch WC included.
Location: Urban. **Surface:** metalled. 01/01-31/12.
Distance: funicular (retour € 1,60) 5 min 2,4km 50m pizzeria 50m.
Remarks: Monitored parking.

Tourist information Orvieto:
U.I.A.T. (Ufficio Informazioni e di Accoglienza Turistica), Piazza Duomo, 24. City on volcanic plateau.
Del Crocifisso del Tufo. Ruins of Etruscan city.

S Panicale 34C2

Area Camper, Viale della Repubblica. **GPS**: n43,02806 e12,10222.

8 € 8/24h € 0,50/180liter Ch € 0,50/kWh.
Surface: grasstiles. 01/01-31/12.
Distance: 100m 100m 50m.
Remarks: Max. 72h.

S Passignano sul Trasimeno 34C1

Airone Area Camper, Lungolago Giappesi.
GPS: n43,18445 e12,14526.

18 € 16-22/24h 2 pers. incl Ch WC € 0,50 included.
Location: Comfortable. **Surface:** grassy.
01/04-31/10.
Distance: 500m beach 150m on the spot 200m 200m.
Remarks: At lake Trasimeno.

S Passignano sul Trasimeno 34C1

Via Europa, SS75bis, km 35,8. **GPS**: n43,18509 e12,14348.

IT

12 € 1,50/h, 20-8h free liter h WC. **Location:** Urban, simple, noisy. **Surface:** asphalted.
01/01-31/12.
Distance: 400m 200m 100m 150m on the spot.
Remarks: At lake Trasimeno.

Perugia 34C2

Il Bove, Via Giovanni Ruggia. **GPS:** n43,09810 e12,38386.

50 € 5/12h, € 18/24h Ch included WC.
Location: Urban. **Surface:** asphalted. 01/01-31/12.
Distance: 1,5km 500m on the spot 100m 200m on the spot.
Remarks: Parking police station, video surveillance, playground.

Tourist information Perugia:
Palazzo dei Priori.
Tue.

San Gemini 34D2

Via della Libertà. **GPS:** n42,61200 e12,54372.

16 € 10/24h Ch WC. **Surface:** metalled.
01/01-31/12.
Distance: 300m 100m 200m.

Sant'Anatolia di Narco 34D2

Purchetta, SP209. **GPS:** n42,73599 e12,83598.
8 free. **Location:** Rural. **Surface:** grassy.
01/01-31/12.
Distance: 900m on the spot on the spot 200m Spoleto/Norcia.

Scheggia e Pascelupo 34D1

Camper Scheggia, Via Campo Sportivo. **GPS:** n43,40007 e12,66674.
€ 12/24h Ch included € 2. **Surface:** gravel.
01/01-31/12.
Distance: 450m 500m.

Spello 34D2

Via Centrale Umbra. **GPS:** n42,99371 e12,66730.

70 € 8/24h Ch. **Location:** Rural. **Surface:** asphalted.
01/01-31/12.
Distance: 500m 1,1km 500m 500m on the spot.
Remarks: Parking sports park.

Spello 34D2

Terme Francescane Village, Via Fonte Citerna.
GPS: n43,00619 e12,62116.
30 € 18-35 Ch € 3 WC included. **Location:** Rural.
Surface: gravel. 01/01-31/12.
Distance: Spello 6km 2,5km.

Spoleto 34D2

Parcheggio Ponciano, Via del Tiro a Segno.
GPS: n42,73687 e12,74212.

20 € 1/h, € 8/24h. **Surface:** gravel. 01/01-31/12.
Distance: 500m 500m 500m.
Remarks: Escalator to city centre.

Spoleto 34D2

Via dei Filosofi. **GPS:** n42,74619 e12,73214.

20 free free. **Location:** Urban. **Surface:** gravel.
01/01-31/12.
Distance: 800m 300m 300m on the spot.

Tourist information Spoleto:
Montefalco. Village worth seeing, parking outside village, narrow streets.
Ponte delle Torri. Aqueduct, 14th century.
Tue, Fri.
Art festival. 01/06-31/07.

Terni 34D2

Piazzale Felice Fatati, SR209. **GPS:** n42,55690 e12,72006.

free Ch € 3. **Location:** Rural. **Surface:** unpaved.
01/01-31/12.
Distance: Terni 7km on the spot on the spot.
Remarks: Along river, nearby waterfalls.

Terni 34D2

Via Lombardo Radice. **GPS:** n42,56634 e12,63577.

€ 4/48h € 0,50 Ch included. **Location:** Urban, noisy.
Surface: asphalted. 01/01-31/12.
Distance: 50m 50m 500m 250m.
Remarks: At cemetery.

Todi 34C2

Area Porta Orvietana, Viale di Montesanto.
GPS: n42,78120 e12,40168.

16 € 15,40/24h, € 3/h Ch. **Surface:** asphalted. Sa-morning market.
Remarks: Elevator (free) to centre.

Torgiano 34C2

Via Perugia. **GPS:** n43,02917 e12,43833.

10 free € 0,05/1liter Ch. **Location:** Urban.
Surface: asphalted. 01/01-31/12.
Distance: 200m 3,5km 200m 300m.
Remarks: Next to sports fields.

Trevi 34D2

Via Costa San Paolo. **GPS:** n42,87829 e12,75221.

20 free Ch free. **Surface:** grasstiles. 01/01-31/12.
Distance: 500m 5,1km 350m on the spot.
Remarks: At swimming pool.

Abruzzo

Anversa degli Abruzzi 34E3

Il Sagittario, Loc. Ponte delle Fornaci. **GPS:** n41,99995 e13,80960.
10 € 12 Ch WC. **Location:** Rural. **Surface:** gravel.
01/01-31/12.
Distance: 1km 1km 1km on the spot on the spot.

Anversa degli Abruzzi 34E3

Bioagriturismo La Porta dei Parchi, Piazza Roma 3.
GPS: n42,00014 e13,79899.

5 € 10, free with a meal Ch WC € 5 included.
Location: Rural. **Surface:** metalled. 01/01-31/12.
Distance: 1km on the spot.

IT

S Barrea 34E3

Barrea Sosta Camper, Strada Regionale 83. **GPS**: n41,76129 e13,98768.
23 € 15-25 € 5 Ch € 3/24h WC included.
Location: Rural. 01/01-31/12.
Distance: 700m on the spot shuttle to centre on the spot on the spot.
Remarks: At the lake, bicycle rental, picnic and barbecue place.

S Campotosto 34D2

Via Lago, SR557. **GPS**: n42,56208 e13,34805.
€ 5 . **Surface:** grassy. 01/01-31/12.
Distance: Campotosto 3km on the spot.
Remarks: At lake Campotosto.

Casalbordino 34F3

Via Alessandrini. **GPS**: n42,19952 e14,61800.
20 € 5. **Location:** Rural. **Surface:** grassy/sand.
01/01-31/12.
Distance: on the spot on the spot on the spot.
Remarks: To be paid at bar in the village.

S Casalbordino 34F3

Area di sosta Ass Villa Sarda, Contr. Piana Sabelli.
GPS: n42,17773 e14,59994.
20 free Ch WC . **Location:** Rural. **Surface:** grassy.
01/01-31/12.
Distance: 1,5km 1km on the spot.

S Cologna Spiaggia 34E2

Area sosta camper Gulliver, Via del Mare, Roseto degli Abruzzi.
GPS: n42,73563 e13,98021.
50 € 15-20 Ch WC included.
Surface: grassy/gravel. 01/04-30/09.
Distance: 800m 100m 350m 200m.
Remarks: Bicycle rental, picnic and barbecue place, playground.

S Fossacesia 34F2

Area Camper, Via Lungomare Sud 168.
GPS: n42,24067 e14,52988.

24 € 10 Ch included. **Surface:** gravel/sand.
01/03-30/11.
Distance: 1km 6,5km on the spot on the spot 5km 1,5km.
Remarks: Pebbled beach.

S Isola del Gran Sasso 34E2

S.Gabriele dell Addolorata. **GPS**: n42,51712 e13,65634.

free Chfree. **Location:** Urban. **Surface:** gravel/sand.
01/01-31/12.
Distance: on the spot 4km on the spot on the spot.
Remarks: Nearby basilica.

S Lanciano 34E2

Area Attrezzata, Strada provinciale Lanciano-Frisa, Lancianovecchia.
GPS: n42,23385 e14,39106.

50 free ChWCfree. **Location:** Urban. **Surface:** asphalted.
01/01-31/12 Sa-morning market.
Distance: 300m (stairs and elevator) 300m 450m.
Remarks: At city walls, upper part of the parking, escalator to city centre.

Tourist information Lanciano:
Historical city with medieval Jewish district, Ripa Sacca.

S L'Aquila 34D2

Via porta Napoli. **GPS**: n42,34175 e13,39510.
10 free Chfree. **Location:** Urban. **Surface:** gravel.
01/01-31/12.
Distance: 700m 500m 2km.

S L'Aquila 34D2

Via Strinella. **GPS**: n42,35323 e13,40708.

10 free Chfree. **Surface:** asphalted. 01/01-31/12.
Distance: 500m.
Remarks: In front of Hotel Federico II, adjacent Parco del Castello.

S Notaresco 34E2

Via Martiri della Libertà. **GPS**: n42,65527 e13,89578.
10 free Chfree against payment. **Location:** Urban.
Surface: asphalted. 01/01-31/12.
Distance: on the spot on the spot 500m.
Remarks: At tennis-courts.

S Ovindoli 34E3

Via Statale. **GPS**: n42,14143 e13,51740.

50 free Chfree. **Location:** Simple.
Distance: 500m 600m 2km.

S Penne 34E2

Agriturismo Il Portico, Contrada Colle Serangelo 26.
GPS: n42,45592 e13,95165.

15 € 10, free with a meal Ch (7x)€ 3 WC included.
Location: Rural. **Surface:** grassy.
01/01-31/12.
Distance: 3km on the spot.
Remarks: Swimming pool (summer).

S Pescasseroli 34E3

Area Camper S.Andrea, Loc. Sant'Andrea, SS83.
GPS: n41,79888 e13,79222.

50 € 17, 2 pers. incl Ch WC € 0,50/5minutes included.
Location: Rural. **Surface:** unpaved.
8-13h, 14.30-20h.
Distance: 1km 1km on the spot.
Remarks: Free shuttle to centre.

Tourist information Pescasseroli:
Parco Nazionale d'Abruzzo. Nature reserve.

S Pineto 34E2

Sand stone beach, Via Tremiti, fraz. Scerne.
GPS: n42,64270 e14,04505.
free ChWC . **Surface:** grassy. 01/05-31/10.
Distance: on the spot on the spot.

S Roccaraso 34E3

Park Hotel Il Poggio, SS17, C.da Poggio, 1, Loc Il Poggio.
GPS: n41,82638 e14,10111.

18 € 20 Ch (18x)included . 01/01-31/12.
Distance: on the spot.
Remarks: Discount longer stays, shuttle bus to ski-piste.

S Roseto degli Abruzzi 34E2

Area di Sosta Camper Romeo, Via degli Orti 13, loc. Cologna Spiaggia.
GPS: n42,72287 e13,98076.

40 € 20/24h Ch (40x)WC € 1 included.
Location: Rural. **Surface:** grassy. 01/01-31/12.
Distance: 200m 750m on the spot 100m 100m.
Remarks: Barbecue place.

S Roseto degli Abruzzi 34E2

Area di sosta Isola del Sole, Piana degli Ulivi.
GPS: n42,66902 e14,01189.

IT

11 € 20 Ch (11x)€ 2 WC included. **Location:** Rural.
Surface: metalled. 01/01-31/12.
Distance: 3km 3km 1km.
Remarks: Swimming pool (summer).

S Roseto degli Abruzzi 34E2

Palazzo dello Sport, Via Ticino. **GPS**: n42,66012 e14,02382.

10 free Chfree. **Surface:** asphalted.
01/01-31/12 Tue.
Distance: 200m 1km 300m 300m.
Remarks: At gymnasium, tuesday market.

S San Demetrio nei Vestini 34E3

La Grotta di Stiffe, Via del Mulino, Fraz. Stiffe.
GPS: n42,25567 e13,54811.

free € 2,50 € 2,50. **Surface:** metalled/sand.
01/01-31/12.
Distance: l'Aquila 18km.

S San Salvo Marina 34F3

Area Sosta Communale per Autocaravan.
GPS: n42,07195 e14,76289.
30 € 16/24h, € 20/48h, € 30/72h ChWCincluded cold shower. **Surface:** grassy. 01/05-15/09.
Distance: 300m 2,2km 300m.

S Santo Stefano di Sessanio 34E2

Ostello del Cavaliere, Piazza Della Giudea.
GPS: n42,34429 e13,64314.
5 guests free . **Surface:** metalled.
Distance: 300m.

S Sant'Egidio alla Vibrata 34E2

Via Campania, Zona industriale. **GPS**: n42,81937 e13,69915.

10 free Chfree. **Location:** Urban. **Surface:** asphalted.
01/01-31/12.
Distance: 1km 200m.
Remarks: Industrial area.

S Torino di Sangro 34F2

Area camper Vitale, Lido le Morgie. **GPS**: n42,20403 e14,60349.
100 € 15/24h Chincluded € 2 WC € 0,50.
Surface: grassy/sand. 01/01-31/12.
Distance: 8km beach 70m 250m on the spot.

S Tortoreto Lido 34E2

Frontemare Easy Park, Via Napoli. **GPS**: n42,78425 e13,94966.
30 € 15 Ch included WC . **Surface:** asphalted.
01/04-01/10.
Distance: beach 200m.
Remarks: Max. 72h.

Tortoreto Lido 34E2

Lungomare Sirena. **GPS**: n42,78863 e13,94989.

6 free. 01/01-31/12.
Distance: beach 100m.
Remarks: Max. 48h.

S Villalago 34E3

SP82b. **GPS**: n41,92255 e13,85621.

13 free Chfree. **Location:** Rural. **Surface:** asphalted.
01/01-31/12.
Distance: on the spot.
Remarks: At lake Scanno, nearby beach and kosk.

Molise

S Campobasso 34F3

Area di sosta Dominick Ferrante, Contrada Macchie 1.
GPS: n41,56886 e14,65118.

20 € 10/24h, € 15/48h Ch included.
Surface: gravel.
Distance: 800m.

S Monteroduni 34E3

Oasi San Nazzaro, Vico 5 del Sole. **GPS**: n41,53448 e14,15924.

40 € 10, free with a meal Ch (6x)included.
Surface: grassy. 01/01-31/12.
Distance: 3,5km Fish lake on the spot.

S Petacciato Marina 34F3

Villagio la Torre, SS16 Adriatica km535,5, Termoli ri Vasto.
GPS: n42,02432 e14,88739.

60 € 10-20 Ch (50x)included WC . **Surface:** gravel/sand.
01/01-31/12.
Distance: on the spot on the spot on the spot.
Remarks: Access via gate next to tower ruins.

S Petacciato Marina 34F3

Parking spiaggia, Via del Mare, SS16. **GPS**: n42,03543 e14,85337.

40 8-20h € 6 against payment. **Location:** Rural.
Surface: asphalted. 01/01-31/12.
Distance: 4,5km 9,5km 50m 100m 300m.
Remarks: Reserved place for motorhomes.

S Petacciato Marina 34F3

Parking Tolomei, Via Marinelle, SS 16. **GPS**: n42,03219 e14,85844.
50 € 15 Chincluded WC € 0,50 . **Location:** Rural.
Surface: gravel. 01/01-31/12.
Distance: Direct access 600m 900m.
Remarks: Shuttle bus.

Puglia

S Alberobello 35D1

Parcheggio Nel Verde, Via Cadore. **GPS**: n40,78266 e17,23418.

60 € 18/24h, € 14/12h, € 10/6h Ch included.
Surface: grassy/gravel. 01/01-31/12.
Distance: Trulli-centre 50m 50m 100m.
Remarks: No camping activities.

Tourist information Alberobello:

Centre of the Trulli-region. Trulli houses are curious houses built without motar.

Thu-morning.

S Bari 35C1

Area Hobby Park Wash, Via Giovanni del Conte.
GPS: n41,11581 e16,88501.
€ 15/24h Ch included . **Location:** Urban.
Surface: metalled. 01/01-31/12.
Distance: centre 500m 700m 800m 600m 200m.
Remarks: Monitored parking.

S Bari 35C1

Gran Parcheggio Alberotanza, Via Alberotaza, 43A.
GPS: n41,09520 e16,87868.

250 € 20 € 0,50/30liter € 2,50 Ch € 0,50/kWh WC.

IT

Location: Urban. **Surface:** asphalted. 01/01-31/12.
Distance: 7,8km 500m 500m 400m.
Remarks: Monitored parking.

Brindisi 35D1
Freeland, SS16 14. **GPS:** n40,60184 e17,95656.
15 € 13 Ch included. **Location:** Urban. **Surface:** metalled.
01/01-31/12.
Distance: 5km.
Remarks: Video surveillance.

Brindisi 35D1
Garage Minnuta, Strada Minnuta 6. **GPS:** n40,63517 e17,91824.
20 € 10 Ch € 3 WC included. **Location:** Urban.
Surface: asphalted. 01/01-31/12.
Distance: 2km 1km.
Remarks: 24/24 surveillance.

Castellana Grotte 35D1
Area Sapori & Sapori, Via Turi. **GPS:** n40,88560 e17,15722.
10 free Ch free. **Location:** Urban. **Surface:** asphalted.
01/01-31/12.
Distance: 1km on the spot 1km 1km.
Remarks: Caves 1,8km.

Castellana Grotte 35D1
Le Grotte di Castellana, SS32. **GPS:** n40,87543 e17,14900.
10 € 5. **Location:** Rural.
Surface: grassy/gravel.
01/01-31/12.
Distance: city centre 2km on the spot 500m.
Remarks: Parking at the caves of Castellana, overnight stay allowed.

Castellana Grotte 35D1
Agriturismo Monte del Vento, Via Alberobello 202.
GPS: n40,83457 e17,24166.
5 € 15/24h, free with a meal Ch included WC.
Location: Rural. **Surface:** unpaved. 01/01-31/12.
Distance: on the spot.

Foggia 34G3
Parking 92. GPS: n41,43430 e15,48063.
€ 10 Ch included.
Distance: 6km.

Gallipoli 35D1
Area Sosta Camper Nuovi Orizzonti, Sp 221 Contrada L'Ariò.
GPS: n40,00286 e18,03374.
40 € 21, Aug € 26 Ch WC included.
Location: Comfortable, quiet. **Surface:** forest soil.
01/01-31/12.
Distance: Gallipoli 5km 1,5km.
Remarks: Free shuttle to beach.

Gallipoli 35D1
Autopark Spiaggia D'oro San Mauro, Loc. Padula Bianca.
GPS: n40,09568 e18,01625.
50 € 20 Ch. **Location:** Quiet. 01/06-30/09.
Distance: Gallipoli 4km 100m.

Gallipoli 35D1
CamperPark Baia Verde, Via Rosa dei Venti, Loc. Baia Verde.
GPS: n40,03375 e18,02088.
70 € 20 Ch included. **Surface:** grassy.
01/06-30/09.
Distance: Gallipoli 4km 200m 200m.

Gallipoli 35D1
Campo delle Bandiere, Loc. Padula Bianca. **GPS:** n40,09681 e18,01297.
€ 15-25 ChWC. **Surface:** sand. 01/06-01/09.
Distance: Sandy beach.

Gallipoli 35D1
La Sosta, Via Beneficati Rossi, Loc. Padula Bianca.
GPS: n40,09454 e18,01572.
€ 10-30 ChWC. **Surface:** sand. 01/01-31/12.
Distance: 50m on the spot.
Remarks: Video surveillance.

Gallipoli 35D1
Via Cimitero. **GPS:** n40,05479 e17,99689.
20 € 10/24h. **Surface:** asphalted. 01/01-31/12.
Distance: centre 400m 650m 400m 200m.

Lequile 35D1
Salento Sosta Camper, Via Preti di Campi 6. **GPS:** n40,28266 e18,13179.
18 € 15/24h Ch. **Location:** Comfortable, quiet.
Surface: gravel. 01/01-31/12.
Distance: city centre Lecce 8km.
Remarks: Bike/car rental.

Lesina 34F3
Oasi, Via Ludovica Ariosto. **GPS:** n41,86472 e15,35806.
15 € 12, Sept-Mar-Apr € 15, May/Aug € 18 Ch WC included. **Surface:** asphalted. 01/01-31/12.
Distance: 300m on the spot 500m.

Lucera 34G3
Via Montello. **GPS:** n41,49987 e15,33223.
100 free. **Location:** Urban. **Surface:** asphalted.
01/01-31/12.
Distance: 900m 300m 500m.
Remarks: At station.

Lucera 34G3
Centro sportivo Casanova, Strada Contrada Casanova.
GPS: n41,48849 e15,26008.
10 € 10 Ch included. **Location:** Isolated. **Surface:** metalled.
01/01-31/12.
Distance: Lucera 9km.
Remarks: At sports centre.

Margherita di Savoia 34G3
Lido Baywatch, Via Barletta. **GPS:** n41,36222 e16,17361.

12 € 20, 01/06-30/09 € 25 Ch WC included.
Surface: gravel. 01/01-31/12.
Distance: 2km on the spot on the spot.

Marina di Felloniche 35D1
Marcheddu Parking village, SP214. **GPS:** n39,79729 e18,33392.
30 € 15-25 Ch WC. **Location:** Rural.
Surface: unpaved. 01/04-15/10.
Distance: 4km on the spot on the spot on the spot on the spot.
Remarks: Barbecue place.

Massafra 35D1
Area di Sosta La Stella, SS7, SS Appia km 633, Le Forche.
GPS: n40,59201 e17,09904.

20 € 15-20 € 2,50 Ch (18x)€ 3 WC included € 1.
Location: Rural. **Surface:** grassy. 01/01-31/12.
Distance: 1km 3km 6km 500m 1km.
Remarks: Beachshuttle € 2.

Mattinata 34G3
Eden Park, Porto di Mattinata, SP53. **GPS:** n41,70667 e16,06556.

30 € 14,60-26,60 ChWC included € 0,50.
Surface: grassy/sand. 01/06-31/08.
Distance: 1km pebbled beach on the spot 1km 1km.

Melendugno 35D1
Area Camper Salento I Faraglioni, SP366 km 20.5, Sant'Andrea.
GPS: n40,25550 e18,43748.
15 € 15-32/24h, 4 pers.incl + tourist tax € 0,50 Ch included WC € 1. **Location:** Rural. **Surface:** unpaved.
01/01-31/12.
Distance: 700m 400m on the spot.
Remarks: Barbecue place, shuttle bus to beach, playground.

Melendugno 35D1
Gran Pasha, Strada provinciale Lecce-Melendugno-San Foca, km.18.
GPS: n40,27724 e18,40510.
50 € 15-25 + tourist tax € 0,50/pp Ch € 3 WC included.
Surface: unpaved. 01/04-30/09.
Distance: 1,5km 1,5km.
Remarks: Bar, barbecue place, free shuttle.

Monopoli 35D1
Area du Sosta Camper Lido Millennium, SP90, Loc. Capitolo, SS16 km850 Uscita Capitolo. **GPS:** n40,90374 e17,35261.

100 € 15-18-23 Ch 6Amp WC included € 1.
Surface: gravel. Easter-30/09.
Distance: 500m 50m 50m 50m.
Remarks: Private beach.

Otranto 35D1
Oasy Park, Via Renis. **GPS:** n40,13795 e18,48922.

50 € 18, Aug € 20, 2 pers. Incl Ch (70x),16Amp WC included € 1 € 4. **Surface:** grassy/gravel. 01/01-31/12.
Distance: 400m 700m 400m 400m.

S Otranto 35D1

Area Camper Fontanelle, Sp366, km28. **GPS**: n40,19159 e18,45494.

20 € 15/24h, Jul-Aug € 25, 4 pers incl. + tourist tax Ch € 3 WC included € 0,50. **Location:** Comfortable, isolated, quiet.
Surface: grassy. 01/04-31/10.
Distance: Otranto 5km beach 400m.
Remarks: Shuttle bus to Otranto, regional products.

S Peschici 34G3

Camper Marina Picola, Loc. Pantanello, Baia di Peschici.
GPS: n41,94528 e16,00528.

45 Apr € 12, May € 13, Jun/Sep € 15, Jul € 20, Aug € 25 Ch included WC € 0,50. **Surface:** grassy/sand. 01/04-30/09.
Distance: 2,5km, walking 800m (stairs) sandy beach 50m 300m.

S Peschici 34G3

AgriCamper Pane e Vino, SS89 km 2,6. **GPS**: n41,92372 e16,01534.
20 € 10 Ch WC. **Surface:** sand.
Distance: 3,5km on the spot on the spot.
Remarks: Borrow cycles for free.

S Peschici 34G3

Area attrezzata per camper Dattoli, Via Spiaggia, SS89.
GPS: n41,94522 e16,01138.
14 € 15-20 Ch WC included € 0,50.
Location: Rural. **Surface:** unpaved.
01/01-31/12.
Distance: Old city 300m (stairs) 100m 100m 1km.

Putignano 35D1

Grotte di Putignano, SS172. **GPS**: n40,85706 e17,10944.
free. 01/01-31/12.

S Rodi Garganico 34G3

Area sosta camper Isola Bella, Via delle More.
GPS: n41,92444 e15,84166.

30 € 15-20, Aug € 25 Ch WC included.
Surface: grassy/sand. 01/06-15/09.
Distance: Lido del Sole 1,5km, Rodi Garganico 3,8km sandy beach 10m on the spot 100m 1,5km.

S San Giovanni Rotondo 34G3

Coppa Cicuta, Strada Comunale Pozzocavo-Tre Carrini.
GPS: n41,69599 e15,70423.

30 € 12 Ch (30x)€ 1,50/night WC included € 10.
Surface: gravel. 01/01-31/12.
Distance: 3km on the spot.
Remarks: Shuttle € 2/pp.

S San Giovanni Rotondo 34G3

Lo Chalet, Viale Padre Pio. **GPS**: n41,70658 e15,69799.
€ 15/24h Ch WC. **Surface:** metalled.
01/01-31/12.
Distance: on the spot.
Remarks: Free shuttle, santuario 300m.

S San Giovanni Rotondo 34G3

Di Cerbo, Circonvallazione Sud, SP45bis. **GPS**: n41,69725 e15,73097.

20 € 5,20/day, € 7,80/night Ch WC € 1,50 € 1.
Surface: asphalted. 01/01-31/12.
Distance: 1km on the spot on the spot on the spot.
Remarks: Shuttle bus.

P San Giovanni Rotondo 34G3

Viale Padre Pio. **GPS**: n41,70679 e15,69927.
150 € 2,50, overnight stay free. **Surface:** asphalted.
Remarks: Shrine Padre Pio 200m.

S San Pietro in Bevagna 35D1

Holiday Area Camper, Via Chidro di Specchiarica, Salento.
GPS: n40,30511 e17,69486.
50 € 15-23 Ch included € 2,50 WC.
Location: Urban. **Surface:** unpaved. 01/06-30/09.
Distance: 2km on the spot 800m.
Remarks: Monitored parking 24/24.

S San Pietro in Bevagna 35D1

La Salina, SP122, Manduria. **GPS**: n40,30121 e17,72630.
30 € 14-21, 4 pers.incl Ch € 2,50 WC included.
Location: Rural. **Surface:** gravel.
01/06-30/09.
Distance: 1km on the spot 450m on the spot on the spot.

S San Pietro in Bevagna 35D1

La Marina, Via Favignana, Manduria. **GPS**: n40,30888 e17,67750.

80 € 20/24h Ch included WC € 0,50. **Surface:** unpaved.
01/06-01/09.
Distance: on the spot 300m 450m.
Remarks: Monitored parking.

S Santa Maria al Bagno 35D1

Area Camper Mondonuovo, Via Torremozza.
GPS: n40,13494 e18,00166.
20 € 15, Aug € 17 Ch. **Surface:** gravel. 01/01-31/12.
Distance: beach 500m 900m.

S Torre Canne di Fasano 35D1

Lido Tavernese, SS379, uscita Torre Canne Sud.
GPS: n40,82023 e17,49875.

100 € 15-22, Aug € 28 Ch (80x)€ 2 WC included € 1.
Location: Rural. **Surface:** grassy. 01/05-30/09.
Distance: 3,5km on the spot 01/07-31/08.

S Torre dell'Orso 35D1

Camper Park Area La Torre. GPS: n40,27824 e18,41413.
20 € 10-35 Ch. 01/06-30/09.
Distance: 700m.
Remarks: Regional products.

S Troia 34G3

Campo della Fiera, Via Sant'Antonio. **GPS**: n41,36158 e15,30616.

30 free Ch free. **Location:** Urban. **Surface:** asphalted.
01/01-31/12.
Distance: 200m 300m 350m.
Remarks: Near the cathedral.

S Vico del Gargano 34G3

Lido Azzurro. GPS: n41,94208 e15,98303.

80 € 15, July € 20, Aug € 25 Ch € 3,(Aug) WC included.
Surface: sand. 01/01-31/12.
Distance: Valazzo 4km Sandy beach 1km (camping).

S Vieste 34G3

Fusilo Rosina, Contrada S.Lucia. **GPS**: n41,91028 e16,12944.

70 Jun-Sep € 15, Jul € 20, Aug € 27,50 Ch (70x)included WC € 0,50. **Location:** Rural. **Surface:** grassy. 01/06-15/09.
Distance: 4km 300m 50m 100m 50m.
Remarks: Barbecue place, playground.

S Vieste 34G3

Area Eden Blu, Lungomare Enrico Mattei.
GPS: n41,85985 e16,17396.
40 € 30/24h Ch WC. **Location:** Rural.
Surface: unpaved. 01/04-31/10.
Distance: on the spot 200m on the spot.
Remarks: Monitored parking 24/24.

Tourist information Vieste:
Mo.

S Zapponeta 34G3

Zapponeta Beach, Via del Mare. **GPS**: n41,45694 e15,96083.

IT

30 € 13, 13/06-10/07, 22/08-11/09 € 14, 11/07-21/08 € 16, 2 pers incl Ch € 3 WCincluded € 1. **Surface:** grassy/metalled.
01/04-30/09.
Distance: 250m on the spot on the spot 500m 500m.
Remarks: Narrow entrance.

Campania

S Bacoli 35B1
Sea Oasi Village, Via Spiaggia Romana. **GPS**: n40,82194 e14,04791.
100 € 18-20, 4 pers.incl Chincluded € 5 € 0,50.
Location: Rural. **Surface:** grassy. 01/01-31/12.
Distance: on the spot on the spot 1km.

S Bacoli 35B1
Sea Oasi Village, Via Strada Romana, loc. Fusaro.
GPS: n40,82194 e14,04791.
± 100 € 15-20/24h, 4 pers.incl Ch € 5 WC € 1.
Surface: grassy/sand.
Distance: on the spot.
Remarks: At the beach.

S Bacoli 35B1
Parco Naturale Agriturismo Fondi di Baia, Via Fondi di Baia.
GPS: n40,81157 e14,07412.

20 € 10 Ch included. **Surface:** asphalted.
01/01-31/12.
Distance: 3km Baia 700m 100m.

S Baia e Latina 35B1
Il Baglio Country Village, Via Sturzo 13. **GPS**: n41,30386 e14,24754.
guests free Ch WC. 01/01-31/12.
Distance: village 2km on the spot.
Remarks: Use of sauna against payment.

S Battipaglia 35C1
Camperstop Lagomare, Via Andrea Doria 1, Fraz. Lago.
GPS: n40,55296 e14,90615.
40 € 20/24h, max. 4 pers Ch ,3kWh WC included.
Surface: grasstiles. 01/01-31/12.
Distance: 100m 50m.

S Benevento 35B1
Sannio Camper Club, Via Domenico Mustilli.
GPS: n41,13141 e14,78960.

50 € 10/24h Ch included. **Location:** Urban.
Surface: metalled. 01/01-31/12.
Distance: 500m 1,8km 300m.

Tourist information Benevento:
Piazza Risorgimento en Piazza Santa Maria. Wed, Sa 8-13h.

S Casalbore 35C1
Agriturismo Le Mainarde, Mainardi 16. **GPS**: n41,24516 e15,00242.
30 € 15 Ch included. **Location:** Rural. **Surface:** asphalted.
01/01-31/12.
Distance: 1,5km on the spot.

S Case del Conte 35C1
Cilento Il Brigantino, Case del Conte Baia Arena.
GPS: n40,23652 e14,95882.
30 € 10-21 € 1,50 Ch € 0,33/h. **Location:** Rural.
Surface: grassy. 01/01-31/12.
Distance: 2km 600m.

S Cava de' Tirreni 35B1
Via Ido Longo, loc. Sant'Arcangelo. **GPS**: n40,69984 e14,69553.
20 free Ch free. **Location:** Urban. **Surface:** grasstiles.
01/01-31/12.
Distance: on the spot 2,3km 300m on the spot.

Tourist information Cava de' Tirreni:
Salerno. City with medieval centre.
Museo Civico, Amalfi. Museum with Tavole Amalfitane, the old Law of the Sea. 8-14h, Sa 8-12h holiday.

S Contursi Terme 35C1
Agriturismo Il Giardino, Loc. Prato. **GPS**: n40,64891 e15,23002.
5 € 15 Ch included. **Location:** Rural.
Surface: metalled. 01/01-31/12.
Distance: 1km 4,4km on the spot.
Remarks: Le Terme Vulpacchio 50m, swimming pool available.

S Marina di Camerota 35C1
Parcheggio Europa, Via Sirene. **GPS**: n40,00302 e15,36493.
€ 18 Ch included. **Surface:** unpaved.
Easter-30/09.
Distance: 300m on the spot on the spot.

S Mondragone 35B1
Dun Area Camper, Via Domiziana, km 15.250.
GPS: n41,13159 e13,86150.
50 € 10-20 Ch. **Surface:** grassy/sand. 01/01-31/12.
Distance: Mondragone 4km on the spot on the spot 3km on the spot.
Remarks: Monitored parking 24/24.

S Napoli 35B1
Parking IPM, Via Colli Aminei 27, Naples (Napoli).
GPS: n40,87038 e14,24616.

50 € 22/24h Chincluded € 2/24h,3Amp. **Location:** Urban.
Surface: asphalted. 01/01-31/12.
Distance: on the spot 1,2km 200m 400m bus R4 centre Napoli 30m.
Remarks: Monitored parking.

S Napoli 35B1
Parking Patry, Via Nuova Poggioreale 120, Naples (Napoli).
GPS: n40,86788 e14,29436.
25 € 24/24h Ch included. **Location:** Urban.
Surface: metalled. 01/01-31/12.
Distance: 2km 350m 450m metro 300m.
Remarks: Monitored parking.

Tourist information Naples (Napoli):
A.A.C.S.T.(Azienda Autonoma di Cura Soggiorno e Turismo), Palazzo Reale, www.regione.campania.it. Capital of the province with many monuments and cultural treasures.
Vesuvio. Volcano, observatorium on western edge of the crater. Visit with guide possible.
Mergellina. Small peninsula with fishing-port and marina.
Teatro San Carlo. Opera building.
Museo Nazionale Archeologico di Napoli, Piazza Museo Nazionale 19. Antique hellenic-roman civilisation. Tue-Su 9-14h.
Palazzo Reale. Royal palace. 9-13.30h Mo.
Duomo San Gennaro. Cathedral with original interior.
Ercolano/Herculaneum. Ancient city buried together with Pompeii. 9-14.45h, holidays 9-18.15h.
Mercato Corso Malta. Mo, Fri.

S Paestum 35C1
Camper Village Maremirtilli, Via Linora di Paestum, SP278.
GPS: n40,37607 e15,00119.
70 € 15-25 Ch WC. **Surface:** grassy. 01/01-31/12.
Distance: on the spot.

S Paestum 35C1
Mediterranea Camper Village, Via Linora di Paestum.
GPS: n40,39570 e14,99817.
30 € 13-20 + € 3/pp tourist tax Ch WCincluded € 3.
Location: Rural. **Surface:** grassy. 01/01-31/12.
Distance: Paestum 3,5km 50m 1,5km 1,5km 400m.
Remarks: Bread-service and meals, playground.

S Paestum 35C1
Camper Park Zone Archeologica, Via Magna Grecia, Capaccio Paestum.
GPS: n40,41851 e15,00697.
30 € 10 Ch. **Location:** Rural. **Surface:** unpaved.
01/01-31/12.
Distance: 300m 1,6km 50m 50m.
Remarks: Paestum Excavations 200m.

S Paestum 35C1
Gli Eucalipti Area di Sosta, Via Linora, 76, Capaccio.
GPS: n40,38565 e15,00308.
25 € 13-18 + € 2,50/pp tourist tax Ch included.
Location: Rural. **Surface:** grassy. 01/05-01/10.
Distance: 4km 50m on the spot on the spot.
Remarks: Shuttle bus.

S Paestum 35C1
Fattoria del Casaro, Via Licinella 5, Capaccio Paestum.
GPS: n40,41504 e15,00505.
20 € 10/24h Ch included.
Distance: 600m beach 1,8km on the spot.
Remarks: Paestum Excavations 300m regional products and bread.

S Paestum 35C1
Camper Park Mandetta, Via Torre di Mare 2.
GPS: n40,41486 e14,98954.
20 € 15-25 Ch WCincluded € 1. **Surface:** unpaved.
01/01-31/12.
Distance: 1km 200m on the spot 250m.

Tourist information Paestum:
A.A.C.S.T.(Azienda Autonoma di Cura Soggiorno e Turismo), Via Magna Grecia, 151. Old city, founded by the Greeks. In the surroundings many vestiges from that time. 9h-sunset.

S Palinuro 35C1
Sosta Camper Palorcio, Via San Sebastiano, 39.
GPS: n40,03831 e15,31236.
35 € 12-22, 08/08-24/08 € 30 Ch WC included.
Surface: grassy. 01/06-30/09.
Distance: 1km.

S Palinuro 35C1
Via Palorcio. **GPS**: n40,03722 e15,30944.
€ 20/24h ChWC included. **Location:** Rural.
Surface: unpaved. 01/01-31/12.
Distance: 3,5km 700m 700m on the spot.

S Pompei 35B1
Camping Pompei, Via Plinio 113. **GPS**: n40,74675 e14,48496.
€ 15,50-20, 2 pers.incl Ch WC included.
Location: Urban.
Surface: grassy.
01/01-31/12.
Remarks: Entrance acient city 150m.

Tourist information Pompei:
Ancient city at the foot of Vesuvius. 9h-sunset holiday.

S Pontecagnano Faiano 35B1
Camper Stop Italy, Via Dei Navigatori. **GPS**: n40,60304 e14,86387.
45 € 12-20 Ch. **Location:** Comfortable.
Surface: grassy. 01/01-31/12.
Distance: 50m 50m on the spot on the spot.

IT

S Pozzuoli 35B1

Castagnaro Park, Via del Castagnaro 1. **GPS**: n40,86939 e14,12150.
85 € 15 Ch (80x)€ 3/24h WC € 1,50 included.
Surface: grassy/gravel.
01/01-31/12.
Distance: 300m 4km 300m 300m 200m.
Remarks: Monitored parking, reservation during Christmas period.
Tourist information Pozzuoli:
Cuma. Archeological site. 9-14.45h, summer 18h.

S Sala Consilina 35C1

Via Santa Maria della Misericordia. **GPS**: n40,41376 e15,56397.
20 € 5/night Ch included. **Surface:** metalled.
01/01-31/12.
Distance: 1,5km 300m 500m 2,5km 1,5km 15km 15km.
Remarks: Behind hotel Vallis Dea.

S Tramonti 35B1

Agriturismo Costiera Amalfitana, Via Falcone, 12 - Frazione Pietre.
GPS: n40,69929 e14,61811.
22 01/09-14/06 € 22, 15/06-31/08 - 23/12-06/01 € 30
Ch WC included. **Location:** Rural, comfortable.
Surface: grassy/gravel. 01/01-31/12.
Distance: 50m 15km 6km on the spot 30m 500m on the spot.
Remarks: Amalfi Coast, regional products.

Basilicata

S Grumento Nova 35C1

Agriturismo Al Parco Verde, Contrada Spineto, Moliterno-Grumento.
GPS: n40,28110 e15,90563.
20 € 20 Ch WC included. **Location:** Rural.
Surface: grassy. 01/06-01/10.
Distance: 8km 2km on the spot 5km on the spot 2km 1km.
Remarks: Archeological site 200m.

S Matera 35C1

Area Camper Matera, SS7, Via Appia. **GPS**: n40,67981 e16,62126.
25 € 14/24h Ch WC included. **Surface:** metalled.
01/01-31/12.
Distance: centre 3,5km.

S Matera 35C1

Parco Serra Venerdì, Via dei Normanni. **GPS**: n40,66814 e16,58960.

12 € 18/24h Ch WC . **Surface:** metalled.
01/01-31/12.
Distance: 1,8km 200m on the spot.

S Metaponto 35C1

Camper parking Nettuno, Viale Magna Grecia, Metaponto Lido.
GPS: n40,35693 e16,83221.

50 € 13/24h, Jul/Aug € 18 Ch WC included € 1.
Surface: grassy/gravel. 01/01-31/12.
Distance: 50m on the spot 300m.
Tourist information Metaponto:
Archeological site. 9h-sunset.

S Nova Siri 35C1

Via Tre Passi nel Delirio. **GPS**: n40,12801 e16,65424.
9 free Ch free . **Location:** Rural. **Surface:** metalled.
01/01-31/12.
Distance: 1,5km 100m 550m on the spot.
Remarks: Video surveillance.

Calabria

S Amantea 35C2

Garden Park Caterina, SS. 18, loc Coreca.
GPS: n39,09383 e16,08508.
10 € 20-25, 4 pers.incl Ch € 2,50 WC included € 1 € 5.
Surface: grassy. 15/06-15/09.
Distance: on the spot on the spot on the spot nearby.

S Bova Marina 35C3

Mafalda's Camper Park, Via Sotto Ferrovia, loc. San Pasquale.
GPS: n37,92422 e15,94800.
20 € 10-20 Ch included . **Surface:** gravel/sand.
Distance: 3km on the spot on the spot 200m 500m.
Remarks: Accessible via unpaved road, video surveillance.

S Camigliatello Silano 35C2

Rifugio dei Peccatori di Gola, Strada per il Lago Cecita, SS17.
GPS: n39,35852 e16,48655.
20 € 15-19 Ch WC. **Location:** Rural. **Surface:** grassy.
01/01-31/12.
Distance: 4,5km 1km on the spot.

S Catanzaro Marina 35D2

Il Chioschetto, Via Carlo Pisacane 24. **GPS**: n38,83321 e16,64862.

10 free . **Location:** Simple. **Surface:** sand.
Distance: Sandy beach.

S Cirella 35C1

Area Camper Ulisse, SS 18 km 270, Diamante.
GPS: n39,72500 e15,80930.

130 € 10-25, 4 pers.incl Ch WC included .
Location: Rural. **Surface:** grassy/sand. 01/04-31/10.
Distance: 800m on the spot on the spot on the spot on the spot on the spot.

S Cirella 35C1

Lido Alexander, SS 18, Diamante. **GPS**: n39,72168 e15,81097.

50 € 8-17, 2 pers. incl. Ch € 3 WC included € 1 € 3.
Location: Rural. **Surface:** grassy/gravel. 01/01-31/12.
Distance: 1,5km on the spot on the spot on the spot on the spot.

S Cirella 35C1

Lido delle Sirene, SS 18, Contr. Riviere. **GPS**: n39,71822 e15,81137.

100 € 13 Ch included € 2 WC . **Location:** Rural.
Surface: grassy.
01/01-31/12.
Distance: 1km on the spot on the spot on the spot 1km.

S Cirella 35C1

Lido Tropical, Viale Glauco, 9, Diamante. **GPS**: n39,69222 e15,81556.

200 € 8-30, 4 pers.incl, dog € 2 Ch included,4Amp
WC . **Location:** Urban. **Surface:** grassy/sand.
01/01-31/12.
Distance: 1,5km on the spot on the spot 200m 200m shuttle to town.
Remarks: Swimming pool available.

S Cirò Marina 35D2

Via Maddalena. **GPS**: n39,35998 e17,12910.
25 € 6, 01/06-31/08 € 12 . **Surface:** unpaved.
01/01-31/12.
Distance: 1,2km 50m.

S Cirò Marina 35D2

Village "Le Casette", Località Difesa Piana. **GPS**: n39,39815 e17,13625.
25 € 15-25 Ch included. **Location:** Rural.
Surface: grassy/sand. 01/01-31/12.
Distance: 4km 300m on the spot

S Cittadella del Capo 35C2

Torre Parise, Via Parise. **GPS**: n39,56580 e15,87399.
16 € 15, Jul/Aug € 18, 3 pers. incl Ch included WC .
Location: Rural. **Surface:** grassy. 01/01-31/12.
Distance: 1,5km 200m 500m 1km 900m.

Remarks: Breakfast-service, swimming pool.

Condofuri Marina 35C3

Agriturismo Antonino Gemelli, Via Salinella 37.
GPS: n37,92372 e15,85150.
20 € 18-24 Ch WC. **Location:** Rural.
Surface: gravel/sand. 01/01-31/12.
Distance: 500m 100m 2km 1km 2,5km.

Corigliano Calabro 35C1

B&B Club Tepee, Contrada Sant'Agata 42, SS106bis > Cantinella.
GPS: n39,64528 e16,39909.
20 € 10 Chincluded WC. **Location:** Rural.
01/01-31/12.
Distance: Corigliano 14km on the spot.

Cropani Marina 35D2

Sena Park, Viale Venezia 34. **GPS:** n38,91143 e16,80963.
25 € 12-28, 2 pers.incl Ch € 3 WC € 0,50 included.
Location: Rural. **Surface:** grassy/sand. 01/01-31/12.
Distance: 500m 400m 400m ristorante/pizzeria 500m station 2km.
Remarks: Playground, washing motorhome € 20.

Crotone 35D2

Hera Lacinia Mare, Via Filippo, 47, Campione III.
GPS: n39,00311 e17,16984.
10 € 20 Chincluded € 5. **Surface:** gravel/metalled.
20/06-01/09.
Distance: on the spot on the spot on the spot 100m 200m.

Morano Calabro 35C1

Via Gaetano Scorza. **GPS:** n39,84098 e16,13731.

0 free. **Surface:** asphalted. 01/01-31/12.
Distance: 200m 7km 200m 200m.
Remarks: Next to church of San Bernardino, panoramic view.

Palmi 35C2

Sosta Camper Prajola, Lungomare Donna Canfora.
GPS: n38,39333 e15,86277.

5 € 15/24h Ch included. **Location:** Simple.
Surface: gravel. 01/01-31/12.
Distance: on the spot.

Praia a Mare 35C1

Nuova Playa, Contr. Fiucci. **GPS:** n39,86885 e15,78943.

5 € 25, peak season € 35 Ch WC included.
Location: Rural. **Surface:** grassy. 01/01-31/12.
Distance: 2km on the spot on the spot 100m 2km.
Remarks: Black sandy beach, in front of Dino island, barbecue place, playground.

Praia a Mare 35C1

Punto Mare, Loc. Fiuzzi. **GPS:** n39,87633 e15,78727.

30 € 6 € 2,50 € 2,50 Ch € 2. **Surface:** grassy.
01/06-30/09.
Distance: 800m 600m 600m 500m 500m on the spot.
Remarks: Along railwayline.

Rossano 35D1

Sosta Camper Il Faro, C. da Foresta Faro Campo Trionto.
GPS: n39,62148 e16,75146.

12 € 18-25, 2 pers. incl. Ch WC included.
Location: Rural, comfortable, isolated. **Surface:** grassy.
01/03-31/10.
Distance: 2km, Rossano 12km Sandy beach on the spot.
Remarks: Regional products.

Santa Maria del Cedro 35C1

Sosta Camper Manuel, Via Lipari ss18. **GPS:** n39,75428 e15,80431.
50 € 15 Ch WC included. **Surface:** grassy.
01/01-31/12.
Distance: 1km on the spot on the spot on the spot on the spot on the spot.

Scalea 35C1

Dolce Vita, Via Fiume Lao 7. **GPS:** n39,79667 e15,79265.

100 € 16-21 Ch € 5 WC € 0,50. **Location:** Rural.
Surface: grassy. 01/05-30/09.
Distance: on the spot on the spot on the spot on the spot 800m on the spot.

Scalea 35C1

Lido Zio Tom, Corso Mediterraneo km 261,7.
GPS: n39,81306 e15,78917.

140 € 10-20 Ch included,4Amp WC € 1. **Location:** Rural.
Surface: grassy/gravel.
15/04-15/10.
Distance: 600m on the spot 300m 400m station 1,5km.
Remarks: Bar, barbecue place, shuttle bus to city centre.

Scalea 35C1

Lido Aqua Mar Sosta Camper Martina, Corso Mediterraneo.
GPS: n39,80092 e15,79087.
€ 20/24h Ch WC € 0,50. 01/01-31/12.
Distance: 2km on the spot 400m 950m on the spot.

Trebisacce 35C1

Blue Marine, Via Lungomare. **GPS:** n39,87512 e16,54189.
30 € 12,50 Ch included. **Location:** Rural.
Surface: unpaved. 01/01-31/12.
Distance: 1km on the spot 500m 850m.

Sardinia

Aglientu 33G2

Oasi Gallura, Localita'Vignola Mare 19, SP 90 km 53.
GPS: n41,12556 e9,06167.

95 € 16-22,50, 2 pers. incl Ch € 3 WC € 5 included.
Location: Comfortable, quiet. **Surface:** grassy/sand.
Distance: 25m sandy beach 50m 100m 100m.

Alghero 33G2

Camperpark I Platani, Ss 291 Km 32,5 S.Maria la Palma - Fertilia.
GPS: n40,60699 e8,27463.

€ 16, 01/06-160/09 € 20-25 Ch ,hot shower € 0,50 € 5 included. **Location:** Comfortable. **Surface:** grassy.
01/01-31/12.
Distance: Alghero 7km 1,5km.
Remarks: Monitored parking 24/24, free shuttle to beach and supermarket, dogs beach.

Alghero 33G2

Paradise Park, Loc. Le Bombarde. **GPS:** n40,59180 e8,25610.

150 € 16-23 Ch WC € 0,50 € 5 included.
Location: Comfortable, quiet. 01/01-31/12.
Distance: 350m 350m on the spot on the spot 50m.

Arborea 33G3

Corsaro Beach, Str. 26 Ovest. **GPS:** n39,80187 e8,54956.

10 € 5-10. **Surface:** forest soil. 15/06-15/09.
Distance: sandy beach 100m 400m.

Arbus 33G3

Spiaggia Scivu, SC Scivu. **GPS:** n39,49426 e8,41444.

IT

+50 free, summer € 12/day, overnight stay free € 1.
Location: Isolated. **Surface:** gravel/sand. 01/01-31/12.
Distance: sandy beach 100m, stairs.
Remarks: Bar.

S Bosa 33G2

S'Abba Drucche Spiagge, SP49 Alghero-Bosa km 38+800.
GPS: n40,31641 e8,47352.

100 € 20 Ch (96x),6Amp WC included € 1 € 5 € 2.
Surface: unpaved. 15/03-30/10.
Distance: on the spot on the spot.
Remarks: Discount longer stays.

Bosa 33G2

Parcheggio Nassiriya, Via Sas Conzas. **GPS**: n40,29472 e8,49922.

±10 free. **Location:** Urban. **Surface:** asphalted. 01/01-31/12.
Distance: 300m 150m.
Remarks: Along river.

S Bosa 33G2

Casa del Vento, SP49. **GPS**: n40,32886 e8,43628.

±5 € 10 Ch included. **Location:** Rural.
Surface: gravel/sand.
Distance: Bosa 8km At the sea, no beach on the spot.
Remarks: Beautiful view, narrow entrance.

S Buggerru 33G3

Area Camper Il Porto, Via Roma. **GPS**: n39,40317 e8,40250.

50 € 5-15, Jul/Aug € 20 Ch € 5. **Surface:** sand.
01/04-31/10.
Distance: 800m on the spot 400m 800m.
Remarks: Beach parking.

S Buggerru 33G3

Punta Sosta San Nicolao, Loc. Cala Domestica.
GPS: n39,41757 e8,41147.

20 € 10 Ch included cold shower. **Surface:** grassy/sand.
01/05-30/10.
Distance: 4km sandy beach 50m 50m.
Remarks: Beach parking.

S Cabras 33G3

Tanca Is Muras, Località Mari Ermi. **GPS**: n39,96226 e8,40324.

€ 12 included. **Location:** Isolated. 01/05-01/10.
Distance: Sandy beach.

S Cagliari 33G3

Campernow, Via Gerolamo Cardano. **GPS**: n39,23580 e9,13832.

10 € 17 Ch WC included. **Location:** Urban, central, noisy. **Surface:** metalled. 20/04-15/10.
Distance: city centre 3km 150m Lidl 100m 100m.

S Cagliari 33G3

Camper Cagliari Park, Via Stanislao Caboni. **GPS**: n39,21024 e9,12772.

150 € 20 Ch € 5 WC included. **Location:** Urban.
Surface: asphalted. 01/01-31/12.
Distance: city centre 1,5km 300m.
Remarks: Monitored parking.

S Cala Gonone 33G2

Palmasera, Viale Bue Marino. **GPS**: n40,27954 e9,62993.

€ 20, Jul/Aug € 25-30 Ch WC € 0,50 € 5 included.
Surface: unpaved. 01/04-31/10.
Distance: 800m 500m ristoro 200m on the spot.
Remarks: Shuttle bus to beach.

Cala Sinzias 33G3

SP18. **GPS**: n39,18912 e9,56273.

10 free, summer € 10. **Surface:** sand. 01/01-31/12.
Distance: sandy beach 50m on the spot.
Remarks: Beach parking, pay in at kiosk.

S Cardedu 33G3

Cucamonga, Marina di Gairo. **GPS**: n39,75397 e9,67130.

±20 € 10 Ch included. **Location:** Rural, isolated, quiet.
Surface: sand. 01/01-31/12.
Distance: pebbled beach 7km.

S Cardedu 33G3

Motorpark I Ginepri. **GPS**: n39,77181 e9,63886.
€ 20 Ch WC included . **Surface:** grassy/gravel.
Distance: 1,8km.
Remarks: Monitored parking 24/24, free shuttle.

S Domus de Maria 33G3

Area Camper Chia, Su Giudeu, Capo Spartivento, Chia.
GPS: n38,89128 e8,86264.

100 € 16-20 Ch WC included € 0,50.
Location: Comfortable. **Surface:** sand. Easter-01/11.
Distance: on the spot 400m 900m.

Golfo Aranci 33G2

Playa Vistas Chulas, Via Cala Moresca. **GPS**: n40,98826 e9,63589.

±20 free. **Location:** Isolated. **Surface:** gravel/sand.
01/01-31/12.
Distance: 2km on the spot on the spot.
Remarks: 1km unpaved road, max. ^3.2m, beach parking, no camping activities.

S Masua 33G3

La Nuova Colonia, Masua Porto Flavia. **GPS**: n39,33409 e8,42052.

IT

50 € 14-17 Ch included free,at restaurant.
Location: Rural, isolated, quiet. **Surface:** unpaved.
01/04-31/10.
Distance: sandy beach 50m, stairs on the spot.
Remarks: Former mineral mines, tour Porto Flavia.

S Nuoro 33G2

P.le Anfiteatro cittadino, Piazza Veneto. **GPS**: n40,31447 e9,32807.

5 free Chfree. **Surface:** asphalted. 01/01-31/12.
Distance: 1,2km.

S Olbia 33G2

Camper service Marina di Cugnana, Località Marina di Cugnana, SP73.
GPS: n41,02042 e9,51441.

30 € 1,50/h, € 25/24h Ch WC included. **Location:** Noisy.
01/05-30/09.
Distance: Olbia 12km on the spot on the spot.
Remarks: Shuttle bus to beach, swimming pool.

S Oristano 33G3

Stadio Tharros, Via Dorando Petri. **GPS**: n39,89710 e8,58927.
Chfree. 01/01-31/12.

S Orosei 33G2

Osalla Beach Garden, Osalla di Orosei. **GPS**: n40,34474 e9,68619.

34 € 15-20 Ch WC included,cold shower.
Location: Comfortable, quiet. **Surface:** gravel/sand.
Easter-31/10.
Distance: 300m on the spot 3,5km.

S Quartu Sant'Elena 33G3

Is Canaleddus, Viale L. da vinci, SP17. **GPS**: n39,17957 e9,36489.

€ 10 . **Surface:** unpaved. 01/05-01/10.
Distance: pebbeled beach 150m on the spot.

Remarks: Beach parking.

S San Nicolò d'Arcidano 33G3

Viale Dei Giardini. **GPS**: n39,68530 e8,64570.

4 free € 4 € 4 Ch€ 4 € 4. **Surface:** asphalted.
01/01-31/12.
Distance: on the spot.

San Teodoro 33G2

Via Donat Cattin. **GPS**: n40,76658 e9,66884.

30 € 1/h, € 4/6h. **Location:** Noisy. **Surface:** asphalted.
Distance: 800m 1,8km 100m.

S Sant'Anna Arresi 33G3

Sosta camper Il Ruscello, Via del Cormorano, loc. Is Pillonis.
GPS: n38,97772 e8,62317.

80 € 16-20 Ch WC € 4 included. **Location:** Rural, comfortable, isolated. **Surface:** grassy/gravel. 01/01-31/12.
Distance: 3,5km on the spot.
Remarks: Shuttle bus to beach.

Siniscola 33G2

Spiaggia di Berchida. **GPS**: n40,48064 e9,80680.

+50 € 10/day. **Location:** Rural, isolated. **Surface:** unpaved.
01/01-31/12.
Distance: on the spot.

Solanas 33G3

Via al Mare. **GPS**: n39,13333 e9,43254.

10 free. **Surface:** sand.
Distance: 300m Sandy beach 300m.
Remarks: Beach parking.

S Sorso 33G2

Camp Site International, Via degli Oleandri, SP 81 km 13, Platamona Lido. **GPS**: n40,81566 e8,46563.

120 € 14-20 Ch WC € 3 included.
Location: Simple. **Surface:** unpaved. 01/04-30/09.
Distance: 350m 2km on the spot.

S Stintino 33G2

La Pineta, Loc. Pozzo S.Nicola, SP34. **GPS**: n40,86843 e8,23610.

40 € 17-19-21 Ch WCincluded hot shower € 1 € 5.
Location: Rural. **Surface:** grassy/sand. 01/01-31/12.
Distance: 3,5km on the spot.

S Tancau sul Mare 33G3

Area attrezzata Costa Orientale, Viale Mare.
GPS: n39,98321 e9,68608.

55 € 10-20, Jul/Aug electricity € 3 Ch WC included
€ 4. **Location:** Comfortable. **Surface:** asphalted/sand.
Easter-31/10.
Distance: Santa Maria Navarese 900m sandy beach 50m 50m
250m. **Remarks:** Shady.

S Tonara 33G3

Ostello delle Gioventù, Via Muggianeddu, 2. **GPS**: n40,02855 e9,17542.
5 € 10/24h Ch included. **Surface:** metalled.
01/01-31/12.
Distance: 500m on the spot.
Remarks: Steep ramp.

S Tortolì 33G3

Tanca Orrì, Lido Orrì. **GPS**: n39,90364 e9,68204.

80 € 16-20 Ch € 2,2Amp WC included,cold shower.
Location: Comfortable. **Surface:** unpaved. 01/01-31/12.
Distance: Tortolì 5km sandy beach 50m 100m.

S Tortolì 33G3

Area Camper Rocce Rosse, Via del Muflone. **GPS**: n39,86865 e9,67924.

IT

70 € 15-25, Aug € 35 € 4. **Location:** Rural. **Surface:** sand.
01/06-30/09.
Distance: Tortolì 9km sandy beach 250m on the spot mini market.
Remarks: Shady.

Tortoli 33G3

Baia Cea, Via del Muflone. **GPS:** n39,86874 e9,68034.

60 € 15-30 Ch WC included. **Location:** Rural.
Surface: sand. 01/05-30/09.
Distance: Tortolì 9km on the spot on the spot.

Valledoria 33G2

Punto Maragnani, Via La Ciaccia, Loc. Maragnani.
GPS: n40,92021 e8,79240.

90 € 15/24h Ch WC included. **Surface:** unpaved.
01/01-31/12.
Distance: 50m 200m.
Remarks: Motorhome washing place.

Villaputzu 33G3

Bella Vista Camper Service, Località Prumari, Porto corallo.
GPS: n39,43820 e9,63243.

50 € 10-25 Ch WC € 1 € 5 included.
Location: Rural. **Surface:** gravel.
Distance: Villaputzu 6km 50m 500m 7km.

Villasimius 33G3

Gli Aranci, Viale dei Carrubi, loc. Pranu Zinnigas.
GPS: n39,15977 e9,50865.

100 € 23 Ch WC included. **Location:** Comfortable, quiet. **Surface:** unpaved. 01/01-31/12.
Distance: 2km 4km 100m Eurospin 1km.

Remarks: Shuttle bus to beach.

Sicily

Agrigento 35B3

Albachiara, Viale Dune, San Leone. **GPS:** n37,24824 e13,60837.
40 € 15-30 Ch WC included . 01/01-31/12.
Distance: on the spot on the spot on the spot.

Agrigento 35B3

Il Pepe Rosa, Strada Statale Occidentale. **GPS:** n37,23082 e13,68551.
20 € 15 Ch WC . **Location:** Rural. **Surface:** gravel.
01/01-31/12.
Distance: 4km.
Remarks: Barbecue place.

Agrigento 35B3

Valle dei Templi, Viale Caduti di Marzabotto. **GPS:** n37,28881 e13,58181.
50 € 5. **Location:** Simple. **Surface:** sand. 01/01-31/12.
Distance: 450m on the spot.
Remarks: Near entrance and pay-desk of Valle dei Templi.

Augusta 35C3

Area Attrezzata Camper Nelly, SS114 - Km 118,5, Contrada Agnone Bagni. **GPS:** n37,31148 e15,09260.
€ 18-22 Ch WC included € 1 € 3. 15/05-15/09.
Distance: 6km 1,5km 180m.

Caccamo 35B3

SS 285, Via Termitana. **GPS:** n37,93410 e13,66115.
10 free Ch free. **Location:** Urban, simple.
Surface: gravel/metalled. 01/01-31/12.
Distance: 900m 300m 650m.
Remarks: At castle.

Caltagirone 35C3

Piazzale San Giovanni, Loc. San Giovanni.
GPS: n37,23949 e14,50717.
10 € 4, overnight stay free Ch included. **Location:** Urban.
Surface: asphalted. 01/01-31/12.
Distance: historical centre 700m 250m.

Caltanissetta 35B3

Via Guastaferro. **GPS:** n37,48959 e14,04515.
25 free Ch free. **Location:** Urban, simple, noisy.
Surface: asphalted. 01/01-31/12.
Distance: 2km on the spot on the spot.
Remarks: Near post office.

Camporotondo Etneo 35C3

Camperlot, Via A. Tripoli. **GPS:** n37,53593 e14,99321.
25 € 10-16 Ch WC . **Location:** Rural.
Surface: grassy/metalled. 01/01-31/12.
Distance: 12km 650m 650m.
Remarks: 20km from Etna, barbecue place, playground.

Castelbuono 35B3

Via Guiseppe Mazzini. **GPS:** n37,93694 e14,09296.
10 free Ch. **Location:** Urban, simple, quiet.
Surface: asphalted. 01/01-31/12.
Distance: 700m 700m.

Castellammare del Golfo 35B3

Playtime, Viale Leonardo da Vinci, SS187.
GPS: n38,02494 e12,89086.
20 € 16/24h Ch included € 2 € 4. **Location:** Rural.
Surface: grassy. 01/01-31/12.
Distance: 200m 1km.
Remarks: Monitored parking 24/24, swimming pool available.

Castelluzzo 35B3

SP16. **GPS:** n38,12220 e12,72524.

free. **Surface:** gravel.
Distance: on the spot.
Remarks: Beach parking, beach train.

Castelluzzo 35B3

Parking Macari, SP16. **GPS:** n38,13564 e12,73638.

free. **Surface:** sand.

Enna 35B3

Ennacamper, C/da S.Giuseppe, Pergusa. **GPS:** n37,52277 e14,29000.
30 € 20/24h € 5 ChService € 5 € 4 . **Location:** Rural, simple. **Surface:** sand. 01/01-31/12.
Distance: Enna 10km.
Remarks: Bicycle rental, free shuttle, cleaning motorhome € 5.

Francavilla di Sicilia 35C3

Maremonti, Via Cappuccini. **GPS:** n37,90855 e15,14347.

±50 gift . **Surface:** unpaved. 01/01-31/12.
Distance: 400m Riverbed.
Remarks: Gole dell'Alcantara 6km.

Furnari 35C2

Sosta CamperTonnarella, Corso Palermo 6.
GPS: n38,13218 e15,12469.

44 € 15-25 Ch WC included € 0,50 € 4.
Location: Simple. **Surface:** gravel. 01/01-31/12.
Distance: on the spot on the spot 150m 250m.
Remarks: Monitored parking, excursion to the Eolie-islands.

Gangi 35B3

SP14. **GPS:** n37,79203 e14,21079.
15 € 15 Ch included . **Surface:** gravel/sand.
01/01-31/12.
Distance: 750m 750m.
Remarks: Monitored parking.

Giardini Naxos 35C3

Parking Lagani, Via Stralcina 22, zona Recanati.
GPS: n37,82092 e15,26753.

IT

30 € 15-30 Ch WCincluded € 1,(summer) € 5.
Location: Urban. **Surface:** metalled. 01/01-31/12.
Distance: on the spot 200m 50m 200m Bus to Taormina 300m.
Remarks: Special tariff for long stay during the winter, bar, view on Etna and Taormina.

S Giardini Naxos 35C3
Eden Parking, Via Stracina. **GPS**: n37,82188 e15,26701.

30 € 7-25 Ch € 0,35/kWh WC € 1. **Surface:** grassy.
01/01-31/12.
Distance: 500m > Taormina.

S Giardini Naxos 35C3
Holiday Sun, Viale Stracina 20. **GPS**: n37,82109 e15,26784.
30 € 7-25 Ch (30x),16Amp WCincluded.
Location: Urban. **Surface:** grassy/gravel. 01/01-31/12.
Distance: 500m beach 500m on the spot > Taormina.

Tourist information Giardini Naxos:
Sa-morning.

S Ispica 35C3
Associazione Camper Club Porto Ulisse.
GPS: n36,69761 e14,98647.
30 € 16/24h Ch. **Surface:** grassy.
Easter-30/09.
Distance: 100m.

S Licata 35B3
Giummarella, Via Salvo D'Acquisto. **GPS**: n37,09943 e13,94267.
30 € 10-20 Ch included. **Surface:** gravel.
01/01-31/12.
Distance: 600m.

S Licata 35B3
Ristorante La Sorgente, Loc. Pisciotto.
GPS: n37,12666 e13,85194.

80 Jun € 15, Jul € 20, Aug € 25 Ch WC included.
Location: Rural. **Surface:** gravel. 01/01-31/12.
Distance: Licata 9km on the spot on the spot.
Remarks: Stairs to sandy beach.

S Marina di Ragusa 35C3
Marina Caravan, Via Portovenere 57. **GPS**: n36,78472 e14,56486.

60 € 15-20 Ch WC € 4 included. **Surface:** grassy.
01/01-31/12.
Distance: 500m 300m 100m 100m 200m.
Remarks: Water/drainage at each pitch, bicycle rental.

S Marina di Ragusa 35C3
Via Falconara. **GPS**: n36,78821 e14,54697.
40 free Chfree WC. **Surface:** asphalted. 01/01-31/12.
Distance: 1km 1km.

S Marsala 35A3
Sibiliana Beach Village, Contrada Fossarunza 205/z 14.
GPS: n37,73520 e12,47497.
100 € 20 Ch WC included. **Surface:** unpaved.
Distance: 50m.

S Marsala 35A3
Nautisub Club S. Teodoro, Contrada Birgi.
GPS: n37,91046 e12,46178.

± 50 € 15-20 Ch € 2,50. **Location:** Rural.
Surface: grassy. 01/05-30/09.
Distance: 5km Sandy beach on the spot.

S Marsala 35A3
Via Colonnello Maltese. **GPS**: n37,79497 e12,43270.
free Chfree. **Location:** Urban. **Surface:** asphalted.
01/01-31/12 Su-morning (market).
Distance: 500m on the spot 450m 200m.

S Marsala 35A3

Camping Lilybeo Village, Contrada Bambina, 131 B/bis.
GPS: n37,74791 e12,49614.
40 € 20, 01/06-15/07 € 25, 16/07-01/09 € 30 Ch (40x),16Amp WC € 5 included.
Surface: grassy/metalled. 01/01-31/12.
Distance: 7km 10km 3km 3km 700m 1km 100m 3km.
Remarks: Possibility for reservation.

S Mineo 35C3
Le Bave di Bacco, Strada Provinciale 86. **GPS**: n37,24137 e14,72239.
guests free. **Location:** Rural, simple, isolated.
Surface: grassy. 01/01-31/12.
Distance: 5km.

S Montallegro 35B3
Vizzi Parking, Via Lungomare, SP87. **GPS**: n37,38206 e13,30932.
€ 15 € 3 Ch € 2. **Surface:** gravel. 01/06-01/10.
Distance: 100m.

S Montallegro 35B3
Agriturismo Torre Salsa, Bove Marina.
GPS: n37,37583 e13,32222.

20 € 17-24, 2 pers incl., 1 pers + € 5 € 4 Ch according consumption WC € 1 € 6 € 1,50/h. **Location:** Rural.
Surface: grassy. 01/01-31/12.
Distance: 700m on the spot.
Remarks: Also pitches on the beach without service, estate 300 acres, hiking and mountain bike trails.

S Montevago 35B3
Agricamper Villa dei Pini, Via Piersanti Mattarella.
GPS: n37,70083 e12,98000.
€ 15 Ch included. 01/01-31/12.
Distance: 200m.

S Montevago 35B3
Centro Terme Acqua Pia, Loc. Acque Calde. **GPS**: n37,70602 e12,98092.
20 2 days-1night € 15 + € 15/pp € 3. 01/04-31/10.
Remarks: Including access spa resort.

S Motta Camastra 35C3
S185, fraz. Ficarazzi. **GPS**: n37,88870 e15,17633.

10 € 15 Ch WC included. **Location:** Rural.
Surface: grassy/gravel. 01/01-31/12.
Distance: 300m 1km.
Remarks: In front of entrance of Gole dell'Alcantara.

S Noto 35C3
Airone, Via San Corrado, Lido di Noto. **GPS**: n36,85916 e15,11555.

50 Jun/Sep € 14-16, Aug € 20 Ch € 2 WC hot shower € 0,50. **Surface:** grassy/sand. 01/04-30/09.
Distance: 100m 100m 750m Bus to Noto 100m.

S Noto 35C3
Eucalyptus Park, Via delle Sabbie d'Oro, Lido di Noto.
GPS: n36,85605 e15,11372.
48 € 16/24h Ch WC. **Location:** Urban.
Surface: gravel. 01/01-31/12.
Distance: on the spot 300m 400m 300m.

S Noto 35C3
Il Canneto, Viale Lido di Noto, Lido di Noto.
GPS: n36,86083 e15,11944.

55 € 10-18 Chincluded € 2 WC.
Location: Urban. **Surface:** grassy/sand.
01/01-31/12.
Distance: on the spot 200m 1,2km.

IT

Remarks: Bread-service and meals, direct access to the sandy beach.

Noto 35C3

NotoParking, Contrada Faldino, Noto. **GPS**: n36,88353 e15,08595.

40 € 18 Ch included € 3 WC € 1. **Location:** Rural. **Surface:** grassy/gravel. 01/01-31/12.
Distance: 1km 3km 5km 200m 200m 150m.
Remarks: Bread-service, organised excursions in the surroundings, free shuttle bus to Noto.

Noto 35C3

Oasi Park Falconara, Viale Ionio, Lido di Noto.
GPS: n36,87001 e15,12872.
50 € 15, 01/06-31/10 € 17-24 Ch WC included.
Surface: gravel. 01/01-31/12.
Distance: Noto 4km beach 700m pizzeria 50m.
Remarks: Shuttle bus to Noto and beach.

Noto 35C3

Parcheggio Calamosche, Oasi di Vendicari.
GPS: n36,81611 e15,09888.

40-50 € 15 WC included. **Surface:** grassy.
01/06-30/09.
Distance: Noto 10km 20 min walking bar/restaurant.

Oliveri 35C2

Azimut Sosta Camper, Corso Cristoforo Colombo.
GPS: n38,12840 e15,05833.
100 € 12-22 Ch (100x),6Amp WC included.
Location: Rural, comfortable. **Surface:** grassy/gravel.
01/03-31/10.
Distance: 500m, Tindari 1,2km 2,5km beach 50m 50m 50m 200m 10m 100m 100m 200m.
Remarks: Monitored parking, barbecue place.

Pachino 35C3

Area camper Venere, Contrada Granelli. **GPS**: n36,70100 e15,02790.
€ 20-26, 5 pers. incl Ch WC included.
Surface: unpaved. 01/06-30/09.
Distance: Sandy beach.

Pachino 35C3

Dragomar, Strada Marzamemi Portopalo di Capo Passero, Marzamemi.
GPS: n36,72732 e15,12083.

30 € 12-21 Ch € 3 WC included. **Surface:** gravel.
01/01-31/12.
Distance: on the spot 400m 600m.
Remarks: Seaview, no beach.

Palermo 35B3

Green Car Palermo, Via Quarto dei Mille 11b.
GPS: n38,11016 e13,34307.
25 € 20/24h Ch included. **Location:** Rural, simple.
Surface: asphalted. 01/01-31/12.
Distance: piazza Indipendenza 300m 50m 50m 200m.
Remarks: Monitored parking 24/24.

Palermo 35B3

Parcheggio Saiwash, Via Gaetano Costa 25. **GPS**: n38,09137 e13,33543.
€ 15/24h Ch included.
Location: Urban. **Surface:** metalled.
01/01-31/12.
Distance: historical centre 3km 2km 750m 750m 100m.
Remarks: Monitored parking 24/24.

Palermo 35B3

Parking Giotto, Piazzale John Lennon. **GPS**: n38,13240 e13,33148.
36 € 20/24h Ch included free. **Location:** Central.
Surface: asphalted. 01/01-31/12.
Remarks: 3 nights stay 10% discount.

Palermo 35B3

Parking Ospedale Cervello, Via Trabucco. **GPS**: n38,15619 e13,31354.
free . **Location:** Urban, simple, isolated. **Surface:** metalled.
01/01-31/12.
Distance: on the spot 1,5km 2km 400m.
Remarks: Nearby hospital.

Palermo 35B3

Parking Pippo Uscè, Via Giuseppe Paratore 40.
GPS: n38,09588 e13,37198.
40 € 15/24h Ch included. **Location:** Urban.
Surface: metalled. 01/01-31/12.
Distance: city centre 3km 400m 300m 100m.

Palermo 35B3

Via Uditore 17. **GPS**: n38,13140 e13,32515.
20 € 18 Ch included WC . **Location:** Urban.
Surface: gravel. 01/01-31/12.
Distance: 4km 200m 150m bus 110 > centre.
Remarks: Monitored parking, barbecue place, shuttle bus to city centre.

Palermo 35B3

Piazza Alcide De Gasperi. **GPS**: n38,15170 e13,33944.
free. **Location:** Urban. **Surface:** asphalted.
01/01-31/12.
Distance: 3,5km on the spot 350m bus 101/106 > centre.
Remarks: Nearby stadium.

Palermo 35B3

Freesbee Parking, Via Imperatore Federico 116.
GPS: n38,14722 e13,35277.
100 € 15-18 Ch included € 3/24h WC € 1.
Location: Urban. **Surface:** asphalted. 01/01-31/12.
Distance: Cathedral Palermo 400m 2km 50m 1km 150m.
Remarks: At motorhome dealer, 24/24 surveillance.

Tourist information Palermo:

U.I.A.T. (Ufficio Informazioni e di Accoglienza Turistica), Piazza Castelnuovo, 34, www.regione.sicilia.it/turismo. Capital of Sicilly, port and economical heart of the Island.
San Giovanni degli Eremiti.
Santa Catarina.
Vucciria, Via Cassari-Argenteria. Palermo's most famous, picturesque and historic market.

Piano San Paolo 35C3

Terra Nostra, Via Piano San Paolo 27. **GPS**: n37,16016 e14,52840.
20 € 20 Ch included . **Location:** Rural. **Surface:** sand.
01/01-31/12.
Distance: on the spot on the spot on the spot.

Piazza Armerina 35B3

Via G. Lo Giudice. **GPS**: n37,38711 e14,37041.
free. **Location:** Urban, simple. **Surface:** asphalted.
01/01-31/12.
Distance: 200m 50m 50m.

Piazza Armerina 35B3

Agricamper Valle Dell'Elsa, SS65. **GPS**: n37,30173 e14,39605.
12 € 15/24h Ch WC included. **Location:** Rural, comfortable, isolated, quiet. **Surface:** metalled. 01/01-31/12.
Distance: Piazza Armerina 20km on the spot.
Remarks: At swimming pool.

Piazza Armerina 35B3

Agriturismo Agricasale, Contrada Ciavarina.
GPS: n37,34032 e14,38840.
40 € 15 Ch included WC . **Location:** Rural, comfortable, isolated, quiet. **Surface:** unpaved.
01/01-31/12.
Distance: Piazza Armerina 13km bar/restaurant.
Remarks: Swimming pool € 3/pppd.

Piazza Armerina 35B3

Agriturismo Gigliotto, SS 117bis km60. **GPS**: n37,29051 e14,38721.
20 € 20, 01/04-31/10 € 30 Ch WC included.
Location: Rural, comfortable, quiet. **Surface:** gravel.
01/01-31/12.
Distance: Piazza Armerina 13km.
Remarks: Swimming pool incl.

Piazza Armerina 35B3

SP90. **GPS**: n37,36805 e14,33421.
20 € 3-15/24h Ch included. **Location:** Rural, simple.
Surface: unpaved. 01/01-31/12.
Distance: Piazza Armerina 4,5km 400m.
Remarks: Villa Romana del Casale 400m.

Porto Empedocle 35B3

Punta Piccola Park, Scala dei Turchi, SP68.
GPS: n37,28916 e13,49250.

99 € 15-20, 01/07-31/08 € 23 Ch (65x) WC € 1 included. **Surface:** gravel. 01/01-31/12.
Distance: 2,5km on the spot 200m 1km.
Remarks: Shopping service, direct access to the sandy beach.

Tourist information Porto Empedocle:

Valle dei Templi, Agrigento. The Valley of The Temples, archeology.

Portopalo di Capo Passero 35C3

Cicogna, Via Carlo Alberto, 2. **GPS**: n36,68333 e15,13638.
20 Jun/Sep € 12, Jul/Aug € 16 Ch (20x)included .
Surface: gravel.
Distance: 50m sandy beach 300m.

Pozzallo 35C3

Il Giardino di Epicuro, SP67. **GPS**: n36,73128 e14,86240.

50 € 20 Ch (22x)€ 3 cold shower. **Surface:** grassy/sand.
01/05-30/09.
Distance: 500m on the spot 50m 300m.
Remarks: Sandy beach.

Pozzallo 35C3

Salvamar, Zona Porto di Pozzallo. **GPS**: n36,71541 e14,82240.

30 11/09-31/05 € 15, 01/06-10/09 € 20 2 pers. incl Ch included. **Surface:** grassy. 01/01-31/12.
Distance: 200m 500m 1km.

Realmonte 35B3

Sosta camper Zanzibar, C/o Capo Rossello.
GPS: n37,29495 e13,45438.

100 Jul € 10/24h, Aug € 22/24h Ch WC included € 1,hot

shower € 1. **Location:** Rural. **Surface:** gravel.
summer.
Distance: sandy beach on the spot 150m.
Remarks: Bus to Valle dei Templi (€ 7/pp, min. 4 pers).

S Reitano 35B3

Via Lungomare Colonna. **GPS**: n38,01407 e14,33081.
70 € 10 Ch € 0,50. **Location:** Simple.
15/07-18/09.
Distance: 500m on the spot.

S Ribera 35B3

Kamemi, SS115, Secca Grande. **GPS**: n37,43840 e13,24469.
Camperstop € 10 Ch. 01/01-31/12 01/08-24/08 No Camperstop.

S Roccalumera 35C3

Park Jonio, Via Collegio, SS114 Roccalumera > Nizza di Sicilia.
GPS: n37,97943 e15,39752.

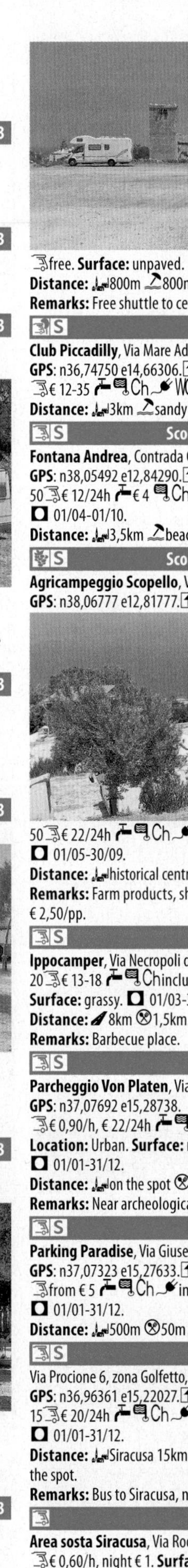

60 € 11-17, Jul/Aug € 15-20, 3 pers. incl Ch (60x).
Surface: gravel.
Distance: within walking distance 250m Bar/snack on the spot. **Remarks:** In front of Centro Sportivo.

S San Giovanni La Punta 35C3

Entertainmentcity Isivillage, Via Fisichelli 63.
GPS: n37,58929 e15,08612.
guests free WC. **Location:** Rural. **Surface:** asphalted.
01/01-31/12.
Distance: 1,5km on the spot 550m.

S San Vito Lo Capo 35B3

Al Faro, Via Faro 36. **GPS**: n38,18472 e12,73277.

30 € 18-30 Ch included hot shower € 1.
Surface: asphalted/grassy. 01/05-31/10.
Distance: 1km on the spot 300m 1km.
Remarks: Terrace on the sea, no beach, sandy beach 400m.

S San Vito Lo Capo 35B3

Parking camper Giovanni, Via Savoia 13.
GPS: n38,16222 e12,73666.

90 € 12-18 Ch (90x) WC € 0,50 € 5 included.
Surface: gravel. 01/01-31/12.
Distance: 300m 1,4km 1km 1km.
Remarks: Free shuttle to beach.

S San Vito Lo Capo 35B3

Monte Monaco, Via del Secco, 80. **GPS**: n38,17438 e12,74552.
€ 12, Jun € 15, Jul € 20, Aug € 25 Ch WC € 1.
Surface: gravel. 01/04-31/10.
Distance: 850m 300m 300m 850m.

San Vito Lo Capo 35B3

Via la Piana. **GPS**: n38,16886 e12,74307.

free. **Surface:** unpaved.
Distance: 800m 800m.
Remarks: Free shuttle to centre.

S Scicli 35C3

Club Piccadilly, Via Mare Adriatico, Donnalucata.
GPS: n36,74750 e14,66306.
€ 12-35 Ch WC. 01/01-31/12.
Distance: 3km sandy beach 100m.

S Scopello 35B3

Fontana Andrea, Contrada Ciauli, SS 187.
GPS: n38,05492 e12,84290.
50 € 12/24h € 4 Ch € 2. **Location:** Rural. **Surface:** grassy.
01/04-01/10.
Distance: 3,5km beach 300m 500m.

S Scopello 35B3

Agricampeggio Scopello, Via Finanzierè Vincenzo Mazzarell.
GPS: n38,06777 e12,81777.

50 € 22/24h Ch included € 1. **Surface:** gravel.
01/05-30/09.
Distance: historical centre 200m 1,5km 100m 400m.
Remarks: Farm products, shuttle to beach and Riserva dello Zingaro € 2,50/pp.

S Siracusa 35C3

Ippocamper, Via Necropoli del Fusco 18. **GPS**: n37,09855 e15,18905.
20 € 13-18 Ch included WC € 1 € 3. **Location:** Rural.
Surface: grassy. 01/03-31/10.
Distance: 8km 1,5km.
Remarks: Barbecue place.

S Siracusa 35C3

Parcheggio Von Platen, Via Augusto Von Platen 38.
GPS: n37,07692 e15,28738.
€ 0,90/h, € 22/24h Ch (5x)included WC.
Location: Urban. **Surface:** metalled.
01/01-31/12.
Distance: on the spot 700m 500m on the spot.
Remarks: Near archeological site and museum, shuttle € 1/pp.

S Siracusa 35C3

Parking Paradise, Via Giuseppe Agnello 1.
GPS: n37,07323 e15,27633.
from € 5 Ch included. **Surface:** grassy/metalled.
01/01-31/12.
Distance: 500m 50m 500m.

S Siracusa 35C3

Via Procione 6, zona Golfetto, Fontane Bianche.
GPS: n36,96361 e15,22027.
15 € 20/24h Ch WC included. **Surface:** unpaved.
01/01-31/12.
Distance: Siracusa 15km on the spot 800m 600m on the spot.
Remarks: Bus to Siracusa, natural swimming pool in sea.

Siracusa 35C3

Area sosta Siracusa, Via Rodi 15. **GPS**: n37,06436 e15,28710.
€ 0,60/h, night € 1. **Surface:** asphalted. 01/01-31/12.
Distance: Ortigia 500m 50m.

S Siracusa 35C3

Agriturismo Terrauzza sul Mare, Via Blanco 8.
GPS: n37,01169 e15,28736.
15 € 15/24h Ch included. **Location:** Rural. **Surface:** sand.
01/01-31/12.
Distance: 100m 1,5km.

Remarks: Regional products.

S Sutera 35B3

Piazza Rettore Carruba. **GPS**: n37,52450 e13,72960.
free Ch. **Location:** Urban. **Surface:** asphalted.
01/01-31/12.
Distance: on the spot on the spot 300m.

S Taormina 35C3

Sosta Camper Pier Giovanni, Trappitello, Via Spagnuolo.
GPS: n37,82196 e15,24502.

15 € 10-20 Ch WC included. **Surface:** grassy/metalled.
01/01-31/12.
Distance: 500m 4km 300m 300m.
Remarks: Shuttle bus to city centre.

S Terme Vigliatore 35C2

Area Trinacria, Via Lungomare Marchesana.
GPS: n38,14018 e15,14596.

120 € 15, Aug € 18 Ch included. **Surface:** grassy.
01/01-31/12.
Distance: 50m pizzeria 200m 200m.
Remarks: Excursion to the Eolie-islands.

S Trapani 35B3

Hotel Le Saline, SP21 km4, contrada Nubia-Paceco.
GPS: n37,98304 e12,53106.
20 € 15-20 Ch. **Surface:** metalled.
01/01-31/12.

IT

Luxembourg

Capital: Luxembourg
Government: Grand duchy
Official Language: French, German, Luxembourgish
Population: 582.291 (2016)
Area: 2,586 km²

General information
Calling code: 00352
General emergency: 112
Currency: Euro

Regulations for overnight stays
Parking overnight and camping by public road is forbidden. Motorhome-service only on campsites.

Additional public holidays 2018
May 1 Labor day
June 23 National Holiday
August 15 Assumption of the Virgin Mary
November 1 All Saints' Day

Time Zone
Winter (Standard Time) GMT+1
Summer (DST) GMT+2

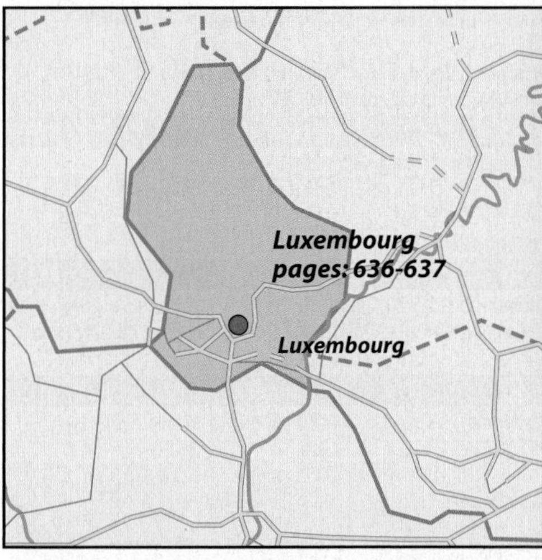

Berdorf 16E1

Camperhafen Martbusch, 3, Beim Martbusch.
GPS: n49,82660 e6,34599.

9 € 8-10 € 1/100liter Ch € 0,50/kWh € 3 included.
Location: Rural, comfortable, quiet. **Surface:** asphalted.
01/01-31/12.
Distance: 500m on the spot 7km 500m on the spot on the spot.
Remarks: Max. 2 nights, check in at reception campsite.

Bleesbrück 16E1

Camping Bleesbrück, 1, Bleesbreck. **GPS**: n49,87270 e6,18940.

3 € 15 Ch WC included.
Location: Rural, simple, noisy. **Surface:** grassy.
01/04-15/10.
Distance: 2,5km on the spot 2,5km.
Remarks: Arrival >18h departure <9h, if not camping tariff.

Diekirch 16E1

Camping de la Sûre, Route de Gilsdorf.
GPS: n49,86597 e6,16489.

9 € 16 + € 1,50/pp tourist tax, dog € 2,50 Ch WC included sanitary only summer € 3 free. **Location:** Comfortable, central.
Surface: grasstiles/grassy. 01/01-31/12.
Distance: 100m 100m 100m (permit € 4/month) 100m 100m.
Remarks: Max. 2 days, water closed during wintertime.

Tourist information Diekirch:
Conservatoire National de véhicules historique, 20-22, rue de Stavelot. Exhibition of historical vehicles.
10-18h Mo.
Musée National de l'histoire militaire, 10, Bamertal. War museum.
Tue-Su 10-18h Mo.
Rue de Marché. Tue 8-12h.
Al Dikkirch. Folk festival. 2nd week Jul.

Dudelange 16E1

Parking Gare-Usines. GPS: n49,47176 e6,07772.

8 free Ch free. **Location:** Simple, noisy.
Surface: grasstiles/grassy. 01/01-31/12.
Distance: 1km 4,1km near train station.
Remarks: Well situated for visiting Luxembourg city, 20min by train, max. 48h.

Tourist information Dudelange:
Musée National des Mines de Fer, Carreau de la Mine, Rumelange. History of the mines.

Ermsdorf 16E1

Neumühle. GPS: n49,83917 e6,22503.
€ 16-20,50 Ch WC € 4 included.
Location: Rural, comfortable, isolated, quiet. **Surface:** grassy.
15/03-31/10.
Distance: 1km on the spot 6km.

Heiderscheid 16E1

Camperhafen Fuussekaul, Fuussekaul 4.
GPS: n49,87806 e5,99278.
35 € 10, Jul/Aug € 15 Ch (35x),16Amp WC included € 1/5minutes € 4/2,50 € 4,90/day. **Location:** Luxurious, isolated, quiet. **Surface:** grasstiles/metalled. 01/01-31/12.
Distance: 1km 8km 8km 5km on the spot on the spot on the spot on the spot.

Tourist information Heiderscheid:
Heischter Mart. Traditional market. end Jul.

Heiderscheidergrund 16E1

Camping Bissen, 11, Millewee. **GPS**: n49,90495 e5,95595.
3 € 10, 10/07-15/08 € 15 Ch included.
Surface: gravel. 01/01-31/12.
Distance: on the spot on the spot.
Remarks: Quick-Stop: >17h - <10h, along river.

Hoscheid 11E3

Hotel-Restaurant Des Ardennes, Haaptstrooss.
GPS: n49,94675 e6,08084.

4 free with a meal WC included.
Location: Simple, quiet. **Surface:** asphalted. 01/02-15/12.
Distance: on the spot on the spot on the spot.
Remarks: Parking behind hotel.

Junglinster 16E1

Rue Emile Nilles. **GPS**: n49,70421 e6,25123.

3 free € 0,10/10liter Ch (4x)€ 0,50/kWh.
Location: Simple. **Surface:** asphalted. 01/01-31/12.
Distance: 200m.

Larochette 16E1

Camping Auf Kengert. **GPS**: n49,80021 e6,19788.
2 € 17-26 Ch included. 01/03-08/11.
Remarks: Quick-Stop: >19h - <9h.

Tourist information Larochette:
Schiessentümpel. Waterfall with three cascades.
Château. Easter-Oct, 10-18h, daily.

Liefrange 16E1

Camperhafen Leifreg, 14, Haaptstrooss. **GPS**: n49,91136 e5,87438.

23 € 10, Jul/Aug € 15 Ch WC included € 1.

Location: Rural, isolated, quiet. **Surface:** grasstiles/metalled.
01/04-01/11.
Distance: on the spot Obersauer Stausee 500m on the spot.

Luxemburg 16E1

Glacis, Boulevard de la Foire /Av. de la Faiencerie.
GPS: n49,61602 e6,12246.

20 Mo-Fr € 1/h. **Location:** Urban, simple, noisy.
Surface: asphalted.
01/01-31/12.
Distance: centre 650m on the spot.
Remarks: Overnight stay allowed.

Tourist information Luxemburg:
Luxembourg City Tourist Office, Place d'Armes, www.lcto.lu. Citadel and fortifications have been changed in parks and walks, especially in the lower city. 01/04-31/10 Mo-Sa 9-19h, Su 10-18h, 01/11-31/03 Mo-Sa 9-18h.
Casemates du Bock, Montée de Clausen. Casemates, 21km.
01/03-31/10 10-20.30h.
Musée National d'histoire et d'art, Marché-aux-Poissons. Archeological findings. Tue-Su 10-18h.
Palais Grand Ducal, 17, rue du Marché-aux-Herbes. Ducal palace.
01/07-31/08.
Cathédrale Notre-Dame, Rue Notre Dame.
daily 10-12h, 14-17.30h.
Crypte Archéologique, Montée de Clausen.
01/03-31/10 10-17h. free.
Marché-aux-puces, place d'Armes. Bric-a-brac.
2nd + 4th Sa of the month.
Markt, place Guillaume.
Wed + Sa morning.
Schueberfouer. Folk festival.
30/08-15/09.

Nommern 16E1

Europacamping Nommerlayen, Rue Nommerlayen.
GPS: n49,78450 e6,16414.

13 € 10-20 Ch € 2/2kWh WC € 5,25/4,75 included.
Location: Rural, comfortable, isolated, quiet.
Surface: grasstiles.
01/03-06/11.
Distance: 1km on the spot on the spot 1,5km on the spot.
Remarks: Quick-Stop: >17h - <10h.

Redange/Attert 16E1

Rue de la Piscine 24. **GPS**: n49,76918 e5,89459.

12 free Ch (5x)free. **Location:** Rural, simple, quiet.
Surface: asphalted. 01/01-31/12.
Distance: 800m on the spot.
Remarks: Max. 48h.

Schwebsange 16E1

Camport, Rue du Port. **GPS**: n49,51163 e6,36249.

18 € 10, 2 pers.incl Ch € 2,50 WC € 2 included,at restaurant. **Location:** Rural, comfortable, quiet. **Surface:** grasstiles.
01/04-31/10.
Distance: 500m fishing permit obligatory on the spot on the spot 500m.

Tourist information Schwebsange:
A Possen, 1 rue Aloyse Sandt, Bech-Kleinmacher. Folkore and wine museum. 01/05-31/10 14-19h, 01/03-30/04, 01/11-31/12 Fri-Su 14-19h Mo.

Vianden 16E1

39, rue du Sanatorium. **GPS**: n49,93717 e6,20556.

free. **Location:** Simple, central, quiet.
Surface: asphalted. 01/01-31/12.
Distance: 500m 100m 500m 500m on the spot on the spot on the spot.
Remarks: At the chair-lifts (télesiege).

Tourist information Vianden:
SEO. Large hydro-electric power-station. Easter-Sep 10-20h. free.
Bakkerij museum, 96-98, Grand-Rue. Easter-Oct 11-17h Mo.
Château de Vianden. 10-16 02/11, 25/12, 01/01.
Nessmoort. Nuts market. 2nd Su Oct.
Télesiège. Chair-lift. Easter-Oct.

Wiltz 11E3

Kaul, Rue Joseph Simon. **GPS**: n49,97173 e5,93433.

3 free € 1 Ch. **Location:** Rural, simple, isolated, quiet.
Surface: gravel. 01/01-31/12.
Distance: 500m 500m.
Remarks: Recreation park, near campsite.

Montenegro

Capital: Podgorica
Government: parliamentary republic
Official Language: Montenegrin
Population: 644,578 (2016)
Area: 13,812 km^2

General information
Dialling code: 0382
General emergency: 112
Currency: Euro
Credit cards are accepted almost everywhere.

Regulations for overnight stays
Free overnight stay is not allowed.

Additional public holidays 2018
January 7-8 Christmas (Orthodox)
May 1 Labour Day
May 21 Independence Day
July 13 Statehood Day

Time Zone
Winter (Standard Time) GMT+1
Summer (DST) GMT+2

Bijela 39A4
Zlokovic. **GPS**: n42,45768 e18,66873.
50 € 21 Ch included.
Surface: grassy/sand. 01/03-01/11.
Distance: 2km on the spot on the spot on the spot.

Dobrilovina 39A4
Kamp Eco Oaza. **GPS**: n43,01780 e19,40936.
25 € 15 Ch included. **Location:** Rural. **Surface:** grassy.
01/01-31/12.
Distance: 200m on the spot.

Gusinje 39A4
Krojet. **GPS**: n42,55053 e19,82502.
15 € 10. **Location:** Rural. **Surface:** grassy. 01/04-30/10.
Distance: on the spot.

Kotor 39A4
E65. **GPS**: n42,42761 e18,76881.
20 € 1/h Ch free. **Location:** Urban.
Surface: gravel. 01/01-31/12.
Distance: 500m on the spot on the spot 200m 200m.

Morinj 39A4
Naluka. **GPS**: n42,48694 e18,65214.
40 € 20 Ch included.
Surface: grassy/sand. 01/05-01/10.
Distance: on the spot on the spot 600m.

Petnjica 39A4
Jatak. **GPS**: n42,97815 e19,07510.
10 € 10 Ch included € 2 € 2.
Surface: grassy. 01/06-01/09.
Distance: on the spot.

Petrovac 39A4
Maslina, Buljarica bb 300. **GPS**: n42,19833 e18,96583.
100 € 15,60 Ch included € 3.
Surface: grassy. 01/01-31/12.
Distance: 2km 200m 300m.

Podgorica 39A4
Hostel Izvor. **GPS**: n42,48363 e19,30621.
10 € 15 Ch included.
Surface: concrete. 01/01-31/12.
Distance: on the spot.

Rasova 39A4
Miro Tara-Regata, Djrdjevica Tara. **GPS**: n43,14862 e19,29217.
20 € 15 Ch included.
Surface: grassy/gravel. 01/04-30/10.

Ulcinj 39A4
Miami beach. **GPS**: n41,90870 e19,24978.
30 € 20 Ch included.
Surface: grassy/sand. 01/05-01/10.
Distance: on the spot on the spot on the spot.

Ulcinj 39A4
Safari beach. **GPS**: n41,90466 e19,26533.

130 € 15, 15/6-15/9 € 30 Ch included € 3.
Surface: grassy. 01/01-31/12.
Distance: 7km on the spot on the spot on the spot.

Utjeha-Bušat 39A4
Oliva, Uvala Maslina-Utjeha. **GPS**: n42,01028 e19,15111.
25 € 15 Ch included. **Surface:** grassy. 01/04-30/11.
Distance: on the spot on the spot on the spot.

Utjeha-Bušat 39A4
Utjeha, Uvala Maslina-Utjeha. **GPS**: n42,01012 e19,15095.

20 € 14, 20/6-1/9€ 16 Ch included against payment.
Surface: grassy. 15/04-01/11.
Distance: on the spot on the spot on the spot.

Žabljak 39A4
Kod Boce. **GPS**: n43,14352 e19,11580.
30 € 6 Ch included € 2. **Surface:** grassy/gravel.
15/04-30/10.

Žabljak 39A4
Razvrsje. **GPS**: n43,14443 e19,11510.
20 € 10 Ch included.
Surface: grassy/gravel. 01/01-31/12.
Distance: 900m on the spot.

The Netherlands

Capital: Amsterdam
Government: Constitutional monarchy
Official Language: Dutch
Population: 17,016,967 (2016)
Area: 41,543 km²

General information
Country dial code: 0031
General emergency: 112
Currency: Euro
Credit cards are not accepted everywhere.

Regulations for overnight stays
Wild camping is forbidden in the Netherlands. Several motorhome-friendly municipalities have regulated facilities where overnight parking is allowed.

Additional public holidays 2018
April 2 Easter Monday
April 27 King's day
May 5 Liberation day
May 21 Pentecost Monday
December 26 Boxing day

Time Zone
Winter (Standard Time) GMT+1
Summer (DST) GMT+2

NL

North Holland

Abbenes 9C2

Camperplaats 't Groene Hart, Kaagweg 50.
GPS: n52,22630 e4,61911.

25 € 14 Chincluded (6x)€ 2/24h,10Amp WC€ 0,20 €1 free. **Location:** Rural, comfortable, quiet.
Surface: grassy/gravel. 15/03-01/11.
Distance: 4km 900m 1,5km 1,5km 1,5km 4km Leiden <> Amsterdam on the spot on the spot.
Remarks: Bicycle rental.

Amsterdam 9C1

Amsterdam City Camp, Papaverweg 50 Noord 4.
GPS: n52,39847 e4,90010.

50 € 18, 01/08-31/08 € 21 + tourist tax € 2,50/pp, dog € 1 Ch (30x)€ 4,10Amp included . **Location:** Urban, comfortable. **Surface:** metalled. 01/01-31/12.
Distance: 2km 20m 100m 1km 1,5km 500m.
Remarks: Video surveillance, free ferry to city centre.

Amsterdam 9C1

Fam. Ackermann, Lutkemeerweg 149, Amsterdam-Osdorp.
GPS: n52,36358 e4,77240.

16 € 15, tourist tax incl € 4 Ch € 4/day.
Surface: metalled.
01/01-31/12.
Distance: 10km city centre 2km
Tram > Amsterdam 1,2km.
Remarks: Arrival <18h. Via Osdorperweg, special license.

Tourist information Amsterdam:
VVV, Stationsplein 10 en Leidseplein 1, www.iamsterdam.com. City Card gives entrance to museums, public transport, boattrip on the canals etc., 24h/€ 55, 48h/€ 65, 72h/€ 75, available at VVV.
Canalbus. Boat trip on the canals.
€ 21.
Stelling van Amsterdam. Forts built to protect Amsterdam.
Albert Cuyp, Albert Cuyp. Market with over 260 stalls.
daily 9-17h Su.
Antiek, Noordermarkt.
Sa 9-17h.
Artis, Plantage Kerklaan 38-40. City-zoo.
9-17/18h.
Villa Arena, Arena boulevard. Furniture mall, 50 shops.
Tue-Sa 10-18h, Mo 13-18h.

Andijk 9D1

Jachthaven Andijk, Nieuwe Haven 1. **GPS**: n52,74521 e5,18443.
3 € 10 Ch WC .
Surface: asphalted. 01/05-31/10.
Distance: on the spot on the spot on the spot on the spot on the spot.

De Rijp 9C1

Bloembolbedrijf Stoop, Zuiddijk 34. **GPS**: n52,54813 e4,83416.

4 € 7 € 1/100liter (4x)€ 2/day. **Location:** Rural, simple, quiet. **Surface:** concrete. 01/01-31/12.
Distance: 3km 200m 200m 3km 3km.

Den Helder 7C3

Willemsoord, Willemsoord 47. **GPS**: n52,96134 e4,76856.

40 € 12,50, tourist tax incl Ch (3x)€ 1/2kWh included. **Location:** Simple, central, quiet. **Surface:** metalled.
01/01-31/12.
Distance: 400m 300m 300m 400m 1km 600m.

Remarks: Max. 48h, ferry boat to Texel 500m.

Den Oever 7C3

Haventerrein Oostkade, Oostkade 3. **GPS**: n52,93395 e5,03974.

10 € 10 € 0,50/100liter € 0,50 Ch (8x) WC included.
Location: Motorway, simple, isolated, noisy. **Surface:** metalled.
01/01-31/12.
Distance: 500m 1,4km 200m offshore fishing 500m 500m on the spot.
Remarks: At old harbour, max. 3 days, saturday-morning fishmarket.

Enkhuizen 9D1

Gependam, Dirck Chinaplein. **GPS**: n52,69806 e5,29005.

6 € 10,85 WC € 0,20 € 1.
Location: Urban, simple, central.
Surface: asphalted.
01/01-31/12.
Distance: 1km on the spot on the spot 100m 1km 100m.
Remarks: Max. 48h.

Tourist information Enkhuizen:
Zuiderzeemuseum. Historical little town. 01/04-31/10 10-17h.

NL

Hoorn 9C1

Jachthaven Hoorn, Visserseiland 221. **GPS**: n52,63467 e5,05676.

27 € 14,60 Ch WC € 0,50 included.
Location: Quiet. **Surface:** metalled. 01/04-31/10.
Distance: 500m 2,8km on the spot on the spot 100m on the spot.
Remarks: Check in at harbourmaster.

Huizen 9D2

Recreatieterrein Wolskamer, IJsselmeerstraat.
GPS: n52,30860 e5,24046.

8 free Ch. **Location:** Simple, quiet. **Surface:** grassy.
01/01-31/12.
Distance: 1km 200m 200m 1km Lidl 300m on the spot on the spot.
Remarks: Max. 48h, service at harbourmaster.

Tourist information Huizen:
Sa.

Katwoude 9C1

De Simonehoeve, Wagenweg 2. **GPS**: n52,48620 e5,03196.

10 free. **Location:** Simple. **Surface:** asphalted. 01/01-31/12.
Distance: 2km 2km 2km on the spot 2km 100m.
Remarks: Cheese farm, nearby Hotel Volendam, free guided tour.

Laren 9D2

Sportcomplex De Biezem, Schapendrift 64. **GPS**: n52,25717 e5,23884.

2 free Ch WC. **Surface:** metalled. 01/01-31/12.
Distance: 1km 1km.
Remarks: Max. 1 night.

Medemblik 9D1

Haven Medemblik, Pekelharinghaven 50. **GPS**: n52,77139 e5,11361.

5 € 12,50, 2 pers.incl Ch WC included.
Location: Simple, quiet. **Surface:** metalled. 01/01-31/12.
Distance: 1km 200m on the spot 50m 1km 50m on the spot.
Remarks: Max. 48h, check in at harbourmaster.

Tourist information Medemblik:
Museum Stoomtram. Steam tram museum: Hoorn-Medemblik.

Middenmeer 9C1

Jachthaven Middenmeer, Havenstraat. **GPS**: n52,81236 e4,99112.

12 € 10 Ch WC included € 5/2 € 2.
Location: Comfortable. **Surface:** metalled. 01/01-31/12.
Distance: 500m 1,7km 50m 50m 500m 150m on the spot.
Remarks: Max. 48h, check in at harbourmaster.

Monnickendam 9C1

Jachthaven Waterland, Galgeriet 5a. **GPS**: n52,45920 e5,04059.

6 € 18,50 Ch € 0,50/2kWh WC € 4,50 included.
Location: Urban, simple, quiet. **Surface:** metalled.
30/04-15/10.
Distance: 500-800m on the spot on the spot.
Remarks: Check in at harbourmaster, caution sepkey € 20, bookings in peak season.

Naarden 9D2

Jachthaven Naarden, Onderwal 4. **GPS**: n52,30874 e5,14703.

10 € 17,50 + € 2/pp tourist tax Ch WC € 5/3 included. **Location:** Rural, comfortable, quiet.
Surface: grassy/metalled. 01/01-31/12.
Distance: Naarden-vesting (fortress) 2,3km 600m 500m lake Gooi on the spot on the spot on the spot.

Tourist information Naarden:
Vestingmuseum. Fortress museum. Tue-Fri 10.30-17h, Sa/Su/holidays 12-17h.

Nieuw Vennep 9C2

Allesonda Hoeve, IJweg 1391. **GPS**: n52,28705 e4,62614.
15 € 12,50 Ch included. **Location:** Rural.
Surface: metalled. 01/04-01/10.
Distance: 1,5km 1,5km 1,5km.
Remarks: Only cash payment.

Opperdoes 9C1

Imkerij de Bijenstal, Zwarte pad. **GPS**: n52,76255 e5,08027.

3 € 11,10, 2 pers.incl (2x) € 3,50.
Location: Rural, simple, isolated, quiet. **Surface:** gravel.
Distance: 500m 2km 300m 500m.
Remarks: Boat rental.

Tourist information Opperdoes:
Museum stoomtram, Van Dedemstraat 8, Medemblik. Steam tram museum: Hoorn-Medemblik.

Oudendijk 9C1

Bruin Eetcafé Les Deux Ponts, Slimdijk 2.
GPS: n52,60462 e4,95983.

10 free, use of a meal obligated. **Location:** Rural, simple, quiet.
Surface: gravel. 01/01-31/12 Tue.
Distance: 2km on the spot on the spot on the spot.

Purmerend 9C1

Het Bolwerk, Nieuwstraat. **GPS**: n52,50681 e4,95049.

5 € 6,90 € 1 € 0,15/h free. **Location:** Urban, simple, quiet. **Surface:** metalled.
01/01-31/12 water: 01/11-01/04.

Distance: 200m ⊗200m.
Remarks: Max. 72h, tuesday morning market.

Tourist information Purmerend:
Centrum. Tue.

Schagen 9C1

Jachthaven Schagen, Lagedijkerweg 2B. **GPS**: n52,79088 e4,78746.

21 € 7,50 + € 1,15/pp tourist tax € 0,50/100liter Ch included WC € 0,50 € 4/4 € 1.
Surface: metalled. 01/01-31/12.
Distance: 500m on the spot ⊗400m 500m.
Remarks: Check in at harbourmaster, caution key sanitary building € 15.

Tourist information Schagen:
West Friese Folkloremarkt. Folkore market. Jun-Jul-Aug: Thu.

Slootdorp 7C3

De Tulpentuin, Wierweg 7. **GPS**: n52,85627 e5,01010.

8 € 11,50 Ch (8x)WC included.
Location: Rural, isolated, quiet. **Surface:** metalled.
01/01-31/12.
Distance: Wieringerwerf 2km 2km 500m ⊗2km 2km on the spot on the spot.
Remarks: At tulip grower, regional products.

Stompetoren 9C1

Het Schermer Wapen, Oterlekerweg 3. **GPS**: n52,61285 e4,82096.

4 free, use of a meal obligated. **Location:** Urban, simple.
Surface: gravel. 01/01-31/12 Wed.
Distance: 500m ⊗on the spot 500m.

Texel/De Cocksdorp 7C3

De Krim, Roggeslootweg 6. **GPS**: n53,15110 e4,85996.
10 € 16-26 Ch included. **Surface:** grassy/metalled.
01/01-31/12.

Vijfhuizen 9C2

Camperpark N205, Floriadepark. **GPS**: n52,34190 e4,67972.
100 € 12,50 Ch (20x)€ 2,50 WC included.
Location: Rural. **Surface:** grassy. 01/01-31/12.
Distance: 750m on the spot on the spot on the spot.
Remarks: Bread-service, 24/24 surveillance.

Volendam 9C1

Marinapark Volendam, De Pieterman 1.
GPS: n52,48944 e5,05972.

36 € 14 10-17h, € 20/24h Ch included € 5 .
Location: Comfortable, quiet.
Surface: grasstiles/metalled.
01/01-31/12.
Distance: 1,5km 50m 50m ⊗300m 300m 300m.

Tourist information Volendam:
VVV, Zeestraat 37, www.vvv-volendam.nl. Old fishermen's village.
Volendams Museum, Zeestraat 41. Life and Work in Volendam, 1800-1900.
01/03-30/11 10-17h.

Weesp 9C2

Vecht & Weide, Dammerweg 5c. **GPS**: n52,28729 e5,07152.

8 € 12, tourist tax incl Ch (8x)WC included.
Location: Rural. **Surface:** metalled. 01/01-31/12.
Distance: 4km 400m ⊗400m 3,5km bus 300m on the spot on the spot.
Remarks: Max. 8M.

Wormerveer 9C1

Wandelweg. **GPS**: n52,48936 e4,79485.
5 € 12 Ch . **Location:** Urban. **Surface:** metalled.
01/01-31/12.
Distance: 1km ⊗100m 100m.

Zandvoort 9C1

Boulevard Barnaart. **GPS**: n52,38752 e4,53479.
13 € 22. **Location:** Rural. **Surface:** metalled. 01/01-31/12.
Distance: on the spot on the spot 350m on the spot on the spot.

't Zand 7C3

Camperplaats Molen de Hoop, Parallelweg 33.
GPS: n52,83628 e4,74931.

14 € 15 Ch WC included. **Location:** Rural.
Surface: grasstiles/grassy. 01/01-31/12.
Distance: centre 300m 4km 300m ⊗350m 300m 150m on the spot on the spot.
Remarks: Near mill, money in envelope in mail box, call for entrance code.

Friesland

Akkrum 7D3

Tusken de Marren, Ulbe Twijnstrawei 31. **GPS**: n53,04853 e5,82577.

20 € 15 € 0,50/100liter Ch € 2/night WC € 4/2 included. **Surface:** grassy/metalled. 15/03-01/11.
Distance: 200m on the spot on the spot 700m 500m on the spot.
Remarks: Information at harbourmaster, boat rental.

Anjum 7E2

It Tún-Hûs, Bantswei 1a. **GPS**: n53,37751 e6,12999.

15 € 12 Ch (20x)WC € 1 included.
Location: Rural. **Surface:** grassy/metalled. 01/04-01/11.
Distance: 400m 2km ⊗350m 550m 500m on the spot on the spot.

Appelscha 7E3

De Compagnonshoeve, Vaart Noordzijde 104.
GPS: n52,95222 e6,36278.

10 € 8 Ch € 1,50 included.
Location: Rural, simple, quiet. **Surface:** grassy. 01/01-31/12.
Distance: on the spot 3km on the spot ⊗200m 400m 400m 50m.

Appelscha 7E3

Camperplaats Appelscha, Noorder Es. **GPS**: n52,95459 e6,33619.

10 € 10 € 0,10/20liter Ch (10x)€ 0,50/kWh WC € 0,50 included. **Surface:** grassy/metalled. 01/01-31/12.
Distance: on the spot 5km 900m ⊗on the spot 1km 500m on the spot on the spot.

Balk 7D3

Jachthaven Lutsmond, Sleatemar 1a. **GPS**: n52,90389 e5,59694.

10 € 10 + € 1/pp tourist tax Ch € 3 WC .
Surface: grassy. 01/01-31/12.
Distance: 1km on the spot on the spot ⊗nearby 1km

NL

on the spot on the spot.

Bergum 7E3

Camperterrein Prinses Margriet Kanaal, Opperdijk van Veenweg 22. **GPS**: n53,18643 e6,00176.

25 € 10/night Chincluded € 2/night 1h free, 1 day € 7,50. **Location:** Urban, comfortable, quiet. **Surface:** grassy/metalled. 01/01-31/12.
Distance: 2km 2km on the spot 2km 200m on the spot on the spot on the spot.

Bergum 7E3

W.S.V. Bergumermeer, Bergumerdaam 51. **GPS**: n53,18705 e5,99299.

10 € 11 + € 1/pp tourist tax € 0,50/100liter Ch € 0,50/kWh WC € 0,50/time € 3,50/3,50 included. **Location:** Urban, comfortable, central, quiet. **Surface:** metalled. 01/04-31/10.
Distance: 500m 2,5km 5km on the spot 900m 500m 500m on the spot on the spot.
Remarks: Max. 72h.

Blesdijke 7E3

Stoutenburght, Markeweg 35a. **GPS**: n52,83850 e6,03339.

12 € 10 Ch (12x),6Amp WC included. **Location:** Rural. **Surface:** grassy. 01/01-31/12.
Distance: 5km 2km 2km on the spot on the spot.

Bolsward 7D3

Camperplaats Half-Hichtum, Hichtumerweg 14. **GPS**: n53,07365 e5,52253.

5 € 16 Ch WC € 3,50 included. **Location:** Rural, comfortable, quiet. **Surface:** grassy/metalled. 01/04-15/10.
Distance: 1km 1,3km 6km 500m 1km 1km 200m on the spot on the spot.

Brantgum 7E2

Camperplaats Veldzicht, Veldbuurtsterweg 9. **GPS**: n53,35556 e5,93632.

20 € 11 Ch included. **Location:** Rural, comfortable, isolated, quiet. **Surface:** grassy/metalled. 01/01-31/12.
Distance: Dokkum 7km 2km 3km 3km on the spot on the spot.
Remarks: Ferry boat to Ameland 3km.

Burdaard 7E3

Jachthaven Mounehiem, Mounewei 17. **GPS**: n53,29711 e5,88261.

12 € 12 Ch € 1/night,10Amp WC € 0,50/5minutes € 4,50/2,50 included. **Location:** Rural, comfortable, quiet. **Surface:** grassy/gravel. 01/01-31/12.
Distance: on the spot 2km on the spot on the spot 100m 500m 2km on the spot on the spot.
Remarks: Passerby € 1/100l.

Damwoude 7E3

Camperplaats Prikkebosk, Dammeloane 46. **GPS**: n53,28238 e6,01201. 2 € 10 WC. **Location:** Rural. 01/01-31/12.
Distance: 2km 2km 2km on the spot on the spot.

Dokkum 7E2

Van Kleffenstraat 8. **GPS**: n53,32496 e5,99254.
5 € 14, 2 pers incl Ch WC free. **Location:** Central. **Surface:** grassy/metalled. 01/01-31/12.
Distance: on the spot on the spot 400m 200m 400m on the spot on the spot.
Remarks: Max. 72h.

Drachten 7E3

VV Drachten, Gauke Boelensstraat. **GPS**: n53,10289 e6,08832.

5 free. **Surface:** asphalted. 01/01-31/12.
Distance: 500m on the spot 500m on the spot on the spot.

Drachten 7E3

Jachthaven De Drait, Biskopswei 27, De Wilgen. **GPS**: n53,10244 e6,04549.

15 € 10 Ch € 2 WC € 3,50/3,50 included.
Surface: metalled. 01/01-31/12.
Distance: centre 4km 2,5km 2,5km.
Remarks: Check in at harbourmaster, wifi code at harbour master, boat rental.

Earnewâld 7E3

Eilansgrien. **GPS**: n53,12958 e5,93630.

5 € 5,40 + € 1/pp tourist tax Ch included WC € 0,50 € 3,50,€ 3,50/3,50. **Surface:** asphalted. 01/01-31/12.
Distance: 200m 500m 200m.
Remarks: Max. 72h, sanitary/washing machine at tourist office (Summer season).

Elsloo 7E3

Camperplaats Kale Duinen, Kloosterweg 5. **GPS**: n52,94360 e6,27313. 9 € 12,50 Ch included WC. **Location:** Rural, isolated, noisy. **Surface:** asphalted. 01/01-31/12.
Distance: 2,5km 2,5km on the spot on the spot.

Harlingen 7D3

Tsjerk Hiddesluizen, Nieuwe Vissershaven 17. **GPS**: n53,17938 e5,41731.

10 € 7,50 € 1 Ch (16x)€ 1/2kWh WC.
Surface: asphalted. 01/01-31/12.
Distance: 500m 500m 500m 100m.
Remarks: Max. 72h, laundromat/toilets/shower 500m.

Heerenveen 7E3

Thialf, Pim Mulierlaan 1. **GPS**: n52,93843 e5,94495.

4 free. **Surface:** metalled. 01/01-31/12 during event.
Distance: 2km 2km 2km.
Remarks: On parking ground of skating rink, max. 72h.

Heerenveen 7E3

De Koningshof, Prinsenweg 1. **GPS**: n52,94759 e5,94438.

4 free. **Surface:** asphalted. 01/01-31/12.
Distance: 1km on the spot 4km 500m.
Remarks: Large parking near A32, max. 72h.

Heerenveen 7E3

Gemeentewerf, Venus 4. **GPS**: n52,96663 e5,93502. free. Mon-Fri 9-15u.

Hogebeintum 7D2

Bezoekerscentrum Terp Hegebeintum, Pijpkedijk 4. **GPS**: n53,33612 e5,85266.

NL

4 free. **Location:** Simple, isolated. **Surface:** asphalted.
Distance: 4km.
Remarks: Parking information centre/VVV, highest mound in the Netherlands, max. 2 days, ferry boat to Ameland 3km.

S IJlst 7D3

De Tsjalk, De Tsjalk. **GPS**: n53,00846 e5,62741.

4 € 9,50 WCfree € 0,50/5minutes.
Location: Urban, simple, central, quiet. **Surface:** metalled.
01/01-31/12.
Distance: 200m on the spot 200m 200m 200m on the spot on the spot.

S Jelsum 7D3

Camperplaats Tjem Tjoeg, Aldlansdyk 28. **GPS**: n53,23041 e5,81765.
3 € 5 included. **Location:** Rural. **Surface:** grassy.
01/04-30/09.
Distance: Leeuwarden 5km.

S Joure 7D3

Jachthaven, Grienedyk. **GPS**: n52,97210 e5,78836.

4 € 10 + € 1/pp tourist tax € 0,50/70liter € 3 € 1 € 7,50
Surface: metalled. 01/03-01/11.
Distance: 500m 50m.
Remarks: Max. 72h.

S Kollum 7E3

Jachthaven de Rijd, Cantecleer 2. **GPS**: n53,28727 e6,15139.

12 € 10 Ch 10Amp WC included.
Location: Urban, simple, central, quiet. **Surface:** metalled.
01/05-01/10.
Distance: on the spot on the spot 500m 500m 500m on the spot on the spot.
Remarks: Max. 72h.

S Koudum 7D3

De Kuilart, De Kuilart 1. **GPS**: n52,90305 e5,46706.

10 + 2 € 8 Chincluded € 1/night,6Amp WC € 0,35/5minutes € 4,40/2,35 .
Location: Rural, luxurious, noisy. **Surface:** grassy/metalled.
01/01-07/05, 22/05-05/07, 25/08-31/12 holidays.
Distance: 1,5km on the spot on the spot on the spot 1km 1km on the spot on the spot.
Remarks: Quick-Stop: >17h - <10h, check in at reception.

S Langweer 7D3

Brandweerkazerne, Pontdyk. **GPS**: n52,96000 e5,71972.

4 free free. **Location:** Simple. **Surface:** metalled.
01/01-31/12.
Distance: 500m 500m 500m 500m.
Remarks: Max. 72h.

S Langweer 7D3

Passantenhaven Langweer, Pontdyk. **GPS**: n52,96091 e5,72240.

3 € 7, tourist tax € 0,20/pp € 0,20 Ch € 2 WC € 0,50 € 3,50/3,50 . **Surface:** grassy. 01/04-31/10.
Distance: 500m on the spot on the spot 500m 500m 500m.

S Leeuwarden 7D3

Prinsentuin, Wissesdwinger 1. **GPS**: n53,20528 e5,79659.

2 € 6,50 Ch 6Amp WC € 4,31/3 included.
Location: Urban, comfortable, central, quiet. **Surface:** metalled.
01/01-31/12 sanitary building: 01/11-01/04.
Distance: 500m 2km on the spot on the spot on the spot 400m on the spot on the spot on the spot.
Remarks: Max. 48h.

Leeuwarden 7D3

Harlingertrekweg. **GPS**: n53,19839 e5,77098.

5 € 6. **Location:** Noisy. **Surface:** metalled. 01/01-31/12.
Distance: 1km 1km 1km 500m.
Remarks: Max. 48h.

S Leeuwarden 7D3

Camperplaats Leeuwarden, De Zwemmer 3.
GPS: n53,18445 e5,83748.

12 € 10 € 1 Ch € 2,50/night WC included.
Location: Urban, comfortable, quiet. **Surface:** metalled.
01/01-31/12.
Distance: 5km 2km on the spot on the spot 1km 1km 5km 300m on the spot on the spot.
Remarks: Discount at restaurant, 4th night free, discount museum and theater.

S Leeuwarden 7D3

Leeuwarder Jachthaven, Jachthavenlaan 3.
GPS: n53,19886 e5,83019.

6 € 12,50 Ch WC € 1/5minutes included.
Location: Urban, comfortable, isolated, quiet. **Surface:** grassy/gravel.
01/01-31/12.
Distance: 2,5km 1km on the spot on the spot 500m 500m 300m on the spot on the spot.
Remarks: Check in at harbourmaster.

S Leeuwarden 7D3

Taniaburg, Vierhuisterweg 72. **GPS**: n53,21955 e5,79286.

8 € 13, 2 pers.incl., dog € 1,50 Ch € 2/night,6Amp WC € 2,50,€ 2,50/3 included. **Location:** Rural, comfortable, quiet.
Surface: grassy/gravel. 01/04-01/11.
Distance: 3km 1km on the spot on the spot 500m 500m on the spot on the spot.
Remarks: Canoe and bicycle rental.

S Lemmer 7D3

Jachthaven Lemmer, Plattedijk 4-12. **GPS**: n52,84708 e5,69696.

25 € 13 + tourist tax € 1/pp € 0,50 Ch € 0,50 WC € 0,50 . **Surface:** metalled. 01/01-31/12.
Distance: 1km 2,7km on the spot 1km.

S Lemmer 7D3

Watersportcentrum Tacozijl, Plattedijk 20. **GPS**: n52,85104 e5,68189.

NL

20 € 12,50-21 Ch € 0,50/kWh WC included .
Surface: grassy/metalled. 01/01-31/12.
Distance: centre 2,2km 3km 1,5km on the spot on the spot on the spot.

Tourist information Lemmer:
Ir. D.F. Woudagemaal. The biggest steam pumpingstation of Europe. Tue-Sa 10-17h, Su 13-17h.

S **Lollum** 7D3

Camperplaats Landgoed Hizzard, Hizzaarderlaan 16.
GPS: n53,11913 e5,51428.
2 € 12, tourist tax incl Chincluded (2x)€ 2,50/24h WC € 2,50 . **Location:** Rural. **Surface:** metalled. 01/01-31/12.
Distance: city centre Winsum 3,8km on the spot 3,8km 1,4km on the spot on the spot.

S **Makkum** 7D3

Gemeentehaven Makkum, Workumerdijk 2.
GPS: n53,05329 e5,40317.

2 € 10 ChWC included € 2/2.
+**Location:** Urban, simple, central, noisy. **Surface:** metalled. 01/04-31/10 service: 01/11-01/04.
Distance: 100m on the spot 400m 950m 950m on the spot on the spot.
Remarks: Max. 72h.

S **Mirns** 7D3

De Braamberg, Murnserdyk. **GPS**: n52,85249 e5,48190.

10 € 10 + € 1/pp tourist tax Chincluded € 2 WC .
Location: Rural. **Surface:** gravel. 01/01-31/12.
Distance: beach 250m.

S **Molkwerum** 7D3

Camperplaats 't Seleantsje, 't Seleantsje 2.
GPS: n52,90419 e5,39493.

18 € 10-12 + € 1,25/pp tourist tax Ch WCincluded € 0,50/6minutes € 4/2,50 € 5/day. **Location:** Rural, comfortable, quiet. **Surface:** grasstiles. 15/03-01/11.
Distance: 300m on the spot on the spot on the spot 4km 1km on the spot on the spot.

S **Nes** 7E3

Manege Nes, Burdineweg 2. **GPS**: n53,05468 e5,85558.

10 € 5 Ch € 2/night,16Amp WC included.
Location: Rural, simple, quiet. **Surface:** grassy/metalled. 01/01-31/12.
Distance: 700m 1km 10km 50m 700m 700m 700m on the spot on the spot.
Remarks: At manege.

Nijetrijne 7E3

Paviljoen Driewegsluis, Lindedijk 2a. **GPS**: n52,83261 e5,92467.

customers free. **Surface:** metalled.
Distance: on the spot on the spot on the spot on the spot.

S **Oudega** 7E3

Jachthaven Oudega, Roundeel. **GPS**: n53,12315 e5,99961.

2 €7 € 1/100liter € 1 € 1.
Location: Simple. **Surface:** grassy. 01/04-01/11.
Distance: 200m 200m 200m.
Remarks: Max. 48h.

S **Oudemirdum** 7D3

Landgoed de Syme, Jan Schotanusweі 106a, via Oude Balksterweg.
GPS: n52,85746 e5,51115.

2 €7,50 included € 2,50/night.
Location: Rural, simple, isolated, quiet.
Surface: grassy/metalled. 01/01-31/12.
Distance: 4km 6km 6km 4km 4km on the spot on the spot.

S **Oudeschoot** 7E3

Minicamping 't Woutersbergje, Van Bienemalaan 15-17.
GPS: n52,93544 e5,96009.

7 € 12,90 Ch € 2,50/night,6 Amp WC € 3/2 included. **Location:** Rural, comfortable, central, quiet.
Surface: metalled. 01/01-31/12.
Distance: 3,5km 300m on the spot on the spot.

S **Ried** 7D3

Jachthaven it Kattegat, Berlikumerweg 13. **GPS**: n53,22416 e5,59330.

3 + 4 € 9,50 . **Location:** Rural, simple, quiet.
Surface: grassy/metalled. 01/04-01/10.
Distance: on the spot 500m on the spot on the spot 500m on the spot on the spot.

S **Rohel** 7D3

Aktiviteitenboerderij, Vierhuisterweg 29. **GPS**: n52,90337 e5,84540.

5 € 15 Ch WC included. **Location:** Quiet.
Surface: metalled. 01/01-31/12.
Distance: on the spot on the spot on the spot on the spot.

S **Sint Jacobiparochie** 7D3

Camperpark Zwarte Haan, Nieuwebildtdijk 428.
GPS: n53,30915 e5,63051.
20 € 12,50 Ch (20x),10Amp WC included.
Location: Comfortable, isolated, quiet.
Surface: grassy/metalled. 01/01-31/12.
Distance: 50m, Sint Jacobiparochie 8km 8km Wadden Sea 100m on the spot 5km on the spot on the spot.

S **Sloten** 7D3

Jachthaven Lemsterpoort, Jachthaven 7.
GPS: n52,89265 e5,64486.

10 € 12 € 0,50/100liter Ch € 2,50/24h,6Amp WC € 1/5minutes included. **Location:** Urban, comfortable, quiet.
Surface: grassy/metalled. 01/01-31/12.
Distance: 100m 2km on the spot on the spot 100m 100m 500m on the spot on the spot.

NL

Sneek 7D3

Camperplaats Aquanaut, Selfhelpweg 7. **GPS**: n53,02725 e5,66302.
12 € 15 Ch (12x) WC € 0,50 € 2,50.
Location: Urban. **Surface:** metalled. 01/01-31/12.
Distance: 500m 500m 100m 500m 500m 50m 500m on the spot on the spot.
Remarks: Water closed during wintertime.

Sneek 7D3

Jachthaven Holiday Boatin, Eeltjebaasweg 3.
GPS: n53,01996 e5,69562.

4 € 12 Ch € 1/night,10Amp WC included.
Location: Urban, comfortable, quiet. **Surface:** concrete.
01/01-31/12.
Distance: 3,6km 2km on the spot on the spot 4km 2km, bakery 300m 300m on the spot on the spot.

Sneek 7D3

Amicitia Hotel Sneek, Alexanderstraat.
GPS: n53,02378 e5,67595.

10 € 9,50, free with a meal Ch included.
Surface: metalled. 01/01-31/12.
Distance: 1,5km 400m 8km on the spot.
Remarks: Reservation during Sneek sailing week: info@amicitiahotel.nl, 1st week of August.

Stavoren 7D3

Marina Stavoren Buitenhaven, Suderstrand 2.
GPS: n52,87360 e5,36715.

25 € 12,50 Ch € 2,16Amp WC € 4,50/2,50 included. **Surface:** asphalted. 01/04-31/10.
Distance: Stavoren 500m on the spot on the spot on the spot 500m 500m on the spot on the spot.
Remarks: Max. 3 nights, check in at harbourmaster.

Sumar 7E3

Recreatiecentrum Bergumermeer, Solcamastraat 30.
GPS: n53,19044 e6,02316.

10 € 19,50 Ch WC included.
Location: Rural, luxurious, quiet. **Surface:** grassy/metalled.
01/04-31/10.
Distance: 5km.

Sumar 7E3

Recreatiecentrum Bergumermeer, Solcamastraat-30.
GPS: n53,19044 e6,02316.

1 € 8 17-10h. 01/04-31/10.

Surhuisterveen 7E3

Zwembad Wettervlecke, Badlaan 3. **GPS**: n53,17987 e6,16124.

5 € 5 € 1 € 1 WC included. **Surface:** grassy.
Distance: 500m 500m.

Tersoal 7D3

Watersportbedrijf Lege Geaen, Buorren 2.
GPS: n53,07729 e5,74360.

6 € 12 Ch € 2,50/night WC included.
Location: Rural, comfortable, quiet. **Surface:** grassy/gravel.
01/01-31/12.
Distance: 8km 1,5km on the spot on the spot 1,5km 8km on the spot on the spot.

Wartena 7E3

Jachthaven Wartena, Stukenwei. **GPS**: n53,15145 e5,90532.

10 € 10 € 0,50/100 Ch WC € 1 € 6.
Location: Central.
Surface: grassy/metalled. 01/01-30/11.
Distance: 200m on the spot on the spot 500m 500m on the spot on the spot.
Remarks: Bicycle rental.

Wijnjewoude 7E3

Op Het Eind, Opper Haudmare 2. **GPS**: n53,05441 e6,17790.
2 € 8 € 1 € 1 € 2.
Surface: metalled. 01/01-31/12.
Distance: 2km on the spot on the spot.

Winsum 7D3

Camperplaats Winsum, Skans 12. **GPS**: n53,15177 e5,63111.

4 € 12 Ch included WC. **Location:** Simple.
01/01-31/12.

Wommels 7D3

Jachthaven Wommels, Terp 14. **GPS**: n53,10957 e5,58765.

8 € 11 Ch WC included € 0,50.
Location: Simple. **Surface:** grassy/metalled. 01/04-01/10.
Distance: 300m on the spot 100m.
Remarks: Market 100m, museum 200m.

Tourist information Wommels:
Tue-morning.

Workum 7D3

Jachthaven Bouwsma, Moleburren 11. **GPS**: n52,98230 e5,45518.

10 € 10-12,50 + € 1/pp tourist tax Ch € 2,50/night,6 Amp WC € 2 € 1/7minutes € 8/0 included.
Location: Urban, central, quiet.
Surface: grassy/metalled.
01/04-31/10.
Distance: 750m 1,5km on the spot 500m 500m 200m on the spot on the spot.
Remarks: Bicycle rental.

Tourist information Workum:
Jopie Huisman Museum, Noard 6. Autodidact, paintings and drawings. € 8,50.

Woudsend 7D3

Recreatiecentrum De Rakken, Lynbaen 10.
GPS: n52,94649 e5,62732.

15 € 17,50 + € 1/pp tourist tax Ch WC included € 4,50/2,50. **Surface:** grassy/metalled. 15/03-15/10.
Distance: 200m 2,5km 200m 200m 200m.

Ypecolsga 7D3

Camperplaats Waterloo, Nr. 19. **GPS**: n52,92758 e5,59549.

NL

13 € 10,50, 2 pers.incl Ch WC € 1,50/pp,use sanitary € 1,50/pp € 4,50,€ 4,50/2 included.
Surface: grasstiles. 01/03-01/11.
Distance: 3km 1km 1km 3,5km 3,5km nearby on the spot.

Zurich 7D3

Camperplaats Zurich, Caspar di Roblesdijk 3.
GPS: n53,11235 e5,39335.

3 € 3. **Location:** Urban, simple, central, noisy.
Surface: metalled. 01/01-31/12.
Distance: on the spot 1,5km on the spot on the spot on the spot on the spot.
Remarks: Max. 72h.

Zwaagwesteinde 7E3

Camperpark Kuikhorne, Kuikhornsterweg 31.
GPS: n53,24124 e6,01875.

25 € 10, 2 pers.incl € 1/100liter Ch € 2 WC € 0,50 € 4/3. **Surface:** asphalted/grassy. 01/01-31/12.
Distance: 2km on the spot 2km, pizzeria within walking distance 2km on the spot on the spot.
Remarks: Max. 72h, boat rental.

Groningen

Appingedam 7F2

Camperplaats Appingedam, Farmsumerweg 21.
GPS: n53,32062 e6,86689.

10 free free € 1/kWh,10Amp. **Location:** Urban, simple, central, noisy.
Surface: metalled. 01/01-31/12.
Distance: 750m Damsterdiep 500m 500m on the spot on the spot on the spot.
Remarks: Max. 72h.

Tourist information Appingedam:
Solwerderstraat. Sa 09-16h.

Blijham 7F3

Camperpark Turfstee, Turfweg 28. **GPS**: n53,11118 e7,02912.

55 € 10 + € 0,75 tourist tax Ch WC € 0,50/5minutes € 7,50/0 included. **Location:** Rural, comfortable, isolated.
Surface: grassy/gravel. 01/01-31/12.
Distance: 3km 3km 3km on the spot on the spot.

Delfzijl 7F2

Zeebadweg, Zeebadweg. **GPS**: n53,33582 e6,92650.

8 free Chfree € 1.
Distance: 500m on the spot on the spot 100m 300m.
Remarks: Max. 48h.

Doezum 7E3

Landgoed Jonker, Provincialeweg 133a.
GPS: n53,20411 e6,26018.

60 € 10, 2 pers.incl Ch (20x)€ 2/day,4Amp WC included.
Location: Luxurious.
Surface: grassy/metalled.
25/03-01/10.
Distance: 1,5km on the spot on the spot on the spot.

Tourist information Doezum:
Abel Tasman Kabinet, Kompasstraat 1, Grootegast. Local archaeological museum seafarer Abel Tasman. Thu-Sa 13.30-16.30h.

Finsterwolde 7F3

Minicamping B&B Kostverloren 11, Kostverloren 11.
GPS: n53,21356 e7,16193.
2 € 11 € 2 € 2,50/day WC included.
Location: Rural, comfortable, isolated, quiet. **Surface:** gravel.
01/04-01/11.
Distance: 4km 4km 4km 4km on the spot on the spot.

Groningen 7E3

Sportcentrum Kardinge, Bieskemaar. **GPS**: n53,23946 e6,59680.

15 tourist tax. **Location:** Rural, simple, quiet.
Surface: metalled. 01/01-31/12.
Distance: 3km 1km on the spot.
Remarks: Max. 72h.

Tourist information Groningen:
Prinsenhof en prinsenhoftuin. 15/03-15/10.

Haren 7E3

De Lijste, Meerweg. **GPS**: n53,16298 e6,57878.
6 free. **Surface:** grassy. 01/01-31/12.
Distance: 1,3km no bathing 250m.
Remarks: Max. 72h.

Lauwersoog 7E2

Lauwersmeerplezier, Kustweg 30. **GPS**: n53,40625 e6,20044.

23 € 17, 2 pers. incl WC € 3 included.
Surface: grassy/metalled. 01/01-31/12.
Distance: 500m on the spot on the spot 500m 500m.

Lauwersoog 7E2

Havenkantoor Lauwersoog, Haven 2.
GPS: n53,40819 e6,19768.

2 € 2/m Ch WC included. **Location:** Urban, simple, quiet. **Surface:** metalled. 01/01-31/12.
Distance: on the spot on the spot on the spot on the spot on the spot.
Remarks: Motorhomes <7m.

Lauwersoog 7E2

Jachthaven Noordergat, Noordergat 1.
GPS: n53,40493 e6,20311.

30 € 15 + € 1,15/pp tourist tax Ch included WC € 0,50/5minutes € 3/2,50.
Location: Rural, simple, quiet. **Surface:** concrete. 01/01-31/12.
Distance: on the spot on the spot on the spot on the spot.

Tourist information Lauwersoog:
Lauwersmeergebied. Breeding area for birds and recreation area.
01/04-31/10 Tue-Su 11-17h.

Leens 7E2

Leenstertillen, Leenstertillen 2. **GPS**: n53,35066 e6,37002.

15 € 12,50 Chservice € 3 included WC € 1.
Location: Rural, simple, quiet. **Surface:** grassy/gravel.
01/01-31/12.
Distance: 1,5km 50m 50m 1,5km 1,6km.
Remarks: Dog € 1,50/night, barbecue place.

Losdorp 7F2

Restaurant Eemshaven, Schafferweg 29.
GPS: n53,37214 e6,84411.

4 consuming is appreciated Ch € 5,customers WC free.
Location: Rural, simple, quiet. **Surface:** metalled.
01/01-31/12 Mo.
Distance: 2km 2km 1km on the spot on the spot.
Remarks: Code wifi in restaurant.

Lutjegast 7E3

't Kompas, Kompasstraat 1. **GPS**: n53,23498 e6,25972.

5 free. **Surface:** metalled. 01/01-31/12.
Distance: 200m on the spot 200m on the spot.
Remarks: Behind the club-building.

Midwolda 7F3

Blauwestadhoeve, Hoofdweg 156. **GPS**: n53,19424 e7,00751.
6 € 10 + € 0,95/pp tourist tax € 2,25 € 1,50 Ch € 1,50 (6x) € 1,45 WC € 1 € 1 € 1,45. **Location:** Rural.
Surface: grassy/metalled. 01/01-31/12.
Distance: 250m 2km 900m 500m 100m 250m 100m on the spot on the spot.

Midwolda 7F3

Jachthaven Midwolda, Strandweg 1. **GPS**: n53,19634 e7,03068.
5 € 11,90, 2 pers.incl € 0,50/100liter Ch € 2/day WC included. **Location:** Rural, comfortable, quiet. **Surface:** grassy.
01/04-31/10.

Distance: city centre 1km on the spot on the spot 1km 500m on the spot.
Remarks: View at Lake Oldambt.

Musselkanaal 7F3

Jachthaven Spoordok, Havenkade 1. **GPS**: n52,92694 e7,01389.

35 € 9,50 + € 0,90/pp tourist tax € 0,50/100liter Ch (35x) WC included. **Location:** Rural, comfortable, quiet.
Surface: grassy/metalled. 01/04-01/11.
Distance: 200m on the spot on the spot on the spot nearby on the spot on the spot.
Remarks: Max. 72h.

Nuis 7E3

Het Knooppunt, Oudeweg 47. **GPS**: n53,15061 e6,31021.

12 € 10 Ch WC included. **Location:** Rural.
Surface: grassy/metalled. 01/04-01/10.
Distance: on the spot 3km 5km 2km 3,5km on the spot on the spot on the spot.
Remarks: Breakfast-service, charging point for electric bicycles.

Onderdendam 7E2

Watersportvereniging Onderdendam, Warffumerweg 12.
GPS: n53,33652 e6,58600.

6 € 6 + € 1/pp Ch (6x) € 2,50 WC included € 0,50.
Location: Simple, quiet. **Surface:** grassy/metalled.
Distance: 500m on the spot on the spot 500m 500m.

Onstwedde 7F3

Holte 9. **GPS**: n53,05021 e7,04459.

5 € 3 Ch included € 2. **Location:** Rural, simple.
Surface: grassy. 01/01-31/12.
Distance: 1km 1km 1km 1km bike junction.

Onstwedde 7F3

Ooldershoeve, Veenhuizen 6.
GPS: n53,02214 e7,01250.
10 € 8, 2 pers.incl + tourist tax € 0,90/pp € 1 Ch € 2 included. **Location:** Rural. **Surface:** grassy. 01/01-31/12.
Distance: 2km 2,5km on the spot on the spot.

Sellingen 7F3

Camperpark Westerwolde, Zevenmeersveenweg 1a.
GPS: n52,95412 e7,13174.

10 € 8 + € 1/pp tourist tax € 1 Ch WC included € 4.
Location: Rural, simple, quiet.
Surface: grassy. 01/01-31/12.
Distance: 1km on the spot 1km 1km on the spot on the spot.
Remarks: Arrival after 7pm.

Slochteren 7F3

Duurswoldje, Edserweg. **GPS**: n53,20051 e6,79020.

7 € 7 Ch included € 1/24h.
Location: Rural, simple, quiet. **Surface:** grassy. 01/01-31/12.
Distance: 500m on the spot on the spot 1km on the spot.
Remarks: Covered picnic area, small stock accommodation.

Stadskanaal 7F3

De Roo Campers, Unikenkade 1. **GPS**: n53,03556 e6,87617.

10 € 5 Ch WC included. **Location:** Rural, simple, quiet.
Surface: grassy.
01/01-31/12.
Distance: 8km 4km on the spot on the spot 8km 8km.

Tourist information Stadskanaal:
Pagedal, www.stadskanaal.nl. Daytime recreation.

Ter Apel 7F3

Jachthaven De Runde, Oosterkade 5. **GPS**: n52,87179 e7,07329.

10 € 7,50 + € 0,75/pp tourist tax € 0,50 Ch € 1 WC € 0,50 € 4,€ 4/2 free,5h. **Location:** Rural, comfortable, quiet.
Surface: grassy/metalled. 01/01-31/12.
Distance: 1km on the spot on the spot on the spot 1km 500m on the spot.
Remarks: Wifi 5h free.

Termunterzijl 7F2

Zeestrand, Schepperbuurt 4a. **GPS**: n53,30173 e7,03085.

NL

15 € 10 Ch WC included € 1 € 4/2 € 2,50.
Surface: metalled. 01/01-31/12.
Distance: 100m 100m 100m 200m 200m.
Remarks: Registration via intercom or phone.

S Veendam 7F3

Borgerswold, Flora 2. **GPS**: n53,10637 e6,84826.

60 € 5 + € 2,50/pp Ch WC included.
Location: Rural, simple, quiet.
Surface: grassy.
01/01-31/12.
Distance: 2km beach 50m on the spot 2km 1km 1,5km on the spot.

Tourist information Veendam:
Museumspoorlijn STAR, Parallelweg 4, Veendam. Museum railway line, tickets available at railwaystation.
round trip € 15.
Veenkoloniaalmuseum, Museumplein 5. History of the peat, shipping and industry.
Tue-Thu 11-17h, Fri-Mo 13-17h 01/09-30/06 Mo.
€ 7,50.

S Winschoten 7F3

Jachthaven de Rensel, Hellingbaan 4. **GPS**: n53,14405 e7,04760.

10 € 11, 2 pers.incl € 0,50 Ch WC included.
Location: Simple, quiet. **Surface:** concrete. 01/01-31/12.
Distance: 800m 200m McDonalds 200m AH.

S Winschoten 7F3

Hotel Café Restaurant Bowling In den Stallen, Oostereinde 10. **GPS**: n53,15371 e7,06528.

10 consuming is appreciated on demand.
Location: Rural, simple, quiet.
Surface: asphalted/metalled.
Distance: 1km 600m 600m on the spot 1km 600m.

Tourist information Winschoten:
Stoomgemaal, Winschoter Oostereinde. Steam-engine 1895.

S Winsum 7E2

Jachthaven/Camping Marenland, Winsumerstraatweg. **GPS**: n53,33177 e6,51015.

10 € 14,50, 2 pers.incl. Ch WC € 6,50/0 included,at restaurant. **Location:** Urban, comfortable, quiet.
Surface: grassy/metalled. 01/04-01/10.
Distance: 300m 200m on the spot on the spot 500m 200m on the spot Pieterpad.

S Zeerijp 7F2

Johanna Hoeve, Groeveweg 1. **GPS**: n53,35058 e6,73776.
10 € 7,50 Ch. **Surface:** grassy.
Distance: 2km.

S Zoutkamp 7E2

Jachthaven Hunzegat, Strandweg 17. **GPS**: n53,34114 e6,29406.

11 € 13 + € 1,15pp tourist tax Ch,dump chem.toilet only with biodegradable liquid (10x) WC included € 0,50 € 7,40/0.
Location: Rural, comfortable, quiet. **Surface:** grassy/metalled.
01/01-31/12.
Distance: 1km on the spot on the spot 500m 500m 300m on the spot.
Remarks: Bread-service.

Tourist information Zoutkamp:
Zeehondencrèche, Hoofdstraat 94a, Pieterburen. Sanctory to cure sick seals. Mo-Fr 9-17h, Sa-Su 10-17h. € 10,50.

S Zuidbroek 7F3

De Broeckhof, W.A. Scholtenweg 18. **GPS**: n53,16118 e6,86054.

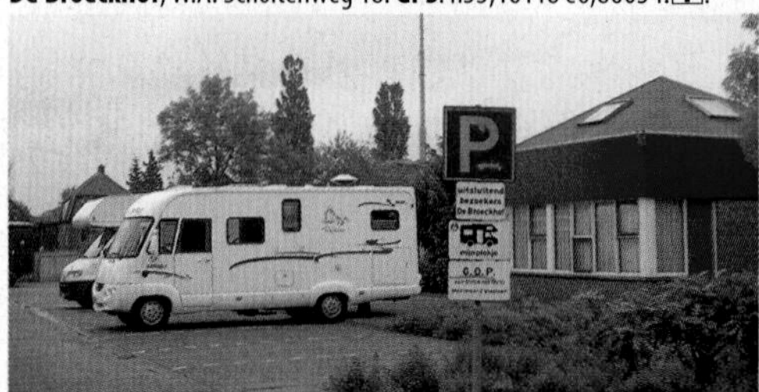

5 free Ch WC € 0,50 € 1 free.
Location: Rural, simple, central, quiet. **Surface:** metalled.
01/01-31/12.
Distance: 500m on the spot on the spot 1km on the spot on the spot on the spot.
Remarks: Max. 72h.

Drenthe

S Barger Compascuum 9F1

Nationale Veenpark, Berkenrode 4. **GPS**: n52,75504 e7,02546.

20 € 7,50 + € 1,20/pp tourist tax included.
Location: Rural, simple, quiet.
Surface: grassy. 01/05-31/10.
Distance: 1km 100m 1km on the spot on the spot.
Remarks: Max. 3x24h, after visiting Veenpark 2nd night free, boat rental.

Tourist information Barger Compascuum:
Veenpark-Wereld van Veen, Berkenrode 4. Life and Work in peat area, 160 acres of nature, peat and villages.
01/04-31/10 10-17h, 01/07-31/08 10-18h.

S Borger 7F3

Nuuverstee, Rolderstraat 4. **GPS**: n52,92633 e6,77447.

9 € 15 Ch (9x),10Amp WC included.
Location: Rural, luxurious. **Surface:** grassy/metalled. 01/01-31/12.
Distance: 800m 600m 2km 500m 600m 1km 500m on the spot on the spot.
Remarks: Bread-service, charging point for electric bicycles, use of sauna against payment.

S Dwingeloo 9E1

Torentjeshoek, Leeuweriksveldweg 1. **GPS**: n52,81927 e6,36077.

6 € 10-19 + € 1,10/pp tourist tax Ch ,10Amp WC included,on camp site. **Location:** Rural, luxurious, quiet.
Surface: grassy/metalled. 01/01-31/12.
Distance: 2km 2km 200m 200m 2km 2km 1km on the spot on the spot.
Remarks: Arrival >16h, departure <11h.

Eelderwolde 7E3

Scandinavisch Dorp, Oude Badweg 1. **GPS**: n53,16984 e6,55391.

5 free. **Location:** Rural, simple, quiet.
Surface: asphalted/grassy.
01/01-31/12 Restaurant: Tue, 01/10-01/04 Mo-Tue.
Distance: 2km 5km 500m on the spot on the spot 2km 200m on the spot on the spot.
Remarks: Guests free.

S Eext 7F3

Schaopvolte, Stationsstraat 60a. **GPS**: n53,00007 e6,72862.

10 € 8,50, tourist tax excl € 1 Ch (6x) € 1/4kWh WC € 0,50 € 4,50 € 2/day. **Location:** Rural, simple, quiet.
Surface: grassy/gravel. 01/04-01/11.
Distance: 2km.

S Elim 9E1

De Barswieke, Barsweg 9. **GPS**: n52,67144 e6,57821.

NL

10 € 6 Chincluded € 1,50 WC € 0,50.
Surface: grassy/metalled. 01/01-31/12.
Distance: 1km 1km.

Emmen 9F1

Kerkhoflaan/Emmalaan. **GPS**: n52,78091 e6,90330.

10 free. **Location:** Urban, simple.
Surface: grassy.
01/01-31/12.
Distance: 1km Albert Heijn 600m.
Remarks: Behind hotel Eden, max. 72h, zoo Emmen 900m.

Tourist information Emmen:
Wildlands Adventure Zoo, Raadhuisplein 99. Zoo.
10-17h.

Erica 9F1

Achter op Erica, Verlengde Herendijk. **GPS**: n52,73006 e6,92256.

15 € 8 Chincluded € 3 € 1.
Location: Rural. **Surface:** grassy. 01/01-31/12.
Distance: 3,5km on the spot on the spot.
Remarks: Closed when frosty, possibility for reservation.

Het Haantje 9F1

Camperplaats 't Haantje, Haantje 8. **GPS**: n52,81539 e6,83443.

30 € 15 + € 1,15/pp tourist tax Ch 6Amp WC against payment included.
Location: Rural. **Surface:** grassy. 30/03-14/10.
Distance: Emmen 7km on the spot.

Hoogersmilde 7E3

De Reeënwissel, Bosweg 23. **GPS**: n52,90450 e6,38490.

€ 12 Chincluded € 1 WC. **Location:** Rural.
Surface: grassy/gravel. 01/01-31/12.

Distance: on the spot 1,3km on the spot on the spot.

Hoogeveen 9E1

Markt. **GPS**: n52,72821 e6,47966.
4 € 7,50. **Location:** Urban. **Surface:** metalled. 01/01-31/12.
Distance: on the spot 100m 50m.
Remarks: Max. 72h.

Hoogeveen 9E1

Terpweg 3. **GPS**: n52,72639 e6,50040.

3 free. **Location:** Rural, simple, isolated. **Surface:** metalled.
01/01-31/12.
Distance: 2km 2,2km 100m 1km 1km.
Remarks: At sports park, max. 72h.

Matsloot 7E3

Camping Pool, Matsloot 1a. **GPS**: n53,19354 e6,44980.

10 € 10 Ch WC included. **Location:** Rural, simple, isolated, quiet. **Surface:** metalled. 01/01-31/12.
Distance: 5km on the spot on the spot on the spot.
Remarks: On Leekster lake.

Meppel 9E1

Jachthaven, Westeinde 32. **GPS**: n52,69615 e6,18096.

15 € 8,10, 2 pers.incl € 0,50 Ch WC € 3/3.
Location: Urban, comfortable, central, quiet. **Surface:** grassy.
01/01-31/12.
Distance: 500m on the spot on the spot on the spot 400m.

Nieuwlande 9F1

Bonenstee, Brugstraat 87. **GPS**: n52,67889 e6,61194.

20 € 7,50, 01/11-31/03 € 6 Ch (6x)€ 1,50 WC € 1 included. **Location:** Rural. **Surface:** grassy/metalled.
01/01-31/12 service 01/11-31/03.
Distance: 2km 4km 4km 2km 2km 100m bike junction on the spot.
Remarks: Max. 72h.

Noord-Sleen 9F1

De Kalverweide, Zweeloërstraat 1. **GPS**: n52,79330 e6,79475.

10 € 12 Ch WC included.
Location: Rural, comfortable, quiet. **Surface:** grassy. 01/01-31/12.
Distance: 500m on the spot on the spot.
Remarks: Use of sauna against payment.

Oosterhesselen 9F1

Sauna Hesselerbrug, Verlengde Hoogeveensevaart 32.
GPS: n52,73535 e6,72029.

use of sauna obligatory. **Surface:** metalled.
Distance: 4km 4km.

Ruinen 9E1

De Wiltzangh, Witteveen 2. **GPS**: n52,78140 e6,36581.

10 € 12,50, tourist tax incl Ch € 0,50/kWh WC € 4,50 included. **Surface:** grassy/sand. 01/01-31/12.
Distance: 2km 2km on the spot 2km on the spot on the spot.

Schoonloo 7F3

Camping BuitenGewoon, Elperstraat 16. **GPS**: n52,90114 e6,67965.
€ 10 ChWC.
Distance: 1,5km.

Ufelte 9E1

De Blauwe Haan, Weg achter de es 11.
GPS: n52,80220 e6,27264.

6 € 10 excl. tourist tax Ch € 2,50/night,10Amp WC included. **Location:** Rural, luxurious, quiet.
Surface: grassy/metalled. 01/04-31/10.
Distance: 5km 2km 3km 3km 2,5km 5km 2km on the spot on the spot.

Westerbork 7F3

Landgoed het Timmerholt, Gagelmaat 4.
GPS: n52,86850 e6,61748.

NL

4 € 10, 19/07-02/08 € 12,50 Ch included WC € 1,50/pppd € 1,50/pppd € 3,90/2,75 h. **Location:** Rural, luxurious, quiet. **Surface:** grassy/metalled. 01/01-31/12.
Distance: 2km 4km on the spot on the spot on the spot 2km 2km on the spot on the spot.
Remarks: Water closed during wintertime.

Tourist information Westerbork:
Herinneringscentrum Kamp Westerbork, Oosthalen 8, Hooghalen. Mo-Fri 10-17h, Sa-Su 11-17h, 01/07-31/08 and holidays 11-17h.

Wijster 9E1
Grondsels, Grondselweg 7. **GPS**: n52,80143 e6,49025.

10 € 5 Ch € 2 WC included. **Location:** Rural, simple, isolated, quiet. **Surface:** grassy/metalled.
15/03-31/10.
Distance: 3km on the spot 3km 5km on the spot.

Overijssel

Almelo 9F1
Stationsstraat. **GPS**: n52,35827 e6,65589.
3 free. **Location:** Urban. **Surface:** metalled. 01/01-31/12.
Distance: 600m.

Tourist information Almelo:
Markt- en Centrumplein. Thu 8.30-14h, Sa 8.30-17h.

Bathmen 9E2
Prinses Margrietlaan. **GPS**: n52,25025 e6,29927.

2 free. **Location:** Urban, simple, central, quiet.
Surface: metalled. 01/01-31/12.
Distance: 1km 2,5km 1km 1km on the spot on the spot.
Remarks: Parking gymnasium.

Belt Schutsloot 9E1
Café-Restaurant de Belt, Havezatheweg 4. **GPS**: n52,66774 e6,05189.

10 free for clients. **Surface:** asphalted.
01/01-31/12.
Distance: 3km 1km 1km on the spot 3km.
Remarks: North of Zwartsluis, at Belter- and Beulakerwijde.

Bentelo 9F2
De Bentelose Esch, Eschweg 2. **GPS**: n52,21250 e6,67010.

25 € 15, 2 pers.incl Ch (25x) WC € 2 included.
Location: Rural, luxurious, quiet. **Surface:** grassy/gravel.
15/03-01/11.
Distance: 2km 5km 2km 2km 400m on the spot on the spot.

Beuningen 9F1
De Nijenhaer, Nijenhaerweg 25. **GPS**: n52,34471 e6,99325.

15 € 12,50 Ch WC included. **Location:** Rural.
Surface: grassy. 01/01-31/12.
Distance: 3km on the spot on the spot.

Borne 9F2
De Aak. **GPS**: n52,30197 e6,75906.
1 free. **Location:** Urban. **Surface:** metalled. 01/01-31/12.
Distance: 200m 200m 500m.

Dalfsen 9E1
Stationsweg 4. **GPS**: n52,49944 e6,25949.

5 free. **Location:** Rural, simple, central, quiet.
Surface: grasstiles. 01/01-31/12.
Distance: 500m 500m 800m on the spot on the spot on the spot.
Remarks: Max. 48h.

Dalfsen 9E1
Starnbosch, Sterrebosweg 4. **GPS**: n52,47538 e6,26336.

7 € 10 + € 0,85/pp tourist tax Ch (8x) WC included € 0,40/5minutes € 5/0,50 € 1/1h. **Location:** Rural, comfortable, quiet. **Surface:** grassy/sand. 01/01-31/12.
Distance: 4km on the spot 4km 3,3km on the spot on the spot.
Remarks: Max. 48h.

De Lutte 9F2
Erve Velpen, Beuningerstraat 25. **GPS**: n52,33224 e7,01197.

20 € 7, tourist tax € 1/pp Ch € 2/day € 1/8minutes included. **Location:** Rural, comfortable, isolated, quiet.
Surface: grassy. 01/01-31/12.
Distance: 4km 300m bike junction on the spot.

Dedemsvaart 9E1
Camperplaats Dedemsvaart, Langewijk 112.
GPS: n52,60435 e6,45108.

10 € 6,50 € 1,50 € 2,50,16Amp .
Location: Urban. **Surface:** metalled. 01/01-31/12.
Distance: 700m 300m 200m.
Remarks: Max. 48h.

Den Ham 9E1
De Linderbeek, Zomerweg 56. **GPS**: n52,44526 e6,49870.

4 € 12,50 Ch WC € 5 included. 01/04-01/10.
Distance: on the spot on the spot.
Remarks: Max. 7 nights, € 2,50 discount on presentation of the guide 2012.

Diepenheim 9E2
Camperpark Ravenhorst/Diepenheim, Esweg 6.
GPS: n52,18307 e6,57872.

30 € 12,50 2p incl. + tourist tax Ch (30x),6Amp WC € 1 included. **Location:** Rural, luxurious, quiet.
Surface: grassy/metalled. 15/03-01/11.
Distance: 2km 2km 2km on the spot on the spot.
Remarks: Money in envelope in mail box.

Diepenheim 9E2
't Holt, Hengevelderweg 1A. **GPS**: n52,19500 e6,59186.

3 € 5, free for clients Ch free.
Surface: metalled.

NL

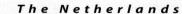

01/01-31/12.
Distance: 3km on the spot on the spot 3km on the spot.
Remarks: Golf court (pitch+putt).

Diepenheim 9E2

In de Kokkerieje, Grotestraat 94. **GPS**: n52,19923 e6,55452.

free with a meal. Mo-Tue.
Distance: on the spot 1km 500m.
Remarks: Parking behind restaurant.

Enschede 9F2

De Loeks, Moorvenweg 2a. **GPS**: n52,17757 e6,86599.

15 € 18,50, dog € 1 Ch (15x)WC € 2 included.
Location: Rural, luxurious, isolated, quiet. **Surface:** grassy/metalled.
01/01-31/12 sanitary 01/11-31/03.
Distance: 3km 2km 2km on the spot on the spot.

Enschede 9F2

Diekmanterrein, Weggelhorstweg. **GPS**: n52,20543 e6,90096.

5 free. **Location:** Urban, simple, isolated, quiet. **Surface:** asphalted.
01/01-31/12.
Distance: 2km 1,4km on the spot.

Enter 9E2

Werfstraat. **GPS**: n52,29808 e6,58271.

3 free. **Location:** Urban, simple. **Surface:** grassy/gravel.
01/01-31/12.
Distance: 600m on the spot on the spot 600m 700m on the spot on the spot.
Remarks: Max. 72h.

Geesteren 9F1

Zalencentrum Spalink, Koelenbeekweg 10. **GPS**: n52,44060 e6,69555.

15 € 8,50 Ch WC. **Surface:** grassy/gravel.

01/01-31/12.
Distance: 3,5km on the spot 3,5km on the spot on the spot.
Remarks: Guests free.

Geesteren 9F1

Land van Maas en Webbink, Vinckenweg 83.
GPS: n52,43513 e6,67557.
8 € 5. **Location:** Rural, quiet.
Surface: gravel. 01/01-31/12.
Distance: 5km 7km 1km 50m 500m on the spot on the spot.

Genemuiden 9E1

Koppel. **GPS**: n52,62355 e6,03678.
2 free. **Location:** Urban. **Surface:** metalled. 01/01-31/12.
Distance: 200m 250m 800m.

Giethoorn 9E1

Passantenhaven de Zuiderkluft, Vosjacht 1G.
GPS: n52,72134 e6,07449.

30 € 12, 2 pers.incl., 01/11-01/04 € 6 € 0,50/100liter Ch € 1/2kWh WC € 0,50 € 4/4 .
Surface: grassy/gravel. 01/01-31/12.
Distance: 1km on the spot on the spot.
Remarks: Check in at harbourmaster, water closed during wintertime.

Giethoorn 9E1

Camperplaats Haamstede, Kanaaldijk 17.
GPS: n52,72828 e6,07570.

40 € 10, 2 pers.incl € 0,50 Ch € 3 WC € 0,50 included.
Location: Rural, comfortable, central, quiet.
Surface: grassy. 01/04-31/10.
Distance: 2km 1km 20m 1km 1km on the spot on the spot.
Remarks: Arrival <21h.

Giethoorn 9E1

Camperresort Bodelaeke, Vosjacht 10A.
GPS: n52,71703 e6,07668.
99 € 10, 2 pers. incl. € 0,50/100liter Ch € 3,16Amp WC € 6/4 included.
Location: Rural, comfortable. **Surface:** grasstiles/grassy.
15/03-15/11.
Distance: 1km on the spot on the spot.

Tourist information Giethoorn:
VVV, Eendrachtsplein 1, www.kopvanoverijssel.nl. Village in nature reserve De Weerribben, Dutch Venice, boat trips possible.

Gramsbergen 9F1

Jachthaven 't Hooge Holt, Kanaaldijk West 2b.
GPS: n52,60563 e6,67462.
10 € 10 € 1 Ch € 1/24h.
Surface: grassy. 01/04-01/10.
Distance: 1km on the spot on the spot 1km 900m 900m on the spot on the spot.

Haaksbergen 9F2

Henk Pen Caravans en Kampeerauto's, Westsingel 2.
GPS: n52,14917 e6,71167.

2 free free. **Location:** Simple, noisy.
Surface: asphalted. 01/01-31/12.
Distance: 1km on the spot on the spot 1km.
Remarks: Motorhome dealer.

Haaksbergen 9F2

Camping Scholtenhagen, Scholtenhagenweg 30.
GPS: n52,14820 e6,72467.

24 € 10 Ch (24x)WC € 0,90 € 5,25 included.
Location: Rural, luxurious, quiet. **Surface:** grassy. 01/01-31/12.
Distance: 2km 7km 3km on the spot 2,5km 1km on the spot on the spot.
Remarks: Max. 72h, bread-service, excl use swimming pool.

Hardenberg 9E1

De Kuserbrink, Parkweg. **GPS**: n52,57746 e6,62927.

4 € 10 € 0,50/100liter Ch (4x)€ 1/kWh.
Location: Rural, comfortable, central, quiet. **Surface:** grasstiles.
01/01-31/12.
Distance: centre 500m on the spot on the spot.
Remarks: Max. 72h.

Hardenberg 9E1

Fam. Pullen, Allemansweg 1a, Collendoorn.
GPS: n52,58845 e6,59146.

20 € 10 Ch included. **Location:** Rural, comfortable, isolated, quiet. **Surface:** grassy. 01/01-31/12.
Distance: 3km 3km bike junction on the spot.
Remarks: Dog on leads.

Hasselt 9E1

Jachthaven de Molenwaard, Van Nahuysweg 151.
GPS: n52,59367 e6,08741.

NL

10 € 8,50, tourist tax € 0,70/pp Ch (10x)€ 2/night WC € 0,50/6minutes € 3,75/3,75 included.
Location: Luxurious, quiet. **Surface:** metalled. 01/01-31/12.
Distance: 500m on the spot on the spot 500m 500m 500m on the spot on the spot.
Remarks: Check in at harbourmaster.

Heeten 9E1

De Baanbreker, Speelmansweg 8. **GPS**: n52,36026 e6,31190.

10 € 4,50 Ch . **Surface:** metalled. 01/01-31/12.
Distance: 2km 2km 2km on the spot on the spot.
Remarks: Max. 48h.

Hellendoorn 9E1

Camperplaats Hancate, Zuidelijke Kanaaldijk.
GPS: n52,43418 e6,44060.

10 € 10 Ch (4x) included. **Location:** Rural, simple, quiet. **Surface:** grassy. 01/01-31/12.
Distance: 5km on the spot 100m 200m on the spot on the spot.

Hengelo 9F2

Jachthaven Hengelo, Kanaalweg 8. **GPS**: n52,25123 e6,76216.
6 € 10 + € 1/pp tourist tax Ch included.
Location: Rural. **Surface:** grassy/metalled. 01/05-01/10.
Distance: 3km on the spot on the spot 3km on the spot on the spot.
Remarks: Max. 72h, max. 7m.

Hengelo 9F2

Camperplaats Eulerhook, Vöckersweg 19.
GPS: n52,24652 e6,75365.

15 € 10 Ch (15x) WC included. **Location:** Rural, comfortable, noisy. **Surface:** metalled. 01/01-31/12.
Distance: 4km 2km 500m 4km 3km 1km on the spot on the spot.
Remarks: Nearby motorway.

Hertme 9F2

Camperpark Rabo Scheele, Hertmerweg 37.
GPS: n52,32663 e6,74691.

25 € 12, 2 pers.incl Ch WC included.
Location: Rural, comfortable, quiet. **Surface:** grassy/metalled.
01/01-31/12.
Distance: Hertme 500m, Borne 2km 100m 500m 2km 2km on the spot on the spot.

Holten 9E2

Camperplaats Holten, Schreursweg 5. **GPS**: n52,27862 e6,44847.
25 € 11 Ch included.
Location: Rural. 01/04-31/10.
Distance: 2km 2km 500m on the spot on the spot.

Holten 9E2

Camperplaats Lookerland, Rijssenseweg 34A.
GPS: n52,28515 e6,43866.

20 € 10 Ch (10x)included WC free. **Location:** Rural, quiet. **Surface:** grassy/metalled.
01/04-31/09.
Distance: 1,3km 3km 1,3km 1,3km 100m on the spot Pieterpad.
Remarks: Money in envelope in mail box.

Tourist information Holten:
VVV, Dorpsstraat 27, www.vvvholten.nl.

Kampen 9E1

Burgemeester Berghuisplein 1. **GPS**: n52,55268 e5,91356.

25 € 7,50 ChWCincluded € 0,50/6minutes.
Location: Urban, comfortable, central, quiet.
Surface: metalled.
01/01-31/12.
Distance: historical centre 500m 1,5km 1,5km 900m 1km on the spot on the spot.
Remarks: Max. 72h, entrance code sanitary building at town hall.

Tourist information Kampen:
VVV, Oudestraat 151, www.vvvkampen.nl. Former Hanseatic town on the Ijssel.

Losser 9F2

Brilmansdennen, Bookholtlaan. **GPS**: n52,26927 e7,01378.

3 free. **Surface:** metalled. 01/01-31/12.
Distance: 1km.
Remarks: At sports park, max. 72h.

Nieuwleusen 9E1

Camperplaats Vechtdal, Den Hulst 20. **GPS**: n52,59193 e6,29324.
12 € 15, 2 pers.incl ChWC included. 22/01-16/12.
Distance: 800m 800m on the spot on the spot.
Remarks: Bread-service.

Nieuwleusen 9E1

Koninging Julianalaan. **GPS**: n52,58213 e6,28076.

3 free. **Location:** Urban, simple.
Surface: metalled. 01/01-31/12.
Distance: 300m on the spot on the spot.
Remarks: Max. 48h.

Nijverdal 9E1

De Wilgenweard, Sportlaan 6. **GPS**: n52,37118 e6,46538.

3 € 5 + € 0,75/pp tourist tax.
Surface: metalled. 01/01-31/12.
Distance: 500m on the spot on the spot on the spot 500m 200m on the spot on the spot.

Ommen 9E1

Landgoed De Stekkenkamp, Beerzerweg 3.
GPS: n52,51128 e6,43933.

8 € 7,50 + € 0,80/pp tourist tax € 0,50/4minutes Ch (8x) included. **Location:** Rural, simple, quiet. **Surface:** grasstiles/grassy.
01/01-31/12.
Distance: 1,2km 1,2km 1,2km 1,2km 1,2km 1,2km on the spot on the spot.
Remarks: At historical farmhouse, max. 72h.

Overdinkel 9F2

Camperplaats Skop'nboer, Schaapskooiweg 2.
GPS: n52,24692 e7,03581.

25 € 15 Ch WC included. **Location:** Rural, luxurious, quiet. **Surface:** grasstiles/grassy. 01/01-31/12.
Distance: 3km 3km on the spot on the spot.

Steenwijk 9E1

Jachthaven, Houthaven. **GPS**: n52,78627 e6,10006.

20 € 10 € 1. **Surface:** grassy. 01/01-31/12.
Distance: 1km on the spot on the spot 300m.

NL

Remarks: Check in at harbourmaster.

Tubbergen 9F1

De Vlaskoel, Sportlaan 3. **GPS**: n52,41043 e6,78316.

2 free free. **Location:** Simple. **Surface:** metalled.
01/01-31/12.
Distance: 500m 600m 600m on the spot on the spot.
Remarks: At swimming pool.

Vollenhove 9E1

De Haven. **GPS**: n52,68277 e5,94862.

6 € 12 Ch € 1 WC € 0,50. **Surface:** metalled.
01/01-31/12.
Distance: 100m 100m 1km.
Remarks: Check in at harbourmaster.

Vollenhove 9E1

Recreatiecentrum 't Akkertien, Op de Voorst, Noordwal 3.
GPS: n52,67609 e5,93914.

20 € 8 Ch included € 4. 01/01-31/12.
Distance: 900m on the spot on the spot 400m peak season.

Wierden 9E1

De Huurne, Zandinksweg 22. **GPS**: n52,35003 e6,57474.

10 € 10 Ch included. 01/01-31/12.
Distance: 2km 3km 2km 700m on the spot on the spot.
Remarks: Max. 3 nights, max 3,5t.

Wierden 9E1

Wijngaard Baan, Kloosterhoeksweg 15. **GPS**: n52,32172 e6,56709.

24 € 12 Ch WC included. **Surface:** metalled.
01/01-31/12.

Distance: 3km on the spot on the spot 3km on the spot on the spot.
Remarks: Vineyard.

Wijhe 9E1

Passantenhaven, Veerweg. **GPS**: n52,38639 e6,12830.

10 € 6, tourist tax € 0,50/pp ChWC included.
Location: Simple, central. **Surface:** asphalted/metalled.
24/04-02/11.
Distance: 500m on the spot on the spot 500m 500m on the spot on the spot.
Remarks: Max. 3 nights.

Tourist information Wijhe:
Marktplein. Tue-morning.

Zwartsluis 9E1

Voetbalvereniging DESZ, Clingellanden. **GPS**: n52,63850 e6,07536.

15 € 10, 2 pers.incl Ch. **Surface:** gravel.
Distance: 400m.
Remarks: Service at marina.

Tourist information Zwartsluis:
Stoomgemaal Mastenbroek, Kamperzeedijk 5, Genemuiden. Pumping-engine, 1856.

Zwolle 9E1

Turfmarkt. **GPS**: n52,51326 e6,10380.

7 mo-sa 8-18h € 5/day, free overnight stay.
Location: Urban, simple, central. **Surface:** metalled. 01/01-31/12.
Distance: 800m 1km 650m on the spot on the spot.
Remarks: Max. 72h.

Zwolle 9E1

Jachthaven de Hanze, Holtenbroekerdijk 44.
GPS: n52,53122 e6,07345.

15 € 10, tourist tax incl Ch (15x)€ 0,50/kWh WC € 1/7minutes included. **Location:** Rural, comfortable, central, quiet. **Surface:** grassy/metalled. 01/01-31/12.
Distance: 2,5km 2km on the spot on the spot 1km 1km 500m on the spot on the spot.
Remarks: Max. 72h.

Zwolle 9E1

Agnietenplas, Haersterveerweg 29A. **GPS**: n52,53779 e6,13169.
80 € 16,50, 2 pers.incl + tourist tax € 0,60/pp € 1/kWh .

Location: Rural. **Surface:** grassy. 01/01-31/12.
Distance: 3km on the spot on the spot.
Remarks: Caution sepkey € 20.

Tourist information Zwolle:
Sassenpoort, Koestraat 46. Medieval gate building. Wed-Fri 14-17h, Sa/Su/holidays 12-17h.

Flevoland

Almere 9D2

Marina Muiderzand, IJmeerdijk 4. **GPS**: n52,34155 e5,13493.

10 (01/10-30/04 2 pl) € 14,50 Ch WC € 5/3 included
Surface: asphalted. 01/01-31/12.
Distance: 8km on the spot on the spot on the spot on the spot 1km.
Remarks: Check in at harbourmaster.

Tourist information Almere:
VVV, De Diagonaal 199, www.vvvalmere.nl.
Stadhuisplein. Wed, Sa 9-16h.
Biologische Boerenmarkt, Kempenhaanpad 14, www.stadsboerderijalmere.nl. Sa 9.30-13h.

Almere-Haven 9D2

WSV Almere, Sluiskade 11. **GPS**: n52,33257 e5,21715.

40 € 15,50, 2 pers. incl Ch (12x)€ 0,50/2kWh WC € 5 included. **Location:** Urban, simple. **Surface:** grassy.
01/03-01/11.
Distance: on the spot on the spot 200m on the spot.

Almere-Haven 9D2

Haven, Sluis. **GPS**: n52,33366 e5,22170.

2 € 7 ChWC € 0,50.
Surface: metalled.
02/05-04/09.
Distance: on the spot 1km on the spot on the spot 1km.
Remarks: Max. 72h, check in at harbourmaster.

Tourist information Almere-Haven:
De Brink. Fri 9-16h.

Emmeloord 9D1

Camperplaats Emmeloord, Casteleynsweg 1.
GPS: n52,73981 e5,77235.
12 € 9, 2 pers. incl Ch € 2/day included.
Surface: grassy. 11/04-31/10.
Distance: 4,9km 150m.
Remarks: 2 bicylces available.

Lelystad 9D1

P Houtribhoek, Houtribslag. **GPS**: n52,54762 e5,45666.

NL

4 free.
Surface: metalled.
01/01-31/12.
Distance: 2km on the spot on the spot on the spot 2km.
Remarks: Max. 48h.

Tourist information Lelystad:
Oostvaardersplassen. 6000 acres of lakes, mud fields, reed swamps, hiking route 5km and cycle route 35km.
Batavia Stad, Bataviaplein 60. Outlet-shopping.
daily 10-18h.
free, parking € 3.

Luttelgeest 9D1
Camping Craneburcht, Kuinderweg 52. **GPS**: n52,78304 e5,84331.

10 € 13,50 + € 0,75/pp tourist tax € 2 WC.
Surface: metalled. 01/03-30/11 winter: Mo-Tue.
Distance: 200m on the spot 7km.
Remarks: Arrival >17h, departure <10h.

Nagele 9D1
Afslag Nagele, Han Stijkelweg 11. **GPS**: n52,65034 e5,68610.

20 € 12 Ch € 2/night WC included free.
Location: Comfortable, isolated, quiet. **Surface:** grassy/metalled.
01/01-31/12.
Distance: 3km.
Remarks: Max. 5 days.

Urk 9D1
Haven, Burgemeester Schipperkade. **GPS**: n52,66040 e5,59975.

20 € 15 Ch (18x)WC included.
Surface: metalled.
01/01-31/12.
Distance: 200m 100m 100m, bakery 300m.

Tourist information Urk:
VVV, Wijk 2 2, www.vvvflevoland.nl. Old fishermen's village, former island.
Het Oude Raadhuis, Wijk 2 2. Regional museum.
01/04-31/10 Mo-Fr 10-17h, Sa 10-16h, 01/03-30/11 Mo-Sa 10-16h.
Urkerhard.
Sa 8.30-13h.
Stegentocht/Ginkiestocht. Guided walk, reservation at Touristinfo Urk.

Zeewolde 9D2
Camperpark De Wielewaal, Wielseweg 9. **GPS**: n52,25981 e5,43727.

50 € 12, 2 pers.incl, tourist tax € 1/pp, dog € 1 Ch included € 2 WC against payment.
Surface: metalled. 01/01-31/12.
Distance: 7km on the spot on the spot 7km.

Gelderland

Aalten 9F2
't Noorden, Lichtenvoordsestraatweg 44.
GPS: n51,93402 e6,58206.

4 € 10 € 1/80liter Ch (4x)included.
Location: Rural, simple, noisy.
Surface: gravel. 01/01-31/12.
Distance: 700m on the spot on the spot.

Tourist information Aalten:
Wijngoed De Hennepe, Romienendiek 3, www.wijngoeddehennepe.nl. Guided tour and tastery. shop Tue-Fr 13.30h-sunset, Sa 10h, guided tour/tasting Jul/Aug We 15h.
Hoge Blik. Thu 8-12h.

Aerdt 9E2
De Aerdtse Wacht, Heuvelakkersestraat 18.
GPS: n51,88634 e6,08861.

4 € 10 € 1/80liter Ch included. **Location:** Rural, comfortable, isolated, quiet. **Surface:** metalled. 01/01-31/12.
Distance: 1km 1,5km 1,5km on the spot on the spot on the spot on the spot on the spot on the spot.

Almen 9E2
De Nieuwe Aanleg, Scheggertdijk 10. **GPS**: n52,16711 e6,29744.

12 € 12,50 € 0,75/100liter Ch (12x)included WC € 1/5minutes . **Location:** Rural, comfortable, quiet.
Surface: metalled. 01/01-31/12.
Distance: 2km on the spot on the spot on the spot 2km on the spot on the spot on the spot.
Remarks: At the Twentekanaal.

Tourist information Almen:
Dorpsstraat. Small week market. Tue 11-13h.

Apeldoorn 9E2
Malkander, Dubbelbeek 38. **GPS**: n52,18305 e5,96673.

4 free. **Location:** Simple, isolated. **Surface:** metalled.
01/01-31/12, 15-09h.
Distance: 2km 150m 1km on the spot.
Remarks: At swimming pool, max. 72h.

Apeldoorn 9E2
Willem Alexanderlaan 651. **GPS**: n52,20974 e5,95899.
8 € 8,80/24h. **Location:** Urban. **Surface:** metalled.
01/01-31/12.
Distance: 400m 4,5km 700m 900m 300m on the spot on the spot.
Remarks: Max. 72h.

Tourist information Apeldoorn:
Marktplein. Wed 8-13h, Sa 8-17h.

Appeltern 9D3
Strand Maaslanden, Hamsestraat 2. **GPS**: n51,83107 e5,56193.

10 € 10 Ch included WC € 1.
Location: Rural. **Surface:** grassy/metalled.
Distance: 2km on the spot on the spot on the spot on the spot.
Remarks: Boat rental, bicycle rental, show-garden Appeltern 3km.

Appeltern 9D3
Herberg 't Mun, Molenstraat 10, Blauwe Sluis.
GPS: n51,84048 e5,56360.

50 € 5 Ch (12x)€ 2,6Amp WC included.
Location: Rural, simple, isolated, quiet.
Surface: grassy/metalled. 01/01-31/12.
Distance: 2km 300m Trout farm on the spot 2km on the spot on the spot on the spot.
Remarks: Show-garden Appeltern 3km.

Arnhem 9E2
Nieuwe Kade. **GPS**: n51,97327 e5,91593.

4 € 9 € 2,50 Ch (4x)€ 0,50/kWh WC .
Location: Urban, simple, central, quiet.
Surface: metalled. 01/01-31/12.
Distance: 1km 4,7km 200m 1km 1km on the spot on the spot.
Remarks: Along the Rhine river, max. 48h, service at petrol station n51,970749 e5,94796.

Tourist information Arnhem:
Jansplaats. Small week market. Tue 7.30-15h.

Barneveld 9D2

De Grote Glind, Scherpenzeelseweg 158. **GPS**: n52,11540 e5,53775.
7 € 15, 2 pers.incl Ch included WC . **Location:** Rural.
Surface: grassy. 01/05-30/09.
Distance: Barneveld 5km 600m.
Remarks: At museum.

Bemmel 9E2

Dijkstraat/Wardstraat. **GPS**: n51,88972 e5,90972.

3 free. **Location:** Urban, simple, central, quiet.
Surface: metalled. 01/01-31/12.
Distance: 400m 400m 400m 400m on the spot on the spot.
Remarks: Max. 72h.

Borculo 9E2

Hambroekplas/Berkelpalace, Hambroekweg 10.
GPS: n52,11573 e6,53758.

4 € 10 € 1/80liter Ch (4x)included. **Location:** Rural, simple, noisy. **Surface:** grassy/gravel. 01/03-31/10.
Distance: 500m 150m 50m 500m on the spot on the spot.

Borculo 9E2

Bruggink Campers, Kamerlingh Onnestraat 19.
GPS: n52,12281 e6,52682.

3 free on demand. **Location:** Urban, simple, noisy.
Surface: metalled. 01/01-31/12, 18-9h.
Distance: 1,5km 2km 500m 1,5km 1,5km on the spot.

Bredevoort 9F2

P2, recreatieplas Slingeplas, Kruittorenstraat 10b.
GPS: n51,94722 e6,62318.

8 € 10 € 1/80liter Ch (8x)included.
Location: Rural, simple, quiet. **Surface:** metalled. 01/04-01/10.
Distance: 500m 100m 400m 500m on the spot.
Remarks: Max. 72h.

Tourist information Bredevoort:
VVV, Markt 8. City with half-timbered houses.
Book market. 3rd Sa of the month 10-17.

Culemborg 9D2

Jachthaven de Helling, Beusichemsedijk.
GPS: n51,96117 e5,22148.

20 € 16,50 + tourist tax Ch WC € 0,50 € 4/4 included. **Surface:** grassy/sand. 01/04-01/11.
Distance: 500m on the spot on the spot 100m 500m 1,5km.
Remarks: Check in at harbourmaster.

De Heurne 9E2

De Haar, Caspersstraat 14. **GPS**: n51,89802 e6,50035.

18 € 10 € 1/80liter Ch (15x) included.
Location: Rural, comfortable, quiet.
Surface: grassy. 01/01-31/12.
Distance: 1km 8km 1km on the spot on the spot.
Remarks: Filling station gas bottles 300m.

Doesburg 9E2

Jachthaven Doesburg, Turfhaven. **GPS**: n52,01109 e6,13368.

6 € 7,50 Ch (6x)€ 0,50/kWh WC € 0,50/4minutes.
Location: Urban, comfortable, central, quiet. **Surface:** concrete.
01/01-31/12.
Distance: 500m 4km on the spot 500m 1km 500m on the spot on the spot.
Remarks: Check in at harbourmaster.

Doornenburg 9E2

Kerkstraat. **GPS**: n51,89416 e6,00129.

3 free. **Location:** Rural, quiet. **Surface:** metalled.
01/01-31/12.
Distance: 400m 200m cafetaria 200m 400m on the spot.
Remarks: Max. 3 days, view on castle Doornenburg.

Emst 9E2

Recreatiepark 't Smallert, Smallertsweg 8.
GPS: n52,30910 e5,98126.

20 € 5 free. **Surface:** metalled. 01/01-31/12.
Distance: 2km 200m 200m on the spot on the spot on the spot.
Remarks: Check in on arrival.

Ermelo 9D2

Camperpark Strand Horst, Buitenbrinkweg 82.
GPS: n52,31181 e5,56643.

40 € 14-16, 2 pers. incl € 1 Ch (50x)WC € 0,50/6minutes included. **Location:** Rural, comfortable, noisy.
Surface: grassy/metalled. 01/03-01/11.
Distance: 4km 50m 200m 200m 500m 4km.

Garderen 9D2

Hotel Restaurant Overbosch, Hooiweg 23.
GPS: n52,22577 e5,70504.

10 € 7,50 € 2,50/24h .
Location: Rural, simple, quiet. **Surface:** gravel. 01/01-31/12.
Distance: 1km on the spot 1km on the spot on the spot on the spot.
Remarks: Use of a meal desired.

Garderen 9D2

Gasterij Zondag, Apeldoornsestraat 163-165.
GPS: n52,21443 e5,70696.

10 free . **Location:** Rural.
Surface: gravel.
01/01-31/12 Restaurant: Tue.
Distance: 2km 3,5km on the spot on the spot on the spot.
Remarks: Max. 1 night, entrance next to restaurant, restaurant visit appreciated.

Geldermalsen 9D2

Kostverlorenkade. **GPS**: n51,88507 e5,29030.

NL

1 free. **Surface:** metalled.
Distance: 100m 3,6km on the spot on the spot on the spot.
Remarks: Parking at departure excursion boat.

Gendringen 9E2

Willem Alexanderplein. **GPS:** n51,86999 e6,37948.

2 free. **Location:** Urban, simple, central. **Surface:** asphalted.
01/01-31/12.
Distance: 200m 100m 500m.
Remarks: Max. 72h.

Gendringen 9E2

Diekshuus, Ulftseweg 4a. **GPS:** n51,87412 e6,38586.

8 € 10 € 1/80liter Ch (4x)included. **Location:** Rural, simple, quiet. **Surface:** gravel. 01/01-31/12.
Distance: 600m 600m on the spot on the spot.
Remarks: At manege.

Gendt 9E2

Camperpark Lingewaard, Zandvoort 64. **GPS:** n51,88619 e5,95008.

20 € 14, 2 pers incl € 1/100liter Ch (20x)€ 0,50/kWh WC € 1 € 1 free. **Location:** Rural. **Surface:** grassy/gravel.
01/01-31/12.
Distance: 2km 5km 1,2km 200m 100m 2km on the spot 300m on the spot on the spot.

Gorssel 9E2

De Vlinderhoeve, Bathmenseweg 7. **GPS:** n52,21825 e6,26255.

5 € 14 Ch WC € 6/2 included. **Location:** Rural, luxurious, isolated, quiet.
Surface: forest soil.
01/04-31/10.

Distance: 4,5km 5km on the spot on the spot on the spot.
Remarks: To be paid at campsite.

Groenlo 9F2

Camping Marveld, Elshofweg 6. **GPS:** n52,03604 e6,63134.
6 € 10 € 1/80liter Ch (4x)included. **Location:** Urban, simple. **Surface:** metalled. 01/01-31/12.
Distance: 1km 500m.

Harderwijk 9D2

P Parkweg, Parkweg. **GPS:** n52,34088 e5,62977.

3 free. **Location:** Urban, simple. **Surface:** metalled.
01/01-31/12.
Distance: 1,2km 3km 1,3km 800m.

Hattem 9E1

Jachthaven Hattem, Geldersedijk 20. **GPS:** n52,47699 e6,06945.

22 € 10 + € 1,25/pp tourist tax Ch (4x)€ 2/24h WC € 0,50 € 4/4 included. **Location:** Urban, comfortable, central, quiet.
Surface: grasstiles/grassy.
01/01-31/12.
Distance: 200m on the spot on the spot 200m 200m 50m on the spot on the spot.
Remarks: Max. 72h, check in at harbourmaster, bread-service.

Heerde 9E1

Brasserie Meet & Eat, Eperweg 55. **GPS:** n52,37084 e6,02079.

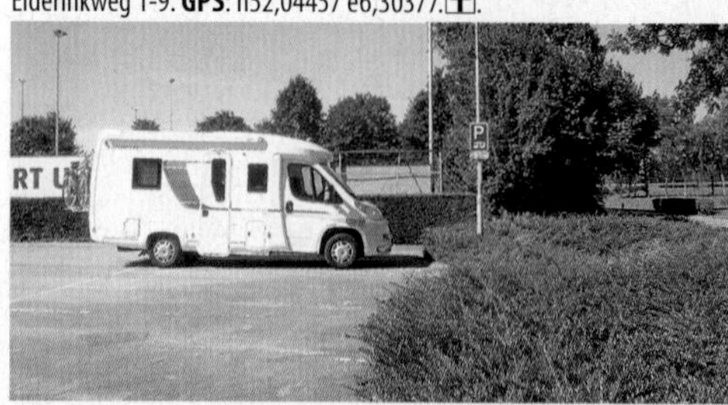

10 free, use of a meal desired (2x)included WC .
Surface: grassy/gravel.
Su (01/10-30/04).
Distance: 3km 1,5km 1,5km on the spot 2km 100m.

Hengelo 9E2

Elderinkweg 1-9. **GPS:** n52,04457 e6,30377.

2 free. **Location:** Rural, simple. **Surface:** asphalted.
01/01-31/12.
Distance: 500m 100m.
Remarks: Next to sports fields, max. 24h.

Heteren 9D2

Steenkuil, N837. **GPS:** n51,95456 e5,73094.

3 free. **Location:** Rural, simple, isolated, quiet.
Surface: gravel/metalled.
01/01-31/12.
Distance: 2km 2km 2km 2km on the spot on the spot.
Remarks: Max. 72h.

Heteren 9D2

Landgoed Overbetuwe, Uilenburgsestraat 3. **GPS:** n51,94853 e5,77266.
10 € 12 € 2 Ch€ 2 € 2 WC€ 2 .
Surface: grassy.
01/01-31/12.
Distance: 2km.

Huissen 9E2

Looveer. **GPS:** n51,93578 e5,94467.

3 free. **Location:** Simple, central. **Surface:** grasstiles/metalled.
01/01-31/12.
Distance: 200m 200m 200m 200m on the spot 500m on the spot on the spot.
Remarks: Max. 72h.

Hurwenen 9D3

Het Uilennest, Groenestraat 2a. **GPS:** n51,81367 e5,31880.

16 € 12,50 Ch WC included. **Surface:** grassy/metalled.
01/01-31/12. **Distance:** 600m on the spot 600m on the spot on the spot.
Remarks: Reservation in winter peak season, charging point for electric bicycles.

Kerkwijk 9D3

Hippisch Centrum Bommelerwaard, Jan Stuversdreef 1-3.
GPS: n51,78876 e5,19929.

5 € 10 WC included. **Surface:** metalled.
01/01-31/12.
Distance: 2km 1,5km 1,5km 1,5km.

Lathum 9E2

Jachthaven 't Eiland, De Muggenwaard 16.
GPS: n51,98819 e6,04462.

NL

15 € 15, 2 pers.incl Ch (20x)WC included.
Location: Rural, comfortable, quiet. **Surface:** grassy/metalled.
01/01-31/12.
Distance: 1km 5km on the spot on the spot on the spot 1km 500m on the spot.
Remarks: Max. 48h.

Lichtenvoorde 9E2

Zieuwentseweg. **GPS**: n51,99067 e6,55990.

4 € 10 € 1/80liter Ch (4x)included.
Location: Urban, simple, central. **Surface:** gravel/sand.
01/01-31/12.
Distance: 500m on the spot 500m 100m.
Remarks: Next to sports centre.

Maasbommel 9D3

Eeterij 't Pont, Veerweg 1. **GPS**: n51,81963 e5,54507.

10 € 10 **Location:** Rural. **Surface:** grassy/gravel.
01/01-31/12.
Distance: 750m on the spot on the spot.
Remarks: Along the Meuse river, beautiful view.

Maasbommel 9D3

Saletmeubelen, Kapelstraat 30. **GPS**: n51,82459 e5,53193.

5 € 10 Ch included. 01/01-31/12.
Distance: 300m 1km 1km 1km 300m.

Megchelen 9E3

Theetuin, B&B Vita Verde, Nieuweweg 10. **GPS**: n51,83895 e6,38022.

3 € 10 included. **Surface:** grassy/gravel. 01/01-31/12.
Distance: 500m 5km 500m 4km on the spot on the spot.
Remarks: Bread-service.

Meteren 9D3

Restaurant 3 Zussen, Rijksstraatweg 80. **GPS**: n51,85722 e5,28033.

5 free.
Distance: on the spot.
Remarks: Use of a meal desired.

Millingen a/d Rijn 9E3

't Crumpse Hoekje, Crumpsestraat 28.
GPS: n51,85624 e6,03145.

12 € 8, 2 pers.incl € 1/90liter Ch (12x)€ 2/day WC € 1/6minutes included. **Location:** Rural, luxurious, isolated, quiet. **Surface:** gravel. 01/01-31/12.
Distance: 1,4km 2km 1,4km 1,4km 1,5km on the spot.

Neede 9F2

Café restaurant De Olde Mölle, Diepenheimseweg 21.
GPS: n52,14153 e6,61035.

8 € 10 € 1/80liter Ch .
Surface: metalled. 01/01-31/12.
Distance: 1km on the spot.
Remarks: Max. 72h.

Neede 9F2

Camperpark Achterhoek, Diepenheimseweg 44.
GPS: n52,18023 e6,58588.

24 € 14,50, 04/07-23/08 € 16, 2 pers.incl Ch (24x)WC € 0,12/minutes € 5,50/3,50 included. **Location:** Rural, comfortable, noisy. **Surface:** grassy. 25/03-25/09.
Distance: 4,5km on the spot on the spot 4,5km on the spot on the spot.
Remarks: To be paid at campsite, bread-service, bicycle rental.

Nijkerk 9D2

Camperplaats Nijkerk, Watergoorweg 31.
GPS: n52,22641 e5,47711.

4 free Chfree. **Location:** Urban, simple, noisy. **Surface:** metalled.
01/01-31/12.
Distance: 500m 2km 2km 500m 500m 500m 200m on the spot on the spot.

Nunspeet 9D1

Camperplaats De Zwaan, Hardenbrinkweg 46.
GPS: n52,37901 e5,75363.

35 € 13 Ch (45x)WC € 3/3 included.
Location: Rural, luxurious, quiet. **Surface:** grasstiles/grassy.
01/01-31/12.
Distance: 2,5km 3,5km 2,5km 2,5km 1km 2km 900m Zwanenroute on the spot.
Remarks: No arrival on Sunday.

Nunspeet 9D1

Routiers Nunspeet, Rijksweg A28. **GPS**: n52,36199 e5,77061.

3 free WC . **Surface:** asphalted. 01/01-31/12.
Remarks: Use of sanitary free with a meal.

Tourist information Nunspeet:
Thu-morning.

Otterlo 9D2

De Wije Werelt, Arnhemseweg 100-102. **GPS**: n52,08592 e5,77319.

50 € 18-25 Ch (10x)WC included € 5/2 € 3,50/day.
Location: Rural, simple.
Surface: grassy.
01/01-31/12.
Distance: 500m 500m on the spot campsite supermarket on the spot on the spot on the spot.

Tourist information Otterlo:
M Kröller Müller Museum. Collection.

Poederoijen 9C3

Slot Loevestein, Loevestein 1. **GPS**: n51,81722 e5,02086.
4 free. 01/01-31/12.
Distance: 6km 6km 6km on the spot on the spot.

Putten 9D2

Brinkstraat. **GPS**: n52,26244 e5,60756.

NL

2 free. **Location:** Urban, simple, central. **Surface:** metalled. 01/01-31/12.
Distance: 200m 300m 300m 250m on the spot on the spot.
Remarks: Max. 48h.

Putten 9D2

Camperplaats De Driest, Driestweg 10. **GPS:** n52,23386 e5,61533.
15 voluntary contribution. 01/01-31/12.
Distance: 2,5km on the spot on the spot.
Remarks: Max. 72h.

Tourist information Putten:
Wed.

Rekken 9F2

Grensovergang, Oldenkotseweg. **GPS:** n52,09783 e6,75568.

5 € 5. **Surface:** metalled. 01/01-31/12.
Distance: on the spot on the spot on the spot.
Remarks: Max. 72h, cycle and hiking routes.

Ressen 9E2

De Woerdt, Woerdsestraat 4. **GPS:** n51,88867 e5,87215.

15 € 7,50 + € 1/pp tourist tax (10x)€ 1.
Location: Rural. **Surface:** grassy/metalled.
01/01-31/12.
Distance: 2km 3,6km 2km.
Remarks: Regional products, pitches in the orchard.

Ruurlo 9E2

Camping Tamaring, Wildpad 3. **GPS:** n52,10239 e6,44257.

2 € 10 € 1/80liter Ch (4x)included. **Location:** Rural, simple, quiet. **Surface:** gravel/metalled. 01/01-31/12.
Distance: 2km on the spot on the spot.
Remarks: Max. 8M.

Silvolde 9E2

Parking de Paasberg, Terborgseveld. **GPS:** n51,91633 e6,37194.

4 free. **Location:** Urban, simple, quiet. **Surface:** metalled.
01/01-31/12.
Distance: city centre 1km 300m.
Remarks: Parking at swimming pool, max. 72h.

Sinderen 9E2

NatuurlijkBUITEN, Toldijk 11. **GPS:** n51,91297 e6,42384.

2 € 12 € 1/80liter (2x) included.
Location: Rural, comfortable, isolated, quiet. **Surface:** grassy/gravel.
01/01-31/12.
Distance: 3km 3km on the spot 3km 3km 2km on the spot on the spot.
Remarks: Bread-service + breakfast-service, bicycle rental.

Sinderen 9E2

Biezenhof, Kapelweg 42a. **GPS:** n51,90424 e6,45180.

4 € 10 € 1/80liter Ch included. **Location:** Rural, simple, quiet. **Surface:** gravel. 01/01-31/12.
Distance: 4km 4km 4km on the spot.

Steenderen 9E2

Camperplaats Landlust, Landlustweg 2.
GPS: n52,06086 e6,18866.

12 € 12,50, 2 pers.incl Ch (12x) WC included.
Location: Rural, luxurious, central, quiet. **Surface:** grassy/metalled.
01/01-31/12.
Distance: on the spot 1,5km 300m 150m 150m on the spot on the spot.

Stokkum 9E2

Camping Brockhausen, Eltenseweg 20. **GPS:** n51,87778 e6,21167.

4 € 10 € 1/80liter Ch (4x)included € 2,50/day.
Location: Rural, simple. **Surface:** gravel. 01/01-31/12.

Distance: 800m 500m 2,5km 2km on the spot on the spot.
Remarks: Bread-service.

Terschuur 9D2

Camperplaats Groot Westerveld, Leemweg 2.
GPS: n52,16819 e5,53239.

4 € 7,50 Ch € 2,50/night,10Amp WC included.
Location: Rural, simple, quiet. **Surface:** grassy/metalled.
01/03-30/09.
Distance: 1,5km 4km 2km 3km 2km 1km on the spot on the spot.

Terwolde 9E2

Dorpsstraat 53, N792. **GPS:** n52,28173 e6,09962.

2 free. **Location:** Simple, central, quiet. **Surface:** metalled.
01/01-31/12.
Distance: 100m on the spot on the spot on the spot on the spot.

Tiel 9D2

Parking Waalkade, Waalkade. **GPS:** n51,88518 e5,44079.

4 € 8,30. **Surface:** asphalted. 01/01-31/12.
Distance: 500m on the spot on the spot on the spot 500m on the spot.
Remarks: Max. 2 nights, cash payment.

Tiel 9D2

Restaurant de Betuwe, Hoog Kellenseweg 7.
GPS: n51,90391 e5,44286.
10 € 8. **Surface:** asphalted. 01/01-31/12.
Distance: 2km on the spot.

Tolkamer 9E3

Europakade, Europakade. **GPS:** n51,85122 e6,09938.

15 € 7,50 + € 0,90/pp tourist tax (6x)€ 1/kWh.
Location: Simple, central, quiet. **Surface:** metalled.
01/01-31/12 high water.
Distance: 200m 150m 200m 500m on the spot on the spot.
Remarks: Max. 48h.

Tolkamer 9E3

Jachthaven de Bijland, Zwarteweg 2. **GPS:** n51,85923 e6,09775.

NL

20 € 8/day, € 10/night Ch WC € 1/4minutes included.
Location: Rural, comfortable, central. **Surface:** grassy.
15/04-15/10.
Distance: 200m 200m on the spot on the spot.

Tolkamer 9E3

De Swaenebloem, Bijland 3. **GPS:** n51,86235 e6,07937.

15 € 11,20 Ch (12x)€ 1,50/day WC included.
Location: Rural, comfortable, quiet.
Surface: grassy. 01/01-31/12.
Distance: 3,5km 100m on the spot on the spot 3,5km 3km on the spot on the spot.
Remarks: Charging point for electric bicycles.

Twello 9E2

Jachtlustplein 7. **GPS:** n52,23439 e6,09847.

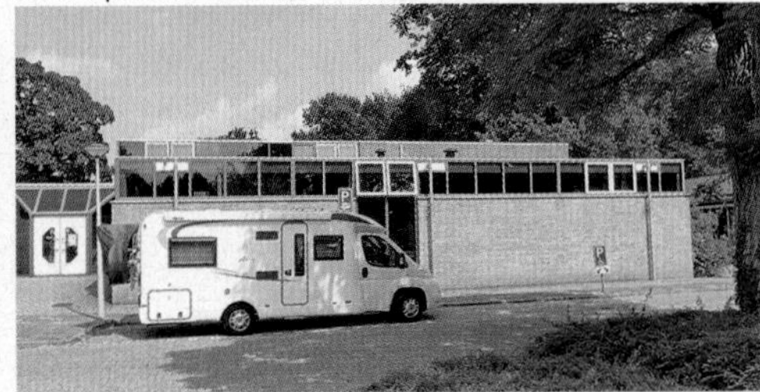

1 free. **Location:** Urban, simple, central, quiet. **Surface:** metalled.
01/01-31/12.
Distance: 100m 100m 100m on the spot on the spot on the spot.

Varik 9D3

Pleisterplaats Bol Varik, Waalbandijk 8. **GPS:** n51,82589 e5,37829.

5 € 8, tourist tax incl free. 01/01-31/12.
Distance: 50m 500m 100m.
Remarks: Max. 48h, check in at restaurant.

Varsseveld 9E2

Pallandtbad, Grutterinkpad. **GPS:** n51,94345 e6,46691.

3 free. **Location:** Urban, simple, central. **Surface:** metalled.
01/01-31/12.
Distance: 200m 200m 200m 200m.
Remarks: Behind swimming pool, max. 24h.

Vierakker 9E2

Hanzestadcampers, Vierakkersestraatweg 19.
GPS: n52,10659 e6,24122.

3 € 7,50 Ch (3x) included.
Location: Rural, simple, quiet. **Surface:** gravel. 01/01-31/12.
Distance: 500m 1km 500m 500m on the spot on the spot.

Voorst 9E2

De Adelaar, Rijksstraatweg 49. **GPS:** n52,17760 e6,14150.

12 € 13 free Ch (12x)€ 2,50 WC € 0,50 € 4/4 included. **Location:** Rural, luxurious, quiet.
Surface: grassy/metalled. 01/01-31/12.
Distance: 500m 7km on the spot on the spot 150m 1km on the spot.
Remarks: Incl. use camp-site facilities, playground.

Voorst 9E2

Boerderij de Kolke, Klarenbeekseweg 30. **GPS:** n52,17355 e6,13318.

16 € 7,90 Ch (16x)€ 1/kWh included.
Location: Rural, comfortable, central, quiet. **Surface:** grassy/metalled.
01/01-31/12.
Distance: 1km 500m.
Remarks: Regional products.

Voorthuizen 9D2

Ackersate, Harremaatweg 26. **GPS:** n52,18683 e5,62547.

5 € 23 Ch WC included € 1 € 5,50,on camp site .
Location: Rural, simple. **Surface:** metalled.
01/04-27/10.
Distance: 1,3km 4,2km on the spot on the spot on the spot on the spot.

Wageningen 9D2

Pabstendam. **GPS:** n51,96107 e5,65923.
3 free. **Surface:** grasstiles. 01/01-31/12.
Distance: 650m 650m.
Remarks: Nearby port.

Westendorp 9E2

Recreatieoord Hippique, Doetinchemseweg 141.
GPS: n51,94964 e6,42084.

4 € 10 € 1/80liter Ch (8x) WC € 5/day € 5 included.
Location: Rural, luxurious. **Surface:** grasstiles.
01/01-31/12.
Distance: 500m 2km 3km 1,5km 3km 1,5km on the spot on the spot.
Remarks: Arrival 9><20h.

Wijchen 9D3

Oude Klapstraat 80. **GPS:** n51,80840 e5,72140.
2 free. **Surface:** metalled. 01/01-31/12.
Distance: 500m.

Wilp 9E2

Kampeerhoeve Bussloo, Grotenhuisweg 50. **GPS:** n52,20883 e6,10961.

10 € 11-13,50, tourist tax incl Ch (10x) € 3,50/day € 5/4 included. **Location:** Rural, luxurious, isolated, quiet.
Surface: grassy/metalled. 01/01-31/12.
Distance: 4,5km 2km 400m 400m 1km 4,5km on the spot on the spot.
Remarks: Use sanitary facilities at campsite.

Winterswijk 9F2

Landgoed Kreil, Heenkamppieperweg 1.
GPS: n51,93734 e6,67493.

2 € 10 € 1/80liter Ch included against payment.
Location: Rural, simple, isolated, quiet. **Surface:** metalled.
01/03-31/10.
Distance: Breedevoort 4,5km Located on estate.

Winterswijk 9F2

Camping Ten Hagen, Waliënsestraat 139A.
GPS: n51,99131 e6,71898.

4 € 10 € 1/80liter Ch (4x)included € 3/24h
Location: Rural, simple, isolated, quiet. **Surface:** grassy.
01/01-31/12.
Distance: city centre 3km 3km 2km on the spot on the spot.
Remarks: Max. 24h, manufacturer of wooden clogs.

Winterswijk 9F2

Het Winkel, De Slingeweg 20. **GPS:** n51,95176 e6,73621.

NL

4 € 10 € 1/80liter Ch (4x)included. **Location:** Rural, simple, quiet. **Surface:** gravel/sand. 01/01-31/12.
Distance: 4,5km on the spot on the spot on the spot.

Winterswijk 9F2

Vreehorst, Vreehorstweg 43. **GPS**: n51,95028 e6,69251.

4 € 10 € 1/80liter Ch (4x)included. **Location:** Rural, simple, quiet. **Surface:** sand. 01/01-31/12.
Distance: 3,6km on the spot on the spot.

Zaltbommel 9D3

De Beersteeg, Beersteeg. **GPS**: n51,81040 e5,24083.

6 free. **Surface:** metalled. 01/01-31/12.
Distance: centre 600m 2,5km 250m.

Zelhem 9E2

Carpoolplaats, Stikkenweg/N330. **GPS**: n51,99893 e6,34541.

2 free. **Location:** Rural, simple, noisy. **Surface:** asphalted. 01/01-31/12.
Distance: 1km.
Remarks: Max. 24h.

Zutphen 9E2

Houtwal. **GPS**: n52,13609 e6,19747.

8 € 2, overnight stay free € 1/80liter (8x)€ 1/kWh.
Location: Urban, simple, quiet. **Surface:** metalled. 01/01-31/12.
Distance: 1km.
Remarks: Nearby police station, max. 48h, beautiful view.

Zutphen 9E2

IJsselkade. **GPS**: n52,13953 e6,19154.

2 € 1,30/h, >18.00h free. **Location:** Urban, simple, central, noisy. **Surface:** metalled. 01/01-31/12.
Distance: 1km.
Remarks: Motorhome max. 6m, max. 48h.

Tourist information Zutphen:
Groenmarkt-Houtmarkt-Zaadmarkt. Thu 8-12h, Sa 8-17h.
Lange Hofstraat. Farmers market. Thu 8-13h.

Utrecht

Amersfoort 9D2

Aan de Eem, Grote Koppel. **GPS**: n52,16083 e5,38286.

3 € 1,10/meter WC included.
Location: Urban, noisy. **Surface:** metalled. 01/01-31/12.
Distance: 600m 500m 500m on the spot.
Remarks: At fire-station, max. 24h.

Tourist information Amersfoort:
VVV, Breestraat 1, www.vvvamersfoort.nl.

Baarn 9D2

De Zeven Linden, Zevenlindenweg 4. **GPS**: n52,19721 e5,24838.

3 € 19 € 2,50 Ch.
Location: Simple. **Surface:** metalled. 01/04-01/11.
Distance: 2km 1km 2km 300m on the spot on the spot.

Tourist information Baarn:
Brink. Tue 8.30-14h.

Bunnik 9D2

Buitengoed de Boomgaard, Parallelweg 9.
GPS: n52,06065 e5,19943.

16 € 18-19 ChWC € 2.
Surface: metalled.
26/03-15/10.
Distance: 3km 800m.
Remarks: Arrival >17h departure <10h check in at reception next morning, use camp-site facilities allowed.

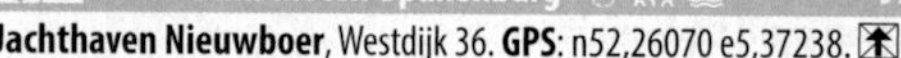

Bunschoten-Spakenburg 9D2

Jachthaven Nieuwboer, Westdijk 36. **GPS**: n52,26070 e5,37238.

8 € 18, 2 pers. incl Ch WC € 3,50 included.
Location: Rural, comfortable, quiet. **Surface:** grassy.
01/01-31/12.
Distance: 800m 6km 100m 700m 700m 700m on the spot on the spot.

IJsselstein 9C2

Jachthaven Marnemoende, Noord IJsseldijk 107b.
GPS: n52,04583 e5,01861.

3 € 15 Ch WC € 4/2 included.
Location: Rural, luxurious, quiet. **Surface:** gravel. 01/01-31/12.
Distance: 2km on the spot on the spot on the spot 2km 2km on the spot.

Leusden 9D2

De Mof, Arnhemseweg 95. **GPS**: n52,10654 e5,41445.

5 free, use of a meal desired.
Location: Rural, simple. **Surface:** gravel.
01/01-31/12 Mon, Tue.
Distance: 4km 4km on the spot on the spot on the spot.
Remarks: First check in at restaurant.

Mijdrecht 9C2

Rondweg. **GPS**: n52,20804 e4,86879.

4 free. **Location:** Urban, simple, noisy. **Surface:** metalled.
01/01-31/12.
Distance: 500m 500m 500m 500m.
Remarks: Max. 48h.

Rhenen 9D2

Restaurant 3 Zussen, Kerkewijk-zuid 115. **GPS**: n52,00682 e5,54006.

5 free. **Location:** Rural, simple. **Surface:** asphalted.
01/01-31/12.

NL

Distance: 1km Veenendaal on the spot 1km on the spot on the spot on the spot.
Remarks: Use of a meal desired.

Vianen 9D2

Kanaalweg, P1. **GPS:** n51,99549 e5,09620.

4 free. **Surface:** metalled. 01/01-31/12.
Distance: 500m.
Remarks: During events: Hazelaarplein, max. 48h.

Vianen 9D2

Ponthoeve, Buitenstad 58. **GPS:** n51,99829 e5,09035.

6 free. **Location:** Rural, simple.
Surface: metalled.
01/01-31/12.
Distance: centre 400m 300m 800m 900m on the spot on the spot.
Remarks: Max. 6m, max. 72h, inclining pitches.

Tourist information Vianen:
VVV, Voorstraat 97, www.vvv-vianen.nl. Historical centre.
Voorstraat (zuid). Wed 10-16h.

Werkhoven 9D2

Camperplaats aan het Dorp, Herenstraat 98.
GPS: n52,01759 e5,24344.

7 € 15 Ch (7x) WC free. **Location:** Rural.
Surface: gravel. 01/01-31/12.
Distance: 800m 300m on the spot on the spot on the spot.

Wijk bij Duurstede 9D2

P2, Inudatiekanaal. **GPS:** n51,97100 e5,35100.

3 € 10, 2 pers.incl WC. **Location:** Rural, simple, quiet.
Surface: asphalted. 01/01-31/12.
Distance: 200m 200m 500m on the spot on the spot.
Remarks: At harbour.

South Holland

Alblasserdam 9C3

Camperpark Kinderdijk, Marineweg 3a.
GPS: n51,85971 e4,65816.

44 € 17, tourist tax incl Ch WC included.
Location: Central. **Surface:** metalled.
01/02-27/12.
Distance: on the spot 2km on the spot on the spot 300m 200m on the spot on the spot.
Remarks: World Heritage site Kinderdijk, 19 mills, 5km, waterbus ferry 300m.

Tourist information Alblasserdam:
Werelderfgoed Kinderdijk, Nederwaard 1, Kinderdijk. World famous mill-area. 12/03-30/10 9-17.30, 31/10-30/12 11-16.
Wilgenplein. Mo-afternoon.

Bleiswijk 9C2

Jan van de Heidenstraat. **GPS:** n52,01415 e4,53411.

2 free. **Location:** Urban. **Surface:** metalled. 01/01-31/12.
Distance: 300m 5km 500m Jumbo 400m.
Remarks: Next to fire-station.

Bleskensgraaf 9C3

Farm Nescio, Elzenweg 19. **GPS:** n51,85674 e4,75266.

8 € 14 Ch WC included. **Location:** Rural, comfortable, isolated, quiet. **Surface:** metalled. 01/01-31/12.
Distance: 2,5km 1,5km 1,5km 1km 2,5km.
Remarks: Possibility of guided tour.

Delft 9C2

Delftse Hout, Korftlaan 5. **GPS:** n52,01772 e4,37945.

20 € 24-28 Ch (20x)€ 3,50/24h WC € 6,50 included. **Location:** Urban, comfortable, central.
Surface: grasstiles/metalled. 26/03-01/11.
Distance: 2km 1,2km 1km 1km 1km 1km summer > centre on the spot on the spot.
Remarks: Check in at reception campsite.

Tourist information Delft:
VVV, Hippolytusbuurt 4, www.delft.nl. Historical centre with canals and merchant houses. church 01/03-31/10 Mo-Sa 9-18h, 01/11-28/02 Mo-Sa 11-16h.

Den Haag 9C2

Camperpark Den Haag, Valutapad, The Hague (Den Haag).
GPS: n52,05282 e4,38013.

100 € 15,95 + tourist tax € 2,05/pp Ch (30x)€ 3,75/24h, 10Amp WC included.
Location: Urban, comfortable. **Surface:** grassy/metalled.
01/01-31/12.
Distance: 7km 1,7km 12km 1km 1km 500m.
Remarks: Bread-service.

Tourist information The Hague (Den Haag):
VVV, Spui 68, www.denhaag.com. Government city and royal residence.
Bezoekerscentrum Binnenhof, Binnenhof 8a. Guided tours in government buildings. Mo-Sa 10-16h. € 5-10.
Madurodam, George Maduroplein 1. Miniature Holland.

Dordrecht 9C3

Camperplaats Stadswerven, Maasstraat.
GPS: n51,81793 e4,68750.

12 Mo-Sa € 6,50/24h, Su free € 1/60liter Ch.
Location: Simple, quiet. **Surface:** metalled. 01/01-31/12.
Distance: city centre 3km 5km on the spot on the spot 3km 1km waterbus.
Remarks: Max. 72h, near Noah's Ark.

Dordrecht 9C3

Weeskinderendijk 5. **GPS:** n51,80861 e4,65611.

2 € 1/4h, first 24h free. **Location:** Urban, simple, noisy.
Surface: metalled. 01/01-31/12.
Distance: 500m 500m 500m 100m.
Remarks: Max. 72h.

Dordrecht 9C3

Jachthaven Westergoot, Baanhoekweg 1. **GPS:** n51,81518 e4,72467.
15 € 10 Ch € 2 WC € 0,50/7minutes € 5.
Distance: on the spot.

Giessenburg 9C3

Boerenterras De Groot, A.M.A. Langeraadweg 9.
GPS: n51,85327 e4,92205.

6 € 10 Ch WC included. **Location:** Rural, simple, isolated, quiet. **Surface:** concrete. 01/01-31/12.
Distance: 1,5km 3km on the spot 1,5km 3,5km on the spot.

Giessenburg 9C3

Halfomhoeve, Bovenkerkseweg 76/78. **GPS:** n51,84628 e4,87548.

NL

5 € 10 Ch WC included. **Location:** Rural, simple, isolated, quiet. **Surface:** concrete. 01/05-15/10.
Distance: 2km 3km on the spot 1,5km 1,5km on the spot on the spot.

Giessenburg 9C3

Landscheiding Giessenburg, Landscheiding 1.
GPS: n51,84753 e4,92294.

10 € 10 Ch WC included.
Location: Rural, comfortable, isolated, quiet.
Surface: grassy/metalled. 01/01-31/12.
Distance: 2km 2km 2km on the spot on the spot.

Gorinchem 9C3

WSV Merwede, Buiten de Waterpoort 8.
GPS: n51,82697 e4,96477.

16 € 12 Ch included € 0,50 € 5/4.
Location: Comfortable, isolated, quiet.
Surface: gravel/metalled.
01/01-31/12.
Distance: 500m on the spot on the spot 300m 1km on the spot.
Remarks: Max. 72h, check in at harbourmaster.

Tourist information Gorinchem:
VVV, Grote Markt 17, www.gorinchem.nl. Historical centre with city walls.
Slot Loevestein, Loevestein 1, Poederoijen. Castle, 14th century.
Grote Markt.
Mo 8.30-12.30h.

Gouda 9C2

Parking Klein Amerika, Fluwelensingel. **GPS:** n52,01185 e4,71576.

30 € 8 Ch (12x) WC included.
Location: Urban, simple, quiet. **Surface:** metalled.
01/01-31/12.
Distance: 300m.
Remarks: Max. 3 days.

Tourist information Gouda:
VVV, Markt 35, www.vvvgouda.nl. Historical centre with 300 monuments, famous for its Gouda-cheese.
Kaaswaag, Markt. History of the Gouda cheese, cheesetasting.
01/04-30/09 13-17h, Thu 10-17h. € 7,50.
Markt. Thu 8.30-13h, Sa 8.30-17h.

Montmartre, Markt. Antiques and flea market. 01/05-30/09 We 9-17h.

Goudriaan 9C2

Boerderij de Verwondering, De Hoogt 14.
GPS: n51,89150 e4,90741.

2 € 10 Ch included. **Location:** Rural, simple, isolated. **Surface:** concrete.
Distance: 2,5km 7km.

Hillegom 9C2

De Vosse, Vosselaan. **GPS:** n52,29541 e4,59122.
3 free. **Surface:** metalled. 01/01-31/12.
Distance: centre 1,3km 1km 1km.
Remarks: At swimming pool, max. 3 days.

Hoek van Holland 9B2

Koningin Emmaboulevard. **GPS:** n51,97822 e4,12091.
5 free. **Surface:** asphalted.
Distance: on the spot 150m 750m.

Hoogblokland 9C2

Landwinkel De Bikkerhoeve, Bazeldijk 66. **GPS:** n51,89716 e4,99563.

6 € 10 Ch WC included. **Location:** Rural, simple, isolated, quiet. **Surface:** concrete. 01/03-31/10.
Distance: 2km 1,4km 2km 2km on the spot on the spot.

Langerak 9C2

Camperplaats Langerak, Melkweg 3. **GPS:** n51,92069 e4,89975.
3 € 15 WC . **Location:** Rural.
Surface: metalled.
Distance: on the spot on the spot.
Remarks: Max. 8M, bicycle rental.

Leerdam 9C2

De Galgenwaard, Lingedijk 8a, Oosterwijk.
GPS: n51,87451 e5,07311.

3 € 8 included € 2 WC. **Location:** Rural, simple, quiet.
Surface: metalled. 01/04-01/10.
Distance: Leerdam 2km on the spot on the spot 300m Along the river Linge.
Remarks: Opening hours 7-22h, passenger ferry across the Linge.

Leerdam 9C2

Groenzoom, Lingedijk. **GPS:** n51,88288 e5,08670.

3 free. **Location:** Urban, simple. **Surface:** metalled.
01/01-31/12.
Distance: 2,5km 2,5km 2,5km on the spot.
Remarks: In front of Lingedijk 27, max. 72h, small pitches.

Leerdam 9C2

Parking Glasmuseum, Lingedijk. **GPS:** n51,88676 e5,08699.

2 free. **Location:** Rural, simple. **Surface:** asphalted.
01/01-31/12.
Distance: 1km on the spot 1km on the spot.

Leerdam 9C2

Jachthaven Oude Horn, Sundsvall 1. **GPS:** n51,88984 e5,09532.

3 free. **Location:** Urban, simple. **Surface:** gravel.
01/01-31/12.
Distance: 300m 300m 300m.
Remarks: Max. 72h.

Leiden 9C2

P Haagweg, Haagweg 6. **GPS:** n52,15963 e4,47852.

15 € 12/24h.
Location: Urban. **Surface:** metalled.
01/01-31/12.
Distance: 800m 800m 800m Free bus to centre.
Remarks: Along railwayline, video surveillance, free shuttle (till 2am).

Lexmond 9C2

De Fruithof, Achthoven 39. **GPS:** n51,97414 e5,00254.
2 € 12 included. **Location:** Rural. **Surface:** metalled.
Distance: 150m on the spot on the spot on the spot.
Remarks: Max. 7m.

Maassluis 9B2

Camperplaats Maassluis, Govert van Wijnkade 50.
GPS: n51,91628 e4,24535.

3 free free. **Surface:** asphalted. 01/01-31/12.
Distance: city centre 1km 500m 1,2km 450m on the spot on the spot.
Remarks: Max. 48h.

Nieuwland 9C2

De Griênduil, Geer 25. **GPS:** n51,90106 e5,02622.

NL

4 € 10, 4 pers.incl. + tourist tax € 1/pp Ch WC included.
Location: Simple, quiet. **Surface:** gravel.
01/01-31/12.
Distance: on the spot 2km 4km on the spot on the spot.
Remarks: In winter limited services.

Noordeloos 9C2

Huis den Dool, Botersloot 67. **GPS:** n51,91170 e4,95995.
3 € 12,50 Ch included. **Location:** Rural.
Distance: on the spot on the spot.
Remarks: Charging point for electric bicycles.

Numansdorp 9C3

Fort Buitensluis, Fortlaan 10. **GPS:** n51,71727 e4,43866.

5 € 20 Ch € 2/night WC € 0,50 € 1 included.
Surface: unpaved. 01/04-01/10.
Distance: 1,5km 5km on the spot on the spot 1,5km 1,5km 2,5km on the spot on the spot.
Remarks: At Hollands Diep, golf court 3km.

Oostvoorne 9B2

Jachthaven Geijsman, Zanddijk 5. **GPS:** n51,92438 e4,10811.
€ 15 Ch included,10Amp WC . **Surface:** metalled.
01/04-01/10.
Distance: 500m on the spot on the spot.

Oud Beijerland 9C3

De Oude Tol, Randweg 31a. **GPS:** n51,82933 e4,39585.

4 free. **Location:** Rural, simple, isolated, quiet.
Surface: asphalted.
01/01-31/12.
Distance: 2km on the spot 100m on the spot on the spot.
Remarks: Arrival >16h, max. 24h.

Ouddorp 9B3

Drive-in Camperpark Klepperduinen, Vrijheidsweg 1.
GPS: n51,81724 e3,89850.

51 € 8,50-10,65/12h, € 15-21,50/24h + tourist tax € 0,95/pp, dog € 2,50/day Ch (51x)€ 4/24h WC included .
Location: Rural, luxurious, isolated, quiet. **Surface:** grassy/metalled.
01/01-31/12.
Distance: 500m 1km on the spot on the spot on the spot.

Pernis 9C2

Casa E Parking, Ring 156 -158. **GPS:** n51,88581 e4,39008.

5 € 15 Ch WC € 2/2 included. **Surface:** metalled.
01/01-31/12.
Distance: Rotterdam 11km 300m 300m 100m.

Poeldijk 9B2

Booma Recreatie, Vredebestlaan 14b. **GPS:** n52,02464 e4,21242.

10 € 6 Ch included (10x)€ 2/day. **Location:** Rural, simple, quiet. **Surface:** gravel. 01/01-31/12.
Distance: 800m 50m 800m 800m 800m on the spot on the spot.

Roelofarendsveen 9C2

Groencentrum De Veense Bukker, Hazenpad 1.
GPS: n52,19336 e4,61475.
10 € 12,50, 2 pers.incl included € 2,16Amp.
Location: Rural, isolated, quiet.
Surface: unpaved. 01/01-31/12.
Distance: 2km 1km 2km 2km.

Sassenheim 9C2

Jachthaven Jonkman, Jonkman 1. **GPS:** n52,22074 e4,54476.

6 € 15 € 0,50 Ch € 1 WC € 0,50 € 5 included.
Location: Comfortable. **Surface:** grassy/gravel. 15/03-01/11.
Distance: 2km 1km on the spot on the spot on the spot 2km on the spot.
Remarks: Check in at harbourmaster.

Schiedam 9C2

Doeleplein 1. **GPS:** n51,91972 e4,40111.

2 € 6,60. **Location:** Urban, simple, central, quiet.
Surface: metalled. 01/01-31/12.
Distance: 500m 1,5km on the spot on the spot 500m 500m 500m.
Remarks: Max. 72h.

Schiedam 9C2

Noordvest 40. **GPS:** n51,91926 e4,39372.

6 € 7. **Location:** Urban, simple, central, quiet. **Surface:** metalled.
01/01-31/12.
Distance: city centre 100m.
Remarks: Max. 72h.

Tourist information Schiedam:
Het Jenever Museum, Lange Haven 74-76. Making distilled spirits.
Tue-Su 12-17h.
Lange Kerkstraat. Fri 9-16h.

Streefkerk 9C2

Camperplaats Streefkerk, Middenpolderweg 2a.
GPS: n51,91266 e4,81287.
5 € 12,50 Ch WC included . **Location:** Rural.
Surface: metalled.

Strijensas 9C3

Jachthaven Strijensas, Sassendijk 6. **GPS:** n51,71472 e4,58735.

6 € 7 € 0,50/100liter Ch € 2,50 WC € 1 included.
Surface: asphalted. 01/01-31/12.
Distance: 500m on the spot on the spot on the spot.
Remarks: Max. 72h.

Vlaardingen 9C2

Parking Deltabrug, Oosthavenkade 81. **GPS:** n51,90364 e4,34769.

4 free. **Location:** Urban, noisy. **Surface:** metalled.
01/01-31/12.
Distance: 1km on the spot 50m 100m 500m.
Remarks: Along railwayline, max. 48h.

Wijngaarden 9C3

't Koeiestalletje, Westeinde 26. **GPS:** n51,84378 e4,74631.

5 € 8 Ch service € 2 WC . **Location:** Rural.
Surface: metalled. 01/01-31/12 Su.
Distance: 5km 5km 5km on the spot on the spot.
Remarks: Charging point for electric bicycles, regional products.

Zevenhoven 9C2

Camperplaats Zevenhoven, Noordeinde 36.
GPS: n52,19475 e4,77305.

NL

5 € 10 included. **Location:** Rural, comfortable.
Surface: grassy/metalled. 01/01-31/12.
Distance: 1km 1km on the spot on the spot.

Zuid-Beijerland 9C3

WSV de Hitsert, Hitsertse Kade 8. **GPS**: n51,73826 e4,36529.

6 € 16,50 Ch WC included € 0,50 . **Location:** Quiet.
Surface: grassy/metalled. 01/05-01/11.
Distance: 900m on the spot on the spot on the spot 900m on the spot on the spot.
Remarks: Max. 72h, max. 8M.

Zealand

Axel 11B1

P Watertoren, Kinderdijk 4. **GPS**: n51,25972 e3,91028.

2 free. **Location:** Urban, simple, noisy. **Surface:** metalled.
01/01-31/12.
Distance: 800m on the spot on the spot 500m on the spot on the spot.
Remarks: Max. 24h.

Tourist information Axel:
Noordstraat. Sa 8-16h.

Breskens 9A3

Roompot Recreatie, Nieuwe Sluisweg. **GPS**: n51,40193 e3,54420.

10 € 14 Ch included WC . **Location:** Rural, comfortable, quiet. **Surface:** metalled. 01/01-31/12.
Distance: 500m 400m 100m 100m on the spot on the spot.
Remarks: Servicepoint at camping Zeebad, ferry to Vlissingen 500m (pedestrian/bicycles).

Graauw 11B1

Zandbergsestraat. **GPS**: n51,32519 e4,10420.

7 free. **Location:** Rural, simple, quiet. **Surface:** gravel/sand.
01/01-31/12.
Distance: 400m 400m on the spot.
Remarks: Max. 72h.

Groede 11A1

De Ploeg, Parking Zuid, Voorstraat 47. **GPS**: n51,38232 e3,51268.

40 € 5 17-10h, € 12,50/24h Ch (35x)€ 2,50/night WC . **Location:** Comfortable, central, quiet.
Surface: grasstiles/metalled. 01/04-01/10 22-7h.
Distance: 100m 3km 100m 100m 100m > Terneuzen on the spot on the spot.
Remarks: Caution € 10, sanitary/washing machine at campsite.

Groede 11A1

Strandcamping Groede, Zeeweg 1. **GPS**: n51,39632 e3,48719.

50 € 1/h. **Location:** Rural, simple, quiet. **Surface:** gravel.
01/01-31/12.
Distance: Groede 3km sandy beach 200m 60m on the spot on the spot on the spot.
Remarks: Max. 1 night.

Hansweert 9B3

Westhavendijk. **GPS**: n51,44483 e4,00629.

5 free. **Location:** Rural, simple, isolated, quiet. **Surface:** asphalted.
01/01-31/12.
Distance: 250m 4km on the spot 200m on the spot on the spot.

Hulst 11B1

Parkeerterrein Havenfort, Havenfort. **GPS**: n51,27700 e4,04912.

15 € 0,80/h, mo-sa 9-17h, su 12-18h.
Surface: metalled. 01/01-31/12.
Distance: on the spot 25m 150m 150m 200m on the spot on the spot.
Remarks: Max. 72h, shops open on Sunday.

Hulst 11B1

De Bourgondiër, Tolweg 109. **GPS**: n51,26410 e3,98915.
20 € 17,50-20 Ch WC included . **Location:** Rural.
Surface: gravel/metalled. 01/01-31/12.
Distance: 4km 10km 1500 on the spot 4km 500m on the spot on the spot.
Remarks: Playground.

Tourist information Hulst:
VVV, Grote Markt 19, www.bezoekhulst.nl. Fortified city with city walls, shops open on Sunday.

Kamperland 9B3

Camperpark Zeeland, Campensweg 5.
GPS: n51,57495 e3,65236.

102 € 15,50-19,50, 2 pers. incl. € 0,20/min Ch (75x)€ 4/24h, 16Amp WC € 0,25/min € 6/4 included
Location: Rural, luxurious, quiet. **Surface:** grassy/gravel.
01/01-31/12.
Distance: 3km 2km 50m 50m 100m 4km 2km on the spot on the spot.

Kamperland 9B3

Roompot Beach Resort, Mariapolderseweg 1.
GPS: n51,58972 e3,71666.

20 € 6 10-17h, € 14 17-10h Ch WC € 4,50/1,20 .
Surface: asphalted. 01/01-31/12.
Distance: 3km 500m 500m 500m 500m 1km.

Kloosterzande 11B1

Hulsterweg. **GPS**: n51,36555 e4,02121.

2 free. **Location:** Rural, simple, central, quiet. **Surface:** metalled.
01/01-31/12.
Distance: 500m 80m 700m on the spot on the spot.

Kruiningen 9B3

Landwinkel de Plantage, Kaasgat 4a. **GPS**: n51,46865 e4,04445.

15 € 12,50 Ch € 2,50/night,10Amp WC included.
Surface: grassy. 01/01-31/12.
Distance: 3km 3km 3km 3km on the spot 1km on the spot on the spot.

Middelburg 9A3

Hof van Tange, Hof van Tange. **GPS**: n51,49688 e3,60474.

6 € 9,50, Su/holidays free WC € 0,50.
Location: Simple, central, quiet. **Surface:** gravel/sand.
01/01-31/12 1st week Aug.
Distance: 500m 5km 500m 300m on the spot on the spot on the spot.
Remarks: Motorhome <6m, max. 48h.

Middelburg 9A3

Oude Veerseweg. **GPS**: n51,50071 e3,62842.

5 free € 1 Ch (4x)€ 4. **Location:** Comfortable, central, quiet. **Surface:** metalled. 01/01-31/12.
Distance: 1km 100m 500m 1km on the spot.

Middelburg 9A3

Kanaalweg. **GPS**: n51,49432 e3,61519.

3 € 9,50. **Location:** Urban, simple, central, noisy.
Surface: concrete. 01/01-31/12.
Distance: 500m on the spot on the spot 500m on the spot.
Remarks: Max. 48h.

Oosterland 9B3

Wok van Zeeland, Rijksweg 6. **GPS**: n51,65767 e4,05336.

3 free. **Location:** Simple, isolated, noisy. **Surface:** asphalted.
01/01-31/12.
Distance: 2km on the spot.
Remarks: Only overnight stays.

Oostkapelle 9A3

De Pekelinge, Landmetersweg 1. **GPS**: n51,55725 e3,55139.
20 € 22,50-30,50 Ch included.
Location: Simple, isolated, quiet. **Surface:** gravel/sand.
27/03-01/11.
Distance: nearby nearby on the spot on the spot.
Remarks: Arrival >20h departure <10h, max. 1 night.

Paal 11B1

Jachthaven, Zeedijk van de van Alsteinpolder.
GPS: n51,35331 e4,10937.

4 free. **Location:** Rural. **Surface:** asphalted/metalled.
01/01-31/12.
Distance: 100m on the spot on the spot on the spot on the spot on the spot.
Remarks: Max. 72h.

Renesse 9B3

Camping International, Scharendijkseweg 8.
GPS: n51,74030 e3,78967.

20 € 20, 11/07-22/09 € 35 Ch (16x)WC included € 5/3,50 € 2. **Location:** Rural. **Surface:** metalled.
04/03-01/11.
Distance: 1,5km 2,5km on the spot on the spot on the spot 1,5km on the spot on the spot.

Sas van Gent 11B1

Kanaaleiland, Oostkade. **GPS**: n51,22527 e3,80246.

2 free. **Surface:** metalled.
Distance: 100m 100m 100m.
Remarks: Max. 24h.

Tourist information Sas van Gent:
Keizer Karelplein. Tue 9-16h.

Terneuzen 11B1

Rooseveltlaan. **GPS**: n51,32840 e3,85391.

4 free. **Location:** Rural. **Surface:** asphalted. 01/01-31/12.
Distance: 2,1km on the spot on the spot.
Remarks: Max. 24h.

Tourist information Terneuzen:
Portaal van Vlaanderen, Zeevaartweg 11. Interactive Visitors Centre at the Terneuzen Locks, guided tour and boat excursions.
Markt. Sa 9-16h.

Tholen 9B3

Jachthaven, Contre Escarpe 4. **GPS**: n51,53112 e4,22390.

4 € 10,50 + € 1/pp tourist tax Ch € 1,50/24h WC € 5 included. **Surface:** metalled. 01/01-31/12.
Distance: 100m 100m 100m.
Remarks: Max. 72h.

Vogelwaarde 11B1

Populierenstraat. **GPS**: n51,32562 e3,97758.

2 free. **Location:** Urban, simple, quiet. **Surface:** metalled.
01/01-31/12.
Distance: 1km 400m on the spot on the spot.

Westdorpe 11B1

De Baeckermat, Bernhardstraat. **GPS**: n51,22917 e3,82167.

2 free. **Location:** Rural, simple, quiet. **Surface:** metalled.
01/01-31/12.
Distance: 500m on the spot 100m 500m on the spot on the spot on the spot.
Remarks: Max. 24h.

Wolphaartsdijk 9B3

Camping 't Veerse Meer, Veerweg. **GPS**: n51,54325 e3,81253.

7 € 15/22 Ch (5x)WC on camp site on camp site included. **Location:** Rural, comfortable, isolated, quiet.
Surface: metalled. 01/01-31/12 15/11-15/12.
Distance: 1,5km 100m 100m 100m on the spot on the spot on the spot.

Zaamslag 11B1

Campererf de Feijter, Zaamslagsedijk 6. **GPS**: n51,31953 e3,93574.
€ 10,50 Ch on demand ,16Amp included.
Location: Rural, isolated, quiet. **Surface:** grassy.
01/01-31/12.
Distance: 3km 3km 3km.

Zierikzee 9B3

De Zandweg, Zandweg 30. **GPS**: n51,65691 e3,91210.

NL

12 € 12,50 Ch (12x),10Amp included.
Location: Rural, comfortable, central, noisy. **Surface:** asphalted.
01/01-31/12.
Distance: 800m on the spot on the spot 350m 1km 350m on the spot.
Remarks: Service passerby € 3.

North Brabant

S Asten 11E1

Camperpark Wetland, Tureluurweg 7. **GPS**: n51,36687 e5,84214.

50 € 9 + € 1,35/pp tourist tax Ch (37x)€ 2 WC € 2/2 included. **Location:** Rural. **Surface:** grassy/metalled.
01/01-31/12.
Distance: 2km 4km 9km 5km 2km 1,5km on the spot on the spot.
Remarks: Located in nature reserve De Groote Peel.

Bakel 9D3

Sporthal de Beek, De Beekakker 13a. **GPS**: n51,50061 e5,74377.

2 free. **Location:** Urban, simple. **Surface:** metalled.
01/01-31/12.
Distance: 500m on the spot on the spot.
Remarks: At gymnasium.

Bergen op Zoom 9B3

De Boulevard. **GPS**: n51,48405 e4,27941.

8 free. 01/01-31/12.
Remarks: Max. 72h.

Bergen op Zoom 9B3

De Boulevard Noord. **GPS**: n51,48735 e4,27708.

5 free. **Surface:** metalled. 01/01-31/12.

Distance: 1km 3,8km on the spot on the spot.
Remarks: Max. 72h. On the level of restaurant 'La Playa'.

Tourist information Bergen op Zoom:
De Markiezenhof, Steenbergsestraat 8. Medieval palace built in the late 15th century. Tue-Su 11-17h.

Best 9D3

Carpoolplaats De Wilg. **GPS**: n51,52106 e5,39423.

3 free. **Location:** Motorway, isolated.
Surface: metalled. 01/01-31/12.
Distance: 500m 150m on the spot on the spot.
Remarks: Max. 24h.

S Boxtel 9D3

Dennenoord, Dennendreef 5. **GPS**: n51,59770 e5,28661.

4 € 12,50 + € 1/pp tourist tax Ch WC € 4 included.
Location: Rural, simple, isolated.
Surface: metalled. 01/01-31/12.
Distance: 4km 4km.
Remarks: Max. 3 nights.

Breda 9C3

Nijverheidssingel 391. **GPS**: n51,58793 e4,76366.
6 € 4. **Surface:** metalled.
01/01-31/12.
Distance: 900m 800m 900m 200m.

Tourist information Breda:
VVV, Willemstraat 17-19, www.vvvbreda.nl. Many historical bldg. And castles.

S Budel 11D1

Camperplaats Budel, Heikantstraat 16. **GPS**: n51,26163 e5,59007.

25 € 9,50 Ch € 2,50/day,4Amp WC included.
Location: Urban. **Surface:** grasstiles/grassy. 01/01-31/12.
Distance: 800m 2km 600m 800m 800m 600m on the spot on the spot.
Remarks: Max. 72h, video surveillance, barbecue place, charging point for electric bicycles.

S De Heen 9B3

Akkermans leisure&golf, Heensemolenweg 23.
GPS: n51,60654 e4,24547.

5 € 12,50 Ch (16x)WC included .
Location: Rural, comfortable, isolated, quiet.

Surface: asphalted/metalled. 01/01-31/12.
Distance: on the spot on the spot on the spot.

S Dorst 9C3

Recreatiepark 't Haasje, Klein Oosterhout 1A.
GPS: n51,60945 e4,88918.

7 € 22,10-26,50 Ch (10x) € 0,24 € 3,80/1,80 included. **Location:** Rural. **Surface:** grassy/metalled.
01/01-31/12.
Distance: 4km on the spot 100m on the spot on the spot on the spot on the spot.

S Drimmelen 9C3

Camperpark Jachthaven Biesbosch, Nieuwe Jachthaven 5.
GPS: n51,70750 e4,81008.
18 € 13,50, 15/06-15/09 € 16,50 Ch € 3/24h WC € 5/1,50 included .
Surface: asphalted/grassy.
01/01-31/12.
Distance: 1km on the spot 200m on the spot on the spot on the spot.
Remarks: Barbecue place.

S Drunen 9D3

Camperpark Drunen, Sportlaan 14. **GPS**: n51,67224 e5,14156.

20 € 15,50, 2 pers.incl + tourist tax € 1/pp Ch WC included. **Location:** Comfortable. **Surface:** metalled.
01/01-31/12.
Distance: centre 2,3km 4km on the spot national park Drunense Dunes.
Remarks: At sports park, breakfest-service, incl. access swimming pool.

S Eindhoven 9D3

P+R Meerhoven, Sliffertsestraat 304. **GPS**: n51,43507 e5,42444.

10 first 24h € 3, € 5/24h Ch WC free.
Location: Simple. **Surface:** metalled. 01/01-31/12.
Distance: 4km on the spot 200m 500m on the spot on the spot on the spot.
Remarks: Free bicycles available.

Escharen 9D3

Bar Bistro De Brouwketel, Hoogeweg 9.
GPS: n51,74152 e5,73376.

15 free. **Surface:** grassy/metalled. 01/01-31/12.

Etten-Leur 9C3

Jachthaven Turfvaart, Westpolderpad 6. **GPS**: n51,59512 e4,65102.

5 € 10, 01/04-01/10 € 15 € 0,50/100liter Ch WC € 1 included. **Surface:** grassy/metalled. 01/01-31/12.
Distance: 1,5km on the spot 500m.

Tourist information Etten-Leur:
Mo-morning.

Geertruidenberg 9C3

WSV Geertruidenberg, Statenlaan 15. **GPS**: n51,70362 e4,86311.

6 € 10 Ch WC included. **Location:** Comfortable, quiet. **Surface:** gravel. 01/01-31/12.
Distance: 500m 3km on the spot on the spot 500m.
Remarks: Max. 3 days, max. 9m, only cash payment.

Gemert 9D3

St.Gerardusplein. **GPS**: n51,55354 e5,69109.

2 free. **Location:** Urban, simple. **Surface:** gravel.
01/01-31/12.
Distance: on the spot 300m 200m 100m on the spot on the spot.

Gemert 9D3

Koksehoeve, Koksedijk 25. **GPS**: n51,57380 e5,65846.

10 free, use of a meal obligated. **Location:** Rural, simple, isolated, quiet. **Surface:** metalled. 01/01-31/12.
Distance: 2km.

Grave 9D3

Gemaal van Sasse/Kazematten, Mars en Wijthdijk.
GPS: n51,76859 e5,73085.
2 free. **Location:** Rural. **Surface:** metalled. 01/01-31/12.
Distance: 2,5km 2,5km 2,5km on the spot on the spot.

Grave 9D3

Het Arsenaal, Trompetterstraat. **GPS**: n51,75925 e5,73769.
1 free. **Surface:** metalled. 01/01-31/12.
Distance: 200m 200m 50m 200m.

Heeswijk-Dinther 9D3

Hotel-Restaurant de Leygraaf, Meerstraat 45A.
GPS: n51,66445 e5,47511.

4 € 11,20 WC included.
Location: Rural, comfortable.
Surface: grassy.
01/01-31/12.
Distance: 1,5km 6km on the spot on the spot on the spot.
Remarks: Check in on arrival, use sanitary only during opening hours.

Helenaveen 9E3

Oude Hoeven, Soemeersingel 99. **GPS**: n51,40951 e5,90594.

5 € 7,50, 2 pers. incl Ch € 1,50 . **Location:** Quiet.
Surface: grassy. 01/04-01/11.
Distance: on the spot on the spot.
Remarks: Max. 72h, money in envelope in mail box.

Helmond 9D3

Parking Beatrixlaan, Beatrixlaan. **GPS**: n51,48100 e5,64870.

6 € 3/24h. **Location:** Urban, simple, quiet. **Surface:** metalled.
01/01-31/12.
Distance: 300m 500m 300m 500m on the spot on the spot on the spot.
Remarks: Castle 500m.

Hoogerheide 9B3

METO parking, Huijbergseweg. **GPS**: n51,42318 e4,33452.
5 free. **Location:** Simple. **Surface:** metalled.
01/01-31/12.
Distance: 800m 800m 800m.

Hoogerheide 9B3

Fa. Broos, Buitendreef 4, De Kooi. **GPS**: n51,42522 e4,34656.

5 free (3x)free.
Location: Rural, simple, isolated. **Surface:** metalled.
01/01-31/12.
Distance: 3km 3km 3km 3km on the spot on the spot.

Hulten 9C3

Restaurant Stad Parijs, Rijksweg 6. **GPS**: n51,56996 e4,96446.

15 free € 0,75. **Location:** Rural, simple, quiet. **Surface:** asphalted.
01/01-31/12.
Distance: on the spot.
Remarks: Free, use of a meal obligated.

Linden 9E3

Jachthaven 't Loo, Hardweg 15. **GPS**: n51,75182 e5,82740.

11 € 12,50-22,50 Ch € 2,50/day WC € 1 € 4/3 included. **Surface:** grassy. 01/01-31/12.
Distance: on the spot on the spot on the spot on the spot on the spot on the spot.
Remarks: Check in at harbourmaster 9-12h, 15-18h, caution key sanitary building € 20.

Molenschot 9C3

Camperplaats De Trekvogel, Broekstraat 72.
GPS: n51,57277 e4,89423.

12 € 16 Ch (12x) WC included. **Location:** Rural.
Surface: grassy/metalled. 01/01-31/12.
Distance: 200m on the spot on the spot.

Nuenen 9D3

Sportpark RKSV Nuenen, Pastoorsmast 14.
GPS: n51,46317 e5,56277.

NL

5 free. **Location:** Rural, simple, isolated. **Surface:** grassy.
01/01-31/12 July.
Distance: 1,7km 800m 900m.
Remarks: Max. 5 days a month.

S Oijen 9D3
Speciaalbierbrouwerij Oijen, Oijensebovendijk.
GPS: n51,81049 e5,53126.

3 € 10, free with a meal included. **Location:** Rural, simple, quiet. **Surface:** grassy/gravel. 01/01-31/12.
Distance: on the spot on the spot on the spot on the spot on the spot.

S Oirschot 9D3
Camperplaats Oirschot, De Rijt. **GPS:** n51,50064 e5,32366.

28 € 13 Ch (28x)€ 2 included.
Surface: gravel.
01/01-31/12.
Distance: 1km on the spot 1km 900m.
Remarks: Max. 72h.

Tourist information Oirschot:
VVV, Sint Odulphusstraat 11, www.vvvoirschot.nl. City with 100 monumental buildings, hiking and biking routes.
01/01-31/12.
Museum de Vier Quartieren, Sint Odulphusstraat 11. Regional museum. Tue-Su 13-16.30h.

S Oosteind 9C3
Camperplaats Oosteind, Ter Horst 19. **GPS:** n51,64705 e4,88326.

4 € 8 Ch included. **Location:** Rural, comfortable, isolated.
Surface: grassy. 01/01-31/12.
Distance: 2km 1km 500m.

S Oss 9D3
Van Venrooy Motorhomes, Galliërsweg 39.
GPS: n51,75981 e5,55642.

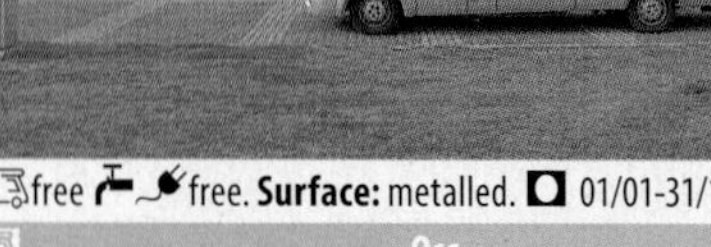

2 free free. **Surface:** metalled. 01/01-31/12.

Oss 9D3
Sportpark Rusheuvel. GPS: n51,77743 e5,52295.

free. **Surface:** metalled. 01/01-31/12.
Distance: 750m 750m AH 500m.
Remarks: Max. 3 nights.

S Oudenbosch 9C3
Het Oude Bossche veld, Moerdijksestraat 1. **GPS:** n51,59558 e4,54117.

15 € 15,20, tourist tax incl Ch included.
Surface: grassy/metalled. 01/04-01/11.
Distance: city centre 1km 600m 1km 1km on the spot on the spot.
Remarks: Max. 72h, possibility for reservation.

S Overloon 9E3
Van Well, Roosendaalseweg 1. **GPS:** n51,56377 e5,91995.

15 € 6,50 Ch € 2 included.
Location: Quiet. **Surface:** grassy. 01/01-31/12.
Distance: 2,5km 4km 2km 2,5km 2,5km 2,5km on the spot on the spot.

Raamsdonksveer 9C3
De Uilendonck, Lageweg 8, Raamsdonk. **GPS:** n51,68540 e4,91380.

3 free. **Location:** Rural, simple, isolated, quiet. **Surface:** metalled.

01/01-31/12.
Distance: 1km on the spot.

Raamsdonksveer 9C3
Kloosterweg 1. **GPS:** n51,68908 e4,87582.

4 free. **Surface:** metalled.
Distance: 800m on the spot 800m.
Remarks: Parking at sports park.

S Reusel 11D1
De Wekker, Wilhelminalaan 97. **GPS:** n51,36187 e5,17339.

5 Free, use of a meal obligated. **Location:** Simple, quiet.
Surface: sand. 01/01-31/12 Tue.
Distance: on the spot.

S Roosendaal 9C3
Mobildrôme, Argon 31-33, Oud Gastel. **GPS:** n51,56333 e4,46278.

8 free € 0,50 Ch € 0,50.
Surface: metalled.
Distance: 2km 1,1km 2km.

Tourist information Roosendaal:
Rosada, A17, afrit 19. Factory outlet.

S Schijndel 9D3
De Schootse Hoeve, Schootsehoef 2. **GPS:** n51,60668 e5,42324.
15 € 13 Ch (4x)included. **Location:** Rural.
Surface: grassy/metalled. 01/01-31/12.
Distance: 2km 500m.

Tourist information Schijndel:
Sa 10-14h.

Veghel 9D3
Hoogstraat. **GPS:** n51,61530 e5,53818.
2 free. **Location:** Urban, simple, central, noisy. **Surface:** metalled.

01/01-31/12.
Distance: 100m 100m 100m. **Remarks:** Max. 72h.

S Vessem 9D3

Eurocamping Vessem, Zwembadweg 1. **GPS**: n51,41197 e5,27490.

40 € 7, 19/03-31/10 € 10 € 1/80liter Ch € 0,60/kWh € 0,50 € 1/day.
Location: Rural. **Surface:** grassy. 01/01-31/12.
Distance: 1,5km 7km 5km on the spot 1,5km on the spot 300m on the spot on the spot.

S Vianen 9E3

Ons Plekske, Berkenkamp 59. **GPS**: n51,71602 e5,84489.

25 € 13, 2 pers.incl Ch WC € 3/3 included.
Location: Luxurious, quiet. **Surface:** grassy. 01/01-31/12.
Distance: on the spot 3,5km 2,6km 2,6km on the spot on the spot. **Remarks:** Monitored parking 24/24.

S Wijk en Aalburg 9D3

Bakkerij Hardeman, Torenstraat 4. **GPS**: n51,75976 e5,13123.

5 € 3 Ch € 2 WC € 7,50 included. 01/01-31/12.
Distance: on the spot on the spot.

S Zundert 9C3

Museum de Scooter, Heischoorstraat 4. **GPS**: n51,49025 e4,64532.

10 € 12 Ch WC included. 01/01-31/12.
Distance: 2,8km A1 7km on the spot on the spot.
Remarks: Reservation during flower parade: museum@lambretta-nl.net.

Limburg

S Afferden 9E3

Roland, Rimpelt 17. **GPS**: n51,63766 e6,03035.
38 € 8 Ch (20x)€ 2/day,6Amp WC included € 0,50 € 4,50/2,50 € 5/day. **Location:** Rural. **Surface:** grassy.
01/04-31/10.
Distance: 1,5km 1km 300m 1,5km 2km on the spot on the spot.
Remarks: Max. 72h, dog € 4, sanitary/washing machine at campsite.

Brunssum 11E1

Schutterspark P1, Heidestraat 20. **GPS**: n50,94582 e5,98385.

10 free. **Surface:** metalled. 01/01-31/12.
Distance: 1,5km 100m Schuttershuuske.
Remarks: Max. 72h, barefoot path.

Gennep 9E3

Martinusplein. **GPS**: n51,69985 e5,97206.

5 free. **Location:** Urban, simple, quiet.
Surface: metalled. 01/01-31/12.
Distance: 100m 4,6km 200m 150m bakery 100m, supermarket 250m on the spot on the spot.
Remarks: Max. 72h.

S Grathem 11E1

Camperplaats Twins, Hunselerdijk 8. **GPS**: n51,22052 e5,86561.
10 € 10 WC . **Location:** Rural. **Surface:** grassy.
01/01-31/12.
Distance: 3km on the spot.

S Grubbenvorst 9E3

Het Kompas, Meerlosebaan 7. **GPS**: n51,42861 e6,12889.

38 € 10 Ch (39x),4Amp included.
Location: Rural. **Surface:** grassy/gravel. 01/03-30/11.
Distance: 2km 500m 2km 2km 1km on the spot on the spot. **Remarks:** Money in envelope in mail box.

Heel 11E1

De Tump, Heelderweg 13. **GPS**: n51,17698 e5,88315.

5 € 7. **Surface:** grassy. 01/05-31/10.
Distance: 1km on the spot.
Remarks: Max. 48h.

S Ittervoort 11E1

Camperplaats Ittervoort, Brigittastraat 31.
GPS: n51,17565 e5,82228.

15 € 10, 2 pers. incl. Ch included € 2,50 WC € 1/day.
Location: Rural, simple. **Surface:** grassy. 01/01-31/12.
Distance: Ittervoort 500m, Thorn 2km 2,6km on the spot Jan Linders 750m. **Remarks:** Vineyard Thorn 600m.

S Kessel 11E1

Camperplaats Kessel, Hazenakkerweg 1. **GPS**: n51,29856 e6,05009.

18 € 12, 2 pers.incl Ch (18x)€ 2,50/24h WC included.
Location: Rural. **Surface:** asphalted/grassy. 01/01-31/12.
Distance: city centre 200m 10km 100m 200m 500m 300m on the spot on the spot.
Remarks: Max. 8M.

S Landgraaf 11E1

Camperplaats Landgraaf, Tunnelweg 1a. **GPS**: n50,87217 e6,02288.

28 € 10 € 0,50/50liter Ch (18x)€ 0,50/kWh included . **Location:** Rural. **Surface:** grassy/gravel.
01/01-31/12. **Distance:** 300m 3km 3km 3km 300m 300m 1,6km 150m 50m 50m 250m.

NL

Landgraaf 11E1

De Watertoren, Kerkveldweg 1. **GPS**: n50,91016 e6,07300.

6 € 10, peak season € 15 + € 0,90/pp tourist tax € 1/90liter Ch included. **Location:** Simple, isolated, quiet.
Surface: grassy/gravel. 01/01-31/12.
Distance: 2km.

Maasbree 11E1

Camperplaats Rooth, Rooth. **GPS**: n51,36820 e6,08374.
15 € 12 Ch (18x) WC. **Location:** Rural, comfortable. **Surface:** grassy/sand. 01/04-01/11.
Distance: 3km 4km 2km 500m 3km 700m on the spot on the spot.
Remarks: Max. 72h.

Maasbree 11E1

Restaurant Boszicht, Provincialeweg 2. **GPS**: n51,36395 e6,07980.

3 Free, use of a meal obligated. **Location:** Simple, noisy.
Surface: gravel.
Distance: 2km 2km on the spot.

Maastricht 11D2

Camperplaats Maastricht, Bosscherweg 35. **GPS**: n50,87286 e5,68179.
100 € 15 € 0,50/50liter Ch (67x)€ 0,50/kWh,16Amp.
Surface: grassy/gravel. 01/01-31/12.
Distance: 2,9km 100m 800m 600m 50m on the spot on the spot.

Maastricht 11D2

Maastricht Marina, Hoge Weerd 20. **GPS**: n50,82389 e5,69944.

24 € 18,50 Ch (20x),6Amp WC € 3,50/2,50 included. **Surface:** gravel/metalled. 03/02-31/12.
Distance: 1,5km 2,8km 50m 50m 50m 1,5km 800m on the spot on the spot.

Remarks: Arrival < 19h.

Meijel 11E1

Nieuwehof, Vieruitersten 25. **GPS**: n51,35410 e5,89717.
29 € 10 + € 1/pp tourist tax Ch WC included on demand. **Location:** Rural, comfortable, quiet.
Surface: grassy/sand. 01/01-31/12.
Distance: 1,8km 14km on the spot on the spot.

Milsbeek 9E3

Toeristisch knooppunt de Diepen, Zwarteweg 60.
GPS: n51,73788 e5,95510.

4 free. **Surface:** grassy/sand.
Distance: on the spot.
Remarks: Next to Eethuis de Diepen.

Neer 11E1

Jachthaven Hanssum, Hanssum 40b. **GPS**: n51,25778 e6,00361.

12 € 12,50 Ch WC € 0,50. **Surface:** grassy/metalled.
Distance: 3km on the spot 200m.
Remarks: Max. 48h, service near marina.

Neer 11E1

Café Restaurant Boothuis de Troost, Hanssum 47.
GPS: n51,25964 e6,00380.

4 € 7,50, guests free. **Surface:** metalled.

Nieuw Bergen 9E3

Camperplaats Bos&Heide, Op de Paal 4. **GPS**: n51,59008 e6,07269.

25 € 7, tourist tax € 1/pp included Ch (15x)€ 2 WC.
Surface: grassy. 01/03-31/10.
Distance: 1,5km 2km 1,5km 1,5km.
Remarks: Located in nature reserve Maasduinen.

Ospel 11D1

De Peeldijk, Plattepeeldijk 19. **GPS**: n51,30504 e5,79827.
8 € 10 Ch included,16Amp. **Location:** Rural.
Surface: metalled. 01/01-31/12.
Distance: city centre 1,5km.
Remarks: Max. 72h.

Ottersum 9E3

Bier-Café Restaurant Old Inn, Siebengewaldseweg 13.
GPS: n51,68935 e6,00728.

20 free. **Surface:** metalled. 01/01-31/12.
Distance: 3km 500m.

Plasmolen 9E3

Eldorado, Witteweg 18. **GPS**: n51,73284 e5,91639.

13 € 14,50-17 + € 1/pp tourist tax € 0,50/100liter Ch (13x) € 0,50/kWh WC € 1 € 3 € 5/24h.
Location: Rural, comfortable, quiet.
Surface: grassy.
01/01-31/12 Service: winter.
Distance: 200m 8km on the spot on the spot 200m 200m on the spot on the spot.
Remarks: Check in at Eldorado Boatshop Witteweg 9, max. 72h.

Roermond 11E1

Helenawerf Watersport, Maasboulevard 101.
GPS: n51,19356 e5,98039.
20 € 12,50 WC. **Surface:** gravel. 01/02-01/12.
Distance: 500m 200m on the spot on the spot.
Remarks: Possibility for reservation.

Sittard 11E1

De Nieuwe Hateboer, Sportcentrumlaan. **GPS**: n51,00794 e5,88150.

10 free Ch WC use sanitary facilities at swimming pool.
Surface: asphalted. 01/01-31/12.
Distance: 2km 6,2km 2km 2km 100m on the spot.
Remarks: At swimming pool, register via SMS (licence plate number) +31 6 27 82 55 82, max. 48h.

Thorn 11E1

Waterstraat. **GPS**: n51,15860 e5,84403.

3 € 2,50/9-18h. **Surface:** gravel. 01/01-31/12.
Distance: 150m 150m.
Remarks: Max. 24h.

Tourist information Thorn:
VVV, Wijngaard 14, www.lekker-genieten.nl. The white village, with historical centre and Gothic collegiate church.

NL

S Valkenburg 11E2

Camperplaats Valkenburg Valkenburg aan de Geul

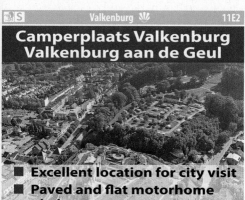

- Excellent location for city visit
- Paved and flat motorhome pitches
- Use swimming pool included

www.camperplaatsvalkenburg.nl
info@camperplaatsvalkenburg.nl

Camperplaats Valkenburg aan de Geul, Heunsbergerweg 1. **GPS**: n50,86037 e5,83148.
40 € 15-25 € 1/100liter Ch (30x)€ 0,60/kWh,16Amp WCincluded € 0,70 € 4,75/2,25 € 2,50/24h.
Location: Rural, comfortable, quiet. **Surface:** grassy/metalled.
01/01-31/12.
Distance: 500m 2km 1,5km 1,5km on the spot 500m 500m on the spot on the spot.
Remarks: Maastricht 15km.

P Valkenburg 11E2

Burgemeester Henssingel. **GPS**: n50,86361 e5,83725.

6 € 1,70/h, max. € 7.
Surface: metalled.
01/01-31/12.
Distance: 300m.

Tourist information Valkenburg:
VVV, Th.Dorrenplein 5, www.vvvzuidlimburg.nl. Popular holiday resort.
Gemeentegrot, Cauberg 4. Marl caves.
M Steenkolenmijn, Daalhemerweg 31. Visiting a gallery of a mine.
01/04-30/11 10-17, 01/11-07/01 + weekend, guided tour 12h, 13h, 14h and 15h.

S Venlo 9E3

Camperplaats De Boswesels Venlo

- Located in nature reserve
- Free wifi access
- Electricity/water/drainage at each pitch

www.camperkampeerplaatsvenlo.nl
info@camperkampeerplaatsvenlo.nl

Camperplaats de Boswesels, Weselseweg/Kikvorstraat. **GPS**: n51,39270 e6,19990.
16 € 10 + € 2/pp tourist tax Ch (16x) included.
Location: Rural, simple.
Surface: grassy. 01/04-01/11.
Distance: 1km 500m 1,5km 1,5km on the spot on the spot.

Remarks: Charging point for electric bicycles.

S Venlo 9E3

WSV De Maas, Jachthavenweg 50. **GPS**: n51,39245 e6,14854.

20 € 13 € 2,10Amp WC € 3/2 included.
Surface: metalled. 01/03-30/11.
Distance: Venlo centre 4km 3,5km on the spot 500m.
Remarks: Max. 48h, check in at harbourmaster, free bicycles available, free ferry to city centre.

S Weert 11D1

Suffolkweg Zuid 30. **GPS**: n51,25435 e5,69283.

20 € 12 Chincluded € 2. **Surface:** gravel/metalled.
Remarks: Max. 72h.

S Well 9E3

Jachthaven 't Leuken, De Kamp 7a. **GPS**: n51,56361 e6,06360.

30 € 10 Ch WC included.
Location: Simple, quiet. **Surface:** grassy. 01/04-01/11.
Distance: Well 2km 11km on the spot on the spot on the spot on the spot on the spot.
Remarks: Walking and bicycle area, acquatic sports area.

NL

Norway

Capital: Oslo
Government: parliamentary constitutional monarchy
Official Language: Norwegian
Population: 5,232,929 (2016)
Area: 323,787 km²

General information
Dialling code: 0047
General emergency: 112
Currency: Norwegian krone (NOK),
€ 1 = NOK 9,50, NOK 1 = € 0,10
£1 = NOK 10,80, NOK 1 = £0.09 (October 2017)
Credit cards are accepted almost everywhere.

Regulations for overnight stays
In general wild camping is allowed, you must hold at least 150 metres from the nearest house or cabin.

Camping Key Europe is obligatory when using campsites: the card can be purchased at any campsite for NOK 160 (± € 17/£15), valid for one year.

Additional public holidays 2018
March 30 Good Friday
April 2 Easter Monday
May 17 Constitution Day
May 21 Pentecost Monday
July 29 St. Olaf's Day

Time Zone
Winter (Standard Time) GMT+1
Summer (DST) GMT+2

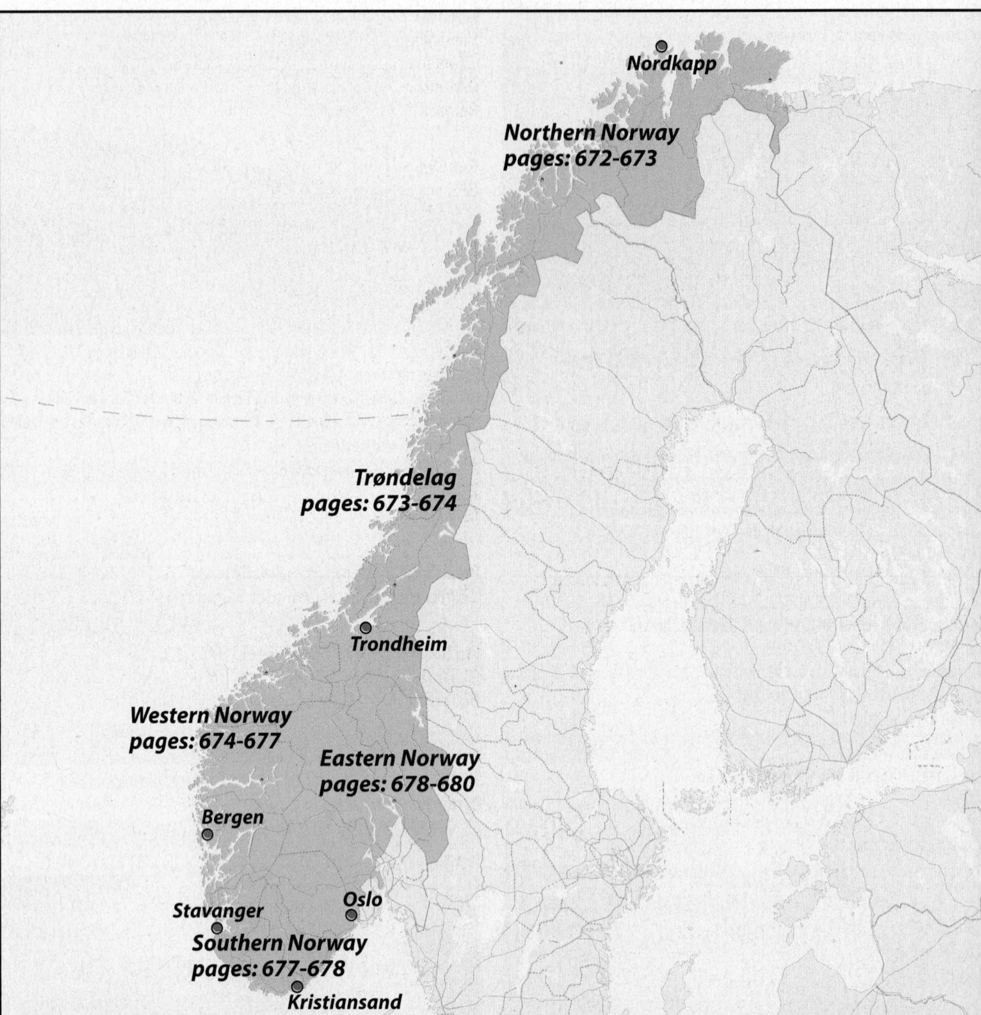

NO

Northern Norway

Båstad 3A2
Eggumsveien. **GPS**: n68,30729 e13,65160.
30 NOK 100 WC.
Location: Rural, isolated, quiet. **Surface:** asphalted.
Distance: on the spot on the spot.
Remarks: Check in at cafe.

Bodø 3A3
Bobilparkering Sentrum, Hålogalandsgata 11.
GPS: n67,27866 e14,41026.
4 NOK 10/h, overnight stay free Chfree.
01/01-31/12.
Distance: 500m.

Botnhamn 3A2
Sjark- Og Småbåtforening. GPS: n69,50743 e17,90753.
5 NOK 75 Ch NOK 50. **Surface:** concrete.
Distance: on the spot on the spot on the spot on the spot.

Brønnøysund 4B1
Brønnøy havn, Havnegata. **GPS**: n65,47271 e12,20725.
free. **Surface:** gravel. 01/01-31/12 snow.
Distance: on the spot on the spot on the spot.
Remarks: At shopping centre.

Brønnøysund 4B1
Statiol, Valveien 48. **GPS**: n65,47919 e12,21634.
NOK 130 Ch.
Distance: on the spot on the spot 200m.
Remarks: Behind petrol station.

Evenes 3A2
Evenes Lofoten, Nerveien 654. **GPS**: n68,45810 e16,70223.

10 NOK 170 Chincluded (10x)NOK 30/day WC.
Location: Rural, simple. **Surface:** gravel. 01/01-31/12.
Distance: on the spot on the spot on the spot.
Remarks: Money in envelope in mail box, use of sauna against payment.

Fauske 3A3
Fauske Parkering AS. GPS: n67,25741 e15,38421.

NOK 150 Ch included.
Surface: asphalted. water disconnected in winter.
Distance: 700m on the spot on the spot on the spot.
Remarks: Max. 24h, money in envelope in mail box.

Fiskåbygd 4A3
Statoil, Van ylven. **GPS**: n62,08607 e5,57917.

6 free Ch. **Location:** Rural, simple, simple.
Surface: asphalted. 01/01-31/12.
Distance: on the spot on the spot on the spot 300m 100m.
Remarks: At petrol station, max. 3 days.

Hammerfest 3B1
Jernbanetrasken. **GPS**: n70,66290 e23,67571.
10 NOK 200 Ch included. **Surface:** asphalted.
01/05-30/09.
Distance: on the spot on the spot 300m.
Remarks: Behind the hotel.

Hattfjelldal 4C1
RV 73. **GPS**: n65,59578 e13,99090.
60 free Chfree. **Surface:** asphalted.
Distance: 100m.

Hovden 3A3
Hovden-Halsa, E 17. **GPS**: n66,72466 e13,69884.

10 free Ch WC free. **Location:** Rural, simple.
Surface: asphalted. 01/01-31/12.
Distance: 10km on the spot on the spot on the spot.

Husøy i Senja 3A2

Fylkesveg. **GPS**: n69,54522 e17,67056.
6 NOK 100.
Distance: on the spot on the spot.

Innhavet 3A3

Innhavet bobilparkering. **GPS**: n67,96367 e15,92576.

NOK 200 Ch included.
Surface: gravel. 01/01-31/12.
Distance: on the spot on the spot on the spot 150m.
Remarks: To be paid at petrol station.

Jøkelfjord 3B1

Jøkelfjord Bobilcamping. **GPS**: n70,06207 e21,92987.
10 NOK 100 Ch NOK 50.
Distance: on the spot on the spot.

Kabelvåg 3A2

Kabelvåg Feriehus & Camping, Mølnosveien.
GPS: n68,21747 e14,44541.
25 NOK 240 Ch NOK 40 NOK 50.
Surface: gravel/metalled. 01/01-31/12.
Distance: 2,5km on the spot on the spot.
Remarks: Canoe rental.

Kirkenes 3C1

Havneveien. **GPS**: n69,72754 e30,07291.

free Ch. **Surface:** asphalted.
Distance: 1km on the spot on the spot 100m.

Kleppstad 3A2

Lofoten Bobilcamping, Lyngvær. **GPS**: n68,22915 e14,21571.
NOK 125 NOK 40 WC. 01/05-15/09.
Distance: on the spot.

Lødingen 3A2

Båtforeningen. **GPS**: n68,41249 e16,00871.
NOK 120 (18x)NOK 30 WC NOK 20. **Surface:** grassy/gravel.
Distance: on the spot on the spot 1km 1km.
Remarks: Money in envelope in mail box.

Melbu 3A2

Melbu Båtforenings, Neptunveien. **GPS**: n68,49493 e14,81248.
NOK 150 included. **Surface:** gravel.
Distance: on the spot on the spot 900m.

Mo i Rana 3A3

E6. **GPS**: n66,30462 e14,12296.
Ch.

Narvik 3A2

Turist Parking, Brugata. **GPS**: n68,44172 e17,41705.
free. **Surface:** asphalted.

Oksfjordhamn 3B1

Oksfjord Båtforening. **GPS**: n69,90620 e21,32404.
NOK 100 Ch WC. **Surface:** gravel.

Skaland 3A2

Senjatrollet, Finnsæter. **GPS**: n69,41020 e17,26334.
20 free Ch. **Location:** Isolated.

Skutvik 3A3

Skutvik Båtforening. **GPS**: n68,01368 e15,33414.
NOK 100. **Surface:** grassy.
Distance: on the spot on the spot.

Sommarøy 3A2

Skipsholmvegen. **GPS**: n69,63335 e17,99490.
voluntary contribution Ch. **Surface:** gravel.
Distance: 1km on the spot on the spot 800m.
Remarks: At the beach.

Stokkvägen 3A3

Grønsvik Kystfort, Aldesundveien, Fv17.
GPS: n66,34991 e13,00156.

8 free WC. **Location:** Rural, simple. **Surface:** asphalted.
01/01-31/12.
Distance: on the spot 300m on the spot.

Storforshei 3A3

Polarsirkel-Senteret, Saltfjellet. **GPS**: n66,55175 e15,32134.
free. **Location:** Isolated, quiet. **Surface:** asphalted.

Stø 3A2

Stø Bobilcamp. **GPS**: n69,01984 e15,10762.
13 NOK 180 Ch WC. **Surface:** gravel. 01/05-15/09.
Distance: on the spot on the spot on the spot.

Svolvær 3A2

Bobilcamp Svolvær, Purkholmen. **GPS**: n68,22733 e14,56016.

30 NOK 250 Ch WC included. **Location:** Urban, simple. **Surface:** gravel/metalled. 01/01-31/12.
Distance: 200m on the spot 200m 200m 200m on the spot on the spot.

Svolvær 3A2

Vestfjord Hotell Lofoten, Fiskergata 46. **GPS**: n68,22949 e14,56492.

28 NOK 250 (34x) WC included NOK 5.
Distance: 200m on the spot on the spot 400m 250m 2km 2km.

Utskarpen 3A3

Flostrandveien. **GPS**: n66,31917 e13,31009.

7 free. **Location:** Rural. **Surface:** asphalted/grassy.
Distance: on the spot on the spot on the spot.

Utskarpen 3A3

Flostrandveien
GPS: n66,31387 e13,28420.

Vestpollen 3A2

Vestpollen, E10. **GPS**: n68,31583 e14,71576.

8 free. **Location:** Rural, simple.
Surface: asphalted. 01/01-31/12.
Distance: 3km on the spot on the spot.

Vevelstad 4B1

Steinmo Bobilparkering, Fv17. **GPS**: n65,60550 e12,36637.
NOK 100. **Location:** Isolated, quiet. **Surface:** grassy/gravel.
Distance: on the spot on the spot.

Øvergård 3B2

Hatteng, E 6. **GPS**: n69,27228 e19,93653.

12 free Ch WC. **Location:** Rural, simple. **Surface:** metalled.
01/01-31/12.
Distance: 4km on the spot on the spot 4km.

Trøndelag

Grong 4B1

Fv391. **GPS**: n64,46587 e12,31143.

5 free. **Surface:** asphalted.
Distance: 100m 100m 400m.
Remarks: Picnic area.

Heimdal 4B2

Sandmoen Bobilparkering, Sandmoflata 6.
GPS: n63,33155 e10,35678.

26 NOK 100-200 Ch (13x)NOK 100 WC included NOK 20 NOK 50/24h. **Location:** Simple, noisy.
Surface: asphalted. 01/01-31/12.
Distance: on the spot on the spot.
Remarks: Check in at reception, breakfast-service.

Inderøy 4B2

Inderøy Bobilcamp, Sakshangvegen. **GPS**: n63,87790 e11,26847.

NO

14 NOK 100 free. **Location:** Rural, simple, isolated, quiet.
Surface: gravel. 01/01-31/12.
Distance: 1,5km 300m on the spot.
Remarks: Pay at restaurant.

S **Inderøy** 4B2

Kjerknesvågen Kai, Vågavegen 650. **GPS**: n63,91311 e11,19049.

10 NOK 200 Ch WCincluded NOK 20. **Location:** Simple, quiet. **Surface:** gravel.
01/01-31/12 1st and 3rd weekend July.
Distance: on the spot on the spot on the spot.

S **Leksvik** 4B2

Hammerbergvegen. **GPS**: n63,66747 e10,61449.

14 NOK 150 included. **Location:** Urban, simple.
Surface: asphalted. 01/01-31/12.
Distance: 500m on the spot on the spot on the spot 1km.
Remarks: Pay at restaurant.

S **Oppdal** 4B2

Trollheimsporten Turistsenter, Festa. **GPS**: n62,61610 e9,47695.

8 NOK 150 Ch WCincluded NOK 10/4minutes.
Location: Rural, comfortable, quiet. **Surface:** asphalted.
Distance: 12km on the spot on the spot on the spot.
Remarks: Sauna incl..

S **Rennebu** 4B2

Berkåk Veikro, Mjukliveien 1. **GPS**: n62,83215 e10,01117.

8 NOK 200 Ch WCincluded NOK 50.
Location: Urban, simple, noisy. **Surface:** gravel. 01/01-31/12.
Distance: on the spot on the spot 100m.

S **Rinnan** 4B2

Rinnleirets Bobilcamp, E6. **GPS**: n63,76421 e11,43589.

50 NOK 165 Ch (16x)included WC NOK 20.
Location: Rural, simple, noisy. **Surface:** gravel.
01/01-31/12.
Distance: on the spot on the spot on the spot.
Remarks: Money in envelope in mail box.

Trofors 4B1

Store Svenningvatn. **GPS**: n65,32528 e13,37714.
NOK 80. **Location:** Rural, isolated, quiet. **Surface:** gravel.
Distance: Trofors 25km on the spot on the spot.
Remarks: Money in envelope in mail box.

Trondheim 4B2

Øya Stadion, Klostergata. **GPS**: n63,42565 e10,38172.

20 free. **Location:** Urban, simple. **Surface:** asphalted.
01/01-31/12.
Distance: 1km on the spot 1km 200m.
Remarks: At stadium, max. 24h.

Western Norway

S **Ålesund** 4A2

Hjelsetgaarden Motorhome, Sorenskriver Bullsgate.
GPS: n62,47670 e6,16110.

45 NOK 250 (30x)WC included. **Location:** Urban, comfortable. **Surface:** asphalted. 01/01-31/12.
Distance: on the spot on the spot on the spot 50m 150m 200m.

S **Åndalsnes** 4A2

Rauma, Isfjordsvegen. **GPS**: n62,56659 e7,69109.

20 free . **Location:** Urban, simple. **Surface:** asphalted.
01/01-31/12.
Distance: 300m 100m 100m 200m 300m.
Remarks: Whale safari.

S **Askvoll** 4A3

Askvoll Småbåtlag, Rv608. **GPS**: n61,34679 e5,06360.

15 NOK 125 Ch NOK 35 WCincluded NOK 10 NOK 50.
Location: Simple, quiet. **Surface:** gravel. 01/01-31/12.
Distance: 300m on the spot on the spot on the spot 300m.

S **Austrheim** 4A3

Åvika, Njøtevegen 292. **GPS**: n60,75028 e5,00472.
20 Ch WC. **Location:** Rural. 01/01-31/12.

S **Austrheim** 4A3

Mastrevikane. **GPS**: n60,78828 e4,94098.
NOK 120 . **Surface:** asphalted. 01/01-31/12.
Distance: 1km on the spot on the spot.

S **Austrheim** 4A3

Kjelstraumen vertshus, Austrheimsvegen. **GPS**: n60,79825 e4,93908.
20 NOK 150 (15x) WC . 01/01-31/12.
Distance: on the spot on the spot 300m.

S **Averøy** 4A2

Atlanterhavsveien. **GPS**: n63,01244 e7,42807.

15 NOK 210 NOK 20 Ch NOK 30 WC NOK 20/20.
Location: Rural, comfortable. **Surface:** gravel.
Distance: on the spot on the spot on the spot on the spot.
Remarks: Boat rental.

S **Bergen** 4A3

Bergenshallen, Vilhelm Bjerknes vei 24. **GPS**: n60,35421 e5,35876.

28 NOK 150/24h Chincluded . **Location:** Urban, simple. **Surface:** asphalted. 01/05-31/08.
Distance: 5km 500m on the spot.
Remarks: Max. 48h.

Bokn 5A1

Langtid, Langtid. **GPS**: n59,16978 e5,45382.

25 free. **Location:** Rural, simple. **Surface:** metalled.
01/01-31/12.
Distance: 100m 100m.
Remarks: Parking at ferry-boat.

S **Bokn** 5A1

Føresvikvegen 580. **GPS**: n59,23255 e5,43919.
4 NOK 50 (2x)NOK 50.
Location: Rural, simple. **Surface:** asphalted. 01/01-31/12.
Distance: on the spot on the spot on the spot on the spot on the spot.

NO

Remarks: To be paid at supermarket.

Bremanger 4A3

Iglandsvik Marina. GPS: n61,83631 e4,93487.

20 NOK 200 included NOK 30/40.
Location: Simple, quiet. **Surface:** gravel. 01/01-31/12.
Distance: on the spot on the spot 500m 300m on the spot.

Bru 5A1

Sokn Marina, Åmøyveien. **GPS:** n59,05210 e5,67691.
30 NOK 180 Ch WC . 01/01-31/12.
Distance: on the spot on the spot.

Bryne 5A2

Abobil.no, Vesthagen 11. **GPS:** n58,72057 e5,64894.

25 free Ch (25x)free.
Surface: asphalted. 01/01-31/12.
Distance: 1km 800m 800m 1km.
Remarks: At motorhome dealer.

Egersund 5A2

Nordre Eigerøy, Ytstebrødveien. **GPS:** n58,45522 e5,90852.
NOK 150 included.
Location: Isolated. **Surface:** grassy. 01/01-31/12.
Distance: 5,5km on the spot on the spot 5,5km on the spot.

Egersund 5A2

Ved taxi-stasjon, Jernbaneveien. **GPS:** n58,45373 e6,00243.
10 free. **Surface:** asphalted.
Distance: 300m on the spot on the spot 300m.

Erfjord 5A1

Hålandsosen, Riksveg. **GPS:** n59,34806 e6,23703.
free. **Location:** Isolated, quiet. **Surface:** gravel.
Distance: on the spot on the spot 200m.

Florø 4A3

Bobilparkering Florø, Strandavegen 19. **GPS:** n61,60061 e5,02252.

NOK 60-150.
Location: Simple. **Surface:** asphalted. 01/01-31/12.
Distance: 600m on the spot 100m 100m.
Remarks: Pay at tourist office.

Fosnavåg 4A2

Gerhard Voldnes veg. **GPS:** n62,33913 e5,63907.

free (10x)NOK 50.
Distance: 800m on the spot on the spot 300m 800m.
Remarks: Coins at town hall.

Gurskøy 4A2

Leikong bubilparkering, Riksveg. **GPS:** n62,25072 e5,78544.

6 NOK 100/24h Ch included. **Surface:** gravel.
Distance: on the spot on the spot on the spot.
Remarks: Money in envelope in mail box, beautiful view.

Haugesund 5A1

Kvalsvik, Skjelavikvegen. **GPS:** n59,43541 e5,24054.

5 free. **Location:** Simple. **Surface:** gravel/metalled.
Distance: 4km on the spot on the spot on the spot.

Hebnes 5A1

Joker Vatlandsvåg kai. GPS: n59,41009 e6,01843.
NOK 100 . 01/01-31/12.
Distance: on the spot on the spot takeaway restaurant on the spot.

Husnes 5A1

Husnes Båtlag, Onarheimsvegen. **GPS:** n59,87187 e5,76195.

NOK 150 Ch included NOK 50 WC NOK 10 NOK 40 free.
Location: Rural, simple. **Surface:** metalled.
01/01-31/12.
Distance: 1,5km on the spot on the spot 1,5km.
Remarks: Golf court 300m.

Isfjorden 4A2

Gjerdset Turistsenter, Gjerdsetbygda. **GPS:** n62,57868 e7,56713.

5 NOK 100 WC included.
Location: Rural, comfortable. **Surface:** gravel.
Distance: 13km 200m 200m 100m.

Jørpeland 5A1

Jørpeland Bobilparkering. GPS: n59,01757 e6,04377.
NOK 150 NOK 50 WC . **Surface:** asphalted.
Distance: 500m on the spot on the spot 450m.

Klokkarvik 4A3

Kleppe Båtlag, Kleppholmen. **GPS:** n60,18462 e5,15163.

30 NOK 100 Ch (10x)NOK 50 WC NOK 10 included.
Location: Simple. **Surface:** asphalted. 01/01-31/12.
Distance: 6km on the spot on the spot.

Kristiansund 4A2

Freiveien. **GPS:** n63,12188 e7,72856.

10 free. **Location:** Rural, simple.
Surface: gravel. 01/01-31/12.
Distance: on the spot on the spot on the spot on the spot.

Kristiansund 4A2

Kristiansund Småbåtlag, Freiveien 50. **GPS:** n63,11713 e7,73168.

5 NOK 7-35, overnight stay free. **Location:** Urban, simple.
Surface: asphalted. 01/01-31/12.
Distance: 1km on the spot on the spot on the spot.

Kulleseid 5A1

Kulleseidkanalen, Kulleseidkanalen. **GPS:** n59,74194 o5,23481.
10 NOK 100 NOK 50
01/01-31/12.
Distance: on the spot 300m.

Måløy 4A3

Småbåthavn, Gate 1 vagsoy. **GPS:** n61,93236 e5,11212.

10 NOK 200 WC included . **Location:** Urban, central.
Surface: asphalted.
Distance: on the spot on the spot on the spot on the spot on the spot.
Remarks: Behind Aldi-süd.

Matre 5A1

Matre Havn, Matre Havn. **GPS:** n59,84352 e5,98434.

NO

6 NOK 100 included NOK 50 WC.
Location: Rural, isolated, quiet. **Surface:** asphalted. 01/01-31/12.
Distance: on the spot on the spot.
Remarks: Money in envelope in mail box.

Nesflaten 5B1

Fylkesveg. **GPS**: n59,64471 e6,80223.
3 free. **Surface:** asphalted. 01/01-31/12.
Distance: on the spot on the spot.
Remarks: At the quay.

Norheimsund 4A3

Rosselandsvegen. **GPS**: n60,37007 e6,10616.

8 free WC. **Location:** Rural, simple. **Surface:** asphalted.
01/01-31/12.
Distance: 2,5km on the spot on the spot 100m on the spot on the spot.
Remarks: Nearby waterfalls.

Norheimsund 4A3

Norheimsund Badstrand, Sandvegen 36.
GPS: n60,36869 e6,14811.

20 free WC. **Location:** Urban, simple.
Surface: gravel. 01/01-31/12.
Distance: 200m on the spot on the spot 200m 200m on the spot on the spot.

Norheimsund 4A3

Norheimsund Badstrand, Sandvegen 36.
GPS: n60,36869 e6,14811.
20 free WC. **Location:** Urban, simple. **Surface:** gravel.
01/01-31/12.
Distance: 200m on the spot on the spot 200m 200m on the spot on the spot.

Odda 4A3

Odda bobilcamp, Røldalsvegen. **GPS**: n60,07144 e6,54865.
40 NOK 150 included. **Surface:** asphalted.
Distance: on the spot on the spot.
Remarks: Max. 3 days.

Rennesøy 5A1

GPS: n59,13787 e5,59161.
free. **Surface:** asphalted.
Distance: on the spot on the spot.

Rognaldsvåg 4A3

Rognaldsvåg Bobilparkering. GPS: n61,56494 e4,79580.
8 NOK 150 WC. **Surface:** gravel. 01/01-31/12.
Distance: 150m 150m on the spot.

Rosendal 5A1

Skåla Vika, Skålafjæro. **GPS**: n59,98528 e6,00708.

80 NOK 175 Ch NOK 25 included.
Location: Rural, simple. **Surface:** gravel. 01/01-31/12.
Distance: 200m on the spot on the spot 200m.
Remarks: Money in envelope in mail box.

Sand 5A1

Hydrokaien, Nordenden. **GPS**: n59,48516 e6,24756.
6 free WC. **Surface:** asphalted.
Distance: 300m on the spot on the spot 800m 300m on the spot.
Remarks: At museum.

Sand 5A1

Stasjon XY. GPS: n59,47590 e6,28913.
Ch.
Remarks: At petrol station.

Sandeid 5A1

Kai. GPS: n59,54198 e5,86770.

5 NOK 100 NOK 25 NOK 10. **Location:** Rural, simple.
Surface: asphalted. 01/01-31/12.
Distance: on the spot on the spot on the spot.
Remarks: Money in envelope in mail box.

Sauda 5A1

Bobil Havn, Treaskjæret. **GPS**: n59,64480 e6,33716.
15 NOK 100 Ch WC.
Distance: 1,2km on the spot on the spot 1,2km 1,2km 100m.
Remarks: At the quay.

Skånevik 5A1

Fylkesveg. **GPS**: n59,73385 e5,92672.

8 NOK 150 Ch included WC.
Location: Urban, simple. **Surface:** gravel. 01/01-31/12.
Distance: 500m on the spot on the spot 400m.

Skare 5B1

Skare Kommune Odda, Riksveg 13 144 langs E 134.
GPS: n59,88666 e6,65612.

50 NOK 100 Ch included. **Location:** Motorway, simple.
Surface: gravel. 01/01-31/12.
Distance: 6km on the spot on the spot on the spot.
Remarks: Money in envelope in mail box, service 2km.

Sveio 5A1

Victors Bobil camping, Fylkesveg. **GPS**: n59,53016 e5,44353.

NOK 250-300 Ch WC included.
Location: Rural, isolated. **Surface:** grassy/gravel. 01/04-31/10.
Distance: 9km on the spot on the spot 9km.
Remarks: Small pitches.

Svelgen 4A3

Svelgen Hotell, Granden. **GPS**: n61,76978 e5,29393.

7 free. **Location:** Simple. **Surface:** asphalted. 01/01-31/12.
Distance: on the spot on the spot on the spot 200m on the spot.

Sykkylven 4A2

Sykkylven Småbåthamn, Ullavikvegen. **GPS**: n62,39679 e6,58192.
NOK 90 NOK 30 WC. **Surface:** asphalted.
Distance: 500m on the spot on the spot 500m 500m.

Sæbøvik 5A1

Halsnøy Samfunnshus, Riksveg. **GPS**: n59,79431 e5,71196.

12 NOK 100 Ch included NOK 50 WC NOK 30.
Location: Rural, simple. **Surface:** asphalted.
01/01-31/12 water disconnected in winter.
Distance: on the spot on the spot on the spot 200m.

Tau 5A1

Tau Båtforening, Kvernvegen. **GPS**: n59,06086 e5,91343.
8 NOK 150 Ch WC included. 01/01-31/12.
Distance: on the spot on the spot 1km 1km.

Tjøvåg 4A2

Laternen Marina. GPS: n62,31388 e5,70805.

NOK 100 (4x)NOK 25 NOK 20 NOK 30.
Location: Comfortable. **Surface:** gravel. 01/01-31/12.
Distance: 5km on the spot on the spot on the spot.
Remarks: Boat rental.

Tresfjord 4A2

Småbåthavn. GPS: n62,52520 e7,13085.

NO

4 NOK 150 NOK 30 NOK 30 Ch NOK 30 WC.
Location: Rural, simple, quiet. **Surface:** gravel.
Distance: 100m on the spot on the spot 100m.
Remarks: At petrol station.

S Urangsvåg 5A1

Fylkesveg. **GPS**: n59,84002 e5,15190.
6 NOK 180 Ch WC included. **Surface:** asphalted.
Distance: on the spot on the spot.

S Vikedal 5A1

Vikedal Båthavn, Riksveg. **GPS**: n59,49632 e5,89837.

30 NOK 100 Ch NOK 50 WC included NOK 30.
Location: Rural, simple. **Surface:** metalled.
01/01-31/12.
Distance: 200m on the spot on the spot 200m 200m.
Remarks: Money in envelope in mail box.

S Viksdalen 4A3

GPS: n61,39096 e6,26945.

6 NOK 150 Ch included. **Location:** Rural, simple, isolated, quiet. **Surface:** gravel. 01/01-31/12.
Distance: 12km on the spot on the spot 12km.
Remarks: Dead end street, narrow road, boat rental.

Ølen 5A1

Fjellstøl Skianlegg, Helgaland. **GPS**: n59,58853 e5,88857.

30 NOK 40. **Location:** Rural, simple. **Surface:** gravel.
01/01-31/12.
Distance: 6km on the spot on the spot.
Remarks: Money in envelope in mail box.

S Ølen 5A1

Båtlag, Fylkesveg. **GPS**: n59,60748 e5,81448.

10 NOK 140 included WC NOK 30.
Location: Rural, simple. **Surface:** gravel. 01/01-31/12.
Distance: 150m on the spot on the spot 300m 600m.
Remarks: Money in envelope in mail box.

S Ølensvåg 5A1

Ask Bobilparkering, Gjerdevikvegen 46.
GPS: n59,59728 e5,75857.

30 NOK 100 Ch (12x)NOK 30 included. **Location:** Rural, luxurious. **Surface:** gravel. 01/01-31/12.
Distance: 1km on the spot on the spot.
Remarks: Money in envelope in mail box, barbecue place.

S Øydegard 4A2

Riksvei, E39 70. **GPS**: n62,98958 e7,88272.

10 free WC free. **Location:** Rural, simple, isolated, quiet.
Surface: asphalted.
Distance: on the spot on the spot.

Southern Norway

S Åmli 5B2

Dølemo. **GPS**: n58,71102 e8,34497.
NOK 150 Ch WC . **Location:** Isolated, quiet.
Surface: grassy. 01/01-31/12.
Distance: on the spot on the spot.

S Åmli 5B2

Pan Garden, Tveit 38. **GPS**: n58,74697 e8,50946.
10 NOK 100 NOK 50 NOK 30. **Location:** Isolated, quiet.
Distance: on the spot on the spot on the spot.

Borhaug 5B2

Lista Fyr, Toppveien 10. **GPS**: n58,10943 e6,56863.
free. 01/01-31/12.
Distance: 1,5km.
Remarks: At lighthouse, max. 2 nights.

S Borhaug 5B2

Borshavn. **GPS**: n58,10081 e6,58335.
NOK 200 Ch WC . **Surface:** asphalted.
Distance: on the spot on the spot.
Remarks: Max. 1 day.

S Eidstod 5B1

Eidstod Kommune Vrådal, Vråliosvegen.
GPS: n59,32570 e8,48630.

20 free Ch free. **Location:** Rural, simple.
Surface: gravel/sand. 01/01-31/12.
Distance: on the spot on the spot on the spot on the spot on the spot.

S Farsund 5B2

Farsund Bobil Camp, Ferjeveien. **GPS**: n58,09439 e6,81278.
NOK 175 . **Surface:** metalled. 01/01-31/12
Service: winter.
Distance: 500m on the spot on the spot 500m 1,5km.

S Flekkefjord 5B2

Flekkefjord Bobilcamp, Tollbodbrygga. **GPS**: n58,29267 e6,66296.

25 NOK 250 Ch (16x)included WC .
Surface: gravel. 01/01-31/12.
Distance: 850m on the spot 850m 200m.
Remarks: Pay at shop.

S Grimstad 5B2

Sørlandets Caravansenter, Grøm Næringspark 2.
GPS: n58,34011 e8,56658.
3 free Ch free. **Location:** Simple.
Distance: 1km 200m 1km 1km.
Remarks: At motorhome dealer, max. 24h.

S Hidrasund 5B2

Kirkehavn. **GPS**: n58,22896 e6,52919.
NOK 150 Ch.
Location: Isolated, quiet. **Surface:** asphalted. 01/01-31/12.
Distance: 2km on the spot 2km 1km on the spot.

S Hornes 5B2

Mineralparken Bobilcamp, Mineralvegen 1.
GPS: n58,54993 e7,77542.
40 NOK 200 Ch NOK 20 NOK 40/40 included.
Surface: grassy.
Distance: 700m on the spot on the spot.
Remarks: Bread-service in summer period.

Kviteseid 5B1

Kviteseid, Garverivegen. **GPS**: n59,40275 e8,48675.

5 free. **Location:** Rural, simple. **Surface:** gravel.
01/01-31/12.
Distance: on the spot on the spot on the spot on the spot on the spot on the spot on the spot on the spot.

S Lillesand 5B2

Lillesand gjesthavn, Kokkenes. **GPS**: n58,24745 e8,38349.
25 NOK 200 Ch included WC . **Surface:** asphalted.
Service: winter.
Distance: 500m on the spot on the spot 200m 500m.

S Lindesnes 5B2

Spangereidveien. **GPS**: n58,03998 e7,15014.

2 NOK 150 WC NOK 20 NOK 45/45.
Distance: on the spot on the spot on the spot.
Remarks: Boat rental.

S Mandal 5B2

Mandal Havn, Havnegata. **GPS**: n58,02440 e7,45566.
10 NOK 180 . **Surface:** asphalted.
Distance: 400m on the spot 400m 1km.

S Mysen 5D1

Jernbanegaten 17. **GPS**: n59,55266 e11,32510.
8 free Ch free. **Location:** Urban. **Surface:** metalled.
01/01-31/12.
Distance: on the spot 500m 500m.

NO

Remarks: Max. 48h.

Risør 5C2

Tjenngata. **GPS**: n58,72093 e9,22567.

NOK 20/h, NOK 100/day included NOK 10 NOK 30/30. **Surface:** grassy. 01/01-31/12 Service: winter.
Distance: 600m 500m 500m 600m.

Snig 5B2

Snig, Stegganskogen R460. **GPS**: n58,05313 e7,27103.

6 free WC. **Location:** Rural, simple. **Surface:** gravel.
01/01-31/12.
Distance: 4,5km on the spot on the spot on the spot on the spot.

Valle 5B1

Sanden Såre. **GPS**: n59,27128 e7,46221.
NOK 150-200 Ch. **Location:** Rural, isolated, quiet.
Surface: grassy.
Distance: 10km on the spot on the spot.
Remarks: Nearby waterfalls.

NO

Eastern Norway

Brandbu 4B3

Tegneseriemuseet, Rosendalsvegen. **GPS**: n60,41719 e10,50940.
4 NOK 100 NOK 50. **Surface:** asphalted. 01/03-01/10.
Distance: 500m 400m 300m.
Remarks: At museum.

Bøverdalen 4A3

Leirvassbu. **GPS**: n61,54917 e8,24694.
NOK 200 WC. **Location:** Isolated, quiet. 20/06-30/09.
Remarks: Accessible via toll road (NOK 60).

Dalen 5B1

Bobilparkering Dalen Bryggje. **GPS**: n59,44515 e8,02292.

NOK 200-280 Ch WC included.
Surface: metalled.
Distance: 900m on the spot on the spot on the spot.
Remarks: Money in envelope in mail box.

Dovre 4B2

Krymsdalhyte. **GPS**: n62,08557 e9,64947.

free. **Location:** Isolated. **Surface:** grassy.
01/01-31/12.
Distance: on the spot 300m on the spot.
Remarks: Accessible via toll road (NOK 80), national Park 'Rondane'.

Etnedal 4B3

Sebu Røssjøen, Lenningsvegen. **GPS**: n61,12502 e9,71475.
free.
Distance: on the spot.

Flatdal 5B1

Kvåle Din gard, Kvålevegen. **GPS**: n59,56042 e8,56248.
5 NOK 200 Ch WC. **Location:** Rural, quiet. **Surface:** grassy.
01/01-31/12.
Distance: on the spot on the spot.

Fredrikstad 5C1

Gjestehavn, Frederikstad Dokka 1c. **GPS**: n59,21423 e10,92512.

15 NOK 250 Ch WC NOK 40 included.
Location: Urban, simple, central, quiet. **Surface:** asphalted.
01/04-01/10.
Distance: 300m on the spot on the spot 300m 150m on the spot on the spot.

Gjøvik 4B3

Gjøvik Marina, Bryggevegen. **GPS**: n60,79555 e10,70116.
25 NOK 50 Ch. **Surface:** gravel. 15/06-13/09.
Distance: on the spot on the spot McDonalds 300m.
Remarks: To be paid at petrol station.

Halden 5D1

Slippen Brygge, Kiellands gate 22. **GPS**: n59,11539 e11,38128.

20 NOK 150 included. **Location:** Urban, simple, quiet.
Surface: asphalted/gravel. 01/01-31/12.
Distance: historical centre 500m on the spot on the spot 500m 800m on the spot on the spot.
Remarks: Money in envelope in mail box.

Hamar 4B3

Hamar båtforening, Brygga. **GPS**: n60,78846 e11,07138.
20 NOK 120 Ch (6x).
Surface: asphalted. 01/06-30/09.
Distance: 300m on the spot on the spot 1km 400m.

Holmestrand 5C1

Hagemannsveien. **GPS**: n59,48048 e10,32933.
free. **Surface:** asphalted.
Distance: on the spot on the spot.
Remarks: At harbour.

Holmestrand 5C1

Hakan Bobilhavn, Weidemannsgate 13.
GPS: n59,48921 e10,32294.

40 NOK 150 Ch NOK 2,80/kWh WC included.
Location: Urban, simple, quiet. **Surface:** asphalted.
01/06-15/09.
Distance: 200m on the spot on the spot on the spot 300m.

Horten 5C1

Horten Gjestehavn, Tollbugata 2. **GPS**: n59,41302 e10,48695.

14 NOK 200 WC included.
Location: Urban, simple, central, quiet. **Surface:** asphalted.
01/01-31/12 service: 16/09-31/03.
Distance: on the spot on the spot on the spot 100m 600m on the spot.

Hov 4B3

Fjordvegen 27. **GPS**: n60,69915 e10,33972.
2 NOK 100 Ch. **Surface:** grassy.
Distance: on the spot on the spot.

Høvringen 4B3

Rondane Haukliseter Fjellhotell. **GPS**: n61,88853 e9,48745.
NOK 200 Ch WC. **Surface:** grassy.
Distance: 1km 1km.
Remarks: Use of sauna against payment.

Kongsberg 5C1

Glabak. **GPS**: n59,67205 e9,64166.
5 NOK 170. **Surface:** asphalted. 01/01-31/12.
Distance: on the spot 400m 550m on the spot.
Remarks: At swimming pool.

Kragerø 5C1

Allemannsveien. **GPS**: n58,87553 e9,41766.
NOK 150. **Surface:** unpaved.
Distance: on the spot 100m.

Kvelde 5C1

Roppestad, Farrisveien 863. **GPS**: n59,15310 e9,90844.

10 free Ch WC free. **Location:** Rural, simple, isolated, quiet.
Surface: grassy. 15/05-15/09.
Distance: 18km 50m 50m on the spot.
Remarks: Max. 2 days.

Langesund 5C1

Bobilparkering Smietangen, Cudrios gate 17.
GPS: n59,00220 e9,74905.

8 free. **Location:** Simple, central. **Surface:** concrete.
01/01-31/12.
Distance: 200m on the spot 200m.
Remarks: Temporary stopover.

Larvik 5C1

Indre Havn, Strandpromenaden. **GPS**: n59,04892 e10,03361.

17 NOK 150 or € 15 Ch included.
Location: Urban, simple, central, quiet. **Surface:** asphalted.
01/01-31/12.
Distance: 200m on the spot on the spot 500m 500m 500m on the spot.
Remarks: Money in envelope in mail box.

Lillehammer 4B3

Lysgårdsbakkene, Lysgårdsvegen 55. **GPS**: n61,12431 e10,48914.
NOK 70/24h. **Surface:** metalled.
Distance: 250m.

Lunde 5C1

Hogga Sluser, Gamle Strengenvegen. **GPS**: n59,30216 e9,04331.
12 NOK 150 Ch included NOK 10.
Distance: on the spot on the spot.

Moss 5C1

Bobilhavn, Værftsgata 3. **GPS**: n59,43486 e10,65141.

14 NOK 150 Ch WC included.
Location: Urban, comfortable, central, quiet. **Surface:** asphalted.
01/01-31/12.
Distance: 500m 3km on the spot on the spot 300m 100m on the spot.
Remarks: Max. 3 days.

Mysusæter 4B3

Mysuseter Fjellstue. **GPS**: n61,81161 e9,68463.
NOK 40. **Surface:** metalled.

Notodden 5C1

Notodden Bobilcamp, Heddalsvegen. **GPS**: n59,55876 e9,24851.
13 NOK 150 Ch (13x)included WC NOK 10 NOK 20.
Surface: metalled. 01/01-31/12.
Distance: 1km on the spot on the spot on the spot 250m.

Notodden 5C1

Heddalsvegen. **GPS**: n59,55981 e9,24834.
NOK 20 Ch WC NOK 10 NOK 20. 01/01-31/12.

Oslo 4B3

Øvreseterveien. **GPS**: n59,98130 e10,67166.

15 . **Location:** Rural. **Surface:** gravel.
Distance: 3km on the spot on the spot 3km 200m on the spot.

Oslo 4B3

Sjølyst Marina, Drammensveien 164. **GPS**: n59,92026 e10,67506.

250 NOK 300 Ch WC included .
Location: Urban, simple, central, noisy. **Surface:** asphalted.
01/06-20/09.
Distance: 6km on the spot on the spot on the spot on the spot.

Oslo 4B3

Bogstad Camp, Ankerveien 117. **GPS**: n59,96293 e10,64203.

38 NOK 285, 4 pers.incl Ch NOK 60/day WC NOK 15 NOK 40/40 included. **Location:** Comfortable, quiet.
Surface: grassy/gravel. 01/01-31/12.
Distance: city centre 6km 700m 700m on the spot on the spot on the spot on the spot.

Rauland 5B1

Raulandsfjell. **GPS**: n59,72005 e8,00510.
14 NOK 180-250 WC . 01/01-31/12.
Distance: 5km on the spot on the spot on the spot.
Remarks: At ski-lift.

Sandefjord 5C1

Sandefjord Bobil havn, Sandefjordsveien 5.
GPS: n59,12506 e10,22108.

16 NOK 260 Ch included.
Location: Urban, simple, quiet. **Surface:** asphalted. 01/01-31/12.
Distance: 700m on the spot on the spot 700m 1km on the spot on the spot.
Remarks: Max. 72h.

Sarpsborg 5D1

Tindlund bobilparkering, Neie Tidlundsveien.
GPS: n59,27326 e11,04667.

6 NOK 100 (4x). **Location:** Urban, simple.
Surface: gravel.
Distance: 1,3km.

Sarpsborg 5D1

Stamsaas Fritid, Vogtsvei 40. **GPS**: n59,28532 e11,08414.

10 free free. **Location:** Urban, simple, noisy. **Surface:** asphalted.
01/01-31/12.
Distance: 1km 350m.
Remarks: Service during opening hours.

Seljord 5B1

Flatin Gard, Flatingrendi 3. **GPS**: n59,50725 e8,63964.
40 NOK 100, NOK 200 service incl WC .
Distance: 100m 100m.

Siljan 5C1

Sporevann. **GPS**: n59,38476 e9,69584.
10 free. **Location:** Simple, isolated.
Distance: 11km on the spot on the spot.

Skien 5C1

Fritidspark, Moflatveien 59. **GPS**: n59,18510 e9,59698.

14 NOK 200 Ch WC NOK 20 included.
Location: Rural, simple, central, quiet. **Surface:** asphalted.
01/04-01/10.
Distance: historical centre 500m on the spot 500m on the spot.
Remarks: Check in at hotel, breakfast-service.

Skien 5C1

Teg Seil, Bøleveien 4. **GPS**: n59,19634 e9,62039.

10 NOK 150. **Location:** Urban, simple, quiet.
Surface: asphalted. 01/05-30/09.
Distance: 700m on the spot on the spot 400m on the spot.
Remarks: At sailmaker.

Skreia 4B3

Hersjøen. **GPS**: n60,54498 e11,03309.
NOK 45. **Location:** Isolated, quiet. **Surface:** grassy.
Distance: on the spot on the spot 6,5km.

Tyristrand 4B3

Stall Myhre, Holleiaveien 263. **GPS**: n60,11111 e10,07194.
NOK 100. **Location:** Isolated, quiet. **Surface:** grassy.
01/03-01/10.
Distance: 3,5km.
Remarks: At horse farm.

Tønsberg 5C1

Storgaten, Storgatan 1. **GPS**: n59,26323 e10,41569.

NO

8 NOK 150 Ch WC included. **Location:** Urban, simple, noisy. **Surface:** asphalted.
Distance: on the spot 100m 300m on the spot.
Remarks: Max. 2 days.

Tønsberg 5C1

Fjordgaten, Fjordgatan 15. **GPS**: n59,27390 e10,40009.

23 NOK 150 included. **Location:** Rural, simple, quiet. **Surface:** gravel. 01/01-31/12.
Distance: 1km 50m 50m on the spot on the spot.

Tønsberg 5C1

Messeområdet, Stenmalveien 32. **GPS**: n59,28069 e10,41015.

12 free. **Location:** Rural, simple, quiet. **Surface:** asphalted. 01/01-31/12.
Distance: 2km 2km 2km on the spot on the spot.
Remarks: At the skating rink, picnic area.

Tønsberg 5C1

Shell, Kjelleveien 28. **GPS**: n59,27879 e10,40092.
Ch.

Ulefoss 5C1

Norsjø Golfpark, Romnesvegen 98. **GPS**: n59,30248 e9,26511.
NOK 50.
Distance: 4km.
Remarks: At golf court.

Uvdal 4B3

Uvdal resort. **GPS**: n60,26515 e8,78849.
NOK 150. **Surface:** grassy.
Distance: on the spot on the spot.

Vågå 4B3

Steinhole fjellcamp. **GPS**: n61,62293 e8,99682.
NOK 50. **Location:** Isolated, quiet. **Surface:** grassy.

Voll 5C1

Ole"s Kios og gatekjøkken, Svanvikveien 653.
GPS: n59,12797 e9,51008.

12 NOK 150 Ch WC included.
Location: Rural, simple, quiet. **Surface:** gravel. 01/01-31/12.
Distance: 1km on the spot on the spot on the spot on the spot on the spot on the spot.
Remarks: Check in on arrival, regional products.

NO

Poland

Capital: Warsaw
Government: parliamentary republic
Official Language: Polish
Population: 38,523,261(2016)
Area: 311,888 km²

General information
Dialling code: 0048
General emergency: 112
Currency: Zloty (PLN)
€ 1 = 4,24 PLN, 1 PLN = € 0,23
£1 = 4,82 PLN, 1PLN = £0.20 (October 2017)
Credit cards are accepted almost everywhere.

Regulations for overnight stays
Free overnight stay is not allowed. On private property with permission of the owner.

Additional public holidays 2018
January 6 Epiphany
May 3 Constitution Day
May 31 Corpus Christi
August 15 Assumption of Mary
November 1 All Saints' Day
November 11 Independence Day

Time Zone
Winter (Standard Time) GMT+1
Summer (DST) GMT+2

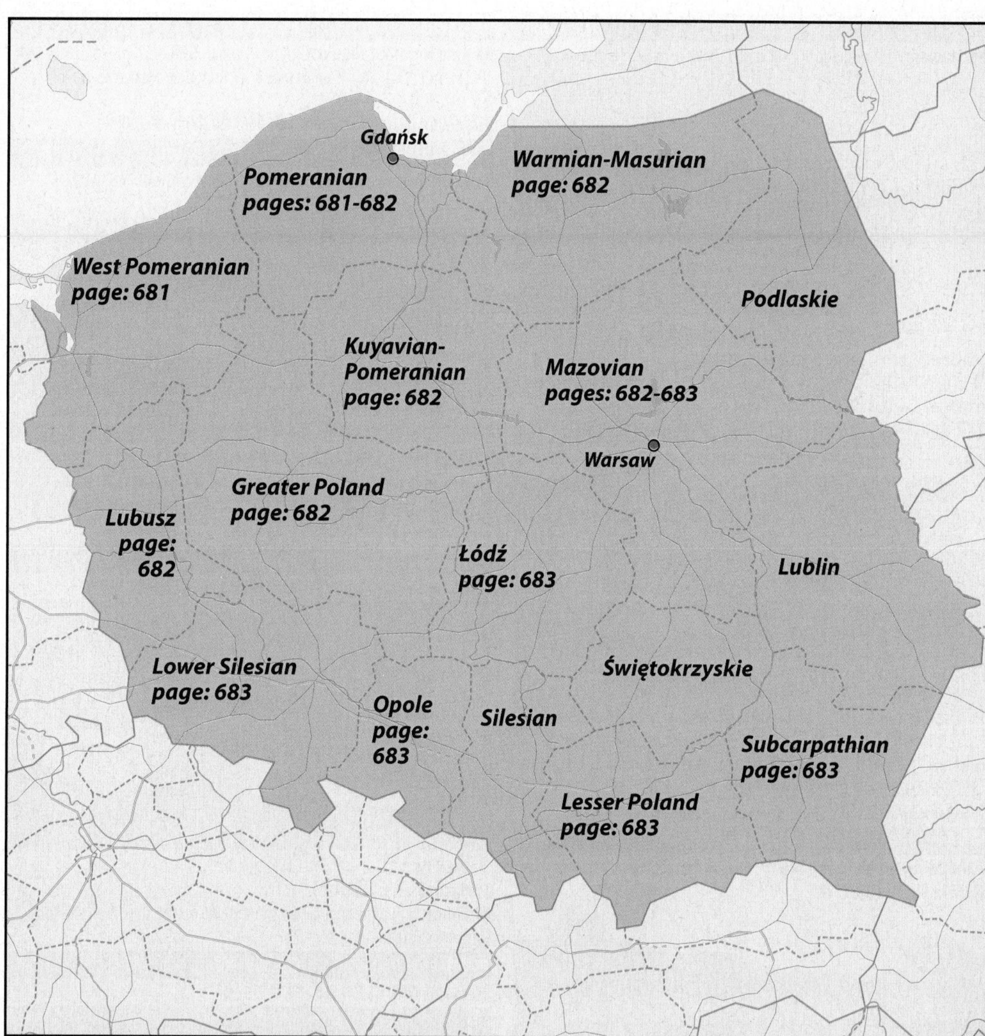

PL

West Pomeranian

Czaplinek 38A1

Drawtur, Ul. Pieciu Pomostów 1. **GPS**: n53,57671 e16,21984.

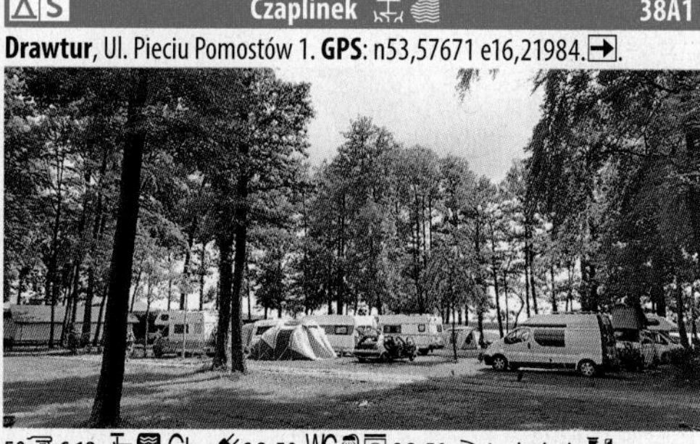

50 € 12 Ch € 2,50 WC € 3,50 included.
Location: Rural, noisy. **Surface:** grassy.
Distance: 2km 50m on the spot on the spot 2km.
Remarks: Dog € 2/day.

Miedzywodzie 6H3

Narcyz, Armii Krajowej 33. **GPS**: n54,00376 e14,69290.

8 € 20 Ch WC on demand included.
Location: Rural, central, noisy. **Surface:** grassy.
01/05-01/10.
Distance: 100m 800m 600m 100m 100m 50m.
Remarks: Breakfest-service.

Miroslawiec 38A2

Hotel Park Reduta Napoleona, Lowicz Walecki 60.
GPS: n53,33081 e16,02333.

30 € 8,50 € 2,25 Ch € 7,50 WC € 2,50 included.
Location: Rural, isolated, quiet. **Surface:** grassy.
01/01-31/12.
Distance: 5km 100m 500m 50m 700m.

Szczecin 8H2

Hotel Panorama, Ul.Radosna 60. **GPS**: n53,36420 e14,61550.

10 € 17 on demand included WC .
Location: Urban, simple. **Surface:** metalled. 01/01-31/12.
Distance: 10km 1km on the spot 1km on the spot.

Wolin 8H1

Fam. Lafrentz, Gogolice 20, Gogolice. **GPS**: n53,83300 e14,62262.

13 € 12 Ch included. **Location:** Rural, quiet.
Surface: gravel. 01/01-31/12.
Distance: 1,4km 500m 50m 1,4km 1,4km 1,4km.

Pomeranian

Gdańsk 38B1

Akademia Muzycna, Lakowa 1-2. **GPS**: n54,34561 e18,66357.

15 € 1-1,50/h. **Location:** Urban, central.
Surface: grassy/metalled. 01/01-31/12.
Distance: 100m 100m 100m.

Malbork 38B1

Camping Nogat 197, Ul. Parkowa 3. **GPS**: n54,04653 e19,03877.
30 € 19 Ch WC included .
Location: Rural. **Surface:** grassy/metalled. 01/05-30/09.
Distance: 1,5km on the spot on the spot on the spot on the spot.

Malbork 38B1

Nad Stawem, Ul. Solskiego 10. **GPS**: n54,04285 e19,02536.

30 € 12 Ch € 2,50 WC included.
Location: Urban, central. **Surface:** grassy.
01/03-01/11.
Distance: 200m 50m 200m.

Parchowo 38A1

Kalex, Jamnowski Mlyn 15. **GPS**: n54,22644 e17,63750.

10 € 14 Ch WC € 2 € 2 included.
Location: Rural, isolated, quiet. **Surface:** grassy/sand.
01/04-01/11.
Distance: 5km on the spot on the spot 5km.

Wierzbna 38A2

De Vuijle vaetdoek "carpe Diem", 66-340 Przytoczna.
GPS: n52,56639 e15,81722.

70 € 17,50 Ch WC included. **Location:** Rural, simple, isolated. **Surface:** grassy. 01/05-01/09.

Zagaje 38A1

Gosciniec Zagaje, Zagaje 1. **GPS**: n54,00583 e17,12778.
6 € 20 WC included. **Location:** Rural.
Surface: grassy. 01/01-31/12.
Distance: 4km 200m on the spot 4km on the spot on the spot.

Warmian-Masurian

Dobre Miasto 38B1

Garnizonowa 16. **GPS**: n53,98594 e20,41430.
3 free. **Location:** Simple. **Surface:** metalled.
01/01-31/12.
Distance: 1km.
Remarks: At swimming pool.

Gierloz 38C1

Wolf's Liar - Wilczy Szaniec, 11-400 Kętrzyn.
GPS: n54,07925 e21,49309.

10 € 12,50 included WC. **Location:** Rural, simple, comfortable. 01/01-31/12.
Distance: on the spot.
Remarks: Former headquarters of Hitler.

Mikolajki 38C1

Parking Hotelik Caligula, Ul.Jana Pawla II. **GPS**: n53,80278 e21,57444.
20 € 14 Ch on demand included. **Surface:** gravel.
01/01-31/12.
Distance: 100m 200m 500m 200m 200m.

Milolyn 38B1

Mazur, Ul Twarda 28a, Milomlyn. **GPS**: n53,76583 e19,84639.

4 € 7,50 € 1 € 1 Ch € 1 € 1.
Location: Rural, quiet. **Surface:** grassy. 01/01-31/12.
Distance: 500m 500m 1km 1km 400m 200m 500m 100m 100m.

Mrągowo 38C1

Camping Seeblick, Ruska Wieś 1. **GPS**: n53,94226 e21,32047.

30 € 15 Ch WC included.
Surface: grassy. 01/01-31/12.
Distance: on the spot on the spot on the spot on the spot.
Remarks: Bread-service.

Osetno 38B1

Osetno 16. **GPS**: n53,41562 e19,31729.

20 € 7,50 Ch WC on demand included.
Location: Rural, simple, isolated. **Surface:** grassy.
01/01-31/12.
Distance: 12km 30km 800m 800m 1km 100m on the spot.
Remarks: Bread-service.

Paslek 38B1

Kemping Bezplatny, 526. **GPS**: n53,98052 e19,62524.

100 € 12,50 included WC. **Location:** Rural, simple, isolated. **Surface:** grassy. 01/01-31/12.
Distance: 10km 10km on the spot 10km on the spot on the spot.

Piecki 38C1

Restaurant Krutynska, Krutyn 72. **GPS**: n53,68807 e21,43075.
20 € 13 Ch included. **Location:** Rural. **Surface:** grasstiles.
01/01-31/12.
Distance: 300m 300m.

Pieniezno 38B1

Caravanparc Pieniezno, 14-520. **GPS**: n54,23454 e20,13697.

20 € 10 Ch WC included on demand.
Location: Rural, quiet. **Surface:** grassy. 01/01-31/12.
Distance: 1km 800m 800m 500m.

Sorkwity 38C1

Haus am see, Janowo 1. **GPS**: n53,83495 e21,20284.
5 € 10-15 Ch included. **Location:** Rural.
Surface: grassy. 01/01-31/12.
Distance: 500m 50m 1km.

Tolkmicko 38B1

Swietokanska. **GPS**: n54,32367 e19,52264.

10 € 5 included WC € 0,50 € 2.
Location: Rural, noisy. **Surface:** metalled. 01/01-31/12.
Distance: 100m 50m on the spot 100m 100m.

Łukta 38B1

Plichta 9. **GPS**: n53,75989 e20,05300.
20 € 5 € 1.
Location: Rural. **Surface:** grassy. 01/04-01/11.

Lubusz

Owince 8H3

Fisch Camp, Wolności 40. **GPS**: n52,53517 e14,89269.

30 € 12 Ch WC included € 1/1day.
Location: Rural. **Surface:** grassy. 01/01-31/12.

Greater Poland

Biskupice 38A2

WojciechSzczepanski, Jankowo-Mlyn 23. **GPS**: n52,44965 e17,16442.
20 € 20 Ch included. **Location:** Rural. **Surface:** grassy.
01/01-31/12.

Poznań 38A2

Hotel-Camping Malta, Ul. Krańcowa 98. **GPS**: n52,40331 e16,98434.
40 € 18-22,50 Ch WC included.
Surface: grassy/metalled. 01/01-31/12.
Distance: on the spot on the spot 1km on the spot on the spot.
Remarks: Video surveillance.

Kuyavian-Pomeranian

Toruń 38B2

Camping Tramp, Kujawska 14. **GPS**: n52,99925 e18,60755.
40 € 16 Ch € 4,50 WC included.
Location: Rural, noisy. **Surface:** grassy/metalled.
01/05-01/10.
Distance: 200m 2,5km on the spot on the spot.

Mazovian

Warszawa 38C2

Parking, 1 Sierpinia, Warsaw (Warszawa). **GPS**: n52,19189 e20,98069.
10 € 10 € 2 € 2 Ch € 3 € 5. **Location:** Urban.

PL

Surface: metalled. 01/01-31/12.
Distance: city centre 5,5km 2km 100m 500m 300m.

Warszawa 38C2

Parking, Wybrzeze Gdanskie, Warsaw (Warszawa).
GPS: n52,25133 e21,01469.
15 € 25. **Location:** Urban. **Surface:** metalled. 01/01-31/12.
Distance: city centre 3km 5km on the spot on the spot 250m.

Lower Silesian

Karpacz 38A3

Rezydencja Holandia, Ul.Konstytucji 3-go Maja 67.
GPS: n50,77345 e15,74734.
15 € 5 € 1 € 1 Ch free € 1. **Location:** Rural.
Surface: metalled. 01/01-31/12.
Distance: 1km 900m.

Uciechów 38A3

Camping Forteca, Ul.Wroclawska 12. **GPS**: n50,75572 e16,69438.
50 € 17 Ch € 3,50,16Amp included. **Surface:** grassy.
01/04-01/10.
Distance: 4km 100m.
Remarks: Bread-service.

Opole

Gora Swietej Anny 38B3

P Najem Pokoi, Ul.Strzelecka 2A. **GPS**: n50,45785 e18,16895.
20 € 10 Ch included. 01/01-31/12.
Distance: 600m 100m.

Naklo 38B3

Fam Urban, Ul Strzelecka 91. **GPS**: n50,57790 e18,12715.
10 € 12 Ch WC included.
Location: Rural. **Surface:** grassy.
Distance: 400m 100m.

Łódź

Lipce Reymontowskie 38C2

Bumerang, Chlebow 3. **GPS**: n51,92795 e19,92847.
8 € 12 Ch included € 3.
Location: Rural. **Surface:** grassy. 01/01-31/12.

Lesser Poland

Gaj 38C4

Camping Korona, Ul. Myslenicka 32. **GPS**: n49,96229 e19,89294.
30 € 15 Ch WC included. **Location:** Rural.
Surface: grassy/metalled. 01/01-31/12.
Remarks: Bread-service, video surveillance.

Kraków 38C4

Guesthaus Apis, Ul.Podgorki 60. **GPS**: n49,98885 e19,96210.
5 € 15 Ch WC included.
Surface: metalled.
01/01-31/12.
Distance: 50m 400m.

Kraków 38C4

Elcamp, Ul.Tyniecka 118e. **GPS**: n50,03418 e19,87658.
10 € 7 € 1,20 Ch € 1,20 . **Surface:** grassy/gravel.
01/01-31/12.
Distance: Kraków 5km 100m.

Oswiecim 38B4

Auschwitz Parking, Stanislaw-Leszezynskiej 11.
GPS: n50,02867 e19,20111.
10 € 10 € 2,50. **Surface:** metalled. 01/01-31/12.
Remarks: Near Auswitz-Birkenau memorial and museum.

Sękowa 38C4

DW977. **GPS**: n49,62666 e21,19565.
5 free free. **Location:** Isolated. **Surface:** grasstiles.
01/01-31/12.
Distance: 1,5km 1,5km.
Remarks: Next to sports fields.

Wieliczka 38C4

Salt Mine, Edwarda Dembowskiego 22. **GPS**: n49,98542 e20,05338.
20 € 7,50. **Location:** Urban. **Surface:** gravel/sand.
01/01-31/12.
Distance: 1,5km 400m 50m 500m.

Subcarpathian

Wetlina 38D4

Górna Wetlinka, 38-608. **GPS**: n49,14740 e22,52028.
15 € 15 Ch included € 3.
Location: Rural. 01/04-01/10.
Distance: 200m on the spot on the spot.

PL

Portugal

Capital: Lisbon
Government: Parliamentary democracy
Official Language: Portuguese
Population: 10,833,816 (2016)
Area: 92,212 km²

General information
Dialling code: 00351
General emergency: 112
Currency: Euro
Payments by credit card are accepted almost everywhere.

Regulations for overnight stays
If there is no local prohibition wild camping is allowed, max. 48h, exept in urban areas and drinking water protection areas.

Additional public holidays 2018
January 6 Epiphany
March 30 Good Friday
April 25 Liberationday
May 1 Labor Day
May 31 Corpus Christi
June 10 National Holiday
August 15 Assumption of the Virgin Mary
October 5 Republic day
November 1 All Saints' Day
December 8 Immaculate Conception

Time Zone
Winter (Standard Time) GMT+0
Summer (DST) GMT+1

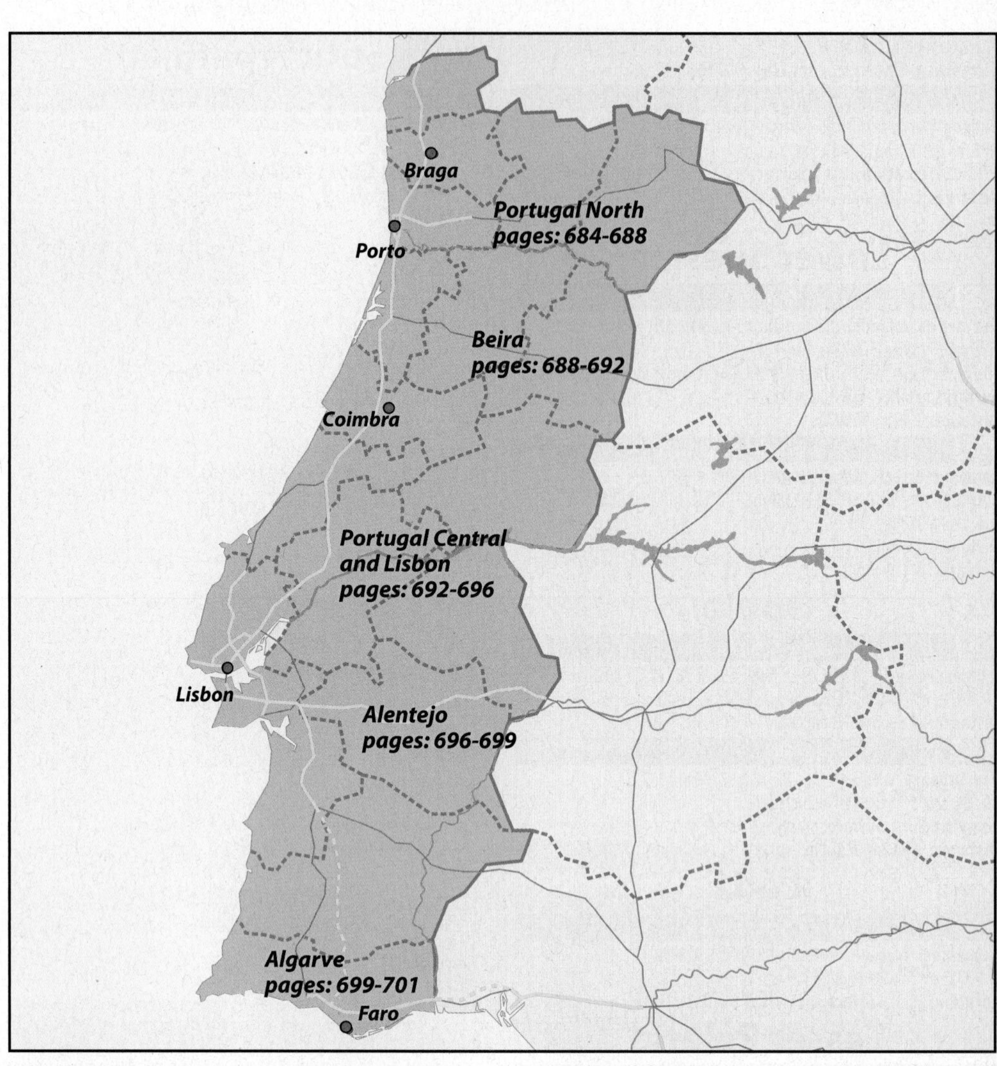

PT

Portugal North

Aguçadoura 29B3

Aguaçadoura Futebol Clube. GPS: n41,44389 w8,77722.

5 free. **Location:** Rural, simple. **Surface:** gravel/sand.
01/01-31/12.
Distance: 500m 50m 500m 500m.
Remarks: Parking at the beach.

Amarante 29C3

Av. Alexandre Herculano. **GPS**: n41,27286 w8,07178.

Surface: metalled.
Distance: 800m on the spot on the spot 50m.
Remarks: Parking near sports centre.

Amarante 29C3

GPS: n41,27020 w8,07708.

Surface: metalled. Wed.
Distance: on the spot on the spot.
Remarks: Market square along the river.

Amarante 29C3

Penedo da Rainha, São Gonçalo. **GPS**: n41,28031 w8,06925.
€ 10,90-22 Ch . 04/01-30/11.
Distance: 1km on the spot on the spot 1km.

Tourist information Amarante:
Museu Municipal Amadeu de Souza Cardoso, Alameda Teixeira Pascoaes. Modern art.

Arcos de Valdevez 29C3

N202. **GPS**: n41,84749 w8,41524.

10 free. **Location:** Rural, simple. **Surface:** metalled.
01/01-31/12.
Distance: 300m.
Remarks: Along the Vez river.

Avintes 29B3

Parque Biológico de Gaia, Rue da Cunha.
GPS: n41,09730 w8,55414.

9 € 4 + € 4 /pp, entrance park incl Ch included WC free,at reception.
Location: Luxurious, quiet. **Surface:** grasstiles. 01/01-31/12.
Distance: 10km 800m 100m > Porto.
Remarks: Check in at reception.

Barcelos 29C3

R.Rosa Ramalho. **GPS**: n41,52829 w8,61547.

12 free. **Location:** Rural, simple. **Surface:** metalled.
01/01-31/12.
Distance: centre 800m 3,5km on the spot.
Remarks: Parking swimming pool.

Tourist information Barcelos:
Museu de Olaria de Barcelos, R. Cónego Joaquim Gaiolas. Ceramics and archeology. Tue-Su 10-12.30h, 14-18h, Thu 10-18h.

Bico 30B1

R. Vasco da Gama. **GPS**: n40,73016 w8,64747.

30 free. **Location:** Rural, simple, isolated, quiet.
Surface: metalled. 01/01-31/12.
Distance: 300m on the spot on the spot on the spot.
Remarks: In fishing port.

Braga 29C3

Bom Jesus do Monte. **GPS**: n41,55278 w8,38137.

25 free Ch WC free. **Location:** Urban, simple. **Surface:** concrete.
01/01-31/12.
Distance: 6km 20m 100m.
Remarks: Parking at funicular railway.

Braga 29C3

Sameiro. **GPS**: n41,53928 w8,36743.

10 free. **Location:** Simple.
Surface: gravel/sand.
Remarks: Parking at place of pilgrimage.

Tourist information Braga:
Semana Santa. Procession.
week before Easter.
Parque Nacional da Peneda-Gerês.
Hiking routes.

Bragança 29D3

Parque de Merendas, Rue Miguel Torga. **GPS**: n41,80417 w6,74611.

30 free Ch free.
Location: Rural, comfortable, quiet.
Surface: metalled.
01/01-31/12.
Distance: 200m 200m 200m.
Remarks: P below the castle, 01/07-15/09, max. 24h, beautiful view.

Tourist information Bragança:
Medival upper city and castle.
Museu Militar.
9-11.45h, 14-18.15h.
Parque Natural de Montesinho. Nature reserve.

Caminha 29B3

Largo da Feira. **GPS**: n41,87490 w8,84113.

10 free. **Location:** Urban, simple. **Surface:** metalled.
01/01-31/12.
Distance: 500m 100m.

Carrazeda de Ansiães 29D3

Rua Engenheiro Camilo de Mendonça. **GPS**: n41,24498 w7,30386.
Ch. 01/01-31/12.
Remarks: Parking swimming pool.

Carregal do Sal 30C1

Quinta de Cabriz. **GPS**: n40,42465 w8,01856.
free. **Surface:** unpaved.
Distance: on the spot.
Remarks: Portugal Tradicional, max. 24h.

Carregal do Sal 30C1

Luzio, Arruamento Urbano a Sul da Vila. **GPS**: n40,43116 w7,99471.

3 free Ch free. **Location:** Simple.
Surface: grassy. 01/01-31/12.
Distance: 1km.
Remarks: Behind petrol station.

Castelo do Neiva 29B3

Av, de Santoinho. **GPS**: n41,67501 w8,78243.

Chaves 29C3

Alameda do Trajano. **GPS**: n41,73694 w7,46917.

6 free. **Location:** Urban, simple. **Surface:** metalled.
01/01-31/12.
Distance: historical centre 300m 8,6km 100m 100m.
Remarks: Along the Tâmega river.

Chaves 29C3

Quinta do Rebentão, Vila Nova de Veiga. **GPS**: n41,70127 w7,50013.
100 € 16,40-20,40 Ch WC . 01/01-30/11.
Distance: 4km 400m 1km 800m.

Tourist information Chaves:
Torre de Mengem. Military museum.

Covas 29C3

Parque Campismo de Covas, Lugar de Pereiras.
GPS: n41,88758 w8,69497.
€ 5,30-8 Ch WC . 01/01-31/12.

Covas 29C3

Quinta do Retiro, Lugar Quinta do Retiro s/n. **GPS**: n40,35230 w7,91583.
5 01/09-30/06 € 17,50, 01/07-31/08 € 22 Ch (5x),10Amp WC € 1/1 included. **Surface:** grassy. 01/01-31/12.
Distance: 800m 3km 3km 3km 8km on the spot.

Entre-os-Rios 29C3

GPS: n41,08357 w8,29322.

4 WC Lunchroom & co.
Location: Simple, central, noisy. 01/01-31/12.
Distance: 100m on the spot on the spot 100m 100m.
Remarks: Parking along the Douro river.

Espinho 29B3

GPS: n40,98916 w8,6452.

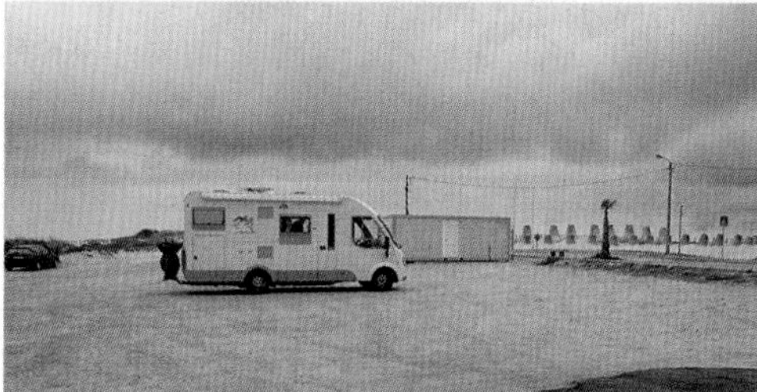

+10 free free,beach. **Location:** Rural, simple, isolated, quiet.
Surface: gravel/sand. 01/01-31/12.
Distance: 1km 25m 1km 1km.
Remarks: Beach parking.

Espinho 29B3

Municipal de Espinho, Zona da Ribeira dos Mochos.
GPS: n41,01402 w8,63743.
€ 18,90-23,30 Ch WC . 01/01-31/12.

Esposende 29B3

Forte de S.João Baptiste, Rue do Farol. **GPS**: n41,54222 w8,79111.

5 free free.
Location: Urban, simple. **Surface:** asphalted.
01/01-31/12.
Distance: 1,5km on the spot on the spot 1,5km.
Remarks: Parking at lighthouse, free wifi for clients restaurant.

Esposende 29B3

Parque de Campismo de Fão, Lírios - Fão. **GPS**: n41,50778 w8,77833.
Ch WC . 01/01-31/12.
Distance: 500m 500m on the spot 500m.

Freixo de Espada a Cinta 30D1

Espaço Multiusos, R. do Samiteiro de Cima.
GPS: n41,08826 w6,81751.

12 free Ch (12x)free.
Surface: metalled. 01/01-31/12.
Distance: 900m 900m 900m.
Remarks: Arrival <18h.

Freixo de Numão 30D1

Area de autocaravanas Jean Pierre Rossi, Sebarigos.
GPS: n41,06000 w7,22111.

PT

30 € 5/night Ch WC included.
Surface: metalled.
Distance: 900m ⊗500m 500m.

Gerês 29C3

Vila do Gerês. **GPS**: n41,73538 w8,15969.

4 free free. **Location:** Rural, simple, isolated, quiet.
Surface: asphalted. 01/01-31/12.
Distance: 1km ⊗on the spot.

Gondomar 29C3

Medas, Gavinho - Medas. **GPS**: n41,03917 w8,42694.
€ 26-32 Ch WC. 01/01-31/12.

Gosende 30C1

Cooperativa Capuchinhas CRL, Campo Benfeito.
GPS: n40,99799 w7,9269.
free. **Surface:** unpaved.
01/01-31/12.
Distance: 5,1km.
Remarks: Portugal Tradicional.

Guilhufe 29C3

EM594. **GPS**: n41,19541 w8,31605.

8 free Chfree. **Location:** Simple, noisy. **Surface:** metalled.
01/01-31/12.
Distance: 1km 1,6km ⊗1km 1km.

Izeda 29D3

Largo do Toural. **GPS**: n41,56750 w6,72333.

30 free Chfree. **Location:** Rural, simple, central, quiet.
Surface: metalled. 01/01-31/12.
Distance: centre ⊗200m 200m.

Lamego 30C1

Parque Lamego, N2, Lugar da Raposeira.
GPS: n41,09016 w7,82214.

40 € 5 + € 3/pp Ch € 4/day WC.
Location: Luxurious, isolated, quiet. **Surface:** unpaved.
01/01-31/12. **Distance:** 1,2km 4,5km ⊗500m 2km on the spot. **Remarks:** Baker every morning, beautiful view, near Caves da Raposeira, sale of wines.

Lamego 30C1

GPS: n41,09501 w7,80372.

free. **Surface:** metalled. 01/01-31/12.
Distance: on the spot ⊗on the spot on the spot.
Remarks: At the foot of monumental stairs of the Santuari.

Tourist information Lamego:
Bodega Raposeira. free.
Nossa Senhora dos Remédios. Pilgrimage in Portugal, most important festivity of the country. end Aug-beginning Sep.

Lordelo 29C3

R. da Igreja 350. **GPS**: n41,23472 w8,41139.

20 free Chfree. **Location:** Simple, quiet.
Surface: gravel/sand. 01/01-31/12.
Distance: 400m ⊗400m 400m.

Macedo de Cavaleiros 29D3

Rua das Piscinas. **GPS**: n41,53756 w6,95715.

8 free € 2/100liter Ch € 2/1h. **Location:** Urban, simple, central, quiet. **Surface:** asphalted.
01/01-31/12.
Distance: 200m ⊗200m 300m on the spot.

Macedo de Cavaleiros 29D3

Barragem do Azibo, Frada da Pegada. **GPS**: n41,58333 w6,89944.

10 free. **Location:** Rural, simple, quiet. **Surface:** metalled.
01/01-31/12.
Distance: 2km Sandy beach ⊗on the spot.
Remarks: At barrage, guarded during summer period.

Matosinhos 29B3

Av. de Praia. **GPS**: n41,26044 w8,72434.

10 free. **Location:** Simple, noisy. **Surface:** metalled.
01/01-31/12.
Distance: 200m ⊗200m 600m on the spot.
Remarks: Beach parking.

Matosinhos 29B3

Municipal de Angeiras. **GPS**: n41,26722 w8,71972.
€ 18,50-29 Ch. 01/01-31/12.
Remarks: Service only € 3,15-5,40.

Melgaço 29C2

Porta de Lamas de Mouro, Lamas de Mouro.
GPS: n42,05202 w8,19413.
free. **Surface:** metalled.

Melgaço 29C2

Rua do Mercado. **GPS**: n42,11549 w8,26095.

6 free. **Location:** Rural, simple. 01/01-31/12.
Distance: ⊗on the spot.

Miranda do Douro 29E3

Av. Eduardo Quero. **GPS**: n41,49167 w6,27333.

free. **Surface:** metalled.
Distance: 25m ⊗200m.
Remarks: Near city wall.

Miranda do Douro 29E3

Largo do Cestelo. **GPS**: n41,49611 w6,275.

free. **Surface:** metalled.
Distance: on the spot ⊗50m 50m.
Remarks: Parking near ruins of castle.

Mirandela 29D3

Largo Cardal. **GPS**: n41,48685 w7,18391.

PT

15 free Fon. **Location:** Rural, simple, central, noisy.
Surface: asphalted. 01/01-31/12.
Distance: centre on the spot on the spot on the spot on the spot on the spot.
Remarks: Large parking along the river.

Mirandela 29D3

Três Rios-Maravilha.
GPS: n41,50683 w7,19716.
€ 16,50-21,50 Ch WC.
02/02-01/12.

Tourist information Mirandela:
Museu municipal. Modern Portuguese painting art. free.
Villa Flôr. Village museum. free.

Mogadouro 29D3

Mogadouro, Complexo Desportivo Municipal. **GPS:** n41,33528 w6,71861.
€ 13-15 Ch WC. 01/04-30/09.
Distance: 500m on the spot 500m.

Mondim de Basto 29C3

Area Mondim de Basto. **GPS:** n41,41199 w7,95137.

30 free Chfree. **Location:** Urban, simple, central.
Surface: metalled. 01/01-31/12.
Distance: 300m 300m 300m.
Remarks: Friday market.

Montalegre 29C3

Rua João Rodrigues Cabrilho. **GPS:** n41,82280 w7,78684.
free Chfree. **Surface:** metalled. 01/01-31/12.
Distance: 500m.

Murça 29C3

Murça-Estádio, Variante à N15. **GPS:** n41,40421 w7,44994.

free. **Surface:** asphalted. 01/01-31/12.
Distance: 500m 300m.
Remarks: At footballstadium.

Nelas 30C1

Paço dos Cunhas de Santar, Largo do Paço, Santar.
GPS: n40,57229 w7,89154.
free.
Remarks: Portugal Tradicional, max. 24h, vineyard/restaurant, awning and generator prohibited.

Parada 29C3

Santuàrio. **GPS:** n41,68806 w8,20167.

Paredes de Coura 29C3

R. Bombeiros Voluntários 1. **GPS:** n41,91060 w8,55826.

46 € 12/24h, € 21/48h Ch (21x)WC included.
Location: Rural. **Surface:** metalled. 01/01-31/12.
Distance: 150m 13km 500m 150m 30m 50m.
Remarks: Video surveillance.

Peso da Régua 29C3

Parque de pernoita de autocaravanas.
GPS: n41,15570 w7,78058.
16 € 3 Ch free. **Surface:** metalled. 01/01-31/12.
Distance: 1km 100m.

Peso da Régua 29C3

Parque Ovar, Av. de Ovar. **GPS:** n41,16278 w7,79222.

4 free (4x)WCfree,150m. **Location:** Urban, simple, central, noisy.
Surface: asphalted. 01/01-31/12.
Distance: on the spot 4km on the spot on the spot on the spot.

Ponte de Lima 29C3

Alameda de São João. **GPS:** n41,77052 w8,5847.

15. **Location:** Urban, simple. **Surface:** metalled.
01/01-31/12.
Distance: 300m on the spot.
Remarks: Along river.

Póvoa de Varzim 29B3

Rio Alto, Estela. **GPS:** n41,46277 w8,77369.
€ 19-32 Ch WC. 01/01-31/12.
Remarks: Service passerby € 3,50-6.

Queimadela 29C3

Parque de Campismo do Baragem. **GPS:** n41,50379 w8,16216.
Ch. **Surface:** grassy/metalled. 01/01-31/12.
Distance: 100m 100m on the spot.

Santa Maria da Feira 30B1

GPS: n40,91972 w8,54306.

5 free. **Location:** Rural, simple, quiet. **Surface:** gravel/sand.
01/01-31/12.
Distance: 600m 600m.
Remarks: Parking at castle.

São Romão do Corgo 29C3

Quinta de Bourça, Lugar de Vila Nova. **GPS:** n41,44348 w7,9932.
free € 2,50 € 2,50. **Location:** Rural.
Distance: 11km.

Remarks: Portugal Tradicional.

Soajo 29C3

M530. **GPS:** n41,87197 w8,2633.

5 free. **Location:** Rural, simple. **Surface:** metalled.
01/01-31/12.
Distance: 100m 100m.
Remarks: Parking near school.

Torre de Moncorvo 30D1

Moncorvão. **GPS:** n41,18083 w7,04167.
9 free Chfree. **Surface:** metalled. 01/01-31/12.
Distance: 1,5KM.
Remarks: At sports park.

Valadares-SP do Sul 30C1

Cooperativa Mimos, Largo do Cruzeiro 1. **GPS:** n40,75704 w8,19997.

3 free. **Location:** Simple. **Surface:** grassy.
01/01-31/12.
Distance: on the spot.
Remarks: Portugal Tradicional.

Valpaços 29D3

Do Rabaçal, Rua Gago Coutinho. **GPS:** n41,63222 w7,24778.
€ 15-19 Ch WC. 01/01-31/12.

Venda Nova 29C3

Av. Prof. Dr. Anibal Cavaco Silva, Rio Tinto. **GPS:** n41,17530 w8,54159.
3 free Chfree. **Location:** Urban. **Surface:** asphalted.
01/01-31/12.
Distance: on the spot metro F.

Viana do Castelo 29B3

Praia do Cabadelo, Av. do Cabedelo. **GPS:** n41,68388 w8,83333.
20 free Chfree. **Surface:** metalled. 01/01-31/12.
Distance: 400m on the spot 100m.

Viana do Castelo 29B3

Rua de Lima. **GPS:** n41,69534 w8,81875.

15 free. **Location:** Urban, simple.
Surface: metalled/sand.
Distance: centre 700m.
Remarks: Large parking along the Limia river.

Tourist information Viana do Castelo:
Campo do Costelo. Market. Fri.
Romaria da Nossa Senhora da Agonia. Procession with Gigantes (giants). 3rd week Aug.

Vila Chã 29B3

Sol de Vila Chã, Rua do Sol, Facho. **GPS:** n41,29825 w8,73263.
Ch. 01/01-31/12.
Distance: 300m 10m on the spot 100m.

Vila do Conde 29B3

Av. Júlio Graça. **GPS:** n41,34476 w8,74541.

PT

20 free. **Location:** Urban, simple, central, noisy. **Surface:** metalled.
01/01-31/12.
Distance: 400m 150m 150m 200m 400m.
Remarks: Along the Este river.

Vila do Conde 29B3

Av. Marques de Sa Bandiera. **GPS**: n41,34270 w8,74587.

20 free. **Location:** Urban, simple, central. **Surface:** gravel/sand.
01/01-31/12.
Distance: 500m on the spot 200m 400m.
Remarks: Parking at sea.

Vila Nova de Cerveira 29B2

Av. dos Pescadores. **GPS**: n41,93823 w8,74685.

4 free Ch free. **Location:** Rural, simple.
Surface: asphalted. 01/01-31/12.
Distance: historical center 150m river-beach.
Remarks: Near Minho river and public pool park.

Vila Nova de Foz Côa 30D1

Autocross, N102. **GPS**: n41,06727 w7,15496.
free Ch free. **Location:** Isolated, quiet.
Distance: 2km.

Vila Nova de Foz Côa 30D1

Rua Engenheiro Eugénio Nobre. **GPS**: n41,08028 w7,14806.
+50 free. **Location:** Rural. 01/01-31/12.
Distance: 500m 500m.

Vila Nova de Gaia 29B3

Madalena, Rua de Cerro, Praia de Madalena. **GPS**: n41,10750 w8,65556.
€ 18,30-28,80 Ch WC.
01/01-31/12.
Remarks: Service only € 3,15-5,40.

Tourist information Vila Nova de Gaia:
City of the port wine, at the left bank of the river Douro, Port houses can be visited daily.

Vila Real 29C3

Municipal de Vila Real, Rua Dr. Manuel Cardona, Quinta da Carreira.
GPS: n41,30333 w7,73667.
€ 13,20-20,90 Ch WC.
01/01-31/12.

Tourist information Vila Real:
Solar de Mateus. Baroque country house, 18th century, known from label of the Matheus wine.

Vilartão 29D3

Parque de campismo o tempo parou, Rua da Bandera.
GPS: n41,76445 w7,21006.
12 € 10 Ch WC. **Location:** Rural. **Surface:** unpaved.
01/01-31/12.
Remarks: Swimming pool.

Vinhais 29D3

GPS: n41,83381 w7,00271.

6 free Ch free. **Location:** Urban, simple. **Surface:** gravel.
01/01-31/12.
Distance: 200m 100m.
Remarks: Nearby swimming pool.

Beira

Aldeia da Ponte 30D1

Caminho do Freguil. **GPS**: n40,41092 w6,87159.

4 free Ch free. **Location:** Rural, simple.
Surface: metalled. 01/01-31/12.
Distance: 300m.
Remarks: Near old Roman bridge.

Almeida 30D1

Rua da Guerreira. **GPS**: n40,72753 w6,90402.

free WC. **Surface:** metalled. 01/01-31/12.
Remarks: At fort-castle.

Anadia 30B1

Rua Seabras de Castro. **GPS**: n40,44056 w8,4375.

free. **Surface:** asphalted.
Distance: 100m 100m.

Aveiro 30B1

Parque de S João, Canal São Roque. **GPS**: n40,64328 w8,65859.

10 free free. **Surface:** grasstiles. 01/01-31/12.
Distance: 200m 25m 200m 200m.
Remarks: Parking at the Canal and A25.

Tourist information Aveiro:
Ecomuseu da Troncalhada, Canal das Pirâmides. Salt-making.
summer.
Museu de Aveiro, Av. Sta. Joana Princesa. Collection baroque art.

Tue-Su 10-17.30h.

Barril de Alva 30C1

EM517-1. **GPS**: n40,28611 w7,96167.

50 free Ch € 1 WC free. **Location:** Rural, simple, quiet.
Surface: unpaved. 01/01-31/12.
Distance: 500m river-beach on the spot.

Barriosa 30C1

Poço da Broca. **GPS**: n40,29366 w7,75376.

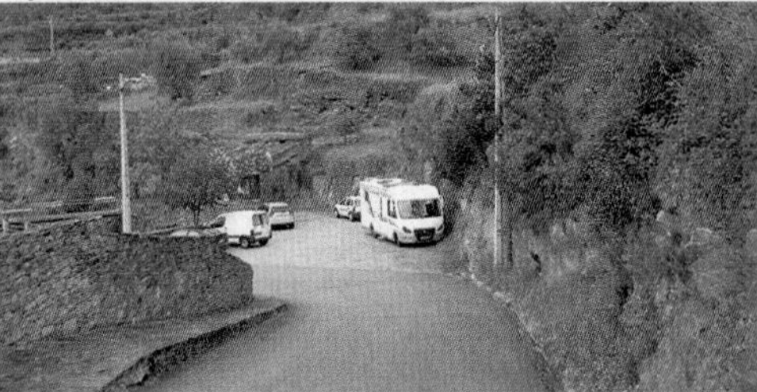

free. **Location:** Rural.
Distance: on the spot on the spot.
Remarks: Portugal Tradicional, restaurant and regional products for sale.

Belmonte 30C2

Parque de Santiago, N345. **GPS**: n40,21835 w7,20459.

4 free Ch WC free. **Surface:** metalled. 01/01-31/12.
Distance: 500m on the spot 150m on the spot.

Castelo Bom 30D1

Avenida Santa Maria, N16. **GPS**: n40,61261 w6,83398.

3 free. **Location:** Rural, simple.
Surface: metalled. 01/01-31/12.
Distance: on the spot.
Remarks: Less suitable for motorhomes >6,5m, typical village nearby spanish border.

Castelo Branco 30C2

Municipal de Castel Branco, N18. **GPS**: n39,85815 w7,49351.
Ch WC. 02/01-15/11.

Tourist information Castelo Branco:
Castelo. Ruins of castle of the Templars.
Alameda da Liberdade. Mo.

Castelo de Paiva 29C3

R. Emidio Navarro. **GPS**: n41,03955 w8,27406.

PT

50 free Ch WC free. **Location:** Simple, central, quiet. **Surface:** metalled. 01/01-31/12.
Distance: on the spot on the spot on the spot.
Remarks: Market square.

S Castelo Mendo 30D1

P5, N16. **GPS**: n40,59444 w6,94833.

3 free free. **Location:** Rural, simple. **Surface:** grassy/sand. 01/01-31/12.
Distance: on the spot 6,8km.

Castelo Rodrigo 30D1

GPS: n40,87778 w6,96611.

free. **Surface:** sand.
Remarks: At the entrance of fort.

Celorico da Beira 30C1

GPS: n40,63389 w7,40472.

10. **Location:** Isolated. **Surface:** metalled.
Distance: 2km.
Remarks: Parking sports park.

Cinfães 29C3

GPS: n41,07167 w8,08719.

10 free. **Surface:** metalled. 01/01-31/12.
Distance: 100m 100m 100m.

S Coimbra 30B1

Parque do Choupalinho, Av. Inês de Castro.
GPS: n40,19970 w8,42905.

20 free Ch free. **Surface:** metalled.
01/01-31/12.
Remarks: Max. 24h.

Tourist information Coimbra:
Portugal dos Pequeninos. Miniature Portugal.
9-19h.

S Coimbrão 30B2

Praia do Pedrógão. GPS: n39,91500 w8,95.
€ 15,60-18,20 Ch WC. 16/02-15/12.
Distance: 50m on the spot on the spot 10m.

S Condeixa 30B1

Av. Bombeiros Voluntarios de Condeixa. **GPS**: n40,11291 w8,49336.

6 free Ch free. **Surface:** asphalted. 01/01-31/12.
Distance: 500m on the spot 300m.
Remarks: Max. 48h, market Friday-morning.

Condeixa 30B1

Conímbriga, Praça da Republiça Condeixa.
GPS: n40,09895 w8,4894.

5 free. **Location:** Simple. **Surface:** grassy/metalled.
01/01-31/12.
Remarks: Parking next to archaeological site.

S Covas do Monte-SP do Sul 30C1

Covas do Monte.
GPS: n40,88873 w8,09823.
free free.
Distance: 250m.
Remarks: Portugal Tradicional.

S Escalos de Baixo 30C2

Hanmar, Estrada National 352. **GPS**: n39,89917 w7,40028.

20 € 8, May-Aug € 10 Ch WC included.
Surface: grassy. 01/01-31/12.
Distance: 1km 1km.

S Estarreja 30B1

R. Dr. Antonio Madureira. **GPS**: n40,75417 w8,56611.

6 € 2/48h Ch included. **Location:** Urban, simple, central.
Surface: metalled. 01/01-31/12.
Distance: on the spot on the spot on the spot.
Remarks: Check in Cafe Piscina, Ag. Seguros Rebelo, tuesday market 100m.

S Estarreja 30B1

Ribeira do Maurão. **GPS**: n40,81328 w8,61588.

6 free € 2 Ch. **Location:** Rural, simple, isolated, quiet.
Surface: metalled. 01/01-31/12.
Distance: on the spot on the spot.
Remarks: Nature reserve.

S Figueira da Foz 30B1

Av. de Espanha. **GPS**: n40,14856 w8,86791.

30 € 0,80/h, overnight stay free WC. **Surface:** asphalted.
01/01-31/12.
Distance: on the spot on the spot 100m.

Figueira da Foz 30B1

R.do Cabedelo. **GPS**: n40,14403 w8,86395.

10. **Location:** Simple. **Surface:** sand. 01/01-31/12.
Distance: on the spot on the spot.
Remarks: Beach parking.

S Figueira da Foz 30B1

Jumbo, Av. Francisco de Sá Carneiro. **GPS**: n40,16413 w8,8413.
Ch free. 01/01-31/12.
Remarks: At petrol station.

S Fratel 30C2

Vila Velha de Ródão. **GPS**: n39,63250 w7,74694.

10 free Ch free. **Surface:** grassy. 01/01-31/12.
Distance: 200m 1km 300m 300m.

PT

Fundão 30C2

Quinta do Convento. GPS: n40,13276 w7,51205.
150 € 13-17 Ch WC. 01/01-31/12.

Furadouro 30B1

Praia do Furadouro. GPS: n40,87645 w8,67381.

30 free WC 50m. **Location:** Rural, simple, quiet. **Surface:** asphalted. 01/01-31/12.
Distance: on the spot 300m 300m.
Remarks: Beach parking.

Guarda 30C1

Parque Pólis, Rua da Direcção Geral de Viação.
GPS: n40,54894 w7,24083.

20 free Ch free.
Location: Simple. **Surface:** metalled. 01/01-31/12.
Distance: historical centre 4km 2,4km 700m.
Remarks: Recreation park.

Guarda 30C1

Rossio de Valhelhas. GPS: n40,40333 w7,40528.
Ch. 01/05-30/09.
Distance: 50m 300m 150m 100m.

Tourist information Guarda:
Medieval city.

Idanha-a-Nova 30C2

Municipal de Idanha-a-Nova, Albufeira da Barragem Marechel Carmona. **GPS:** n39,95056 w7,18722.
€ 11-14 Ch WC. 01/01-31/12.
Distance: 50m on the spot on the spot 8km.
Remarks: Service only € 2,60-4,40.

Idanha-a-Velha 30C2

N332. **GPS:** n39,99830 w7,1445.

Tourist information Idanha-a-Velha:
Archeological tour.

Ilhavo 30B1

Av. Infante Dom Henrique, Praia da Barra. **GPS:** n40,64375 w8,74456.

30 free. **Surface:** metalled. 01/01-31/12.
Distance: 300m 300m.

Ilhavo 30B1

Costa Nova do Prado. **GPS:** n40,61222 w8,74917.

7 free. **Surface:** metalled. 01/01-31/12.
Distance: on the spot on the spot on the spot on the spot.
Remarks: Beach parking.

Ilhavo 30B1

Av Ns.da Saude. **GPS:** n40,61417 w8,75222.
Ch WC. 01/01-31/12.

Tourist information Ilhavo:
M Museu Histórico da Vista Alegre, Fábrica de Porcelanas da Vista Alegre. Collection of porcelain. Tue-Fri 9-18h, Sa-Su 9-12.30h, 14-17h. M Museu Marítimo de Ílhavo, Av. Dr. Rocha Madahil. Shipping museum. Tue-Fri 10-12.30h, 14.30-18h, Sa-Su 14.30-17.30h.

Lorvão 30C1

Rua do Malhao. **GPS:** n40,25896 w8,31468.

10 free Ch free. **Surface:** metalled.
Distance: on the spot.

Luso 30B1

GPS: n40,38639 w8,38139.

10 free. **Surface:** metalled. 01/01-31/12.
Remarks: Parking next to Hotel de Terme.

Tourist information Luso:
Mata Nacional do Buçaco. Nature reserve.

Mira 30B1

Praia de Mira. GPS: n40,44472 w8,79806.
Ch WC. 16/01-15/11.
Remarks: Service only € 3,15-5,40.

Miranda do Corvo 30B2

Rua Porto Mourisco. **GPS:** n40,08803 w8,33232.

8 free Ch free. **Location:** Rural.
Surface: asphalted. 01/01-31/12.
Distance: 700m.

Oleiros 30C2

R. Dr. Barata Relvas. **GPS:** n39,92056 w7,91389.
free Ch free. **Surface:** metalled. 01/01-31/12.

Pardilhó 30B1

Parque de Merendas, R. Joaquim Maria Resende.
GPS: n40,80111 w8,63472.

15 € 2/48h Ch included. **Location:** Rural, comfortable, isolated, quiet. **Surface:** metalled. 01/01-31/12.
Distance: 600m on the spot on the spot.
Remarks: Max. 48h, check in at bar (service).

Penacova 30C1

Bairro de Carrazedos. **GPS:** n40,26722 w8,28306.

10 free Ch WC free.
Surface: metalled. 01/01-31/12.
Distance: 400m 3km 800m 400m.

Penamacor 30C2

Lazer de Benquerença, Benquerença. **GPS:** n40,22938 w7,22136.

10 free Ch free. **Location:** Rural, simple, quiet.
Surface: gravel/sand. 01/01-31/12.
Distance: 2km on the spot.

Pinhel 30D1

GPS: n40,77389 w7,06194.

Distance: on the spot on the spot.
Remarks: At townhall.

Praia de Mira 30B1

Praia da Mira. **GPS:** n40,45800 w8,8025.

6 free.
Location: Simple. **Surface:** metalled. 01/01-31/12.
Distance: on the spot.
Remarks: Beach parking.

Praia de Mira 30B1

GPS: n40,44620 w8,80447.

PT

20 free. **Surface:** sand.
Distance: 500m.
Remarks: Beach parking.

S Praia de Quiaos 30B1

Praia de Quiaos. **GPS**: n40,22034 w8,89116.

15 free. **Location:** Simple. **Surface:** metalled.
01/01-31/12.
Remarks: Beach parking.

S Sabugal 30D1

Rua do Cemitério. **GPS**: n40,34843 w7,08653.

6 free Chfree. **Surface:** metalled. 01/01-31/12.
Distance: 500m 400m.

S Sangalhos 30B1

R. Mercado 150. **GPS**: n40,48639 w8,47528.

20 free Chfree. **Location:** Simple. **Surface:** metalled.
01/01-31/12.
Remarks: At sports centre.

S Santa Ovaia 30C1

Ponte das Três Entradas, Avô. **GPS**: n40,30667 w7,87139.
€ 13-14,50 WC .
Surface: grassy.
01/01-31/12.
Distance: 10m on the spot on the spot on the spot 10m.

S São João da Pesqueira 29C3

Restaurant Carocha, N222. **GPS**: n41,15120 w7,42378.
50 free Chfree. **Location:** Isolated. **Surface:** unpaved.
01/01-31/12.
Distance: 1km on the spot.
Remarks: Next to restaurant and Port wine cellar Cave Cadão.

S Sao Joao de Areias 30C1

Terra de Iguanas, Estrada principal 76, Vila Dianteira.
GPS: n40,39045 w8,08574.

4 € 10 Ch WC included. **Location:** Rural, comfortable, quiet. **Surface:** sand. 01/01-31/12.
Distance: 2km 1km 1,2km 2km 400m 2km on the spot.
Remarks: Max. 3 nights, swimming pool incl., vegetables and fruit from the garden.

S São Pedro do Sul 30C1

Termas São Pedro do Sul, N46. **GPS**: n40,74056 w8,08639.

6 free Chfree. **Location:** Simple. **Surface:** asphalted.
01/01-31/12.
Distance: 1km.
Remarks: Max. 48h.

S Sertã 30C2

R. Amaro Vicente Martins. **GPS**: n39,79729 w8,09588.

4 free Chfree. **Location:** Simple. **Surface:** asphalted.
01/01-31/12.
Distance: 500m 3km 50m.
Remarks: At sports park.

Sertã 30C2

Palácio da Justiça, R. Baden Powell. **GPS**: n39,80028 w8,09944.

free. **Location:** Simple. **Surface:** gravel/sand.
01/01-23/12.
Distance: 100m 3km 50m 100m.

S Sertã 30C2

Albergue do Bonjardim, Quinta da Portela, Nesperal.
GPS: n39,81306 w8,16278.

6 € 6 Ch (4x)€ 4 WC € 5 included.
Location: Luxurious, isolated. **Surface:** grassy/gravel.
01/04-01/11. **Distance:** 500m 2km 2,5km 500m

50m on the spot. **Remarks:** Sauna, steam bath and covered pool € 7,50, breakfast € 7,50, wine tasting.

Tabua 30C1

Piscina. **GPS**: n40,36306 w8,03.

3 free. **Surface:** metalled.

Tabua 30C1

Rua Aurora Jesus Goncalves. **GPS**: n40,36306 w8,02278.

10 free. **Surface:** metalled.

Trancoso 30C1

Parque Sportivo. **GPS**: n40,77160 w7,35621.

3 free. **Surface:** metalled.

Trancoso 30C1

Av. Heróis de São Marcos. **GPS**: n40,77583 w7,35056.

10 . **Surface:** metalled.
Distance: 50m.
Remarks: Note: Friday market day.

S Vagos 30B1

Praia da Vagueira. **GPS**: n40,54944 w8,77056.
20 € 7,50, 01/10-31/05 € 5 Ch € 2 € 0,50.
Surface: sand. 01/01-31/12.
Distance: on the spot.
Remarks: Service passerby € 2,50.

S Vagos 30B1

Vagueira, Gafanha da Boa Hora. **GPS**: n40,55806 w8,74528.
€ 16-25 Ch WC . 01/01-31/12.
Distance: 1km on the spot 1km 500m.
Remarks: Service only € 2,60-4,40.

Vagueira 30B1

Rua Arménio, Praia da Vagueira. **GPS**: n40,56506 w8,76697.

PT

20 free. **Surface:** metalled.
Distance: 200m sandy beach 50m.
Remarks: Beach parking.

S Vila Nova de Oliveirinha 30C1

Quinta do Tapadinho, Rua dos Brandões. **GPS**: n40,36520 w7,92195.

5 € 13,25 € 2/100liter Ch (5x)€ 5/24h,10Amp WC € 4 included. **Surface:** grassy/sand. 01/01-31/12.
Distance: 1km 6km 1km 8km 1km on the spot.

S Vila Pouca da Beira 30C1

Despinheiro, Avenida Principal. **GPS**: n40,30159 w7,9257.

4 € 8, 2 pers.incl WC € 1 € 4. **Location:** Rural, isolated, quiet. **Surface:** grassy. 01/01-31/12.
Distance: 500m 2km 2km 800m on the spot on the spot.

S Vilar Formoso 30D1

Zaza, Avenida das Tilia's, N332. **GPS**: n40,61528 w6,83833.

12 € 5/24h € 2 Ch (12x)€ 3/day. **Location:** Simple.
Surface: asphalted/gravel. 01/01-31/12.
Distance: 500m baker on site.

S Viseu 30C1

Av. Europa. **GPS**: n40,66533 w7,91681.
8 free Chfree.
Surface: asphalted.
01/01-31/12.
Distance: on the spot 6km.

Tourist information Viseu:
Centre of Vinho do Dão.
Museu municipal, Castro Daire. Etnographical collection.

Portugal Central and Lisbon

S A-dos-Cunhados 30A2

R. Monsenhor José Fialho. **GPS**: n39,15222 w9,30083.

10 free Chfree. **Location:** Simple, quiet. **Surface:** asphalted.
01/01-31/12.
Distance: 100m 6km beach 7km 200m.

S Abrantes 30B2

Aquapolis, São Joao. **GPS**: n39,45489 w8,18977.

10 free Chfree. **Location:** Rural, simple. **Surface:** metalled.
01/01-31/12.
Distance: 3km 4,7km on the spot 100m 6km.
Remarks: Service 100m.

S Abrantes 30B2

Aquapolis, São Joao. **GPS**: n39,45347 w8,19072.

2 free Ch free. **Surface:** metalled.
Distance: 3km 4,8km Sandy beach.
Remarks: Along the Tagus river.

Abrantes 30B2

Largo do Pralvo. **GPS**: n39,44956 w8,18968.

10 free. **Location:** Urban, simple, quiet. **Surface:** metalled.
01/01-31/12.
Distance: 1km 6,5km on the spot 1km 1km.
Remarks: Along the Tagus river.

Abrantes 30B2

Parque Urbano de São Lourenço, São Vincente.
GPS: n39,47530 w8,21541.

10 free. **Location:** Rural, simple, quiet. **Surface:** grassy/gravel.
01/01-31/12.
Distance: centre 2,4km 4,4km 50m 1,8km.
Remarks: Max. 48h.

Tourist information Abrantes:
Posto de Turismo, Esplanada 1º de Maio, www.cm-abrantes.pt. City with historical centre.

S Alenquer 30B3

Alenquer camping, Casal das Pedras. **GPS**: n39,05917 w9,02833.
4 € 13-15,50 Ch € 2,50 . 01/01-31/12.
Distance: on the spot on the spot.

Almada 30A3

Costa de Caparicia, R. Eduardo Luis. **GPS**: n38,56691 w9,19308.

10 free. **Location:** Simple. **Surface:** sand.
Distance: on the spot on the spot on the spot.

Almourol 30B2

Castelo de Almourol, Praia do Ribatejo. **GPS**: n39,46295 w8,38297.

10 free. **Location:** Simple. **Surface:** metalled.
Distance: 2km 4km on the spot 2km.
Remarks: On the banks of the Tejo river, parking castle.

Arruda dos Vinhos 30B3

Casal da Pevide. **GPS**: n38,99861 w9,08417.

3 free. **Location:** Urban, simple, noisy. **Surface:** asphalted.
01/01-31/12.
Distance: 2km on the spot on the spot.
Remarks: Parking Intermarché.

Assafora 30A3

Pic-nic area, Estr. de São Julião. **GPS**: n38,91167 w9,41138.

4 free. **Location:** Rural, simple, quiet. **Surface:** metalled.
01/01-31/12.
Distance: 800m on the spot.

S Baleal 30A2

Estrada do Baleal. **GPS**: n39,37240 w9,33702.

30 free free. **Location:** Rural, simple, quiet. **Surface:** asphalted.

PT

01/01-31/12.
Distance: 2km on the spot on the spot on the spot 2km on the spot.
Remarks: Parking next to bar restaurant in village square, not recommended at the weekend.

S Batalha 30B2

Parque Cónego M. Simões Inácio, Rua Cerca Conventual.
GPS: n39,66134 w8,82516.

15 free Ch free. **Location:** Urban, simple, quiet.
Surface: asphalted. 01/01-31/12 Mo.
Distance: 100m on the spot.
Remarks: At football ground/tennis, max. 48h.

Cabo Espichel 30A3

P Cabo Espichel. **GPS**: n38,42031 w9,21353.

free. **Location:** Rural, isolated. **Surface:** sand.
01/01-31/12.
Distance: Sesimbra 13km At the sea.
Remarks: Beautiful view.

Cascais 30A3

Cap Raso. **GPS**: n38,71134 w9,48498.

free. **Location:** Rural, simple, quiet. **Surface:** sand.
01/01-31/12.
Distance: 6km on the spot 6km on the spot on the spot.

Cascais 30A3

Ponta da Gate, Estrada do Guincho. **GPS**: n38,72769 w9,47555.

10 free. **Location:** Simple, quiet. **Surface:** gravel.
01/01-31/12.
Distance: 8km on the spot on the spot on the spot 8km on the spot.

S Cascais 30A3

Guincho, Areia, Guincho. **GPS**: n38,72167 w9,46639.
€ 19,50-42,30 ChWC. 01/01-31/12.
Remarks: Service only € 3,15-5,40.

S Castanheira de Pera 30C2

Variante à Nacional 236. **GPS**: n40,00847 w8,20467.
20 free Ch. 01/01-31/12.
Distance: 900m 700m 900m.
Remarks: Service 700m GPS N40,002978 W-8,206685.

S Cerradas 30A3

Estrada Á-dos-Serrados. **GPS**: n38,91798 w9,38292.

20 free Chfree. **Location:** Rural, simple, quiet.
Surface: gravel. 01/01-31/12.
Distance: on the spot 5km on the spot.
Remarks: At gymnasium, max. 48h.

S Constância 30B2

Estrada National. **GPS**: n39,47670 w8,34365.

20 free Chfree. **Location:** Rural, comfortable, quiet.
Surface: metalled. 01/01-31/12.
Distance: 500m 2,3km on the spot on the spot 500m 300m.
Remarks: Along the Zêzere river.

S Corroios 30A3

Avenida Amélia Rey Colaço. **GPS**: n38,63155 w9,1562.
20 free Chfree. **Location:** Urban. **Surface:** metalled.
01/01-31/12.
Distance: on the spot 1km 800m station 1,5km.

S Coruche 30B3

Area autocaravana, Rua 5 de Outubro. **GPS**: n38,96139 w8,51944.

100 free Chfree. **Surface:** metalled. 01/01-31/12 last Sa of the month.
Distance: on the spot on the spot.

S Costa da Caparica 30A3

Caravanismo da Costa da Caparica, Santo António da Caparica.
GPS: n38,65389 w9,23833.
€ 18,89-36 Ch WC. 01/01-31/12.
Distance: 500m on the spot on the spot 100m.
Remarks: Service only € 3,15-5,40.

S Dois Portos 30A3

R. da Azenha. **GPS**: n39,03689 w9,18098.

4 free free. **Location:** Simple, quiet. **Surface:** metalled.
01/01-31/12.
Distance: on the spot.

S Ericeira 30A3

Municipal de Mil Regos, N247, Casal do Moinho Velho.
GPS: n38,97778 w9,41861.
€ 13-17 Ch WC. 01/01-31/12.
Remarks: Service in front of campsite.

Tourist information Ericeira:
Aldeia Museu de José Franco, Sobreiro. Miniature village. 9-19h. free.

S Fátima 30B2

Rua de Sao Vicente de Paulo. **GPS**: n39,63389 w8,67111.

6 free WCfree. **Location:** Urban, simple, quiet.
Surface: asphalted. 01/01-31/12.
Distance: 1km 3,2km 100m 1km.
Remarks: May 12-13 festivities.

S Foz do Arelho 30B2

Av. do Mar. **GPS**: n39,42828 w9,22055.

120 € 3 ChWC € 1 included. **Location:** Rural, simple, quiet. **Surface:** unpaved. 01/01-31/12.
Distance: 1km 50m 50m 1,5km on the spot on the spot.
Remarks: Beach parking.

S Lisbon 30A3

Municipal de Lisboa-Monsanto, Monsanto, Estrada da Circunvalação.
GPS: n38,72472 w9,20805.
€ 24-30 Ch WC.
01/01-31/12.
Distance: 3km on the spot on the spot 50m.

Tourist information Lisbon:
Lisboa Card. Card gives entrance to museums, public transport, available at: Rua Jardim do Regedor 50 (10-18), Mosteiros do Jeronimos, Museu dos Coches. € 18,50/24h, € 31,50/48h, € 39/72h.
Market. Tue, Sa.
32 Covered markets, most important market: Av. 24 de Julho.
6-14h
Su.
Campo de Sta Clara. Flea market.
Rua de São Bento. Antiques market.
Arena near metro Campo Pequeno. 01/05-30/09 Thu.
Feira Popular. Fairground, opposite the Entrecampos metro.
01/05-30/09.
Oceanário, Parque das Nações. Aquarium. 10-19h. € 15,30.
Chiado. Elegant shopping district. elevator 7-24h.

S Mação 30C2

Campo de Feiras, Av. Vicente Mirrado. **GPS**: n39,55723 w7,99303.

10 free Ch WCfree. **Location:** Urban, simple.
Surface: metalled. 01/01-31/12.
Distance: 500m 6km 500m 500m.
Remarks: Max. 48h.

S Mafra 30A3

R. Arieiro. **GPS**: n38,95451 w9,33555.

PT

4 free € 1/80liter Ch. **Location:** Urban, simple, central, quiet. **Surface:** asphalted. 01/01-31/12.
Distance: 1,5km 2km on the spot.
Remarks: Max. 24h.

Tourist information Mafra:
Posto do turismo, Palácio Nacional de Mafra - Torreão Sul, Terreiro D. João V, www.cm-mafra.pt/turismo.
Parque Tapada Nacional, Portão do Codeçal. Safaripark. 10-19h.

Marinha Grande 30B2

Praia Velha, São Pedro de Moel. **GPS:** n39,76974 w9,02752.

10 free. **Location:** Rural, simple, quiet. **Surface:** metalled. 01/01-31/12.
Distance: 5km 100m 100m 50m.
Remarks: Beach parking.

Marinha Grande 30B2

ORBITUR São Pedro de Moel, São Pedro de Moel.
GPS: n39,75806 w9,02583.
Ch. **Location:** Rural. **Surface:** grassy/sand. 01/01-31/12.
Remarks: Service only € 3,15-5,40.

PT

Mira de Aire 30B2

Av. Mota Pinto. **GPS:** n39,54240 w8,70347.

12 free Ch free. **Location:** Simple, quiet.
Surface: asphalted. 01/01-31/12.
Distance: 500m 500m.
Remarks: Steep entrance road, caves 1,8km.

Montalvo 30B2

Horta Do Casinha, Rua Circulação de Montalvinho.
GPS: n39,48550 w8,30765.
6 free Ch . **Location:** Rural, simple, quiet.
Surface: grassy. 16/12-01/01.
Distance: on the spot.
Remarks: Narrow entrance.

Montijo 30B3

GPS: n38,70286 w8,97665.

50 free. **Surface:** metalled.
Distance: 800m 200m 100m 200m 2km.
Remarks: Parking at ferry-boat to Lisbon.

Nazaré 30B2

Rua Nossa Senhora da Vitória. **GPS:** n39,64696 w9,06936.

20 € 10 € 3 Ch. **Location:** Rural, isolated, quiet.
Surface: metalled. 01/01-31/12.
Distance: on the spot on the spot.
Remarks: Max. 24h.

Nazaré 30B2

Avenue do Municipio. **GPS:** n39,59741 w9,0696.

20 free. **Location:** Urban. **Surface:** asphalted. 01/01-31/12.
Distance: 200m 250m 250m 250m 750m.

Obidos 30B2

Casa Azzurra, Rua do's Cumeiras 10. **GPS:** n39,39250 w9,16947.

10 € 8 € 2/100liter Ch € 2/night WC € 1 € 4/4 € 1/day. **Location:** Rural, comfortable, isolated.
Surface: grassy/metalled. 01/01-31/12.
Distance: 4km on the spot 4km 4km on the spot on the spot.
Remarks: Service passerby € 5, barbecue place, swimming pool available.

Obidos 30B2

Rue do Ginasio. **GPS:** n39,35628 w9,15672.

20 € 6/24h Ch included. **Location:** Rural, simple, quiet.
Surface: gravel/sand. 01/01-31/12.
Distance: 500m 1km 500m 500m.
Remarks: Service passerby € 2.

Odrinhas 30A3

Parque Autocaravanas Odrinhas, Rua do Castanhal 9.
GPS: n38,88312 w9,37491.

40 € 8 Ch € 3,50/day WC € 1 € 4,50 included. **Location:** Rural, comfortable, quiet. **Surface:** gravel/sand. 01/01-31/12.
Distance: on the spot on the spot on the spot on the spot.
Remarks: Repair possibilities motorhome, swimming pool available.

Outeiro da Cabeça 30B2

Rua do Pavilhão Gimnodesportivo. **GPS:** n39,19306 w9,1825.

5 free Ch free. **Location:** Rural, simple, isolated.
Surface: gravel. 01/01-31/12.
Distance: 300m 2,5km 300m 300m.

Palmela 30B3

GPS: n38,56664 w8,90032.

6 free. **Location:** Urban, simple, quiet. **Surface:** sand. 01/01-31/12.
Remarks: Parking at castle.

Pataias 30B2

Intermarché. GPS: n39,66041 w9,0151.

10 free Ch free . **Location:** Rural, simple, quiet.
Surface: asphalted. 01/01-31/12.
Distance: 200m on the spot on the spot on the spot.
Remarks: Parking Intermarché, max. 48h.

Peniche 30A2

ASA Peniche - Motorhome Park, Rua da Liberdade 12.
GPS: n39,36622 w9,37917.

60 € 5 Ch (60x)€ 3 WC € 0,50 € 1 4,50/2,50 included. **Location:** Urban, luxurious, central.
Surface: metalled. 01/01-31/12.
Distance: city centre 1km 3,1km 600m 200m 300m 200m 1,2km 1,6km 1,6km.
Remarks: Arrival <19.30h, bread-service, video surveillance, picnic and barbecue place.

Peniche 30A2

Av. Porto De Pesca. **GPS:** n39,35852 w9,37752.
50 free. **Location:** Urban, simple, central. **Surface:** asphalted. 01/01-31/12.
Distance: 500m 900m 1km 500m 500m 500m.
Remarks: At fire-station and marina.

Peniche 30A2

Farol do Cabo Cavoeiro, Caminho do Farol.
GPS: n39,35989 w9,4082.

5 free. **Location:** Rural, simple, isolated. **Surface:** metalled.
01/01-31/12.
Distance: 5km 300m on the spot 3km.
Remarks: At lighthouse.

Peniche 30A2

R. de Liberdade. **GPS**: n39,36577 w9,37417.

10 free. **Location:** Rural, simple. **Surface:** sand.
01/01-31/12.
Distance: 1,7km 50m 200m 200m.

Peniche 30A2

Peniche Praia, Estrada Marginal Norte. **GPS**: n39,36959 w9,392.

23 € 9, Jul/Aug € 15 Ch WC included € 6,20/4,50 . **Location:** Rural, comfortable, quiet. **Surface:** grassy.
01/01-31/12.
Distance: 1,5km At the sea on the spot on the spot 1,5km on the spot 1,5km.

Tourist information Peniche:
Fortaleza de Peniche. Bathing resort.
Posto de Turismo, Rua Alexandre Herculano, www.cm-peniche.pt. Bathing resort.

Póvoa e Meadas 30C2

Barragem de Nisa, M1007. **GPS**: n39,48394 w7,5476.

10 free ChWC free. **Location:** Rural, simple, isolated, quiet. **Surface:** grasstiles/grassy. 01/01-31/12.
Distance: 4km 4km.

Póvoa e Meadas 30C2

Casa Carita, Rua de Santo Antonio. **GPS**: n39,50532 w7,53139.

4 € 5 included. **Location:** Rural, simple, isolated. **Surface:** grassy/sand. 01/01-31/12.

Distance: 500m 500m.

Praia de Santa Cruz 30A2

GPS: n39,14418 w9,37482.

50 free WC free. **Location:** Rural, simple. **Surface:** asphalted.
01/01-31/12.
Distance: 300m 20m on the spot 300m.
Remarks: Parking at the beach or near the cliffs.

Ribamar 30A3

R. do Cacho Longo, São Lourençio. **GPS**: n39,01120 w9,42078.

10 free. **Location:** Rural, simple, isolated. **Surface:** gravel.
01/01-31/12.
Distance: 2km Sandy beach on the spot 6km.

Salir do Porto 30B2

Casa da Duna, Rua Dom Fernando. **GPS**: n39,49939 w9,1517.
50 free Ch € 2 € 2 WC € 5 . **Surface:** grassy.
01/01-31/12.
Distance: 1,5km 200m on the spot on the spot on the spot.

Salvaterra de Magos 30B3

Parque d'Escaroupim, RN 118. **GPS**: n39,02378 w8,79209.
16 free Ch . **Location:** Urban. **Surface:** metalled.
01/01-31/12.
Distance: on the spot 500m 200m.

São Mamede 30B2

Rua de São Martinho. **GPS**: n39,62238 w8,71536.

10 free Ch free. **Location:** Urban, simple, quiet.
Surface: metalled.
Distance: on the spot 200m 200m.

São Martinho do Porto 30B2

Av. Marigal. **GPS**: n39,50176 w9,14132.

15 free. **Location:** Rural, simple, noisy. **Surface:** metalled.
01/01-31/12.
Distance: 1,4km 5,5km sandy beach 50m 50m 850m on the spot.

Setúbal 30B3

Ecoparque Do Outão, N10-4. **GPS**: n38,50328 w8,92858.
60 € 6, 2 pers.incl Ch included WC. **Location:** Rural.
Surface: grassy. 01/01-31/12.
Distance: 4km on the spot 3km.
Remarks: Monitored parking.

Tourist information Setúbal:
Posto Municipal de Turismo, Rua de Santa Maria, Apartado 80, www.mun-setubal.pt. Bathing resort.
Festas Bocageanas. Local celebration. 15/09.

Sintra 30A3

Avenida Conde Sucena, São Pedro de Penaferrim.
GPS: n38,78883 w9,37473.

10 € 7 Ch included. **Location:** Rural, simple, quiet.
Surface: asphalted. 01/01-31/12.
Distance: 2km on the spot.
Remarks: At footballstadium.

Tomar 30B2

Av. Gen. Bernardo Faria. **GPS**: n39,59972 w8,41306.

free WC. **Location:** Simple. **Surface:** gravel/sand.
01/01-31/12.
Distance: 200m 200m 300m.
Remarks: Nearby railway station.

Tourist information Tomar:
Sinagoga de Tomar, Museu Luso-Hebraico, Rua Dr. Joaquim Jacinto, 75. Synagogue and Jewish Portuguese history.
free.
Convento de Cristo. Fortified monastery.
Festa dos Tabuleiros.
Whitsuntide.
Barragem de Castelo de Bode. Artificial lake, 15km east of the city.

Torres Vedras 30A2

Municipal da Praia de Santa Cruz. **GPS**: n39,13444 w9,37472.
Ch WC . 01/01-31/12.

Turcifal 30A3

Largo Brigadeiro França Borges. **GPS**: n39,04288 w9,26581.

5 free Ch free. **Location:** Urban, central, quiet.
Surface: metalled. 01/01-31/12.
Distance: on the spot on the spot on the spot.

Vermoil 30B2

R. Vale de Fojo, Pombal. **GPS**: n39,85080 w8,66125.

5 free Ch free. **Surface:** gravel/sand. 01/01-31/12.
Distance: 200m 300m 300m.
Remarks: At cemetery.

PT

Vila Nova da Barquinha 30B2

Parque De Pernoita, Largo do Primeiro de Dezembro.
GPS: n39,45763 w8,43297.

10 free ChWC free. **Location:** Rural, simple, quiet.
Surface: metalled.
Distance: 100m on the spot on the spot on the spot 150m on the spot on the spot on the spot.
Remarks: Along the Tagus river.

Alentejo

Alcácer do Sal 30B3

Barragem Pego do Altar, Alcácer do Sal > N253 > Montemoro o Novo > N380. **GPS**: n38,42055 w8,39384.

15 free ChWC free. **Location:** Rural. **Surface:** sand.
01/01-31/12.
Distance: Alcácer do Sal 13km on the spot 100m.

Alcácer do Sal 30B3

Rua do Cabo da Vila.
GPS: n38,36903 w8,50276.
free. 01/01-31/12.
Distance: Old city 600m 5,6km 400m.
Remarks: Near arena.

Tourist information Alcácer do Sal:
Little town on the Rio Sado.

Almograve 31B1

Avenida da Praia. **GPS**: n37,65303 w8,80059.

30 free free. **Location:** Simple. **Surface:** grasstiles.
01/01-31/12.
Distance: on the spot.

Alvito 31B1

Rua de Tapadinha. **GPS**: n38,25917 w7,99222.
free.
Remarks: At swimming pool.

Avis 30C3

Municipal Albufeira do Maranhão, Barragam Albufeira do Maranhão.
GPS: n39,05682 w7,91145.
€ 8-12 Ch WC.
Distance: on the spot.
Remarks: Service only € 1,90.

Beja 31B1

Parque da Cidade, Rua de Lisboa. **GPS**: n38,02204 w7,87371.

3 free. **Location:** Urban. **Surface:** gravel/metalled.
01/01-31/12.
Distance: 900m 100m 250m 250m 100m on the spot on the spot.

Tourist information Beja:
Villa Romana de Pisões. Roman ruins.
Festa de S. Lourenço e Sta. Maria. Annual fair. 2nd week Aug.

Campo Maior 30C3

Barragem do Caia. **GPS**: n39,00308 w7,14219.

.

Castelo de Vide 30C2

Estr. de São Vincente. **GPS**: n39,41028 w7,44917.

free. **Location:** Rural, quiet. **Surface:** metalled.
01/01-31/12.
Distance: 1km 300m.
Remarks: At stadium.

Castelo de Vide 30C2

Rua Luís de Camões. **GPS**: n39,41583 w7,45778.

free. **Location:** Urban, simple, central.
Surface: concrete.
01/01-31/12.
Remarks: Near city wall.

Tourist information Castelo de Vide:
www.cm-castelo-vide.pt. Historical centre with medieval citadel.

Cavaleiro 31B1

Cabo Sardano. **GPS**: n37,59810 w8,80608.

30 free. **Location:** Simple. **Surface:** sand. 01/01-31/12.
Distance: on the spot.
Remarks: At lighthouse.

Comporta 30B3

GPS: n38,37849 w8,78544.

40 free Chfree. **Location:** Urban, simple, quiet.
Surface: gravel/sand. 01/01-31/12.
Distance: 250m 1km 250m 250m.

Comporta 30B3

GPS: n38,38308 w8,78712.

±6 free. **Location:** Urban, simple, quiet. **Surface:** gravel/sand.
01/01-31/12.
Distance: 250m 1km 300m 500m.
Remarks: Near church.

Elvas 30C3

Intermarché, Rue Paco Bandera. **GPS**: n38,87458 w7,18429.

15 free Chfree. **Surface:** asphalted. 01/01-31/12.
Distance: historical centre 1,7km on the spot.
Remarks: At petrol station and supermarket, max. 48h.

Elvas 30C3

GPS: n38,87766 w7,17763.

. **Surface:** metalled.
Remarks:
Parking at aqueduct.

Tourist information Elvas:
Fortified city.

Estrela 31C1

Aldeia de Estrela, Cais. **GPS**: n38,26637 w7,38906.
5 free. **Location:** Rural, simple. **Surface:** gravel/sand.
Distance: on the spot.

Estremoz 30C3

Rossio Marquês de Pombal. **GPS**: n38,84320 w7,58672.

PT

10 free. **Location:** Urban, simple, central. **Surface:** metalled.
01/01-31/12.
Distance: on the spot 50m 50m.

Tourist information Estremoz:
Market. Sa.

Evora 30C3

GPS: n38,57529 w7,90519.

free. **Location:** Urban, simple, noisy. **Surface:** gravel/metalled.
01/01-31/12.
Distance: 1km 500m 500m.
Remarks: Parking university, illuminated.

Evora 30C3

Avenida Condas De Vilalva. **GPS:** n38,57592 w7,91491.

Location: Urban, noisy. **Surface:** metalled.
01/01-31/12.
Distance: 1km.

Evora 30C3

Lago da Porta de Avis. **GPS:** n38,57672 w7,91096.

free.
Location: Urban, simple, noisy.
Surface: gravel/metalled.
01/01-31/12.
Distance: 1,5km.
Remarks: Parking at aqueduct.

Tourist information Evora:
Posto de Turismo, Praça do Geraldo, www.cm-evora.pt.
City with historical centre.
Igreja de S. Francisco, Capela dos Ossos. Chapel of the bones.
8-18h
12-14h.
Tue.

Ferreira do Alentejo 31B1

GPS: n38,05675 w8,11955.

free. **Surface:** asphalted.
Distance: 500m 100m 1km 1,5km.
Remarks: Parking sports park.

Grândola 31B1

Parque de Grândola. **GPS:** n38,18525 w8,564.

7 free Ch. **Location:** Simple.
Surface: asphalted. 01/01-31/12.
Distance: 1km 7,4km 600m 500m 1,4km.
Remarks: At sports grounds.

Lousal 31B1

Rua 25 Abril. **GPS:** n38,03591 w8,42908.

6 free Chfree. **Surface:** gravel. 01/01-31/12.
Distance: 15km 250m 400m bakery on the spot.
Remarks: At the site of the old mines of Lousal.

Luz 31C1

R. de Mourão. **GPS:** n38,34278 w7,37389.

free Chfree. **Surface:** metalled.

Marvão 30C2

N359-6. **GPS:** n39,39434 w7,3736.

12 free Chfree. **Location:** Rural, simple, quiet.
Surface: grassy/gravel. 01/01-31/12.
Distance: on the spot 500m.

Melides 31B1

Praia de Melides. GPS: n38,12897 w8,79262.

Surface: metalled. 01/01-31/12.
Distance: Melides 6,2km Sandy beach on the spot.

Mértola 31C1

N122/IC27. **GPS:** n37,64250 w7,65833.

10 free. 01/01-31/12.
Distance: 200m 200m.

Mértola 31C1

Rua dos Bombeiros Voluntários.
GPS: n37,64114 w7,66326.
10 free.
Surface: gravel/sand.
Remarks: At fire-station.

Tourist information Mértola:
Convento São Francisco. Former convent, exposition room and atelier. 10-17h.

Messejana 31B1

GPS: n37,83167 w8,24694.

50 €7 €2 Ch WC. **Location:** Rural. **Surface:** metalled.
01/01-31/12.
Distance: on the spot 10km 400m.
Remarks: Barbecue place, swimming pool.

Mina de São Domingos 31C1

Rua Catarina Eufémia. **GPS:** n37,67052 w7,50194.
free €2 Ch.

Mina de São Domingos 31C1

Praia Fluvial, R265. **GPS:** n37,67228 w7,50418.

20 free. **Location:** Simple. **Surface:** metalled/sand.
Distance: 750m 50m.
Remarks: At recreation area, marked pitches.

Monsaraz 30C3

GPS: n38,44250 w7,38003.

PT

±15 free. **Location:** Quiet. **Surface:** metalled. 01/01-31/12.
Distance: 100m 100m.
Remarks: Near city wall, beautiful view.

S Monsaraz 30C3

Rue da Fonte.
GPS: n38,45317 w7,38117.
€ 3,50 Ch.
Mo-Fr 8-21h, Sa-Su 8-12h.
Remarks: Call for the key.

Tourist information Monsaraz:
www.monsaraz.com.pt/. Small medieval town.

S Montargil 30B3

Ponte de Sôr. **GPS**: n39,09972 w8,145.
70 € 30-37 Ch. WC . 01/01-31/12.
Remarks: Service only € 3-5.

S Montemor-o-Novo 30B3

A6-IP7. **GPS**: n38,61856 w8,07924.

2 free. **Location:** Motorway, simple, quiet.
Surface: asphalted/metalled. 01/01-31/12.
Remarks: Note: toll ticket is valid for 12 hours!.

Odeceixe 31B1

GPS: n37,43750 w8,79833.

30 free. **Location:** Simple. **Surface:** sand. 01/01-31/12.
Distance: 6km on the spot.
Remarks: Beach parking.

S Pedrogão do Alentejo 31C1

Alqueva Camping-Car Park, Estrada nacional 258, Km38,5.
GPS: n38,11705 w7,63571.

25 first night € 7,50, € 6 each additional night Ch.
Location: Rural. **Surface:** gravel. 01/01-31/12.
Distance: 1km 1km 1km 1km on the spot on the spot on the spot.

Ponte de Sôr 30C2

Avenida da Liberdade. **GPS**: n39,24996 w8,00824.

10 free. **Location:** Rural, simple, central, noisy.
Surface: concrete. 01/01-31/12.
Distance: on the spot 100m 100m.

Porto Covo 31B1

Rua Francisco Albino. **GPS**: n37,85225 w8,78874.
30 free. **Surface:** metalled. 01/01-31/12.
Distance: centre 250m 750m.

Porto Covo 31B1

Forte do Pessegueiro, Praia da Ilha. **GPS**: n37,49389 w8,47268.

10 . **Location:** Simple. **Surface:** sand. 01/01-31/12.
Distance: 4km on the spot.
Remarks: Parking at castle.

Porto Covo 31B1

Praia Grande, Rua do Mar. **GPS**: n37,85054 w8,79299.

15 . **Location:** Simple. **Surface:** gravel.
Distance: 1km 100m 100m 1km.
Remarks: Beach parking.

S Redondo 30C3

Zona Industrial. **GPS**: n38,64521 w7,54266.

50 free Chfree. **Location:** Urban, simple.
Surface: gravel/sand. 01/01-31/12.
Distance: 400m 400m 100m.

Reguengos de Monsaraz 30C3

N255. **GPS**: n38,43077 w7,53315.

free. **Surface:** asphalted.
Remarks: Parking at swimming pool.

S Reguengos de Monsaraz 30C3

Campo 25 de Abril. **GPS**: n38,42150 w7,53534.

€ 3,50 Ch.
Remarks: Next to fire-station.

Santa Clara-e-Velha 31B1

Barragem de Santa Clara. GPS: n37,51303 w8,44024.

free. **Location:** Isolated. **Surface:** metalled/sand.
Distance: on the spot.
Remarks: Follow 'Pousada/Zona recreitiva balnear'.

S Santiago do Cacém 31B1

Rua das Nogueiras. **GPS**: n38,01276 w8,69453.

7 free Chfree. **Surface:** grasstiles.
Distance: 600m 100m 600m.
Remarks: At swimming pool.

S Santo António das Areias 30C2

Camping Asseiceira, Asseiceira. **GPS**: n39,41012 w7,34062.
10 € 16-20 Ch. WC . **Surface:** grassy.
01/01-31/10.

São Martinho das Amoreiras 31B1

N503. **GPS**: n37,56250 w8,34139.

free. **Surface:** metalled.
Remarks: At barrage.

S Terrugem 30C3

Largo Joaquim Codero Vinaigre. **GPS**: n38,84556 w7,34861.

10 free Chfree. **Location:** Rural, simple, quiet.
Surface: asphalted.
Distance: 300m.

S Vila Nova de Santo André 31B1

Intermarché. GPS: n38,06521 w8,77951.
5 free Chfree € 4/2. **Surface:** metalled.
01/01-23/12.
Distance: on the spot.
Remarks: At petrol station.

S Vila Nova de Santo André 31B1

Praia de Santo André, Lagoa de Santo Andre.
GPS: n38,11396 w8,79552.

PT

±15 free. Location: Simple.
Surface: sand. 01/01-23/12.
Distance: 5km on the spot on the spot bakery 1km.
Remarks: Beach parking.

S Vila Viçosa 30C3

Avenida do Alandroal. **GPS**: n38,76988 w7,4154.

10 € 3 € 2 Ch. **Location:** Rural, simple, quiet.
Surface: asphalted. 01/01-31/12.
Distance: 1km 100m.
Remarks: At fire-station, monitored parking.

Vila Viçosa 30C3

Largo Gago Coutinho. **GPS**: n38,77661 w7,42034.

10 free. **Location:** Urban, simple, central. **Surface:** sand.
01/01-31/12.
Distance: 250m 25m 100m.

Algarve

S Albufeira 31B2

Parque da Galé, Rua do Barranco Vale Rabelho.
GPS: n37,09347 w8,31125.

28 € 8 Ch (28x) included. **Location:** Comfortable.
Surface: unpaved. 01/01-31/12.
Distance: 600m 1,8km 200m 500m.

S Albufeira 31B2

Parque da Palmeira, Rua da Palmeira. **GPS**: n37,09829 w8,24339.

90 € 8 Ch WC € 4,50 included. **Location:** Urban.
Surface: gravel. 01/01-31/12.
Distance: Old city 1,7km 7km 1,5km 800m Lidl bus terminal 300m.

S Albufeira 31B2

Park Falesia, Estrada do Alfarmar. **GPS**: n37,09036 w8,16044.

30 € 12 Ch € 0,50 included.
Surface: gravel. 01/01-31/12.
Distance: 4km 500m 1km 500m 200m.
Remarks: Video surveillance.

Tourist information Albufeira:
Posto de Turismo, R. 5 de Outubro 4, www.cm-albufeira.pt. 10-20h. ZooMarine, N125. Attractions park, dolphinarium, aquarium. 10-20h.

S Alcoutim 31C2

Estrada da Pousada da Juventude. **GPS**: n37,47500 w7,47472.
free Chfree. **Surface:** sand.
01/01-31/12.
Distance: 500m 200m.
Remarks: Next to 'Centro de Saude'.

Tourist information Alcoutim:
Fortified city. 9-17.30h.

S Aljezur 31A1

Largo do Mercado. **GPS**: n37,31611 w8,80278.

10 free WCfree. **Location:** Simple.
Surface: metalled. 01/01-31/12.
Distance: 200m 500m.

Altura 31C2

Av. 24 de Junho. **GPS**: n37,17456 w7,49373.
20 free. **Location:** Urban. **Surface:** grassy/sand.
01/01-31/12.
Distance: 600m 1,5km 1km 1km.

S Alvor 31B2

Zona para autocaravanas, Praia de Alvor.
GPS: n37,12482 w8,59506.

150 € 4,50, June-Sep € 7 Chincluded. **Location:** Central.
Surface: sand. 01/01-31/12.
Distance: centre 400m 100m on the spot.

S Ameixial 31B2

Estacionamento de Autocaravannas. **GPS**: n37,36539 w7,97165.
10 free Chfree. **Location:** Rural, isolated, quiet.
Surface: unpaved. 01/01-31/12.

S Budens 31A2

Figueira Caravan Park, R. da Fonte. **GPS**: n37,07300 w8,84519.
35 € 7,50-10 Ch ,10Amp included. **Location:** Rural, comfortable. **Surface:** gravel.
01/01-23/12.
Distance: Budens 2,5km 1,8km 250m Intermarché Budens.
Remarks: Discount longer stays.

Budens 31A2

Praia Boca do Rio. **GPS**: n37,06563 w8,82434.

20 free. **Location:** Simple. **Surface:** sand. 01/01-31/12.
Distance: 2,2km 50m.
Remarks: Forbidden during Summer period.

Cabo de São Vicente 31A2

N268. **GPS**: n37,02361 w8,995.

8 free. **Surface:** metalled. 01/01-31/12.
Distance: Sagres 6km.
Remarks: Parking at lighthouse.

S Caldas de Monchique 31B2

Parque Rural Autocaravanas Vale da Carrasqueira, Barracão 190.
GPS: n37,27667 w8,54333.

14 € 12,50/24h Ch WC included .
Location: Rural, comfortable. **Surface:** gravel.
Distance: on the spot.

Carrapateira 31A2

Praia de Amado. **GPS**: n37,19623 w8,90156.

30 free. **Location:** Simple. **Surface:** gravel.
Distance: Carrapateira 2km 100m on the spot.
Remarks: Beach parking, no camping activities.

Carrapateira 31A2

Praia de Bordeira. **GPS**: n37,19735 w8,90726.

10 free. **Location:** Simple. **Surface:** metalled.
Distance: Carrapateira 2,5km.
Remarks: Parking near the cliffs.

Carvoeiro 31B2

Estr. do Farol. **GPS**: n37,08774 w8,44285.

PT

8. **Location:** Isolated. **Surface:** sand.
Distance: 500m on the spot.
Remarks: Parking at lighthouse.

Carvoeiro 31B2

Praia Marinha. **GPS**: n37,09026 w8,41254.

free. **Location:** Isolated. **Surface:** unpaved.
04/01-31/12.
Distance: 4km on the spot.
Remarks: Beach parking, beautiful view.

Castro Marim 31C2

Av. Dr. José Afonso Gomes. **GPS**: n37,21984 w7,44434.

± 20 free € 2 Ch. **Surface:** gravel. 01/01-31/12 2nd Sa of the month.
Distance: 1,3km 50m.
Remarks: Coins at the shops in the village.

Falésia 31B2

Algarve Motorhome Park, Praia da Falésia.
GPS: n37,09015 w8,16015.
55 € 8/24h Ch € 2 included. **Location:** Luxurious.
Surface: gravel. 01/01-31/12.
Distance: 850m on the spot 250m.

Faro 31B2

Avenida Calouste Gulbenkian. **GPS**: n37,02599 w7,94692.
8 free. **Location:** Isolated. **Surface:** metalled.
01/01-31/12.
Distance: city centre 1,5km 600m 600m.
Remarks: Along railwayline.

Faro 31B2

Doca de Faro. **GPS**: n37,02551 w7,94657.

15 free. **Location:** Urban, simple. **Surface:** metalled.
01/01-31/12.
Distance: 600m.

Faro 31B2

Parking Largo de São Francisco. **GPS**: n37,01132 w7,93184.

±6 free. **Surface:** metalled.
Distance: centre 400m 300m.

Fuseta 31B2

Casa Da Avo Nina, Rua da Ponte Grande. **GPS**: n37,05544 w7,74975.
6 € 10 Ch included. **Location:** Urban. **Surface:** grassy.
01/01-31/12.
Distance: on the spot 300m 650m station 300m.

Lagos 31B2

Area de servico, Junto ao Estadio Municipal de Lagos.
GPS: n37,11563 w8,678.

20 € 3, from 4th night € 2,50 € 2/100 Ch WC free.
Surface: gravel. 01/01-31/12.
Distance: city centre 2km 7,3km 2,3km McDonalds 450m.
Remarks: Check in and pay at reception stadio, market 1st Saturday each month.

Tourist information Lagos:
M Museu Municipal, Rua General Alberto da Silveira. Regional museum. 9.30-12.30h, 14-17h holiday.

Manta Rota 31C2

Praia de Manta Rota, Quinta Manta Rota 15.
GPS: n37,16513 w7,52096.

80 € 4,50 Ch € 2,50/12h included.
Surface: metalled. 16/09-30/06.
Distance: on the spot 6,5km 100m 100m 500m.

Moncarapacho 31B2

Route 66. **GPS**: n37,08313 w7,76494.
40 € 8 Ch WC € 3 included. **Location:** Rural, comfortable, isolated. **Surface:** gravel/sand.
01/01-31/12.
Distance: 2,5km 3km on the spot.

Moncarapacho 31B2

Área de Repouso Furnalha, EM 516. **GPS**: n37,08065 w7,8085.
12 € 8 Ch WC . **Location:** Rural. 01/01-31/12.
Distance: 2km 1,5km.

Moncarapacho 31B2

Caravanas Algarve. **GPS**: n37,09502 w7,77427.

20 € 8,50 Ch WC .
Surface: gravel.
01/01-31/12.

Distance: 1km beach 6km 1km on the spot on the spot.

Odeleite 31C2

Almada D´Ouro Club-Algarve, M1063, Alcarias-Odeleite.
GPS: n37,33187 w7,46865.

10 + 20 € 4,50 € 2,50 Ch € 2,50 € 5 included.
Location: Isolated, quiet. **Surface:** gravel. 01/01-31/12.
Distance: Odeleite 2,3km on the spot.
Remarks: At hunting club, discount longer stays.

Paderne 31B2

Motorhome Friends, Centieira. **GPS**: n37,15643 w8,20972.

21 € 5 Ch (9x)€ 3,50 WC € 5 included.
Location: Rural. **Surface:** grassy/gravel. 16/09-31/05.
Distance: 1km 10km on the spot.
Remarks: Max. 48h, bicycle rental € 5, car rental € 15.

Paderne 31B2

Cm 1177 920N. **GPS**: n37,16801 w8,20897.

12 free Ch free. **Surface:** metalled. 01/01-31/12.
Distance: 1km 1km.

Pêra 31B2

Mikki's Place, Sitio das Arreias. **GPS**: n37,12781 w8,32305.

100 € 8-10,50 Ch € 2,50/day WC on demand included. **Location:** Rural, comfortable, isolated, quiet.
Surface: gravel/metalled. 01/01-31/12.
Distance: 2km 3km on the spot 2km.

Pêra 31B2

KM 64 Parque de Autocaravanas, ES125, km64.
GPS: n37,12420 w8,32607.
50 € 3 € 2 Ch included € 3.
Surface: asphalted. 01/06-01/10.
Distance: 1,5km 4km.

Pereiro 31C2

Parque de autocaravanismo do Pereiro, Pereiro.
GPS: n37,44695 w7,5924.
16 free Ch free WC. **Surface:** unpaved.
01/01-31/12.
Distance: 500m on the spot.
Remarks: Baker every morning.

Quarteira 31B2

Estrada Fonte Santa, M527-2. **GPS**: n37,07322 w8,07716.

PT

100 € 2/24h € 2 Ch € 2.
Surface: gravel.
01/01-31/12.
Distance: 2km 6,8km sandy beach 2,5km 50m 150m Lidl on the spot.
Remarks: Tue 17h-Wed 17h adjacent parking because of Gypsy Market.

S Sagres 31A2

Fortaleze de Sagres. GPS: n37,00523 w8,94545.

50 free WC. **Surface:** asphalted. 01/01-31/12.
Distance: 500m.
Remarks: At fort-castle.

S São Bartolomeu de Messines 31B2

Camperstop Messines. GPS: n37,27979 w8,24133.

40 € 6, 01/07-31/08 € 7,50 Ch WC € 4/4 included.
Location: Rural, quiet. **Surface:** gravel. 01/01-31/12.
Distance: 6,5km 6,4km 1,2km.
Remarks: Shopping service.

S São Bartolomeu de Messines 31B2

Rua António Aleixo. **GPS:** n37,25514 w8,2847.

4 free Ch free. **Location:** Rural. **Surface:** gravel.
01/01-31/12.
Distance: centre 150m 2,7km.
Remarks: Monday regional market.

S Silves 31B2

Algarve Motorhome Park Silves, N124. **GPS:** n37,18722 w8,45158.

50 € 5/24h Ch € 2 included. 01/01-31/12.
Distance: 1km 800m.

S Silves 31B2

Club Autocaravana Vacaria, N124. **GPS:** n37,21834 w8,36924.

15 € 5 Ch € 1/24h WC € 1 included.
Location: Rural, comfortable, isolated. **Surface:** gravel/metalled.
01/01-31/12.
Distance: 9km 100m.

S Silves 31B2

Parque do Castelo, Rua do Encalhe. **GPS:** n37,19388 w8,43614.
40 first night € 5, € 4,50 each additional night, >10m + € 1 Ch € 2,50/24h,6Amp WC € 0,50 included. **Surface:** gravel.
01/09-31/05.
Distance: centre 500m 500m Lidl 550m on the spot.

S Silves 31B2

Estação de serviço para autocaravanas municipal.
GPS: n37,18527 w8,44551.
€ 3 Ch free. **Surface:** gravel. 01/01-31/12.
Distance: centre 650m 650m 450m.

Silves 31B2

Barregem do Arade, N124-3. **GPS:** n37,23960 w8,37699.

10 free. **Location:** Isolated.
Surface: sand.
Distance: Silves 10km.

Tourist information Silves:
Museu Municipal de Arqueologia. Archeological findings.
Castello. 9-18h.
Festival da cerveja. Beer festival. July.

S Tavira 31B2

Parque de Autocaravanes. GPS: n37,13637 w7,64013.

20 € 9,90 Ch WC € 2 included.
Surface: grassy/gravel. 15/09-15/06 summer.
Distance: 1km.
Remarks: Swimming pool.

Tourist information Tavira:
Castello. Mo-Fri 8-17.30h.

Vila do Bispo 31A2

Praia da Barriga, N1265. **GPS:** n37,09970 w8,94445.

free. **Surface:** asphalted.
Distance: Vila do Bispo 3,8km on the spot.
Remarks: Beach parking.

S Vila do Bispo 31A2

Sagres, Cerro da Moita. **GPS:** n37,02278 w8,94583.
550 € 30-38 Ch WC . 01/01-31/12.
Distance: 2km on the spot on the spot 500m.

S Vila Real de Santo António 31C2

Avenida de República. **GPS:** n37,19955 w7,4153.

70 € 4,50 Ch € 5/24h included.
Surface: metalled/sand. 01/01-31/12.
Distance: 500m on the spot.

PT

Romania

Capital: Bucharest
Government: semi presidential republic
Official Language: Romanian
Population: 21,599,736 (2016)
Area: 238,391 km^2

General information
Dialling code: 0040
General emergency: 112
Currency: Leu (RON)
€ 1 = 4,59 RON, 1 RON = € 0,21
£1 = 5,22 RON, 1 RON = £0.19 (October 2017)
Credit card are mostly accepted in the main cities.

Regulations for overnight stays
Wild camping is allowed with permission from land owner/manager or local government.

Additional public holidays 2018
April 8-9 Orhodox Easter
May 1 Labour Day
August 15 Assumption of Mary
November 1 All Saints' Day
November 30 Saint Andrew's Day
December 1 National Holiday

Time Zone
Winter (Standard Time) GMT+2
Summer (DST) GMT+3

Transylvania pages: 702-703
Moldavia page: 703
Banat page: 703
Wallachia page: 703
Dobruja page: 703
Bucharest

RO

Transylvania

Aurel Vlaicu 39B2

Camping Aurel Vlaicu, Str. Pricipala 155. **GPS**: n45,91424 e23,27938.

€ 12,50 Ch € 2,50 WC included.
Location: Rural. **Surface:** grassy. 15/04-30/09.
Distance: 250m 250m 100m 300m 250m.

Baile Felix 39B1

Camping Apollo. GPS: n46,99608 e21,98056.
€ 14 Ch WC included. 01/01-31/12.
Distance: 100m 400m 100m.

Blăjel 39C2

Camping Doua Lumi, Strada Tudor Vladimirescu 87-89.
GPS: n46,21032 e24,32478.

15 € 13 Ch € 3 WC included.
Surface: grassy. 01/04-15/10.
Distance: 10km.

Borșa 39B1

Camping Borșa Turism, Strada Pietroasa 9. **GPS**: n47,64769 e24,66889.
4 € 3,50 + € 3,50/pp Ch WC € 3,50 included.
Location: Urban. **Surface:** gravel. 01/01-31/12.
Distance: 1km 1,5km 900m on the spot.

Bran 39C2

Vampire camping, Soholstr. **GPS**: n45,52787 e25,37183.

€ 15 Ch € 3,50 WC included.
Location: Rural. **Surface:** grassy. 01/04-01/11.
Distance: 650m.

Cârța 39C2

Camping de Oude Wilg, Str. Prundului 311. **GPS**: n45,78332 e24,56700.

€ 11 € 2,50 Ch € 2,50 WC included € 3,50/3,50.
Location: Rural. **Surface:** grassy.
Distance: 500m 500m on the spot on the spot.

Gârbova 39B2

Poarta Oilor, Str. Eminescu 573. **GPS**: n45,85933 e23,72019.
€ 17 Ch WC included. **Location:** Rural.
Surface: grassy. 01/05-30/09.

Gilău 39B1

Camping Eldorado. GPS: n46,76748 e23,35381.

€ 13 Ch € 2,50 WC included.
Surface: grassy. 15/04-15/10.
Distance: 15km 50m 750m.

Miniș 39B2

Camping Route Roemenië, Minis 298. **GPS**: n46,13356 e21,59788.

from € 12,50 € 1,50 € 2,50 Ch € 2,75 WC included € 4.
Location: Rural. **Surface:** grassy. 15/04-15/09.
Distance: 1km.

Mureș 39C1

Camping Mustang, Câmpu Cetății 16/A. **GPS**: n46,66750 e25,00361.
€ 11,50 Ch WC € 2,50 included. **Location:** Rural.
Surface: grassy. 01/04-31/10.
Distance: 3km 500m 400m.

Nireş 39B1

Camping Zwaluwnest, Com. Mica 42A. **GPS**: n47,11918 e23,96788.

€ 11 Ch € 2,50 WC included € 4/4.
Location: Rural. **Surface:** grassy. 01/04-15/10.

Ocna Sibiului 39B2

Strada Mihai Viteazul 90. **GPS**: n45,88040 e24,04437.
20 € 5 € 1 € 2. **Surface:** grassy. 01/04-01/10.
Distance: 800m.

Remetea 39B2

Camping Turul, Bihor 8. **GPS**: n46,73443 e22,34436.

€ 11,50 Ch € 2,50 WC included.
Location: Rural. **Surface:** grassy.
Distance: 100m 700m 900m.

Richis 39C2

Camping La Curtea Richvini. **GPS**: n46,09797 e24,48066.
€ 10 Ch € 3 WC included € 4. **Location:** Rural.
Surface: grassy.

Vişeu de Sus 39B1

Gara CFF Mocanita, Strada Cerbului 5. **GPS**: n47,71461 e24,44282.

€ 9 Ch WC according consumption included.
Surface: metalled. 01/01-31/12.
Distance: 1,5km.

Zărneşti 39C2

Alpin Ranch, Strada Pinului 13. **GPS**: n45,57861 e25,34389.

€ 12 Ch WC included. **Location:** Rural.
Surface: grassy.
Distance: 800m.

Moldavia

Dărmăneşti 39C1

Camperland, Calea Trotusului 272. **GPS**: n46,40150 e26,48267.

€ 15 Ch WC € 3,25 included.
Surface: grassy. 15/04-15/10.
Distance: 400m.

Fundu Moldovei 39C1

Camping de Vuurplaats, Strada Principale 130.
GPS: n47,53417 e25,41528.

24 € 14,75 Ch € 2,75 WC € 4 included.
Location: Rural. **Surface:** grassy. 01/04-01/10.
Distance: on the spot on the spot.
Remarks: Barbecue place.

Dobruja

Jupiter 39D2

Camping Popas Zodiac, Gala Galaction str 49.
GPS: n43,85860 e28,59960.
€ 16,50 - € 19,25 Ch included . **Surface:** grassy.
01/05-31/10.
Distance: 200m 200m 100m.

Murighiol 39D2

La doi Sturioni, Str. Portului 2. **GPS**: n45,03632 e29,16677.

10 € 12 Ch included. **Location:** Simple.
Surface: unpaved. 01/05-01/10.
Distance: 200m 200m.

Murighiol 39D2

Pension Laguna Albastra. **GPS**: n45,03824 e29,18161.
25 € 12 Ch included. **Location:** Simple. **Surface:** grassy.
01/04-15/10.
Distance: on the spot on the spot on the spot.

Navodari 39D2

GPM Camping Holiday. **GPS**: n44,27467 e28,61774.

30 € 16 Ch included . 25/04-30/09.
Distance: on the spot on the spot on the spot.

Banat

Mehadia 39B2

Camping Hercules, DN6. **GPS**: n44,86918 e22,38774.
5 € 15 Ch WC .
Distance: on the spot 500m on the spot on the spot.

Wallachia

Bucharest 39C2

Casa Albă, Padurea Baneasa, pe Aleea Privighetorilor 31 - 35.
GPS: n44,51734 e26,09249.

20 Ch WC . **Location:** Isolated, quiet.
Surface: asphalted. 01/01-31/12.
Distance: 10km 5km 800m on the spot.

Paclele Mici 39C2

Popasul La Hangar, 108. **GPS**: n45,34711 e26,70928.
5 € 7 Ch included. **Location:** Simple.
Surface: gravel/sand. 01/01-31/12.
Distance: on the spot.

RO

Sweden

Capital: Stockholm
Government: parliamentary constitutional monarchy
Official Language: Swedish
Population: 9,880,604 (2016)
Area: 450,295 km²

General information
Dialling code: 0046
General emergency: 112
Currency: Swedish Krona (SEK)
€ 1 = SEK 9,74, SEK 1 = € 0,10
£1 = SEK 11,07, SEK 1 = £0.09 (October 2017)
Credit cards are accepted almost everywhere.

Regulations for overnight stays
In general wild camping is allowed, not in private gardens and agricultural land.

Camping Key Europe is obligatory when using campsites: the card can be purchased at any campsite for SEK 160 (± € 16,50/ £15), valid for one year.

Additional public holidays 2018
March 30 Good Friday
April 2 Easter Monday
May 1 Labour Day
June 6 National day
June 22-23 Midsummer
December 13 Saint Lucy's Day

Time Zone
Winter (Standard Time) GMT+1
Summer (DST) GMT+2

SE

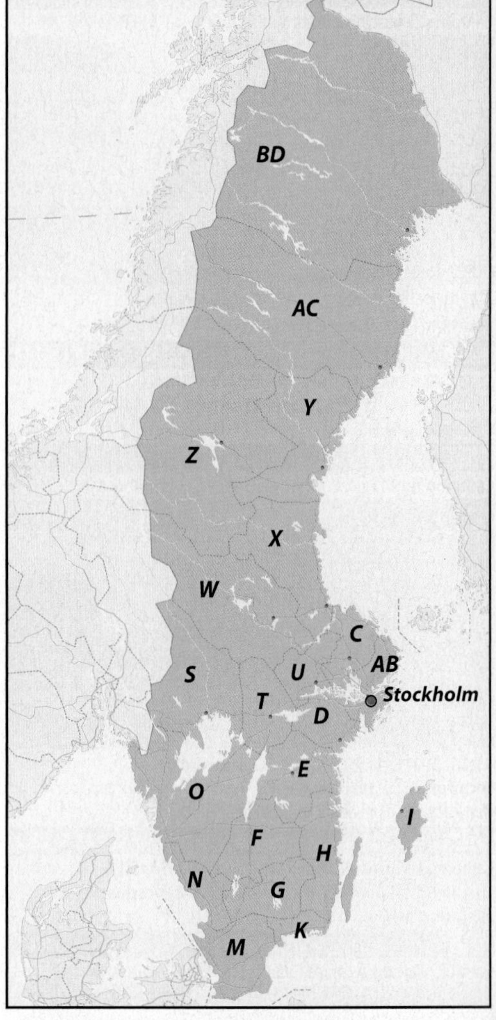

Stockholm

S Norrtälje 4D3
Nässelgrundet 7. **GPS**: n59,68147 e18,81752.
3 SEK 200. **Surface:** grassy.
Distance: Norrtälje 19km on the spot on the spot.
Remarks: Canoe and boat rental.

S Skarpnäck 5G1
Ställplatsstockholm, Flatens Skogsväg 30.
GPS: n59,24822 e18,16159.
48 SEK 180 Ch.
Distance: Stockholm 15km.

S Stockholm 5G1
Långholmens Husbilscamping Stockholm, Skutskepparvägen 1.
GPS: n59,32021 e18,03200.
76 SEK 250, 19/06-30/08 SEK 280 Ch included WC SEK 5.
Location: Urban. **Surface:** metalled. 13/05-13/09.
Distance: 4km 200m 500m.

S Stockholm 5G1
Tantolundens Husbilscamping Stockholm, Ringvägen 24.
GPS: n59,31241 e18,05299.
14 SEK 250, 19/06-30/08 SEK 280 WC included.
Location: Urban. **Surface:** gravel. 01/01-31/12.
Distance: 5km 2km 350m.

Stockholm 5G1
Strandvägen. **GPS**: n59,33124 e18,08595.
SEK 15/h, overnight stay free. **Surface:** asphalted.
Distance: 1km on the spot 300m.
Remarks: At the quay.

Västerbotten

Byske 4D1
E45. **GPS**: n64,94809 e21,18009.
free. **Location:** Rural, simple, isolated, noisy.
Distance: 1,7km 1,5km 1,7km.

Klimpfjäll 4C1
Stekenjokk. **GPS**: n65,09030 e14,45897.
free. **Location:** Isolated, quiet.
Surface: unpaved. With snow.
Distance: on the spot on the spot on the spot.

Marsfjäll 4C1
Trappstegsforsen. **GPS**: n64,95526 e15,46639.
free. **Location:** Isolated, quiet. **Surface:** gravel.
Distance: 7km on the spot.

S Sävar 4D1
Sävar Rastplats, Skomakarvägen. **GPS**: n63,89191 e20,53027.

free Ch free. **Surface:** asphalted.
Distance: 2km 100m 1,7km.

S Skellefteå 4D1
Ställplats Campus, Laboratorgränd. **GPS**: n64,74601 e20,95595.
10 SEK 100 WC included.
Location: Urban. **Surface:** metalled.
20/06-14/08.
Distance: 1km on the spot on the spot 100m on the spot.

S Tärnaby 4C1
Joeström. **GPS**: n65,74384 e15,08882.
voluntary contribution. **Location:** Rural. **Surface:** grassy.
Distance: 10km on the spot on the spot.

S Vilhelmina 4C1
Meselefors Rastplats, E45. **GPS**: n64,43398 e16,78733.
2 free Ch free.
Distance: on the spot on the spot.
Remarks: Max. 12h.

Vormsele 4C1
Blåviksjöns, Blå vägen. **GPS**: n64,82994 e18,03335.
free. **Location:** Isolated, quiet. **Surface:** asphalted.
Distance: Vormsele 47km on the spot on the spot.

Norrbotten

S Gällivare 3B3
Lappeasuando. **GPS**: n67,49093 e21,12025.

free Ch WC free.
Location: Isolated, quiet. **Surface:** asphalted.
Distance: Gällivare 56km 200m 200m.

S Jävrebyn 4D1
Jävrefyrens väg. **GPS**: n65,14339 e21,50862.

SEK 50 Ch. **Location:** Rural. **Surface:** grassy/gravel.
Distance: on the spot on the spot 500m.

S Jokkmokk 3B3
Polcirkeln. **GPS**: n66,55058 e19,76375.

SEK 100 Ch SEK 40 WC included.
Location: Rural. **Surface:** asphalted/grassy.
Distance: 2km on the spot.

Jokkmokk 3B3

Laponia Rastplats, E45. **GPS**: n66,64258 e19,82465.

free. **Surface:** grassy/gravel.
Distance: 5km 100m.

Moskosel 3B3

E45. **GPS**: n65,95231 e19,51979.

free Ch free.
Distance: 10km on the spot on the spot.
Remarks: Along river.

Nikkala 3C3

Båtklubben Bothnia, Haparandahamn 65.
GPS: n65,77154 e23,90442.
SEK 100 SEK 40. **Surface:** asphalted/grassy.
Distance: on the spot on the spot.
Remarks: Borrow cycles for free, use of sauna against payment.

Övre Soppero 3B2

Ryssäjoki Naturrastplats. GPS: n68,15435 e21,78256.

. **Location:** Rural, isolated. **Surface:** unpaved.
Distance: 8km on the spot on the spot.

Porjus 3B3

Strömgatan. **GPS**: n66,95671 e19,80798.
free. **Surface:** asphalted.
Distance: 500m.
Remarks: In front of fire-station.

Vittangi 3B2

Rastplats Suptallen. GPS: n67,66938 e21,40521.
free.
Distance: 15km.

Uppsala

Älvkarleby 4D3

Älvkarleby Turist & Konferenshotell, Västanåvägen 54.
GPS: n60,56518 e17,43796.
20 SEK 100 WC.
Distance: 100m on the spot.
Remarks: Pay at reception.

Öregrund 4D3

Kyrkogatan. **GPS**: n60,33958 e18,43672.
5 SEK 120. **Surface:** asphalted. 01/01-31/12.
Distance: 200m on the spot on the spot 350m 200m.

Öregrund 4D3

GPS: n60,34091 e18,44107.
3 free free WC. **Surface:** asphalted.
Distance: on the spot on the spot on the spot 100m 200m.

Uppsala 4D3

Stallängsgatan. **GPS**: n59,84446 e17,65698.
10 SEK 180 (10x) WC included.
Surface: gravel. 01/01-31/12.
Distance: 2km 600m.

Södermanland

Eskilstuna 5F1

Sundbyholms Gästhamn, Sundbyholm. **GPS**: n59,44749 e16,62593.
6 SEK 150 SEK 40.
Distance: on the spot on the spot on the spot on the spot.
Remarks: Next to castle.

Mariefred 5F1

Mariefreds gästhamnen, Gripsholmsvägen.
GPS: n59,25793 e17,22160.
4 SEK 260 WC. **Surface:** asphalted. 01/01-31/12.
Distance: on the spot 200m 200m.

Mariefred 5F1

Statoil, Storgatan 18. **GPS**: n59,25944 e17,21805.
2 free . **Surface:** asphalted. 01/01-31/12.

Nyköping 5F1

Nyköpings hamn, Spelhagsvägen. **GPS**: n58,74460 e17,01524.
10 free Ch.
Distance: 1km.
Remarks: Max. 2 days, service 100m.

Oxelösund 5F1

Femöre Marina, Fiskehamnsvägen 12. **GPS**: n58,65830 e17,11123.
15 SEK 150 Ch (10x)SEK 50. **Surface:** gravel.
Distance: 3km on the spot on the spot on the spot.

Strängnäs 5F1

Strängnäs Gästhamn, Storgatan 38. **GPS**: n59,37860 e17,02599.
13 SEK 150, 01/05-31/08 SEK 200 (13x) WC included.
01/01-31/12.
Distance: on the spot on the spot on the spot 200m.
Remarks: Max. 48h.

Trosa 5G1

Trosa Gästhamn, Uddbergagatan 1. **GPS**: n58,89090 e17,55360.
8 SEK 160 Ch included WC.
Distance: on the spot on the spot 200m 1km.
Remarks: Use of sauna against payment.

Östergötland

Borensberg 5F1

Kaffeteriet, Magasinsgatan 7. **GPS**: n58,55885 e15,27995.

35 SEK 195 Ch (19x) WC included.
Location: Rural, simple, isolated, quiet. **Surface:** gravel.
01/04-15/10.
Distance: 550m on the spot on the spot on the spot 550m.
Remarks: At Göta Canal.

Borensberg 5F1

Glasbruket, Kanalvägen 17. **GPS**: n58,55909 e15,30322.

5 SEK 185 (8x)SEK 30 WC. **Location:** Rural, simple, isolated, quiet. **Surface:** grassy. 01/05-30/09.

Distance: 1,5km 1,5km.
Remarks: At Göta Canal.

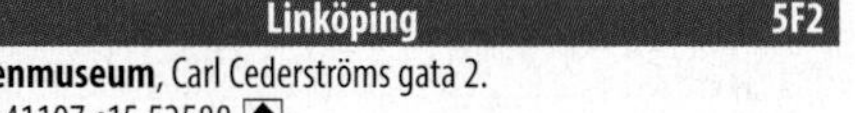

Linköping 5F2

Flygvapenmuseum, Carl Cederströms gata 2.
GPS: n58,41107 e15,52588.

20 free. **Location:** Rural, simple, isolated, quiet.
Surface: grassy. 01/01-31/12.
Distance: 1km 1km on the spot.
Remarks: Parking museum.

Ljungsbro 5F1

Vetra Kloster Golfklubb, Veda gård 2. **GPS**: n58,52862 e15,51955.

6 SEK 150 (6x) WC included.
Location: Rural, isolated, quiet. **Surface:** gravel. 01/04-31/10.
Distance: 3km on the spot.
Remarks: At golf court.

Mantorp 5F2

Östgöta Camping-Gruppen, Möllersbrunnsvägen 3.
GPS: n58,36089 e15,28313.

24 SEK 100 WC. **Location:** Rural, simple, isolated, quiet.
Surface: gravel. 01/01-31/12.
Distance: 1km 800m 800m.
Remarks: At motorhome dealer.

Mjölby 5E2

Mjölby Golfklubb, Blixberg Miskarp. **GPS**: n58,30753 e15,10125.

5 SEK 100 WC.
Location: Rural, isolated, quiet. **Surface:** gravel. 01/04-31/10.
Distance: on the spot on the spot.
Remarks: At golf court.

Motala 5E1

Södra Hamnen, Fabriksgatan 12 H. **GPS**: n58,52979 e15,03811.

20 SEK 200 Ch WC included.
Location: Urban, simple, central, quiet. **Surface:** grassy.
01/01-31/12.
Distance: 1km on the spot on the spot 500m on the

SE

spot.

Motala 5E1

Borenshults slussar, Verkstadsvägen 114.
GPS: n58,55550 e15,07820.

6 SEK 150 (6x)SEK 50/night WC included.
Location: Rural, simple, quiet. **Surface:** gravel. 01/05-31/08.
Distance: on the spot on the spot.
Remarks: Nearby sluices, at Göta Canal.

Motala 5E1

Café Mallboden, Varvsgatan 17. **GPS**: n58,54829 e15,06689.

5 SEK 200 (4x) WC included.
Location: Simple, quiet. **Surface:** grassy. 01/05-30/09.
Remarks: At Göta Canal.

Norrköping 5F1

Bråvikens Golfklubb, Drurövägen. **GPS**: n58,60259 e16,32305.

6 SEK 100 WC .
Location: Rural. **Surface:** asphalted. 01/04-31/10.
Distance: on the spot on the spot on the spot.

Norrköping 5F1

Söderköping Golfklubb, Alsätersvägen 40.
GPS: n58,49662 e16,16989.

8 SEK 150 WC. **Location:** Rural, simple, isolated, quiet.
Surface: asphalted. 01/04-31/10.
Distance: on the spot on the spot.
Remarks: Golf court.

Norsholm 5F1

Kapten Bille´s, Slussvägen. **GPS**: n58,50818 e15,97840.

14 SEK 185 WC included. **Location:** Rural, simple, isolated, quiet. **Surface:** gravel/metalled. 01/05-30/09.
Distance: on the spot on the spot 100m on the spot.
Remarks: At Göta Canal.

Ödeshög 5E2

Hästholmens hamn, Hamngatan. **GPS**: n58,27904 e14,63522.

5 SEK 120 SEK 50/day WC included.
Location: Urban, simple, quiet. **Surface:** asphalted.
Distance: 500m on the spot on the spot on the spot 1km on the spot.

Skänninge 5E2

Gripenbergs gårdsbutik, Gripenberg 1. **GPS**: n58,40659 e15,08026.

SEK 150 SEK 25/night WC included .
Location: Rural, simple, isolated. **Surface:** grassy. 01/01-31/12.
Distance: 1,5km 2km 1,5km on the spot.

Söderköping 5F1

Bergaskolan, Skepparvägen. **GPS**: n58,48097 e16,33524.

22 SEK 185 Ch WC included. **Location:** Rural, simple, isolated, quiet. **Surface:** gravel. 12/04-29/09.
Distance: 500m on the spot on the spot 500m on the spot.
Remarks: At former school, service on campsite.

Söderköping 5F1

Kanalmagasinet AB, Mem. **GPS**: n58,47923 e16,41422.

4 SEK 185 WC included. **Location:** Rural, simple, isolated, quiet. **Surface:** grassy. 01/05-30/09.
Distance: on the spot on the spot on the spot on the spot.
Remarks: Pay at Kanalmagasinet.

Vadstena 5E2

Vadstena Golfklubb, Kungs Starby 801. **GPS**: n58,42509 e14,89430.

20 SEK 200 (8x) WC included. **Location:** Rural, isolated, quiet. **Surface:** gravel. 01/04-31/10.
Distance: 3,2km on the spot on the spot.
Remarks: At golf court.

Vadstena 5E2

Vadstena Ställplats, Krönangsgatan 7.
GPS: n58,44496 e14,87933.

30 SEK 100, May-Sep SEK 130 Ch SEK 30/night WC .
Location: Urban, simple, central, quiet. **Surface:** grassy.
01/01-31/12 Service: winter.
Distance: 400m on the spot on the spot on the spot 500m on the spot.

Vreta Kloster 5F1

Bergs Slussar Vandrarhem, Oscars Slussar 2.
GPS: n58,48524 e15,52970.

25 SEK 185 Ch WC included . **Location:** Rural, simple, isolated, quiet. **Surface:** grassy. 01/04-30/09.
Distance: 500m 100m 500m on the spot.
Remarks: At Göta Canal.

Jönköping

Aneby 5E2

Wiredaholm Golf & Konferens, Nobyvägen.
GPS: n57,91294 e14,64571.

6 SEK 100 WC included. **Location:** Rural, isolated, quiet.
Surface: grassy. 01/04-30/09.
Distance: on the spot on the spot.
Remarks: At golf court.

Bredaryd 5E3

Pelles, Sunnaryd Solbacka. **GPS**: n57,01704 e13,69058.
2 SEK 200 WC SEK 50. **Surface:** grassy/gravel.
01/01-31/12.
Remarks: Breakfast-service.

Gränna 5E2

Gränna Hamn, Hamnvägen. **GPS**: n58,02728 e14,46070.

30 SEK 200 Ch (20x),10Amp WC included .
Location: Rural, comfortable, isolated, quiet. **Surface:** asphalted.
01/01-31/12.
Distance: 800m 100m 100m 400m on the spot on the spot.

Gränna 5E2

Gränna Hamn, Amiralsvägen. **GPS**: n58,02868 e14,45960.

20 SEK 120. **Location:** Rural, simple, isolated, quiet. **Surface:** asphalted. 01/01-31/12.
Distance: 600m 100m 100m 100m on the spot on the spot.

Gränna 5E2

BauerGårdens, Bunn. **GPS**: n57,93629 e14,49227.

100 SEK 250 Ch (70x) WC included. **Location:** Rural, simple, isolated, quiet. **Surface:** gravel. 10/04-01/12.
Distance: on the spot on the spot on the spot.

Hult 5F2

Ställplats Lyckarps, RV 40. **GPS**: n57,63577 e15,09830.

19 € 10 Ch included (10x) SEK 3. **Location:** Rural, simple, isolated, quiet. **Surface:** gravel. 01/05-31/10.
Distance: 8km 200m on the spot.

Jönköping 5E2

Hyltena Natt-Camp, Hyltena 50. **GPS**: n57,66595 e14,18246.

10 SEK 125 included WC. **Location:** Rural, simple, noisy. **Surface:** asphalted. 01/01-31/12.
Distance: Jönköping 15km 500m 500m 500m on the spot.
Remarks: Quick-Stop.

Mullsjö 5E2

Ryfors Golf Club. GPS: n57,90524 e13,82475.
SEK 150 WC. **Location:** Isolated, quiet. **Surface:** grassy.
Distance: 4,5km.
Remarks: At golf court.

Rydaholm 5E3

Skeda Strand, Skeda gård 1. **GPS**: n57,03727 e14,18147.

10 SEK 120 (6x) SEK 30/night,10Amp WC included. **Location:** Rural, simple, isolated, quiet. **Surface:** gravel. 01/01-31/12.
Distance: on the spot on the spot on the spot on the spot.
Remarks: Boat rental.

Rydaholm 5E3

Lady & Lufsen Ställplats Husbil, Krusebacken. **GPS**: n56,98089 e14,22967.

10 SEK 100 Ch SEK 15/night . **Location:** Rural, simple, isolated, quiet. **Surface:** grassy. 15/05-15/09.
Distance: 5km on the spot 5km on the spot.
Remarks: Max. 2 nights.

Sandhem 5E2

Kyrkekvarn Sörgården, Kyrkekvarn 2. **GPS**: n57,99581 e13,84571.

10 SEK 180 Ch WC included. **Location:** Rural, isolated, quiet. **Surface:** grassy/gravel. 01/04-31/10.
Distance: 6km.
Remarks: Canoe rental.

Sandhem 5E2

Kohagens Badplats. GPS: n57,98724 e13,77696.
3 free Ch free. **Location:** Rural. **Surface:** gravel. 01/01-31/12.
Distance: on the spot on the spot.
Remarks: At lake.

Tenhult 5E2

Ställplats Bogla, Bogla 29. **GPS**: n57,74284 e14,28935.

30 SEK 100 Ch included (20x) SEK 20. **Location:** Rural, isolated, quiet. **Surface:** gravel. 01/01-31/12.
Distance: Jönköping 5km.

Vrigstad 5E3

Timjan Café & Restaurang, Flahult 2. **GPS**: n57,31552 e14,29112.

6 SEK 100 SEK 50.
Location: Rural, simple, isolated, quiet. **Surface:** gravel.
Distance: on the spot on the spot.

Kronoberg

Diö 5E3

Sutareboda. GPS: n56,60767 e14,23700.
SEK 100. **Location:** Rural.
Distance: Diö 5km.

Växjö 5E3

Askelövsgatan Parkering, Askelövsgatan. **GPS**: n56,87743 e14,79634.

5 9-18h SEK 5/h, overnight stay free.
Location: Urban, simple, central, quiet. **Surface:** asphalted. 01/01-31/12.
Distance: 500m 350m 300m 500m on the spot.

Kalmar

Bläsinge 5F3

Bläsinge Hamn. GPS: n56,62015 e16,70076.

15 SEK 100 (14x) WC included. **Location:** Rural, simple, isolated, quiet. **Surface:** grassy/gravel. 01/01-31/12.
Distance: on the spot on the spot on the spot 15km.
Remarks: Money in envelope in mail box.

Borgholm 5F3

Stug o Fiske, Verkstadsgatan 5. **GPS**: n56,86841 e16,66309.

29 SEK 150 free Ch (20x) WC included.
Location: Rural, comfortable, quiet. **Surface:** grassy/gravel. 24/03-10/10.
Distance: 2km on the spot on the spot 2km.
Remarks: Pay at restaurant.

Borgholm 5F3

Lindby Boden, Lindby Bygata 23. **GPS**: n56,81571 e16,70548.

SE

50 SEK 70 included (5x). **Location:** Rural, simple, isolated, quiet. **Surface:** grassy. 01/01-31/12.
Distance: Borgholm 10km 10km 10km on the spot on the spot.
Remarks: Money in envelope in mail box.

Borgholm 5F3

Slot Borgholm, Sollidenvägen 5. **GPS**: n56,86975 e16,64785.

20 SEK 100. **Location:** Rural, simple, isolated, quiet. **Surface:** gravel. 01/01-31/12.
Distance: 2km 2km 2km.
Remarks: Service 2,5km GPS N56,88224 E16,66190.

Borgholm 5F3

Hamnvägen. **GPS**: n56,88301 e16,64790.

40 SEK 140 Ch WC included.
Location: Urban, simple, central, quiet. **Surface:** grassy. 01/01-31/12.
Distance: on the spot on the spot on the spot 200m 200m.
Remarks: Service 500m.

Byxelkrok 5F2

Byxelkrok, Neptunivägen. **GPS**: n57,34969 e17,03601.

15 SEK 100. **Location:** Rural, simple, isolated, quiet. **Surface:** forest soil.
Distance: 4km 100m 100m 4km 4km.
Remarks: Money in envelope in mail box.

Byxelkrok 5F2

Oskarshamn, Neptunivägen. **GPS**: n57,32767 e17,00812.

8 SEK 140 Ch WC included. **Location:** Rural, simple, noisy. **Surface:** gravel. 15/05-30/09.
Distance: 500m on the spot on the spot on the spot 500m.
Remarks: Check in at harbourmaster.

Degerhamn 5F3

Gräsgårds hamn. **GPS**: n56,31722 e16,53167.

25 SEK 80 included (20x). **Location:** Rural, simple, isolated, quiet. **Surface:** grassy. 01/01-31/12.
Distance: 15km on the spot 15km 15km.
Remarks: Pay in at kiosk.

Degerhamn 5F3

Degerhamns Ställplats & Hamn. **GPS**: n56,35723 e16,40734.

40 free. **Location:** Rural, simple, isolated, quiet. **Surface:** grassy. 15/04-18/10.
Distance: 1,5km on the spot on the spot 300m 1,5km.

Färjestaden 5F3

Köpsenter, Brovägen. **GPS**: n56,65293 e16,47138.

17 free. **Location:** Urban, simple, central, noisy. **Surface:** asphalted. 01/01-31/12.
Distance: 500m 50m 50m 50m on the spot.
Remarks: At shopping centre, max. 1 night.

Figeholm 5F2

Figeholms Båtklubb, Vasakajen. **GPS**: n57,37267 e16,55416.

8 SEK 150 Ch (8x)SEK 20/24h WC included.
Location: Rural, comfortable, central, quiet. **Surface:** asphalted. 01/01-31/12.
Distance: 100m on the spot 200m.
Remarks: Pay at harbourmaster.

Fliseryd 5F3

Ställplats Jungnerholmarna, Jungnerholmarna.
GPS: n57,13000 e16,25587.

10 SEK 90 Ch (6x) WC included.
Location: Rural, comfortable, central, quiet. **Surface:** grassy. 01/01-31/12.
Distance: 500m on the spot on the spot 1,5km on the spot.
Remarks: Check in and key electricity at supermarket.

Grönhögen 5F3

Ventlinge Stellplats, Ventlinge 118. **GPS**: n56,28372 e16,40681.

20 SEK 120 Ch (8x) WC included.
Location: Rural, comfortable, quiet. **Surface:** grassy. 01/04-01/11.
Distance: 1,5km 300m 300m 1,5km 1,5km.
Remarks: At golf court, farm products.

Grönhögen 5F3

Grönhögens hamn, Fiskaregränd. **GPS**: n56,26652 e16,39722.

30 SEK 150 Ch (28x) WC included SEK 15.
Location: Rural, comfortable, quiet. **Surface:** grassy. 01/01-31/12.
Distance: on the spot 50m on the spot 500m 500m on the spot on the spot.
Remarks: Golf court 1km.

Hjorted 5F2

Vattencafé "Vattenfronten", Blankaholm.
GPS: n57,59028 e16,52972.

8 SEK 140 included SEK 40/24h WC.
Location: Rural. **Surface:** grassy/gravel. 01/01-31/12.
Distance: 300m on the spot on the spot 300m.
Remarks: To be paid at bar.

Kalmar 5F3

Ölandskajen, ölandskajen 1. **GPS**: n56,66030 e16,36130.

SE

18 SEK 160 SEK 40/24h WC included.
Location: Urban, simple, central, noisy.
Surface: asphalted.
01/01-31/12 water disconnected in winter.
Distance: 200m 1km on the spot 200m 200m on the spot.
Remarks: Pay and coins at tourist office, historical centre.

S Kalmar 5F3
Svinö. GPS: n56,68111 e16,38079.

20 free Ch WC free. **Location:** Rural, simple, isolated, noisy.
Surface: gravel. 01/01-31/12 Service: winter.
Distance: 4km 200m on the spot on the spot 4km 4km 5km on the spot.
Remarks: Dogs beach.

Kalmar 5F3
Elevatorkajen, Skeppsbrogatan 49. **GPS**: n56,66360 e16,37060.

6 SEK 5/h, overnight stay free.
Location: Urban, simple, central, quiet.
Surface: asphalted.
01/01-31/12.
Distance: 100m 1km on the spot 200m 200m 400m.
Remarks: Service 4km GPS N56,68111 E16,38079, historical centre.

S Köpingsvik 5F3
Kårehamns Fiskaffär. GPS: n56,95623 e16,88755.

40 SEK 140 Ch (25x) WC included.
Location: Rural, comfortable, isolated, quiet. **Surface:** gravel.
01/01-31/12.
Distance: 15km 100m on the spot on the spot 15km.
Remarks: Service 200m.

Löttorp 5G2
Böda, Bödahamnsvägen. **GPS**: n57,24052 e17,07503.

50 SEK 140 Ch (10x)SEK 20/24h WC included.
Location: Rural, comfortable, quiet. **Surface:** grassy/gravel.
01/01-31/12.
Distance: 1km on the spot on the spot 1km.

S Mönsterås 5F3
Hamnen Mönsterås, Hamngatan. **GPS**: n57,04151 e16,44874.

13 SEK 125 Ch (8x) WC included.
Location: Urban, comfortable, quiet. **Surface:** asphalted.
01/01-31/12.
Distance: 100m on the spot on the spot 100m.
Remarks: At the quay, code internet at tourist office.

S Nabelund 5G2
Nabelundsvägen 1. **GPS**: n57,34882 e17,08904.

40 SEK 140 Ch (4x) WC included.
Location: Rural, simple, isolated, quiet. **Surface:** grassy/gravel.
01/01-31/12.
Distance: 7km on the spot on the spot 7km 7km.
Remarks: Pay at harbourmaster.

S Oskarshamn 5F2
Oskarshamns gästhamn, Norra Strandgatan.
GPS: n57,26768 e16,45516.

10 SEK 100-150 Ch WC included.
Location: Urban, simple, central, noisy.
Surface: asphalted.
01/01-31/12.
Distance: 500m on the spot on the spot 500m 500m 400m.
Remarks: Pay at harbourmaster, service 2km GPS N57,27830 E16,47543.

Sandvik 5F3
Gästhamnen Sandvik, Stenhuggarvägen.
GPS: n57,07143 e16,85335.

30 SEK 160 Ch (30x) WC included.
Location: Rural, comfortable, quiet.
Surface: gravel. 01/01-31/12.
Distance: 100m on the spot on the spot on the spot 50m.

S Stora Rör 5F3
Stora Rörs Hamn, Stora Rörsvägen. **GPS**: n56,75654 e16,52817.

8 SEK 160 (6x) WC included. **Location:** Rural, simple, quiet.
Surface: asphalted. 01/01-31/12.
Distance: on the spot on the spot on the spot on the spot 100m.
Remarks: Pay at shop.

S Storebrö 5F2
Stellplats Storbro Sportclub, Ulvekarrsvägen.
GPS: n57,59367 e15,83992.

20 SEK 150 (4x) WC included.
Location: Rural, simple, quiet. **Surface:** gravel. 01/01-31/12.
Distance: 300m.
Remarks: Money in envelope in mail box.

S Storebrö 5F2
Tobo Golgklubb camping, Fredensborg 133.
GPS: n57,57566 e15,81154.

10 SEK 100 Ch (10x) WC included. **Location:** Rural, simple, isolated, quiet. **Surface:** gravel. 01/01-31/12.
Distance: 7km 50m 7km.
Remarks: Payment and sanitary facilities at Golfclub.

Timmernabben 5F3
Festplatsen Timmernabben, Botsmansvägen.
GPS: n56,97350 e16,44028.

SE

30 SEK 150 (20x) WC included. Location: Rural, simple, quiet. Surface: grassy/gravel. 01/01-31/12.
Distance: 100m on the spot on the spot 1km 1km.

S Torngärd 5F3

Parkeerterrein Natuurreservaat, Fagelvägen.
GPS: n56,33169 e16,54289.

6 SEK 40 WC included. **Location:** Rural, simple, quiet.
Surface: gravel. 01/01-31/12.
Distance: 15km on the spot 15km 15km 15km.
Remarks: Bird reserve, money in envelope in mail box.

S Tuna 5F2

Ställplats Tuna, Lillgatan. **GPS**: n57,57716 e16,10351.

12 SEK 100 SEK 60 Ch (4x) WC SEK 10/time.
Location: Rural, simple, central, quiet. **Surface:** gravel.
01/01-31/12.
Distance: 2,5km 100m on the spot.
Remarks: Money in envelope in mail box, moose park 9km, tourist train.

S Västervik 5F2

Ställplats Sågen, Värmeverksgatan. **GPS**: n57,75138 e16,65541.

45 SEK 100 Ch included (15x) SEK 40. **Location:** Urban, simple, central, quiet.
Surface: gravel. 01/01-31/12.
Distance: 1,5km on the spot on the spot 800m.
Remarks: Money in envelope in mail box, service 1,5km GPS N57.74120 E16.66293.

S Västervik 5F2

Barlastsudden Sea Port, Barlastgatan 11.
GPS: n57,75464 e16,65149.
19 SEK 100 SEK 50. **Surface:** gravel. 22/06-30/09.
Distance: 1km on the spot on the spot.

Vimmerby 5F2

Astrid Lindgrens Värld, Fabriksgatan 8.
GPS: n57,67514 e15,84151.

200 SEK 200. **Location:** Urban, simple, central.
Surface: asphalted. 01/01-31/12.
Distance: 1km 1km 1,3km.
Remarks: Quick-Stop: >19h - <8h.

Gotland

S Burgsvik 5G2

Ställplats Sandkvie, Öja Sandkvie 173. **GPS**: n57,01533 e18,31373.
35 SEK 120 Ch SEK 30 WC.
Surface: grassy. 01/01-31/12.
Distance: 4km 2km on the spot.

S Fårö 5G2

Lauterhorns. GPS: n57,95249 e19,07995.
15 SEK 100, 01/06-31/08 SEK 120 SEK 10/20liter (8x) SEK 30.
Surface: gravel.
Distance: on the spot.

Gotlands Tofta 5G2

Tofta Beach, Malvavägen 17. **GPS**: n57,49233 e18,13133.
250 SEK 130. 15/04-18/10.

S Visby 5G2

Park and Stay, Gutevägen. **GPS**: n57,62855 e18,28034.
35 SEK 169 Ch. **Surface:** gravel. 15/04-18/10.
Distance: 700m.

Blekinge

S Hasslö 5F3

Garpahamnen Hasslö, Hamnvägen. **GPS**: n56,09990 e15,47368.
SEK 130 WC.
Distance: on the spot on the spot.

S Hasslö 5F3

Hasslö Stugby, Fiskaregårdsvägen 2. **GPS**: n56,10227 e15,47770.

6 SEK 200 included SEK 10 SEK 40.
Location: Rural, simple, isolated, quiet. **Surface:** grassy/gravel.
01/01-31/12.
Distance: on the spot on the spot on the spot 300m on the spot.

Karlshamn 5F3

Hamnplan, Hamngatan 2A. **GPS**: n56,16520 e14,86522.

6 free. **Location:** Urban, simple, central, quiet. **Surface:** asphalted.
01/01-31/12 during event.
Distance: 500m on the spot 500m 500m.
Remarks: Max. 24h.

Karlshamn 5F3

Saltsjöbadsvägen. **GPS**: n56,15835 e14,87974.

free. **Location:** Rural, isolated. **Surface:** gravel.
Distance: 2,5km.

Karlshamn 5F3

Stationsvägen. **GPS**: n56,17563 e14,86610.
free. **Surface:** asphalted. 01/01-31/12.
Distance: 800m 800m 800m on the spot.
Remarks: Near train station.

S Karlshamn 5F3

Ställplats Väggaviken, Saltsjöbadsvägen.
GPS: n56,15840 e14,88486.

30 SEK 180 Ch included WC. **Location:** Rural, simple, isolated, quiet. **Surface:** gravel. 01/06-31/08.
Distance: 2km on the spot 2km on the spot.

S Karlshamn 5F3

Svaneviks småbåtshamn, Idrottsvägen.
GPS: n56,15692 e14,88850.

12 SEK 180 Ch WC included. **Location:** Rural, simple, isolated, quiet. **Surface:** gravel. 01/06-31/08.
Distance: 3km on the spot on the spot on the spot.
Remarks: Pay at harbourmaster.

Karlshamn 5F3

Kreativum Science Center, Strömmavägen 28.
GPS: n56,19288 e14,85211.

5 free. **Location:** Rural, simple, isolated, quiet. **Surface:** asphalted.
01/01-31/12.
Distance: 4km 800m.
Remarks: At museum, check in on arrival.

S Karlskrona 5F3

Karlskrona Stadsmarina, Östra Hamngatan.
GPS: n56,16548 e15,59390.

24 SEK 180 ,10Amp WC included.
Location: Urban, simple, central, quiet.
Surface: asphalted. 01/01-31/12.
Distance: 1km on the spot on the spot 200m 1km.
Remarks: Pay at harbourmaster, out of season less pitches.

S Karlskrona 5F3

Argongatan. **GPS**: n56,16988 e15,59426.
Ch.

S Ramdala 5F3

Brofästet Senoren gårdsbutik, Svartnabbsvägen.
GPS: n56,13769 e15,74035.

SE

28 SEK 100 Chincluded SEK 50/night WC.
Location: Rural, simple, isolated, quiet. **Surface:** grassy.
01/04-30/09.
Distance: 7km on the spot on the spot 1,5km on the spot.
Remarks: Next to The viking village.

Ronneby 5F3

Ronneby Golfklubb, Reddvägen 14. **GPS**: n56,18962 e15,29355.

21 SEK 75 Ch (6x)SEK 75/night WC.
Location: Rural, simple, isolated, quiet. **Surface:** gravel.
01/01-31/12.
Distance: 2km on the spot on the spot.
Remarks: At golf court.

Ronneby 5F3

Ställplats-Fridhemsvägen, Fridhemsvägen.
GPS: n56,20776 e15,28109.

5 free. **Location:** Urban, central. **Surface:** asphalted.
01/01-31/12.
Distance: 300m 100m 400m 300m on the spot on the spot.

Ronneby 5F3

Ronneby Hamn, Östra Piren. **GPS**: n56,17527 e15,30177.

20 SEK 150 included. **Location:** Rural, simple, isolated, quiet. **Surface:** metalled. 01/01-31/12.
Distance: 3km on the spot on the spot 1,5km on the spot.
Remarks: Service at Ronneby Rönninge.

Sölvesborg 6H1

Hörviks gästhamn, Kustvägen, Hörvik. **GPS**: n56,04139 e14,76556.

33 SEK 150 ChWC. **Location:** Rural, simple, isolated.
Surface: gravel. 01/04-15/10.
Distance: 12km on the spot on the spot 300m 200m on the spot.

Sölvesborg 6H1

Torsö hamn, Oastensvägen, Västra Torsö. **GPS**: n55,99952 e14,64871.

6 SEK 150 WC included. **Location:** Rural, simple, isolated, quiet. **Surface:** grassy. 01/01-31/12.
Distance: 7km on the spot on the spot on the spot.

Sölvesborg 6H1

Krokås gästhamn, Krokåsvägen 1. **GPS**: n56,04890 e14,75669.

8 SEK 100 (8x)SEK 20/night.
Location: Urban, simple, isolated, quiet. **Surface:** grassy/gravel.
01/05-31/08.
Distance: 15km on the spot on the spot 1,5km on the spot.

Sölvesborg 6H1

Nogersunds gästhamn, Östra Hamnvägen, Nogersunds.
GPS: n56,00509 e14,73863.

30 SEK 160 Ch included WC. **Location:** Rural, simple, isolated, quiet. **Surface:** grassy. 01/01-31/12.
Distance: 11km on the spot on the spot on the spot.

Sölvesborg 6H1

Sölveborgs golfbana, Ljunganabbevägen.
GPS: n56,04428 e14,59946.

10 SEK 200 WC included.
Location: Rural, simple, isolated, quiet. **Surface:** grassy.
Distance: 7km on the spot on the spot.
Remarks: At golf court.

Sturkö 5F3

Ekenabben. **GPS**: n56,10142 e15,63803.
8 SEK 135 SEK 30/night. **Location:** Rural, simple, isolated, quiet. **Surface:** asphalted. 01/04-30/09.
Distance: 7km on the spot on the spot on the spot on the spot.

Sturkö 5F3

Ställplats Sanda, Strandvägen. **GPS**: n56,11966 e15,65123.
6 SEK 135 SEK 30/night. **Location:** Rural, simple, isolated, quiet. **Surface:** asphalted. 01/04-30/09.

Distance: on the spot on the spot 1,5km on the spot.

Torhamn 5F3

Sandhamn Marine, Brändaskärsvägen 4.
GPS: n56,09351 e15,85479.

50 SEK 100, 01/05-30/09 SEK 175 Ch (30x)WC SEK 50 included. **Location:** Rural, comfortable, isolated, quiet.
Surface: gravel. 01/01-31/12.
Distance: 1km on the spot on the spot on the spot.
Remarks: Borrow cycles for free.

Skåne

Åhus 6G1

Strandvillan, Kolonivägen 62. **GPS**: n55,94443 e14,32109.

16 SEK 150 WC included. **Location:** Rural, simple, isolated, quiet. **Surface:** grassy. 01/01-31/12.
Distance: 2km 700m.

Åhus 6G1

Åhus husbilsparkering, Kantarellvägen 3.
GPS: n55,93721 e14,31622.

30 SEK 150. **Location:** Urban. **Surface:** forest soil.
01/01-31/12.
Distance: 1,5km 400m 200m 1,5km.

Anderslöv 6G2

Lady's Hage, Sörbyvägen 100. **GPS**: n55,44392 e13,32986.

20 SEK 100. **Location:** Rural, simple, isolated, quiet.
Surface: grassy. 01/01-31/12.
Distance: 900m 1km 900m on the spot.

Ängelholm 5E3

Sibirienvägen. **GPS**: n56,23618 e12,81852.

SE

8 free. WC free. **Surface:** grassy.
Distance: 4km 100m 4km on the spot on the spot.
Remarks: Nature reserve.

S Ängelholm 5E3

Ängelholms Föreningshamn, Segelvägen 9.
GPS: n56,26704 e12,84138.
30 SEK 150 (16x)included.
01/06-06/12.
Distance: 5km on the spot on the spot on the spot 5km.
Remarks: Max. 48h, pay at harbourmaster.

Båstad 5E3

Italienska vägen. **GPS**: n56,43383 e12,83132.
SEK 50. **Surface:** grassy. 01/01-31/12.
Distance: 1km 400m 500m.

S Borrby 6G1

Catrinegården, Borrby 1223. **GPS**: n55,46673 e14,21090.

4 SEK 120 Ch (4x)SEK 30/night WC.
Location: Rural, simple, isolated, quiet. **Surface:** grassy.
01/01-31/12.
Distance: 2,5km on the spot 2,5km on the spot on the spot.

S Bromölla 6H1

Skåneporten Bromölla, Kristianstadsvägen.
GPS: n56,06414 e14,49689.

20 free WC. **Location:** Rural, simple, isolated, noisy.
Surface: asphalted. 01/01-31/12.
Distance: 200m on the spot 1km on the spot.
Remarks: Service to be paid at campsite.

Fjälkinge 6G1

Tosteberga Ängar, Tostebergavägen. **GPS**: n56,01567 e14,45466.

6 free. **Location:** Rural, simple, isolated, quiet.
Surface: forest soil. 01/01-31/12.
Distance: 2km.
Remarks: Nature reserve.

S Fjälkinge 6G1

Tosteberga Hamn, Bodavägen 185. **GPS**: n55,99759 e14,44539.

15 SEK 150 WC included. **Location:** Rural, comfortable, isolated, quiet. **Surface:** grassy/gravel. 01/01-31/12.
Distance: on the spot on the spot.

S Gärsnäs 6G1

Ekogården, Skräddaröd 126. **GPS**: n55,60681 e14,23481.

35 SEK 150 Ch (16x)WC included.
Location: Rural, isolated, quiet.
Surface: grassy. 01/04-30/09.
Distance: Gärsnäs 10km.

S Höllviken 6F2

Falsterbokanalens Båtklubb, Västra hamnplan 1.
GPS: n55,41011 e12,93200.

8 SEK 200 Ch (8x)included WC.
Location: Rural, isolated, quiet. **Surface:** asphalted.
01/05-30/09.
Distance: on the spot on the spot on the spot.

S Höllviken 6F2

Ställplats Foteviken, Museivägen 27. **GPS**: n55,42774 e12,95213.

15 SEK 200, SEK 100 without service Ch (4x) WC.
Location: Rural, simple, isolated, quiet. **Surface:** grassy.
01/02-30/11.
Distance: 1km on the spot 1km 1km on the spot.
Remarks: At museum.

Jonstorp 5E3

Bläsinge Gård, Gamla Södåkravägen 127. **GPS**: n56,23770 e12,65567.
20 SEK 150 SEK 50. **Surface:** gravel. 01/01-31/12.

Kristianstad 6G1

Sommarlust Ishall, Kanalgatan 100. **GPS**: n56,04442 e14,16646.

30 free. **Location:** Urban, simple. **Surface:** asphalted.
01/01-31/12.
Distance: 2km 400m 300m on the spot on the spot.
Remarks: Max. 24h.

S Landskrona 6F1

Lundåkrahamnen, Stuverigatan 43. **GPS**: n55,86171 e12,85009.

48 SEK 180 Ch WC included.
Location: Rural, simple, quiet. **Surface:** grassy.
01/01-31/12.
Distance: 2km on the spot on the spot 300m on the spot on the spot.
Remarks: Arrival <22h, monitored parking.

S Landskrona 6F1

Gammeleksgården, Rosenhällsvägen 40.
GPS: n55,92197 e12,84515.

6 SEK 150 Ch WC included on demand.
Location: Rural, simple, noisy. **Surface:** gravel. 01/01-31/12.
Distance: on the spot on the spot.
Remarks: Arrival >18h, departure <10h, check in at B&B <22h, breakfast € 6.

S Limhamn 6F1

Lagunen, Vakgatan 9. **GPS**: n55,59593 e12,93305.

25 SEK 180 Ch WC included.
Location: Rural, simple, quiet.
Surface: gravel. 01/01-31/12.
Distance: 5km on the spot 5km 5km on the spot on the spot.

S Limhamn 6F1

Limhamns Småbåtshamn, Bryggövägen.
GPS: n55,58358 e12,91824.

40 SEK 220 Ch WC included.
Location: Rural, simple, quiet. **Surface:** grasstiles.
01/01-31/12 Service: winter.
Distance: 700m, Malmö 6km on the spot on the spot on the spot on the spot on the spot.

Löderup 6G2

Kåseberga Ställplats, Ales väg 2. **GPS**: n55,38863 e14,06322.

SE

48 SEK 120. **Location:** Rural, isolated, quiet.
Surface: grassy. 01/04-31/10.
Distance: on the spot 300m on the spot.

Malmö 6F1

Andelshamnen Lagunen, Vaktgatan 9. **GPS**: n55,59611 e12,93278.
10 SEK 180/night Ch WC . **Location:** Urban.
Surface: grassy/sand. 01/01-31/12.
Distance: centre 4km on the spot.
Remarks: Borrow cycles for free.

Näsum 5E3

Ställplats Axeltorp, Olofströmsvägen 177-11.
GPS: n56,14389 e14,52012.

22 SEK 100 (10x)SEK 20 included.
Location: Rural. **Surface:** grassy. 01/01-31/12.
Distance: 4km on the spot on the spot on the spot on the spot.
Remarks: At the lake, boat rental.

Örkelljunga 5E3

Bengt i Örkelljunga, Skåneporten 2. **GPS**: n56,28548 e13,33957.

20 SEK 50 SEK 15 Ch SEK 50.
Surface: grassy. 01/01-31/12.
Distance: 4km on the spot 1km.
Remarks: At motorhome dealer, max. 24h, pay at reception.

Osby 5E3

Spegeldammen, Hässleholmsvägen. **GPS**: n56,36871 e13,98441.
free.
Distance: 1,6km on the spot.
Remarks: Max. 2 nights.

Simrishamn 6G1

Camping car parking Hammarlunda, Gislövshammar.
GPS: n55,49015 e14,30745.

30 SEK 120 Ch included WC. **Location:** Rural, simple, isolated, quiet. **Surface:** grassy. 01/01-31/12.
Distance: 8km 700m 700m 2,5km on the spot on the spot.

Simrishamn 6G1

Österlens GK, Williams väg 20, Djupadal. **GPS**: n55,61208 e14,28146.

8 SEK 250 WC included.
Location: Rural, isolated, quiet. **Surface:** gravel. 01/04-31/10.
Distance: 400m 500m on the spot on the spot.
Remarks: At golf court.

Simrishamn 6G1

Småbåtshamnen. **GPS**: n55,56035 e14,34906.

7 SEK 205 Ch (5x)SEK 2/kWh WC .
Location: Rural, simple, central, quiet. **Surface:** asphalted.
01/01-31/12.
Distance: 500m on the spot on the spot on the spot on the spot on the spot.
Remarks: Tallycard.

Simrishamn 6G1

Tobisviks Camping, Tobisvägen 1. **GPS**: n55,56792 e14,33708.

50 SEK 120-200 Ch WC . **Location:** Rural, comfortable, isolated, quiet. **Surface:** grassy. 01/01-31/12.
Distance: 3km on the spot on the spot on the spot.

Skanör 6F2

Skanör hamn, Hamnvägen 1. **GPS**: n55,41608 e12,83168.

10 SEK 220 (10x),10Amp WC included.
Location: Rural, simple, isolated, quiet. **Surface:** gravel.
22/04-01/10.
Distance: on the spot on the spot on the spot 1km on the spot.
Remarks: Discount longer stays.

Smygehamn 6G2

Köpmansmagasinet, Smyge strandväg. **GPS**: n55,33978 e13,36172.

40 free. **Location:** Rural, simple, isolated, quiet. **Surface:** grassy.
01/01-31/12.
Distance: on the spot on the spot 200m on the spot on the spot.

Trelleborg 6G2

Trelleborgs turist Parkering, Strandridaregatan.
GPS: n55,37536 e13,12004.

free, night SEK 100 Ch WC (summer).
Location: Rural, simple, isolated. **Surface:** gravel.
01/01-31/12.
Distance: 2km on the spot on the spot 1,5km 800m on the spot.

Yngsjö 6G1

Gamla Skolan, Yngsjövägen 1065. **GPS**: n55,84441 e14,20019.

SEK 200 WC included. **Location:** Simple, isolated.
Surface: gravel. 01/05-30/09.
Distance: 1,5km.
Remarks: Breakfast-service.

Ystad 6G2

Västerleden 129. **GPS**: n55,42472 e13,78694.

10 free. **Location:** Rural, isolated, quiet.
Surface: grassy. 01/01-31/12.
Distance: on the spot on the spot on the spot.
Remarks: Max. 24h.

Ystad 6G2

Ystads Marina, Segelgatan 1. **GPS**: n55,42666 e13,81730.

28 free, night SEK 150 Ch (16x)SEK 10/2kWh WC SEK 10/4minutes SEK 10 .
Location: Urban, simple, central, quiet. **Surface:** gravel.
01/06-15/09.
Distance: 1km on the spot on the spot on the spot on the spot on the spot on the spot.
Remarks: Caution SEK 50.

Halland

Falkenberg 5D3

Falkenbergs Båtsällskap, Gröningevägen 3.
GPS: n56,89360 e12,49318.
25 € 18 Ch included. **Location:** Urban. **Surface:** metalled.
01/05-01/09.
Distance: city centre 1,5km on the spot on the spot 1km

SE

on the spot.

Falkenberg 5D3

Lövstavikens Båtförening, Sanddynevägen 58.
GPS: n56,89329 e12,46795.
20 SEK 160 Ch WC included.
Surface: grassy/gravel.
Distance: 3km on the spot.

Fjärås 5D3

Tjolöholms Slott, Tjolöholms byväg. **GPS**: n57,40173 e12,10161.
SEK 100. **Surface:** grassy/gravel. 01/01-31/12.
Distance: on the spot.
Remarks: At castle, max. 2 days.

Fjärås 5D3

Skårs Gård, Förlandavägen. **GPS**: n57,40081 e12,26869.
6 SEK 140 WC included. **Location:** Rural.
Distance: 11km.

Frillesås 5D3

Espenäsvägen. **GPS**: n57,31674 e12,15298.
5 SEK 100. **Surface:** grassy. 01/04-01/10.
Distance: 1,5km on the spot.
Remarks: Money in envelope in mail box.

Gullbrandstorp 5E3

Strandgården, Skarviksvägen 2. **GPS**: n56,69518 e12,68550.
8 SEK 250 included.
Distance: on the spot on the spot.
Remarks: Max. 3 days, golf court 300m.

Halmstad 5E3

Citycamp Halmstad, Styrmansgatan. **GPS**: n56,66682 e12,86145.
50 SEK 120, 01/06-31/08 SEK 140.
Distance: on the spot.

Halmstad 5E3

Halmstad Segelsällskap, Grötviksvägen. **GPS**: n56,64191 e12,77782.
10 SEK 150 included.

Ullared 5D3

Ställplats Ullared, Värnamovägen. **GPS**: n57,13232 e12,73472.
100 free, night SEK 90. **Surface:** gravel.
Distance: 1km.
Remarks: Max. 48h.

Unnaryd 5E3

Tiraholms Fisk. **GPS**: n56,94263 e13,64560.
SEK 100 . **Surface:** grassy.
Distance: on the spot on the spot.
Remarks: At small lake, check in on arrival.

Varberg 5D3

Apelvik Strand, Tångkörarvägen, Apelviken.
GPS: n57,08157 e12,26156.

SEK 150 WC .
Distance: on the spot.
Remarks: Beach parking.

Varberg 5D3

Naturum Getterön, Lassavägen 1. **GPS**: n57,12627 e12,25332.

24 SEK 125, 01/06-31/08 SEK 200 included.
Surface: gravel.
Distance: on the spot.
Remarks: Nature reserve.

Varberg 5D3

Getterön Marina, Änggärdev. 1. **GPS**: n57,11399 e12,22588.
21 SEK 170-200 Ch included.
Surface: metalled. 01/01-31/12.
Distance: on the spot on the spot.
Remarks: Monitored parking.

Varberg 5D3

Otto Torells gata 24. **GPS**: n57,11000 e12,24250.
14 SEK 360 Ch WC included.
Location: Urban. **Surface:** concrete. 01/01-31/12.
Distance: 500m 400m 800m.

Värobacka 5D3

Bua hamn, Hamnvägen. **GPS**: n57,23926 e12,11410.
SEK 180, 15/06-15/08 SEK 200 Ch WC .
Surface: asphalted. 01/01-31/12.
Distance: 1km on the spot on the spot 200m 500m.

Västra Götaland

Åmål 5D1

Måkebergsvägen 4. **GPS**: n59,05615 e12,70862.

80 SEK 100 Ch WC included. **Location:** Rural, simple, quiet. **Surface:** grassy/gravel. 01/04-15/10.
Distance: 600m on the spot on the spot 600m 600m on the spot on the spot.
Remarks: Pay at harbourmaster, servicepoint at Camping Örnäs.

Bohus-björkö 5D2

Björkö Hamn, Ljungblomsvägen 7. **GPS**: n57,72812 e11,67751.
SEK 250 included SEK 10 SEK 50. **Surface:** gravel.
01/01-31/12.
Distance: on the spot on the spot on the spot 500m.

Dals Långed 5D1

Ställplats Dals Långed, Christian Aarsruds väg 2.
GPS: n58,92272 e12,30742.

8 SEK 150 Ch WC included. **Location:** Rural, comfortable, quiet. **Surface:** gravel. 01/05-25/10.
Distance: 250m 3km on the spot on the spot 400m 200m on the spot on the spot.

Fiskebäckskil 5D2

Skaftö Golfklubb, Stockeviksvägen 2. **GPS**: n58,23213 e11,45394.
5 SEK 200 included.
Distance: on the spot.
Remarks: At golf court.

Floda 5D2

Öijared Golf, Öjaredsvägen. **GPS**: n57,85467 e12,39777.
. **Surface:** asphalted.
Remarks: At golf court.

Forsvik 5E1

Ställplats Forsvik Göta kanal, Baltzar von Platens väg 18.
GPS: n58,57525 e14,43557.

15 SEK 150 WC included.
Location: Rural, simple, quiet. **Surface:** gravel. 01/05-30/09.
Distance: 2km on the spot on the spot on the spot on the spot.
Remarks: At Göta Canal.

Göteborg 5D2

Lisebergs ställplats Skatås, Skatåsvägen.
GPS: n57,70303 e12,03513.
37 SEK 240/24h Ch included.
Surface: asphalted. 30/05-13/09.
Distance: 750m 750m 750m.

Grebbestad 5D2

SportShopen, Rörvik 1. **GPS**: n58,67683 e11,27572.
50 SEK 150-200 Ch included SEK 50. **Location:** Rural.
Surface: gravel. 01/01-31/12.
Distance: 2km 1,5km on the spot.

Hälsö 5D2

Tjolmenvägen. **GPS**: n57,73152 e11,65794.
15 SEK 180 WC included.
Distance: on the spot on the spot.

Hjo 5E2

Tupp och höna Ställplats, Svebråta Sörgården 3.
GPS: n58,34658 e14,14127.

20 SEK 70 Ch SEK 30 WC . **Location:** Rural, isolated, quiet. **Surface:** gravel. 01/05-30/09.
Distance: on the spot on the spot.

Hjo 5E2

Viktoriagatan. **GPS**: n58,30359 e14,28919.

6 free. **Location:** Urban, simple, central, quiet.
Surface: asphalted. 01/01-31/12.
Distance: 500m 500m 500m 400m 300m on the spot on the spot.

Hjo 5E2

Bisonfarmen i Gate, Mobolet Mohem.
GPS: n58,17747 e14,16246.

15 SEK 150 Ch (10x) WC .
Location: Rural. **Surface:** gravel. 01/05-30/09.
Distance: on the spot on the spot.
Remarks: Beautiful view.

Hjo 5E2

Restaurang Stampens Kvarn, Stampens kvarn 1.
GPS: n58,30745 e14,25516.

SE

6 SEK 140 Ch. SEK 30 WC. **Location:** Rural, comfortable, isolated, quiet. **Surface:** grassy. Easter-30/09.
Distance: 1,5km on the spot on the spot.

Hunnebostrand 5D2

Nordens Ark, Åby säteri. **GPS**: n58,44347 e11,43661.
10 SEK 200. **Location:** Rural, isolated, quiet. **Surface:** unpaved.
01/01-31/12.
Remarks: Parking zoo.

Karlsborg 5E1

Carlsborg Segelsällskap, Västra Varvsgatan 6.
GPS: n58,53998 e14,50208.

40 SEK 180 Ch. WC included.
Location: Rural, simple, quiet. **Surface:** grassy/gravel.
29/04-31/10 during event.
Distance: 300m on the spot 400m 300m on the spot.
Remarks: At the canal.

Kungshamn 5D2

Smögenbrons Rum, Dinglevägen 27. **GPS**: n58,36903 e11,24984.
SEK 100 Ch. 01/06-31/08.
Distance: 1km on the spot on the spot 1km.

Lidköping 5E1

Camp Active Studios, Lovene, Kållands Åsaka 1.
GPS: n58,45263 e13,04888.
20 SEK 150 Ch. (20x)included WC. **Location:** Rural.
Surface: asphalted/gravel. 01/04-30/09.
Distance: 10km on the spot 1,5km.
Remarks: Sports centre, swimming pool.

Lidköping 5E1

Spikens Båtsällskap. **GPS**: n58,68952 e13,20174.
SEK 120 Ch. SEK 30 SEK 5/3minutes. 01/05-30/09.
Distance: Lidköping 25km on the spot on the spot on the spot.

Lyrestad 5E1

Lyrestad Gästhamn, Kanalvägen 9. **GPS**: n58,80324 e14,05703.

25 SEK 150, 17/06-07/08 SEK 175 Ch WC.
Location: Rural, simple, quiet. **Surface:** grassy.
01/06-31/08.
Distance: on the spot on the spot 200m 200m 500m on the spot.
Remarks: At Göta Canal, next to midget golf, caution SEK 100.

Lyrestad 5E1

Norrqvarn Hotell & Konferens, Norrqvarns Slussområde.
GPS: n58,78655 e14,08360.

15 SEK 150 (5x)SEK 25/night WC. **Location:** Rural, simple, isolated, quiet. **Surface:** gravel. 01/01-31/12.
Distance: 3km on the spot on the spot on the spot on the spot.
Remarks: At Göta Canal, check in on arrival, canoe and bicycle rental, restaurant only in summer.

Lysekil 5D2

Valbodalens. **GPS**: n58,28905 e11,43849.
30 SEK 180 (20x)WC included. 25/04-30/09.
Distance: 2km on the spot on the spot.

Lysekil 5D2

Kolholmarnas, Bangårdsgatan. **GPS**: n58,27418 e11,43912.
36 SEK 180.
Distance: 600m 600m 600m.

Mariestad 5E1

Kajgatan 1. **GPS**: n58,71311 e13,81893.

14 SEK 140 SEK 25 WC SEK 30.
Location: Rural, central, quiet. **Surface:** asphalted. 01/01-31/12.
Distance: 300m on the spot on the spot 150m 1km 800m on the spot on the spot.
Remarks: Max. 3 days.

Mariestad 5E1

Mariestads Hamnområde, Hamngatan 58.
GPS: n58,71601 e13,82033.

46 SEK 140 Ch. SEK 25/night,6Amp SEK 30.
Location: Urban, simple, central, quiet. **Surface:** asphalted.
01/01-31/12.
Distance: 800m on the spot on the spot 500m 1km 1km on the spot.
Remarks: Max. 3 days.

Öckerö 5D2

Hönö Röd, Rödvägen. **GPS**: n57,69933 e11,63954.
30 SEK 150 Ch. WC included.
Distance: 300m 300m 500m.

Öckerö 5D2

Hönö Klåva Hamn, Öckerövägen. **GPS**: n57,68345 e11,65156.
SEK 170, 15/06-15/08 SEK 200 included. 01/01-31/12.
Distance: on the spot 500m.

Sjötorp 5E1

Sjötorps Gästhamn, Stenbordsvägen. **GPS**: n58,83716 e13,97865.

30 SEK 185 WC included.
Location: Urban, simple, quiet. **Surface:** gravel. 01/05-30/09.
Distance: 400m on the spot on the spot on the spot on the spot on the spot on the spot.
Remarks: At Göta Canal, caution SEK 200.

Skärhamn 5D2

Hav & Logi Skärhamn, Rövallen 1. **GPS**: n57,97059 e11,55519.
6 SEK 200-300 Ch. WC. **Location:** Rural.
10/04-16/10.
Distance: 2,5km 100m.

Strömstad 5D1

Bojarparkering, Kebalvägen. **GPS**: n58,95115 e11,17330.

30 SEK 100/24h Ch WC included.
Location: Rural, simple, quiet. **Surface:** gravel. 01/01-31/12.
Distance: 3km 1km 200m 300m 3km on the spot on the spot on the spot.
Remarks: Free bus to centre.

Tanumshede 5D1

Brehogsvägen 8. **GPS**: n58,72129 e11,34524.
10 free Ch. WC free. **Location:** Urban. **Surface:** asphalted.
01/01-31/12.
Distance: 2km on the spot on the spot 300m.
Remarks: At shopping centre.

Tidaholm 5E2

Smedjegatan. **GPS**: n58,18130 e13,96792.

2 free. **Location:** Urban, central, quiet.
Surface: asphalted. 01/01-31/12.
Distance: 300m 400m 400m.
Remarks: Max. 48h.

Tidaholm 5E2

Södra Kungsvägen. **GPS**: n58,17838 e13,96083.
2 free. **Location:** Urban, simple, central, quiet. **Surface:** asphalted.
01/01-31/12.
Distance: 300m 50m.
Remarks: Max. 48h.

Töreboda 5E1

Hajstorp Slusscafé & Vandrarhem, Brovaktarstugan 5, Hajstorp.
GPS: n58,74745 e14,10776.

16 SEK 200 Ch. WC included.
Location: Rural, isolated, quiet. **Surface:** gravel. 01/04-30/09.
Distance: 200m on the spot on the spot 400m on the spot.
Remarks: At Göta Canal, max. 3t.

Trollhättan 5D2

Ställplatser Trollhättan, Åkerssjövägen. **GPS**: n58,26531 e12,26549.
16 SEK 150 Ch.
Distance: 2,8km.

Värmland

Årjäng 5D1

Sandaholm Restaurang & Camping, Sanda Sjövik.
GPS: n59,36078 e12,27807.

SE

15 SEK 100 Ch (8x)SEK 40/24h WC included SEK 25/24h.
Location: Rural, simple, quiet. **Surface:** metalled.
01/04-01/10.
Distance: 6km on the spot on the spot on the spot 6km on the spot on the spot.

S Filipstad 5E1
Asphyttans Slussar, Konsul Lundströms väg. **GPS**: n59,61839 e14,18147.
SEK 120 included.
Distance: 12km.
Remarks: Canoe and boat rental.

Hammarö 5E1
Getingbergets Badplats, Sättersvägen 569. **GPS**: n59,29690 e13,56170.
6 SEK 100. **Location:** Rural, isolated, quiet.
Surface: gravel. 01/01-31/12.
Distance: on the spot on the spot.
Remarks: To be paid at golf court GPS N59,30313, E13,542056.

Karlstad 5E1
Sävegatan 2. **GPS**: n59,39329 e13,51467.

25 free. **Location:** Urban, simple, central, noisy.
Surface: asphalted. 01/01-31/12.
Distance: 500m 100m 100m on the spot.

Karlstad 5E1
Trädgårdsgatan. **GPS**: n59,37726 e13,50376.

4 SEK 5/h, SEK 25/day. **Location:** Urban, simple, central, noisy.
Surface: asphalted. 15/04-15/10.
Distance: 500m 1km 500m 500m on the spot on the spot on the spot.
Remarks: Along railwayline, small pitches.

Kil 5E1
Fryksta, Sjöleden. **GPS**: n59,52045 e13,32507.

6 free. **Location:** Rural, simple, isolated, quiet.
Surface: gravel. 01/01-31/12.
Distance: 3km 2km on the spot on the spot on the spot on the spot on the spot.
Remarks: Only overnight stays 18-10h.

S Kristinehamn 5E1
Kristinehamns Gästhamn och Ställplats, Hamnvägen 9.
GPS: n59,31138 e14,09558.
37 SEK 165 Ch (20x)SEK 30 WC included.

Surface: gravel.
Distance: 700m 300m.
Remarks: Next to midget golf.

S Morokulien 4B3
Kungsvägen. **GPS**: n59,93089 e12,24181.
free Ch WC. **Surface:** asphalted/metalled.
Distance: on the spot.
Remarks: Next to petrol station.

S Nysäter 5D1
Nysäters gästhamn, Marknadsvägen.
GPS: n59,28417 e12,78242.

20 SEK 100 WC included.
Location: Rural, comfortable, isolated, quiet. **Surface:** grassy/gravel.
15/05-15/09.
Distance: 500m on the spot on the spot 500m 500m 500m on the spot on the spot.

S Säffle 5D1
Karlsborgsgatan. **GPS**: n59,12405 e12,92426.

10 SEK 100 WC included.
Location: Rural, simple, quiet. **Surface:** gravel. 15/05-15/10.
Distance: 1km 2km on the spot on the spot 1km 900m on the spot on the spot.
Remarks: Check in at harbourmaster.

Säffle 5D1
Medborgarhusets, Magasinsgatan 2. **GPS**: n59,13499 e12,92178.

8 SEK 150 included. **Location:** Urban, simple, noisy.
Surface: asphalted. 15/05-15/10.
Distance: 700m 300m on the spot on the spot 500m on the spot on the spot on the spot.
Remarks: Pay at harbourmaster.

Örebro

S Askersund 5E1
Askersund Citycamp & Gästhamn, Sundsbrogatan 1.
GPS: n58,87879 e14,89928.

20 SEK 230 Ch (20x)included WC.
Location: Urban, simple, central, quiet. **Surface:** gravel.
01/04-01/11.
Distance: 350m on the spot 2km 350m 400m 150m

on the spot.

S Aspabruk 5E1
Aspa Båtklubb, Norrviksvägen 4. **GPS**: n58,75961 e14,80499.

10 SEK 150 Ch WC included.
Location: Rural. **Surface:** gravel. 01/04-30/09.
Distance: 1km on the spot on the spot on the spot on the spot.

S Hällefors 4C3
Lantliv Hjulsjö, Hjulsjö 108. **GPS**: n59,77813 e14,77634.
10 SEK 150 WC included. **Location:** Isolated, quiet.
Surface: grassy.
Distance: on the spot on the spot.
Remarks: At lake, use of sauna against payment.

Västmanland

S Arboga 5F1
Hjälmare Docka. **GPS**: n59,38186 e15,94347.
10 SEK 150 included. **Surface:** grassy. 01/04-15/10.
Distance: on the spot on the spot on the spot.
Remarks: At the canal.

S Lindesberg 5E1
Fotbollsgatan. **GPS**: n59,60157 e15,18676.
10 free Ch free. **Surface:** asphalted. 01/01-31/12.
Distance: centre 2,5km 2,5km 2,5km.
Remarks: Max. 24h.

S Västerås 4D3
Västerås Gästhamn. **GPS**: n59,60190 e16,54648.
15 SEK 200 WC included. 01/01-31/12.
Distance: 500m on the spot on the spot 500m.
Remarks: Pay at harbourmaster.

Dalarna

Ludvika 4C3
Eriksgatan. **GPS**: n60,15020 e15,18936.
free. **Location:** Urban. **Surface:** asphalted. 01/01-31/12.
Distance: on the spot 200m.
Remarks: Max. 24h.

Särna 4C3
Lägerplats, Byvägen. **GPS**: n61,80383 e12,90931.
6 SEK 60. **Location:** Rural. **Surface:** grassy.
Distance: on the spot on the spot.
Remarks: Along river.

Säter 4C3
Säterdalens Folkpark. **GPS**: n60,34854 e15,75439.
free.
Distance: 650m 650m 850m.

S Smedjebacken 4C3
Smedjebackens. **GPS**: n60,13828 e15,41647.
5 SEK 100 Ch. **Surface:** gravel. 01/05-01/10.
Distance: 500m on the spot 200m 500m on the spot on the spot.

S Sollerön 4C3
Sollerö camping, Levsnäs. **GPS**: n60,90048 e14,58318.
18 SEK 80-100 (8x)SEK 30. **Surface:** asphalted.
Distance: on the spot on the spot.
Remarks: Quick-Stop: >18h - <9h.

S Stjärnsund 4C3
Villa Solhem, Bruksallén 17. **GPS**: n60,43421 e16,20744.
11 SEK 200 (4x)SEK 20 WC included.
Distance: on the spot 300m 300m.

Gävleborg

S Axmar 4D3
Axmarbrygga Havskrog, Boskär. **GPS**: n61,04877 e17,15774.
30 SEK 90 Ch SEK 40 WC included SEK 10.
Surface: gravel. 03/04-01/11.
Distance: on the spot on the spot on the spot.
Remarks: Bread-service.

SE

S Gävle 4D3

Hemlingbystugan, Hemlingbyvägen 93. **GPS**: n60,65005 e17,16996.
free WC. **Surface:** asphalted.
Distance: 2km 2km 1,8km.
Remarks: Max. 3 days.

Gävle 4D3

Culinarparkeringen, Drottningsgatan 47, Anderholmen.
GPS: n60,67810 e17,15493.

12 SEK 2/h, overnight stay and weekend free. **Surface:** gravel.

Gävle 4D3

Södra Skeppsbron. **GPS**: n60,67670 e17,15985.

2 free. **Location:** Urban. **Surface:** asphalted. 01/01-31/12.
Distance: on the spot on the spot on the spot on the spot.
Remarks: Max. 48h.

Ockelbo 4C3

Wij Trädgårdar, Vigatan 4. **GPS**: n60,88722 e16,70139.
free. 23/05-06/09.
Distance: 1km.
Remarks: Near mill, max. 3 days.

Västernorrland

S Docksta 4D2

Skuleberget Havscamping, Veåsand 211.
GPS: n63,06659 e18,36723.

42 SEK 250 (42x) WC included.
Location: Isolated, quiet.
Distance: 3km 50m 50m on the spot.

Kvissleby 4D2

Svartvik. **GPS**: n62,31935 e17,36955.

20 free. **Location:** Noisy.
Surface: grassy/gravel. 01/01-31/12.
Distance: on the spot on the spot 500m.

Sandöverken 4D2

Hotell Höga Kusten AB, Hornöberget. **GPS**: n62,80468 e17,95136.

free. **Surface:** asphalted.
Distance: on the spot on the spot.

S Skatan 4D2

Galströmsvägen. **GPS**: n62,19896 e17,49645.
free Ch WC. 01/01-31/12.
Distance: 500m 200m.

Jämtland

S Bispgården 4C2

Rojo Zweden, Sörböle 230. **GPS**: n62,99040 e16,62163.
25 € 10,60 Ch WC included. **Location:** Isolated.
Surface: grassy. 01/05-01/09.
Distance: 8km.

Gällö 4C2

Alma Ångbåt. **GPS**: n62,82794 e15,30652.
SEK 150. **Surface:** grassy.
Distance: on the spot on the spot 300m.

S Hammarstrand 4C2

Zorbcenter, Dödviken 145. **GPS**: n63,14690 e16,17890.

11 SEK 150 (5x)SEK 20 WC included.
Surface: grassy. 01/05-31/09.
Distance: 15km on the spot 1km.
Remarks: Canoe and boat rental.

S Mattmar 4C2

Ångaren Östersund, Södra Arvesund 516. **GPS**: n63,23573 e14,06810.
SEK 60 SEK 60 SEK 20.
Surface: grassy/metalled. 01/01-31/12.
Distance: on the spot on the spot on the spot.

S Svenstavik 4C2

Centrumvägen. **GPS**: n62,76731 e14,43496.
SEK 100 Chfree WC.
Location: Urban. **Surface:** asphalted.
Distance: on the spot on the spot on the spot.

SE

Slovakia

Capital: Bratislava
Government: parliamentary republic
Official Language: Slovak
Population: 5,445,802 (2016)
Area: 49,036 km²

General information
Dialling code: 0421
General emergency: 112
Currency: Euro
Credit cards are accepted almost everywhere.

Regulations for overnight stays
Wild camping is not allowed.

Additional public holidays 2018
January 1 Republic Day
January 6 Epiphany
May 1 Labour Day
May 8 End of World War II
July 5 St. Cyril & St. Methodius Day
August 29 National Uprising Day
September 1 Constitution Day
September 15 Day of Lady Sorrows
November 1 All Saints' Day
November 17 Freedom and Democracy Day

Time Zone
Winter (Standard Time) GMT+1
Summer (DST) GMT+2

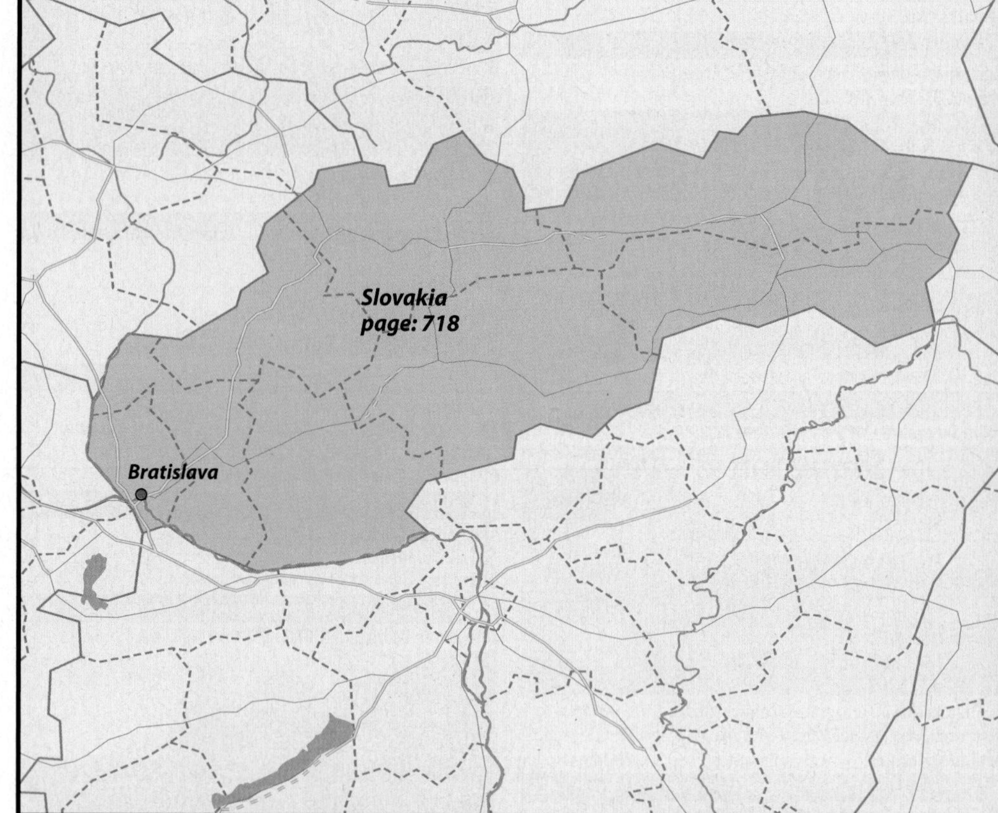

SK

Bratislava

Bratislava 36C1

Camping Zlate Piesky, Senecká cesta 2. **GPS**: n48,18836 e17,18557.
€ 15,80, 2 pers.incl Ch € 3,50 WC included.
Location: Urban. **Surface:** grassy. 01/05-15/10.
Distance: 8km 100m on the spot 200m.

Trnava

Banka 36C1

Camping Pullmann Piestany, Cesta Janka Alexyho 921.
GPS: n48,57609 e17,83444.
€ 8 Ch WC included. **Surface:** grassy.
Distance: 2km on the spot.

Dunajská Streda 36C1

CaravanCamp DS, Kúpelná ulica 21. **GPS**: n47,98689 e17,61150.
15 € 12 Ch WC included.
Location: Rural. **Surface:** grassy. 01/04-01/11.
Distance: 1km 350m 900m.

Šamorín 36C1

Stellplatz Čilistov, Čilistov. **GPS**: n48,01364 e17,30850.

25 € 7 Ch € 3 WC included. **Location:** Rural, simple. **Surface:** grassy/gravel. 01/04-31/10.
Distance: Bratislava 20km 50m 500m 200m.
Remarks: Dog € 4, golf court 2km.

Žilina

Liptovský Ján 38C4

Pension Horec, Starojanka. **GPS**: n49,03709 e19,67526.
15 free. **Location:** Rural. **Surface:** metalled. 01/01-31/12.

Varín 38B4

Autocamp Varin, Doktor Jozefa Tisu 13. **GPS**: n49,20833 e18,87861.
€ 12 Ch € 3,30 WC included.
Location: Rural. **Surface:** grassy. 01/05-11/10.
Distance: on the spot.

Banská Bystric

Brezno 38C4

Sedliacky Dvor, Hliník 7, Rohozná. **GPS**: n48,79535 e19,72869.

20 € 17,25 Ch WC € 3,25 included.
Location: Rural. **Surface:** grassy. 15/04-31/10.
Distance: 7km 1,2km 1,2km 700m on the spot on the spot.
Remarks: Bread-service.

Prešov

Haligovce 38C4

Camping Goralsky Dvor. **GPS**: n49,37984 e20,43972.
€ 10,50 Ch € 3,50 WC included.
Location: Rural. **Surface:** grassy.
Distance: on the spot.

Snina 38D4

Camping Snina, Rybnícka 4483. **GPS**: n48,97384 e22,18919.
25 € 9 Ch included € 2,50 € 0,50 . 15/05-30/09.
Distance: 3km 50m 50m on the spot on the spot.

Vysoké Tatry 38C4

Pension Slnecny Dom, Tatranská Lomnica 287.
GPS: n49,16664 e20,28169.
4 € 10 Ch included. 01/01-31/12.
Distance: on the spot on the spot.

Košice

Vyšný Medzev 38C4

Camping Sokol, Hrdinov SNP 64 - 68. **GPS**: n48,71472 e20,90222.
€ 17,50 Ch € 2,50 WC included.
Location: Motorway. **Surface:** grassy. 01/04-01/10.
Distance: on the spot.

Slovenia

Capital: Ljubljana
Government: parliamentarian republic
Official Language: Slovenian
Population: 1,978,029 (2016)
Area: 20,373 km²

General information
Dialling code: 00386
General emergency: 112
Currency: Euro
Credit card are accepted almost everywhere.

Regulations for overnight stays
There is no regulation against overnight camping, but it is not yet generally accepted. In the National Park Triglav wild camping is forbidden.

Additional public holidays 2018
February 8 Prešern Day - Slovenian cultural festival
April 27 Uprising against the Occupation Day
May 1-2 Labour Day
June 25 National Holiday
August 15 Assumption of the Virgin Mary
October 31 Reformation Day
November 1 All Saints' Day
December 26 Independence Day

Time Zone
Winter (Standard Time) GMT+1
Summer (DST) GMT+2

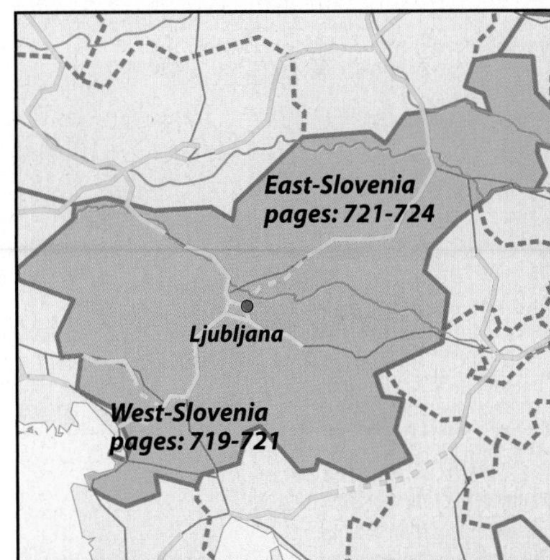

Slovenia West

Bled 36A3
Ljubljanska cesta. **GPS:** n46,36957 e14,11700.
€ 10. **Surface:** metalled. 01/01-31/12.
Distance: city centre 1km 300m 100m.

Bled 36A3
Camping Bled, Kidričeva 10 c. **GPS:** n46,36162 e14,08221.
€ 28,50-31,50 Ch WC.
01/04-15/10.
Distance: on the spot on the spot on the spot on the spot.
Tourist information Bled:
Bled Castle. Exhibition about the history of Bled, during the summer also open-air concerts. 8-17h.
Soteska Vintgar Gorge, TD Gorje, Podhom 0, Gorje. Trail over bridges and galleries along a river.

Bohinjsko jezero 37A1
Kamp Zlatorog, Ukanc 2. **GPS:** n46,27887 e13,83739.
€ 20-30 Ch WC. 25/04-30/09.
Distance: on the spot on the spot 150m.
Tourist information Bohinjsko jezero:
Savica Falls. Water falls.

Bovec 23H1
Alpski turistični center Kanin Bovec, Dvor 43.
GPS: n46,33306 e13,53944.

14 € 20/24h, € 30/36h Ch included.
Location: Rural.
Surface: asphalted.
01/01-31/12
service: 01/11-15/03.
Distance: 1km on the spot on the spot.
Remarks: Max. 36h, payment only with coins.
Tourist information Bovec:
Triglav National Park, Dom Trenta, Soča. Information centre.
Kluže Fortress, Trg golobarskih žrtev 8. Fort above gorge.
Soča Trail, Soča. Hiking trail along the Soca river.

Cerkno 37A1
Kmetija Želinc, Straža 8. **GPS:** n46,10259 e13,94670.
5 € 12. 01/01-31/12.
Distance: on the spot on the spot.

Domžale 37A1
ACG Autocenter Glavan, Češminova ulica 1a.
GPS: n46,14637 e14,60047.

2 free Ch (2x)free,16Amp. **Location:** Urban, simple, central, noisy. **Surface:** asphalted/gravel.
01/01-31/12.
Distance: 100m 3km 500m 300m 150m 150m 500m on the spot on the spot 20km 20km.

Dornberk 37A1
Saksida, Založšče 12a. **GPS:** n45,88963 e13,74751.

15 € 10/pp Ch (15x),16Amp WC included.
Location: Rural, comfortable, isolated. **Surface:** gravel/metalled.
01/01-31/12.
Distance: 1km 350m 350m on the spot 1km 300m on the spot on the spot.
Remarks: Covered picnic area, swimming pool available.

DovjeMojstrana 36A3
Kamne. GPS: n46,46444 e13,95778.
€ 15,20-21 Ch WC. 01/01-31/12.
Distance: 1km 1km.

Hruševje 37A1
Penzion & Camp Mirjam, Razdrto 19. **GPS:** n45,75690 e14,06126.

9 € 12 Ch included WC on demand € 1.
Location: Urban, simple, central, quiet. **Surface:** gravel.
01/05-31/10.
Distance: on the spot 1km 10km 10km 50m on the spot on the spot.

Idrija 37A1
Veri Krajnik, Carl Jakoba ulica 9. **GPS:** n45,99879 e14,02595.

3 € 5 Ch included. **Location:** Rural, simple, isolated, quiet. **Surface:** grassy/gravel. 01/01-31/12.
Distance: 1,5km 1,5km 1,5km 1,5km on the spot on the spot.
Remarks: Narrow entrance.

Ilirska Bistrica 37A1
Grill Danilo, Bazoviška cesta 46. **GPS:** n45,55846 e14,24340.

6 € 13 + tourist tax € 1,04pp Ch (6x),16Amp WC included.
Location: Rural, comfortable, central, quiet. **Surface:** asphalted.
01/01-31/12.
Distance: 500m 10km 20km 50m on the spot 200m 100m 500m on the spot on the spot 20km 20km.

Izola 37A1
Tomažičeva ulica. **GPS:** n45,53230 e13,64861.
10 € 15/24h. **Surface:** asphalted. 01/01-31/12.
Distance: 500m 200m 100m.

Izola 37A1
Cankarjev Drevored. **GPS:** n45,53808 e13,66397.

5 € 15/24h Ch (4x)included,16Amp.
Location: Urban, simple, quiet. **Surface:** asphalted.
01/01-31/12.
Distance: 500m 500m on the spot 500m 500m on the spot on the spot on the spot.

Kamniška Bistrica 36A3
Kamp Alpe. GPS: n46,30543 e14,60794.
10 € 25 Ch WC. 01/05-01/10.

SL

Kobarid 23H1

Koren, Drezneske Ravne 333. **GPS**: n46,25083 e13,58667.

€ 25-30 Ch WC. 01/01-31/12.
Distance: 500m on the spot on the spot on the spot.

Kobarid 23H1

Lazar, Gregorciceva 63. **GPS**: n46,25530 e13,58720.
€ 26 Ch WC. 01/04-31/10.
Distance: on the spot on the spot.

Tourist information Kobarid:
Kobariski muzej, Gregorciceva 1. Museum about the first World War. 01/04-30/09 9-18h, 01/10-31/03 10-17h.
Tolmin Chutes, LTO Sotočje, Petra Skalarja 4, Tolmin. Touristic route along the rapid to the thermal source of the river.

Koper 37A1

Ljubljanska cesta 13. **GPS**: n45,53790 e13,73780.
36 € 10/24h Ch WC included. **Surface:** asphalted.
01/01-31/12.
Distance: city centre 1,5km 2km 300m 300m.
Remarks: Nearby bus station.

Kranj 37A1

Stara Sava, Gregorčičeva ulica. **GPS**: n46,24307 e14,35771.
6 € 10/24h € 0,50/40liter Ch € 0,20/kWh. **Surface:** gravel.
01/01-31/12.
Distance: 200m 200m 100m.

Kranjska Gora 36A3

Borovška cesta. **GPS**: n46,48746 e13,77510.
20 € 15/24h Ch WC included.
Location: Rural. **Surface:** gravel. 01/01-31/12.
Distance: 500m 200m on the spot on the spot on the spot on the spot.
Remarks: To be paid at bar.

Laze v Tuhinju 37A1

Terme Snovik, Snovik 7. **GPS**: n46,22661 e14,70440.
20 € 25 Ch (3x)included. **Surface:** grassy.
01/01-31/12.
Distance: on the spot on the spot.

Ljubljana 37A1

Alo Camp, Peruzzijeva ulica 105.
GPS: n46,02151 e14,52303.

13 € 20-25 Ch (13x)WC included.
Surface: asphalted. 01/01-31/12.
Distance: 3km on the spot 500m 50m on the spot on the spot.
Remarks: Check in at hotel, borrow cycles for free.

Ljubljana 37A1

Pri Kovaču, Cesta II. grupe odredov 82, Dobrunje.
GPS: n46,03162 e14,60386.

10 € 8/night, guests free Ch (20x)€ 2/night,16Amp WC € 0,80 included **Location:** Rural, comfortable, central, quiet. **Surface:** gravel.
01/01-31/12 Restaurant: Tue.
Distance: 8km 2,5km 5km 4km on the spot 100m, bakery 200m 20m on the spot on the spot 400m.

Ljubljana 37A1

Campark, Na Produ 2, Črnuče.
GPS: n46,09974 e14,51672.
36 € 10 Ch € 4 WC.
Surface: metalled. 01/01-31/12.
Distance: 2km 200m 500m 100m on the spot.

Ljubljana 37A1

Camperstop Colonial, Parmova 51.
GPS: n46,06461 e14,50203.
5 € 12 included. 01/01-31/12.
Distance: 2km 100m on the spot 200m on the spot on the spot.
Remarks: Max. 3 nights.

Ljubljana 37A1

Sraka, Masarykova 23a.
GPS: n46,05740 e14,51870.

15 € 15, park € 10 Ch included.
Location: Urban. **Surface:** gravel. 01/01-31/12.
Distance: 1km on the spot 100m on the spot on the spot on the spot.
Remarks: Motorhome washing place.

Ljubljana 37A1

Gostilna Livada, Hladnikova 15.
GPS: n46,03513 e14,50967.
9 free.
01/01-31/12.
Distance: 1km 500m.
Remarks: Free with a meal.

Tourist information Ljubljana:
Ljubljana Tourist Card. Card offers among other things free public transport, free access at museums and discount in restaurants, shops etc. Available at Tourist Office, railway station and several hotels. € 20,70/24h.
Ljubljana Tourist Information Center, Krekov trg 10, www.visitljubljana.com. Capital, historical city with a lot of annual events.
National museum, Muzjeska 1. Archeological and historical museum.
10-18h, Thu 10-20h Mo.
Plecnik museum, Kurunova 4. Architectonic museum in the house of Joze Plecnik. Tue, Thu 10-14h.
Slovene Natural History Museum, Muzjeska 1. Zoological and botanic museum. daily 10-18h, Thu 10-20h Mo.
Ljubljana Castle. Medieval fortress, tourist train at town centre.
01/10-30/04 10-21h, 01/05-30/09 9-22h.
Vodnikov trg. daily, summer 6-18h, winter 6-16h.
Zoo Ljubljana, Večna pot 70. Zoo.
summer 9-19h, winter 9-16h.

Logatec 37A1

Počivališče Lom. **GPS**: n45,89817 e14,25486.
6 free. **Location:** Motorway. **Surface:** asphalted.
Distance: on the spot on the spot on the spot.
Remarks: At petrol station.

Luče 36A3

Camp Smica, Luče 4. **GPS**: n46,36117 e14,73626.
€ 12-16 Ch WC. 01/05-30/10.
Distance: on the spot on the spot 900m.

Lukovica 37A1

Gostilna Furman, Stari trg 19. **GPS**: n46,17026 e14,69233.

10 € 10, € 15 service incl Ch (10x) WC
Location: Urban, simple, central, quiet. **Surface:** gravel.
01/01-31/12.
Distance: on the spot 3km 3km on the spot 200m 100m on the spot on the spot.

Lukovica 37A1

OMV Istrabenz. **GPS**: n46,16690 e14,69380.
2 free Ch free. **Location:** Motorway, noisy.
01/01-31/12.
Distance: on the spot on the spot.
Remarks: Parking petrol station OMV Istrabenz.

Podgrad 37A1

Pension Patrik, Hrušica 100. **GPS**: n45,53257 e14,12055.

8 € 5, tourist tax incl Ch WC € 2,50 € 3,50/3,50 included. **Location:** Quiet. **Surface:** gravel.
01/01-31/12.
Distance: 2,8km 40km 10km 2,8km 2,8km 50m on the spot on the spot.

Portorož 37A1

Marina Portorož, Cesta solinarjev 8. **GPS**: n45,50505 e13,59847.

60 € 17, 15/04-20/09 € 26 + tourist tax € 0,63/pp Ch (64x), 16Amp included **Location:** Urban, simple, quiet.
Surface: gravel. 01/01-31/12.
Distance: 1km on the spot on the spot on the spot on the spot 500m on the spot on the spot.
Remarks: Monitored parking 24/24, swimming pool available.

Tourist information Portorož:
Turistična organizacija Koper, Verdijeva 10, Koper. City with a Venetian past and a lot of curiosities.
Pomorski muzej Sergej Mašera, Cankarjevo nabrežje 3, Piran. Maritime museum. 9-12h, 15-18h, 01/07-31/08 9-12h, 18-21h Mo.

Postojna 37A1

Park Postojnska Jama, Veliki Otok. **GPS**: n45,78066 e14,20322.

20 € 20/24h Ch (20x)included,16Amp.
Location: Rural, simple, quiet.
Surface: concrete.
01/04-30/09.
Distance: 1km 3km 100m 1km on the spot on the spot on the spot.

SL

Remarks: Postojna caves 300m.

Tourist information Postojna:

Križna jama, Bloška polica 7, Grahovo. Largest water caves of Slovenia.

Perdjama Grad. Castle, 16th century and caves.

01/05-30/09 9-18, 01/10-30/04 10-16h.

Postojnska Jama, Jamska cesta 30. Postojna caves.

01/05-30/09 9-18, 01/10-30/04 10-16h.

S Rateče 23H1

Nordijski center Planica. GPS: n46,47708 e13,72418.

6 € 12 Ch WC included. **Surface:** metalled.

01/01-31/12.

S Šenčur 37A1

Camper Stop Cubis, Poslovna cona A 2.

GPS: n46,23855 e14,40769.

14 € 12 Ch (12x) included.

Surface: gravel. 01/01-31/12.

Distance: 1km 150m 1km on the spot.

Remarks: Video surveillance.

S Sežana 37A1

Partizanska cesta 1. **GPS:** n45,70954 e13,87582.

6 free € 0,50/40liter Ch € 0,50/kWh. **Surface:** metalled.

01/01-31/12.

Distance: 200m 200m 200m.

Remarks: Along railwayline.

Škofja Loka 37A1

Škofja Loka- Gorenja vas. **GPS:** n46,16694 e14,30907.

4 7-19h parking rate, overnight stay free.

Location: Urban, simple, central, quiet. **Surface:** asphalted.

01/01-31/12.

Distance: on the spot 200m.

S Šmarje 37A1

Garni Mimosa, Srgaši 38a. **GPS:** n45,50843 e13,70560.

5 € 10 € 8/100liter (1x)included,16Amp WC on demand . **Location:** Urban, simple, central, quiet.

Surface: gravel. 01/01-31/12.

Distance: 6km 50m 50m 100m on the spot on the spot.

S Smlednik 37A1

Hotel Kanu, Valburga 7. **GPS:** n46,16927 e14,42228.

20 € 10 Ch (4x),16Amp WC € 5 included

Location: Rural, isolated, quiet. **Surface:** grasstiles.

01/01-31/12 water disconnected in winter.

Distance: 300m 5km on the spot on the spot on the spot 300m 300m on the spot on the spot 20km 7km.

S Tolmin 37A1

Kamp Siber, Klanec 8. **GPS:** n46,18082 e13,73792.

20 € 8/pp Ch € 3 WC .

Location: Rural. **Surface:** grassy/gravel. 01/01-01/11.

Distance: 1km on the spot on the spot 1km.

Slovenia East

S Braslovče 36B3

Najem & Kamping, Preserje 16b. **GPS:** n46,28915 e15,05524.

20 € 5 Ch (2x)€ 5/day,16Amp included.

Location: Rural, comfortable, isolated, quiet. **Surface:** gravel.

01/01-31/12.

Distance: 1km on the spot on the spot 1km 1km 1km on the spot on the spot 10km 10km.

Remarks: Opening hours 7-22h.

S Brestanica 37B1

Bazen Brestanica, Jetrno selo 2. **GPS:** n46,00124 e15,47492.

4 free Ch . **Surface:** gravel.

Remarks: At swimming pool.

S Brestanica 37B1

Ribiška družina Brestanica, Raztez 1a. **GPS:** n46,00504 e15,49751.

5 free WC .

Location: Isolated, quiet. **Surface:** gravel.

Distance: on the spot on the spot on the spot.

Remarks: Fishpond, check in at restaurant.

S Celje 36B3

Mestini Park Celje, Partizanska Cesta. **GPS:** n46,22550 e15,26082.

6 free € 0,50/40liter Ch € 0,50/kWh. **Surface:** asphalted.

01/01-31/12.

Distance: on the spot on the spot.

S Celje 36B3

Parking Glazija, Ljubljanska cesta 20. **GPS:** n46,23319 e15,25904.

2 € 10 included. **Location:** Urban.

Surface: metalled.

Distance: on the spot.

S Celje 36B3

Glavan Center Karavaninga, Gaji 45. **GPS:** n46,24406 e15,30217.

6 € 5 € 1/100liter Ch (2x)€ 0,50/kWh,16Amp .

Location: Rural, simple, isolated, quiet.

Surface: gravel.

01/01-31/12.

Distance: 3km 4km 4km 200m 2km on the spot on the spot on the spot.

Remarks: At motorhome dealer.

Tourist information Celje:

Jama Pekel, Šempeter. Caves.

Stari Grad Castle. Remainders of castle.

Rimska Nekropola, Šempeter. Roman Necropolis, archeological park.

S Cirkulane 36B3

Herman Lederhaus, Dolane 8. **GPS:** n46,37114 e15,99682.

10 € 10 Ch WC included.

Surface: grassy/gravel. 01/01-31/12.

Distance: on the spot on the spot on the spot 50m.

Remarks: Restaurant and leather factory.

S Dolenjske Toplice 37B1

Dolenjske Toplice, Meniška vas 61. **GPS:** n45,76739 e15,05151.

10 € 8 + € 0,64/pp tourist tax Ch € 2,75 WC included.

Location: Rural, simple, isolated, quiet. **Surface:** grassy/gravel.

01/04-15/10.

Distance: 800m on the spot on the spot 800m 800m on the spot on the spot.

Remarks: Along the Krka river, terme Dolenjske Toplice 800m.

S Dolsko 37A1

Domačija Pr Krač, Dolsko 19. **GPS:** n46,09195 e14,67522.

35 WC . **Surface:** metalled. 01/01-31/12.

Distance: on the spot 550m on the spot on the spot.

Remarks: Regional products.

Hinje 37B1

Domačija Krnc, Hrib pri Hinjah 9. **GPS:** n45,76729 e14,88887.

5 € 15. **Surface:** grassy. 01/01-31/12.

Distance: on the spot.

S Ivančna Gorica 37A1

Turistična vas Pristava, Pristava nad Stično 4.

GPS: n45,98999 e14,82394.

10 € 15 Ch included WC .

Location: Quiet. **Surface:** gravel. 01/01-31/12.

Distance: on the spot on the spot.

Ivanjkovci 36B3

Vinoteka Svetinjska Klet, Svetinje 5.

GPS: n46,46220 e16,16990.

SL

10 free. **Surface:** metalled.
Remarks: Sale of wines.

Jesenice na Dolenjskem 37B1

Gostinstvo Strnisa, Jesenice na Dolenjskem 7c.
GPS: n45,85869 e15,68979.

5 € 6 € 2 Ch € 2,50 WC. **Location:** Urban.
Surface: concrete.
Distance: on the spot.

Kamnica 36B3

Gostilna Koblarjev Zaliv, Na otok 20. **GPS**: n46,56560 e15,61908.

20 free, use of a meal desired free. **Surface:** grassy.
01/01-31/12.
Distance: Maribor 2km on the spot on the spot on the spot 2km 300m.
Remarks: Walking and bicycle area along the Drava river to Maribor centre.

Kocevje 37B1

Turistični Komplex Jezero, Trdnjava 3. **GPS**: n45,64421 e14,87140.

3 € 12 Ch (4x)included WC. **Location:** Simple, isolated, quiet. **Surface:** asphalted. 01/01-31/12.
Distance: 1km 200m 200m on the spot 1km 1km on the spot on the spot.
Remarks: Check in at tourist office, nature reserve.

Kostanjevica na Krki 37B1

Krška cesta. **GPS**: n45,84891 e15,41795.
5 free. **Surface:** grassy/metalled. 01/01-31/12.
Distance: 300m on the spot on the spot 300m.
Remarks: Along river.

Krško 37B1

Raceland, Pesje 30. **GPS**: n45,92977 e15,53500.

50 € 12 WC included.
Location: Rural, isolated, noisy. **Surface:** asphalted.
Distance: on the spot.
Remarks: Parking at Karting.

Krško 37B1

Stadium Matija Gubec, Cesta krških žrtev 130a.
GPS: n45,94691 e15,48832.

30 free. **Surface:** grassy/gravel. 01/01-31/12.

Krško 37B1

Gostilna Stanislava Pečnik, Gunte 8. **GPS**: n45,98645 e15,46572.

2 free. Su.
Distance: on the spot on the spot on the spot.

Laško 37B1

Thermana Park Laško, Zdraviliška cesta 6.
GPS: n46,16188 e15,23132.

16 € 7-10/pp, dog € 4 Chincluded (16x)€ 4/day,16Amp WC **Location:** Urban, simple, central, noisy.
Surface: grasstiles/metalled. 01/01-31/12.
Distance: 700m on the spot 700m on the spot on the spot on the spot on the spot 10km 10km.
Remarks: Max. 24h, check in at reception.

Laško 37B1

Zdraviliške Laško, Zdraviliška cesta 4. **GPS**: n46,15761 e15,23224.

4 € 7-10/pp, dog € 4 Chincluded (4x)€ 4/day,16Amp WC **Location:** Urban, simple, central, noisy.
Surface: asphalted. 01/01-31/12.
Distance: 500m on the spot 500m on the spot on the spot on the spot on the spot 10km 10km.
Remarks: Discount on access terme.

Lendava 36C3

Terme Lendava, Tomsiceve 21A. **GPS**: n46,55396 e16,45813.

90 € 12,50-13,50/pp, dog € 3 Ch € 4 WC € 1/30minutes. **Surface:** asphalted/grassy. 01/01-31/12.
Remarks: Including access spa resort.

Ljutomer 36B3

Gostilna Trnek, Mota 76. **GPS**: n46,55516 e16,21929.

25 guests free Chincluded € 3 WC.
Location: Rural, isolated, quiet. **Surface:** grassy/gravel.
01/01-31/12.
Distance: on the spot on the spot on the spot 1km.
Remarks: Use sanitary only during opening hours.

Mala Nedelja 36B3

Bioterme, Moravci v Slovenskih Goricah 34 b.
GPS: n46,51437 e16,05109.
50 € 8 + € 0,64/pp tourist tax € 0,10/8liter Ch € 0,50/kWh included. **Surface:** grasstiles/grassy. 01/01-31/12.
Distance: 1,5km on the spot on the spot on the spot on the spot.
Remarks: Discount on access terme.

Maribor 36B3

Avtobusna postaja Maribor, Mlinska ulica 1.
GPS: n46,55852 e15,65573.

4 € 10 Ch.
Location: Noisy. **Surface:** asphalted. 01/01-31/12.
Distance: on the spot fast food on the spot on the spot.
Remarks: Nearby bus station P4, check in at tourist office.

Maribor 36B3

Partizanska cesta 50. **GPS**: n46,56315 e15,65819.
9 8-17h € 0,50/h, overnight stay and weekend free.
Surface: asphalted. 01/01-31/12.
Distance: city centre 1km 200m 300m.
Remarks: At station.

Maribor 36B3

Ulica Heroja Staneta. **GPS**: n46,56557 e15,64992.
2 € 16. **Surface:** asphalted.
Distance: on the spot 200m.

Metlika 37B1

Dependansa sobe Metlika, Cesta bratstra in enotnosti 77.
GPS: n45,64663 e15,31778.

SL

3 € 15 + € 0,64/pp tourist tax Ch included.
Location: Urban, simple, central, quiet. **Surface:** asphalted.
01/01-31/12.
Distance: 100m 1km 1km 100m 100m 100m on the spot on the spot.

Moravske Toplice 36B3

Kamp Moravske Toplice, Kranjčeva ulica 12.
GPS: n46,67862 e16,22151.

200 € 32-60 2 pers. Incl., dog € 3 Ch € 4.
Surface: grassy/gravel. 01/01-31/12.
Distance: 400m 100m 200m on the spot on the spot.
Remarks: Including access spa resort 3000.

Tourist information Moravske Toplice:
Goričko Regional Park, Ulica ob igrišču 3, www.park-goricko.org. Information centre.

Murska Sobota 36B3

Lovenjak, Polana 40. **GPS:** n46,68233 e16,13836.
10 € 11,30, 2 pers.incl included. **Surface:** metalled.
01/01-31/12.
Distance: on the spot on the spot on the spot.
Remarks: Free entrance swimming pool, jacuzzi, sauna.

Novo Mesto 37B1

Old Gardening, Skalickega 3. **GPS:** n45,79536 e15,17039.

10 € 15 Ch (10x) WC included.
Location: Comfortable, quiet. **Surface:** grassy/gravel.
01/01-31/12 with mucht snowfall.
Distance: 400m 400m 300m 400m on the spot on the spot.

Novo Mesto 37B1

Pri Belokranjucu, Kandijska cesta 63. **GPS:** n45,79947 e15,17865.

3 € 15 Ch ,16Amp included.
Location: Urban, simple, central, noisy. **Surface:** asphalted.
01/01-31/12.
Distance: 400m 5km 400m on the spot 200m on the spot 200m on the spot on the spot.

Obrežje Jug 37B1

OMV Istrabenz. GPS: n45,85517 e15,68513.
2 free. **Location:** Motorway, noisy.
Distance: on the spot.
Remarks: Parking petrol station OMV Istrabenz.

Ormož 36B3

Bar Ribnik, Ob ribniku 1. **GPS:** n46,40588 e16,15963.

3 free free.
Location: Rural. **Surface:** asphalted. 01/01-31/12.
Distance: on the spot on the spot.

Otočec 37B1

Kamp Otočec. GPS: n45,83794 e15,23821.
40 € 18, 20/06-24/08 € 22 Ch € 3,50 included.
Surface: grassy/gravel. 01/04-30/09.
Distance: 500m on the spot on the spot 500m 500m.
Remarks: Along river.

Pivka 37A1

Park of Military History Pivka, Kolodvorska cesta.
GPS: n45,66812 e14,18779.

8 € 10 Ch included,at restaurant. **Surface:** asphalted.
01/01-31/12.
Distance: 2km on the spot.
Remarks: At museum, video surveillance.

Podbočje 37B1

Turistična kmetija Hribar, Podbočje 36. **GPS:** n45,86190 e15,47110.

5 free. **Surface:** gravel.
Distance: 400m on the spot on the spot on the spot on the spot.

Podčetrtek 37B1

Golf Klub a Podčetrtek Amon, Olimje 24. **GPS:** n46,14400 e15,56493.

20 € 10 + € 1,25/pp tourist tax WC included.
Location: Isolated, quiet. **Surface:** asphalted/gravel.
01/01-31/12 With snow.
Distance: 3km on the spot on the spot on the spot.
Remarks: At golf court, bicycle rental.

Podčetrtek 37B1

Terme Olimia Kamp Natura, Zdravillška cesta 24.
GPS: n46,16529 e15,60522.

15 € 16,50-21,50/pp, dog € 3 Ch € 4,20 WC € 3.
Surface: metalled. 21/04-30/09.
Distance: on the spot on the spot.
Remarks: Including access spa resort.

Tourist information Podčetrtek:
Sedovška Homestead, Aškercev trg 24, Šmarje pri Jelšah. Traditional farmstead.
Rogatec Open-air Museum, Ptujska cesta 23, Rogatec. Open air museum, 18-20th century. 01/04-31/10 Mo.
Božjepotna Marijina cerkev, Sladka Gora, Šmarje pri Jelšah. Pilgrimage church.
Olimje Monastery and Pharmacy, Olimje 82. Monastery and one of the oldest pharmacies in the world.

Podsmreka 37A1

A2. **GPS:** n45,94805 e14,77065.
5 free free. **Location:** Motorway.
Distance: 100m.
Remarks: Guarded parking petrol station Petrol Podsmereka, highway Novo Mesto-Ljubljana.

Prebold 37B1

Dolina, Dolenja Vas 147. **GPS:** n46,24015 e15,08771.
€ 15,50 Ch WC. 01/01-31/12.
Distance: 200m 200m.

Ptuj 36B3

Terme Ptuj, Pot v toplice 9. **GPS:** n46,42109 e15,85585.

20 € 20 + € 1,63/registration + tourist tax Ch (2x),16Amp WC € 5/5 included.
Location: Simple. **Surface:** gravel. 01/01-31/12.
Distance: 800m 3km 500m 100m 1km on the spot 25km.

Tourist information Ptuj:
Maribor Tourist Board, Partizanska 47, Maribor, www.maribor-tourism.si. Old city with historical centre.
Mariborski Grad, Maribor. Castle, 15th century, regional museum. 01/04-31/12 Tue-Sa 9-17h, Su 9-14h Mo.
Ptujski Grad. Castle, 11th century with regional museum. 01/05-31/10 9-18h.

S Rečica ob Savinji 36A3

Menina. **GPS**: n46,31167 e14,90917.
€ 18-22 Ch WC . 01/01-31/12.
Distance: on the spot on the spot 300m.

Tourist information Rečica ob Savinji:
Mozirski gaj, Hribernikova 1, Mozirje. Botanical garden.
01/04-31/10 9-19h.
Musej Premogovništva, Stari jašek - Koroška cesta, Velenje. Coal mining museum.

S Rogaška Slatina 36B3

Eco vila Mila, Kamence 19. **GPS**: n46,20169 e15,62350.
€ 5, 01/04-31/10 € 10 + tourist tax € 1,27 € 0,50/kWh.
Surface: asphalted. 01/01-31/12.
Distance: on the spot.

S Rogla 36B3

Rogla. **GPS**: n46,45259 e15,33117.

€ 12 Ch included. **Surface:** gravel.
Distance: Zreče 10km 200m on the spot on the spot on the spot on the spot.
Remarks: Altitude 1517m.

Sevnica 37B1

Cesta na Grad. **GPS**: n46,00862 e15,31527.
15 free. **Surface:** gravel. 01/01-31/12.
Distance: 500m 500m 500m on the spot.
Remarks: Next to castle.

S Slovenj Gradec 36B3

Camperstop Slovenj Gradec, Ozare 18.
GPS: n46,51418 e15,07678.

6 € 5 Ch (4x) included. **Location:** Comfortable, quiet.
Surface: gravel. 01/01-31/12.
Distance: 500m 500m 500m on the spot.
Remarks: At youth hostel.

S Slovenj Gradec 36B3

Razborca 66. **GPS**: n46,50230 e15,21017.
10 € 10 Ch included WC . **Surface:** gravel.
01/01-31/12.
Distance: on the spot on the spot on the spot on the spot.

Solcava 36A3

Park Logarska Dolina, Logarska Dolina 9.
GPS: n46,41999 e14,64555.

20 € 10. **Location:** Rural, simple, isolated, quiet.
Surface: grassy/gravel. 01/01-31/12.
Distance: 5km on the spot 5km 5km on the spot on the spot on the spot on the spot.
Remarks: Entrance park € 7/pp.

S Stahovica 36A3

Pri Jurju, Kamniska Bistrica 5. **GPS**: n46,32685 e14,58706.

20 € 5 Ch (20x) € 2/day,16Amp WC included € 5/day.
Location: Rural, simple, isolated, quiet. **Surface:** grassy.
01/01-31/12.
Distance: 8km 6km on the spot 8km 300m on the spot on the spot 3km 3km.

S Tepanje 36B3

A1. **GPS**: n46,34776 e15,48695.
5 free free. **Location:** Motorway, noisy.
Distance: on the spot.
Remarks: Guarded parking petrol station Petrol Tepanje I, on both sides of the highway Maribor-Ljubljana.

S Vinica 37B1

Farm Benetič, Vinica 17. **GPS**: n45,46017 e15,25854.
10 € 10 Ch . **Location:** Isolated, quiet. **Surface:** gravel.
01/01-31/12.
Distance: on the spot on the spot on the spot.

S Visnja Gora 37A1

Mestno kopališče, Kopaliska Ulica 25.
GPS: n45,95268 e14,75097.

20 free (1x) WC free. **Location:** Rural, simple, isolated, quiet. **Surface:** asphalted/gravel. 01/01-31/12.
Distance: on the spot 1,7km 1km 200m on the spot on the spot 10km 10km.
Remarks: Check in at swimming pool, service during opening hours.

S Visnja Gora 37A1

PrinceSport&Fun Center, Kopališka ulica 27.
GPS: n45,95207 e14,75201.
€ 10 WC included. **Surface:** grassy/gravel.
01/01-31/12.

S Žalec 36B3

Camperstop Žalec, Mestni trg. **GPS**: n46,25418 e15,16274.

4 free € 0,50/40liter Ch (4x) € 0,50/kWh,16Amp.
Location: Urban, simple, central, quiet. **Surface:** metalled.
01/01-31/12.
Distance: 500m 100m 500m 500m on the spot on the spot.
Remarks: At sports park, caution key service € 20 at hotel.

S Zdole 37B1

Etnoart tourism Špiler, Kostanjek 18. **GPS**: n46,01018 e15,54409.

5 € 10 . **Surface:** grassy. 01/01-31/12.
Distance: on the spot.

S Zdole 37B1

Gostilna pri Dularju, Kostanjek 20. **GPS**: n46,00975 e15,54155.

10 guests free Ch (3x).
Location: Rural, quiet. 01/01-31/12.

S Zgornje Jezersko 36A3

Camperstop Stara Pošta, Zgornje Jezersko 124.
GPS: n46,40240 e14,50673.

9 € 10/pp Ch (16x) € 3/24h WC € 4 included.
Location: Rural, luxurious, quiet. **Surface:** grassy.
01/04-30/09.
Distance: 1km 1km 1km 1km 1km 100m on the spot on the spot.

S Zgornje Jezersko 36A3

Camperstop Šenkova Domačija, Zgornje Jezersko 12.
GPS: n46,40792 e14,51769.

5 € 10, Jul/Aug € 15 Ch (5x) € 3/night WC € 3 included. **Location:** Rural, quiet. **Surface:** gravel/metalled.
01/01-31/12.
Distance: 2km 300m 300m 300m 2km 100m on the spot on the spot on the spot.

S Zreče 36B3

Thermal Spa, Cesta na Roglo 15. **GPS**: n46,37096 e15,39021.

4 € 10 + € 1,30/pp tourist tax Ch included.
Surface: asphalted. 01/01-31/12.
Distance: 300m 300m on the spot 300m.
Remarks: Check in at hotel, 20% reduction swimming pool.

SL

INDEX

INDEX

INDEX